Ashford's Dictionary of Industrial Chemicals

Ashford's Dictionary of Industrial Chemicals

Properties

Production

Uses

Compiled by Robert D. Ashford

Wavelength Publications Ltd

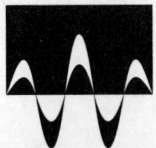

Copyright © 1994 by Wavelength Publications Ltd

British Library Cataloguing in Publication Data
Ashford's Dictionary of Industrial Chemicals:
Properties, Production, Uses
 I. Ashford, Robert D.
 661.003

ISBN 0-9522674-0-3

Publisher   Wavelength Publications Ltd
                     63 Kendal Steps
                     St. George's Fields
                     London W2 2YE, England
                     Tel: (071) 706-1315
                     Fax: (071) 402-0894

Cover Design   Madeleine Bennett
Cover Photograph E. Schrempp/Science Photo Library
Printer   The Bath Press, Avon

To the memory of Henry Francis Douglas Ashford

Preface

The chemical industry may not be the most glamorous sector of the economy but it is one of the most important: almost every aspect of our lives now depends on it in one form or another. Common materials such as plastics, fibres and coatings are today an accepted part of our surroundings and make a major contribution to our quality of life. Most of these products did not exist 100 years ago. They have come about because of basic research, innovation and enterprise by an industry which can justly claim much credit for the improved standard of living that we have today. Mistakes have been made on the way – that is undeniable – but the net effect has been one of considerable benefit to us all.

In view of its enormous contribution to our welfare and way of life, it is sad, and somewhat surprising, to realise just how little of the industry's activities are appreciated by the public at large. There are several reasons for this, most of which can be traced back to cultural and educational priorities that place a greater emphasis on consumption rather than production. A significant factor, however, is the generally secretive nature of chemical companies, many of which only release a minimum amount of information about their activities as a matter of policy. The result is that the world at large often only hears about their products and activities in negative terms, when something goes wrong. Pesticides, for example, have an extremely bad image, associated by many with residual toxins in food or the killing of birds, rather than with their more positive aspects: the alleviation of hunger, and cheap, good-quality food. While these chemicals are undoubtedly of considerable benefit to mankind, they are not perceived as such by the consuming public, mainly because the industry as a whole is reluctant to divulge information and to plead its case in the marketplace.

Even people working within the industry itself suffer from its secretive nature. Most employees in chemical companies have a reasonable idea of the products and processes used in their organisation, but often only a sketchy idea of what is happening in other parts of the industry. In broad terms this means that the company is not fully aware of the range of technical and marketing opportunities open to it, or that it may be at a strategic disadvantage to more astute competitors. All companies need business and market intelligence, but many are not prepared even to contribute to a pool of basic knowledge about the industry because they are unable to assess what information is 'commercially sensitive' and what is not. This means that it is difficult for everyone to gain an overall view of industry and to assess what is happening and where it is going.

This dictionary is intended as a reference book to help you find out about the chemical industry and its products. Its prime function is to provide a concise source for information on the industrial chemicals used today. It has entries on 6,800 different products, including all of the major commodity chemicals, most intermediate products and many of the smaller-volume, 'fine' chemicals used in high-value, speciality items. There is information on plastics, resins, solvents, lubricants, pesticides, drugs, dyes, explosives, plasticisers, antioxidants, stabilisers and a wide range of other 'effect' chemicals of this type. The only area known to the author to be deficient is the dyestuffs, many of which are only referred to by trade name or Colour Index number in the literature. The dyestuff intermediates included in the dictionary are therefore likely to be used as raw materials for more products than the number of listed derivatives might suggest. Chemical warfare agents and illegal drugs have not been covered for obvious reasons.

The basic information provided for each chemical is its structure, a description, alternative names, production, derivatives and uses. Apart from the primary raw materials, all other chemicals mentioned in the production or derivatives sections of a particular entry are also included in the dictionary. This is done deliberately so that the complete 'family tree' of chemicals can be followed through the industry if the reader has sufficient patience. In most cases only a subset of the complete tree is needed. For instance, the raw materials for salicylic acid can be traced backwards through phenol and cumene to benzene, or forwards to acetylsalicylic acid or other downstream products. These raw material–derivative relationships are important in understanding the structure of the industry and of how one chemical is related to another: they provide a map for the flow of chemicals through the industry. Note that only those routes that are currently used in the developed world are included. Technologies which are still at the pilot plant stage or which have not as yet been taken up commercially by industry have been excluded, as have routes that are of historical interest only. Processes that are specific to the CIS countries and China have also been excluded, largely because of the current unreliability of information about these countries in the West. Other countries, such as South Africa and Brazil, in which the chemical industry is structured somewhat differently for strategic reasons, have been included as full participants in the global market.

In compiling the dictionary every effort has been made to be as complete as possible. All sources of information open to the author have been used. These have included reference books, textbooks, magazines, journals, patents, government publications, company literature, product literature and buyers guides, as well as a host of private market research work. A surprisingly large quantity of information on the industry is available in the public domain, although not often presented in the most straightforward, up-to-date or precise way. A major problem is distinguishing between what is speculation and what is fact – and the two are often intermingled to conceal specific information about a company. In other cases the situation is confused because of conflicting, vague or missing information on a particular chemical. In all these cases judgements have had to be made concerning the reliability of the source and the likely method of synthesis used in practice. Often this can be by analogy with related products or by the presence of a clear feedstock or technology position in manufacturers' portfolios. The temptation to simply assume that the obvious laboratory preparation is used in industry has been avoided whereever possible.

The element of judgement means that the information presented in the book should be treated with some caution by readers and viewed more as a personal interpretation of the public and private information available to the author than as the last word on the subject. In spite of considerable effort being made to ensure that information is correct in both substance and detail, there will undoubtedly be errors. Readers are therefore advised to keep this in mind when using the book. The dictionary is not intended as a laboratory or production manual and does not include data on the toxicity or handling of the chemicals listed. The absence of information on these topics should in no way be interpreted as implying that the chemical is free from hazard.

The author would be most grateful to readers who point out errors or omissions in the text so that they can be corrected in future editions of the book. He would also appreciate any suggestions on how the content or presentation could be improved to make the book easier to use or of more direct value to the reader. Such feedback is regarded as a valuable source of constructive criticism and one which will be gratefully acknowledged in future editions. In return, he would be happy to justify his views or discuss the background to a particular statement with anyone who cares to contact him at the publisher's address.

The author wishes to express his sincere gratitude for the encouragement given to him by colleagues, friends and relatives during the long years of this book's gestation. There is a limit to the amount of polite interest that anyone can take in work such as this, particularly when they are not directly involved in the project and only have a passing knowledge of the subject matter. Apologies for being a bore and thanks for their tolerance and understanding are therefore due to all of these folk: they can now have a respite for a few months. Particular thanks goes to Penny Martin for her help with coding the structural diagrams and to staff at the Science Reference Library in London for their assistance and expertise.

Bob Ashford
London, January 1994

Explanatory Note

The dictionary is arranged in alphabetical order by chemical name ignoring all leading number and letter prefixes. This means that entries such as *p*-methyl-benzaldehyde or *N*-methyldicyclohexylamine are all listed under 'm' rather than under 'p' or 'n'. Each chemical is referred to by a name commonly used in industry and does not follow any standard form of nomenclature. Abbreviations (now very common) are expanded to the full name in most cases. The entries for 'MEK' and '2-butanone', for example, both point the reader to 'methyl ethyl ketone' as the prime name for the chemical. For pesticides and drugs, ISO and INN names, respectively, have been used in most instances, while the dyes and pigments are referred to by their Colour Index number, except where trivial chemical names exist. Particular care should be taken with chemicals derived from natural oils, many of which are often named in a fairly loose way by industry – and in this dictionary. Formulae of the type 'C$_{18:2}$' are commonly used by oil and surfactant producers to denote (in this case) an 18 carbon chain containing two double bonds. This nomenclature is used widely in this book.

Entries follow the same pattern to a greater or lesser extent for each chemical. Under each heading are the various alternative names for the chemical, including well-known trade names, abbreviations and the Chemical Abstracts Service number(s). Different names are separated with a semicolon (;). Care should be taken not to confuse this with the comma (,) used as part of chemical names such as in 'magnesia, caustic-calcined'. The names section is followed by a structural formula, underneath which is the atomic formula, molecular weight and a general description of the product. Below this is the subsection headed 'Production' giving the synthetic routes used for the production of the chemical in industry. The 'Production' subsection generally includes raw materials, but not reagents unless these are specifically known. The different chemical products are separated by means of a plus (+) sign; alternative feedstocks are separated with a slash (\).

Information on the way a chemical is produced is provided in one of two ways. Large-tonnage commodity chemicals are usually produced in dedicated plants and often by an individually-named process. In these cases only the process name itself is provided in the brackets immediately following the list of reactants. For other products the production route is indicated by means of reaction signposts which should allow the steps in the synthesis to be worked out from basic chemical principles. Note that the reactants are used in the sequence in which they are written so the first step mentioned refers to reaction on the first chemical or between the first two chemicals. The second reaction step is then on the product of the first reaction, and so on. Occasionally the reaction sequence switches completely to a new reactant, but it is usually obvious when this is occurring so no special indication has been made. Where a chemical is made as a single product, no further information is provided. When it is produced as a coproduct or by-product, however, the associated products are listed after the reaction information, again using the slash (\) separator.

The 'Production' subsection is followed by the 'Derivatives' subsection which simply lists all the other entries in the book in which that chemical is referred to as a raw material. Its purpose is to provide a cross-reference to all the downstream products of the named chemical so that these can be referred to individually. The term 'Derivative' should be interpreted loosely. The final subsection, 'Uses', lists non-chemical and general reagent applications of the product which may not have been mentioned specifically elsewhere.

The English spelling and terminology used in this dictionary is that of the United Kingdom. In most cases it the same as that used in the USA and should present no difficulties for English-speaking people of any nationality. American readers, however, should note the use of 'sulph..' rather than 'sulf..' for sulphur-containing chemicals.

AA *See:* acrylic acid; adipic acid

AAA *See:* acetoacetanilide

AADMC *See:* acetoacet-4-chloro-2,5-dimethoxyanilide

AAMX *See:* acetoacet-2,4-xylidide

AAOA *See:* acetoacet-*o*-anisidide

AAOC *See:* acetoacet-*o*-chloroanilide

AAOT *See:* acetoacet-*o*-toluidide

AAPP *See:* acetoacet-*p*-phenetidide

AAPT *See:* acetoacet-*p*-toluidide

ABFA *See:* azodicarbonamide

abietic acid
[514-10-3]

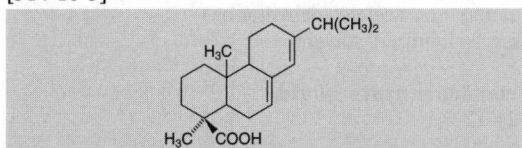

$C_{20}H_{30}O_2$. M: 302.46. Yellow solid. MP: 85°C. Insoluble in water. Commercial grades are mixed products containing abietic acid as the major component.
Production:
• rosin, tall oil (isomerisation)
Derivatives:
calcium rosinate; maleic resins; rosin ester gum; zinc rosinate

ABPA *See:* α-bromopropionic acid

ABS *See:* acrylonitrile-butadiene-styrene copolymers; dodecylbenzenesulphonic acid, branched; dodecylbenzenesulphonic acid, linear

ACA *See:* 2-acetamidocinnamic acid; ammoniacal copper arsenate

7-ACA *See:* 7-aminocephalosporanic acid

ACAC *See:* acetylacetone

ACB *See:* 2-amino-5-chlorobenzophenone

ACE *See:* poly(acrylate-methacrylate) graft copolymers

acebutolol
[37517-30-9]

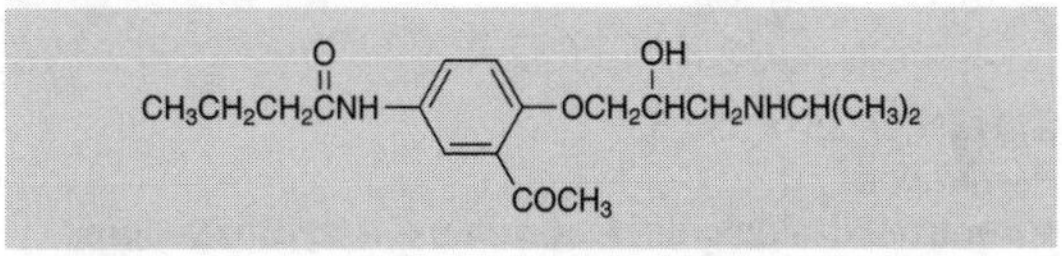

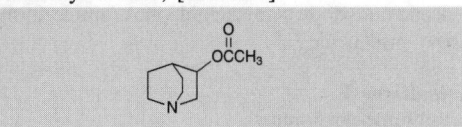

$C_{18}H_{28}N_2O_4$. M: 336.43. Available commercially as the hydrochloride.
Production:
• *n*-butyryl chloride + *p*-aminophenol + acetic acid + epichlorohydrin + isopropylamine (amide formation/esterification/Fries rearrangement/epoxidation/amine formation)
Uses: β-receptor blocker drug

aceclidine
3-quinuclidinyl acetate; [827-61-2]

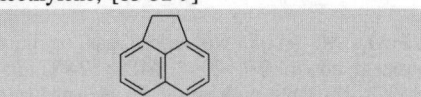

$C_9H_{15}N_1O_2$. M: 169.23.
Production:
• quinuclidin-3-ol + acetic acid (esterification)
Uses: antihypotensive drug

acediasulfone
[80-03-5]; [127-60-6] (sodium salt)

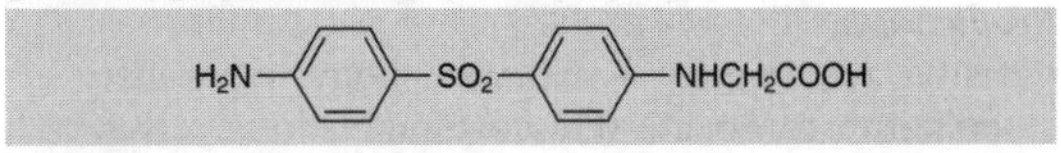

H_2N—⬡—SO_2—⬡—$NHCH_2COOH$

$C_{14}H_{14}N_2O_4S_1$. M: 306.33. Available commercially as the sodium or morpholinium salts.
Production:
• 4,4′-diaminodiphenyl sulphone + chloroacetic acid (amine formation)
Uses: antibacterial drug

acenaphthene
naphthyleneethylene; [83-32-9]

$C_{12}H_{10}$. M: 154.21. Crystalline solid. MP: 92–95°C. BP: 279°C. d: 1.20 kg/l (20°C). Insoluble in water. Soluble in chlorinated and aromatic solvents.
Production:
• fluorene oil (fractionation; coproduced with fluorene/diphenylene oxide)
Derivatives: naphthalic anhydride; Sulphur Brown 52

acenocoumarol
[152-72-7]

$C_{19}H_{15}N_1O_6$. M: 353.33.
Production:
- p-nitrobenzaldehyde + acetone + 4-hydroxycoumarin (Claisen condensation/Michael addition)

Uses: anticoagulant drug

acephate
O,S-dimethyl acetylphosphoramidothioate; [30560-19-1]

$C_4H_{10}N_1O_3P_1S_1$. M: 183.16.
Production:
- acetic anhydride + methamidophos (amide formation)

Uses: insecticide

acesulfame-K
acesulfame-potassium

$C_4H_4K_1N_1O_4S_1$. M: 201.24. White crystals. MP: 250°C. Soluble in water.
Production:
- t-butyl acetoacetate + chlorosulphonyl isocyanate + potassium carbonate (chlorosulphonation/cyclisation/decarboxylation/salt formation)

Uses: artificial sweetener

acetal resins *See:* polyacetal, copolymers; polyacetal, homopolymers

acetaldehyde
ethanal; [75-07-0]

$C_2H_4O_1$. M: 44.05. Colourless gas or liquid with a pungent odour. BP: 20°C. MP: -124°C. d: 0.79 kg/l (15°C). Miscible with water, oxygenated and aromatic solvents.
Production:
- ethylene (Wacker oxidation process)
- ethanol (catalytic dehydrogenation)
- ethanol + oxygen (oxidation)
- acetylene + water (vinylation)
- oxygenates, Fischer-Tropsch, mixed (fractionation;

coproduced with methanol/ethanol/isopropanol/n-butanol/isobutanol/amyl alcohol, primary/acetone/methyl ethyl ketone)
Derivatives:
acetic acid; acetic anhydride; acetoin; 2-acetylpyridine; D-alanine; DL-alanine; benzophenonetetracarboxylate dianhydride; 1,3-butanediol; 3-butyn-2-ol; chloroacetaldehyde; 1-chloroethyl ethyl carbonate; 2-chloro-3-hexyne; cinnamaldehyde; crotonaldehyde; crotonylidene urea; diethyl α-isomalate; ethyl acetate; 2,2′-ethylidene bis(4,6-di-t-butylphenol); glyoxal; 2,5-hexynediol; DL-lactic acid; metaldehyde; methomyl; 2-methylimidazole; p-methylstyrene; paraldehyde; pentaerythritol; peracetic acid; α-picoline; β-picoline; γ-picoline; pyridine; quinaldine; 1,1,3,3-tetramethoxypropane; thiodicarb

acetamide
[60-35-5]

$C_2H_5N_1O_1$. M: 59.07. White crystals. MP: 82°C. BP: 221°C. d: 1.00 kg/l (85°C). Soluble in water and alcohol.
Production:
- ammonium acetate (dehydration)

Uses: solubiliser; solvent

acetamidine hydrochloride
[124-42-5]

$C_2H_7Cl_1N_2$. M: 94.54. Prepared *in situ*. Not a commercially traded product. Dissociates into acetic acid and ammonia on warming. Soluble in water and alcohol.
Production:
- acetonitrile + ammonia + hydrochloric acid (nitrile addition/salt formation)

Derivatives: 4-amino-5-aminomethyl-2-methylpyrimidine; 4-amino-5-bromomethyl-2-methylpyrimidine hydrobromide; sulfisomidine

4-acetamidobenzenesulphonyl chloride
N-acetylsulphanilyl chloride; [121-60-8]

$C_8H_8Cl_1N_1O_3S_1$. M: 233.67. Light brown powder. MP: 146–148°C with decomposition. Hydrolysed by water. Soluble in chlorinated and aromatic solvents.
Production:
- acetanilide + chlorosulphonic acid (chlorosulphonation)

Derivatives: 4-acetylsulphanilamide; salazosulfapyridine; sulfadiazine; sulfadicramide; sulfadimethoxine; sulfaethidole; sulfafurazole; sulfaguanidine; sulfaguanole; sulfalene; sulfamerazine; sulfamethazine; sulfamethizole; sulfamethoxazole; sulfametoxydiazine; sulfamoxole; sulfaperin; sulfaphenazole; sulfapyridine; sulfathiazole; sulfisomidine; sulphaquinoxaline

2-acetamidocinnamic acid
ACA; [5469-45-4]

$C_{11}H_{11}N_1O_3$. M: 205.22. Solid. Available as the dihydrate. MP: 185–186°C. Soluble in water.
Production:
• acetic anhydride + glycine + benzaldehyde (acetylation/condensation)
Derivatives: L-phenylalanine

1-acetamido-8-naphthol-3,6-disulphonic acid
See: N-acetyl-H acid

p-acetamidophenol *See:* paracetamol

acetaminophen *See:* paracetamol

acetanilide
N-phenylacetamide; [103-84-4]

$C_8H_9N_1O_1$. M: 135.17. White, crystalline solid. MP: 113–115°C. BP: 304–307°C. d: 1.21 kg/l (4°C). Soluble in hot water and oxygenated solvents.
Production:
• acetic acid + aniline (amide formation)
Derivatives: 4-acetamidobenzenesulphonyl chloride; p-bromoaniline; p-nitroacetanilide
Uses: analgesic/antipyretic drug

acetazolamide
[59-66-5]

$C_4H_6N_4O_3S_2$. M: 222.25.
Production:
• hydrazine + ammonium thiocyanate + acetic anhydride + ammonia (thiocyanate addition/cyclisation/acetylation/oxidation/sulphonamide formation)
Uses: diuretic/*glaucoma* therapy drug

acetic acid
E260 (EC); [64-19-7]

$C_2H_4O_2$. M: 60.05. Colourless liquid or solid with a characteristic, sharp odour. MP: 16°C. BP: 117–118°C. d: 1.05 kg/l (20°C). Miscible with water and oxygenated solvents. Flash point: 57°C (OC). Also available as a 60% solution in water and in a ~5% solution as vinegar.
Production:
• acetaldehyde (air oxidation)
• acetaldehyde + oxygen (Hoechst-Shawinigan process; coproduced with acetic anhydride)
• acetaldehyde (air oxidation; coproduced with peracetic acid)
• methanol + carbon monoxide (BASF/Monsanto carbonylation processes)
• methanol + carbon monoxide (BP acetyls process; coproduced with acetic anhydride)
• naphtha, heavy (liquid-phase oxidation; coproduced with acetone/methyl ethyl ketone/formic acid/propionic acid)
• n-butane (Celanese LPO process; coproduced with methanol/ethanol/acetone/methyl ethyl ketone/formic acid/propionic acid/n-butyric acid/methyl formate)
• acetic anhydride + cotton linters/bleached wood pulp (acetylation/partial hydrolysis; byproduct of cellulose acetate production)
Derivatives:
acebutolol; aceclidine; acetanilide; acetic anhydride; N-(2-acetoxyethyl)-N-(2-cyanoethyl)aniline; acetyl chloride; N-acetylethanolamine; acrinathrin; aluminium acetate, basic; ammonium acetate; amyl acetate; benzoyl chloride; bornyl acetate; bromoacetic acid; bromoacetyl bromide; n-butyl acetate; s-butyl acetate; 2-t-butylcyclohexyl acetate; 4-t-butylcyclohexyl acetate; 2-s-butyl-1-vinylcyclohexyl acetate; calcium acetate; cellulose triacetate; chloroacetic acid; citronellyl acetate; cobalt acetate; cocoamine acetate; diacetyl fatty acid monoglyceride tartrate; dicyclopentenyl acetate; diethylene glycol monobutyl ether acetate; dimethylacetamide; dodemorph acetate; dodine; ethyl acetate; ethylene glycol monobutyl ether acetate; ethylene glycol monoethyl ether acetate; ethylene glycol monomethyl ether acetate; fatty acid glycerides, acetylated; 3-formylcrotonyl acetate; geranyl acetate; guazatine acetate; 2-hexenyl acetate; 3-hexenyl acetate; hexyl acetate; homoveratric acid; isoamyl acetate; isobornyl acetate; isobutyl acetate; isoheptyl acetate; isononyl acetate; isopropyl acetate; ketene; lavandulyl acetate; lead acetate; L-lysine; magnesium acetate; mercuric acetate; N-methylacetamide; 2-methylbenzothiazole; methyl triacetoxysilane; nickel acetate; peracetic acid; phenethyl acetate; phenyl acetate; 1-phenylethyl acetate; potassium acetate; n-propyl acetate; propylene glycol monoethyl ether acetate; propylene glycol monomethyl ether acetate; sodium acetate; stearylamine acetate; tallowamine acetate; tributyltin acetate; trichloroacetic acid; trifluoroacetic acid; vinyl acetate; vinyltriacetoxysilane; zinc acetate; zirconium acetate

Uses: dyeing auxiliary; etchant (semiconductor manufacture); acidulant (pickles, sauces, ketchup); aluminium brightening agent; laundry sour; Showa Denka allyl alcohol process reagent; Mitsubishi 1,4-butanediol process reagent; solvent (terephthalic acid production)

acetic anhydride
[108-24-7]

(CH₃CO)₂O

$C_4H_6O_3$. M: 102.09. Colourless liquid with an acetic odour. BP: 139°C. MP: -74°C. d: 1.08 kg/l (20°C). Slowly hydrolysed by water and alcohols to acetic acid and esters. Soluble in oxygenated and chlorinated solvents.
Production:
• acetic acid + ketene (addition)
• acetaldehyde + oxygen (Hoechst-Shawinigan process; coproduced with acetic acid)
• methanol + carbon monoxide (BP acetyls process; coproduced with acetic acid)
Derivatives:
acephate; 2-acetamidocinnamic acid; acetazolamide; 4-acetylbiphenyl; acetylcysteine; 2-acetylfuran; *N*-acetyl-H acid; acetylsalicylic acid; 2-acetylthiophene; 4-acetyl-1,1,6-trimethylethanooctahydronaphthalene; Acid Black 60; Acid Red 68; Acid Red 137; Acid Violet 80; L-alanine; amidotrizoic acid; *m*-aminoacetanilide; *p*-aminoacetanilide; anisyl acetate; benzyl acetate; bisacodyl; bromazepam; cedryl acetate; cedryl methyl ketone; cellulose acetate; cellulose acetobutyrate; cellulose propionate; cellulose triacetate; cinnamic acid; cinnamyl acetate; cinoxate; coumarin; decahydro-β-naphthyl acetate; diacetin; 3,5-diacetoxyacetophenone; diethyl 2-(acetamido)malonate; diltiazem; dimethyl benzyl carbinyl acetate; 1,1-dimethylhydrazine; dinoseb acetate; Disperse Blue 79; Disperse Blue 165; Disperse Yellow 77; eugenyl acetate; Food Black 1; guaiyl acetate; 7-hydroxycoumarin; hydroxyethylidene(diphosphonic acid); 2-hydroxy-5-nonylacetophenoxime; iminostilbene; iocetamic acid; iohexol; iotalamic acid; lanolin, acetylated; lanolin alcohol, acetylated; levodopa; linalyl acetate; lorazepam; mafenide; mefluidide; Meldrum's acid; menthyl acetate; metamitron; L-methionine; *p*-methylacetophenone; 2-methyl-5-mercapto-1,3,4-thiadiazole; musk ketone; *p*-nitroacetanilide; 5-nitrofurfural diacetate; nopyl acetate; normorphine; oxazepam; paracetamol; pentaacetylglucose; phenacetin; L-phenylalanine; pinacolone; polyacetal, homopolymers; Reactive Orange 16; salacetamide; starch acetate; sucrose acetate isobutyrate; sucrose octaacetate; sulfacetamide; Sulphur Yellow 1; Sulphur Yellow 9; temazepam; terpinyl acetate; thioacetic acid; thiophene-2,5-dicarboxylic acid; α-tocopheryl acetate; triacetin; tri-*n*-butyl acetylcitrate; α-trichloromethylphenyl carbinyl acetate; triethyl acetylcitrate; triethylene glycol diacetate; L-valine; vetiveryl acetate; vitamin K_1

Uses:
acetic acid chlorination catalyst; aluminium electrolytic polishing agent; acetyl chloride raw material (*in situ* production); acetylation/condensation/dehydration reagent; semiconductor processing reagent

5-acetoacetamidobenzimidazolone

$C_{11}H_{11}N_3O_3$. M: 233.23.
Production:
• diketene + 5-aminobenzimidazolone (amide formation)
Derivatives:
Pigment Orange 36; Pigment Yellow 120; Pigment Yellow 151; Pigment Yellow 154

acetoacetanilide
AAA; [102-01-2]

$C_{10}H_{11}N_1O_2$. M: 177.21. White, crystalline solid. MP: 85–86°C. Slightly soluble in water. Soluble in oxygenated and chlorinated solvents.
Production:
• diketene + aniline (amide formation)
Derivatives:
carboxin; Pigment Orange 15; Pigment Orange 16; Pigment Yellow 1; Pigment Yellow 4; Pigment Yellow 5; Pigment Yellow 12; Solvent Yellow 19

acetoacet-*o*-anisidide
o-acetoacetanisidide; AAOA; [92-15-9]

$C_{11}H_{13}N_1O_3$. M: 207.23.
Production:
• diketene + *o*-anisidine (amide formation)
Derivatives:
Pigment Yellow 17; Pigment Yellow 65; Pigment Yellow 73; Pigment Yellow 74

acetoacet-*o*-chloroanilide
AAOC; [93-70-9]

$C_{10}H_{10}Cl_1N_1O_2$. M: 211.65.

Production:
- diketene + *o*-chloroaniline (amide formation)

Derivatives:
Pigment Yellow 3; Pigment Yellow 63

acetoacet-4-chloro-2,5-dimethoxyanilide
acetoacet-2,5-dimethoxy-4-chloroanilide; AADMC;
[4433-79-8]

$C_{12}H_{14}Cl_1N_1O_4$. M: 271.70.
Production:
- diketene + 4-chloro-2,5-dimethoxyaniline (amide formation)

Derivatives:
Pigment Yellow 83; Pigment Yellow 97

acetoacet-4-chloro-2-methylanilide
acetoacet-4-chloro-*o*-toluidide; [20139-55-3]

$C_{11}H_{12}Cl_1N_1O_2$. M: 225.68.
Production:
- diketene + 2-amino-5-chlorotoluene (amide formation)

Derivatives:
Pigment Yellow 113; Pigment Yellow 171

acetoacet-*N,N*-diethylamide
See: N,N-diethylacetoacetamide

acetoacet-*N,N*-dimethylamide
See: N,N-dimethylacetoacetamide

acetoacet-*N*-methylamide *See: N*-methylacetoacetamide

acetoacet-*p*-phenetidide
AAPP; [122-82-7]

$C_{12}H_{15}N_1O_3$. M: 221.26.
Production:
- diketene + *p*-phenetidine (amide formation)

Derivatives: Pigment Yellow 75

acetoacet-*o*-toluidide
AAOT; [93-68-5]
$C_{11}H_{13}N_1O_2$. M: 191.23.
Production:
- diketene + *o*-toluidine (amide formation)

Derivatives: Pigment Yellow 14

acetoacet-*p*-toluidide
4'-methylacetoacetanilide; AAPT; [1503-54-4]

$C_{11}H_{13}N_1O_2$. M: 191.23. White crystals. MP: 95°C.
Soluble in oxygenated and aromatic solvents.
Production:
- diketene + *p*-toluidine (amide formation)

Derivatives:
Pigment Yellow 55

acetoacet-2,4-xylidide
acetoacet-*m*-xylidide; AAMX; [97-36-9]

$C_{12}H_{15}N_1O_2$. M: 205.26.
Production:
- diketene + 2,4-xylidine (amide formation)

Derivatives:
Pigment Orange 14; Pigment Yellow 13; Pigment Yellow 81; Pigment Yellow 127

2-acetobutyrolactone
α-acetobutyrolactone; 2-acetyl-1,4-butyrolactone;
acetylbutyrolactone; [517-23-7]

$C_6H_8O_3$. M: 128.13.
Production:
- γ-butyrolactone + ethyl acetate (condensation)

Derivatives:
5-(2-hydroxyethyl)-4-methylthiazole; thiamine

acetochlor
2-chloro-*N*-(ethoxyethyl)-6'-ethylacet-*o*-toluidide;
[34256-82-1]

$C_{14}H_{20}Cl_1N_1O_2$. M: 269.77.

Production:
- 2-ethyl-6-methylaniline + formaldehyde + ethanol + chloroacetyl chloride (alkoxymethylation/amide formation)

Uses:
herbicide

acetoguanamine

2,4-diamino-6-methyl-1,3,5-triazine; [542-02-9]

$C_4H_7N_5$. M: 125.13. Solid. MP: 228°C. d: 1.42 kg/l. Slightly soluble in water. Soluble in oxygenated solvents.

Production:
- acetonitrile + dicyandiamide (condensation)

Derivatives: 2-amino-4-methoxy-6-methyltriazine

Uses: comonomer (chemically-resistant/improved-solubility amino resins)

acetoin

acetylmethylcarbinol; 3-hydroxybutan-2-one; [513-86-0]

$C_4H_8O_2$. M: 88.10. Colourless liquid with a pleasant odour. BP: 148°C. MP: 15°C. d: 0.99 kg/l (20°C). Miscible with water and alcohol. Forms a solid dimer on standing which dissociates on heating.

Production:
- acetaldehyde (condensation)

Derivatives: diacetyl; dimethipin; sulfaguanole; sulfamoxole

Uses: flavouring ingredient (margarine)

acetone

dimethyl ketone; 2-propanone; DMK; [67-64-1]

$C_3H_6O_1$. M: 58.08. Colourless, volatile liquid with a characteristic, ethereal odour. BP: 56°C. d: 0.79 kg/l (20°C). Miscible with water as well as most organic solvents and oils. Flash point: -9°C (OC).

Production:
- propylene (Hoechst direct oxidation process)
- isopropanol (vapour-phase dehydrogenation)
- cumene hydroperoxide (acid-catalysed hydrolysis; coproduced with phenol)
- *m*-diisopropylbenzene (oxidation/acid-catalysed hydrolysis; coproduced with resorcinol)
- *p*-diisopropylbenzene (oxidation/acid-catalysed hydrolysis; coproduced with hydroquinone)
- toluene + propylene (Friedel-Crafts alkylation/oxidation/acid-catalysed hydrolysis; coproduced with *m/p*-cresol)
- naphtha, heavy (liquid-phase oxidation; coproduced with methyl ethyl ketone/formic acid/acetic acid/propionic acid)
- *n*-butane (Celanese LPO process; coproduced with methanol/ethanol/methyl ethyl ketone/formic acid/acetic acid/propionic acid/*n*-butyric acid/methyl formate)
- oxygenates, Fischer-Tropsch, mixed (fractionation; coproduced with methanol/ethanol/isopropanol/*n*-butanol/isobutanol/amyl alcohol, primary/acetaldehyde/methyl ethyl ketone)

Derivatives:
acenocoumarol; acetone cyanohydrin; acetone-diphenylamine condensates; alitame; ascorbic acid; bendiocarb; benzylideneacetone; bezafibrate; bisphenol A; bromoform; clofibrate; coumachlor; cycloxydim; diacetone alcohol; 2,2-di(*t*-amylperoxy)propane; dikegulac-sodium; dimethyl benzyl carbinol; dimethyl hexynediol; 5,5-dimethylhydantoin; dobutamine; 6-ethoxy-2,2,4-trimethyl-1,2-dihydroquinoline; etretinate; glafenine; hydramethylnon; *p*-hydroxybenzylacetone; iodoform; iproniazid; isophorone; isopropenyl acetate; *N*-isopropyl-*N'*-phenyl-*p*-phenylenediamine; Meldrum's acid; methylbutynol; α-methylheptenone; β-methylheptenone; 2-methylindole; methyl vinyl ketone; phorone; α-picoline; propachlor; propyphenazone; pseudoionone; sethoxydim; sulfadicramide; 2,2,4-trimethyl-1,2-dihydroquinoline, polymeric

Uses: essential oil extraction solvent; alcohol group protection reagent; solvent (acetylene storage, varnish, lacquers, printing inks, adhesives, cellulose resins)

acetone cyanohydrin

ACH; α-hydroxyisobutyronitrile; 2-hydroxy-2-methylpropanenitrile; [75-86-5]

$C_4H_7N_1O_1$. M: 85.11. Colourless liquid. BP: 82°C. FP: -19°C. d: 0.93 kg/l (20°C). Miscible with water and most organic solvents.

Production:
- acetone + hydrogen cyanide (cyanohydrin formation)

Derivatives: 2,2'-azobisisobutyronitrile; cyanazine; α,α-dimethyl-α-hydroxyacetophenone; methacrylamide sulphate; trimethadione

acetone-1,3-dicarboxylic acid

[542-05-2]

$C_5H_6O_5$. M: 146.09. White, crystalline powder. MP: 135°C with decomposition. Soluble in water and alc-

ohol. Insoluble in chlorinated and aromatic solvents.
Production:
* carbon disulphide + ethyl acetate (thiocarbonyl-ation/hydrolysis)
* methyl γ-chloroacetoacetate + hydrogen cyanide (cyanidation/hydrolysis)

Derivatives: tolmetin

acetone-diphenylamine condensates
ADPA
Mixed product containing quinoline and aromatic amine derivatives.
Production:
* diphenylamine + acetone (carbonyl condensation)

Uses: antioxidant (rubber)

acetonitrile
methyl cyanide; [75-05-8]

CH₃CN

$C_2H_3N_1$. M: 41.05. Colourless liquid with an ethereal odour. BP: 81°C. MP: -45°C. d: 0.79 kg/l (15°C). Miscible with water, oxygenated and chlorinated solvents. Immiscible with aliphatic hydrocarbons.
Production:
* propylene + ammonia (ammoxidation; byproduct of acrylonitrile production)

Derivatives:
acetamidine hydrochloride; acetoguanamine; amantadine; β-aminocrotononitrile; *O,N*-bis(trimethylsilyl)acetamide; 2,4-dihydroxyacetophenone; 2,6-dihydroxyacetophenone; geranonitrile; isoxaben; malononitrile; sulfaphenazole; triethyl orthoacetate; trimethyl orthoacetate
Uses: selective solvent (butadiene extraction); speciality solvent

acetonylacetone
2,5-hexanedione; hexane-2,5-dione; [110-13-4]

$C_6H_{10}O_2$. M: 114.15. Colourless liquid. BP: 190–192°C. MP: -9°C. d: 0.97 kg/l (20°C). Miscible with water and oxygenated solvents.
Production:
* methyl acetoacetate (oxidative coupling/decarboxylation)

Derivatives: glisoxepide; pyrvinium pamoate

p-**acetonylanisole** *See:* *p*-methoxyphenylacetone

acetonylbenzene *See:* phenylacetone

acetophenetidine *See:* phenacetin

acetophenone
acetylbenzene; [98-86-2]

$C_8H_8O_1$. M: 120.15. Colourless liquid with a characteristic odour. MP: 19°C. Slightly soluble in water. Soluble in organic solvents. Flash point: 82°C (OC).
Production:
* cumene hydroperoxide (acid-catalysed hydrolysis; byproduct of phenol/acetone production)

Derivatives: α-chloroacetophenone; dibenzoylmethane; α,4-dichloroacetophenone; 2,4-dichloroacetophenone; 3,5-dihydroxyacetophenone; doxylamine; ethyl methylphenylglycidate; fendiline; *m*-hydroxyacetophenone; mesuximide; D-α-phenylethylamine; 2-phenylindole; sodium 4,4'-bis(4-phenyl-1,2,3-triazol-2-yl)stilbene-2,2'-disulphonate; stearoylbenzoylmethane; tilidine; 2,4,5-trichloroacetophenone
Uses: fragrance ingredient (detergent, technical products)

p-**acetotoluene** *See:* *p*-methylacetophenone

N-(2-acetoxyethyl)-N-(2-cyanoethyl)aniline
3-(*N*-2-acetoxyethylanilino)propionitrile; 3-[(2-acetoxyethyl)phenylamino]propionitrile; [22031-33-0]

$C_{13}H_{16}N_2O_2$. M: 232.28. Liquid. BP: 202–258°C (4.0 kPa).
Production:
* acetic acid + hydroxyethylaniline + acrylonitrile (acetylation/cyanoethylation)

Derivatives: Disperse Orange 30

acetylacetone
pentan-2,4-dione; 2,4-pentanedione; ACAC; [123-54-6]

$C_5H_8O_2$. M: 100.11. Colourless or yellowish liquid. MP: -23°C. BP: 139°C. d: 0.97 kg/l (20°C).
Production:
* isopropenyl acetate (rearrangement)

Derivatives: acetylacetone peroxide; 2-amino-4,6-dimethylpyrimidine; cobalt acetylacetonate; ferric acetylacetonate; nickel acetylacetonate; sulfamethazine
Uses: extraction solvent (mineral processing); metal deactivator (lubricants, fuel)

acetylacetone peroxide
2,4-pentanedione peroxide; Lupersol 224 (Elf-Atochem); Triganox 40 (Akzo)
Mixed product containing α-hydroxy- and α-peroxyhydroperoxides. Commercial grades have 4% active oxygen.

Production:
• acetylacetone + hydrogen peroxide (peroxidation)
Uses: unsaturated polyester resin crosslinking agent

***o*-acetylaniline** *See: o*-aminoacetophenone

***p*-acetylaniline** *See: p*-aminoacetophenone

4-acetylanisole *See:* 4-methoxyacetophenone

4-acetylbiphenyl
4′-phenylacetophenone; [92-91-1]

$$CH_3C(=O)-C_6H_4-C_6H_5$$

$C_{14}H_{12}O_1$. M: 196.25. Solid. MP: 117–119°C. BP: 325°C. Insoluble in water. Soluble in oxygenated solvents.
Production:
• biphenyl + acetic anhydride (Friedel-Crafts acylation)
Derivatives: biphenyl-4-carboxylic acid; bromadiolone

acetyl chloride
[75-36-5]

$$CH_3COCl$$

$C_2H_3Cl_1O_1$. M: 78.49. Colourless liquid with a pungent odour. BP: 52°C. MP: -113°C. d: 1.11 kg/l (20°C). Fumes in moist air. Hydrolysed by water and alcohol. Soluble in oxygenated, chlorinated and aromatic solvents. Acetyl chloride is often produced *in situ* by reaction of acetic anhydride with hydrochloric acid.
Production:
• sodium acetate + sulphur dioxide, pure + chlorine (acid chloride formation)
• acetic acid + benzotrichloride (acid chloride formation; coproduced with benzoyl chloride)
Derivatives:
4-acetyl-1,1-dimethyl-6-*t*-butylindane; 6-acetyl-1,1,2,-3,3,5-hexamethylindane; 6-acetyl-1,1,2,4,4,7-hexamethyltetralin; *o*-aminoacetophenone; *p*-aminoacetophenone; 2-amino-5-methyl-1,3,4-thiadiazole; *t*-butyl peroxyacetate; fenfluramine; flurbiprofen; fluridone; ibuprofen; methyl 3-amino-4-methylthiophene-2-carboxylate; methyl β-naphthyl ketone; naproxen
Uses:
esterification/acid chlorination catalyst

acetylcysteine
N-acetyl-L-cysteine; L-2-acetamido-3-mercaptopropionic acid

$$HSCH_2-\overset{\overset{\displaystyle NHC(=O)CH_3}{|}}{\underset{\underset{\displaystyle H}{|}}{C}}-COOH$$

$C_5H_9N_1O_3S_1$. M: 163.19.

Production:
• L-cysteine + acetic anhydride (amide formation)
Uses: mucolytic/secretolytic drug

4-acetyl-1,1-dimethyl-6-*t*-butylindane
Celestolide (IFF); Crysolide (Givaudan-Roure); [13171-00-1]

$C_{17}H_{24}O_1$. M: 244.38. Solid with a musk-like odour. MP: 77°C.
Production:
• *t*-butylbenzene + isoprene + acetyl chloride (acid-catalysed cyclisation/Friedel-Crafts acylation)
Uses: fragrance ingredient

acetylene
ethyne; [74-86-2]

$$HC\equiv CH$$

C_2H_2. M: 26.04. Colourless gas with an unpleasant odour. Solid sublimes at temperatures above -81°C. Relative density: 0.90 (gas, air=1). Slightly soluble in water. Supplied for welding purposes in cylinders as a solution in acetone or DMF held in a porous calcium silicate matrix. For other purposes the product is used *in situ*.
Production:
• calcium carbide (hydrolysis)
• natural gas + *n*-butane (Hüls electric arc process; coproduced with ethylene)
• natural gas + oxygen (BASF partial combustion process; coproduced with synthesis gas)
• natural gas + oxygen (SBA process; coproduced with synthesis gas)
• natural gas/naphtha, heavy + oxygen (Montecatini autothermic process; coproduced with synthesis gas)
• naphtha, heavy/gasoline, natural/gasoline, dearomatised (steam cracking; byproduct of ethylene/propylene/C_4-stream, steam-cracked/gasoline, pyrolysis/pyrolysis tar production)
• gas oil, light (steam cracking; byproduct of ethylene/propylene/C_4-stream, steam-cracked/gasoline, pyrolysis/pyrolysis tar production)
Derivatives:
acetaldehyde; acetylene black; acrylic acid; bis(aminomethyl)norbornane; buprenorphine; 2-*s*-butyl-1-vinylcyclohexyl acetate; *n*-butyl vinyl ether; 1,4-butynediol; 3-butyn-2-ol; β-carotene; 2-chloro-3-hexyne; chloroprene; 5-cyclohexadecen-1-one; dehydrolinalool; C_{10} dialdehyde; dichloromethylvinylsilane; dimethyl hexyne-

diol; dimethyl hexynol; dimethyl octynediol; empenthrin; ethyl octynol; ethyl vinyl ether; ethynyl cyclohexanol; ethynylestradiol; 3-hexenol; 2,5-hexynediol; isobutyl vinyl ether; mestranol; 3-methoxyestra-2,5-diene-17-ol; methylbutynol; methyl 2-nonynoate; methyl 2-octynoate; methyl pentenynol; methylpentynol; *N*-methyl-*N*-vinylacetamide; methyl vinyl ether; nerolidol; norethisterone; norgestrel; octadecyl vinyl ether; 1-octen-3-ol; phytol; sodium vinyl sulphonate; spironolactone; tetrabromoethane; tetramethyl decynediol; trichloroethylene; vinyl acetate; vinyl bromide; *N*-vinylcarbazole; vinyl chloride; vinyl fluoride; *N*-vinylimidazole; vinyl neodecanoate; vinyl propionate; *N*-vinyl-2-pyrrolidone; vinyltrichlorosilane; vitamin A
Uses: welding gas

acetylene black
carbon black; [1333-86-4]
Black solid. Particles are platelets 40 nm in diameter with a specific surface area of ~65 m^2/g.
Production:
• acetylene (Acetylene Black process)
Uses: electrically-conductive filler (rubber heater pads and tapes); antistatic rubber/plastics filler (conveyor belts, drives, shoe soling); battery electrodes

acetylenedicarboxylic acid
butynedioic acid; [142-45-0]

$$HOOCC \equiv CCOOH$$

C$_4$H$_2$O$_4$. M: 114.06.
Production:
• 1,4-butynediol (alcohol oxidation)
Derivatives: fluoromide

acetylene tetrabromide *See:* tetrabromoethane

acetylene urea *See:* glycoluril

N-acetylethanolamine
N-2-hydroxyethylacetamide; [142-26-7]

$$CH_3CNHCH_2CH_2OH$$

C$_4$H$_9$N$_1$O$_2$. M: 103.12. Liquid or solid. FP: 16°C. Decomposes on heating. Miscible with water.
Production:
• acetic acid + monoethanolamine (amide formation)
Uses: chemical intermediate

2-acetylfuran
α-acetylfuran; 2-furyl methyl ketone; [1192-62-7]

C$_6$H$_6$O$_2$. M: 110.12. Solid. MP: 29–30°C. BP: 173°C.

d: 1.10 kg/l (20°C). Insoluble in water. Soluble in oxygenated solvents.
Production:
• furan + acetic anhydride (Friedel-Crafts acylation)
Derivatives:
cefuroxime; furonazide; maltol; 3-methyl-2-cyclopenten-2-ol-1-one

N-acetyl-H acid
8-acetamido-1-hydroxynaphthalene-3,6-disulphonic acid; 1-acetamido-8-naphthol-3,6-disulphonic acid

C$_{12}$H$_{11}$N$_1$O$_8$S$_2$. M: 361.35.
Production:
• acetic anhydride + H acid (amide formation)
Derivatives: Acid Red 1; Acid Red 138; Acid Violet 7; Acid Violet 12; Direct Blue 67; Direct Red 79; Reactive Blue 13; Reactive Violet 5

6-acetyl-1,1,2,3,3,5-hexamethylindane
Phantolide (PFW); [15323-35-0]

C$_{17}$H$_{24}$O$_1$. M: 244.38. Solid with a musk-like odour. MP: 35°C.
Production:
• *p*-cymene + 2-methyl-2-butene + acetyl chloride (cyclisation/Friedel-Crafts acylation)
Uses: fragrance ingredient

6-acetyl-1,1,2,4,4,7-hexamethyltetralin
acetyl hexamethyltetralin; Fixolide (Givaudan-Roure); Tonalide (PFW); [1506-02-1]

C$_{18}$H$_{26}$O$_1$. M: 258.41. Solid with a musk-like odour. MP: 55°C.
Production:
• *p*-cymene + neohexene/2,3-dimethyl-1-butene + acetyl chloride (acid-catalysed cyclisation/Friedel-Crafts acylation)
Uses: fragrance ingredient

acetylmethylcarbinol *See:* acetoin

β-acetylnaphthalene *See:* methyl β-naphthyl ketone

***m*-acetylphenol** *See: m*-hydroxyacetophenone

***o*-acetylphenol** *See: o*-hydroxyacetophenone

***N*-acetyl-*p*-phenylenediamine** *See: p*-aminoacetanilide

2-acetylpyridine
[1122-62-9]

$C_7H_7N_1O_1$. M: 121.15. Liquid. BP: 192°C. Soluble in oxygenated solvents.
Production:
• picolinic acid + acetaldehyde (carbonyl addition/ decarboxylation)
Derivatives: doxylamine

2-acetylresorcinol *See:* 2,6-dihydroxyacetophenone

4-acetylresorcinol *See:* 2,4-dihydroxyacetophenone

acetylsalicylic acid
2-acetoxybenzoic acid; *O*-acetylsalicylic acid; aspirin; [50-78-2]

$C_9H_8O_4$. M: 180.16. White, crystalline solid. MP: 138–140°C. Slightly soluble in water. Soluble in oxygenated and chlorinated solvents.
Production:
• acetic anhydride + salicylic acid (acetylation)
Derivatives: phenprocoumone
Uses: analgesic/antipyretic drug

4-acetylsulphanilamide
[121-61-9]

$C_8H_{10}N_2O_3S_1$. M: 214.24. Crystalline solid. MP: 216°C. Slightly soluble in water and alcohol.
Production:
• 4-acetamidobenzenesulphonyl chloride + ammonia (sulphonamide formation)
Derivatives: sulfacarbamide; sulfacetamide; sulfathiourea; sulphanilamide

***N*-acetylsulphanilyl chloride**
See: 4-acetamidobenzenesulphonyl chloride

2-acetylthiophene
methyl 2-thienyl ketone; [88-15-3]

$C_6H_6O_1S_1$. M: 126.18. Colourless to light brown liquid. BP: 214°C. MP: 10–12°C. d: 1.17 kg/l (22°C). Slightly soluble in water. Miscible with oxygenated solvents.
Production:
• thiophene + acetic anhydride (acetylation)
Derivatives:
2-thenoic acid; 2-thienylacetic acid

acetyl tri-*n*-butyl citrate *See:* tri-*n*-butyl acetylcitrate

acetyl triethyl citrate *See:* triethyl acetylcitrate

4-acetyl-1,1,6-trimethylethanooctahydronaphthalene
4-acetyl-1,1,6-trimethyl-6,8a-ethano-1,2,3,5,6,7,8,8a-octahydronaphthalene; [32388-56-0]

$C_{17}H_{26}O_1$. M: 246.40. Liquid with a woody odour.
Production:
• hiba oil/thujopsene fraction + acetic anhydride (isomerisation/acetylation)
Uses:
fragrance ingredient

ACH *See:* acetone cyanohydrin

aciclovir
Zorvirax (Burroughs Wellcome); [59277-89-3]

$C_8H_{11}N_5O_3$. M: 225.22.
Production:
• benzoic acid + ethylene oxide + chloromethyl chlorosulphate + guanine (epoxidation/chloromethylation/amine formation/saponification)
Uses: virostatic drug

2,4,8-acid *See:* 2-naphthylamine-4,8-disulphonic acid

Acid Black 1
20470 (CI); [1064-48-8]
$C_{22}H_{14}N_6Na_2O_9S_2$. M: 616.50.

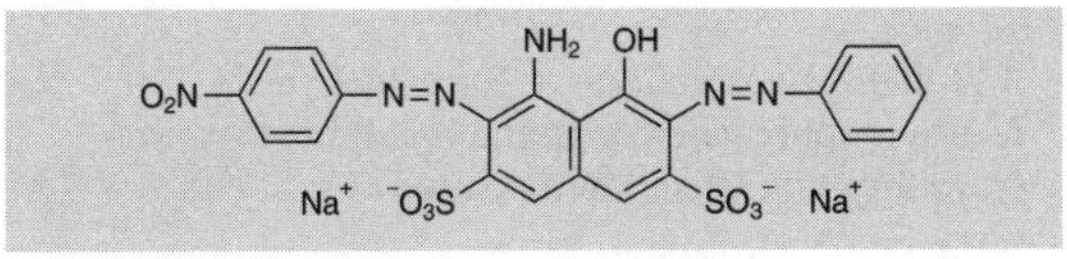

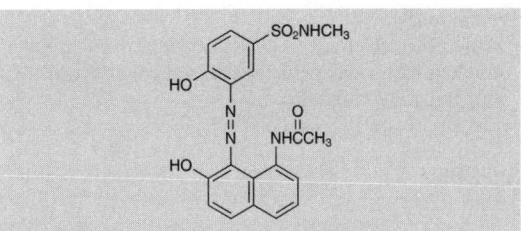

Production:
- *p*-nitroaniline + H acid + aniline (diazotisation/azo coupling/diazotisation/azo coupling)

Derivatives: Acid Green 20

Uses: dye (wool)

Acid Black 52
15711 (CI)

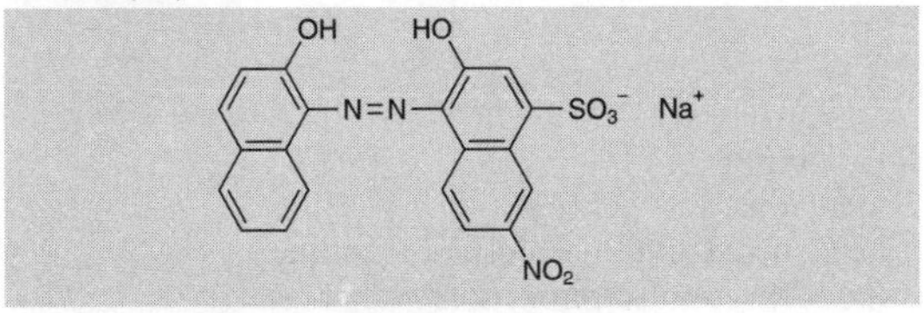

The dye is the 2:1 chromium complex of the displayed structure. $C_{40}H_{20}Cr_1N_6Na_2O_{14}S_2$. M: 970.74.

Production:
- 1-amino-6-nitro-2-naphthol-4-sulphonic acid + β-naphthol + chromium acetate (diazotisation/azo coupling/complex formation)

Uses: dye (wool, silk, polyamide, leather, inks)

Acid Black 58

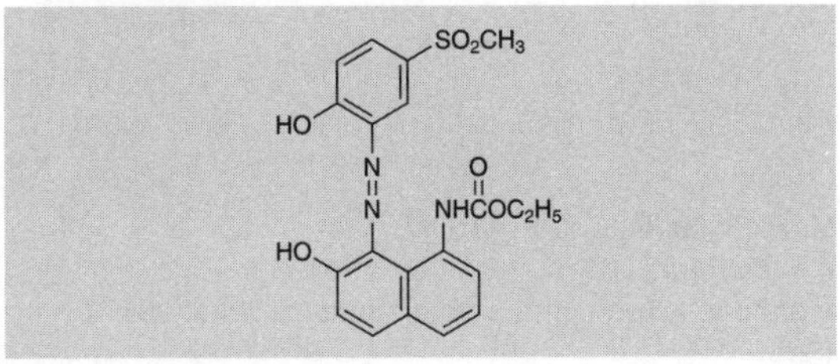

The dye is the 2:1 chromium complex of the displayed structure. $C_{40}H_{34}Cr_1N_6O_{12}S_2$. M: 906.87.

Production:
- 8-amino-2-naphthol + ethyl chloroformate + 2-amino-4-methylsulphonylphenol + chromium acetate (dehydrochlorination/diazotisation/azo coupling/complex formation)

Uses: dye (wool, silk, polyamide, leather)

Acid Black 60
18165 (CI)

The dye is the 2:1 chromium complex of the displayed structure. $C_{38}H_{32}Cr_1N_8O_{10}S_2$. M: 876.84.

Production:
- 1,7-Cleve's acid + acetic anhydride + 2-amino-phenol-4-sulphonic acid + methylamine + chromium sulphate (alkali fusion/amide formation/sulphonamide formation/diazotisation/azo coupling/complex formation)

Uses: dye (wool, silk, polyamide, leather)

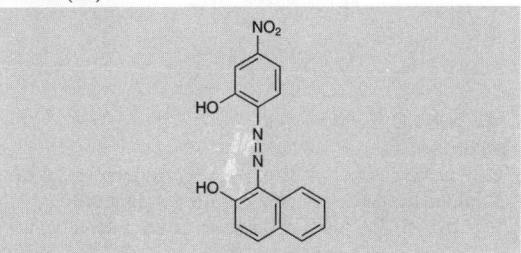

Acid Black 63
12195 (CI)

The dye is the 2:1 chromium complex of the displayed structure. $C_{36}H_{18}Cr_1N_6O_8$. M: 714.57.

Production:
- 2-amino-5-nitrophenol + β-naphthol + chromium acetate (diazotisation/azo coupling/complex formation)

Uses: dye (polyamide fibres)

Acid Blue 1
Food Blue 3 (CI); 42045 (CI)

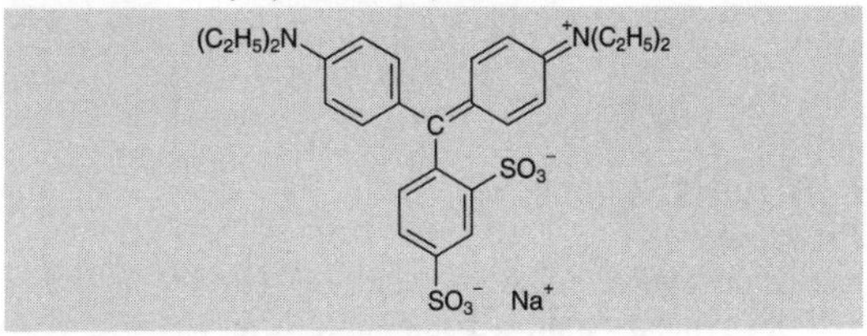

$C_{27}H_{31}N_2Na_1O_6S_2$. M: 566.67.

Production:
- disodium benzaldehyde-2,4-disulphonate + *N,N*-di-ethylaniline (carbonyl condensation/oxidation)

Uses: dye (wool, silk, ink, paper)

Acid Blue 3
patent blue; Food Blue 5 (CI); 42051 (CI); E131 (EC)

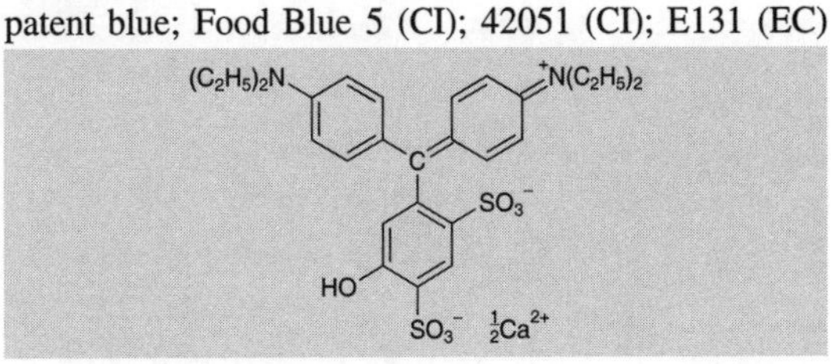

$C_{27}H_{31}Ca_{0.5}N_2O_7S_2$. M: 579.72.

Production:
- *m*-nitrobenzaldehyde + *N,N*-diethylaniline (carbonyl condensation/nitro reduction/diazotisation/hydrolysis/sulphonation/oxidation)

Uses: dye (wool); food colorant

Acid Blue 7
42080 (CI)

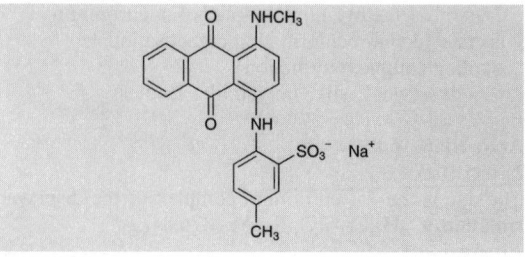

$C_{37}H_{35}N_2Na_1O_6S_2$. M: 690.81.
Production:
- ethylbenzylaniline + disodium benzaldehyde-2,4-di-sulphonate (carbonyl condensation/oxidation)

Uses: dye (wool, silk, polyamide, soap, cosmetics)

Acid Blue 9
Brilliant Blue FCF; Food Blue 2 (CI); Pigment Blue 24 (CI, barium salt); 42090 (CI); 42090:1 (CI, barium salt); 42090:2 (CI, aluminium salt); FD&C Blue No. 1 (FDC); [3844-45-9]

$C_{37}H_{42}N_4O_9S_3$. M: 782.96.
Production:
- benzaldehyde-2-sulphonic acid + *N*-ethyl-*N*-phenylbenzylamine-3-sulphonic acid + ammonium chloride (carbonyl condensation/oxidation/salt formation)

Uses: dye (wool); pigment (printing inks); water-soluble food colorant

Acid Blue 15
42645 (CI)

$C_{42}H_{46}N_3Na_1O_6S_2$. M: 775.96.

Production:
- *N,N*-diethyl-*m*-toluidine + formaldehyde + *N*-ethyl*N*-phenylbenzylamine-3-sulphonic acid (carbonyl condensation/oxidation)

Uses:
dye (wool, silk, leather, shoe cream)

Acid Blue 20
50405 (CI)

R = anilino-.
Production:
- benzenediazonium chloride + aniline (condensation/sulphonation/sodium salt formation)

Uses: acid dye (paper, leather, wax)

Acid Blue 25
62055 (CI)

$C_{20}H_{13}N_2Na_1O_5S_1$. M: 416.37.
Production:
- aniline + bromamine acid (amine formation)
Uses:
dye (wool, silk, polyamide, leather, soap)

Acid Blue 27
61530 (CI)

$C_{22}H_{17}N_2Na_1O_5S_1$. M: 444.43.
Production:
- *p*-toluidine + 1-bromo-4-methylaminoanthraquinone (amine formation/sulphonation)
Uses: dye (wool, polyamide)

Acid Blue 29
20460 (CI)

$C_{22}H_{14}N_6Na_2O_9S_2$. M: 616.49.
Production:
- H acid + *m*-nitroaniline + aniline (diazotisation/azo coupling/diazotisation/azo coupling)

Uses: dye (wool, silk, polyamide, paper)

Acid Blue 40
62125 (CI)

$C_{22}H_{16}N_3Na_1O_6S_1$. M: 473.44.
Production:
- *p*-aminoacetanilide + bromamine acid (amine formation)

Uses: dye (wool, silk, polyamide, paper)

Acid Blue 41
62130 (CI);

$C_{23}H_{18}N_3Na_1O_6S_1$. M: 487.45.
Production:
- *p*-nitroacetanilide + dimethyl sulphate + bromamine acid (methylation/nitro reduction/amine formation)

Uses: dye (wool, silk, polyamide)

Acid Blue 45
63010 (CI)
$C_{14}H_8N_2Na_2O_{10}S_2$. M: 474.32.
Production:
- 1,5-dihydroxyanthraquinone (sulphonation/nitration/nitro reduction)

Derivatives: Disperse Blue 73

Uses: dye (wool, polyamide, plastics)

Acid Blue 62
62045 (CI); [4368-56-3]

$C_{20}H_{18}N_1Na_1O_6S_1$. M: 423.41.
Production:
- cyclohexylamine + bromamine acid (amine formation)

Uses: dye (wool, silk, polyamide)

Acid Blue 74
indigo carmine; indigotine; Food Blue 1 (CI); Pigment Blue 63 (CI, aluminium salt); 73015 (CI); FD&C Blue No. 2 (FDC); E132 (EC); [860-22-0]

$C_{16}H_8N_2Na_2O_8S_2$. M: 466.35.
Production:
- indigo (sulphonation/sodium salt formation)

Uses:
food colorant; pigment (printing inks, pharmaceuticals)

Acid Blue 80
61585 (CI); [4474-24-2]

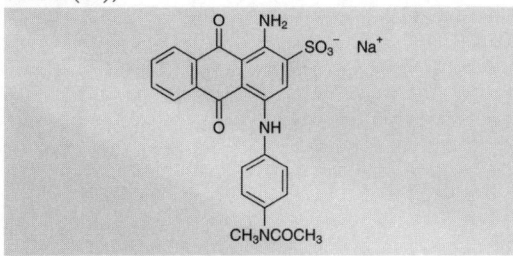

$C_{32}H_{28}N_2Na_2O_8S_2$. M: 678.68.

Production:
• mesidine + quinizarin (amine formation/sulphonation)
Uses:
dye (wool, silk, polyamide)

Acid Blue 92
13390 (CI); [3861-73-2]

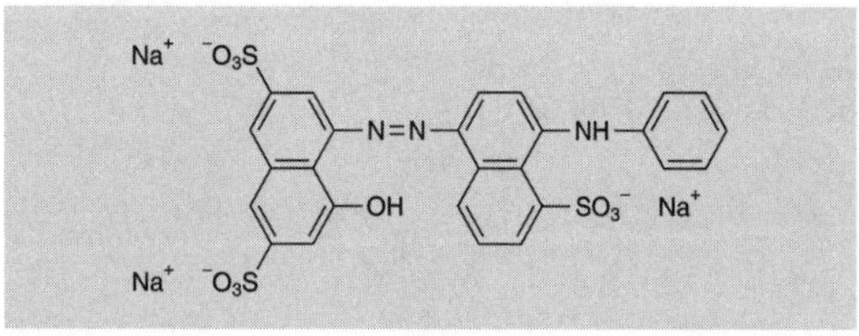

$C_{26}H_{16}N_3Na_3O_{10}S_3$. M: 695.59.
Production:
• H acid + *N*-phenyl-peri acid (diazotisation/azo coupling)
Uses: dye (wool, silk, polyamide)

Acid Blue 93
methyl blue; 42780 (CI)

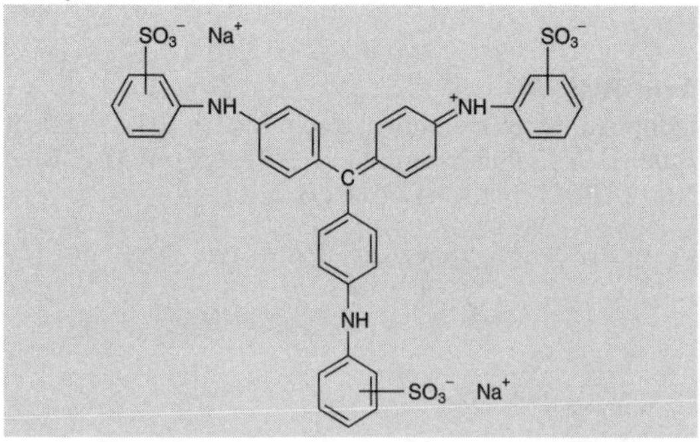

$C_{37}H_{27}N_3Na_2O_9S_3$. M: 799.81.
Production:
• aniline + benzoic acid (condensation/sulphonation)
Uses: dye (wool)

Acid Blue 104
42735 (CI)

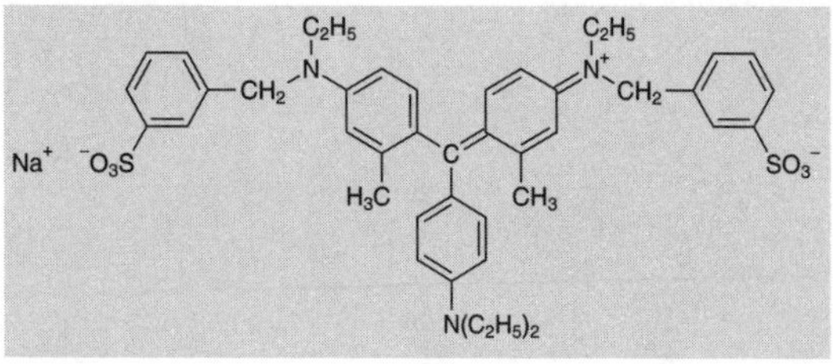

$C_{43}H_{48}N_3Na_1O_6S_2$. M: 789.98.
Production:
• *p*-diethylaminobenzaldehyde + *N*-ethyl-*N*-*m*-tolyl-benzylamine-3-sulphonic acid (carbonyl condensation/oxidation)

Uses:
dye (wool, silk, leather, stains, polish)

Acid Blue 113
26360 (CI); [3351-05-1]

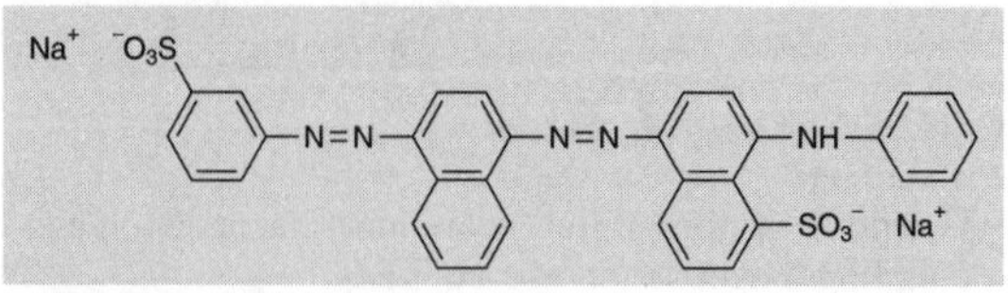

$C_{32}H_{20}N_6Na_2O_6S_2$. M: 694.65.
Production:
• *N*-phenyl-peri acid + 1-naphthylamine + metanilic acid (diazotisation/azo coupling/diazotisation/azo coupling)
Uses:
dye (wool, silk, polyamide, leather)

Acid Blue 118
26410 (CI)

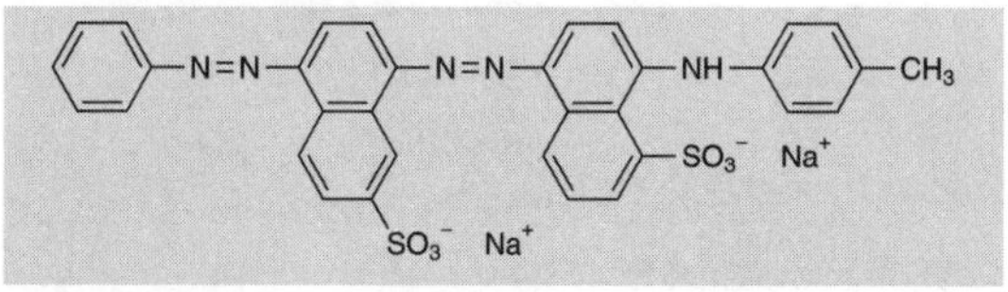

$C_{33}H_{23}N_5Na_2O_6S_2$. M: 695.67.
Production:
• peri acid + *p*-cresol + 1,7-Cleve's acid + aniline (amine formation/diazotisation/azo coupling/ diazotisation/azo coupling)
Uses: dye (wool, silk, leather)

Acid Blue 129
62058 (CI)

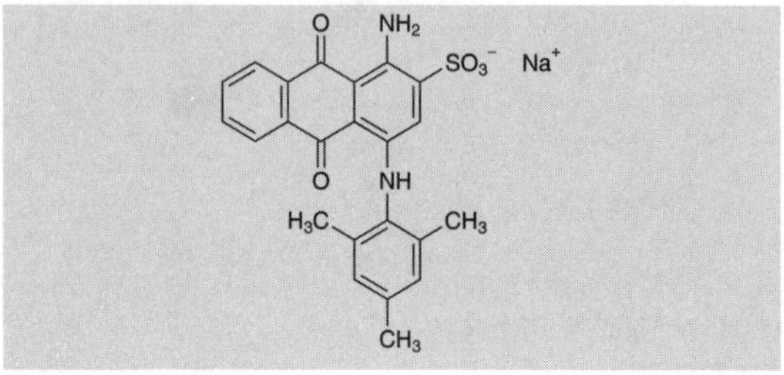

$C_{23}H_{19}N_2Na_1O_5S_1$. M: 458.45.
Production:
• mesidine + bromamine acid (amine formation)
Uses: dye (wool, polyamide)

Acid Blue 138
62075 (CI)
$C_{32}H_{36}N_2Na_2O_8S_2$. M: 686.75.
Production:
• *p*-dodecylaniline + bromamine acid (amine formation/sulphonation)

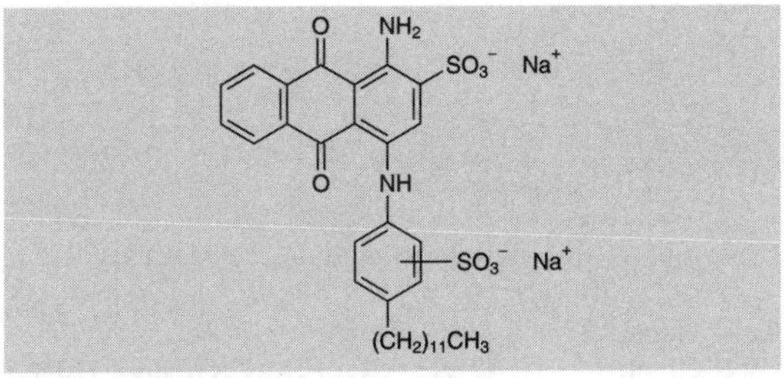

Uses: dye (wool, silk, polyamide)

Acid Blue 145
62070 (CI)

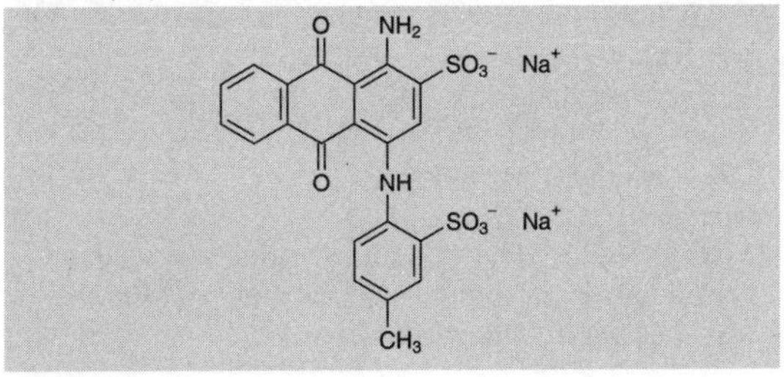

$C_{21}H_{15}N_2Na_2O_8S_2$. M: 533.46.
Production:
• *p*-toluidine + bromamine acid (amine formation/
  sulphonation)
Uses: dye (wool, silk, polyamide)

Acid Blue 158
14880 (CI)

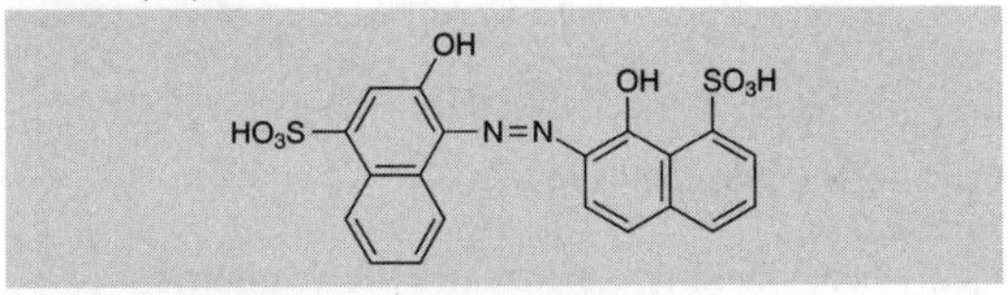

The dye is the 1:1 hydrated chromium complex of the
displayed structure.
Production:
• 1-amino-2-naphthol-4-sulphonic acid + 8-hydroxy-
  naphthalene-1-sulphonic acid + chromium sulphate
  (diazotisation/azo coupling/complex formation)
Uses: dye (wool, silk, polyamide)

Acid Blue 159

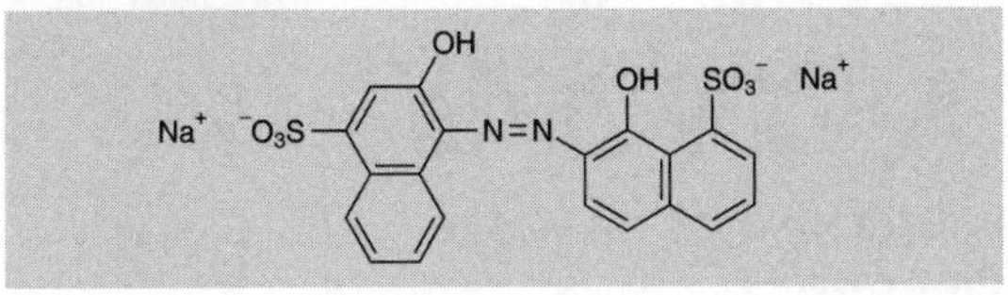

The dye is the 1:1 hydrated chromium complex of the
displayed structure.
Production:
• 1-amino-2-naphthol-4-sulphonic acid + 8-hydroxy-

naphthalene-1-sulphonic acid + chromium sulphate
(diazotisation/azo coupling/complex formation)
Uses: dye (wool)

Acid Blue 213
44512 (CI)

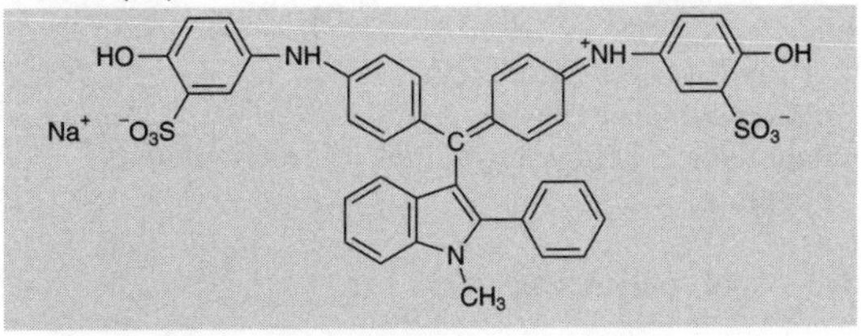

$C_{40}H_{30}N_3Na_1O_8S_2$. M: 767.81.
Production:
• 2-phenylindole + 4,4′-dichlorobenzophenone +
  p-phenetidine (methylation/condensation/
  dehydrochlorination/sulphonation)
Uses:
dye (wool, silk)

Acid Blue 230

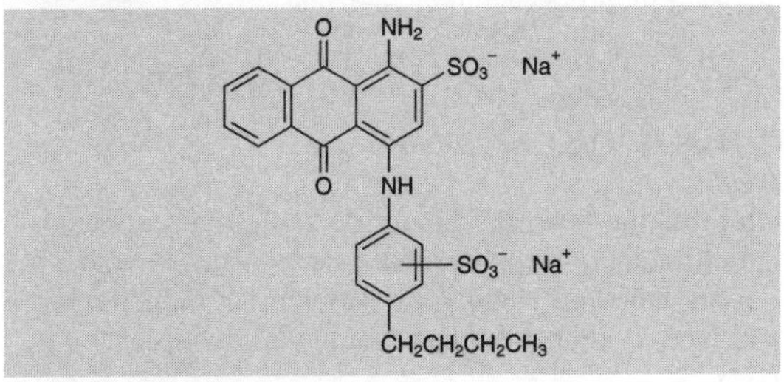

$C_{24}H_{20}N_2Na_2O_8S_2$. M: 574.53.
Production:
• *p*-*n*-butylaniline + bromamine acid (amine
  formation/sulphonation)
Uses:
dye (polyamide, acetate)

Acid Brown 13
10410 (CI)

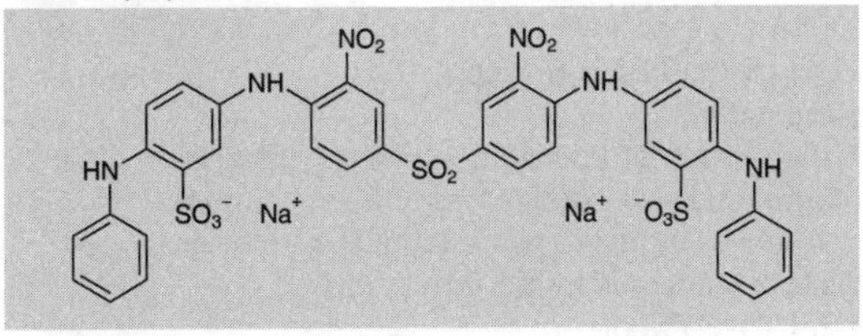

$C_{36}H_{26}N_6Na_2O_{12}S_3$. M: 876.81.
Production:
• *o*-chloronitrobenzene + chlorosulphonic acid +
  4-aminodiphenylamine-2-sulphonic acid (chloro-
  sulphonation/amine formation)
Uses:
dye (wool)

Acid Brown 14
20195 (CI)

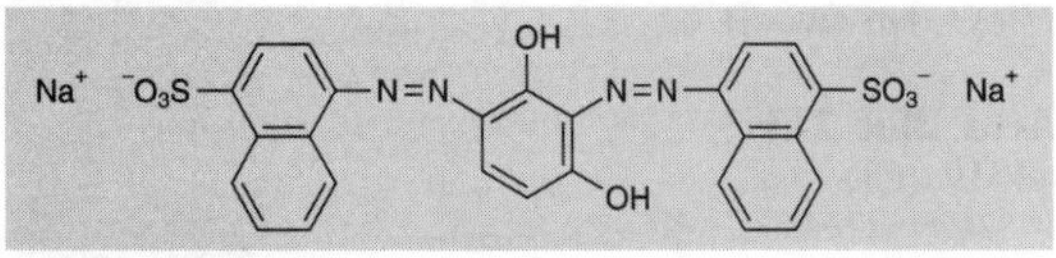

$C_{26}H_{16}N_4Na_2O_8S_2$. M: 622.55.
Production:
- naphthionic acid + resorcinol (diazotisation/azo coupling)

Uses:
dye (wool, polyamide, silk)

Acid Brown 20
17640 (CI); [6369-33-1]

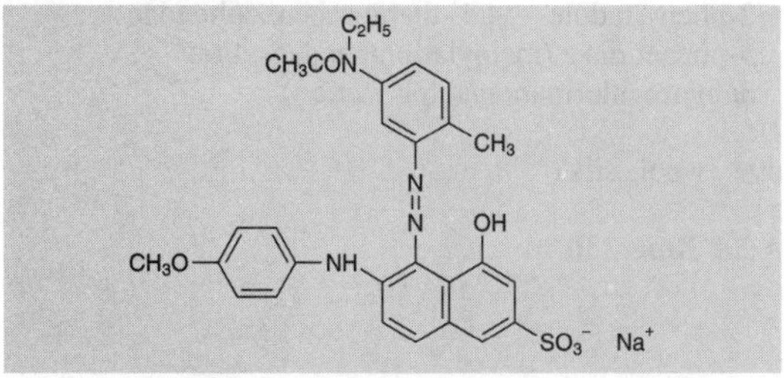

$C_{28}H_{27}N_4Na_1O_6S_1$. M: 570.60.
Production:
- *p*-toluidine + acetic anhydride + diethyl sulphate + hydroquinone monomethyl ether + gamma acid (acetylation/ethylation/nitrosation/nitro reduction/ reductive amination/diazotisation/azo coupling)

Uses:
dye (wool, silk)

Acid Brown 248
10402 (CI)

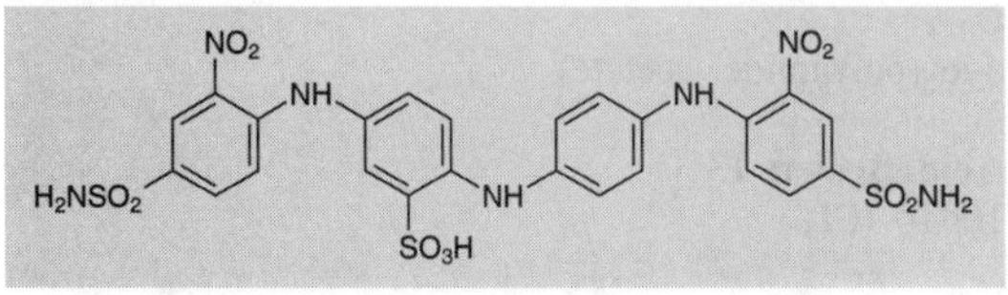

$C_{24}H_{21}N_7O_{11}S_3$. M: 679.66.
Production:
- 4-chloro-3-nitrobenzenesulphonyl chloride + ammonia + 4'-amino-4-nitrodiphenylamine-2-sulphonic acid (sulphonamide formation/ nitro reduction/amine formation)

Uses: dye (wool)

Acid Green 1
10020 (CI); Pigment Green 12 (CI)
$C_{24}H_{15}Fe_1N_3Na_4O_{15}S_3$. M: 829.38.
Production:
- Schaeffer's acid + ferrous sulphate (nitrosation/ complex formation)

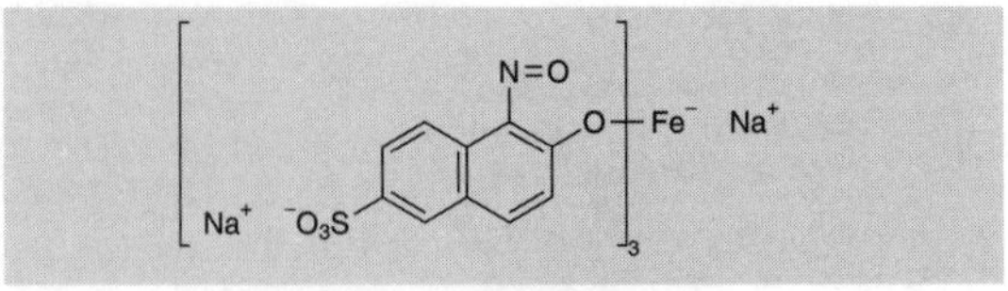

Uses: dye (paper, wool, polyamide, cosmetics)

Acid Green 3
Food Green 1 (CI); 42085 (CI); FD&C Green 1 (FDC)

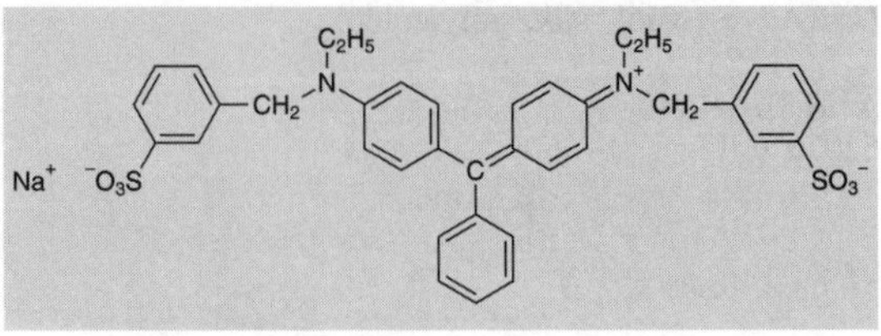

$C_{37}H_{35}N_2Na_1O_6S_2$. M: 690.81.
Production:
- *N*-ethyl-*N*-phenylbenzylamine-3-sulphonic acid + benzaldehyde (carbonyl condensation/oxidation)

Uses: dye (wool, silk, resins)

Acid Green 5
42095 (CI); FD&C Green No. 2 (FDC)

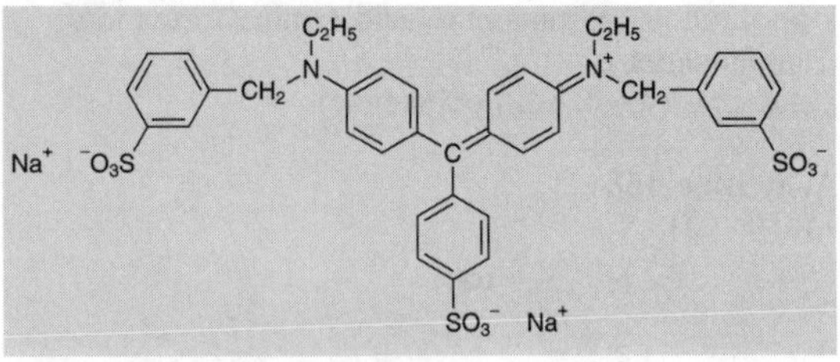

$C_{37}H_{36}N_2Na_2O_9S_3$. M: 794.87.
Production:
- ethylbenzylaniline + benzaldehyde (carbonyl condensation/sulphonation/oxidation)

Uses: dye (wool, silk, polyamide, paper)

Acid Green 9
42100 (CI)

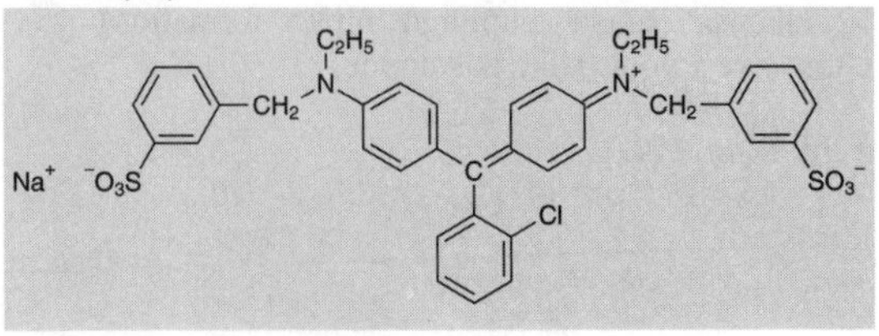

$C_{37}H_{34}Cl_1N_2Na_1O_6S_2$. M: 725.26.
Production:
- *N*-ethyl-*N*-phenylbenzylamine-3-sulphonic acid + *o*-chlorobenzaldehyde (carbonyl condensation/ oxidation)

Uses: dye (wool, silk, polyamide, paper)

Acid Green 16
Naphthalene Green V; 44025 (CI)

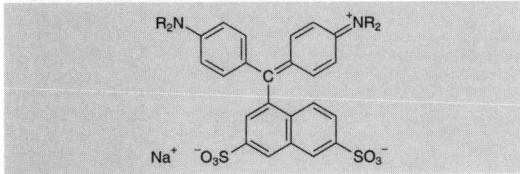

R = methyl, ethyl-.
$C_{27}H_{25}N_2Na_1O_6S_2$. M: 560.62.
Production:
- 4,4′-bis(dimethylamino)benzhydrol + naphthalene-2,7-disulphonic acid (dehydrative coupling)

Uses: dye (wool, silk, polyamide, plastics, paper)

Acid Green 19
Mordant Green 11 (CI); 20440 (CI)

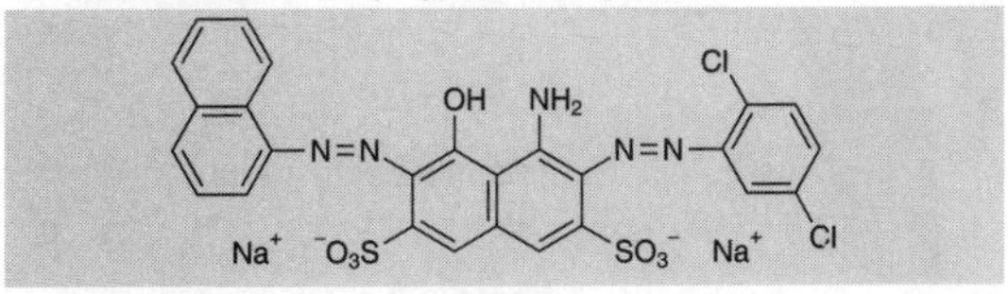

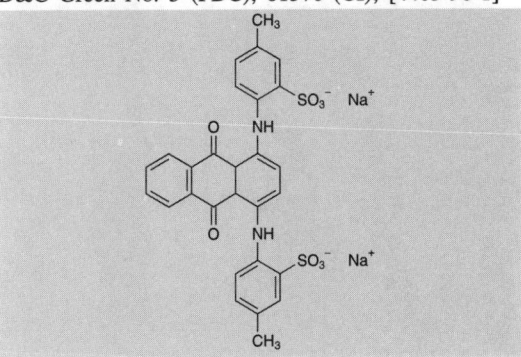

$C_{26}H_{15}Cl_2N_5Na_2O_7S_2$. M: 690.46.
Production:
- 2,5-dichloroaniline + 1-naphthylamine + H acid (diazotisation/azo coupling/diazotisation/azo coupling)

Uses: acid dye (wool/silk)

Acid Green 20
20495 (CI)

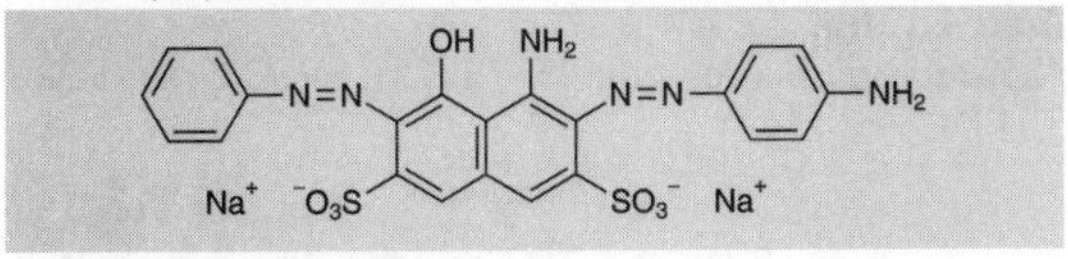

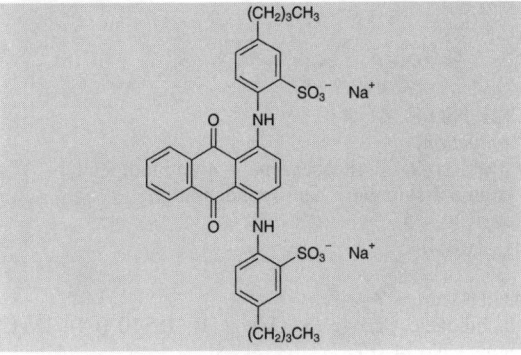

$C_{22}H_{16}N_6Na_2O_7S_2$. M: 586.51.
Production:
- Acid Black 1 (nitro reduction)

Uses: dye (wool, silk, polyamide, leather, paper)

Acid Green 22
42170 (CI)

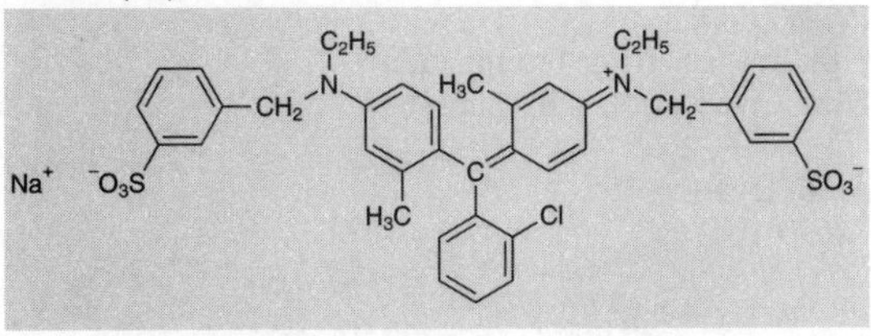

$C_{39}H_{38}Cl_1N_2Na_1O_6S_2$. M: 753.31.
Production:
- N-ethyl-N-m-tolylbenzylamine-3-sulphonic acid + o-chlorobenzaldehyde (condensation/oxidation)

Uses: dye (wool, silk)

Acid Green 25
D&C Green No. 5 (FDC); 61570 (CI); [4403-90-1]

$C_{28}H_{20}N_2Na_2O_8S_2$. M: 622.58.
Production:
- Solvent Green 3 (sulphonation)

Uses: dye (wool, silk, polyamide, paper, stains, soap)

Acid Green 27
61580 (CI)

$C_{34}H_{32}N_2Na_2O_8S_2$. M: 706.74.
Production:
- p-n-butylaniline + quinizarin (amide formation/sulphonation)

Uses: dye (wool)

Acid Green 50
Food Green 4 (CI); 44090 (CI); E142 (EC);

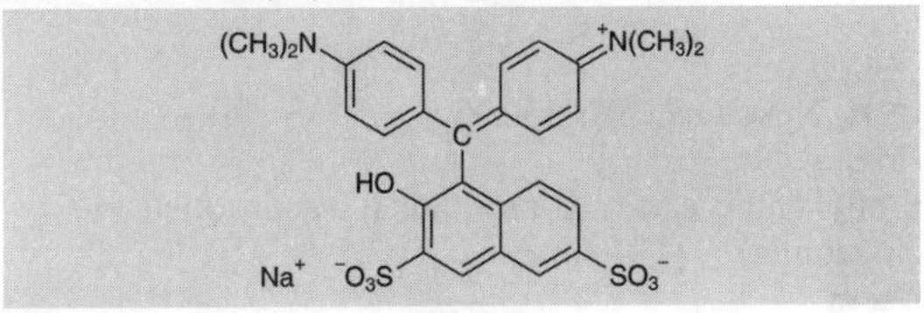

$C_{27}H_{25}N_2Na_1O_7S_2$. M: 576.62.
Production:
- 4,4′-bis(dimethylamino)benzhydrol + R acid (dehydrative coupling)

Uses: dye (wool); food colorant

Acid Green 75

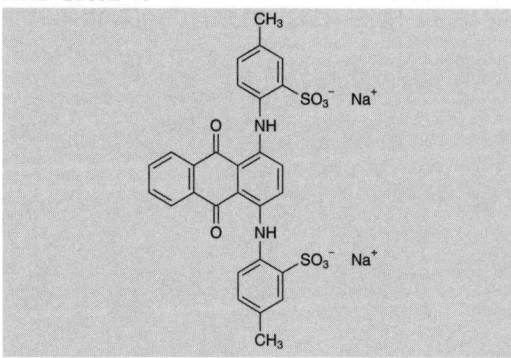

$C_{28}H_{20}N_2Na_2O_8S_2$. M: 622.58.
Production:
• 4B acid + quinizarin (amine formation)
Uses:
dye (wool, polyamide, silk)

Acid Orange 3
10385 (CI); [6373-74-6]

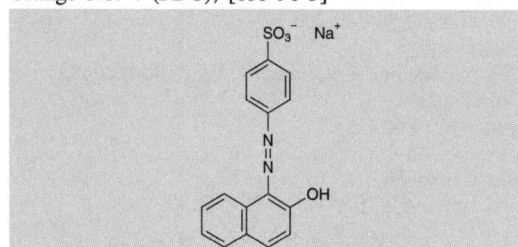

$C_{18}H_{14}N_4O_7S_1$. M: 430.39.
Production:
• 1-chloro-2,4-dinitrobenzene + 4-aminodiphenyl-
amine-2-sulphonic acid (condensation)
Uses:
dye (wool)

Acid Orange 7
Naphthalene Orange G; Orange II; 15510 (CI); D&C
Orange No. 4 (FDC); [633-96-5]

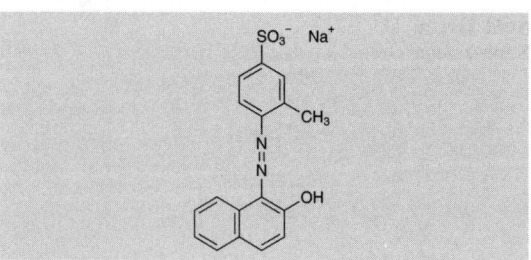

$C_{16}H_{11}N_2Na_1O_4S_1$. M: 350.33.
Production:
• sulphanilic acid + β-naphthol (diazotisation/azo
coupling)
Uses:
dye (wool, silk, polyamide, paper)

Acid Orange 8
15575 (CI)
$C_{17}H_{13}N_2Na_1O_4S_1$. M: 364.35.

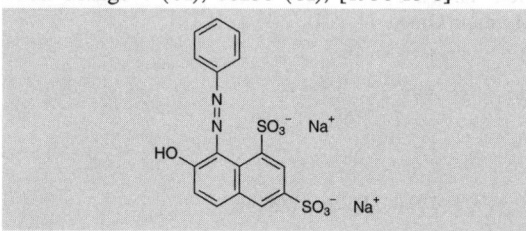

Production:
• 2-aminotoluene-5-sulphonic acid + β-naphthol
(diazotisation/azo coupling)
Uses: dye (wool, silk, polyamide, jute, paper)

Acid Orange 10
Food Orange 4 (CI); 16230 (CI); [1936-15-8]

$C_{16}H_{10}N_2Na_2O_7S_2$. M: 452.37.
Production:
• aniline + G acid (diazotisation/azo coupling)
Uses:
dye (wool, silk, paper, stains, inks)

Acid Orange 11
4′,5′-dibromofluorescein; 45370 (CI); D&C Orange No.
5 (FDC)

$C_{20}H_9Br_2Na_1O_5$. M: 512.08.
Production:
• fluorescein (ring bromination)
Uses: dye (wool, silk, paper)

Acid Orange 19
14690 (CI)

$C_{23}H_{18}N_3Na_1O_6S_2$. M: 519.52.

Production:
- 4-nitrotoluene-2-sulphonic acid + aniline + Nevile-Winther acid (sulphonamide formation/ nitro reduction/diazotisation/azo coupling)

Uses: dye (wool, silk, polyamide)

Acid Orange 20
Orange I; 14600 (CI);

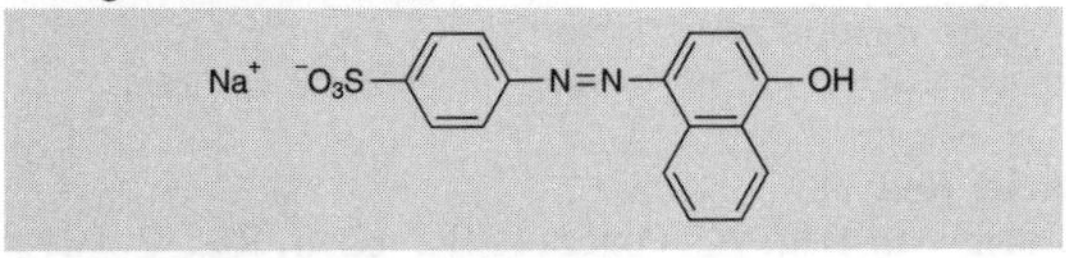

$C_{16}H_{11}N_2Na_1O_4S_1$. M: 350.33.
Production:
- sulphanilic acid + α-naphthol (diazotisation/ azo coupling)

Uses: dye (wool)

Acid Orange 24
20170 (CI); D&C Brown No. 1 (FDC); [1320-07-6]

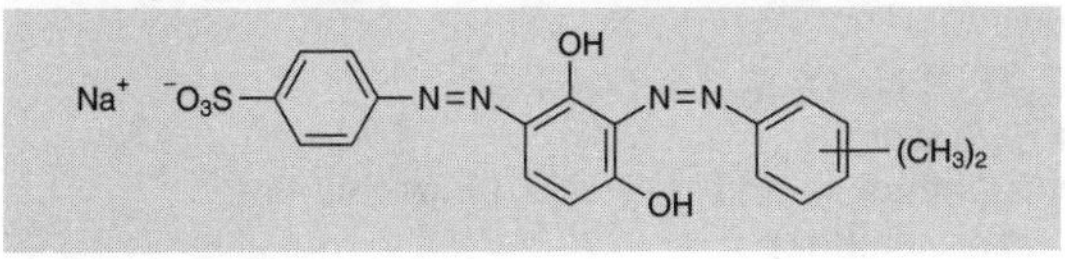

$C_{20}H_{17}N_4Na_1O_5$. M: 416.37.
Production:
- sulphanilic acid + resorcinol + 2,4-xylidine (diazotisation/azo coupling/diazotisation/azo coupling)

Uses: dye (wool, silk, polyamide, shoe cream)

Acid Orange 51
26550 (CI); [8003-88-1]

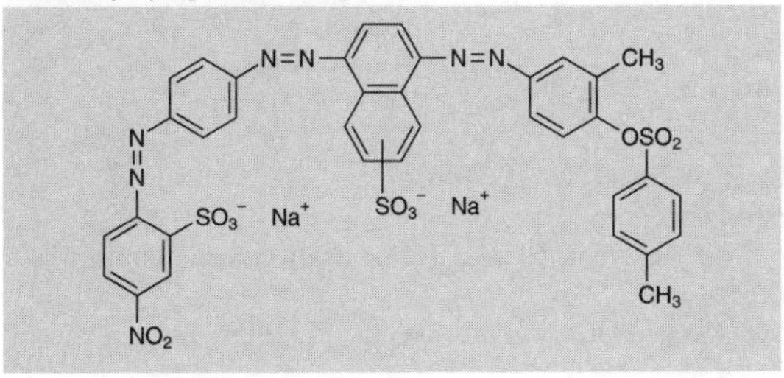

$C_{36}H_{25}N_7Na_2O_{11}S_3$. M: 873.81.
Production:
- o-cresol + p-toluenesulphonyl chloride + 4'-amino-4-nitrodiphenylamine-2-sulphonic acid + Cleve's acid, mixed (diazotisation/dehydrochlorination/azo coupling/diazotisation/azo coupling)

Uses: dye (wool, silk, polyamide, paper, resins)

Acid Orange 60
$C_{16}H_{15}N_5O_4S_1$. M: 373.39.
Production:
- 2-aminophenol-4-sulphonamide + 3-methyl-1-phenyl-5-pyrazolone (diazotisation/azo coupling)

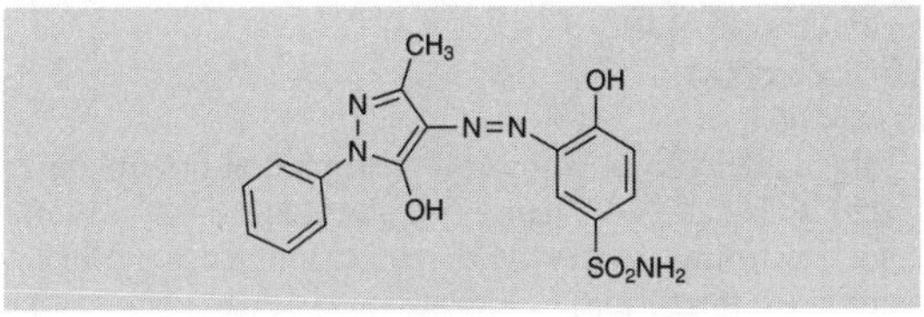

Uses: dye (wool, polyamide)

Acid Orange 67
14172 (CI)

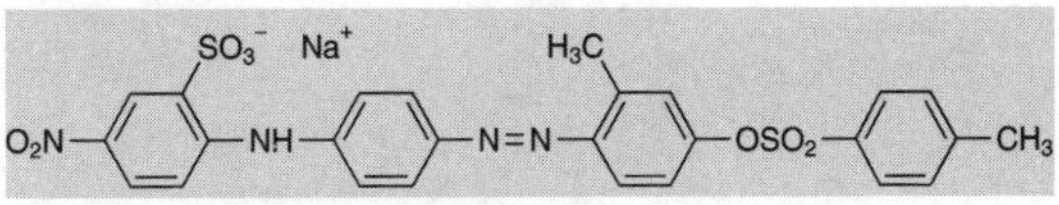

$C_{26}H_{21}N_4Na_1O_8S_2$. M: 604.60.
Production:
- 4'-amino-4-nitrodiphenylamine-2-sulphonic acid + m-cresol + p-toluenesulphonyl chloride (diazotisation/azo coupling/dehydrochlorination)

Uses: dye (wool, silk, polyamide)

Acid Orange 74
Solvent Orange 5 (CI, acid form); 18745 (CI); 18745:1 (CI, acid form)

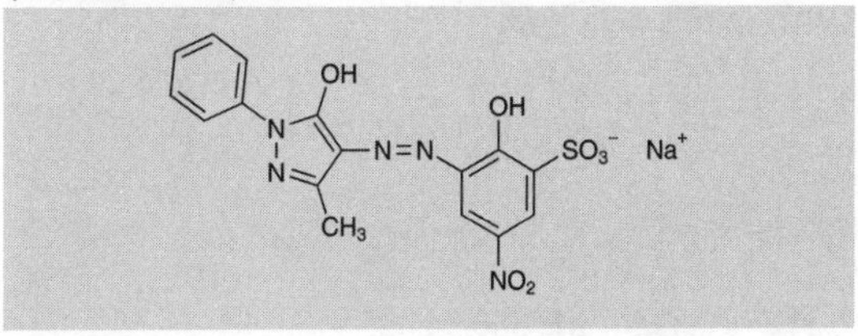

The dye is the 2:1 chromium complex of the displayed structure. $C_{64}H_{20}Cr_1N_{10}Na_2O_{14}S_2$. M: 1315.02.
Production:
- 2-amino-4-nitrophenol-6-sulphonic acid + 3-methyl-1-phenyl-5-pyrazolone + chromium acetate (diazotisation/azo coupling/complex formation)

Uses: dye (wool, polyamide, silk)

Acid Orange 92
12714 (CI); Solvent Orange 42 (CI)

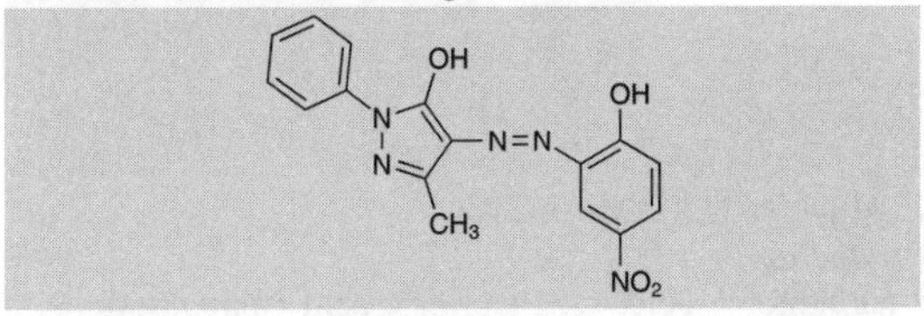

The dye is the 2:1 chromium complex of the displayed structure. $C_{32}H_{22}Cr_1N_{10}O_8$. M: 1457.21.
Production:
- 2-amino-4-nitrophenol + 3-methyl-1-phenyl-5-pyrazolone + chromium acetate (diazotisation/ azo coupling/complex formation)

Uses: dye (polyamide fibres)

Acid Orange 148
Mixed product.
Production:
• salicylaldehyde + 2-amino-4-nitrophenol-6-sulphonic acid + 3-methyl-1-phenyl-5-pyrazolone + chromium acetate (imine formation/diazotization/azo coupling/complex formation)
Uses: dye (wool, polyamide)

Acid Red 1
Red 2G; Food Red 10 (CI); 18050 (CI); E128 (EC);

$C_{18}H_{13}N_3Na_2O_8S_2$. M: 509.42.
Production:
• benzenediazonium chloride + *N*-acetyl-H acid (azo coupling)
Uses:
dye (polyamide); food colorant

Acid Red 4
14710 (CI); [5858-39-9]

$C_{17}H_{13}N_2Na_1O_5S_1$. M: 380.34.
Production:
• *o*-anisidine + Nevile-Winther acid (diazotisation/azo coupling)
Uses: dye (wool, paper)

Acid Red 13
Food Red 4 (CI); 16045 (CI); [2302-96-7]

$C_{20}H_{12}N_2Na_2O_7S_2$. M: 502.43.
Production:
• naphthionic acid + Schaeffer's acid (diazotisation/azo coupling)
Uses: dye (wool, leather, cosmetics)

Acid Red 14
Food Red 3 (CI); Mordant Blue 79 (CI); azorubine; carmoisine; 14720 (CI); E122 (EC)
$C_{20}H_{12}N_2Na_2O_7S_2$. M: 502.43.

Production:
• naphthionic acid + Nevile-Winther acid (diazotisation/azo coupling)
Uses: dye (wool, polyamide, silk); food colorant

Acid Red 18
Cochineal Red A; Ponceau 4R; Food Red 7 (CI); 16255 (CI); E124 (EC)

$C_{20}H_{11}N_2Na_3O_{10}S_3$. M: 604.47.
Production:
• naphthionic acid + G acid (diazotisation/azo coupling)
Uses: dye (wool, polyamide, silk); food colorant

Acid Red 26
Food Red 5 (CI); 16150 (CI)

$C_{18}H_{14}N_2Na_2O_7S_2$. M: 480.42.
Production:
• 2,4-xylidine + R acid (diazotisation/azo coupling)
Uses:
dye (wool, silk, polyamide, paper, inks)

Acid Red 27
amaranth; Food Red 9 (CI); Pigment Red 193 (CI, aluminium salt); 16185 (CI); 16185:1 (CI, aluminium salt); E123 (EC); FD&C Red No. 2 (FDC); [915-67-3]

$C_{20}H_{11}N_2Na_3O_{10}S_3$. M: 604.47.

Production:
• naphthionic acid + R acid (diazotisation/azo coupling)
Uses:
dye (wool, silk); food colorant; pigment (printing inks)

Acid Red 32
17065 (CI); [6360-10-7]

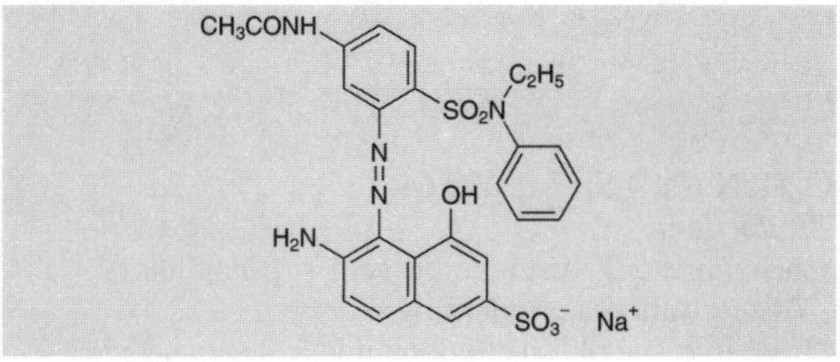

$C_{26}H_{24}N_5Na_1O_7S_2$. M: 605.62.
Production:
• p-aminoacetanilide + N-ethylaniline + gamma acid (chlorosulphonation/sulphonamide formation/diazotisation/azo coupling)
Uses: dye (wool, silk, polyamide)

Acid Red 34
17030 (CI)

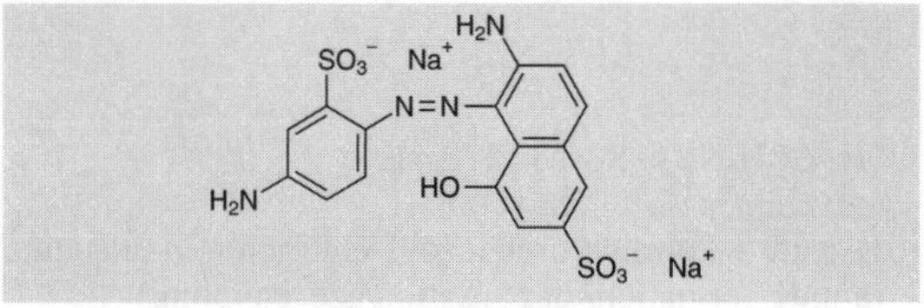

$C_{16}H_{12}N_4Na_2O_7S_2$. M: 482.40.
Production:
• Acid Violet 1 (nitro reduction)
Uses: dye (wool, silk, polyamide)

Acid Red 37
17045 (CI); [6360-07-2]

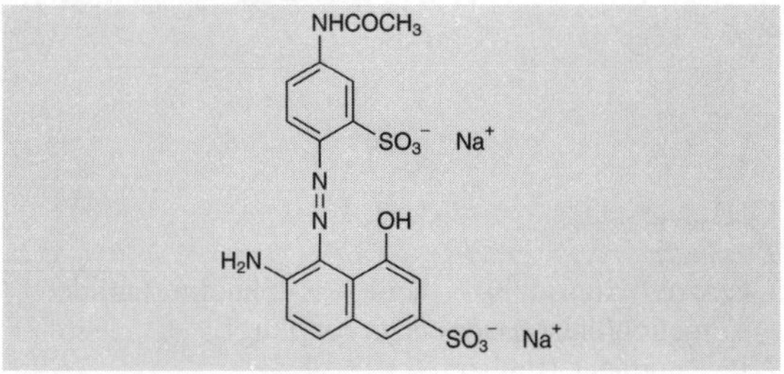

$C_{18}H_{14}N_4Na_2O_8S_2$. M: 524.44.
Production:
• p-aminoacetanilide + gamma acid (sulphonation/diazotisation/azo coupling)
Uses: dye (wool, silk, polyamide, paper, soap, lacquer)

Acid Red 42
17070 (CI); [6245-60-9]

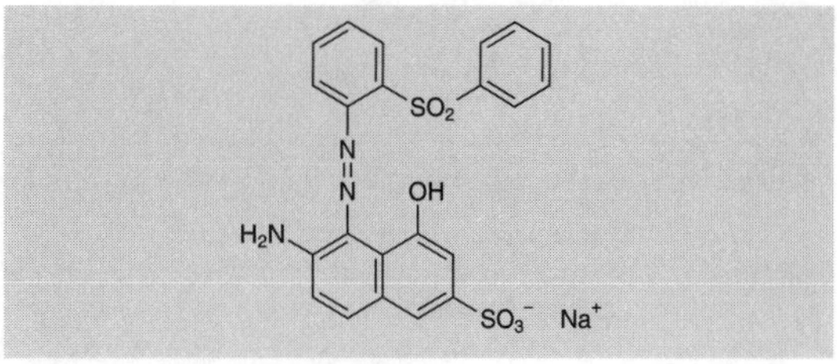

$C_{22}H_{16}N_3Na_1O_6S_2$. M: 505.50.
Production:
• aniline + benzenesulphonyl chloride + gamma acid (sulphonation/diazotisation/azo coupling)
Uses: dye (wool, silk, polyamide)

Acid Red 51
erythrosine; Food Red 14 (CI); Pigment Red 172 (CI, aluminium salt); Solvent Red 140 (CI, free acid); 45430 (CI); 45430:1 (CI, aluminium salt); 45430:2 (CI, free acid); E127 (EC); FD&C Red No. 3 (FDC); [16423-68-0]

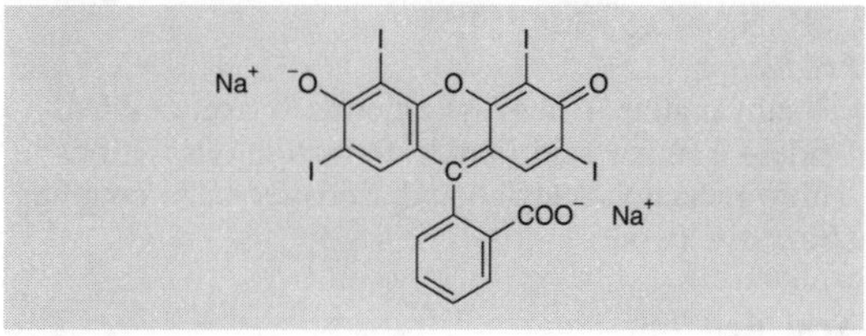

$C_{20}H_6I_4Na_2O_5$. M: 879.86.
Production:
• fluorescein (ring iodination/sodium salt formation)
Uses:
food colorant; photographic sensitising agent; pigment (printing inks)

Acid Red 52
45100 (CI); [3520-42-1]

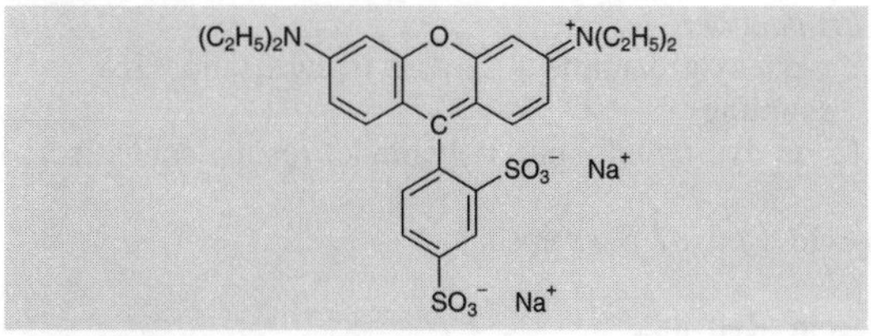

$C_{27}H_{29}N_2Na_2O_8S_2$. M: 619.64.
Production:
• m-diethylaminophenol + disodium benzaldehyde-2,4-disulphonate (carbonyl condensation/ether formation/oxidation)
Uses:
dye (wool, silk, polyamide, paper)

Acid Red 57
17053 (CI)
$C_{24}H_{21}N_4Na_1O_6S_2$. M: 548.57.

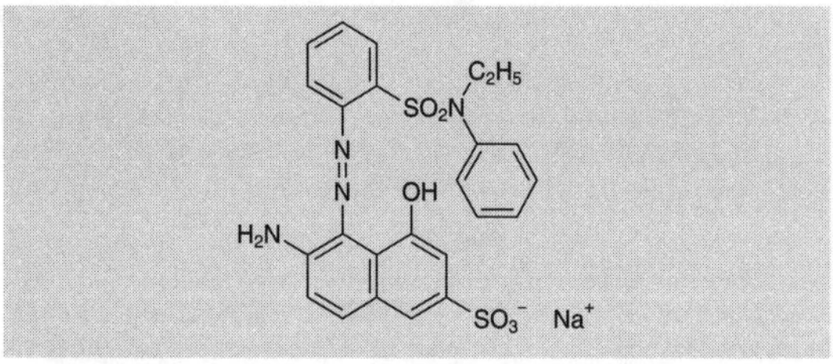

Production:
- orthanilic acid + gamma acid + *N*-ethylaniline
(diazotisation/azo coupling/sulphonamide formation)

Uses: dye (wool, polyamide)

Acid Red 68
17920 (CI); [6369-40-0]

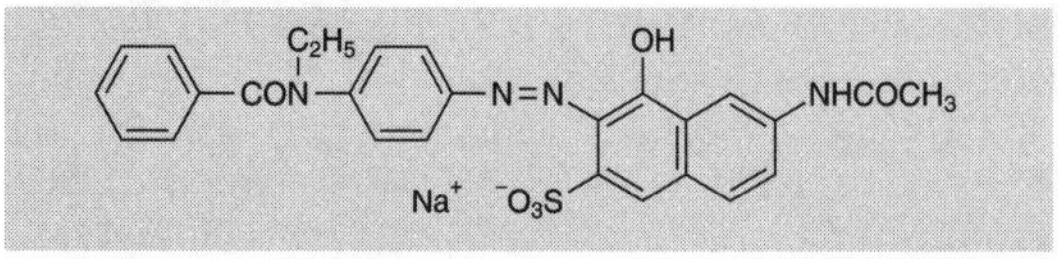

$C_{27}H_{23}N_4Na_1O_6S_1$. M: 554.55.
Production:
- *N*-ethylaniline + benzoyl chloride + acetic anhydride + gamma acid (amide formation/nitrosation/nitro reduction/acetylation/diazotisation/azo coupling)

Uses: dye (wool)

Acid Red 73
27290 (CI)

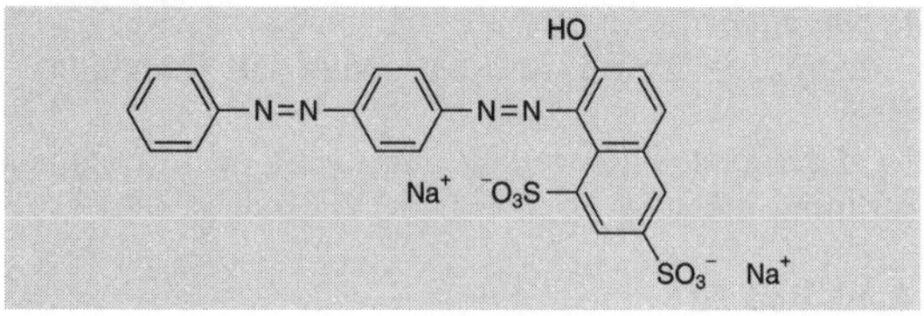

$C_{22}H_{14}N_4Na_2O_7S_2$. M: 556.48.
Production:
- *p*-phenylazoaniline + G acid (diazotisation/azo coupling)

Uses: dye (wool, sulk, polyamide, resins, stains, soap)

Acid Red 87 *See:* eosine

Acid Red 88
15620 (CI); [1658-56-6]

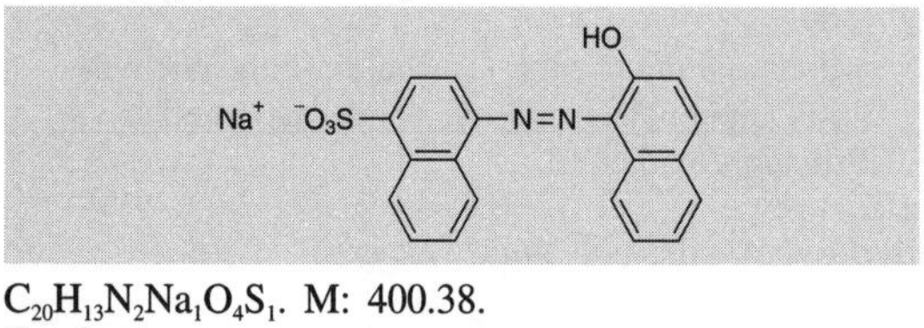

$C_{20}H_{13}N_2Na_1O_4S_1$. M: 400.38.
Production:
- naphthionic acid + β-naphthol (diazotisation/azo coupling)

Uses:
dye (wool, silk, polyamide, paper, jute, stains, soap)

Acid Red 97
22890 (CI); [10169-02-5]

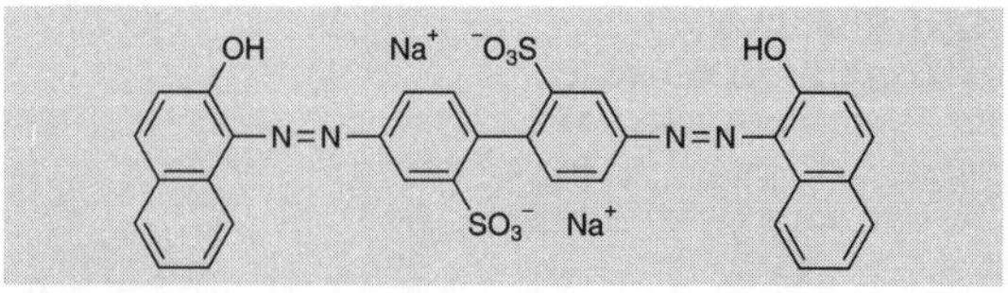

$C_{32}H_{20}N_4Na_2O_8S_2$. M: 698.64.
Production:
- benzidine-2,2'-disulphonic acid + β-naphthol (diazotisation/azo coupling)

Uses: dye (wool, silk, polyamide, jute, paper)

Acid Red 107
Pigment Red 67 (CI, barium salt); 18025 (CI); 18025:1 (CI, barium salt);

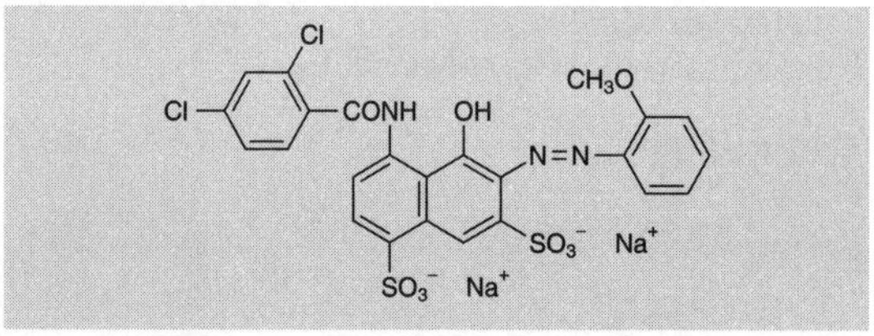

$C_{24}H_{15}Cl_2N_3Na_2O_9S_2$. M: 670.41.
Production:
- K acid + 2,4-dichlorobenzoyl chloride + *o*-anisidine (amide formation/diazotisation/azo coupling)

Uses: pigment (rubber)

Acid Red 108
Pigment Red 66 (CI, barium salt); 18000 (CI); 18000:1 (CI, barium salt)

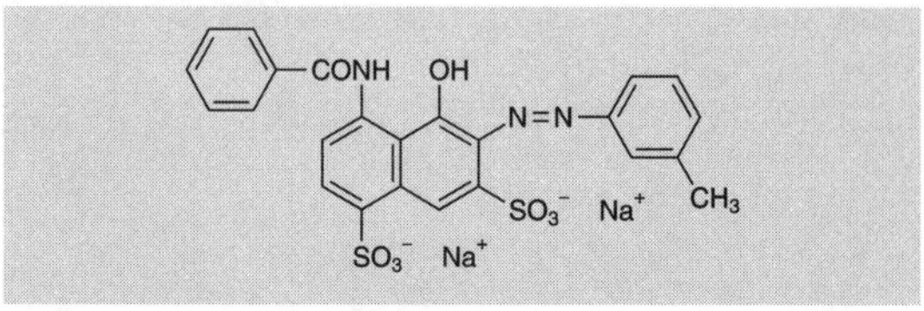

$C_{24}H_{17}N_3Na_2O_8S_2$. M: 585.52.
Production:
- benzoyl chloride + K acid + *m*-toluidine (amide formation/diazotisation/azo coupling)

Uses: pigment (rubber)

Acid Red 114
23635 (CI); [6459-94-5]
$C_{37}H_{28}N_4Na_2O_{10}S_3$. M: 830.82.
Production:
- *o*-tolidine + phenol + G acid + *p*-toluenesulphonyl chloride (diazotisation/azo coupling/diazotisation/azo coupling/dehydrochlorination)

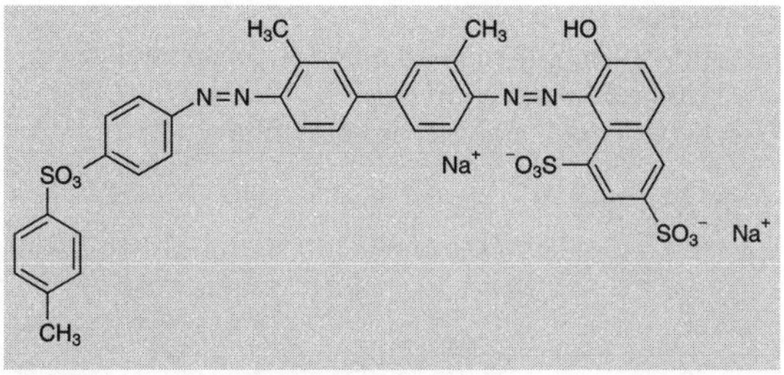

Uses: dye (wool, silk, polyamide)

Acid Red 119

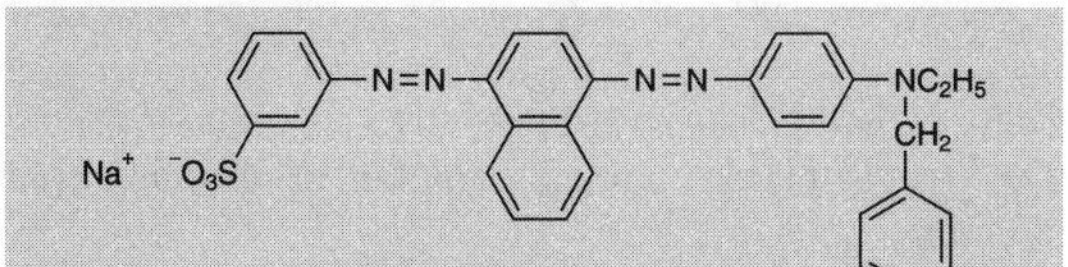

$C_{31}H_{25}N_5Na_2O_6S_2$. M: 673.67.
Production:
- *N*-ethyl-*N*-phenylbenzylamine-3-sulphonic acid + 1-naphthylamine + metanilic acid (diazotisation/ azo coupling/diazotisation/azo coupling)

Uses: dye (wool, polyamide)

Acid Red 137
17755 (CI)

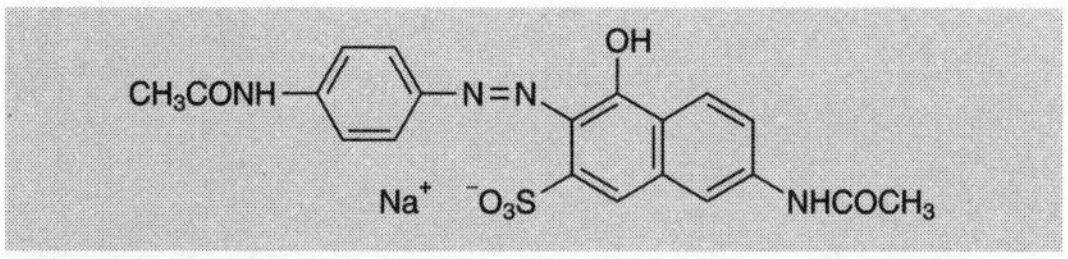

$C_{20}H_{17}N_4Na_1O_6S_1$. M: 464.43.
Production:
- acetic anhydride + J acid + *p*-aminoacetanilide (acetylation/diazotisation/azo coupling)

Uses: dye (paper)

Acid Red 138
18073 (CI)

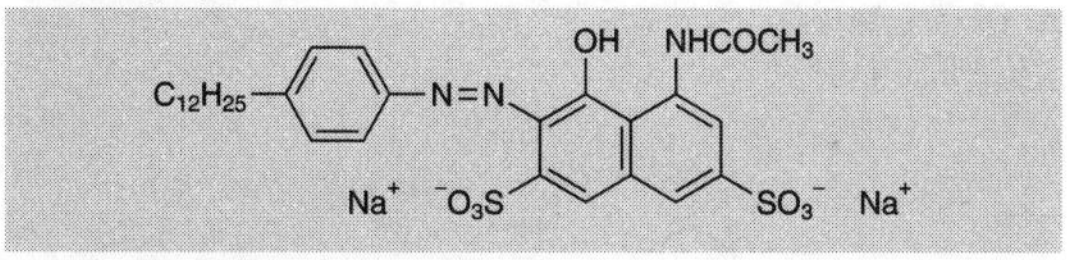

$C_{30}H_{37}N_3Na_2O_8S_2$. M: 677.75.
Production:
- *p*-dodecylaniline + *N*-acetyl-H acid (diazotisation/ azo coupling)

Uses:
dye (wool, silk); pigments intermediate

Acid Red 151
26900 (CI); [6406-56-0]
$C_{22}H_{15}N_4Na_1O_4S_1$. M: 454.44.

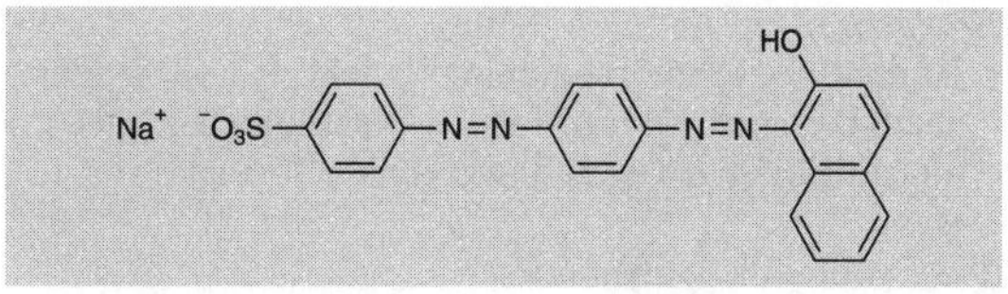

Production:
- 4′-aminoazobenzene-4-sulphonic acid + β-naphthol (diazotisation/azo coupling)

Uses: dye (wool, silk, polyamide, jute)

Acid Red 179
19351 (CI)

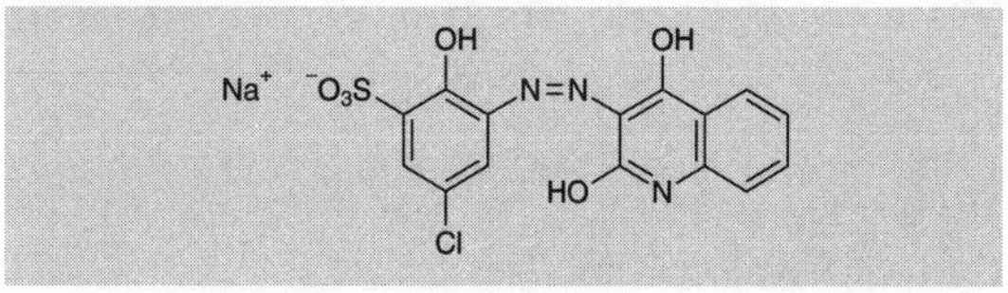

The dye is the chromium complex of the displayed structure.
Production:
- 2-amino-4-chlorophenol-6-sulphonic acid + 2,4-dihydroxyquinoline + chromium acetate (diazotisation/azo coupling/complex formation)

Uses: dye (wool, polyamide, silk)

Acid Red 183
18800 (CI)

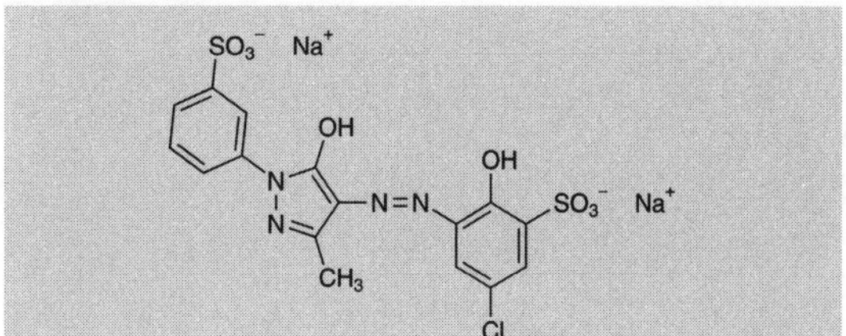

The dye is the chromium complex of the displayed structure.
Production:
- 2-amino-4-chlorophenol-6-sulphonic acid + 1-(3′-sulphophenyl)-3-methylpyrazolone + chromium acetate (diazotisation/azo coupling/complex formation)

Uses: dye (wool, silk)

Acid Red 186
18810 (CI)

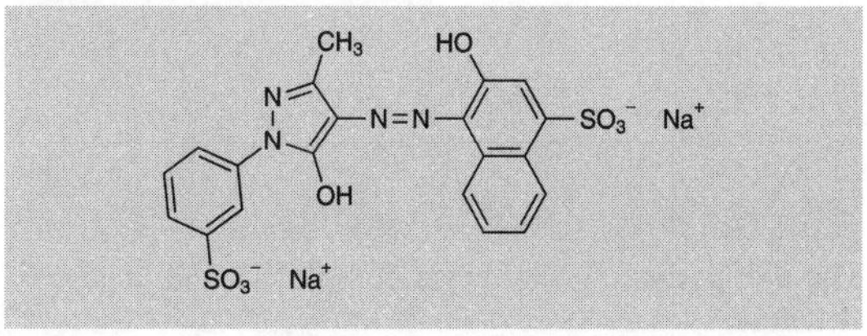

The dye is the chromium complex of the structure.

Production:
- 1-amino-2-naphthol-4-sulphonic acid + 1-(3′-sulpho-phenyl)-3-methylpyrazolone + chromium acetate (diazotisation/azo coupling/complex formation)

Uses:
dye (wool, silk, polyamide)

Acid Red 249
18134 (CI)

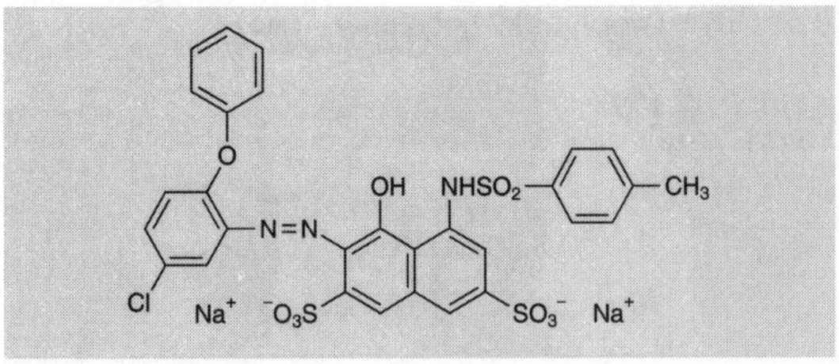

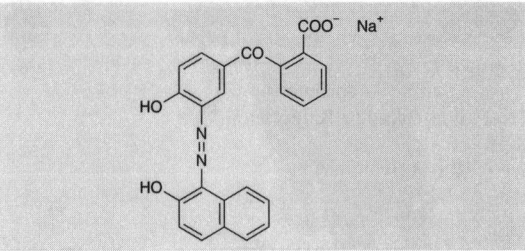

$C_{29}H_{20}Cl_1N_3Na_2O_{10}S_3$. M: 748.11.
Production:
- H acid + p-toluenesulphonyl chloride + 2,5-dichloronitrobenzene + phenol (ether formation/nitro reduction/amide formation/diazotisation/azo coupling)

Uses: dye (wool)

Acid Red 266
17101 (CI)

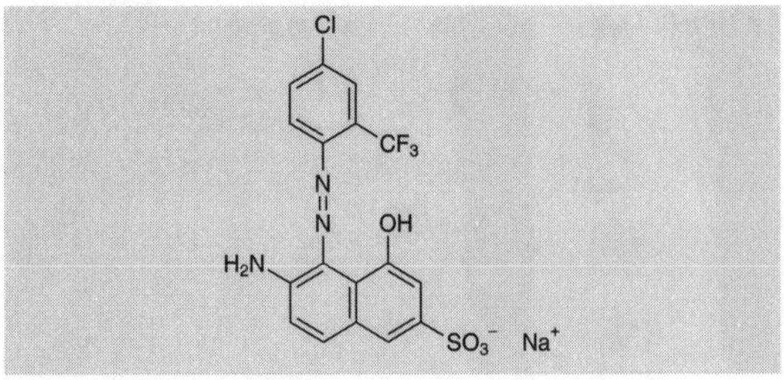

$C_{17}H_{10}Cl_1F_3N_3Na_1O_4S_1$. M: 467.78.
Production:
- 2-amino-5-chlorobenzotrifluoride + gamma acid (diazotisation/azo coupling)

Uses:
dye (polyamide)

Acid Red 296
Solvent Red 102; 15675 (CI)

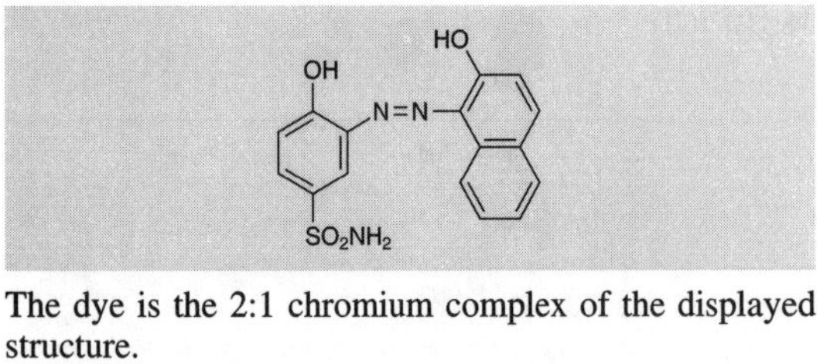

The dye is the 2:1 chromium complex of the displayed structure.
$C_{32}H_{22}Cr_1N_6O_8S_2$. M: 734.69.

Production:
- 2-aminophenol-4-sulphonamide + β-naphthol (diazotisation/azo coupling)

Uses: dye (wool, polyamide, bast fibres)

Acid Red 308

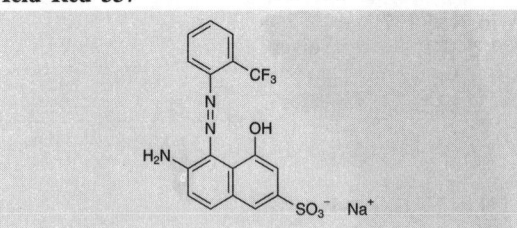

The dye is the 2:1 cobalt complex of the displayed structure.
$C_{48}H_{30}Co_1N_4Na_2O_{10}$. M: 927.70.
Production:
- phthalic anhydride + o-nitrophenol + β-naphthol + cobalt sulphate (Friedel-Crafts acylation/nitro reduction/diazotisation/azo coupling/complex formation)

Uses: dye (wool)

Acid Red 337

$C_{17}H_{11}F_3N_3Na_1O_4S_1$. M: 433.34.
Production:
- o-aminobenzotrifluoride + gamma acid (diazotisation/ azo coupling)

Uses: dye (polyamide)

Acid Violet 1
17025 (CI)

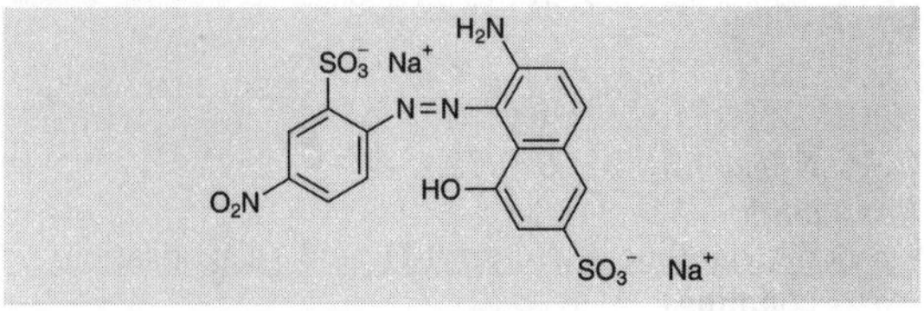

$C_{16}H_{10}N_4Na_2O_9S_2$. M: 512.38.
Production:
- 4-nitroaniline-2-sulphonic acid + gamma acid (diazotisation/azo coupling)

Derivatives: Acid Red 34
Uses: dye (wool)

Acid Violet 3
16580 (CI)

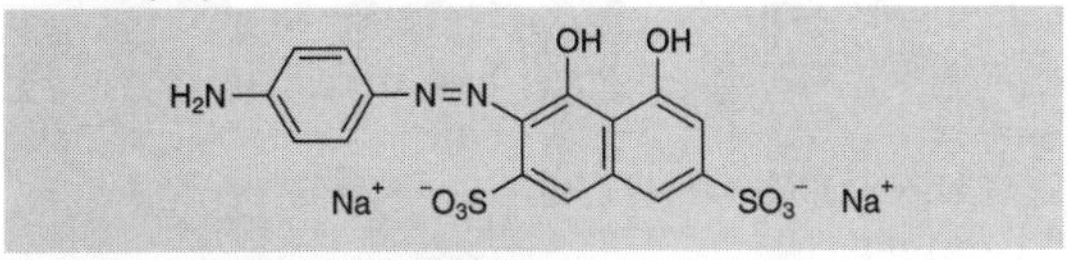

$C_{16}H_{11}N_3Na_2O_8S_2$. M: 483.39.
Production:
- *p*-nitroaniline + chromotropic acid (diazotisation/ azo coupling/nitro reduction)
Uses:
dye (wool, polyamide)

Acid Violet 7
Food Red 11 (CI); 18055 (CI)

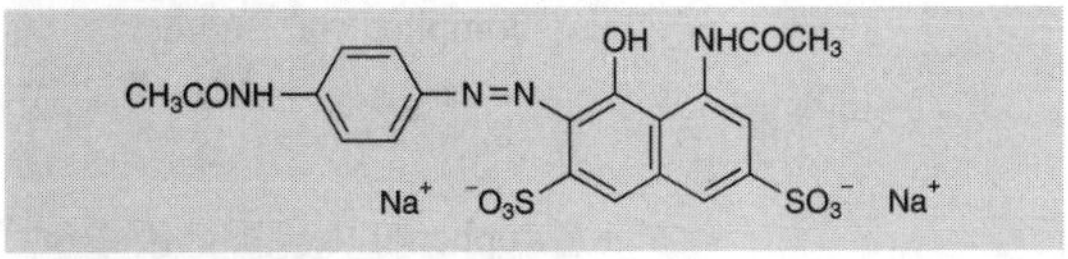

$C_{20}H_{16}N_4Na_2O_9S_2$. M: 566.48.
Production:
- *p*-aminoacetanilide + *N*-acetyl-H acid (diazotisation/azo coupling)
Uses:
dye (wool, polyamide, soap, stains, cosmetics)

Acid Violet 9 *See:* Solvent Violet 10

Acid Violet 12
18075 (CI)

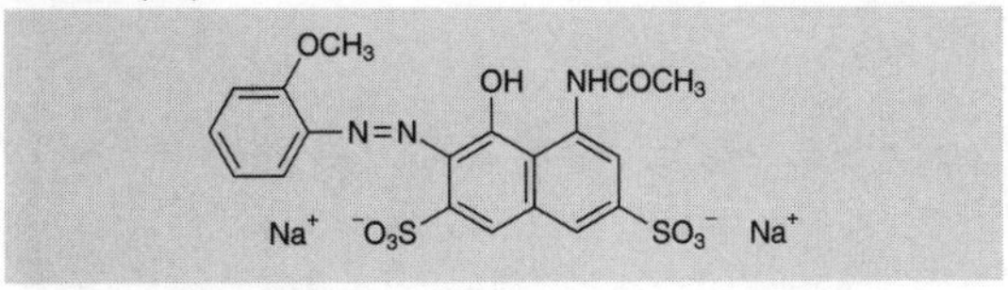

$C_{19}H_{15}N_3Na_2O_9S_2$. M: 539.45.
Production:
- *o*-anisidine + *N*-acetyl-H acid (diazotisation/azo coupling)
Uses: dye (wool, silk, polyamide, leather, paper)

Acid Violet 14
17080 (CI); [4404-39-1]

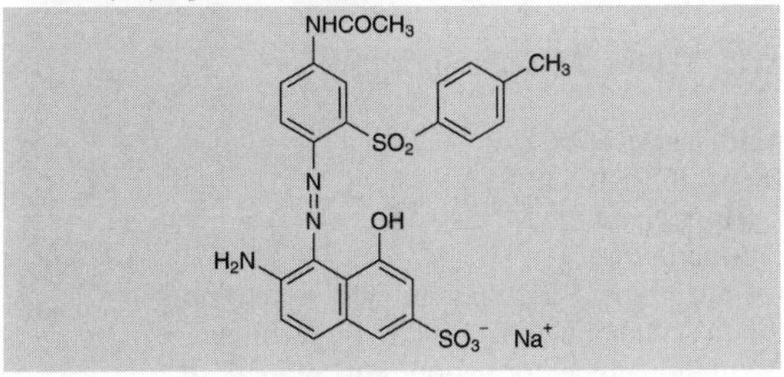

$C_{25}H_{21}N_4Na_1O_7S_2$. M: 576.58.

Production:
- *p*-aminoacetanilide + *p*-toluenesulphonyl chloride + gamma acid (sulphonation/diazotisation/azo coupling)
Uses:
dye (wool, silk, polyamide)

Acid Violet 17
Food Violet 1 (CI); 42650 (CI)

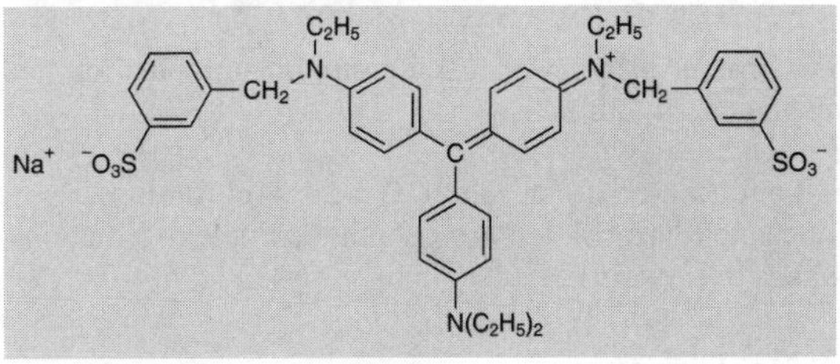

$C_{41}H_{44}N_3Na_1O_6S_2$. M: 761.93.
Production:
- *N*-ethyl-*N*-phenylbenzylamine-3-sulphonic acid + *p*-diethylaminobenzaldehyde (carbonyl condensation/ oxidation)
Uses: dye (wool, silk, paper, soap, inks)

Acid Violet 41
62020 (CI)

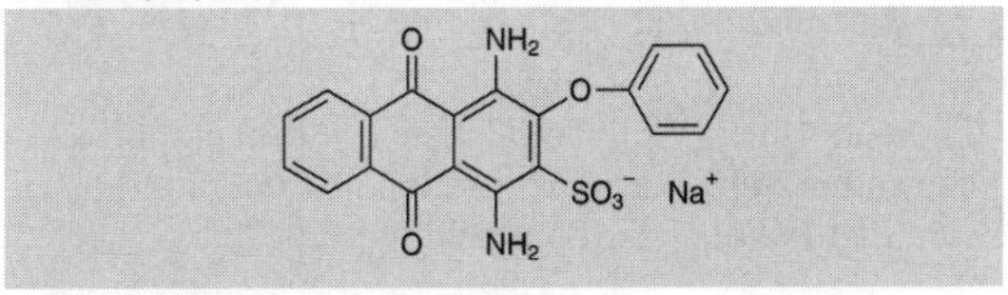

$C_{20}H_{13}N_2Na_1O_6S_1$. M: 432.37.
Production:
- 1,4-diaminoanthraquinone + phenol + sodium sulphite (ring chlorination/ether formation/ sulphonation)
Uses: dye (wool, polyamide)

Acid Violet 49
Food Violet 2 (CI); 42640 (CI)

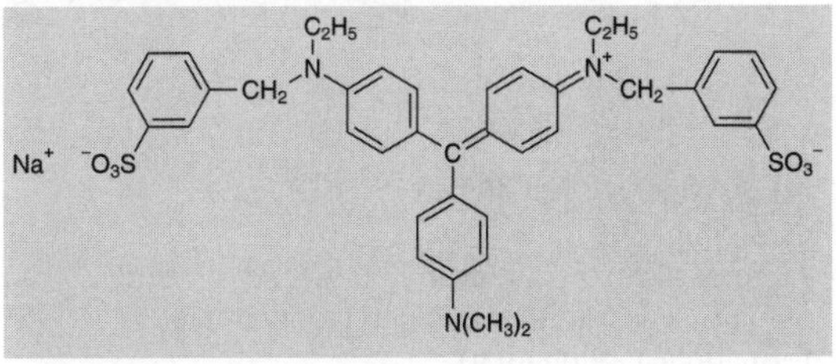

$C_{39}H_{40}N_3Na_1O_6S_2$. M: 733.88.
Production:
- *N*-ethyl-*N*-phenylbenzylamine-3-sulphonic acid + *p*-dimethylaminobenzaldehyde (carbonyl condensation/oxidation)
Uses:
dye (wool, silk, polyamide, leather, paper, ink)

Acid Violet 58
16260 (CI)

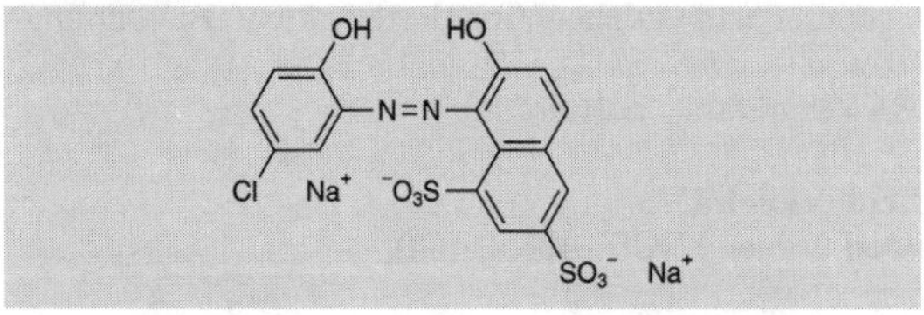

The dye is a hydrated 1:1 chromium complex of the displayed structure.
Production:
• 2-amino-4-chloroanisole + G acid + chromium acetate (diazotisation/azo coupling/complex formation)
Uses: dye (wool)

Acid Violet 78
12205 (CI)

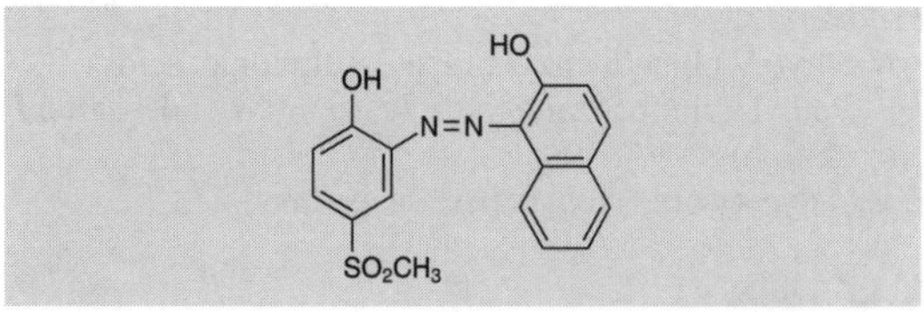

The dye is the 2:1 chromium complex of the displayed structure. $C_{34}H_{24}Cr_1N_4O_8S_2$. M: 732.71.
Production:
• 2-amino-4-methylsulphonylphenol + β-naphthol + chromium sulphate (diazotisation/azo coupling)
Uses: dye (wool, silk, polyamide)

Acid Violet 80

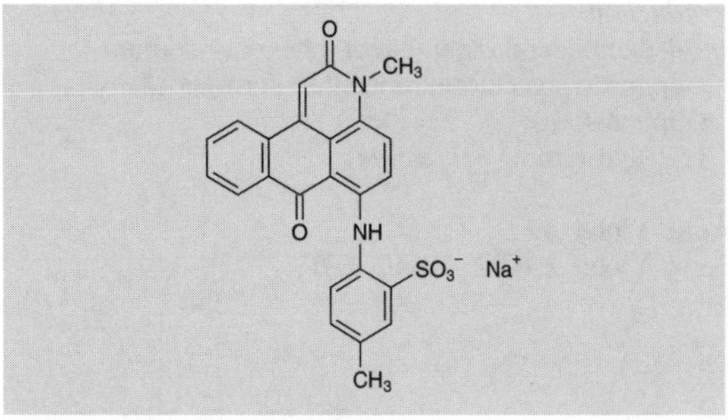

$C_{24}H_{17}N_2Na_1O_5S_1$. M: 468.45.
Production:
• 1-bromo-4-methylaminoanthraquinone + acetic anhydride + *p*-toluidine (acetylation/amine formation/sulphonation)
Uses: dye (wool)

Acid Yellow 3
Quinoline Yellow; Food Yellow 13 (CI); Pigment Yellow 115 (CI, aluminium salt); 47005 (CI); 47005:1 (CI, aluminium salt); D&C Yellow No. 10 (FDC); E104 (EC); [8004-92-0]

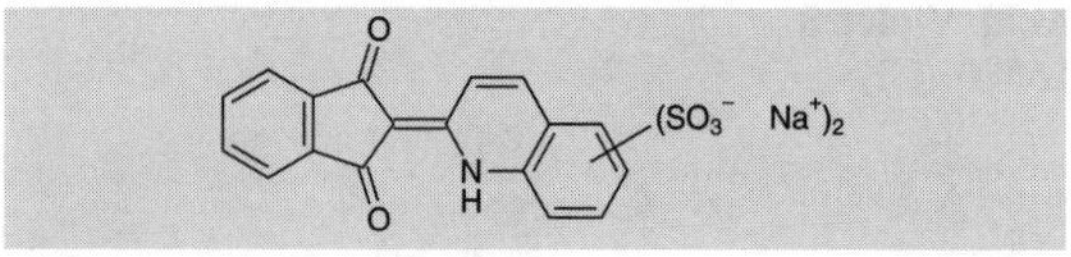

$C_{18}H_9N_1Na_2O_8S_2$. M: 477.38.
Production:
• quinophthalone (sulphonation/sodium salt formation)
Uses: dye (paper, wool, silk); pigment (printing inks); water-soluble food colorant

Acid Yellow 9
See: 4-aminoazobenzene-3,4′-disulphonic acid

Acid Yellow 17
Yellow 2G; 18965 (CI)

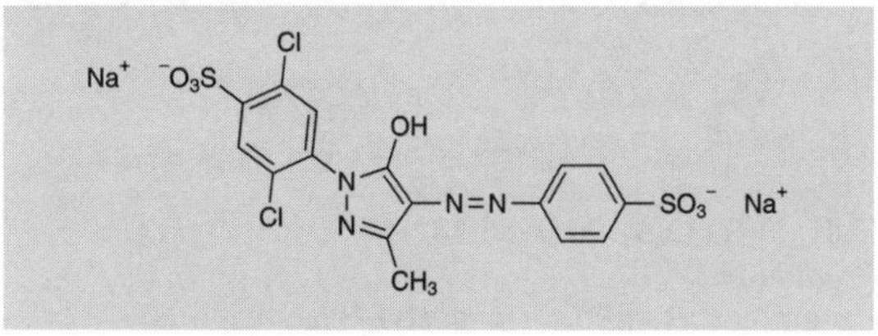

$C_{16}H_{10}Cl_2N_4Na_2O_7S_2$. M: 551.30.
Production:
• sulphanilic acid + 1-(2′,5′-dichloro-4′-sulpho-phenyl)-3-methylpyrazolone (diazotisation/azo coupling)
Uses: dye (wool, polyamide)

Acid Yellow 19
18967 (CI)

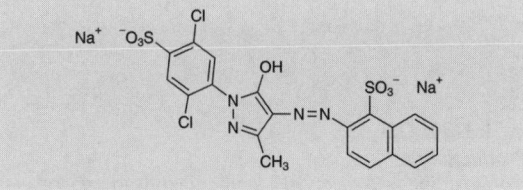

$C_{20}H_{12}Cl_2N_4Na_2O_7S_2$. M: 601.36.
Production:
• Tobias acid + 1-(2′,5′-dichloro-4′-sulphophenyl)-3-methylpyrazolone (diazotisation/azo coupling)
Uses: dye (wool, polyamide)

Acid Yellow 23 *See:* tartrazine

Acid Yellow 25
18835 (CI); [6359-85-9]
$C_{23}H_{20}N_5Na_1O_6S_2$. M: 549.55.
Production:
• 4-nitrotoluene-2-sulphonic acid + aniline + 1-(4′-sulphophenyl)-3-methylpyrazolone (sulphonamide formation/nitro reduction/diazotisation/azo coupling)

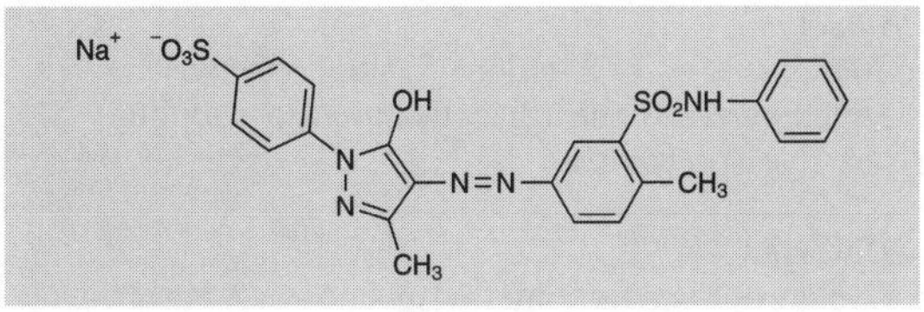

Uses: dye (wool, silk, polyamide, leather)

Acid Yellow 29
18900 (CI)

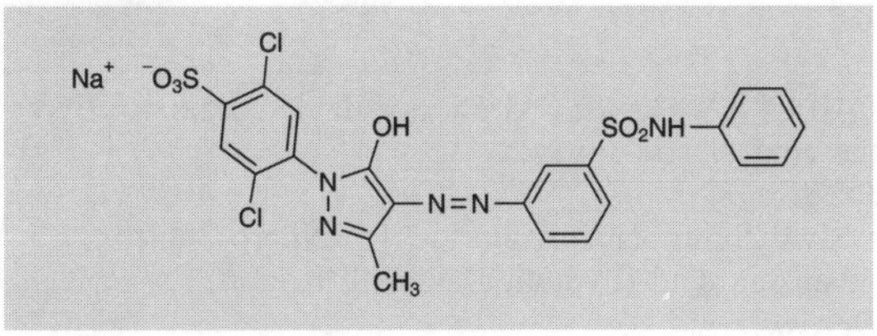

$C_{22}H_{16}Cl_2N_5Na_1O_6S_2$. M: 604.42.
Production:
- metanilic acid + aniline + 1-(2′,5′-dichloro-4′-sulphophenyl)-3-methylpyrazolone (sulphonamide formation/diazotisation/azo coupling)

Uses: dye (wool, polyamide)

Acid Yellow 36
D&C Yellow No. 1 (FDC); 13065 (CI); [587-98-4]

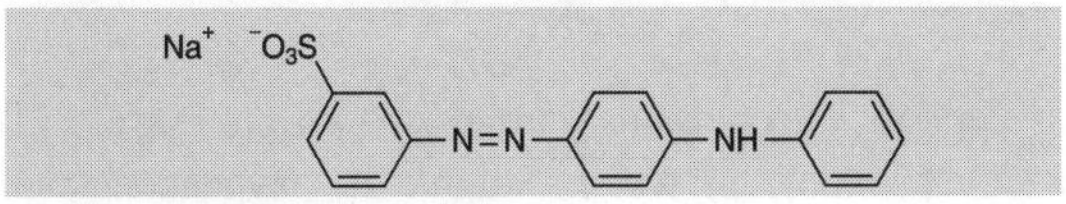

$C_{18}H_{14}N_3Na_1O_3S_1$. M: 375.38.
Production:
- metanilic acid + diphenylamine (diazotisation/azo coupling)

Uses: dye (wool, silk, jute, paper, stain, polish)

Acid Yellow 40
18950 (CI); [6372-96-9]

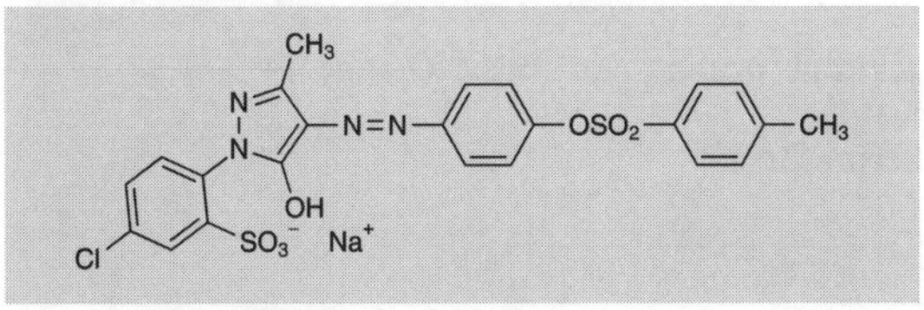

$C_{23}H_{18}Cl_1N_4Na_1O_7S_2$. M: 584.98.
Production:
- p-aminophenol + 1-(4′-chloro-2′-sulphophenyl)-3-methylpyrazolone + p-toluenesulphonyl chloride (diazotisation/azo coupling/dehydrochlorination)

Uses: dye (wool, silk)

Acid Yellow 42
22910 (CI); [6375-55-9]
$C_{32}H_{24}N_8Na_2O_8S_2$. M: 758.70.

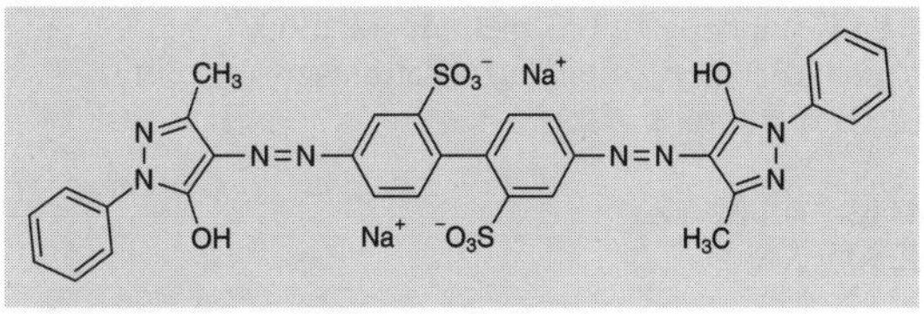

Production:
- benzidine-2,2′-disulphonic acid + 3-methyl-1-phenyl-5-pyrazolone (diazotisation/azo coupling)

Uses: dye (wool, leather)

Acid Yellow 54
19010 (CI)

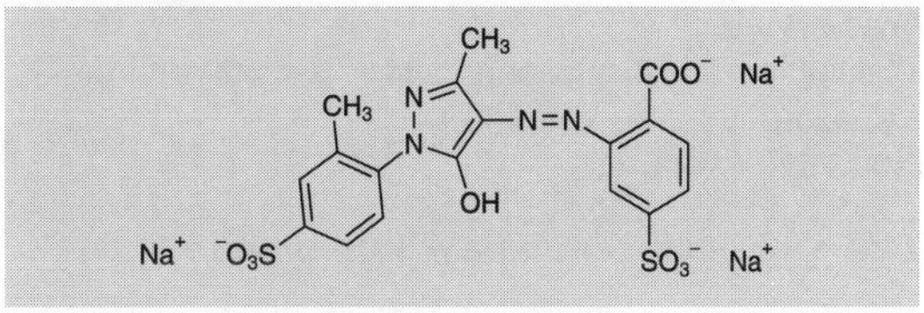

The dye is the 1:1 chromium complex of the displayed structure.
Production:
- o-nitrobenzoic acid + 1-(4′-sulpho-2′-methylphenyl)-3-methylpyrazolone + chromium acetate (sulphonation/nitro reduction/diazotisation/azo coupling)

Uses: dye (wool, silk, polyamide, ink)

Acid Yellow 65
14170 (CI)

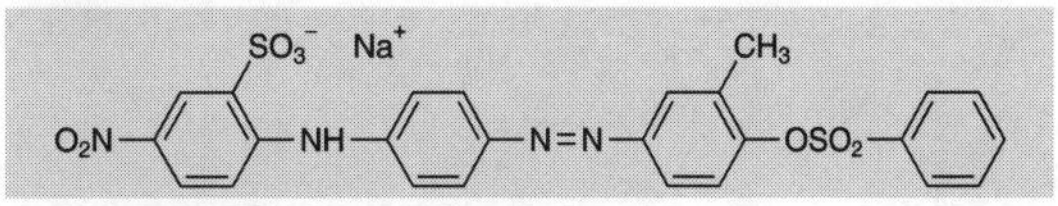

$C_{25}H_{19}N_4Na_1O_8S_2$. M: 590.57.
Production:
- 4′-amino-4-nitrodiphenylamine-2-sulphonic acid + o-cresol + benzenesulphonyl chloride (diazotisation/azo coupling/dehydrochlorination)

Uses: dye (wool, silk, polyamide, leather)

Acid Yellow 73 *See:* fluorescein

Acid Yellow 76
18850 (CI)

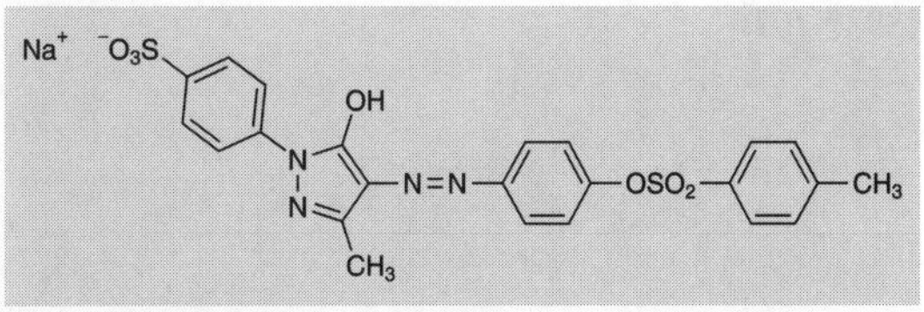

$C_{23}H_{19}N_4Na_1O_7S_2$. M: 550.54.
Production:
- p-aminophenol + p-toluenesulphonyl chloride +

1-(4'-sulphophenyl)-3-methylpyrazolone
(dehydrochlorination/diazotisation/azo coupling)
Uses: dye (wool, silk)

Acid Yellow 87
22905 (CI)

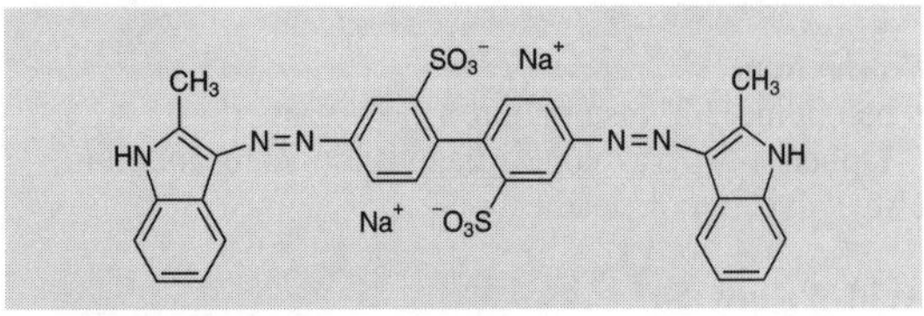

$C_{30}H_{22}N_6Na_2O_6S_2$. M: 672.65.
Production:
• benzidine-2,2'-disulphonic acid + 2-methylindole
   (diazotisation/azo coupling)
Uses: dye (wool, silk)

Acid Yellow 99 *See:* Solvent Yellow 19

Acid Yellow 121 *See:* Solvent Yellow 21

Acid Yellow 127
19005 (CI)

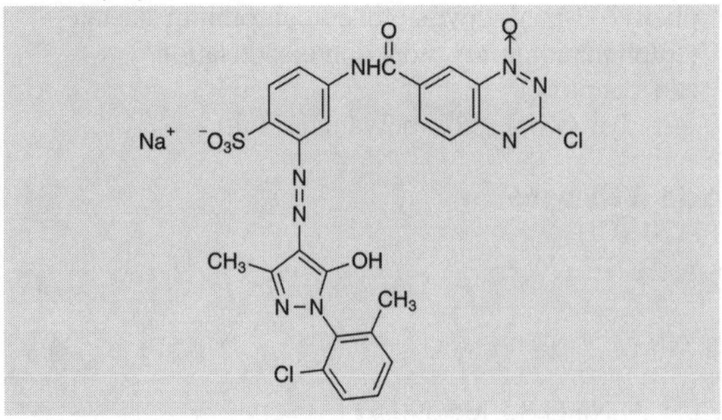

$C_{25}H_{17}Cl_1N_8Na_1O_6S_1$. M: 615.96.
Production:
• *p*-aminobenzoic acid + cyanogen chloride +
   2,4-diaminobenzenesulphonic acid + 1-(6'-chloro-
   2'-methylphenyl)-3-methylpyrazolone
   (nitrosation/condensation/amide formation/
   diazotisation/azo coupling)
Uses: dye (wool, polyamide)

Acid Yellow 200
18930 (CI)

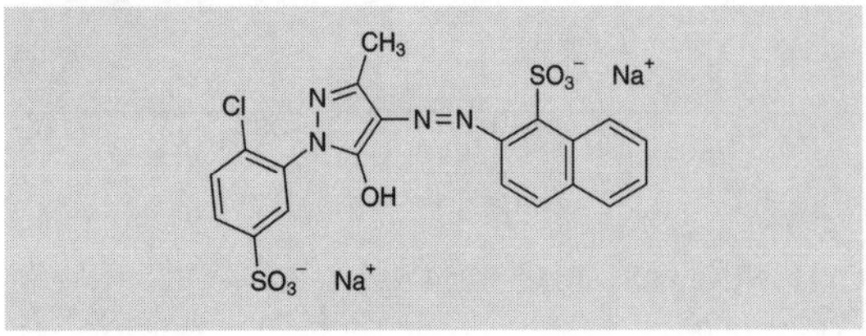

$C_{20}H_{13}Cl_1N_4Na_2O_7S_2$. M: 566.90.

Production:
• Tobias acid + 1-(2'-chloro-5'-sulphophenyl)-
   3-methylpyrazolone (diazotisation/azo coupling)
Uses: dye (polyamide)

acifluorfen
5-[2-chloro-4-(trifluoromethyl)phenoxy]-2-nitrobenzoic
acid; Blazer (BASF); [50594-66-6]

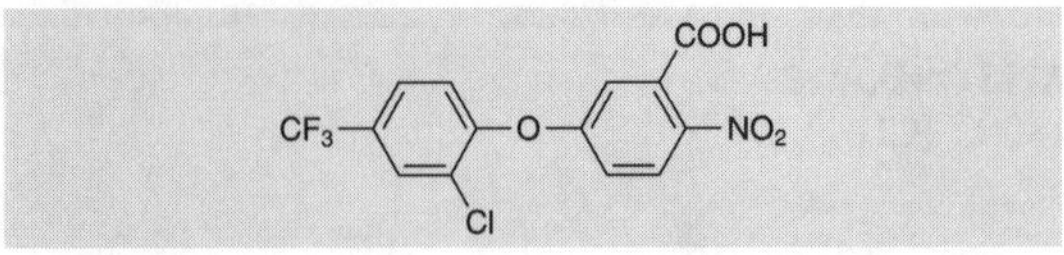

$C_{14}H_7Cl_1F_3N_1O_5$. M: 361.65. Available commercially as
the acid or sodium salt.
Production:
• 3,4-dichlorobenzotrifluoride + 5-chloro-2-nitro-
   benzoic acid (hydration/ether formation)
Derivatives:
fluoroglycofen-ethyl; fomesafen
Uses: herbicide

Aclar *See:* polychlorotrifluoroethylene

aclonifen
[74070-46-5]

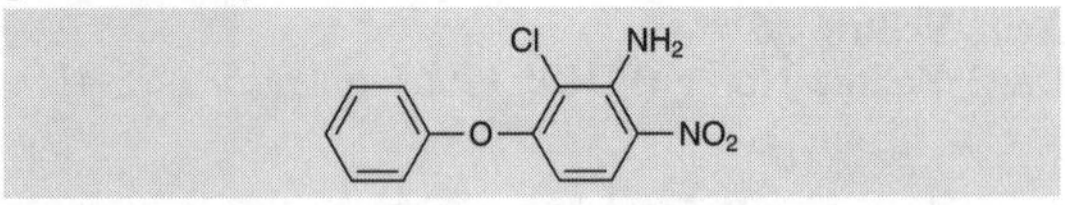

$C_{12}H_9Cl_1N_2O_3$. M: 264.66. Yellow crystals. MP: 81–
82°C. Insoluble in water. Soluble in oxygenated and
aromatic solvents.
Production:
• *p*-chloronitrobenzene + ammonia + phenol
   (chlorination/thermal rearrangement/ammoniation/
   ether formation)
Uses: herbicide

ACN *See:* acrylonitrile

acridine orange *See:* Basic Orange 14

acrinathrin

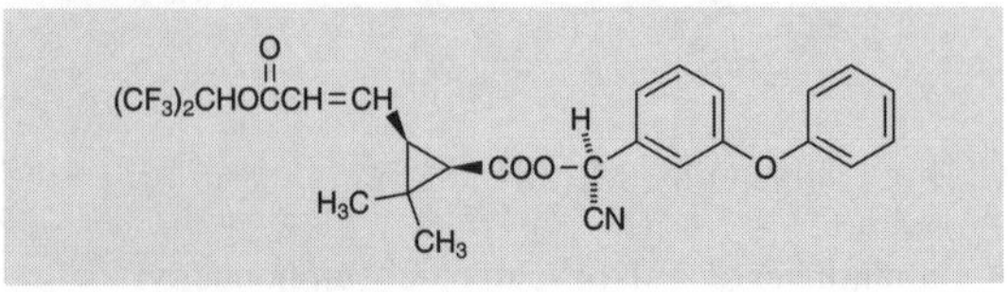

$C_{26}H_{21}F_6N_1O_5$. M: 541.45.
Production:
• hexafluoroisopropanol + acetic acid + (*1R*)-*cis*-
   caronaldehyde + 3-phenoxybenzaldehyde
   cyanohydrin (esterification/condensation/
   dehydration/ esterification)
Uses: acaricide

acrolein

acrylic aldehyde; 2-propenal; [107-02-8]

$$CH_2=CHCHO$$

$C_3H_4O_1$. M: 56.06. Colourless liquid with a penetrating odour. BP: 52–53°C. MP: -87°C. d: 0.42 kg/l (20°C). Soluble in water and oxygenated solvents. The commercial product contains a polymerisation inhibitor such as hydroquinone. When used as a reagent in fine chemical applications, acrolein is usually produced *in situ* from acetaldehyde and aqueous formaldehyde.
Production:
• propylene + oxygen (Sohio gas-phase oxidation process)
• propylene (air oxidation)
Derivatives:
cycloxydim; C_{10} dialdehyde; dimethyl3-cyclohexenecarboxaldehyde; 3,4-epoxycyclohexylmethyl 3,4-epoxycyclohexylcarboxylate; glufosinateammonium; 1,2,6-hexanetriol; 3/4-(4-hydroxy-4-methylpentyl)-3-cyclohexenecarboxaldehyde; DL-methionine; methionine hydroxy analogue; 2-methoxydihydropyran; 3/4-(4-methyl-3-penten-1-yl)-3-cyclohexenecarboxaldehyde; β-picoline; pyridine; sodium polyaldehydocarboxylate; trimethylene glycol; L-tryptophan; violet leaf alcohol
Uses: cellulose fibre crosslinking agent; aquatic biocide (oilfield applications)

acrylamide

[79-06-1]

$$\underset{\displaystyle CH_2=CHCNH_2}{\overset{\displaystyle O}{}}$$

$C_3H_5N_1O_1$. M: 71.08. White solid. MP: 84°C. BP 87°C (0.25 kPa). d: 1.12 kg/l (30°C). Soluble in water and oxygenated solvents. Manufactured and handled as a 50% solution in water, although solid material is also available commercially.
Production:
• acrylonitrile (nitrile hydration)
Derivatives: acrylamide copolymers, cationic; acrylamide-diallyldimethylammonium chloride copolymers; aminoethylpiperazine; acrylic resins, amidated; *N,N*-diethylethylenediamine; dimethylaminoethyl methacrylate-acrylamide copolymers; *N,N'*-methylenebisacrylamide; *N*-methylolacrylamide; polyacrylamide
Uses: carboxylated comonomer (styrene-butadiene latex, acrylic resins)

acrylamide copolymers, cationic
Production:
• acrylamide + 2-dimethylaminoethyl acrylate/3-(methacrylamidopropyl)trimethylammonium chloride/2-dimethylaminoethyl methacrylate/dimethylaminopropyl methacrylamide/trimethylammoniumethyl methacrylate chloride (solution polymerisation)

• acrylamide-sodium acrylate copolymers + 2,3-epoxypropyltrimethylammonium chloride (epoxidation)
Uses: cationic polyelectrolytes (effluent treatment); retention aids/drainage aids (paper production)

acrylamide-diallyldimethylammonium chloride copolymers
[9022-17-7]

Production:
• acrylamide + diallyldimethylammonium chloride (solution polymerisation)
Uses: conditioning agent (shampoos, hair conditioners, cosmetics, toiletries)

acrylamide-sodium acrylate copolymers
polyacrylamide, partially-hydrolysed; poly(acrylamide-sodium acrylate); PHPA

Production:
• polyacrylamide + sodium hydroxide (amide hydrolysis)
Derivatives: acrylamide copolymers, cationic
Uses: anionic flocculants (water treatment); mineral flotation depressant; viscosifier (drilling muds)

2-acrylamido-2-methylpropanesulphonic acid
AMPS (Lubrizol); [15214-89-8]

$C_7H_{13}N_1O_4S_1$. M: 207.25.
Production:
• sodium methallyl sulphonate + acrylonitrile (Ritter reaction)
Uses: comonomer (anionic flocculants/dispersants)

acrylic acid
AA; propenoic acid; [79-10-7]

$$CH_2=CHCOOH$$

$C_3H_4O_2$. M: 72.06. Colourless liquid with an acrid odour. BP: 141°C. MP: 13–14°C. d: 1.40 kg/l (25°C). Miscible with water and oxygenated solvents. Gradually polymerises on standing. Flash point: 68°C (OC).
Production:
• propylene + oxygen (gas-phase oxidation)
• propylene + oxygen (Sohio gas-phase oxidation process; byproduct of acrolein production)

- acetylene + carbon monoxide (Reppe hydrocarbonylation)
- acrylonitrile (nitrile hydrolysis)

Derivatives: acryloyl chloride; allyl acrylate; 2-aminothiazoline-4-carboxylic acid; ammonium polyacrylate; *n*-butyl acrylate; 2-cyanoethyl acrylate; cyclohexyl acrylate; γ-decalactone; dicyclopentenyl acrylate; 2-diethylaminoethyl acrylate; 2-dimethylaminoethyl acrylate; dipropylene glycol diacrylate; epoxy-acrylate resins; 2-(2-ethoxyethoxy)ethyl acrylate; ethyl acrylate; ethylene-acrylic acid copolymers; ethylene-acrylic acid copolymers, ionomeric; ethylene bis(acrylamide); 2-ethylhexyl acrylate; glycerol propoxylate triacrylate; glycidyl acrylate; γ-heptalactone; 1,6-hexanediol diacrylate; 2-hydroxyethyl acrylate; 2-hydroxypropyl acrylate; isobutyl acrylate; isodecyl acrylate; 2-methoxyethyl acrylate; methyl acrylate; neopentyl glycol diacrylate; γ-nonalactone; γ-octalactone; pentaerythritol tetraacrylate; pentaerythritol triacrylate; 2-phenoxyethyl acrylate; polyacrylate resins, crosslinked; poly(acrylic acid); polyester-acrylate resins; sodium β-carboxyethyl acrylate; sodium polyacrylate; sodium polyacrylate, crosslinked; sodium polyaldehydocarboxylate; styrene-butadiene copolymers, carboxylated; tetraethylene glycol diacrylate; tetrahydrofurfuryl acrylate; trimethylolpropane triacrylate; tripropylene glycol diacrylate; γ-undecalactone

Uses: carboxylated comonomer (acrylic, vinyl acetate, styrene-butadiene, nitrile latex); radiation-cured polyester/polyurethane resin comonomer

acrylic fibre *See:* polyacrylonitrile

acrylic resins, amidated

Production:
- styrene + ethyl acrylate + acrylamide + formaldehyde + *n*-butanol (polymerisation/alkoxymethylation)

Uses: epoxy-acrylic coatings (domestic appliances); alkyd-acrylic resins (wood preservatives/stains)

acrylic resins, carboxylated

Production:
- styrene/vinyltoluene + *n*-butyl acrylate/2-ethylhexyl acrylate + methacrylic acid (polymerisation)

Uses: thermosetting acrylic adhesives; thermosetting acrylic finishes (domestic, institutional appliances)

acrylic resins, hydroxylated

R = H, methyl-, R′ = alkyl-.
Production:
- styrene + methyl methacrylate/2-ethylhexyl acrylate/ *n*-butyl acrylate + 2-hydroxyethyl acrylate/2-hydroxyethyl methacrylate (polymerisation)

Uses: epoxy-acrylic stoving lacquers (domestic appliances); alkyd-acrylic resins (wood preservatives, decorative wood stains); isocyanate-cured acrylic coatings (furniture, car refinishing); melamine-acrylic stoving lacquers (domestic appliances); radiation-cured acrylic wood/textile finishes; thermosetting acrylic finishes (vehicles)

acrylic resins, latex

R = H, methyl-, R′ = alkyl-.
Production:
- 2-ethylhexyl acrylate/ethyl acrylate/methyl methacrylate/*n*-butyl acrylate (emulsion polymerisation)

Derivatives:
acrylonitrile-styrene-acrylic ester copolymers; poly-(acrylate-methacrylate) graft copolymers; polyvinyl chloride, high-impact

Uses: binder (non-woven fabrics); brick mastics; concrete admixtures; contact/laminating adhesives; fabric backcoatings/finishes; binder (paper coatings/sizes); tile adhesives; high-speed packaging adhesives; leather finishes; plasticiser (chlorinated rubber paints); pressure-sensitive adhesives; binder (emulsion paints, water-based primers/exterior paints); binder (water-thinnable inks); water-resistance additive (starch adhesives)

acrylic resins, solvent-based

R = H, methyl-, R′ = alkyl-.
Production:
- methyl methacrylate/*n*-butyl acrylate/methyl acrylate/2-ethylhexyl acrylate (polymerisation)

Uses: contact adhesives; lacquer resin (fluorescent-/metallic paints); pressure-sensitive adhesives; protective lacquers (metal components, films)

acrylic rubber
ACM

R = ethyl, *n*-butyl-, R′ = methyl, ethyl-, X = curing site. Elastomers vulcanised by sulphur systems. The vulcanisates are characterised by their excellent heat and oil resistance.
Production:
• ethyl acrylate/*n*-butyl acrylate + 2-methoxyethyl acrylate + allyl glycidyl ether/allyl chloroacetate (emulsion polymerisation)
Uses: automotive seals and components; print rollers

acrylonitrile
propenenitrile; vinyl cyanide; ACN; [107-13-1]

$C_3H_3N_1$. M: 53.06. Colourless liquid with a characteristic odour. BP: 77°C. FP: -83°C. d: 0.81 kg/l (20°C). Solubility in water: 73 g/l water (20°C). Miscible with most organic solvents. Flash point: -5°C (TOC). Toxic and potentially explosive.
Production:
• propylene + ammonia (ammoxidation)
Derivatives:
N-(2-acetoxyethyl)-*N*-(2-cyanoethyl)aniline; acrylamide; 2-acrylamido-2-methylpropanesulphonic acid; acrylic acid; acrylonitrile-butadiene copolymers, amine-terminated; acrylonitrile-butadiene copolymers, carboxyl-terminated; acrylonitrile-butadiene copolymers; acrylonitrile-butadiene-styrene copolymers; acrylonitrile-(ethylene-propylene-diene)-styrene copolymers; acrylonitrile-styrene-acrylic ester copolymers; adiponitrile; β-alanine; 3-[alkoxy(C_8-C_{10})]propylamine; 3-[alkoxy(C_8-C_{10})propyl]-1,3-propanediamine; 3-[alkoxy(C_{12}-C_{15})]propylamine; 3-[alkoxy(C_{12}-C_{15})propyl]-1,3-propanediamine; *N*-alkyl(C_{16}-C_{22})-1,3-propanediamine; aminecyanoethylation adducts; 3-aminopropanol; *N*-(3-aminopropyl)morpholine; *N-t*-butylacrylamide; 3-chloropropionyl chloride; *N*-coco-1,3-propanediamine; *N*-(2-cyanoethyl)-*N*-ethylaniline; 1-(2-cyanoethyl)-2-ethyl-4-methylimidazole; *N*-(2-cyanoethyl)-*N*-ethyl-*m*-toluidine; *N*-(2-cyanoethyl)-*N*-methylaniline; 1,5-diazabicyclo[5.4.0]undec-5-ene; 3-diethylaminopropylamine; dilazep; 3-dimethylaminopropylamine; dipropylenetriamine; Disperse Blue 125; iobenzamic acid; iodoxamic acid; isodecyl-3-oxypropylamine ethoxylates; isotridecyl-3-oxypropylamine; isotridecyl oxypropyl-1,3-propylenediamine; 3-mercaptopropionic acid; 3-methoxypropionitrile; 3-methylaminopropylamine; modacrylic fibre; *N-t*-octylacrylamide; *N*-oleyl-1,3-propanediamine; α-picoline; pipemidic acid; piromidic acid; polyacrylonitrile; polyols, polymer; 1,3-propanediamine; quinolinic acid; starch, acrylamidoglycollic acid-modified; starch-acrylamide graft copolymers; stearyl-1,3-propanediamine; styrene-acrylonitrile copolymers; succinonitrile; *N*-tallow-1,3-propanediamine; thiodipropionic acid; 3,3′-thiodipropionitrile; vinylidene chloride copolymers, latex

acrylonitrile-butadiene copolymers, amine-terminated
ATBN
Viscous liquids. d: 0.94–0.96 kg/l. Acrylonitrile content: 10–16%. M: 1,800–2,400.
Production:
• acrylonitrile + butadiene (solution polymerisation)
Uses: flexible epoxy resin curing agent

acrylonitrile-butadiene copolymers, carboxyl-terminated
CTBN
Viscous liquids. d: 0.95–0.96 kg/l. Acrylonitrile content: 11–26%. M: 3,000–4,000.
Production:
• acrylonitrile + butadiene (solution polymerisation)
Uses: epoxy resin flexibiliser

acrylonitrile-butadiene copolymers
nitrile rubber; NBR; XNBR (carboxylic grades); Chemigum (Goodyear Tire & Rubber); Hycar (B.F. Goodrich); Paracril (Uniroyal Chemical);

Elastomers characterised by their good resistance to oil and petrol, but limited heat resistance. Several grades are offered which vary in molecular weight and monomer content. Acrylonitrile contents are, typically, 25–45%. Terpolymers, containing a small percentage of methacrylic acid or other unsaturated carboxylic acid are common. Vulcanisation is by means of sulphur, peroxides or by crosslinking through carboxyl groups with zinc oxide. Available as slab or crumb.
Production:
• acrylonitrile + butadiene (emulsion polymerisation)
Derivatives:
nitrile rubber, hydrogenated
Uses:
conveyor belts; hydraulic/pneumatic/petrol hoses; PVC/nitrile rubber blends; print blankets; seals/O-rings /shaft packings; shoe-soling (work boots); solvent-based nitrile/phenolic adhesives (structural, electronic applications); tank/container linings; fabric coating latex; glove dipping latex; latex binder (paper/asbestos gaskets, abrasive papers); nitrile-epoxy laminating adhesives; oil/solvent resistant latex binders (non-woven textiles, paper)

acrylonitrile-butadiene-styrene copolymers
poly(acrylonitrile-butadiene-styrene); ABS
Thermoplastic blend produced by polymerisation of acrylonitrile and styrene in the presence of polybuta-

diene. The polymer is characterised by its high impact strength, good heat distortion properties and excellent surface appearance. Techniques are available for electroplating ABS polymer. Several grades are available which vary in impact strength and fire resistance.
Production:
• acrylonitrile + styrene + polybutadiene latex (emulsion polymerisation)
Derivatives:
polyvinyl chloride, high-impact
Uses: automotive fascia panels, door knobs, grilles, fastenings, trim; ABS/PVC blends (fire-retarded automobile and aircraft fittings); ABS/PVC blends (fire-retarded electrical components and housings); ABS/poly(methyl methacrylate) blends; ABS/polycarbonate blends (electrical components and housings); ABS/polysulphone blends (electrical components and housings); office machinery housings/components/fittings; industrial vent/drain/waste piping and fittings; processing aid/impact modifier (polyvinyl chloride); refrigerator fittings/linings; telephone housings

acrylonitrile-(ethylene-propylene-diene)-styrene copolymers
AES; Rovel (Dow Chemical)
Thermoplastic blend produced by polymerisation of acrylonitrile and styrene in the presence of ethylene-propylene-diene latex. The properties of the polymer are similar to those of ABS except for its better heat and light resistance.
Production:
• acrylonitrile + styrene + ethylene-propylene-diene terpolymer, rubber (polymerisation)
Uses:
outdoor equipment housings/fittings

acrylonitrile-styrene-acrylic ester copolymers
ASA; Luran S (BASF)
Thermoplastic blend produced by polymerisation of acrylonitrile and styrene in the presence of acrylic ester latex. d: 1.08 kg/l (20°C). Tensile strength: 50–60 MPa. Tensile modulus: 2,500 MPa. The properties of the polymer are similar to those of ABS except for its better heat and light resistance.
Production:
• acrylonitrile + styrene + acrylic resins, latex (emulsion polymerisation)
Uses: covers/guards (agricultural/outdoor equipment); streetlight housings; road signs

acryloyl chloride
acrylyl chloride; [814-68-6]

$$CH_2=CHCOCl$$

$C_3H_3Cl_1O_1$. M: 90.50. Liquid. BP: 75°C. d: 1.11 kg/l (20°C). Hydrolysed by water. Soluble in chlorinated solvents.

Production:
• acrylic acid (acid chloride formation)
Derivatives: 5-chloro-2-methyl-4-isothiazolinone; 2-(N--ethylperfluorooctylsulphonamido)ethyl acrylate; 2-*n*-octyl-4-isothiazolinone; perfluoroalkyl acrylates

4-(2-acryloyloxyethoxy)-2-hydroxybenzophenone

$C_{18}H_{16}O_5$. M: 312.32.
Production:
• 2,4-dihydroxybenzophenone + 2-hydroxyethyl acrylate (ether formation)
Uses: light stabiliser (plastics)

ACS *See:* ammonium cumene sulphonate

activated carbon
activated charcoal
Available commercially in powder or granular form. The former is used in water treatment, the latter in water and gas purification.
Production:
• hardwood/peat/coconut shells (chemical activation process)
• lignite/coal/hardwood/peat/coconut shells (gas activation process)
Uses: car catalytic converters; vegetable oil/sugar/alcoholic drink decolouring agent; flue gas desulphurisation agent; air purification; dechlorination agent (water treatment)

adamantane
sym-tricyclodecane; [281-23-2]

$C_{10}H_{16}$. M: 136.24. Solid. MP: 266–268°C (sealed tube).
Production:
• dicyclopentadiene (hydrogenation/acid-catalysed rearrangement)
Derivatives: 1-bromoadamantane

ADC *See:* azodicarbonamide

7-ADCA *See:* 7-amino-3-desacetoxycephalosporanic acid

ADD *See:* androstadienedione

adipic acid
butane-1,4-dicarboxylic acid; hexanedioic acid; AA; [124-04-9]

HOOCCH₂CH₂CH₂CH₂COOH

$C_6H_{10}O_4$. M: 146.15. White solid. MP: 151–152°C. d: 1.36 kg/l (25°C). BP: 205°C (1.3 kPa). Soluble in water and oxygenated solvents.
Production:
• cyclohexanol-cyclohexanone, mixed/cyclohexanol + nitric acid, concentrated (oxidative cleavage)
Derivatives:
adipic acid dihydrazide; adipic acid-dimethylamino-hydroxypropyldiethylenetriamine copolymers; adipio-done; adiponitrile; complex ester oils; cyclopentanone; diallyl adipate; dibutoxyethyl adipate; diester oils; di-(2-ethylhexyl) adipate; diisodecyl adipate; diisononyl adipate; diisooctyl adipate; diisopropyl adipate; diisotri-decyl adipate; dimethyl adipate; iocarmic acid; poly-amide 6 terpolymers; polyamide 46; polyamide 66; polyamide 66/610; polyester polyols, linear; polyester polyols, slightly-branched; polyester resins, carboxy-lated; polyester resins, hydroxylated; poly(ether-amide) elastomers; poly(ethylene-adipate); polymeric plastic-isers; poly(*m*-xylyleneadipamide); starch, crosslinked; thioctic acid
Uses:
alkyd resin comonomer; starch crosslinking agent; food buffering agent

adipic acid dihydrazide
[1071-93-8]

H₂NNHCCH₂CH₂CH₂CH₂CNHNH₂

$C_6H_{14}N_4O_2$. M: 174.21.
Production:
• adipic acid + hydrazine (amide formation)
Uses: crosslinked polyurethane resin comonomer; epoxy resin curing agent

adipic acid-dimethylaminohydroxypropyldiethylene-triamine copolymers
polyamide-polyamine-epichlorohydrin resins; Cartaretin F (Sandoz)

$$\left[C(CH_2)_4CNHCH_2CH_2NCH_2CH_2NH \right]_x$$

Production:
• adipic acid + diethylenetriamine + epichlorohydrin + dimethylamine (amide formation/epoxidation/amine formation)
Uses: lubricant/conditioning agent (shampoos, hair con-ditioners); paper wet-strength additives

adipiodone
3,3′-(adipoyldiamino)bis[2,4,6-triiodobenzoic acid]; iodipamide; [606-17-7]
$C_{20}H_{14}I_6N_2O_6$. M: 1139.75. Available commercially as

the free acid or as the *N*-methylglucamine salt.

Production:
• adipic acid + 3-amino-2,4,6-triiodobenzoic acid (amide formation)
Uses: x-ray diagnostic aid

adiponitrile
1,4-dicyanobutane; ADN; [111-69-3]

NCCH₂CH₂CH₂CH₂CN

$C_6H_8N_2$. M: 108.14. Colourless, odourless liquid. BP: 295°C. FP: 2°C. d: 0.97 kg/l (20°C). Very slightly soluble in water. Soluble in alcohol.
Production:
• adipic acid + ammonia (nitrile formation)
• butadiene + hydrogen cyanide (Du Pont HMDA process)
• acrylonitrile (Monsanto electrohydrodimerisation process)
Derivatives: hexamethylenediamine

ADMA *See: N,N*-dimethyl-*p*-phenylenediamine

ADN *See:* adiponitrile

ADPA *See:* acetone-diphenylamine condensates; hydroxyethylidene(diphosphonic acid)

adrenaline *See:* epinephrine

adrenalone
3,4-dihydroxy-ω-(methylamino)acetophenone; [99-45-6]

$C_9H_{11}N_1O_3$. M: 181.20.
Production:
• 3,4-dihydroxy-ω-chloroacetophenone + methylamine (amine formation)
• veratraldehyde + hydrogen cyanide (cyanohydrin formation/alcohol oxidation/nitrile reduction/methylation)
Derivatives:
epinephrine
Uses: haemostatic drug

AEEA *See:* aminoethylethanolamine

AEP *See:* aminoethylpiperazine

AEPD *See:* 2-ethyl-2-aminopropan-1,3-diol

AES *See:* acrylonitrile-(ethylene-propylene-diene)-styrene copolymers

agar
Agar agar; [9002-18-0]
Polysaccharide extracted from *Gelidium* and *Gracilaria* seaweeds in Japan, Taiwan, Korea, Spain, Portugal, Morocco, Chile and the USA.
Uses: microbial fermentation media; laboratory reagent

AGE *See:* allyl glycidyl ether

Agent Orange *See:* 2,4,5-T

AGS acid *See:* alkylene(C_4-C_6)dicarboxylic acids

AHM *See:* ammonium molybdate

AIBN *See:* 2,2′-azobisisobutyronitrile

AKD *See:* alkylketene dimer

Ala *See:* L-alanine

alachlor
2-chloro-2′,6′-diethyl-*N*-methoxymethylacetanilide; Lasso (Monsanto); [15972-60-8]

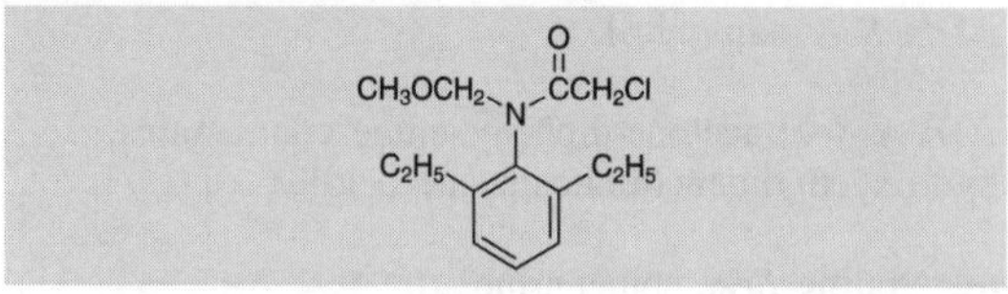

CH_3OCH_2-N-CCH_2Cl (structure with O, C_2H_5, C_2H_5)

$C_{14}H_{20}Cl_1N_1O_2$. M: 269.77.
Production:
• chloromethyl methyl ether + 2,6-diethylaniline + chloroacetyl chloride (amine formation/amide formation)
Uses: herbicide

α-alanine *See:* DL-alanine

β-alanine
β-aminopropionic acid; 3-aminopropionic acid; [107-95-9]

$H_2NCH_2CH_2COOH$

$C_3H_7N_1O_2$. M: 89.10. Crystalline solid. Decomposes when heated above 200°C. Soluble in water. Slightly soluble in alcohol.
Production:
• ammonia + acrylonitrile (cyanoethylation/nitrile hydrolysis)
Derivatives: calcium pantothenate; pentagastrin
Uses: raw material (peptide drugs)

D-alanine
D-2-aminopropionic acid; [338-69-2]

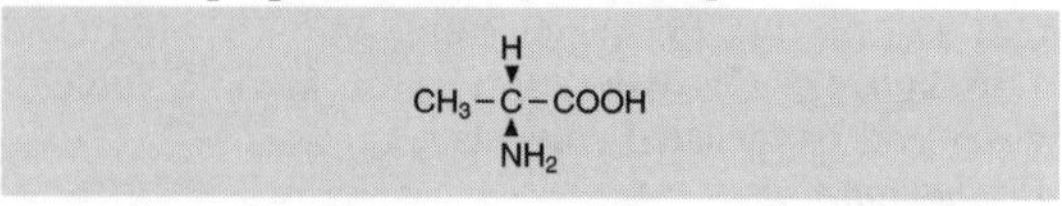

CH_3-C-COOH (structure with H, NH_2)

$C_3H_7N_1O_2$. M: 89.10. Colourless crystals. Decompose on heating above 257°C. d: 1.40 kg/l. Soluble in water.
Production:
• acetaldehyde + hydrogen cyanide + ammonium bicarbonate (Bucherer-Bergs reaction/enzymatic hydrolysis)
Derivatives: alitame

DL-alanine
α-alanine; α-aminopropionic acid; 2-aminopropionic acid; [302-72-7]

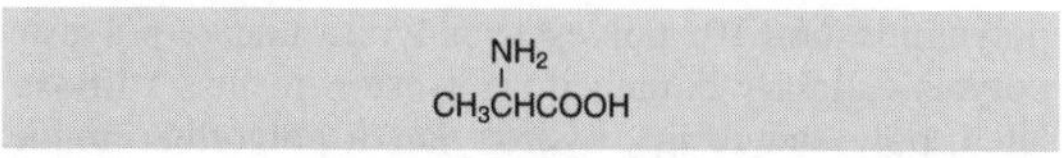

$CH_3CHCOOH$ (structure with NH_2)

$C_3H_7N_1O_2$. M: 89.10. Prisms or needles. MP: 280°C with decomposition. Sublimes at 200°C. d: 1.40 kg/l. Solubility in water: 167 g/l (25°C).
Production:
• acetaldehyde + hydrogen cyanide + ammonia (Strecker synthesis)
Derivatives: L-alanine; procymidone
Uses: sweetener (prepared foods)

L-alanine
Ala; L-α-alanine; L-2-aminopropionic acid; [56-41-7]

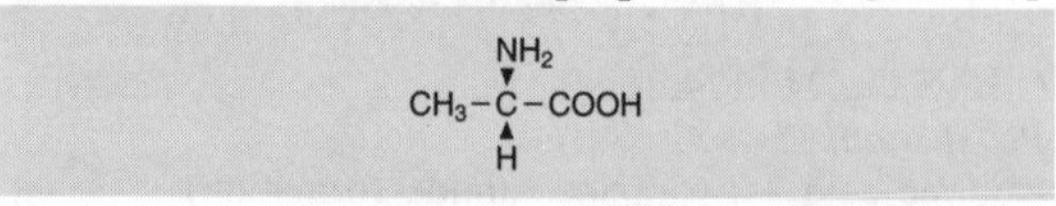

CH_3-C-COOH (structure with NH_2, H)

$C_3H_7N_1O_2$. M: 89.10. This is the naturally-occurring L(+)-enantiomer of alanine. Colourless crystals. Decompose on heating above 257°C. d: 1.40 kg/l. Soluble in water.
Production:
• L-aspartic acid + *Pseudomonas dacunhae* bacteria (microbial conversion)
• DL-alanine + acetic anhydride + *Aspergillus oryzae* mould (acetylation/enzymatic hydrolysis)
Derivatives:
enalapril
Uses: infusion solutions/diagnostic aids; raw material (peptide drugs)

albuterol *See:* salbutamol

alcloxa
[1317-25-5]
$C_4H_9Al_2Cl_1N_4O_7$. M: 314.54.
Production:
• allantoin + aluminium chloride, hexahydrate (salt formation/hydration)

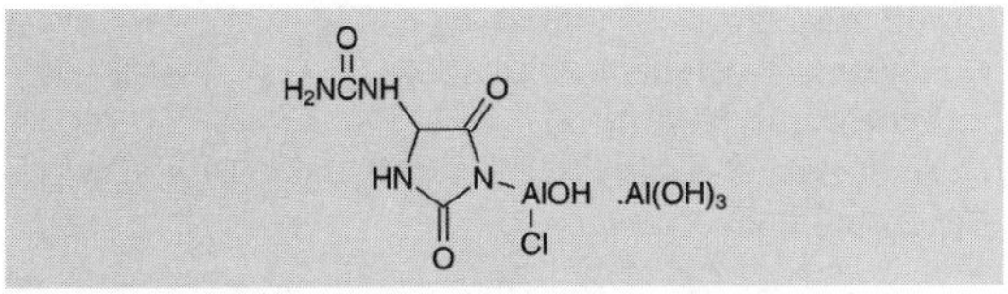

Uses: astringent/antacid/keratolytic drug

β-C$_{14}$ aldehyde

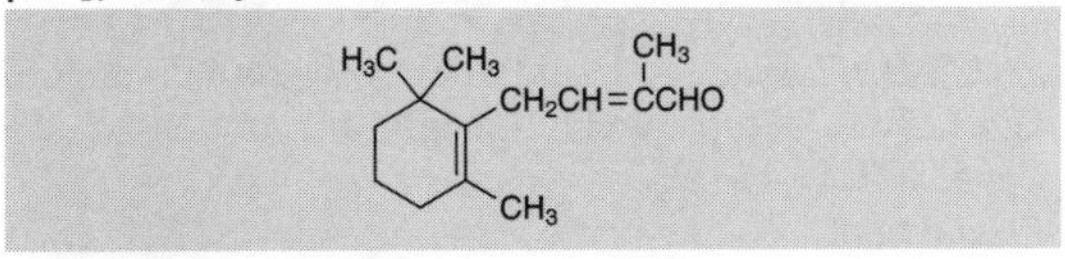

C$_{14}$H$_{22}$O$_1$. M: 206.33.
Production:
• β-ionone + ethyl chloroacetate (Darzens reaction/ ester hydrolysis/decarboxylation)
Derivatives: β-carotene; vitamin A

aldicarb
Temik (Union Carbide); [116-06-3]

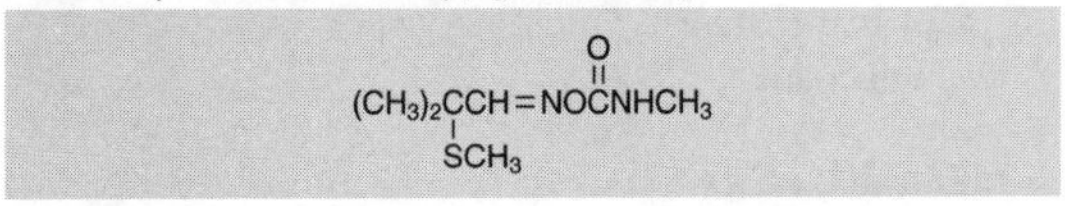

C$_7$H$_{14}$N$_2$O$_2$S$_1$. M: 190.26.
Production:
• isobutyraldehyde + hydroxylamine sulphate + methyl mercaptan + methyl isocyanate (alpha chlorination/oxime formation/sulphide formation/ isocyanate addition)
Derivatives: aldoxycarb
Uses: acaricide/insecticide/nematicide

aldioxa
[5579-81-7]

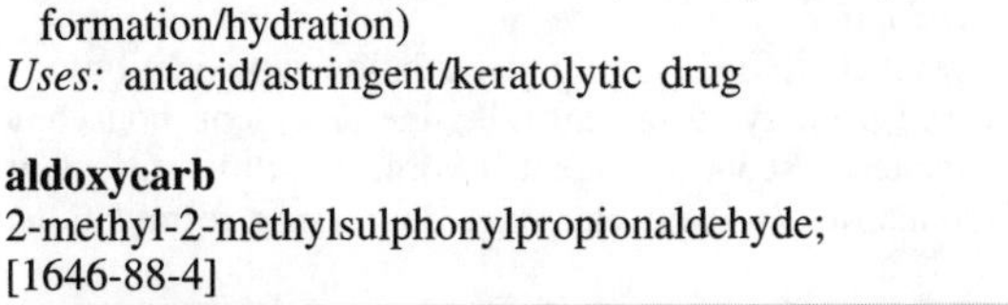

C$_4$H$_7$Al$_1$N$_4$O$_5$. M: 218.10.
Production:
• allantoin + aluminium chloride, hexahydrate (salt formation/hydration)
Uses: antacid/astringent/keratolytic drug

aldoxycarb
2-methyl-2-methylsulphonylpropionaldehyde; [1646-88-4]

C$_7$H$_{14}$N$_2$O$_4$S$_1$. M: 222.26.

Production:
• aldicarb + peracetic acid (oxidation)
Uses: insecticide/nematicide

alfentanil
[71195-58-9]

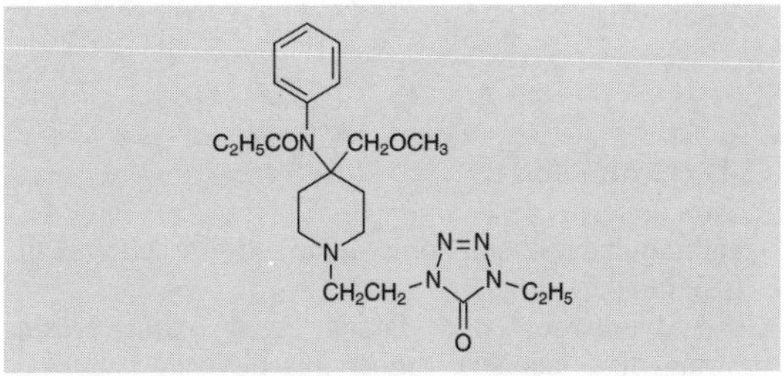

C$_{21}$H$_{32}$N$_6$O$_3$. M: 416.53. Available commercially as the hydrochloride monohydrate.
Production:
• 1-benzyl-4-piperidone + aniline + hydrogen cyanide + propionyl chloride + ethyl isocyanate + sodium azide + ethylene oxide (imine formation/addition/ nitrile hydrolysis/esterification/ester reduction/ methylation/amide formation/condensation/epoxid- ation/amine formation)
Uses: analgesic drug

alginic acid
[9005-32-7]
Polysaccharide. Slightly soluble in water forming acid solutions. Soluble in alkaline solutions. Produced by extraction from kelp (Macrocystis) and oar weeds (Laminaria). The seaweed is harvested and the polymer extracted in the United Kingdom, France, Norway, Canada, the USA, Japan and Korea.
Derivatives: propylene glycol alginate; sodium alginate
Uses: food stabiliser (puddings, creams, mayonnaise); gelling/ binding agent (pharmaceuticals); binder (paper coatings, sizing); plasticiser/binding agent (welding rod coatings); thickening/binding agent (animal feed)

alitame
L-β-aspartyl-N-(2,2,4,4-tetramethyl-3-thietanyl)-D-alaninamide

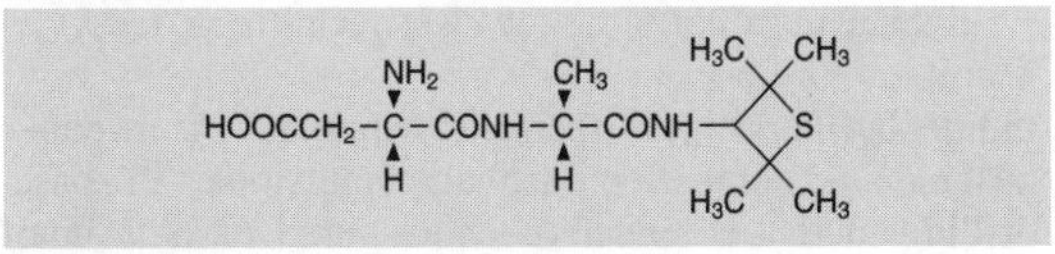

C$_{14}$H$_{25}$N$_3$O$_4$S$_1$. M: 331.44. White, odourless, crystalline powder.
Production:
• nitromethane + acetone + sodium sulphide + D-alanine + L-aspartic acid (carbonyl condensation/ sulphide formation/nitro reduction/amide formation/ amide formation)
Uses: artificial sweetener

alizarin

1,2-dihydroxyanthraquinone; Mordant Red 11 (CI); Pigment Red 83 (CI, calcium lake); 58000 (CI); 58000:1 (CI, calcium lake); [72-48-0]

$C_{14}H_8O_4$. M: 240.21.

Production:
• anthraquinone-2-sulphonic acid, sodium salt (alkali fusion/oxidation)

Uses: dye (wool, silk); laking agent (paints, resins, printing inks, lacquers, rubber, plastics)

Alkali Blue G *See:* Pigment Blue 18, Pigment Blue 61

alkali cellulose

soda cellulose; soda pulp

White solid containing 10–25% water. The cellulose is in a swollen form and can be penetrated by reagents.

Production:
• cotton linters/bleached wood pulp + sodium hydroxide (salt formation)

Derivatives:
diethylaminoethyl cellulose; ethyl cellulose; hydroxyethyl cellulose; hydroxypropyl cellulose; methyl cellulose; sodium carboxymethyl cellulose; sodium cellulose xanthate

alkali lignin

[8068-05-1]

Brown powder.

Production:
• sulphate pulp black liquor (wet refining process)

Uses:
pigments/fillers/clay dispersant (ceramics, paint, paper, pesticides); emulsifier (asphalt emulsions, oil-based drilling muds); extender (phenolic, urea particle board adhesives); leather tanning auxiliary; reinforcing filler (rubber)

n-alkanol(C_7-C_9)

Linevol 79 (Shell)

$$CH_3(CH_2)_nOH$$

n = 6–8. $C_8H_{17}O_1$. M: 129.23. Colourless liquid.

Production:
• 1-hexene/1-octene/*n*-olefins(C_6-C_8) + synthesis gas (hydroformylation)

Derivatives: di-*n*-alkyl(C_7-C_9) phthalate; tri-*n*-alkyl(C_7-C_9) trimellitate

n-alkanol(C_8-C_{10})

octanol/decanol; octyl/decyl alcohol

$$CH_3(CH_2)_nOH$$

n = 7–9. Colourless liquid. BP: 180–240°C. d: 0.82 kg/l (25°C). A typical chain-length distribution is: 43% C_8, 53% C_{10}, 4% C_{12}.

Production:
• ethylene (Alfol/Epal processes; coproduced with *n*-hexanol/*n*-octanol/*n*-decanol/lauryl alcohol, narrow-cut/*n*-alkanol(C_{12}-C_{14})/myristyl alcohol/cetyl alcohol/stearyl alcohol/*n*-alkanol(C_{12}-C_{18})/cetylstearyl alcohol/*n*-alkanol(C_{20+}))
• C_8-C_{10} fatty acids (hydrogenation)

Derivatives: 3-[alkoxy(C_8-C_{10})]propylamine; di-*n*-alkyl-(C_8-C_{10}) phthalate; *n*-nonyl methacrylate; tri-*n*-alkyl-(C_8-C_{10}) trimellitate

Uses: antifoam

n-alkanol(C_9-C_{11})

$$CH_3(CH_2)_nOH$$

n = 8–10. $C_{10}H_{22}O_1$. M: 158.29. Liquid. BP: 215–255°C. d: 0.83 kg/l (20°C). Insoluble in water. Typical chain-length distributions are: 35% C_9, 65% C_{11} or 25% C_9, 50% C_{10}, 25% C_{11} depending on the source of the raw material.

Production:
• 1-octene/1-decene/*n*-olefins(C_8-C_{10}) + synthesis gas (hydroformylation)

Derivatives: *n*-alkanol(C_9-C_{11}) ethoxylates; di-*n*-alkyl-(C_9-C_{11}) phthalate; diester oils

n-alkanol(C_9-C_{11}) ethoxylates

Dobanol 91-6 (Shell); Dobanol 91-12 (Shell); pareth-91 (CTFA)

$$CH_3(CH_2)_mO(CH_2CH_2O)_nH$$

m = 8–10, n = 2–12. Liquids. HLB: 8.1–15.4 (2.5–12 moles EO).

Production:
• *n*-alkanol(C_9-C_{11}) + ethylene oxide (epoxidation)

Uses: primary surfactant (alkaline detergent, household cleaners); scouring agent (wool, textile); surfactant-/emulsifier (solvent cleaning, degreasing formulations)

n-alkanol(C_{12}-C_{13})

Dobanol 23 (Shell)

$$CH_3(CH_2)_nOH$$

n = 11–12.

Production:
• *n*-olefins(C_{11}-C_{12}) + synthesis gas (hydroformylation)
Derivatives: *n*-alkanol(C_{12}-C_{13}) ethoxylates; ammonium lauryl sulphate; dilauryl 1,4-dihydro-2,6-dimethyl-pyridine-3,5-dicarboxylate; dilauryl thiodipropionate; dimethyllaurylamine; disodium laurylsulphosuccinate; lauryl acrylate; lauryl alcohol ethoxylate/propoxylates; lauryl β-aminocrotonate; lauryl chloride; lauryl glycidyl ether; magnesium lauryl sulphate; monoethanolamine lauryl sulphate; sodium lauryl sulphate; triethanolamine lauryl sulphate; zinc didodecyl dithiophosphate

n-alkanol(C_{12}-C_{13}) ethoxylates

$$CH_3(CH_2)_mO(CH_2CH_2O)_nH$$

m = 11–12, n = 2–6.5. Liquid or slurry, depending on the EO content. HLB: 11.9 (6.5 moles EO).
Production:
• *n*-alkanol(C_{12}-C_{13}) + ethylene oxide (epoxidation)
Derivatives: sodium lauryl ether sulphate
Uses: surfactant (household cleaners, detergents)

n-alkanol(C_{12}-C_{14})
lauryl alcohol, broad-cut; lauryl/myristyl alcohol

$$CH_3(CH_2)_nOH$$

n = 11–13. $C_{13}H_{28}O_1$. M: 200.36. White solid. MP: 30°C. BP: 230–300°C. The product is a mixture of C_{12} and C_{14} linear, primary alcohols. The relative proportion of C_{12} to C_{14} varies with the source and processing of the material. Usually C_{12} predominates at 65–70% of the mixture.
Production:
• ethylene (Alfol/Epal processes; coproduced with *n*-hexanol/*n*-octanol/*n*-decanol/*n*-alkanol(C_8-C_{10})/ /lauryl alcohol, narrow-cut/myristyl alcohol/cetyl alcohol/stearyl alcohol/*n*-alkanol(C_{12}-C_{18})/cetylstearyl alcohol/*n*-alkanol(C_{20+}))
• lauric acid, broad cut (hydrogenation)
• methyl laurate (hydrogenation)
Derivatives: *n*-alkanol(C_{12}-C_{14}) ethoxylates; ammonium lauryl sulphate; dilauryl 1,4-dihydro-2,6-dimethyl-pyridine-3,5-dicarboxylate; dilauryl thiodipropionate; dimethyllaurylamine; disodium laurylsulphosuccinate; lauroxy-2-hydroxypropyltrimethylammonium chloride; lauryl acrylate; lauryl alcohol, narrow-cut; lauryl alcohol ethoxylate/propoxylates; lauryl β-aminocrotonate; lauryl chloride; lauryl glycidyl ether; lauryl methacrylate; magnesium lauryl sulphate; monoethanolamine lauryl sulphate; myristyl alcohol; sodium lauryl sulphate; triethanolamine lauryl sulphate; zinc didodecyl dithiophosphate

n-alkanol(C_{12}-C_{14}) ethoxylates

$$CH_3(CH_2)_mO(CH_2CH_2O)_nH$$

m = 11–13, n = 2–8. Liquid/paste.

Production:
• *n*-alkanol(C_{12}-C_{14}) + ethylene oxide (epoxidation)
Derivatives: ammonium lauryl ether sulphate; disodium lauryl ether sulphosuccinate; sodium lauryl ether sulphate; triethanolamine lauryl ether sulphate
Uses:
emulsifier (white oils); surfactant (light-duty liquid cleaners, dishwashing detergents, cold-water detergents)

n-alkanol(C_{12}-C_{15})

$$CH_3(CH_2)_nOH$$

n = 11–14. $C_{13}H_{28}O_1$. M: 200.36. White solid. The product is a mixture of C_{12}, C_{13}, C_{14} and C_{15} linear, primary alcohols. A typical chain-length distribution is: 20% C_{12}, 30% C_{13}, 30% C_{14}, 20% C_{15}.
Production:
• *n*-olefins(C_{11}-C_{14}) + synthesis gas (hydroformylation)
Derivatives: *n*-alkanol(C_{12}-C_{15}) ethoxylates; 3-[alkoxy-(C_{12}-C_{15})]propylamine

n-alkanol(C_{12}-C_{15}) ether phosphoric acid
lauryl ether phosphate

$$\left[CH_3(CH_2)_mO(CH_2CH_2O)_n\right]_x \overset{O}{\underset{\|}{P}}(OH)_{3-x}$$

m = 11–14, n = 2–10, x = 1–2. Colourless to pale yellow liquid or paste.
Production:
• *n*-alkanol(C_{12}-C_{15}) ethoxylates + phosphorus pentoxide (esterification)
Uses: surfactant (detergents, cleaners)

n-alkanol(C_{12}-C_{15}) ethoxylates
pareth-25 (CTFA)

$$CH_3(CH_2)_mO(CH_2CH_2O)_nH$$

m = 11–14, n = 2–11. Colourless liquid, paste or solid. The product is a mixture of C_{12}, C_{13}, C_{14} and C_{15} linear, primary alcohol ethoxylates. A typical chain-length distribution is: 20% C_{12}, 30% C_{13}, 30% C_{14}, 20% C_{15}. HLB: 5.9–13.2 (2–9 moles EO).
Production:
• *n*-alkanol(C_{12}-C_{15}) + ethylene oxide (epoxidation)
Derivatives: *n*-alkanol(C_{12}-C_{15}) ether phosphoric acid; ammonium lauryl ether sulphate; sodium lauryl ether sulphate
Uses: primary surfactant (acid/oxidising cleaners); rolling/cutting fluids (emulsifier); scouring agent (wool); surfactant (household laundry liquid, powder detergents); wetting agent (dust control)

n-alkanol(C_{12}-C_{18})
coco alcohol; coconut alcohol; [68425-37-6]

$$CH_3(CH_2)_nOH$$

n = 11–17. White, soft solid. MP: 18–23°C.

Production:
- ethylene (Alfol/Epal processes; coproduced with *n*-hexanol/*n*-octanol/*n*-decanol/*n*-alkanol(C$_8$-C$_{10}$)/ lauryl alcohol, narrow-cut/myristyl alcohol/ *n*-alkanol(C$_{12}$-C$_{14}$)/cetyl alcohol/stearyl alcohol/cetyl-stearyl alcohol/*n*-alkanol(C$_{20+}$))
- palm kernel methyl ester, topped/methyl cocoate, topped (hydrogenation)

Derivatives:
n-alkanol(C$_{12}$-C$_{18}$) ethoxylates; dimethylcocoamine; lauryl alcohol ethoxylate/propoxylates; monoethanolamine lauryl sulphate; triethanolamine lauryl sulphate

Uses: aluminium rolling oil

n-alkanol(C$_{12}$-C$_{18}$) ethoxylates

CH$_3$(CH$_2$)$_m$(OCH$_2$CH$_2$)$_n$OH

m = 11–17, n = 5–7. White paste.
Production:
- *n*-alkanol(C$_{12}$-C$_{18}$) + ethylene oxide (epoxidation)

Derivatives: ammonium lauryl ether sulphate
Uses: antistatic agent (textile spin finishes); low-foaming surfactant (household, industrial detergents)

n-alkanol(C$_{13}$-C$_{15}$)

CH$_3$(CH$_2$)$_n$OH

n = 12–14. C$_{14}$H$_{30}$O$_1$. M: 214.39. Liquid. BP: 270–298°C. Pour point: -3°C. Flash point: 138°C (PMCC). d: 0.83 kg/l (20°C). Insoluble in water. The chain-length distribution is, typically, 67% C$_{13}$, 33% C$_{15}$.
Production:
- α-olefins(C$_{12}$-C$_{14}$) + synthesis gas (hydroformylation)

Derivatives: *n*-alkanol(C$_{13}$-C$_{15}$) ethoxylates; alkyl(C$_{13}$-C$_{15}$)amine; dimethylalkyl(C$_{13}$-C$_{15}$)amine

n-alkanol(C$_{13}$-C$_{15}$) ethoxylates

CH$_3$(CH$_2$)$_m$O(CH$_2$CH$_2$O)$_n$H

m = 12–14, n = 2–50. Fluid liquid (2 moles EO) to hard wax (50 moles EO). HLB: 5.9–18.1.
Production:
- *n*-alkanol(C$_{13}$-C$_{15}$) + ethylene oxide (epoxidation)

Derivatives:
potassium *n*-alkanol (C$_{13}$-C$_{15}$) ether propylsulphonate; sodium *n*-alkanol (C$_{13}$-C$_{15}$) ether sulphates; sodium lauryl ether sulphate

Uses: surfactant/wetting agent (heavy-duty powder detergents, household/industrial cleaners); emulsifier (pesticides, cleaners); textile scouring/antistatic/dye-levelling agents

n-alkanol(C$_{14}$-C$_{15}$)
Dobanol 45 (Shell)

CH$_3$(CH$_2$)$_n$OH

n = 13–14.

Production:
- *n*-olefins(C$_{13}$-C$_{14}$) + synthesis gas (hydroformylation)

Derivatives:
n-alkanol(C$_{14}$-C$_{15}$) ethoxylates

n-alkanol(C$_{14}$-C$_{15}$) ethoxylates
Dobanol 45 (Shell)

CH$_3$(CH$_2$)$_m$O(CH$_2$CH$_2$O)$_n$H

m = 13–14, n = 7–11. Solid. HLB: 11.6 (7 moles EO), 13.7 (11 moles EO). Soluble in water.
Production:
- *n*-alkanol(C$_{14}$-C$_{15}$) + ethylene oxide (epoxidation)

Uses:
surfactant (heavy-duty powder detergents)

n-alkanol(C$_{16}$-C$_{18}$)
See: cetylstearyl alcohol

n-alkanol(C$_{20+}$)

CH$_3$(CH$_2$)$_n$OH

n ≥ 19. Waxy solid. d: 0.81 kg/l (25°C). Epal process residue contains 66% alcohols and 34% hydrocarbons.
Production:
- ethylene (Alfol/Epal processes; coproduced with *n*-hexanol/*n*-octanol/*n*-decanol/*n*-alkanol(C$_8$-C$_{10}$)/ lauryl alcohol, narrow-cut/myristyl alcohol/ *n*-alkanol(C$_{12}$-C$_{14}$)/cetyl alcohol/stearyl alcohol/cetyl-stearyl alcohol/*n*-alkanol(C$_{12}$-C$_{18}$))

Uses:
textile processing lubricant

alkanol (C$_{30}$-C$_{50}$) ethoxylates
Unithox ethoxylates (Petrolite)

C$_n$H$_{2n+1}$(OCH$_2$CH$_2$)$_x$OH

n = 30–50.
Production:
- polyethylene wax, high-density + ethylene oxide (oxidation/epoxidation)

Uses:
emulsifier (emulsion polymerisation, vegetable oils); antiblocking/release agents

3-[alkoxy(C$_8$-C$_{10}$)]propylamine
alkyl(C$_8$-C$_{10}$)-3-oxypropylamine

CH$_3$(CH$_2$)$_n$OCH$_2$CH$_2$CH$_2$NH$_2$

n = 7–9. A typical chain-length distribution is: 43% C$_8$, 53% C$_{10}$, 4% C$_{12}$.
Production:
- *n*-alkanol(C$_8$-C$_{10}$) + acrylonitrile (cyanoethylation/ nitrile reduction)

Derivatives:
3-[alkoxy(C$_8$-C$_{10}$)propyl]-1,3-propanediamine
Uses: cationic flotation agent (iron ore)

3-[alkoxy(C$_8$-C$_{10}$)propyl]-1,3-propanediamine
N-[alkoxy(C$_8$-C$_{10}$)propyl]-1,3-propylenediamine

$$CH_3(CH_2)_nOCH_2CH_2CH_2NHCH_2CH_2CH_2NH_2$$

n = 7–9. A typical chain-length distribution is: 43% C$_8$, 53% C$_{10}$, 4% C$_{12}$.
Production:
- 3-[alkoxy(C$_8$-C$_{10}$)]propylamine + acrylonitrile (cyanoethylation/nitrile reduction)
Uses: cationic flotation agent (iron ore)

3-[alkoxy(C$_{12}$-C$_{15}$)]propylamine
alkyl(C$_{12}$-C$_{15}$)-3-oxypropylamine

$$CH_3(CH_2)_nOCH_2CH_2CH_2NH_2$$

n = 11–14. A typical chain-length distribution is: 20% C$_{12}$, 30% C$_{13}$, 30% C$_{14}$, 20% C$_{15}$.
Production:
- *n*-alkanol(C$_{12}$-C$_{15}$) + acrylonitrile (cyanoethylation/nitrile reduction)
Derivatives:
3-[alkoxy(C$_{12}$-C$_{15}$)propyl]-1,3-propanediamine
Uses: cationic flotation agent (iron, phosphate ores)

3-[alkoxy(C$_{12}$-C$_{15}$)propyl]-1,3-propanediamine
N-[alkoxy(C$_{12}$-C$_{15}$)propyl]-1,3-propylenediamine

$$CH_3(CH_2)_nOCH_2CH_2CH_2NHCH_2CH_2CH_2NH_2$$

n = 11–14. A typical chain-length distribution is: 20% C$_{12}$, 30% C$_{13}$, 30% C$_{14}$, 20% C$_{15}$.
Production:
- 3-[alkoxy(C$_{12}$-C$_{15}$)]propylamine + acrylonitrile (cyanoethylation/nitrile reduction)
Uses: cationic flotation agent (iron, phosphate ores)

alkyd resins, long-oil
Drying resins containing over 60% fatty acids. Soluble in white spirit and miscible with oils and varnishes.
Production:
- castor oil fatty acids, dehydrated/sunflower acid/safflower acid/linseed fatty acids/soyabean acid/fatty acids, polyunsaturated, conjugated/tobacco seed fatty acids/tall oil fatty acid + phthalic anhydride + glycerol/pentaerythritol (fatty acid process)
- linseed oil/soyabean oil/sunflower oil/castor oil, dehydrated + phthalic anhydride + glycerol (alcoholysis process)
Derivatives: alkyd resins, styreneated/vinyltoluenated; silicone alkyd resins
Uses: alkyd-chlorinated rubber primer paints; alkyd-vinyl copolymer resins (rapid-drying undercoats); binder (decorative undercoat, gloss building paints, printing inks)

alkyd resins, medium-oil
Drying resins containing 40–60% fatty acids.

Production:
- castor oil fatty acids, dehydrated/fatty acids, polyunsaturated, conjugated/safflower acid/linseed fatty acids/soyabean acid/sunflower acid/tobacco seed fatty acids/tall oil fatty acid + phthalic anhydride + glycerol/pentaerythritol (fatty acid process)
- linseed oil/sunflower oil/castor oil, dehydrated/soyabean oil + phthalic anhydride + glycerol (alcoholysis process)
Derivatives: alkyd resins, styrenated/vinyltoluenated
Uses: stoving lacquer modifier; binder (air-dried industrial/floor/decorative paints)

alkyd resins, non-drying
Short oil alkyd resins based on saturated fatty acids.
Production:
- castor oil/coconut oil/lauric acid, broad cut/pelargonic acid + phthalic anhydride + glycerol (esterification)
Uses: alkyd-amino acid-cured resins (industrial and clear wood finishes); alkyd-amino stoving resins (domestic equipment, vehicle finishes); tackifier/plasticiser (rubber, adhesives, cellulose nitrate lacquer)

alkyd resins, short-oil
Drying resins containing 25–45% fatty acids. Soluble in aromatic solvents. Not compatible with drying oils or varnishes.
Production:
- castor oil fatty acids, dehydrated/sunflower acid/fatty acids, polyunsaturated, conjugated/soyabean acid/linseed fatty acids/tall oil fatty acid/tobacco seed fatty acids/safflower acid + phthalic anhydride + glycerol (fatty acid process)
- linseed oil/castor oil, dehydrated/sunflower oil/soyabean oil + phthalic anhydride + glycerol (alcoholysis process)
Uses: air-dried and stoving industrial finishes; stoppers/fillers

alkyd resins, styrenated/vinyltoluenated
Vinyltoluenated alkyd resins dry more quickly and produce more chemically resistant films than unmodified resins.
Production:
- alkyd resins, long-oil/alkyd resins, medium-oil + vinyltoluene/styrene (polymerisation)
Uses: binder (industrial stoving finishes, stoving primers, rapid air-dried finishes); binder (printing inks)

alkyd resins, water-soluble
Alkyd resin containing pendant, hydrophilic amine, hydroxyl or carboxylic acid groups.
Production:
- maleinised oils + phthalic anhydride/trimellitic anhydride + glycerol + triethanolamine/dimethylethanolamine/ammonia (fatty acid process)

- trimethylolpropane/neopentyl glycol/trimethylol-ethane/1,4-cyclohexanedimethanol + castor oil, dehydrated + phthalic anhydride/trimellitic anhydride (alcoholysis process)

Uses:
electrodeposition coatings (automobiles); alkyd-acrylic resins (wood preservatives, decorative wood stains)

alkyl(C_{13}-C_{15})amine
Synprolan 35 (ICI)

$$CH_3(CH_2)_nNH_2$$

n = 12–14. Clear liquid. The chain-length distribution is: 70% C_{13}, 30% C_{15}.
Production:
- *n*-alkanol(C_{13}-C_{15}) + ammonia (direct amination)
Derivatives:
bis(2-hydroxyethyl)alkyl(C_{13}-C_{15})amine
Uses:
corrosion inhibitor (petroleum products); bitumen adhesion promotion agents; mineral flotation agent; pesticide auxiliary; clay surface treatment agent

alkylbenzene, long-chain

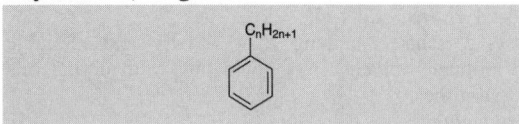

n ≥ 18.
Production:
- α-olefins(C_{18+})/eicosanol + benzene (Friedel-Crafts alkylation)
Derivatives:
alkylbenzene sulphonates, alkali-earth salts
Uses:
synthetic lubricant base oils (refrigeration compressors)

alkylbenzene sulphonates, alkali-earth salts

n ≥ 18, M = calcium, barium, magnesium.
Production:
- alkylbenzene, long-chain + sulphuric acid + calcium hydroxide/barium oxide/barium hydroxide/magnesia, caustic-calcined (sulphonation/salt formation)
Uses: dispersant (motor, marine, industrial lubricants)

alkylbenzene sulphonic acid
See: dodecylbenzenesulphonic acid, branched; dodecylbenzenesulphonic acid, linear

alkyl(C_{13}-C_{15})dimethylamine oxide
Clear liquid containing 30% active matter in water.

$$CH_3(CH_2)_n\overset{\displaystyle CH_3}{\underset{\displaystyle CH_3}{N}}\!\rightarrow\!O$$

n = 12–14.
Production:
- dimethylalkyl(C_{13}-C_{15})amine + hydrogen peroxide (oxidation)
Uses: foam boosters/bodying agents (shampoos, dishwashing liquid, bleach)

alkyl(C_{13}-C_{15})dimethylbenzylammonium chloride

$$C_nH_{2n+1}CH_2N(CH_3)_3^+ \quad Cl^-$$

n = 12–14. Available commercially as 50% or 80% solutions in water.
Production:
- dimethylalkyl(C_{13}-C_{15})amine + benzyl chloride (quaternisation)
Uses: biocide (disinfectants, wood preservatives, oilfield chemicals)

alkylene(C_4-C_6)dicarboxylic acids
AGS acid; DBA acid; nylon waste acid

$$HOOC(CH_2)_nCOOH$$

n = 2–4. $C_5H_8O_4$. M: 132.11. A waste stream from nylon production containing mixed succinic (25–30%), glutaric (42–47%) and adipic acids (25–30%).
Production:
- cyclohexanol-cyclohexanone, mixed/cyclohexanol + nitric acid, concentrated (oxidative cleavage; byproduct of adipic acid production)
Derivatives: alkylene(C_4-C_6) diol; dimethyl alkylene-(C_4-C_6)dicarboxylates; polyester polyols, linear
Uses: flue gas desulphurisation agent (power generation plants)

alkylene(C_4-C_6) diol

$$HO(CH_2)_nOH$$

n = 4–6. $C_5H_{12}O_2$. M: 104.15. A mixture of 1,4-butanediol, 1,5-pentanediol and 1,6-hexanediol.
Production:
- alkylene(C_4-C_6)dicarboxylic acids (hydrogenation)
Derivatives: polyester polyols, linear

alkylketene dimer
AKD

$$CH_3(CH_2)_{15}CH = C-CH(CH_2)_{15}CH_3$$
$$O-C\!\!\diagdown\!\!_O$$

$C_{36}H_{68}O_2$. M: 532.94.

Production:
- stearyl ketene (dimerisation)

Derivatives: distearyl ketone

Uses: paper sizing ingredient

alkyl(C$_9$-C$_{30}$)phenol

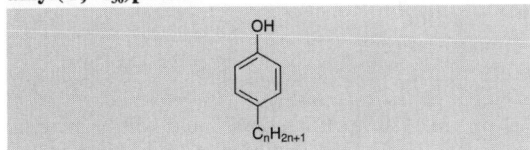

n = 9–30.

Production:
- phenol + propylene (oligomerisation/Friedel-Crafts alkylation)

Derivatives: calcium alkyl salicylates; phenates, alkali-earth salts; phenates, sulphurised, alkali-earth salts

alkylphenol-polyamine adducts

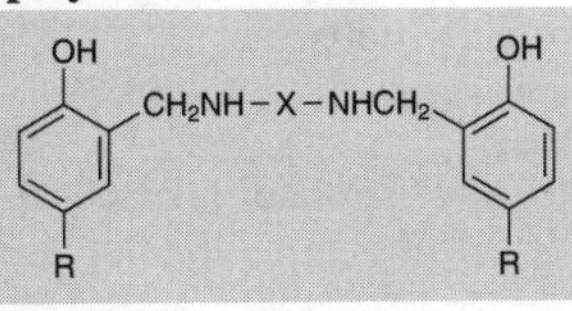

X = polyamine, R = nonyl, dodecyl-.

Production:
- dodecylphenol/nonylphenol + formaldehyde + polyethylenepolyamine (Mannich reaction)

Uses: ashless dispersants (lubricants)

N-alkyl(C$_{16}$-C$_{22}$)-1,3-propanediamine

CH$_3$(CH$_2$)$_n$NHCH$_2$CH$_2$CH$_2$NH$_2$

n = 15–21.

Production:
- fish amine, hydrogenated + acrylonitrile (cyanoethylation/nitrile reduction)

Uses: bitumen adhesion promotion agents

alkyl(C$_{13}$-C$_{15}$)trimethylammonium chloride

CH$_3$(CH$_2$)$_n$N(CH$_3$)$_3^+$ Cl$^-$

n = 12–14. Clear liquid. Available commercially as a 35% solution in water.

Production:
- dimethylalkyl(C$_{13}$-C$_{15}$)amine + methyl chloride (quaternisation)

Uses: cationic emulsifier/biocide (cosmetics); antistatic agent (textile spin finishes)

allantoin

5-ureidohydantoin; [97-59-6]

C$_4$H$_6$N$_4$O$_3$. M: 158.12. Crystalline solid. MP: 230°C with decomposition. Slightly soluble in hot water and alcohol.

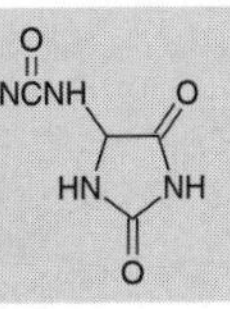

Production:
- glyoxylic acid + urea (condensation)

Derivatives: alcloxa; aldioxa

Uses: wound treatment/antisporiatic drug

allethrin

3-allyl-2-methyl-4-oxocyclopent-2-enylchrysanthemate; [584-79-2]

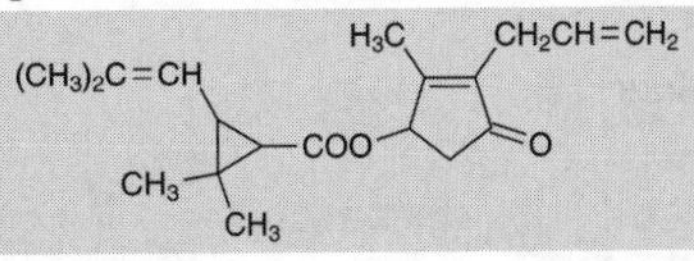

C$_{19}$H$_{26}$O$_3$. M: 302.42. The commercial product is a racemic mixture.

Production:
- allethrolone + (*1RS*)-*cis/trans*-chrysanthemic acid (esterification)

Uses: insecticide

allethrolone

2-allyl-4-hydroxy-3-methylcyclopenten-2-one

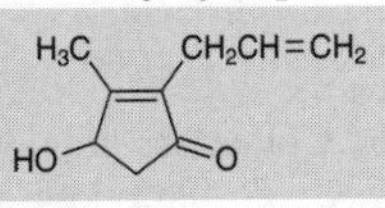

C$_9$H$_{12}$O$_2$. M: 152.19.

Production:
- 5-bromovaleric acid + ethyl acetate + methyl-glyoxal dimethyl acetal (dehydrobromination/ Claisen condensation/carbonyl condensation/ decarboxylation)

Derivatives: allethrin; bioallethrin; *S*-bioallethrin

allopurinol

4-hydroxypyrazolo[3,4-d]pyrimidine; HPP; [315-30-0]

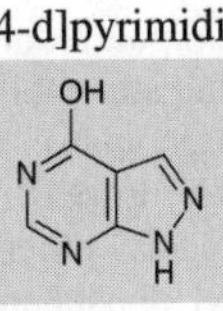

C$_5$H$_4$N$_4$O$_1$. M: 136.11.

Production:
- ethyl cyanoacetate + triethyl orthoformate + hydrazine + formamide (condensation/condensation/ condensation)

Uses: gout treatment drug

alloxydim-sodium

[66003-55-2]

C$_{17}$H$_{24}$N$_1$Na$_1$O$_5$. M: 345.37.

CH$_3$CH$_2$CH$_2$ᴄ=NOCH$_2$CH=CH$_2$

Na$^+$

COOCH$_3$

CH$_3$ CH$_3$

Production:
• diacetone alcohol + dimethyl malonate + *n*-butyryl chloride + hydroxylamine sulphate + allyl chloride (condensation/dehydrochlorination/oxime formation/ether formation)
Uses: herbicide

Allura Red AC *See:* Food Red 17

allyl acrylate

O
‖
CH$_2$=CHCOCH$_2$CH=CH$_2$

C$_6$H$_8$O$_2$. M: 112.13. Liquid. BP: 122°C. d: 1.05 kg/l (20°C). Slightly soluble in water. Soluble in oxygenated solvents.
Production:
• allyl alcohol + acrylic acid (esterification)
Uses: reactive diluent (radiation-cured coatings)

allyl alcohol
2-propen-1-ol; [107-18-6]

CH$_2$=CHCH$_2$OH

C$_3$H$_6$O$_1$. M: 58.08. Colourless liquid with a pungent odour. BP: 95–97°C. d: 0.85 kg/l (20°C). Miscible with water, oxygenated and chlorinated solvents. Gradually polymerises on standing.
Production:
• propylene oxide (isomerisation)
• propylene + oxygen (Showa Denka process)
Derivatives: allyl acrylate; allyl bromide; allyl caproate; allyl chloroacetate; allyl cyanoacrylate; allyl cyclohexylpropionate; allyl enanthate; allyl glycidyl ether; allyl methacrylate; allyl phenoxyacetate; 1,4-butanediol; chlorohydrin; diallyl adipate; diallyl fumarate; diallyl isophthalate; diallyl maleate; diallyl phthalate; diethylene glycol bis(allyl carbonate); epichlorohydrin; glycerol α-allyl ether; 2-hydroperfluoroethyl allyl ether; 2-hydroperfluoropropyl allyl ether; 15-pentadecanolide; propane sultone; triallyl phosphate; triallyl trimellitate; trichlorobutylene oxide

allylamine
3-aminopropene; [107-11-9]

CH$_2$=CHCH$_2$NH$_2$

C$_3$H$_7$N$_1$. M: 57.10. Yellow liquid with a strong ammonia-like odour. BP: 58°C. d: 0.76 kg/l (22°C). Flash point: -12°C (TCC). Soluble in water and oxygenated solvents.

Production:
• allyl chloride + ammonia (amine formation; coproduced with diallylamine/triallylamine)
Derivatives:
γ-aminopropyltriethoxysilane

allyl bromide
3-bromo-1-propene; [106-95-6]

CH$_2$=CHCH$_2$Br

C$_3$H$_5$Br$_1$. M: 120.97. Colourless liquid with a pungent odour. BP: 70–71°C. d: 1.40 kg/l (20°C). Insoluble in water. Miscible with oxygenated and chlorinated solvents.
Production:
• allyl alcohol + hydrobromic acid (alcohol bromination)
Derivatives:
clopenthixol; cyclopentobarbital; cyclopropyl bromide; flupenthixol; levallorphan; methohexital; nalorphine; piproctanyl bromide; tiotixene

allyl caproate
allyl hexanoate; allyl hexoate; [123-68-2]

O
‖
CH$_3$(CH$_2$)$_4$COCH$_2$CH=CH$_2$

C$_9$H$_{16}$O$_2$. M: 156.23. Colourless liquid with a pineapple-like odour. BP: 75°C (2 kPa). d: 0.90 kg/l (20°C). Insoluble in water.
Production:
• allyl alcohol + caproic acid (esterification)
Uses: unsaturated polyester resin comonomer (surface coatings); flavouring ingredient

allyl chloride
3-chloropropene; AC; [107-05-1]

CH$_2$=CHCH$_2$Cl

C$_3$H$_5$Cl$_1$. M: 76.52. Colourless liquid with a pungent odour. FP: -134°C. BP: 45°C. d: 0.94 kg/l (20°C). Slightly soluble in water. Miscible with oxygenated and chlorinated solvents.
Production:
• propylene + chlorine (high-temperature chlorination)
Derivatives:
alloxydim-sodium; allylamine; allyl isothiocyanate; allyl mercaptan; *o*-allylphenol; 1-bromo-3-chloropropane; butalbital; γ-chloropropyltrimethoxysilane; diallylamine; 2,2'-diallylbisphenol A; diallyldimethylammonium chloride; diallyl sulphide; glycerol-1,3-dichlorohydrin; imazalil; metolachlor; naloxone; oxprenolol; pentaerythritol triallyl ether; sodium allyl sulphonate; tetrabromobisphenol A allyl ether; triallylamine; triallyl cyanurate; 2,4,6-tribromophenyl allyl ether; 3-(trimethoxysilyl)propyldimethyloctadecylammonium chloride; trimethylolpropane diallyl ether; valdetamide

allyl chloroacetate
[2916-14-5]

$$ClCH_2COCH_2CH=CH_2$$

$C_5H_7Cl_1O_2$. M: 134.56.
Production:
• allyl alcohol + chloroacetic acid (esterification)
Derivatives: acrylic rubber

allyl cyanoacrylate

$$CH_2=CCOCH_2CH=CH_2 \atop CN$$

$C_7H_7N_1O_2$. M: 137.15. Colourless liquid with a sharp, acrylic odour. Lachrymatory. BP: 78–82°C (1 kPa). d: 1.05 kg/l. Flash point: 82°C.
Production:
• allyl alcohol + cyanoacetic acid + formaldehyde (esterification/carbonyl condensation/thermal depolymerisation)
Uses: cyanoacrylate adhesives (electronics, household, sporting, medical components)

allyl cyclohexylpropionate
allyl 3-cyclohexylpropionate; [2705-87-5]

$$CH_2CH_2COCH_2CH=CH_2$$

$C_{12}H_{20}O_2$. M: 196.29.
Production:
• cinnamic acid + allyl alcohol (hydrogenation/esterification)
Uses: fragrance ingredient

allyl enanthate
allyl heptanoate; allyl heptoate; [142-19-8]

$$CH_3(CH_2)_5COCH_2CH=CH_2$$

$C_{10}H_{18}O_2$. M: 170.25. Colourless liquid with a pineapple-like odour. BP: 210°C. d: 0.89 kg/l (15°C). Insoluble in water.
Production:
• allyl alcohol + *n*-heptanoic acid (esterification)
Uses: fragrance ingredient

allyl glycidyl ether
1,2-epoxy-3-allyloxypropane; AGE; [106-92-3]

$$CH_2-CHCH_2OCH_2CH=CH_2$$

$C_6H_{10}O_2$. M: 114.15. Colourless liquid. BP: 154°C. FP: -100°C. d: 0.97 kg/l (20°C). Slightly soluble in water.
Production:
• allyl alcohol + epichlorohydrin (dehydrochlorination)

Derivatives: acrylic rubber; γ-glycidoxypropyltrimethoxysilane; propylene oxide copolymers, rubber
Uses: polyepichlorohydrin rubber comonomer; unsaturated polyester resin comonomer; crosslinked polyurethane elastomer comonomer

allyl isothiocyanate
allyl mustard oil; mustard oil; [57-06-7]

$$CH_2=CHCH_2NCS$$

$C_4H_5N_1S_1$. M: 99.15. Colourless liquid with a strong, mustard-like odour. BP: 152°C. d: 1.01 kg/l (20°C). Slightly soluble in water. Miscible with alcohol.
Production:
• allyl chloride + potassium thiocyanate (dehydrochlorination)
Derivatives: allylthiourea
Uses: flavouring ingredient

allyl mercaptan
allyl thiol; propene-3-thiol

$$CH_2=CHCH_2SH$$

$C_3H_6S_1$. M: 74.14. Colourless liquid with a garlic-like odour. BP: 90°C. Insoluble in water.
Production:
• allyl chloride + sodium hydrosulphide (dehydrochlorination)
Derivatives:
cycloxydim; γ-mercaptopropyltrimethoxysilane

allyl methacrylate
AMA; [96-05-9]

$$CH_2=CCOCH_2CH=CH_2 \atop CH_3$$

$C_7H_{10}O_2$. M: 126.16.
Production:
• methyl methacrylate + allyl alcohol (transesterification)
Derivatives: γ-methacryloxypropyltrimethoxysilane
Uses: polyester resin comonomer (surface coatings)

allyl mustard oil *See:* allyl isothiocyanate

o-allylphenol
2-allylphenol; [1745-81-9]

$$\overset{OH}{\underset{}{\bigcirc}}CH_2CH=CH_2$$

$C_9H_{10}O_1$. M: 134.18. Liquid.
Production:
• phenol + allyl chloride (ether formation/Claisen rearrangement)

Derivatives:
4,4′-bis(2-allylphenoxy)benzophenone
Uses: polyimide resin comonomer

allyl phenoxyacetate

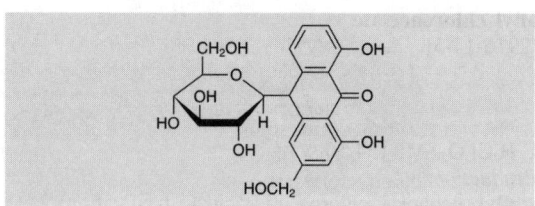

$C_{11}H_{12}O_3$. M: 192.22.
Production:
• allyl alcohol + phenoxyacetic acid (esterification)
Uses: flavouring ingredient

allyl sulphide *See:* diallyl sulphide

allylthiourea
allyl-2-thiourea; thiosinamine (INN); [109-57-9]

$$CH_2=CHCH_2NHCNH_2$$
(with S double-bonded above)

$C_4H_8N_2S_1$. M: 116.17. White crystals with a slight garlic odour. MP: 78°C. d: 1.22 kg/l. Soluble in water and alcohol.
Production:
• allyl isothiocyanate + ammonia (isothiocyanate addition)
Uses: nickel brightening agent; wound treatment drug

almond oil, bitter
Colourless to pale yellow liquid with a benz-aldehyde-like odour. Produced by maceration/steam distillation of bitter almond (*Prunus dulcis* var. *amara*) kernels. d: 1.04 kg/l (25°C). Slightly soluble in water. The unrefined oil contains hydrogen cyanide which is removed chemically.
Uses:
flavouring/fragrance ingredient

almond oil, sweet
Colourless to pale yellow liquid with a benz-aldehyde-like odour. Produced by extraction from sweet almond (*Prunus dulcis*) kernels. d: 1.04 kg/l (25°C). Slightly soluble in water.
Uses: flavouring ingredient

aloe
Dried latex or extract in water of leaves of the Cape Aloe (*Aloe ferox*, grown in South Africa) or the Curacao Aloe (*Aloe barbadensis*, grown in the West Indies).
Derivatives: aloin
Uses: emollient (cosmetics, toiletries)

aloin
[5133-19-7]
$C_{21}H_{22}O_9$. M: 418.40. Yellow, crystalline solid. MP: 148°C. Slightly soluble in water and alcohol.

Production:
• aloe (extraction)
Uses: cathartic drug

alprazolam
[28981-97-7]

$C_{17}H_{13}Cl_1N_4$. M: 308.77.
Production:
• nordazepam + hydrazine + triethyl orthoacetate (thionation/imine formation/condensation)
Uses: anxiolytic drug

alum *See:* aluminium sulphate

alumina, activated

Al_2O_3

Al_2O_3. M: 101.96. Aluminium oxide in the form of porous granules with a high internal surface area. Available in a variety of mesh sizes.
Production:
• alumina trihydrate (calcination)
Uses:
catalyst (alcohol dehydration, olefin isomerisation, Claus process); catalyst support; drying agent; filter medium; chromatographic adsorption agent

alumina, calcined
aluminium oxide; [1344-28-1]

Al_2O_3

Al_2O_3. M: 101.96. White powder. High thermal stability. Insoluble in water.
Production:
• alumina trihydrate (calcination)
Derivatives: alumina, fused; aluminium; aluminium chloride, anhydrous
Uses:
metal polishing compounds; aluminosilicate fibres; glass/enamel ingredient; technical ceramics ingredient; pigment lake base; shock resistant chinaware

alumina, fused
electrocorundum; Saffil (ICI, fibre)

Al_2O_3

Al_2O_3. M: 101.96. White solid. Available either as the finished, shaped object, fibre or in a milled form for use in mixed refractories and ceramics.
Production:
• bauxite/alumina, calcined + metallurgical coke (arc reduction)
Uses: grinding wheels; metal grinding abrasive; polishing papers; aluminium oxide fibres (furnace/kiln linings); refractory bricks (steel/glass furnaces); shaped refractories

alumina, hydrated *See:* alumina trihydrate

alumina, natural *See:* corundum

alumina gel *See:* aluminium hydroxide gel

alumina trihydrate
alumina hydrate; aluminium hydrate; aluminium hydroxide; aluminium trihydroxide; alumina, hydrated; ATH; Lake White; Transparent White; Pigment White 24 (CI); 77002 (CI); [21645-51-2]

$Al_2O_3.H_2O$

$H_2Al_2O_4$. M: 119.98. White powder. Decomposes when heated above 230°C. d: 2.4 kg/l. Insoluble in water.
Production:
• bauxite + sodium hydroxide (Bayer alumina trihydrate process)
Derivatives: alumina, activated; alumina, calcined; aluminium chloride, hexahydrate; aluminium fluoride; aluminium formate, basic; aluminium nitrate; aluminium phosphate, monobasic; aluminium sulphate; aluminium titanate; cobalt blue; cobalt green; polyaluminium chloride; sodium alum; sodium aluminate; sodium aluminium phosphate
Uses: petroleum refining/chemical production catalyst; glass/ceramic/enamel ingredient; filler/pigment (artificial marble); fire-retardant filler (thermoplastics, thermosetting resins, foamed rubber, latex); toothpaste abrasive; antiskid coatings (packaging); binders (alumina/aluminosilicate refractory fibres); pigment (printing inks); pitch collection additive (paper mill water)

aluminium
Pigment Metal 1 (CI); [7429-90-5]

Al

Al_1. M: 26.98. Silvery-white, ductile metal available in bar, sheet, wire, leaf and powder form. Forms an oxide film on the surface in moist air which protects the metal from corrosion. MP 660°C. BP: 2,327°C. d: 2.70 kg/l.

Production:
• alumina, calcined (Hall-Heroult electrolytic reduction process)
Derivatives: aluminium acetate, basic; aluminium chloride, anhydrous; aluminium chlorohydrate; aluminium nitride; aluminium octoate; aluminium phosphide; calcium; chromium; diethylaluminium chloride; ethylaluminium dichloride; ethylaluminium sesquichloride; ferroboron; ferromolybdenum; ferrovanadium; titanium diboride; triethylaluminium; triisobutylaluminium; tri-*n*-octylaluminium
Uses:
aluminium packaging/cooking foil; blowing agent (lightweight building materials); aluminium bronze ingredient (ship propellers, fittings, automobile engine components, plastic moulding dies); lustering pigment (decorative, priming, industrial paints); pigment (heat-resistant paints, reflective bitumen paints); aluminium/zinc casting alloy ingredient (engine components); aluminium power cable alloy raw material; aluminium wrought alloy raw material (vehicle body parts); reagent (aluminothermic process); sprayed metal coatings; steel calorising agent

aluminium acetate, basic
aluminium diacetate; aluminium subacetate; hydroxyaluminium diacetate; mordant rouge; [142-03-0]

$(CH_3COO)_2AlOH$

$C_4H_7Al_1O_5$. M: 162.07. White, amorphous powder. Soluble in water if freshly prepared forming acidic solutions. MP: 54°C. The product is stabilised with boric acid. 8–25% solutions in water are also sold.
Production:
• aluminium + acetic acid (salt formation)
Uses: antiperspirant; embalming fluid ingredient; mordant/laking agent; textile waterproofing/fireproofing agent

aluminium chloride, anhydrous
aluminium trichloride, anhydrous; [7446-70-0]

$AlCl_3$

Al_1Cl_3. M: 133.34. Off-white, hygroscopic powder. d: 2.44 kg/l (25°C). Sublimes at 178°C. Solubility in water: 700 g/l water (15°C). Soluble in hydrochloric acid and organic solvents.
Production:
• aluminium + chlorine (reaction)
• alumina, calcined + chlorine + metallurgical coke (reaction)
Derivatives: aluminium isopropoxide; aluminium octoate; lithium aluminium hydride
Uses: catalyst (Friedel-Crafts reactions, dehydrogenation, decarboxylation, oxidation, amination, petroleum reforming, olefin polymerisation); titanium arc welding flux; aluminium alloy secondary smelting reagent

aluminium chloride, basic
See: aluminium chlorohydrate; polyaluminium chloride

aluminium chloride, hexahydrate
aluminium chloride hydrate; [7784-13-6]

$$AlCl_3.6H_2O$$

$H_{12}Al_1Cl_3O_6$. M: 241.43. Colourless, deliquescent crystals. Loses water on heating. Highly soluble in water producing acidic solutions.
Production:
• alumina trihydrate + hydrochloric acid (neutralisation)
Derivatives: alcloxa; aldioxa; aluminium chlorohydrate; aluminium distearate
Uses: creaseproof textile finishing agent; deodorant/ antiperspirant ingredient; polyamide flame-resistant treatment reagent; crude oil refining agent; textile dyeing auxiliary; synthetic fibre antistatic treatments; wood preservative

aluminium chlorohydrate
aluminium chloride, basic; dialuminium chloride pentahydroxide; [12042-91-0]

$$Al_2(OH)_5Cl$$

$H_5Al_2Cl_1O_5$. M: 174.44. White powder (dihydrate) or solution in water. The product is defined by the ratio OH:Al which is 2.5 in this case. Basic aluminium chloride products with lower OH:Al ratios are called polyaluminium chloride (*qv*).
Production:
• aluminium chloride, hexahydrate (electrolysis)
• aluminium chloride, hexahydrate + aluminium (reaction)
Derivatives:
aluminium monostearate; sucralfate
Uses: deodorant/antiperspirant ingredient

aluminium diacetate *See:* aluminium acetate, basic

aluminium diformate *See:* aluminium formate, basic

aluminium distearate
monohydroxyaluminium distearate; [300-92-5]

$$[CH_3(CH_2)_{16}COO]_2AlOH$$

$C_{36}H_{71}Al_1O_5$. M: 610.94. White powder. MP: 145°C. Insoluble in water and alcohol. Gels mineral and vegetable oils.
Production:
• aluminium chloride, hexahydrate + sodium stearate (salt formation)
Uses: gelling agent (cosmetics); polymers/coatings additive; amino resin processing lubricant

aluminium fluoride
aluminium trifluoride; [7784-18-1]

$$AlF_3$$

Al_1F_3. M: 83.97. White, anhydrous crystals. Sublimes at 1,272°C. Solubility in water: 5.6 g/l (25°C).
Production:
• alumina trihydrate + hydrogen fluoride (salt formation)
• alumina trihydrate + hexafluorosilicic acid/hydrofluoric acid (salt formation/calcination)
Uses:
aluminium electrolysis adjunct; flux (glass, enamel, ceramics production)

aluminium formate, basic
aluminium diformate; [51575-25-8]

$$(HCOO)_2AlOH$$

$C_2H_3Al_1O_5$. M: 134.01.
Production:
• alumina trihydrate + formic acid (salt formation)
Uses: textile waterproofing agent

aluminium hydroxide gel
alumina gel; aluminium hydroxide, colloidal
Al_2O_3. M: 101.96.
Production:
• aluminium sulphate + sodium hydroxide (salt formation)
Uses: gastric medicines

aluminium isopropoxide
[555-31-7]

$$[(CH_3)_2CHO]_3Al$$

$C_9H_{21}Al_1O_3$. M: 204.25. White, hygroscopic solid. MP: 118°C. Soluble in most organic solvents.
Production:
• aluminium chloride, anhydrous + isopropanol (dehydrochlorination)
Derivatives:
aluminium tristearate
Uses: reagent (Meerwein-Ponndorf reduction, Oppenauer oxidation, grease lubricants production)

aluminium monostearate
dihydroxyaluminium monostearate; [7047-84-9]

$$CH_3(CH_2)_{16}\overset{O}{\overset{\|}{C}}OAl(OH)_2$$

$C_{18}H_{37}Al_1O_4$. M: 344.48. Pale yellow powder. MP: 155°C. Insoluble in water or alcohol.
Production:
• aluminium chlorohydrate + sodium stearate (salt formation)
Uses:
gelling agent (pharmaceuticals); lubricant (textile fibres, unsaturated polyester resin)

aluminium nitrate
[7784-27-2]

$Al(NO_3)_3$

$Al_1N_3O_9$. M: 212.99. Available as the nonahydrate. White crystals. MP: 73°C. Decomposes on heating above 150°C. Solubility in water: 637 g/l water (25°C) forming acidic solutions.
Production:
• alumina trihydrate + nitric acid (salt formation)
Uses:
corrosion inhibitor; leather tanning auxiliary; actinide extraction agent

aluminium nitride
[24304-00-5]

AlN

Al_1N_1. M: 40.99.
Production:
• aluminium + nitrogen (thermal conversion)
Uses: integrated circuit housing ceramics

aluminium octoate
aluminium 2-ethylhexanoate; [6028-57-5]

$(C_6H_{13}CH_2COO)_3Al$

$C_{24}H_{45}Al_1O_6$. M: 456.59.
Production:
• aluminium chloride, anhydrous + 2-ethylhexanoic acid (salt formation)
• aluminium + 2-ethylhexanoic acid (electrolysis)
Uses: thickening agent (gasoline)

aluminium phosphate, monobasic

$Al(H_2PO_4)_3$

$H_6Al_1O_{12}P_3$. M: 317.94.
Production:
• alumina trihydrate + phosphoric acid, pure (salt formation)
Uses: binder (refractories); anticorrosion pigment raw material

aluminium phosphide
[20859-73-8]

AlP

Al_1P_1. M: 57.95. Dark yellow or grey crystals. Stable up to 1,000°C. Reacts with water or moisture in air releasing phosphine.
Production:
• aluminium + phosphorus + water (reaction/hydrolysis)
Uses: grain fumigant/insecticide/rodenticide

aluminium potassium sulphate
potash alum; potassium alum; potassium aluminium sulphate; [10043-67-1] (anhydrous); [7784-24-9] (tetracosahydrate)

$Al_2(SO_4)_3.K_2SO_4$

$Al_2K_2O_{16}S_4$. M: 516.41. White, crystalline solid or powder with 24 moles water of crystallisation. This is lost when heated above 65°C. Melts at 93°C and becomes anhydrous above 200°C. d: 1.73 kg/l. Soluble in water forming acidic solutions. Kainite and alunite are natural mineral forms of potash alum mined in various parts of the world.
Production:
• bauxite + potassium sulphate + sulphuric acid (salt formation)
Uses: cement/plaster hardener; dyeing auxiliary; flocculant (water treatment, sugar clarification); gelatine/protein glues hardening agent; baking powder ingredient; leather tanning auxiliary; mordant; reagent (pulp/paper production)

aluminium silicate, fused *See:* mullite

aluminium silicate, precipitated
[1327-36-2]

$Al_2O_3.SiO_2$

$Al_2O_5Si_1$. M: 162.04. White powder. d: 2.1 kg/l. Particle size: 5–30 nm. BET surface area: 35–100 m²/g. Similar products incorporating some sodium are also produced as sodium aluminium silicate. Clay minerals such as montmorillonite and kaolinite are natural forms of aluminium silicate. Mullite, cyanite, andalusite and sillimanite are manufactured minerals based on different ratios of aluminium and silicon oxide.
Production:
• aluminium sulphate + sodium silicate (salt formation)
Uses: extender (emulsion paints); filler (rubber, shoesoling, paper, printing inks)

aluminium subacetate *See:* aluminium acetate, basic

aluminium sulphate
alum; cake alum; papermakers' alum; patent alum; [10043-01-3]

$Al_2(SO_4)_3$

$Al_2O_{12}S_3$. M: 342.14. Available commercially as the octadecahydrate, which is a white, crystalline or granular solid. Loses water of crystallisation on heating. d: 1.69 kg/l. Soluble in water. Aluminium sulphate is also sold as a solution in water. Iron-free grades of aluminium sulphate are made from alumina trihydrate instead of bauxite or kaolin.
Production:
• alumina trihydrate/bauxite/clay + sulphuric acid (Dorr process)

Derivatives: aluminium hydroxide gel; aluminium silicate, precipitated; fosetyl-aluminium; polyaluminium chloride
Uses: oils/fats/soaps/grease clarifying agent; concrete waterproofing agents/retarders; dyeing/tanning auxiliary; flocculant (water treatment); gelatine hardening agent; photographic chemical; catalyst raw material; reagent (titanium dioxide post-treatment); retention aids/dry strength additives/water resistance improvers (paper production); waterproofing/fireproofing agent (textiles)

aluminium titanate

$$Al_2TiO_5$$

$Al_2O_5Ti_1$. M: 181.85.
Production:
• alumina trihydrate + titanium dioxide, hydrate (calcination)
Uses: ceramic components (internal combustion engines)

aluminium tristearate
[637-12-7]

$$[CH_3(CH_2)_{16}COO]_3Al$$

$C_{54}H_{105}Al_1O_6$. M: 877.40. White solid. MP: 115°C. Insoluble in water and alcohol. Gels mineral and vegetable oils.
Production:
• aluminium isopropoxide + stearic acid (salt formation)
Uses: gelling agent (deodorants, cleansing lotions, sticks); waterproofing agent (paper, textile coatings)

AMA *See:* allyl methacrylate

amantadine
[768-94-5]; [665-66-7] (hydrochloride); [31377-23-8] (sulphate)

$C_{10}H_{17}N_1$. M: 151.26. Available commercially as the free base or the hydrochloride, sulphate or fumarate salts.
Production:
• 1-bromoadamantane + acetonitrile (Ritter reaction)
Derivatives: tromantadine
Uses: antiviral/antiparkinsonian drug

amaranth *See:* Acid Red 27

ambazone
[539-21-9]
$C_8H_{11}N_7S_1$. M: 237.29.

Production:
• *p*-benzoquinone + aminoguanidine bicarbonate + thiosemicarbazide (imide formation/imide formation)
Uses: antibacterial drug

ambroxol
[18683-91-5]

$C_{13}H_{18}Br_2N_2O_1$. M: 378.10. Available commercially as the hydrochloride.
Production:
• *o*-nitrobenzaldehyde + paracetamol (hydrogenation/ isomer separation/amide hydrolysis/nitro reduction/ ring bromination/amine formation)
Uses: expectorant drug

amdinocillin *See:* mecillinam

ametryn
2-ethylthio-4-isopropylamino-6-methylthio-1,3,5-triazine; [834-12-8]

$C_9H_{17}N_5S_1$. M: 227.34.
Production:
• 2-methylmercapto-4,6-dichlorotriazine + ethylamine + isopropylamine (amine formation/amine formation)
Uses: herbicide

amfepramone
diethylpropion; [90-84-6]; [134-80-5] (hydrochloride)

$C_{13}H_{19}N_1O_1$. M: 205.30. Available commercially as the hydrochloride.
Production:
• propiophenone + diethylamine (alpha bromination/ amine formation)
Uses: anorexic drug

amidol *See:* 2,4-diaminophenol dihydrochloride

amidotrizoic acid
3,5-diacetamido-2,4,6-triiodobenzoic acid; diatrizoic

acid; [117-96-4]; [737-31-5] (sodium salt)

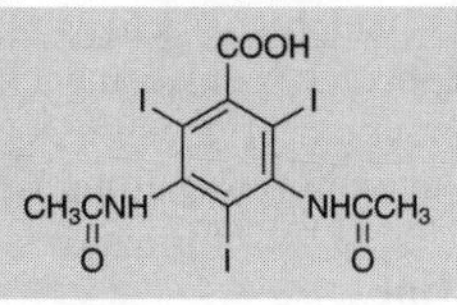

$C_{11}H_9I_3N_2O_4$. M: 613.91. Available commercially as the sodium or N-methylglucamine salt.
Production:
• 3,5-diaminobenzoic acid + acetic anhydride (acetylation/ring iodination)
Derivatives:
metrizoic acid
Uses: x-ray diagnostic aid

amiloride
[2609-46-3]

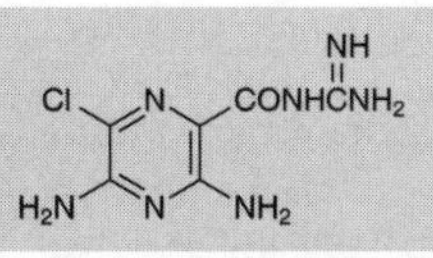

$C_6H_8Cl_1N_7O_1$. M: 229.63. Available commercially as the hydrochloride or in mixtures with hydrochlorothiazide.
Production:
• lumazine + methanol + guanidine hydrochloride (amide hydrolysis/esterification/chlorination/ammoniation/amide formation)
Uses: diuretic drug

amine-cyanoethylation adducts

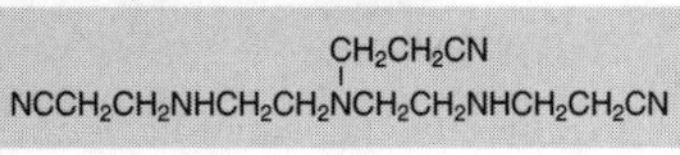

$C_{13}H_{22}N_6$. M: 262.36.
Production:
• diethylenetriamine + acrylonitrile (addition)
Uses: epoxy resin curing agent

m-aminoacetanilide
3-acetamidoaniline; N-acetyl-m-phenylenediamine; 3-aminoacetanilide; [102-28-3]

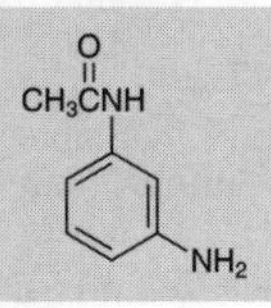

$C_8H_{10}N_2O_1$. M: 150.18.
Production:
• acetic anhydride + m-nitroaniline (amide formation/nitro reduction)
Derivatives:
Reactive Yellow 3
Uses: dyestuffs intermediate

p-aminoacetanilide
4-acetamidoaniline; N-acetyl-p-phenylenediamine; 4-aminoacetanilide; [122-80-5]

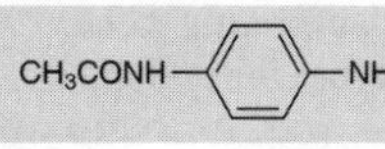

$C_8H_{10}N_2O_1$. M: 150.18. Needles. MP: 162°C. BP: 267°C. Slightly soluble in water. Soluble in oxygenated solvents.
Production:
• acetic anhydride + p-phenylenediamine (acetylation)
• p-nitroacetanilide (nitro reduction)
Derivatives:
Acid Blue 40; Acid Red 32; Acid Red 37; Acid Red 137; Acid Violet 7; Acid Violet 14; Direct Black 80; Direct Red 23; Disperse Yellow 3; Pigment Orange 38

o-aminoacetophenone
o-acetylaniline; 2-aminoacetophenone; [551-93-9]

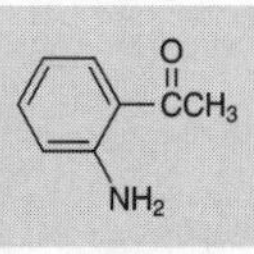

$C_8H_9N_1O_1$. M: 135.17. Yellow solid. MP: 20°C. BP: 253–255°C with slight decomposition. Insoluble in water. Soluble in oxygenated solvents.
Production:
• aniline + acetyl chloride (Friedel-Crafts acylation; coproduced with p-aminoacetophenone)
Derivatives: flutriafol

p-aminoacetophenone
p-acetylaniline; 4-aminoacetophenone; [99-92-3]

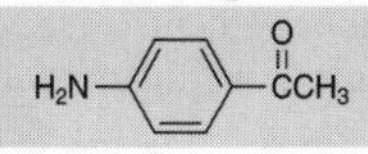

$C_8H_9N_1O_1$. M: 135.17. Yellow crystalline solid. MP: 105–107°C. BP: 293°C. Soluble in hot water and oxygenated solvents.
Production:
• aniline + acetyl chloride (Friedel-Crafts acylation; coproduced with o-aminoacetophenone)
Derivatives: clenbuterol

4-amino-5-aminomethyl-2-methylpyrimidine
5-aminomethyl-2-methylpyrimidin-4-ylamine dihydrochloride; 2-methyl-4-amino-5-aminomethylpyrimidine; [874-43-1]

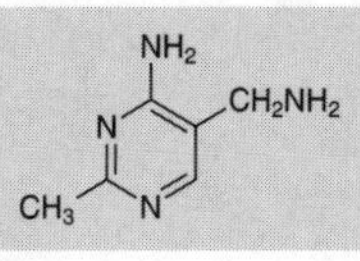

$C_6H_{10}N_4$. M: 138.18.
Production:
• acetamidine hydrochloride + cyanoacetamide +

triethyl orthoformate (condensation/nitrile reduction)
Derivatives: thiamine

2-aminoanisole-4-sulphonic acid
3-amino-4-methoxybenzenesulphonic acid; 2-methoxy-aniline-5-sulphonic acid; 4-methoxymetanilic acid

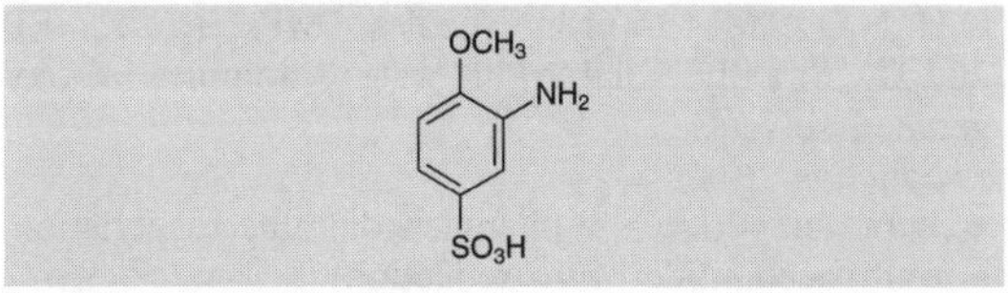

$C_7H_9N_1O_4S_1$. M: 203.22.
Production:
• 2-aminophenol-4-sulphonic acid (methylation)
Derivatives:
N-*n*-butyl-3-amino-4-methoxybenzenesulphonamide;
N,N-diethyl-3-amino-4-methoxybenzenesulphonamide;
Direct Red 83; 5-(β-hydroxyethylsulphonyl)-2-methoxy-aniline

1-aminoanthraquinone
[82-45-1]

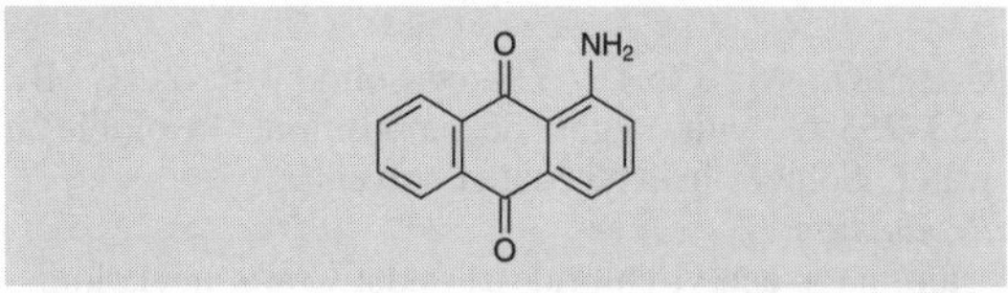

$C_{14}H_9N_1O_2$. M: 223.23. Red needles. MP: 250–252°C.
Insoluble in water. Soluble in oxygenated, chlorinated and aromatic solvents.
Production:
• anthraquinone-1-sulphonic acid, sodium salt + ammonia (sulphonate displacement)
• anthraquinone (nitration/nitro reduction)
Derivatives:
1-amino-4-benzamidoanthraquinone; anthrapyrazolone; 1-benzamido-4-chloroanthraquinone; 1-benzamido-4-hydroxyanthraquinone; bromamine acid; 1-bromo-4-methylaminoanthraquinone; 1,4-diaminoanthraquinone; Disperse Yellow 77; Solubilised Vat Yellow 7; Vat Black 8; Vat Black 25; Vat Green 3; Vat Green 8; Vat Red 48; Vat Yellow 20; Vat Yellow 26; Vat Yellow 28

2-aminoanthraquinone
[117-79-3]

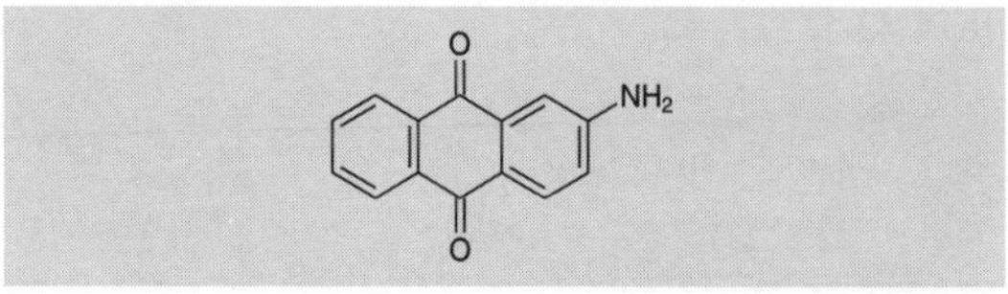

$C_{14}H_9N_1O_2$. M: 223.23. Red needles. MP: 289–292°C.
Insoluble in water. Soluble in oxygenated and aromatic solvents.

Production:
• anthraquinone-2-sulphonic acid, sodium salt + ammonia (sulphonate displacement)
Derivatives: 2-amino-3-bromoanthraquinone; 2-amino-1-chloroanthraquinone; indanthrone

4-aminoantipyrine
4-amino-2,3-dimethyl-1-phenyl-3-pyrazolin-5-one; 4-amino-1,5-dimethyl-2-phenyl-3-pyrazolone; 4-amino-phenazone; ampyrone; [83-07-8]

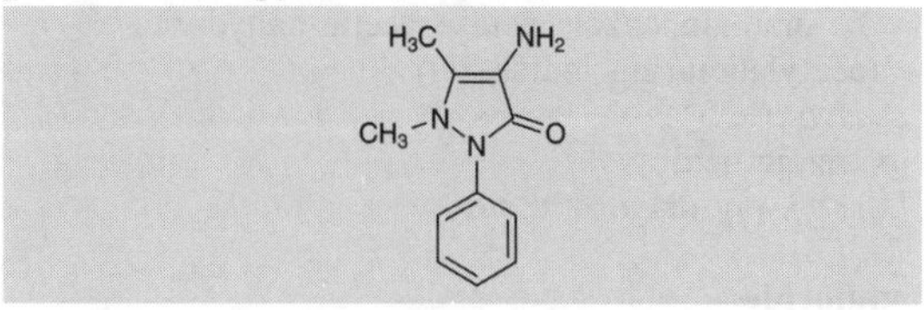

$C_{11}H_{13}N_3O_1$. M: 203.24. Pale yellow, crystalline solid.
MP: 107–109°C. Soluble in water and alcohol.
Production:
• phenazone + sodium nitrite (nitrosation/nitro reduction)
Derivatives: dipyrone; nifenazone

4-aminoazobenzene *See:* *p*-phenylazoaniline

4-aminoazobenzene-3,4′-disulphonic acid
4-phenylazoaniline-2,4′-disulphonic acid; Acid Yellow 9 (CI); Food Yellow 2 (CI); 13015 (CI); [101-50-8]

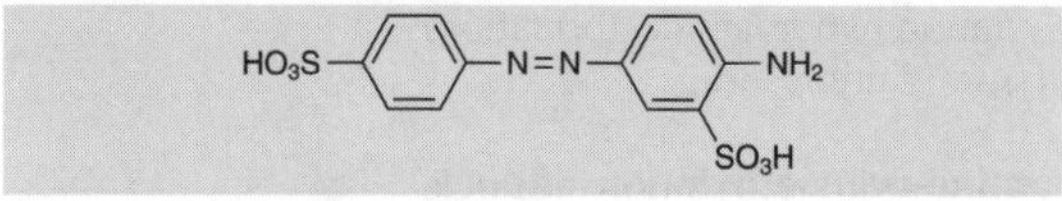

$C_{12}H_{11}N_3O_6S_2$. M: 357.36.
Production:
• *p*-phenylazoaniline (sulphonation)
Derivatives:
Direct Red 80; Reactive Brown 1
Uses: dye (wool)

4′-aminoazobenzene-4-sulphonic acid
4-(4′-aminophenylazo)benzenesulphonic acid; [104-23-4]

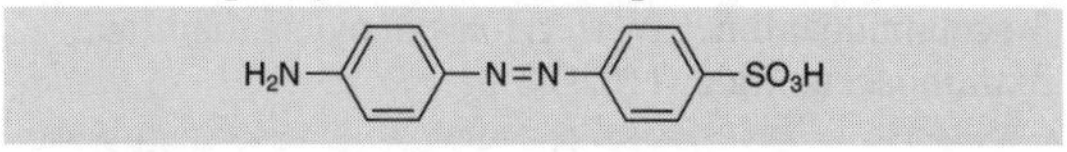

$C_{12}H_{11}N_3O_3S_1$. M: 277.30.
Production:
• sulphanilic acid + aniline (sulphonation)
Derivatives:
Acid Red 151; Direct Red 81; Direct Red 153; Mordant Orange 6

o-aminoazotoluene
toluazotoluidine; 4-(2-tolylazo)-*o*-toluidine; Azoic Diazo Component 4 (CI, hydrochloride); Solvent Yellow 3 (CI); 11160 (CI); 37210 (CI, hydrochloride); [97-56-3]; [2298-13-7]

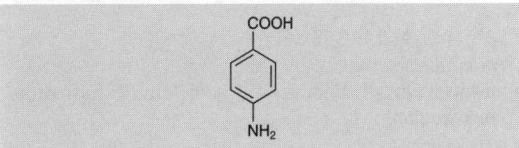

$C_{14}H_{15}N_3$. M: 225.29.
Production:
• *o*-toluidine (diazotisation/azo coupling)
Uses: azoic dye diazo component

p-aminobenzamide

$C_7H_8N_2O_1$. M: 136.15. Solid. MP: 183°C. Slightly soluble in water. Soluble in oxygenated solvents.
Production:
• *p*-nitrobenzoic acid + ammonia (amide formation/ nitro reduction)
Derivatives:
Pigment Red 170; Pigment Red 187; Pigment Red 222

1-amino-4-benzamidoanthraquinone

$C_{21}H_{14}N_2O_3$. M: 342.35.
Production:
• 1-aminoanthraquinone + benzoyl chloride (amide formation/nitration/nitro reduction)
Derivatives: Vat Black 27; Vat Orange 17

1-amino-5-benzamidoanthraquinone
1-benzamido-5-aminoanthraquinone; [117-06-6]

$C_{21}H_{14}N_2O_3$. M: 342.35. Solid. MP: 244–245°C.
Production:
• anthraquinone-1-sulphonic acid, sodium salt + benzoyl chloride + ammonia (nitration/nitro reduction/amide formation/sulphonate displacement)
Derivatives: Vat Brown 3; Vat Orange 15; Vat Orange 17; Vat Yellow 10; Vat Yellow 13; Vat Yellow 23

2-aminobenzenesulphonic acid *See:* orthanilic acid

3-aminobenzenesulphonic acid *See:* metanilic acid

4-aminobenzenesulphonic acid *See:* sulphanilic acid

5-aminobenzimidazolone
5-aminobenzimidazol-2-one

$C_7H_7N_3O_1$. M: 149.15.
Production:
• *o*-phenylenediamine + phosgene (phosgenation/ nitration/nitro reduction)
Derivatives: 5-acetoacetamidobenzimidazolone; 5-(2′-hydroxy-3′-naphthoyl)aminobenzimidazolone

m-aminobenzoic acid
3-aminobenzoic acid; [99-05-8]

$C_7H_7N_1O_2$. M: 137.15. Yellow, crystalline solid. MP: 172–174°C. d: 1.51 kg/l (20°C). Soluble in hot water and oxygenated solvents.
Production:
• *m*-nitrobenzoic acid (nitro reduction)
Derivatives:
3-amino-2,4,6-triiodobenzoic acid; Direct Blue 93; Direct Orange 29; Direct Yellow 49; suramin sodium

o-aminobenzoic acid *See:* anthranilic acid

p-aminobenzoic acid
4-aminobenzoic acid; PABA; [150-13-0]

$C_7H_7N_1O_2$. M: 137.15. White, crystalline solid. MP: 188–189°C. Slightly soluble in water. Soluble in oxygenated solvents.
Production:
• *p*-nitrobenzoic acid (nitro reduction)
Derivatives: Acid Yellow 127; Direct Orange 102; glycerol mono-4-aminobenzoate; poly(*p*-benzhydrazoterephthalamide); 1,3-propylene glycol di-(*p*-aminobenzoate); tetracaine
Uses:
UV absorber

m-aminobenzotrifluoride

3-aminobenzotrifluoride; 3-(trifluoromethyl)aniline;
[98-16-8]

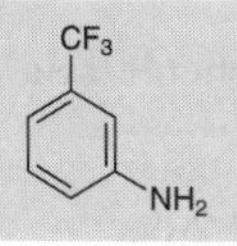

$C_7H_6F_3N_1$. M: 161.13. Liquid. BP: 187–189°C.
Production:
• benzotrichloride (nitration/halogen exchange/nitro
  reduction)
Derivatives: 2-ethylsulphonyl-5-trifluoromethylaniline;
flufenamic acid; fluometuron; fluorosalan; flurochloridone; hydroflumethiazide; *m*-hydroxybenzotrifluoride;
niflumic acid; norflurazon; 2-(trifluoromethyl)phenothi-
azine; trifluperidol; Vat Blue 21

o-aminobenzotrifluoride

2-aminobenzotrifluoride; 2-(trifluoromethyl)aniline;
[88-17-5]

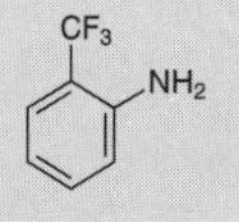

$C_7H_6F_3N_1$. M: 161.13.
Production:
• *o*-nitrotoluene (side-chain chlorination/fluorination/
  nitro reduction)
Derivatives: Acid Red 337; 2-amino-5-chlorobenzotri-
fluoride; Pigment Yellow 154

N-*m*-aminobenzoyl-J acid

2-*m*-aminobenzamido-5-naphthol-7-sulphonic acid

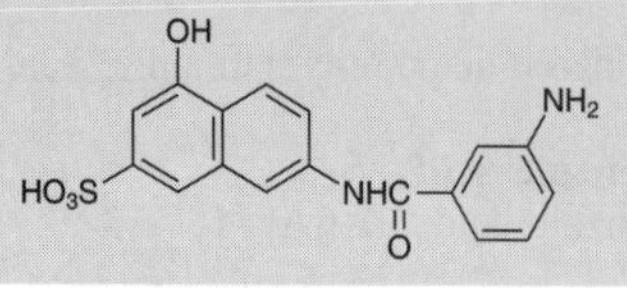

$C_{17}H_{14}N_2O_5S_1$. M: 358.36.
Production:
• *m*-nitrobenzoyl chloride + J acid (amide formation/
  nitro reduction)
Derivatives:
Diazo Brilliant Scarlet ROD; Direct Orange 75; Direct
Red 118; Direct Red 153

4-amino-*N*-benzylpiperidine

[50541-93-0]

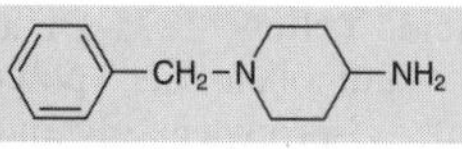

$C_{12}H_{18}N_2$. M: 190.28.
Production:
• 1-benzyl-4-piperidone + ammonia (ammoniation)

Derivatives: astemizole; domperidone; 1-(4-piperidyl)-
2-benzodiazolinone

4-aminobiphenyl-3-sulphonic acid

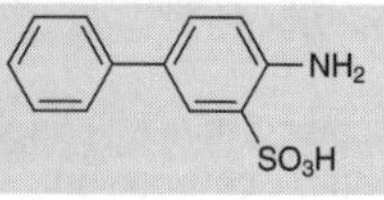

$C_{12}H_{11}N_1O_3S_1$. M: 249.29.
Production:
• biphenyl (nitration/nitro reduction/sulphonation)
Derivatives: Direct Green 13

2-amino-3-bromoanthraquinone

3-amino-2-bromoanthraquinone; [6337-00-4]

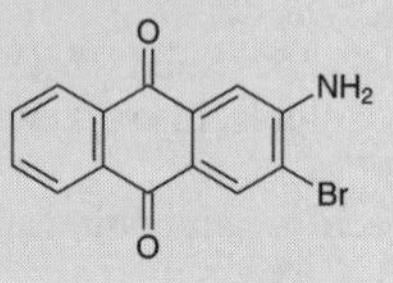

$C_{14}H_8Br_1N_1O_2$. M: 302.12. Solid. MP: 235–303°C.
Production:
• 2-aminoanthraquinone (ring bromination)
Derivatives: Vat Blue 30; Vat Red 10

1-amino-4-bromoanthraquinone-2-sulphonic acid

See: bromamine acid

1-amino-2-bromo-4-hydroxyanthraquinone

[116-82-5]

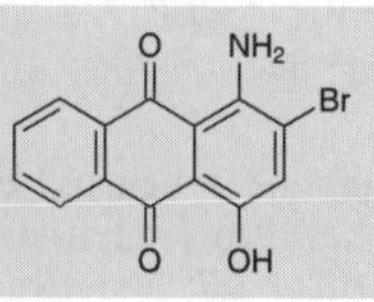

$C_{14}H_8Br_1N_1O_3$. M: 318.12.
Production:
• 1-amino-4-hydroxyanthraquinone (ring bromination)
Derivatives: Disperse Red 60

4-amino-5-bromomethyl-2-methylpyrimidine hydro-bromide

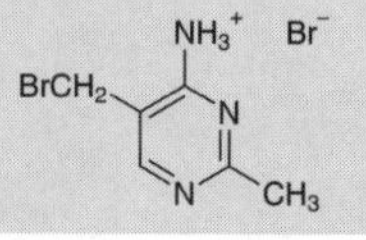

$C_6H_9Br_2N_3$. M: 282.97.
Production:
• ethyl 3-ethoxypropionate + triethyl orthoformate +
  acetamidine hydrochloride + ammonia + hydrogen
  bromide, anhydrous (carbonyl condensation/
  condensation/amine formation/deethylation/
  alcohol bromination)
Derivatives: thiamine

2-amino-3-bromo-5-nitrobenzonitrile
[17601-94-4]

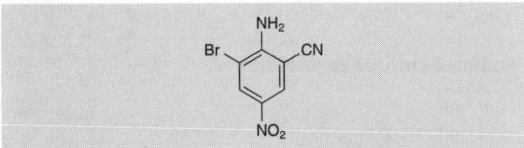

$C_7H_4Br_1N_3O_2$. M: 242.03. Solid. MP: 185–186°C.
Production:
• 2-amino-5-nitrobenzonitrile (ring bromination)
Derivatives:
Disperse Blue 183

2-aminobutanol
2-amino-1-butanol; [96-20-8]; [5856-62-2] ((+)-enantiomer)

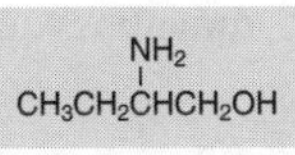

$$CH_3CH_2CHCH_2OH \overset{NH_2}{|}$$

$C_4H_{11}N_1O_1$. M: 89.14. Liquid. BP: 178°C. MP: -2°C.
d: 0.94 kg/l (20°C). Miscible with water. Soluble in oxygenated solvents. Also available as the pure (+)-enantiomer product.
Production:
• 1-nitropropane + formaldehyde (hydroxymethylation/ nitro reduction)
Derivatives: ethambutol
Uses:
coupling solvent (soluble oils, wax emulsions, creams)

3-amino-5-*t*-butylisoxazole
5-*t*-butyl-3-isoxazolamine; [55809-36-4]

$(CH_3)_3C$

$C_7H_{12}N_2O_1$. M: 140.19.
Production:
• cyanopinacolone + hydroxylamine sulphate (amidine formation/cyclisation)
Derivatives:
isouron

2-amino-4-*t*-butylphenol
5-*t*-butyl-2-hydroxyaniline; [1199-46-8]

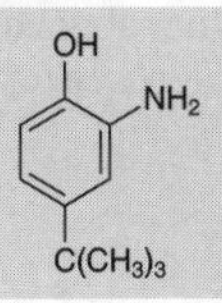

$C(CH_3)_3$

$C_{10}H_{15}N_1O_1$. M: 165.24.
Production:
• *p-t*-butylphenol (nitration/nitro reduction)
Derivatives:
Fluorescent Brightener 184; Fluorescent Brightener 354

6-aminocaproic acid
ε-aminocaproic acid; 6-aminohexanoic acid (INN); [60-32-2]

$$H_2NCH_2CH_2CH_2CH_2CH_2COOH$$

$C_6H_{13}N_1O_2$. M: 131.18. White crystals. MP: 202°C. Soluble in water. Insoluble in alcohol. Commercially available as the free base, the hydrochloride and the hydrobromide derivatives.
Production:
• caprolactam (amide hydrolysis)
Derivatives: guanethidine
Uses: haemostatic drug

7-aminocephalosporanic acid
7-ACA; [957-68-6]

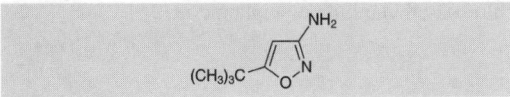

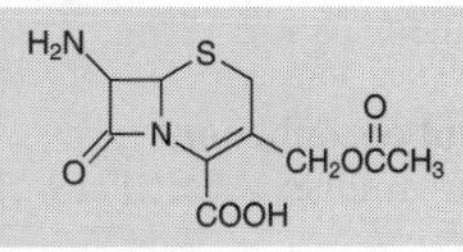

$C_{10}H_{12}N_2O_5S_1$. M: 272.28.
Production:
• cephalosporin C (hydrolysis)
• cephalosporin C (chlorination/ether formation/hydrolysis)
Derivatives: cefacetrile; cefalotin; cefamandole; cefapirin; cefazedone; cefazolin; cefmenoxime; cefoperazone; cefotaxime; cefotetan; cefotiam; cefsulodin; ceftazidime; ceftizoxime; ceftriaxone; cefuroxime

2-amino-4-chloroanisole
5-chloro-*o*-anisidine; 5-chloro-2-methoxyaniline; Fast Red RC base; Azoic Diazo Component 10 (CI); 37120 (CI)

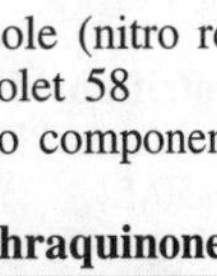

$C_7H_8Cl_1N_1O_1$. M: 157.60. Needles. MP: 82°C. Soluble in oxygenated solvents. Available commercially as the free base or as the hydrochloride salt.
Production:
• 4-chloro-2-nitroanisole (nitro reduction)
Derivatives: Acid Violet 58
Uses: azoic dye diazo component

2-amino-1-chloroanthraquinone

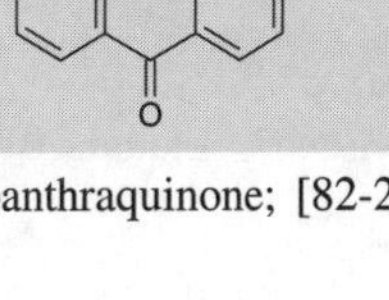

1-chloro-2-aminoanthraquinone; [82-27-9]

$C_{14}H_8Cl_1N_1O_2$. M: 257.67. Solid. MP: 230–235°C.
Production:
• 2-aminoanthraquinone (ring chlorination)
Derivatives: flavanthrone

3-amino-4-chlorobenzamide

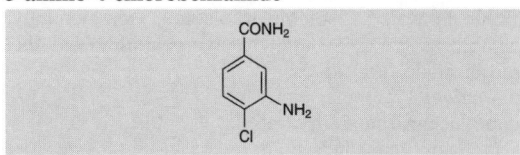

$C_7H_7Cl_1N_2O_1$. M: 170.60.
Production:
• 4-chloro-3-nitrobenzoic acid + ammonia (amide formation/nitro reduction)
Derivatives: Pigment Orange 38

2-amino-5-chlorobenzophenone
2-benzoyl-4-chloroaniline; ACB; [719-59-5]

$C_{13}H_{10}Cl_1N_1O_1$. M: 231.68. Solid. MP: 98–100°C.
Production:
• p-chloroaniline + benzoyl chloride (Friedel-Crafts acylation)
Derivatives: chlordiazepoxide; clorazepate; diazepam; nitrazepam; nordazepam

2-amino-5-chlorobenzotrifluoride
[445-03-4]

$C_7H_5Cl_1F_3N_1$. M: 195.57.
Production:
• o-aminobenzotrifluoride (ring chlorination)
Derivatives:
Acid Red 266; triflumizole

3-amino-4-chlorobenzotrifluoride
Fast Orange RD base; Azoic Diazo Component 49 (CI); 37050 (CI); [121-50-6]

$C_7H_5Cl_1F_3N_1$. M: 195.57. Liquid. BP: 82–83°C (0.9 kPa).

Production:
• p-chlorobenzotrifluoride (nitration/nitro reduction)
Derivatives: Pigment Red 242

5-amino-2-chlorobenzotrifluoride
[320-51-4]

$C_7H_5Cl_1F_3N_1$. M: 195.57.
Production:
• o-chlorobenzotrifluoride (nitration/nitro reduction)
Derivatives:
cloflucarban; flucofenuron

4-amino-2-chloro-6,7-dimethoxyquinazoline
[23680-84-4]

$C_{10}H_{10}Cl_1N_3O_2$. M: 239.66.
Production:
• veratraldehyde + ammonia + sodium cyanate (nitration/carbonyl oxidation/amide formation/nitro reduction/cyclisation/chlorination/ammoniation)
Derivatives: prazosin

5-amino-2-chloroethylbenzene-4-sulphonic acid
3-amino-6-chloroethylbenzene-4-sulphonic acid;
4-chloro-3-ethylaniline-6-sulphonic acid

$C_8H_{10}Cl_1N_1O_3S_1$. M: 235.69.
Production:
• ethylbenzene (sulphonation/ring chlorination/nitration/nitro reduction)
Derivatives: Pigment Orange 46; Pigment Red 200

2-amino-5-chloro-2′-fluorobenzophenone
2-fluoro-2′-amino-5′-chlorobenzophenone; [784-38-3]

$C_{13}H_9Cl_1F_1N_1O_1$. M: 249.67.
Production:
• anthranilic acid + p-chloroaniline (Balz-Schiemann

reaction/acid chloride formation/Friedel-Crafts acylation)
Derivatives: clonazepam; flunitrazepam; flurazepam

2-amino-4-chlorophenol

o-amino-*p*-chlorophenol; 4-chloro-2-aminophenol;
5-chloro-2-hydroxyaniline; [95-85-2]

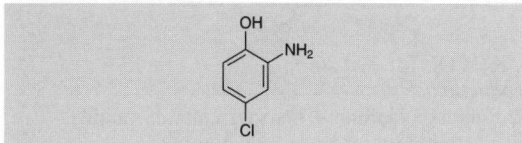

$C_6H_6Cl_1N_1O_1$. M: 143.58. Light tan crystals. MP: 138°C
with decomposition. Slightly soluble in water. Soluble
in oxygenated solvents.
Production:
• 4-chloro-2-nitrophenol (nitro reduction)
Derivatives: chlorzoxazone; Mordant Blue 13
Uses: dyestuffs intermediate

2-amino-4-chlorophenol-6-sulphonic acid

3-amino-5-chloro-2-hydroxybenzenesulphonic acid;
2-hydroxy-5-chloroaniline-3-sulphonic acid; [88-23-3]

$C_6H_6Cl_1N_1O_4S_1$. M: 223.64.
Production:
• 4-chloro-2-nitrophenol (sulphonation/nitro reduction)
Derivatives:
Acid Red 179; Acid Red 183; Mordant Black 7; Mordant Black 38; Mordant Red 19

2-amino-3-chlorotoluene

2-chloro-6-methylaniline; 3-chloro-*o*-toluidine; [87-60-5]

$C_7H_8Cl_1N_1$. M: 141.60.
Production:
• *o*-toluidine (ring chlorination; byproduct of
  2-amino-5-chlorotoluene production)
Derivatives:
1-(6'-chloro-2'-methylphenyl)-3-methylpyrazolone
Uses: dyestuffs intermediate

2-amino-4-chlorotoluene

5-chloro-2-methylaniline; 4-chloro-*o*-toluidine; Fast Red
KB base; Azoic Diazo Component 32 (CI); 37090
(CI); [6259-42-3]
$C_7H_8Cl_1N_1$. M: 141.60. Available commercially as the
free base or as the hydrochloride salt.

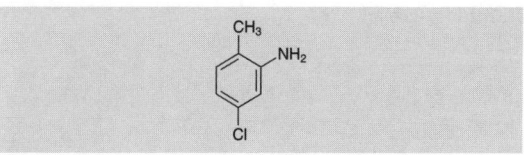

Production:
• *p*-chlorotoluene (nitration/nitro reduction)
Uses: azoic dye coupling component

2-amino-5-chlorotoluene

5-chloro-2-toluidine; 5-chloro-*o*-toluidine; Azoic Diazo
Component 11 (CI); 37085 (CI)

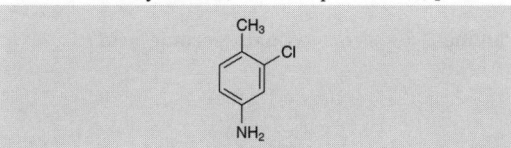

$C_7H_8Cl_1N_1$. M: 141.60. Crystalline solid. MP: 27–30°C.
BP: 241°C. Insoluble in water. Soluble in hot alcohol.
Production:
• *o*-toluidine (ring chlorination)
Derivatives: acetoacet-4-chloro-2-methylanilide; 4-chloro-3'-hydroxy-2'-naphth-*m*-toluidide; 5-chloro-3'-hydroxy-2'-naphth-*o*-toluidide; Pigment Red 7

4-amino-2-chlorotoluene

3-chloro-4-methylaniline; 2-chloro-*p*-toluidine; [95-74-9]

$C_7H_8Cl_1N_1$. M: 141.60. Solid/liquid. MP: 26°C. BP:
242–244°C. Insoluble in water.
Production:
• 2-chloro-4-nitrotoluene (nitro reduction)
Derivatives: 2B acid; chlorotoluron; pentanochlor

4-amino-2-chlorotoluene-5-sulphonic acid *See:* 2B acid

5-amino-2-chlorotoluene-4-sulphonic acid

2-chloro-5-aminotoluene-4-sulphonic acid; CLT acid;
[88-53-9]

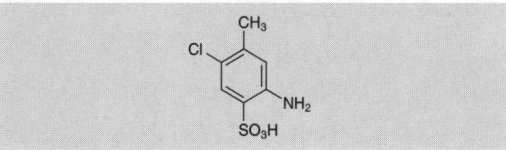

$C_7H_8Cl_1N_1O_3S_1$. M: 221.66.
Production:
• *p*-toluenesulphonic acid (ring chlorination/nitration/
  nitro reduction)
Derivatives: Pigment Red 52; Pigment Red 53

o-amino-*p*-cresol

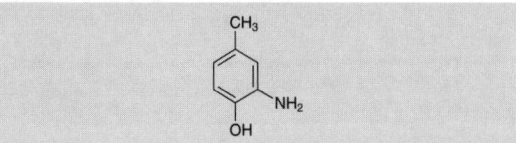

3-amino-4-hydroxytoluene; 2-amino-4-methylphenol; 2-hydroxy-5-methylaniline; [95-84-1]
$C_7H_9N_1O_1$. M: 123.16. Crystalline solid. MP: 135–137°C. Sublimes. Slightly soluble in water and aromatic solvents. Soluble in oxygenated solvents.
Production:
• *p*-cresol (nitration/nitro reduction)
Derivatives: Fluorescent Brightener 135

β-aminocrotononitrile

3-aminocrotononitrile; diacetonitrile

$$NH_2$$
$$CH_3C=CHCN$$

$C_4H_8N_1O_2$. M: 102.11.
Production:
• acetonitrile (condensation)
Derivatives: 5-amino-3-methyl-1-phenylpyrazole; 1,4-butanediol β-aminocrotonate; lauryl β-aminocrotonate; pyridoxine; sulfisomidine; thiodiglycol di-β-aminocrotonate

7-amino-3-desacetoxycephalosporanic acid
7-ADCA

$C_8H_{10}N_2O_3S_1$. M: 214.24.
Production:
• benzylpenicillin + peracetic acid (oxidation/esterification/rearrangement/saponification)
Derivatives: cefadroxil; cefalexin; cefradine

3-amino-2,5-dichlorobenzoic acid *See:* chloramben

2-amino-2′,5-dichlorobenzophenone
[2958-36-3]

$C_{13}H_9Cl_2N_1O_1$. M: 266.13.
Production:
• *p*-chloroaniline + *o*-chlorobenzoyl chloride (Friedel-Crafts acylation)
Derivatives: lorazepam; triazolam

4′-amino-2′,5′-diethoxybenzanilide
N-benzoyl-2,5-diethoxy-*p*-phenylenediamine; Fast Blue BB base; Azoic Diazo Component 20 (CI); 37175 (CI); [120-00-3]

$C_{17}H_{20}N_2O_3$. M: 300.36.
Production:
• 2,5-diethoxyaniline + benzoyl chloride (amide formation/nitration/nitro reduction)
Uses: azoic dye diazo component

4-amino-1-diethylaminopentane
1-diethylamino-4-aminopentane; 5-diethylamino-2-aminopentane; novoldiamine; [140-80-7]

$$NH_2$$
$$CH_3CHCH_2CH_2CH_2N(C_2H_5)_2$$

$C_9H_{22}N_2$. M: 158.29. Liquid with an unpleasant odour. BP: 200°C. d: 0.82 kg/l (20°C). Soluble in water and alcohol.
Production:
• 5-diethylamino-2-pentanone + ammonia (reductive amination)
Derivatives:
chloroquine; mepacrine

2-amino-5-diethylaminotoluene
5-diethylamino-2-aminotoluene; Developer CD2 (Kodak);

$C_{11}H_{18}N_2$. M: 178.27. Available commercially as the hydrochloride.
Production:
• *N,N*-diethyl-*m*-toluidine + sodium nitrite (nitrosation/nitro reduction)
Uses: photographic developing agent

7-(4-amino-6-diethylaminotriazin-2-yl)amino-3-phenylcoumarin
Tinopal 3525 (Ciba-Geigy)

$C_{22}H_{22}N_6O_2$. M: 402.46.
Production:
• 7-amino-3-phenylcoumarin + cyanuric chloride +

diethylamine + ammonia (amine formation/amine formation/amine formation)
Uses: fluorescent brightening agent (plastics)

4-amino-2,5-dimethoxybenzenesulphonic acid

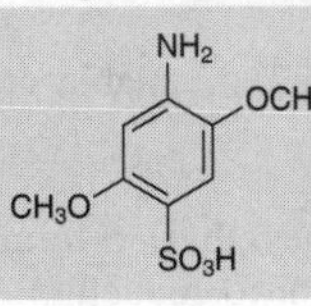

$C_8H_{11}N_1O_5S_1$. M: 233.25.
Production:
• 2,5-dimethoxyaniline (sulphonation)
Derivatives: 2,5-dimethoxy-5-(β-hydroxyethylsulphonyl)aniline; Pigment Violet 32; Pigment Yellow 97

4-amino-2,3-dimethyl-1-phenyl-3-pyrazolin-5-one
See: 4-aminoantipyrine

2-amino-4,6-dimethylpyrimidine

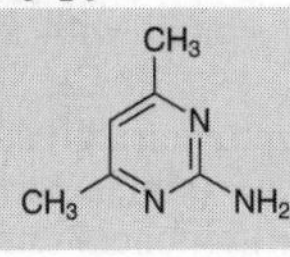

$C_6H_9N_3$. M: 123.16.
Production:
• acetylacetone + guanidine carbonate (condensation)
Derivatives: sulfometuron-methyl

6-amino-1,3-dimethyluracil
[6642-31-5]

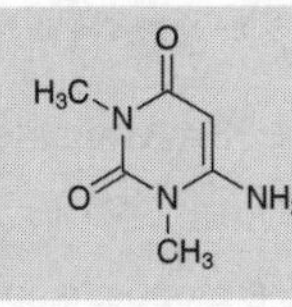

$C_6H_9N_3O_2$. M: 155.16. Cream powder. MP: 292–297°C. Very slightly soluble in water.
Production:
• ethyl cyanoacetate + N,N'-dimethylurea (condensation)
Derivatives:
bamifylline; theophylline; urapidil

p-aminodiphenylamine
N-phenyl-p-phenylenediamine; Diphenyl Black Base P; Azoic Diazo Component 22 (CI); 37240 (CI); [101-54-2]

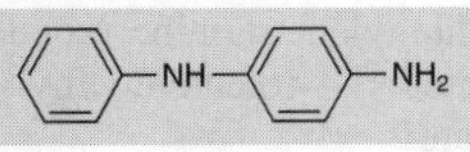

$C_{12}H_{12}N_2$. M: 184.24. Purple needles. MP: 75°C. BP: 364°C. Insoluble in water. Soluble in oxygenated solvents.

Production:
• aniline + p-chloronitrobenzene (amine formation/ nitro reduction)
Derivatives: N-hexyl-N'-phenyl-p-phenylenediamine; N-isopropyl-N'-phenyl-p-phenylenediamine
Uses: azoic dye diazo component

4-aminodiphenylamine-2-sulphonic acid
5-amino-2-anilinobenzenesulphonic acid; [91-30-5]

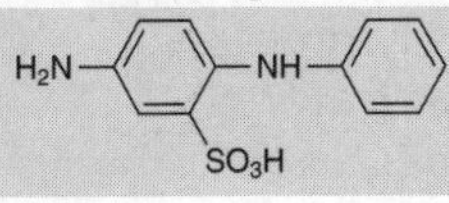

$C_{12}H_{12}N_2O_3S_1$. M: 264.30.
Production:
• aniline + 2-chloro-5-nitrobenzenesulphonic acid (amine formation/nitro reduction)
Derivatives:
Acid Brown 13; Acid Orange 3; Direct Blue 106

2-aminoethanol *See:* monoethanolamine

2-(2-aminoethoxy)ethanol
diethylene glycol amine; DGA; Diglycolamine (Texaco Chemical); [929-06-6]

$$H_2NCH_2CH_2OCH_2CH_2OH$$

$C_4H_{11}N_1O_2$. M: 105.14. Colourless liquid with a mild, ammoniacal odour. BP: 221°C. FP: -12°C. d: 1.06 kg/l (20°C). Miscible in water, alcohol and aromatics. Immiscible with aliphatic hydrocarbons.
Production:
• diethylene glycol + ammonia (amine formation; byproduct of morpholine production)
Derivatives:
2-(2-dimethylaminoethoxy)ethanol
Uses: hydrogen sulphide/carbon dioxide extraction solvent (gas processing)

N-(2-aminoethyl)-γ-aminopropyltrimethoxysilane
[1760-24-3]

$$H_2NCH_2CH_2NHCH_2CH_2CH_2Si(OCH_3)_3$$

$C_8H_{22}N_2O_3Si_1$. M: 222.37. Liquid. BP: 259°C. d: 1.04 kg/l (25°C). Flash point: 138°C (PMCC).
Production:
• ethylenediamine + γ-chloropropyltrimethoxysilane (amine formation)
Uses: plastics coupling agent

aminoethyl behenyl imidazoline

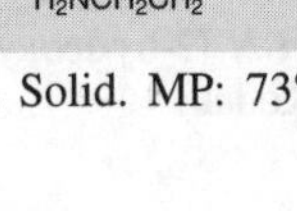

$C_{26}H_{53}N_3$. M: 407.73. Solid. MP: 73°C.

Production:
• behenic acid + diethylenetriamine (condensation)
Uses: corrosion inhibitor/demulsifier (crude oil processing); emulsifier (pesticides); anticaking agent; bitumen emulsifier; surfactant (acid cleaners)

3-amino-*N*-ethylcarbazole
3-amino-9-ethylcarbazole

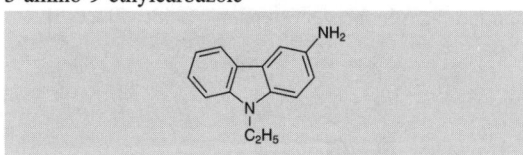

$C_{14}H_{14}N_2$. M: 210.27.
Production:
• *N*-ethylcarbazole (nitration/nitro reduction)
Derivatives: Direct Blue 108; Pigment Violet 23; Pigment Violet 37

aminoethyl cocoyl imidazoline

R = coco-. Solid. MP: 43°C.
Production:
• coconut acid + diethylenetriamine (condensation)
Uses: corrosion inhibitor/demulsifier (crude oil processing); emulsifier (pesticides); anticaking agent; bitumen emulsifier; surfactant (acid cleaners)

aminoethylethanolamine
N-(2-hydroxyethyl)ethylenediamine; AEEA; [111-41-1]

$$H_2NCH_2CH_2NHCH_2CH_2OH$$

$C_4H_{12}N_2O_1$. M: 104.15. Liquid with a strong ammoniacal odour. BP: 242–246°C. Pour point: -39°C. d: 1.03 kg/l (20°C). Flash point: 132°C (PMCC). Miscible with water, alcohol and acetone.
Production:
• ethylenediamine + ethylene oxide (epoxidation)
• monoethanolamine + ammonia (ammoniation; coproduced with ethylenediamine/diethylenetriamine/piperazine/*N*-hydroxyethylpiperazine/aminoethylpiperazine)
Derivatives:
capryl imidazoline; caprylyl imidazoline; cocoyl imidazoline; hydroxyethylethylenediaminetriacetic acid, trisodium salt; isostearyl imidazoline; lauryl imidazoline; oleyl imidazoline; stearyl imidazoline; tall oil hydroxyethyl imidazoline; *N,N,N'*-trimethylaminoethylethanolamine

2-amino-5-[*N*-ethyl-*N*-(2-hydroxyethyl)amino]toluene
Developer CD4 (Kodak)

$C_{11}H_{18}N_2O_1$. M: 194.27. Available commercially as the bisulphate.
Production:
• *N*-ethyl-*N*-(2-hydroxyethyl)-*m*-toluidine + sodium nitrite (nitrosation/nitro reduction)
Uses: photographic developing agent

2-amino-5-[*N*-ethyl-*N*-(2-methoxyethyl)amino]toluene

$C_{12}H_{20}N_2O_1$. M: 208.30. Available commercially as the bisulphate.
Production:
• *N*-ethyl-*m*-toluidine/ethylene glycol monomethyl ether + sodium nitrite (amine formation/nitrosation/nitro reduction)
Uses: photographic developing agent

2-amino-5-[*N*-ethyl-*N*-(2-methylsulphonaminoethyl)-amino]toluene
Developer CD3 (Kodak)

$C_{12}H_{21}N_3O_2S_1$. M: 271.38. Available commercially as the 2:3 bisulphate salt.
Production:
• *N*-ethyl-*m*-toluidine + monoethanolamine + methanesulphonyl chloride (sulphonamide formation/amine formation/nitrosation/nitro reduction)
Uses: photographic developing agent

aminoethyl oleyl imidazoline

$C_{22}H_{43}N_3$. M: 349.60. Liquid. Pour point: <-25°C.
Production:
• oleic acid + diethylenetriamine (condensation)
Derivatives: 1-methyl-1-(oleamidoethyl) oleylimidazoline methosulphate
Uses: corrosion inhibitor/demulsifier (crude oil processing); emulsifier (pesticides); anticaking agent; bitumen emulsifier; surfactant (acid cleaners)

aminoethylpiperazine
1-(2-aminoethyl)piperazine; *N*-aminoethylpiperazine;
1-(1-piperazinyl)-2-aminoethane; AEP; [140-31-8]

HN⟨piperazine⟩N–CH₂CH₂NH₂

$C_6H_{15}N_3$. M: 129.21. Clear liquid with a mild, ammoniacal odour. MP: -18°C. BP: 222°C. d: 0.98 kg/l
(20°C). Miscible with water, alcohols, ether and aromatic solvents. Corrosive to copper.
Production:
• ethylene dichloride + ammonia (amine formation;
  coproduced with ethylenediamine/diethylenetri-
  amine/triethylenetetramine/tetraethylenepentamine/
  polyethylenepolyamine/piperazine)
• monoethanolamine + ammonia (ammoniation;
  coproduced with ethylenediamine/diethylene-
  triamine/piperazine/*N*-hydroxyethylpiperazine/
  aminoethylethanolamine)
• piperazine + acrylamide (Michael addition/Hofmann
  degradation)
Derivatives: fatty acid imidazoline polyamines
Uses: epoxy resin curing agent

2-amino-2-ethyl-1,3-propanediol
See: 2-ethyl-2-aminopropan-1,3-diol

aminoethyl tallow imidazoline

R–⟨imidazoline⟩
H₂NCH₂CH₂

R = tallow-. Solid. MP: 43°C.
Production:
• tallow acid + diethylenetriamine (condensation)
Derivatives: 1-methyl-1-(tallowamidoethyl)tallowimid-
azoline methosulphate
Uses: corrosion inhibitor/demulsifier (crude oil processing); emulsifier (pesticides); anticaking agent; bitumen
emulsifier; surfactant (acid cleaners)

amino-G acid
2-aminonaphthalene-6,8-disulphonic acid; 7-aminonaph-
thalene-1,3-disulphonic acid; 2-naphthylamine-6,8-di-
sulphonic acid; [86-65-7]

H₂N–⟨naphthalene⟩–SO₃H / SO₃H

$C_{10}H_9N_1O_6S_2$. M: 303.31. Crystalline solid. MP: 274°C.
Soluble in water.
Production:
• G acid + ammonia (Bucherer reaction)
Derivatives: Direct Orange 72; Direct Yellow 118; ga-
mma acid; Mordant Yellow 20

aminoguanidine bicarbonate
aminoguanidium hydrogen carbonate; [2582-30-1]

$$\underset{H_2NCNHNH_2}{\overset{\overset{NH_2^+}{\|}}{}} \quad HCO_3^-$$

$C_2H_8N_4O_3$. M: 136.11. Solid. MP: 169–179°C with decomposition.
Production:
• cyanamide + hydrazine (condensation)
Derivatives:
ambazone; 3-amino-1,2,4-triazole; epirizole; tetrazene
Uses: photographic chemical

1-amino-4-hydroxyanthraquinone
Disperse Red 15 (CI); 60710 (CI)

⟨anthraquinone structure with O, NH₂, O, OH⟩

$C_{14}H_9N_1O_3$. M: 239.23.
Production:
• 1-benzamido-4-hydroxyanthraquinone (amide
  hydrolysis)
• 1-chloro-4-hydroxyanthraquinone + ammonia
  (ammoniation)
Derivatives: 1-amino-2-bromo-4-hydroxyanthraquinone;
Vat Red 28
Uses: dye (polyamide, polyester, polyacrylonitrile)

3-amino-4-hydroxybenzenesulphonic acid
See: 2-aminophenol-4-sulphonic acid

4-amino-2-hydroxybenzoic acid
See: *p*-aminosalicylic acid

5-amino-2-hydroxybenzoic acid
See: 5-aminosalicylic acid

8-amino-2-hydroxynaphthalene
See: 8-amino-2-naphthol

2-amino-5-hydroxynaphthalene-1,7-disulphonic acid
See: sulpho-J acid

4-amino-5-hydroxynaphthalene-1,3-disulphonic acid
See: Chicago acid

4-amino-5-hydroxynaphthalene-1,7-disulphonic acid
See: K acid

5-amino-4-hydroxynaphthalene-2,7-disulphonic acid
See: H acid

6-amino-1-hydroxynaphthalene-3,5-disulphonic acid
See: sulpho-J acid

1-amino-2-hydroxynaphthalene-4-sulphonic acid
See: 1-amino-2-naphthol-4-sulphonic acid

1-amino-8-hydroxynaphthalene-4-sulphonic acid
See: S acid

4-amino-3-hydroxynaphthalene-1-sulphonic acid
See: 1-amino-2-naphthol-4-sulphonic acid

6-amino-4-hydroxynaphthalene-2-sulphonic acid
See: gamma acid

7-amino-4-hydroxynaphthalene-2-sulphonic acid
See: J acid

1-amino-4-hydroxy-2-phenoxyanthraquinone
See: Disperse Red 60

3-amino-4-hydroxytoluene *See:* o-amino-p-cresol

5-aminoisophthalic acid
aniline-3,5-dicarboxylic acid

$C_8H_7N_1O_4$. M: 181.16.
Production:
• 5-nitroisophthalic acid (nitro reduction)
Derivatives: Pigment Yellow 120
Uses: photographic coupling agent intermediate

DL-2-aminoisovaleric acid *See:* DL-valine

4-amino-3-methoxyazobenzene-3'-sulphonic acid, sodium salt

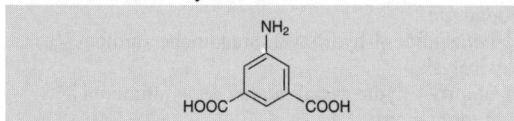

$C_{13}H_{12}N_3Na_1O_4S_1$. M: 329.31.
Production:
• metanilic acid + o-anisidine (diazotisation/azo coupling/sodium salt formation)
Derivatives:
Direct Yellow 44; Direct Yellow 118

3-amino-4-methoxybenzenesulphonic acid
See: 2-aminoanisole-4-sulphonic acid

3-amino-4-methoxybenzenesulphon-N-n-butylamide
*See: N-n-*butyl-3-amino-4-methoxybenzenesulphonamide

3-amino-4-methoxybenzoic acid
3-amino-p-anisic acid; [2840-26-8]
$C_8H_9N_1O_3$. M: 167.17.

Production:
• 4-methoxybenzoic acid (nitration/nitro reduction)
Derivatives:
Pigment Red 146; Pigment Red 147; Pigment Red 176; Pigment Red 184; Pigment Red 187

2-amino-6-methoxybenzothiazole
6-methoxy-2-aminobenzothiazole; 6-methoxybenzothiazol-2-ylamine; [1747-60-0]

$C_8H_8N_2O_1S_1$. M: 180.22.
Production:
• potassium thiocyanate + p-anisidine (Kaufmann reaction)
Derivatives:
Basic Blue 41; Basic Blue 54

4-amino-4'-methoxydiphenylamine
N-(4-anilino)-p-anisidine; Azoic Diazo Component 35 (CI); 37255 (CI); [6254-98-4]

$C_{13}H_{14}N_2O_1$. M: 214.26. Available as the free base and as the bisulphate salt.
Production:
• p-anisidine + 2-chloro-5-nitrobenzenesulphonic acid (amine formation/nitro reduction/desulphonation)
Uses:
azoic dye diazo component

N-(4-amino-5-methoxy-2-methylphenyl)benzamide
4'-amino-6'-methyl-m-benzanisidide; Fast Violet B base; Azoic Diazo Component 41 (CI); 37165 (CI); [27761-27-9]

$C_{15}H_{16}N_2O_2$. M: 256.30.
Production:
• p-cresidine + benzenesulphonyl chloride + benzoyl chloride (amine formation/nitration/nitro reduction/amide formation/hydrolysis)
Uses:
azoic dye diazo component

2-amino-4-methoxy-6-methyltriazine

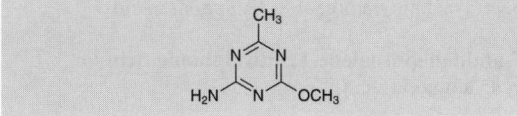

$C_5H_8N_4O_1$. M: 140.14.
Production:
• acetoguanamine + *O*-methylisourea sulphate
  (condensation)
Derivatives: chlorsulfuron; metsulfuron-methyl

3-amino-4-methoxytoluene *See:* p-cresidine

5-amino-4-methoxytoluene-2-sulphonic acid
2-amino-4-methylanisole-5-sulphonic acid; [6471-78-9]

$C_8H_{11}N_1O_4S_1$. M: 217.25.
Production:
• *p*-cresidine (sulphonation)
Derivatives: Food Red 17; Pigment Red 185
Uses: dyestuffs intermediate

3-amino-4-methylbenzoic acid
3-amino-*p*-toluic acid

$C_8H_9N_1O_2$. M: 151.17. MP: 166–168°C.
Production:
• *p*-toluic acid (nitration/nitro reduction)
Derivatives: Pigment Red 221; suramin sodium
Uses: dyestuffs intermediate

2-aminomethyl-1-ethylpyrrolidine

$C_7H_{16}N_2$. M: 128.22.
Production:
• *N*-methylpyrrolidone + nitromethane (carbonyl
  condensation/hydrogenation)
Derivatives: sulpiride

2-amino-2-methylisopentamide
2-amino-2,3-dimethylbutyramide; 2-methyl-2-aminoiso-
pentamide
$C_6H_{14}N_2O_1$. M: 130.19.

Production:
• methyl isopropyl ketone + hydrogen cyanide +
  ammonia (Strecker synthesis/nitrile hydration)
Derivatives: imazamethabenz-methyl; imazapyr-isopropylammonium; imazaquin-ammonium; imazethapyr

5-amino-3-methyl-1-phenylpyrazole
[1131-18-6]

$C_{10}H_{11}N_3$. M: 173.22.
Production:
• β-aminocrotononitrile + aniline (condensation)
Derivatives: Direct Red 180
Uses: dyestuffs intermediate

2-amino-2-methyl-1,3-propanediol
[115-69-5]

$C_4H_{11}N_1O_2$. M: 105.14. Crystalline solid. MP: 110°C.
Soluble in water forming alkaline solutions.
Production:
• nitroethane + formaldehyde (hydroxymethylation/
  nitro reduction)
Uses: emulsifier (cosmetics, polishes, cleaners)

2-amino-2-methyl-1-propanol
isobutanolamine; AMP; [124-68-5]

$C_4H_{11}N_1O_1$. M: 89.14. Liquid/solid. MP: 30–31°C. BP:
165°C. d: 0.93 kg/l (20°C). Miscible with water
forming alkaline solutions. Soluble in alcohol.
Production:
• 2-methyl-2-nitropropanol (nitro reduction)
Derivatives: 2-dimethylamino-2-methyl-1-propanol; 4,4-
dimethyl oxazolidine; 2-[(hydroxymethyl)amino]-2-me-
thylpropanol
Uses: emulsifier (creams, lotions, oils, waxes); pigment
dispersant (emulsion paints); amine soaps (metalworking fluids)

2-amino-6-methylpyridine
2-amino-6-picoline; [1824-81-3]
$C_6H_8N_2$. M: 108.14. Pale yellow, hygroscopic, crystall-

ine solid. M: 40–45°C. Soluble in water, oxygenated, chlorinated and aromatic solvents.

Production:
• α-picoline + sodamide (Chichibabin reaction)
Derivatives: nalidixic acid

2-amino-4-methylsulphonylphenol
2-hydroxy-5-methylsulphonylaniline; [80-23-9]

$C_7H_9N_1O_3S_1$. M: 187.22.
Production:
• o-nitrophenol + methanesulphonyl chloride (sulphonation/nitro reduction)
Derivatives: Acid Black 58; Acid Violet 78

2-amino-5-methyl-1,3,4-thiadiazole
[1603-91-4]

$C_3H_5N_3S_1$. M: 115.15.
Production:
• acetyl chloride + semicarbazide hydrochloride (condensation)
Derivatives: sulfamethizole

6-amino-1-methyluracil
[2434-53-9]

$C_5H_7N_3O_2$. M: 141.13.
Production:
• ethyl cyanoacetate + N-methylurea (condensation)
Derivatives: propentofylline; theobromine

α-aminonaphthalene *See:* 1-naphthylamine

2-aminonaphthalene-1,5-disulphonic acid
See: 2-naphthylamine-1,5-disulphonic acid

2-aminonaphthalene-4,8-disulphonic acid
See: 2-naphthylamine-4,8-disulphonic acid

2-aminonaphthalene-6,8-disulphonic acid
See: amino-G acid

4-aminonaphthalene-1,5-disulphonic acid
See: 1-naphthylamine-4,8-disulphonic acid

7-aminonaphthalene-1,3-disulphonic acid
See: amino-G acid

1-aminonaphthalene-5-sulphonic acid
See: 1-naphthylamine-5-sulphonic acid

2-aminonaphthalene-1-sulphonic acid
See: Tobias acid

4-aminonaphthalene-1-sulphonic acid
See: naphthionic acid

5-aminonaphthalene-1-sulphonic acid
See: 1-naphthylamine-5-sulphonic acid

5-aminonaphthalene-2-sulphonic acid
See: 1,6-Cleve's acid

6-aminonaphthalene-2-sulphonic acid
See: Broenner's acid

8-aminonaphthalene-1-sulphonic acid *See:* peri acid

8-aminonaphthalene-2-sulphonic acid
See: 1,7-Cleve's acid

8-aminonaphthalene-1,3,5-trisulphonic acid
See: 8-naphthylamine-1,3,5-trisulphonic acid

8-aminonaphthalene-1,3,6-trisulphonic acid
See: Koch acid

8-amino-2-naphthol
8-amino-2-hydroxynaphthalene; 1-amino-7-naphthol; [118-46-7]

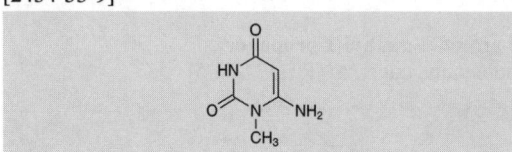

$C_{10}H_9N_1O_1$. M: 159.19. Needles. MP: 206°C. Soluble in hot water and oxygenated solvents.
Production:
• 1,7-Cleve's acid (alkali fusion)
Derivatives: Acid Black 58; Mordant Black 38

8-amino-1-naphtholactam *See:* naphtholactam

6-amino-1-naphthol-3,5-disulphonic acid
See: sulpho-J acid

8-amino-1-naphthol-3,5-disulphonic acid *See:* K acid

8-amino-1-naphthol-3,6-disulphonic acid *See:* H acid

8-amino-1-naphthol-5,7-disulphonic acid
See: Chicago acid

1-amino-2-naphthol-4-sulphonic acid
1-amino-2-hydroxynaphthalene-4-sulphonic acid;
4-amino-3-hydroxynaphthalene-1-sulphonic acid;
[116-63-2]

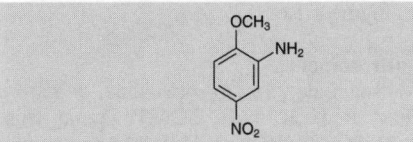

$C_{10}H_9N_1O_4S_1$. M: 239.25.
Production:
• 1-nitroso-2-naphthol (nitro reduction/sulphonation)
Derivatives: Acid Blue 158; Acid Blue 159; Acid Red 186; 1amino-6-nitro-2-naphthol-4-sulphonic acid; Mordant Red 7

4-amino-5-naphthol-1-sulphonic acid
See: S acid

6-amino-4-naphthol-2-sulphonic acid
See: gamma acid

7-amino-4-naphthol-2-sulphonic acid
See: J acid

2-amino-4-nitroanisole
2-methoxy-5-nitroaniline; 4-nitro-*o*-anisidine; 5-nitro-2-methoxyaniline; Fast Scarlet R base; Azoic Diazo Component 13 (CI); 37130 (CI); [97-52-9]

$C_7H_8N_2O_3$. M: 168.15.
Production:
• 2,4-dinitroanisole (partial nitro reduction)
Derivatives: Pigment Red 23

2-amino-5-nitroanisole
2-methoxy-4-nitroaniline; Azoic Diazo Component 5 (CI); 37125 (CI);

$C_7H_8N_2O_3$. M: 168.15. Pale yellow needles. MP: 139°C.
Production:
• 2-chloro-4-nitroaniline + methanol (ether formation)
Derivatives: Pigment Red 171; Pigment Yellow 74

4-amino-3-nitroanisole
4-methoxy-2-nitroaniline; Fast Bordeaux GP base; Azoic Diazo Component 1 (CI); 37135 (CI); [96-96-8]

$C_7H_8N_2O_3$. M: 168.15. Dark red powder. MP: 123°C. Soluble in water and oxygenated solvents.
Production:
• *p*-anisidine (nitration)
Derivatives:
pamaquine; Pigment Yellow 65; primaquine

2-amino-5-nitrobenzenesulphonic acid
See: 4-nitroaniline-2-sulphonic acid

2-amino-5-nitrobenzoic acid
See: 5-nitroanthranilic acid

2-amino-5-nitrobenzonitrile
2-cyano-4-nitroaniline; [17420-30-3]

$C_7H_5N_3O_2$. M: 163.14.
Production:
• 5-nitroanthranilic acid + ammonia (nitrile formation)
Derivatives:
2-amino-3-bromo-5-nitrobenzonitrile; Disperse Red 73

4′-amino-4-nitrodiphenylamine-2-sulphonic acid
2-(*p*-aminoanilino)-5-nitrobenzenesulphonic acid;
[91-29-2]

$C_{12}H_{11}N_3O_5S_1$. M: 309.29.
Production:
• 2-chloro-5-nitrobenzenesulphonic acid +
p-nitroaniline (amine formation/partial nitro reduction)
Derivatives: Acid Brown 248; Acid Orange 51; Acid Orange 67; Acid Yellow 65

1-amino-6-nitro-2-naphthol-4-sulphonic acid

$C_{10}H_8N_2O_6S_1$. M: 284.23.

Production:
• 1-amino-2-naphthol-4-sulphonic acid (nitration)
Derivatives: Acid Black 52; Mordant Black 11

2-amino-4-nitrophenol
[99-57-0]

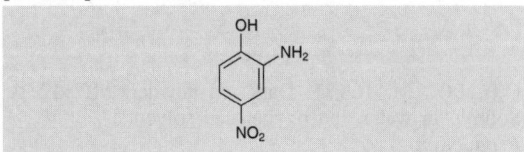

$C_6H_6N_2O_3$. M: 154.13. Orange crystals. MP: 143–145°C. Slightly soluble in water. Soluble in oxygenated solvents.
Production:
• 2,4-dinitrophenol (nitro reduction)
Derivatives: Acid Orange 92; Mordant Brown 1; Mordant Brown 33

2-amino-5-nitrophenol
2-hydroxy-4-nitroaniline; [121-88-0]

$C_6H_6N_2O_3$. M: 154.13.
Production:
• 2-chloro-4-nitroaniline (hydrolysis)
Derivatives: Acid Black 63; Sulphur Red 7

2-amino-4-nitrophenol-6-sulphonic acid
2-hydroxy-5-nitroaniline-3-sulphonic acid; [96-67-3]

$C_6H_6N_2O_6S_1$. M: 234.18.
Production:
• 2,4-dinitrophenol (sulphonation/partial nitro reduction)
Derivatives:
Acid Orange 74; Acid Orange 148; Solvent Yellow 19

2-amino-5-nitrothiazole
[121-66-4]

$C_3H_3N_3O_2S_1$. M: 145.13.
Production:
• 2-aminothiazole (nitration)
Derivatives: Basic Blue 119; Disperse Blue 102; Disperse Blue 339; niridazole; Serisol Blue RD
Uses: anthelmintic drug

2-amino-4-nitrotoluene
5-nitro-*o*-toluidine; Fast Scarlet G base; Azoic Diazo Component 12 (CI); 37105 (CI); [99-55-8]

$C_7H_8N_2O_2$. M: 152.15. Yellow, crystalline solid. MP: 107°C. Slightly soluble in water. Soluble in oxygenated solvents.
Production:
• dinitrotoluene (nitro reduction)
Derivatives:
lucanthone; Pigment Red 8; Pigment Red 17; Pigment Red 22; Sulphur Yellow 1
Uses: azoic dye diazo component

2-amino-5-nitrotoluene
2-methyl-4-nitroaniline; *p*-nitro-*o*-toluidine; Fast Red RL base; Azoic Diazo Component 34 (CI); 37100 (CI); [99-52-5]

$C_7H_8N_2O_2$. M: 152.15. Yellow, crystalline solid. MP: 131–133°C. Soluble in water, oxygenated and aromatic solvents.
Production:
• *o*-toluidine (nitration)
Derivatives: Pigment Red 12

4-amino-3-nitrotoluene
4-methyl-2-nitroaniline; 2-nitro-*p*-toluidine; *m*-nitro-*p*-toluidine; Fast Red GL base; MNPT; Azoic Diazo Component 8 (CI); 37110 (CI); [119-32-4]

$C_7H_8N_2O_2$. M: 152.15. Red crystals. MP: 115–116°C. Soluble in hot water and alcohol.
Production:
• *p*-toluidine (nitration)
• *m*-nitro-*p*-cresol (ammoniation)
Derivatives:
m-nitrotoluene; Pigment Orange 6; Pigment Red 3; Pigment Red 13; Pigment Yellow 1

5-aminoorotic acid
[7164-43-4]
$C_5H_5N_3O_4$. M: 171.11.

Production:
• 6-methyluracil (side-chain oxidation/nitration/nitro reduction)
Derivatives: dipyridamole

6-aminopenicillanic acid
6-APA; [551-16-6]

$C_8H_{12}N_2O_3S_1$. M: 216.26. Crystals. MP: 206–208°C with decomposition. Soluble in acid.
Production:
• benzylpenicillin (enzymatic hydrolysis)
Derivatives: amoxicillin; ampicillin; azidocillin; carbenicillin; ciclacillin; cloxacillin; dicloxacillin; epicillin; flucloxacillin; mecillinam; meticillin; oxacillin; pheneticillin; propicillin; temocillin; ticarcillin

o-aminophenetole *See:* o-phenetidine

p-aminophenetole *See:* p-phenetidine

m-aminophenol
3-aminophenol; 3-hydroxyaniline; *m*-hydroxyaniline; MAP; [591-27-5]

$C_6H_7N_1O_1$. M: 109.14. Crystals. MP: 124–126°C. Soluble in hot water and oxygenated solvents.
Production:
• resorcinol + ammonia (amine formation)
• metanilic acid (alkali fusion)
Derivatives: 7-amino-3-phenylcoumarin; *p*-aminosalicylic acid; desmedipham; flutolanil; formetanate hydrochloride; karbutilate; mepronil; phenmedipham

o-aminophenol
2-aminophenol; 2-hydroxyaniline; *o*-hydroxyaniline; [95-55-6]

$C_6H_7N_1O_1$. M: 109.14. Colourless needles. MP: 174–177°C. Sublimes. Slightly soluble in water and alcohol.

Production:
• o-nitrophenol (nitro reduction)
Derivatives:
2-benzoxazolethiol; benzoxazolone; 1,4-bis(benzoxazol-2-yl)naphthalene; 4,4′-bis(benzoxazol-2-yl)stilbene; chlorquinaldol; Fluorescent Brightener 190
Uses: dyestuffs intermediate

p-aminophenol
4-aminophenol; 4-hydroxyaniline; *p*-hydroxyaniline; Oxidative Base 6 (CI); [123-30-8]

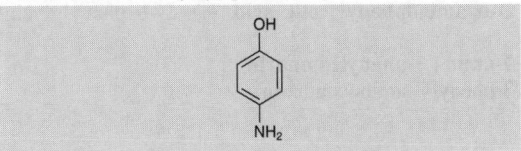

$C_6H_7N_1O_1$. M: 109.14. White or reddish flakes. Discoloured by light and air. MP: 188–190°C. Sublimes. Slightly soluble in water and alcohol.
Production:
• p-nitrophenol (nitro reduction)
• nitrobenzene (catalytic reduction/rearrangement)
Derivatives:
acebutolol; Acid Yellow 40; Acid Yellow 76; *N*-benzyl-*p*-aminophenol hydrochloride; *N*-butyryl-*p*-aminophenol; *N*-(4-hydroxyphenyl)glycine; *N*-lauroyl-*p*-aminophenol; *N*-methyl-*p*-aminophenol; paracetamol; *N*-pelagonoyl-*p*-aminophenol; *N*-stearoyl-*p*-aminophenol; Sulphur Black 11; Sulphur Green 1; Sulphur Green 9; Sulphur Green 11; Sulphur Red 10; triglycidyl-*p*-aminophenol
Uses: dyestuffs intermediate; photographic developer

2-aminophenol-4-sulphonamide
o-aminophenol-p-sulphonamide; [98-32-8]

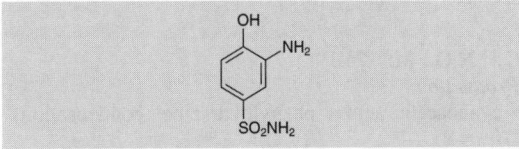

$C_6H_8N_2O_3S_1$. M: 188.21.
Production:
• 2-aminophenol-4-sulphonic acid + ammonia (acetylation/sulphonamide formation/amide hydrolysis)
Derivatives:
Acid Orange 60; Acid Red 296; Direct Violet 66

2-aminophenol-4-sulphonic acid
3-amino-4-hydroxybenzenesulphonic acid; *o*-aminophenol-*p*-sulphonic acid; 2-hydroxyaniline-5-sulphonic acid; [98-37-3]
$C_6H_7N_1O_4S_1$. M: 189.20. Brown, crystalline solid. MP: 155°C. Slightly soluble in water.
Production:
• p-phenolsulphonic acid (nitration/nitro reduction)

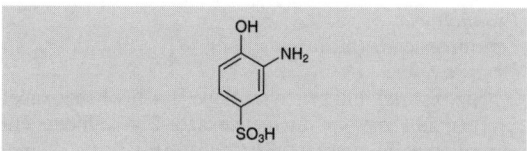

Derivatives: Acid Black 60; 2-aminoanisole-4-sulphonic acid; 2-aminophenol-4-sulphonamide; Mordant Black 9; Mordant Brown 13; Mordant Red 5; Mordant Violet 5; Reactive Red 6

D-α-aminophenylacetic acid *See:* D-α-phenylglycine

7-amino-3-phenylcoumarin
3-phenyl-7-aminocoumarin

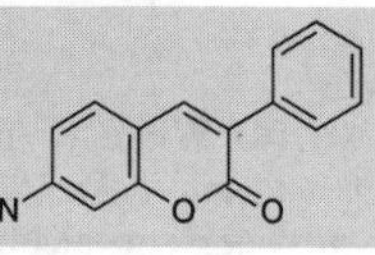

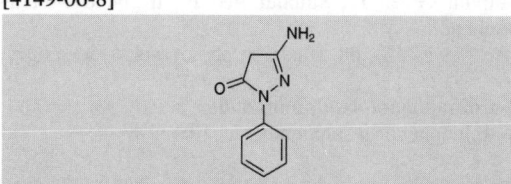

$C_{15}H_{11}N_1O_2$. M: 237.26.
Production:
• benzyl cyanide + ethyl formate + *m*-aminophenol (carbonyl condensation/Pechmann reaction)
Derivatives:
7-(4-amino-6-diethylaminotriazin-2-yl)amino-3-phenylcoumarin; 7-(4-chloro-6-diethylaminotriazin-2-yl)amino-3-phenylcoumarin

3-amino-1-phenyl-5-pyrazolone
[4149-06-8]

$C_9H_9N_3O_1$. M: 175.19.
Production:
• cyanoacetic acid + phenylhydrazine (condensation)
Uses:
photographic coupling agent intermediate

aminophylline *See:* theophylline

2-aminopropane-1,3-diol

$C_3H_9N_1O_2$. M: 91.11.
Production:
• nitromethane + formaldehyde (nitration/nitro reduction)
Derivatives: 1,3-dimercaptoisopropyldimethylamine
Uses:
alkyd/unsaturated polyester/epoxy resin comonomer

3-aminopropanol
propanolamine; [156-87-6]

$H_2NCH_2CH_2CH_2OH$

$C_3H_9N_1O_1$. M: 75.11. Liquid. BP: 187–190°C. FP: 11°C. d: 1.46 kg/l (25°C). Soluble in water and oxygenated solvents.
Production:
• water + acrylonitrile (cyanoethylation/nitrile reduction)
Derivatives: 3-(2-chloroethyl)aminopropanol hydrochloride; cyclophosphamide; 3-dimethylaminopropanol; domperidone; pantothenol

α-aminopropionic acid *See:* DL-alanine

3-aminopropyldiethylamine
See: 3-diethylaminopropylamine

3-aminopropyldimethylamine
See: 3-dimethylaminopropylamine

N-(3-aminopropyl)morpholine
APM; [123-00-2]

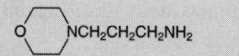

$C_7H_{16}N_2O_1$. M: 144.22. Colourless liquid. BR: 215–230°C. FP: -15°C. d: 0.98 kg/l (20°C). Soluble in water and most organic solvents. Flash point: 100°C (PMCC).
Production:
• morpholine + acrylonitrile (cyanoethylation/nitrile reduction)
Derivatives: styrene-fumarate copolymers

γ-aminopropyltriethoxysilane
[919-30-2]

$H_2NCH_2CH_2CH_2Si(OC_2H_5)_3$

$C_9H_{23}N_1O_3Si_1$. M: 221.38.
Production:
• trichlorosilane + allylamine + ethanol (hydrosilation/dehydrochlorination)
Derivatives: bis(2-hydroxyethyl)-γ-aminopropyltriethoxysilane; γ-ureidopropyltriethoxysilane
Uses: plastics coupling agent

2-aminopyridine
α-pyridylamine; [92-67-1]

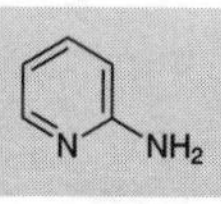

$C_5H_6N_2$. M: 94.11. Colourless to pale yellow lumps or flakes. MP: 55–60°C. BP: 204°C. Soluble in water, oxygenated and chlorinated solvents.

Production:
• pyridine + sodamide (Chichibabin reaction)
Derivatives:
azamethiphos; 1-azaphenothiazine; 2,6-diaminopyridine; fenyramidol; mepyramine; piroxicam; salazosulfapyridine; sulfapyridine; tripelennamine

3-aminopyridine
β-pyridylamine; [462-08-8]

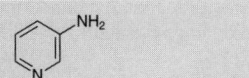

$C_5H_6N_2$. M: 94.11. White crystals. MP: 64°C. BP: 250–252°C. Soluble in water and oxygenated solvents.
Production:
• nicotinonitrile (Ritter reaction)
Derivatives: 3-hydroxypyridine; pirenzepine

4-aminopyridine
γ-pyridylamine; [504-24-5]

$C_5H_6N_2$. M: 94.11. Needles. MP: 158–160°C. Soluble in water and oxygenated solvents.
Production:
• pyridine (peroxidation/nitration/nitro reduction)
Derivatives: 4-dimethylaminopyridine; pinacidil

2-aminopyrimidine
[109-12-6]

$C_4H_5N_3$. M: 95.10. Solid. MP: 123–126°C. Sublimes. Soluble in water.
Production:
• propargyl alcohol + guanidine hydrochloride (oxidative condensation)
Derivatives:
buspirone; sulfadiazine; sulfametoxydiazine

5-aminosalicylic acid
5-amino-2-hydroxybenzoic acid; [89-57-6]

$C_7H_7N_1O_3$. M: 153.15.
Production:
• salicylic acid (nitration/nitro reduction)
Derivatives: Direct Green 28

p-aminosalicylic acid
4-amino-2-hydroxybenzoic acid; 4-aminosalicylic acid; 2-hydroxy-4-aminobenzoic acid; PAS; PASA; [65-49-6]

$C_7H_7N_1O_3$. M: 153.15. Crystalline solid. MP: 150°C with decomposition. Slightly soluble in water. Soluble in acid and alkali solutions. Available commercially as the free acid and as the sodium dihydrate salt.
Production:
• m-aminophenol + potassium bicarbonate (Kolbe-Schmitt reaction)
Derivatives: bromopride; metoclopramide; xipamide
Uses: tuberculostatic drug

4-aminostilbene-2-sulphonic acid
[6265-01-6]

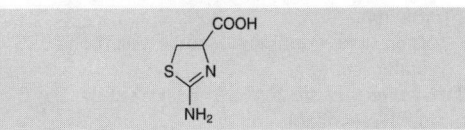

$C_{14}H_{13}N_1O_3S_1$. M: 275.32.
Production:
• 4-nitrotoluene-2-sulphonic acid + benzaldehyde (Knoevenagel condensation/nitro reduction)
Derivatives:
Fluorescent Brightener 46

2-aminothiazole
thiazol-2-ylamine; 2-thiazylamine; [96-50-4]

$C_3H_4N_2S_1$. M: 100.13. Yellow crystals. MP: 92°C. Soluble in hot water.
Production:
• chloroacetaldehyde + thiourea (condensation)
Derivatives:
2-amino-5-nitrothiazole; Basic Red 29; sulfathiazole
Uses: thyroid hormone drug

2-aminothiazoline-4-carboxylic acid
ATC

$C_4H_6N_2O_2S_1$. M: 146.16.
Production:
• acrylic acid + chlorine + thiourea (addition/condensation)
Derivatives: L-cysteine

2-aminothiophenol
2-mercaptoaniline; [137-07-5]

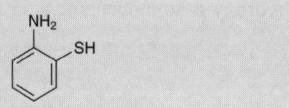

C₆H₇N₁S₁. M: 125.20.
Production:
• hydrogen sulphide + *o*-chloronitrobenzene
  (thiolation/nitro reduction)
Derivatives:
diltiazem; 2-methylbenzothiazole; orthanilic acid

aminothiourea *See:* thiosemicarbazide

***m*-aminotoluene** *See: m*-toluidine

***o*-aminotoluene** *See: o*-toluidine

***p*-aminotoluene** *See: p*-toluidine

2-aminotoluene-5-sulphonic acid
6-aminotoluene-3-sulphonic acid

C₇H₉N₁O₃S₁. M: 187.22.
Production:
• *o*-toluidine (sulphonation)
Derivatives:
Acid Orange 8; 1-(6′-chloro-2′-methyl-4′-sulphophenyl)-
4-methylpyrazolone; 1-(4′-sulpho-2′-methylphenyl)-3-
methylpyrazolone

4-aminotoluene-3-sulphonic acid *See:* 4B acid

3-amino-1,2,4-triazole
aminotriazole; amitrole; ATA; [61-82-5]

C₂H₄N₄. M: 84.08. Crystalline powder. MP: 157–159°C.
Soluble in water and alcohol.
Production:
• formic acid + aminoguanidine bicarbonate
  (condensation)
Derivatives: Basic Red 22; Basic Yellow 25; 3-salicyl-
amido-1,2,4-triazole
Uses: herbicide

3-amino-2,4,6-triiodobenzoic acid
2,4,6-triiodo-*m*-aminobenzoic acid; [3119-15-1]
C₇H₄I₃N₁O₂. M: 514.83.

Production:
• *m*-aminobenzoic acid (ring iodination)
Derivatives:
adipiodone; iobenzamic acid; iodoxamic acid; ioglycamic acid; iotroxic acid

aminotris(methylene phosphonic acid)
AMP; ATMP

C₃H₁₂N₁O₉P₃. M: 299.05. Available commercially as an
aqueous solution with a 50% acid content. Also available as a 29% acid solution of the pentasodium salt.
Production:
• ammonia + formaldehyde + phosphorous acid
  (Mannich reaction)
Uses:
pigments/fillers/clay dispersant (ceramics, paint, paper);
scale inhibitor/chelant (boilers, cooling towers, oilfield
water systems); sequestrant (liquid laundry detergents,
industrial cleaners)

ω-aminoundecanoic acid
11-aminoundecanoic acid; [2432-99-7]

H₂N(CH₂)₁₀COOH

C₁₁H₂₃N₁O₂. M: 201.31.
Production:
• undecylenic acid + hydrogen bromide, anhydrous +
  ammonia (anti-Markownikoff addition/amine formation)
Derivatives:
polyamide 11; poly(ether-amide) elastomers

amitraz
N,N-bis(2,4-xylyliminomethyl)methylamine;
[33089-61-1]

C₁₉H₂₃N₃. M: 293.41.
Production:
• 2,4-xylidine + triethyl orthoformate + methylamine
  (imine formation/amine formation)
Uses: acaricide/insecticide

amitriptyline
C₂₀H₂₃N₁. M: 277.41. The product is available as the
free base or hydrochloride.

CHCH₂CH₂N(CH₃)₂

Production:
• dibenzosuberone + 3-dimethylaminopropyl chloride hydrochloride (Grignard reagent formation/Grignard reaction/dehydration)
Uses:
antidepressant drug

amitrole *See:* 3-amino-1,2,4-triazole

ammoidin *See:* methoxsalen

ammonia
[7664-41-7]

NH₃

H_3N_1. M: 17.03. Colourless liquified gas with a characteristic, pungent odour. BP: -33°C. MP: -78°C. d: 0.597 (gas, air=1). Soluble in water forming alkaline solutions. Soluble in oxygenated solvents. Also available as a solution in water.
Production:
• synthesis gas + water + air (shift reaction/carbon dioxide removal/desulphurisation/Haber-Bosch process)
Derivatives:
acetamidine hydrochloride; acetazolamide; 4-acetylsulphanilamide; Acid Brown 248; aclonifen; acrylonitrile; adiponitrile; β-alanine; DL-alanine; alkyd resins, water-soluble; alkyl(C_{13}-C_{15})amine; allylamine; allylthiourea; 1-aminoanthraquinone; 2-aminoanthraquinone; *p*-aminobenzamide; 1-amino-5-benzamidoanthraquinone; 4-amino-*N*-benzylpiperidine; 4-amino-5-bromomethyl-2methylpyrimidine hydrobromide; 3-amino-4-chlorobenzamide; 4-amino-2-chloro-6,7-dimethoxyquinazoline; 4-amino-1-diethylaminopentane; 7-(4-amino-6-diethylaminotriazin-2-yl)amino-3-phenylcoumarin; aminoethylethanolamine; aminoethylpiperazine; amino-G acid; 1-amino-4-hydroxyanthraquinone; 2-amino-2-methylisopentamide; 2-amino-5-nitrobenzonitrile; *m*-aminophenol; 2-aminophenol-4-sulphonamide; aminotris(methylene phosphonic acid); ω-aminoundecanoic acid; ammonia, aqueous; ammoniacal copper arsenate; ammonium acetate; ammonium bicarbonate; ammonium bifluoride; ammonium bisulphite; ammonium borate; ammonium bromide; ammonium carbamate; ammonium caseinate; ammonium citrate, dibasic; ammonium cumene sulphonate; ammonium *O,O*-dicresyl dithiophosphate; ammonium ferric citrate; ammonium fluoborate; ammonium fluosilicate; ammonium formate; ammonium lauryl ether sulphate; ammonium lauryl sulphate; ammonium molybdate; ammonium nitrate; ammonium nonylphenol ether sulphates; ammonium oleate; ammonium paratungstate; ammonium pentaborate; ammonium perchlorate; ammonium perfluorooctoate; ammonium picrate; ammonium polyacrylate; ammonium polyphosphate, solution; ammonium stearate; ammonium sulphamate; ammonium sulphate; ammonium sulphide; ammonium sulphite; ammonium thiocyanate; ammonium thioglycollate; aniline; L-aspartic acid; aztreonam; benzimide; benzo-isothiazolin-3-one; benzonitrile; benzthiazuron; benzylamine; bisamine A; bitoscanate; boron nitride; Broenner's acid; bumetanide; buphenine; *n*-butylamine; *s*-butylamine; caprolactam; carbamazepine; carbomethoxybenzenesulphonyl isocyanate; cartap; chloramine-B; chloramphenicol; chloridazon; chloroacetonitrile; 5-chloroaniline-2,4-disulphonamide; 2-chlorobenzenesulphonyl isocyanate; 4-chlorobutyronitrile; 2-chloro-5-chlorosulphonylbenzenesulphonamide; 2-chloro-4-nitroaniline; 4-chloro-2-nitroaniline; chlorpropamide; chlorthalidone; cilastatin; citrazinic acid; clonazepam; clopamide; cocoamine; copper hydroxide; cupric oxide; cuprous oxide; cyanazine; cyanoacetamide; cyclohexane-1,4-diisocyanate; cyclohexylamine; cyclopentylamine; cyclopropylamine; cyromazine; DL-cysteine hydrochloride; diallylamine; 1,4-diaminoanthraquinone; 3,3'-diaminobenzidine; 1,12-diaminododecane; 2,6-diaminopyridine; diammonium phosphate; diamylamine; diazepam; diazinon; diazoxide; dibenzylamine; di-*n*-butylamine; di-*s*-butylamine; 3,5-dichloroaniline; 2,6-dichlorobenzonitrile; 2,4-dichloro-5-sulphamoylbenzoic acid; dicocoamine; dicyclohexylamine; diethanolamine; diethylamine; diethylenetriamine; *N,N*-diethylethylenediamine; di-(2-ethylhexyl)amine; 1,3-diiminoisoindoline; diisobutylamine; diisopropanolamine; diisopropylamine; dilauryl 1,4-dihydro-2,6-dimethylpyridine-3,5-dicarboxylate; dimethylamine; 1,1-dimethylhydrazine; dinitramine; 2,4-dinitroaniline; di-*n*-propylamine; dipropylenetriamine; di-*o*-tolylguanidine; di-(trimethylsilyl)amine; *p*-dodecylaniline; erucamide; ethionamide; ethosuximide; ethylamine; ethylenediamine; ethylenediaminetetraacetic acid, ammonium ferric salt; *N*-ethylethylenediamine; 2-ethylhexylamine; 2-ethyl-4-methylimidazole; *N*-ethylmorpholine; 2-(*N*-ethylperfluorooctylsulphonamido)ethyl phosphate, ammonium salt; etrimfos; fish amine; fish amine, hydrogenated; flubendazole; flucytosine; flunitrazepam; Fluorescent Brightener 204; fluoroacetamide; flurazepam; fomesafen; formamide; fosamine-ammonium; furfurylamine; furosemide; glibenclamide; glipizide; glisoxepide; glufosinate-ammonium; glycine; guanidine carbonate; guazatine acetate; *n*-hexadecylamine; hexamethylenetetramine; hexythiazox; hydrazine; hydroflumethiazide; hydrogen cyanide; 5-(2-hydroxyethyl)-4-methylthiazole; *N*-hydr-oxyethylpiperazine; hydroxylamine sulphate; *p*-hydroxyphenylacetonitrile; D-α-(4-hydroxyphenyl)glycine; 4-hydroxy-2,2,6,6-tetramethylpiperidine; imazaquin-ammonium; imidazole; iminodiacetic acid; iohexol; isonicotinamide; isophoronediamine; isophthalodinitrile; isopropylamine; isoxsuprine; laurylamine; lenacil; levodopa; L-lysine;

mafenide; mebendazole; menadoxime; meprobamate; mercuric chloride, ammoniated; methacrylonitrile; methamidophos; methocarbamol; methylamine; methyldopa; methylenebis(maleimide); 2-methyl-5-ethylpyridine; methyl hydrazine; 2-methylimidazole; methylol carbamate resins; 4-methylthiazole; methyprylon; metiram; mexiletine; monoammonium phosphate; monoethanolamine; monoisopropanolamine; morpholine; nicardipine; nickel carbonate, basic; nicotinonitrile; nifedipine; nimodipine; nitrazepam; nitrendipine; nitric oxide; nitrilotriacetic acid; o-nitroaniline; p-nitroaniline; 5-nitroanthranilic acid; nitrophosphate; nonylphenol polyether amines; norephedrine; octodrine; n-octylamine; oleamide; oleylamine; oryzalin; oxytocin; pendimethalin; pentagastrin; perylimide; phenolic resins, amino-substituted; DL-phenylalanine; L-phenylalanine; p-phenylene diisocyanate; 2-phenylethylamine; D-α-phenylethylamine; D-α-phenylglycine; phthalimide; phthalodinitrile; picloram; α-picoline; β-picoline; γ-picoline; pinacidil; piperazine; piracetam; polyether polyols, flexible, amineterminated; polyethylenepolyamine; polystyrene, crosslinked, aminated; polystyrene, crosslinked, phosphonated; potassium gold cyanide; prodiamine; 1,2-propanediamine; 1,3-propanediamine; n-propylamine; propyzamide; prothionamide; pyrazinamide; pyridine; 3-pyridino-4-methyl-6-hydroxy-2-pyridone chloride; pyrrole; pyrrolidine; 2-pyrrolidone; Reactive Blue 7; Reactive Blue 13; Reactive Orange 13; Reactive Red 12; rimantidine; salicylamide; sodamide; sodium carbonate; sodium saccharin; soya amine; stearamide; stearylamine; succinimide; succinonitrile; sulfalene; sulfamethoxazole; sulpiride; tallowamine; taurine; n-tetradecylamine; tetraethylenepentamine; tetrahydrophthalimide; thiafensulfuron-methyl; thiamazole; Tobias acid; p-toluenesulphonamide; tolycaine; trialkyl(C_8-C_{10})amine; triallylamine; 1,3,5-triamino-2,4,6-trinitrobenzene; triamylamine; tribenzylamine; tri-n-butylamine; 3,5,6-trichloro-2-pyridone; tricrotonylidenetetramine; triethanolamine; triethylamine; triethylenediamine; triethylenetetramine; tri-n-hexylamine; triisooctylamine; triisopropanolamine; trimethylamine; trimethylhexamethylenediamine; tri-n-octylamine; urea; DL-valine; Vat Red 28; veratryl cyanide; xipamide; 2,6-xylidine; 3,5-xylidine; zinc ammonium chloride; zirconium hydroxide
Uses:
extraction solvent; fertiliser; microbial fermentation nutrient; refrigerant fluid

ammonia, aqueous
ammonia liquor; ammonium hydroxide; [1336-21-6]

$$NH_3.nH_2O$$

H_3N_1. M: 17.03. Colourless liquid with a pungent odour. Available with 15–35% ammonia content. d: 0.88 kg/l (35% w/w ammonia, 20°C).
Production:
• ammonia (dissolution)

Uses: etchant (semiconductor manufacture); industrial cleaning agent; hair dyeing/tinting ingredient; household cleaner/detergent ingredient; photographic/printing reagent; amine soap ingredient (metalworking fluids); stabiliser (natural rubber latex, paints, paper coatings)

ammoniacal copper arsenate
ACA
Production:
• ammonia + copper sulphate/copper carbonate, basic + arsenic pentoxide (salt formation)
Uses:
wood preservative

ammonium acetate
[631-61-8]

$$CH_3CO^- \quad NH_4^+$$

$C_2H_7N_1O_2$. M: 77.09. White, crystalline solid. MP: 112–114°C. Very slightly soluble in water. Soluble in oxygenated solvents.
Production:
• acetic acid + ammonia (neutralisation)
Derivatives: acetamide
Uses: diaphoretic/diuretic drug; analytical reagent; microbial fermentation nutrient

ammonium alum
aluminium ammonium sulphate; ammonium aluminium sulphate; [7784-25-0]

$$NH_4Al(SO_4)_2$$

$H_4Al_1N_1O_8S_2$. M: 237.14. The commercial product is the dodecahydrate. Colourless crystals or powder. MP: 94°C. d: 1.64 kg/l. Solubility in water: 150 g/l water (20°C) forming slightly acidic solutions.
Production:
• bauxite + sulphuric acid + ammonium sulphate (salt formation)
Uses: electroplating bath ingredient; gelatine hardening agent; mordant; tanning auxiliary; textile fireproofing agent; water treatment chemical

ammonium aluminium sulphate
See: ammonium alum

ammonium biborate *See:* ammonium borate

ammonium bicarbonate
ammonium hydrogen carbonate; [1066-33-7]

$$NH_4HCO_3$$

$C_1H_5N_1O_3$. M: 79.06. White crystals. Gradual decomposition at 25–60°C. d: 1.57 kg/l. Soluble in water.
Production:
• ammonia + carbon dioxide (salt formation)

Derivatives: D-alanine; ammonium carbonate; ammonium sulphate; ammonium zirconyl carbonate; L-cysteine; 5,5-dimethylhydantoin; hydroxylamine sulphate; magnesium carbonate, basic; manganese carbonate; mephenytoin; DL-methionine; phenytoin
Uses:
buffering agent (acid neutralisation reactions); amino resin curing agent; baking powder ingredient; blowing agent (polyvinyl chloride, rubber); leaching agent (uranium ores); reagent (Bucherer synthesis); textile auxiliary; yeast fermentation nutrient

ammonium bichromate *See:* ammonium dichromate

ammonium bifluoride
ammonia white acid; ammonium hydrogen fluoride; [1341-49-7]

$$NH_4HF_2$$

$H_5F_2N_1$. M: 57.05. White crystals. MP: 125°C. Readily soluble in water forming acidic solutions which etch glass.
Production:
• ammonia + hydrogen fluoride (salt formation)
Derivatives: cryolite
Uses:
etchant (semiconductor manufacture); aluminium etchant/brightening agent; industrial cleaning agent; wool flame-resistance treatment reagent; oil-well acidising reagent; sterilising agent (brewing, bottling industry); surface treatment agent (magnesium alloys)

ammonium bisulphite
[10192-30-0]

$$NH_4HSO_3$$

$H_5N_1O_3S_1$. M: 99.11. Usually sold as a pale yellow, 65% solution in water which has a sulphur dioxide odour. d: 1.35 kg/l (20°C).
Production:
• ammonia + sulphur dioxide, raw (salt formation)
Uses: photographic bleach fixer bath component; oxygen scavenger (oilfield chemical treatments); caramel production

ammonium borate
ammonium biborate; diammonium tetraborate

$$(NH_4)_2O.2B_2O_3$$

$H_8B_4N_2O_7$. M: 191.30. The commercial product is the tetrahydrate. Crystalline solid. d: 1.58 kg/l. Soluble in water.
Production:
• ammonia + boric acid (salt formation)
Uses:
fireproofing agent (wood, textiles); glaze/enamel/ceramics ingredient; soap/cleaner ingredient

ammonium bromide
[12124-97-9]

$$NH_4Br$$

$H_4Br_1N_1$. M: 97.94. White, crystalline solid. Sublimes when heated. d: 2.33 kg/l (15°C). Solubility in water: 680 kg/l water (10°C).
Production:
• hydrobromic acid + ammonia (salt formation)
Uses: fire-retardant additive; photographic chemical

ammonium carbamate
[1111-78-0]

$$\overset{O}{\overset{\|}{NH_2CO^-}} \quad NH_4^+$$

$C_1H_6N_2O_2$. M: 78.07. Crystalline powder. MP: 425°C (sealed tube). Volatile and thermally unstable at room temperature, releasing ammonia. Soluble in water and alcohol.
Production:
• ammonia + carbon dioxide (reaction)
• ammonium carbonate + ammonia + carbon dioxide (reaction)
Derivatives: ammonium carbonate
Uses: neutralisation/amination reagent

ammonium carbonate
ammonium bicarbonate/carbamate; [506-87-6]

$$NH_4HCO_3/NH_4CONH_2$$

$C_1H_8N_2O_3$. M: 96.08. White, crystalline solid comprising an equimolar mixture of ammonium bicarbonate and ammonium carbamate.
Production:
• ammonium bicarbonate + ammonium carbamate (blending)
Derivatives:
ammonium carbamate; cupric oxide; cuprous oxide
Uses: blowing agent (foamed plastics/rubber); baking powder ingredient; photographic chemical; reagent (carbon monoxide absorption processes); detergent builder

ammonium caseinate
An alkaline dispersion of casein in water.
Production:
• casein + ammonia (salt formation)
Uses: adhesives (beer bottle labelling pastes); foil-paper laminating adhesives; adhesives (wooden doors); binder (paper coatings); protective colloid (emulsion polymerisation)

ammonium chloride
sal ammoniac; [12125-02-9]

$$NH_4Cl$$

$H_4Cl_1N_1$. M: 53.49. White, crystalline powder. Sublimes

without melting. Bulk density: 0.8–0.9 kg/l. Solubility in water: 272 kg/l solution (20°C) forming acidic solutions.

Production:
- ammonium sulphate + sodium chloride, natural (salt formation)
- limestone + sodium chloride, natural + ammonia (ammonia-soda process; byproduct of sodium carbonate production)

Derivatives:
Acid Blue 9; ammonium metavanadate; Basic Yellow 2; Basic Yellow 37; chromium oxide; etridiazole; guanidine hydrochloride; hydroxylamine hydrochloride; poly(fluoroalkoxyphosphazene) elastomers

Uses:
curing agent (formaldehyde-based adhesives); yeast fermentation nutrient; fertiliser ingredient; tin plating/galvanising flux; blowing agent; dry-cell batteries; etchants/cleaner ingredient; explosives ingredient; photographic chemical; tanning auxiliary

ammonium citrate, dibasic

$$CH_2COO^- \quad NH_4^+$$
$$HOCCOOH$$
$$CH_2COO^- \quad NH_4^+$$

$C_6H_{14}N_2O_7$. M: 226.18. White granules. d: 1.48 kg/l. Solubility in water: 1.0 kg/l water (20°C) forming acidic solutions.

Production:
- ammonia + citric acid (salt formation)

Uses:
food additive; analytical reagent (fertilisers); electrodeless nickel coating reagent

ammonium cumene sulphonate
ACS; [37475-88-0]

$$(CH_3)_3CH \text{—} \bigcirc \text{—} SO_3^- \quad NH_4^+$$

$C_9H_{15}N_1O_3S_1$. M: 217.29. Available commercially as a 60% solution in water.

Production:
- cumenesulphonic acid + ammonia (salt formation)

Uses:
hydrotrope (liquid detergents, cleaners)

ammonium decaborate *See:* ammonium pentaborate

ammonium dichromate
ammonium bichromate; [7789-08-4]

$$(NH_4)_2Cr_2O_7$$

$H_8Cr_2N_2O_7$. M: 252.05. Orange-red crystals. Decomposes on heating to 180°C releasing nitrogen. d: 2.15 kg/l (25°C). Solubility in water: 308 g/l water (15°C) forming acidic solutions.

Production:
- ammonium sulphate + sodium dichromate (salt formation)

Derivatives:
chromium dioxide

Uses: fireworks ingredient; lithographic/photoengraving reagent; wood preservative

ammonium *O,O*-dicresyl dithiophosphate
Aerofloat 241 (American Cyanamid);

$C_{14}H_{18}N_1O_2P_1S_2$. M: 327.40.

Production:
- phosphorus pentasulphide + cresylic acid + ammonia (condensation)

Uses:
flotation collector (sulphide ores)

ammonium ferric citrate
ferric ammonium citrate

$$CH_2COO^-$$
$$HOCCOO^- \quad mFe^{3+}.nNH_4^+$$
$$CH_2COO^-$$

Available commercially as a brown grade, containing 20.5–22.5% Fe, or as a green grade containing ~16% Fe. Both types are deliquescent and very soluble in water.

Production:
- ferric chloride + ammonia + citric acid (salt formation)

Uses: blueprint developing agent; dietary supplement ingredient

ammonium fluoborate

$$NH_4BF_4$$

$H_4B_1F_4N_1$. M: 104.84. White, crystalline solid. Sublimes on heating. d: 1.87 kg/l (15°C). Soluble in water.

Production:
- ammonia + fluoboric acid (salt formation)

Uses:
electroplating bath ingredient; etchant (semiconductor manufacture); reagent (Balz-Schliemann reactions); surface treatment agent (aluminium)

ammonium fluosilicate
ammonium hexafluorosilicate; ammonium silicofluoride; [1309-32-6]

$$(NH_4)_2SiF_6$$

$H_8F_6N_2Si_1$. M: 178.15. Crystalline solid. Decomposes on heating. Solubility in water: 200 g/l water (20°C).

Production:
• ammonia + hexafluorosilicic acid (salt formation)
Uses:
glass frosting agent; wood preservative; soldering flux

ammonium formate
[540-69-2]

$$HCO^- \quad NH_4^+$$

$C_1H_5N_1O_2$. M: 63.06. Deliquescent white granules. MP: 116°C. d: 1.28 kg/l. Highly soluble in water and alcohol.
Production:
• ammonia + formic acid (salt formation)
Uses: reagent (carbon monoxide absorption processes)

ammonium hexafluorosilicate
See: ammonium fluosilicate

ammonium lauryl ether sulphate
ammonium laureth sulphate (CTFA)

$$CH_3(CH_2)_{11}(OCH_2CH_2)_nOSO_3^- \quad NH_4^+$$

n = 2–3. Available commercially as a 25% or 60% solution in water, sometimes with ethanol as a solubilising agent.
Production:
• n-alkanol(C_{12}-C_{14}) ethoxylates/n-alkanol(C_{12}-C_{15}) ethoxylates/n-alkanol(C_{12}-C_{18}) ethoxylates + ammonia (sulphation/salt formation)
Uses: surfactant (light-duty liquid detergents, hair shampoo, bubble bath); foaming agent (plasterboard, lightweight concrete production)

ammonium lauryl sulphate
[2235-54-3]

$$CH_3(CH_2)_{11}OSO_3^- \quad NH_4^+$$

Available commercially as 25–35% solutions in water.
Production:
• n-alkanol(C_{12}-C_{14})/n-alkanol(C_{12}-C_{13}) + ammonia (sulphation/salt formation)
Uses: foaming agent (firefighting foams); surfactant (light-duty liquid cleaners, dishwashing detergents); surfactant (shampoos, bubble baths)

ammonium mercaptoacetate
See: ammonium thioglycollate

ammonium metavanadate
ammonium vanadate

$$NH_4VO_3$$

$H_4N_1O_3V_1$. M: 116.98. Colourless crystals. Decomposes on heating with release of ammonia. d: 2.33 kg/l. Solubility in water: 6 g/l (25°C).

Production:
• ammonium chloride + vanadium pentoxide (salt formation)
Uses: dyeing auxiliary; glaze/ceramics ingredient; wood stains; photographic developer ingredient; tin/vanadium yellow pigments

ammonium molybdate
ammonium heptamolybdate; ammonium paramolybdate; molybdic acid; AHM; [12027-67-7]

$$(NH_4)_6Mo_7O_{24}$$

$H_{24}Mo_7N_6O_{24}$. M: 1163.79. Available commercially as the tetrahydrate. Colourless or yellowish crystals. Releases water when heated to 90°C. Solubility in water: 430 g/l water, forming an acidic solution.
Production:
• molybdenum trioxide + ammonia (salt formation)
Derivatives:
molybdenum; phosphomolybdic acid
Uses: catalyst raw material (hydrodesulphurisation, ammoxidation, oxidation); fertiliser trace element additive

ammonium nitrate
AN; [6484-52-2]

$$NH_4NO_3$$

$H_4N_2O_3$. M: 80.04. Colourless, hygroscopic prills which decompose when heated above 210°C. d: 1.72 kg/l. Soluble in water and alcohol. Grades intended for explosive use are porous so that they can be mixed with diesel oil to produce ammonium nitrate-fuel oil (ANFO). Ammonium nitrate is sold for fertiliser applications as straight ammonium nitrate (AN), as ammonium sulphate-nitrate (ASN) or as calcium-ammonium nitrate (CAN, 'Nitrochalk', 'Calnitro'). AN is sold as an aqueous solution in USA, mixed with urea (UAN). There are restrictions on the sale of pure AN in many countries.
Production:
• nitric acid + ammonia (salt formation)
• apatite + nitric acid + ammonia + carbon dioxide (calcium separation process; byproduct of nitrophosphate production)
Derivatives:
cyclonite; guanidine nitrate; nitrous oxide; octogen
Uses:
explosives; fertiliser; calcium ammonium nitrate/ammonium sulphate nitrate fertilisers; raw material (DSM hydroxylamine phosphate process)

ammonium nonylphenol ether sulphate

$$C_9H_{19}-\langle\rangle-(CH_2CH_2O)_nSO_3^- \quad NH_4^+$$

n = 5–25. Available commercially as 30% solutions in water.

Production:
- nonylphenol ethoxylates + ammonia (sulphation/salt formation)

Uses: emulsifier (emulsion polymerisation)

ammonium oleate
[544-60-5]

$$CH_3(CH_2)_7CH=CH(CH_2)_7COO^-\ NH_4^+$$

$C_{18}H_{37}N_1O_2$. M: 299.51. Yellow paste. Soluble in water.
Production:
- oleic acid + ammonia (salt formation)

Uses: emulsifier (cosmetics)

ammonium paramolybdate
See: ammonium molybdate

ammonium paratungstate
ammonium tungstate; APT

$$(NH_4)_6W_7O_{24}$$

$H_{24}N_6O_{24}W_7$. M: 1779.16.
Production:
- tungsten ore concentrates + hydrochloric acid + ammonia (acid leaching/salt formation)

Derivatives:
tungsten; tungsten trioxide

ammonium pentaborate
ammonium decaborate

$$NH_4B_5O_8$$

$H_4B_5N_1O_8$. M: 200.09. The commercial product is the tetrahydrate. White, crystalline powder. Solubility in water: 70 g/l water (15°C).
Production:
- ammonia + boric acid (salt formation)

Uses:
electrolytic capacitors; fire-retardant (wood, textiles, paper); starch viscosifier (paper coatings)

ammonium perchlorate
APC; [7790-98-9]

$$NH_4ClO_4$$

$H_4Cl_1N_1O_4$. M: 117.49. White, crystalline solid. Decomposes explosively on heating to 345–350°C. Solubility in water: 200 g/l solution (25°C).
Production:
- sodium perchlorate + ammonia (salt formation)

Uses: oxidising agent (rocket propellant, pyrotechnics)

ammonium perfluorooctoate
Fluorad FC-143 (3M)

$$CF_3(CF_2)_6COO^-\ NH_4^+$$

$C_8H_4F_{15}N_1O_2$. M: 431.10.

Production:
- perfluorooctanoic acid + ammonia (salt formation)

Uses: emulsifier (fluoropolymer production); photographic chemical

ammonium persulphate
ammonium peroxydisulphate; [7727-54-0]

$$(NH_4)_2S_2O_8$$

$H_8N_2O_8S_2$. M: 228.19. White, crystalline solid. Decomposes on heating releasing oxygen. Solubility in water: 794 g/l water (20°C) with slow decomposition.
Production:
- ammonium sulphate + sulphuric acid (electrolytic oxidation)

Derivatives: cadmium sulphate; hydrogen peroxide; potassium persulphate; sodium persulphate; starch, thermochemically-converted

Uses:
etchant (printed circuit boards); oxidising agent (dyestuffs); photographic chemical; polymerisation initiator (latex, polyacrylonitrile, styrene copolymers); hair colouring agent; textile bleach stabiliser

ammonium phosphate, dibasic
See: diammonium phosphate

ammonium phosphate, monobasic
See: monoammonium phosphate

ammonium picrate
[131-74-8]

$C_6H_6N_4O_7$. M: 246.14. Yellow crystals. Decompose on heating without melting. d: 1.72 kg/l. Soluble in water and oxygenated solvents.
Production:
- picric acid + ammonia (salt formation)

Uses: explosives/rocket propellant

ammonium polyacrylate

Pale yellow liquid containing, typically, 30% active matter in water. Solutions are alkaline. d: 1.12 kg/l (20°C).
Production:
- acrylic acid + ammonia (aqueous polymerisation)

Uses: pigment dispersant (water-based paints, ceramics, paper); stabiliser (emulsion polymerisation); wetting agent (cement/pigment manufacture)

ammonium polymethacrylate

$$\left[CH_2-\underset{\underset{COO^-\ NH_4^+}{|}}{\overset{\overset{CH_3}{|}}{C}} \right]_x$$

Pale yellow liquid comprising a 30% solution in water. d: 1.12 kg/l (20°C). Viscosity: 50 mPa.s (25°C). pH: 8.5–9.0 (5% solution).
Production:
• methacrylic acid + ammonia (aqueous polymerisation)
Uses:
cement admixture; pigments/fillers/clay dispersant (ceramics, paint, paper); thickening agent (natural rubber latex)

ammonium polyphosphate, solid
[68333-79-9]

$$\left[\overset{O^-\ NH_4^+}{\underset{\underset{O}{\|}}{P}}-O \right]_n$$

$H_4N_1O_3P_1$. M: 97.01. White powder. Starts decomposing at 250°C, rapidly at 300°C. Often sold as a 45% w/w solution in water.
Production:
• urea + phosphoric acid, pure (thermal combination)
• diammonium phosphate + phosphorus pentoxide (disproportionation)
Uses:
fire-retardant additive (paints, mastics, polyurethane foam, rubber, chipboard); intumescent paint ingredient

ammonium polyphosphate, solution

$$\left[\overset{O^-\ NH_4^+}{\underset{\underset{O}{\|}}{P}}-O \right]_n$$

$H_4N_1O_3P_1$. M: 97.01.
Production:
• ammonia + phosphoric acid, crude (TVA and Swift processes)
Uses: fertiliser

ammonium rhodanide *See:* ammonium thiocyanate

ammonium stearate
[1002-89-7]

$$CH_3(CH_2)_{16}COO^-\ \ NH_4^+$$

$C_{18}H_{39}N_1O_2$. M: 301.52. Yellow paste. Soluble in water.
Production:
• ammonia + stearic acid (neutralisation)
Uses: emulsifier (cosmetics)

ammonium sulphamate
AMS; Amcide (Albright and Wilson); Ammate (Du Pont); [7773-06-0]

$$NH_2SO_3^-\ \ NH_4^+$$

$H_6N_2O_3S_1$. M: 114.12.
Production:
• ammonia + sulphamic acid (salt formation)
Uses: electroplating bath ingredient; fire-retardant (textiles, paper, wood); herbicide; urea-formaldehyde resin latent catalyst

ammonium sulphate
[7783-20-2]

$$(NH_4)_2SO_4$$

$H_8N_2O_4S_1$. M: 132.13. White, crystalline solid. Decomposes on heating to 100°C releasing ammonia. d: 1.77 kg/l (20°C). Solubility in water: 706 g/l water (0°C).
Production:
• coal + sulphuric acid (high-temperature carbonisation; byproduct of metallurgical coke production)
• coal (low-temperature carbonisation; byproduct of semicoke production)
• methacrylamide sulphate (hydrolysis; byproduct of methacrylic acid production)
• methanol + methacrylamide sulphate (alcoholysis; byproduct of methyl methacrylate production)
• nitric oxide + ammonium bicarbonate + sulphur dioxide, pure + ammonia (Raschig hydroxylamine process; byproduced with hydroxylamine sulphate production)
• nitric oxide + hydrogen + sulphuric acid (nitric oxide reduction process; byproduct of hydroxylamine sulphate production)
• cyclohexanone oxime + ammonia + oleum (Beckmann rearrangement; byproduct of caprolactam production)
• formamide (amide hydrolysis; byproduct of formic acid production)
• ammonia + sulphuric acid (salt formation)
• ammonia + tail gases, sulphuric acid plants/tail gases, power stations (desulphurisation)
Derivatives:
ammonium alum; ammonium chloride; ammonium dichromate; ammonium persulphate; chromium; chromium oxide; cuprous oxide; nitrophosphate; Prussian Blue
Uses: fermentation nutrient; fire extinguishant powder; fire-retardant (textiles, wood, paper); aluminium etchant ingredient; microbial fermentation nutrient; photographic chemical; textile/leather auxiliary

ammonium sulphide
ammonium polysulphide

$$(NH_4)_2S_x$$

Clear, yellow aqueous solution with a strong odour of ammonia and hydrogen sulphide. Contains approximately 10% w/w H_2S.

Production:
• ammonia + hydrogen sulphide + sulphur (salt formation)
Uses: froth flotation agent; analytical reagent; photographic chemical

ammonium sulphite
[10196-04-0]

$(NH_4)_2SO_3$

$H_8N_2O_3S_1$. M: 116.13. Available as the monohydrate. White crystals. Loses water of crystallisation and gradually oxidised when heated in air. Solubility in water: 1.0 kg/l (12°C). d: 1.41 kg/l.
Production:
• sulphur dioxide, pure + ammonia (salt formation)
Derivatives: ammonium thiosulphate
Uses: photographic bleach fixer bath component; reducing agent (pharmaceuticals, hair preparations)

ammonium thiocyanate
ammonium rhodanide; [1762-95-4]

NH_4SCN

$C_1H_4N_2S_1$. M: 76.11. White, hygroscopic, crystalline powder. MP: 149–150°C. Soluble in water and alcohol. Also available as a 50% aqueous solution.
Production:
• ammonia + carbon disulphide (salt formation)
• ammonia + sodium thiocyanate (salt formation)
Derivatives: acetazolamide; guanidine carbonate; *N*-isopropyl-*N'*-*t*-butylthiourea; potassium thiocyanate; sodium thiocyanate; thiosemicarbazide; tramazoline
Uses: corrosion inhibitor (metal treatment); dispersant (animal glue, proteins); photographic chemical; textile dyeing/printing auxiliary

ammonium thioglycollate
ammonium mercaptoacetate; [5421-46-5]

$HSCH_2COO^-$ NH_4^+

$C_2H_7N_1O_2S_1$. M: 109.15. Colourless to pale-pink liquid. Available commercially as a 30–59% solution in water. d: 1.10 kg/l (30% solution, 20°C), 1.19 kg/l (59% solution, 20°C). Solutions are neutral or alkaline, depending on the intended application.
Production:
• ammonia + thioglycollic acid (salt formation)
Uses: cold permanent hair waving reagent

ammonium thiosulphate
[7783-18-8]

$(NH_4)_2S_2O_3$

$H_8N_2O_3S_2$. M: 148.20. White crystals. Decomposes at 150°C. Soluble in water. Sold commercially as solid or in solution.

Production:
• ammonium sulphite + sulphur (salt formation)
Uses: photographic fixer ingredient

ammonium tungstate *See:* ammonium paratungstate

ammonium vanadate *See:* ammonium metavanadate

ammonium zirconyl carbonate

$(NH_4)_3ZrOH(CO_3)_3$

$C_3H_{13}N_3O_{10}Zr_1$. M: 342.36. Commercially available as a solution in water. Solutions decompose on heating producing ammonia, carbon dioxide and zirconia.
Production:
• ammonium bicarbonate + zirconium carbonate, basic (salt formation)
Uses:
insolubilising agent (starch, casein, soya protein paper binders); textile waterproofing/fungicidal treatments

amoxicillin
amoxycillin; [26787-78-0]; [61336-70-7] (trihydrate)

$C_{16}H_{19}N_3O_5S_1$. M: 365.41. Available commercially as the anhydrous or trihydrate salts.
Production:
• D-α-(4-hydroxyphenyl)glycine + 6-aminopenicillanic acid (Dane salt formation/amide formation/hydrolysis)
Uses: antibacterial drug

AMP *See:* aminotris(methylene phosphonic acid); 2-amino-2-methyl-1-propanol

t-**AMP** *See:* p-t-amylphenol

amphetamine
α-methylphenethylamine; 1-methyl-2-phenylethylamine; 1-phenyl-2-aminopropane; [300-62-9]

$C_9H_{13}N_1$. M: 135.21. Available commercially as the racemic free base, phosphate or sulphate salts. Also available as the separate (+)- or (−)-enantiomers. Manufacture is restricted in most countries.
Production:
• phenylacetone + hydroxylamine sulphate (oxime formation/hydrogenation)
Uses:
nerve stimulant drug

ampicillin
[69-53-4]; [69-52-3] (sodium salt); [7177-48-2] (tri-hydrate)

$C_{16}H_{19}N_3O_4S_1$. M: 349.41. Available commercially as the anhydrous or trihydrate acid, or as the sodium salt.
Production:
• D-α-phenylglycine + 6-aminopenicillanic acid
  (Dane salt formation/amide formation/hydrolysis)
Derivatives: azlocillin; bacampicillin; mezlocillin; piperacillin; pivampicillin; talampicillin
Uses: antibacterial drug

AMPS
See: 2-acrylamido-2-methylpropanesulphonic acid

ampyrone *See:* 4-aminoantipyrine

AMS *See:* α-methylstyrene, ammonium sulphamate

amsonic acid
See: 4,4'-diaminostilbene-2,2'-disulphonic acid

amyl acetate
primary amyl acetate

$C_7H_{14}O_2$. M: 130.19. Colourless liquid. BP: 149°C. FP: -100°C. d: 0.87 kg/l (20°C). Slightly soluble in water. Flash point: 38°C (TCC).
Production:
• amyl alcohol, primary + acetic acid (esterification)
Uses: solvent (lacquers)

amyl alcohol, active *See:* 2-methyl-1-butanol

amyl alcohol, primary

$C_5H_{12}O_1$. M: 88.15. Mixed product, the composition of which varies with the source. Primary amyl alcohol from fusel oil is composed of isoamyl alcohol and 2-methyl-1-butanol. That produced by hydroformylation/hydrogenation of n-butenes contains 2-methyl-1-butanol and n-amyl alcohol. It is a colourless liquid. BP: 133°C. FP: -90°C. d: 0.81 kg/l (20°C). Slightly soluble in water. Soluble in most organic solvents. Flash point: 45°C (TCC).
Production:
• pentaldehydes, mixed (hydrogenation)
• fusel oil (fractionation)

• oxygenates, Fischer-Tropsch, mixed (fractionation; coproduced with methanol/ethanol/isopropanol/n-butanol/isobutanol/acetaldehyde/acetone/methyl ethyl ketone)
Derivatives: amyl acetate; n-amyl alcohol; amyl phosphoric acid; diamylamine; 2-methyl-1-butanol; potassium amyl xanthate; sodium diamylsulphosuccinate
Uses: solvent (paints, lacquers, printing inks)

n-amyl alcohol
1-pentanol; primary n-amyl alcohol; [71-41-0]

$$CH_3CH_2CH_2CH_2CH_2OH$$

$C_5H_{12}O_1$. M: 88.15. Colourless liquid with a mild, characteristic odour. BP: 137–139°C. FP: -78°C. d: 0.82 kg/l (20°C). See also amyl alcohol, primary.
Production:
• amyl alcohol, primary (fractionation; coproduced with 2-methyl-1-butanol)
Derivatives:
n-amyl bromide; γ-octalactone; triamylamine
Uses: extraction solvent (mineral processing); process solvent

t-amyl alcohol
2-methyl-2-butanol; t-pentanol; [75-85-4]

$C_5H_{12}O_1$. M: 88.15. Colourless liquid with a pleasant odour. BP: 100–102°C. FP: -12°C. Slightly soluble in water. Miscible with most organic solvents.
Production:
• C_5-stream, refinery (hydration)
Uses: process solvent

amyl aldehyde *See:* valeraldehyde

amylanthraquinone
[32588-54-8]

$C_{19}H_{18}O_2$. M: 278.35.
Production:
• isoamylene + phthalic anhydride + benzene
  (Friedel-Crafts alkylation/condensation)
Derivatives: hydrogen peroxide

α-amylase, bacterial
E.C.3.2.1.1 (Enzyme Commission); [9000-90-2]
Enzyme used to liquify starch by aiding dispersion and partially hydrolysing the amylose and amylopectin

components. *B. licheniformis* produces a heat-stable form of α-amylase which can be used at temperatures of 90–105°C. The *B. amyloliquefaciens* grades require a temperature of 70–85°C for optimum performance.

Production:
- microbial fermentation medium + *Bacillus licheniformis* bacteria/*Bacillus amyloliquefaciens* bacteria (fermentation)

Derivatives: glucose syrup; maltodextrin
Uses: reagent (paper size pretreatment)

α-amylase, fungal

E.C.3.2.1.1 (Enzyme Commission); [9000-90-2]
Extract containing α-amylase with some protease. Operates in the pH range 5.0–6.0 at 55–60°C. Used for saccharification of acid or enzyme-liquified starch to produce glucose.

Production:
- mould fermentation medium + *Aspergillus niger* mould/*Aspergillus oryzae* mould (fermentation)

Derivatives:
glucose syrup
Uses: starch hydrolysis reagent (food production)

n-amyl bromide

[110-53-2]

$$CH_3CH_2CH_2CH_2CH_2Br$$

$C_5H_{11}Br_1$. M: 151.04. Liquid. BP: 130°C. MP: -95°C. d: 1.22 kg/l (20°C). Insoluble in water. Soluble in oxygenated solvents.

Production:
- *n*-amyl alcohol (bromidation)

Derivatives: methyl 2-octynoate
Uses: photographic coupling agent intermediate

α-amylcinnamaldehyde

α-amyl cinnamic aldehyde; jasmine aldehyde; α-pentylaldehyde; 2-pentyl-3-phenyl-2-propenal; [122-40-7]

$$CHO$$
$$\bigcirc\!\!-CH=C(CH_2)_4CH_3$$

$C_{14}H_{18}O_1$. M: 202.29. Pale yellow liquid with a floral odour.

Production:
- benzaldehyde + *n*-heptaldehyde (aldol condensation)

Uses: fragrance/flavouring ingredient

β-amylene *See:* 2-methyl-2-butene

t-amyl hydroperoxide

$$CH_3$$
$$CH_3CH_2CO-OH$$
$$CH_3$$

$C_5H_{12}O_2$. M: 104.15. Decomposes on heating with a 10-hour half-life at 172°C.

Production:
- isoamylene + hydrogen peroxide (peroxidation)

Derivatives: *t*-amyl peroxybenzoate; *t*-amyl peroxy-2-ethylhexanoate; *t*-amyl peroxy-2-ethylhexylcarbonate; *t*-amyl peroxyneodecanoate; *t*-amyl peroxyneoheptanoate; *t*-amyl peroxypivalate; 1,1-di(*t*-amylperoxy)cyclohexane; 2,2-di(*t*-amylperoxy)propane; ethyl 3,3-bis(*t*-amylperoxy)butyrate

t-amyl methyl ether
TAME

$$CH_3$$
$$CH_3CH_2COCH_3$$
$$CH_3$$

$C_6H_{14}O_1$. M: 102.18. Liquid. BP: 88°C. d: 0.79 kg/l. Solubility in water: 12 g/l solution. Octane number: 105–115 (RON), 95–105 (MON).

Production:
- C_5-stream, refinery + methanol (ether formation)

Uses: petrol blending component

amyl nitrite *See:* isoamyl nitrite

amyloglucosidase *See:* glucoamylase

t-amyl peroxybenzoate

$$CH_3 \quad O$$
$$CH_3CH_2CO-OC-\!\!\bigcirc$$
$$CH_3$$

$C_{12}H_{16}O_3$. M: 208.26. Decomposes on heating with a 10-hour half-life at 100°C.

Production:
- *t*-amyl hydroperoxide + benzoyl chloride (esterification)

Uses: unsaturated polyester resin crosslinking agent; polymerisation initiator

t-amyl peroxy-2-ethylhexanoate

t-amyl peroxyoctoate

$$CH_3 \quad C_2H_5$$
$$C_2H_5CO-OCCH(CH_2)_3CH_3$$
$$CH_3 \quad O$$

$C_{13}H_{26}O_3$. M: 230.35.

Production:
- *t*-amyl hydroperoxide + 2-ethylhexanoyl chloride (dehydrochlorination)

Uses: vinyl polymerisation initiator

t-amyl peroxy-2-ethylhexylcarbonate

$$CH_3 \quad O$$
$$C_2H_5CO-OCOCH_2CH(CH_2)_3CH_3$$
$$CH_3 \quad C_2H_5$$

$C_{14}H_{28}O_4$. M: 260.37. Decomposes on heating with a

10-hour half-life at 98°C.
Production:
• *t*-amyl hydroperoxide + 2-ethylhexyl chloroformate (dehydrochlorination)
Uses: polymerisation initiator

t-amyl peroxyneodecanoate

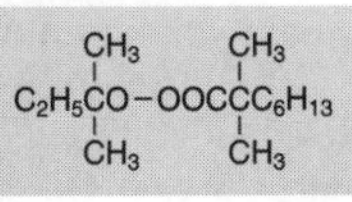

$$CH_3 \quad\quad CH_3$$
$$C_2H_5CO-OOCCC_6H_{13}$$
$$CH_3 \quad\quad CH_3$$

$C_{15}H_{30}O_3$. M: 258.40.
Production:
• *t*-amyl hydroperoxide + neodecanoyl chloride (esterification)
Uses: vinyl polymerisation initiator

t-amyl peroxyneoheptanoate
Esperox 747M (Witco)

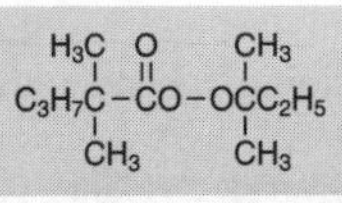

$$H_3C \quad O \quad\quad CH_3$$
$$C_3H_7C-CO-OCC_2H_5$$
$$CH_3 \quad\quad CH_3$$

$C_{12}H_{24}O_3$. M: 216.32. Available as a solution containing 75% peroxide with a 10-hour half-life at 47°C.
Production:
• *t*-amyl hydroperoxide + neoheptanoyl chloride (dehydrochlorination)
Uses: polymerisation initiator

t-amyl peroxyoctoate
See: *t*-amyl peroxy-2-ethylhexanoate

t-amyl peroxypivalate

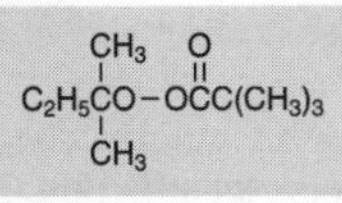

$$CH_3 \quad O$$
$$C_2H_5CO-OOCC(CH_3)_3$$
$$CH_3$$

$C_{10}H_{20}O_3$. M: 188.27.
Production:
• *t*-amyl hydroperoxide + pivaloyl chloride (esterification)
Uses: vinyl polymerisation initiator

p-t-amylphenol
t-AMP; Pentaphen 61 (Elf-Atochem)

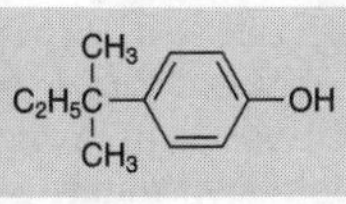

$$CH_3$$
$$C_2H_5C-\phenyl-OH$$
$$CH_3$$

$C_{11}H_{16}O_1$. M: 164.25. White crystals. MP 93°C. BP: 265–267°C. Slightly soluble in water.
Production:
• isoamylene + phenol (Friedel-Crafts alkylation)
Derivatives:
phenolic resins, oil-soluble, oil-reactive
Uses: disinfectant

amyl phosphoric acid
amyl acid phosphate

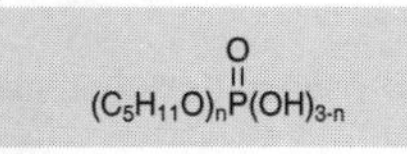

$$O$$
$$\|$$
$$(C_5H_{11}O)_nP(OH)_{3-n}$$

n = 1–2. Mixed product.
Production:
• amyl alcohol, primary + phosphorus pentoxide (esterification)
Uses: surfactant (industrial cleaners)

amyris oil
Yellow liquid with a sandalwood-like odour. Produced by steam distillation of wood from *Amyris balsamifera* tree. d: 0.96 kg/l (20°C). Soluble in alcohol. Produced mainly in the West Indies.
Uses:
perfume ingredient

AN *See:* ammonium nitrate

anatase
Anatase ore from Brazil (the prime source) contains 30–40% TiO_2 and can be used directly in the sulphate process for titanium dioxide production. The ore is upgraded for titanium dioxide production by the chloride route.
Derivatives: titanium dioxide; titanium dioxide, hydrate; titanium tetrachloride

ancymidol
α-cyclopropyl-4-methoxy-α-(pyrimidin-5-yl)benzyl alcohol; [12771-68-5]

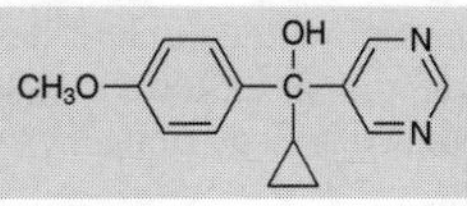

$$CH_3O-\phenyl-C(OH)-pyrimidine$$

$C_{15}H_{16}N_2O_2$. M: 256.30.
Production:
• anisole + cyclopropane carboxylic acid + 5-bromopyrimidine (acid chloride formation/ Friedel-Crafts acylation/Grignard reagent formation/Grignard reaction)
Uses: plant growth regulator

androstadienedione
androsta-1,4-diene-3,17-dione; ADD; [897-06-3]

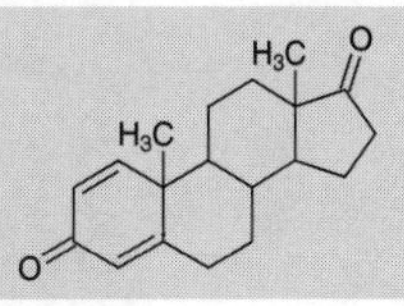

$C_{19}H_{24}O_2$. M: 284.40.
Production:
• phytosterols, mixed/cholesterol/ergosterol + *Mycobacterium phlei* bacteria (microbial conversion)

• prasterone (hydrogenation/alcohol oxidation/alpha bromination/dehydrobromination)
Derivatives:
betamethasone; cortisone; dexamethasone; estrone

androstenolone *See:* prasterone

anethole
p-methoxypropenylbenzene; *p*-propenylanisole; [104-46-1]

CH₃O—⟨ ⟩—CH=CHCH₃

$C_{10}H_{12}O_1$. M: 148.21. White crystals with anise odour. MP: 22–23°C. BP: 234–237°C. The commercial product is a mixture of the *cis*- and *trans*-isomers. Insoluble in water. Soluble in alcohol.
Production:
• pine oil (fractionation; coproduced with α-terpineol)
• pine oil (fractionation; coproduced with dipentene/ 3-carene)
• anisole + propionyl chloride (Friedel-Crafts acylation /carbonyl reduction/dehydration)
Uses: flavouring ingredient (alcoholic drinks, mouth-care products)

anhydrite
calcium sulphate, anhydrous; gypsum, dead-burned

CaSO₄

$Ca_1O_4S_1$. M: 136.14. Whitish solid. MP: 1,360°C with dissociation. d: 2.96 kg/l. Solubility in water: 2.0 g/l (25°C). Soluble anhydrite (anhydrite III, hexagonal calcium sulphate) is an allotrope used as a drying agent. It is produced by calcining gypsum at 300°C in an electric oven.
Production:
• fluorspar + sulphuric acid (acidification; byproduct of hydrogen fluoride production)
• gypsum (calcination)
Uses:
filler; hard plaster; artificial marble; wall plaster

anilazine
2,4-dichloro-6-(2-chloroanilino)-1,3,5-triazine; [101-05-3]

$C_9H_5Cl_3N_4$. M: 275.53.
Production:
• cyanuric chloride + *o*-chloroaniline (amine formation)
Uses: fungicide

aniline
[62-53-3]

$C_6H_7N_1$. M: 93.14. Pale yellow liquid. BP: 184°C. MP: -6°C. d: 1.02 kg/l (20°C). Solubility in water: 35 g/kg solution (25°C). Miscible with oxygenated and aromatic solvents. Flash point: 76°C (CC).
Production:
• nitrobenzene + iron (nitro reduction)
• phenol + ammonia (amine formation)
Derivatives: acetanilide; acetoacetanilide; Acid Black 1; Acid Blue 20; Acid Blue 25; Acid Blue 29; Acid Blue 93; Acid Blue 118; Acid Orange 10; Acid Orange 19; Acid Red 42; Acid Yellow 25; Acid Yellow 29; alfentanil; *o*-aminoacetophenone; *p*-aminoacetophenone; 4'-aminoazobenzene-4-sulphonic acid; *p*-aminodiphenylamine; 4-aminodiphenylamine-2-sulphonic acid; 5-amino-3-methyl-1-phenylpyrazole; arsanilic acid; bamipine; Basic Orange 1; Basic Red 2; *p*-benzoquinone; *N*-benzylaniline; bromazepam; buprofezin; butylideneaniline; cyclohexylamine; 4,4'-diaminodiphenylmethane, crude; 4,4'-diaminodiphenyl sulphone; *N,N'*-diaryl-*p*-phenylenediamine; dichlofluanid; diclofenac; dicyclohexylamine; 2,6-diethylaniline; *N,N*-diethylaniline; *N,N*-di(2-hydroxyethyl)aniline; *N,N*-dimethylaniline; diphenylguanidine; *N,N'*-diphenyl-*p*-phenylenediamine; Direct Green 28; Direct Orange 29; Direct Orange 34; Direct Orange 102; Direct Red 4; Direct Red 16; Direct Red 31; Disperse Orange 3; Disperse Red 22; Disperse Yellow 14; Disperse Yellow 16; Disperse Yellow 33; Disperse Yellow 42; *N*-ethylaniline; fenfuram; fentanyl; Fluorescent Brightener 9; Fluorescent Brightener 28; Fluorescent Brightener 32; Fluorescent Brightener 136; Fluorescent Brightener 142; Fluorescent Brightener 182; Fluorescent Brightener 204; Fluorescent Brightener DM; Fluorescent Brightener DMEA; fluorobenzene; fluspirilene; hydroxyethylaniline; 3-hydroxy-2-naphthanilide; iobenzamic acid; 2-mercaptobenzothiazole; *N*-methylaniline; oxyphenbutazone; *p*-phenylazoaniline; *N*-phenylgamma acid; *N*-phenylglycine; phenyl isocyanate; phenyl isothiocyanate; *N*-phenylmaleimide; *N*-phenyl-α-naphthylamine; *N*-phenyl-β-naphthylamine; Pigment Blue 18; Pigment Blue 61; Pigment Red 146; Pigment Red 147; Pigment Red 176; Pigment Red 184; Pigment Violet 19; Pigment Yellow 97; propachlor; propham; pyroquilon; pyrvinium pamoate; quinaldine; Reactive Red 2; Reactive Red 3; salicylanilide; Solvent Black 5; Solvent Blue 3; Solvent Yellow 14; Solvent Yellow 56; sotalol; sulphanilic acid; Sulphur Yellow 1; thenalidine; thiocarbanilide; 2,4,6-tribromoaniline; 2,2,4-trimethyl-1,2-dihydroquinoline, polymeric; trimethylphenylammonium hydroxide; triphenylmethane triisocyanate; 2,6-xylidine

aniline-3,5-dicarboxylic acid
See: 5-aminoisophthalic acid

aniline-2,5-disulphonic acid
2-amino-*p*-benzenedisulphonic acid; [98-44-2]

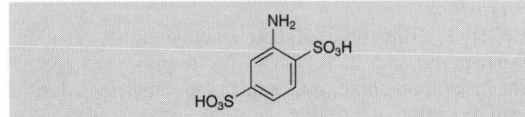

$C_6H_7N_1O_3S_1$. M: 173.20. Available as the dihydrate. Needles. Decompose on heating above 120°C. Soluble in water and alcohol.
Production:
• 4-chloro-3-nitrobenzenesulphonyl chloride (hydrolysis/sulphonation/nitro reduction)
• *m*-nitrobenzenesulphonic acid (sulphonation/nitro reduction)
Derivatives:
Direct Blue 78; Fluorescent Brightener 103

aniline-3-(β-hydroxyethyl)sulphone
See: *m*-(β-hydroxyethylsulphonyl)aniline

aniline-4-(β-hydroxyethyl)sulphone
See: *p*-(β-hydroxyethylsulphonyl)aniline

aniline-2-sulphonic acid *See:* orthanilic acid

aniline-3-sulphonic acid *See:* metanilic acid

aniline-4-sulphonic acid *See:* sulphanilic acid

Aniline Yellow *See:* *p*-phenylazoaniline

2-anilino-5-naphthol-7-sulphonic acid
See: N-phenyl-J acid

6-anilino-4-naphthol-2-sulphonic acid
See: N-phenylgamma acid

anilofos
S-4-chloro-N-isopropylcarbaniloylmethyl *O,O*-dimethyl phosphorodithioate; [64249-01-0]

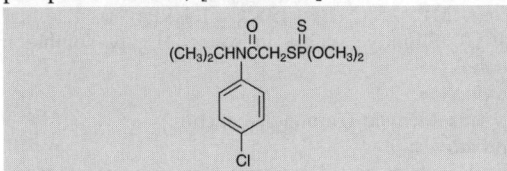

$C_{13}H_{19}Cl_1N_1O_3P_1S_2$. M: 367.85.
Production:
• *p*-chloroaniline + isopropanol + chloroacetyl chloride + *O,O*-dimethyl dithiophosphoric acid (amine formation/amide formation/dehydrochlorination)
Uses: herbicide

animal glue
bone glue; hide glue
Hard, yellow to dark amber solid containing 10–15% water. d: 1.27 kg/l. Soluble in water. Animal glue is similar to gelatine (*qv*) in that both are the hydrolysis products of collagen. With animal glue, however, temperatures are higher and the reaction less controlled so that shorter peptide chain-lengths and higher impurity levels are produced. The latter comprise principally inorganic salts and fats.
Production:
• bone, green/bone, degreased (acid extraction)
• hide pieces + hydrochloric acid (acid extraction)
Derivatives:
L-arginine; L-asparagine; L-leucine; protein hydrolysates; L-tyrosine
Uses: adhesives (bookbinding, grinding disks, sandpapers); binder (match heads); paper gaskets; paper /textile sizing ingredient; plasticiser (rubber)

p-anisaldehyde
p-anisic aldehyde; 4-methoxybenzaldehyde; [123-11-5]

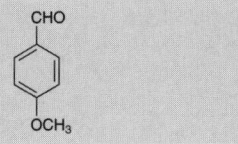

$C_8H_8O_2$. M: 136.15. Colourless liquid with a pleasant, floral odour. BP: 249°C. MP: 1°C. d: 1.12 kg/l (15°C). Insoluble in water. Soluble in oxygenated solvents.
Production:
• *p*-methoxytoluene + manganese dioxide (side-chain oxidation)
• *p*-hydroxybenzaldehyde (methylation)
• anisole (Vilsmeier reaction)
Derivatives: anisoin; anisyl alcohol; cinoxate; diltiazem; dobutamine; 2-ethylhexyl *p*-methoxycinnamate; methyl 2-carbomethoxy-4′-methoxycinnamate; sodium anisaldehyde bisulphite
Uses: fragrance/flavouring ingredient

anise oil
aniseed oil; [8007-70-3]
Colourless to pale yellow liquid. Produced by distillation of anise (*Pimpinella anisum*) seeds. d: 0.98–0.99 kg/l (20°C). Slightly soluble in water. Soluble in alcohol.
Uses: food/drink/toothpaste flavouring ingredient

p-anisic acid *See:* 4-methoxybenzoic acid

anisic alcohol *See:* anisyl alcohol

o-anisidine
2-aminoanisole; *o*-aminoanisole; 2-methoxyaniline; [90-04-0]

C₇H₉N₁O₁. M: 123.16. Yellow liquid. BP: 250–252°C. MP: 5°C. d: 1.09 kg/l (20°C). Almost insoluble in water. Miscible with oxygenated solvents.
Production:
• *o*-nitroanisole (nitro reduction)
Derivatives:
acetoacet-*o*-anisidide; Acid Red 4; Acid Red 107; Acid Violet 12; 4-amino-3-methoxyazobenzene-3'-sulphonic acid, sodium salt; Diazo Brilliant Scarlet ROD; Direct Red 24; Direct Red 26; Direct Red 72; Direct Yellow 49; Disperse Orange 29; 3-hydroxy-2-naphth-*o*-anisidide; 1-(2-methoxyphenyl)piperazine hydrochloride; Pigment Red 222; Solvent Red 1

p-anisidine
4-aminoanisole; *p*-aminoanisole; 4-methoxyaniline; [104-94-9]

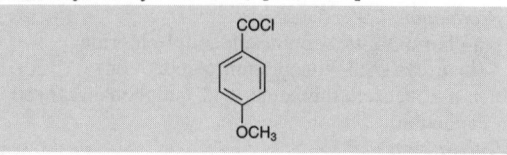

C₇H₉N₁O₁. M: 123.16. Solid. MP: 57–60°C. BP: 244°C. Slightly soluble in water. Soluble in oxygenated solvents.
Production:
• *p*-chloronitrobenzene + methanol (ether formation/ nitro reduction)
Derivatives: 2-amino-6-methoxybenzothiazole; 4-amino-4'-methoxydiphenylamine; 4-amino-3-nitroanisole; Basic Yellow 28; Disperse Blue 125; Disperse Blue 165; 3-hydroxy-2-naphth-*p*-anisidide; indomethacin; mepacrine; Pigment Red 190; Pigment Yellow 170

anisoin
4,4'-dimethoxybenzoin; [119-52-8]

C₁₆H₁₆O₄. M: 272.31.
Production:
• *p*-anisaldehyde (condensation)
Uses:
photoinitiator (radiation-cured lacquers, inks)

anisole
methoxybenzene; methyl phenyl ether; [100-66-3]
C₇H₈O₁. M: 108.14. Liquid with a pleasant odour. BP: 153–154°C. MP: -37°C. d: 0.99 kg/l (20°C). Insoluble in water. Soluble in oxygenated solvents.

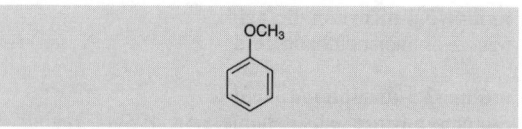

Production:
• phenol + dimethyl sulphate (methylation)
Derivatives:
ancymidol; anethole; *p*-anisaldehyde; Disperse Blue 73; methoxychlor; tamoxifen

anisoyl chloride
p-methoxybenzoyl chloride; [100-07-2]

C₈H₇Cl₁O₂. M: 170.60.
Production:
• 4-methoxybenzoic acid (acid chloride formation)
Derivatives: Vat Violet 17
Uses: amino group protection reagent

anisyl acetate
4-methoxybenzyl acetate; [104-21-2]

C₁₀H₁₂O₃. M: 180.21. Colourless liquid with sweet odour. BP: 133°C (1.5 kPa). d: 1.11 kg/l (20°C). Soluble in alcohol.
Production:
• anisyl alcohol + acetic anhydride (esterification)
Uses: flavouring ingredient

anisyl alcohol
anise alcohol; anisic alcohol; 4-methoxybenzyl alcohol; [105-13-5]

C₈H₁₀O₂. M: 138.17. Colourless liquid with floral odour. MP: 25°C. BP: 135°C (1.4 kPa). d: 1.11 kg/l (20°C). Slightly soluble in water. Highly soluble in alcohol.
Production:
• *p*-anisaldehyde (carbonyl reduction)
Derivatives:
anisyl acetate; anisyl formate; mepyramine; pentazocine; phenazocine
Uses: flavouring/fragrance ingredient

anisyl formate
4-methoxybenzyl formate; [122-91-8]
C₉H₁₀O₃. M: 166.18. Colourless liquid with sweet

odour. BP: 136°C (1.3 kPa). d: 1.11 kg/l (20°C). Soluble in alcohol.

CH₃O—⟨⟩—CH₂OCH (O)

Production:
• anisyl alcohol + formic acid (esterification)
Uses: flavouring ingredient

annatto
E190(b) (EC); [1393-63-1]
Orange solid. Produced by extraction from the pulp surrounding the seeds of the annatto tree (*Bixa orellana*) which is grown in Brazil, Kenya, Zaire and the Cameroons.
Uses: food colorant (butter, cheese, margarine)

antazoline
[91-75-8]; [2508-72-7] (hydrochloride); [3131-32-6] (methane sulphonate)

C₁₇H₁₉N₃. M: 265.36. Available commercially as the free base, hydrochloride or methane sulphonate.
Production:
• chloroacetonitrile + ethylenediamine + *N*-benzyl-aniline (condensation/amine formation)
Uses:
antihistamine drug

anthracene
[120-12-7]

C₁₄H₁₀. M: 178.23. Pale yellow leaves. MP: 216–217°C. d: 1.25 kg/l (25°C). Insoluble in water. Soluble in oxygenated, chlorinated and aromatic solvents.
Production:
• anthracene oil (fractionation)
Derivatives: anthraquinone; benzoctamine; maprotiline; Vat Green 7

anthracene oil
tar oil, coal; [8002-29-7]
Tar fraction. BR: 270–340°C.
Production:
• coal tar, crude (alkali extraction/fractionation; co-produced with light oil/carbolic oil/naphthalene fraction//creosote oil/fluorene oil/coal tar pitch/tar acid liquor)
Derivatives:
anthracene; carbon black
Uses: road tars; tar oil wash (fruit tree sprays)

anthracite
Hard, jet-black coal with a high carbon content and calorific value. Bulk density: 0.80–0.93 kg/l.
Derivatives: silicon carbide
Uses: domestic fuel; filter medium (water treatment)

anthralin
1,8-dihydroxyanthrone; Dithranol (INN); [480-22-8]

C₁₄H₁₀O₃. M: 226.23. Available commercially as the free alcohol or as the triacetate derivative.
Production:
• 1,8-dihydroxyanthraquinone (reduction)
Uses: antipsoriatic drug

anthranilic acid
2-aminobenzoic acid; *o*-aminobenzoic acid; [118-92-3]

C₇H₇N₁O₂. M: 137.15. White or light tan crystalline powder. MP: 146–148°C. Soluble in hot water and oxygenated solvents.
Production:
• isatoic anhydride (decarboxylation)
Derivatives: 2-amino-5-chloro-2'-fluorobenzophenone; benzazimide; Disperse Yellow 77; 2,2'-dithiodibenzoic acid; methyl anthranilate; Mordant Brown 40; Mordant Red 9; Mordant Yellow 8; Pigment Red 208; Pigment Yellow 151; Solvent Yellow 21; thiosalicylic acid; Vat Violet 13

anthrapyrazolone
1,9-pyrazolanthrone; 70615 (CI)

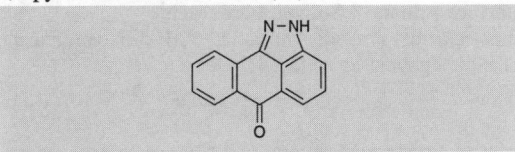

C₁₄H₈N₂O₁. M: 220.22.
Production:
• 1-aminoanthraquinone (diazotisation/reduction/acid-catalysed dehydration)
Derivatives: Vat Black 8; Vat Red 13

anthraquinone
9,10-anthraquinone; [84-65-1]
C₁₄H₈O₂. M: 208.21. Pale yellow, crystalline solid. MP: 283–285°C. BP: 377°C. d: 1.44 kg/l (20°C). Insoluble in water.

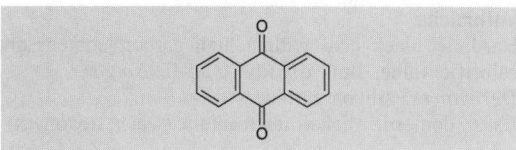

Production:
- anthracene + sodium dichromate + sulphuric acid (chromate oxidation)
- anthracene (gas-phase oxidation)
- anthracene + nitric acid, concentrated (nitric acid oxidation process)
- *o*-benzoylbenzoic acid (acid-catalysed condensation)
- naphthoquinone + butadiene (Kawasaki process)

Derivatives:
1-aminoanthraquinone; anthraquinone-1,5-disulphonic acid; anthraquinone-1,8-disulphonic acid; anthraquinone-2,6-disulphonic acid; anthraquinone-2,7-disulphonic acid; anthraquinone-1-sulphonic acid, sodium salt; anthraquinone-2-sulphonic acid, sodium salt; anthrone; benzanthrone

Uses: wood pulping reagent

anthraquinone-1,5-disulphonic acid
ρ acid; rho acid; [117-14-6]

$C_{14}H_8O_8S_2$. M: 368.33. Off-white, crystalline solid. MP: 310°C with decomposition. Soluble in water.

Production:
- anthraquinone (mercury-catalysed sulphonation; coproduced with anthraquinone-1,8-disulphonic acid)

Derivatives:
1,5-diaminoanthraquinone; 1,5-dichloroanthraquinone; 1,5-dihydroxyanthraquinone

anthraquinone-1,8-disulphonic acid
azine acid; χ acid; chi acid; 9,10-dioxoanthracene-1,8-disulphonic acid; [82-48-4]

$C_{14}H_8O_8S_2$. M: 368.33. Available as the pentahydrate. Yellow needles. MP: 293°C with decomposition. Slightly soluble in water.

Production:
- anthraquinone (mercury-catalysed sulphonation; coproduced with anthraquinone-1,5-disulphonic acid)

Derivatives:
1,8-dihydroxyanthraquinone

anthraquinone-2,6-disulphonic acid
2,6-anthraquinonedisulphonic acid; [84-50-4]

$C_{14}H_8O_8S_2$. M: 368.33.

Production:
- anthraquinone (sulphonation; coproduced with anthraquinone-2-sulphonic acid, sodium salt/ anthraquinone-2,7-disulphonic acid)

Derivatives: Vat Red 48

anthraquinone-2,7-disulphonic acid
9,10-dioxoanthracene-2,7-disulphonic acid; [84-49-1]

$C_{14}H_8O_8S_2$. M: 368.33.

Production:
- anthraquinone (sulphonation; coproduced with anthraquinone-2-sulphonic acid, sodium salt/ anthraquinone-2,6-disulphonic acid)

Uses:
dyestuffs intermediate

anthraquinone-1-sulphonic acid, sodium salt
[128-56-3]

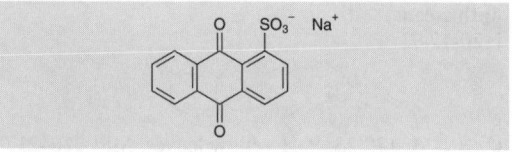

$C_{14}H_7Na_1O_5S_1$. M: 310.25.

Production:
- anthraquinone (sulphonation/sodium salt formation)

Derivatives:
1-aminoanthraquinone; 1-amino-5-benzamidoanthraquinone; 1-chloroanthraquinone; Disperse Red 9; Disperse Red 22; 1-hydroxyanthraquinone

anthraquinone-2-sulphonic acid, sodium salt
silver salt; [84-48-0]

$C_{14}H_7Na_1O_5S_1$. M: 310.25. Yellow, crystalline solid. MP: >350°C. Soluble in water.

Production:
- anthraquinone (sulphonation; coproduced with anthraquinone-2,6-disulphonic acid/anthraquinone-2,7-disulphonic acid)

Derivatives: alizarin; 2-aminoanthraquinone

anthrarufin *See:* 1,5-dihydroxyanthraquinone

anthrone
9,10-dihydro-9-oxoanthracene; [90-44-8]

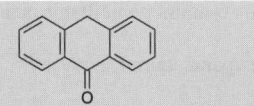

$C_{14}H_{10}O_1$. M: 194.23. Colourless crystals. MP: 152–154°C. Insoluble in water. Soluble in organic solvents.
Production:
- anthraquinone (reduction)

Derivatives: melitracen
Uses: analytical reagent

antimony
[7440-36-0]

Sb

Sb_1. M: 121.75. Silvery-white, brittle metal. d: 6.68 kg/l. MP: 630.7°C. Stable to air and moisture.
Production:
- copper-lead smelter flue dust (sublimation/leaching)
- antimony-containing sulphide ores/antimony trisulphide (blast furnace smelting)
- antimony trioxide (reduction)

Uses: cast iron ingredient; lead-antimony-tin alloys (battery plates, casting applications); lead alloying ingredient (solder, pewter, white metal, shotgun pellets); lead-antimony alloys (battery plates, roofing, radiation protection, ammunition)

antimony chloride *See:* antimony trichloride

antimony diamyldithiocarbamate

$$\left[(C_5H_{11})_2N\overset{\overset{\displaystyle S}{\|}}{C}S\right]_3 Sb$$

$C_{33}H_{66}N_3S_6Sb_1$. M: 819.04.
Production:
- diamylamine + carbon disulphide + antimony trioxide (salt formation)

Uses: antiwear additive (gear oils, greases)

antimony oxide *See:* antimony trioxide

antimony pentachloride
[7647-18-9]
Cl_5Sb_1. M: 299.01. Colourless oily liquid. MP: 3°C. Decomposes on heating. d: 2.35 kg/l (20°C). Fumes

in air. Hydrolysed by dissolution in water.

SbCl₅

Production:
- antimony trichloride + chlorine (reaction)

Derivatives:
antimony pentoxide
Uses: chlorination catalyst

antimony pentasulphide
[1315-04-4]

Sb₂S₅

S_5Sb_2. M: 403.82. Yellow to red amorphous solid of indefinite composition. Insoluble in water.
Production:
- antimony trisulphide + sulphur + sodium hydroxide (reaction)

Uses: fireworks ingredient; vulcanisation accelerator

antimony pentoxide
[1314-60-9]

Sb₂O₅

O_5Sb_2. M: 323.49. Yellow powder. Decomposes on heating to 380°C. Commercial product also sold as a dispersion in water or organic solvent.
Production:
- antimony pentachloride (hydrolysis)

Uses:
fire-retardant additive (clear polyester plastics/fibres)

antimony potassium tartrate
potassium antimony tartrate; tartar emetic; [28300-74-5]

COO–CHO–Sb, CHO, COO⁻ K⁺

$C_8H_4K_2O_{12}Sb_2$. M: 613.81. Available as the trihydrate. Colourless, efflorescent, crystalline solid. Loses water on heating above 100°C. Soluble in water.
Production:
- potassium bitartrate + antimony trioxide (salt formation)

Uses:
anthelmintic drug; mordant (textile/leather dyeing)

antimony sulphide *See:* antimony trisulphide

antimony trichloride
antimony chloride; [10025-91-9]

SbCl₃

Cl_3Sb_1. M: 228.11. Colourless, deliquescent crystals. Fumes in air. d: 3.14 kg/l (20°C). MP: 73°C. Solubility in water: 99 g/l (25°C).

Production:
• antimony trisulphide + hydrochloric acid
  (chlorination)
Derivatives:
antimony pentachloride; antimony tris(isooctyl thioglycollate); diphenylantimony 2-ethylhexanoate
Uses: catalyst; dyeing auxiliary; steel bronzing agent

antimony trifluoride
[7783-56-4]

$$SbF_3$$

F_3Sb_1. M: 178.74. White crystals. MP: 280°C. BP:
346°C. Soluble in water with partial hydrolysis.
Production:
• antimony trioxide + hydrofluoric acid (reaction)
Uses: fluorination reaction catalyst

antimony trioxide
antimony oxide; Pigment White 11 (CI); [1309-64-4]

$$Sb_2O_3$$

O_3Sb_2. M: 291.50. White, crystalline solid. MP: 656°C.
d: 5.67 kg/l. Slightly soluble in water. The mineral
valentinite is a natural source of antimony oxide used
for the production of antimony metal.
Production:
• antimony-containing sulphide ores/antimony
  trisulphide (ore roasting)
Derivatives:
antimony; antimony diamyldithiocarbamate; antimony
potassium tartrate; antimony trifluoride; chrome antimony titanium buff; titanium nickel yellow
Uses: fire-retardant additive (halogenated plastics); fire-
retardant additive (unsaturated polyester resins); opacifying ingredient (glass, porcelain, pottery glazes); pigment (paints)

antimony tris(isooctyl thioglycollate)

$$Sb\left[SCH_2\overset{O}{\overset{\|}{C}}OC_8H_{17}\right]_3$$

$C_{30}H_{57}O_6S_3Sb_1$. M: 731.72.
Production:
• antimony trichloride + isooctyl thioglycollate
  (dehydrochlorination)
Uses: polyvinyl chloride heat stabiliser

antimony trisulphide
antimony sulphide; [1345-04-6]

$$Sb_2S_3$$

S_3Sb_2. M: 339.69. Grey-black crystalline solid. MP:
550°C. Insoluble in water. Stibnite is the natural
mineral form of antimony trisulphide. It is available
as ore concentrates contain >45% antimony produced
as byproducts of copper, silver and gold production.

Production:
• antimony sulphide ore concentrates (liquation)
Derivatives:
antimony; antimony pentasulphide; antimony trichloride; antimony trioxide
Uses: coloured glass ingredient; raw material (safety
matches, fireworks, explosives)

antipyrine *See:* phenazone

6-APA *See:* 6-aminopenicillanic acid

APAP *See:* paracetamol

apatite, defluorinated
phosphate, defluorinated; tricalcium phosphate, defluorinated
Produced principally in the USA and the CIS. Standard
grades contain 40–42% P_2O_5.
Production:
• apatite + quartz (calcination)
Uses: animal feed additive

APB *See:* polybutene-1, atactic

APC *See:* ammonium perchlorate

APM *See:* aspartame; *N*-(3-aminopropyl)morpholine

APO *See:* triethylenephosphoramide

APP *See:* polypropylene, atactic

apricot kernel oil
apricot nut oil
Colourless to pale yellow oil. Produced by macer-
ation/steam distillation of apricot (*Prunus armeniaca*)
kernels. Similar to bitter almond oil.
Uses:
fragrance/flavouring ingredient

APT *See:* ammonium paratungstate

arachis oil *See:* peanut oil

***m*-aramid** *See:* poly(*m*-phenyleneisophthalamide)

***p*-aramid** *See:* poly(*p*-phenyleneterephthalamide)

L-arginine
L-amino-4-guanidovaleric acid; Arg; [74-79-3];
[1119-34-2] (hydrochloride)

$$H_2NCNHCH_2CH_2CH_2-\overset{NH_2}{\underset{H}{C}}-COOH \quad (NH)$$

$C_6H_{14}N_4O_2$. M: 174.21. Available commercially as the

naturally-occurring L(+)-enantiomer in the form of the anhydrous or dihydrate free base or hydrochloride salt. Crystalline solid. Decomposes on heating above 240°C. Soluble in water.
Production:
- microbial fermentation medium + *Corynebacterium glutamicum* bacteria (fermentation/separation; byproduct of L-glutamic acid production)
- animal glue (hydrolysis/extraction; coproduced with L-tyrosine/L-leucine/L-asparagine)

Derivatives:
thymopentin
Uses: infusion solutions/diagnostic aids; raw material (peptide drugs)

argon
[7440-37-1]

Ar

Ar_1. M: 39.95. Colourless inert gas. BP: -186°C. Soluble in water and organic solvents.
Production:
- air (cryogenic separation; byproduct of oxygen/ nitrogen production)

Uses: inert filler gas (light bulbs, fluorescent tubes, instruments); shielding gas (aluminium, stainless steel welding); blanketing gas (zirconium /titanium refining)

Armstrong's acid
See: naphthalene-1,5-disulphonic acid

aromatics, mixed
benzol, hydrogenated; BTX
Mixed hydrocarbon stream comprising mainly benzene, toluene and xylene, the relative proportions of which vary with the source of the aromatics. Reformate feedstocks produce a stream comprising, typically, 10% benzene, 45% toluene, 7% *p*-xylene, 16% *m*-xylene and 9% *o*-xylene. The remainder is ethylbenzene and higher aromatics. Pyrolysis gasoline gives an aromatics stream containing 45–50% benzene, 30–35% toluene and 10–15% xylene, together with some ethylbenzene and styrene. The output of the Cyclar process is, typically, 25% benzene, 43% toluene, 23% xylene and 9% C_{9+} aromatics from an LPG feedstock. Mixed aromatics from coal carbonisation contain 67% benzene, 16% toluene, 6% xylene and ethylbenzene, and 7% C_{9+} aromatics.
Production:
- gasoline, pyrolysis, hydrogenated/reformate (solvent extraction; coproduced with gasoline, dearomatised)
- liquified petroleum gas (BP-UOP Cyclar process)
- benzole (sulphuric acid refining)
- benzole + coke oven gas (hydrorefining)

Derivatives:
C_{9+} aromatics; benzene; toluene; xylene, mixed

C_{9+} aromatics
Liquid. BP: 160–285°C. Mixed aromatic hydrocarbon stream comprising 45–55% trimethylbenzene isomers (mesitylene, cumene, durene, propylbenzene, indane and others) plus heavier aromatics.
Production:
- aromatics, mixed (separation; coproduced with benzene/toluene/xylene, mixed)

Derivatives:
C_{10+} aromatics; hydrocarbon resins, C_9 aromatic types; trimethylbenzene fraction

C_{10+} aromatics
heavy aromatic naphtha; HAN
Mixed hydrocarbon stream mainly consisting of naphthalene and alkyl naphthalene. BR: 215–285°C.
Production:
- C_{9+} aromatics (fractionation; coproduced with trimethylbenzene fraction)

Derivatives: dimethylnaphthalene fraction; methylnaphthalene fraction; naphthalene fraction
Uses: pesticide carrier; solvent (tank cleaning, petroleum additives, oilfield chemicals)

arsanilic acid
p-aminobenzenearsonic acid; [98-50-0]

$C_6H_8As_1N_1O_3$. M: 217.06.
Production:
- aniline + arsenic acid (reaction)

Uses: growth stimulant (pigs, poultry)

arsenic
[7440-38-2]

As

As_1. M: 74.92. Shiny, grey, semi-metallic solid. Sublimes at 615°C without melting. d: 5.73 kg/l (25°C). Insoluble in water.
Production:
- arsenic trioxide + metallurgical coke (reduction)

Derivatives: arsine
Uses: copper/lead alloying ingredient

arsenic acid
orthoarsenic acid; [7778-39-4]

H_3AsO_4

$H_3As_1O_4$. M: 141.94. Available as the hemihydrate. White, hygroscopic, crystalline solid. MP: 35°C. Releases water when heated above 160°C forming arsenic pentoxide. d: ~2.2 kg/l. Soluble in water.
Production:
- arsenic trioxide + nitric acid (oxidation/hydration)

Derivatives: arsanilic acid; arsenic pentoxide

Uses: glass production clarifying agent; defoliant (cotton); glass raw material; reducing agent

arsenic pentoxide
[1303-28-2]

As_2O_5

As_2O_5. M: 229.83. White, amorphous lumps. Deliquescent. MP: ~300°C with decomposition. d: 4.32 kg/l. Soluble in water and alcohol.
Production:
• arsenic trioxide (air oxidation)
• arsenic acid (dehydration)
Derivatives: ammoniacal copper arsenate; copper arsenate, chromated
Uses: coloured glass ingredient

arsenic trioxide
arsenious trioxide; white arsenic; [1327-53-3]

As_2O_3

As_1O_3. M: 122.92. White, amorphous lumps, cubic or monoclinic crystals. MP: 272°C (cubic form), 312°C (monoclinic form). All forms sublime at 125–150°C. Highly toxic. Soluble in water.
Production:
• lead refinery anode slimes/copper smelter flue dust/ copper-lead smelter flue dust (sublimation/leaching)
Derivatives:
arsenic; arsenic acid; arsenic pentoxide; disodium methylarsonate; monosodium methylarsonate; 3-nitro-4-hydroxyphenylarsonic acid; 10,10'-oxybisphenoxyarsine; sodium cacodylate
Uses: Nokes froth flotation reagent component; glass raw material; rodenticide

arsine
[7784-42-1]

AsH_3

H_3As_1. M: 77.94. Colourless gas with an unpleasant, garlic-like odour. Highly toxic. MP: -117°C. BP: -62°C. Slightly soluble in water.
Production:
• arsenic + sodium/zinc (alloy formation/hydration)
Uses: semiconductor dopant

ASA *See:* acrylonitrile-styrene-acrylic ester copolymers

ascorbic acid
vitamin C; E300 (EC); [50-81-7]

$C_6H_8O_6$. M: 176.12. White, crystalline solid. MP: 190–

192°C with decomposition. d: 1.65 kg/l. Soluble in water. Slightly soluble in oxygenated solvents. The commercial product is the natural L(+)-enantiomer.
Production:
• L-sorbose + acetone (acetal formation/oxidation/ rearrangement)
Derivatives: ascorbyl palmitate; calcium ascorbate; sodium ascorbate
Uses: dietary supplement ingredient; antioxidant (food); preservative (photographic developers)

ascorbyl palmitate
E304 (EC); [137-66-6]

$C_{22}H_{38}O_7$. M: 414.53. White to pale yellow powder. Fat-soluble derivative of ascorbic acid.
Production:
• palmitic acid + ascorbic acid (esterification)
Uses: antioxidant (processed meat)

L-asparagine
L-α-aminosuccinamic acid; Asn; [70-47-3]; [74144-37-9] (sulphate)

$C_4H_8N_2O_3$. M: 132.12. Available commercially as the naturally-occurring L(−)-enantiomer monohydrate. Crystalline solid. MP: 234°C. d: 1.54 kg/l (15°C). Slightly soluble in water.
Production:
• animal glue (hydrolysis/extraction; coproduced with L-tyrosine/L-arginine/L-leucine)
Uses: infusion solutions/diagnostic aids; raw material (peptide drugs)

aspartame
L-aspartyl-L-phenylalanine methyl ester; APM; [53906-69-7]; [22839-47-0]

$C_{14}H_{18}N_2O_5$. M: 294.29. Available as the anhydrous or hemihydrate salts. Colourless crystals. MP: 246°C.
Production:
• DL-phenylalanine + methanol + L-aspartic acid (esterification/enzymatic coupling)
• L-phenylalanine + methanol + L-aspartic acid (esterification/amide formation)
Uses: artificial sweetener

L-aspartic acid
L-aminosuccinic acid; Asp; [617-45-8]

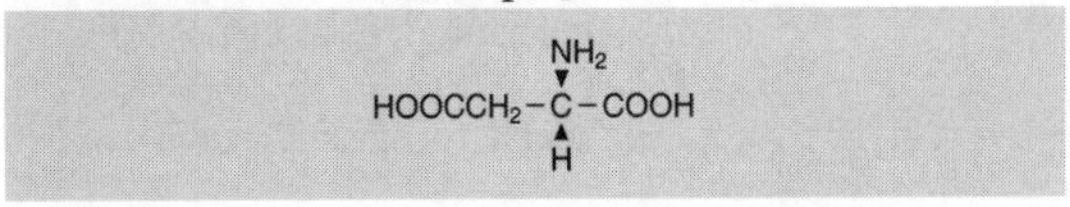

$$\underset{\underset{H}{\overset{\overset{NH_2}{|}}{|}}{HOOCCH_2 - C - COOH}}$$

$C_4H_7N_1O_4$. M: 133.11. White, crystalline solid comprising the L(+)-enantiomer. MP: >300°C with decomposition. Slightly soluble in water.
Production:
• fumaric acid + ammonia + *Escherichia coli*
  bacteria (microbial conversion)
Derivatives:
L-alanine; alitame; aspartame; oxytocin; pentagastrin;
L-phenylalanine; thymopentin
Uses: raw material (peptide drugs)

asphalt *See:* bitumen

asphaltite
bitumen, natural; burmudez pitch; gilsonite
Black solid. Softening point: 135–195°C (gilsonite), 170°C (manjak), >195°C (rafaelite and grahamite). d: 1.04–1.15 kg/l. Asphaltites are natural bitumens with a low rock content. Solubility in CS_2: >95%. Gilsonite and grahamite are mined in the USA, raphaelite in Argentina, burmudez pitch in Venezuela and manjak (glance pitch) in the West Indies.
Derivatives:
carbon, moulded
Uses: oil-based drilling muds filtrate control agents; barrier coatings (building boards, explosives, automobile underseal); foundry mould binder; bitumen paint ingredient; binder (printing inks); raw material (petroleum coke production)

aspirin *See:* acetylsalicylic acid

astemizole
[68844-77-9]

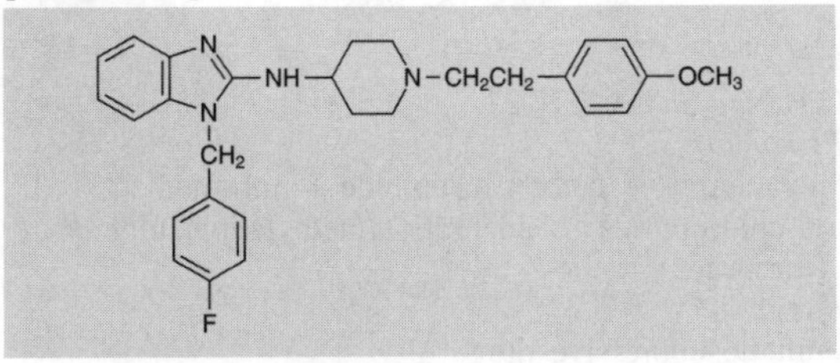

$C_{28}H_{31}F_1N_4O_1$. M: 458.59.
Production:
• *o*-nitroaniline + carbon disulphide + 4-amino-
  N-benzylpiperidine + 4-fluorobenzyl chloride +
  2-(*p*-methoxyphenyl)ethanol (thiocarbonylation/
  thiocyanate addition/nitro reduction/condensation/
  amine formation/decarboxylation/amine formation)
Uses: antihistamine drug

asulam
methyl 4-aminophenylsulphonylcarbamate; [3337-71-1]

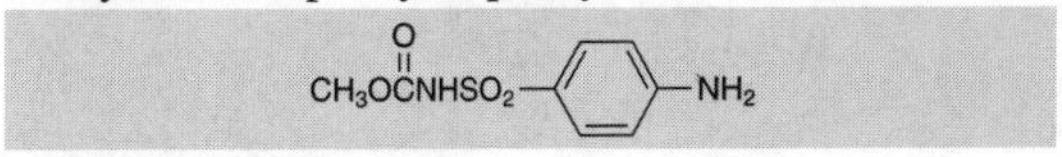

$C_8H_{10}N_2O_4S_1$. M: 230.24.
Production:
• sulphanilamide + methyl chloroformate
  (dehydrochlorination)
Uses: herbicide

ATA *See:* 3-amino-1,2,4-triazole

ATBN *See:* acrylonitrile-butadiene copolymers, amine-terminated

ATC *See:* 2-aminothiazoline-4-carboxylic acid

atenolol
[29122-68-7]

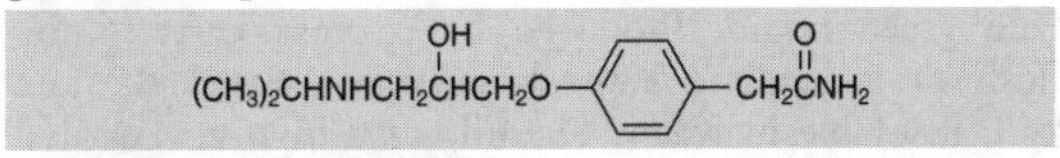

$C_{14}H_{22}N_2O_3$. M: 266.34.
Production:
• *p*-hydroxyphenylacetonitrile + epichlorohydrin +
  isopropylamine (epoxidation/amine formation/nitrile
  hydration)
Uses: antianginal drug

ATH *See:* alumina trihydrate

atmospheric residue *See:* long residue

ATMP *See:* aminotris(methylene phosphonic acid)

atrazine
2-ethylamino-4-isopropylamino-6-chloro-1,3,5-triazine;
[1912-24-9]

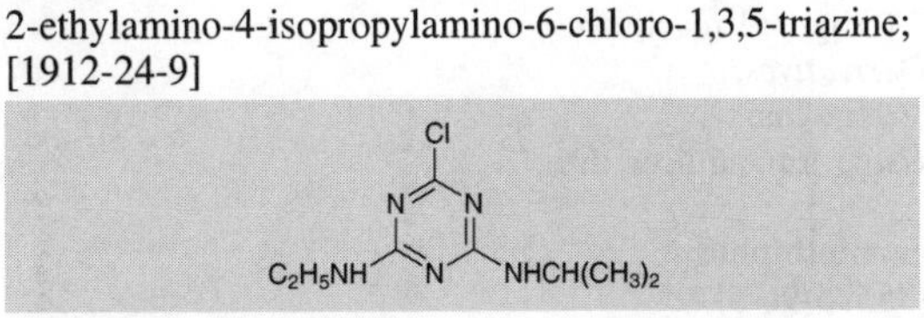

$C_8H_{12}Cl_1N_5$. M: 215.69.
Production:
• cyanuric chloride + ethylamine + isopropylamine
  (dehydrochlorination/dehydrochlorination)
Uses:
herbicide

atropine
DL-hyoscyamine
$C_{17}H_{23}N_1O_3$. M: 289.38. Extracted with scopolamine from thorn apple (*Datura stramonium*) fruit. Available commercially as the hydrochloride, methyl nitrate and sulphate salts.

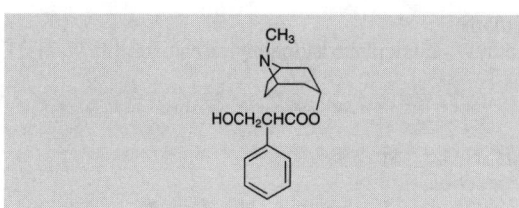

Derivatives:
ipratropium bromide
Uses: anticholinergic drug

attapulgite *See:* fuller's earth

aureomycin *See:* chlortetracycline

avermectin *See:* ivermectin

avocado oil
[8024-32-6]
Pale green liquid. Produced by expression from the flesh of avocado (*Persea americana*) pears. d: 0.91 kg/l. Insoluble in water. The oil has a high unsaturated fatty acid content.
Uses: emollient (cosmetics)

azacyclonol
[115-46-8]

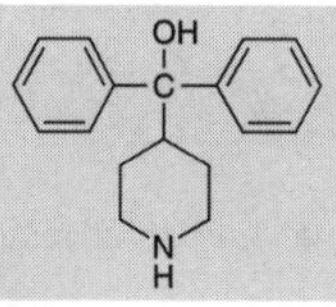

$C_{18}H_{21}N_1O_1$. M: 267.38.
Production:
• ethyl isonipecotinate + phenylmagnesium bromide (Grignard reaction)
Derivatives:
terfenadine
Uses: tranquilliser drug

azamethiphos
[35575-96-3]

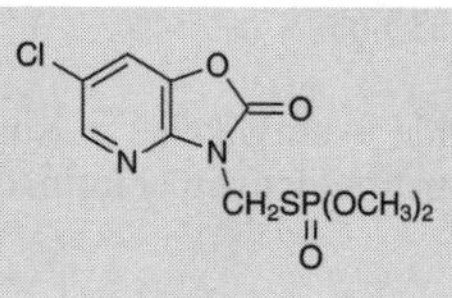

$C_9H_{10}Cl_1N_2O_5P_1S_1$. M: 324.66.
Production:
• 2-aminopyridine + phosgene + formaldehyde + *O,O*-dimethyl dithiophosphoric acid (ring chlorination/base-catalysed hydrolysis/phosgenation/chloromethylation/dehydrochlorination/hydrolysis)
Uses: insecticide

1-azaphenothiazine
pyridine[2,3,b]-benzo-1,4-thiazine

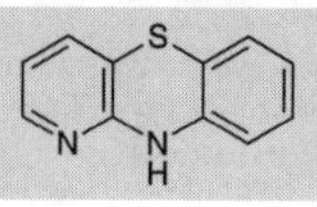

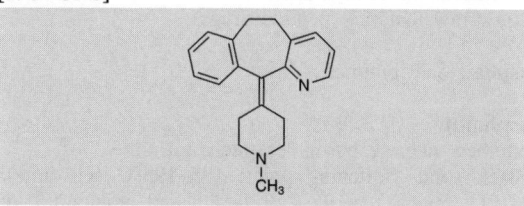

$C_{11}H_8N_2S_1$. M: 200.25.
Production:
• 2-aminopyridine + chlorobenzene + sulphur (amine formation/thionation)
Derivatives:
isothipendyl; pipazetate; prothipendyl

azatadine
[3964-81-6]

$C_{20}H_{22}N_2$. M: 290.41. Available as the free base or as the dimaleate salt.
Production:
• nicotinic acid + phthalic anhydride + isonipecotic acid (condensation/cyclisation/condensation/decarboxylation)
Uses:
antihistamine drug

azathioprine
[446-86-6]

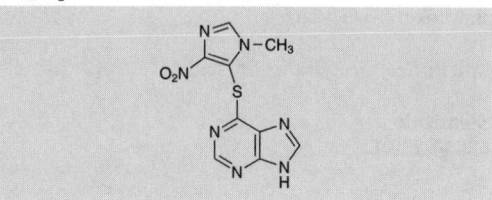

$C_9H_7N_7O_2S_1$. M: 277.27.
Production:
• cyanamide + carbon disulphide + nitromethane + 6-chloropurine (condensation/methylation/sulphide formation)
Uses:
immunosuppressive drug

azelaic acid
1,7-nonanedioic acid; [123-99-9]

HOOCCH$_2$CH$_2$CH$_2$CH$_2$CH$_2$CH$_2$CH$_2$COOH

$C_9H_{16}O_4$. M: 188.23. Crystalline solid. MP: 96–102°C. d: 1.02 kg/l (110°C). Acid value: 580–598 mg KOH/g. Commercial products have 80–90% C_9 dibasic acid

content. Slightly soluble in cold water. Soluble in hot water and oxygenated solvents.
Production:
- oleic acid (ozonolysis; coproduced with pelargonic acid)

Derivatives: complex ester oils; diester oils; di-(2-ethylhexyl) azelate; diisooctyl azelate; polyamide 6 terpolymers; polyamide 69; polyazelaic polyanhydride; polyester polyols, linear; poly(ether-amide) elastomers; polymeric plasticisers
Uses: alkyd resin comonomer; thermoplastic polyamide resin comonomer (hot-melt adhesives)

azidocillin
[17243-38-8]

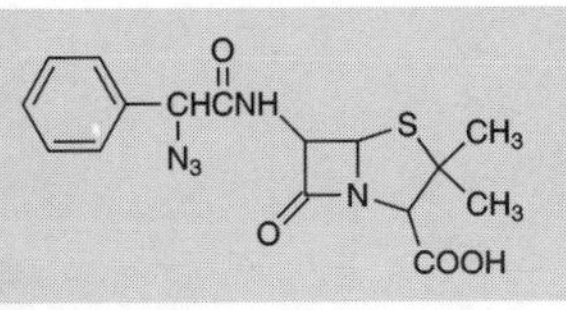

$C_{16}H_{17}N_5O_4S_1$. M: 375.42.
Production:
- D-mandelic acid + sodium azide + 6-aminopenicillanic acid (alcohol bromination/azide formation/amide formation)
Uses: antibacterial drug

azinphos-ethyl
S-3,4-dihydro-4-oxo-1,2,3-benzotriazin-3-ylmethyl *O,O*-diethyl phosphorodithioate; [2642-71-9]

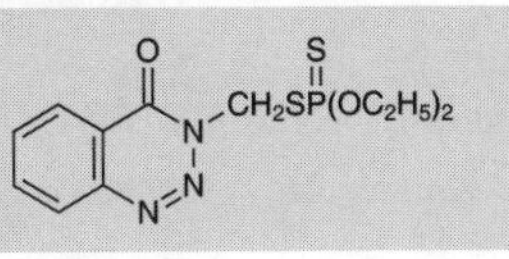

$C_{12}H_{16}N_3O_3P_1S_2$. M: 345.38.
Production:
- benzazimide + formaldehyde + *O,O*-diethyl dithiophosphoric acid (chloromethylation/dehydrochlorination)
Uses: acaricide/insecticide

azinphos-methyl
S-3,4-dihydro-4-oxo-1,2,3-benzotriazin-3-ylmethyl *O,O*-dimethylphosphorodithioate; [86-50-0]

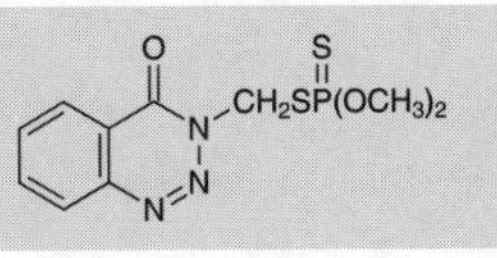

$C_{10}H_{12}N_3O_3P_1S_2$. M: 317.33.
Production:
- benzazimide + formaldehyde + *O,O*-dimethyl dithiophosphoric acid (chloromethylation/dehydrochlorination)
Uses: acaricide/insecticide

aziprotryne
2-azido-4-isopropylamino-6-methylthio-1,3,5-triazine; [4658-28-0]

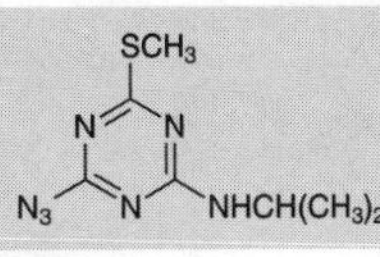

$C_7H_{11}N_7S_1$. M: 225.28.
Production:
- 2-methylmercapto-4,6-dichlorotriazine + isopropylamine + sodium azide (amine formation/amine formation)
Uses: herbicide

aziridine *See:* ethyleneimine

azlocillin
[37091-66-0]

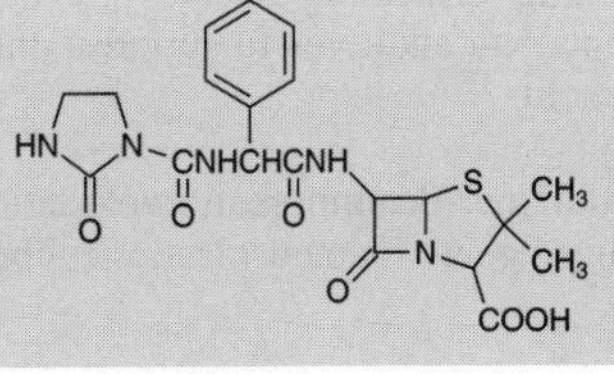

$C_{20}H_{23}N_5O_6S_1$. M: 461.49.
Production:
- ethylene urea + ethyl chloroformate + ampicillin (dehydrochlorination/amide formation)
Uses:
antibacterial drug

1,1′-azobisformamide
See: azodicarbonamide

2,2′-azobisisobutyronitrile
AIBN; [78-67-1]

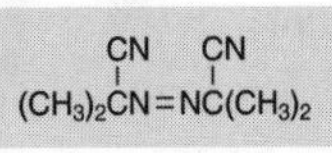

$C_8H_{12}N_4$. M: 164.22. Crystalline solid. MP: 103–104°C with decomposition. Soluble in alcohol.
Production:
- acetone cyanohydrin + hydrazine (amine formation/oxidation)
Uses:
blowing agent (foamed plastics/rubber); free radical reaction initiator

azocyclotin
tri(cyclohexyl)-1H-1,2,4-triazol-1-yltin; [41083-11-8]
$C_{20}H_{35}N_3Sn_1$. M: 436.21.
Production:
- cyclohexyl chloride + stannic chloride + 1,2,4-triazole (dechlorination/dehydrochlorination)

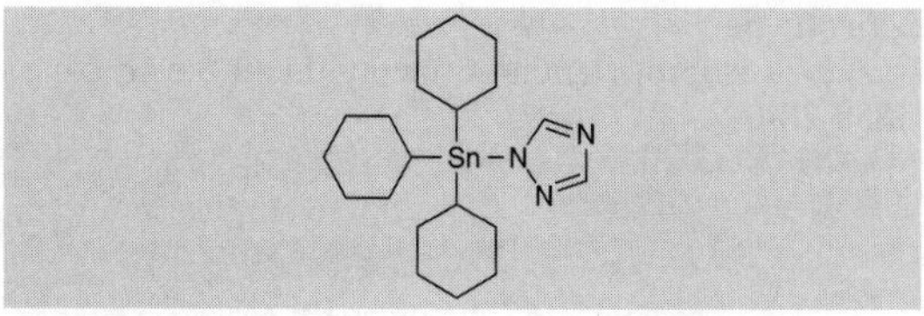

Uses: acaricide

azodicarbonamide

1,1'-azobisformamide; ABFA; ADC; [123-77-3]

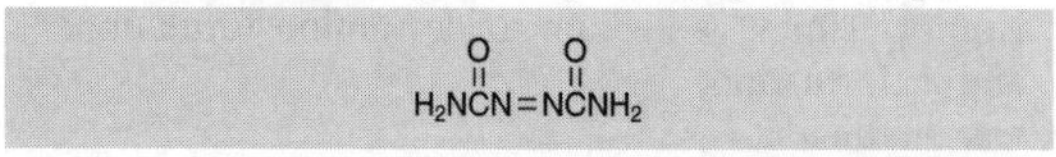

$C_2H_4N_4O_2$. M: 116.08. Pale yellow or orange, crystalline powder. Starts decomposing at 140°C producing 190 ml/g of nitrogen and carbon monoxide. d: 1.65 kg/l. Insoluble in most organic solvents. Also available in various modified forms, usually as a paste in plasticiser containing dispersing agents, kickers, auxiliary blowing agents and additives to suppress the formation of cyanuric acid.

Production:
• urea + hydrazine (deammoniation/oxidation)

Uses: blowing agent (foamed plastics/rubber)

aztreonam

[78110-38-0]

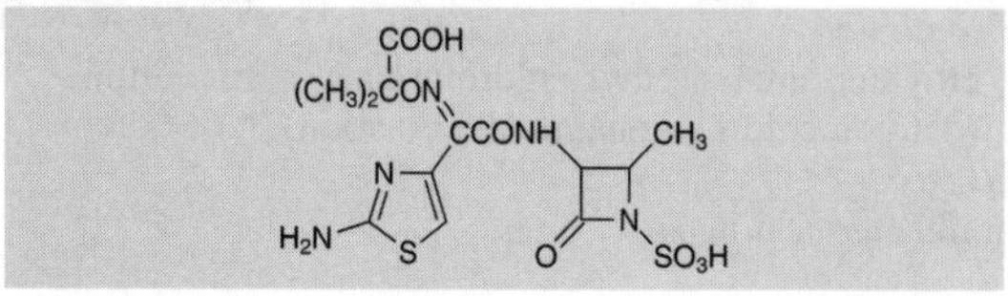

$C_{13}H_{17}N_5O_8S_2$. M: 435.43.

Production:
• L-threonine + ammonia + chlorosulphonic acid + ethyl γ-chloroacetoacetate + thiourea + methacrylic acid (multistep synthesis)

Uses: antibacterial drug

bacampicillin
[50972-17-3]

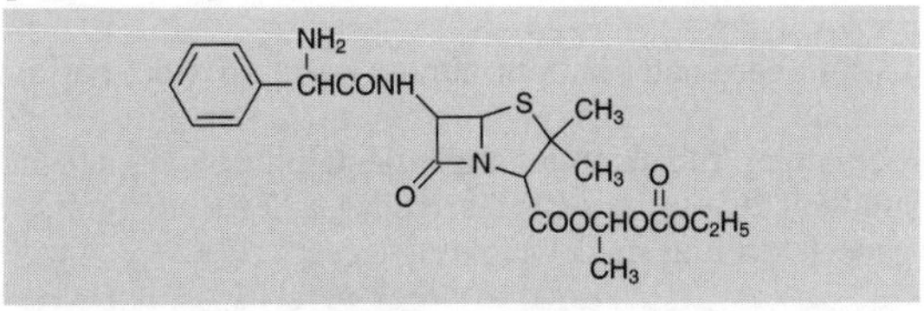

$C_{21}H_{27}N_3O_7S_1$. M: 465.52. Available commercially as the free base or hydrochloride.
Production:
• ampicillin + 1-chloroethyl ethyl carbonate (Dane salt formation/esterification/hydrolysis)
Uses: antibacterial drug

2B acid
4-amino-2-chlorotoluene-5-sulphonic acid; 4-amino-6-chlorotoluene-3-sulphonic acid; [88-51-7]

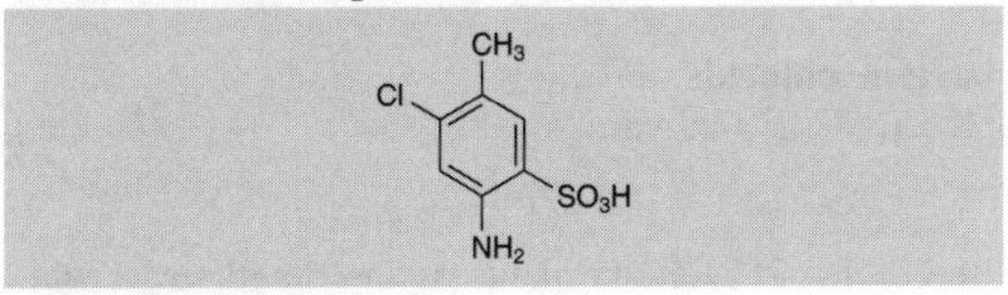

$C_7H_8Cl_1N_1O_3S_1$. M: 221.66.
Production:
• 4-amino-2-chlorotoluene (sulphonation)
Derivatives:
Pigment Red 48

4B acid
4-aminotoluene-3-sulphonic acid; [88-44-8]

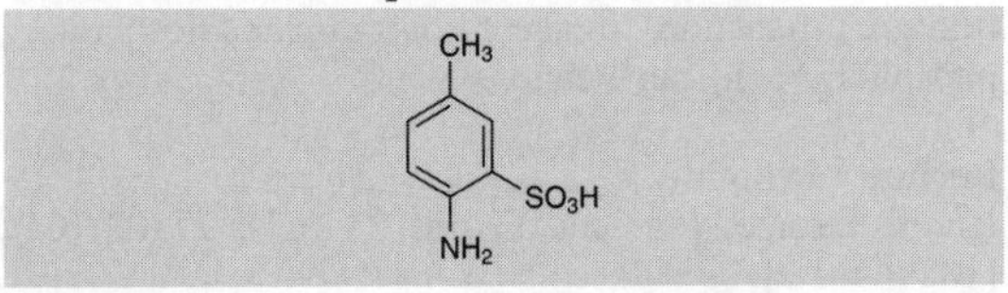

$C_7H_9N_1O_3S_1$. M: 187.22. Pale yellow needles. MP: 131–132°C with decomposition. Slightly soluble in water.
Production:
• *p*-toluidine (sulphonation)
Derivatives:
Acid Green 75; Direct Red 24; Pigment Red 57

bagasse
Fibrous sugarcane residue after extraction of the juice. Contains about 25% pentosans.
Derivatives:
furfural
Uses: fuel; fibreboard/paper

balsam, Canada
Exuded yellow liquid oleoresin of the Canadian balsam tree (*Abies balsamea*). d: 1.53 kg/l (20°C). Insoluble in water. Producing areas are Canada and northern USA.
Uses: lens assembly/microscopy cement

balsam, copaiba
Exuded yellow liquid oleoresin from *Copaifera* trees which grow in the Amazon and Orinoco regions of South America. Insoluble in water. Soluble in oxygenated, aromatic and chlorinated solvents.
Uses: perfume fixative (soaps); fine varnish ingredient; fragrance ingredient

balsam, Peru
Exuded dark-brown liquid oleoresin with a pleasant odour from *Myroxylon pereirae* trees growing in El Salvador. d: 1.15–1.17 kg/l. Insoluble in water.
Derivatives: Peru balsam oil

balsam, tolu
Exuded yellow or brown oleoresin from the *Toluifera balsamum* tree which grows in Venezuela, Columbia, Ecuador and Peru. Its main constituents are the benzyl esters of cinnamic and benzoic acids. Insoluble in water. Soluble in oxygenated, aromatic and chlorinated solvents.
Uses:
flavouring ingredient (confectionery, pharmaceuticals)

bamifylline
[2016-63-9]

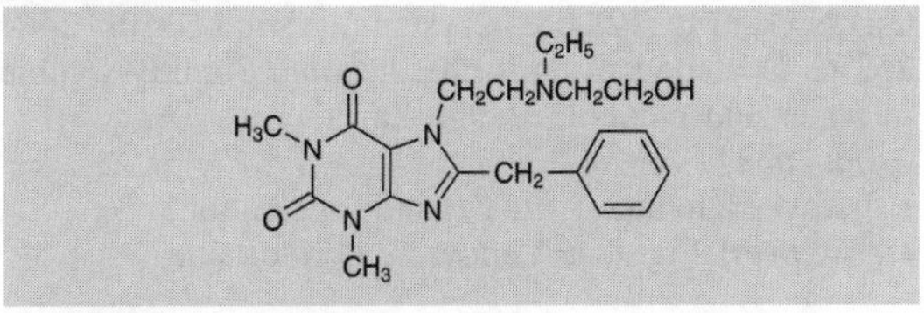

$C_{20}H_{27}N_5O_3$. M: 385.48.
Production:
• 6-amino-1,3-dimethyluracil + phenylacetyl chloride + ethylene oxide + *N*-ethylethanolamine (nitrosation/nitro reduction/condensation/epoxidation/amine formation)
Uses: bronchodilator drug

bamipine
[4945-47-5]
$C_{19}H_{24}N_2$. M: 280.41.
Production:
• 1-methyl-4-piperidone + aniline + benzyl chloride (reductive amination/amine formation)

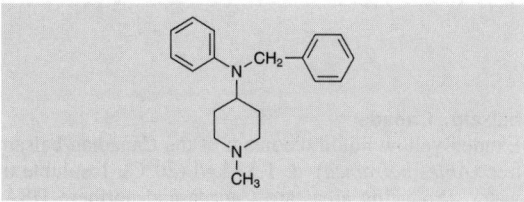

Uses: antihistamine drug

banana oil *See:* isoamyl acetate

BAP *See: N*-benzyl-*p*-aminophenol hydrochloride

barbital
5,5-diethylbarbituric acid

$C_8H_{12}N_2O_3$. M: 184.20. Available commercially as the free acid or its sodium salt.
Production:
• diethyl malonate + ethyl chloride + urea (dehydrochlorination/condensation)
Uses: sleep-inducing drug

barbituric acid
hexahydropyrimidine-2,4,6-trione; malonylurea; 2,4,6-trihydroxypyrimidine; [67-52-7]

$C_4H_4N_2O_3$. M: 128.08. Crystalline solid. MP: 248–252°C. Decomposes on further heating. Slightly soluble in water and alcohol. Soluble in ether.
Production:
• diethyl malonate + urea (amide formation)
Derivatives: Pigment Yellow 139; riboflavin

barite
barium sulphate; barytes; heavy spar

$BaSO_4$

$Ba_1O_4S_1$. M: 233.40. Barite is a natural mineral mined in many parts of the world, sometimes in association with fluorspar.
Derivatives: barium sulphide
Uses: filler (plastics, rubber, paint); glass ingredient; drilling mud weighting agent

barium carbonate
[513-77-9]
$C_1Ba_1O_3$. M: 197.35. White powder. Insoluble in water.

$BaCO_3$

d: 4.29 kg/l. Decomposes when heated to 1,400°C. Occurs naturally as the mineral witherite.
Production:
• barium sulphide + carbon dioxide (salt formation)
Derivatives:
barium chromate; barium nitrate; barium oxide; barium titanate
Uses: clay tile/ceramics ingredient; phosphor glass ingredient (television, CRT screens); filler (photographic paper); drilling mud weighting agent

barium chlorate
[13477-00-4]

$Ba(ClO_3)_2$

$Ba_1Cl_2O_6$. M: 304.24. Available as the monohydrate. Colourless crystals. Loses water of crystallisation above 120°C. Solubility in water: 300 g/l water (20°C).
Production:
• barium chloride + sodium chlorate (salt formation)
Uses: match head/fireworks/explosives ingredient

barium chloride
[10361-37-2] (anhydrous)

$BaCl_2$

Ba_1Cl_2. M: 208.25. Available as the dihydrate, a white crystalline solid which loses its water of crystallisation at 100°C. d: 3.10 kg/l. Solubility in water: 395 g/l water (0°C). Also available as the anhydrous product.
Production:
• barium sulphide + hydrochloric acid (salt formation)
Derivatives: barium chlorate; blanc fixe; petroleum sulphonates, alkali-earth salts
Uses: case hardening/heat treatment salts; flux (magnesium production); reagent (barium lake formation); phosphoric acid purification agent

barium chromate
lemon chrome; Pigment Yellow 31 (CI); 77103 (CI); [10294-40-3]

$BaCrO_4$

$Ba_1Cr_1O_4$. M: 253.34. Greenish-yellow crystals. d: 4.50 kg/l. Insoluble in water.
Production:
• barium carbonate + chromic acid (salt formation)
Uses: pigment (pipe jointing compounds)

barium hydroxide
[17194-00-2]

$Ba(OH)_2$

$H_2Ba_1O_2$. M: 171.36. Available as the octahydrate which is a white, crystalline solid which melts in its

water of crystallisation at 78°C. d: 2.18 kg/l. Slightly soluble in water.
Production:
• barium sulphide (air oxidation)
Derivatives: alkylbenzene sulphonates, alkali-earth salts; barium peroxide; barium ricinoleate; barium stearate; barium-zinc heat stabilisers; cadmium-barium heat stabilisers; dialkylaryl sulphonates, alkali-earth salts; ferrite; phenates, alkali-earth salts; phenates, sulphurised, alkali-earth salts; polybutene thiophosphonate propoxylates, alkali-earth salts
Uses: filler (paper, sealants); reagent (vegetable oil, sugar production); vulcanisation accelerator

barium metaborate
barium borate; Busan 11-M1 (Buckman Laboratories); Butrol 23 (Buckman Laboratories); [37228-06-1]

$$BaO.B_2O_3$$

$B_2Ba_1O_4$. M: 222.96.
Production:
• barium oxide + sodium borate (salt formation)
Uses: fire/mould-resistant additive (paints, plastics, textiles, paper)

barium nitrate
[10022-31-8]

$$Ba(NO_3)_2$$

$Ba_1N_2O_6$. M: 261.34. Colourless crystals. MP: 592°C. d: 3.24 kg/l. Solubility in water: 50 g/l water (0°C).
Production:
• barium sulphide/barium carbonate + nitric acid (salt formation)
Derivatives: barium oxide
Uses: fireworks/explosives ingredient; enamels

barium oxide
barium monoxide; [1304-28-5]

$$BaO$$

Ba_1O_1. M: 153.34. White to grey, crystalline powder. MP: 1,923°C. d: 5.70 kg/l. Dissolves in water forming barium hydroxide.
Production:
• barium carbonate + metallurgical coke (calcination)
• barium nitrate (calcination)
Derivatives:
alkylbenzene sulphonates, alkali-earth salts; barium metaborate; barium peroxide; barium stearate; barium-zinc heat stabilisers; cadmium-barium heat stabilisers; dialkylaryl sulphonates, alkali-earth salts; phenates, alkali-earth salts; phenates, sulphurised, alkali-earth salts; polybutene thiophosphonate propoxylates, alkali-earth salts
Uses: fluorescent pigment (paints, plastics); fireworks ingredient; solvent/gas desiccant

barium peroxide
barium dioxide; [1304-29-6]

$$BaO_2$$

Ba_1O_2. M: 169.34. Greyish-white powder. Insoluble in water but combines with it to form the octahydrate.
Production:
• barium oxide (air oxidation)
• barium hydroxide + hydrogen peroxide (peroxidation)
Uses:
dehydration agent (water-sensitive adhesives/sealants); textile bleach

barium ricinoleate
barium 12-hydroxyoleate

$$\left[CH_3(CH_2)_5\overset{\underset{|}{OH}}{C}HCH_2CH=CH(CH_2)_7COO\right]_2Ba$$

$C_{36}H_{66}Ba_1O_6$. M: 732.36.
Production:
• barium hydroxide + ricinoleic acid (salt formation)
Uses: polyvinyl chloride heat stabiliser

barium stearate
[6865-35-6]

$$\left[CH_3(CH_2)_{16}COO\right]_2Ba$$

$C_{36}H_{70}Ba_1O_4$. M: 704.30.
Production:
• stearic acid + barium hydroxide/barium oxide (salt formation)
Uses: polyvinyl chloride heat stabiliser

barium sulphate *See:* barite; blanc fixe

barium sulphide
black ash; [21109-95-5]

$$BaS$$

Ba_1S_1. M: 169.40. Yellowish-white powder. Sublimes in hot water with decomposition. Reacts with acid producing hydrogen sulphide.
Production:
• barite + coal (reduction)
Derivatives: barium carbonate; barium chloride; barium hydroxide; barium nitrate; blanc fixe; lithopone; sodium sulphide; zinc sulphide
Uses: skin/hide depilatory agent; fluorescent pigment (paints, plastics); iron reducing agent (aluminium sulphate production); small-scale hydrogen sulphide generation material

barium titanate
[12047-27-7]

$$BaTiO_3$$

$Ba_1O_3Ti_1$. M: 233.24.

Production:
• barium carbonate + titanium dioxide, hydrate (thermal conversion)
Uses:
electroceramic capacitors; heat-sensitive conductors

barium toner *See:* Pigment Red 49

barium-zinc heat stabilisers
Production:
• barium oxide/barium hydroxide/zinc oxide + 2-ethylhexanoic acid/C_8-C_{10} fatty acids/isodecanoic acid/neodecanoic acid/lauric acid, broad cut/stearic acid/naphthenic acid/benzoic acid/dodecylphenol + 2-ethylhexyl epoxystearate/isooctyl epoxystearate/ isooctyl epoxytallate (salt formation)
Uses: polyvinyl chloride heat stabiliser

barytes *See:* barite

Basic Blue 1
Pigment Blue 9 (CI, PMTA salt); 42025 (CI); 42025:1 (CI, PMTA salt);

$C_{23}H_{24}Cl_2N_2$. M: 399.36.
Production:
• *N,N*-dimethylaniline + *o*-chlorobenzaldehyde (carbonyl condensation/oxidation)
Uses: dye (polyacrylonitrile); pigment (printing ink)

Basic Blue 3
Maxilon Blue 5G (Ciba-Geigy)

The dye is the zinc chloride double salt of the displayed structure.
Production:
• *N,N*-diethyl-*m*-anisidine + *m*-diethylaminophenol + zinc chloride (nitrosation/condensation/salt formation)
Uses: dye (polyacrylonitrile)

Basic Blue 6
Meldola's Blue; 51175 (CI); [7057-57-0]; [966-62-1]
The dye is the zinc chloride double salt of the displayed structure. Reddish-blue solid. Soluble in water and ethanol.
Production:
• *N,N*-dimethyl-*p*-nitrosoaniline + β-naphthol + zinc chloride (condensation/salt formation)

Uses: dye (cotton, leather)

Basic Blue 7
Victoria Blue; Brilliant Blue; Solvent Blue 5 (CI, free base); Pigment Blue 1 (CI, PMTA salt); Pigment Blue 62 (CI, CFA salt); 42595 (CI, chloride salt); 42595:1 (CI, free base); 42595:2 (CI, PMTA salt)

$C_{33}H_{40}Cl_1N_3$. M: 514.15. The chloride and PMTA salts are produced from the oxidised form of this triarylmethine *leuco* base.
Production:
• 4,4'-bis(diethylamino)benzophenone + *N*-ethyl-1-naphthylamine (carbonyl condensation)
Uses: basic dye (paper); pigment (printing inks); solvent dye (ballpen inks, printer ribbons)

Basic Blue 9
52015 (CI); Methylene Blue; methylthionine chloride; Solvent Blue 8 (CI); [61-73-4]

The dye is the zinc chloride double salt of the displayed structure. Dark green crystals. Soluble in water. Slightly soluble in ethanol.
Production:
• *N,N*-dimethyl-*p*-phenylenediamine + sodium thiosulphate + *N,N*-dimethylaniline + zinc chloride (thiosulphonation/oxidation/salt formation)
Uses: nickel plating brightening agent; antiseptic; basic dye (leather, acrylic fibre)

Basic Blue 22
61512 (CI)
$C_{22}H_{29}N_3O_6S_1$. M: 463.54.
Production:
• 3-dimethylaminopropylamine + 1-bromo-4-methylaminoanthraquinone + dimethyl sulphate (amine formation/quaternisation)

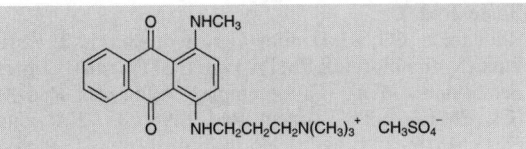

Uses: dye (polyacrylonitrile)

Basic Blue 26 *See:* Solvent Blue 4

Basic Blue 41
11154 (CI); [12270-13-2]

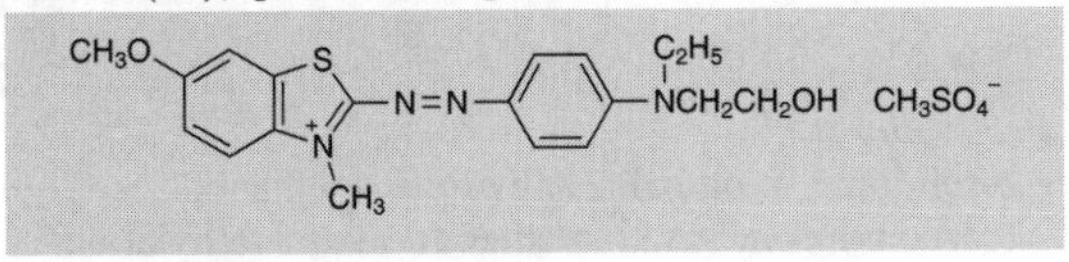

$C_{20}H_{26}N_4O_6S_2$. M: 482.58.
Production:
• 2-amino-6-methoxybenzothiazole + *N*-ethyl-
  N-(2-hydroxyethyl)aniline + dimethyl sulphate
  (diazotisation/azo coupling/methylation)
Uses:
dye (polyacrylonitrile)

Basic Blue 54
11052 (CI)

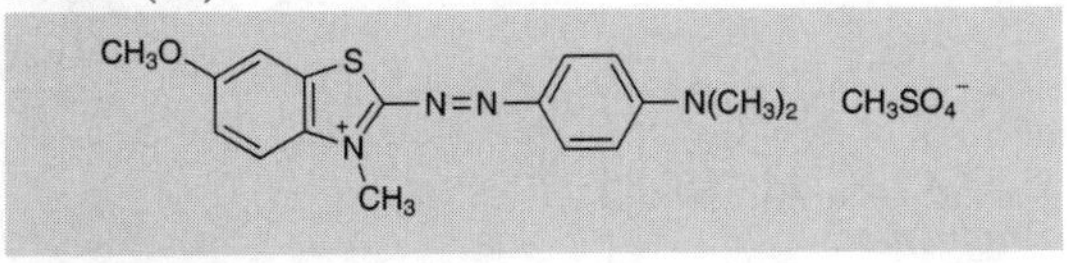

$C_{18}H_{22}N_4O_5S_2$. M: 438.53.
Production:
• 2-amino-6-methoxybenzothiazole + *N,N*-dimethyl-
  aniline + dimethyl sulphate (diazotisation/azo
  coupling/quaternisation)
Uses:
dye (polyacrylonitrile)

Basic Blue 119

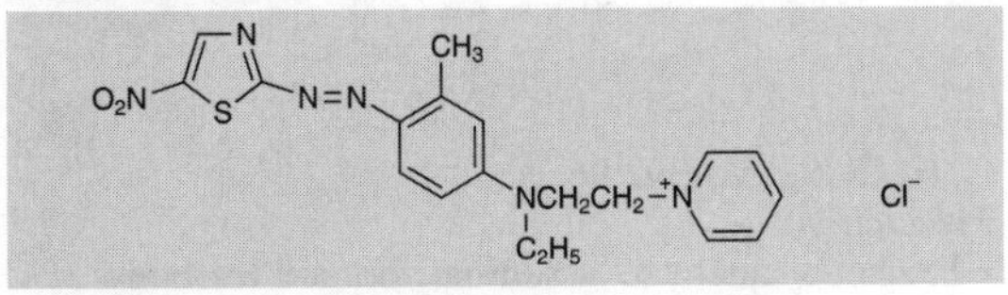

$C_{19}H_{21}Cl_1N_6O_2S_1$. M: 432.93.
Production:
• 2-amino-5-nitrothiazole + *N*-ethyl-*N*-(2-hydroxy-
  ethyl)-*m*-toluidine + pyridine (diazotisation/azo
  coupling/quaternisation)
Uses:
dye (polyacrylonitrile)

Basic Brown 1
Bismarck Brown; Solvent Brown 41 (CI, free base);

21000 (CI); 21000:1 (CI, free base)

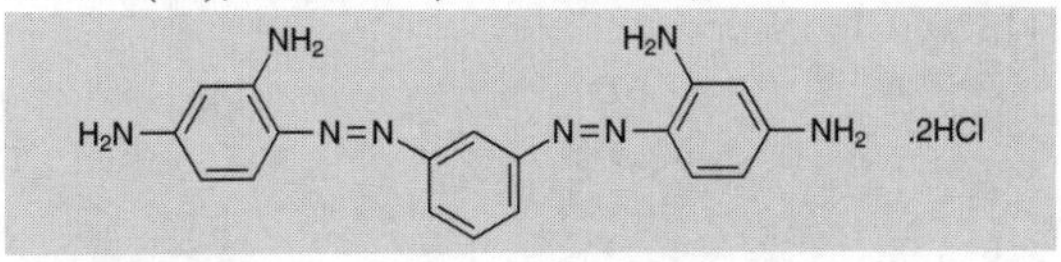

Mixed product, the main component of which is shown
in the formula.
Production:
• *m*-phenylenediamine + sodium nitrite (diazotisation/
  azo coupling)
Derivatives: Direct Brown 44
Uses:
basic dye (cotton); solvent dye (wood stains, varnishes)

Basic Green 1
Pigment Green 1 (CI, PMTA salt); 42040 (CI);
42040:1 (CI, PMTA salt)

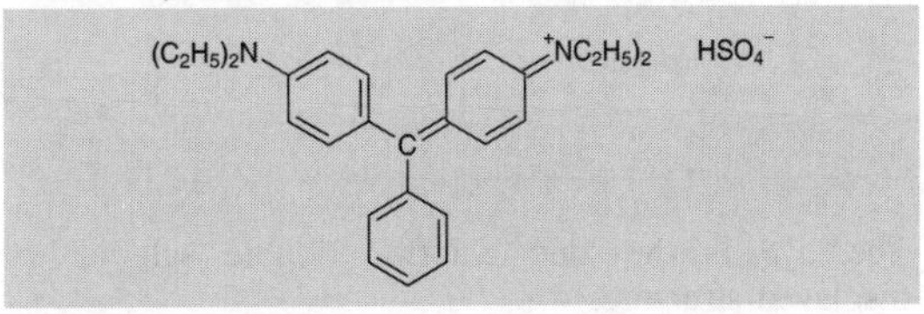

$C_{27}H_{34}N_2O_4S_1$. M: 482.64.
Production:
• *N,N*-diethylaniline + benzaldehyde (carbonyl
  condensation/oxidation)
Uses:
Pigment Green 2 component; dye (wool, silk, poly-
amide, polyvinyl chloride, jute, cotton, leather, poly-
acrylonitrile); pigment (printing inks)

Basic Green 4
Malachite Green; Solvent Green 1 (CI, free base);
Pigment Green 4 (CI, PMTA salt); 42000 (CI, zinc
sulphate salt); 42000:1 (CI, free base); 42000:2 (CI,
PMTA salt); [569-64-2]

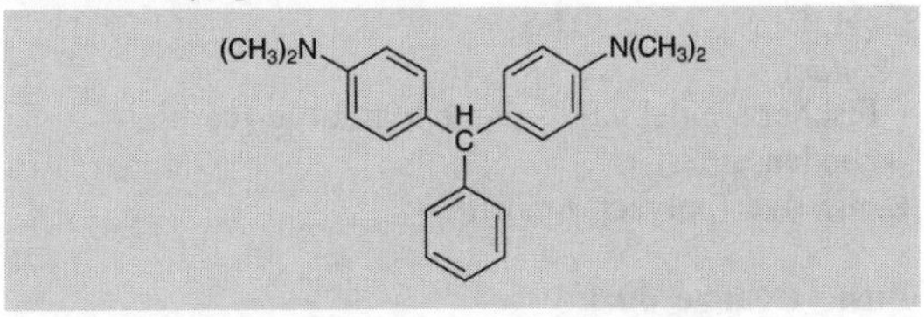

$C_{23}H_{25}N_2$. M: 329.46. The zinc sulphate and PMTA
salts are produced from the oxidised form of this
triarylmethine *leuco* base.
Production:
• benzaldehyde + *N,N*-dimethylaniline (carbonyl
  condensation)
• *N,N*-dimethylaniline + benzotrichloride
  (dehydrochlorination/reduction)
Uses:
basic dye (acrylic fibre); pigment (printing inks); solvent dye (ballpen ink, printer ribbons)

Basic Orange 1
11320 (CI)

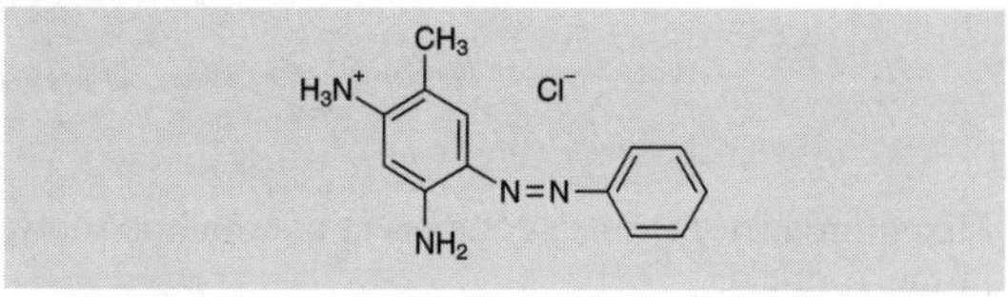

$C_{13}H_{15}Cl_1N_4$. M: 262.74.
Production:
- aniline + 2,4/2,6-diaminotoluene (diazotisation/azo coupling)

Uses: dye (cotton, bast, paper, leather, printing ink)

Basic Orange 14
acridine orange; Solvent Orange 15 (CI, free base); 46005 (CI); 46005:1 (CI, free base)

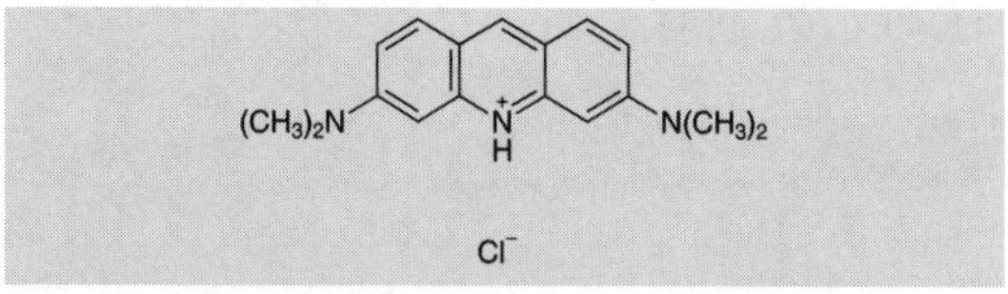

The dye is the zinc chloride double salt of the displayed structure.
Production:
- bis(p-dimethylaminophenyl)methane + zinc chloride (nitration/nitro reduction/cyclisation/oxidation/salt formation)

Uses: basic dye (bast, leather, silk); solvent dye (inks)

Basic Orange 21
48035 (CI)

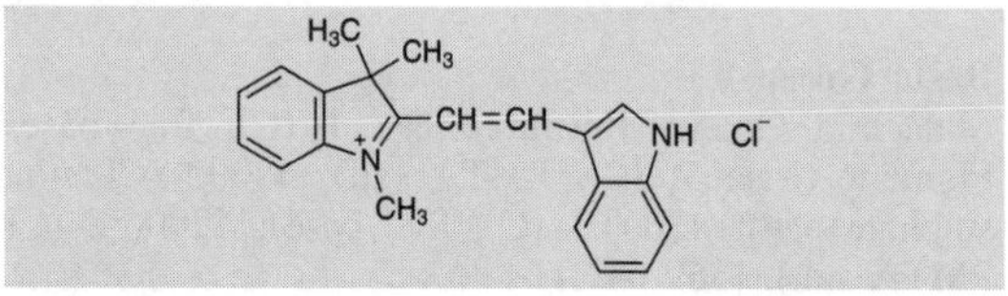

$C_{21}H_{21}Cl_1N_2$. M: 336.86.
Production:
- Fischer's aldehyde + 2-methylindole (carbonyl condensation)

Uses: dye (polyacrylonitrile)

Basic Orange 30:1

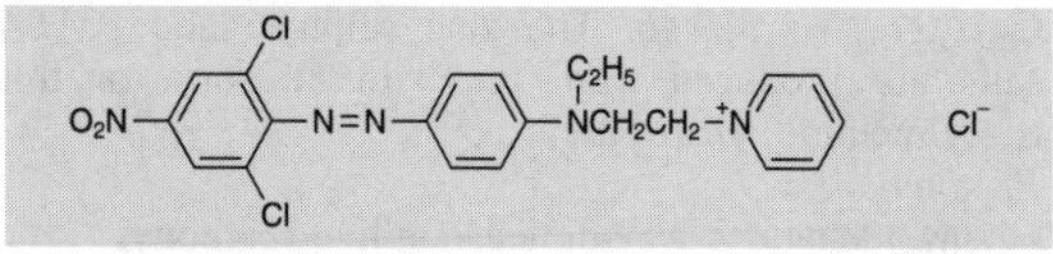

$C_{21}H_{20}Cl_3N_5O_2$. M: 480.79.
Production:
- 2,6-dichloro-4-nitroaniline + N-ethyl-N-(2-hydroxyethyl)aniline + pyridine (diazotisation/azo coupling/quaternisation)

Uses: dye (polyacrylonitrile)

Basic Red 1
Rhodamine 6G; Rhodamine GG (hydrochloride); Fanal Pink (hydrochloride); PMTA Pink (PMTA salt); Copper Ferrocyanide Pink (CFA complex); Pigment Red 81 (CI, PMTA salt); Pigment Red 169 (CI, CFA complex); 45160 (CI, hydrochloride); 45160:1 (CI, PMTA salt); 45160:2 (CI, CFA complex);

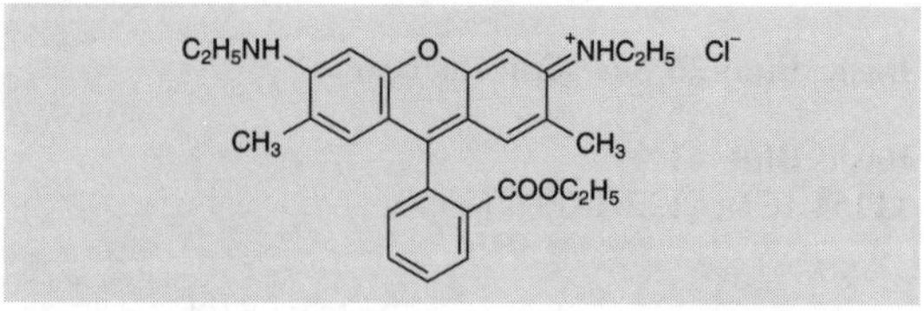

Production:
- o-toluidine + phthalic anhydride + ethanol (carbonyl condensation/ether formation/ethylation/oxidation)

Uses:
pigment (printing inks, lacquers, paper coatings)

Basic Red 2
50240 (CI)

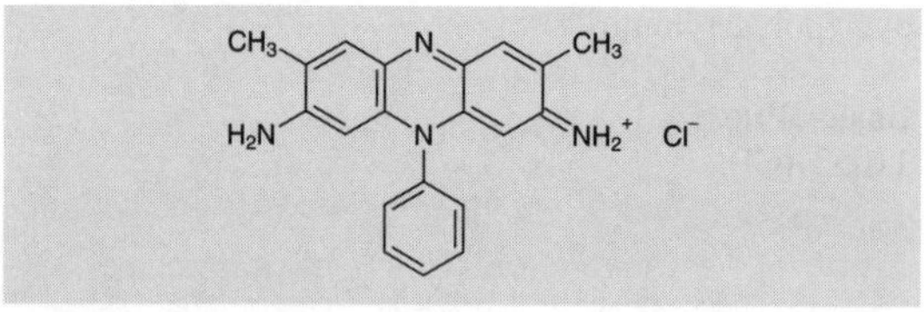

$C_{20}H_{19}Cl_1N_4$. M: 350.85.
Production:
- aniline + o-toluidine (diazotisation/azo coupling/reduction/oxidative coupling/amine formation/amine formation)

Uses: dye (cotton, wool, silk, leather, paper, solvents)

Basic Red 12
Astraphloxine FF; 48070 (CI)

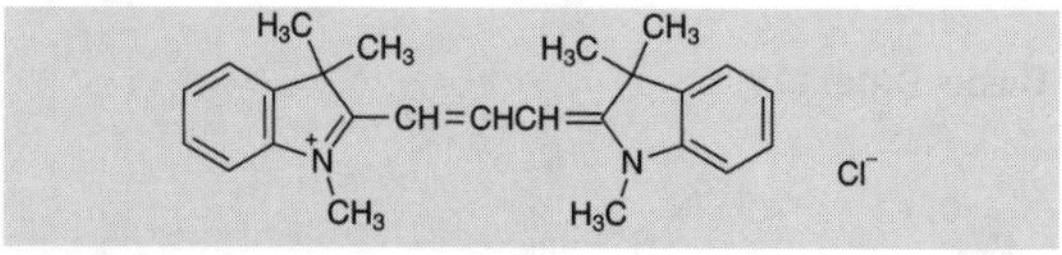

$C_{25}H_{29}Cl_1N_2$. M: 392.96.
Production:
- Fischer's aldehyde + sodium formate (carbonyl condensation/decarboxylation)

Uses: dye (cotton, bast, acetate, nylon, paper, leather)

Basic Red 14

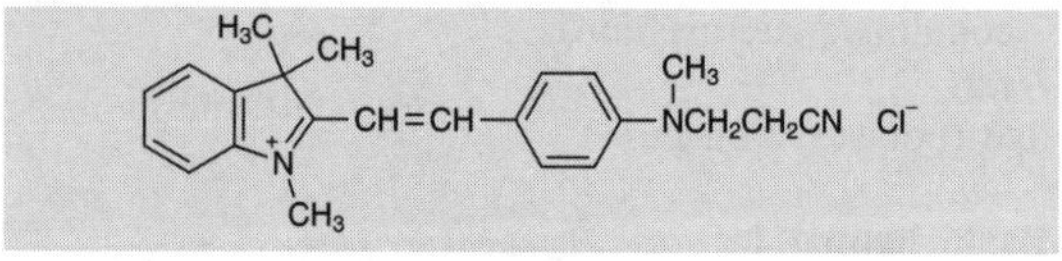

$C_{23}H_{26}Cl_1N_3$. M: 379.93.

Production:
- N-(2-cyanoethyl)-N-methylaniline + formaldehyde + Fischer's base (Vilsmeier reaction/carbonyl condensation)

Uses: dye (polyacrylonitrile)

Basic Red 18
11085 (CI)

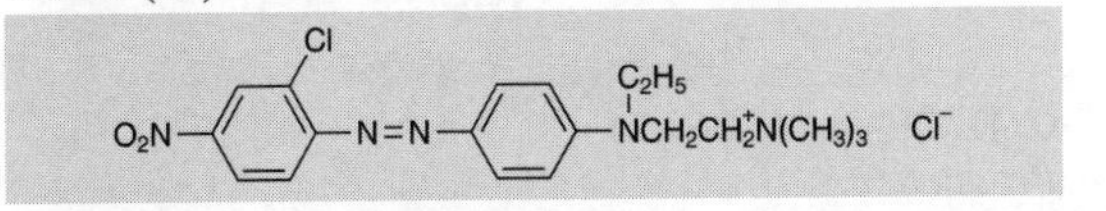

C$_{19}$H$_{25}$Cl$_2$N$_5$O$_2$. M: 426.36.
Production:
- N-ethyl-N-(2-hydroxyethyl)aniline + trimethylamine + 2-chloro-4-nitroaniline (quaternisation/ diazotisation/azo coupling)

Uses: dye (polyacrylonitrile)

Basic Red 18:1

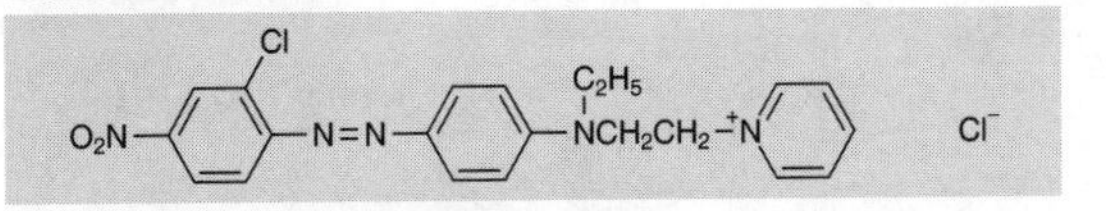

C$_{21}$H$_{21}$Cl$_2$N$_5$O$_2$. M: 446.34.
Production:
- 2-chloro-4-nitroaniline + N-ethyl-N-(2-hydroxy-ethyl)aniline + pyridine (diazotisation/azo coupling/quaternisation)

Uses: dye (polyacrylonitrile)

Basic Red 22
Maxilon Red BL; 11055 (CI); [12221-52-2]

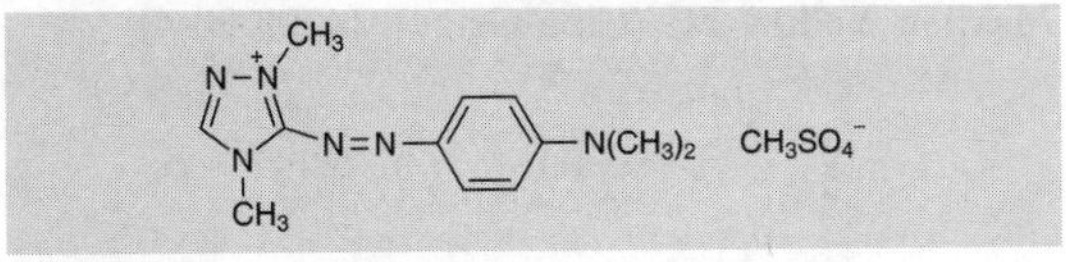

C$_{13}$H$_{20}$N$_6$O$_4$S$_1$. M: 356.40.
Production:
- N,N-dimethylaniline + 3-amino-1,2,4-triazole + dimethyl sulphate (diazotisation/azo coupling/quaternisation)

Uses: dye (polyacrylonitrile)

Basic Red 29
11460 (CI)

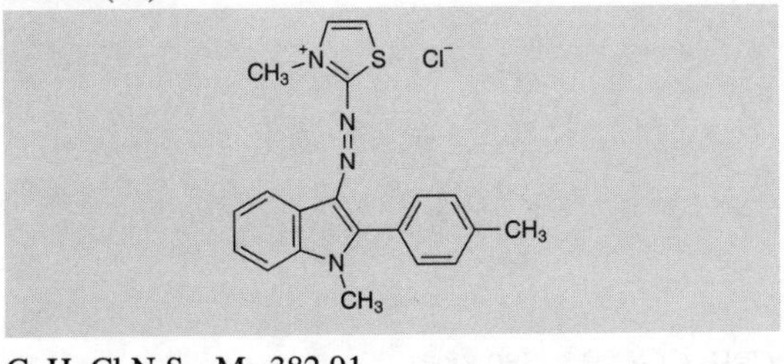

C$_{20}$H$_{19}$Cl$_1$N$_4$S$_1$. M: 382.91.

Production:
- 2-aminothiazole + N-methyl-2-p-tolylindole + methyl chloride (diazotisation/azo coupling/methylation)

Uses: dye (polyacrylonitrile)

basic slag
Thomas slag
Ground blast furnace slag containing 10–20% P$_2$O$_5$ and a range of trace elements.
Production:
- iron ore + metallurgical coke + limestone (blast furnace smelting; byproduct of iron production)

Uses: fertiliser ingredient

Basic Violet 1
methyl violet; Solvent Violet 8 (CI, free base); Pigment Violet 3 (CI, PMTA salt); Pigment Violet 27 (CI, CFA complex); 42535 (CI, chloride salt); 42535:1 (CI, free base); 42535:2 (CI, PMTA salt); 42535:3 (CI, CFA complex); [8004-87-3]

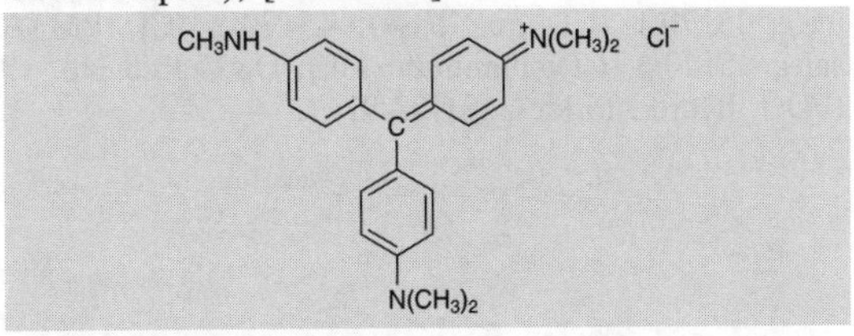

C$_{24}$H$_{28}$Cl$_1$N$_3$. M: 393.95. Mixed product based on a triphenylmethine structure with each molecule containing 4–6 N-methyl groups.
Production:
- N,N-dimethylaniline (oxidative coupling)

Uses: pigment (paints, printing inks); solvent dye (ballpen inks, printer ribbons, lacquers)

Basic Violet 3
Crystal Violet; Gentian Violet; Solvent Violet 9 (CI, free base); Pigment Violet 39 (CI, PMA salt); 42555 (CI, chloride salt); 42555:1 (CI, free base); 42555:2 (CI, PMA salt); [548-62-9]

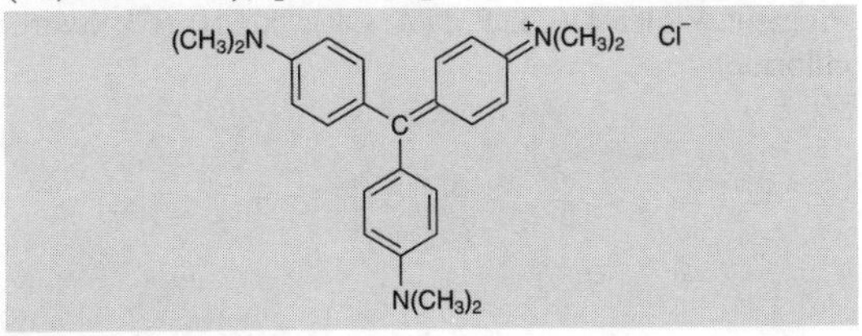

C$_{25}$H$_{30}$Cl$_1$N$_3$. M: 407.98.
Production:
- N,N-dimethylaniline + phosgene (condensation)
Uses:
basic dye (cotton, paper); pigment (printing inks); solvent dye (ballpen inks, printer ribbons, rotogravure inks); topical antiseptic

Basic Violet 4
Pigment Blue 14 (CI, PMTA salt); 42600 (CI);
42600:1 (CI, PMTA salt)

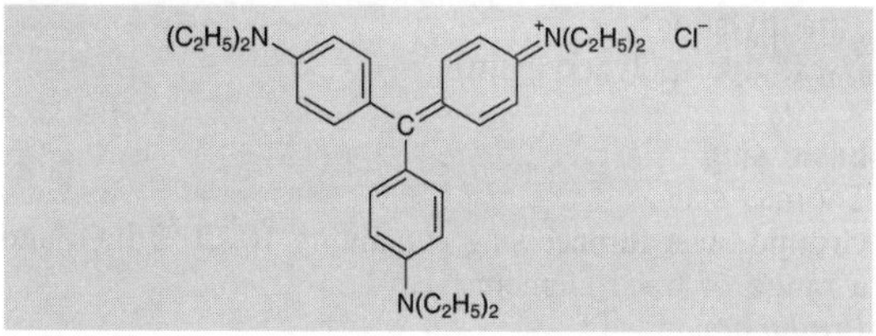

$C_{31}H_{42}Cl_1N_3$. M: 492.15.
Production:
• N,N-diethylaniline + phosgene (condensation)
Uses:
dye (cotton); pigment (paper)

Basic Violet 10
Rhodamine B (hydrochloride); Solvent Red 49 (CI,
free base); Pigment Violet 1 (CI, PMTA salt); Pigment
Red 173 (CI, aluminium salt); 45170 (CI, hydrochloride); 45170:1 (CI, free base); 45170:2 (CI, PMTA
salt); 45170:3 (CI, aluminium salt); D&C Red No. 19
(FDC, hydrochloride); [81-88-9]

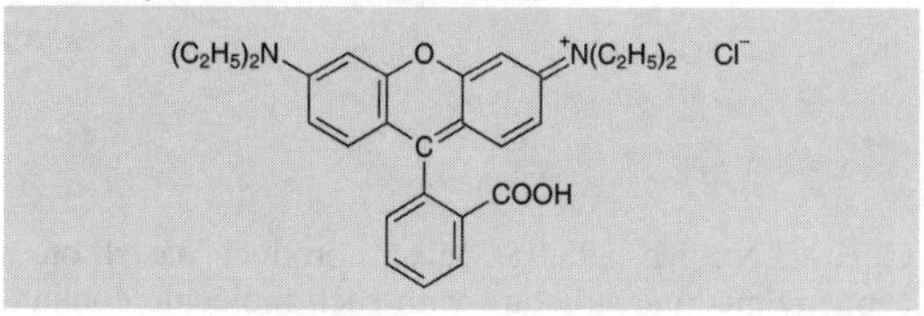

$C_{28}H_{32}N_2O_3$. M: 444.58. The structure shows the oxidised form of this triarylmethine *leuco* base.
Production:
• m-diethylaminophenol + phthalic anhydride
  (condensation)
Uses: basic dye (paper, leather); pigment (paints,
printing inks); solvent dye (ballpen inks, printer ribbon,
solvents)

Basic Violet 14
fuchsine; magenta; Solvent Red 41 (CI, free base);
Pigment Violet 4 (CI, PMTA salt); 42510 (CI, hydrochloride)

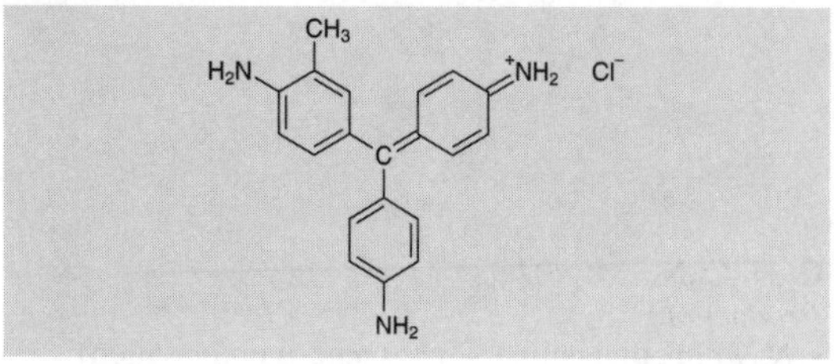

$C_{20}H_{20}Cl_1N_3$. M: 337.85.
Production:
• p-toluidine + o-toluidine + nitrobenzene (condens-
  ation/nitro reduction)

Derivatives: Solvent Blue 3
Uses: dye (polyacrylonitrile)

Basic Violet 16
48013 (CI)

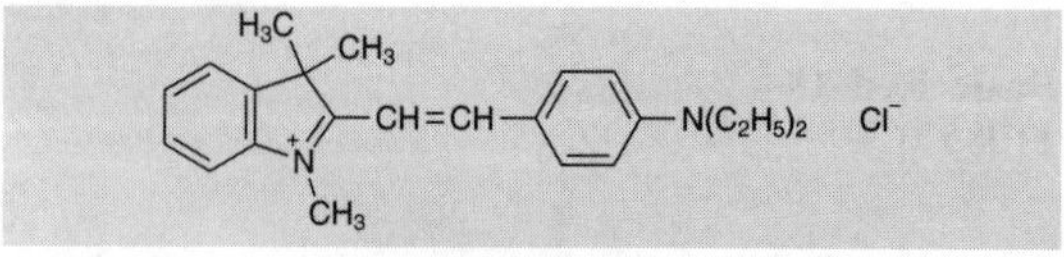

$C_{23}H_{29}Cl_1N_2$. M: 368.94.
Production:
• Fischer's base + p-diethylaminobenzaldehyde
  (carbonyl condensation)
Uses: dye (polyacrylonitrile)

Basic Yellow 2
Auramine O; Solvent Yellow 34 (CI, free base);
Pigment Green 3 (CI, PMTA salt); 41000 (CI, hydrochloride); 41000:1 (CI, free base); 41000:2 (CI, PMTA
salt);

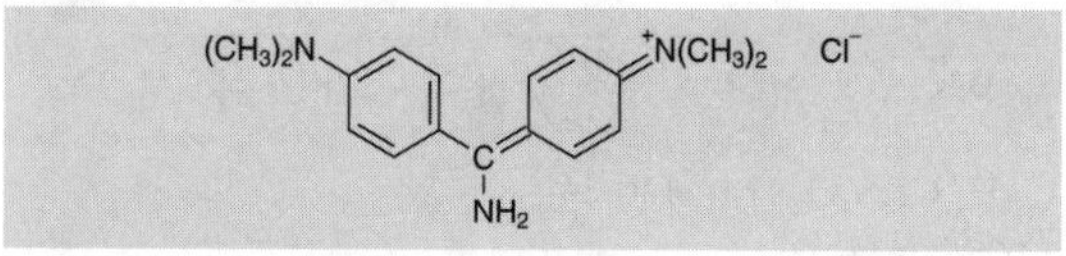

$C_{17}H_{22}Cl_1N_3$. M: 303.84.
Production:
• bis(p-dimethylaminophenyl)methane + ammonium
  chloride (condensation)
Uses: dye (cotton, paper, silk)

Basic Yellow 11
Maxilon Yellow 5G (Ciba-Geigy); [4208-80-4]

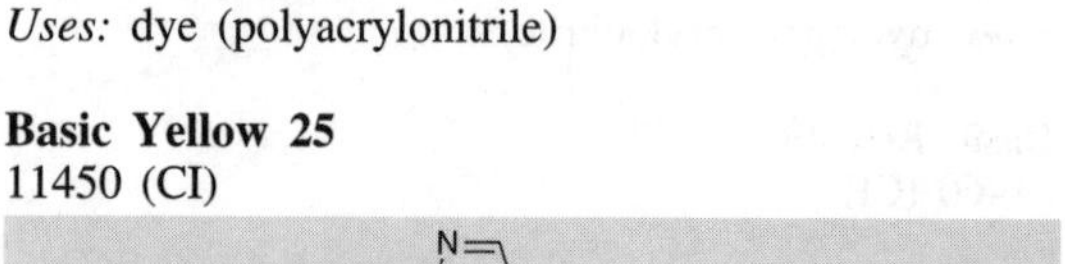

$C_{21}H_{26}N_2O_6S_1$. M: 434.50.
Production:
• Fischer's aldehyde + 2,4-dimethoxyaniline (con-
  densation/salt formation)
Uses: dye (polyacrylonitrile)

Basic Yellow 25
11450 (CI)

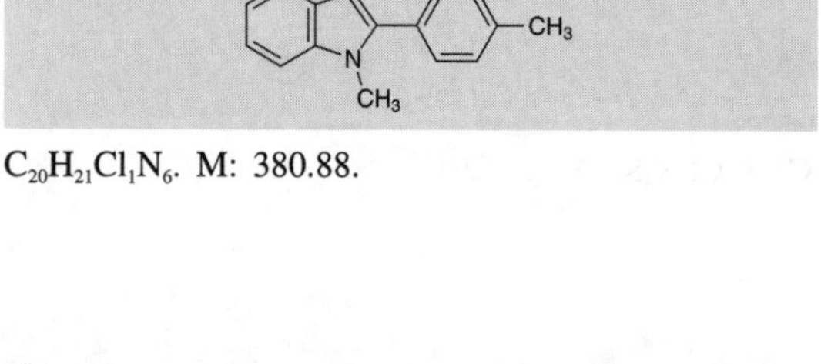

$C_{20}H_{21}Cl_1N_6$. M: 380.88.

Production:
- 3-amino-1,2,4-triazole + *N*-methyl-2-*p*-tolylindole + methyl chloride (diazotisation/azo coupling/quaternisation)

Uses: dye (acrylic, acetate fibres)

Basic Yellow 28
48054 (CI)

$C_{21}H_{27}N_3O_5S_1$. M: 433.52.
Production:
- *p*-anisidine + Fischer's base + dimethyl sulphate (diazotisation/imine formation/methylation)

Uses:
dye (polyacrylonitrile)

Basic Yellow 37
41001 (CI)

$C_{21}H_{30}Cl_1N_3$. M: 359.94.
Production:
- *N,N*-diethylaniline + formaldehyde + ammonium chloride (condensation/reductive coupling)

Uses: dye (paper, printing inks)

bauxite
Natural ore made up of aluminium and iron oxides and hydrates. The Al_2O_3 content is typically 55–60%. The major producing countries are Australia, Jamaica and Surinam.
Derivatives:
alumina, fused; alumina trihydrate; aluminium potassium sulphate; aluminium sulphate; ammonium alum
Uses:
alumina cement raw material

bay oil
myrcia oil; [8006-78-8]
Yellow liquid with a pleasant odour. Produced by steam distillation of the leaves of the bay tree (*Pimenta acris*). d: 0.96 kg/l (20°C). The main constituent of the oil is eugenol (50%). Insoluble in water. Soluble in alcohol.
Uses:
fragrance ingredient/emollient (cosmetics, toiletries)

BBAB *See:* 1,4-bis(bromoacetoxy)-2-butene

BBP *See:* *n*-butyl benzyl phthalate

BCF *See:* bromochlorodifluoromethane

BCP *See:* 1-bromo-3-chloropropane

BDA *See:* benzyldimethylamine

BDMA *See:* benzyldimethylamine; 1,4-butanediol dimethacrylate

BDO *See:* 1,4-butanediol

behenalkonium chloride
See: behenyldimethylbenzylammonium chloride

behenamidopropyl betaine

$C_{29}H_{58}N_2O_3$. M: 482.79.
Production:
- behenamidopropyldimethylamine + sodium chloroacetate (quaternisation)

Uses: foam stabiliser/viscosifier (cosmetics, household cleaners)

behenamidopropyldimethylamine

$C_{27}H_{56}N_2O_1$. M: 424.76. Solid.
Production:
- behenic acid + 3-dimethylaminopropylamine (amide formation)

Derivatives: behenamidopropyl betaine

behenamine oxide *See:* dimethylbehenylamine oxide

behenic acid
docosanoic acid; [112-85-6]

$C_{22}H_{44}O_2$. M: 340.59. White, crystalline solid with faint odour. Titre: 70–74°C. Typical chain-length distributions are: 4% C_{18}, 5% C_{20}, 89% C_{22}, 2% C_{24} for a narrow-cut grade and 5% C_{16}, 12% C_{18}, 8% C_{20}, 74% C_{22}, 1% C_{24} for a broad-cut grade.
Production:
- erucic acid (hydrogenation)

Derivatives:
aminoethyl behenyl imidazoline; behenamidopropyldimethylamine; glycerol tribehenate; pentaerythritol tetrabehenate
Uses: plastics processing lubricant

behentrimonium chloride
See: behenyltrimethylammonium chloride

behenyl alcohol
1-docosanol; [661-19-8]

$$CH_3(CH_2)_{21}OH$$

$C_{22}H_{46}O_1$. M: 326.61. Colourless waxy solid. MP: 71°C. Insoluble in water. Soluble in oxygenated solvents. The chain-length distribution is 70–90% C_{22} with the remainder principally C_{18} and C_{20}. The precise distribution varies with the raw material source.
Production:
• erucic acid (hydrogenation)
Uses: water evaporation reduction agent

behenyldimethylbenzylammonium chloride
behenalkonium chloride (CTFA)

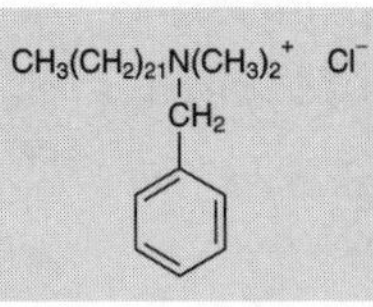

$$CH_3(CH_2)_{21}N(CH_3)_2{}^+ \quad Cl^-$$
$$\overset{|}{CH_2}$$

$C_{31}H_{58}Cl_1N_1$. M: 480.26. Available as a paste containing 25% active matter in propylene glycol.
Production:
• dimethylbehenylamine + benzyl chloride (quaternisation)
Uses: emulsifier/softening agent/emollient (hair rinses, skin creams, lotions)

behenyltrimethylammonium chloride
behentrimonium chloride (CTFA)

$$CH_3(CH_2)_{21}N(CH_3)_3{}^+ \quad Cl^-$$

$C_{25}H_{54}Cl_1N_1$. M: 404.16. Available as a paste containing 25% active matter in propylene glycol. Also available as a blend with cetylstearyl alcohol.
Production:
• dimethylbehenylamine + methyl chloride (quaternisation/quaternisation)
Uses: emulsifier/softening agent/emollient (hair rinses, skin creams, lotions)

benalaxyl
methyl *N*-phenylacetyl-*N*-2,6-xylyl-DL-alaninate; [71626-11-4]

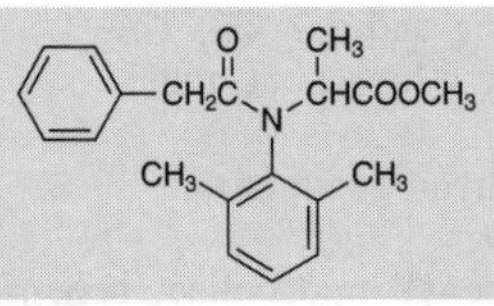

$C_{20}H_{23}N_1O_3$. M: 325.41.
Production:
• phenylacetyl chloride + 2,6-xylidine + methyl α-chloropropionate (amide formation/amide formation)
Uses: fungicide

benazolin
4-chloro-2-oxobenzothiazolin-3-ylacetic acid; [3813-05-6]; [67338-65-2] (potassium salt)

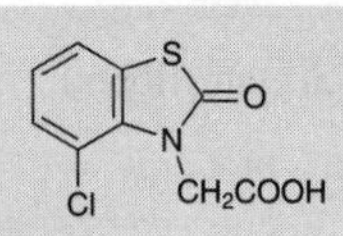

$C_9H_6Cl_1N_1O_3S_1$. M: 243.67.
Production:
• *o*-chloroaniline + potassium thiocyanate + ethyl chloroacetate (thiocyanate addition/condensation/dehydrochlorination)
Derivatives: benazolin-ethyl
Uses: herbicide

benazolin-ethyl
ethyl 4-chloro-2,3-dihydro-2-oxobenzothiazol-3-ylacetate; [25059-80-7]

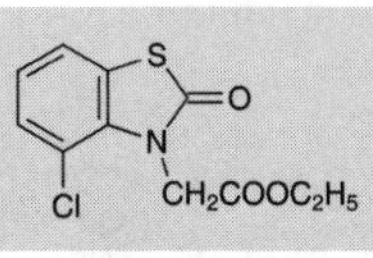

$C_{11}H_{10}Cl_1N_1O_3S_1$. M: 271.72.
Production:
• ethanol + benazolin (esterification)
Uses: herbicide

bendiocarb
2,2-dimethyl-1,3-benzodioxol-4-yl methylcarbamate; [22781-23-3]

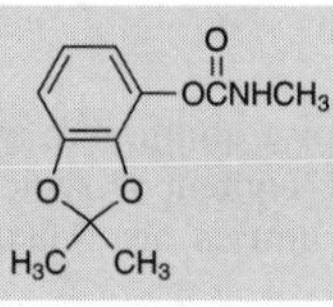

$C_{11}H_{13}N_1O_4$. M: 223.23.
Production:
• pyrogallol + acetone + methyl isocyanate (acetal formation/isocyanate addition)
Uses: insecticide

bendioxide *See:* bentazone

benfluralin
N-butyl-*N*-ethyl-2,6-dinitro-4-trifluoromethylaniline; Balan (Eli Lilly); [1861-40-1]

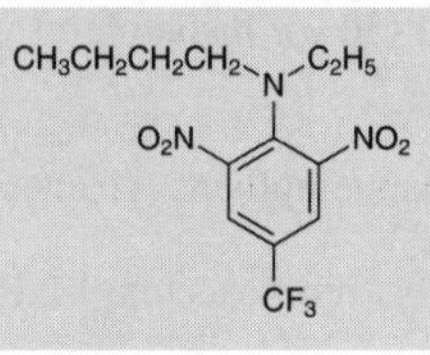

$C_{13}H_{16}F_3N_3O_4$. M: 335.28.

Production:
- 4-chloro-3,5-dinitrobenzotrifluoride + *n*-butylethyl-amine (dehydrochlorination)

Uses: herbicide

benfuracarb
[82560-54-1]

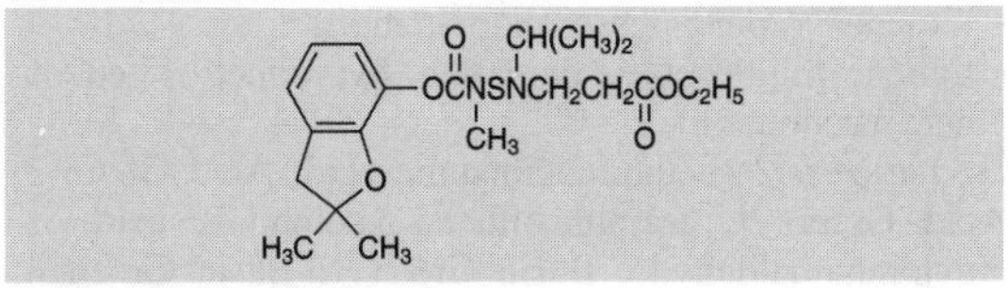

$C_{20}H_{30}N_2O_5S_1$. M: 410.52.
Production:
- isopropylamine + ethyl acrylate + carbofuran + sulphur dichloride (carboxyethylation/dehydro-chlorination/dehydrochlorination)

Uses: insecticide

benomyl
methyl 1-(butylcarbamoyl)benzimidazol-2-ylcarbamate; Benlate (Du Pont); [17804-35-2]

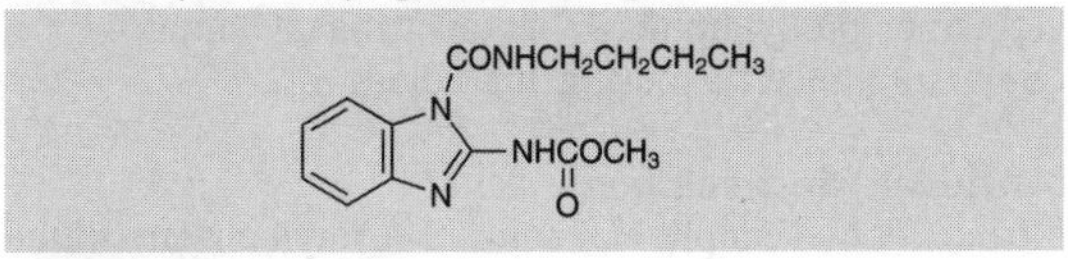

$C_{14}H_{18}N_4O_3$. M: 290.32.
Production:
- carbendazim + *n*-butyl isocyanate (isocyanate addition)

Uses: fungicide

benoxaprofen
[67434-14-4]

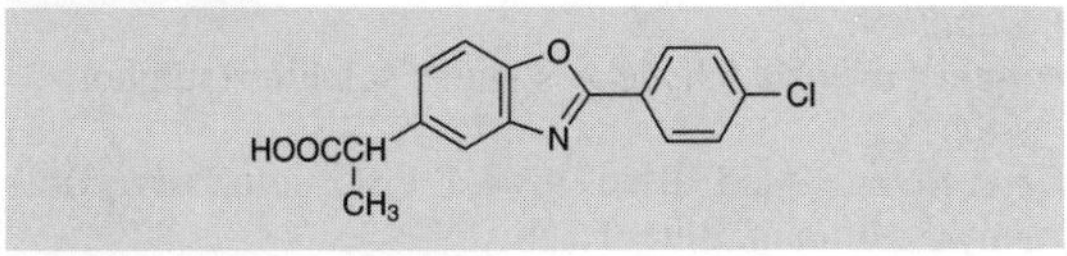

$C_{16}H_{12}Cl_1N_1O_3$. M: 301.74.
Production:
- *p*-hydroxyphenylacetonitrile + methyl iodide + *p*-chlorobenzoyl chloride (dehydroiodination/nitration/nitro reduction/condensation/nitrile hydrolysis)

Uses: antiinflammatory/analgesic drug

benoxinate *See:* oxybuprocaine

benperidol
[2062-84-2]
$C_{22}H_{24}F_1N_3O_2$. M: 381.45.
Production:
- 1-(4-piperidyl)-2-benzodiazolinone + 4-chloro-4′-fluorobutyrophenone (amine formation)

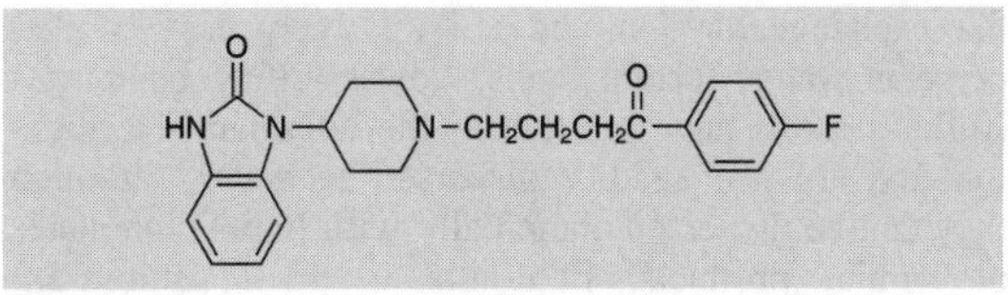

Uses:
analgesic/neuroleptic drug

bensulide
O,O-diisopropyl *S*-2-phenylsulphonylaminoethyl phos-phorodithioate; [741-58-2]

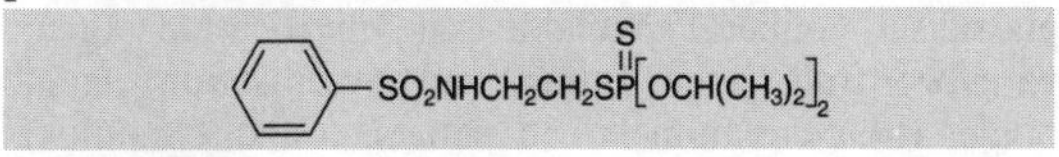

$C_{14}H_{24}N_1O_4P_1S_3$. M: 397.51.
Production:
- benzenesulphonyl chloride + monoethanolamine + *O,O*-diisopropyl phosphorodithioic acid (sulphon-amide formation/dehydrochlorination)

Uses: herbicide

bensultap
S,S′-2-dimethylaminotrimethylene di(benzenethiosulph-onate); [17606-31-4]

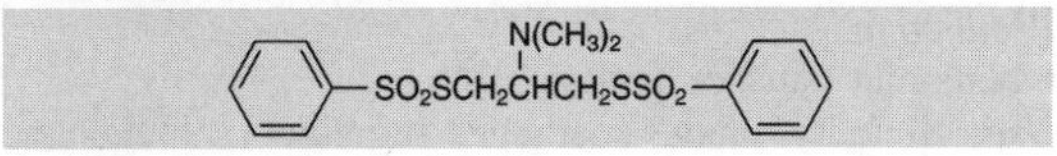

$C_{17}H_{21}N_1O_4S_4$. M: 431.63.
Production:
- 1,3-dimercaptoisopropyldimethylamine + benzene-sulphonyl chloride (dehydrochlorination)

Uses: insecticide

bentazone
bendioxide; 3-isopropyl-1H-2,1,3-benzothiadiazin-4-one 2,2-dioxide; [25057-89-0]

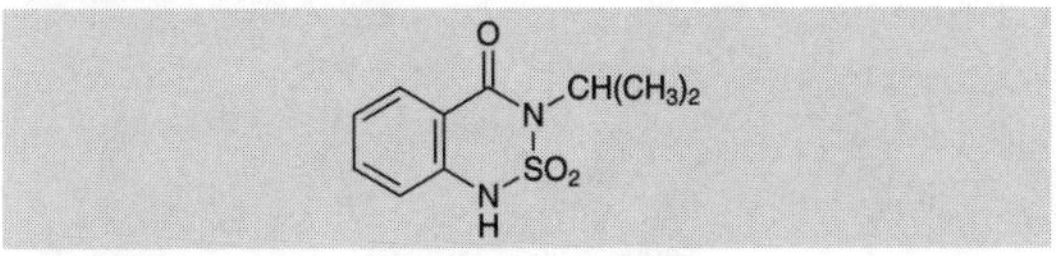

$C_{10}H_{12}N_2O_3S_1$. M: 240.28.
Production:
- methyl anthranilate + isopropylamine + chloro-sulphonic acid (amide formation/chlorosulphonation)

Uses: herbicide

bentonite
[1302-78-9]
Natural montmorillonite clay made up of alumino-silicate layers in which silicon or aluminium atoms are surrounded tetrahedrally and octahedrally by oxygen atoms. Binding between the layers with tetrahedrally-arranged atoms is relatively weak allowing interlayer cations to be exchanged with the surrounding medium. High-swelling ('Wyoming') bentonites have sodium as

the exchangeable ion and are relatively easy to disperse in water, forming gels. Low-swelling bentonites (fuller's earth) have calcium as the dominant interlayer ion and are less readily dispersed in water, although they can be dispersed chemically with lignosulphonates or similar products. Bentonite is often sodium-exchanged or acid-activated prior to use in order to obtain the right swelling characteristics. It is mined in many different countries around the world. The USA, Greece and Germany are the largest producers.

Derivatives: bentonite, organophilic

Uses: cat litter; petroleum refining catalyst; ceramics plasticiser; mineral/vegetable oil clarification agent; wine/beer/fruit juice fining and stabilisation agent; binder (iron ore/animal feed pellets, foundry moulds); creams/cosmetics ingredient; insecticide filler/carrier; thichening agent (water-thinned paints); abrasive/thickening agent (soap, cleaners); soil conditioner; suspension agent (diaphragm wall, tunnel construction); viscosifier (drilling muds)

bentonite, organophilic
Bentone (NL Corporation)
Bentonite treated with fatty amines to render the surface oil-wettable.
Production:
• bentonite (surface treatment)
Uses: foundry sands; cosmetics ingredient; thickening agent (lubricant greases, paints, oil-based drilling muds)

1,2-benzacenaphthene *See:* fluoranthene

benzalacetone *See:* benzylideneacetone

benzal chloride
benzyl dichloride; benzylidene chloride; α,α-dichlorotoluene; [98-87-3]

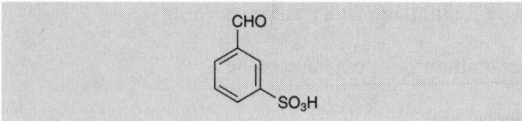

$C_7H_6Cl_2$. M: 161.04. Colourless liquid with a pungent odour. BP: 205°C. MP: -16°C. d: 1.25 kg/l (15°C). Insoluble in water. Miscible with most organic solvents.
Production:
• toluene (side-chain chlorination; coproduced with benzyl chloride/benzotrichloride)
Derivatives: benzaldehyde

benzaldehyde
[100-52-7]
$C_7H_6O_1$. M: 106.13. Colourless liquid with an almond-like odour. BP: 178–179°C. MP: -26°C. d: 1.04 kg/l (15°C). Slightly soluble in water. Miscible with most organic solvents.

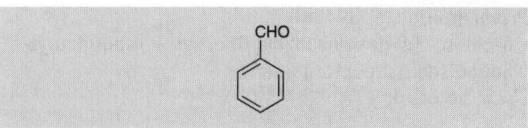

Production:
• benzal chloride (hydrolysis)
• toluene (vapour-phase air oxidation)
• toluene (liquid-phase oxidation; byproduct of benzoic acid production)
Derivatives: 2-acetamidocinnamic acid; Acid Green 3; Acid Green 5; 4-aminostilbene-2-sulphonic acid; α-amylcinnamaldehyde; Basic Green 1; Basic Green 4; benzaldehyde-3-sulphonic acid; benzathine; benzoin; benzoyl cyanide; benzyl alcohol; benzylamine; benzyl benzoate; benzylideneacetone; *N*-benzylmethylamine; bromadiolone; cinnamaldehyde; cinnamic acid; *N,N'*-dibenzaloxalyldihydrazide; dibenzoylmethane; dibenzylamine; L-ephedrine; ethyl 3-phenylglycidate; fendiline; α-hexylcinnamaldehyde; DL-mandelic acid; α-methylcinnamaldehyde; methyl cinnamate; 5-methyl-3-phenylisoxazole-4-carboxylic acid; norephedrine; oxetacaine; 3-phenoxybenzaldehyde; DL-phenylalanine; D-α-phenylglycine; prenylamine; tebutam; tribenzylamine
Uses: fragrance/flavouring ingredient

benzaldehyde-2-sulphonic acid
o-benzaldehydesulphonic acid; 2-formylbenzenesulphonic acid

$C_7H_6O_4S_1$. M: 186.19. Crystalline solid. Soluble in water.
Production:
• *o*-chlorobenzaldehyde + sodium sulphite (sulphonation)
Derivatives: Acid Blue 9; 4,4'-bis(2-sulphostyryl)biphenyl; Mordant Blue 3
Uses:
nickelplating brightening agent; dyestuffs intermediate

benzaldehyde-3-sulphonic acid
m-benzaldehydesulphonic acid; 3-formylbenzenesulphonic acid

$C_7H_6O_4S_1$. M: 186.19.
Production:
• benzaldehyde (sulphonation)
Derivatives: *N*-ethyl-*N*-phenylbenzylamine-3-sulphonic acid; *N*-ethyl-*N*-*m*-tolylbenzylamine-3-sulphonic acid

benzalkonium chloride
See: dimethylcocobenzylammonium chloride

1-benzamido-4-chloroanthraquinone

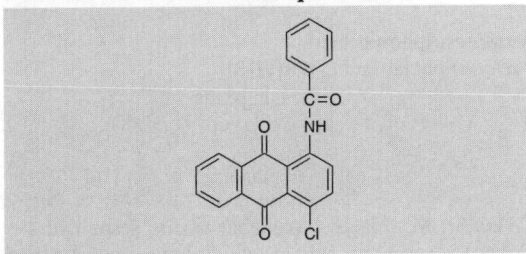

$C_{21}H_{12}Cl_1N_1O_3$. M: 361.79.
Production:
• 1-aminoanthraquinone + benzoyl chloride (amide formation/ring chlorination)
Derivatives:
Vat Black 27; Vat Brown 3

1-benzamido-4-hydroxyanthraquinone
[6409-74-1]

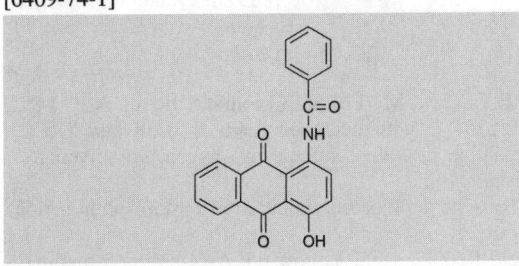

$C_{21}H_{13}N_1O_4$. M: 343.34.
Production:
• 1-aminoanthraquinone + benzoyl chloride (amide formation/sulphonation/alkali fusion)
Derivatives:
1-amino-4-hydroxyanthraquinone

benzanthrone
[82-05-3]

$C_{17}H_{10}O_1$. M: 230.27. Yellow needles. MP: 165–172°C. Insoluble in water. Available commercially in grades of 80–99% purity.
Production:
• anthraquinone + glycerol (carbonyl condensation/acid-catalysed coupling)
Derivatives:
3-bromobenzanthrone; dibenzanthrone; 3,9-dibromobenzanthrone; 16,17-dihydroxydibenzanthrone

benzathine
DBED; *N,N'*-dibenzylethylenediamine; [140-28-3]

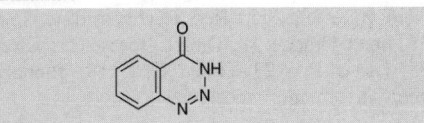

$C_{16}H_{20}N_2$. M: 240.35.
Production:
• benzaldehyde + ethylenediamine (reductive amination)
Uses: penicillin adjunct

benzazimide
4-ketobenztriazine

$C_7H_5N_3O_1$. M: 147.14.
Production:
• anthranilic acid + ammonia + sodium nitrite (amide formation/diazotisation)
Derivatives: azinphos-ethyl; azinphos-methyl

benzene
[71-43-2]

C_6H_6. M: 78.12. Colourless liquid with a characteristic, aromatic odour. BP: 80°C. MP: 5°C. d: 0.88 kg/l (15°C). Very slightly soluble in water. Miscible with most organic solvents. Flash point: -10°C.
Production:
• aromatics, mixed (separation; coproduced with xylene, mixed/toluene/C_{9+} aromatics)
• toluene (hydrodealkylation)
• toluene (disproportionation; coproduced with xylene, mixed)
Derivatives:
alkylbenzene, long-chain; amylanthraquinone; benzene-1,3-disulphohydrazide; benzenesulphonic acid; benzenesulphonyl chloride; benzophenone; *o*-benzoylbenzoic acid; biphenyl; bromobenzene; *t*-butylbenzene; chlorobenzene; *p*-chlorobenzophenone; clotrimazole; cumene; cyclohexane; *o*-dichlorobenzene; *p*-dichlorobenzene; 2,2-diethoxyacetophenone; *m*-diisopropylbenzene; *p*-diisopropylbenzene; α,α-dimethyl-α-hydroxyacetophenone; diphenylantimony 2-ethylhexanoate; di-(phenylmercury) dodecenylsuccinate; diphenylmethane; dodecylbenzene, branched; dodecylbenzene, linear; ethylbenzene; fenbutatin oxide; hexachlorobenzene; 1-hydroxycyclohexyl phenyl ketone; lindane; maleic anhydride; 2-methylbenzophenone; 3-methylbenzophenone; nitrobenzene; phenethyl alcohol; phenylmercuric propionate; phenylmercury acetate; phenyltoloxamine; phosphenyl chloride; propiophenone; proquazone; resorcinol;

terphenyl; α-trichloromethylphenyl carbinyl acetate; 1,3,5-trinitrobenzene; trityl chloride

benzenediazonium chloride
[100-34-5]

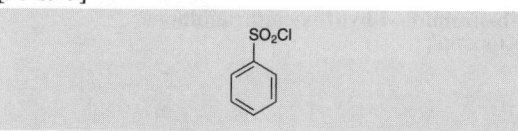

$C_6H_5Cl_1N_2$. M: 140.57. Needles. Slightly soluble in water. Soluble in oxygenated solvents. Highly toxic. Potentially explosive. Manufactured *in situ*. Not a commercially traded product.
Derivatives:
Acid Blue 20; Acid Red 1; chrysoidine; Direct Black 3; Direct Orange 18; Direct Orange 26; Direct Orange 75; Direct Red 23; Direct Red 118; phenazopyridine; phenylhydrazine; riboflavin

benzene-1,3-dicarboxylic acid *See:* isophthalic acid

benzene-1,4-dicarboxylic acid *See:* terephthalic acid

benzene-1,3-disulphohydrazide
1,3-benzenedisulphohydrazide

$C_6H_{10}N_4O_4S_2$. M: 266.31. Solid. Decomposes at 115°C. Sold as a 50% paste in chloroparaffin.
Production:
• benzene + sulphuryl chloride + hydrazine (chlorosulphonation/sulphonamide formation)
Uses: blowing agent (foamed rubber)

benzenesulphinic acid
[618-41-7]

$C_6H_6O_2S_1$. M: 142.18. Solid. MP: 85°C. Decomposes on heating above 100°C. Soluble in hot water and oxygenated solvents.
Production:
• benzenesulphonyl chloride (sulphonate reduction)
Uses:
nickelplating brightening agent

benzenesulphohydrazide
[80-17-1]

$C_6H_8N_2O_2S_1$. M: 172.20.

Production:
• benzenesulphonyl chloride + hydrazine (dehydrochlorination)
Uses: blowing agent (foamed rubber)

benzenesulphonic acid
phenylsulphonic acid; [98-11-3]

$C_6H_6O_3S_1$. M: 158.18. Available as the sesquihydrate. Colourless needles. MP: 43°C. Soluble in water and alcohol. Slightly soluble in benzene.
Production:
• benzene (sulphonation)
Uses: nickelplating brightening agent

benzenesulphonyl chloride
[98-09-9]

$C_6H_5Cl_1O_2S_1$. M: 176.62. Colourless liquid. MP: 14°C. BP: 251°C with decomposition. d: 1.38 kg/l (15°C). Insoluble in water. Soluble in oxygenated solvents.
Production:
• benzene + chlorosulphonic acid (chlorosulphonation)
Derivatives:
Acid Red 42; Acid Yellow 65; N-(4-amino-5-methoxy-2-methylphenyl)benzamide; bensulide; bensultap; benzenesulphinic acid; benzenesulphohydrazide; N-n-butylbenzenesulphonamide; chloramine-B; Direct Blue 67; perfluidone; thiophenol
Uses: ether formation reagent

benzene-1,3,5-tricarboxylic acid *See:* trimesic acid

benzhydrol
diphenylcarbinol; [91-01-0]

$C_{13}H_{12}O_1$. M: 184.24. Colourless needles. MP: 66–68°C. BP: 297–298°C. Slightly soluble in cold water. Soluble in oxygenated and chlorinated solvents.
Production:
• benzophenone (carbonyl reduction)
Derivatives:
cinnarizine; diphenhydramine; diphenylpyraline

benzhydryl cyanide *See:* diphenylacetonitrile

benzidine-3,3′-dicarboxylic acid
[2130-56-5]

$C_{14}H_{12}N_2O_4$. M: 272.26.
Production:
• *o*-nitrobenzoic acid (benzidine rearrangement)
Derivatives: Direct Blue 93

benzidine-2,2′-disulphonic acid
4,4′-diaminobiphenyl-2,2′-disulphonic acid; [117-61-3]

$C_{12}H_{10}O_6S_2$. M: 314.33. Flakes. MP: 175°C with decomposition. Slightly soluble in water.
Production:
• *m*-nitrobenzenesulphonic acid (benzidine rearrangement)
Derivatives: Acid Red 97; Acid Yellow 42; Acid Yellow 87; Mordant Yellow 26

benzil
dibenzoyl; [134-81-6]

$C_{14}H_{10}O_2$. M: 210.23. Yellow, crystalline solid. MP: 94–96°C. BP: 346–348°C with decomposition. d: 1.23 kg/l (15°C). Insoluble in water. Soluble in most organic solvents.
Production:
• benzoin (alcohol oxidation)
Derivatives: benzilic acid; phenytoin
Uses: photoinitiator (radiation-cured lacquers, inks)

benzil diethyl acetal
benzil diethyl ketal; 2,2-diethoxy-2-phenylacetophenone

$C_{18}H_{20}O_3$. M: 284.36.
Production:
• benzoin + sodium ethoxide (acetal formation/oxidation)
Uses: photoinitiator (radiation-cured lacquers, inks)

benzil dimethyl acetal
benzil dimethyl ketal; 2,2-dimethoxy-2-phenylacetophenone; Irgacure 651 (Ciba-Geigy)

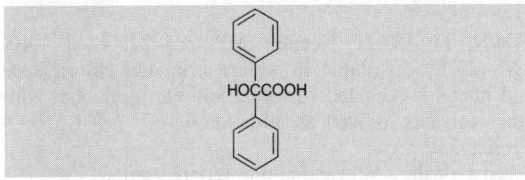

$C_{16}H_{16}O_3$. M: 256.31.
Production:
• benzoin + sodium methoxide (acetal formation/oxidation)
Uses: photoinitiator (radiation-cured lacquers, inks)

benzilic acid
diphenylglycollic acid; 2-hydroxy-2,2-diphenylacetic acid

$C_{14}H_{12}O_3$. M: 228.25. Off-white needles. MP: 151°C. Changes to deep red colour at higher temperature. Soluble in alcohol and hot water.
Production:
• benzil (base-catalysed rearrangement)
Derivatives: clidinium bromide; diphenylacetic acid

benzimidazole-2-thiol *See:* 2-mercaptobenzimidazole

benzine *See:* naphtha, heavy

benzite *See:* 1,3,5-trinitrobenzene

benzocaine *See:* ethyl *p*-aminobenzoate

benzoctamine
[17243-39-9]

$C_{18}H_{19}N_1$. M: 249.36.
Production:
• anthracene + ethylene + methylamine (Vilsmeier reaction/cycloaddition/reductive amination)
Uses: tranquilliser/anxiolytic drug

***p*-benzodiazine** *See:* quinoxaline

benzodihydropyrone *See:* dihydrocoumarin

1,2-benzodioxole
1,2-methylenedioxybenzene
$C_7H_6O_2$. M: 122.13.

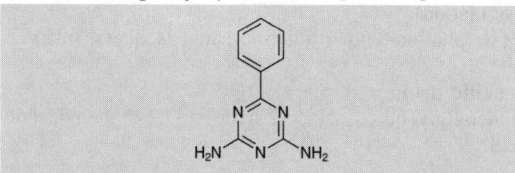

Production:
• catechol + methylene bromide (ether formation)
Derivatives: 3,4-methylenedioxyaniline; piperonal

benzoguanamine
2,4-diamino-6-phenyl-*sym*-triazine; [91-76-9]

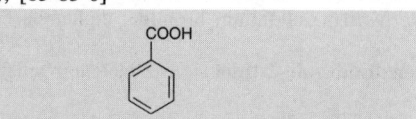

C₉H₉N₅. M: 187.20. Needles. MP: 225–228°C. d: 1.40 kg/l (25°C). Insoluble in water, aromatic, chlorinated and many oxygenated solvents. Soluble in alcohol and ether solvents as well as dilute acid.
Production:
• benzonitrile + dicyandiamide (condensation)
Uses:
amino resin comonomer (moulding compounds)

benzoic acid
E210 (EC); [65-85-0]

C₇H₆O₂. M: 122.13. White crystals. MP: 122–123°C. Sublimes. BP: 249°C. Slightly soluble in water. Soluble in oxygenated, chlorinated and aromatic solvents. Available commercially as technical or food grades.
Production:
• toluene (liquid-phase oxidation)
• *p*-xylene (side-chain oxidation/hydrogenation; byproduct of terephthalic acid production)
Derivatives:
aciclovir; Acid Blue 93; barium-zinc heat stabilisers; benzoyl chloride; benzyl benzoate; *n*-butyl benzoate; cadmium-barium heat stabilisers; cadmium-zinc heat stabilisers; calcium benzoate; caprolactam; Crystal Violet Lactone; cyclohexanecarboxylic acid; denatonium benzoate; 3,5-dichlorobenzoyl chloride; diethylene glycol dibenzoate; 3,5-dihydroxybenzoic acid; 3,5-dinitrobenzoic acid; dipropylene glycol dibenzoate; ethyl benzoate; *n*-hexyl benzoate; phenol; Pigment Blue 18; Pigment Blue 56; Pigment Blue 61; piperocaine; potassium benzoate; pyridate; sodium benzoate; Solvent Blue 3; 2,2,4-trimethyl-1,3-pentanediol isobutyrate benzoate
Uses:
alkyd resin modifier; preservative (soft drinks, mouth-

wash, toothpaste); polyvinyl chloride heat costabilisers; vulcanisation retarder

benzoin
2-hydroxy-2-phenylacetophenone; [119-53-9]

C₁₄H₁₂O₂. M: 212.25. Crystalline solid. MP: 134–136°C. BP: 343–344°C. Insoluble in water. Soluble in hot alcohol and acetone.
Production:
• benzaldehyde (condensation)
Derivatives: benzil; benzil diethyl acetal; benzil dimethyl acetal; benzoin *n*-butyl ether; benzoin ethyl ether; benzoin isopropyl ether
Uses: photoinitiator (radiation-cured lacquers, inks)

benzoin *n*-butyl ether
n-butyl benzoin ether; 2-*n*-butyl-2-phenylacetophenone

C₁₈H₂₀O₂. M: 268.36.
Production:
• benzoin + *n*-butyl chloride (ether formation)
Uses: photoinitiator (radiation-cured lacquers, inks)

benzoin ethyl ether
2-ethoxy-2-phenylacetophenone; ethyl benzoin ether

C₁₆H₁₆O₂. M: 240.31.
Production:
• benzoin + diethyl sulphate (ethylation)
Uses: photoinitiator (radiation-cured lacquers, inks)

benzoin isopropyl ether
2-isopropoxy-2-phenylacetophenone; isopropyl benzoin ether

C₁₇H₁₈O₂. M: 254.33.
Production:
• benzoin + propylene (ether formation)
Uses: photoinitiator (radiation-cured lacquers, inks)

benzoisothiazolin-3-one
1,2-benzoisothiazolin-3-one; BIT; Proxel CRL (ICI);
[2634-33-5]

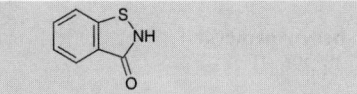

$C_7H_5N_1O_1S_1$. M: 151.19.
Production:
• 2,2'-dithiodibenzoic acid + ammonia (amide form-
ation/oxidation)
Uses: biocide

benzole
Crude, mixed aromatic stream from coal carbonisation
comprising, typically: 67% benzene, 16% toluene, 6%
xylenes and ethylbenzene, and 7% C_{9+} aromatics. Dienes and sulphur have to be removed before being processed further.
Production:
• coal (high-temperature carbonisation; byproduct of
metallurgical coke production)
• coal (low-temperature carbonisation; byproduct of
semicoke production)
• light oil (acid extraction/alkali extraction)
Derivatives: aromatics, mixed

benzonitrile
phenyl cyanide; [100-47-0]

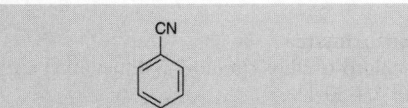

$C_7H_5N_1$. M: 103.13. Colourless liquid with an almond-
like odour. BP: 191°C. FP: -13°C. d: 1.34 kg/l (20°C).
Insoluble in water. Miscible with most organic
solvents.
Production:
• toluene + ammonia (ammoxidation)
Derivatives:
benzoguanamine; benzylamine; 5-phenyltetrazole

benzophenone
diphenyl ketone; [119-61-9]

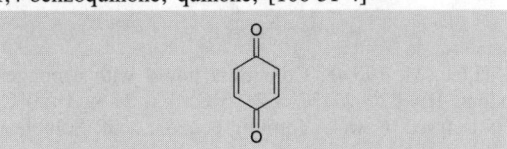

$C_{13}H_{10}O_1$. M: 182.22. Crystalline solid with a floral
odour. MP: 48–49°C. BP: 305°C. Insoluble in water.
Soluble in oxygenated and chlorinated solvents.
Production:
• benzene + benzoyl chloride (Friedel-Crafts acylation)
Derivatives: benzhydrol; diphenylacetonitrile; ethyl
2-cyano-3-phenylcinnamate; perhexiline; phenytoin
Uses: fragrance ingredient/fixative; photoinitiator (radiation-cured lacquers, inks)

benzophenone-1 *See:* 2,4-dihydroxybenzophenone

benzophenone-3
See: 2-hydroxy-4-methoxybenzophenone

benzophenone-4 *See:* 2-hydroxy-4-methoxybenzophen-
one-5-sulphonic acid

benzophenone-12
See: 2-hydroxy-4-octoxybenzophenone

benzophenone-2-carboxylic acid
See: o-benzoylbenzoic acid

benzophenonetetracarboxylate dianhydride
3,3',4,4'-benzophenonetetracarboxylate dianhydride;
BTDA; [2421-28-5]

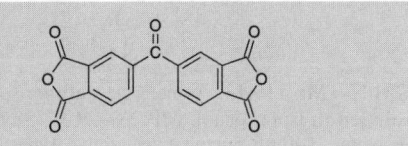

$C_{17}H_6O_7$. M: 322.23.
Production:
• acetaldehyde + o-xylene (carbonyl condensation/
side-chain oxidation)
Derivatives:
polyimide resins, prepolymers; poly(imide-sulphone)

1,2-benzopyrone *See:* coumarin

p-benzoquinone
1,4-benzoquinone; quinone; [106-51-4]

$C_6H_4O_2$. M: 108.10. Solid. MP: 113–115°C. Insoluble
in water and aliphatic hydrocarbons. Soluble in oxygenated solvents.
Production:
• aniline + sodium dichromate + sulphuric acid
(chromate oxidation)
Derivatives: ambazone; ethofumesate; hydroquinone
Uses: oxidation/dehydrogenation reagent

1,4-benzoquinone dioxime *See:* p-quinonedioxime

1,4-benzoquinone monooxime *See:* p-nitrosophenol

benzotetronic acid *See:* 4-hydroxycoumarin

benzothiazolyl disulphide
See: 2,2'-dibenzothiazyl disulphide

benzothienocycloheptanone
4-oxo-9,10-dihydro-(benzo[4,5]cyclohepta)thiophene

$C_{13}H_{10}O_1S_1$. M: 214.28.
Production:
- 2-thienylacetic acid + phthalic anhydride (carbonyl condensation/decarboxylation/reduction/dehydration)

Derivatives:
ketotifen; pizotifen

benzotriazole
1,2,3-benzotriazole; Cobratec (PMC); [95-14-7]

$C_6H_5N_3$. M: 119.13. White, crystalline solid or 50% solution in isopropanol. MP: 98–99°C. Slightly soluble in water. Soluble in most organic solvents.
Production:
- *o*-phenylenediamine + sodium nitrite (diazotisation)

Uses:
photographic antifogging agent; copper corrosion inhibitor

benzotrichloride
α,α,α-trichlorotoluene; [98-07-7]

$C_7H_5Cl_3$. M: 195.48. Colourless liquid with a pungent odour. BP: 220–221°C. FP: -5°C. d: 1.37 kg/l (20°C). Hydrolysed by water forming benzoic acid. Soluble in oxygenated and aromatic solvents.
Production:
- toluene (side-chain chlorination; coproduced with benzyl chloride/benzal chloride)

Derivatives:
acetyl chloride; *m*-aminobenzotrifluoride; Basic Green 4; benzotrifluoride; benzoyl chloride; propionyl chloride

benzotrifluoride
1-(trifluoromethyl)benzene; α,α,α-trifluorotoluene; [98-08-8]

$C_6H_5F_3$. M: 134.10. Colourless liquid. BP: 100–103°C. MP: -29°C. d: 1.19 kg/l (20°C). Insoluble in water.

Production:
- benzotrichloride + hydrogen fluoride (fluorination)

Derivatives: fenfluramine; fluridone

2-benzoxazolethiol
[2382-96-9]

$C_7H_5N_1O_1S_1$. M: 151.19.
Production:
- *o*-aminophenol + carbon disulphide (thiocarbonylation)

Uses: photographic coupling agent intermediate

benzoxazolone
2-oxobenzoxazole; [59-49-4]

$C_7H_5N_1O_2$. M: 135.13. Needles. MP: 141–142°C. Slightly soluble in water. Soluble in oxygenated solvents.
Production:
- *o*-aminophenol + phosgene (phosgenation)

Derivatives:
fenoxaprop-ethyl; phosalone
Uses: dyestuffs intermediate

benzoximate
3-chloro-α-ethoxyimino-2,6-dimethoxybenzyl benzoate; [29104-30-1]

$C_{18}H_{18}Cl_1N_1O_5$. M: 363.79.
Production:
- 2,6-dimethoxybenzoic acid + hydroxylamine sulphate + diethyl sulphate + benzoyl chloride (ring chlorination/oxime formation/ethylation/esterification)

Uses: acaricide

o-benzoylbenzoic acid
benzophenone-2-carboxylic acid; [85-52-9]

$C_{14}H_{10}O_3$. M: 226.23. White, crystalline solid. MP: 127–129°C. Soluble in oxygenated solvents and hot benzene.

Production:
• phthalic anhydride + benzene (Friedel-Crafts acylation)
Derivatives:
anthraquinone; nefopam

benzoyl chloride
[98-88-4]

$C_7H_5Cl_1O_1$. M: 140.57. Hygroscopic liquid with a pungent odour. BP: 197–199°C. MP: -1°C. d: 1.21 kg/l (25°C). Hydrolysed by water and alcohol. Miscible with oxygenated and aromatic solvents.
Production:
• benzoic acid + benzotrichloride (disproportionation)
• acetic acid + benzotrichloride (acid chloride formation; coproduced with acetyl chloride)
• propionic acid + benzotrichloride (acid chloride formation; coproduced with propionyl chloride)
Derivatives:
Acid Red 68; Acid Red 108; 1-amino-4-benzamido-anthraquinone; 1-amino-5-benzamidoanthraquinone; 2-amino-5-chlorobenzophenone; 4′-amino-2′,5′-diethoxy-benzanilide; N-(4-amino-5-methoxy-2-methylphenyl)benz-amide; t-amyl peroxybenzoate; 1-benzamido-4-chloro-anthraquinone; 1-benzamido-4-hydroxyanthraquinone; benzophenone; benzoximate; benzoyl cyanide; benzoyl peroxide; benzoylprop-ethyl; t-butyl peroxybenzoate; 5-chloro-2-hydroxybenzophenone; dibenzopyrenequin-one; 2,5-di-(benzoylperoxy)-2,5-dimethylhexane; di-benzoylp-quinonedioxime; 2,4-dihydroxybenzophenone; Direct Green 13; Direct Red 81; flamprop-methyl; flamprop-M-isopropyl; 2-hydroxy-5-nonylbenzophen-oxime; p-phenylbenzophenone; Reactive Red 4; tamoxi-fen; 2,3,4-trihydroxybenzophenone mono-2,1,5-diazo-ester; Vat Blue 21; Vat Violet 15; Vat Yellow 3
Uses:
amino group protection/benzoylation reagent

benzoyl cyanide
[613-90-1]

$C_8H_5N_1O_1$. M: 131.14. Solid. MP 32°C. BP: 206–208°C. Insoluble in water. Soluble in oxygenated solvents.
Production:
• benzoyl chloride + sodium cyanide (cyanidation)
• benzaldehyde + hydrogen cyanide (cyanohydrin formation/alcohol oxidation)
Derivatives:
methyl phenylglyoxylate

benzoyl peroxide
dibenzoyl peroxide; BP; BPO; [94-36-0]

$C_{14}H_{10}O_4$. M: 242.24. Granules, powder or paste with 35–100% peroxide content. The product has a 10-hour half-life at 71°C.
Production:
• benzoyl chloride + hydrogen peroxide (dehydro-chlorination)
Uses:
unsaturated polyester resin/silicone rubber curing agent; flour bleach; bulk polyvinyl chloride/poly(methyl meth-acrylate) polymerisation initiator

benzoylprop-ethyl
ethyl 2-(N-benzoyl-3,4-dichloroanilino)propionate; [22212-55-1]

$C_{18}H_{17}Cl_2N_1O_3$. M: 366.26.
Production:
• ethyl α-chloropropionate + 3,4-dichloroaniline + benzoyl chloride (amide formation/amine formation)
Uses: herbicide

benzthiazuron
1-benzothiazol-2-yl-3-methylurea; [1929-88-0]

$C_9H_9N_3O_1S_1$. M: 207.25.
Production:
• 2-mercaptobenzothiazole + ammonia + methyl isocyanate (ammoniation/isocyanate addition)
Uses: herbicide

benzyl acetate
[140-11-4]

$C_9H_{10}O_2$. M: 150.18. Colourless liquid with a fruity odour. BP: 213–215°C. MP: -50°C. d: 1.06 kg/l (20°C). Insoluble in water. Miscible with oxygenated solvents.
Production:
• benzyl alcohol + acetic anhydride (esterification)
Uses:
flavouring/fragrance ingredient

benzylacetone

1-phenyl-3-butanone; 4-phenylbutan-2-one; [2550-26-7]

$C_{10}H_{12}O_1$. M: 148.21. Colourless liquid with a floral odour. BP: 235–237°C. d: 0.99 kg/l (20°C). Soluble in oxygenated solvents.

Production:
- benzylideneacetone (hydrogenation)

Derivatives: buphenine; dimethyl phenethyl carbinol; labetalol; 5-phenyl-3-methyl-2-pentenonitrile

Uses: fragrance ingredient

benzyl alcohol

[100-51-6]

$C_7H_8O_1$. M: 108.14. Colourless liquid with a mild, aromatic odour. BP: 205–206°C. MP: -15°C. Slightly soluble in water. Miscible with oxygenated and chlorinated solvents.

Production:
- benzyl chloride + sodium carbonate (hydration)
- benzaldehyde (hydrogenation)

Derivatives: benzyl acetate; benzyl benzoate; benzyl bromoacetate; benzyl chloroformate; benzyl cinnamate; benzyl isovalerate; benzyl methacrylate; benzyl nicotinate; benzyl phenylmalonate; benzyl propionate; benzyl salicylate

Uses:
epoxy resin curing agent; degreasing agent (rug cleaners); dyeing auxiliary (wool, polyamide, leather); photographic developer ingredient; solvent (ballpoint pen inks); fragrance/flavouring solvent

benzylamine

aminotoluene; [100-46-9]

$C_7H_9N_1$. M: 107.16. Pale amber liquid. BP: 182–185°C. FP: <-30°C. d: 0.98 kg/l (20°C). Soluble in water forming alkaline solutions. Miscible with oxygenated solvents.

Production:
- benzaldehyde + ammonia (reductive ammoniation; coproduced with dibenzylamine/tribenzylamine)
- benzonitrile (hydrogenation)

Derivatives:
1-benzyl-3-carbethoxy-4-piperidone hydrochloride; benzyldimethylamine; biotin; fenoterol; labetalol; mafenide;

reproterol; theodrenaline

Uses: corrosion inhibitor (metalworking fluids); base-catalysis reagent; stabiliser (antibiotics)

N-benzyl-p-aminophenol hydrochloride

BAP

$C_{13}H_{14}Cl_1N_1O_1$. M: 235.71.

Production:
- p-aminophenol + benzyl chloride (amine formation)

Uses: photographic developing agent

N-benzylaniline

[103-32-2]

$C_{13}H_{13}N_1$. M: 183.25. Crystalline solid. MP: 37°C. BP: 306°C. Insoluble in water. Soluble in oxygenated and chlorinated solvents.

Production:
- aniline + benzyl chloride (amine formation)

Derivatives: antazoline; ethylbenzylaniline

Uses: dyestuffs intermediate

benzylbenzene *See:* diphenylmethane

benzyl benzoate

[120-51-4]

$C_{14}H_{12}O_2$. M: 212.25. Liquid or solid with a pleasant odour. MP: 18–20°C. BP: 323–324°C. d: 1.12 kg/l (25°C). Insoluble in water. Soluble in oxygenated and chlorinated solvents.

Production:
- benzyl alcohol + benzoic acid (transesterification)
- benzaldehyde (Tishchenko reaction)

Uses: fragrance/flavouring ingredient; scabicide lotions

benzyl bromoacetate

Merbac-35 (Merck)

$C_9H_9Br_1O_2$. M: 229.07.

Production:
- bromoacetic acid + benzyl alcohol (esterification)

Uses: preservative (water-based paints)

benzyl-t-butylamine

N-(t-butyl)benzylamine; [3378-72-1]

$C_{11}H_{17}N_1$. M: 163.27. Liquid. BP: 114°C (3.5 kPa). Insoluble in water.

CH₂NHC(CH₃)₃

Production:
• benzyl chloride + *t*-butylamine (amine formation)
Derivatives:
salbutamol; terbutaline

benzyl *n*-butyl phthalate *See:* *n*-butyl benzyl phthalate

1-benzyl-3-carbethoxy-4-piperidone hydrochloride
1-benzyl-3-ethoxycarbonyl-4-piperidone; ethyl *N*-benzyl-4-piperidone-3-carboxylate hydrochloride

$C_{15}H_{20}Cl_1N_1O_3$. M: 297.78.
Production:
• benzylamine + ethyl acrylate (carboxyethylation/condensation)
Derivatives: 1-benzyl-4-piperidone; droperidol; 1-(4-piperidyl)-2-benzodiazolinone

benzyl chloride
α-chlorotoluene; [100-44-7]

CH₂Cl

$C_7H_7Cl_1$. M: 126.59. Colourless liquid with a pungent odour. BP: 178–180°C. FP: -41°C. d: 1.11 kg/l (20°C). Insoluble in water. Miscible with most organic solvents.
Production:
• toluene (side-chain chlorination; coproduced with benzotrichloride/benzal chloride)
Derivatives:
alkyl(C_{13}-C_{15})dimethylbenzylammonium chloride; bamipine; behenyldimethylbenzylammonium chloride; benzyl alcohol; *N*-benzyl-*p*-aminophenol hydrochloride; *N*-benzylaniline; benzyl-*t*-butylamine; *o*-benzyl-*p*-chlorophenol; benzyl cyanide; benzyldimethylamine; benzyl isoeugenol; benzyl mercaptan; 1-benzyl-2-methylimidazole; benzyltriethylammonium chloride; benzyltrimethylammonium chloride; bephenium hydroxynaphthoate; *n*-butyl benzyl phthalate; cetyldimethylbenzylammonium chloride; denatonium benzoate; dextropropoxyphene; diazepam; 3,5-dibenzoxyacetophenone; dibenzyl disulphide; dimethindene; dimethyl benzyl carbinol; dimethylcocobenzylammonium chloride; dimethyl-

laurylbenzylammonium chloride; dimethylstearylbenzylammonium chloride; doxepin; ethylbenzylaniline; iprobenfos; myristyldimethylbenzylammonium chloride; nicardipine; oleylbenzyldimethylammonium chloride; oxyphenbutazone; tiocarbazil; 2,2,4-trimethyl-1,3-pentanediol benzyl phthalate; tripelennamine

benzyl chloroformate
benzyl chlorocarbonate; [501-53-1]

CH₂OCCl

$C_8H_7Cl_1O_2$. M: 170.60. Liquid. Decomposes on heating above 30°C. MP: -18°C. Decomposed by water forming hydrochloric acid.
Production:
• benzyl alcohol + phosgene (phosgenation)
Uses:
amino group protection reagent

***o*-benzyl-*p*-chlorophenol**
2-benzyl-4-chlorophenol; 5-chloro-2-hydroxydiphenylmethane; clorophene; OBCP; [120-32-1]

OH
CH₂
Cl

$C_{13}H_{11}Cl_1O_1$. M: 218.68. White to brown flakes. MP: 48°C. Insoluble in water. Soluble in oxygenated solvents.
Production:
• *p*-chlorophenol + benzyl chloride (Friedel-Crafts alkylation)
Uses: biocide

benzyl cinnamate
phenylmethyl 3-phenyl-2-propenoate; [103-41-3]

CH=CHCOCH₂

$C_{16}H_{14}O_2$. M: 238.29. White crystals with balsam-like odour. MP: 39°C, BP: 244°C (0.7 kPa). d: 1.11 kg/l (15°C). Insoluble in water. Soluble in alcohol.
Production:
• benzyl alcohol + cinnamic acid (esterification)
Uses: perfume fixative

benzyl cyanide
phenylacetonitrile; α-tolunitrile; [140-29-4]

$C_8H_7N_1$. M: 117.16. Liquid with an aromatic odour.

BP: 233–234°C. FP: -24°C. d: 1.02 kg/l (20°C). Insoluble in water. Miscible with oxygenated solvents.
Production:
• benzyl chloride + sodium cyanide (cyanidation)
Derivatives:
7-amino-3-phenylcoumarin; 5-benzyl-3-furylmethyl alcohol; dicycloverine; diphenoxylate; disopyramide; fluridone; oxabetrinil; pentoxyverine; pethidine; pheniramine; phenylacetic acid; phenylacetone; 2-phenylethylamine; phoxim; tolazoline; triamterene

benzyldimethylamine
N,N-dimethylbenzylamine; BDA; BDMA; [103-83-3]

$C_9H_{13}N_1$. M: 135.21. Colourless to pale yellow liquid. BP: 183–184°C. d: 0.915 kg/l (0°C). Slightly soluble in hot water and alcohol. Soluble in ether.
Production:
• benzyl chloride + dimethylamine (amine formation)
• benzylamine + dimethyl sulphate (methylation)
Derivatives:
myristyldimethylbenzylammonium chloride
Uses: polyurethane/polyester resin catalyst; corrosion inhibitor/neutralising agent; epoxy resin curing agent

5-benzyl-3-furylmethyl alcohol
2-benzyl-4-furylmethyl alcohol; 5-benzyl-3-(hydroxymethyl)furan; [20416-09-5]

$C_{12}H_{12}O_2$. M: 188.23.
Production:
• benzyl cyanide + ethyl succinyl chloride + ethyl formate (condensation/nitrile hydrolysis/decarboxylation/diacetal formation/carbonyl condensation/condensation)
Derivatives:
bioresmethrin; kadethrin; resmethrin

benzyl 2-hydroxybenzoate
See: benzyl salicylate

benzylideneacetone
benzalacetone; 4-phenyl-3-buten-2-one; 4-phenylbutenone; [122-57-6]

$C_{10}H_{10}O_1$. M: 146.19. Flakes with a pleasant odour. MP: 38–39°C. BP: 261°C. d: 1.04 kg/l (15°C). Insoluble in water. Soluble in oxygenated, chlorinated and aromatic solvents.

Production:
• benzaldehyde + acetone (carbonyl condensation)
Derivatives: benzylacetone; warfarin

benzyl isoeugenol

$C_{17}H_{18}O_2$. M: 254.33. White, crystalline powder with a floral odour. Soluble in alcohol.
Production:
• benzyl chloride + eugenol (ether formation)
Uses: perfume ingredient

benzyl isovalerate
[103-38-8]

$C_{12}H_{16}O_2$. M: 192.26. Liquid with a heavy, floral odour. BP: 245°C.
Production:
• benzyl alcohol + isovaleric acid (esterification)
Uses: fragrance ingredient

benzyl mercaptan
benzylthiol; [100-53-8]

$C_7H_8S_1$. M: 124.20. Colourless liquid with an unpleasant odour. BP: 194–195°C. d: 1.06 kg/l (15°C). Insoluble in water. Soluble in oxygenated solvents.
Production:
• benzyl chloride + sodium hydrosulphide (thiolation)
Derivatives:
thioctic acid

benzyl methacrylate

$C_{11}H_{12}O_2$. M: 176.22.
Production:
• benzyl alcohol + methyl methacrylate (transesterification)
Uses: vinyl/acrylic resin comonomer

N-benzylmethylamine
N-methylbenzylamine; [103-67-3]
$C_8H_{11}N_1$. M: 121.19. Colourless to pale yellow liquid. BP: 184–190°C. MP: <-24°C. d: 0.94 kg/l (20°C). Insoluble in water.

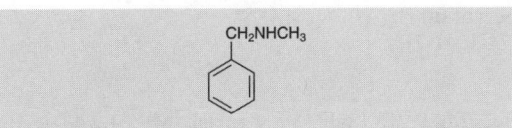

Production:
• methylamine + benzaldehyde (reductive amination)
Derivatives:
synephrine
Uses: rubber/epoxy adhesives compounding ingredient; methylamination reagent

1-benzyl-2-methylimidazole

$C_{11}H_{12}N_2$. M: 172.23.
Production:
• 2-methylimidazole + benzyl chloride (amide formation)
Uses: polyester-epoxy powder coating curing agent

benzyl nicotinate
[94-44-0]

$C_{13}H_{11}N_1O_2$. M: 213.24.
Production:
• benzyl alcohol + nicotinic acid (esterification)
Uses: hyperemic drug

benzylpenicillin
benzylpenicillinic acid; penicillin G; [1406-05-9]

$C_{16}H_{18}N_2O_4S_1$. M: 334.39. White powder. Sparingly soluble in water. Soluble in most organic solvents. Available commercially as the acid, sodium salt or methyl ester.
Production:
• mould fermentation medium + potassium phenylacetate + *Penicillium chrysogenum* mould (fermentation)
Derivatives: 7-amino-3-desacetoxycephalosporanic acid; 6-aminopenicillanic acid; penicillamine
Uses: antibacterial drug

benzyl phenylmalonate
phenylmalonic acid, benzyl ester; MBPM; [25774-02-1]

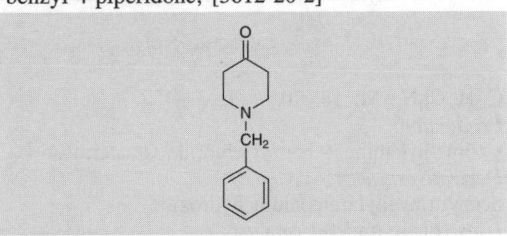

$C_{16}H_{14}O_4$. M: 270.29. Solid.
Production:
• benzyl alcohol + phenylacetic acid + triethyl orthoformate (esterification/condensation)
Derivatives: carbenicillin

1-benzyl-4-piperidone
N-benzyl-4-piperidone; [3612-20-2]

$C_{12}H_{15}N_1O_1$. M: 189.26.
Production:
• 1-benzyl-3-carbethoxy-4-piperidone hydrochloride (decarboxylation)
Derivatives:
alfentanil; 4-amino-*N*-benzylpiperidine; 4-(4-chlorophenyl)-4-hydroxypiperidine; fentanyl; fluspirilene; penfluridol; trifluperidol

benzyl propionate
[122-63-4]

$C_{10}H_{12}O_2$. M: 164.21.
Production:
• benzyl alcohol + propionic acid (esterification)
Uses: fragrance ingredient

benzyl salicylate
benzyl 2-hydroxybenzoate; [118-58-1]

$C_{14}H_{12}O_3$. M: 228.25. Viscous, colourless liquid with balsam-like odour. BP: 186–188°C (1.3 kPa), d: 1.18 kg/l (20°C). Soluble in oxygenated solvents. Slightly soluble in water.
Production:
• benzyl alcohol + salicylic acid (esterification)
Uses: sunscreening agent (cosmetics); fragrance/flavouring ingredient

benzyltriethylammonium chloride
triethylbenzylammonium chloride; BETEC; [56-37-1]

$C_{13}H_{22}Cl_1N_1$. M: 227.78. Solid. MP: 197–199°C with decomposition. Also available commercially as a 60% solution in water.
Production:
• triethylamine + benzyl chloride (quaternisation)
Uses: phase-transfer catalyst

benzyltrimethylammonium chloride
trimethylbenzylammonium chloride; BTMAC; [56-93-9]

$C_{10}H_{16}Cl_1N_1$. M: 185.70.
Production:
• trimethylamine + benzyl chloride (quaternisation)
Derivatives:
benzyltrimethylammonium hydroxide
Uses: phase-transfer catalyst

benzyltrimethylammonium hydroxide
trimethylbenzylammonium hydroxide; BTMA-OH; Triton B (Rohm and Haas); [100-85-6]

$C_{10}H_{17}N_1O_1$. M: 167.26. Available commercially as a 40% solution in methanol.
Production:
• benzyltrimethylammonium chloride + sodium hydroxide (salt formation)
Uses: cyanoethylation/condensation catalyst

bephenium hydroxynaphthoate
[7181-73-9]; [3818-50-6]

$C_{28}H_{29}N_1O_4$. M: 443.55.
Production:
• phenol + 2-dimethylaminoethyl chloride hydrochloride + benzyl chloride + β-oxynaphthoic acid (amine formation/quaternisation/salt formation)
Uses: anthelmintic drug

bergamot oil
Greenish-yellow liquid with a pleasant odour. Produced by expression of bergamot orange (*Citrus bergamia*) fruit peel. d: 0.88 kg/l (20°C). The main terpene constituents of the oil are (−)-linalyl acetate and linalool.
Uses:
fragrance ingredient (perfumes, toiletries)

beryllium
[7440-41-7]

Be

Be_1. M: 9.01. Light, grey metal. MP: 1,279°C. BP: 2,970°C. d: 1.85 kg/l. The metal is relatively corrosion-resistant due to the presence of an oxide layer on its surface. Toxic.
Production:
• beryllium hydroxide + hydrogen fluoride + magnesium (salt formation/reduction)
Uses: aircraft brakes; x-ray windows; neutron reflectors

beryllium hydroxide
beryllium hydrate; [13327-32-7]

Be(OH)₂

$H_2Be_1O_2$. M: 43.03.
Production:
• low-grade beryllium ores (leaching)
• beryl (sulphate extraction process)
• beryl (fluoride process)
Derivatives: beryllium; beryllium oxide
Uses: nickel/aluminium/magnesium alloying ingredient; beryllium-copper alloys (electrical contacts, springs, dies, bellows, welding disks)

beryllium oxide
beryllia; [1304-56-9]

BeO

Be_1O_1. M: 25.01. White powder. High thermal stability.
Production:
• beryllium hydroxide (calcination)
Uses: beryllium alloy ingredient; electronic oxide ceramics ingredient; refractory ceramics raw material (nuclear reactors)

betahistine
[5638-76-6]; [5579-84-0] (hydrochloride)

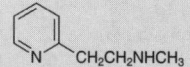

$C_8H_{12}N_2$. M: 136.20. Available commercially as the hydrochloride or mesylate salts.
Production:
• α-picoline + formaldehyde + methylamine (aminomethylation)
Uses: vasodilator drug

betaine
[107-43-7]; [17671-50-0] (citrate); [590-46-5] (hydrochloride)

(CH₃)₃⁺NCH₂COO⁻

$C_5H_{11}N_1O_2$. M: 117.15. Available commercially as the

anhydrous or monohydrate salts. Also available as the hydrochloride and citrate derivatives. Solubility of the anhydrous salt: 1,600 g/l water (20°C) forming slightly alkaline solutions.
Production:
• trimethylamine + chloroacetic acid (quaternisation)
Uses: lipotropic drug

betamethasone
[378-44-9]

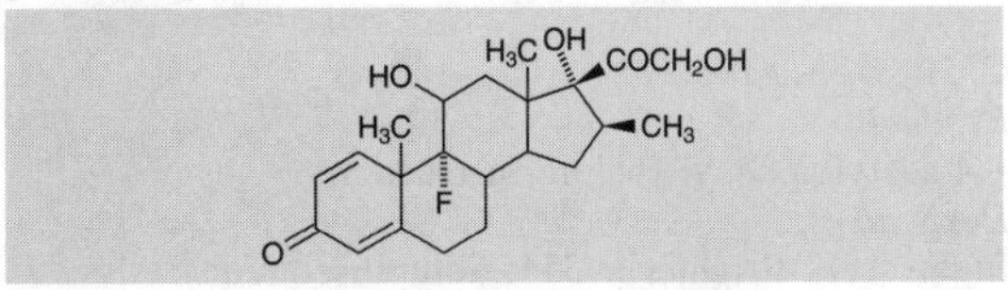

$C_{22}H_{29}F_1O_5$. M: 392.46. Available commercially as the alcohol and as the 17-valerate, 17-benzoate, 17,21-dipropionate, disodium 21-phosphate salt.
Production:
• androstadienedione (multistep synthesis; coproduced with dexamethasone)
Uses:
antiinflammatory drug

BETEC *See:* benzyltriethylammonium chloride

bezafibrate
[41859-67-0]

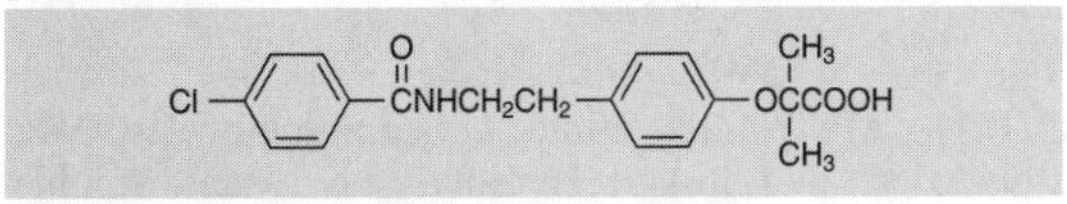

$C_{19}H_{20}Cl_1N_1O_4$. M: 361.83.
Production:
• tyramine + *p*-chlorobenzoyl chloride + acetone + chloroform (amide formation/condensation)
Uses: lipid reduction drug

BGE *See:* *n*-butyl glycidyl ether

BHA *See:* *t*-butylhydroxyanisole

BHC *See:* lindane

BHMT *See:* bis(hexamethylene)triamine

BHT *See:* 2,6-di-*t*-butyl-*p*-cresol

bicine *See:* sodium dihydroxyethylglycine

bicyclo[2.2.1]hept-2-ene *See:* norbornene

bifenox
methyl 5-(2,4-dichlorophenoxy)-2-nitrobenzoate;
[42576-02-3]
$C_{14}H_9Cl_2N_1O_5$. M: 342.13.

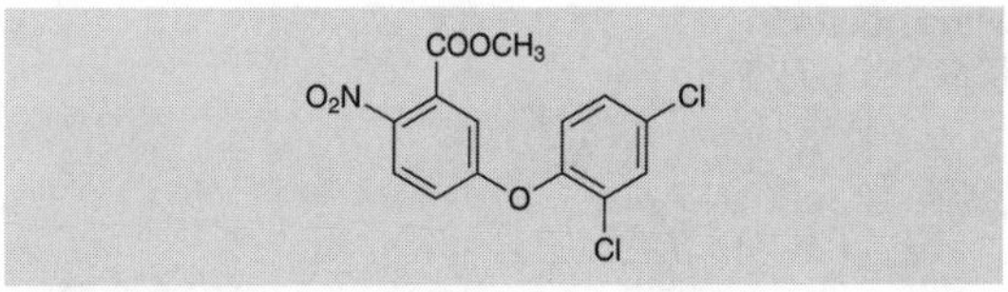

Production:
• 5-chloro-2-nitrobenzoic acid + methanol + 2,4-dichlorophenol (esterification/ether formation)
Uses: herbicide

bifenthrin
[82657-04-3]

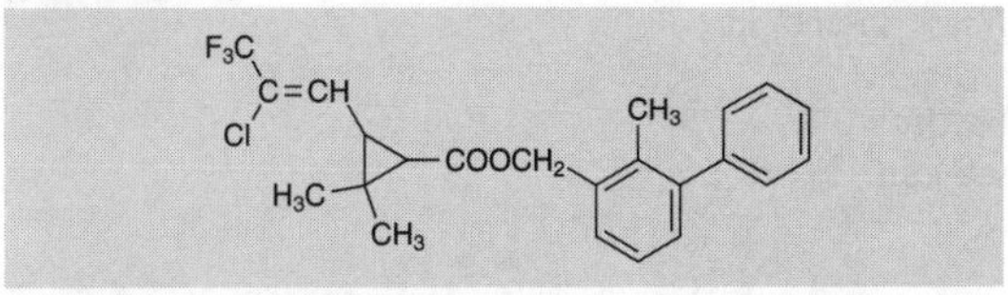

$C_{23}H_{22}Cl_1F_3O_2$. M: 422.87. Mixed isomer product with a *cis*-cyclopropane ring.
Production:
• 2-methyl-3-phenylbenzyl alcohol + 3-(2-chloro-3,3,3-trifluoropropenyl)-2,2-dimethylcyclopropane-carboxylic acid (esterification)
Uses: insecticide/acaricide

BIIR *See:* butyl rubber, brominated

bioallethrin
[584-79-2]

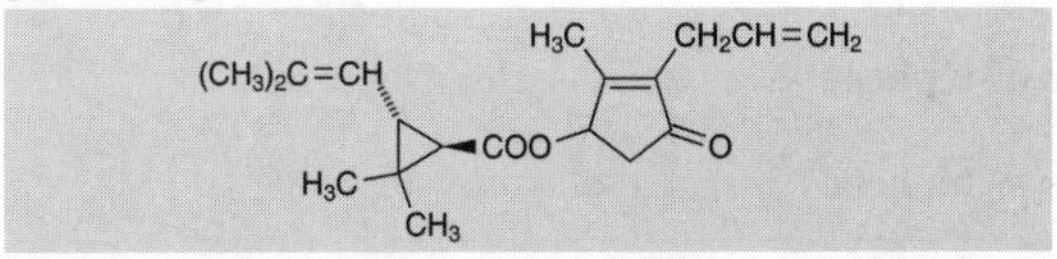

$C_{19}H_{26}O_3$. M: 302.42. Amber liquid. d: 1.00 kg/l. Insoluble in water. Soluble in oxygenated and hydrocarbon solvents.
Production:
• allethrolone + (*1R*)-*trans*-chrysanthemic acid (esterification)
Uses: insecticide

S-bioallethrin
[28434-00-6]

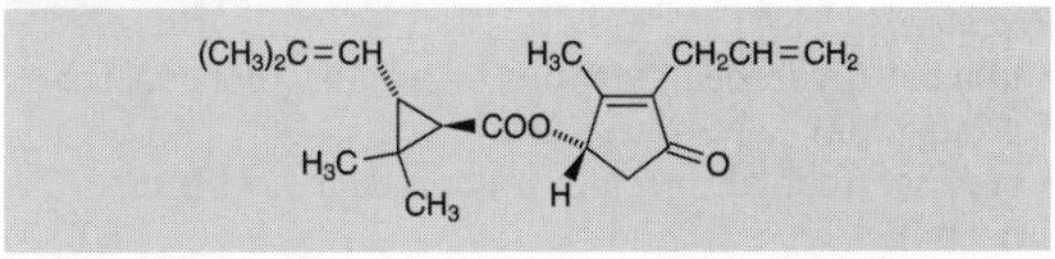

$C_{19}H_{26}O_3$. M: 302.42.
Production:
• allethrolone + (*1R*)-*trans*-chrysanthemic acid (racemate separation/esterification)
Uses:
insecticide

bioresmethrin
[28434-01-7]

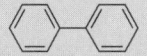

$C_{22}H_{26}O_3$. M: 338.45. Amber liquid or solid. MP: 30–35°C. Insoluble in water. Soluble in oxygenated and hydrocarbon solvents.
Production:
• 5-benzyl-3-furylmethyl alcohol + (*1R*)-*trans*-chrysanthemic acid (esterification)
Uses: insecticide

biotin
vitamin H; [58-85-5]

$C_{10}H_{16}N_2O_3S_1$. M: 244.31. Needles. MP: 230–232°C. Soluble in water and alcohol.
Production:
• fumaric acid + benzylamine + phosgene + diethyl malonate + thioacetic acid + cyclopropyl bromide (Hoffmann-La Roche synthesis)
Uses:
food additive; microbial fermentation nutrient

***o,o′*-biphenol** *See:* 2,2′-dihydroxybiphenyl

***p,p′*-biphenol** *See:* 4,4′-dihydroxybiphenyl

biphenyl
diphenyl; E230 (EC); [92-52-4]

$C_{12}H_{10}$. M: 154.21. White to pale yellow, fused solid or molten liquid. Distinctive odour. MP: 69–71°C. BP: 255°C. d: 1.04 kg/l (20°C). Insoluble in water. Soluble in oxygenated and chlorinated solvents. Flash point: 113°C (PMCC).
Production:
• toluene (hydrodealkylation; byproduct of benzene production)
• benzene (dehydrogenation; coproduced with terphenyl)
• xylenol, mixed (fractionation/alkali extraction; coproduced with *o*-phenylphenol)
Derivatives:
4-acetylbiphenyl; 4-aminobiphenyl-3-sulphonic acid; 4,4′-bis(2-sulphostyryl)biphenyl; difenacoum; diflunisal; 4,4′-dihydroxybiphenyl; fenbufen; *p*-phenylbenzophen-

one; *o*-phenylphenol; *p*-phenylphenol; tetrakis(2,4-di-*t*-butylphenyl)-4,4′-biphenyl diphosphonite
Uses:
dye carrier; fungicide (citrus fruit packaging); heat-transfer fluid

biphenyl-4-carboxylic acid
4-carboxybiphenyl; *p*-phenylbenzoic acid; [92-92-2]

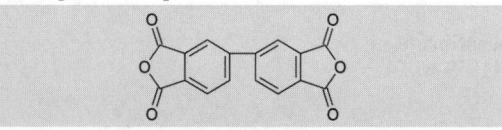

$C_{13}H_{10}O_2$. M: 198.22.
Production:
• 4-acetylbiphenyl (haloform reaction)
Derivatives:
Fluorescent Brightener 354; Solubilised Vat Yellow 7; Vat Yellow 10

biphenyl-2,2′-dicarboxylic acid *See:* diphenic acid

biphenyl-2,2′-diol *See:* 2,2′-dihydroxybiphenyl

biphenyl-4,4′-diol *See:* 4,4′-dihydroxybiphenyl

biphenyl-3,3′,4,4′-tetracarboxylic dianhydride
BPDA; [2420-87-3]

$C_{16}H_6O_6$. M: 294.22. White, crystalline powder. MP: 299–301°C. d: 1.56 kg/l. Hydrolysed by water. Soluble in hot *N,N*-dimethylformamide, *N*-methyl-2-pyrrolidone and dimethyl sulphoxide.
Production:
• 4-chloro-*o*-xylene (Ullmann reaction/side-chain oxidation)
Derivatives: polyimide resins, prepolymers

2,2′-bipyridine
2,2′-dipyridyl; [366-18-7]

$C_{10}H_8N_2$. M: 156.18. Crystalline solid. MP: 69–71°C. BP: 272–273°C. Slightly soluble in water. Soluble in oxygenated solvents.
Production:
• pyridine + nickel (oxidative coupling)
Derivatives:
diquat dibromide
Uses: analytical reagent

bisacodyl
4,4′-(2-pyridylmethylene)bisphenol diacetate; [603-50-9]
$C_{22}H_{19}N_1O_4$. M: 361.40.

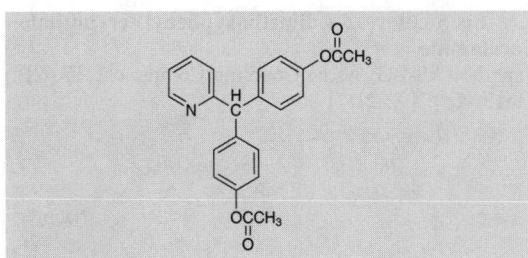

Production:
- α-picoline + phenol + acetic anhydride (side-chain oxidation/carbonyl addition/acetylation)

Uses: laxative drug

4,4′-bis(2-allylphenoxy)benzophenone

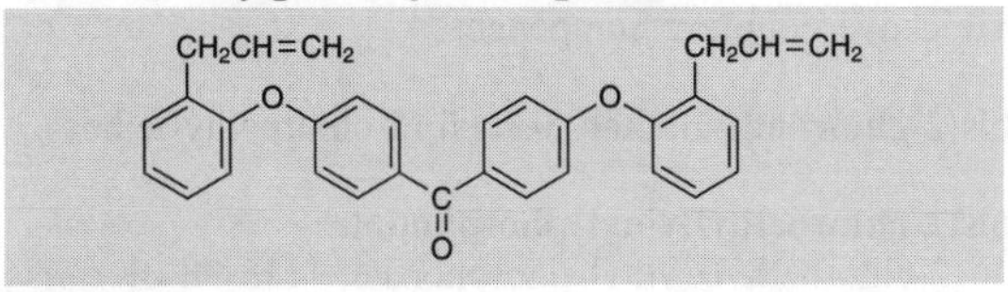

$C_{31}H_{26}O_3$. M: 446.55.

Production:
- 4,4′-difluorobenzophenone + *o*-allylphenol (ether formation)

Derivatives:
bismaleimide prepolymers

Uses: bismaleimide prepolymer comonomer

bisamine A
2,2′-bis(*p*-aminophenyl)propane

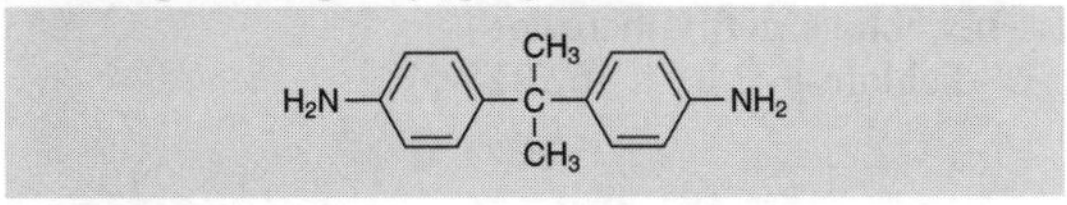

$C_{15}H_{18}N_2$. M: 226.31.

Production:
- bisphenol A + ammonia (ammoniation)

Uses: amorphous polyamide comonomer

bis(*p*-aminocyclohexyl)methane
4,4′-diaminodicyclohexylenemethane; 4,4′-methylene biscyclohexylamine; PACM; [1761-71-3]

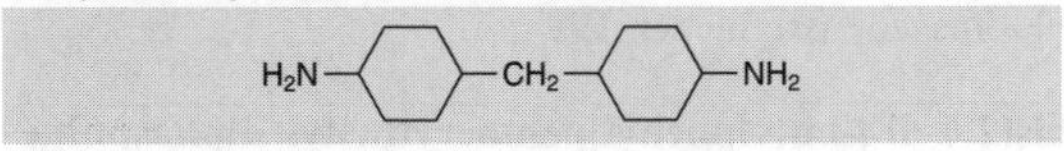

$C_{13}H_{26}N_2$. M: 210.36. Colourless liquid. d: 0.92 kg/l (25°C). Amine value: 530 mg KOH/g.

Production:
- 4,4′-diaminodiphenylmethane, crude (hydrogenation)

Derivatives: 4,4′-diisocyanatodicyclohexylmethane; methylenebis(dimethylcyclohexylamine)

Uses: amorphous polyamide comonomer; epoxy resin curing agent

bis(2-aminoethyl)amine *See:* diethylenetriamine

1,3-bis(aminomethyl)cyclohexane

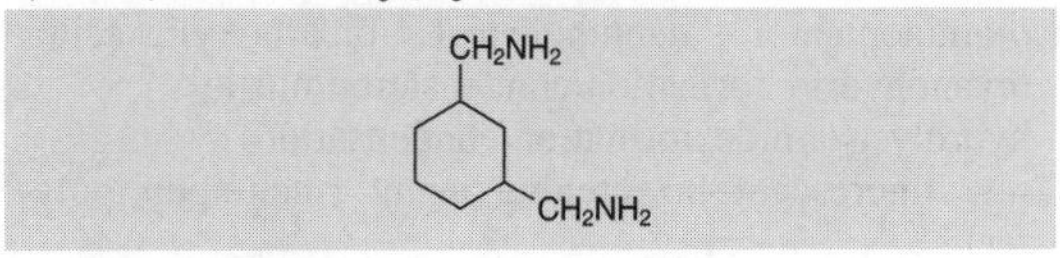

$C_8H_{18}N_2$. M: 142.24.

Production:
- *m*-xylylenediamine (hydrogenation)

Derivatives: xylene diisocyanate, hydrogenated

bis(4-amino-3-methylcyclohexyl)methane
4,4′-bis(2-methylcyclohexylamine); 4,4′-diamino-3,3′-dimethyldicyclohexylenemethane

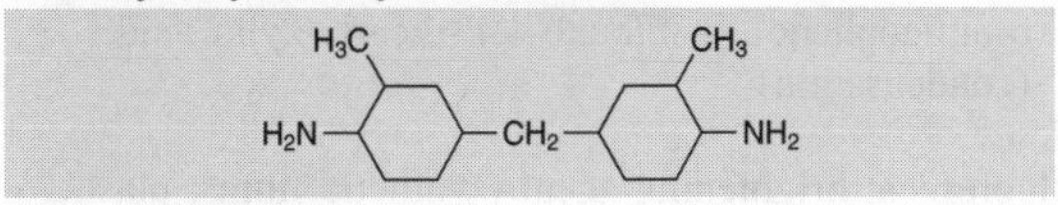

$C_{15}H_{30}N_2$. M: 238.41.

Production:
- *o*-toluidine + formaldehyde (carbonyl condensation/hydrogenation)

Derivatives:
polyamide TR55

Uses: amorphous polyamide comonomer

bis(aminomethyl)norbornane

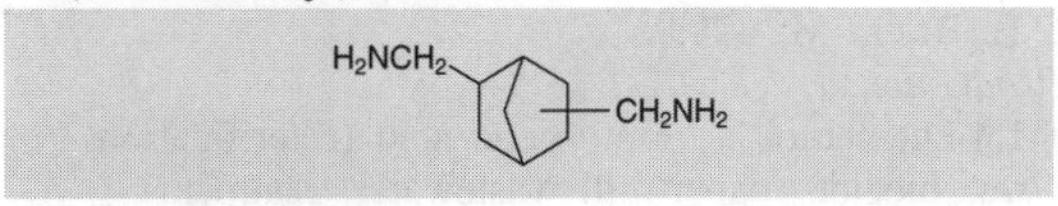

$C_9H_{18}N_2$. M: 154.26.

Production:
- dicyclopentadiene + acetylene + hydrogen cyanide (cycloaddition/addition/nitrile reduction)

Derivatives: polynorbornamide

1,2-bis(2-aminophenylthio)ethane

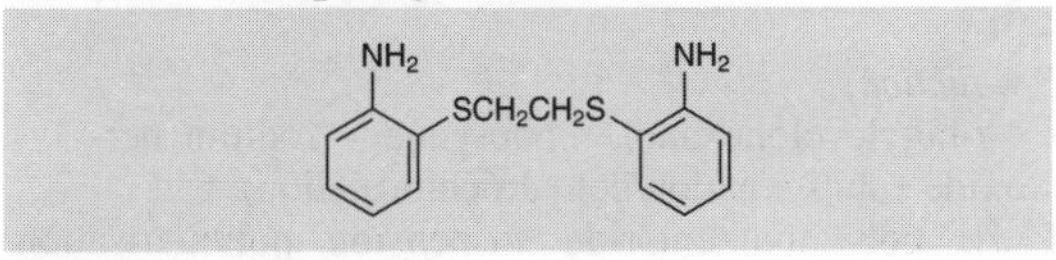

$C_{14}H_{16}N_2S_2$. M: 276.42.

Production:
- *o*-chloronitrobenzene + 1,2-ethanedithiol (dehydrochlorination/nitro reduction)

Uses: cast polyurethane elastomer curing agent

1,4-bis(benzoxazol-2-yl)naphthalene
Hostalux KCB (Hoechst); [5089-22-5]

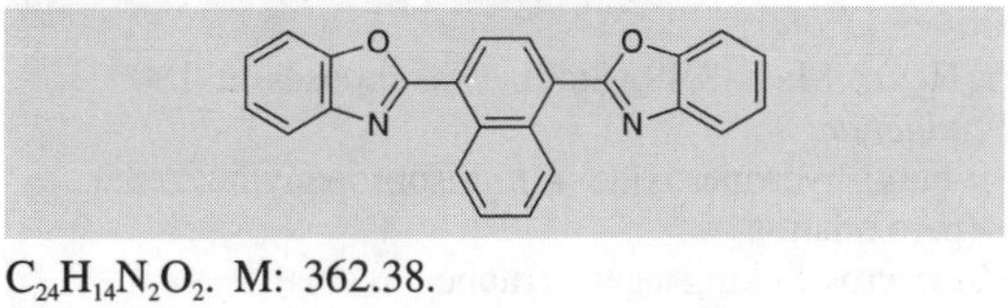

$C_{24}H_{14}N_2O_2$. M: 362.38.

Production:
- *o*-aminophenol + naphthalene-1,4-dicarboxylic acid (cyanohydrin formation/condensation/nitrile hydrolysis/amide formation/condensation)

Uses: fluorescent brightening agent (melt-spun polyester)

4,4′-bis(benzoxazol-2-yl)stilbene
[1533-45-5]

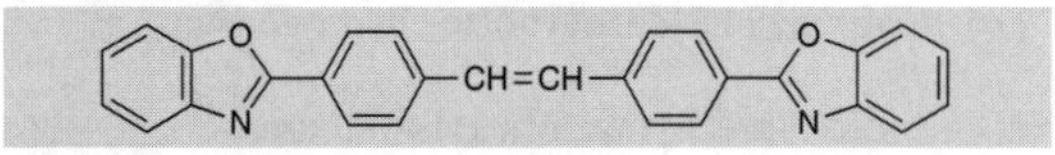

$C_{28}H_{18}N_2O_2$. M: 414.46.
Production:
- *o*-aminophenol + stilbene-4,4′-dicarboxylic acid (condensation)

Uses:
fluorescent brightening agent (synthetic fibres, plastics)

2,5-bis(benzoxazol-2-yl)thiophene
See: Fluorescent Brightener 190

1,4-bis(bromoacetoxy)-2-butene
1,4-di-(bromoacetoxy)butenediol; BBAB

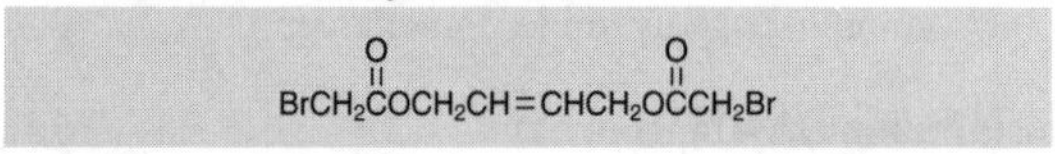

$$BrCH_2COCH_2CH=CHCH_2OCCH_2Br$$

$C_8H_{10}Br_2O_4$. M: 329.98.
Production:
- 1,4-butenediol + bromoacetic acid (esterification)

Uses: biocide (paper-mill wastewater treatment)

bis(4-*t*-butylcyclohexyl) peroxydicarbonate
Perkadox 16 (Akzo)

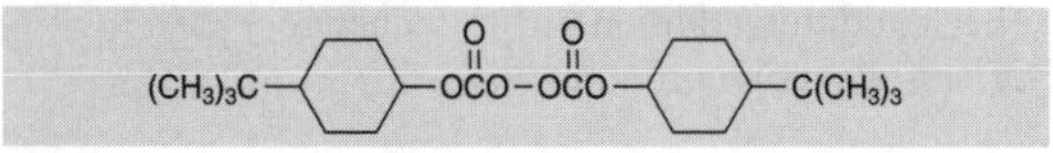

$$(CH_3)_3C—\bigcirc—OCO-OCO—\bigcirc—C(CH_3)_3$$

$C_{22}H_{38}O_6$. M: 398.53. Powder. Half-life is 10-hours at 44°C.
Production:
- 4-*t*-butylcyclohexanol + phosgene + sodium peroxide (phosgenation/dehydrochlorination)

Uses: polyvinyl chloride suspension polymerisation initiator

1,4-bis(*t*-butylperoxyisopropyl)benzene
bis(*t*-butylperoxy)-α,α′-diisopropylbenzene; Perkadox 14 (Akzo); Peroximon F (EniChem)

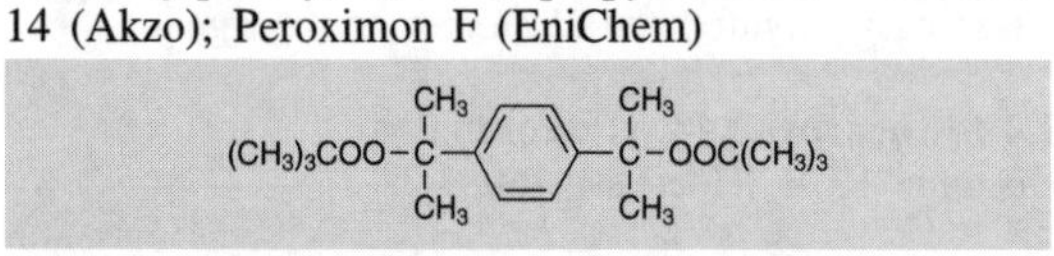

$C_{20}H_{34}O_4$. M: 338.49. Solid. Decomposes at 180°C.
Production:
- *t*-butyl hydroperoxide + *p*-diisopropenylbenzene (peroxidation)

Uses: crosslinking agent (rubber, resins)

N,N′-bis(5-chloro-2,4-dimethoxyphenyl)terephthalodiacetamide
Naphthol AS-LG; Azoic Coupling Component 35 (CI); 37615 (CI); [92-21-7]

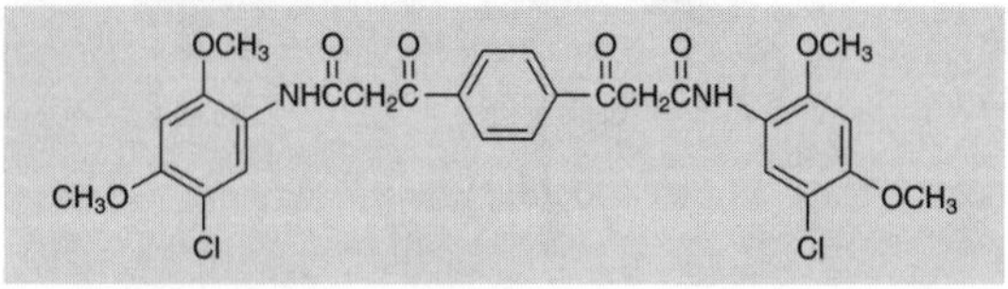

$C_{28}H_{26}Cl_2N_2O_8$. M: 589.43.
Production:
- dimethyl terephthalate + ethyl acetate + 5-chloro-2,4-dimethoxyaniline (Claisen condensation/amide formation)

Uses:
azoic dye coupling component

bis(2-chloroethyl)ether *See:* di-(2-chloroethyl)ether

bis(2-chloroethyl)vinyl phosphonate
di-(2-chloroethyl) vinyl phosphonate; [115-98-0]

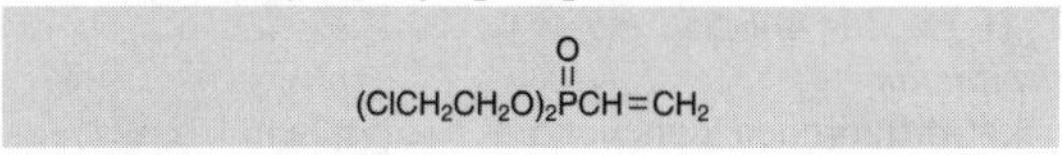

$$(ClCH_2CH_2O)_2PCH=CH_2$$

$C_6H_{11}Cl_2O_3P_1$. M: 233.04.
Production:
- tris(2-chloroethyl) phosphite (Arbusov rearrangement/dehydrochlorination)

Uses:
fire-retarded vinyl latex comonomer

1,4-bis(chloromethyl)benzene
α,α′-dichloro-*p*-xylene; [623-25-6]

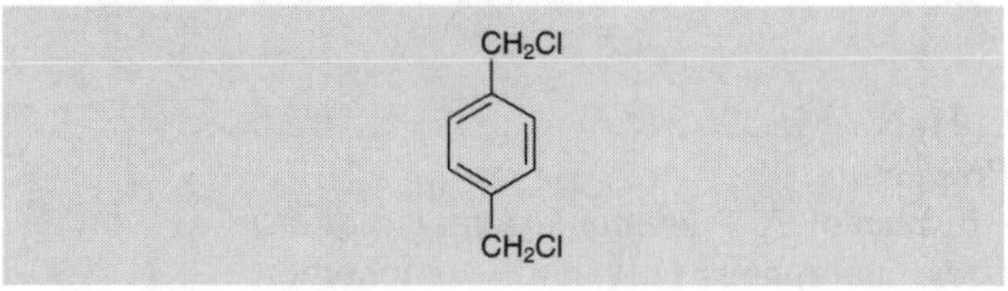

$C_8H_8Cl_2$. M: 175.06.
Production:
- *p*-xylene (side-chain chlorination)

Derivatives:
Fluorescent Brightener 199

bis(2,4-di-*t*-butylphenyl)pentaerythrityl diphosphite
Ultranox 624 (Borg-Warner Chemicals); [26741-53-7]

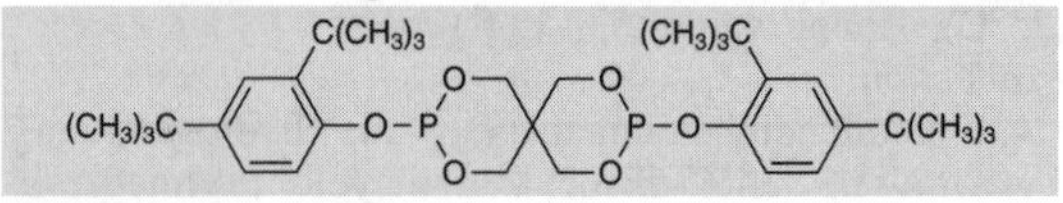

$C_{33}H_{50}O_6P_2$. M: 604.70.
Production:
- 2,4-di-*t*-butylphenol + pentaerythritol + phosphorus trichloride (dehydrochlorination/dehydrochlorination)

Uses: antioxidant (plastics)

4,4′-bis(diethylamino)benzophenone
tetraethyldiaminobenzophenone; [90-93-7]

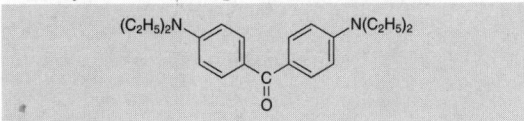

$C_{21}H_{28}N_2O_1$. M: 324.46. Flakes. MP: 95°C. Soluble in hot alcohol.
Production:
• *N,N*-diethylaniline + phosgene (phosgenation)
Derivatives: Basic Blue 7
Uses: photoactivator (printing inks, lacquers)

4,4′-bis(dimethylamino)benzhydrol
Michler's hydrol; tetramethyldiaminobenzhydrol; tetramethyldiaminodiphenylcarbinol; [119-58-4]

$C_{17}H_{22}N_2O_1$. M: 270.38. Pale green, crystalline solid. MP: 95°C. Insoluble in water. Soluble in oxygenated and aromatic solvents.
Production:
• bis(*p*-dimethylaminophenyl)methane (oxidation)
Derivatives: Acid Green 16; Acid Green 50

4,4′-bis(dimethylamino)benzophenone
Michler's ketone; tetramethyldiaminobenzophenone; [90-94-8]

$C_{17}H_{20}N_2O_1$. M: 268.36. White flakes. MP: 172°C. Insoluble in water. Soluble in aromatic solvents.
Production:
• *N,N*-dimethylaniline + phosgene (phosgenation)
Derivatives: Crystal Violet Lactone; Solvent Blue 4

2,2-bis(β-dimethylaminoethyl) ether
2,8-dimethyl-2,8-diaza-5-oxanonane; Dabco BL-11 (Air Products and Chemical); ZF-22 (Texaco Chemical)

$$(CH_3)_2NCH_2CH_2OCH_2CH_2N(CH_3)_2$$

$C_8H_{20}N_2O_1$. M: 160.26. Liquid with a mild, ammoniacal odour. Sold as a solution in dipropylene glycol.
Production:
• dimethylamine + diethylene glycol (amine formation)
Uses: polyurethane foam catalyst

bis(*p*-dimethylaminophenyl)methane
4,4′-bis(dimethylamino)diphenylmethane; *N,N,N′,N′*-tetramethyl-4,4′-diaminodiphenylmethane; Michler's base;

[101-61-1]

$C_{17}H_{22}N_2$. M: 254.38. Solid. MP: 87°C. BP: 390°C. Insoluble in water. Soluble in hot alcohol, ether and aromatic solvents.
Production:
• *N,N*-dimethylaniline + formaldehyde (carbonyl condensation)
Derivatives:
Basic Orange 14; Basic Yellow 2; 4,4′-bis(dimethylamino)benzhydrol
Uses: antioxidant (lubricants)

N,N′-bis(1,4-dimethylpentyl)-*p*-phenylenediamine
diheptyl-*p*-phenylenediamine; 77PD; Santoflex 77 (Monsanto); [3081-14-9]

$C_{20}H_{36}N_2$. M: 304.52.
Production:
• *p*-phenylenediamine + methyl isoamyl ketone (reductive amination)
Uses: antioxidant (motor fuels, rubber)

bis[*O*-ethyl-(3,5-di-*t*-butyl-4-hydroxybenzyl)phosphonic acid], calcium salt

$C_{32}H_{52}Ca_1O_8P_2$. M: 666.79.
Production:
• 2,6-di-*t*-butylphenol + formaldehyde + phosphorous acid + ethanol + calcium hydroxide (chloromethylation/dehydrochlorination/dehydrochlorination/salt formation)
Derivatives: bis[*O*-ethyl-(3,5-di-*t*-butyl-4-hydroxybenzyl)phosphonic acid], nickel salt
Uses: antioxidant (plastics)

bis[*O*-ethyl-(3,5-di-*t*-butyl-4-hydroxybenzyl)phosphonic acid], nickel salt
Irgastab 2001 (Ciba-Geigy)

$C_{32}H_{52}Ni_1O_8P_2$. M: 685.42.

Production:
- bis[*O*-ethyl-(3,5-di-*t*-butyl-4-hydroxybenzyl)-phosphonic acid], calcium salt + nickel oxide, black (salt formation)

Uses: light stabiliser (plastics)

2,5-bis(2-ethylhexanoylperoxy)-2,5-dimethylhexane
USP-245 (Witco)

$$(CH_3)_2CO-OCCH(CH_2)_3CH_3$$
$$\overset{|}{CH_2} \quad C_2H_5$$
$$\overset{|}{CH_2} \quad C_2H_5$$
$$(CH_3)_2CO-OCCH(CH_2)_3CH_3$$

$C_{24}H_{46}O_6$. M: 430.62. Liquid. Decomposes when heated with a 10-hour half-life at 68°C.
Production:
- 2,5-dimethylhexane-2,5-dihydroperoxide + 2-ethylhexanoyl chloride (esterification)

Uses: unsaturated polyester resin crosslinking agent; polymerisation initiator

bis(2-ethylhexyl) hydrogen phosphate
dioctyl phosphate; dioctyl phosphoric acid; D2EHPA (Henkel); DEHPA (Mobil Oil); [298-07-7]

$$\left[CH_3(CH_2)_3\overset{\overset{\displaystyle C_2H_5}{|}}{CH}CH_2O\right]_2 \overset{\overset{\displaystyle O}{\|}}{P}OH$$

$C_{16}H_{35}O_4P_1$. M: 322.43.
Production:
- 2-ethylhexanol + phosphorus oxychloride (dehydrochlorination)

Uses: extraction agent (zinc, cobalt, rare earth, uranium processing); extreme-pressure additive (metalworking fluids); textile lubricant/antistatic agent

bis(2-ethylhexyl) peroxydicarbonate
Lupersol 223 (Elf-Atochem); Trigonox E4P (Akzo)

$$CH_3(CH_2)_3\overset{|}{\underset{C_2H_5}{CH}}CH_2O\overset{\overset{\displaystyle O}{\|}}{C}O-O\overset{\overset{\displaystyle O}{\|}}{C}OCH_2\overset{|}{\underset{C_2H_5}{CH}}(CH_2)_3CH_3$$

$C_{18}H_{34}O_6$. M: 346.46. Available commercially as 40% and 75% solutions in mineral spirit. The product as a 10-hour half-life of 44°C.
Production:
- sodium peroxide + 2-ethylhexyl chloroformate (dehydrochlorination)

Uses: polymerisation initiator

4,4-bis(*p*-fluorophenyl)butyl chloride
$C_{16}H_{15}Cl_1F_2$. M: 280.75.
Production:
- cyclopropane carboxylic acid + ethanol + *p*-bromofluorobenzene (esterification/Grignard reagent formation/Grignard reaction/alcohol reduction)

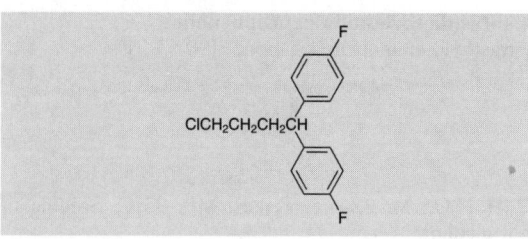

Derivatives:
fluspirilene; lidoflazine; penfluridol; pimozide

bis(hexamethylene)triamine
BHMT; [143-23-7]

$$H_2N(CH_2)_6NH(CH_2)_6NH_2$$

$C_{12}H_{29}N_3$. M: 215.38.
Production:
- adiponitrile (nitrile reduction; byproduct of hexamethylenediamine production)

Derivatives: polyamide resins, reactive

bis(2-hydroxyethyl)alkyl(C_{13}-C_{15})amine

$$CH_3(CH_2)_nN(CH_2CH_2OH)_2$$

n = 12–14. Liquid. Cloud point: 10°C.
Production:
- alkyl(C_{13}-C_{15})amine + ethylene oxide (epoxidation)

Derivatives:
bis(2-hydroxyethyl)alkyl(C_{13}-C_{15})amine oxide

bis(2-hydroxyethyl)alkyl(C_{13}-C_{15})amine oxide

$$CH_3(CH_2)_n\overset{\overset{\displaystyle O}{\uparrow}}{N}(CH_2CH_2OH)_2$$

n = 12–14. Clear liquid containing 27.5% active matter in water.
Production:
- bis(2-hydroxyethyl)alkyl(C_{13}-C_{15})amine + hydrogen peroxide (oxidation)

Uses: foam boosters/stabilisers (shampoos, dishwashing liquid, detergents)

bis(2-hydroxyethyl)-γ-aminopropyltriethoxysilane

$$(HOCH_2CH_2)_2NCH_2CH_2CH_2Si(OC_2H_5)_3$$

$C_{13}H_{31}N_1O_5Si_1$. M: 309.48.
Production:
- γ-aminopropyltriethoxysilane + ethylene oxide (epoxidation)

Uses: plastics coupling agent

bis(2-hydroxyethyl)cocoamine
PEG-2 cocoamine

$$RN(CH_2CH_2OH)_2$$

R = coco-. $C_{16}H_{35}N_1O_2$. M: 273.47. Liquid. MP: -2°C.

d: 0.87 kg/l (25°C). HLB: 10.2. A typical chain-length distribution is: 5% C_8, 5% C_{10}, 50% C_{12}, 10% C_{16}, 10% C_{18}.
Production:
• cocoamine + ethylene oxide (epoxidation)
Derivatives: bis(2-hydroxyethyl)cocoamine oxide
Uses: emulsifier; antistatic agent (plastics)

bis(2-hydroxyethyl)cocoamine oxide
N,N-di-(2-hydroxyethyl)cocoamine oxide

$$RN(CH_2CH_2OH)_2 \quad (N{\uparrow}O)$$

R = coco-. $C_{16}H_{35}N_1O_3$. M: 289.47. Clear liquid. A typical chain-length distribution is: 5% C_{10}, 50% C_{12}, 20% C_{14}, 10% C_{16}, 10% C_{18}. Often sold as a 39% solution in water.
Production:
• bis(2-hydroxyethyl)cocoamine + hydrogen peroxide (oxidation)
Uses: foam boosters (bubble-baths); hydrotrope/thickening agent (hypochlorite cleaners); thixotropic agent (water-based paints)

bis(2-hydroxyethyl)isotridecyl-3-oxypropylamine

$$C_{12}H_{25}CH_2OCH_2CH_2CH_2N(CH_2CH_2OH)_2$$

$C_{20}H_{43}N_1O_3$. M: 347.57.
Production:
• isotridecyl-3-oxypropylamine + ethylene oxide (epoxidation)
Uses: cationic emulsifier; corrosion inhibitor

bis(2-hydroxyethyl)oleylamine
N,N-di-(2-hydroxyethyl)oleylamine oxide

$$CH_3(CH_2)_7CH=CH(CH_2)_8N(CH_2CH_2OH)_2$$

$C_{22}H_{45}N_1O_2$. M: 355.61. Viscous liquid. HLB: 9.9.
Production:
• oleylamine + ethylene oxide (epoxidation)
Uses: corrosion inhibitor; emulsifier (wax, soluble oils, pesticides, cleaners, bitumen, silicone oils); antistatic agent (textile spin finishes, paper processing, plastics); wetting/dispersing agent (electrostatic paints, inks, dyes, pigments)

bis(2-hydroxyethyl)tallowamine
PEG-2 tallow amine (CTFA)

$$RN(CH_2CH_2OH)_2$$

R = tallow-. $C_{22}H_{47}N_1O_2$. M: 357.63. Liquid/paste. MP: 23°C. d: 0.92 kg/l (25°C). HLB: 9.8. A typical chain-length distribution is: 5% C_{14}, 30% C_{16}, 65% C_{18}.
Production:
• tallowamine + ethylene oxide (epoxidation)
Derivatives: bis(2-hydroxyethyl)tallowamine oxide
Uses: cationic emulsifier

bis(2-hydroxyethyl)tallowamine oxide
N,N-di-(2-hydroxyethyl)tallowamine oxide

$$RN(CH_2CH_2OH)_2 \quad (N{\uparrow}O)$$

R = tallow-. $C_{22}H_{47}N_1O_3$. M: 373.63. Clear liquid or paste. A typical chain-length distribution is: 5% C_{14}, 30% C_{16}, 65% C_{18}. The product is often sold as a 39% or 49% solution in water.
Production:
• bis(2-hydroxyethyl)tallowamine + hydrogen peroxide (oxidation)
Uses:
thickening agent (acid cleaners)

N,N'-bis(3-hydroxy-2-naphthoyl)dianisidine
N,N'-bis(2-hydroxy-3-naphthoyl)-3,3'-benzidine; *N,N'*-bis(2-hydroxy-3-naphthoyl)dianisidine; Naphthol AS-BR; Azoic Coupling Component 3 (CI); 37575 (CI); [91-92-9]

$C_{36}H_{28}N_2O_6$. M: 584.62.
Production:
• β-oxynaphthoic acid + *o*-dianisidine (amide formation)
Uses: azoic dye coupling component

N,N'-bis(2-hydroxypropyl)-2-methylpiperazine

$C_{11}H_{24}N_2O_2$. M: 216.32.
Production:
• ethylenediamine + propylene oxide (epoxidation/amine formation)
Uses: polyurethane foam catalyst

bismaleimide prepolymers

R = aromatic diamine. Thermosetting resins cured at 200–260°C.
Production:
• maleic anhydride/nadic anhydride + 4,4'-diaminodiphenylmethane, crude/4,4'-oxydianiline/*m*-phenylenediamine/*p*-phenylenediamine + 2,2'-diallylbis-

phenol A/4,4′-bis(2-allylphenoxy)benzophenone (imide formation)
Uses: high-performance adhesives/laminates (aerospace, aircraft, defence)

bis(2-methoxyethyl) ether
See: diethylene glycol dimethyl ether

1,4-bis(methoxymethyl)benzene

CH_3OCH_2—⟨benzene ring⟩—CH_2OCH_3

$C_{10}H_{14}O_2$. M: 166.22.
Production:
• dimethyl terephthalate + dimethyl sulphate (ester reduction/methylation)
Derivatives: phenylene-phenolic resins

N,N′-bis(2-methoxy-5-methylphenyl) urea

$C_{17}H_{20}N_2O_3$. M: 300.36.
Production:
• *p*-cresidine + phosgene (phosgenation)
Derivatives:
Direct Orange 72; Direct Red 79; Direct Yellow 34

N,N′-bis(methoxymethyl)urone
dihydroxymethylurone dimethyl ether; [7388-44-5]

CH_3OCH_2N—⟨ring⟩—NCH_2OCH_3

$C_7H_{14}N_2O_4$. M: 190.20.
Production:
• methanol + formaldehyde + urea (condensation)
Uses: permanent-press textile finishing agent

bismethylenedianiline maleimide
BMI (Itoh Oil Chemicals)

$C_{21}H_{14}N_2O_4$. M: 358.35.
Production:
• 4,4′-diaminodiphenylmethane, crude + maleic anhydride (imide formation)
Uses:
bismaleimide prepolymer resins (high-performance aircraft adhesives)

bis(2-morpholinoethyl)ether
2,2′-dimorpholinodiethyl ether; DMDEE

O⟨morpholine⟩$N-CH_2CH_2OCH_2CH_2-N$⟨morpholine⟩O

$C_{12}H_{24}N_2O_3$. M: 244.33. Liquid with mild, ammoniacal odour. BP: 309°C. FP: -28°C. d: 1.10 kg/l (20°C).
Production:
• morpholine + diethylene glycol (amine formation)
Uses: polyurethane foam catalyst

bismuth
[7440-69-9]

Bi

Bi_1. M: 208.98. Soft, brittle, grey metal with a slightly reddish colour. MP: 271°C. BP: 1,564°C. d: 9.8 kg/l. Highly diamagnetic showing a strong Hall effect. Available as lumps, powder, shot, rod and as single crystal disks.
Production:
• lead bullion (pyrometallurgical refining/Parkes process/Betterton-Kroll process; byproduct of lead production)
• lead bullion (electrochemical refining; byproduct of lead production)
Derivatives: bismuth nitrate
Uses: aluminium/special steel additive; malleable iron additive; low melting alloy ingredient (fusible safety plugs, fuses, solder); semiconductors/rectifiers

bismuth dimethyldithiocarbamate
Bismate (Vanderbilt Chemical); [21260-46-8]

$$\left[(CH_3)_2NC\overset{S}{\underset{\|}{S}}\right]_3 Bi$$

$C_9H_{18}Bi_1N_3S_6$. M: 569.64. Brownish-yellow powder. MP: >300°C. d: 2.1 kg/l. Insoluble in water and hydrocarbon solvents.
Production:
• sodium dimethyldithiocarbamate + bismuth nitrate (salt formation)
Uses: vulcanisation accelerator

bismuth nitrate

$Bi(NO_3)_3$

$Bi_1N_3O_9$. M: 394.99. Available as the pentahydrate. Colourless, deliquescent crystals with an odour of nitric acid. d: 2.83 kg/l. Hydrolysed by water to the subnitrate.
Production:
• bismuth + nitric acid (salt formation)
Derivatives:
bismuth dimethyldithiocarbamate; bismuth oxide; bismuth oxychloride; bismuth subgallate; bismuth subnitrate

bismuth oxide
bismuth trioxide; [1304-76-3]

$$Bi_2O_3$$

Bi_2O_3. M: 465.96. Yellow powder. MP: 820°C. d: 8.9 kg/l. Insoluble in water.
Production:
• bismuth nitrate + sodium hydroxide (salt formation)
Uses:
catalyst component; enamels/ceramics

bismuth oxychloride
bismuth chloride oxide; [7787-59-9]

$$BiOCl$$

$Bi_1Cl_1O_1$. M: 260.43. White, crystalline powder. High melting point. d: 7.72 kg/l. Insoluble in water.
Production:
• bismuth nitrate + sodium chloride, refined (salt formation)
Uses:
pigment (cosmetics); synthetic pearl polishing medium

bismuth subgallate
bismuth gallate, basic; bismuth 3,4,5-trihydroxybenzoate, basic; BSG; [99-26-3]

$C_7H_5Bi_1O_6$. M: 354.09. Yellow powder. Insoluble in water.
Production:
• bismuth nitrate + gallic acid (salt formation)
Uses: gastrointestinal/antieczema drug

bismuth subnitrate
bismuth oxynitrate; [1304-85-4]
White, hygroscopic, crystalline powder. Releases water when heated above 105°C, decomposing at 260°C. d: 4.92 kg/l (20°C). Insoluble in water. The exact composition of this chemical varies with the manufacturing process.
Production:
• bismuth nitrate (hydrolysis)
Uses:
enamel flux; cosmetics ingredient

2,4-bis(*n*-octylthio)-6-(4-hydroxy-3,5-di-*t*-butylanilino)-1,3,5-triazine
Irganox 565 (Ciba-Geigy)
$C_{33}H_{56}N_4O_1S_2$. M: 588.97.
Production:
• cyanuric chloride + 2,6-di-*t*-butylphenol + *n*-octyl mercaptan (nitration/nitro reduction/amine formation/sulphide formation)

Uses: antioxidant (lubricants, rubber)

bisphenol A
diphenylolpropane; 4,4'-isopropylidenediphenol; BPA; DPP; [80-05-7]

$C_{15}H_{16}O_2$. M: 228.29. White crystals or flakes. MP: 154–156°C. BP: 220°C (0.5 kPa). d: 1.20 kg/l (25°C). Insoluble in water. Soluble in oxygenated solvents.
Production:
• phenol + acetone (carbonyl condensation)
Derivatives:
bisamine A; bisphenol A diglycidyl ether; bisphenol A dimethacrylate; bisphenol A glycidyl ether prepolymers; bisphenol A propoxylates; cyanate ester resins; 2,2'-diallylbisphenol A; di-(2-hydroxyethyl)bisphenol A; di-(2-hydroxypropyl)bisphenol A; 4,4'-methylenebiscyclohexanol; polyarylate, amorphous; polycarbonate; polyester carbonate; poly(ether-imide); polysulphone; tetrabromobisphenol A
Uses: phenolic resin comonomer; antioxidant (plastics)

bisphenol A diglycidyl ether
epoxide resins; epoxy resins; dian resins; DGEBA; DGEBPA; Epikote 828 (Shell)

$C_{21}H_{24}O_4$. M: 340.42. Colourless liquid. d: 1.16 kg/l (20°C). Viscosity: 100–150 poise (25°C).
Production:
• bisphenol A + epichlorohydrin (dehydrochlorination)
Derivatives:
bisphenol A glycidyl ether prepolymers; epoxy-acrylate resins; epoxy ester resins; melamine-epoxy resins; polyols, epoxy dispersion; vinyl ester resins
Uses: polyvinyl chloride heat costabilisers

bisphenol A dimethacrylate
4,4'-isopropylidenediphenyl dimethacrylate; [3253-39-2]
$C_{23}H_{24}O_4$. M: 364.44.
Production:
• methyl methacrylate + bisphenol A (transesterification)

Uses: crosslinked acrylic resin comonomer

bisphenol A glycidyl ether prepolymers
epoxide resins; epoxy resins

n = 1–15. For n = 0 see bisphenol A diglycidyl ether. Viscous liquids or solids depending on the molecular weight. The resins are cured by reaction with amines, anhydrides or mercaptans when used for adhesive, encapsulation or structural purposes. They are also cured with polyester, phenolic or amino resin when used in surface coating applications.
Production:
• bisphenol A/bisphenol A diglycidyl ether + epichlorohydrin (condensation)
Derivatives:
epoxy-acrylate resins; epoxy ester resins; glycidyl-amine adducts; melamine-epoxy resins; phenolic-epoxy resins
Uses: cable jointing compounds; carboxyl-terminated thermosetting acrylic resin curing agent; electrical generator/motor insulation; electrical/electronic encapsulation; electrostatic powder coatings; epoxy-pitch coatings (marine paints); fibre-reinforced laminates (aircraft, chemical plant, tooling); adhesives (household, office, general industrial use); concrete adhesives/groutings; heavy electrical transformers/switchgear castings; heavy-duty road surfaces (runways, bridge paving); alkyd-amino resin modifier; moulding powders (high temperature electronic applications); nitrile-epoxy laminating adhesives; patterns/jigs/moulds; printed circuit boards; self-levelling/trowelled flooring systems; two-pot paints (anticorrosion, aircraft, marine, steel pipe coatings)

bisphenol AF
4,4′-hexafluoroisopropylidenediphenol; [1478-61-1]

$C_{15}H_{10}F_6O_2$. M: 336.23.
Production:
• hexafluoroacetone + phenol (condensation)
Derivatives:
bisphenol AF dimethacrylate
Uses: fluoroelastomer crosslinking agent

bisphenol AF dimethacrylate
1,1,1,3,3,3-hexafluoro-2,2-bis(4-methacryloxyphenyl)-propane

$C_{23}H_{18}F_6O_4$. M: 472.38.
Production:
• bisphenol AF + methacrylyl chloride (esterification)
Uses: crosslinked fluoroelastomer comonomer

bisphenol A propoxylates
Gerodiol (Rhone-Poulenc)

m+n = 3–16. Liquid at high PO content, solid at low PO content.
Production:
• bisphenol A + propylene oxide (epoxidation)
Uses:
alkyd/unsaturated polyester resin comonomer

bisphenol F diglycidyl ether

$C_{19}H_{20}O_4$. M: 312.37. Mixed product consisting of the 2,2′-, 4,4′- and 2,4′-isomers.
Production:
• phenol + formaldehyde + epichlorohydrin (condensation/ether formation)
Uses: epoxy resin comonomer

bisphenol H *See:* 4,4′-methylenebiscyclohexanol

bisphenol H diglycidyl ether

$C_{21}H_{36}O_4$. M: 352.52.
Production:
• 4,4′-methylenebiscyclohexanol + epichlorohydrin (ether formation)
Uses:
epoxy resin comonomer (weather-resistant applications)

bisphenol S *See:* 4,4′-dihydroxydiphenyl sulphone

4,4′-bis(2-sulphostyryl)biphenyl
[27344-41-8] (disodium salt)

$C_{28}H_{20}Na_2O_6S_2$. M: 562.57.

Production:
- biphenyl + benzaldehyde-2-sulphonic acid (chloro-methylation/Wittig reaction)

Uses: fluorescent brightening agent (detergents)

N,N'-bis(2,2,6,6-tetramethyl-4-piperidyl)-1,6-hexa-methylenediamine

Chimassorb 944 (Chimosa); [70624-18-9]

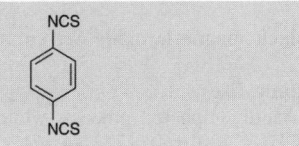

$C_{24}H_{50}N_4$. M: 394.69.
Production:
- 4-hydroxy-2,2,6,6-tetramethylpiperidine + hexa-methylenediamine (amine formation)

Derivatives:
hindered-amine cyanurates, polymeric
Uses: light stabiliser (plastics)

bisthiosemi

1,1'-methylenebis(thiosemicarbazide); [39603-48-0]

$$H_2NCNHNHCH_2NHNHCNH_2$$

$C_3H_{10}N_6S_2$. M: 194.28.
Production:
- thiosemicarbazide + formaldehyde (condensation)

Uses: rodenticide

bis(tri-*n*-butyltin)oxide *See:* tri-*n*-butyltin oxide

O,N-bis(trimethylsilyl)acetamide

$CH_3C\overset{OSi(CH_3)_3}{\underset{NSi(CH_3)_3}{}}$

$C_7H_{22}N_1O_1Si_2$. M: 192.44.
Production:
- acetonitrile + hexamethyldisiloxane (nitrile addition)

Uses:
silylating agent (chemical analysis, pharmaceutical synthesis)

BIT *See:* benzoisothiazolin-3-one

bitertanol

1-(biphenyl-4-yloxy)-3,3-dimethyl-1-(1H-1,2,4-triazol--1-yl)butan-2-ol; [55179-31-2]

$(CH_3)_3CCHCHO$—

$C_{20}H_{23}N_3O_2$. M: 337.42.

Production:
- *p*-phenylphenol + α-chloropinacolone + 1,2,4-triazole (dehydrochlorination/amine formation/carbonyl reduction)

Uses: fungicide

bithionol

2,2'-thiobis(4,6-dichlorophenol); 6,6'-thiobis(2,4-di-chlorophenol); [97-18-7]

$C_{12}H_6Cl_4O_2S_1$. M: 356.05.
Production:
- 2,4-dichlorophenol + sulphur dichloride (sulphide formation)

Uses:
anthelmintic drug

bitoscanate

phenylene-1,4-dithiocyanate; [4044-65-9]

$C_8H_4N_2S_2$. M: 192.26.
Production:
- *p*-phenylenediamine + carbon disulphide + ammonia (addition/oxidation)

Uses:
anthelmintic drug

bitumen

asphalt (USA)

Dark brown or black solid. Light brown 'albino' bitumens are also produced from some crude oils. Softening point: 25–170°C (Ring and Ball Method). Air oxidation, producing 'blown' bitumen, is used to form bitumens with higher penetration and softening points. For applications such as road making bitumen is sold as a blend with sand or aggregate as 'asphalt'. Natural asphalt - mixtures of rock and bitumen - are mined in various parts of the world. These ores generally contain a low bitumen content, typically, <10%. Deposits of higher-grade lake asphalt are also known, such as the Trinidad pitch lake. Here the bitumen content is about 50%. See also asphaltite and tar sands.

Production:
- long residue (vacuum distillation; coproduced with gas oil, vacuum/lubricant oils, distillates/short residue)

- short residue (solvent deasphalting; coproduced with deasphalted oil)
- short residue (Duo-Sol process; coproduced with brightstock)

Derivatives: carbon fibre
Uses:
canal/reservoir/sea defence linings; alkyd-modified aluminium bituminous paints; asphalt cutbacks (road repairs, surface dressing); asphalt emulsion binders (road repairs, surface dressing); asphalt mastics (road, roof, pathway surfacing); vehicle underbody sealants; binder (coal briquettes); construction adhesives; hot-laid asphalt roads; mineshaft/tunnel linings; paper sizing/coating emulsions; protective coatings (pipelines, submerged, underground steelwork); roofing/flooring membrane emulsions

bitumen, natural *See:* asphaltite

black ash *See:* barium sulphide

black copper *See:* copper, blister

black cyanide *See:* calcium cyanide

black magnetic oxide *See:* iron oxide black

blanc fixe
barium sulphate; process white; Pigment White 21 (CI); 77120 (CI); [7727-43-7]

$BaSO_4$

$Ba_1O_4S_1$. M: 233.40.
Production:
- barium sulphide + sodium sulphate (salt formation)
- barium chloride + sulphuric acid (salt formation)

Uses:
filler/pigment (floor coverings, paints, plastic foams); pigment/colour lake base (printing inks)

blasticidin S
[2079-00-7]

$C_{17}H_{26}N_8O_5$. M: 422.45.
Production:
- microbial fermentation medium + *Streptomyces griseochromogenes* bacteria (fermentation/extraction)

Uses: fungicide

bleached wood pulp
α-cellulose
The physical properties and constituents of wood pulp

vary with the species of tree from which it is derived and the processing method. Of importance for chemical processing is the α-cellulose content. Sulphite paper pulps contain ~89% α-cellulose and sulphate pulps a somewhat lower value. Further refining can be used to increase this level to almost pure α-cellulose.
Derivatives:
alkali cellulose; cellulose acetate; cellulose acetobutyrate; cellulose propionate; cellulose triacetate
Uses: filler

bleaching powder
lime, chlorinated
Grey-white powder with a strong chlorine odour. Tropical bleaching powder is a stabilised form of bleaching powder formed by the addition of calcium oxide to the standard product.
Production:
- calcium hydroxide + chlorine (salt formation)

Uses: sanitising agent (drinking water); tanning auxiliary; textile/laundry bleach

BMI *See:* bismethylenedianiline maleimide

BMP *See:* *m*-phenylenebismaleimide

BNPD *See:* 2-bromo-2-nitropropane-1,3-diol

bois de rose oil
rosewood oil
Colourless to pale yellow liquid. produced by steam distillation of wood from *Aniba rosaeodora* var. *amazonica*. d: 0.88 kg/l (20°C). Soluble in alcohol. The main constituent of this oil is linalool. It is produced mainly in Brazil.
Uses: perfume ingredient

BON acid *See:* β-oxynaphthoic acid

bone ash

$Ca_5OH(PO_4)_3$

$H_1Ca_5O_{13}P_3$. M: 502.32. Powder primarily consisting of basic calcium phosphate approximating to the formula above. Synthetic bone ash is also produced.
Production:
- bonemeal (calcination)

Uses: mould coatings (copper, stainless steel, bronze, aluminium casting); bone china raw material

bone char
bone black; bone charcoal
Predominantly tricalcium phosphate with about 10% carbon.
Production:
- bone, degreased (calcination)

Uses: sugar/solvent decolouring agent; filter medium

bone glue *See:* animal glue

bonemeal
Production:
• bone, degreased/bone, green (acid extraction; byproduct of animal glue production)
Derivatives: bone ash
Uses: fertiliser ingredient; animal feed supplement

boracic acid *See:* boric acid

borax *See:* sodium borate

Bordeaux mixture
[8011-63-0]

$$[Cu(OH)_2]_x.CaSO_4$$

Production:
• copper sulphate + calcium hydroxide (addition)
Uses: fungicide

boric acid
boracic acid; orthoboric acid; [10043-35-3]

$$H_3BO_4$$

$H_3B_1O_4$. M: 77.83. White, waxy solid. MP: 131°C. Releases water forming metaboric acid when heated further. d: 1.44 kg/l (15°C). Solubility in water: 63.5 g/l water (30°C).
Production:
• sodium borate + sulphuric acid (neutralisation)
Derivatives:
ammonium borate; ammonium pentaborate; boron carbide; boron oxide; boron trifluoride; ferroboron; fluoboric acid; 2,2′-oxybis(4,4,6-trimethyl)-1,3,2-dioxaborinane; Pigment Green 18; potassium pentaborate; potassium tetraborate; trimethyl borate; tris(triethylene glycol monomethyl ether)borate; zinc borate
Uses: buffering agent (chromeplating, aluminium anodising); oxidation catalyst; welding/brazing flux component; domestic insecticide; fire-retardant (wood, paper); antiseptic; preservative (natural rubber latex); Sol-gel glass process raw material

borneol
2-bornanol; bornyl alcohol; [507-70-0]

$C_{10}H_{18}O_1$. M: 154.25. Borneol is the *endo* isomer of the displayed structure. Available commercially as the (−)-enantiomer. MP: 208°C. d: 1.01 kg/l (20°C). Soluble in alcohol, oxygenated and aromatic solvents.
Production:
• bornyl acetate (ester hydrolysis)
Uses: fragrance ingredient

bornyl acetate
[76-49-3]

$C_{12}H_{20}O_2$. M: 196.29. Colourless liquid with a camphor-like odour. BP: 223°C. d: 0.98 kg/l (20°C).
Production:
• β-pinene + acetic acid (esterification)
Derivatives:
borneol
Uses: fragrance ingredient (soap, household products)

boron carbide
[12069-32-8]

$$B_4C$$

C_1B_4. M: 55.25. Hard, black, crystalline particles. d: 2.6 kg/l. MP: 2,350°C.
Production:
• boric acid + metallurgical coke (thermal reduction)
• boron oxide + magnesium + metallurgical coke (reduction)
Derivatives:
boron trichloride
Uses: abrasion-resistant nozzles and surfaces; polishing papers; grinding wheel abrasive; metal composite reinforcing fibre (armourplating)

boron nitride
[10043-11-5]

$$BN$$

B_1N_1. M: 24.82. Hard, white, crystalline particles. MP: 3,000°C. Boron nitride exists in a hexagonal form, with a graphite-like structure, and in a cubic form with a diamond-like structure. High-pressure, high-temperature treatment of hexagonal boron nitride produces the cubic form. It is the hardest material know after diamond.
Production:
• boron oxide + ammonia (reaction)
Uses:
grinding wheel abrasive; high-temperature lubricants; metal melting crucibles; refractory linings (rocket motors, plasma torches)

boron oxide
boric oxide; [1303-86-2]

$$B_2O_3$$

B_2O_3. M: 69.62. Colourless, hygroscopic, glassy solid. d: 2.46 kg/l. MP: 450°C.
Production:
• boric acid (thermal dehydration)

Derivatives:
boron carbide; boron nitride; ferroboron; titanium di-boride
Uses: flux; acidic catalyst; glass raw material

boron trichloride
[10294-34-5]

$$BCl_3$$

B_1Cl_3. M: 117.17. Colourless liquid/gas. BP: 12°C. Soluble in water with decomposition.
Production:
• boron carbide + chlorine (chlorination)
Uses:
catalyst; semiconductor dopant; boron vapour deposition raw material (boron fibres)

boron trifluoride
boron fluoride; [7637-07-2]

$$BF_3$$

B_1F_3. M: 67.80. Colourless gas. BP: -101°C. Highly soluble in water with decomposition.
Production:
• sodium borate + fluorspar + oleum (reaction)
• boric acid + hydrofluoric acid (reaction)
Derivatives:
boron trifluoride etherate; boron trifluoride monoethylamine; diethylamine borane; dimethylamine borane
Uses:
Friedel-Crafts reaction/esterification catalyst; Ziegler catalyst component

boron trifluoride etherate

$$BF_3.O(C_2H_5)_2$$

$C_4H_{10}B_1F_3O_1$. M: 141.92. Liquid. BP: 125–126°C. d: 1.13 kg/l (25°C). Fumes in moist air. Hydrolysed by water.
Production:
• boron trifluoride + diethyl ether (complex formation)
Uses: alkylation/acylation/condensation catalyst

boron trifluoride monoethylamine
ethylamine-boron trifluoride; [75-23-0]

$$BF_3.NH_2C_2H_5$$

$C_2H_7B_1F_3N_1$. M: 112.89.
Production:
• boron trifluoride + ethylamine (complex formation)
Uses: epoxy resin curing agent

bourbonal *See:* ethyl vanillin

BP *See:* benzoyl peroxide

BPA *See:* bisphenol A

BPDA
See: biphenyl-3,3′,4,4′-tetracarboxylic dianhydride

BPH *See:* 2,2′-methylenebis(4-methyl-6-*t*-butylphenol)

BPI *See:* *m*-phenylenebismaleimide

BPIC *See:* *t*-butyl peroxyisopropylcarbonate

BPMC *See:* fenobucarb

BPO *See:* benzoyl peroxide

BR *See:* polybutadiene, latex; polybutadiene, rubber

BRA *See:* 2,4-dihydroxybenzoic acid

brass
Copper-zinc alloy. Cartridge brass contains 70% Cu, 30% Zn and 60/40 brass, 60% Cu, 40% Zn. Free-cutting brass is a Cu-Zn-Pb alloy containing 2–5% lead. Aluminium, iron, tin and manganese are minor constituents of certain types of brass.
Production:
• copper + zinc + lead bullion (melt blending)
Uses:
cartridge brass (ammunition cases); free-cutting brass (machined components, screws); 60-40 brass (ornaments, handles, fittings)

Bremen Blue *See:* copper carbonate, basic

brightstock
Highly viscous lubricant base oils produced from paraffinic crude oils. Pour point: -18°C. d: ~0.88 kg/l. Viscosity at 40°C: ~400 mm²/s. Viscosity index: 100–115. The paraffin content is typically 70% with the majority of the remainder being naphthenic hydrocarbons.
Production:
• deasphalted oil (solvent extraction)
• short residue (Duo-Sol process; coproduced with bitumen)
• lubricant oils, distillates (hydrocracking; coproduced with lubricant oils, hydrocracked)
Uses:
cable lubricants; cylinder oils; 2-stroke oils; thickening agent (heavy engine oils)

brine *See:* sodium chloride, natural

British gum *See:* dextrin

brodifacoum
3-[3-(4′-bromobiphenyl-4-yl)-1,2,3,4-tetrahydro-1-naphthyl]-4-hydroxycoumarin; [56073-10-0]
$C_{31}H_{23}Br_1O_3$. M: 523.42.

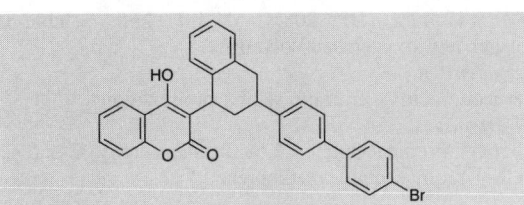

Production:
• difenacoum (ring bromination)
Uses: rodenticide

Broenner's acid

2-aminonaphthalene-6-sulphonic acid; 6-aminonaphthalene-2-sulphonic acid; 2-naphthylamine-6-sulphonic acid; [93-00-5]

$C_{10}H_9N_1O_3S_1$. M: 223.04.
Production:
• Schaeffer's acid + ammonia (ammoniation)
Derivatives: Direct Red 4; Direct Red 72; Direct Red 73; Mordant Yellow 3

bromacil

5-bromo-3-s-butyl-6-methyluracil; [314-40-9]

$C_9H_{13}Br_1N_2O_2$. M: 261.11.
Production:
• s-butylamine + sodium cyanate + ethyl acetoacetate + bromine (cyanate addition/condensation/alpha bromination)
Uses: herbicide

bromadiolone

3-[3-(4′-bromobiphenyl-4-yl)-3-hydroxy-1-phenyl-propyl]-4-hydroxycoumarin; broprodifacoum; [28772-56-7]

$C_{30}H_{23}Br_1O_4$. M: 527.41.
Production:
• benzaldehyde + 4-acetylbiphenyl + 4-hydroxycoumarin (carbonyl condensation/condensation/carbonyl reduction/ring bromination)
Uses: rodenticide

bromamine acid

1-amino-4-bromoanthraquinone-2-sulphonic acid;
1-bromo-4-aminoanthraquinone-3-sulphonic acid;
[116-81-4]

$C_{14}H_8Br_1N_1O_5S_1$. M: 382.17.
Production:
• 1-aminoanthraquinone + chlorosulphonic acid + bromine (chlorosulphonation/ring bromination)
Derivatives:
Acid Blue 25; Acid Blue 40; Acid Blue 41; Acid Blue 62; Acid Blue 129; Acid Blue 138; Acid Blue 145; Acid Blue 230; Direct Green 28; Pigment Red 177; Reactive Blue 2; Reactive Blue 4; Reactive Blue 19; Reactive Blue 94

bromazepam

[1812-30-2]

$C_{14}H_{10}Br_1N_3O_1$. M: 316.15.
Production:
• aniline + picolinic acid + acetic anhydride + ethyl glycinate hydrochloride (Friedel-Crafts acylation/acetylation/ring bromination/amide hydrolysis/condensation)
Uses:
anxiolytic/sedative drug

bromelain

E.C.3.4.22.5 (Enzyme Commission); [9001-00-7]
Dried extract of pineapple (*Ananas comosus*) fruit and stems.
Uses:
beer chillproofing agent; meat tenderiser; food texturising agent

bromhexine

bromhexidine; [3572-43-8]; [611-75-6] (hydrochloride)

$C_{14}H_{20}Br_2N_2$. M: 376.13. Available commercially as the free base or as the hydrochloride salt.

Production:
- *o*-nitrobenzaldehyde + *N*-methylcyclohexylamine (reductive amination/nitro reduction/ring bromination)

Uses: expectorant drug

bromine

[7726-95-6]

Br₂

Br₂. M: 159.81. Reddish-brown, mobile liquid with a pungent odour. BP: 59°C. FP: -7°C. d: 3.09 kg/l (20°C). Solubility in water: 35 g/l water (20°C).

Production:
- seawater + chlorine (cold debromination process)
- natural brines/brine, residual + chlorine (hot debromination process)

Derivatives:
bromacil; bromamine acid; bromoacetic acid; bromoacetyl bromide; *p*-bromoaniline; bromobenzene; bromochlorodifluoromethane; bromochloromethane; bromoform; 2-bromo-2-nitropropane-1,3-diol; α-bromopropionic acid; 5-bromopyrimidine; β-bromostyrene; *N*-bromosuccinimide; bromotrifluoromethane; butyl rubber, brominated; chlorbromuron; cyanogen bromide; cyclopropyl bromide; decabromodiphenyl oxide; dibromobutanediol-epichlorohydrin adduct; 1,3-dibromo-5,5-dimethylhydantoin; dibromoethyldibromocyclohexane; ethylene bis(5,6-dibromonorbornane-2,3-dicarboximide); ethylene dibromide; halothane; hexabromocyclododecane; hydrogen bromide, anhydrous; methylene bromide; naled; octabromodiphenyl oxide; pentabromodiphenyl oxide; potassium bromate; tetrabromobisphenol A; tetrabromoethane; tetrabromophthalic anhydride; tralomethrin; 2,4,6-tribromoaniline; 2,4,6-tribromophenol

Uses:
ring bromination reagent; water disinfectant

bromine chloride

[13863-41-7]

BrCl

Br₁Cl₁. M: 115.35. Reddish-brown liquid or gas. BP: 5°C. Decomposes at 10°C. Soluble in water with hydrolysis.

Production:
- methylene chloride + bromine (bromination; byproduct of bromochloromethane/methylene bromide production)

Derivatives:
1-bromo-3-chloro-5,5-dimethylhydantoin

Uses: wastewater treatment chemical

bromoacetic acid

MBAA; monobromoacetic acid; [79-08-3]

BrCH₂COOH

C₂H₃Br₁O₂. M: 138.94. Hygroscopic, crystalline solid.

MP: 47–49°C. BP: 208°C. d: 1.93 kg/l. Soluble in water and oxygenated solvents.

Production:
- acetic acid + bromine (alpha bromination)

Derivatives:
benzyl bromoacetate; 1,4-bis(bromoacetoxy)-2-butene; ethyl bromoacetate; methoprene

bromoacetyl bromide

[598-21-0]

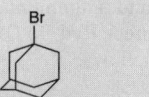

C₂H₂Br₂O₁. M: 201.85. Liquid. BP: 148–150°C. d: 2.31 kg/l (22°C). Hydrolysed by water.

Production:
- acetic acid + bromine (alpha bromination)

Derivatives:
cefotetan; labetalol; sotalol

1-bromoadamantane

[768-90-1]

C₁₀H₁₅Br₁. M: 215.13.

Production:
- adamantane (bromination)

Derivatives: amantadine; rimantidine

p-bromoaniline

4-bromoaniline; [106-40-1]

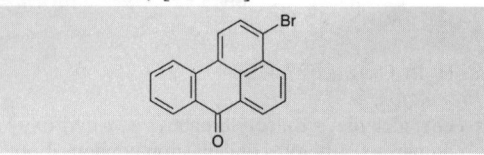

C₆H₆Br₁N₁. M: 172.03. Crystalline solid. MP: 62–64°C. Insoluble in water. Soluble in oxygenated solvents.

Production:
- acetanilide + bromine (ring bromination/amide hydrolysis)

Derivatives: metobromuron; resorantel

3-bromobenzanthrone

bromobenzanthrone; [81-96-9]

C₁₇H₉Br₁O₁. M: 309.16. Yellow needles. MP: 160–164°C. Soluble in alcohol.

Production:
- benzanthrone (ring bromination)

Derivatives: Vat Green 3

bromobenzene
phenyl bromide; [108-86-1]

$C_6H_5Br_1$. M: 157.01. Colourless liquid with an aromatic odour. BP: 155–156°C. MP: -30°C. d: 1.50 kg/l (20°C). Insoluble in water. Miscible with most organic solvents.
Production:
- benzene + bromine (ring bromination)

Derivatives:
bromopropylate; clobazam; fenoprofen; flurbiprofen; phenylmagnesium bromide
Uses: speciality solvent

***p*-bromobenzyl cyanide**
4-bromobenzyl cyanide; 4-bromophenylacetonitrile; [16532-79-9]

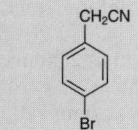

$C_8H_6Br_1N_1$. M: 196.05. Pale yellow, crystalline solid. MP: 47–49°C. Insoluble in water. Soluble in aromatic solvents.
Production:
- *p*-toluidine + potassium bromide + sodium cyanide (diazotisation/Sandmeyer reaction/side-chain chlorination/cyanidation)

Derivatives:
brompheniramine

bromobutide
2-bromo-3,3-dimethyl-*N*-(1-methyl-1-phenylethyl)butyramide; [74712-19-9]

$(CH_3)_3CCHCHNHC \underset{\underset{CH_3}{|}}{\overset{\overset{O}{\|}}{}}$

$C_{15}H_{22}Br_1N_1O_1$. M: 312.25.
Production:
- isobutylene + trimethyl orthoacetate + 2-phenyl-2-propylamine (condensation/alpha bromination/amide formation)

Uses: herbicide

α-bromobutyric acid
2-bromobutyric acid; [80-58-0]

$CH_3CH_2CHCOOH$ (Br)

$C_4H_7Br_1O_2$. M: 167.00. Colourless, oily liquid. BP: 181°C (34 kPa). Decomposes on further heating. FP: -4°C. Soluble in oxygenated solvents. The commercial product is a racemic mixture.
Production:
- *n*-butyric acid (alpha bromination)

Derivatives: 2-phenoxybutyric acid

***p*-bromochlorobenzene**
1-bromo-4-chlorobenzene; [106-39-8]

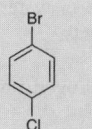

$C_6H_4Br_1Cl_1$. M: 191.45. Crystalline solid. MP: 66–68°C. BP: 196°C. d: 1.58 kg/l (71°C). Insoluble in water. Soluble in aromatic and chlorinated solvents.
Production:
- chlorobenzene (ring bromination)

Derivatives: 4-(4-chlorophenyl)-4-hydroxypiperidine

bromochlorodifluoromethane
R12B1; BCF (ICI); Halon 1211; [353-59-3]

CF_2ClBr

$C_1Br_1Cl_1F_2$. M: 165.36. Colourless, almost odourless, liquified gas. BP: 1°C. d: 1.85 kg/l (15°C).
Production:
- chlorodifluoromethane + bromine (bromination)

Uses: fire extinguishant gas

1-bromo-3-chloro-5,5-dimethylhydantoin
3-bromo-1-chloro-5,5-dimethylhydantoin; Halobrom (Dead Sea Bromine)

$C_5H_6Br_1Cl_1N_2O_2$. M: 241.46.
Production:
- 5,5-dimethylhydantoin + bromine chloride (halogenation)

Uses: biocide (cooling water systems, swimming pools)

bromochloromethane
chlorobromomethane; CBM; [74-97-5]

CH_2BrCl

$C_1H_2Br_1Cl_1$. M: 129.38. Colourless liquid. BP: 68°C. FP: -88°C. d: 1.91 kg/l (25°C). Very slightly soluble in water.

Production:
- methylene chloride + bromine (bromination; coproduced with methylene bromide)

Derivatives: chlormephos

Uses:
fire extinguishant fluid; process solvent

1-bromo-3-chloropropane
3-bromo-1-chloropropane; trimethylene chlorobromide; BCP; [109-70-6]

BrCH$_2$CH$_2$CH$_2$Cl

C$_3$H$_6$Br$_1$Cl$_1$. M: 157.43. Liquid. BP: 142–145°C. d: 1.46 kg/l (25°C). Insoluble in water. Soluble in oxygenated and chlorinated solvents.

Production:
- allyl chloride + hydrogen bromide, anhydrous (addition)

Derivatives:
cyclomethycaine; fluphenazine; opipramol; pentoxifylline; perphenazine; piperocaine; prochlorperazine; propentofylline; reproterol; trazodone; trifluoperazine; urapidil; verapamil

2-bromo-2-chloro-1,1,1-trifluoroethane *See:* halothane

bromocyclopropane *See:* cyclopropyl bromide

6-bromo-2,4-dinitroaniline
[1817-73-8]

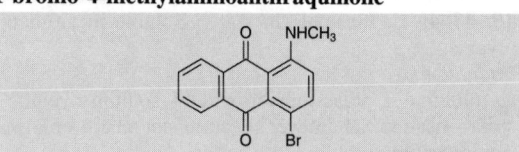

C$_6$H$_4$Br$_1$N$_3$O$_4$. M: 262.02. Solid. MP: 148–150°C.

Production:
- 2,4-dinitroaniline (ring bromination)

Derivatives:
Disperse Blue 79

Uses: dyestuffs intermediate

bromofenoxim
3,5-dibromo-4-hydroxybenzaldehyde 2,4-dinitrophenyloxime; [13181-17-4]

C$_{13}$H$_7$Br$_2$N$_3$O$_6$. M: 461.02.

Production:
- *p*-hydroxybenzaldehyde + hydroxylamine sulphate + 1-chloro-2,4-dinitrobenzene (ring bromination/imine formation/ether formation)

Uses: herbicide

p-bromofluorobenzene
4-fluorobromobenzene; [460-00-4]

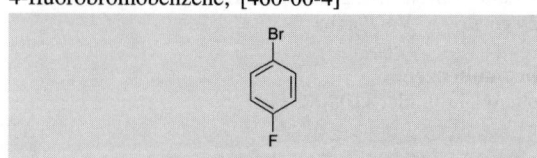

C$_6$H$_4$Br$_1$F$_1$. M: 175.00. Liquid. BP: 152–155°C. MP: -17°C. d: 1.49 kg/l (20°C). Insoluble in water. Soluble in oxygenated solvents.

Production:
- fluorobenzene (ring bromination)

Derivatives: 4,4-bis(*p*-fluorophenyl)butyl chloride; flusilazole; flutriafol

bromoform
tribromomethane; [75-25-2]

CHBr$_3$

C$_1$H$_1$Br$_3$. M: 252.73. Liquid with chloroform-like odour. BP: 146–150°C. MP: 8°C. d: 2.89 kg/l (20°C). Slightly soluble in water. Miscible with oxygenated, chlorinated and aromatic solvents.

Production:
- acetone + bromine (haloform reaction)

Derivatives:
(*1R*)-*cis*-3-(2,2-dibromovinyl)-2,2-dimethylcyclopropanecarboxylic acid

Uses: high-density solvent (mineral separation)

1-bromo-4-methylaminoanthraquinone

C$_{15}$H$_{10}$Br$_1$N$_1$O$_2$. M: 316.15. Bright red needles. MP: 194°C. Soluble in oxygenated solvents.

Production:
- 1-aminoanthraquinone + dimethyl sulphate (methylation/ring bromination)

Derivatives:
Acid Blue 27; Acid Violet 80; Basic Blue 22

5-bromo-5-nitro-1,3-dioxane
Bronidox L (Henkel); [30007-47-7]

C$_4$H$_6$Br$_1$N$_1$O$_4$. M: 212.00.

Production:
- 2-bromo-2-nitropropane-1,3-diol + formaldehyde (condensation)

Uses: preservative

2-bromo-2-nitropropane-1,3-diol
BNPD; bronopol; [52-51-7]

$$O_2NC(CH_2OH)_2 \overset{Br}{|}$$

$C_3H_6Br_1N_1O_4$. M: 199.99. Off-white, crystalline powder. MP: >110°C. Bulk density: 0.72 kg/l. Soluble in water and alcohol. Insoluble in aliphatic hydrocarbons.
Production:
• nitromethane + formaldehyde + bromine (hydroxy-methylation/bromination)
Derivatives: 5-bromo-5-nitro-1,3-dioxane
Uses: bactericide (cosmetics, toiletries); biocide (metalworking fluids)

4-bromophenylacetonitrile
See: p-bromobenzyl cyanide

bromopride
[4093-35-0]

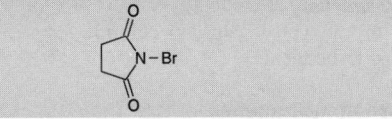

$C_{14}H_{22}Br_1N_3O_2$. M: 344.25.
Production:
• *p*-aminosalicylic acid + *N,N*-diethylethylenediamine (acetylation/methylation/ring bromination/amide formation/amide hydrolysis)
Uses: antiemetic/stomach therapy drug

α-bromopropionic acid
2-bromopropanoic acid; ABPA; [598-72-1]

$$CH_3CHCOOH \overset{Br}{|}$$

$C_3H_5Br_1O_2$. M: 152.97. Crystalline solid. MP: 25–26°C. BP: 204°C. d: 1.70 kg/l (20°C). Soluble in water and oxygenated solvents.
Production:
• propionic acid + bromine (alpha bromination)
Derivatives: carticaine; naproxen; prilocaine

bromopropylate
isopropyl 4,4′-dibromobenzilate; [18181-80-1]

$C_{17}H_{16}Br_2O_3$. M: 428.13.

Production:
• bromobenzene + chloral + isopropanol (carbonyl condensation/oxidation/esterification)
Uses: acaricide

2-bromopyridine
[109-04-6]

$C_5H_4Br_1N_1$. M: 157.99. Liquid. BP: 192–194°C. d: 1.66 kg/l (15°C). Insoluble in water. Soluble in most organic solvents.
Production:
• pyridine (ring bromination)
Derivatives:
carbinoxamine; chloropyramine; triprolidine

5-bromopyrimidine
[4595-59-9]

$C_4H_3Br_1N_2$. M: 158.97.
Production:
• uracil + bromine (ring bromination/hydrogenation)
Derivatives:
ancymidol; fenarimol; flurprimidol; nuarimol

β-bromostyrene
w-bromostyrene; bromostyrol; [103-64-0]

$C_8H_7Br_1$. M: 183.05. Liquid with a strong, hyacinth-like odour.
Production:
• cinnamic acid + bromine (addition/dehydrobromination/decarboxylation)
Uses:
fragrance ingredient

N-bromosuccinimide
NBS; [128-08-5]

$C_4H_4Br_1N_1O_2$. M: 177.98. Crystalline solid. MP: 178°C with slight decomposition. d: 2.10 kg/l. Slightly soluble in water.
Production:
• succinimide + bromine (bromination)
Uses:
bromination/alcohol oxidation reagent

bromotrifluoromethane
R13B1; Halon 1301; [75-63-8]

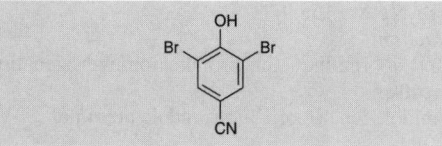

CF₃Br

$C_1Br_1F_3$. M: 148.90. Colourless, liquified gas. BP: -58°C. d: 1.58 kg/l (25°C).
Production:
• chlorotrifluoromethane/trifluoromethane + bromine (bromination)
Derivatives: flurprimidol
Uses: fire extinguishant gas

5-bromovaleric acid
5-bromopentanoic acid; [2067-33-6]

BrCH₂CH₂CH₂CH₂COOH

$C_5H_9Br_1O_2$. M: 181.02.
Production:
• 2-methoxydihydropyran + hydrobromic acid (hydrolysis/addition)
Derivatives: allethrolone

bromoxynil
3,5-dibromo-4-hydroxybenzonitrile; [1089-84-5]

$C_7H_3Br_2N_1O_1$. M: 276.92.
Production:
• *p*-hydroxybenzonitrile (ring bromination)
Derivatives:
bromoxynil octanoate
Uses: herbicide

bromoxynil octanoate
2,6-dibromo-4-cyanophenyl octanoate; [1689-99-2]

$C_{15}H_{17}Br_2N_1O_2$. M: 403.12.
Production:
• bromoxynil + caprylyl chloride (esterification)
Uses: herbicide

brompheniramine
dexbrompheniramine ((+)-enantiomer); [86-22-6]; [132-21-8] ((+)-enantiomer); [980-71-2] (hydrogen maleate)
$C_{16}H_{19}Br_1N_2$. M: 319.24. Available commercially as the racemic mixture or (+)-enantiomer maleate salts.
Production:
• *p*-bromobenzyl cyanide + 2-chloropyridine + 2-dimethylaminoethyl chloride hydrochloride

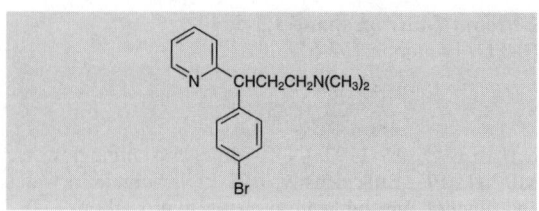

(condensation/condensation/nitrile hydrolysis/decarboxylation)
Uses: antihistamine drug

BRON *See:* dibenzosuberone

bronopol *See:* 2-bromo-2-nitropropane-1,3-diol

broprodifacoum *See:* bromadiolone

brucine
dimethoxystrychnine; [357-57-3]; [4845-99-2] (sulphate)
$C_{23}H_{26}N_2O_4$. M: 394.47. Alkaloid extracted from *Strychnos nux-vomica* seeds. Available as the free base or as the sulphate salt.
Uses:
alcohol denaturant; racemate separation agent

BSG *See:* bismuth subgallate

t-**BTA** *See:* *t*-butyltoluenediamine

BTDA *See:* benzophenonetetracarboxylate dianhydride

BTMAC *See:* benzyltrimethylammonium chloride

BTX *See:* aromatics, mixed

bufexamac
[2438-72-4]

CH₃CH₂CH₂CH₂O— —CH₂CNHOH

$C_{12}H_{17}N_1O_3$. M: 223.28.
Production:
• *p*-hydroxyacetophenone + *n*-butyl bromide + hydroxylamine sulphate (ether formation/Willgerodt reaction/amide formation)
Uses:
antiinflammatory/analgesic drug

bumetanide
[28395-03-1]

$C_{17}H_{20}N_2O_5S_1$. M: 364.41.

Production:
- 4-chloro-3-nitrobenzoic acid + chlorosulphonic acid + ammonia + phenol + *n*-butanol (chlorosulphonation/sulphonamide formation/ether formation/nitro reduction/amine formation)

Uses: diuretic drug

buphenine

nylidrin; [447-41-6]; [849-55-8] (hydrochloride)

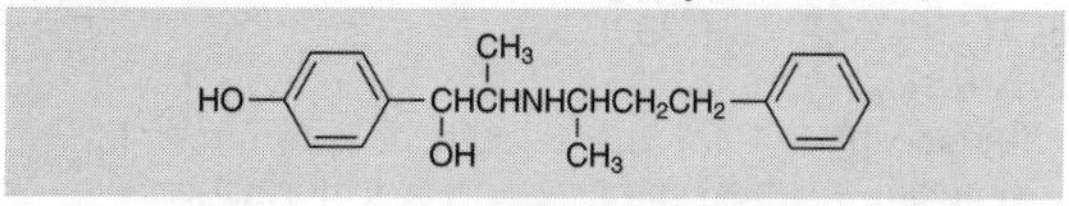

$C_{19}H_{25}N_1O_2$. M: 299.42. Available commercially as the hydrochloride.
Production:
- benzylacetone + ammonia + *p*-hydroxypropiophenone (reductive ammoniation/alpha bromination/amine formation/carbonyl reduction)

Uses:
vasodilator drug

bupirimate

5-butyl-2-ethylamino-6-methylpyrimidin-4-yl dimethylsulphamate; [41483-43-6]

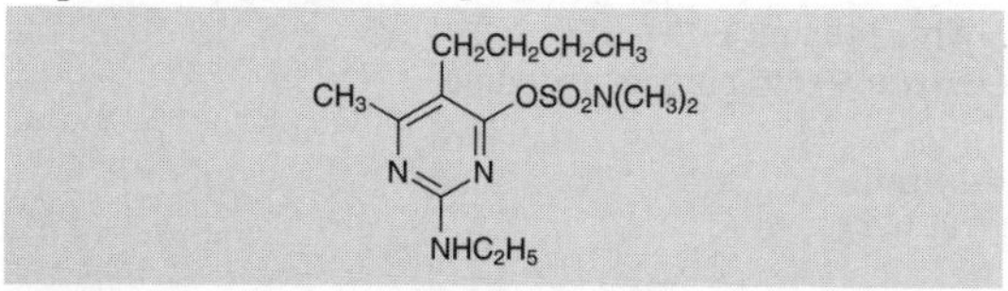

$C_{13}H_{24}N_4O_3S_1$. M: 316.42.
Production:
- ethirimol + dimethylsulphamyl chloride (sulphonation)

Uses: fungicide

bupivacaine

[2180-92-9]; [18010-40-7] (hydrochloride)

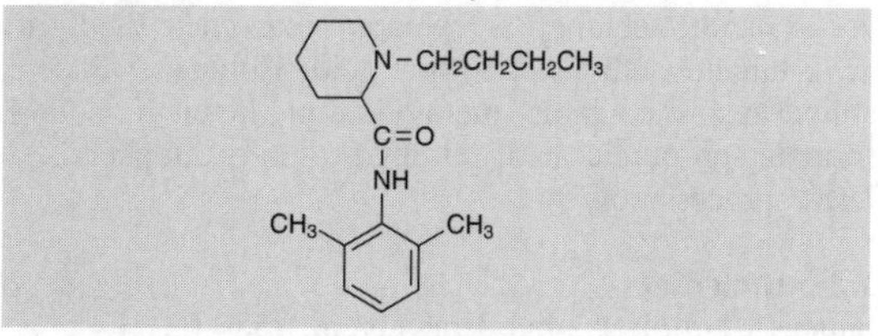

$C_{18}H_{28}N_2O_1$. M: 288.43. Available commercially as the free base or hydrochloride.
Production:
- picolinic acid + 2,6-xylidine + *n*-butyl bromide (amide formation/quaternisation/hydrogenation)

Uses:
local anaesthetic drug

buprenorphine

[52485-79-7]
$C_{29}H_{41}N_1O_4$. M: 467.66.

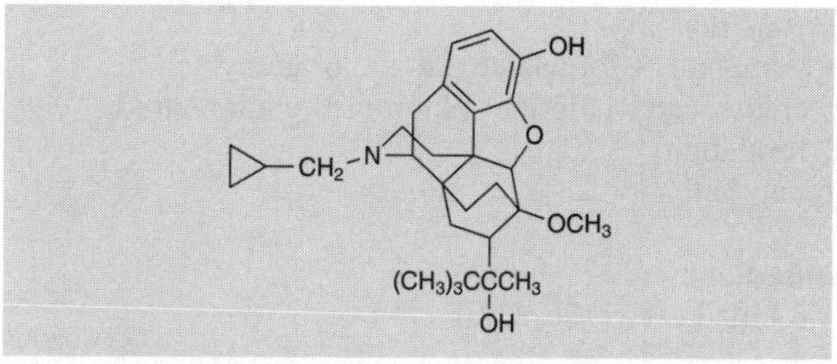

Production:
- pinacolone + acetylene + thebaine + cyclopropylmethyl bromide (ethynylation/Diels-Alder cycloaddition/hydrogenation/demethylation/amine formation/demethylation)

Uses: analgesic drug

buprofezin

2-*t*-butylimino-3-isopropyl-5-phenyl-1,3,5-thiadiazinan-4-one; [69327-76-0]

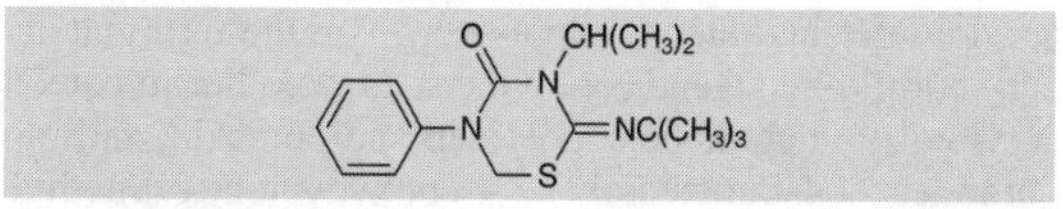

$C_{16}H_{23}N_3O_1S_1$. M: 305.44.
Production:
- aniline + formaldehyde + phosgene + *N*-isopropyl-*N'*-*t*-butylthiourea (imine formation/phosgenation/condensation)

Uses:
acaricide/insecticide

buspirone

[36505-84-7]

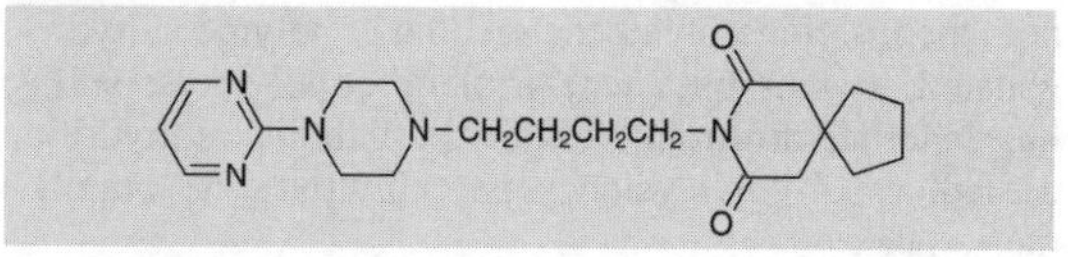

$C_{21}H_{31}N_5O_2$. M: 385.51. Available commercially as the hydrochloride.
Production:
- 2-aminopyrimidine + diethanolamine + 4-chlorobutyronitrile + 3,3-tetramethyleneglutaric acid (amine formation/amine formation/nitrile reduction/amide formation)

Uses: tranquilliser drug

butachlor

N-butoxymethyl-2-chloro-2',6'-diethylacetanilide; [23184-66-9]

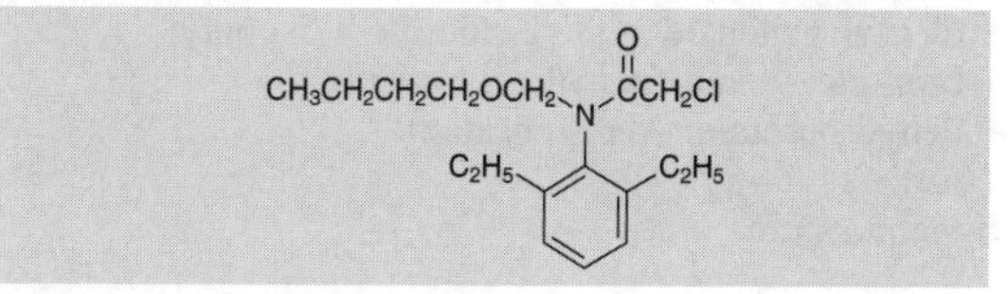

$C_{17}H_{26}Cl_1N_1O_2$. M: 311.86.

Production:
- *n*-butanol + formaldehyde + 2,6-diethylaniline + chloroacetyl chloride (chloromethylation/amide formation)

Uses: herbicide

butadiene
1,3-butadiene; [106-99-0]

$$CH_2=CHCH=CH_2$$

C_4H_6. M: 54.09. Colourless gas. BP: -4°C. FP: -109°C. d: 0.62 kg/l (20°C). Soluble in most organic solvents.
Production:
- C_4-stream, steam-cracked/C_4-stream, refinery (solvent extraction; coproduced with raffinate I)
- raffinate II (Texas Petrochemicals Oxo-D process/ Phillips O-X-D process)
- *n*-butane (catalytic dehydrogenation)

Derivatives:
acrylonitrile-butadiene copolymers, amine-terminated; acrylonitrile-butadiene copolymers, carboxyl-terminated; acrylonitrile-butadiene copolymers; adiponitrile; anthraquinone; 1,4-butanediol; 3,4-epoxycyclohexylmethyl 3,4-epoxycyclohexylcarboxylate; 3,4-epoxy-6-methylcyclohexylmethyl 3,4-epoxy-6-methylcyclohexane carboxylate; ethylidene norbornene; 1,4-hexadiene; *n*-octanol; 1,2-polybutadiene; polybutadiene, hydrogenated; polybutadiene, hydroxyl-terminated; polybutadiene latex; polybutadiene rubber; polybutadiene oil; sebacic acid; squalane; styrene-butadiene copolymers, carboxylated; styrene-butadiene copolymers, high-styrene; styrene-butadiene copolymers, latex; styrene-butadiene copolymers, rubber; styrene-butadiene block copolymers, branched; styrene-butadiene random copolymers, hydrogenated; styrene-butadiene triblock copolymers; sulfolane; tetrahydrofuran; tetrahydrophthalic anhydride; trimedlure; 4-vinylcyclohexene; vinylpyridine copolymers, latex

butadiene rubber *See:* polybutadiene, rubber

butalbital
[77-26-9]

$C_{11}H_{16}N_2O_3$. M: 224.26.
Production:
- diethyl malonate + allyl chloride + isobutyl bromide + urea (dehydrochlorination/ dehydrobromination/cyclisation)

Uses:
hypnotic drug

butamben *See:* *n*-butyl *p*-aminobenzoate

butamifos
O-ethyl *O*-6-nitro-*m*-tolyl *s*-butylphosphoramidothioate; [36335-67-8]

$C_{13}H_{21}N_2O_4P_1S_1$. M: 332.35.
Production:
- thiophosphoryl chloride + ethanol + 6-nitro-*m*-cresol + *s*-butylamine (dehydrochlorination/ dehydrochlorination/dehydrochlorination)

Uses: herbicide

butane, mixed

$$C_4H_{10}$$

Gas processing plant or refinery stream containing mainly isobutane and *n*-butane. The proportion of each varies with the source. The unreacted stream from refinery raffinate II processes is usually mixed butanes.
Production:
- liquified petroleum gas (fractionation; coproduced with propane)

Derivatives: *n*-butane; isobutane

n-butane
[106-97-8]

$$CH_3CH_2CH_2CH_3$$

C_4H_{10}. M: 58.12. Colourless gas. BP: 0°C. d: 0.58 kg/l (25°C). Slightly soluble in water. Flash point: -73°C.
Production:
- butane, mixed (fractionation; coproduced with isobutane)

Derivatives:
acetic acid; acetone; acetylene; butadiene; *n*-butyric acid; ethanol; ethylene; formic acid; isobutane; maleic anhydride; methanol; methyl ethyl ketone; methyl formate; propionic acid; tetrahydrofuran; thiophene
Uses: process solvent

1,2-butanediol
butane-1,2-diol; 1,2-butylene glycol; [584-03-2]

$C_4H_{10}O_2$. M: 90.12. Colourless liquid. BP: 195–197°C. FP: -10°C. Miscible with water. Soluble in alcohol.
Production:
- 1,2-butylene oxide (hydration)
- butadiene + oxygen + hydrogen (Mitsubishi process; byproduct of 1,4-butanediol/tetrahydrofuran production)

Uses: dyestuffs intermediate

1,3-butanediol
butane-1,3-diol; 1,3-butylene glycol; [107-88-0]

$$CH_3CHCH_2CH_2OH$$
$$|$$
$$OH$$

$C_4H_{10}O_2$. M: 90.12. Colourless liquid. BP: 207°C. d: 1.00 kg/l (20°C). Soluble in water and oxygenated solvents.
Production:
• acetaldehyde (aldol condensation/hydrogenation)
Derivatives:
1,3-butanediol dimethacrylate; polyester resins, carboxylated; polyester resins, hydroxylated; polymeric plasticisers; polyurethane, cast elastomers
Uses:
oil-free alkyd/unsaturated polyester resin comonomer

1,4-butanediol
butane-1,4-diol; 1,4-butylene glycol; 1,4-BDO; BDO; [110-63-4]

$$HOCH_2CH_2CH_2CH_2OH$$

$C_4H_{10}O_2$. M: 90.12. Colourless liquid or solid. MP: 19°C. BP: 137–138°C (2.7 kPa). Miscible with water, ethanol and acetone.
Production:
• 1,4-butynediol (hydrogenation)
• butadiene + oxygen + hydrogen (Mitsubishi process; coproduced with tetrahydrofuran)
• allyl alcohol + synthesis gas (Arco hydroformylation process)
• maleic anhydride (hydrogenation; coproduced with tetrahydrofuran)
Derivatives:
1,4-butanediol β-aminocrotonate; 1,4-butanediol diglycidyl ether; 1,4-butanediol dimethacrylate; γ-butyrolactone; copolyester, thermoplastic elastomers; 1,4-dibromobutane; 1,4-dichlorobutane; 4,4′-diphenylmethane diisocyanate polyether prepolymers; Disperse Yellow 99; montan ester waxes; 12-oxa-16-hexadecanolide; poly(butylene terephthalate); polyester polyols, linear; polyester resins, linear, medium molecular weight; polymeric plasticisers; polyurethane, cast elastomers; polyurethane, thermoplastic elastomers; pyrrolidine; tetrahydrofuran
Uses: elastomeric fabric coatings; polyurethane chain-extender; solvent (Shell Higher Olefin process)

1,4-butanediol β-aminocrotonate

$$CH_3C=CHCOOCH_2CH_2CH_2CH_2OOCCH=CCH_3$$
$$|\qquad\qquad\qquad\qquad\qquad\qquad\qquad |$$
$$NH_2\qquad\qquad\qquad\qquad\qquad\qquad NH_2$$

$C_{12}H_{20}N_2O_4$. M: 256.30.
Production:
• 1,4-butanediol + β-aminocrotononitrile (nitrile hydrolysis/esterification)
Uses: polyvinyl chloride heat stabiliser

1,4-butanediol diglycidyl ether
1,4-bis(2,3-epoxypropoxy)butane; [2425-79-8]

$$CH_2-CHCH_2OCH_2CH_2CH_2CH_2OCH_2CH-CH_2$$

$C_{10}H_{18}O_4$. M: 202.25. Colourless liquid. d: 1.11 kg/l (25°C).
Production:
• 1,4-butanediol + epichlorohydrin (dehydrochlorination)
Uses: reactive diluent (epoxy resins)

1,3-butanediol dimethacrylate
[1189-08-8]

$$CH_2=CCOOCHCH_2CH_2OOCC=CH_2$$
$$|\qquad\qquad |\qquad\qquad\qquad\qquad |$$
$$CH_3\qquad CH_3\qquad\qquad\qquad CH_3$$

$C_{12}H_{18}O_4$. M: 226.27. Liquid. d: 1.01 kg/l (25°C). Insoluble in water. Flash point: 124°C (COC). Commercial products contain hydroquinone methyl ether or similar polymerisation inhibitors.
Production:
• 1,3-butanediol + methyl methacrylate (transesterification)
Uses: peroxide crosslinking coactivator

1,4-butanediol dimethacrylate
BDMA; 1,4-butylene glycol dimethacrylate

$$CH_2=CCOCH_2CH_2CH_2CH_2OCC=CH_2$$
$$|\qquad\qquad\qquad\qquad\qquad\qquad\qquad |$$
$$CH_3\qquad\qquad\qquad\qquad\qquad\qquad CH_3$$

$C_{12}H_{18}O_4$. M: 226.27. Colourless liquid with a mild odour. Slightly soluble in water. Miscible with oxygenated solvents.
Production:
• 1,4-butanediol + methyl methacrylate (transesterification)
Uses: polyvinyl chloride plastisol comonomer; acrylic/vinyl resin crosslinking agent; anaerobic adhesives (threadlock compounds, casting sealants)

2,3-butanedione *See:* diacetyl

1-butanethiol *See:* *n*-butyl mercaptan

2-butanethiol *See:* *s*-butyl mercaptan

n-butanol
1-butanol; *n*-butyl alcohol; [71-36-3]

$$CH_3CH_2CH_2CH_2OH$$

$C_4H_{10}O_1$. M: 74.12. Colourless liquid. BP: 117–119°C. MP: -90°C. d: 0.81 kg/l (20°C). Solubility in water: 74 g/kg solution (20°C). Miscible with most organic solvents. Flash point: 52°C (TCC).

Production:
- *n*-butyraldehyde (hydrogenation)
- propylene + synthesis gas (Shell hydroformylation process; coproduced with isobutanol/2-ethylhexanol)
- crotonaldehyde (hydrogenation)
- oxygenates, Fischer-Tropsch, mixed (fractionation; coproduced with methanol/ethanol/isopropanol/ isobutanol/amyl alcohol, primary/acetaldehyde/ acetone/methyl ethyl ketone)

Derivatives:
acrylic resins, amidated; bumetanide; butachlor; *n*-butyl acetate; *n*-butyl acrylate; *n*-butylamine; *n*-butyl benzoate; *n*-butyl benzyl phthalate; *n*-butyl bromide; *n*-butyl chloride; *n*-butyl chloroformate; *n*-butyl cyanoacetate; butyl 2-cyano-3-methyl-*p*-methoxycinnamate; *n*-butyl 4,4-di-(*t*-butylperoxy)valerate; *n*-butyl diphenyl phosphate; *n*-butyl glycidyl ether; *n*-butyl glycollate; *n*-butyl 4-hydroxybenzoate; *n*-butyl isodecyl phthalate; *n*-butyl lactate; *n*-butyl methacrylate; *n*-butyl nitrite; *n*-butyl octyl phthalate; *n*-butyl oleate; *n*-butyl *p*-aminobenzoate; *n*-butyl phosphoric acid; *n*-butyl propionate; *n*-butyl ricinoleate; *n*-butyl stearate; *n*-butyl thioglycollate; *n*-butyl titanate; *n*-butyl vinyl ether; 2,4-D-butyl; 2,4-DB-butyl; di-*n*-butylamine; di-*n*-butyl butylphosphonate; di-*n*-butyl ether; di-*n*-butyl fumarate; di-*n*-butyl maleate; di-*n*-butyl phthalate; di-*n*-butyl sebacate; di-*n*-butyl succinate; diethylene glycol monobutyl ether; ethylene glycol monobutyl ether; fluazifop-butyl; fluazifop-P-butyl; flurenol-butyl; γ-heptalactone; melamineformaldehyde resins, butylated; oxalic acid; Pigment Red 208; tetra-*n*-butylammonium hydrogen sulphate; tri-*n*-butylamine; tri-*n*-butyl citrate; tri-*n*-butyl phosphate; triethylene glycol monobutyl ether; urea-formaldehyde resins, butylated; zinc di-*n*-butyl dithiophosphate; zirconium butoxide

Uses:
extraction solvent (mineral processing); solvent/cosolvent (resins, gums, waxes, lacquer thinners, paints, printing inks)

s-butanol
butan-2-ol; *s*-butyl alcohol; methylethylcarbinol; SBA; [78-92-2]

$$OH$$
$$|$$
$$CH_3CH_2CHCH_3$$

$C_4H_{10}O_1$. M: 74.12. Colourless liquid. BP: 99–101°C. d: 0.81 kg/l (20°C). Solubility in water: 363 g/kg solution (25°C). Flash point: 25°C (CC).
Production:
- raffinate II (hydration)

Derivatives:
s-butyl acetate; *s*-butylamine; di-*s*-butylamine; methyl ethyl ketone; sodium *O,O*-di-*s*-butyl dithiophosphate
Uses:
petrol octane booster; solvent (paints, lacquers, industrial cleaners)

t-butanol
t-butyl alcohol; 2-methyl-2-propanol; GTBA (gasoline grade); TBA; [75-65-0]

$$(CH_3)_3COH$$

$C_4H_{10}O_1$. M: 74.12. Colourless liquid or solid with a pleasant odour. BP: 81–83°C. FP: 24°C. d: 0.78 kg/l (25°C). Soluble in water. Miscible with most organic solvents. Flash point: 11°C (CC).
Production:
- *t*-butyl hydroperoxide + propylene (Arco TBA-PO process; coproduced with propylene oxide)
- isobutylene (hydration)

Derivatives: *t*-butyl acetoacetate; *t*-butyl glycidyl ether; *t*-butyl hypochlorite; isobutylene; methacrolein; methyl *t*-butyl ether; pentagastrin; propylene glycol mono-*t*-butyl ether; trimedlure
Uses: flavouring/fragrance ingredient; solvent (ethylene-vinyl acetate production); petrol octane booster

2-butanone *See:* methyl ethyl ketone

1-butene
but-1-ene; butene-1; [25167-67-3]

$$CH_3CH_2CH=CH_2$$

C_4H_8. M: 56.10. Colourless, liquified gas. BP: -6°C. FP: -15°C. d: 0.59 kg/l (25°C). Insoluble in water. Soluble in oxygenated and hydrocarbon solvents.
Production:
- raffinate II (fractionation)
- ethylene (Ziegler oligomerisation; coproduced with 1-hexene/1-octene/1-decene/1-dodecene/α-olefins-(C_{12}-C_{14})/α-olefins(C_{14}-C_{16})/α-olefins(C_{16}-C_{18})/ α-olefins(C_{18+}))
- ethylene (Alphabutol process)

Derivatives: 1,2-butylene oxide; *n*-butyl mercaptan; *s*-butyl mercaptan; *o*-*s*-butylphenol; polybutene-1; polyethylene, high-density; polyethylene, linear low-density; tri-n-butylaluminium; tri-*n*-butylphosphine

1,4-butenediol
2-butene-1,4-diol; but-2-ene-1,4-diol; [110-64-5]

$$HOCH_2CH=CHCH_2OH$$

$C_4H_8O_2$. M: 88.10. Colourless liquid. BP: 232–235°C. FP: 7°C. d: 1.07 kg/l. Soluble in water and oxygenated solvents. The commercial product is predominantly the *cis*-isomer.
Production:
- 1,4-butynediol (reduction)

Derivatives: 1,4-bis(bromoacetoxy)-2-butene; endosulphan; 3-formylcrotonyl acetate; pyridoxine

n-butenes, mixed *See:* raffinate II

butesin *See:* *n*-butyl *p*-aminobenzoate

butizide
buthiazide; [2043-38-1]

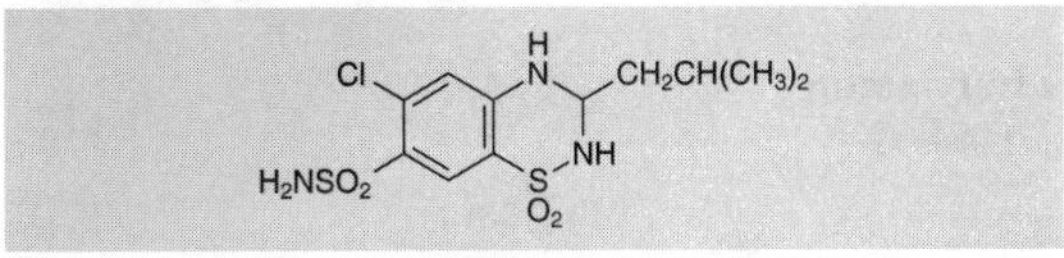

$C_{11}H_{16}Cl_1N_3O_4S_2$. M: 353.85.
Production:
- isovaleraldehyde + 5-chloroaniline-2,4-disulphon-amide (carbonyl condensation)

Uses: diuretic/antihypertensive drug

butocarboxim
3-(methylthio)-2-butanone *O*-(methylcarbamoyl)oxime; [34681-10-2]

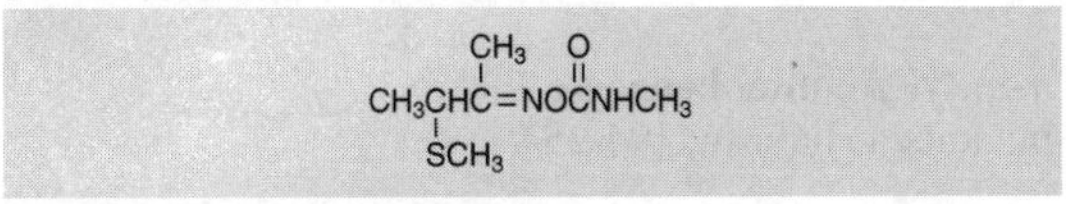

$C_7H_{14}N_2O_2S_1$. M: 190.26.
Production:
- methyl ethyl ketone + hydroxylamine sulphate + methyl mercaptan + methyl isocyanate (alpha chlorination/oxime formation/sulphide formation/isocyanate addition)

Derivatives:
butoxycarboxim

Uses: insecticide

butoxycarboxim
3-methylsulphonylbutanone *O*-methylcarbamoyloxime; [34681-23-7]

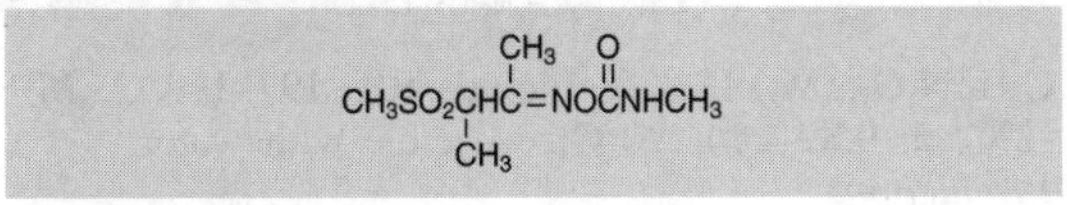

$C_7H_{14}N_2O_4S_1$. M: 222.26.
Production:
- butocarboxim + peracetic acid (oxidation)

Uses: insecticide/acaricide

2-*n*-butoxyethanol
See: ethylene glycol monobutyl ether

butoxyethyl *p*-dimethylaminobenzoate
2-*n*-butoxyethyl-4-(dimethylamino)benzoate; Quantacure BEA (Shell)

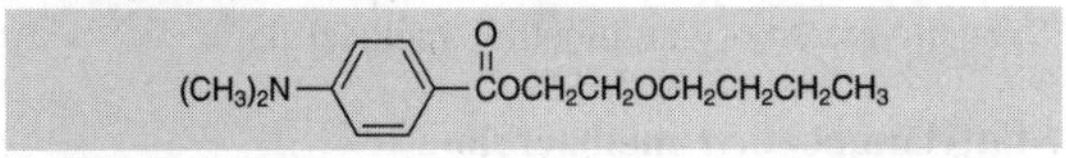

$C_{15}H_{23}N_1O_3$. M: 265.35.
Production:
- *p*-dimethylaminobenzoic acid + ethylene glycol monobutyl ether (esterification)

Uses:
photoactivator (printing inks, lacquers)

butralin
N-s-butyl-4-*t*-butyl-2,6-dinitroaniline; [33629-47-9]

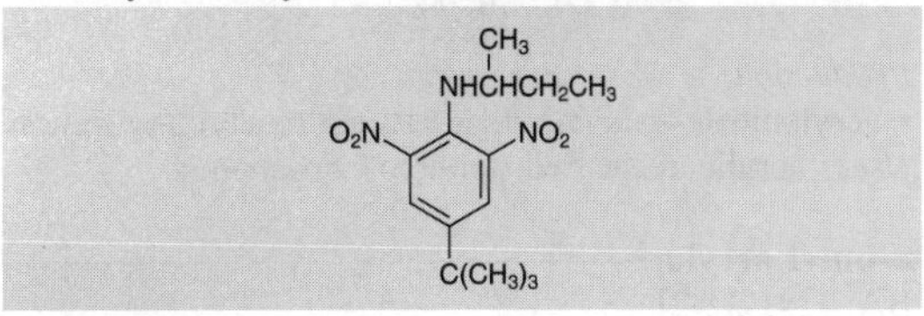

$C_{14}H_{21}N_3O_4$. M: 295.34.
Production:
- *p-t*-butylphenol + *s*-butylamine (nitration/amine formation)

Uses: herbicide

n-butyl acetate
butyl acetate; [123-86-4]

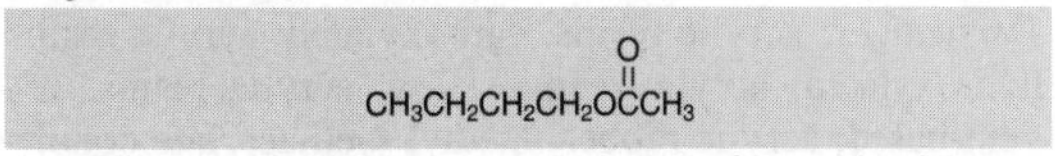

$C_6H_{12}O_2$. M: 116.17. Colourless liquid with a strong, fruity odour. BP: 124–127°C. d: 0.88 kg/l (20°C). Solubility in water: 7 g/l (20°C). Miscible with most organic solvents. Flash point: 25°C (TCC).
Production:
- *n*-butanol + acetic acid (esterification)

Derivatives: n-butyl cyanoacetate
Uses: flavouring ingredient; solvent (adhesives, cellulose nitrate lacquers/printing inks)

s-butyl acetate
[105-46-4]

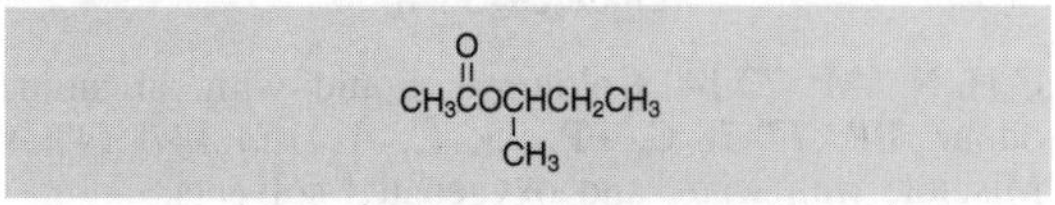

$C_6H_{12}O_2$. M: 116.17. Colourless liquid. BP: 112°C. d: 0.87 kg/l (20°C). Slightly soluble in water. Soluble in oxygenated solvents. Flash point: 31°C (TOC).
Production:
- *s*-butanol + acetic acid (esterification)

Uses: solvent (varnish, adhesives)

t-butyl acetoacetate

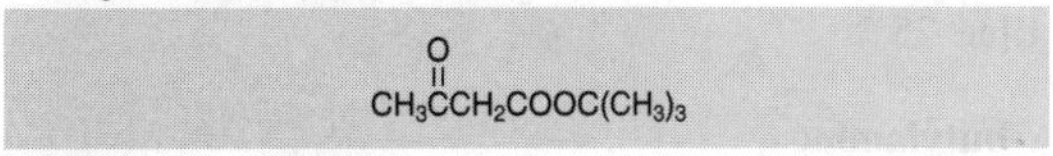

$C_8H_{14}O_3$. M: 158.20.
Production:
- *t*-butanol + diketene (esterification)

Derivatives: acesulfame-K

N-t-butylacrylamide
[107-58-4]
$C_7H_{13}N_1O_1$. M: 127.19. White, crystalline solid. MP: 129°C. d: 1.02 kg/l (30°C). Soluble in oxygenated solvents.

$$CH_2=CHCNHC(CH_3)_3$$
(with O double bond)

Production:
• acrylonitrile + isobutylene (Ritter reaction/hydration)
Uses: acrylic resin hydrophobic comonomer

n-butyl acrylate
BA; [141-32-2]

$$CH_2=CHCOCH_2CH_2CH_2CH_3$$
(with O double bond)

$C_7H_{12}O_2$. M: 128.18. Colourless liquid. BP: 149°C. FP: -64°C. d: 0.90 kg/l (20°C). Solubility in water: 1.4 g/l (20°C).
Production:
• *n*-butanol + acrylic acid (esterification)
Derivatives: acrylic resins, carboxylated; acrylic resins, hydroxylated; acrylic resins, latex; acrylic resins, solvent-based; acrylic rubber; methyl methacrylate copolymers, high molecular weight; styrene-acrylic copolymers; vinyl acetate-butyl acrylate copolymers; vinyl chloride-acrylic ester copolymers
Uses: acrylic resin comonomer

n-butyl alcohol *See:* *n*-butanol

t-butyl alcohol *See:* *t*-butanol

n-butylamine
monobutylamine; MNBA; [109-73-9]

$$CH_3CH_2CH_2CH_2NH_2$$

$C_4H_{11}N_1$. M: 73.14. Colourless liquid with an amine odour. BP: 77–78°C. FP: -50°C. d: 0.74 kg/l (4°C). Miscible with water and oxygenated solvents.
Production:
• *n*-butanol + ammonia (ammoniation; coproduced with di-*n*-butylamine/tri-*n*-butylamine)
Derivatives: N-*n*-butylaminoethanol; N-*n*-butyl-3-amino-4-methoxybenzenesulphonamide; *n*-butylaminonickel-2,2′-thiobis(4-*t*-octylphenol); N-*n*-butylbenzenesulphonamide; N-*n*-butyldiethanolamine; *n*-butylethylamine; *n*-butyl isocyanate; di-*n*-butylthiourea; neburon; Solvent Blue 35

s-butylamine
2-aminobutane; [13952-84-6]

$$CH_3$$
$$C_2H_5CHNH_2$$

$C_4H_{11}N_1$. M: 73.14. Colourless liquid with an ammoniacal odour. BP: 63°C. FP: -104°C. d: 0.79 kg/l (4°C). Miscible with water and oxygenated solvents.
Production:
• *s*-butanol + ammonia (amine formation; coproduced with di-*s*-butylamine)

Derivatives: bromacil; butamifos; butralin; N,N′-di-*s*-butyl-*p*-phenylenediamine

t-butylamine
[75-64-9]

$$(CH_3)_3CNH_2$$

$C_4H_{11}N_1$. M: 73.14. Colourless liquid. BP: 44–46°C. MP: -72°C. d: 0.70 kg/l (20°C). Miscible with water and most organic solvents.
Production:
• isobutylene + hydrogen cyanide (Ritter reaction)
Derivatives: benzyl-*t*-butylamine; *t*-butylaminoethanol; N-*t*-butyl-2-benzothiazolesulphenamide; carazolol; celiprolol; clenbuterol; N-isopropyl-N′-*t*-butylthiourea; karbutilate; nadolol; terbacil; terbuthylazine; timolol

n-butyl *p*-aminobenzoate
butamben; butesin; [94-25-7]

$$CH_3CH_2CH_2CH_2OC-\bigcirc-NH_2$$
(with O double bond)

$C_{11}H_{15}N_1O_2$. M: 193.25. Solid. MP: 58°C. Insoluble in water. Soluble in oxygenated, chlorinated and aromatic solvents.
Production:
• *n*-butanol + *p*-nitrobenzoic acid (esterification/nitro reduction)
Uses: local anaesthetic drug

N-*n*-butylaminoethanol
n-butylethanolamine; [111-75-1]

$$CH_3CH_2CH_2CH_2NHCH_2CH_2OH$$

$C_6H_{15}N_1O_1$. M: 117.20. Liquid. BP: 197–199°C. MP: -2°C. d: 0.89 kg/l (20°C). Miscible with water.
Production:
• *n*-butylamine + ethylene oxide (epoxidation; coproduced with N-*n*-butyldiethanolamine)
Uses: textile auxiliary

t-butylaminoethanol
2-(*t*-butylamino)ethanol; [4620-70-6]

$$(CH_3)_3CNHCH_2CH_2OH$$

$C_6H_{15}N_1O_1$. M: 117.20.
Production:
• *t*-butylamine + ethylene oxide (epoxidation)
Derivatives: *t*-butylaminoethyl methacrylate

t-butylaminoethyl methacrylate
[3775-90-4]

$$CH_2=CCOCH_2CH_2NHC(CH_3)_3$$
$$CH_3$$
(with O double bond)

$C_{10}H_{19}N_1O_2$. M: 185.27. Liquid. BP: 93°C. FP: <-70°C.

d: 0.91 kg/l (25°C). Solubility in water: 18 g/l (20°C).
Production:
- *t*-butylaminoethanol + methyl methacrylate (transesterification)

Uses:
acrylic resin comonomer

N-*n*-butyl-3-amino-4-methoxybenzenesulphonamide
2-amino-4-*n*-butylaminosulphonylanisole; 3-amino-4-methoxybenzenesulphon-*N*-*n*-butylamide; Fast Red SW base; Azoic Diazo Component 14 (CI); 37151 (CI); [80-22-8]

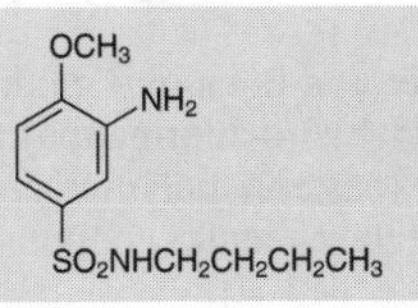

$C_{11}H_{18}N_2O_3S_1$. M: 258.33.
Production:
- 2-aminoanisole-4-sulphonic acid + *n*-butylamine (sulphonamide formation)

Uses: azoic dye coupling component

n-butylaminonickel-2,2′-thiobis(4-*t*-octylphenol)
Cyasorb UV1084 (American Cyanamid)

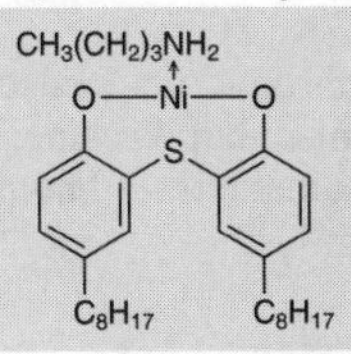

$C_{32}H_{51}N_1Ni_1O_2S_1$. M: 572.54. Pale green powder. MP: 259–261°C.
Production:
- 2,2′-thiobis(4-*t*-octylphenol) + nickel sulphate + *n*-butylamine (complex formation)

Uses: light stabiliser (plastics)

p-*n*-butylaniline
4-*n*-butylaniline; [104-13-2]

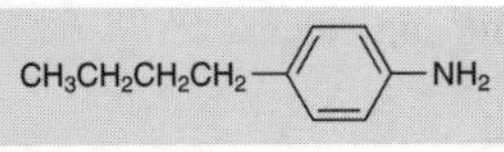

$C_{10}H_{15}N_1$. M: 149.24.
Production:
- *n*-butylbenzene (nitration/nitro reduction)

Derivatives:
Acid Blue 230; Acid Green 27

2-*t*-butylanthraquinone
[84-47-9]
$C_{18}H_{16}O_2$. M: 264.33.
Production:
- *t*-butylbenzene + phthalic anhydride (Friedel-Crafts acylation/cyclisation)

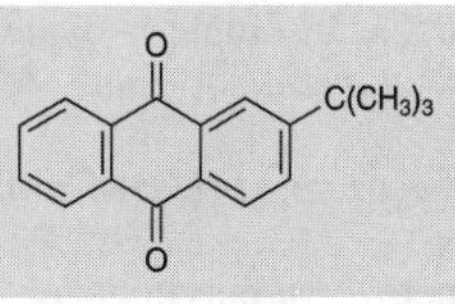

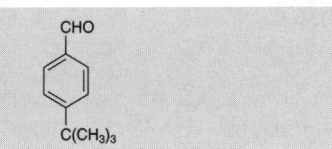

Uses: reagent (hydrogen peroxide production)

butylate
S-ethyl diisobutylthiocarbamate; [2008-41-5]

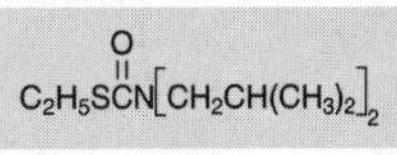

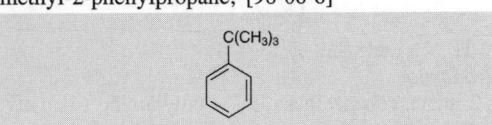

$C_{11}H_{23}N_1O_1S_1$. M: 217.37.
Production:
- diisobutylamine + ethyl chlorothioformate (dehydrochlorination)

Uses: herbicide

p-*t*-butylbenzaldehyde
TBB; [939-97-9]

$C_{11}H_{14}O_1$. M: 162.23.
Production:
- *p*-*t*-butyltoluene (side-chain oxidation)

Derivatives:
4-*t*-butyl-α-methylhydrocinnamaldehyde

Uses: fragrance ingredient

n-butylbenzene
[104-51-8]

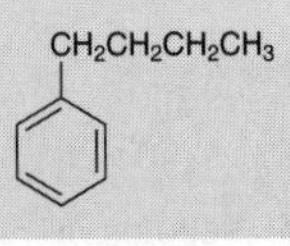

$C_{10}H_{14}$. M: 134.22. Liquid. BP: 183°C. MP: -88°C. d: 0.86 kg/l (20°C). Insoluble in water. Flash point: 71°C (TOC).
Production:
- toluene + propylene (potassium-catalysed alkylation; coproduced with isobutylbenzene)

Derivatives: *p*-*n*-butylaniline

t-butylbenzene
2-methyl-2-phenylpropane; [98-06-6]

$C_{10}H_{14}$. M: 134.22. Colourless liquid. BP: 166–169°C.

d: 0.87 kg/l (20°C). Insoluble in water. Miscible with oxygenated and aromatic solvents.
Production:
• isobutylene + benzene (Friedel-Crafts alkylation)
Derivatives:
4-acetyl-1,1-dimethyl-6-*t*-butylindane; 2-*t*-butylanthraquinone; 4′-*t*-butyl-4-chlorobutyrophenone

N-n-butylbenzenesulphonamide
benzenesulphon-*n*-butylamide; [3622-84-2]

$C_{10}H_{15}N_1O_2S_1$. M: 213.30. Yellow liquid. d: 1.15 kg/l (25°C).
Production:
• benzenesulphonyl chloride + *n*-butylamine (sulphonamide formation)
Uses: plasticiser (polyamide resins)

n-butyl benzoate
[136-60-7]

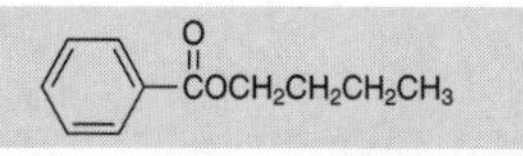

$C_{11}H_{14}O_2$. M: 178.23. Oily liquid. BP: 250°C. MP: -22°C. Insoluble in water. Soluble in oxygenated solvents.
Production:
• *n*-butanol + benzoic acid (esterification)
Uses: dye carrier (polyester); fragrance ingredient

p-t-butylbenzoic acid
4-*t*-butylbenzoic acid; [98-73-7]

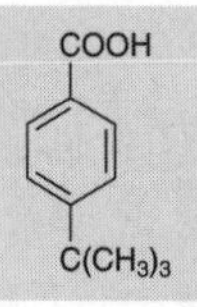

$C_{11}H_{14}O_2$. M: 178.23. Needles. MP: 164°C. Insoluble in water. Soluble in oxygenated and aromatic solvents.
Production:
• *p-t*-butyltoluene (side-chain oxidation)
Uses:
alkyd resin chain stopper; corrosion inhibitor

N-t-butyl-2-benzothiazolesulphenamide
benzothiazyl-2-*t*-butylsulphenamide; TBBS; [95-31-8]

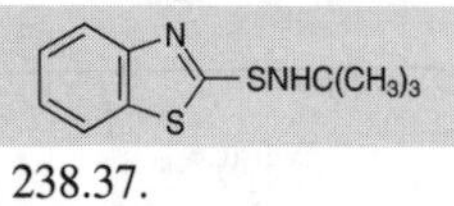

$C_{11}H_{14}N_2S_2$. M: 238.37.
Production:
• 2-mercaptobenzothiazole + *t*-butylamine (oxidative coupling)
Uses: vulcanisation accelerator

n-butyl benzyl phthalate
BBP; benzyl *n*-butyl phthalate; Santicizer 160 (Monsanto); Unimoll BB (Bayer); [85-68-7]

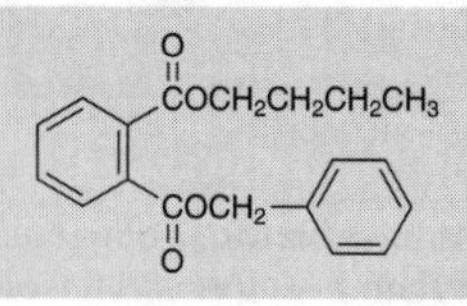

$C_{19}H_{20}O_4$. M: 312.37. Colourless liquid. BP: 235–255°C (1.3 kPa). Pour point: -35°C. d: 1.12 kg/l. Insoluble in water.
Production:
• benzyl chloride + *n*-butanol + phthalic anhydride (esterification/dehydrochlorination)
Uses: plasticiser (castable polyurethanes, polyvinyl acetate adhesives/sealants/caulks, polyvinyl chloride flooring/plastisols)

n-butyl bromide
[109-65-9]

$C_4H_9Br_1$. M: 137.01. Colourless liquid. BP: 101–104°C. MP: -112°C. d: 1.27 kg/l (25°C). Insoluble in water. Soluble in oxygenated solvents.
Production:
• *n*-butanol + hydrobromic acid (alcohol bromination)
Derivatives: bufexamac; bupivacaine; butylscopolamine bromide; oxybuprocaine; tetra-*n*-butylammonium bromide; tetracaine

n-butyl *n*-butyryllactate
n-butyl butyryllactate; [7492-70-8]

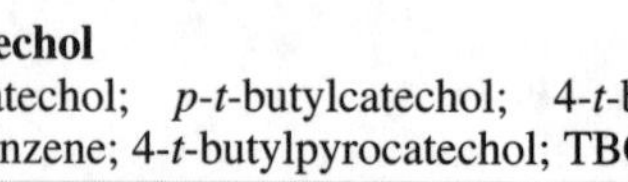

$C_{11}H_{20}O_4$. M: 216.28. Colourless liquid. Insoluble in water. Soluble in oxygenated solvents.
Production:
• *n*-butyl lactate + *n*-butyryl chloride (esterification)
Uses: flavouring ingredient

t-butylcatechol
4-*t*-butylcatechol; *p-t*-butylcatechol; 4-*t*-butyl-1,2-dihydroxybenzene; 4-*t*-butylpyrocatechol; TBC; [98-29-3]

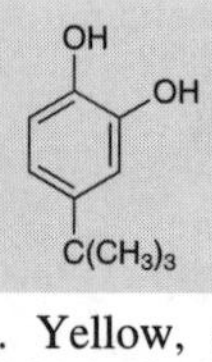

$C_{10}H_{14}O_2$. M: 166.22. Yellow, crystalline solid. MP: 50°C. BP: 285°C. d: 1.04 kg/l (60°C). Forms conjugate solutions with water at *t*-butylcatechol concentrations over 20%. Soluble in oxygenated, chlorinated and

aromatic solvents. Flash point: 160°C (PMCC). Also available commercially as a liquid containing 15% water or methanol.
Production:
• catechol + isobutylene (Friedel-Crafts alkylation)
Uses: chain transfer agent (chloroprene production); antioxidant; polymerisation inhibitor

Butyl Cellosolve *See:* ethylene glycol monobutyl ether

n-butyl chloride
1-chlorobutane; [109-69-3]

$$CH_3CH_2CH_2CH_2Cl$$

$C_4H_9Cl_1$. M: 92.56. Colourless liquid. BP: 77–78°C. d: 0.89 kg/l (20°C). Insoluble in water. Miscible with oxygenated solvents.
Production:
• *n*-butanol + hydrochloric acid (alcohol chlorination)
Derivatives:
benzoin *n*-butyl ether; *n*-butyllithium; *n*-butylmagnesium chloride; diethyl *n*-butylmalonate; diethylene glycol dibutyl ether; dimethirimol; ethirimol; hexaconazole; methyl *n*-amyl ketone; myclobutanil; tetra-*n*-butyltin
Uses:
solvent (oils, fats, waxes)

t-butyl chloroacetate

$$\underset{\displaystyle O}{ClCH_2\overset{\displaystyle \parallel}{C}OC(CH_3)_3}$$

$C_6H_{11}Cl_1O_2$. M: 150.61. Liquid. BP: 155°C with decomposition. Hydrolysed by water.
Production:
• isobutylene + chloroacetic acid (esterification)
Uses: reagent (Darzen reaction)

4′-*t*-butyl-4-chlorobutyrophenone
[43076-61-5]

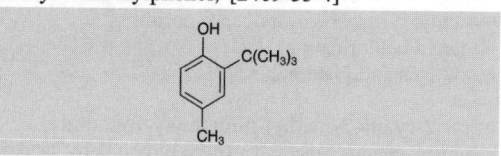

$C_{14}H_{19}Cl_1O_1$. M: 238.75.
Production:
• 4-chlorobutyryl chloride + *t*-butylbenzene (Friedel-Crafts acylation)
Derivatives: terfenadine

n-butyl chloroformate
n-butyl chlorocarbonate; [592-34-7]

$$\underset{\displaystyle O}{CH_3CH_2CH_2CH_2O\overset{\displaystyle \parallel}{C}Cl}$$

$C_5H_9Cl_1O_2$. M: 136.57.
Production:
• *n*-butanol + phosgene (dehydrochlorination)
Derivatives: furathiocarb

2-*t*-butyl-*p*-cresol
2-*t*-butyl-4-methylphenol; [2409-55-4]

$C_{11}H_{16}O_1$. M: 164.25. Solid. MP: 55°C. Insoluble in water. Soluble in oxygenated solvents.
Production:
• *m/p*-cresol + isobutylene (Friedel-Crafts alkylation; coproduced with 6-*t*-butyl-*m*-cresol)
• *p*-cresol + isobutylene (Friedel-Crafts alkylation)
Derivatives: 2,6-di-*t*-butyl-*p*-cresol; 2,2′-dicyclopentadienylbis(6-*t*-butyl-4-methylphenol); 2-(2-hydroxy-3-*t*-butyl-5-methylphenyl)-5-chlorobenzotriazole; 2,2′-methylenebis(4-methyl-6-*t*-butylphenol); 2,2′-thiobis(4-methyl-6-*t*-butylphenol)

6-*t*-butyl-*m*-cresol
2-*t*-butyl-5-methylphenol; 6-*t*-butyl-3-methylphenol; MBMC; [88-60-8]

$C_{11}H_{16}O_1$. M: 164.25. Colourless liquid or solid. FP: 23°C. BP: 244°C. d: 0.92 kg/l (80°C).
Production:
• *m/p*-cresol + isobutylene (Friedel-Crafts alkylation; coproduced with 2-*t*-butyl-*p*-cresol)
Derivatives:
4,4′-butylidene bis(6-*t*-butyl-*m*-cresol); 4,4′-thiobis(2-*t*-butyl-5-methylphenol); 1,1,3-tris(5-*t*-butyl-4-hydroxy-2-methylphenyl)butane

t-butylcumyl peroxide
Interox BCUP (Interox); Luperco 801 (Elf-Atochem); Trigonox T (Akzo)

$C_{13}H_{20}O_2$. M: 208.30. Liquid. Decomposes at 180°C.
Production:
• *t*-butyl hydroperoxide + α-methylstyrene (peroxidation)
Uses: crosslinking agent (rubber, resins)

n-butyl cyanoacetate
[5459-58-5]

$$\underset{\displaystyle O}{NCCH_2\overset{\displaystyle \parallel}{C}OCH_2CH_2CH_2CH_3}$$

$C_7H_{11}N_1O_2$. M: 141.18.

Production:
- *n*-butanol + cyanoacetic acid (esterification)
- *n*-butyl acetate + cyanogen chloride (dehydrochlorination)

Uses: cyanoacrylate adhesives

butyl 2-cyano-3-methyl-*p*-methoxycinnamate
n-butyl 2-cyano-3-methyl-3-(*p*-methoxyphenyl)acrylate;
UV Absorber 317 (Bayer)

$C_{16}H_{19}N_1O_3$. M: 273.34. Pale yellow liquid.
Production:
- cyanoacetic acid + *n*-butanol + 4-methoxyaceto-phenone (esterification/Cope reaction)

Uses: light stabiliser (plastics)

4-*t*-butylcyclohexanol
[98-52-2]

$C_{10}H_{20}O_1$. M: 156.27.
Production:
- *p*-*t*-butylphenol (hydrogenation)

Derivatives: bis(4-*t*-butylcyclohexyl) peroxydicarbonate;
4-*t*-butylcyclohexyl acetate

2-*t*-butylcyclohexyl acetate
[20298-69-5] (*cis*-isomer); [20298-70-8] (*trans*-isomer)

$C_{12}H_{22}O_2$. M: 198.31. Colourless liquid with a fruity odour. d: 0.94 kg/l (25°C). The commercial product is a mixture of *cis*- and *trans*-isomers.
Production:
- *o*-*t*-butylphenol + acetic acid (esterification)

Uses: fragrance ingredient (soap, household products)

4-*t*-butylcyclohexyl acetate
Vertenex; [32210-23-4]

$C_{12}H_{22}O_2$. M: 198.31. Colourless liquid with a strong odour.
Production:
- 4-*t*-butylcyclohexanol + acetic acid (esterification)

Uses: fragrance ingredient (soap)

n-butyl 4,4-di-(*t*-butylperoxy)valerate
Interox NBV (Interox); Trigonox 17 (Akzo)

$$\left[(CH_3)_3COO\right]_2 CCH_2CH_2CO(CH_2)_3CH_3$$

$C_{17}H_{34}O_6$. M: 334.45.
Production:
- levulinic acid + *n*-butanol + *t*-butyl hydroperoxide (esterification/ketal formation)

Uses: crosslinking agent (resins)

N-n-butyldiethanolamine
2,2'-butyliminodiethanol; [102-79-4]

$$CH_3CH_2CH_2CH_2N(CH_2CH_2OH)_2$$

$C_8H_{19}N_1O_2$. M: 161.25. Liquid. BP: 264–278°C. Pour point: -45°C. d: 0.97 kg/l (20°C). Miscible with water.
Production:
- *n*-butylamine + ethylene oxide (epoxidation; coproduced with *N*-*n*-butylaminoethanol)

Uses:
textile auxiliary

6-*t*-butyl-2,4-dimethylphenol
2-*t*-butyl-4,6-dimethylphenol; 6-*t*-butyl-*m*-xylenol;
[1879-09-0]

$C_{12}H_{18}O_1$. M: 178.27.
Production:
- 2,4-xylenol + isobutylene (Friedel-Crafts alkylation)

Derivatives: oxymetazoline; 1,3,5-tris(4-*t*-butyl-3-hydr-oxy-2,6-dimethylbenzyl)isocyanurate

Uses:
antioxidant (rubber, motor fuels)

n-butyl diphenyl phosphate

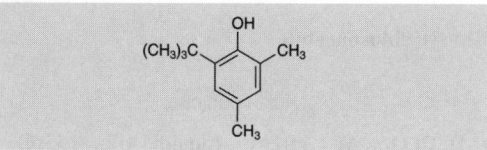

$C_{16}H_{19}O_4P_1$. M: 306.30.
Production:
- *n*-butanol + phenol + phosphorus oxychloride (dehydrochlorination/dehydrochlorination)

Uses:
aircraft hydraulic fluids

1,2-butylene glycol *See:* 1,2-butanediol

1,3-butylene glycol *See:* 1,3-butanediol

1,4-butylene glycol *See:* 1,4-butanediol

1,2-butylene oxide

1,2-butene oxide; butylene oxide; 1,2-epoxybutane; [106-88-7]

$$CH_3CH_2CH-CH_2$$

$C_4H_8O_1$. M: 72.10. Colourless liquid. BP: 63°C. FP: <-50°C. d: 0.82 kg/l (25°C). Solubility in water: 95 g/l water (25°C). Soluble in oxygenated solvents.
Production:
• 1-butene + chlorine (hypochlorination/dehydrochlorination)
Derivatives:
1,2-butanediol; 2,4-D-2-hydroxybutyl; MCPA-(2-hydroxybutyl)
Uses: oil-soluble polyalkylene glycol comonomer (motor, transmission, gear oils); stabiliser (chlorinated solvents)

n-butyl epoxystearate

n-butyl 9,10-epoxystearate

$$CH_3(CH_2)_7CH-CH(CH_2)_7COCH_2CH_2CH_2CH_3$$

$C_{22}H_{42}O_3$. M: 354.58. Liquid. d: 0.94 kg/l.
Production:
• *n*-butyl oleate + peracetic acid/performic acid (epoxidation)
Uses:
polyvinyl chloride costabiliser/plasticiser

n-butylethanolamine *See: N-n*-butylaminoethanol

n-butylethylamine

ethyl-*n*-butylamine; EBA; [13360-63-9]

$$CH_3CH_2CH_2CH_2NHC_2H_5$$

$C_6H_{15}N_1$. M: 101.20. Liquid. BP: 111°C. FP: -78°C. d: 0.74 kg/l (4°C). Soluble in water and oxygenated solvents.
Production:
• ethanol + *n*-butylamine (amine formation)
Derivatives:
benfluralin; pebulate

n-butyl glycidyl ether

BGE; [2426-08-6]

$$CH_3CH_2CH_2CH_2OCH_2CH-CH_2$$

$C_7H_{14}O_2$. M: 130.19. Colourless liquid with an unpleasant odour. BP: 164°C. d: 0.93 kg/l (25°C). Viscosity: 20 cP (25°C). Soluble in water.
Production:
• *n*-butanol + epichlorohydrin (dehydrochlorination)
Uses:
reactive diluent (epoxy resins)

t-butyl glycidyl ether

$$(CH_3)_3COCH_2CH-CH_2$$

$C_7H_{14}O_2$. M: 130.19.
Production:
• *t*-butanol + epichlorohydrin (dehydrochlorination)
Uses:
reactive diluent (epoxy resins)

n-butyl glycollate

n-butyl hydroxyacetate

$$HOCH_2COCH_2CH_2CH_2CH_3$$

$C_6H_{12}O_3$. M: 132.17.
Production:
• *n*-butanol + glycollic acid (esterification)
Uses: levelling agent (varnishes)

t-butylhydrazinium chloride

[7400-27-3]

$$(CH_3)_3CNHNH_3^+ \ Cl^-$$

$C_4H_{13}Cl_1N_2$. M: 124.60.
Production:
• isobutylene + hydrazine (addition)
Uses:
blowing agent (foamed plastics)

t-butyl hydroperoxide

TBHP; [75-91-2]

$$(CH_3)_3COOH$$

$C_4H_{10}O_2$. M: 90.12. The commercial product is a 70% solution in water.
Production:
• isobutane + oxygen (liquid-phase oxidation)
• isobutylene + hydrogen peroxide (peroxidation)
Derivatives:
1,4-bis(*t*-butylperoxyisopropyl)benzene; *t*-butanol; *t*-butylcumyl peroxide; *n*-butyl 4,4-di-(*t*-butylperoxy)valerate; *t*-butyl monoperoxymaleate; *t*-butyl peroxyacetate; *t*-butyl peroxybenzoate; *t*-butyl peroxycrotonate; *t*-butyl peroxy-2-ethylhexanoate; *t*-butyl peroxy-2-ethylhexylcarbonate; *t*-butyl peroxyisopropylcarbonate; *t*-butyl peroxyneodecanoate; *t*-butyl peroxyneoheptanoate; *t*-butyl peroxypivalate; *t*-butyl peroxy-*o*-toluate; di-t-butyl peroxide; 2,2-di-(*t*-butylperoxy)butane; 1,1-di(*t*-butylperoxy)cyclohexane; 2,5-di-(*t*-butylperoxy)-2,5-dimethylhex-3-yne; 1,1-di(*t*-butylperoxy)-3,3,5-trimethylcyclohexane; ethyl 3,3-bis(*t*-butylperoxy)butyrate; propylene oxide
Uses: latex polymerisation initiator

5-*t*-butyl-2-hydroxyaniline

See: 2-amino-4-*t*-butylphenol

t-butylhydroxyanisole
BHA; E320 (EC); hydroxyanisole, butylated; [25013-16-5]

$C_{11}H_{16}O_2$. M: 180.25. White, waxy beads. MP: 48–58°C. BP: 263–272°C. Insoluble in water. Soluble in oxygenated solvents, fats and oils. The commercial product is a mixture of 2-*t*-butyl-4-methylphenol and 3-*t*-butyl-4-methylphenol.
Production:
• hydroquinone monomethyl ether + isobutylene (Friedel-Crafts alkylation)
Uses: antioxidant (oils, fats, prepared foods, food packaging, animal feed)

n-butyl 4-hydroxybenzoate
butylparaben; [94-26-8]

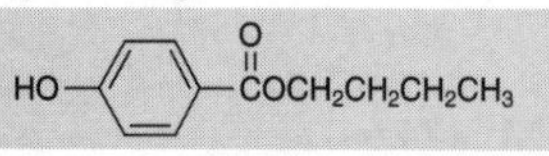

$C_{11}H_{14}O_3$. M: 194.23. White, crystalline powder. MP: 67–69°C. Insoluble in water. Soluble in oxygenated solvents.
Production:
• *n*-butanol + *p*-hydroxybenzoic acid (esterification)
Uses:
preservative (food, pharmaceuticals)

t-butyl hypochlorite

(CH₃)₃COCl

$C_4H_9Cl_1O_1$. M: 108.56. Pale yellow liquid with an unpleasant odour. Manufactured *in situ*. Not a traded product.
Production:
• *t*-butanol + chlorine (reaction)
Uses:
alkoxychlorination/alcohol dehydration reagent

butylideneaniline
butyraldehyde aniline; BAA; [4275-07-4]

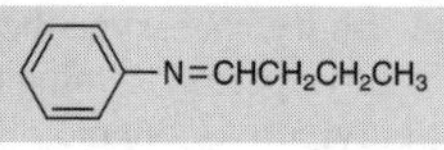

$C_{10}H_{13}N_1$. M: 147.22.
Production:
• *n*-butyraldehyde + aniline (carbonyl condensation)
Uses: vulcanisation accelerator

4,4′-butylidene bis(6-*t*-butyl-*m*-cresol)
Oxi-Chek 414 (Ferro)
$C_{26}H_{38}O_2$. M: 382.59.

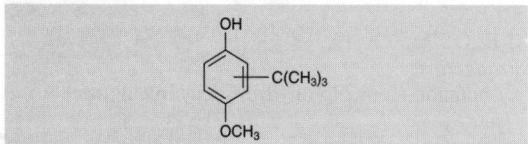

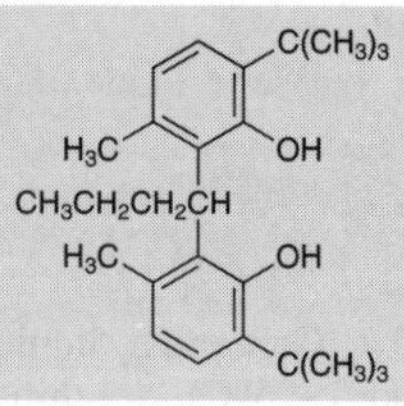

Production:
• 6-*t*-butyl-*m*-cresol + *n*-butyraldehyde (carbonyl condensation)
Uses: antioxidant (plastics, adhesives)

n-butyl isocyanate
[111-36-4]

CH₃CH₂CH₂CH₂NCO

$C_5H_9N_1O_1$. M: 99.13.
Production:
• *n*-butylamine + phosgene (phosgenation)
Derivatives: benomyl; tolbutamide

n-butyl isodecyl phthalate

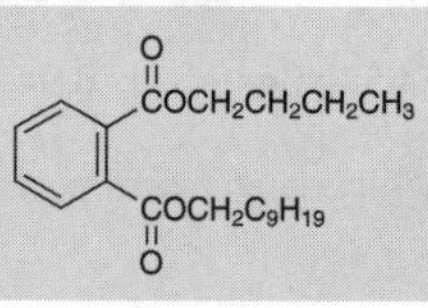

$C_{22}H_{34}O_4$. M: 362.51. Liquid. BP: 220°C (0.67 kPa). MP: <-50°C. d: 0.99 kg/l. Insoluble in water.
Production:
• *n*-butanol + isodecanol + phthalic anhydride (esterification)
Uses: plasticiser (vinyl resins)

n-butyl lactate
[138-22-7]

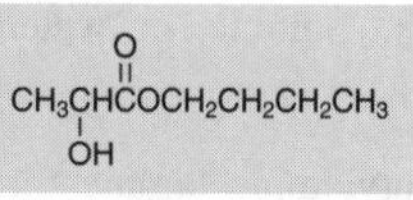

$C_7H_{14}O_3$. M: 146.19. Colourless liquid. BP: 188°C. MP: -43°C. d: 0.98 kg/l (20°C). Slightly soluble in water. Miscible with oxygenated solvents.
Production:
• *n*-butanol + DL-lactic acid (esterification)
Derivatives:
n-butyl *n*-butyryllactate
Uses: solvent

n-butyllithium
[109-72-8]

CH₃CH₂CH₂CH₂Li

$C_4H_9Li_1$. M: 64.05. Liquid. BP: 150°C with decomposition. Decomposed by water. Flammable.

Production:
• *n*-butyl chloride + lithium (reaction)
Derivatives:
perhexiline; tetrafluoro-*p*-methylbenzyl alcohol
Uses: solution polymerisation initiator (polyolefin elastomers); Grignard-type reagent

n-butylmagnesium chloride
[693-04-9]

$$CH_3CH_2CH_2CH_2MgCl$$

$C_4H_9Cl_1Mg_1$. M: 116.87. Available commercially as a 2–3 molar solution in THF.
Production:
• *n*-butyl chloride + magnesium (Grignard reagent formation)
Derivatives: tetra-*n*-butyltin
Uses:
linear low-density polyethylene catalyst component

n-butyl mercaptan
1-butanethiol; [109-79-5]

$$CH_3CH_2CH_2CH_2SH$$

$C_4H_{10}S_1$. M: 90.18. Liquid with an unpleasant odour. BR: 97–101°C. MP: -116°C. d: 0.84 kg/l (15°C). Slightly soluble in water. Soluble in oxygenated solvents.
Production:
• 1-butene + hydrogen sulphide (anti-Markownikov addition)
Derivatives: perfluorobutanesulphonic acid; *S,S,S*-tributyl phosphorotrithioate

s-butyl mercaptan
2-butanethiol; butane-2-thiol; [513-53-1]

$$CH_3CH_2\underset{\underset{CH_3}{|}}{C}HSH$$

$C_4H_{10}S_1$. M: 90.18. Liquid with an unpleasant odour. BP: 84–88°C. MP: -165°C. d: 0.83 kg/l (15°C). Slightly soluble in water. Soluble in oxygenated solvents.
Production:
• raffinate II + hydrogen sulphide (addition)
Derivatives: cadusafos

t-butyl mercaptan
t-butylthiol; 2-methyl-2-propanethiol; [75-66-1]

$$(CH_3)_3CSH$$

$C_4H_{10}S_1$. M: 90.18. Liquid with an unpleasant odour. BR: 62–69°C. FP: -1°C. d: 0.80 kg/l (15°C). Slightly soluble in water. Soluble in oxygenated solvents.
Production:
• isobutylene + hydrogen sulphide (addition)
Derivatives: *t*-butyl polysulphide; terbufos
Uses: gas odorant

n-butyl methacrylate
butyl methacrylate; [97-88-1]

$$CH_2{=}\underset{\underset{CH_3}{|}}{C}\overset{\overset{O}{||}}{C}OCH_2CH_2CH_2CH_3$$

$C_8H_{14}O_2$. M: 142.20. Colourless liquid. BP: 163–171°C. d: 0.89 kg/l (25°C). Insoluble in water. Flash point: 66°C (COC). Commercial products contain hydroquinone methyl ether or a similar polymerisation inhibitor.
Production:
• *n*-butanol + methyl methacrylate (transesterification)
Derivatives: methyl methacrylate copolymers, high molecular weight; polymethacrylates, oil-soluble; polymethacrylates, oil-soluble dispersants
Uses:
acrylic resin comonomer

4-*t*-butyl-α-methylhydrocinnamaldehyde
2-methyl-3-(*p*-*t*-butylphenyl)propanal; α-methyl-β-(*p*-*t*-butylphenyl)propionaldehyde; Lilestralis (Bush Boake Allen); Lilial (Givaudan-Roure); Lysmeral (BASF); [80-54-6]

$$(CH_3)_3C{-}\langle\ \rangle{-}CH_2\underset{\underset{CH_3}{|}}{C}HCHO$$

$C_{14}H_{20}O_1$. M: 204.31. Pale yellow liquid with a floral odour. BP: 120–127°C (0.8 kPa). d: 0.94 kg/l (20°C). Insoluble in water.
Production:
• *p*-*t*-butylbenzaldehyde + propionaldehyde (aldol condensation/dehydration/hydrogenation)
• α-methylcinnamaldehyde + isobutylene (hydrogenation/Friedel-Crafts alkylation/alcohol oxidation)
Derivatives:
fenpropidin; fenpropimorph
Uses: fragrance ingredient (soap, toiletries)

2-*t*-butyl-4-methylphenol *See:* 2-*t*-butyl-*p*-cresol

2-*t*-butyl-5-methylphenol *See:* 6-*t*-butyl-*m*-cresol

6-*t*-butyl-3-methylphenol *See:* 6-*t*-butyl-*m*-cresol

t-butyl monoperoxymaleate
Esperox 41-25 (Witco)

$$(CH_3)_3CO{-}O\overset{\overset{O}{||}}{C}CH{=}CHCOOH$$

$C_8H_{12}O_5$. M: 188.19. Available as a solution containing 25% peroxide with a 10-hour half-life at 87°C.
Production:
• *t*-butyl hydroperoxide + maleic anhydride (esterification)
Uses:
polyester crosslinking agent; polymerisation initiator

n-butyl nitrite
butyl nitrite

$$CH_3CH_2CH_2CH_2ON=O$$

$C_4H_9N_1O_2$. M: 103.12.
Production:
• *n*-butanol + sodium nitrite (nitrosation)
Derivatives:
glibornuride; metaraminol
Uses: alpha carbonylation/diazotisation reagent

n-butyl octyl phthalate

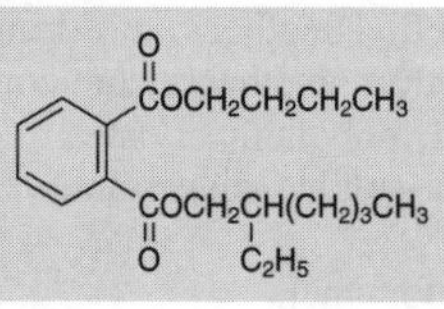

$C_{20}H_{30}O_4$. M: 334.46. Colourless liquid. BP: 225°C
(0.67 kPa). MP: <-50°C. d: 0.99 kg/l (25°C). Insoluble
in water. Miscible with most organic solvents.
Production:
• *n*-butanol + 2-ethylhexanol + phthalic anhydride
  (esterification)
Uses: plasticiser (vinyl resins)

n-butyl oleate
butyl oleate; [142-77-8]

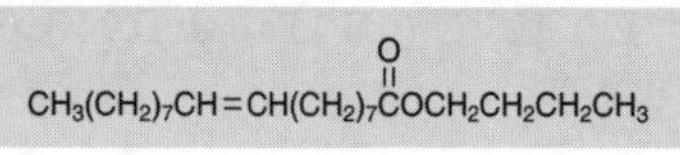

$$CH_3(CH_2)_7CH=CH(CH_2)_7COCH_2CH_2CH_2CH_3$$

$C_{22}H_{42}O_2$. M: 338.58. Pale yellow liquid. Pour point:
-21°C. d: 0.87 kg/l (20°C). Flash point: 200°C (COC).
Insoluble in water.
Production:
• *n*-butanol + oleic acid (esterification)
Derivatives:
n-butyl epoxystearate
Uses: emulsifier/bodying agent/emollient (toiletries,
cosmetics); lubricity additive (rolling oils); plasticiser
(surface coatings)

butylparaben *See:* n-butyl 4-hydroxybenzoate

t-butyl peroxyacetate
t-butyl peracetate; Triganox F-C50 (Akzo); [107-71-1]

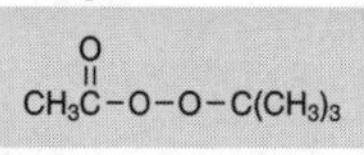

$C_6H_{12}O_3$. M: 132.17. Available as a 50% solution in
mineral spirit. The product has a 10-hour half-life at
103°C.
Production:
• *t*-butyl hydroperoxide + acetyl chloride (dehydrochlorination)
Uses:
silicon rubber curing agent

t-butyl peroxybenzoate
t-butyl perbenzoate; Esperox 10 (Witco); [614-45-9]

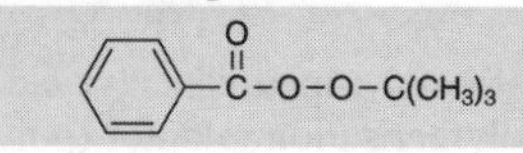

$C_{11}H_{14}O_3$. M: 194.23. Liquid. The product has a
10-hour half-life at 104°C.
Production:
• *t*-butyl hydroperoxide + benzoyl chloride (dehydrochlorination)
Uses:
silicon rubber curing agent; polyester crosslinking agent

t-butyl peroxycrotonate
Esperox 13M (Witco)

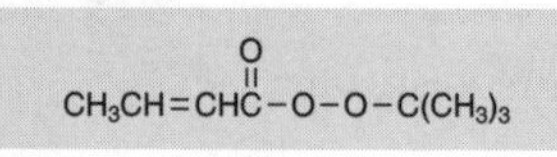

$$CH_3CH=CHC-O-O-C(CH_3)_3$$

$C_8H_{14}O_3$. M: 158.20. Available as a solution containing
75% peroxide with a 10-hour half-life at 98°C.
Production:
• *t*-butyl hydroperoxide + crotonic acid (acid chloride
  formation/dehydrochlorination)
Uses: polyester crosslinking agent; polymerisation
initiator

t-butyl peroxy-2-ethylhexanoate
t-butyl peroctoate; *t*-butyl peroxyoctoate; [62695-55-0]

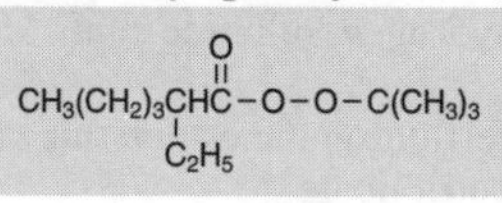

$C_{12}H_{24}O_3$. M: 216.32. Liquid or 50% solution in
di-2-ethylhexyl phthalate or mineral spirit. The peroxide has a 10-hour half-life at 72°C.
Production:
• *t*-butyl hydroperoxide + 2-ethylhexanoyl chloride
  (dehydrochlorination)
Uses: unsaturated polyester resin crosslinking agent;
polymerisation initiator

t-butyl peroxy-2-ethylhexylcarbonate

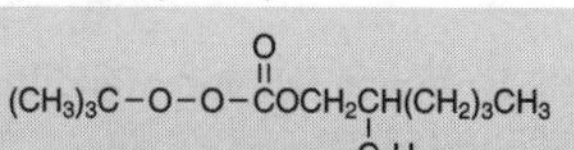

$C_{13}H_{26}O_4$. M: 246.35. Decomposes on heating with a
10-hour half-life at 100°C.
Production:
• *t*-butyl hydroperoxide + 2-ethylhexyl chloroformate
  (dehydrochlorination)
Uses: polymerisation initiator

t-butyl peroxyisopropylcarbonate
O,O-t-butyl isopropylmonoperoxycarbonate; BPIC;
TBIC; Lupersol TBIC-M75 (Elf-Atochem); Triganox
BPIC (Akzo); [2372-21-6]

$$(CH_3)_3C-O-O-\overset{\overset{\displaystyle O}{\|}}{C}OCH(CH_3)_2$$

$C_8H_{16}O_4$. M: 176.22. The product has a 10-hour half-life at 99°C.
Production:
- *t*-butyl hydroperoxide + isopropyl chloroformate (dehydrochlorination)

Uses: vinyl polymerisation initiator

t-butyl peroxyneodecanoate
Esperox 33M (Witco)

$$(CH_3)_3C-O-O-\overset{\overset{\displaystyle O}{\|}}{C}-\overset{\overset{\displaystyle CH_3}{|}}{\underset{\underset{\displaystyle CH_3}{|}}{C}}C_6H_{13}$$

$C_{14}H_{28}O_3$. M: 244.37. Available commercially as a 75% solution in organic solvent. The product has a 10-hour half-life at 47°C.
Production:
- *t*-butyl hydroperoxide + neodecanoyl chloride (esterification)

Uses: polymerisation initiator

t-butyl peroxyneoheptanoate
Esperox 750M (Witco)

$$(CH_3)_3C-O-O-\overset{\overset{\displaystyle O}{\|}}{C}-\overset{\overset{\displaystyle CH_3}{|}}{\underset{\underset{\displaystyle CH_3}{|}}{C}}C_3H_7$$

$C_{11}H_{22}O_3$. M: 202.30. Available as a solution containing 75% peroxide with a 10-hour half-life at 50°C.
Production:
- *t*-butyl hydroperoxide + neoheptanoyl chloride (dehydrochlorination)

Uses: polymerisation initiator

t-butyl peroxypivalate
Esperox 31M (Witco); Lupersol 11 (Elf-Atochem)

$$(CH_3)_3C-O-O-\overset{\overset{\displaystyle O}{\|}}{C}C(CH_3)_3$$

$C_9H_{18}O_3$. M: 174.24. Available commercially as a 75% solution in organic solvent. The product as a 10 hour half-life at 55°C.
Production:
- *t*-butyl hydroperoxide + pivaloyl chloride (esterification)

Uses: polymerisation inhibitor

t-butyl peroxy-*o*-toluate
Esperox 497M (Witco)
$C_{12}H_{16}O_3$. M: 208.26. Available as a solution containing 75% peroxide with a 10-hour half-life at 97°C.
Production:
- *t*-butyl hydroperoxide + *o*-toluoyl chloride (dehydrochlorination)

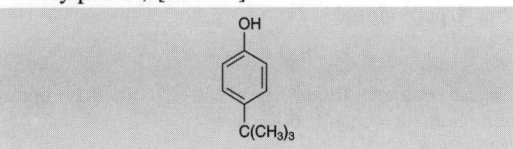

Uses:
polyester crosslinking agent; polymerisation initiator

o-s-butylphenol
OSBP; [89-72-5]

$C_{10}H_{14}O_1$. M: 150.22. Amber-coloured liquid. BP: 224–237°C. MP: 14°C. d: 0.98 kg/l (20°C). Insoluble in water. Soluble in oxygenated solvents.
Production:
- phenol + 1-butene (orthoalkylation)

Derivatives:
2-*s*-butyl-1-vinylcyclohexyl acetate; dinoseb; fenobucarb

o-t-butylphenol
2-*t*-butylphenol; OTBP; [88-18-6]

$C_{10}H_{14}O_1$. M: 150.22. Amber-coloured liquid. BP: 224°C. MP: -6°C. d: 0.98 kg/l (20°C). Insoluble in water. Soluble in oxygenated solvents.
Production:
- isobutylene + phenol (orthoalkylation; coproduced with 2,6-di-*t*-butylphenol)

Derivatives: 2-*t*-butylcyclohexyl acetate; dinoterb; ethylene glycol bis[3,3-bis(3-*t*-butyl-4-hydroxyphenyl)butyrate]; 2,2′-methylenebis(4-ethyl-6-*t*-butylphenol)

p-t-butylphenol
4-*t*-butylphenol; [98-54-4]

$C_{10}H_{14}O_1$. M: 150.22. Needles. MP: 96–98°C. BP: 238°C. Soluble in hot water and oxygenated solvents.
Production:
- phenol + isobutylene (Friedel-Crafts alkylation; coproduced with 2,4-di-*t*-butylphenol)

Derivatives: 2-amino-4-*t*-butylphenol; butralin; 4-*t*-butylcyclohexanol; *t*-butylphenyl diphenyl phosphate; *p-t*-butylphenyl salicylate; phenolic resins, oil-soluble, oil-reactive; propargite

t-butylphenyl diphenyl phosphate
diphenyl *t*-butylphenyl phosphate

$C_{22}H_{23}O_4P_1$. M: 382.39.
Production:
• *p*-*t*-butylphenol + phenol + phosphorus oxychloride
  (dehydrochlorination)
Uses:
fire-resistant engineering plastic plasticiser

p-*t*-butylphenyl salicylate
TBS; [87-18-3]

$C_{17}H_{18}O_3$. M: 270.33.
Production:
• *p*-*t*-butylphenol + salicylic acid (esterification)
Uses: light stabiliser (plastics)

n-butyl phosphoric acid
n-butyl acid phosphate; [12788-93-1]

$\left[CH_3(CH_2)_3O \right]_n \overset{O}{\underset{\|}{P}}(OH)_{3-n}$

m = 1–2. Colourless liquid. d: 1.12 kg/l (25°C). Insoluble in water. Soluble in oxygenated solvents and
aromatics.
Production:
• *n*-butanol + phosphorus pentoxide (esterification)
Uses:
ingredient (industrial cleaning agents); curing agent
(acid-catalysed paint systems)

t-butyl polysulphide

$(CH_3)_3CS_nC(CH_3)_3$

n = 5.5 average. Liquid. BP: 236°C with decomposition. Sulphur content: 60% w/w.
Production:
• *t*-butyl mercaptan + sulphur (sulphurisation)
Uses: extreme-pressure additive (metalworking fluids)

n-butyl propionate
[590-01-2]

$CH_3CH_2\overset{O}{\underset{\|}{C}}OCH_2CH_2CH_2CH_3$

$C_7H_{14}O_2$. M: 130.19. Colourless liquid with a fruity

odour. BP: 147°C. FP: -89°C. d: 0.88 kg/l (20°C).
Slightly soluble in water. Soluble in oxygenated sol-
vents.
Production:
• *n*-butanol + propionic acid (esterification)
Uses: fragrance/flavouring ingredient; solvent (lacquers)

4-*t*-butylpyrocatechol *See:* *t*-butylcatechol

n-butyl ricinoleate
butyl ricinoleate

$CH_3(CH_2)_5\overset{OH}{\underset{|}{C}}HCH_2CH=CH(CH_2)_7\overset{O}{\underset{\|}{C}}O(CH_2)_3CH_3$

$C_{22}H_{42}O_3$. M: 354.58.
Production:
• *n*-butanol + ricinoleic acid (esterification)
Uses: plasticiser (cellulosic, vinyl acetate resins)

butyl rubber
IIR; isobutylene-isoprene copolymers

$\left[CH_2-\overset{CH_3}{\underset{CH_3}{\underset{|}{\overset{|}{C}}}} \right]_x \left[CH_2CH=\overset{CH_3}{\overset{|}{C}}CH_2 \right]_y$

Elastomers vulcanised by highly accelerated sulphur
systems. The vulcanisates have low air permeability
and low resilience at ambient temperatures but these
increase rapidly as the temperature is raised. The
polymer consists of 98% isobutylene and 2% isoprene.
Available as rubber bails and as latex, formed by
mechanical emulsification of the solid rubber.
Production:
• isobutylene + isoprene (cationic polymerisation)
Derivatives:
butyl rubber, brominated; butyl rubber, chlorinated
Uses:
cable insulation/jacketing; caulks/sealants; latex (non-
woven fabrics binders, fabric coatings); laminating adhesives (polyethylene film); latex (protective coatings,
adhesives, sealants); pressure-sensitive adhesives; roofing membranes; sealing/pipe wrapping/electrical tapes;
self-curing cements; tyre inner tubes/liners/curing bladders; wax/plastic additive

butyl rubber, brominated
BIIR; Bromobutyl (Exxon Chemical)

$\left[CH_2-\overset{CH_3}{\underset{CH_3}{\underset{|}{\overset{|}{C}}}} \right]_x \left[CH_2CH=\overset{CH_3}{\overset{|}{C}}CH \overset{}{\underset{Br}{\underset{|}{}}} \right]_y$

Elastomer vulcanised by sulphur systems. The vulcanisate is characterised by its low gas permeability, its
good weather/ozone resistance and better chemical/heat
resistance than butyl rubber.
Production:
• butyl rubber + bromine (bromination)

Uses:
conveyor belts/hosing/antivibration mounts; food/ drug
seals; adhesives; tyre inner tubes/liners/curing bladders

butyl rubber, chlorinated
CIIR; Chlorobutyl (Exxon Chemical)

$$\left[CH_2-\underset{\underset{CH_3}{|}}{\overset{\overset{CH_3}{|}}{C}}\right]_x \left[CH_2CH=\underset{\underset{Cl}{|}}{\overset{\overset{CH_3}{|}}{C}}CH\right]_y$$

Elastomer vulcanised by sulphur systems. The vulcanisate is characterised by its low gas permeability, its
good weather/ozone resistance and better chemical/heat
resistance than butyl rubber. The polymer contains
1–2% chlorine, usually substituted at a position allylic
to the double bond.
Production:
• butyl rubber + chlorine (chlorination)
Uses: conveyor belts/hosing/antivibration mounts; food/
drug seals; adhesives; tyre inner tubes/liners

butylscopolamine bromide
N-butylhyoscinium bromide; [149-64-4]

$$CH_3CH_2CH_2CH_2-\overset{+}{\underset{\underset{O}{|}}{N}}\overset{CH_3}{\underset{}{}}\quad Br^-$$

$$\underset{\underset{CH CH_2 OH}{\overset{|}{}}}{O-C=O}$$

$C_{21}H_{30}Br_1N_1O_4$. M: 440.38.
Production:
• scopolamine + *n*-butyl bromide (quaternisation)
Uses: antispasmodic drug

n-butyl stearate
butyl stearate; [123-95-5]

$$\underset{\underset{CH_3(CH_2)_{16}COCH_2CH_2CH_2CH_3}{}}{\overset{O}{\overset{\|}{}}}$$

$C_{22}H_{44}O_2$. M: 340.59. Colourless liquid. Pour point:
21°C. BP: 210–235°C (1.0 kPa). Saponification value:
170–180 mg KOH/g. d: 0.85 kg/l (20°C). Insoluble in
water. Soluble in hydrocarbon oils.
Production:
• *n*-butanol + stearic acid (esterification)
Uses:
emollient (cosmetics); lubricant (textile spin finishes);
plasticiser/flow improver (plastics, rubber, lacquers)

n-butyl thioglycollate

$$\underset{\underset{HSCH_2COCH_2CH_2CH_2CH_3}{}}{\overset{O}{\overset{\|}{}}}$$

$C_6H_{12}O_2S_1$. M: 148.23. Colourless liquid. BP: 85–88°C
(2.0 kPa). d: 1.03 kg/l (20°C).

Production:
• *n*-butanol + thioglycollic acid (esterification)
Uses: unsaturated polyester resin curing agent

n-butyltin trichloride
[1118-46-3]

$$CH_3CH_2CH_2CH_2SnCl_3$$

$C_4H_9Cl_3Sn_1$. M: 282.16.
Production:
• tetra-*n*-butyltin + stannic chloride (Kocheshkov
redistribution)
Derivatives: monobutyltin sulphide; monobutyltin tris-
(isooctylthioglycollate); monobutyltin tris(2-mercapto-
ethyl oleate)
Uses: fabric waterproofing agent

n-butyltin tris(isooctylmercaptoacetate)
See: monobutyltin tris(isooctylthioglycollate)

butyl titanate
TBT; tetrabutyl orthotitanate; titanium butylate; titanium tetrabutoxide; [5593-70-4]

$$(CH_3CH_2CH_2CH_2O)_4Ti$$

$C_{16}H_{36}O_4Ti_1$. M: 340.37. Pale yellow, viscous liquid.
BP: 185°C (14 kPa). Pour point: <-70°C. d: 1.00 kg/l
(20°C). Soluble in aliphatic, aromatic, chlorinated and
oxygenated solvents.
Production:
• *n*-butanol + titanium tetrachloride
(dehydrochlorination)
Uses: esterification/alcoholysis catalyst; alkyd/epoxy/
silicone resin crosslinking agent; Ziegler catalyst component; high temperature coatings ingredient; glass surface treatment agent

p-t-butyltoluene
4-*t*-butyltoluene; TBT; [98-51-1]

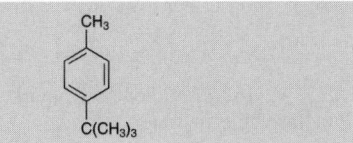

$C_{11}H_{16}$. M: 148.25. Colourless liquid. BP: 198–199°C.
d: 0.86 kg/l (20°C). Insoluble in water. Soluble in oxygenated and aromatic solvents.
Production:
• isobutylene + toluene (Friedel-Crafts alkylation)
Derivatives:
p-*t*-butylbenzaldehyde; *p*-*t*-butylbenzoic acid

t-butyltoluenediamine
$C_{11}H_{18}N_2$. M: 178.27.
Mixed product containing 80% 5-*t*-butyl-2,4-diamino-
toluene and 20% 3-*t*-butyl-2,6-diaminotoluene.

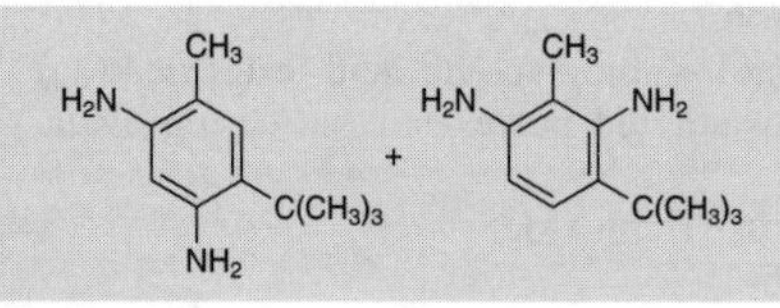

Production:
• 2,4/2,6-diaminotoluene + isobutylene (Friedel-Crafts alkylation)
Uses: polyurethane catalyst

2-*s*-butyl-1-vinylcyclohexyl acetate

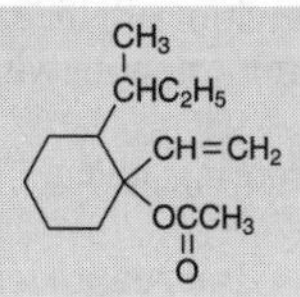

$C_{14}H_{24}O_2$. M: 224.34.
Production:
• *o*-*s*-butylphenol + acetylene + acetic acid (hydrogenation/alcohol oxidation/ethynylation/hydrogenation/esterification)
Uses: fragrance ingredient

n-butyl vinyl ether
BVE; vinyl *n*-butyl ether; [111-34-2]

$$CH_2=CHOCH_2CH_2CH_2CH_3$$

$C_6H_{12}O_1$. M: 100.17.
Production:
• acetylene + *n*-butanol (ethynylation)
Uses: acrylic/vinyl acetate resin comonomer

5-*t*-butyl-*m*-xylene
5-*t*-butyl-1,3-dimethylbenzene; 1,3-dimethyl-5-*t*-butyl-benzene; [98-19-1]

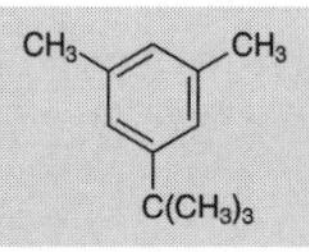

$C_{12}H_{18}$. M: 162.27. Colourless liquid. BP: 201°C (19.5 kPa). Insoluble in water.
Production:
• *m*-xylene + isobutylene (Friedel-Crafts alkylation)
Derivatives: musk ketone; musk xylol; xylometazoline

6-*t*-butyl-*m*-xylenol *See:* 6-*t*-butyl-2,4-dimethylphenol

butynedioic acid *See:* acetylenedicarboxylic acid

1,4-butynediol
2-butyne-1,4-diol; butynediol; [110-65-6]

$$HOCH_2C\equiv CCH_2OH$$

$C_4H_6O_2$. M: 86.09. Hygroscopic flakes. MP: 54°C. BP:

238°C. Miscible with water, alcohol and acetone. Soluble in ethyl acetate.
Production:
• acetylene + formaldehyde (ethynylation)
Derivatives:
acetylenedicarboxylic acid; 1,4-butanediol; 1,4-butene-diol; dibromobutanediol-epichlorohydrin adduct; di-(2-hydroxyethyl)butynediol; mucochloric acid
Uses: nickelplating brightening agent; corrosion inhibitor (acid pickling); stabiliser (chlorinated solvents)

3-butyn-2-ol
1-butyn-3-ol; 3-hydroxy-1-butyne; methylpropynol; [2028-63-9]

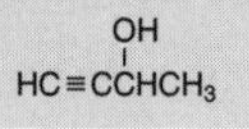

$C_4H_6O_1$. M: 70.09. Liquid. BP: 108–111°C. MP: -39°C. Soluble in water and oxygenated solvents. Also available commercially as a 55% aqueous solution.
Production:
• acetylene + acetaldehyde (ethynylation)
Derivatives:
chlorbufam
Uses: aroma chemicals intermediate

n-butyraldehyde
n-butanal; [123-72-8]

$$CH_3CH_2CH_2CHO$$

$C_4H_8O_1$. M: 72.10. Colourless liquid with a pungent odour. BP: 75°C. MP: -96°C. d: 0.80 kg/l (20°C). Solubility in water: 71 g/kg solution (25°C). Miscible with organic solvents. Flash point: -12°C (TCC).
Production:
• propylene + synthesis gas (hydroformylation; coproduced with isobutyraldehyde)
Derivatives:
n-butanol; butylideneaniline; 4,4'-butylidene bis(6-*t*-butyl-*m*-cresol); butyraldoxime; *n*-butyric acid; *n*-butyronitrile; 2-ethylhexaldehyde; 2-ethylhexanol; 2-hexenal; polyvinyl butyral; trimethylolpropane

butyraldehyde aniline *See:* butylideneaniline

butyraldoxime
butyraldehyde oxime; [110-69-0]

$$CH_3CH_2CH_2CH=NOH$$

$C_4H_9N_1O_1$. M: 87.12. Liquid. BP: 152°C. MP: -30°C. d: 0.92 kg/l (20°C). Soluble in water and oxygenated solvents.
Production:
• *n*-butyraldehyde + hydroxylamine sulphate (oxime formation)
Uses:
antiskinning agent (paints, printing inks)

n-butyric acid
butanoic acid; [107-92-6]

$$CH_3CH_2CH_2COOH$$

$C_4H_8O_2$. M: 88.10. Colourless liquid with an unpleasant odour. BP: 162–165°C. MP: -6°C. d: 0.96 kg/l (20°C). Miscible with water and oxygenated solvents.
Production:
- *n*-butyraldehyde (carbonyl oxidation)
- *n*-butane (Celanese LPO process; coproduced with methanol/ethanol/acetone/methyl ethyl ketone/formic acid/acetic acid/propionic acid/methyl formate)

Derivatives:
α-bromobutyric acid; *N*-butyryl-*p*-aminophenol; *n*-butyryl chloride; cellulose acetobutyrate; dimethyl benzyl carbinyl butyrate; di-*n*-propyl ketone; ethyl butyrate; geranyl butyrate; isoamyl butyrate; *n*-propyl butyrate

γ-butyrolactone
butyrolactone; dihydro-2(3H)-furanone; GBL; [96-48-0]

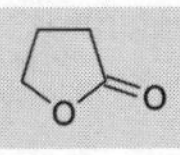

$C_4H_6O_2$. M: 86.09. Liquid. BP: 204–206°C. MP: -43°C. d: 1.12 kg/l. Miscible with water and most organic solvents. Insoluble in aliphatic hydrocarbons. Flash point: 98°C (OC).
Production:
- 1,4-butanediol (dehydrogenation)

Derivatives:
2-acetobutyrolactone; 4-chlorobutyryl chloride; 2,4-DB; 4-indol-3-ylbutyric acid; MCPB-sodium; *N*-methylpyrrolidone; ofurace; 2-pyrrolidone

n-butyronitrile
n-propyi cyanide; NBN; [109-74-0]

$$CH_3CH_2CH_2CN$$

$C_4H_7N_1$. M: 69.11. Liquid. BP: 115–117°C. FP: -112°C. d: 0.79 kg/l (4°C). Slightly soluble in water. Miscible with oxygenated solvents. Flash point: 85°C (TOC).
Production:
- *n*-butyraldehyde + hydroxylamine sulphate (oxime formation/dehydration)

Uses: solvent

N-butyryl-*p*-aminophenol
4-hydroxybutyranilide; Suconox-4 (Hexcel); [101-91-7]

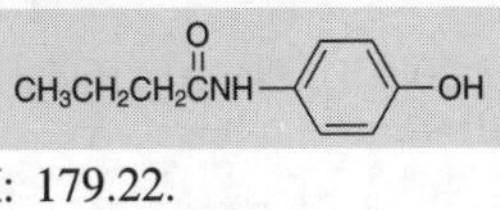

$$CH_3CH_2CH_2CNH \text{—} \text{—} OH$$

$C_{10}H_{13}N_1O_2$. M: 179.22.
Production:
- *n*-butyric acid + *p*-aminophenol (amide formation)

Uses:
antioxidant (plastics)

n-butyryl chloride
n-butanoyl chloride; [141-75-3]

$$CH_3CH_2CH_2CCl$$

$C_4H_7Cl_1O_1$. M: 106.55. Colourless liquid with an unpleasant odour. BP: 101–105°C. MP: <-70°C. d: 1.03 kg/l (15°C). Hydrolysed by water and alcohol.
Production:
- *n*-butyric acid (acid chloride formation)

Derivatives:
acebutolol; alloxydim-sodium; *n*-butyl *n*-butyryllactate; cycloxydim; linalyl butyrate; sethoxydim

C

cadmium
[7440-43-9]

Cd

Cd$_1$. M: 112.40. Silver-white, slightly bluish metal. MP: 321°C. BP: 770°C. d: 8.65 kg/l (25°C). Insoluble in water. Available commercially as granules, ingots, powder, shot, foil, rod, wire and as single crystals.
Production:
• cadmium concentrates + metallurgical coke (thermal reduction)
Derivatives:
cadmium chloride; cadmium nitrate; cadmium oxide; cadmium sulphate
Uses: bearing alloy ingredient; copper electrical cable alloy ingredient; fusible alloy/brazing metal/solder ingredient

cadmium-barium heat stabilisers
Available as formulated products in powder or liquid form. The powders are primarily fatty acid metal salts mixed with polyol synergists and phenolic antioxidants. They are combined with liquid components such as phosphites and epoxy plasticisers at the time of use. Liquid stabilisers are supplied with the phosphite component pre-blended into the mix.
Production:
• barium oxide/barium hydroxide/cadmium sulphate + 2-ethylhexanoic acid/isodecanoic acid/neodecanoic acid/C$_8$-C$_{10}$ fatty acids/lauric acid, broad cut/naphthenic acid/benzoic acid/dodecylphenol + zinc 2-ethylhexanoate (salt formation)
Uses: polyvinyl chloride heat stabiliser

cadmium carbonate
[513-78-0]

CdCO$_3$

C$_1$Cd$_1$O$_3$. M: 172.41. White powder. Decomposes when heated above 500°C. d: 4.26 kg/l. Insoluble in water.
Production:
• cadmium sulphate + sodium carbonate (salt formation)
Derivatives: cadmium red; cadmium yellow

cadmium chloride
[10108-64-2]

CdCl$_2$

Cd$_1$Cl$_2$. M: 183.31. Available as the anhydrous or hemipentahydrate salts. The anhydrous grade is white crystals. MP: 568°C. Soluble in water. The hemipentahydrate grade consists of colourless, efflorescent crystals. Soluble in water. Cadmium chloride is also sold as a 20% solution in water.
Production:
• cadmium + hydrochloric acid (salt formation)
• cadmium + chlorine (reaction)
Uses: dyeing/printing auxiliary

cadmium diethyldithiocarbamate
Cadmate (Vanderbilt Chemical); [14239-68-0]

$\left[(C_2H_5)_2N\overset{\displaystyle S}{\overset{\|}{C}}S\right]_2 Cd$

C$_{10}$H$_{20}$Cd$_1$N$_2$S$_4$. M: 408.94. White powder. MP: 70°C. Insoluble in water.
Production:
• cadmium sulphate + sodium diethyldithiocarbamate (salt formation)
Uses: vulcanisation accelerator

cadmium nitrate
[10325-94-7]

Cd(NO$_3$)$_3$

Cd$_1$N$_2$O$_6$. M: 236.40. Available as the tetrahydrate. White, crystalline powder. MP: 59°C. Solubility in water: 2,150 g/l water (20°C).
Production:
• cadmium + nitric acid (salt formation)
Uses: red porcelain glaze ingredient; nickel-cadmium batteries

cadmium oxide
[1306-19-0]

CdO

Cd$_1$O$_1$. M: 128.40. Dark brown, crystalline solid or powder. Sublimes at 1540°C. d: 6.95 or 8.15 kg/l. Insoluble in water.
Production:
• cadmium (air oxidation)
Uses: oxidation/hydrogenation catalyst; cadmium plating reagent; silver alloy ingredient; raw material (glass, ceramics, phosphors, semiconductors); vulcanisation accelerator

cadmium red
Pigment Orange 20 (CI); Pigment Red 108 (CI); 77196 (CI); 77202 (CI)

CdS.nCdSe

Series of pigments which range in colour from orange to reddish-blue, depending on the sulphur:selenium ratio.

Production:
• cadmium carbonate + sulphur + sodium selenite (calcination)
Uses:
pigment (paints, lacquers, enamels, pottery decoration)

cadmium sulphate
[13477-20-8] (hydrate)

$$3CdSO_4$$

$Cd_1O_4S_1$. M: 208.46. Octahydrate: Colourless crystals. d: 3.09 kg/l. Loses water on heating, forming the monohydrate. Solubility in water: 1.13 kg/l (0°C). Also sold as a 20% solution in water.
Production:
• cadmium + ammonium persulphate (salt formation)
Derivatives:
cadmium-barium heat stabilisers; cadmium carbonate; cadmium diethyldithiocarbamate; cadmium-zinc heat stabilisers
Uses: cadmium plating reagent

cadmium yellow
Pigment Yellow 37 (CI); 77199 (CI); [20548-54-3]

$$CdS$$

Series of pigments which range from lemon yellow to orange-red.
Production:
• cadmium carbonate + sodium sulphide (salt formation/calcination)
• cadmium carbonate + zinc oxide + sulphur (calcination)
Uses: pigment (paints, printing inks)

cadmium-zinc heat stabilisers
Available as formulated products containing a blend of fatty acid metal salts, costabilisers and antioxidants.
Production:
• cadmium sulphate/zinc oxide + 2-ethylhexanoic acid/isodecanoic acid/neodecanoic acid/C_8-C_{10} fatty acids/lauric acid, broad cut/stearic acid/naphthenic acid/benzoic acid/dodecylphenol + soyabean oil, epoxidised/isooctyl epoxystearate/isooctyl epoxytallate (salt formation)
Uses: polyvinyl chloride heat stabiliser

cadusafos
S,S-di-*s*-butyl *O*-ethyl phosphorodithioate; [95465-99-9]

$$\underset{C_2H_5OP(SCHC_2H_5)_2}{\overset{O\ \ CH_3}{\|\ \ |}}$$

$C_{10}H_{23}O_2P_1S_2$. M: 270.39.
Production:
• *s*-butyl mercaptan + phosphorus trichloride + ethanol + hydrogen peroxide (dehydrochlorination/dehydrochlorination/oxidation)

Uses:
insecticide/nematicide

caffeine
1,3,7-trimethylxanthine; [58-08-2]

$C_8H_{10}N_4O_2$. M: 194.20. White, crystalline solid. Sublimes at 178°C. MP: 236°C. Slightly soluble in water and alcohol.
Production:
• theophylline + dimethyl sulphate (methylation)
• coffee beans (extraction)
Uses: diuretic/analeptic drug

cake alum *See:* aluminium sulphate

calamus oil
Yellow or brown viscous liquid. Produced by steam distillation of the roots of sweet flag (*Acorus calamus*) d: 0.96 kg/l (25°C). Soluble in ethanol. Oil from different sources varies considerably in composition. The main producing regions are North America, India and Europe.
Uses:
flavouring ingredient (fortified wines); perfume ingredient

calciferol
ergocalciferol; vitamin D_2; [50-14-6]

$C_{28}H_{44}O_1$. M: 396.66.
Production:
• ergosterol (photochemical conversion)
Uses: antirachitic drug; rodenticide

calcite
calcium carbonate, natural; whiting; Paris white; E170 (EC); Pigment White 18 (CI); 77220 (CI); [1317-65-3]

$$CaCO_3$$

$C_1Ca_1O_3$. M: 100.09. Relatively pure, naturally-occurring calcium carbonate. White, crystalline powder. d: 2.70–2.72 kg/l. Ground calcite has a mean particle size of 6–20 μ.
Uses:
filler (plastics, rubber, caulks, sealants); filler/pigment (paper coatings, paint, adhesives, inks)

calcium

[7440-70-2]

Ca

Ca$_1$. M: 40.08. Silver-white, ductile metal tarnished by air to give a grey surface. MP: 850°C. BP: 1,440°C. d: 1.54 kg/l (25°C). Reacts with water producing hydrogen.
Production:
• calcium oxide + aluminium (thermal reduction)
Derivatives: calcium hydride
Uses:
deoxiding agent (steel, copper, magnesium, tantalum and lead production); lead-calcium alloys (batteries); reducing agent (zirconium, thorium, uranium, rare earth production)

calcium acetate

E263 (EC); [62-54-4]

CH$_3$COO$^-$ $\frac{1}{2}$Ca^{2+}

C$_4$H$_6$Ca$_1$O$_4$. M: 158.17. White, hygroscopic, crystalline solid. Decomposes when heated above 160°C. d: 1.50 kg/l. Soluble in water.
Production:
• calcium hydroxide + acetic acid (salt formation)
Uses: esterification catalyst; preservative (bread, bakery goods, casein); tanning auxiliary

calcium alkylbenzenesulphonate

$$\left[CH_3(CH_2)_{11} - \!\!\bigcirc\!\!- SO_3^- \right]_2 Ca^{2+}$$

C$_{36}$H$_{58}$Ca$_1$O$_6$S$_2$. M: 691.06. Clear, brown, viscous solution containing 60–70% active matter in water.
Production:
• dodecylbenzenesulphonic acid, linear + calcium hydroxide (salt formation)
Uses: emulsifier/wetting agent (pesticides)

calcium alkyl salicylates

n = 7–28. Salicylates are usually supplied as a mixed additive package with sulphonates and antioxidants all dissolved in mineral oil. They are often in an 'over-based' form containing stabilised micelles of calcium carbonate.
Production:
• alkyl(C$_9$-C$_{30}$)phenol/nonylphenol/dodecylphenol + carbon dioxide + calcium hydroxide (Kolbe-Schmitt reaction/salt formation)
Uses: detergent additive (lubricants)

calcium ascorbate

E302 (EC); [5743-27-1]

C$_{12}$H$_{14}$Ca$_1$O$_{12}$. M: 390.31. White, crystalline powder. Soluble in water. Insoluble in alcohol. The commercial product is the natural L(+)-enantiomer monohydrate.
Production:
• ascorbic acid + calcium hydroxide (salt formation)
Uses: antioxidant/colour fixative (prepared meat, dairy, baby products)

calcium benzoate

E213 (EC); [2090-05-3]

C$_{14}$H$_{10}$Ca$_1$O$_4$. M: 282.31. Available as the trihydrate. White powder. Loses water of crystallisation at 110°C. d: 1.44 kg/l. Slightly soluble in water. Not approved for food use in the USA.
Production:
• benzoic acid + calcium hydroxide (salt formation)
Uses: food preservative; preservative (prepared foods, cosmetics)

calcium bisulphite

calcium hydrogen sulphite; [13780-03-5]

Ca(HSO$_3$)$_2$

H$_2$Ca$_1$O$_6$S$_2$. M: 202.22. Produced in situ at pulp mills.
Production:
• limestone + sulphur dioxide, raw (salt formation)
Uses: raw material (sulphite pulp process)

calcium borate, natural

colmanite; ulexite
Natural ore. The commercially exploited calcium borate minerals are colmanite (2CaO.3B$_2$O$_3$.5H$_2$O) and ulexite (Na$_2$O.2CaO.5B$_2$O$_3$.16H$_2$O). These are sold as mined or as refined products.
Derivatives: sodium borate
Uses: flux (glass, enamel, ceramics production); metallurgical flux; glass raw material

calcium bromide

[7789-41-5]

CaBr$_2$

Br$_2$Ca$_1$. M: 199.89. White powder. MP: 760°C. d: 3.3 kg/l. Solubility in water: 1.44 kg/l water. Calcium bromide for oilfield applications is usually sold as a

53% w/w solution in water with a density of 1.7 g/l. It is also sold in solution with zinc bromide.
Production:
• calcium hydroxide + hydrobromic acid (salt formation)
Uses: oil-well drilling/completion fluids

calcium carbide
[75-20-7]

CaC₂

C₂Ca₁. M: 64.10. Grey-black lumps. MP: 2,300°C. d: 2.34 kg/l (15°C). Decomposed by water forming acetylene. Commercial grades contain about 80% calcium carbide.
Production:
• calcium oxide + metallurgical coke (electrothermal reduction)
Derivatives: acetylene; calcium cyanamide
Uses: desulphurising agent (pig iron production)

calcium carbonate, precipitated
whiting; CCP; Pigment White 18 (CI); 77220 (CI); E170 (EC); [471-34-1]

CaCO₃

C₁Ca₁O₃. M: 100.09. White powder. Available commercially with either an aragonite or calcite crystal structure. d: 2.83 kg/l (aragonite), 2.71 kg/l (calcite). Decomposes at 825°C releasing carbon dioxide. Insoluble in water. Commercial grades are often coated with stearic acid.
Production:
• calcium hydroxide + carbon dioxide (salt formation)
• calcium chloride + sodium carbonate (salt formation)
Uses:
filler/pigment (paint, adhesives, sealants, printing inks, paper coatings); polyvinyl chloride impact modifier/processing aid/filler; mineral supplement; antacid drug; reinforcing filler (rubber)

calcium caseinate
Production:
• casein + calcium hydroxide (salt formation)
Uses:
adhesives (wooden doors, panels, laminates)

calcium chloride
[10043-52-4]

CaCl₂

Ca₁Cl₂. M: 110.99. Available commercially as 95% anhydrous, 70% dihydrate or as a 35–40% solution in water. Anhydrous grade: Greyish-white, hygroscopic powder or flakes. MP: 772°C. d: 2.16 kg/l (25°C). Solubility in water: 600 g/l water (0°C). Dihydrate:

Greyish-white, hygroscopic solid or flakes. MP: 176°C. d: 1.83 kg/l (25°C).
Production:
• limestone + sodium chloride, natural + ammonia (ammonia-soda process; byproduct of sodium carbonate production)
• propylene + chlorine + calcium hydroxide (hypochlorination/dehydrochlorination; byproduct of propylene oxide production)
• natural brines + calcium oxide (precipitation; coproduced with magnesium hydroxide)
• limestone + hydrochloric acid (neutralisation)
Derivatives:
calcium carbonate, precipitated; calcium silicate; petroleum sulphonates, alkali-earth salts
Uses:
oil-well drilling muds/completion fluids; concrete setting accelerators; aircraft deicing agent; drying agent; dust binder/road consolidation agent (construction, mining); Downs cell eutectic additive; froth flotation agent; reagent (calcium lake formation); refrigerant brines

calcium citrate
E333 (EC); tricalcium dicitrate; [813-94-5]

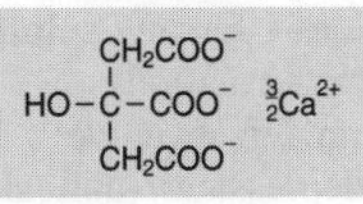

$$HO-\overset{\underset{\displaystyle CH_2COO^-}{|}}{\underset{\underset{\displaystyle CH_2COO^-}{|}}{C}}-COO^- \quad \tfrac{3}{2}Ca^{2+}$$

C₁₂H₁₀Ca₃O₁₄. M: 498.44. Available commercially as the tetrahydrate. White crystals. Loses water of crystallisation at 100°C, decomposing at 230°C. Soluble in water. Insoluble in alcohol.
Production:
• citric acid + calcium hydroxide (salt formation)
Uses: acidity regulator (flour, jams, soft drinks, confectionery)

calcium cyanamide
nitro-lime; [156-62-7]

CaCN₂

C₁Ca₁N₂. M: 80.10. Dark grey lumps containing 21% nitrogen. MP: ~1340°C. d: 2.29 kg/l.
Production:
• calcium carbide + nitrogen (reaction)
Derivatives: calcium cyanide; cyanamide
Uses: fertiliser; iron/steel hardening additive

calcium cyanide
black cyanide; [592-01-8]

Ca(CN)₂

C₂Ca₁N₂. M: 92.11. Usually supplied as an alkaline solution in water.
Production:
• calcium cyanamide (thermal rearrangement)

Uses: flotation depressant; mineral extractant reagent (gold, silver)

calcium cyclamate

calcium cyclohexylsulphamate; [139-06-0]

$C_{12}H_{24}Ca_1N_2O_6S_2$. M: 396.53. Available as the monohydrate. White, crystalline solid with a strong, sweet taste. Soluble in water. Insoluble in most organic solvents.

Production:
• cyclohexylamine + sulphur trioxide + calcium hydroxide (sulphonation/neutralisation)

Uses: artificial sweetener

calcium ferrocyanide

yellow prussiate of calcium

$$Ca_2Fe(CN)_6$$

$C_6Ca_2Fe_1N_6$. M: 292.12. Available as the undecahydrate. Yellow crystals. Solubility in water: 620 g/l water (20°C). Insoluble in alcohol.

Production:
• calcium hydroxide + ferrous sulphate + hydrogen cyanide (complex formation)

Derivatives: sodium ferrocyanide

Uses: flotation depressant; anticaking agent (salt); heavy metal scavenger

calcium fluoride *See:* fluorspar

calcium formate

[544-17-2]

$$HCOO^-\ \tfrac{1}{2}Ca^{2+}$$

$C_2H_2Ca_1O_4$. M: 130.12. White or pale yellow, crystalline powder with a weak, caramel-like odour. d: 2.02 kg/l. Solubility in water: 170 g/l water (20°C).

Production:
• calcium hydroxide + synthesis gas (base-catalysed carbonylation)
• acetaldehyde + formaldehyde (aldol condensation/ Cannizzaro reaction; byproduct of pentaerythritol production)

Derivatives: formic acid

Uses: concrete setting accelerators; silage fermentation additive; tanning auxiliary

calcium gluconate

[299-28-5]

$$\left[HOCH(CHOH)_4COO^-\right]_2 Ca^{2+}$$

$C_{12}H_{22}Ca_1O_{14}$. M: 430.38. Available as the monohydrate. White powder or granules. Releases water on heating with some decomposition. Soluble in hot water. Slow dissolution and less solubility in cold water.

Production:
• sodium gluconate + calcium hydroxide (salt formation)

Uses: calcium replenisher drug; food additive

calcium hydride

[57308-10-8]

$$CaH_2$$

H_2Ca_1. M: 42.10. Grey powder. d: 1.7 kg/l. Decomposed by water with the release of hydrogen.

Production:
• calcium + hydrogen (reaction)

Derivatives:
titanium hydride; zirconium hydride

Uses: drying agent; raw material (hydrogen production); reducing agent

calcium hydroxide

lime; lime, hydrated; lime, slaked; [1305-62-0]

$$Ca(OH)_2$$

$H_2Ca_1O_2$. M: 74.10. White powder. Bulk density: 0.48 kg/l. Slightly soluble in water forming alkaline solutions.

Production:
• calcium oxide (slaking)

Derivatives:
alkylbenzene sulphonates, alkali-earth salts; bis[*O*-ethyl- -(3,5-di-*t*-butyl-4-hydroxybenzyl)phosphonic acid], calcium salt; bleaching powder; Bordeaux mixture; calcium acetate; calcium alkylbenzenesulphonate; calcium alkyl salicylates; calcium ascorbate; calcium benzoate; calcium bromide; calcium carbonate, precipitated; calcium caseinate; calcium citrate; calcium cyclamate; calcium ferrocyanide; calcium formate; calcium gluconate; calcium hypochlorite; calcium hypophosphite; calcium lactate; calcium laurate; calcium lignosulphonate; calcium montanate; calcium naphthenate; calcium peroxide; calcium plumbate; calcium polysulphide; calcium propionate; calcium rosinate; calcium stearate; calcium stearoyl-2-lactylate; calcium tartrate; calcium zinc molybdate; citric acid; copper tallate; dialkylaryl sulphonates, alkali-earth salts; dicalcium phosphate; epichlorohydrin; ethylenediaminetetraacetic acid, calcium disodium salt; gypsum; lithium carbonate; lithium hydroxide; monocalcium phosphate; phenates, alkali-earth salts; phenates, sulphurised, alkali-earth salts; phosphine; polyaluminium chloride; polybutene thiophosphonate propoxylates, alkali-earth salts; propylene oxide; tricalcium phosphate; trimethylphenyl-ammonium hydroxide

Uses:
oil-well drilling mud ingredient; building mortars, plasters, outside rendering materials; calcium silicate bricks; sugar clarification agent; soil conditioner/acidity

controller; soil consolidation agent; depilatory agent (skin/hide production); vulcanisation activator; water treatment chemical

calcium hypochlorite
HTH (Olin); [7778-54-3]

$$Ca(OCl)_2$$

$Ca_1Cl_2O_2$. M: 142.99. White granules with a chlorine odour. The product should contain at least 65% available chlorine.
Production:
• calcium hydroxide + chlorine + sodium hypochlorite (Olin process)
• calcium hydroxide + chlorine + sodium carbonate (PPG process)
Uses:
sanitising agent (drinking water); swimming pool disinfectant; tanning auxiliary; textile/laundry bleach; wastewater treatment chemical

calcium hypophosphite
[7789-79-9]

$$Ca(H_2PO_2)_2$$

$H_4Ca_1O_4P_2$. M: 170.06. Greyish-white powder. Decomposes on heating above 300°C releasing phosphine. Solubility in water: 154 g/l water (25°C) producing slightly acidic solutions.
Production:
• calcium hydroxide + phosphorus (salt formation)
Uses: corrosion inhibitor; reducing agent (electrodeless nickel plating)

calcium lactate
E327 (EC); [814-80-2]

$$\underset{}{CH_3}\overset{OH}{\underset{}{C}}HCOO^- \ \tfrac{1}{2}Ca^{2+}$$

$C_6H_{10}Ca_1O_6$. M: 218.22. Available as the pentahydrate. White, crystalline powder. Loses water of crystallisation at 120°C. Soluble in water.
Production:
• DL-lactic acid + calcium hydroxide (salt formation)
Uses:
buffering agent (prepared foods, bakery products)

calcium laurate
[4696-56-4]

$$\left[CH_3(CH_2)_{10}COO\right]_2 Ca$$

$C_{24}H_{46}Ca_1O_4$. M: 438.71.
Production:
• lauric acid, broad cut + calcium hydroxide (salt formation)
Uses:
polyvinyl chloride heat stabiliser

calcium lignosulphonate
calcium lignin sulphonate; [8061-52-7]
Brown powder or 50% solution in water.
Production:
• sulphite pulp waste liquor + calcium hydroxide (salt formation/separation)
Uses: concrete admixtures; dispersant (oil-well drilling muds)

calcium montanate
Solid. MP: 123°C.
Production:
• montanic acid + calcium hydroxide (salt formation)
Uses: plastics processing lubricant

calcium naphthenate
Production:
• naphthenic acid + calcium hydroxide (salt formation)
Uses: corrosion inhibitor (marine lubricants); paint drier

calcium orthophosphate *See:* tricalcium phosphate

calcium oxide
lime; quicklime; [1305-78-8]

$$CaO$$

Ca_1O_1. M: 56.08. Greyish-yellow, hygroscopic lumps. MP: 2,572°C. d: 3.34 kg/l. Soluble in water forming calcium hydroxide.
Production:
• limestone (calcination)
• gypsum (Mueller-Kuehne process; coproduced with sulphur dioxide, raw)
Derivatives: calcium; calcium carbide; calcium chloride; calcium hydroxide; calcium zirconate; calcium zirconyl silicate; magnesium hydroxide; sodium hydroxide; zirconia
Uses: ground consolidation; pH control (ore/chemical processing); sand-lime bricks/building materials; bauxite processing reagent; reagent (magnesium production); steel manufacturing reagent; water treatment chemical

calcium pantothenate
D-*N*-(2,4-dihydroxy-3,3-dimethyl-1-oxobutyl)-β-alanine, calcium salt; [137-08-6]

$$\left[(CH_3)_2\overset{CH_2OH}{\underset{OH}{C}}CHCONHCH_2CH_2COO\right]_2 Ca$$

$C_{18}H_{32}Ca_1N_2O_{10}$. M: 476.54. White, crystalline solid. Decomposes above 195°C. Soluble in water. Both the racemic and the (+)-isomers are available commercially.
Production:
• pantolactone + β-alanine (amide formation)
Uses: animal feed additive

calcium peroxide
[1305-79-9]

$$CaO_2$$

Ca_1O_2. M: 72.08. Yellow-white powder. Decomposes above 200°C. Insoluble in water. Available oxygen: 13–22%, depending on grade.
Production:
• calcium hydroxide + hydrogen peroxide (salt formation)
Uses: disinfectant (seed/grain); dough conditioner

calcium phosphate, dibasic *See:* dicalcium phosphate

calcium phosphate, monobasic
See: monocalcium phosphate

calcium phosphate, tribasic *See:* tricalcium phosphate

calcium plumbate
[12013-69-3]

$$2CaO.PbO_2$$

$Ca_2O_4Pb_1$. M: 351.35. Light-brown pigment. d: 5.7 kg/l. Its use in paint is controlled in many countries. Technical grades are orange-brown, crystalline solids.
Production:
• calcium hydroxide + litharge (calcination)
Uses: anticorrosion pigment (primer paints); match head/fireworks/explosives ingredient

calcium polysulphide
lime sulphur; [1344-81-6]

$$CaS_n$$

Produced as an aqueous solution by dissolving sulphur in a lime suspension.
Production:
• calcium hydroxide + sulphur (reaction)
Uses: acaricide/fungicide

calcium propionate
E282 (EC); [4075-81-4]

$$CH_3CH_2COO^- \quad \tfrac{1}{2}Ca^{2+}$$

$C_6H_{10}Ca_1O_4$. M: 186.23. Colourless, crystalline solid. Soluble in water. Slightly soluble in alcohol.
Production:
• propionic acid + calcium hydroxide (salt formation)
Uses: preservative (bread, bakery goods)

calcium pyrophosphate
dicalcium pyrophosphate; [7790-76-3]

$$Ca_2P_2O_7$$

$Ca_2O_7P_2$. M: 254.10. White powder. MP: 1,350°C. d: 3.09 kg/l. Insoluble in water.

Production:
• dicalcium phosphate (thermal dehydration)
Uses:
toothpaste abrasive; animal feed supplement; pharmaceutical ingredient; white bone china ingredient

calcium rosinate
calcium abietate; calcium resinate; rosin, lime-hardened; limed rosin; [9007-13-0]
Solid. Softening point: 115–165°C. Metal content ranges from 2–7%.
Production:
• abietic acid/rosin, gum/rosin, wood/rosin, tall oil/rosin, polymerised + calcium hydroxide (salt formation)
Uses: binder (printing inks, wood varnishes)

calcium silicate
Microcal (Crosfield Chemicals); [10101-39-0]
$Ca_1O_4Si_1$. M: 132.17. White powder. $CaO:SiO_2$ ratio typically 1:3.5. d: 2.10 kg/l (25°C). High surface area and absorption power. Insoluble in water.
Production:
• calcium chloride + sodium silicate (precipitation)
Uses:
flattening/thickening agent (oil-based paints); chromatographic adsorption agent; antiblocking agent (plastics)

calcium silicate slag
Production:
• apatite + metallurgical coke + quartz (electric furnace reduction; byproduct of phosphorus production)
Uses: road building material

calcium stearate
[1592-23-0]

$$\left[CH_3(CH_2)_{16}COO\right]_2Ca$$

$C_{36}H_{70}Ca_1O_4$. M: 607.04.
Production:
• stearic acid + calcium hydroxide (salt formation)
Uses:
cement/stucco additive; explosives compounding ingredient; emulsifier (hair creams); external polyvinyl chloride/rubber processing lubricant; fabric waterproofing agent; polyvinyl chloride heat stabiliser; paper coating lubricant; foundry mould release agent; wax ingredient

calcium stearoyl-2-lactylate
E482 (EC)

$$CH_3(CH_2)_{16}\overset{\overset{\displaystyle O}{\|}}{C}OCHCOO^- \quad \tfrac{1}{2}Ca^{2+} \atop CH_3$$

$C_{42}H_{78}Ca_1O_8$. M: 751.15. Off-white flakes or powder. MP: 45–60°C.

Production:
- stearic acid + DL-lactic acid + calcium hydroxide (esterification/salt formation)

Uses:
dough conditioner; emulsifier (cosmetics)

calcium sulphate hemihydrate
plaster of Paris

$$CaSO_4 \cdot \tfrac{1}{2}H_2O$$

$Ca_1O_4S_1$. M: 136.14. Whitish powder. Loses water when heated above 163°C. Solubility in water: 3.0 g/l (25°C).
Production:
- gypsum (calcination)
- apatite + sulphuric acid (wet phosphoric acid hemihydrate process; coproduced with phosphoric acid, crude)

Uses: medical/mould casts; stucco; wall plaster

calcium superphosphate
superphosphate, normal; superphosphate, single; NSP

$$Ca(H_2PO_4)_2/CaSO_4$$

Impure mixture containing monocalcium phosphate and calcium sulphate. 18–22% P_2O_5 content. Bulk density: 0.97 kg/l (granular grades), 0.8 kg/l (non-granular grades).
Production:
- apatite + sulphuric acid (salt formation)

Uses: fertiliser ingredient

calcium tartrate
calcium-L-tartrate

$$\begin{array}{c} HOCHCOO^- \\ | \\ HOCHCOO^- \end{array} \; Ca^{2+}$$

$C_4H_4Ca_1O_6$. M: 188.14. Available as the tetrahyrate. White powder. Slightly soluble in water.
Production:
- grape press cakes/wine lees + calcium hydroxide (extraction/salt formation)

Derivatives: tartaric acid
Uses: food preservative; antacid drug

calcium toner *See:* Pigment Red 49

calcium triple superphosphate
TSP

$$Ca(H_2PO_4)_2$$

Impure mixture containing monocalcium phosphate as the main ingredient. 45–47% P_2O_5 content. Soluble in water.
Production:
- apatite + phosphoric acid, crude (reaction)

Uses: fertiliser ingredient

calcium zinc molybdate
molybdenum white; Moly-White 212 (PMC)

$$CaO.iZnO.mMoO_3.nH_2O$$

White powder. d: 3.00 kg/l. Insoluble in water.
Production:
- calcium hydroxide + zinc oxide + molybdenum trioxide (salt formation)

Uses: anticorrosion pigment (protective paints)

calcium zirconate
[12013-47-7]

$$CaO.ZrO_2$$

$Ca_1O_3Zr_1$. M: 179.30. White solid. MP: 2,550°C. d: 4.78 kg/l. Insoluble in water.
Production:
- calcium oxide + zircon (alkali fusion)

Derivatives:
zirconium sulphate, basic
Uses: refractories raw material

calcium zirconyl silicate
calcium zirconium silicate

$$CaO.ZrO_2.SiO_2$$

$Ca_1O_5Si_1Zr_1$. M: 239.38. White, high-melting solid. Insoluble in water.
Production:
- calcium oxide + zircon (alkali fusion)

Derivatives: zirconia
Uses: refractories raw material

Calgon *See:* sodium hexametaphosphate

calomel *See:* mercurous chloride

camomile oil
chamomile oil; [8015-92-7]
Blue-green oil which turns brown on exposure to light and air. Produced by steam distillation of different varieties of camomile flowers. German grades are produced from *Matricaria chamomilla*, Roman grades from *Anthemis nobilis*. d: 0.94 kg/l. Soluble in alcohol. Mainly produced in northern and eastern Europe.
Uses:
perfume ingredient

camphene
[79-92-5]

$C_{10}H_{16}$. M: 136.24. Crystalline solid. MP: 51–52°C. BP: 158–160°C. Insoluble in water. Soluble in ether, cyclohexane and chlorinated solvents.

Production:
- α-pinene (acid-catalysed rearrangement)

Derivatives: isobornyl acetate; isocamphylcyclohexanol

campholenic aldehyde

$C_{10}H_{16}O_1$. M: 152.24.
Production:
- α-pinene + peracetic acid (epoxidation/rearrangement)

Uses: fragrance ingredient

camphor

2-camphanone; 1,7,7-trimethylbicyclo[2,2,1]heptan-2-one; [76-22-2]

$C_{10}H_{16}O_1$. M: 152.24. Colourless solid with a characteristic odour. MP: 180°C. BP: 204°C. d: 0.99 kg/l (25°C). Sublimes. Soluble in aromatic and oxygenated solvents. Available as the (+)-isomer and as the racemic mixture.
Production:
- camphor oil (fractionation)
- isobornyl acetate (ester hydrolysis/dehydrogenation)

Derivatives: 10-camphoric acid; D-camphorsulphonic acid; glibornuride; heptopargil

Uses: fragrance ingredient (incense, technical products); moth repellant; plasticiser (cellulose nitrate explosives)

10-camphoric acid
[5394-83-2]

$C_{10}H_{16}O_4$. M: 200.24. Crystalline solid. MP: 186–188°C. d: 1.19 kg/l. Soluble in hot water, oxygenated and chlorinated solvents. Available commercially as the D(+)-enantiomer.
Production:
- camphor (oxidation)

Uses: racemate separation agent

camphor oil

Cinnamomum camphora oil
Colourless to yellow-brown liquid with a camphor or safrole odour. Available in three grades which differ in their boiling ranges: white camphor oil (d: ~0.87 kg/l), yellow camphor oil (d: ~0.97 kg/l, BP: >200°C) and

brown camphor oil (d: ~1.07 kg/l). They are obtained by fractionation of the crude oil. Brown camphor oil contains no camphor and is used as a substitute for sassafras oil. The crude oil is extracted from the wood of the camphor tree (*Cinnamomum camphora*) which is grown in the Far East.
Derivatives:
camphor
Uses: fragrance ingredient (technical products); cough medicine ingredient; solvent (paints, lacquers); topical analgesic drug

D-camphorsulphonic acid

$C_{10}H_{16}O_4S_1$. M: 232.30. Solid. MP: 195°C with decomposition. Soluble in water. Insoluble in ether.
Production:
- camphor (sulphonation)

Uses: racemate separation agent

cananga oil *See:* ylang-ylang oil

candelilla wax
[8006-44-8]
Yellow, brittle solid. MP: 70°C. Acid value: 14 mg KOH/g. Saponification value: 55 mg KOH/g. Insoluble in water. The wax is obtained by hot water/acid extraction of *Euphorbia antisyphilitica* shrubs which grow in Coahuila and Chihuahua states of Mexico. Its major constituents are a hydrocarbon fraction (50%) containing a C_{31} alkane, wax esters (28%) and free alcohols (13%).
Uses:
wax ingredient; cosmetics/chewing gum ingredient

canola oil *See:* rapeseed oil

CAP *See:* cellulose propionate

capraldehyde *See:* n-decaldehyde

capric acid
decanoic acid; n-decanoic acid; decoic acid; n-decoic acid; decylic acid; [334-48-5]

$C_{10}H_{20}O_2$. M: 172.27. Pale yellow solid. Titre: 27–32°C. Acid value: 320–330 mg KOH/g. d: 0.88 kg/l (4°C). Insoluble in water. Grades containing 90–100% C_{10} are available commercially.
Production:
- C_8-C_{10} fatty acids (fractionation; coproduced with caprylic acid)

Derivatives: capryl imidazoline; ethyl caprate

caproaldehyde *See: n*-hexaldehyde

caproamphocarboxyglycinate

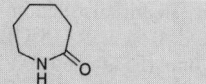

$C_{18}H_{31}N_2Na_1O_5$. M: 378.44. Available as a 43% solution in water.
Production:
• capryl imidazoline + sodium chloroacetate (dehydrochlorination)
Uses: amphoteric surfactant (toilet soaps/cleaners)

caproamphocarboxypropionate

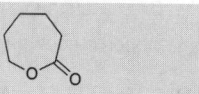

$C_{20}H_{25}N_2Na_1O_5$. M: 396.41. Available as a 39% solution in water.
Production:
• capryl imidazoline + methyl acrylate (carboxyethylation/hydrolysis)
Uses: amphoteric surfactant (toilet soaps/cleaners)

caprocol *See:* hexylresorcinol

caproic acid
hexanoic acid; [142-62-1]

$$CH_3(CH_2)_4COOH$$

$C_6H_{12}O_2$. M: 116.17. Colourless, oily liquid with a goat-like odour. MP: -2°C. BP: 202–203°C. d: 0.92 kg/l (20°C). Solubility in water: 11 g/l water (20°C).
Production:
• C_8-C_{10} fatty acids (fractionation; byproduct of capric acid/caprylic acid production)
• *n*-hexaldehyde (oxidation)
Derivatives:
allyl caproate; ethyl caproate; hexylresorcinol

caprolactam
ε-caprolactam; 2-oxohexamethyleneimine; [105-60-2]

$C_6H_{11}N_1O_1$. M: 113.17. White, hygroscopic, crystalline solid with a characteristic odour. MP: 69°C. BP: 267°C. d: 1.02 kg/l (77°C). Soluble in water, oxygenated and chlorinated solvents.
Production:
• benzoic acid + hydrogen + nitrosyl hydrogen sulphate (SNIA caprolactam process)
• cyclohexanone oxime + ammonia + oleum (Beckmann rearrangement)

Derivatives: 6-aminocaproic acid; caprolactam disulphide; 1,5-diazabicyclo[5.4.0]undec-5-ene; polyamide 6; polyamide 6 terpolymers; poly(ether-amide) elastomers; polynorbornamide
Uses: isocyanate blocking agent; polyamide 6 casting material

caprolactam disulphide
N,N'-dithiobis(hexahydro-2H-azepinone); CLD

$C_{12}H_{20}N_2O_2S_2$. M: 288.43.
Production:
• caprolactam + sulphur monochloride (chlorosulphurisation)
Uses: vulcanisation agent

caprolactone
ε-caprolactone; hexan-6-olide; [502-44-3]

$C_6H_{10}O_2$. M: 114.15. Colourless liquid. BP: 235°C. FP: -1°C. d: 1.08 kg/l (20°C). Miscible with water.
Production:
• cyclohexanone + peracetic acid (peroxidation)
Derivatives:
cilastatin; polycaprolactone diols

capryl aldehyde *See: n*-octaldehyde

caprylic acid
n-octanoic acid; [124-07-2]

$$CH_3(CH_2)_6COOH$$

$C_8H_{16}O_2$. M: 144.22. Colourless, oily liquid. MP: 16°C. BP: 237°C. d: 0.91 kg/l (20°C). Slightly soluble in water. Soluble in oxygenated solvents. A typical technical grade contains 95% C_8, 4% C_{10} and 1% C_{12}.
Production:
• C_8-C_{10} fatty acids (fractionation; coproduced with capric acid)
Derivatives:
caprylyl chloride; caprylyl imidazoline; ethyl caprylate; *n*-octylamine; perfluorooctanoic acid

capryl imidazoline

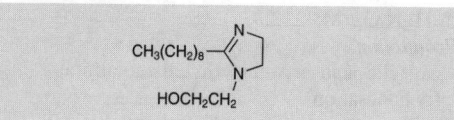

$C_{14}H_{28}N_2O_1$. M: 240.38.

Production:
• capric acid + aminoethylethanolamine (condensation)
Derivatives:
caproamphocarboxyglycinate; caproamphocarboxypropionate

caproamphocarboxyglycinate
[7702-01-4]

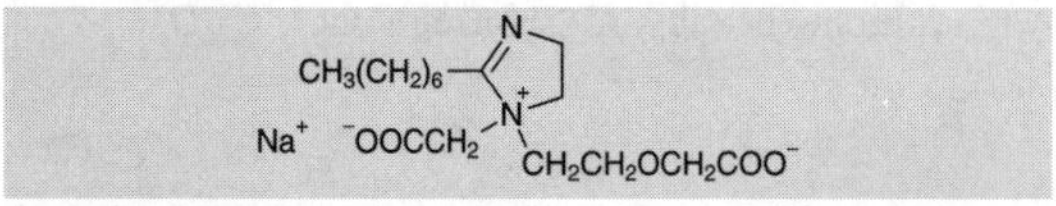

$C_{16}H_{27}N_2Na_1O_5$. M: 350.39. Available as solutions containing 35–50% active matter.
Production:
• caprylyl imidazoline + sodium chloroacetate (ether formation/quaternisation)
Uses: low-foaming surfactant (machine washing, steam cleaning, hard-surface detergents)

caproamphocarboxypropionate

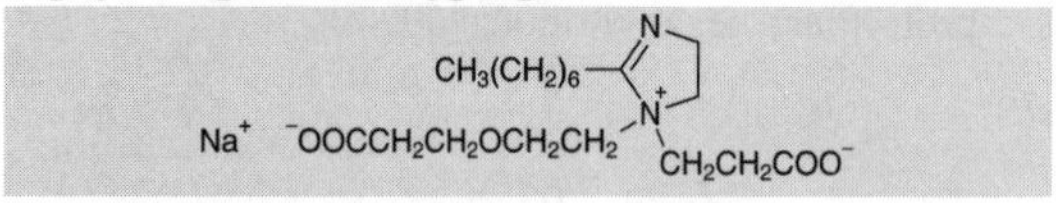

$C_{18}H_{31}N_2Na_1O_5$. M: 378.44. Available as a 38.5% solution in water.
Production:
• caprylyl imidazoline + methyl acrylate (carboxyethylation/hydrolysis)
Uses: low-foaming wetting agent (steam cleaners, bottle washing compounds)

caprylyl chloride
n-octanoyl chloride

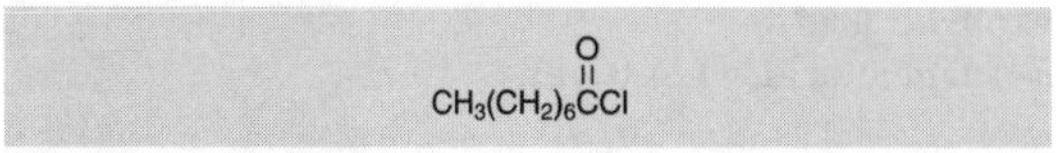

$C_8H_{15}Cl_1O_1$. M: 162.66. Liquid. BP: 196°C. MP: -63°C. d: 0.96 kg/l (20°C).
Production:
• caprylic acid (acid chloride formation)
Derivatives: bromoxynil octanoate; ioxynil octanoate

caprylyl imidazoline
caprylyl hydroxyethyl imidazoline (CTFA)

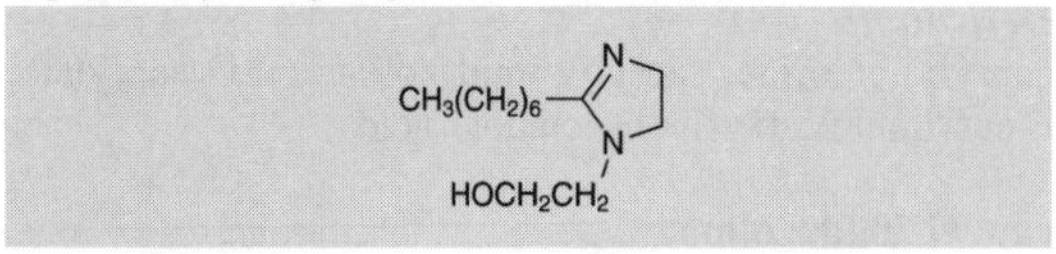

$C_{12}H_{24}N_2O_1$. M: 212.33.
Production:
• caprylic acid + aminoethylethanolamine (condensation)
Derivatives: capryloamphocarboxyglycinate; caprylo-amphocarboxypropionate

captafol
1,2,3,6-tetrahydro-*N*-(1,1,2,2-tetrachloroethylthio)phthalimide; [2425-06-1]

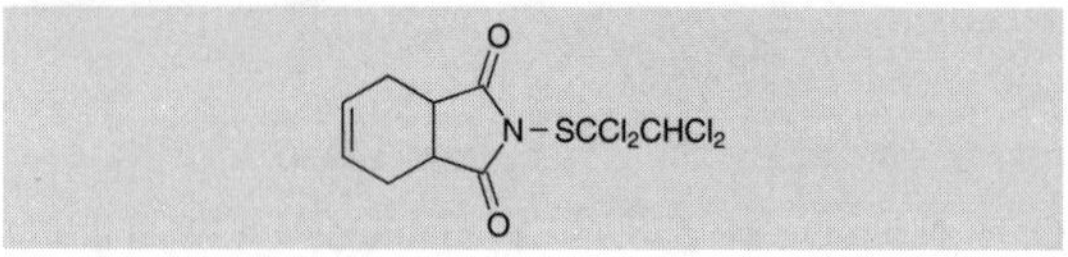

$C_{10}H_9Cl_4N_1O_2S_1$. M: 349.06.
Production:
• trichloroethylene + sulphur dichloride + tetrahydrophthalimide (addition/dehydrochlorination)
Uses: fungicide

captan
N-(trichloromethylthio)cyclohex-4-ene-1,2-dicarboximide; [133-06-2]

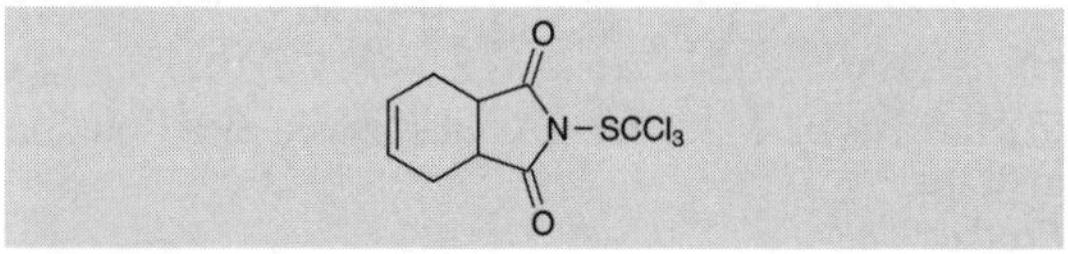

$C_9H_8Cl_3N_1O_2S_1$. M: 300.59.
Production:
• tetrahydrophthalimide + trichloromethanesulphenyl chloride (dehydrochlorination)
Uses: fungicide; plastics biostabiliser

captopril
[62571-86-2]

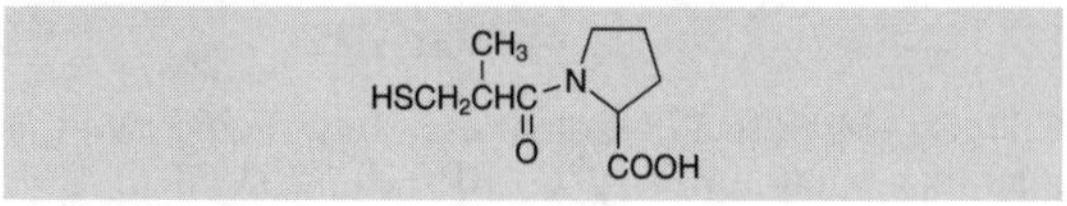

$C_9H_{15}N_1O_3S_1$. M: 217.29.
Production:
• thioacetic acid + methacrylic acid + L-proline (carboxyethylation/amide formation/racemate separation/deacetylation)
Uses: antihypertensive drug

caraway oil
[8000-42-8]
Colourless or pale yellow oil with a caraway odour. Produced by steam distillation of caraway (*Carvum carvi*) seeds. d: 0.91 kg/l (15°C). Its major constituents are (+)-carvone (55%) and (+)-limonene (40%). The major producing countries are Poland and Hungary.
Uses: food/drink flavouring ingredient

carazolol
[57775-29-8]
$C_{18}H_{22}N_2O_2$. M: 298.39.
Production:
• carbazole + epichlorohydrin + *t*-butylamine (sulphonation/alkali fusion/ether formation/epoxidation)

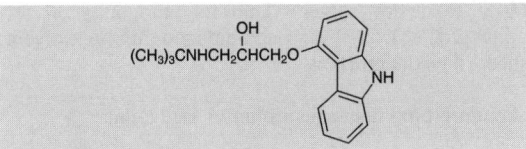

Uses: antianginal/antihypertensive drug

carbamazepine
5H-dibenz[b,f]azepine-5-carboxamide; [298-46-4]

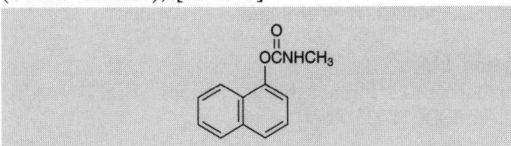

$C_{15}H_{12}N_2O_1$. M: 236.27.
Production:
• iminostilbene + phosgene + ammonia (phosgenation/dehydrochlorination)
Uses:
analgesic/antiepileptic drug

carbanil *See:* phenyl isocyanate

carbaryl
1-naphthyl methylcarbamate; Dicarbam (BASF); Sevin (Union Carbide); [63-25-2]

$C_{12}H_{11}N_1O_2$. M: 201.23.
Production:
• α-naphthol + methyl isocyanate (isocyanate addition)
Uses: insecticide

carbazole
[86-74-8]

$C_{12}H_9N_1$. M: 167.21. Crystalline solid. MP: 243–245°C. Insoluble in water. Soluble in acetone.
Production:
• anthracene oil (fractionation; byproduct of anthracene production)
Derivatives: carazolol; N-ethylcarbazole; Vat Blue 43; N-vinylcarbazole

carbendazim
methyl benzimidazol-2-ylcarbamate; MBC
[10605-21-7]
$C_9H_8N_3O_2$. M: 190.18. Available commercially as the free acid or as the phosphate salt.

Production:
• cyanamide + methyl chloroformate + o-phenylene-diamine (dehydrochlorination/condensation)
Derivatives: benomyl
Uses: fungicide

carbenicillin
[4697-36-3]; [4800-94-6] (disodium salt)

$C_{17}H_{18}N_2O_6S_1$. M: 378.39. Available commercially as the disodium salt.
Production:
• benzyl phenylmalonate + 6-aminopenicillanic acid (amide formation/hydrogenation)
Uses: antibacterial drug

carbetamide
(R)-1-(ethylcarbamoyl)ethyl carbanilate; [16118-49-3]

$C_{12}H_{16}N_2O_3$. M: 236.27.
Production:
• D-lactic acid + ethylamine + phenyl isocyanate (amide formation/isocyanate addition)
Uses: herbicide

carbetapentane *See:* pentoxyverine

carbinoxamine
levocarbinoxamine ((−)-enantiomer);
[486-16-8]; [3505-38-2] (hydrogen maleate)

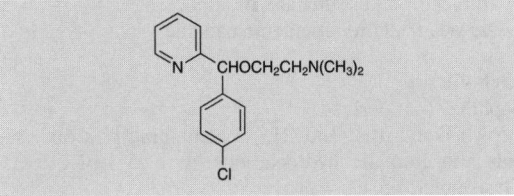

$C_{16}H_{19}Cl_1N_2O_1$. M: 290.79. Available commercially as the racemic mixture or (−)-enantiomer maleate.
Production:
• 2-bromopyridine + 2-dimethylaminoethyl chloride hydrochloride + p-chlorobenzaldehyde (Grignard reagent formation/Grignard reaction/ether formation)
Uses: antihistamine drug

carbocromen
chromonar; [804-10-4]

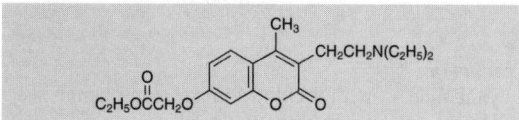

$C_{20}H_{27}N_1O_5$. M: 361.44. Available commercially as the hydrochloride.
Production:
- ethyl acetoacetate + 2-diethylaminoethyl chloride hydrochloride + resorcinol + ethyl bromoacetate (dehydrochlorination/esterification/carbonyl condensation/dehydrobromination)

Uses: vasodilator drug

carbocysteine
3-carboxymethylthioalanine; [638-23-3]

$C_5H_9N_1O_4S_1$. M: 179.19.
Production:
- L-cysteine + chloroacetic acid (dehydrochlorination)

Uses: respiratory tract drug

carbodiimide *See:* cyanamide

carbofuran
Furadan (FMC); [1563-66-2]

$C_{12}H_{15}N_1O_3$. M: 221.26.
Production:
- o-nitrophenol + methallyl chloride + methyl isocyanate (dehydrochlorination/nitro reduction/ diazotisation/hydration/isocyanate addition)

Derivatives:
benfuracarb; carbosulphan; furathiocarb
Uses: acaricide/insecticide/nematicide

carbolic oil
naphtha, coal-derived
Brown liquid. BR: 160–215°C containing phenols, cresols and aromatic hydrocarbons. d: 0.93 kg/l (15°C). Flash point: 45°C.
Production:
- coal tar, crude (alkali extraction/fractionation; coproduced with light oil/creosote oil/naphthalene fraction/fluorene oil/anthracene oil/coal tar pitch/tar acid liquor)

Derivatives:
coumarone-indene resin

Uses: extraction solvent (Duo-Sol lubricating oil refining process); coal tar pitch/bitumen fluxing solvent; sheep dips/disinfectants

carbomethoxybenzenesulphonyl isocyanate

$C_9H_7N_1O_5S_1$. M: 241.22.
Production:
- 2,2'-dithiodibenzoic acid + methanol + ammonia + phosgene (thiol oxidation/esterification/sulphonamide formation/phosgenation)

Derivatives: metsulfuron-methyl; sulfometuron-methyl

carbon *See:* charcoal

carbon, moulded
Production:
- metallurgical coke/asphaltite/carbon black/coal tar pitch/graphite, natural/needle coke (carbonisation)

Derivatives: graphite, manufactured
Uses: chemical handling equipment/components; electric motor brushes/contacts; electrodes (electrolysis); furnace lining material; moulds/crucibles (metal, glass, ceramic industries); welding/arc electrodes

carbon black
channel black; furnace black; Pigment Black 7 (CI); 77266 (CI); [1333-86-4]
Production:
- heavy cycle oil/pyrolysis tar/anthracene oil (furnace black process)
- natural gas (thermal black process)
- coal tar pitch (gas black process)

Derivatives: carbon, moulded; titanium carbide; tungsten carbide
Uses: light stabiliser/antioxidant/conductive filler (plastics); pigment (paints, printing inks, plastics); reinforcing filler/pigment (tyres, rubber goods)

carbon dioxide
E290 (EC); [124-38-9]

CO_2

C_1O_2. M: 44.01. Colourless, odourless, liquified gas or white, solid lumps. Sublimes at -78°C. Triple point: -57°C (510 kPa). Relative density: 1.53 (gas, air=1). Soluble in water. Carbon dioxide produced by as a byproduct of ammonia production requires treatment to remove hydrogen sulphide if produced by gasification or partial oxidation.
Production:
- synthesis gas + water (shift reaction/solvent extraction; coproduced with hydrogen)

- natural gas (air oxidation)
- natural gas (separation)
- limestone (calcination; byproduct of calcium oxide production)
- fermentation byproduct gases (extraction)

Derivatives:

ammonium bicarbonate; ammonium carbamate; barium carbonate; calcium alkyl salicylates; calcium carbonate, precipitated; *m*-cresotic acid; *o*-cresotic acid; cyanamide; dicamba; diflunisal; *N,N'*-dimethylurea; ethylene carbonate; *p*-hydroxybenzoic acid; α-hydroxynaphthoic acid; lead carbonate, basic; magnesia, causticcalcined; magnesium carbonate, basic; nickel carbonate, basic; nitrophosphate; β-oxynaphthoic acid; potassium bicarbonate; potassium carbonate; propantheline bromide; propylene carbonate; salicylic acid; sodium bicarbonate; sodium dichromate; tetrafluoro-*p*-methylbenzyl alcohol; tetramethylurea; urea

Uses:

carbonated drinks; enhanced oil recovery driver gas; low-alcohol beer/decaffeinated coffee/vegetable oil extraction solvent; fire extinguishant gas; food freezing/refrigeration agent; aerosol propellant; blanketing gas (chemical/food/matallurgical production, welding); industrial refrigeration

carbon disulphide
carbon bisulphide; [75-15-0]

$$CS_2$$

C_1S_2. M: 76.14. Colourless liquid with an unpleasant odour. BP: 46°C. MP: -112°C. d: 1.26 kg/l (20°C). Toxic. Slightly soluble in water. Miscible with most organic solvents. Flash point: -30°C (CC).

Production:

- natural gas + sulphur (reaction)
- metallurgical coke + sulphur (reaction; coproduced with hydrogen sulphide)

Derivatives:

acetone-1,3-dicarboxylic acid; ammonium thiocyanate; antimony diamyldithiocarbamate; astemizole; azathioprine; 2-benzoxazolethiol; bitoscanate; cefotetan; *N*-cyanoimido-*S,S*-dimethyldithiocarbamate; di-*n*-butylthiourea; dicyclohexylcarbodiimide; diethylthiourea; 2,5-dimercapto-1,3,4-thiadiazole; *N,N'*-dimethyldiphenylthiuram disulphide; dipentamethylenethiuram tetrasulphide; dithianon; di-*o*-tolylguanidine; di-*o*-tolylthiourea; ethidimuron; ethylenethiourea; 5-(2-hydroxyethyl)-4-methylthiazole; lead diamyldithiocarbamate; 2-mercaptobenzimidazole; 2-mercaptobenzothiazole; 2-mercaptomethylbenzimidazole; metam-sodium; 1-methylamino-1-methylthio-2-nitroethylene; 2-methyl-5-mercapto-1,3,4-thiadiazole; 4-methylthiazole; metiram; metribuzin; nabam; nickel di-*n*-butyldithiocarbamate; *N*-oxydiethylenedithiocarbamyl-*N'*-oxydiethylenesulphenamide; phenyl isothiocyanate; piperidinium pentamethylenedithiocarbamate; potassium amyl xanthate; potassium ethyl xanthate; potassium isopropyl xanthate; propineb; sodium cellulose xanthate; sodium diethyldithiocarbamate; sodium dimethyldithiocarbamate; sodium isobutyl xanthate; sodium isopropyl xanthate; starch, sodium xanthate; thiamine; thiocarbanilide; thiophosgene; trichloromethanesulphenyl chloride; tricyclazole; zinc diamyldithiocarbamate; zinc dibenzyldithiocarbamate; zinc di-*n*-butyldithiocarbamate; zinc ethylphenyldithiocarbamate; zinc pentamethylenedithiocarbamate

Uses:

process solvent

carbon fibre
graphite fibre (HM grades)

Available in various grades: high tensile (HT) carbon fibres from acrylic (PAN) fibre have tensile strengths of 2.5–6.0 GPa and elastic moduli of 250–500 GPa. High modulus (HM) carbon fibres from mesophase pitch have elastic moduli up to 830 GPa. Lower grade products are made from isotropic pitch and regenerated cellulose. Low performance carbon wool and felts are also available by straightforward pyrolysis of cotton wool or woven cloth.

Production:

- coal tar pitch/bitumen (pyrolysis)
- cellulose, regenerated (pyrolysis)
- polyacrylonitrile (pyrolysis)

Uses:

fibre-reinforced laminates (aircraft fuselage, missiles, sports equipment)

carbon monoxide
[630-08-0]

$$CO$$

C_1O_1. M: 28.01. Colourless gas. BP: -191°C. MP: -205°C. d: 0.814 kg/l (-190°C). Toxic. Slightly soluble in water. Soluble in oxygenated and chlorinated solvents.

Production:

- synthesis gas (cryogenic separation; coproduced with hydrogen)
- synthesis gas (Tenneco Cosorb/Uhde selective absorption processes)

Derivatives:

acetic acid; acetic anhydride; acrylic acid; carbon tetrafluoride; carbonyl sulphide; cyanoacetic acid; diethyl malonate; diisopropyl malonate; dimethyl carbonate; dimethylformamide; dimethyl malonate; 2,2-dimethylpentanoic acid; ethyl formate; 2-ethyl-2-methylbutanoic acid; formamide; formic acid; glycollic acid; ibuprofen; iron pentacarbonyl; *p*-isopropylbenzaldehyde; magnesium chloride; *p*-methylbenzaldehyde; methyl formate; molybdenum hexacarbonyl; neodecanoic acid; neoheptanoic acid; nickel tetracarbonyl; oxalic acid; perfluoro(methyl vinyl ether); phosgene; pivalic acid; propionic acid

carbon tetrachloride
CTC; [56-23-5]

$$CCl_4$$

C_1Cl_4. M: 153.82. Colourless liquid with a sweet odour. BP: 76°C. FP: -23°C. d: 1.60 kg/l (20°C). Non-flammable. Insoluble in water. Miscible with alcohol and ether.
Production:
• methyl chloride + chlorine (thermal chlorination; coproduced with chloroform/methylene chloride)
• natural gas + hydrogen chloride, anhydrous/oxygen (Lummus oxychlorination process; coproduced with chloroform/methyl chloride/methylene chloride)
• natural gas + hydrogen chloride, anhydrous (oxychlorination; coproduced with chloroform/methylene chloride)
• ethane/propane + chlorine (chlorinolysis; coproduced with perchloroethylene)
Derivatives:
dichlorodifluoromethane; (*1RS*)-*cis*-3-(2,2-dichlorovinyl)-2,2-dimethylcyclopropanecarboxylic acid; perchloroethylene; trichlorobutylene oxide; trichlorofluoromethane; trityl chloride
Uses: solvent (chlorination reactions)

carbon tetrafluoride
tetrafluoromethane; [75-73-0]

$$CF_4$$

C_1F_4. M: 88.00. Colourless, inert gas.
Production:
• carbon monoxide + fluorine (fluorination)
Uses: inert filler gas (electrical switchgear); refrigerant

carbonyl sulphide
carbon oxysulphide; [463-58-1]

$$COS$$

$C_1O_1S_1$. M: 60.07. Liquified gas. BP: -50°C. MP: -139°C. d: 1.19 kg/l (-53°C). Very slightly soluble in water.
Production:
• carbon monoxide + sulphur (addition)
Derivatives: fenothiocarb; hexythiazox; methidathion; thiobencarb; tiocarbazil; tri-allate

carbosulphan
2,3-dihydro-2,2-dimethylbenzofuran-7-yl (dibutylaminothio)methylcarbamate; [55285-14-8]

$C_{20}H_{32}N_2O_3S_1$. M: 380.55.

Production:
• carbofuran + sulphur dichloride + di-*n*-butylamine (dehydrochlorination/dehydrochlorination)
Uses: insecticide

carboxin
Vitavax (Uniroyal Chemical); [5234-68-4]

$C_{12}H_{11}N_1O_2S_1$. M: 233.29.
Production:
• acetoacetanilide + 2-mercaptoethanol (alpha chlorination/condensation)
Derivatives: oxycarboxin
Uses: fungicide

carboxymethylcellulose
See: sodium carboxymethyl cellulose

carboxymethyl starch

$$R-OCH_2COO^-\ Na^+$$

R = starch-.
Production:
• starch + sodium chloroacetate (ether formation)
Uses: paper sizing; protective colloid (emulsion paints); thickening agent (polyvinyl acetate adhesives)

cardamom oil
cardomon oil; [8000-66-6]
Characteristic to pale yellow liquid with a characteristic odour. Produced by steam distillation of cardomom (*Elettaria cardamomum*) seed. d: 0.93 kg/l (25°C). Insoluble in water. Soluble in alcohol. The main constituents of the oil are 1,8-cineole and α-terpinyl acetate. The prime producing areas are India, Sri Lanka and South-East Asia.
Uses: food/drink flavouring ingredient

3-carene
Δ^3-carene; [13466-78-9]

$C_{10}H_{16}$. M: 136.24.
Production:
• pine oil (fractionation; coproduced with dipentene/anethole)
Uses: solvent

carmine
carminic acid; cochineal; E120 (EC); [1390-65-4] (aluminium lake)

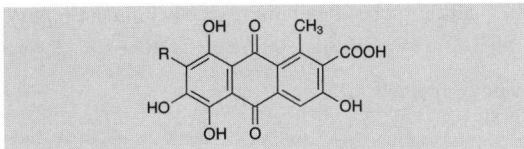

R = glucose. $C_{22}H_{20}O_{13}$. M: 492.39. Red powder. Water extract of *Dactylopius coccus* insects which live on cacti mainly grown in Peru. Sparingly soluble. Carminic acid content: 40–60%.
Uses: food/cosmetics colorant

carminic acid *See:* carmine

carmoisine *See:* Acid Red 14

carnauba wax
Pale yellow to brown brittle solid. Softening point: 82–84°C. Acid value: 2.5–5.0 mg KOH/g. Saponification value: 79–85 mg KOH/g. Consists mainly of long-chain wax esters. Obtained from South American palm tree (*Copernicia cerifera*) leaves.
Uses:
carbon paper ingredient; car/floor/shoe polish ingredient; cosmetics/pharmaceuticals ingredient; paraffin wax modifier

carob gum *See:* locust bean gum

(*1R*)-*cis*-caronaldehyde

C_7H_{10}O_3. M: 142.16.
Production:
• (*1RS*)-*trans*-chrysanthemic acid (hydration/lactone formation/hydrolysis/ozonolysis)
Derivatives:
acrinathrin; (*1R*)-*cis*-3-(2,2-dibromovinyl)-2,2-dimethyl-cyclopropanecarboxylic acid; kadethrinic acid

Caro's acid *See:* peroxysulphuric acid

β-carotene
carotene; E160(a) (EC); [7235-40-7]

$C_{40}H_{56}$. M: 536.89. Red or purple crystals. Insoluble in water. Soluble in ether and vegetable oils.
Production:
• β-C_{14} aldehyde + ethyl vinyl ether + propionaldehyde + acetylene (multistep synthesis)

• β-ionone + acetylene + C_{10} dialdehyde (ethynylation/Wittig reaction)
Uses:
food colorant

carrageenan
carrageenin; E407 (EC); Irish moss; [9000-07-1]
White to beige powder. Polysaccharide gum. M: 100,000–1,000,000. Soluble in water forming viscous solutions. Produced by Irish moss (*Gigartina stellata* or *Chondrus crispis* seaweed).
Uses:
thickening/gelling agent (milk/dairy products)

cartap
[15263-53-3]; [15263-52-2] (hydrochloride)

$C_7H_{15}N_3O_2S_2$. M: 237.35.
Production:
• 1,3-dimercaptoisopropyldimethylamine + phosgene + ammonia (phosgenation/dehydrochlorination)
Uses: insecticide

carticaine
[23964-58-1]

$C_{13}H_{20}N_2O_3S_1$. M: 284.37. Available commercially as the hydrochloride.
Production:
• α-bromopropionic acid + methyl 3-amino-4-methyl-thiophene-2-carboxylate + *n*-propylamine (amide formation/amine formation)
Uses:
local anaesthetic drug

carvacrol
2-hydroxy-*p*-cymene; isopropyl-*o*-cresol; 5-isopropyl-2-methylphenol; [499-75-2]

$C_{10}H_{14}O_1$. M: 150.22. Colourless liquid with a herbal odour. BP: 237–238°C. d: 0.98 kg/l (20°C). Insoluble in water. Soluble in oxygenated solvents.
Production:
• *o*-cresol + propylene (Friedel-Crafts alkylation)
Uses:
disinfectant/antiseptic

(–)-carvone

carvone; (–)-1,8-*p*-menthadien-6-one; [6485-40-1]

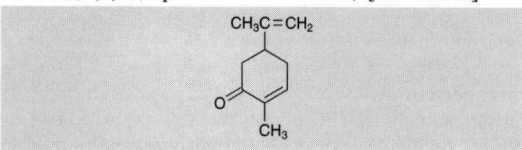

$C_{10}H_{14}O_1$. M: 150.22. Pale yellow liquid with a herbal, minty odour. BP: 230°C. d: 0.96 kg/l (20°C). Insoluble in water. Miscible with alcohol. The product is the natural (–)-enantiomer and is the main component of spearmint oil.
Production:
• (+)-limonene + nitrosyl chloride (addition/ dehydrochlorination/imine hydrolysis)
Uses: flavouring ingredient (food, drinks, mouth-care products)

casamino acid *See:* protein hydrolysates

casein

milk protein; [9000-71-9]
White powder consisting of mixed phosphoproteins from milk. Isoelectric point: 4.6. Soluble in alkaline solutions.
Production:
• skimmed milk (acid-selective precipitation process)
• skimmed milk (rennet process)
Derivatives: ammonium caseinate; calcium caseinate; casein plastics; protein hydrolysates; sodium caseinate
Uses: adhesives (beer bottle labelling pastes); foil-paper laminating adhesives; animal feed ingredient; binder (paper coatings); imitation cheese, coffee whiteners, prepared foods, bakery products; protective colloid (emulsion polymerisation); stabiliser (rosin paper sizes); textile finishing agent

casein plastics

Horn-like solid produced by blending casein with pigments and clarifying agents, followed by extrusion, shaping and then hardening in formaldehyde solution.
Production:
• casein + formaldehyde (dry process)
Uses: buttons/buckles/hair slides

cashew nutshell glycidyl ether

$C_{24}H_{38}O_2$. M: 358.56.
Production:
• cashew nutshell oil + epichlorohydrin (ether formation)

Uses: nitrile rubber flexibiliser; reactive diluent (epoxy resins)

cashew nutshell oil

CNSL

$C_{21}H_{34}O_1$. M: 302.50. Brown liquid. BP: 223–227°C (1.3 kPa). d: 0.93 kg/l (20°C). The main component of the oil is caradanol, 3-(*n*-penta-8′-decenyl)phenol.
Production:
• cashew nutshells (extraction)
Derivatives:
cashew nutshell glycidyl ether; cashew nutshell-phenol condensate diglycidyl ether

cashew nutshell-phenol condensate diglycidyl ether

NC-514 (Cardolite)

$C_{33}H_{48}O_4$. M: 508.74.
Production:
• cashew nutshell oil + phenol + epichlorohydrin (Friedel-Crafts alkylation/ether formation)
Uses: epoxy resins (surface coatings)

cassia oil *See:* cinnamon oil, Chinese

castor oil

[8001-79-4]
Pale yellow liquid. d: ~0.95 kg/l (20°C). Saponification value: 175–185 mg KOH/g. Iodine value: 80–90 g I₂/100 g. Insoluble in water. Soluble in oxygenated solvents. The main component of the oil is ricinoleic acid glyceride (85%). The castor oil (*Ricinus communis*) shrub is cultivated in many tropical and semi-tropical countries.
Derivatives: alkyd resins, non-drying; castor oil, blown; castor oil, dehydrated; castor oil, hydrogenated; castor oil, sulphated; castor oil ethoxylates; factice; glycerol monoricinoleate; methyl ricinoleate; polyurethane, low-resilience elastomers; ricinoleic acid
Uses: cosmetics/pharmaceuticals ingredient; lubricity additive (motor fuels, lubricants); plasticiser (resins, lacquers, printing inks)

castor oil, blown

Viscous oil which has been bodied by blowing air through the oil.

Production:
- castor oil (air oxidation)

Uses: plasticiser (paints, lacquers)

castor oil, dehydrated

dehydrated castor oil; DCO
$C_{54}H_{98}O_6$. M: 843.36. Pale yellow oil. Acid value: 195–200 mg KOH/g. Iodine value: 165–175 g I_2/100 g. A typical chain-length distribution is : 6% $C_{18:1}$, 90% $C_{18:2}$, of which 70% is conjugated. Dehydrated castor oil alkyd resins are produced directly from castor oil which dehydrates during the reaction.

Production:
- castor oil (dehydration)

Derivatives:
alkyd resins, long-oil; alkyd resins, medium-oil; alkyd resins, short-oil; alkyd resins, water-soluble; castor oil fatty acids, dehydrated; cyclopentadienised oils; dimer acid; isostearic acid; maleinised oils; trimer acid

Uses: drying oil (printing inks)

castor oil, hydrogenated

glyceryl tri(12-hydroxystearate); [8001-78-3]

$$CH_3(CH_2)_5CH(CH_2)_{10}COOCH \overset{\displaystyle OH}{\underset{\displaystyle OH}{\,|\,}} \quad \begin{matrix} OH \\ | \\ CH_2OOC(CH_2)_{10}CH(CH_2)_5CH_3 \\ OH \\ | \\ CH_2OOC(CH_2)_{10}CH(CH_2)_5CH_3 \end{matrix}$$

$C_{57}H_{110}O_9$. M: 939.50. Hard wax. MP: 85°C. Insoluble in water.

Production:
- castor oil (hydrogenation)

Derivatives:
castor oil ethoxylates

Uses: plastics processing lubricant; thixotropic agent (water-based paints)

castor oil, sulphated

alizarin oil; castor oil, sulphonated; Turkey red oil; [72-48-0]
Viscous liquid. Acid value: 175–180 mg KOH/g. Contains 8.0–8.5% combined SO_3. Soluble in water.

Production:
- castor oil (sulphonation/sodium salt formation)

Uses:
emulsifier (water-based paints, metalworking fluids); flotation collector (phosphate ores); lubricant (amino resins, starch adhesives)

castor oil, sulphonated *See:* castor oil, sulphated

castor oil ethoxylates

PEG castor oil
Appearance varies from pale yellow liquid to white solid as ethoxylate chain-length increases within the range 5–100 moles EO. HLB: 3.8–16.5 (5–100 moles EO).

Production:
- castor oil/castor oil, hydrogenated + ethylene oxide (epoxidation)

Uses: emulsifier (cosmetics, pesticides, metalworking fluids, household products, detergent formulations, dye carriers, textile spin finishes); antistatic agent/dispersant/dyeing auxiliary (textile processing)

castor oil fatty acids, dehydrated

$$CH_3(CH_2)_5CH=CHCH=CH(CH_2)_7COOH$$

$C_{18}H_{32}O_2$. M: 280.46. Yellow liquid. Titre: -8–+11°C depending on grade. Chain-length distribution varies with the source and treatment of the castor oil in the range: 25–63% conjugated $C_{18:2}$, 19–47% unconjugated $C_{18:2}$, 6–12% $C_{18:1}$ and 3–11% saturated acid.

Production:
- castor oil, dehydrated (hydrolysis)

Derivatives:
alkyd resins, long-oil; alkyd resins, medium-oil; alkyd resins, short-oil; epoxy ester resins

catechol

1,2-dihydroxybenzene; *o*-dihydroxybenzene; pyrocatechol; 76500 (CI); [120-80-9]

$C_6H_6O_2$. M: 110.12. White, crystalline powder. Discoloured by light and air. MP: 101–105°C. BP: 245°C. d: 1.34 kg/l (20°C). Bulk density: 0.64 kg/l. Soluble in water and oxygenated solvents.

Production:
- tar acid liquor (fractionation; coproduced with tar acids, crude/resorcinol fraction)
- phenol + hydrogen peroxide (oxidation; coproduced with hydroquinone)

Derivatives:
1,2-benzodioxole; *t*-butylcatechol; cloethocarb; 3,4-dihydroxy-ω-chloroacetophenone; epinephrine; ethyl vanillin; guaiacol; homoveratric acid; levodopa; oxprenolol; propoxur; viloxazine

Uses:
antioxidant (perfumes, essential oils); fur/leather dyeing reagent

caustic potash *See:* potassium hydroxide

caustic soda *See:* sodium hydroxide

CBM *See:* bromochloromethane

CBS *See:* N-cyclohexyl-2-benzothiazolesulphenamide

CCA *See:* copper arsenate, chromated

CCC *See:* chlormequat chloride

CCP *See:* calcium carbonate, precipitated

CDA *See:* cyclododecane

CDAC *See:* cetyldimethylbenzylammonium chloride

CDOL *See:* cyclododecanol

CDON *See:* cyclododecanone

CDT *See:* 1,5,9-cyclododecatriene

CEA *See:* N-ethylcyclohexylamine

cedarleaf oil
Pale yellow oil with a strong camphoric odour. Produced by steam distillation of *Thuja occidentalis* leaves. d: 0.91 kg/l (25°C). Soluble in ethanol. Produced in Canada and north USA.
Uses: perfume ingredient

cedarwood oil, Chinese
Reddish-brown liquid/paste with cedar odour. d: ~0.96 kg/l (20°C). Soluble in alcohol. The main component of the oil is cedrol. It is extracted from *Cupressus funebris* which grows in China.
Production:
• *Cupressus funebris* wood (steam distillation)
Uses: fragrance ingredient

cedarwood oil, Texas
Reddish-brown liquid/paste with cedar odour. d: ~0.96 kg/l (20°C). Soluble in alcohol. The main component of the oil is cedrol (40%). It is extracted from Texas cedar (*Juniperus mexicana*) which grows in the USA.
Production:
• Texas cedar wood (steam distillation)
Derivatives: α-cedrene fraction; cedrol
Uses: fragrance ingredient

cedarwood oil, Virginia
Yellow liquid/paste with cedar odour. d: ~0.95 kg/l (20°C). Soluble in alcohol. The main component of the oil is cedrol (40%). It is extracted from red cedar (*Juniperus virginiana*) wood which is grown in the south-eastern USA.
Production:
• red cedar wood (steam distillation)
Derivatives: cedrol; thujopsene fraction
Uses: fragrance ingredient

cedrene epoxide
$C_{15}H_{24}O_1$. M: 220.35.
Production:
• cedrol + peracetic acid (dehydration/epoxidation)

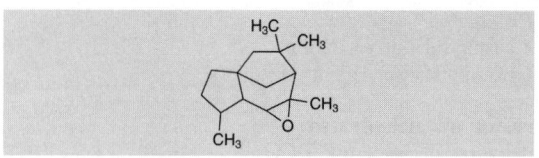

Uses: fragrance ingredient

α-cedrene fraction
[469-61-4] (pure product)

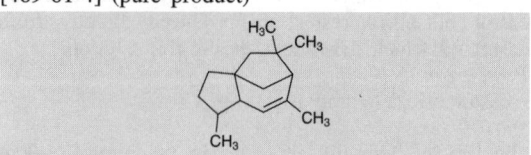

$C_{15}H_{24}$. M: 204.35. Fraction remaining from Texas cedar oil after the removal of cedrol.
Production:
• cedarwood oil, Texas (fractionation; coproduced with cedrol)
Derivatives:
cedryl methyl ketone

cedrol
[77-53-2]

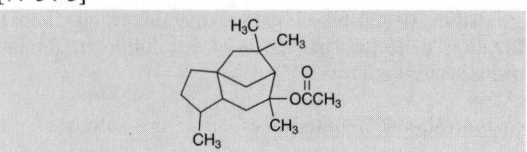

$C_{15}H_{26}O_1$. M: 222.37. White needles. MP: 86°C. Soluble in oxygenated solvents.
Production:
• cedarwood oil, Texas (fractionation; coproduced with α-cedrene fraction)
• cedarwood oil, Virginia (fractionation; coproduced with thujopsene fraction)
Derivatives:
cedrene epoxide; cedryl acetate
Uses: fragrance ingredient

cedryl acetate
[77-54-3]

$C_{17}H_{28}O_2$. M: 264.41. Yellow liquid with a woody odour.
Production:
• cedrol + acetic anhydride (esterification)
Uses:
fragrance ingredient

cedryl methyl ketone
acetylcedrene; [68039-35-0]

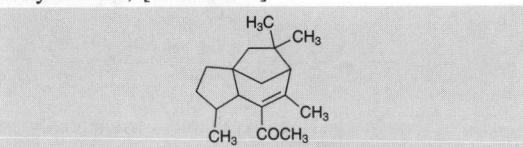

$C_{17}H_{26}O_1$. M: 246.39. Mixed product consisting of acetylated terpenes from cedarwood oil. Cedryl methyl ketone is the main component of the mixture.
Production:
• α-cedrene fraction + acetic anhydride (acetylation)
Uses: fragrance ingredient

cefacetrile
cephacetrile; [10206-21-0]; [23239-41-0] (sodium salt)

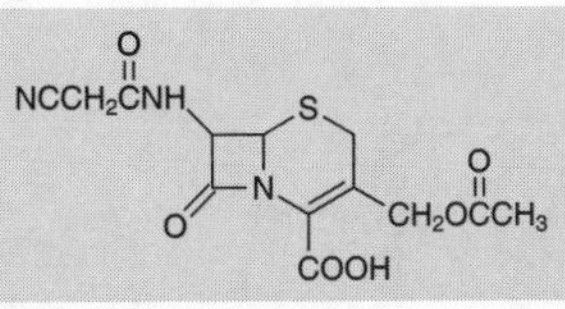

$C_{13}H_{13}N_3O_6S_1$. M: 339.31. Available commercially as the sodium salt.
Production:
• cyanoacetic acid + 7-aminocephalosporanic acid (amide formation)
Uses: antibacterial drug

cefaclor
[70356-03-5]

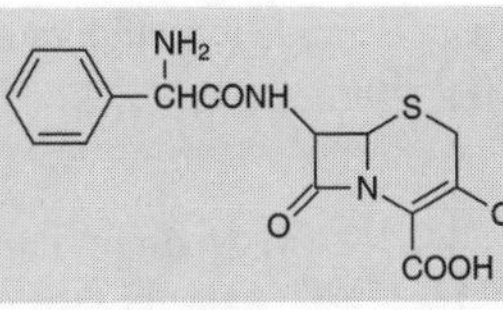

$C_{15}H_{14}Cl_1N_3O_4S_1$. M: 367.80.
Production:
• cefalotin + D-α-phenylglycine (multistep synthesis)
Uses: antibacterial drug

cefadroxil
[66592-87-8]

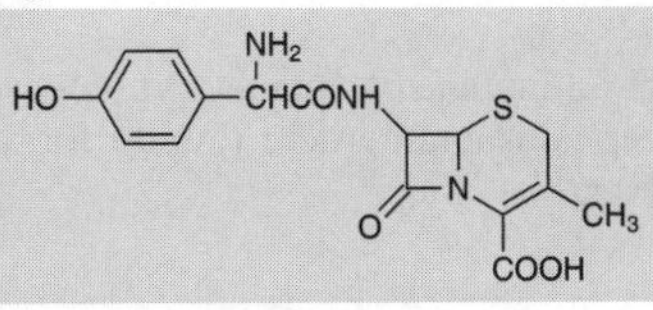

$C_{16}H_{17}N_3O_5S_1$. M: 363.39.
Production:
• D-α-(4-hydroxyphenyl)glycine + 7-amino-3-desacetoxycephalosporanic acid (Dane salt formation/amide formation/hydrolysis)
Uses: antibacterial drug

cefalexin
cephalexin; [15686-71-2]

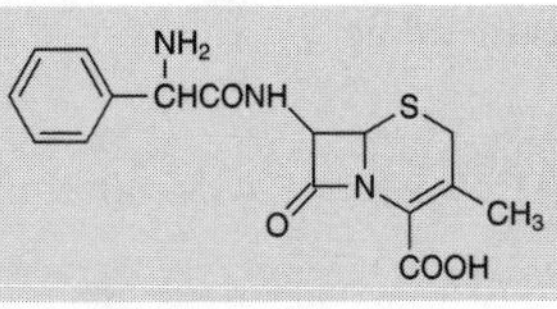

$C_{16}H_{17}N_3O_4S_1$. M: 347.40.
Production:
• D-α-phenylglycine + 7-amino-3-desacetoxycephalosporanic acid (Dane salt formation/amide formation/hydrolysis)
Uses:
antibacterial drug

cefaloridine
cephaloridine; [50-59-9]

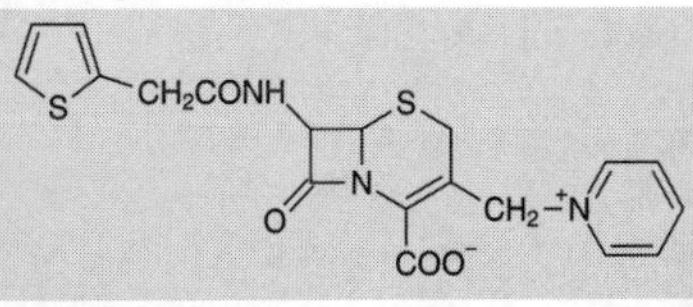

$C_{19}H_{17}N_3O_4S_2$. M: 415.50.
Production:
• cefalotin + pyridine (deacetylation)
Uses: antibacterial drug

cefalotin
cephalothin; [153-61-7]; [58-71-9] (sodium salt)

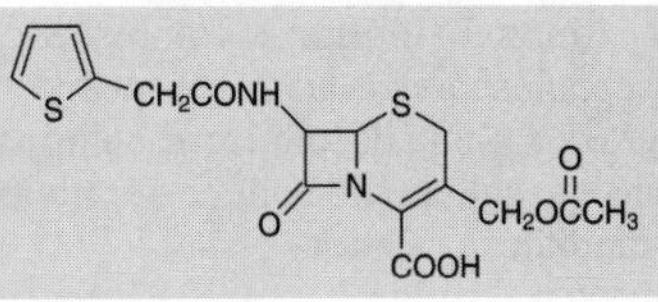

$C_{16}H_{16}N_2O_6S_2$. M: 396.44.
Production:
• 2-thienylacetic acid + 7-aminocephalosporanic acid (amide formation)
Derivatives:
cefaclor; cefaloridine
Uses: antibacterial drug

cefamandole
[34444-01-4]

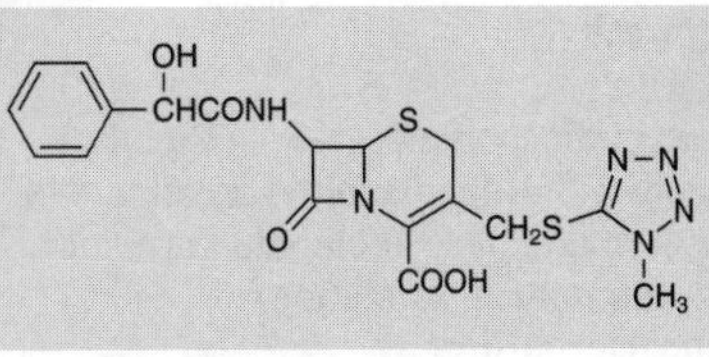

$C_{18}H_{18}N_6O_5S_2$. M: 462.50.
Production:
• D-mandelic acid + 7-aminocephalosporanic acid +

5-thio-1-methyltetrazole (sulphide formation/amide formation)

Uses: antibacterial drug

cefapirin

cephapirin; [21593-23-7]; [24356-60-3] (sodium salt)

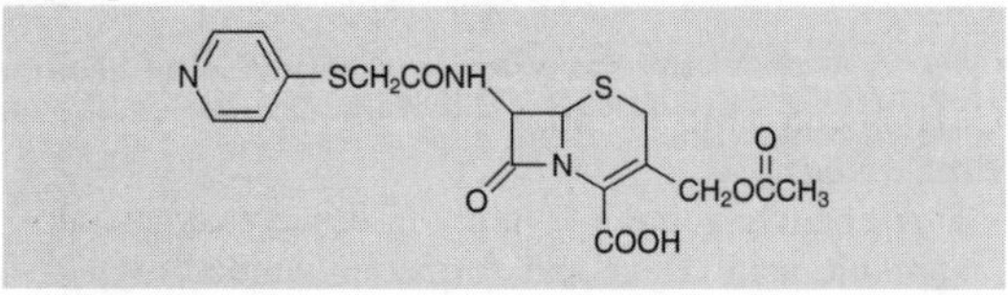

$C_{17}H_{17}N_3O_6S_2$. M: 423.47. Available commercially as the sodium salt.

Production:
- pyridine/thionyl chloride + thioglycollic acid + 7-aminocephalosporanic acid (ring chlorination/thiolation/amide formation)

Uses: antibacterial drug

cefazedone

[56187-47-4]

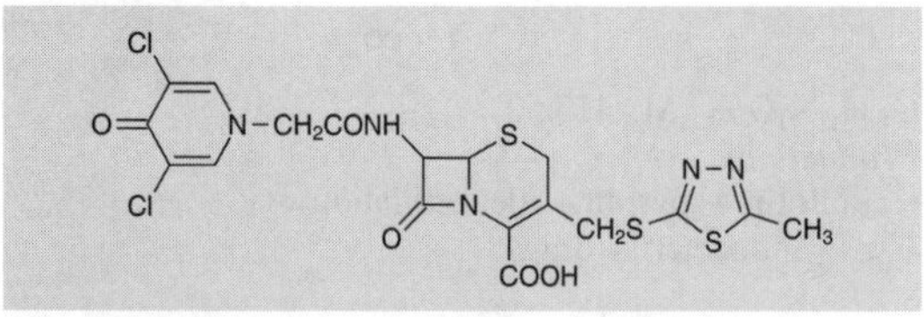

$C_{18}H_{15}Cl_2N_5O_5S_3$. M: 548.44.

Production:
- pyridine + thionyl chloride + chloroacetic acid + 7-aminocephalosporanic acid + 2-methyl-5-mercapto-1,3,4-thiadiazole (ring chlorination/hydration/ring chlorination/amine formation/sulphide formation/amide formation)

Uses: antibacterial drug

cefazolin

[25953-19-9]; [27164-46-1] (sodium salt)

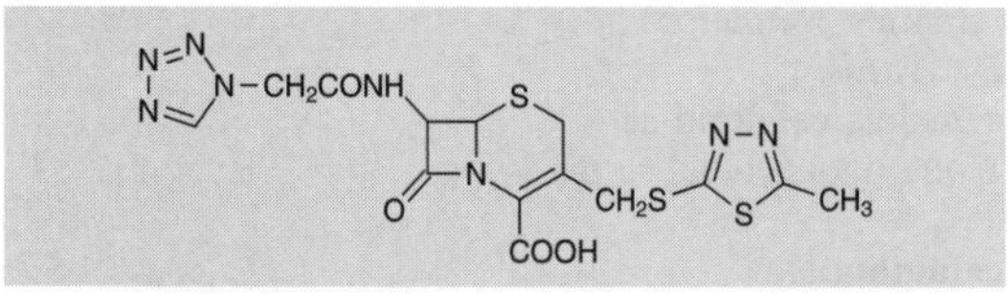

$C_{14}H_{14}N_8O_4S_3$. M: 454.51. Available commercially as the sodium salt.

Production:
- 7-aminocephalosporanic acid + 2-methyl-5-mercapto-1,3,4-thiadiazole + glycine + sodium azide + formaldehyde (sulphide formation/condensation/amide formation)

Uses: antibacterial drug

cefmenoxime

[65085-01-0]; [75738-58-8] (hydrochloride)

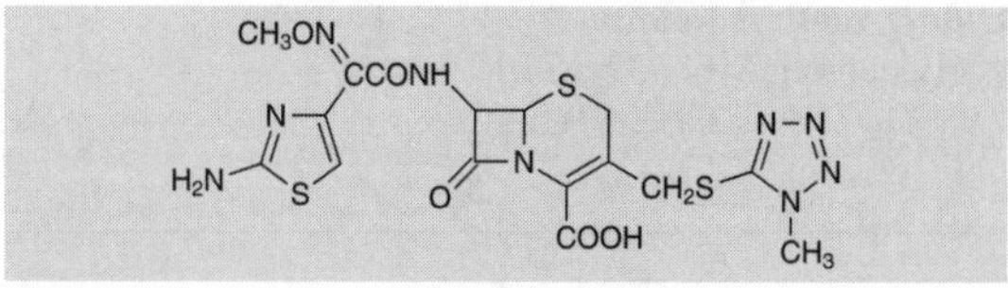

$C_{16}H_{17}N_9O_5S_3$. M: 511.56. Available commercially as the free base or as the hydrochloride salt.

Production:
- 7-aminocephalosporanic acid + 5-thio-1-methyl-tetrazole + ethyl 2-(2-aminothiazolyl)methoxyimino-acetate (sulphide formation/amide formation)

Uses: antibacterial drug

cefoperazone

[62893-19-0]

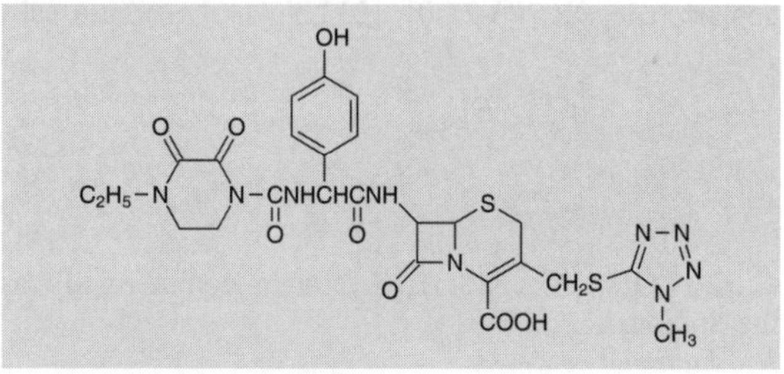

$C_{25}H_{27}N_9O_8S_2$. M: 645.67.

Production:
- 7-aminocephalosporanic acid + 5-thio-1-methyl-tetrazole + *N*-ethylethylenediamine + diethyl oxalate + ethyl chloroformate + D-α-(4-hydroxy-phenyl)glycine (sulphide formation/condensation/dehydrochlorination/amide formation/amide formation)

Uses: antibacterial drug

cefotaxime

[63527-52-6]; [64485-93-4] (sodium salt)

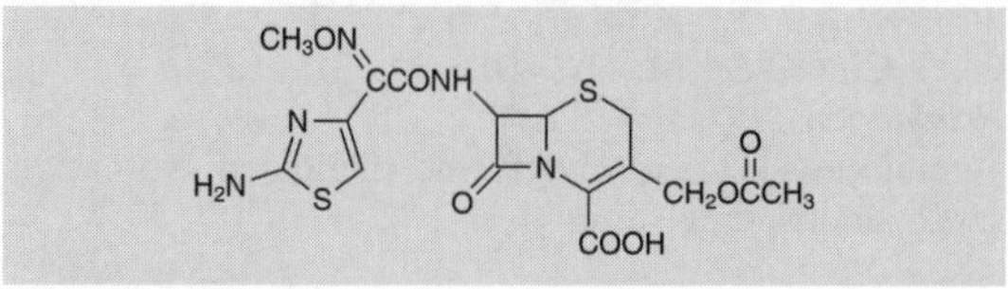

$C_{16}H_{17}N_5O_7S_2$. M: 455.48. Available commercially as the sodium salt.

Production:
- ethyl 2-(2-aminothiazolyl)methoxyiminoacetate + 7-aminocephalosporanic acid (amide formation)

Uses: antibacterial drug

cefotetan

[69712-56-7]

$C_{17}H_{17}N_7O_8S_4$. M: 575.63. Available commercially as the disodium salt.

Production:
- methyl cyanoacetate + carbon disulphide + 7-aminocephalosporanic acid + bromoacetyl

bromide + 5-thio-1-methyltetrazole (nitrile
hydration/condensation/amide formation/sulphide
formation/sulphide formation)

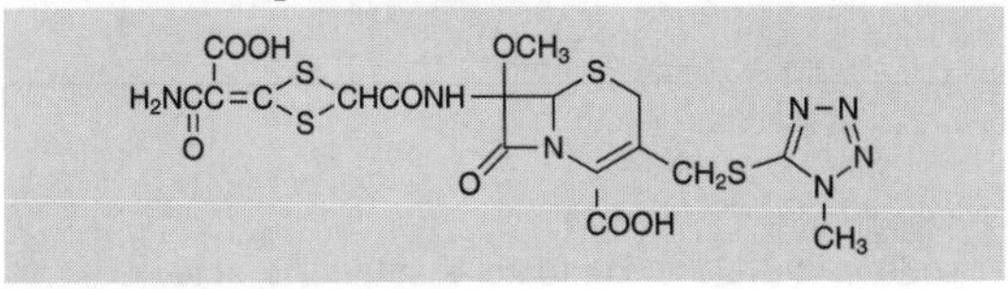

Uses: antibacterial drug

cefotiam
[61622-34-2]

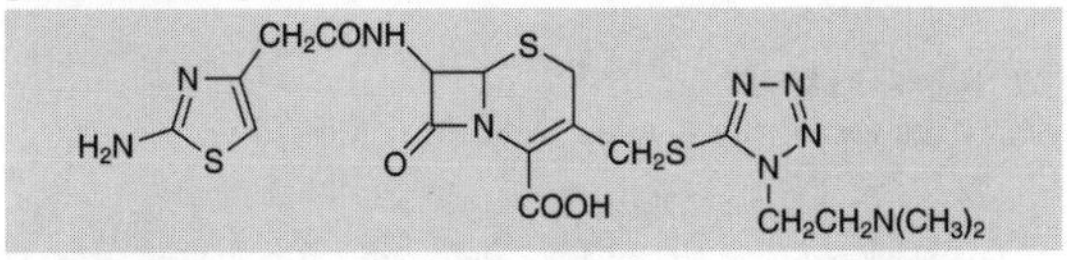

$C_{18}H_{23}N_9O_8S_3$. M: 589.62. Available commercially as
the dihydrochloride.
Production:
- ethyl γ-chloroacetoacetate + thiourea + 7-amino-
  cephalosporanic acid + 5-thio-1-(β-dimethylaminoethyl)tetrazole (condensation/sulphide formation/
  amide formation)
Uses: antibacterial drug

cefoxitin
[35607-66-0]

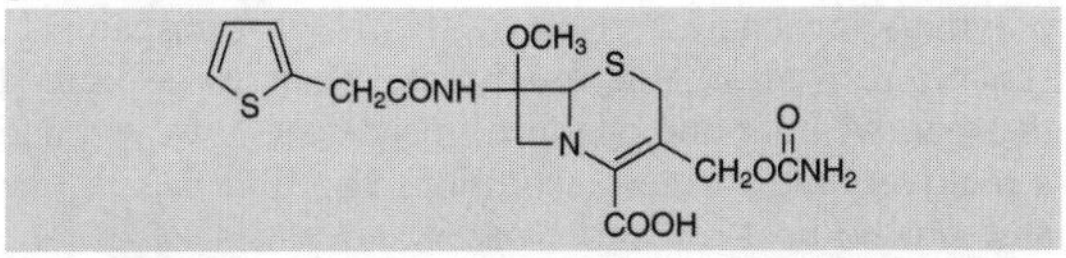

$C_{16}H_{17}N_3O_7S_2$. M: 427.46. Available commercially as
the sodium salt.
Production:
- cephamycin C + 2-thienylacetic acid (chlorination/
  ether formation/hydrolysis/amide formation)
Uses:
antibacterial drug

cefradine
cephradine; [38821-53-3]

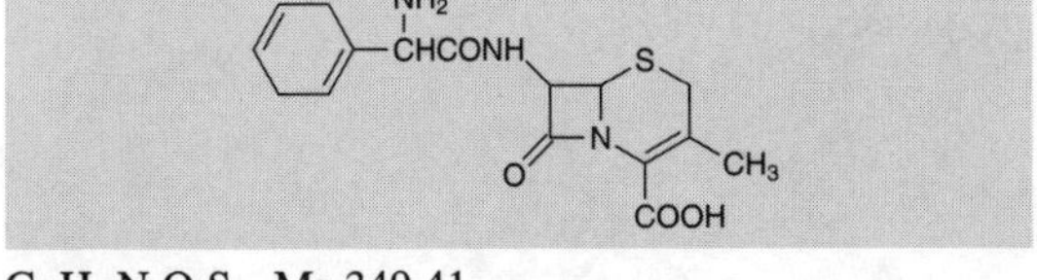

$C_{16}H_{19}N_3O_4S_1$. M: 349.41.
Production:
- D-α-phenylglycine + 7-amino-3-desacetoxycephalo-
  sporanic acid (Birch reduction/Dane salt formation/
  amide formation/hydrolysis)
Uses:
antibacterial drug

cefsulodin
[62587-73-9]

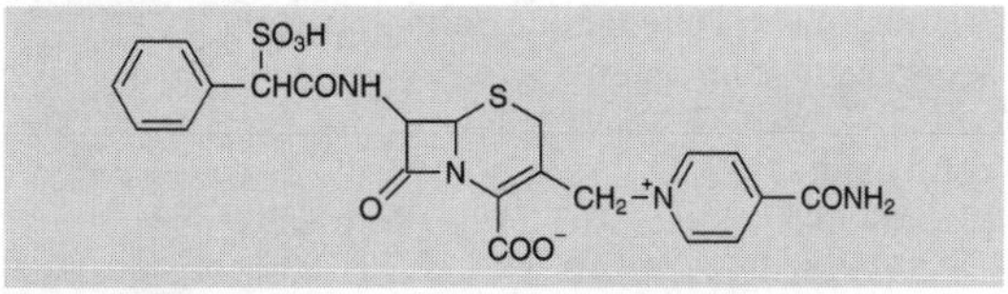

$C_{22}H_{20}N_4O_5S_2$. M: 484.55. Available as the sodium salt.
Production:
- phenylacetic acid + 7-aminocephalosporanic acid +
  isonicotinamide (sulphonation/amide formation/
  deacetylation)
Uses: antibacterial drug

ceftazidime
[72558-82-8]

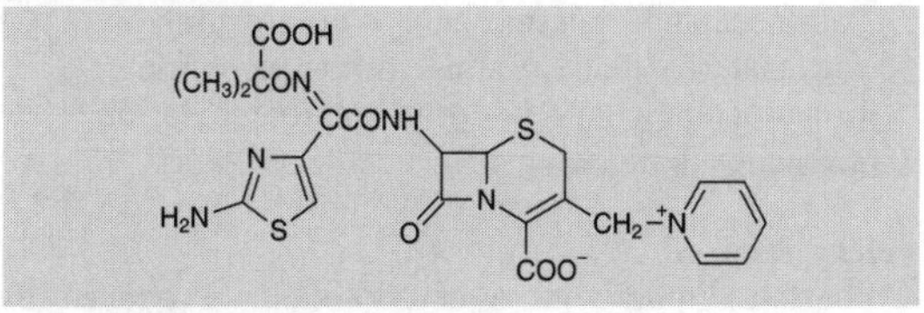

$C_{22}H_{22}N_6O_7S_2$. M: 546.58.
Production:
- ethyl acetoacetate + thiourea/sodium nitrite + methacrylic acid + pyridine + 7-aminocephalosporanic
  acid (multistep synthesis)
Uses: antibacterial drug

ceftizoxime
[68401-81-0]

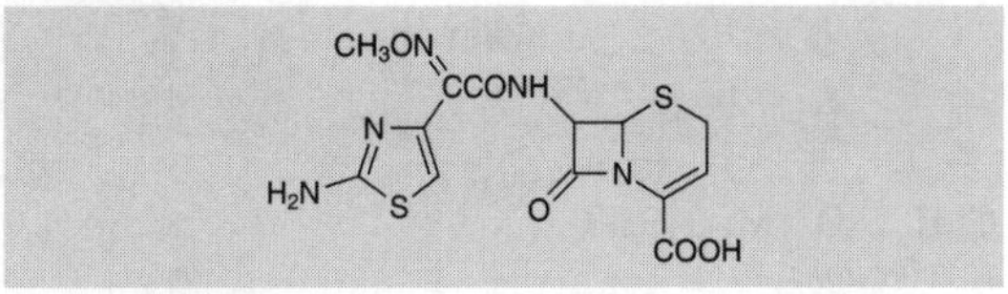

$C_{13}H_{13}N_5O_5S_2$. M: 383.39. Available commercially as
the sodium salt.
Production:
- 7-aminocephalosporanic acid + ethyl 2-(2-amino-
  thiazolyl)methoxyiminoacetate (multistep synthesis)
Uses: antibacterial drug

ceftriaxone
[73384-59-5]

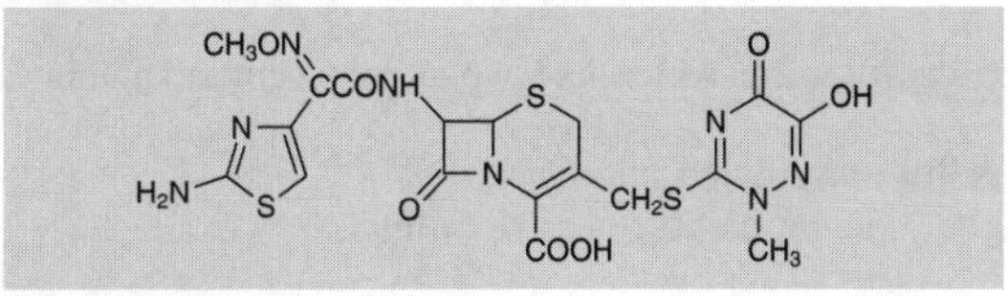

$C_{18}H_{18}N_8O_7S_3$. M: 554.58.
Production:
- 7-aminocephalosporanic acid + ethyl 2-(2-amino-

thiazolyl)methoxyiminoacetate + thiosemicarbazide + oxalic acid (sulphide formation/condensation/ amine methylation/amide formation)
Uses: antibacterial drug

cefuroxime
[55268-75-2]; [56238-63-2] (sodium salt)

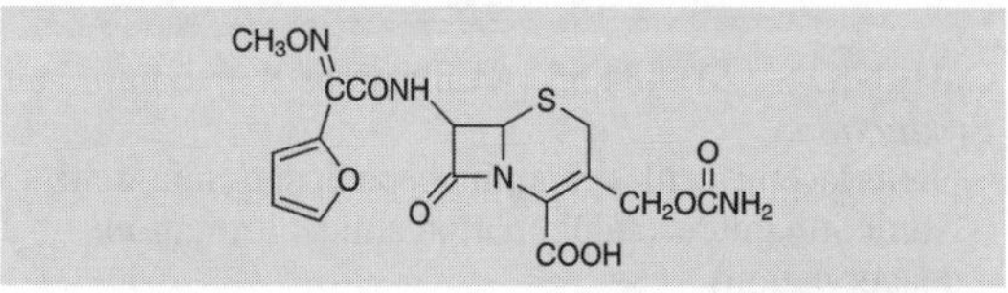

$C_{16}H_{16}N_4O_8S_1$. M: 424.39. Available commercially as the sodium salt or as the 1-acetoxyethyl ester.
Production:
• 2-acetylfuran + hydroxylamine hydrochloride + 7-aminocephalosporanic acid + chlorosulphonyl isocyanate (oxidation/imine formation/amide formation/enzymatic hydrolysis/carbamoylation)
Uses: antibacterial drug

celery seed oil
Colourless liquid with a celery odour. Produced by steam distillation of celery (*Apium graveolens*) seed. d: 0.88 kg/l (20°C). Soluble in alcohol. The major constituent of the oil is (+)-limonene (>50%). It is produced in France, India and USA.
Uses:
flavouring ingredient

celiprolol
[56980-93-9]

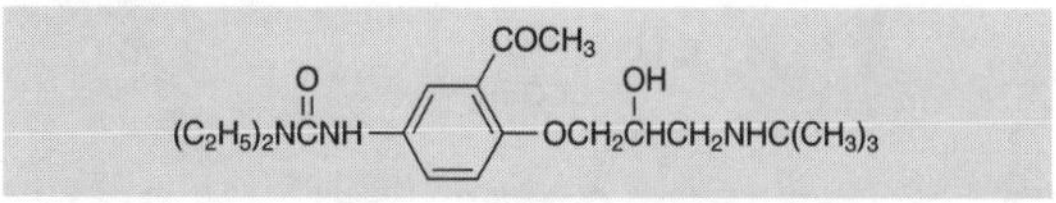

$C_{20}H_{33}N_3O_4$. M: 379.50.
Production:
• *o*-hydroxyacetophenone + epichlorohydrin + *t*-butyl-amine + diethylcarbamoyl chloride (nitration/ether formation/epoxidation/nitro reduction/dehydro-chlorination)
Uses: antihypertensive/*angina pectoris* drug

cellaburate *See:* cellulose acetobutyrate

cellophane *See:* cellulose, regenerated

α-cellulose *See:* bleached wood pulp; cotton linters

cellulose, polyanionic
See: sodium carboxymethyl cellulose

cellulose, regenerated
cellophane; rayon; viscose rayon; [9006-02-4]
Transparent film or fibre. d: 1.51 kg/l.

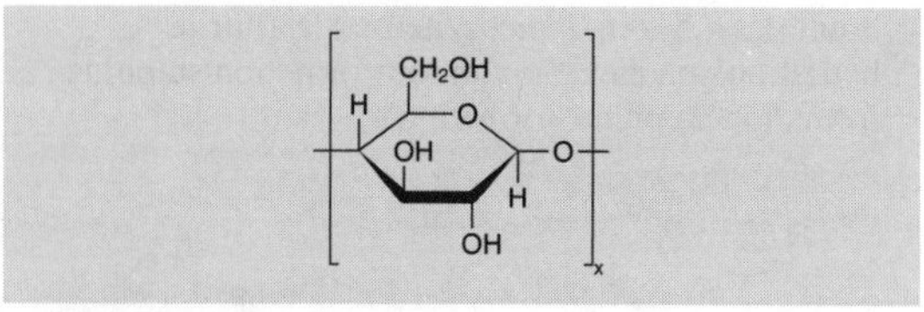

Production:
• sodium cellulose xanthate + sulphuric acid (hydrolysis)
Derivatives: carbon fibre
Uses: cellulose sponges; textile fibres; wrapping film (food, tobacco)

cellulose acetate
secondary cellulose acetate; CA; [9004-35-7]

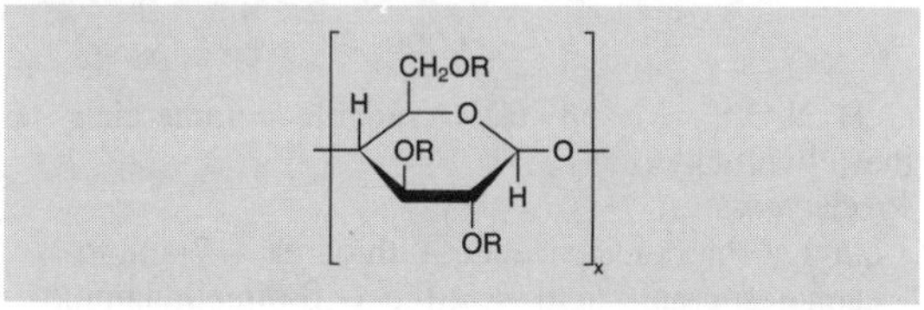

R = H, acetyl-, x = 175–360. Thermoplastic available as compounded granules, sheet, film or fibre. d: 1.27–1.32 kg/l. Tensile strength: 40–70 MPa. Elongation at break: 20–45%. Grades vary in molecular weight, plasticiser content and degree of acetylation. The latter varies from 2.2 to 3.0 (cellulose triacetate). The polymers are characterised by their high transparency, scratch resistance and toughness. They have limited thermal, weather and chemical resistance, however, and a relatively high water absorption. The fibre is silk-like and can be heat-set into creases and pleats.
Production:
• acetic anhydride + bleached wood pulp/cotton linters (acetylation/partial hydrolysis)
Uses: lacquer resin (wood, metal, paper, leather); strippable coatings; textile fibres; transparent household articles (combs, buckles, buttons, pens); 'safety' cinematographic film; transparent packaging films/sheeting; transparent tool grips

cellulose acetobutyrate
cellaburate (INN); cellulose acetate butyrate; CAB; [9004-36-8]

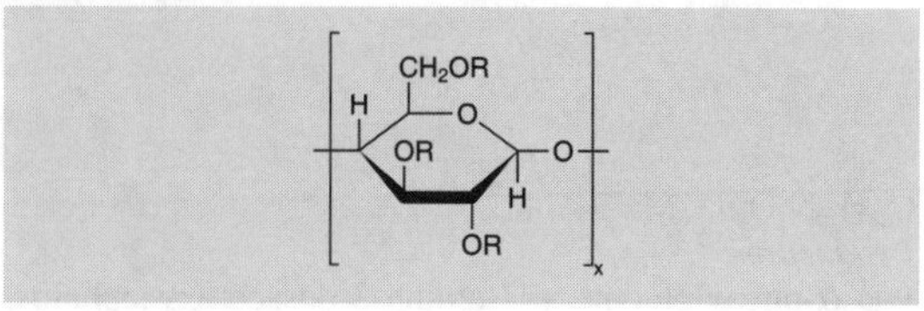

R = acetyl, butyryl-. Thermoplastic. d: 1.15–1.21 kg/l. Tensile strength: 20–40 MPa. Elongation at break: 10–50%. The polymers are characterised by their high transparency, scratch resistance and toughness. They

have limited thermal, weather and chemical resistance, however, and a relatively high water absorption.
Production:
• cotton linters/bleached wood pulp + *n*-butyric acid + acetic anhydride (esterification)
Uses: moulded tool handles/knobs/toys/vehicle parts; lacquer resin (wood, wire, paper, plastics); pipe coatings (oil/water/gas pipelines); fluidised-bed dip coatings

cellulose gum *See:* sodium carboxymethyl cellulose

cellulose methyl ether *See:* methyl cellulose

cellulose nitrate
celluloid; collodion; cordite; guncotton; nitrocellulose; nitrocotton; CN; [9004-70-0]

R = H, NO$_2$. Grades with a nitrogen content of 10.5–12.2% are used for surface coating applications and, at the lower end of this range, for celluloid. Both are generally used in a plasticised form. Celluloid is highly inflammable and has poor chemical resistance, but offers excellent transparency and rigidity. Explosives are produced from material with a nitrogen content >12.7%.
Production:
• cotton linters (nitration)
Uses: explosives; sheet (knife handles, table-tennis balls, spectacle frames); lacquer resin; binder (flexographic inks)

cellulose propionate
cellulose acetopropionate; CAP; CP;

R = acetyl, propionyl-. Thermoplastic. d: 1.18–1.23 kg/l. Tensile strength: 15–40 MPa. Elongation at break: 45–65%. The polymers are characterised by their high transparency, scratch resistance and toughness. They have limited thermal, weather and chemical resistance, however, and a relatively high water absorption.
Production:
• cotton linters/bleached wood pulp + propionic acid + acetic anhydride (esterification)
Uses: lacquer resin; moulded tool handles/automobile components; sunglasses/spectacle frames

cellulose triacetate
triacetate; CA; Tricel (Courtaulds); [9012-09-3]

R = acetyl-, x = 175–360. Thermoplastic available as cast film or fibre. Its properties are similar to those of cellulose acetate.
Production:
• bleached wood pulp/cotton linters + acetic acid + acetic anhydride (acetylation)
Uses: electrical insulation films; photographic film; textile fibres

cellulose xanthate *See:* sodium cellulose xanthate

CEPA *See:* ethephon

cephacetrile *See:* cefacetrile

cephalosporin C
[61-24-5]

C$_{16}$H$_{21}$N$_3$O$_8$S$_1$. M: 415.42.
Production:
• mould fermentation medium + *Cephalosporium acremonium* mould (fermentation)
Derivatives: 7-aminocephalosporanic acid
Uses: antibacterial drug

cephalothin *See:* cefalotin

cephamycin C

C$_{16}$H$_{23}$N$_4$O$_9$S$_1$. M: 447.44.
Production:
• mould fermentation medium + *Streptomyces lactamdurans* mould (fermentation)
Derivatives: cefoxitin
Uses: antibacterial drug

ceresin
[8001-75-0]
White or yellow solid. MP: 68–72°C. Insoluble in

water. Soluble in most organic solvents. The product is a mixture of paraffin and microcrystalline waxes, sometimes with a small proportion of carnauba wax to raise the melting point.
Uses: candle wax; coating wax (packaging, textiles); electrical insulation impregnation wax; heat-seal/hot melt flow additive; shoe/car polish ingredient

cerium oxide
ceric oxide; cerium dioxide; [1306-38-3]

$$CeO_2$$

Ce_1O_2. M: 172.12. Brownish-white, high-melting solid. d: 7.13 kg/l. Insoluble in water.
Production:
• rare earth oxide (solvent extraction; coproduced with lanthanum-praseodymium-neodymium oxide concentrate/samarium oxide)
• rare earth oxide, hydrate (solvent extraction; coproduced with didymium oxide/lanthanum oxide/samarium oxide)
Uses:
television/bottle glass decolouring agent; polishing/grinding pastes

CETAC *See:* cetyltrimethylammonium chloride

cetalkonium chloride
See: cetyldimethylbenzylammonium chloride

cetrimonium bromide
See: cetyltrimethylammonium bromide

cetrimonium chloride
See: cetyltrimethylammonium chloride

cetyl alcohol
1-hexadecanol; hexadecyl alcohol; palmityl alcohol; [36653-82-4]

$$CH_3(CH_2)_{15}OH$$

$C_{16}H_{34}O_1$. M: 242.45. White, waxy solid. MP: 48–50°C. d: 0.82 kg/l (50°C). Insoluble in water. Soluble in oxygenated solvents. A typical chain-length distribution is: 96% C_{16}. Broad-cut fractions are called either cetylstearyl or myristyl alcohol.
Production:
• palmitic acid/methyl palmitate (hydrogenation)
• cetylstearyl alcohol (fractionation; coproduced with stearyl alcohol)
• ethylene (Alfol/Epal processes; coproduced with *n*-hexanol/*n*-octanol/*n*-decanol/*n*-alkanol(C_8-C_{10})/ lauryl alcohol, narrow-cut/myristyl alcohol/ *n*-alkanol(C_{12}-C_{14})/cetylstearyl alcohol/stearyl alcohol/*n*-alkanol(C_{12}-C_{18})/*n*-alkanol(C_{20+}))
Derivatives: cetyl alcohol propoxylates; cetyl bromide; cetyl chloride; cetyl chloroformate; cetyl alcohol eth-

oxylates; cetyl palmitate; cetyl stearate; dimethylcetylamine
Uses: emollient/emulsifier (cosmetics, pharmaceuticals)

cetyl alcohol ethoxylates
ceteth (CTFA); polyethylene glycol monocetyl ether

$$CH_3(CH_2)_{15}(OCH_2CH_2)_nOH$$

n = 2–20. White solid. HLB: 5.3–15.7 (2–20 moles EO).
Production:
• cetyl alcohol + ethylene oxide (epoxidation)
Uses: emulsifier (cosmetics)

cetyl alcohol propoxylates
polypropylene glycol monocetyl ether; PPG cetyl ether

$$CH_3(CH_2)_{15}O(\overset{\overset{\displaystyle CH_3}{|}}{CH}CH_2O)_nH$$

n = 10–50.
Production:
• cetyl alcohol + propylene oxide (epoxidation)
Uses: emollient (cosmetics, toiletries)

cetyl bromide
1-bromohexadecane; *n*-hexadecyl bromide; [112-82-3]

$$CH_3(CH_2)_{15}Br$$

$C_{16}H_{33}Br_1$. M: 305.34. Solid or liquid. MP: 15°C. d: 1.99 kg/l. Insoluble in water.
Production:
• cetyl alcohol + hydrogen bromide, anhydrous (alcohol bromination)
Derivatives: cetylpyridinium bromide; cetyltrimethylammonium bromide

cetyl chloride
1-chlorohexadecane; *n*-hexadecyl chloride; [4860-03-1]

$$CH_3(CH_2)_{15}Cl$$

$C_{16}H_{33}Cl_1$. M: 260.89. Yellow liquid. MP: 12°C. d: 0.86 kg/l (20°C). Insoluble in water. Flash point: 164°C (PMCC). The commercial product contains, typically, 93% C_{16}.
Production:
• cetyl alcohol + hydrogen chloride, anhydrous (alcohol chlorination)
Derivatives: N-cetyl ethylmorpholinium ethosulphate; cetylpyridinium chloride; cetyltrimethylammonium chloride; dimethylcetylamine

cetyl chloroformate
[26272-90-2]

$$CH_3(CH_2)_{15}O\overset{\overset{\displaystyle O}{\|}}{C}Cl$$

$C_{17}H_{33}Cl_1O_2$. M: 304.90. Liquid. MP: 14°C.

Production:
• cetyl alcohol + phosgene (phosgenation)
Uses: peroxide initiator intermediate

cetyldimethylamine *See:* dimethylcetylamine

cetyldimethylbenzylammonium chloride
CDAC; cetalkonium chloride; dimethylhexadecylbenzyl-ammonium chloride; [122-18-9]

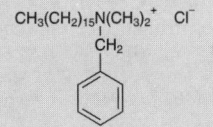

$C_{25}H_{46}Cl_1N_1$. M: 396.10. White, crystalline powder. MP: 58–60°C. Soluble in water and oxygenated solvents.
Production:
• dimethylcetylamine + benzyl chloride (quaternisation)
Uses: medical disinfectant; wetting agent/emulsifier/biocide (textile/leather auxiliaries)

N-cetyl ethylmorpholinium ethosulphate
quaternium-25 (CTFA); CME; Barquat CME (Lonza)

$C_{24}H_{51}N_1O_5S_1$. M: 465.73. Available commercially as a pure product or as an amber, 35% solution in water.
Production:
• morpholine + cetyl chloride + diethyl sulphate (amine formation/quaternisation)
Uses: antistatic agent/lubricant (textile spin finishes)

cetyloleyl alcohol
Pale yellow liquid produced using a special catalyst system for the hydrogenation of coconut methyl ester. The chain-length distribution is, typically: 35% $C_{16:0}$, 70% $C_{18:1}$.
Production:
• C_{14}-C_{18} fatty acids, methyl ester (selective hydrogenation)
Derivatives: cetyloleyl alcohol ethoxylates; sodium cetyloleyl sulphate

cetyloleyl alcohol ethoxylates
polyethylene glycol monocetyloleyl ether

$$RO(CH_2CH_2O)_nH$$

R = cetyloleyl-, n = 2–10. Paste or solid. The products contain 2–10 moles EO and range in colour from pale yellow to white at higher EO contents. HLB: 14 (13 moles EO).
Production:
• cetyloleyl alcohol + ethylene oxide (epoxidation)

Derivatives: cetyloleyl ether phosphoric acid
Uses: emulsifier (hydrocarbon oils, waxes); antistatic agent (textile spin finishes)

cetyloleyl ether phosphoric acid

$$\left[RO(CH_2CH_2O)_n\right]_x \overset{O}{\underset{\|}{P}}(OH)_{3-x}$$

R = cetyloleyl-, n = 2–10, x = 1–2.
Production:
• cetyloleyl alcohol ethoxylates + phosphorus pentoxide (esterification)
Uses: emulsifier/lubricity additive/corrosion inhibitor (metalworking fluids); surfactant (low-foaming detergents/cleaners)

cetyl palmitate
cetin; [540-10-3]

$$CH_3(CH_2)_{14}\overset{O}{\underset{\|}{C}}O(CH_2)_{15}CH_3$$

$C_{32}H_{64}O_2$. M: 480.86. Waxy solid. MP: 54°C. d: 0.99 kg/l (20°C). Insoluble in water. Soluble in oxygenated solvents.
Production:
• cetyl alcohol + palmitic acid (esterification)
Uses: internal polyvinyl chloride processing lubricant

cetylpyridinium bromide
[140-72-7]

$C_{21}H_{38}Br_1N_1$. M: 384.44.
Production:
• pyridine + cetyl bromide (quaternisation)
Uses: topical antiseptic/disinfectant

cetylpyridinium chloride
1-hexadecylpyridinium chloride; CPC; [123-03-5]; [6004-24-6] (monohydrate)

$C_{21}H_{38}Cl_1N_1$. M: 339.99. White powder. MP: 77–83°C. Soluble in water, oxygenated and chlorinated solvents.
Production:
• pyridine + cetyl chloride (quaternisation)
Uses:
antiseptic; preservative (cosmetics, pharmaceuticals)

cetyl stearate
[1190-63-2]

$$CH_3(CH_2)_{16}\overset{O}{\underset{\|}{C}}O(CH_2)_{15}CH_3$$

$C_{34}H_{68}O_2$. M: 508.91. White solid. MP: 56°C.

Production:
- cetyl alcohol + stearic acid (esterification)

Uses: emollient/lubricant (cosmetics); antistatic agent/plastics processing lubricant

cetylstearyl alcohol

n-alkanol(C_{16}-C_{18}); cetearyl alcohol (CTFA); stearyl-cetyl alcohol

$$CH_3(CH_2)_nOH$$

n = 15–17. $C_{18}H_{38}O_1$. M: 270.50. White solid. MP: 50–54°C. A typical chain-length distribution is: 4% C_{14}, 25% C_{16}, 70% C_{18}.

Production:
- ethylene (Alfol/Epal processes; coproduced with *n*-hexanol/*n*-octanol/*n*-decanol/*n*-alkanol(C_8-C_{10})/ lauryl alcohol, narrow-cut/myristyl alcohol/ *n*-alkanol(C_{12}-C_{14})/cetyl alcohol/stearyl alcohol/ *n*-alkanol(C_{12}-C_{18})/*n*-alkanol(C_{20+}))
- C_{14}-C_{18} fatty acids, methyl ester (hydrogenation)

Derivatives: cetyl alcohol; cetylstearyl alcohol ethoxylates; cetylstearyl stearate; stearyl alcohol

Uses: pearlescent shampoo ingredient; plastics processing lubricant

cetylstearyl alcohol ethoxylates

ceteareth (CTFA); polyoxyl cetostearyl ether

$$RO(CH_2CH_2O)_nH$$

R = cetylstearyl-, n = 3–50. Soft solids. Commercial products contain 3–50 moles EO. HLB: 7.3 (3 moles EO), 15.6 (20 moles EO).

Production:
- cetylstearyl alcohol + ethylene oxide (epoxidation)

Derivatives: cetylstearyl ether phosphoric acid

Uses: emulsifier (fatty amines, amides); emulsifier (oils, solvents, waxes); antistatic agent/lubricant (wool carding, textile spin finishes); hydrophobic fibre lubricant

cetylstearyl ether phosphoric acid

$$\left[RO(CH_2CH_2O)_n\right]_x \overset{O}{\underset{\|}{P}}(OH)_{3-x}$$

R = cetylstearyl-, n = 3–10, x = 1–2. White or buff hard wax. The products contain 3–10 moles EO.

Production:
- cetylstearyl alcohol ethoxylates + phosphorus pentoxide (esterification)

Uses: extreme-pressure/emulsifier/corrosion inhibitor additives (metalworking fluids); antistatic agent (plastics); surfactant (detergents, cleaners)

cetylstearyl stearate

Pale yellow solid. Solidification point: 55–56°C. d: 0.82 kg/l (80°C). Insoluble in water. Flash point: 250°C (COC).

$$CH_3(CH_2)_{16}\overset{O}{\underset{\|}{C}}OR$$

R = cetylstearyl-.

Production:
- cetylstearyl alcohol + stearic acid (esterification)

Uses: emollient/bodying agent (cosmetics, toiletries)

cetyltrimethylammonium bromide

cetrimonium bromide (CTFA); hexadecyltrimethylammonium bromide; trimethylcetylammonium bromide; CTAB; HTAB; [57-09-0]

$$CH_3(CH_2)_{15}N(CH_3)_3{}^+ \quad Br^-$$

$C_{19}H_{42}Br_1N_1$. M: 364.46. White powder. MP: 240°C. Soluble in water and oxygenated solvents.

Production:
- dimethylcetylamine + methyl bromide (quaternisation)
- trimethylamine + cetyl bromide (quaternisation)

Uses: antiseptic/disinfectant; antistatic agent (textile spin finishes)

cetyltrimethylammonium chloride

cetrimonium chloride (CTFA); CETAC; [112-02-7]

$$CH_3(CH_2)_{15}N(CH_3)_3{}^+ \quad Cl^-$$

$C_{19}H_{42}Cl_1N_1$. M: 320.01. Available as a 25% or 50% solution in water.

Production:
- *n*-hexadecylamine + methyl chloride (quaternisation)
- trimethylamine + cetyl chloride (quaternisation)

Uses: coagulant (antibiotic production); conditioning agent (hair products); antistatic agent (textile spin finishes); softening agent (textile finishes)

CFC-11 *See:* trichlorofluoromethane

CFC-12 *See:* dichlorodifluoromethane

CFC-13 *See:* chlorotrifluoromethane

CFC-113 *See:* 1,1,2-trichloro-1,2,2-trifluoroethane

CFC-114 *See:* 1,2-dichloro-1,1,2,2-tetrafluoroethane

CFC-115 *See:* chloropentafluoroethane

CHA *See:* cyclohexylamine

channel black *See:* carbon black

charcoal

carbon

C_1. M: 12.01. Black, friable solid. Available as lumps, briquettes and powder.

Production:
- pinewood logs (carbonisation)
- hardwood (carbonisation)

Uses:
case hardening salts; animal feed additive; barbecue/ heating fuel; soil conditioning agent; thermal reduction reagent (metal production)

CHDM *See:* 1,4-cyclohexanedimethanol

chestnut extract
tannin
Dried extract of chestnut wood containing a high proportion of tannin. Italy is the main producing country.
Production:
- chestnut wood (aqueous extraction)

Uses: tanning agent

chi acid *See:* anthraquinone-1,8-disulphonic acid

Chicago acid
1-amino-8-hydroxynaphthalene-2,4-disulphonic acid;
4-amino-5-hydroxynaphthalene-1,3-disulphonic acid;
8-amino-1-naphthol-5,7-disulphonic acid

$C_{10}H_9N_1O_7S_2$. M: 319.31. Grey paste. Soluble in water.
Production:
- 1-naphthylamine-4,8-disulphonic acid
  (sulphonation/alkali fusion)

Derivatives: Direct Blue 1
Uses: dyestuffs intermediate

Chinese Blue *See:* Prussian Blue

Chinese White *See:* zinc oxide

chinomethionat
6-methyl-1,3-dithiolo[4,5-b]quinoxalin-2-one; oxythioquinox; quinomethionate; [2439-01-2]

$C_{10}H_6N_2O_1S_2$. M: 234.30.
Production:
- 3,4-diaminotoluene + oxalyl chloride + phosgene
  (condensation/thiolation/phosgenation)

Uses: acaricide/fungicide

chlomethoxyfen
5-(2,4-dichlorophenoxy)-2-nitroanisole; [32861-85-1]
$C_{13}H_9Cl_2N_1O_4$. M: 314.13.

Production:
- 2,4-dichloronitrobenzene + sodium methoxide +
  2,4-dichlorophenol (ether formation/ether formation)

Uses: herbicide

chloracetic acid *See:* chloroacetic acid

chloral
trichloroacetaldehyde; [75-87-6]

Cl_3CCHO

$C_2H_1Cl_3O_1$. M: 147.39. Liquid with a pungent odour. BP: 97–98°C. FP: -57°C. d: 1.51 kg/l (20°C). Soluble in water and alcohol forming hydrates and alcoholates.
Production:
- ethanol + sodium hypochlorite (chlorination)

Derivatives: bromopropylate; chloral hydrate; chloralose; chloramphenicol; cloethocarb; DDT; dichlorvos; heptenophos; methoxychlor; thiamphenicol; trichlorfon; trichlormethiazide; α-trichloromethylphenyl carbinyl acetate; triforine

chloral hydrate
[302-17-0]

$Cl_3CCH(OH)_2$

$C_2H_3Cl_3O_2$. M: 165.40.
Production:
- chloral (hydration)

Uses: hypnotic/sedative drug

chloralose
(R)-1,2-O-(2,2,2-trichloroethylidene)-α-D-glucofuranose;
[15879-93-3]

$C_8H_{11}Cl_3O_6$. M: 309.53.
Production:
- D-glucose + chloral (acetal formation)

Uses: bird repellant; rodenticide

chloramben
3-amino-2,5-dichlorobenzoic acid; [133-90-4]
$C_7H_5Cl_2N_1O_2$. M: 206.04.
Production:
- 2,5-dichloroaniline + sodium cyanide (Sandmeyer
  reaction/nitrile hydrolysis/nitration/nitro reduction)

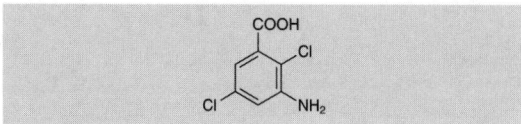

Uses: herbicide

chloramine-B
[127-52-6]

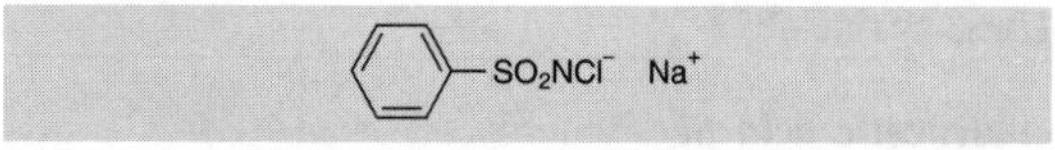

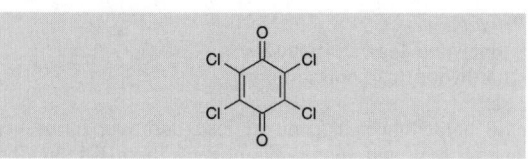

$C_6H_5Cl_1N_1Na_1O_2S_1$. M: 213.62. Available as the sesqui-hydrate. Odourless, white, crystalline solid. Available chlorine content: 29.5%. Decomposes on heating above 170°C. Slightly soluble in water.
Production:
• benzenesulphonyl chloride + ammonia + sodium hypochlorite (sulphonamide formation/chlorination)
Uses: disinfectant/antiseptic

chloramine-T
sodium *p*-toluenesulphochloramine; tosylchloramide sodium (INN); [127-65-1]

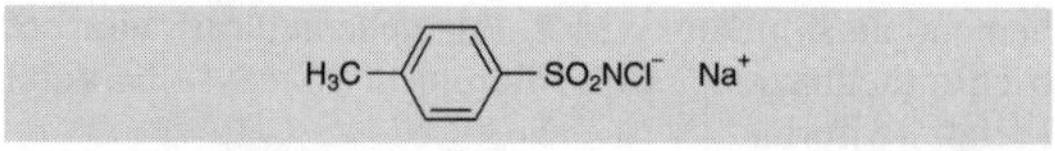

H₃C—〈benzene〉—SO₂NCl⁻ Na⁺

$C_7H_7Cl_1N_1Na_1O_2S_1$. M: 227.65. Available as the mono-hydrate. White, crystalline solid. Slowly decomposes in moist air. Available chlorine content: 25% w/w. Solubility in water: 120 g/l solution (25°C).
Production:
• *p*-toluenesulphonamide + sodium hypochlorite (chlorination)
Uses: disinfectant/preservative

chloramizol *See:* imazalil

chloramphenicol
[56-75-7]

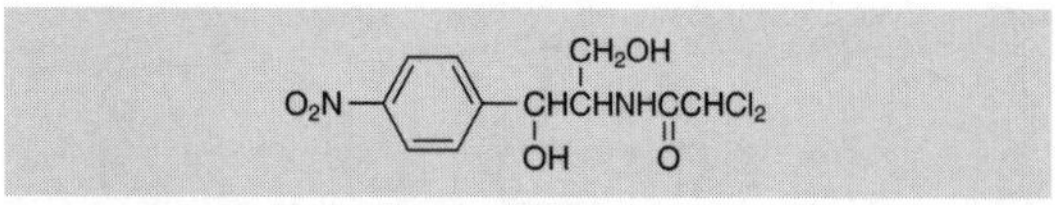

O₂N—〈benzene〉—CHCHNHCCHCl₂ with CH₂OH, OH, O

$C_{11}H_{12}Cl_2N_2O_5$. M: 323.13.
Production:
• cinnamyl alcohol + ammonia + chloral (hypobromination/amine formation/racemate separation/amide formation/nitration)
• *p*-nitrobenzaldehyde + glycine + chloral (condensation/racemate separation/esterification/ester reduction/amide formation)
Uses: antibacterial drug

chloranil
tetrachloro-*p*-benzoquinone; [118-75-2]
$C_6Cl_4O_2$. M: 245.88.

Production:
• 2,4,6-trichlorophenol (hydration/ring chlorination)
• hydroquinone (ring chlorination)
Derivatives:
Direct Blue 106; Direct Blue 108; Direct Blue 109; Pigment Violet 23; Pigment Violet 37; Sulphur Red 7
Uses: dehydrogenation reagent

chlorbromuron
3-(4-bromo-3-chlorophenyl)-1-methoxy-1-methylurea; [13360-45-7]

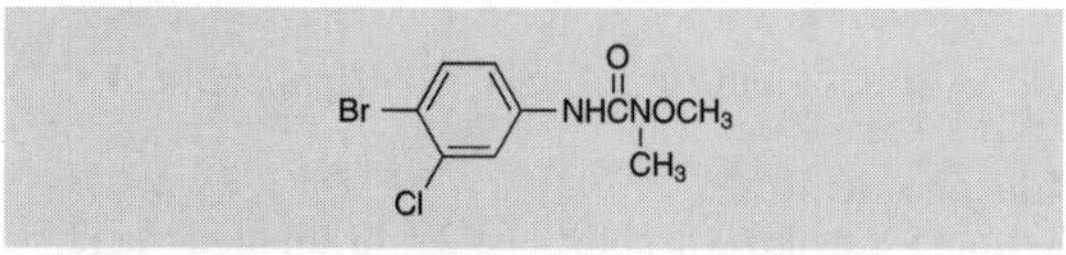

Br—〈benzene〉—NHCNOCH₃ with Cl, O, CH₃

$C_9H_{10}Br_1Cl_1N_2O_2$. M: 293.54.
Production:
• *m*-chloroaniline + phosgene + *N,O*-dimethyl-hydroxylamine + bromine (phosgenation/isocyanate addition/ring bromination)
Uses: herbicide

chlorbufam
1-methylprop-2-ynyl 3-chlorophenylcarbamate; [1967-16-4]

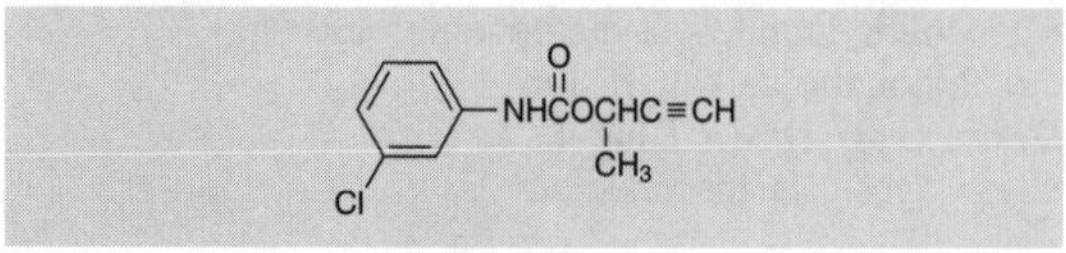

〈benzene〉—NHCOCHC≡CH with Cl, O, CH₃

$C_{11}H_{10}Cl_1N_1O_2$. M: 223.66.
Production:
• *m*-chloroaniline + phosgene + 3-butyn-2-ol (phosgenation/isocyanate addition)
Uses: herbicide

chlordane
1,2,4,5,6,7,8,8-octachloro-2,3,3a,4,7,7a-hexahydro-4,7-methanoindene; [57-74-9]

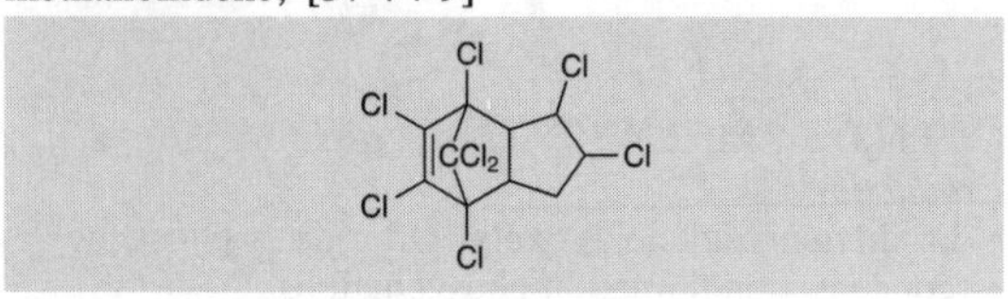

$C_{10}H_6Cl_8$. M: 409.78.
Production:
• hexachlorocyclopentadiene + dicyclopentadiene + chlorine (Diels-Alder cycloaddition/addition)
Uses: insecticide

chlordiazepoxide

Librium (Hoffmann-La Roche); [58-25-3];

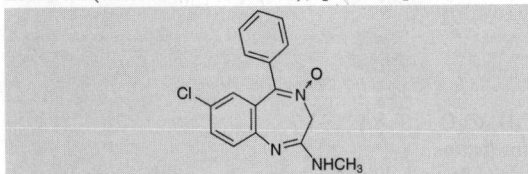

$C_{16}H_{14}Cl_1N_3O_1$. M: 299.76. Available commercially as the free base or as the hydrochloride salt.
Production:
• 2-amino-5-chlorobenzophenone + hydroxylamine sulphate + chloroacetyl chloride + methylamine (imine formation/amide formation/cyclisation/amine formation/rearrangement)
Derivatives: oxazepam
Uses: anxiolytic/sedative drug

chlorendic anhydride *See:* HET anhydride

chlorethephon *See:* ethephon

chlorex *See:* di-(2-chloroethyl)ether

chlorfenvinfos

2-chloro-1-(2,4-dichlorophenyl)vinyl diethyl phosphate; [470-90-6]

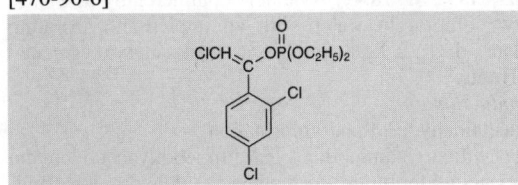

$C_{12}H_{14}Cl_3O_4P_1$. M: 359.57.
Production:
• α,α,2,4-tetrachloroacetophenone + triethyl phosphite (Perkow reaction)
Uses: insecticide/acaricide

chlorflurenol-methyl

chlorflurecol-methyl; [2536-31-4]

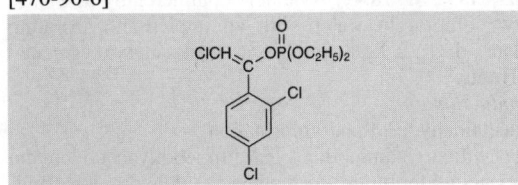

$C_{15}H_{11}Cl_1O_3$. M: 274.70.
Production:
• 9,10-phenanthrenequinone + methanol (ring chlorination/rearrangement/esterification)
Uses: plant growth regulator/herbicide

chlorhexidine

[55-56-1]
$C_{22}H_{30}Cl_2N_{10}$. M: 505.46. Generally used in the form of its digluconate, dihydrochloride or diacetate salt.

Production:
• *p*-chloroaniline + sodium dicyanamide + hexamethylenediamine (amidine formation/amidine formation)
Uses: medical disinfectant

chloridazon

pyrazon; [1698-60-8]

$C_{10}H_8Cl_1N_3O_1$. M: 221.64.
Production:
• mucochloric acid + phenylhydrazine + ammonia (condensation/amine formation)
Uses: herbicide

chlorine

[7782-50-5]

Cl_2. M: 70.91. Yellowish-green gas or liquified gas with a pungent odour. BP: -34°C. MP: -101°C. d: 1.468 kg/l (366.5 kPa, 0°C). Highly toxic. Slightly soluble in water. Soluble in aqueous alkali.
Production:
• sodium chloride, natural (mercury cell electrolysis; coproduced with sodium hydroxide)
• sodium chloride, natural (diaphram cell electrolysis; coproduced with sodium hydroxide)
• sodium chloride, natural (membrane cell electrolysis; coproduced with sodium hydroxide)
• potassium chloride (mercury cell electrolysis; coproduced with potassium hydroxide)
• potassium chloride (membrane cell electrolysis; coproduced with potassium hydroxide)
• hydrochloric acid (electrolysis)
• hydrochloric acid + oxygen (modified Deacon process/Kellogg Kel-chlor oxidation process)
• sodium chloride, refined (Downs process; coproduced with sodium)
• magnesium chloride (melt electrolysis; coproduced with magnesium)
• manganese dioxide + hydrogen chloride, anhydrous (Weldon process; byproduct of manganous chloride production)
• potassium chloride + nitric acid (salt formation; byproduct of potassium nitrate production)
Derivatives:
acetyl chloride; allyl chloride; aluminium chloride, anhydrous; 2-aminothiazoline-4-carboxylic acid; anti-

mony pentachloride; bleaching powder; boron trichloride; bromine; 1,2-butylene oxide; *t*-butyl hypochlorite; butyl rubber, chlorinated; cadmium chloride; calcium hypochlorite; carbon tetrachloride; chlordane; chlorine dioxide; chloroacetic acid; chloroform; 3-chloro-2-hydroxy-5-trifluoromethylpyridine; chloroparaffin; chloroprene; α-chloropropionic acid; 2-chloropyridine; clopyralid; cupric chloride; cyanogen chloride; dichlone; 2,4-dichloroacetophenone; dichlorodifluoromethane; 1,3-dichloro-5,5-dimethylhydantoin; 2,4-dichlorophenol; α,α-dichloropropionic acid; dicofol; *O,O*-diethyl phosphorochlorothioate; *O,O*-dimethyl phosphorochlorothioate; *O,O*-di-*n*-propyl phosphorochlorothioate; epichlorohydrin; ethyl chloride; ethylene dichloride; ferric chloride; ferric sulphate; fonofos; glycerol-1,3-dichlorohydrin; heptachlor; hexachlorocyclopentadiene; hydrogen chloride, anhydrous; 2-hydroxy-5-(trifluoromethyl)pyridine; iodine; iodine monochloride; isoflurane; lead dioxide; lindane; magnesium chloride; manganous chloride; mercuric chloride; mercurous chloride; methallyl chloride; methylene chloride; methyl sulphenyl chloride; *n*-monochloroparaffins(C_{10}-C_{13}); *n*-monochloroparaffins(C_{11}-C_{14}); mucochloric acid; pentachlorophenol; perchloroethylene; phosgene; phosphorus pentachloride; phosphorus trichloride; picloram; polyethylene, chlorinated; polyethylene, chlorosulphonated; potassium ferricyanide; propylene oxide; raffinate I; rare earth chloride; rubber, chlorinated; silicon tetrachloride; sodium hypochlorite; sodium perchlorate; stannic chloride; stannous chloride; starch, oxidised; sulphur dichloride; sulphur monochloride; sulphuryl chloride; terbacil; thionyl chloride; thiophosgene; titanium dioxide; titanium tetrachloride; tri-allate; trichloroacetic acid; 2,4,5-trichloroacetophenone; 1,1,1-trichloroethane; 1,1,2-trichloroethane; trichloroethylene; trichlorofluoromethane; trichloroisocyanuric acid; trichloromethanesulphenyl chloride; 2,4,6-trichlorophenol; vanadium oxychloride; vanadium tetrachloride; zinc chloride; zirconium tetrachloride
Uses:
ring chlorination/oxidation reagent; water disinfectant

chlorine dioxide
[10049-04-4]

ClO₂

Cl_1O_2. M: 67.45. Brownish-red gas. BP: 10°C. Soluble in water. Highly explosive. Manufactured in solution with water and handled as a 10–15% mixture with an inert gas.
Production:
• sodium chlorate + sulphur dioxide, pure + sulphuric acid (Erco/Hooker processes)
• chlorine (Kesting electrolytic process)
• sodium chlorite + chlorine (oxidation)
Derivatives: sodium chlorite
Uses: pulp bleaching agent; water/effluent treatment

chlormephos
S-(chloromethyl) *O,O*-diethyl phosphorodithionate; [24934-91-6]

ClCH₂SP(OC₂H₅)₂

$C_5H_{12}Cl_1O_2P_1S_2$. M: 234.70.
Production:
• *O,O*-diethyl dithiophosphoric acid + bromochloromethane (dehydrobromination)
Uses: insecticide

chlormequat chloride
chlorocholine chloride; 2-chloroethyltrimethylammonium chloride; CCC; [999-81-5]

(CH₃)₃⁺NCH₂CH₂Cl Cl⁻

$C_5H_{13}Cl_2N_1$. M: 158.07.
Production:
• trimethylamine + ethylene dichloride (dehydrochlorination)
Uses: plant growth regulator

chloroacetaldehyde
[107-20-0]

ClCH₂CHO

$C_2H_3Cl_1O_1$. M: 78.49. Available commercially as a 45% w/w solution in water with an unpleasant, irritating odour. d: 1.22 kg/l. Soluble in water and oxygenated solvents.
Production:
• acetaldehyde (alpha chlorination)
Derivatives: 2-aminothiazole; citronelloxyacetaldehyde; L-cysteine; fenfuram; mercaptoacetaldehyde; *N*-methylaminoacetaldehyde dimethyl acetal; oxabetrinil; thiamazole; triflumizole

chloroacetic acid
chloracetic acid; monochloroacetic acid; MCA; [79-11-8]

ClCH₂COOH

$C_2H_3Cl_1O_2$. M: 94.49.
Production:
• acetic acid + chlorine (alpha chlorination)
• trichloroethylene (acid-catalysed hydrolysis)
Derivatives:
acediasulfone; allyl chloroacetate; betaine; *t*-butyl chloroacetate; carbocysteine; cefazedone; chloroacetyl chloride; cyanoacetic acid; 2,4-D; diethyl malonate; 3,4-dihydroxy-ω-chloroacetophenone; 2,4-dihydroxyquinoline; diisopropyl malonate; dimethyl malonate; diodone; Direct Red 180; ethyl chloroacetate; glycollic acid; *N*-(4-hydroxyphenyl)glycine; indol-3-ylacetic acid; ioglycamic acid; iotroxic acid; meclofenoxate; 2-methoxyacetic acid; methyl chloroacetate; 2-methyl-4-chloro-

phenoxyacetic acid; (2-naphthyloxy)acetic acid; nitrofurantoin; phenoxyacetic acid; Pigment Red 88; prothoate; sodium chloroacetate; 2,4,5-T; thioglycollic acid; thioindigo; Vat Orange 5; Vat Red 1

chloroacetone
1-chloropropan-2-one; [78-95-5]

$$CICH_2CCH_3$$

$C_3H_5Cl_1O_1$. M: 92.52. Liquid with a pungent, irritating odour. Discolours on storage. BP: 118–120°C. d: 1.13 kg/l (20°C). Miscible with oxygenated and chlorinated solvents. Stabilised with calcium carbonate.
Production:
• methyl acetoacetate (alpha chlorination/decarboxylation)
Derivatives: hydroprene; methoprene; 4-methylthiazole; mexiletine; zomepirac
Uses: enzyme inactivator; riot control gas

chloroacetonitrile
[107-14-2]

$$CICH_2CN$$

$C_2H_2Cl_1N_1$. M: 75.50. Colourless, lachrymatory liquid with a pungent odour. BP: 124–126°C. d: 1.20 kg/l. Insoluble in water. Soluble in alcohol.
Production:
• methyl chloroacetate + ammonia (nitrile formation)
Derivatives:
antazoline; cyanoacetic acid; fenoxazoline; guanethidine; thidiazuron

α-chloroacetophenone
phenacyl chloride; [532-27-4]

$$CCH_2Cl$$

$C_8H_7Cl_1O_1$. M: 154.60. White crystals. MP: 54–56°C. BP: 243–244°C. Insoluble in water. Soluble in oxygenated and aromatic solvents.
Production:
• acetophenone (alpha chlorination)
Uses: riot control gas

chloroacetyl chloride
chloracetyl chloride; [79-04-9]

$$CICH_2COCl$$

$C_2H_2Cl_2O_1$. M: 112.95. Colourless liquid with a pungent odour. BP: 105–106°C. d: 1.50 kg/l (20°C). Hydrolysed by water and alcohol.
Production:
• chloroacetic acid (acid chloride formation)
Derivatives: acetochlor; alachlor; anilofos; butachlor; chlordiazepoxide; clemastine; clemizole; clonazepam;

denatonium benzoate; diethatyl-ethyl; dimethachlor; flunitrazepam; flurazepam; flurochloridone; formothion; lidocaine; lidoflazine; lorazepam; mecarbam; metazachlor; metolachlor; nitrazepam; nordazepam; ofurace; omethoate; oxetacaine; piperophos; pirenzepine; praziquantel; pretilachlor; propachlor; propanidid; pyroquilon; salbutamol; synephrine; tolycaine; triazolam; tromantadine

m-chloroaniline
3-amino-1-chlorobenzene; 3-chloroaniline; [108-42-9]

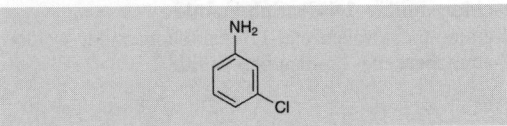

$C_6H_6Cl_1N_1$. M: 127.58. Liquid. BP: 230–231°C. FP: -10°C. d: 1.22 kg/l (20°C). Insoluble in water. Soluble in oxygenated solvents.
Production:
• *m*-chloronitrobenzene (nitro reduction)
Derivatives:
chlorbromuron; chlorbufam; 5-chloroaniline-2,4-disulphonamide; 2-chlorophenothiazine; 1-(3-chlorophenyl)piperazine hydrochloride; chlorpropham; 3,10-dichloroquinacridone; 4,7-dichloroquinoline; *N,N*-di-(2-hydroxyethyl)-*m*-chloroaniline; Mordant Orange 26

o-chloroaniline
2-amino-1-chlorobenzene; 2-chloroaniline; Azoic Diazo Component 44 (CI); [95-51-2]

$C_6H_6Cl_1N_1$. M: 127.58. Liquid. BP: 210–211°C. MP: 0°C. d: 1.21 kg/l (20°C). Insoluble in water. Soluble in aqueous acid and oxygenated solvents.
Production:
• *o*-chloronitrobenzene (nitro reduction)
Derivatives:
acetoacet-*o*-chloroanilide; anilazine; benazolin; Disperse Orange 138; drazoxolon; 4,4′-methylenebis(2-chloroaniline); Pigment Yellow 60

p-chloroaniline
4-amino-1-chlorobenzene; 4-chloroaniline; [106-47-8]

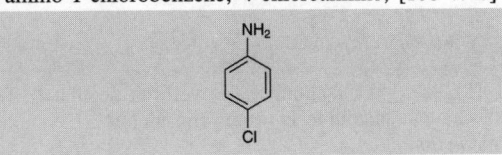

$C_6H_6Cl_1N_1$. M: 127.58. Crystals. MP: 68–71°C. BP: 230–232°C. d: 1.43 kg/l (15°C). Soluble in hot water and oxygenated solvents.

Production:
- *p*-chloronitrobenzene (nitro reduction)

Derivatives:
2-amino-5-chlorobenzophenone; 2-amino-5-chloro-2′-fluorobenzophenone; 2-amino-2′,5-dichlorobenzophenone; anilofos; chlorhexidine; *p*-chlorophenyl isocyanate; 1-(4′-chloro-2′-sulphophenyl)-3-methylpyrazolone; diazepam; diazoxide; 2,9-dichloroquinacridone; 6-dimethylamino-1,2-dimethylquinolinium iodide; monalide; Pigment Green 10; Pigment Red 8; Vat Red 32

5-chloroaniline-2,4-disulphonamide
4-amino-6-chlorobenzene-1,3-disulphonamide; 4-chloro-2-aminobenzene-1,5-disulphonamide

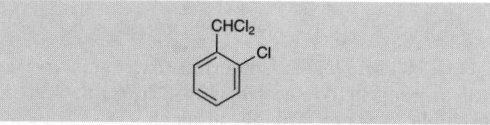

$C_6H_8Cl_1N_3O_4S_2$. M: 285.73.

Production:
- *m*-chloroaniline + chlorosulphonic acid + ammonia (chlorosulphonation/sulphonamide formation)

Derivatives: butizide; chlorothiazide; cyclopenthiazide; hydrochlorothiazide; polythiazide; trichlormethiazide

1-chloroanthraquinone
[82-44-0]

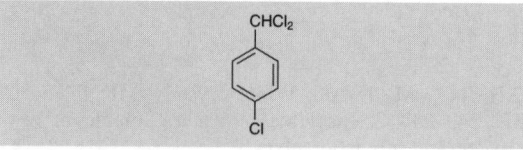

$C_{14}H_7Cl_1O_2$. M: 242.66. Yellow needles. MP: 162°C. Insoluble in water. Soluble in oxygenated solvents.

Production:
- anthraquinone-1-sulphonic acid, sodium salt + sodium chlorate (sulphonate displacement)

Derivatives: Disperse Red 9; Disperse Red 22; Vat Brown 1; Vat Brown 44; Vat Yellow 28

2-chloroanthraquinone
[131-09-9]

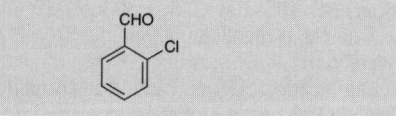

$C_{14}H_7Cl_1O_2$. M: 242.66. Pale yellow needles. MP: 207–210°C. Insoluble in water and alcohol.

Production:
- 2-(4-chlorobenzoyl)benzoic acid (Friedel-Crafts acylation)

Uses: dyestuffs intermediate

chloroauric acid

HAuCl₄

$H_1Au_1Cl_4$. M: 339.79. Yellow, hygroscopic crystals. d: 3.9 kg/l. Soluble in water.

Production:
- gold + hydrochloric acid + nitric acid (salt formation)

Derivatives: potassium gold cyanide

Uses: gold plating/gilding reagent; photographic toning reagent

chloroazodin
dichloroazodicarbonamidine; [502-98-7]

$C_2H_4Cl_2N_6$. M: 183.00.

Production:
- guanidine nitrate + sodium hypochlorite (chlorination)

Uses: medical antiseptic

o-chlorobenzal chloride

$C_7H_5Cl_3$. M: 195.48. Not a commercially traded product.

Production:
- *o*-chlorotoluene (side-chain chlorination; coproduced with *o*-chlorobenzotrichloride)

Derivatives: *o*-chlorobenzaldehyde

p-chlorobenzal chloride

$C_7H_5Cl_3$. M: 195.48. Not a commercially traded product.

Production:
- *p*-chlorotoluene (side-chain chlorination; coproduced with *p*-chlorobenzotrichloride/*p*-chlorobenzyl chloride)

Derivatives: *p*-chlorobenzaldehyde

o-chlorobenzaldehyde
2-chlorobenzaldehyde; [89-98-5]

$C_7H_5Cl_1O_1$. M: 140.57. Pale yellow liquid. BP:

212–214°C. FP: 11°C. d: 1.25 kg/l (20°C). Slightly soluble in water. Soluble in oxygenated and aromatic solvents.
Production:
• *o*-chlorobenzal chloride (dehydrochlorination)
Derivatives:
Acid Green 9; Acid Green 22; Basic Blue 1; benzaldehyde-2-sulphonic acid; *o*-chlorobenzalmalononitrile; 3-(2-chlorophenyl)-5-methylisoxazole-4-carboxylic acid; clomazone; Solvent Red 22

p-chlorobenzaldehyde
4-chlorobenzaldehyde; [104-88-1]

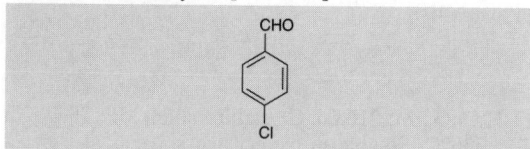

$C_7H_5Cl_1O_1$. M: 140.57. White solid. MP: 45–47°C. BP: 213–214°C. Insoluble in water. Soluble in oxygenated solvents.
Production:
• *p*-chlorobenzal chloride (hydrolysis)
Derivatives:
carbinoxamine; *p*-chlorobenzylamine; coumachlor; pencycuron; robenidine; sulindac; uniconazole
Uses:
dyestuffs intermediate

o-chlorobenzalmalononitrile
CS; [2698-41-1]

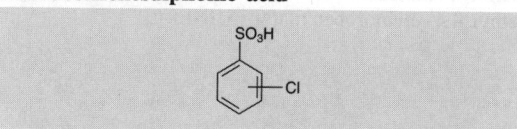

$C_{10}H_5Cl_1N_2$. M: 188.61. White, crystalline solid. MP: 95°C. BP: 312°C. Slightly soluble in water. Soluble in oxygenated and chlorinated solvents.
Production:
• *o*-chlorobenzaldehyde + malononitrile (carbonyl condensation)
Uses:
riot-control agent

chlorobenzene
monochlorobenzene; [108-90-7]

$C_6H_5Cl_1$. M: 112.56. Colourless liquid with a characteristic, penetrating odour. BP: 132°C. MP: -45°C. d: 1.11 kg/l (20°C). Insoluble in water. Miscible with oxygenated, chlorinated and aromatic solvents. Flash point: 28°C (CC).

Production:
• benzene + hydrogen chloride, anhydrous (Gulf oxychlorination process; coproduced with *o*-dichlorobenzene/*p*-dichlorobenzene)
Derivatives: 1-azaphenothiazine; *p*-bromochlorobenzene; chlorobenzenesulphonic acid; *p*-chlorobenzenesulphonyl chloride; 2-(4-chlorobenzoyl)benzoic acid; 1-chloro-2,4-dinitrobenzene; *o*-chloronitrobenzene; *p*-chloronitrobenzene; 2-chlorophenothiazine; (*RS*)-α-(4-chlorophenyl)isovaleric acid; DDT; 2,4'-dichlorobenzophenone; 4,4'-dichlorobenzophenone; dichlorodiphenylsilane; 4,4'-dichlorodiphenyl sulphone; Fluorescent Brightener 121; Fluorescent Brightener 312; hexythiazox; phenol; *N*-phenyl-J acid; phenylmagnesium chloride; *N*-phenyl--peri acid; *o*-phenylphenol; *p*-phenylphenol; tetradifon; trichlorophenylsilane; 2-(trifluoromethyl)phenothiazine; triphenylphosphine
Uses: process solvent

chlorobenzenesulphonic acid

$C_6H_5Cl_1O_3S_1$. M: 192.62. Mixed product containing *o*- and *p*-isomers.
Production:
• chlorobenzene (sulphonation)
Uses:
electroplating electrolyte

o-chlorobenzenesulphonyl chloride

$C_6H_4Cl_2O_2S_1$. M: 211.07.
Production:
• chlorobenzene + chlorosulphonic acid (chlorosulphonation; byproduct of *p*-chlorobenzenesulphonyl chloride production)
Derivatives:
2-chlorobenzenesulphonyl isocyanate

p-chlorobenzenesulphonyl chloride
4-chlorophenylsulphonyl chloride; [98-60-2]

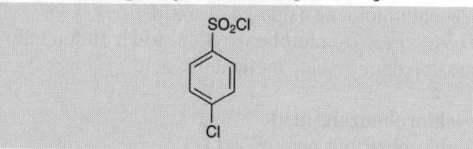

$C_6H_4Cl_2O_2S_1$. M: 211.07. Crystalline solid. MP: 55°C. Hydrolysed by water and alcohol. Soluble in oxygenated and aromatic solvents.

Production:
- chlorobenzene + chlorosulphonic acid (chloro-sulphonation)

Derivatives: 2-chloro-5-chlorosulphonylbenzenesulphon-amide; 4-chloro-3-nitrobenzenesulphonyl chloride; chlorpropamide; oryzalin; tiotixene

2-chlorobenzenesulphonyl isocyanate

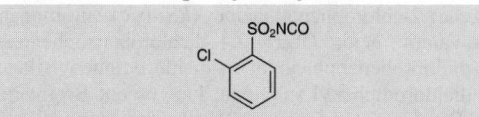

$C_7H_4Cl_1N_1O_3S_1$. M: 217.63.
Production:
- *o*-chlorobenzenesulphonyl chloride + ammonia + phosgene (sulphonamide formation/phosgenation)

Derivatives: chlorsulfuron

chlorobenzilate

ethyl 4,4′-dichlorobenzilate; [510-15-6]

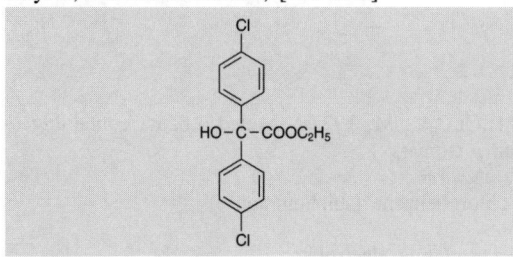

$C_{16}H_{14}Cl_2O_3$. M: 325.20.
Production:
- dicofol + diethyl sulphate (hydrolysis/esterification)

Uses: acaricide

o-chlorobenzoic acid

2-chlorobenzoic acid; [118-91-2]

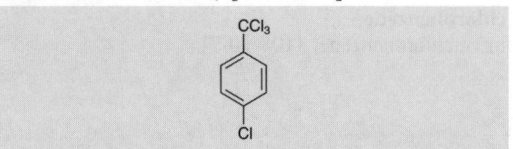

$C_7H_5Cl_1O_2$. M: 156.57. White, crystalline solid. MP: 138–140°C. d: 1.54 kg/l (20°C). Insoluble in water. Soluble in oxygenated solvents.
Production:
- *o*-chlorobenzoyl chloride (hydration)
- *o*-chlorotoluene (side-chain oxidation)

Derivatives: *o*-chlorobenzoyl chloride; flufenamic acid; meclofenamic acid; mefenamic acid

p-chlorobenzoic acid

4-chlorobenzoic acid; [74-11-3]
$C_7H_5Cl_1O_2$. M: 156.57. Crystalline solid. MP: 239–241°C. Insoluble in water. Soluble in oxygenated solvents.

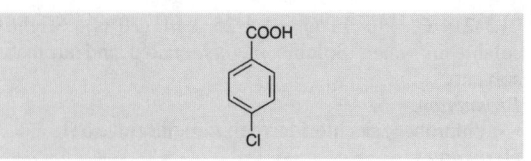

Production:
- *p*-chlorobenzotrichloride (hydrolysis)

Derivatives: 4-chloro-3-nitrobenzoic acid; isobutyl 4-chloro-3,5-diaminobenzoate

p-chlorobenzophenone

4-chlorobenzophenone; 4-chlorophenyl phenyl ketone; [134-85-0]

$C_{13}H_9Cl_1O_1$. M: 216.66. Crystalline solid. MP: 75–77°C. BP: 330°C. Soluble in oxygenated solvents.
Production:
- benzene + *p*-chlorobenzoyl chloride (Friedel-Crafts acylation)

Derivatives: chlorophacinone; chlorphenoxamine; clemastine; hydroxyzine; mebendazole
Uses: photoinitiator (radiation-cured lacquers, inks)

o-chlorobenzotrichloride

2-chlorobenzotrichloride; 2-chloro-α,α,α-trichlorotolu-ene; [2136-89-2]

$C_7H_4Cl_4$. M: 229.92. Colourless solid or liquid. MP: 29–30°C. BP: 260–264°C. d: 1.51 kg/l (25°C). Hydrolysed by hot water. Soluble in most organic solvents.
Production:
- *o*-chlorotoluene (side-chain chlorination; coproduced with *o*-chlorobenzal chloride)

Derivatives: *o*-chlorobenzotrifluoride; *o*-chlorobenzoyl chloride

p-chlorobenzotrichloride

4-chlorobenzotrichloride; [5216-25-1]

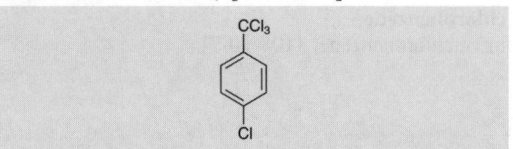

$C_7H_4Cl_4$. M: 229.92. Liquid with a pungent odour. BP: 245°C. Insoluble in water. Soluble in oxygenated and aromatic solvents.
Production:
- *p*-chlorotoluene (side-chain chlorination; coproduced with *p*-chlorobenzyl chloride/*p*-chlorobenzal chloride)

Derivatives: *p*-chlorobenzoic acid; *p*-chlorobenzotrifluoride; *p*-chlorobenzoyl chloride

o-chlorobenzotrifluoride
2-chlorobenzotrifluoride; [88-16-4]

$C_7H_4Cl_1F_3$. M: 180.55.
Production:
• *o*-chlorobenzotrichloride + hydrogen fluoride
  (fluorination)
Derivatives:
5-amino-2-chlorobenzotrifluoride; penfluridol

p-chlorobenzotrifluoride
4-chlorobenzotrifluoride; 4-(trifluoromethyl)chlorobenzene; [98-56-6]

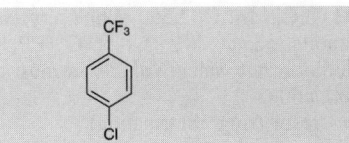

$C_7H_4Cl_1F_3$. M: 180.55. Liquid. BP: 136–138°C. d: 1.35 kg/l (15°C).
Production:
• *p*-chlorobenzotrichloride + hydrogen fluoride
  (fluorination)
Derivatives: 3-amino-4-chlorobenzotrifluoride; 4-chloro-3,5-dinitrobenzotrifluoride; flupenthixol

2-(4-chlorobenzoyl)benzoic acid
[85-56-3]

$C_{14}H_9Cl_1O_3$. M: 260.67. Solid. MP: 147–148°C. Slightly soluble in hot water. Soluble in oxygenated and aromatic solvents.
Production:
• chlorobenzene + phthalic anhydride (Friedel-Crafts
  acylation)
Derivatives:
2-chloroanthraquinone; chlorthalidone; mazindol

o-chlorobenzoyl chloride
2-chlorobenzoyl chloride; [609-65-4]
$C_7H_4Cl_2O_1$. M: 175.02. Colourless, hygroscopic liquid. BP: 232–234°C. FP: -5°C. Hydrolysed by water and alcohol. Soluble in oxygenated solvents.
Production:
• *o*-chlorobenzotrichloride (dehydrochlorination)

• *o*-chlorobenzoic acid (acid chloride formation)

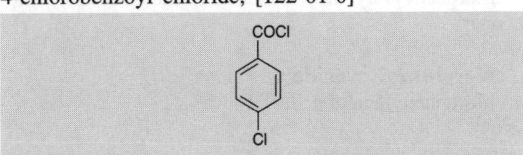

Derivatives: 2-amino-2',5-dichlorobenzophenone; *o*-chlorobenzoic acid; clofentezine; clotrimazole; nuarimol

p-chlorobenzoyl chloride
4-chlorobenzoyl chloride; [122-01-0]

$C_7H_4Cl_2O_1$. M: 175.02. Solid or liquid. MP: 14–16°C. BP: 221°C. d: 1.38 kg/l (20°C). Hydrolysed by water.
Production:
• *p*-chlorobenzotrichloride (hydration)
Derivatives: benoxaprofen; bezafibrate; *p*-chlorobenzophenone; *p*-chlorobenzoyl peroxide; clopamide; 2,4'-dichlorobenzophenone; 4,4'-dichlorobenzophenone; indomethacin; zomepirac

p-chlorobenzoyl peroxide
Interox CLBP (Interox); Percadox PS (Akzo); [94-17-7]

$C_{14}H_8Cl_2O_4$. M: 311.12.
Production:
• *p*-chlorobenzoyl chloride + hydrogen peroxide
  (dehydrochlorination)
Uses: crosslinking agent (resins)

p-chlorobenzylamine
[104-86-9]

$C_7H_8Cl_1N_1$. M: 141.60. Liquid. BP: 104–106°C (1.9 kPa). Insoluble in water. Soluble in oxygenated solvents.
Production:
• *p*-chlorobenzaldehyde + hydroxylamine sulphate
  (oxime formation/reduction)
Derivatives:
chloropyramine; clemizole

p-chlorobenzyl chloride
4-chlorobenzyl chloride; 4,α-dichlorotoluene;
[104-83-6]
$C_7H_6Cl_2$. M: 161.04. Colourless needles. MP: 31°C. BP: 214°C. Insoluble in water. Soluble in oxygenated solvents.

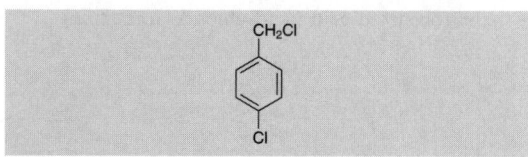

Production:
• *p*-chlorotoluene (side-chain chlorination; coproduced with *p*-chlorobenzotrichloride/*p*-chlorobenzal chloride)
Derivatives:
p-chlorobenzyl cyanide; econazole; paclobutrazol; thiobencarb

p-chlorobenzyl cyanide
4-chlorophenylacetonitrile; [140-53-4]

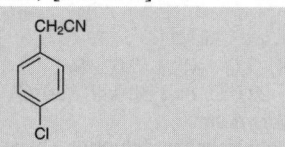

$C_8H_6Cl_1N_1$. M: 151.60.
Production:
• *p*-chlorobenzyl chloride + sodium cyanide (cyanidation)
Derivatives: chlorphenamine

2-chloro-1,3-butadiene *See:* chloroprene

4-chlorobutyronitrile
3-chloropropyl cyanide; 3-cyanopropyl chloride; [628-20-6]

ClCH₂CH₂CH₂CN

$C_4H_6Cl_1N_1$. M: 103.55. Liquid. BP: 195–197°C. Insoluble in water. Soluble in oxygenated solvents.
Production:
• 4-chlorobutyryl chloride + ammonia (nitrile formation)
Derivatives: buspirone

4-chlorobutyryl chloride
4-chlorobutanoyl chloride; γ-chlorobutyryl chloride; [4635-59-0]

ClCH₂CH₂CH₂COCl

$C_4H_6Cl_2O_1$. M: 141.00. Liquid. BP: 114–116°C (14 kPa). FP: -47°C. Hydrolysed by water.
Production:
• γ-butyrolactone + thionyl chloride (chlorination)
Derivatives:
4′-*t*-butyl-4-chlorobutyrophenone; 4-chlorobutyronitrile; 4-chloro-4′-fluorobutyrophenone; kadethrinic acid

2-chloro-5-chlorosulphonylbenzenesulphonamide
chlorsulphonylsulphonamide; [61450-06-4]
$C_6H_5Cl_2N_1O_4S_2$. M: 290.16.

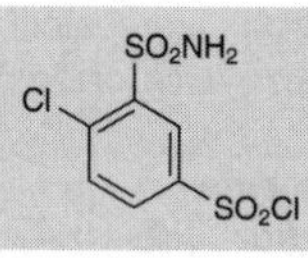

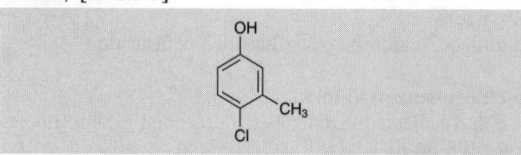

Production:
• *p*-chlorobenzenesulphonyl chloride + ammonia (sulphonamide formation/chlorosulphonation)
Derivatives:
mefruside

p-chloro-*m*-cresol
2-chloro-5-hydroxytoluene; 4-chloro-3-methylphenol; PCMC; [59-50-7]

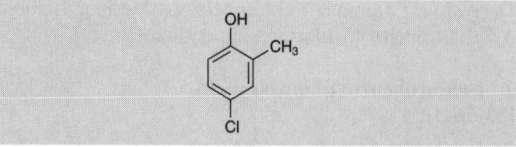

$C_7H_7Cl_1O_1$. M: 142.59. White crystals with a mild, phenolic odour. MP: 64–66°C. BP: 235°C. Slightly soluble in hot water. Soluble in most organic solvents.
Production:
• *m*-cresol (ring chlorination)
Uses:
antiseptic/biocide/preservative/disinfectant

p-chloro-*o*-cresol
4-chloro-2-methylphenol; 2-methyl-4-chlorophenol; PCOC; [1570-64-5]

$C_7H_7Cl_1O_1$. M: 142.59. Pale yellow solid with a chlorophenolic odour. MP: 46–47°C. BP: 232°C. d: 1.20 kg/l (50°C). Sparingly soluble in water. Soluble in aqueous alkali, oxygenated and aromatic solvents. Flash point: 106°C (PMCC).
Production:
• *o*-cresol (ring chlorination)
Derivatives:
MCPB-sodium; mecoprop; mecoprop-P; 2-methyl-4-chlorophenoxyacetic acid

7-(4-chloro-6-diethylaminotriazin-2-yl)amino-3-phenylcoumarin
Tinopal SFG (Ciba-Geigy)

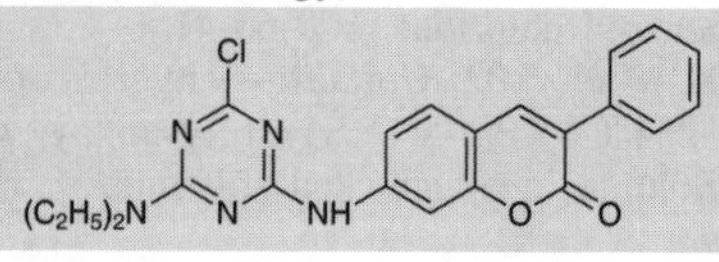

$C_{22}H_{20}Cl_1N_5O_2$. M: 421.88.

Production:
- 7-amino-3-phenylcoumarin + cyanuric chloride + diethylamine (amine formation/amine formation)

Uses: fluorescent brightening agent (plastics)

1-chloro-1,1-difluoroethane
HCFC-142b; R142b; [75-68-3]

$$CH_3CF_2Cl$$

$C_2H_3Cl_1F_2$. M: 100.49. Liquified gas. BP: -9°C. MP: -131°C. Flammable.

Production:
- 1,1,1-trichloroethane + hydrogen fluoride (halogen exchange; coproduced with 1,1-dichloro-1-fluoroethane)

Derivatives: vinylidene fluoride

chlorodifluoromethane
Freon 22 (Du Pont); HCFC-22; R22; [75-45-6]

$$CHF_2Cl$$

$C_1H_1Cl_1F_2$. M: 86.47. Colourless, liquified gas with an ethereal odour. BP: -41°C. Slightly soluble in water. Non-flammable.

Production:
- chloroform + hydrogen fluoride (halogen exchange; coproduced with dichlorofluoromethane)

Derivatives: bromochlorodifluoromethane; flucythrinate; tetrafluoroethylene

Uses: R-502 refrigerant gas component; refrigerant gas

4-chloro-2,5-dimethoxyaniline
2-amino-5-chlorohydroquinone dimethyl ether; [6358-64-1]

$C_8H_{10}Cl_1N_1O_2$. M: 187.63.

Production:
- 2,5-dimethoxyaniline (ring chlorination)

Derivatives: acetoacet-4-chloro-2,5-dimethoxyanilide; 4-chloro-2,5-dimethoxy-3'-hydroxy-2'-naphthanilide

5-chloro-2,4-dimethoxyaniline
4-amino-6-chlororesorcinol dimethyl ether; [97-50-7]

$C_8H_{10}Cl_1N_1O_2$. M: 187.63.

Production:
- resorcinol dimethyl ether (nitration/ring chlorination)

Derivatives: N,N'-bis(5-chloro-2,4-dimethoxyphenyl)-terephthalodiacetamide; 5-chloro-2,4-dimethoxy-3'-hydroxy-2'-naphthanilide

4-chloro-2,5-dimethoxy-3'-hydroxy-2'-naphthanilide
3-hydroxy-2-naphth-4'-chloro-2',5'-dimethoxyanilide; Naphthol AS-LC; Azoic Coupling Component 23 (CI); 37555 (CI); [4273-92-1]

$C_{19}H_{16}Cl_1N_1O_4$. M: 357.80.

Production:
- β-oxynaphthoic acid + 4-chloro-2,5-dimethoxy-aniline (amide formation)

Derivatives: Pigment Red 146

Uses: azoic dye coupling component

5-chloro-2,4-dimethoxy-3'-hydroxy-2'-naphthanilide
3-hydroxy-2-naphth-5'-chloro-2',4'-dimethoxyanilide; Azoic Coupling Component 12 (CI); 37550 (CI); [92-72-8]

$C_{19}H_{16}Cl_1N_1O_4$. M: 357.80.

Production:
- β-oxynaphthoic acid + 5-chloro-2,4-dimethoxy-aniline (amide formation)

Derivatives: Pigment Red 5; Pigment Red 187

4-chloro-1,2-dimethylbenzene *See:* 4-chloro-*o*-xylene

1-chloro-3,3-dimethyl-2-butanone
See: α-chloropinacolone

4-chloro-3,5-dimethylphenol *See:* 4-chloro-3,5-xylenol

3-chloro-2,2-dimethylpropanoyl chloride
See: monochloropivaloyl chloride

6-chloro-2,4-dinitroaniline
2-chloro-4,6-dinitroaniline; 2,4-dinitro-6-chloroaniline; [3531-19-9]

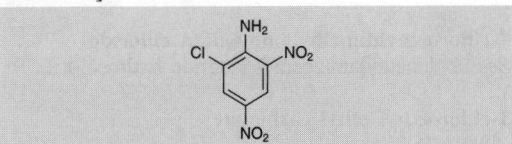

$C_6H_4Cl_1N_3O_4$. M: 217.57. Solid. MP: 154–156°C.

Production:
• 2,4-dinitroaniline (ring chlorination)
Derivatives: Disperse Blue 125
Uses: dyestuffs intermediate

1-chloro-2,4-dinitrobenzene
2,4-dinitrochlorobenzene; [97-00-7]

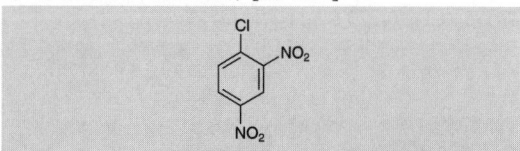

$C_6H_3Cl_1N_2O_4$. M: 202.55. Pale yellow needles with an almond-like odour. MP: 47–50°C. BP: 315°C. Insoluble in water. Soluble in hot alcohol, oxygenated and aromatic solvents.
Production:
• chlorobenzene (nitration)
Derivatives: Acid Orange 3; bromofenoxim; 2,4-dinitroaniline; 2,4-dinitroanisole; 2,4-dinitrofluorobenzene; 2,4-dinitrophenol; Disperse Yellow 9; Disperse Yellow 14

4-chloro-3,5-dinitrobenzotrifluoride
[393-75-9]

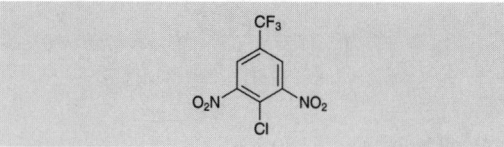

$C_7H_2Cl_1F_3N_2O_4$. M: 270.55.
Production:
• *p*-chlorobenzotrifluoride (nitration)
Derivatives: benfluralin; ethalfluralin; fluchloralin; flumetralin; profluralin; trifluralin

2-chloroethanol *See:* ethylene chlorohydrin

3-(2-chloroethyl)aminopropanol hydrochloride
β-(3-hydroxypropylamino)ethyl chloride hydrochloride

$ClCH_2CH_2NH_2CH_2CH_2CH_2OH$ Cl^-

$C_5H_{13}Cl_2N_1O_1$. M: 174.07.
Production:
• 3-aminopropanol + ethylene oxide + diethyl carbonate + hydrochloric acid (epoxidation/alcohol protection/alcohol chlorination)
Derivatives: ifosfamide; trofosfamide

2-chloroethyldimethylammonium chloride
See: 2-dimethylaminoethyl chloride hydrochloride

1-chloroethyl ethyl carbonate
[50893-36-2]
$C_5H_9Cl_1O_3$. M: 152.57.

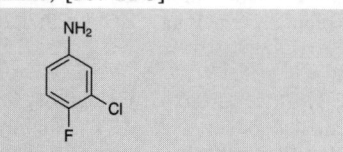

Production:
• acetaldehyde + ethyl chloroformate (addition)
Derivatives:
bacampicillin

5-(2-chloroethyl)-4-methylthiazole *See:* clomethiazole

2-chloroethylphosphonic acid *See:* ethephon

2-chloroethyltrimethylammonium chloride
See: chlormequat chloride

3-chloro-4-fluoroaniline
4-fluoro-3-chloroaniline; [367-21-5]

$C_6H_5Cl_1F_1N_1$. M: 145.57. Liquid. MP: 44–46°C.
Production:
• 3,4-dichloronitrobenzene + sodium fluoride (halogen exchange/nitro reduction)
Derivatives:
flamprop-methyl; flamprop-M-isopropyl; norfloxacin

2-chloro-6-fluorobenzaldehyde
6-chloro-2-fluorobenzaldehyde; 2-fluoro-6-chlorobenzaldehyde; 6-fluoro-2-chlorobenzaldehyde; [387-45-1]

$C_7H_4Cl_1F_1O_1$. M: 158.56.
Production:
• 2-chloro-6-fluorotoluene (side-chain oxidation)
Derivatives:
3-(2-chloro-6-fluorophenyl)-5-methylisoxazole-4-carboxylic acid; flumetralin

4-chloro-4'-fluorobutyrophenone
γ-chloro-4-fluorobutyrophenone; [3874-54-2]

$C_{10}H_{10}Cl_1F_1O_1$. M: 200.64.
Production:
• 4-chlorobutyryl chloride + fluorobenzene (Friedel-Crafts acylation)
Derivatives:
benperidol; droperidol; haloperidol; trifluperidol

3-(2-chloro-6-fluorophenyl)-5-methylisoxazole-4-carboxylic acid
FCIMC acid (Shell); [3919-74-2]

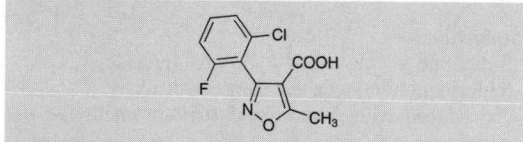

$C_{11}H_7Cl_1F_1N_1O_3$. M: 255.64. Solid.
Production:
• 2-chloro-6-fluorobenzaldehyde + methyl acetoacetate + hydroxylamine hydrochloride
  (Knoevenagel condensation/chlorination/cyclisation)
Derivatives:
flucloxacillin

2-chloro-6-fluorotoluene
2-fluoro-6-chlorotoluene

$C_7H_6Cl_1F_1$. M: 144.58. Liquid. BP: 154–156°C.
Production:
• 2,6-dichlorotoluene (halogen exchange)
Derivatives:
2-chloro-6-fluorobenzaldehyde

chloroform
trichloromethane; [67-66-3]

$CHCl_3$

$C_1H_1Cl_3$. M: 119.38. Colourless, volatile liquid. BP: 61°C. d: 1.48 kg/l (25°C). Insoluble in water. Miscible with most organic solvents. Commercial grades are generally stabilised with a little ethanol.
Production:
• natural gas + hydrogen chloride, anhydrous/oxygen (Lummus oxychlorination process; coproduced with methyl chloride/methylene chloride/carbon tetrachloride)
• natural gas + hydrogen chloride, anhydrous (oxychlorination; coproduced with methylene chloride/carbon tetrachloride)
• methyl chloride + chlorine (thermal chlorination; coproduced with methylene chloride/carbon tetrachloride)
Derivatives:
bezafibrate; chlorodifluoromethane; clofibrate; dichlorofluoromethane; dodecylsalicylaldoxime; *p*-hydroxybenzaldehyde; nonylsalicylaldoxime; salicylaldehyde; triethyl orthoformate; trifluoromethane; trimethyl orthoformate
Uses:
pharmaceuticals/natural oil extraction solvent; non-flammable solvent (pharmaceuticals, perfumes)

2-chloro-3-hexyne
2-chlorohex-3-yne

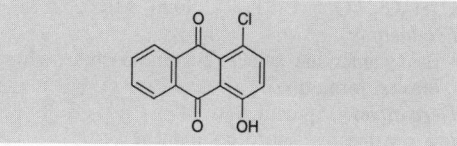

$C_6H_9Cl_1$. M: 116.59.
Production:
• diethyl sulphate + acetylene + acetaldehyde (ethynylation/ethynylation/chlorination)
Derivatives: methohexital

chlorohydrin
1-chloro-2,3-propanediol; 3-chloropropane-1,2-diol; glyceryl-α-monochlorohydrin; [96-24-2]

$C_3H_7Cl_1O_2$. M: 110.54. Colourless or pale yellow liquid. BP: 213°C with decomposition. d: 1.32 kg/l (20°C). Soluble in water and oxygenated solvents.
Production:
• allyl alcohol (hypochlorination)
• epichlorohydrin (dehydrochlorination)
Derivatives:
diprophylline; glycerol α-allyl ether; guaifenesin; iohexol

5-chloro-2-hydroxyaniline
See: 2-amino-4-chlorophenol

1-chloro-4-hydroxyanthraquinone
[82-42-8]

$C_{14}H_7Cl_1O_3$. M: 258.66.
Production:
• *p*-chlorophenol + phthalic anhydride (condensation)
Derivatives:
1-amino-4-hydroxyanthraquinone; 1,4-diaminoanthraquinone; Disperse Blue 72; quinizarin

5-chloro-2-hydroxybenzoic acid
See: 5-chlorosalicylic acid

5-chloro-2-hydroxybenzophenone
HCB; 2-hydroxy-5-chlorobenzophenone; [85-19-8]

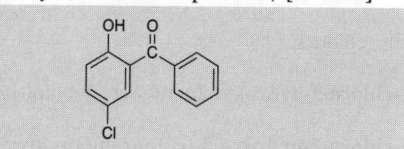

$C_{13}H_9Cl_1O_2$. M: 232.66. Yellow powder. MP: 93–95°C.

Production:
- *p*-chlorophenol + benzoyl chloride (Friedel-Crafts acylation)

Uses: light stabiliser (vinylidene chloride-vinyl chloride copolymers)

4-chloro-3′-hydroxy-2′-naphth-*m*-toluidide

3-hydroxy-2-naphth-4′-chloro-2′-methylanilide; Naphthol AS-TR; Azoic Coupling Component 8 (CI); 37525 (CI); [92-76-2]

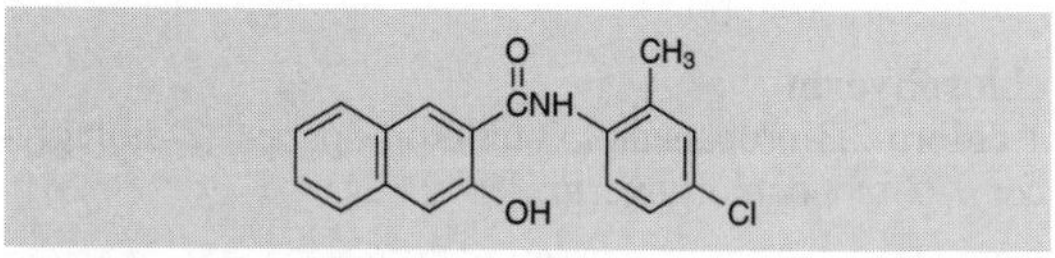

$C_{18}H_{14}Cl_1N_1O_2$. M: 311.77.
Production:
- β-oxynaphthoic acid + 2-amino-5-chlorotoluene (amide formation)

Derivatives: Pigment Red 7
Uses: azoic dye coupling component

5-chloro-3′-hydroxy-2′-naphth-*o*-toluidide

3-hydroxy-2-naphth-5′-chloro-2′-methylanilide; Naphthol AS-KB; Azoic Coupling Component 21; 37526 (CI); [135-63-7]

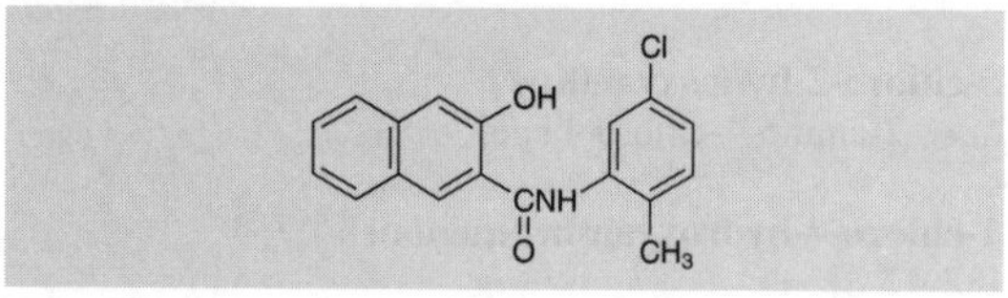

$C_{18}H_{14}Cl_1N_1O_2$. M: 311.77. Solid. MP: 237°C.
Production:
- β-oxynaphthoic acid + 2-amino-5-chlorotoluene (amide formation)

Derivatives: Pigment Red 147
Uses: azoic dye diazo component

3-chloro-2-hydroxypropyltrimethylammonium chloride

[3327-22-8]

$C_6H_{15}Cl_2N_1O_1$. M: 188.11. Available commercially as a 60–65% solution in water.
Production:
- trimethylamine + epichlorohydrin (quaternisation/ hydrolysis)

Derivatives: lauroxy-2-hydroxypropyltrimethylammonium chloride

2-chloro-5-hydroxytoluene *See:* *p*-chloro-*m*-cresol

3-chloro-2-hydroxy-5-trifluoromethylpyridine

$C_6H_3Cl_1F_3N_1O_1$. M: 197.54.

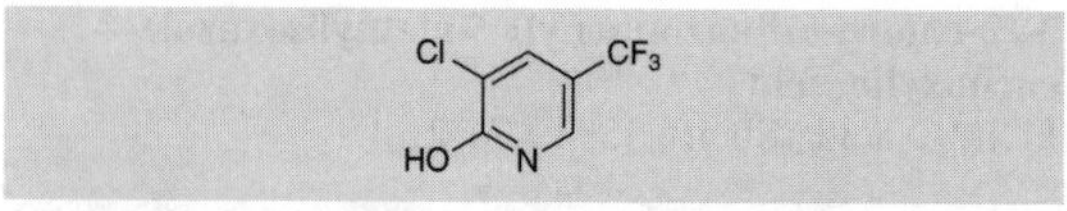

Production:
- β-picoline + chlorine + hydrogen fluoride (chlorination/halogen exchange/hydrolysis; coproduced with 2-hydroxy-5-(trifluoromethyl)-pyridine)

Derivatives: haloxyfop-ethoxyethyl

2-chloro-6-methylaniline *See:* 2-amino-3-chlorotoluene

3-chloro-4-methylaniline *See:* 4-amino-2-chlorotoluene

5-chloro-2-methylaniline *See:* 2-amino-4-chlorotoluene

1-chloro-2-methylanthraquinone

[129-35-1]

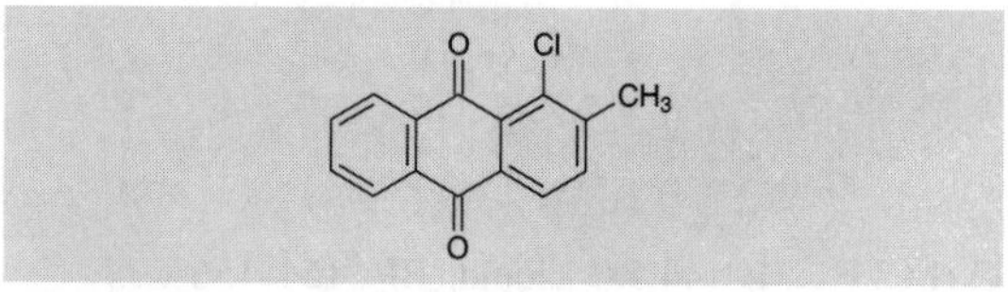

$C_{15}H_9Cl_1O_2$. M: 256.68. Solid. MP: 148–150°C.
Production:
- 2-methylanthraquinone (ring chlorination)

Derivatives:
pyranthrone; Vat Blue 21; Vat Red 35

chloromethyl chlorosulphate

[49715-04-0]

$C_1H_2Cl_2O_3S_1$. M: 165.00. Not a traded product. Manufactured *in situ* only.
Production:
- paraformaldehyde + chlorosulphonic acid (chlorosulphonation)

Derivatives:
aciclovir
Uses: O-chlorosulphonation reagent

5-chloro-2-methyl-4-isothiazolinone

Kathon 886 MW (Rohm and Haas); methylchloroisothiazolinone (CTFA)

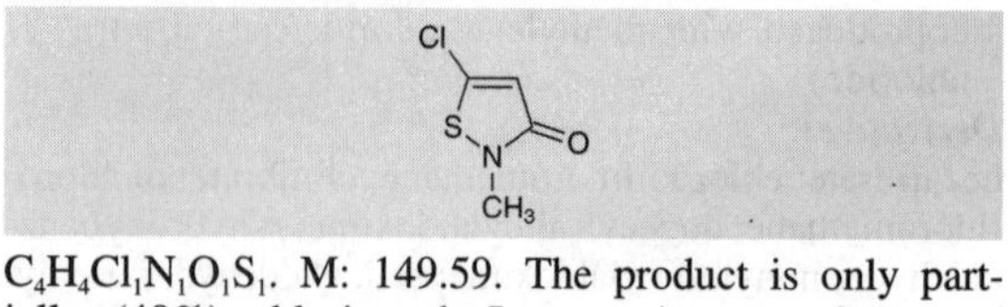

$C_4H_4Cl_1N_1O_1S_1$. M: 149.59. The product is only partially (40%) chlorinated. It comprises a mixture of 5-chloro-2-methyl-4-isothiazoline with 2-methyl-4-isothiazoline sold as a solution containing 24% active matter.

Production:
• acryloyl chloride + methylamine + sulphur
  dichloride (amide formation/sulphide formation)
Uses: biocide (metalworking fluids, cooling water
systems, paper production)

chloromethyl methyl ether
methyl chloromethyl ether; CMME; [107-30-2]

$$CH_3OCH_2Cl$$

$C_2H_5Cl_1O_1$. M: 80.51. Colourless liquid. BP: 59°C. MP:
-103°C. d: 1.06 kg/l (20°C). Soluble in oxygenated
solvents. Hydrolysed by water. Not a generally traded
product.
Production:
• methanol + formaldehyde + hydrogen chloride,
  anhydrous (reaction)
Derivatives: alachlor; phenolic resins, amino-substituted; polystyrene, crosslinked, aminated; polystyrene,
crosslinked, hydroxyethyldimethylbenzylammoniated;
polystyrene, crosslinked, phosphonated; polystyrene,
crosslinked, trimethylbenzylammoniated
Uses: chloromethylation reagent

1-chloromethylnaphthalene
α-chloromethylnaphthalene; α-naphthylmethyl chloride;
[86-52-2]

$$CH_2Cl$$

$C_{11}H_9Cl_1$. M: 176.64. Crystalline solid. MP: 32°C. BP:
291–292°C. Insoluble in water. Soluble in oxygenated,
chlorinated and aromatic solvents.
Production:
• α-methylnaphthalene (side-chain chlorination)
Derivatives: naftidrofuryl; naftifine; α-naphthoic acid;
naphthylacetonitrile

4-chloro-2-methylphenol *See:* p-chloro-o-cresol

4-chloro-3-methylphenol *See:* p-chloro-m-cresol

1-(6'-chloro-2'-methylphenyl)-3-methylpyrazolone

$C_{11}H_{11}Cl_1N_2O_1$. M: 222.67.
Production:
• 2-amino-3-chlorotoluene + diketene (diazotisation/
  reduction/condensation)
Derivatives: Acid Yellow 127

chloromethyl pivalate
[18997-19-8]

$$(CH_3)_3CCOCH_2Cl$$

$C_6H_{11}Cl_1O_2$. M: 150.61.
Production:
• pivaloyl chloride + formaldehyde (addition)
Derivatives: pivampicillin; pivmecillinam

3-chloro-2-methylpropyldimethylamine *See:* 3-di-
methylamino-2-methylpropyl chloride hydrochloride

1-(6'-chloro-2'-methyl-4'-sulphophenyl)-4-methyl-
pyrazolone

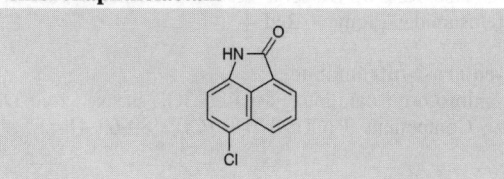

$C_{11}H_{10}Cl_1N_2Na_1O_4S_1$. M: 324.71.
Production:
• 2-aminotoluene-5-sulphonic acid + diketene (ring
  chlorination/diazotisation/azo reduction/condensation)
Derivatives: Reactive Yellow 17

4-chloronaphtholactam

$C_{11}H_6Cl_1N_1O_1$. M: 203.63.
Production:
• α-naphthoic acid (nitration/nitro reduction/amide
  formation/ring chlorination)
Derivatives: naphtholactam blue
Uses: dyestuffs intermediate

chloroneb
1,4-dichloro-2,5-dimethoxybenzene; [2675-77-6]

$C_8H_8Cl_2O_2$. M: 207.06.
Production:
• 1,2,4,5-tetrachlorobenzene + methanol (ether
  formation)
Uses: fungicide

2-chloronicotinic acid

2-chloroniacin; 2-chloropyridine-3-carboxylic acid;
[2942-59-8]

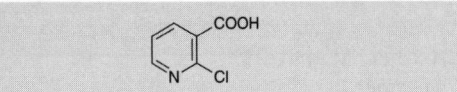

$C_6H_4Cl_1N_1O_2$. M: 157.56.
Production:
• nicotinic acid (oxidation/rearrangement/alcohol chlorination)
Derivatives: diflufenican; niflumic acid

2-chloro-4-nitroaniline

2-chloro-*p*-nitroaniline; *o*-chloro-*p*-nitroaniline; 4-nitro-2-chloroaniline; *p*-nitro-*o*-chloroaniline; [121-87-9]

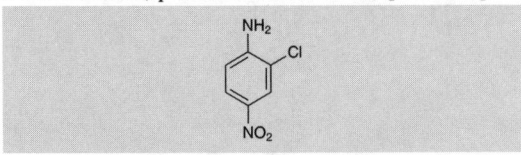

$C_6H_5Cl_1N_2O_2$. M: 172.57. Yellow needles. MP: 105–107°C. Slightly soluble in water. Soluble in oxygenated and aromatic solvents.
Production:
• 3,4-dichloronitrobenzene + ammonia (ammoniation)
Derivatives: 2-amino-5-nitroanisole; 2-amino-5-nitrophenol; Basic Red 18; Basic Red 18:1; dimefuron; Disperse Red 5; Disperse Red 13; Disperse Red 65; niclosamide; Pigment Red 4

4-chloro-2-nitroaniline

p-chloro-*o*-nitroaniline; Fast Red 3GL base; Azoic Diazo Component 9 (CI); 37040 (CI); [89-63-4]

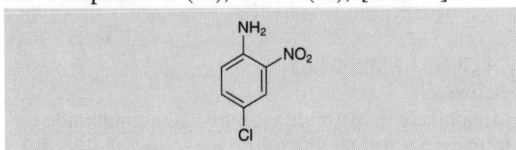

$C_6H_5Cl_1N_2O_2$. M: 172.57. Orange crystals. MP: 116–118°C. Soluble in oxygenated solvents.
Production:
• 2,5-dichloronitrobenzene + ammonia (ammoniation)
Derivatives: 4-chloro-*o*-phenylenediamine; clobazam; Pigment Orange 36; Pigment Red 6; Pigment Red 14; Pigment Yellow 3; Pigment Yellow 73; Pigment Yellow 75

4-chloro-2-nitroanisole

[89-21-4]
$C_7H_6Cl_1N_1O_3$. M: 187.59. yellow needles. MP: 98°C. Soluble in alcohol.
Production:
• 2,5-dichloronitrobenzene + methanol (ether formation)
Derivatives: 2-amino-4-chloroanisole

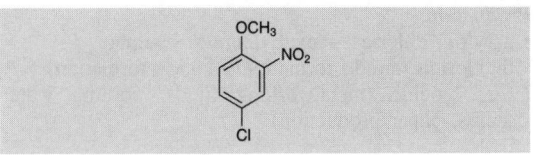

Uses: dyestuffs intermediate

m-chloronitrobenzene

1-chloro-3-nitrobenzene; 3-nitro-1-chlorobenzene; *m*-nitrochlorobenzene; [121-73-3]

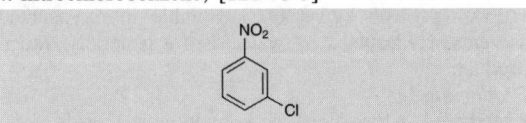

$C_6H_4Cl_1N_1O_2$. M: 157.56. Pale yellow, crystalline solid. MP: 44–46°C. BP: 235–236°C. d: 1.53 kg/l (20°C). Insoluble in water. Soluble in oxygenated, chlorinated and aromatic solvents.
Production:
• nitrobenzene (ring chlorination)
Derivatives: *m*-chloroaniline; poly[(3,4′-diphenyl ether)-(*p*-phenyleneterephthalamide)]

o-chloronitrobenzene

2-chloro-1-nitrobenzene; 2-nitro-1-chlorobenzene; *o*-nitrochlorobenzene; OCNB; [88-73-3]

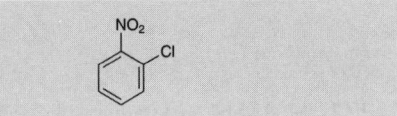

$C_6H_4Cl_1N_1O_2$. M: 157.56. Yellow needles. MP: 32–33°C. BP: 246°C. d: 1.37 kg/l (20°C). Insoluble in water. Soluble in oxygenated and aromatic solvents.
Production:
• chlorobenzene (nitration; coproduced with *p*-chloronitrobenzene)
Derivatives: Acid Brown 13; 2-aminothiophenol; 1,2-bis(2-aminophenylthio)ethane; *o*-chloroaniline; clemizole; dibenzepin; 3,3′-dichlorobenzidine dihydrochloride; domperidone; *o*-nitroaniline; *o*-nitroanisole; *o*-nitrophenol; *o*-phenetidine; 1-(4-piperidyl)-2-benzodiazolinone

p-chloronitrobenzene

1-chloro-4-nitrobenzene; 4-nitro-1-chlorobenzene; *p*-nitrochlorobenzene; PCNB; [100-00-5]

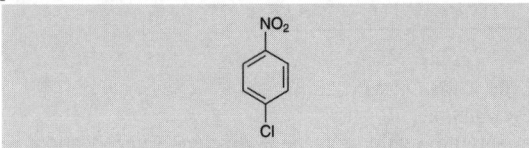

$C_6H_4Cl_1N_1O_2$. M: 157.56. Yellow crystals. MP: 83–84°C. BP: 242°C. d: 1.52 kg/l. Insoluble in water.

Soluble in hot alcohol, oxygenated and aromatic solvents.
Production:
• chlorobenzene (nitration; coproduced with *o*-chloronitrobenzene)
Derivatives:
aclonifen; *p*-aminodiphenylamine; *p*-anisidine; *p*-chloroaniline; 2-chloro-5-nitrobenzenesulphonic acid; chloroxuron; difenoxuron; *p*-fluoroaniline; *p*-nitroaniline; *p*-nitrophenol; 4,4′-oxydianiline; *p*-phenetidine

2-chloro-5-nitrobenzenesulphonic acid
4-chloro-1-nitrobenzene-3-sulphonic acid; 4-nitro-1-chlorobenzene-2-sulphonic acid; [96-73-1]

$C_6H_4Cl_1N_1O_5S_1$. M: 237.61.
Production:
• *p*-chloronitrobenzene (sulphonation)
Derivatives:
4-aminodiphenylamine-2-sulphonic acid; 4-amino-4′-methoxydiphenylamine; 4′-amino-4-nitrodiphenylamine-2-sulphonic acid; 4,4′-diaminodiphenylamine-2-sulphonic acid

4-chloro-3-nitrobenzenesulphonyl chloride
2-chloronitrobenzene-5-sulphonyl chloride; 2-nitrochlorobenzene-4-sulphonyl chloride; [97-08-5]

$C_6H_3Cl_2N_1O_4S_1$. M: 256.07.
Production:
• *p*-chlorobenzenesulphonyl chloride (nitration)
Derivatives: Acid Brown 248; aniline-2,5-disulphonic acid; 1-(2′-chloro-5′-sulphophenyl)-3-methylpyrazolone; Disperse Yellow 33; Disperse Yellow 42

2-chloro-4-nitrobenzoic acid
o-chloro-*p*-nitrobenzoic acid; 4-nitro-2-chlorobenzoic acid; [99-60-5]

$C_7H_4Cl_1N_1O_4$. M: 201.57.
Production:
• 2-chloro-4-nitrotoluene (side-chain oxidation)
Uses: dyestuffs intermediate

4-chloro-3-nitrobenzoic acid
p-chloro-*m*-nitrobenzoic acid; 3-nitro-4-chlorobenzoic acid; [96-99-1]

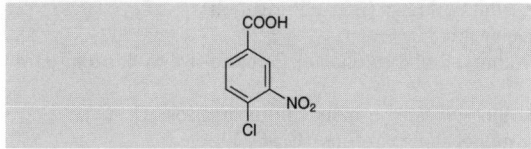

$C_7H_4Cl_1N_1O_4$. M: 201.57. White powder. MP: 181–183°C. d: 1.64 kg/l (20°C). Soluble in hot water.
Production:
• *p*-chlorobenzoic acid (nitration)
Derivatives: 3-amino-4-chlorobenzamide; bumetanide; flubendazole

5-chloro-2-nitrobenzoic acid
[2516-95-2]

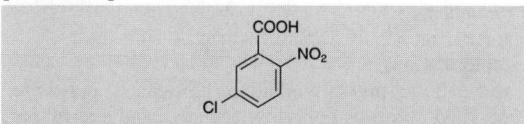

$C_7H_4Cl_1N_1O_4$. M: 201.57. Solid. MP: 138–140°C. Slightly soluble in water. Soluble in oxygenated solvents.
Production:
• *m*-chlorotoluene (nitration/side-chain oxidation)
Derivatives: acifluorfen; bifenox

4-chloro-2-nitrophenol
2-nitro-*p*-chlorophenol; [89-64-5]

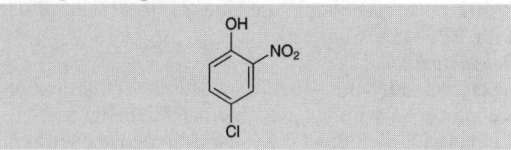

$C_6H_4Cl_1N_1O_3$. M: 173.56. Yellow crystals. MP: 88–89°C. Slightly soluble in water. Soluble in oxygenated and chlorinated solvents.
Production:
• *p*-dichlorobenzene (nitration/hydrolysis)
Derivatives: 2-amino-4-chlorophenol; 2-amino-4-chlorophenol-6-sulphonic acid
Uses: dyestuffs intermediate

2-chloro-4-nitrotoluene
o-chloro-*p*-nitrotoluene; 4-nitro-2-chlorotoluene; [121-86-8]

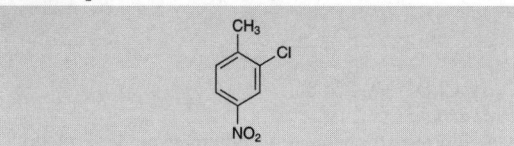

$C_7H_6Cl_1N_1O_2$. M: 171.59. Crystalline solid. MP: 65°C.

BP: 260°C. Insoluble in water. Soluble in oxygenated solvents.
Production:
• *p*-nitrotoluene (ring chlorination)
Derivatives:
4-amino-2-chlorotoluene; 2-chloro-4-nitrobenzoic acid

chloro-oil *See:* *n*-monochloroparaffins (C$_{10}$-C$_{13}$); *n*-monochloroparaffins (C$_{11}$-C$_{14}$);

chloroparaffin
paraffin, chlorinated; wax, chlorinated
Pale yellow liquid or, occasionally, powder. Several grades available varying in viscosity and chlorine content. d: 1.16–1.63 kg/l (25°C). Viscosity range: 200–5x10^6 mPa.s (25°C). Chlorine content: 42–77%. Insoluble in water and alcohol. Soluble in most organic solvents.
Production:
• *n*-paraffins (C$_{14}$-C$_{18}$)/paraffin wax + chlorine (chlorination)
Uses: extreme-pressure additive (lubricants); plasticiser (polyvinyl chloride, polyvinyl acetate, synthetic rubber, chlorinated rubber paints, sealants); fire-retardant additive (plastics, rubbers); leather fat-liquoring agent; tackifier (adhesives, sealants); textile backcoating

chloropentafluoroethane
CFC-115; R115; [76-15-3]

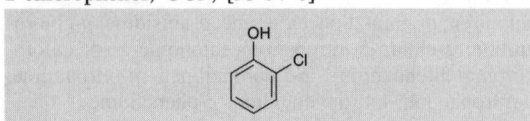

CF$_3$CF$_2$Cl

C$_2$Cl$_1$F$_5$. M: 154.46. Colourless, odourless, liquified gas. R-502 is an azeotropic mixture of R-22 and R-115 with BP: -45.6°C.
Production:
• perchloroethylene + hydrogen fluoride (fluorination; coproduced with 1,1,2-trichloro-1,2,2-trifluoro-ethane/1,2-dichloro-1,1,2,2-tetrafluoroethane/tetra-chlorodifluoroethane)
Uses:
R-502 refrigerant gas component

chlorophacinone
2-[2-(4-chlorophenyl)-2-phenylacetyl]indan-1,3-dione; [3691-35-8]

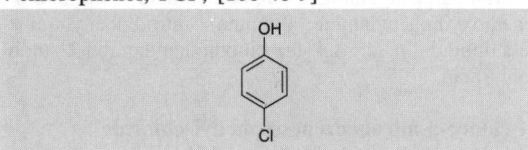

C$_{23}$H$_{15}$Cl$_1$O$_3$. M: 374.82.
Production:
• *p*-chlorobenzophenone + sodium cyanide + methyl acetate + dimethyl phthalate (cyanohydrin

formation/alcohol reduction/condensation/condensation)
Uses: rodenticide

o-chlorophenol
2-chlorophenol; OCP; [95-57-8]

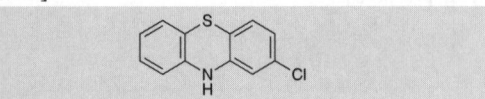

C$_6$H$_5$Cl$_1$O$_1$. M: 128.56. Pale yellow liquid with a carbolic odour. BP: 175°C. FP: 8°C. d: 1.27 kg/l (20°C). Sparingly soluble in water. Soluble in aqueous alkali, oxygenated and aromatic solvents. Flash point: 93°C (PMCC).
Production:
• phenol + sodium hypochlorite (ring chlorination)
Derivatives: profenofos
Uses: fire-retarded phenolic resin comonomer; dyestuffs intermediate

p-chlorophenol
4-chlorophenol; PCP; [106-48-9]

C$_6$H$_5$Cl$_1$O$_1$. M: 128.56. Yellow solid with a chloro-phenolic odour. MP: 42°C. BP: 220°C. d: 1.26 kg/l (45°C). Sparingly soluble in water. Soluble in aqueous alkali, oxygenated and aromatic solvents. Flash point: 102°C (PMCC).
Production:
• phenol + sulphuryl chloride (ring chlorination)
Derivatives:
o-benzyl-*p*-chlorophenol; 1-chloro-4-hydroxyanthraquin-one; 5-chloro-2-hydroxybenzophenone; 2-(4-chloro-phenoxy)propionic acid; chloroxuron; clofibrate; di-chlorophen; fenoxycarb; fluazifop-P-butyl; meclofen-oxate; sulcofenuron; triadimefon
Uses: dyestuffs intermediate; adhesion promotion agent

2-chlorophenothiazine
[92-39-7]

C$_{12}$H$_8$Cl$_1$N$_1$S$_1$. M: 233.71.
Production:
• *m*-chloroaniline + chlorobenzene + sulphur (amine formation/thiolation)
Derivatives: chlorpromazine; levomepromazine; perphenazine; prochlorperazine; thioridazine

2-(4-chlorophenoxy)propionic acid
[3307-39-9]

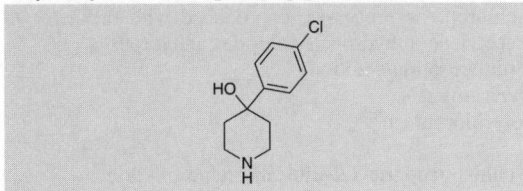

$C_9H_9Cl_1O_3$. M: 200.62.
Production:
• *p*-chlorophenol + α-chloropropionic acid (ether formation)
Derivatives: diclofop-methyl; fenoxaprop-ethyl; fluazifop-butyl; haloxyfop-ethoxyethyl; quizalofop-ethyl

4-chlorophenylacetonitrile *See: p*-chlorobenzyl cyanide

4-chloro-*o*-phenylenediamine
[95-83-0]

$C_6H_7Cl_1N_2$. M: 142.59. Crystalline solid. MP: 72–74°C. Slightly soluble in water. Soluble in oxygenated solvents.
Production:
• 4-chloro-2-nitroaniline (nitro reduction)
Derivatives: 2-(2-hydroxy-3-*t*-butyl-5-methylphenyl)-5-chlorobenzotriazole; 2-(2-hydroxy-3,5-di-*t*-butylphenyl)-5-chlorobenzotriazole; quizalofop-ethyl

4-(4-chlorophenyl)-4-hydroxypiperidine
4-hydroxy-4-(4-chlorophenyl)piperidine; [39512-49-7]

$C_{11}H_{14}Cl_1N_1O_1$. M: 211.69.
Production:
• *p*-bromochlorobenzene + magnesium + 1-benzyl-4-piperidone (Grignard reagent formation/Grignard reaction/amine dealkylation)
Derivatives: haloperidol; loperamide

p-chlorophenyl isocyanate
4-chlorophenyl isocyanate; [104-12-1]

$C_7H_4Cl_1N_1O_1$. M: 153.57.

Production:
• *p*-chloroaniline + phosgene (phosgenation)
Derivatives: cloflucarban; diflubenzuron; monolinuron; triclocarban

(*RS*)-α-(4-chlorophenyl)isovaleric acid
(*RS*)-2-(4-chlorophenyl)isopropylacetic acid; [2012-74-0]

$C_{11}H_{13}Cl_1O_2$. M: 212.67.
Production:
• isobutyroyl chloride + chlorobenzene + methyl chloroacetate (Friedel-Crafts acylation/Darzens reaction/hydrolysis/decarboxylation/carbonyl oxidation)
Derivatives: (*S*)-α-(4-chlorophenyl)isovaleric acid; fenvalerate

(*S*)-α-(4-chlorophenyl)isovaleric acid
(*S*)-2-(4-chlorophenyl)isopropylacetic acid

$C_{11}H_{13}Cl_1O_2$. M: 212.67.
Production:
• (*RS*)-α-(4-chlorophenyl)isovaleric acid (racemate separation)
Derivatives: esfenvalerate

3-(2-chlorophenyl)-5-methylisoxazole-4-carboxylic acid
CIMC acid (Shell); [23598-72-3]

$C_{11}H_8Cl_1N_1O_3$. M: 237.64. Solid.
Production:
• *o*-chlorobenzaldehyde + methyl acetoacetate + hydroxylamine hydrochloride (Knoevenagel condensation/chlorination/cyclisation)
Derivatives:
cloxacillin

chloro-*o*-phenylphenol
4/6-chloro-2-phenylphenol; monochloro-2-phenylphenol; MCOPP

$C_{12}H_9Cl_1O_2$. M: 220.65. Pale amber, viscous liquid. BP: 250–300°C with decomposition. d: 1.25 kg/l (20°C).

Flash point: 132°C (PMCC). Miscible with oxygenated and aromatic solvents. Slightly soluble in water. The product is primarily 4-chloro-2-phenylphenol with 10–15% of the 6-chloro derivative.
Production:
• *o*-phenylphenol (ring chlorination)
Uses: antiseptic

1-(3-chlorophenyl)piperazine hydrochloride
[65369-76-8]

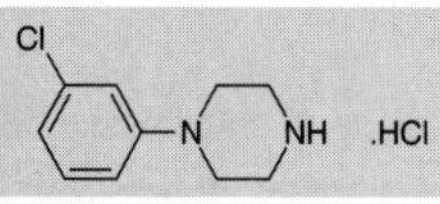

$C_{10}H_{14}Cl_2N_2$. M: 233.14. White, crystalline solid. Slightly soluble in water, isopropanol, acetone and toluene. Soluble in methanol.
Production:
• *m*-chloroaniline + diethanolamine + hydrochloric acid (amine formation/salt formation)
Derivatives: trazodone

4-chlorophenylsulphonyl chloride
See: p-chlorobenzenesulphonyl chloride

4-chlorophthalic anhydride
4-CPAN; [118-45-6]

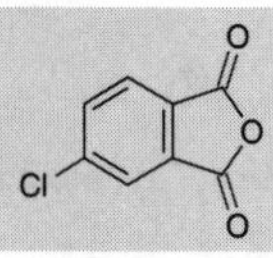

$C_8H_3Cl_1O_3$. M: 182.56. White, crystalline powder. MP: 96–98°C. Soluble in oxygenated, chlorinated and aromatic solvents. Hydrolysed by water.
Production:
• 4-chloro-*o*-xylene (side-chain oxidation)
Derivatives: 2-chlorothioxanthone; 4-fluorophthalic anhydride

chloropicrin
trichloronitromethane; [76-06-2]

$$CCl_3NO_2$$

$C_1Cl_3N_1O_2$. M: 164.38.
Production:
• nitromethane (alpha chlorination)
Uses:
grain fumigant/soil insecticide; dyestuffs oxidation reagent

α-chloropinacolone
1-chloro-3,3-dimethyl-2-butanone; [13547-70-1]

$$(CH_3)_3CCCH_2Cl$$

$C_6H_{11}Cl_1O_1$. M: 134.61.

Production:
• pinacolone (alpha chlorination)
Derivatives: bitertanol; cyanopinacolone; diclobutrazol; diniconazole; paclobutrazol; thiofanox; triadimefon; uniconazole

chloroplatinic acid
hexachloroplatinic acid; hydrogen hexachloroplatinate; Speier's catalyst; [16941-12-1]

$$H_2PtCl_6$$

$H_2Cl_6Pt_1$. M: 409.83. Available as a red, crystalline solid, MP: 60°C, d: 2.43 kg/l, or as a solution in water.
Production:
• platinum + hydrochloric acid + nitric acid (complex formation)
Uses: RTV addition-cured, two-component silicone rubber catalyst; platinum plating reagent; photographic chemical; catalyst raw material

chloroprene
2-chloro-1,3-butadiene; 2-chlorobutadiene; β-chloroprene; [126-99-8]

$C_4H_5Cl_1$. M: 88.53. Colourless liquid. BP: 59–60°C. MP: -130°C. d: 0.95 kg/l (20°C). Insoluble in water. Miscible with most organic solvents. See also polychloroprene.
Production:
• C_4-stream, steam-cracked + chlorine (BP/Du Pont chloroprene processes; coproduced with raffinate I)
• acetylene + hydrogen chloride, anhydrous (dimerisation/addition)
Derivatives:
polychloroprene

3-chloropropane-1,2-diol *See:* chlorohydrin

3-chloropropene *See:* allyl chloride

α-chloropropionic acid
(*RS*)-2-chloropropionic acid; [598-78-7]

$C_3H_5Cl_1O_2$. M: 108.52. Colourless liquid. BP: 183–187°C. MP: <-20°C. d: 1.26 kg/l (20°C). Miscible with water and oxygenated solvents. The commercial product is a racemic mixture.
Production:
• propionic acid + chlorine (alpha chlorination)
Derivatives:
2-(4-chlorophenoxy)propionic acid; (*S*)-α-chloropropionic acid; dichlorprop; ethyl α-chloropropionate;

hexythiazox; mecoprop; methyl α-chloropropionate; napropamide; 2-phenoxypropionic acid

(S)-α-chloropropionic acid
(−)-2-chloropropionic acid; [7474-05-7]

$$CH_3-\overset{\overset{H}{\downarrow}}{\underset{Cl}{C}}-COOH$$

$C_3H_5Cl_1O_2$. M: 108.52.
Production:
• α-chloropropionic acid (enantiospecific enzymatic dechlorination)
• D-lactic acid (alcohol chlorination)
Derivatives: flamprop-M-isopropyl; fluazifop-P-butyl; mecoprop-P

3-chloropropionyl chloride
3-chloropropanoyl chloride; [625-36-5]

$$\overset{\overset{O}{\parallel}}{ClCH_2CH_2CCl}$$

$C_3H_4Cl_2O_1$. M: 126.97. Yellow, hygroscopic liquid. BP: 143–145°C. MP: -32°C. d: 1.33 kg/l (15°C). Slightly soluble in water. Soluble in chlorinated and oxygenated solvents.
Production:
• acrylonitrile (cyanoethylation/hydrolysis)
Derivatives: Fluorescent Brightener 121; Fluorescent Brightener 312; 1-phenyl-3-pyrazolidone; pyroquilon

3-chloropropyl cyanide *See:* 4-chlorobutyronitrile

3-chloropropyldimethylammonium chloride
See: 3-dimethylaminopropyl chloride hydrochloride

γ-chloropropyltrimethoxysilane
[2530-87-2]

$$ClCH_2CH_2CH_2Si(OCH_3)_3$$

$C_6H_{15}Cl_1O_3Si_1$. M: 198.73. Liquid. BP: 196°C. d: 1.08 kg/l (25°C). Insoluble in water. Flash point: 45°C (COC).
Production:
• allyl chloride + trichlorosilane + methanol (hydrosilation/dehydrochlorination)
Derivatives:
N-(2-aminoethyl)-γ-aminopropyltrimethoxysilane
Uses:
plastics coupling agent (epoxy resins, polystyrene)

6-chloropurine
[87-42-3]
$C_5H_3Cl_1N_4$. M: 154.55. Greenish-yellow powder. MP: >300°C. Soluble in hot water and oxygenated solvents.
Production:
• hypoxanthine (chlorination)

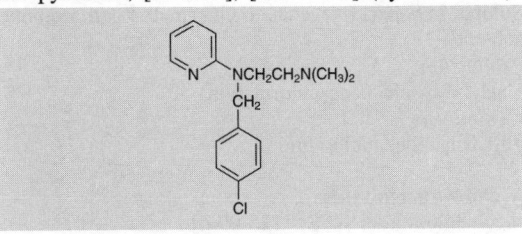

Derivatives: azathioprine; 6-mercaptopurine

chloropyramine
halopyramine; [59-32-5]; [6170-42-9] (hydrochloride)

$C_{16}H_{20}Cl_1N_3$. M: 289.81. Available commercially as the free base or hydrochloride.
Production:
• 2-bromopyridine + p-chlorobenzylamine + 2-dimethylaminoethyl chloride hydrochloride (amine formation/amine formation)
Uses:
antihistamine drug

2-chloropyridine
[109-09-1]

$C_5H_4Cl_1N_1$. M: 113.54. Liquid. BP: 167–170°C. Slightly soluble in water. Soluble in oxygenated solvents.
Production:
• pyridine + chlorine (ring chlorination)
Derivatives:
brompheniramine; chlorphenamine; disopyramide; pheniramine; sodium 2-pyridinethiol-N-oxide; trazodone

2-chloropyridine-3-carboxylic acid
See: 2-chloronicotinic acid

chloroquine
7-chloro-4-(4-diethylamino-1-methylbutylamino)quinoline; [54-05-7]

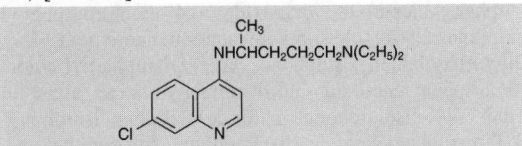

$C_{18}H_{26}Cl_1N_3$. M: 319.88.
Production:
• 4,7-dichloroquinoline + 4-amino-1-diethylaminopentane (amine formation)
Uses: antimalarial/antirheumatic drug

5-chlorosalicylic acid

5-chloro-2-hydroxybenzoic acid; [321-14-2]

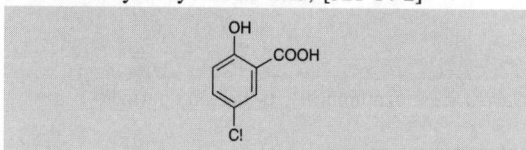

$C_7H_5Cl_1O_3$. M: 172.57. Needles. MP: 173–174°C. Soluble in water, oxygenated, chlorinated and aromatic solvents.
Production:
• salicylic acid (ring chlorination)
Derivatives:
glibenclamide; niclosamide

N-chlorosuccinimide

succinchlorimide; NCS; [128-09-6]

$C_4H_4Cl_1N_1O_2$. M: 133.53. White, crystalline powder with a chlorine odour. 52% available chlorine. Solubility in water: 14 g/l solution (25°C).
Production:
• succinimide (chlorination)
Uses: bactericide

chlorosulphonic acid

chlorosulphuric acid; [7790-94-5]

ClSO₃H

$H_1Cl_1O_3S_1$. M: 116.52. Colourless liquid. BP: 151–152°C with decomposition. FP: -81°C. d: 1.75 kg/l (20°C). Hydrolysed violently by water. Miscible with 100% sulphuric acid, acetic acid and chlorinated solvents. Reacts with most oxygenated solvents.
Production:
• sulphur trioxide + hydrogen chloride, anhydrous (addition)
Derivatives:
4-acetamidobenzenesulphonyl chloride; Acid Brown 13; aztreonam; benzenesulphonyl chloride; bromamine acid; bumetanide; 5-chloroaniline-2,4-disulphonamide; *p*-chlorobenzenesulphonyl chloride; chloromethyl chlorosulphate; clopamide; diazoxide; 4,4′-dichlorodiphenyl sulphone; 2,4-dichloro-5-sulphamoylbenzoic acid; 4,4′-dihydroxydiphenyl sulphone; dimethylsulphamyl chloride; diphenylene oxide-3,6-disulphohydrazide; diphenyl ether 4,4′-bis(sulphonyl chloride); diphenylsulphone-3,3′-disulphohydrazide; disul-sodium; furosemide; glibenclamide; glipizide; glisoxepide; hydroflumethiazide; mafenide; sodium 2-chloroethanesulphonate; tetradifon; *p*-toluenesulphonyl chloride; xipamide
Uses:
chlorosulphonation reagent

chlorosulphonyl isocyanate

[1189-71-5]

ClSO₂NCO

$C_1Cl_1N_1O_3S_1$. M: 141.53.
Production:
• sulphur trioxide + cyanogen chloride (reaction)
Derivatives:
acesulfame-K; cefuroxime
Uses: carbamoylation reagent

1-(2′-chloro-5′-sulphophenyl)-3-methylpyrazolone

$C_{10}H_9Cl_1N_2O_4S_1$. M: 288.70.
Production:
• 4-chloro-3-nitrobenzenesulphonyl chloride + diketene (nitro reduction/diazotisation/reduction/condensation)
Derivatives: Acid Yellow 200

1-(4′-chloro-2′-sulphophenyl)-3-methylpyrazolone

1-(4-chloro-2-sulphophenyl)-3-methyl-5-pyrazolone

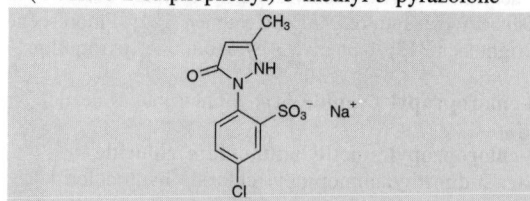

$C_{10}H_9Cl_1N_2O_4S_1$. M: 288.70.
Production:
• *p*-chloroaniline + diketene (sulphonation/diazotisation/reduction/condensation)
Derivatives:
Acid Yellow 40

1-chloro-1,2,2,2-tetrafluoroethane

R124

CHClFCF₃

$C_2H_1Cl_1F_4$. M: 136.47.
Production:
• 1,1-dichloro-2,2,2-trifluoroethane + hydrogen fluoride (halogen exchange; coproduced with pentafluoroethane)
Uses: refrigerant gas

chlorothalonil

tetrachloroisophthalonitrile; [1897-45-6]
$C_8Cl_4N_2$. M: 265.91.

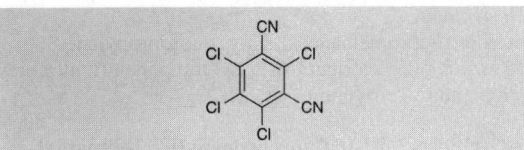

Production:
• isophthalodinitrile (ring chlorination)
Uses: fungicide

chlorothiazide
[58-94-6]; [7085-44-1] (sodium salt)

$C_7H_6Cl_1N_3O_4S_2$. M: 295.73. Available commercially as the acid or sodium salt.
Production:
• formamide + 5-chloroaniline-2,4-disulphonamide (carbonyl condensation)
Uses: diuretic drug

2-chlorothioxanthone
2-chloro-9-thioanthone; 2-chlorothioxanthen-9-one; [86-39-5]

$C_{11}H_7Cl_1O_1S_1$. M: 222.69. Yellow powder.
Production:
• 4-chlorophthalic anhydride + thiophenol (imine formation/Hofmann degradation/diazotisation/ sulphide formation/cyclisation)
Derivatives:
chlorprothixene; clopenthixol
Uses:
photoinitiator (radiation-cured lacquers, inks)

chlorothymol
4-chloro-5-methyl-2-isopropylphenol; [89-68-9]

$C_{10}H_{13}Cl_1O_1$. M: 184.66. White crystals. MP: 62–64°C. Solubility in water: 1 g/l (25°C). Soluble in oxygenated solvents.
Production:
• thymol (ring chlorination)
Uses: disinfectant

α-chlorotoluene *See:* benzyl chloride

m-chlorotoluene
[108-41-8]

$C_7H_7Cl_1$. M: 126.59. Colourless liquid. BP: 160–162°C. MP: -48°C. d: 1.07 kg/l (20°C). Insoluble in water. Soluble in oxygenated, chlorinated and aromatic solvents.
Production:
• *m*-toluidine (diazotisation/Sandmeyer reaction)
Derivatives: 5-chloro-2-nitrobenzoic acid

o-chlorotoluene
2-chlorotoluene; [95-49-8]

$C_7H_7Cl_1$. M: 126.59. Liquid. BP: 157–159°C. FP: -34°C. d: 1.08 kg/l (20°C). Insoluble in water. Soluble in most organic solvents.
Production:
• *o/p*-chlorotoluene (isomer separation; coproduced with *p*-chlorotoluene)
Derivatives:
o-chlorobenzal chloride; *o*-chlorobenzoic acid; *o*-chloro-benzotrichloride; *m*-cresol; *o*-cresol; 2,4-dichlorotoluene; 2,6-dichlorotoluene

o/p-chlorotoluene

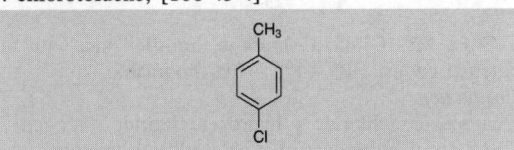

$C_7H_7Cl_1$. M: 126.59. Mixed isomer product used as the feedstock for cresol production.
Production:
• toluene (ring chlorination)
Derivatives:
o-chlorotoluene; *p*-chlorotoluene; *m/p*-cresol; *o*-cresol
Uses: solvent (adhesives)

p-chlorotoluene
4-chlorotoluene; [106-43-4]

$C_7H_7Cl_1$. M: 126.59. Liquid. BP: 161–163°C. MP:

7–8°C. d: 1.07 kg/l (20°C). Insoluble in water. Soluble in most organic solvents.
Production:
• *o/p*-chlorotoluene (isomer separation; coproduced with *o*-chlorotoluene)
Derivatives: 2-amino-4-chlorotoluene; *p*-chlorobenzal chloride; *p*-chlorobenzotrichloride; *p*-chlorobenzyl chloride; 2,4-dichlorotoluene; 3,4-dichlorotoluene

2-chloro-*p*-toluidine *See:* 4-amino-2-chlorotoluene

5-chloro-2-toluidine *See:* 2-amino-5-chlorotoluene

chlorotoluron
3-(3-chloro-4-methylphenyl)-1,1-dimethylurea; [15545-48-9]

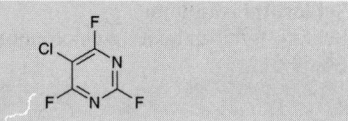

$C_{10}H_{13}Cl_1N_2O_1$. M: 212.67.
Production:
• 4-amino-2-chlorotoluene + dimethylcarbamoyl chloride (isocyanate addition)
Uses: herbicide

1-chloro-2,2,2-trifluoroethane

CH₂ClCF₃

$C_2H_2Cl_1F_3$. M: 118.48.
Production:
• trichloroethylene + hydrogen fluoride (halogen exchange)
Derivatives: halothane; 1,1,1,2-tetrafluoroethane

chlorotrifluoroethylene
CTFE; TFCE; trifluorochloroethylene; [79-38-9]

CF₂=CFCl

$C_2Cl_1F_3$. M: 116.46. Colourless gas. BP: -28°C. Decomposed by water.
Production:
• 1,1,2-trichloro-1,2,2-trifluoroethane (dechlorination)
Derivatives: enflurane; polychlorotrifluoroethylene; poly(ethylene-chlorotrifluoroethylene)

chlorotrifluoromethane
CFC-13; Freon 13 (Du Pont); R13; [75-72-9]

CF₃Cl

$C_1Cl_1F_3$. M: 104.45. Colourless, liquified gas with an ethereal odour. BP: -81°C. Non-flammable.
Production:
• carbon tetrachloride + hydrogen fluoride (halogen exchange; byproduct of dichlorodifluoromethane-/trichlorofluoromethane production)

Derivatives:
bromotrifluoromethane; 3,3,3-trifluoropropylene
Uses: R-503 refrigerant gas component; ultra-low temperature refrigerant

3-(2-chloro-3,3,3-trifluoropropenyl)-2,2-dimethyl-cyclopropanecarboxylic acid

$C_9H_{10}Cl_1F_3O_2$. M: 242.62. The product has a (*1RS*)-*cis* configuration around the cyclopropane ring.
Production:
• methyl 3,3-dimethyl-4-pentenoate + 1,1,1-trichloro-2,2,2-trifluoroethane (addition/dehydrochlorination/dehydrochlorination)
Derivatives: bifenthrin; cyhalothrin; tefluthrin

5-chloro-2,4,6-trifluoropyrimidine
[697-83-6]

$C_4Cl_1F_3N_2$. M: 168.49.
Production:
• 5-nitroso-2,4,6-triaminopyrimidine + hydrogen fluoride + cuprous chloride (diazotisation/azo fluorination/nitro reduction/diazotisation/Sandmeyer reaction)
Derivatives: Reactive Blue 94
Uses: dyestuffs intermediate (Levafix/Drimalan/Verofix reactive dyes)

chlorotrimethylsilane
trimethylchlorosilane; [75-77-4]

(CH₃)₃SiCl

$C_3H_9Cl_1Si_1$. M: 108.64. Colourless liquid. BP: 56–58°C. d: 0.86 kg/l (25°C). Hydrolysed by water with the release of hydrogen chloride. Soluble in chlorinated solvents.
Production:
• silicon, metallurgical grade + methyl chloride (Direct process; coproduced with dichlorodimethyl-silane/trichloromethylsilane/dichloromethylsilane)
Derivatives:
di-(trimethylsilyl)amine; hexamethyldisiloxane
Uses: silylating agent

chloroxuron
3-[4-(4-chlorophenoxy)phenyl]-1,1-dimethylurea; [1982-47-4]

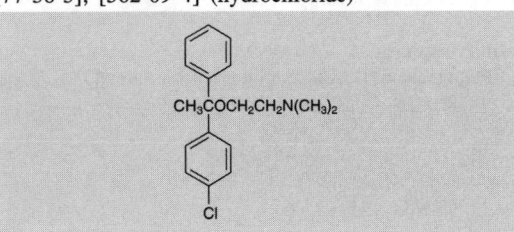

$C_{15}H_{15}Cl_1N_2O_2$. M: 290.74.
Production:
• *p*-chlorophenol + *p*-chloronitrobenzene + dimethyl-carbamoyl chloride (ether formation/nitro reduction/dehydrochlorination)
Uses: herbicide

4-chloro-*o*-xylene
4-chloro-1,2-dimethylbenzene; [615-60-1]

$C_8H_9Cl_1$. M: 140.61. Liquid. BP: 194°C. MP: -6°C. d: 1.07 kg/l (15°C). Insoluble in water. Soluble in aromatic solvents.
Production:
• *o*-xylene (ring chlorination)
Derivatives:
biphenyl-3,3',4,4'-tetracarboxylic dianhydride; 4-chlorophthalic anhydride; 4,4'-oxydiphthalic anhydride; 3,4-xylenol

4-chloro-3,5-xylenol
4-chloro-3,5-dimethylphenol;   chloroxylenol   (INN); *p*-chloro-*m*-xylenol; PCMX; [88-04-0]

$C_8H_9Cl_1O_1$. M: 156.61. White to cream, crystalline solid with a chlorophenolic odour. MP: 114°C. BP: 246°C. Very slightly soluble in hot water. Soluble in aqueous alkali, oxygenated and aromatic solvents. Flash point: 135°C (PMCC).
Production:
• 3,5-xylenol (ring chlorination)
Uses: disinfectant/antiseptic

chlorphenamine
chlorpheniramine; dexchlorpheniramine ((+)-enantiomer); [132-22-9]; [25523-97-1] ((+)-enantiomer); [113-92-8] (hydrogen maleate)

$C_{16}H_{19}Cl_1N_2$. M: 274.79. Available commercially as the

racemic mixture or the (+)-enantiomer maleate salts.
Production:
• *p*-chlorobenzyl cyanide + 2-chloropyridine + 2-dimethylaminoethyl chloride hydrochloride (condensation/condensation/nitrile hydrolysis/decarboxylation)
Uses:
antihistamine drug

chlorphenoxamine
[77-38-3]; [562-09-4] (hydrochloride)

$C_{18}H_{22}Cl_1N_1O_1$. M: 303.84. Available commercially as the free base or hydrochloride.
Production:
• *p*-chlorobenzophenone + methylmagnesium chloride + 2-dimethylaminoethyl chloride hydrochloride (Grignard reaction/ether formation)
Uses:
anticholinergic drug

chlorphonium chloride
tributyl(2,4-dichlorobenzyl)phosphonium chloride; [115-78-6]

$C_{19}H_{32}Cl_3P_1$. M: 397.80.
Production:
• 2,4-dichlorobenzyl chloride + tri-*n*-butylphosphine (dehydrochlorination)
Uses:
plant growth regulator

chlorpromazine
[50-53-3]; [69-09-0] (hydrochloride)

$C_{17}H_{19}Cl_1N_2S_1$. M: 318.86. Available commercially as the free base or hydrochloride.
Production:
• 2-chlorophenothiazine + 3-dimethylaminopropyl chloride hydrochloride (amine formation)
Uses:
neuroleptic/antiemetic drug

chlorpropamide
[94-20-2]

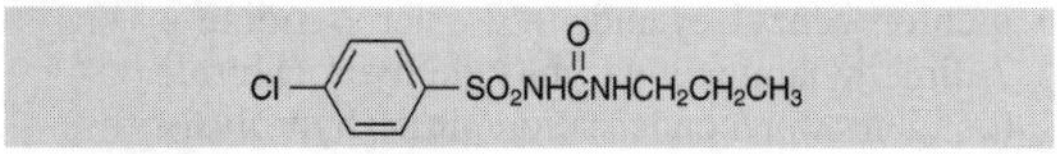

$C_{10}H_{13}Cl_1N_2O_3S_1$. M: 276.73.
Production:
- *p*-chlorobenzenesulphonyl chloride + ammonia + ethyl chloroformate + *n*-propylamine (sulphonamide formation/dehydrochlorination/urea formation)

Uses: antidiabetic drug

chlorpropham
CIPC; isopropyl 3-chlorophenylcarbamate; [101-21-3]

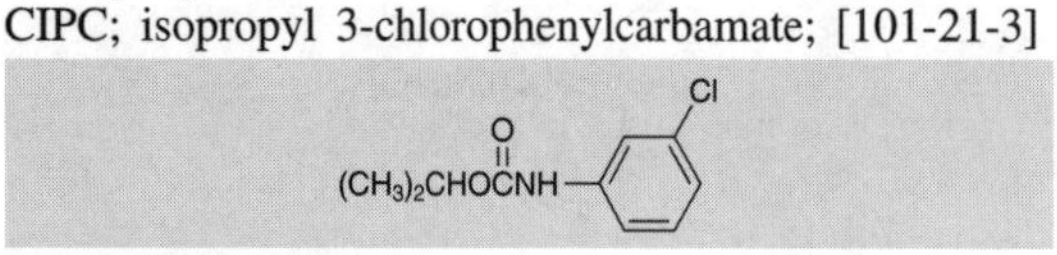

$C_{10}H_{12}Cl_1N_1O_2$. M: 213.67.
Production:
- *m*-chloroaniline + isopropyl chloroformate (dehydrochlorination)

Uses:
herbicide/potato sprouting inhibitor

chlorprothixene
[113-59-7]

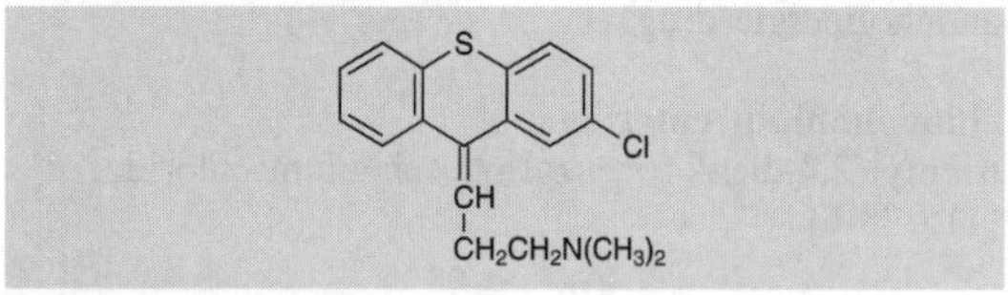

$C_{18}H_{18}Cl_1N_1S_1$. M: 315.86.
Production:
- 2-chlorothioxanthone + 3-dimethylaminopropyl chloride hydrochloride (Grignard reagent formation/Grignard reaction/dehydration)

Uses: neuroleptic drug

chlorpyrifos
O,O-diethyl *O*-3,5,6-trichloro-2-pyridyl phosphorothioate; [2921-88-2]

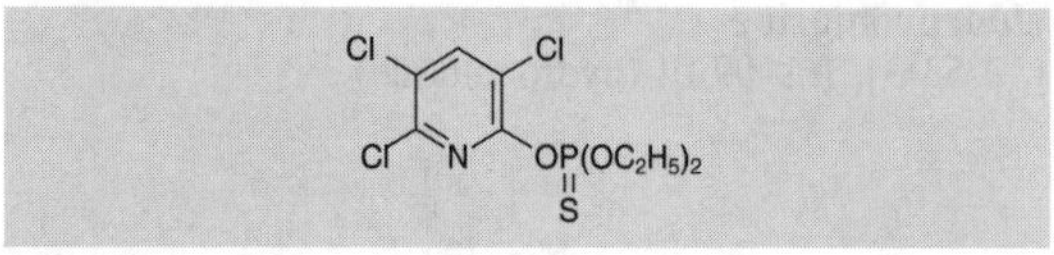

$C_9H_{11}Cl_3N_1O_3P_1S_1$. M: 350.59.
Production:
- 3,5,6-trichloro-2-pyridone + *O,O*-diethyl phosphorochlorothioate (dehydrochlorination)

Uses: insecticide

chlorpyrifos-methyl
O,O-dimethyl *O*-3,5,6-trichloro-2-pyridyl phosphorothioate; [5598-13-0]

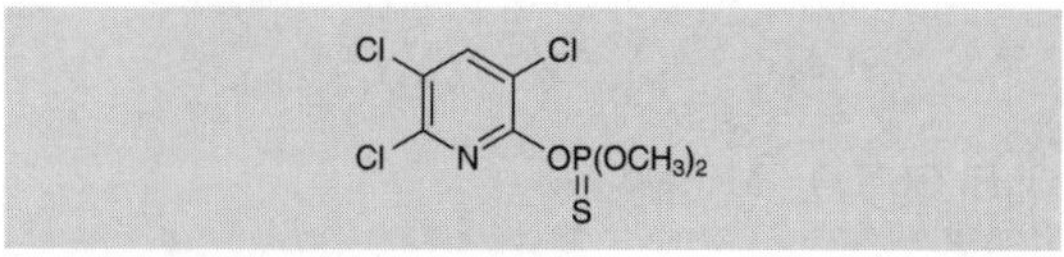

$C_7H_7Cl_3N_1O_3P_1S_1$. M: 322.54.
Production:
- 3,5,6-trichloro-2-pyridone + *O,O*-dimethyl phosphorochlorothioate (dehydrochlorination)

Uses:
acaricide/insecticide

chlorquinaldol

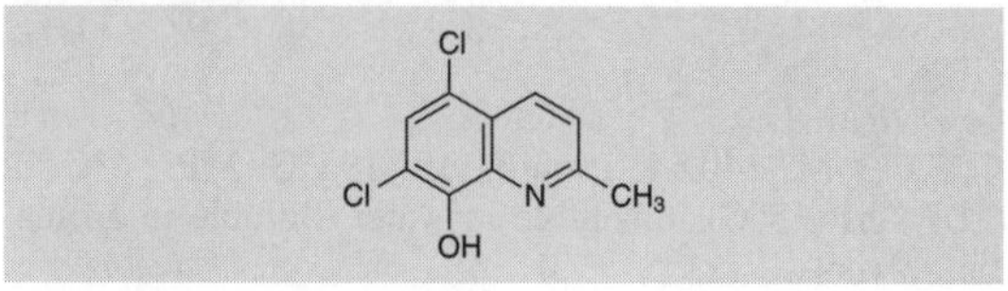

$C_{10}H_7Cl_2N_1O_1$. M: 228.09.
Production:
- *o*-aminophenol + crotonaldehyde (Skraup synthesis/chlorination)

Uses:
antibacterial drug

chlorsulfuron
1-(2-chlorophenylsulphonyl)-3-(4-methoxy-6-methyl-1,3,5-triazin-2-yl)urea; Glean (Du Pont); [64902-72-3]

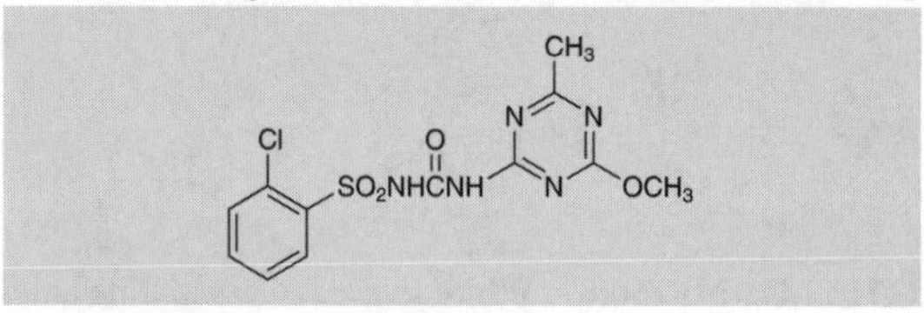

$C_{12}H_{12}Cl_1N_5O_4S_1$. M: 357.77.
Production:
- 2-chlorobenzenesulphonyl isocyanate + 2-amino-4-methoxy-6-methyltriazine (isocyanate addition)

Uses: herbicide

chlortetracycline
aureomycin; [57-62-5]; [64-72-2] (hydrochloride)

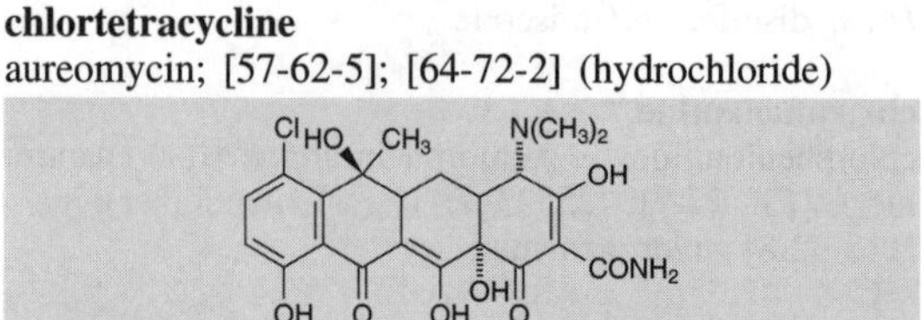

$C_{22}H_{23}Cl_1N_2O_8$. M: 478.87. Available as the free base or as the hydrochloride salt.
Production:
- microbial fermentation medium + *Streptomyces aureofaciens* bacteria (fermentation)

Derivatives:
tetracycline

chlorthal-dimethyl
dimethyl tetrachloroterephthalate; [1861-32-1]

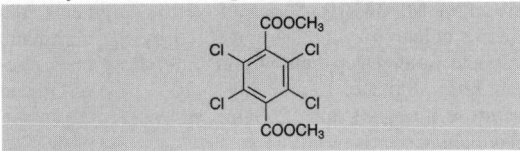

$C_{10}H_6Cl_4O_4$. M: 331.97.
Production:
• dimethyl terephthalate (ring chlorination)
Uses: herbicide

chlorthalidone
[77-36-1]

$C_{14}H_{11}Cl_1N_2O_4S_1$. M: 338.76.
Production:
• 2-(4-chlorobenzoyl)benzoic acid + sulphur dioxide, pure + ammonia (nitration/nitro reduction/ diazotisation/chlorosulphonation/carbonyl condensation/amide formation)
Uses:
diuretic drug

chlorzoxazone
5-chlorobenzoxazolone; [95-25-0]

$C_7H_4Cl_1N_1O_2$. M: 169.57.
Production:
• 2-amino-4-chlorophenol + formic acid (amide formation/cyclisation)
Uses: muscle relaxant drug

chlozolinate
ethyl 3-(3,5-dichlorophenyl)-5-methyl-2,4-dioxo-1,3-oxa-zolidine-5-carboxylate; [72391-46-9]

$C_{13}H_{11}Cl_2N_1O_5$. M: 332.14.
Production:
• diethyl α-isomalate + 3,5-dichloroaniline + phosgene (amide formation/condensation)
Uses: fungicide

Chocolate Brown HT *See:* Food Brown 3

cholecalciferol *See:* vitamin D_3

cholesterol
[57-88-5]

$C_{27}H_{46}O_1$. M: 386.67. White, crystalline solid. MP: 145–149°C. BP: 360°C with some decomposition. d: 1.07 kg/l (20°C). Almost insoluble in water. Soluble in hot alcohol and ethers.
Production:
• cattle spinal cords (solvent extraction)
• lanolin alcohol (separation; coproduced with lanosterol)
Derivatives: androstadienedione; 7-dehydrocholesterol
Uses: emulsifier (cosmetics, pharmaceuticals)

choline chloride
[67-48-1]

$(CH_3)_3^+NCH_2CH_2OH$ Cl^-

$C_5H_{14}Cl_1N_1O_1$. M: 139.62. Available commercially as a pure, crystalline solid, a 60% dry feed grade or as a 70% aqueous solution. Soluble in water and alcohol.
Production:
• trimethylamine + hydrochloric acid + ethylene oxide (salt formation/epoxidation)
Uses: animal feed supplement; lipotropic drug

CHP *See:* cumene hydroperoxide

chrome alum
chromium potassium sulphate; potassium chromium sulphate; [10141-00-1]

$KCr(SO_4)_2$

$Cr_1K_1O_8S_2$. M: 283.22. Available commercially as the dodecahydrate. Dark reddish-violet crystals. MP: 89°C. Loses water on heating to 400°C. d: 1.83 kg/l (25°C). Solubility in water: 200 g/l (20°C).
Production:
• potassium dichromate + sulphur dioxide, pure (salt formation)
Derivatives: chromium phosphate
Uses:
photographic gelatine/glue hardening agent; leather tanning auxiliary; textile mordant

chrome antimony titanium buff
buff rutile; chrome titanate; Pigment Brown 24 (CI); Pigment Yellow 118 (CI); 77310 (CI); 77894 (CI)
Buff coloured powder containing, typically, 85% TiO_2,

10% Sb_2O_3, 5% Cr_2O_3.

$(Ti,Cr,Sb)O_2$

Production:
• chromium oxide + antimony trioxide + titanium dioxide, hydrate (calcination)
Uses: pigment (resins, lacquers)

chrome green
Brilliant Green; Brunswick green; Grass Green; Pigment Green 15 (CI); 77601 (CI)
A range of green pigments formed by blending different proportions of the two components. Prussian blue content: 2–35%. Bronze green pigments are also produced by addition of iron oxide pigments.
Production:
• chrome yellow + Prussian Blue (blending)
Uses: pigment (green industrial maintenance paints)

chrome iron brown
iron chrome brown; Pigment Brown 29 (CI); 77500 (CI); Sicopal Brown K2795 (BASF)

$(Fe,Cr)_2O_3$

$Cr_2Fe_2O_3$. M: 263.68.
Production:
• iron oxide red + sodium dichromate (calcination)
Uses: plastics colorant

chrome lignosulphonate
chromium lignosulphonate
Brown powder. d: 0.73 kg/l. Soluble in water forming an acidic solution.
Production:
• sulphite pulp waste liquor + ferrochrome + sulphuric acid (salt formation)
Uses: dispersant (oil-well drilling muds)

chrome orange
lead chromate
Orange powder. d: 5.9–6.2 kg/l. The product is a mixture of lead chromate and lead hydroxide.
Production:
• lead nitrate/lead acetate + sodium dichromate (salt formation)
Derivatives: lead silicochromate, basic
Uses: pigment (paints)

chrome oxide, green *See:* chromium oxide

chrome scarlet *See:* Pigment Red 104

chrome titanate *See:* chrome antimony titanium buff

chrome yellow
lead chromate; Pigment Yellow 34 (CI); 77600 (CI); 77603 (CI); [7758-97-6]

$PbCrO_4.nPbSO_4$

$Cr_1O_4Pb_1$. M: 323.19. Series of yellow pigments, the precise colour of which is governed by the chromate: sulphate ratio. Deep yellow and red-yellow hues contain little sulphate. Lemon hues, 20–30% $PbSO_4$ and primrose hues, 40–50% $PbSO_4$.
Production:
• lead nitrate/lead acetate + sodium dichromate + sulphuric acid (salt formation)
Derivatives:
chrome green
Uses: pigment (industrial maintenance paints, printing inks, plastics)

chromic acetate, basic *See:* chromium acetate

chromic acid
chromium(VI) oxide; chromium trioxide; [7738-94-5]

CrO_3

Cr_1O_3. M: 100.00. Dark red flakes. MP: 197°C. Decomposes on heating above 250°C. d: 2.70 kg/l. Soluble in water.
Production:
• sodium dichromate + sulphuric acid (reaction)
Derivatives: barium chromate; copper arsenate, chromated; zinc tetroxychromate
Uses: ABS etchant; photographic chemical; aluminium anodising reagent; chrome electroplating/zinc colourless conversion coatings reagent; side-chain oxidation reagent

chromic chloride
chromium trichloride; [10025-73-7]

$CrCl_3$

Cl_3Cr_1. M: 158.36. Available commercially as the hexahydrate. Dark green, deliquescent crystals. d: 1.85 kg/l. Soluble in water producing violet (dilute) or green (concentrated) acidic solutions.
Production:
• chromium sulphate + hydrochloric acid (salt formation)
Derivatives: methacrylatochromic chloride
Uses: corrosion inhibitor; dye chromating reagent; steel chromising reagent; textile mordant

chromic fluoride
[7788-97-8] (anhydrous)

CrF_3

Cr_1F_3. M: 108.99. Available as anhydrous or tetrahydrate grades.
Production:
• chromium sulphate + hydrofluoric acid (salt formation)

Derivatives:
Solvent Yellow 19
Uses: corrosion inhibitor (paints); dyestuff chromating reagent; mordant

chromic sulphate *See:* chromium sulphate

chromite
chromium ore
Chromite is an ore mined in South Africa, Russia and several other countries. It is sold as lump material after rough sorting or concentration. Chromite is a mixed ore containing chromium, iron, aluminium, magnesium and other elements on smaller quantities. For chemical use, ores with a high chromium and iron content are used. For refractory applications, high chromium and aluminium contents are required. For steel a high chromium and magnesium content is needed.
Derivatives:
ferrochrome; potassium chromate; sodium chromate
Uses:
chrome-magnesite refractory bricks; ferrochrome production; refractory ceramics ingredient

chromium
[7440-47-3]

Cr

Cr_1. M: 52.00. Blue-white, hard metal. MP: 1,875°C. d: 7.19 kg/l. Corrosion resistant to air and water. Attacked by non-oxidising acids and alkalis.
Production:
• chromium oxide + aluminium (reduction)
• chromium oxide + metallurgical coke (Simplex process)
• ferrochrome + sulphuric acid + ammonium sulphate (Elkem process)
Uses:
cobalt-chromium stellite alloys (extrusion dies/turbine blades/valve seats); cobalt-chromium-tungsten alloys (cemented carbide cutting tools); nickel chromium alloys (jet engine parts, electrical heating elements)

chromium acetate
chromic acetate, basic; [1066-30-4]

$\overset{O}{\overset{\|}{(CH_3CO)_2Cr(OH)}}$

$C_6H_9Cr_1O_6$. M: 229.13. Available commercially as a violet solution, paste or dry solid. Soluble in water.
Production:
• chromium sulphate + sodium acetate (salt formation)
Derivatives:
Acid Black 52; Acid Black 58; Acid Black 63; Acid Orange 74; Acid Orange 92; Acid Orange 148; Acid Red 179; Acid Red 183; Acid Red 186; Acid Violet 58; Acid Yellow 54

chromium dioxide
[12018-01-8]

CrO_2

Cr_1O_2. M: 84.00. Dark brown or black ferromagnetic powder. d: 4.98 kg/l. Decomposes on heating forming chromic oxide.
Production:
• ammonium dichromate (calcination/reduction)
Uses: magnetic recording tape/disks

chromium oxide
chrome oxide, green; chromic oxide; chromium oxide, green; Pigment Green 17 (CI); 77288 (CI); Sicopal Green 9996 (BASF); [1308-38-9]

Cr_2O_3

Violet crystals containing ~30% Cr. Insoluble in water.
Production:
• sodium dichromate + ammonium chloride/ ammonium sulphate (reduction)
• sodium dichromate + sulphur + metallurgical coke/ hardwood/molasses (calcination)
Derivatives:
chrome antimony titanium buff; chromium
Uses:
stainless steel polishing abrasive; pigment (concrete, roofing tiles, enamels, ceramics, plastics, paints)

chromium phosphate
chromic phosphate; [7789-04-0]

$CrPO_4$

$Cr_1O_4P_1$. M: 146.97. Green pigment. d: 2.15 kg/l. Insoluble in water.
Production:
• chrome alum + disodium phosphate (precipitation)
Uses: dehydrogenation catalyst; anticorrosion pigment (primer paints)

chromium sulphate
chromic sulphate; [10101-53-8]

$Cr_2(SO_4)_3$

$Cr_2O_{12}S_3$. M: 392.17. Green flakes. Loses water of crystallisation when heated above 100°C. d: 1.87 kg/l (15°C). Soluble in water. Available commercially as solid material (pentadecahydrate) or as a solution in water.
Production:
• ferrochrome + sulphuric acid (salt formation)
Derivatives:
Acid Black 60; Acid Blue 158; Acid Blue 159; Acid Violet 78; chromic chloride; chromic fluoride; chromium acetate; Solvent Yellow 21
Uses:
chrome plating reagent; tanning agent; textile mordant

chromium sulphate, basic
chromic sulphate, basic

$$CrOHSO_4$$

$H_1Cr_1O_5S_1$. M: 165.06. Dark-green granules, soluble in water. Commercial products contain 25% Cr_2O_3 mixed with sodium sulphate.
Production:
- sodium dichromate + sulphuric acid + molasses/ glucose syrup (reduction)
- sodium dichromate + sulphur dioxide, pure (reduction)
- aniline + sodium dichromate + sulphuric acid (chromate oxidation; byproduct of *p*-benzoquinone production)
- anthracene + sodium dichromate + sulphuric acid (chromate oxidation; byproduct of anthraquinone production)
- montan wax + sulphuric acid + sodium dichromate (chromate oxidation; byproduct of montanic acid production)
Uses:
tanning agent

chromoglycic acid *See:* cromolyn

chromonar *See:* carbocromen

chromotropic acid
1,8-dihydroxynaphthalene-3,6-disulphonic acid; 4,5-di-hydroxynaphthalene-2,7-disulphonic acid; [148-25-4]

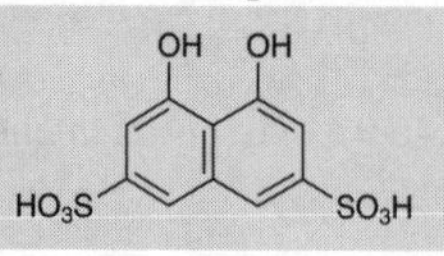

$C_{10}H_8O_8S_2$. M: 320.29. White, crystalline solid. Soluble in water. Insoluble in alcohol.
Production:
- H acid (Bucherer reaction)
Derivatives:
Acid Violet 3; Direct Blue 84; Mordant Blue 13

(1R)-trans-chrysanthemic acid
(+)-*trans*-chrysanthemic acid

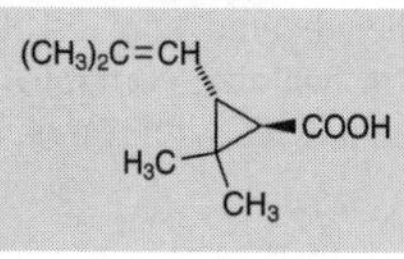

$C_{10}H_{16}O_2$. M: 168.24.
Production:
- dimethyl hexanediol + ethyl diazoacetate (dehydration/chiral catalytic addition)
- (1RS)-*trans*-chrysanthemic acid (racemate separation)
Derivatives:
bioallethrin; *S*-bioallethrin; bioresmethrin

(1RS)-cis/trans-chrysanthemic acid
chrysanthemummonocarboxylic acid; [10453-89-1]

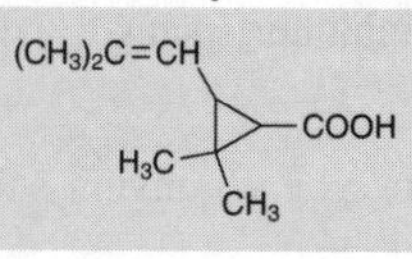

$C_{10}H_{16}O_2$. M: 168.24. The commercial product is a racemic mixture.
Production:
- dimethyl hexanediol + ethyl diazoacetate (dehydration/addition)
Derivatives:
allethrin; phenothrin; resmethrin; tetramethrin

(1RS)-trans-chrysanthemic acid

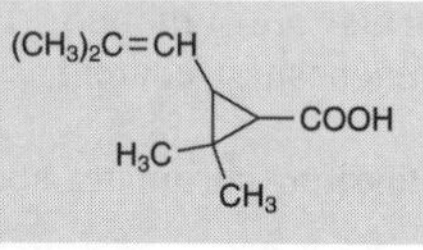

$C_{10}H_{16}O_2$. M: 168.24. Mixed enantiomers with a *trans* configuration in the cyclopropane ring.
Production:
- 3-methyl-2-buten-1-ol + thiophenol + methyl 3-methyl-2-butenoate (sulphide formation/oxidation/ addition/cyclisation)
Derivatives: (1R)-*cis*-caronaldehyde; (1R)-*trans*-chry-santhemic acid; empenthrin

chrysazine *See:* 1,8-dihydroxyanthraquinone

chrysoidine
Basic Orange 2 (CI, hydrochloride); Solvent Orange 3 (CI, free base); 11270 (CI, hydrochloride); 11270:1 (CI, free base); [532-82-1]

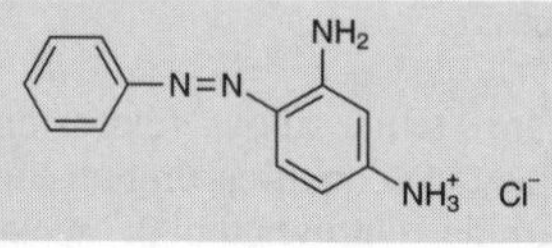

$C_{12}H_{13}Cl_1N_4$. M: 248.71. Red-brown powder. MP: 117–119°C. Soluble in water and oxygenated solvents.
Production:
- *m*-phenylenediamine + benzenediazonium chloride (azo coupling)
Uses: dye (cotton, silk, varnish, printing inks)

ciclacillin
cyclacillin; [3485-14-1]

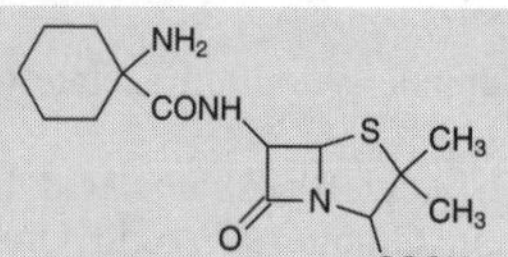

$C_{15}H_{23}N_3O_4S_1$. M: 341.42.

Production:
- cyclohexanone + 6-aminopenicillanic acid (Strecker synthesis/amide formation)

Uses: antibacterial drug

cilastatin
[82009-34-5]

$C_{16}H_{26}N_2O_5S_1$. M: 358.45.
Production:
- isobutylene + ethyl diazoacetate + ammonia + caprolactone + sodium cyanide + L-cysteine (addition/racemate separation/amide formation/bromination/cyanidation/nitrile hydrolysis/amine formation/amine formation)

Uses:
antibacterial drug adjunct

CIMC acid *See:* 3-(2-chlorophenyl)-5-methylisoxazole-4-carboxylic acid

cimetidine
[51481-61-9]

$C_{10}H_{16}N_6S_1$. M: 252.34. Available commercially as the free base or hydrochloride.
Production:
- 4-hydroxymethyl-5-methylimidazole hydrochloride + 2-mercaptoethylamine hydrochloride + N-cyano-imido-S,S-dimethyldithiocarbamate + methylamine (sulphide formation/amine formation/amine formation)

Uses: ulcer therapy drug

cimetropium bromide
[51598-60-8]

$C_{21}H_{28}Br_1N_1O_4$. M: 438.36.
Production:
- scopolamine + cyclopropylmethyl bromide (quaternisation)

Uses: antispasmodic drug

cinene *See:* (+)-limonene

cineole *See:* eucalyptol

cinnamaldehyde
cinnamal; cinnamic aldehyde; 3-phenylpropenal; [104-55-2]

$C_9H_8O_1$. M: 132.16. Yellow liquid with a strong, cinnamon odour. BP: 125–128°C (1.5 kPa). d: 1.05 kg/l (25°C). Insoluble in water. Miscible with oxygenated and chlorinated solvents.
Production:
- benzaldehyde + acetaldehyde (aldol condensation)

Derivatives:
cinnamonitrile; cinnamyl alcohol; 3-phenylpropanol; 3-phenylpropionaldehyde
Uses:
fragrance/flavouring ingredient

cinnamic acid
3-phenyl-2-propenoic acid; [621-82-9]; [140-10-3] (*trans*-isomer)

$C_9H_8O_2$. M: 148.16. White solid. MP: 133–134°C. BP: 300°C. d: 1.24 kg/l (20°C). The commercial product is the *trans*-isomer.
Production:
- benzaldehyde + acetic anhydride + sodium acetate (Perkin condensation)

Derivatives:
allyl cyclohexylpropionate; benzyl cinnamate; β-bromostyrene; cinnamoyl chloride; hydrocinnamic acid; methyl cinnamate; phenethyl cinnamate; L-phenylalanine

cinnamonitrile
[4360-47-8]

$C_9H_7N_1$. M: 129.17. Colourless crystals or viscous liquid with a spicy odour. MP: 22°C (*trans*-form), -4°C (*cis*-form). Commercial product is an isomer mixture with BP: 253–254°C, typically.
Production:
- cinnamaldehyde + hydroxylamine sulphate (oxime formation/dehydration)

Uses: fragrance ingredient

cinnamon leaf oil
cinnamon oil
Brown liquid with cinnamon-like odour produced by steam distillation of *Cinnamomum zeylanicum* leaves grown mainly in Sri Lanka and the Seychelles. The product composition varies somewhat from source to

source. d: ~1.05 kg/l (20°C). Soluble in oxygenated solvents.
Derivatives: eugenol
Uses: flavouring/fragrance ingredient

cinnamon oil, Chinese
cassia oil
Reddish-brown liquid with a cinnamon-like odour. Produced by steam distillation of *Cinnamomum cassia* leaves and twigs. d: 1.06 kg/l (20°C). Soluble in alcohol. The main constituent is cinnamaldehyde (85%). Produced primarily in China.
Uses: fragrance/flavouring ingredient

cinnamon oil, Sri Lankan
cinnamon bark oil
Yellow liquid with a cinnamon odour. Produced by steam distillation of the bark of the cinnamon (*Cinnamomom zeylanicum*) bush. d: 1.02 kg/l (25°C). Soluble in ethanol. The main constituent of the oil is cinnamaldehyde (60%) and eugenol (5–10%). Sri Lanka is the main producing country.
Uses: perfume ingredient

cinnamoyl chloride
[102-92-1]

$C_9H_7Cl_1O_1$. M: 166.61. Yellowish crystals. MP: 35–37°C. BP: 257°C. d: 1.16 kg/l (45°C). Insoluble in water. Soluble in hot alcohol. The commercial product is the *trans*-isomer.
Production:
• cinnamic acid (acid chloride formation)
Derivatives:
polyvinyl cinnamate
Uses: analytical reagent

cinnamyl acetate
cinnamic acetate; [103-54-8]

$C_{11}H_{12}O_2$. M: 176.22. Colourless liquid with a floral odour.
Production:
• cinnamyl alcohol + acetic anhydride (esterification)
Uses:
flavouring/fragrance ingredient

cinnamyl alcohol
cinnamic alcohol; 3-phenyl-2-propen-1-ol; [104-54-1]

$C_9H_{10}O_1$. M: 134.18.

Production:
• cinnamaldehyde (Meerwein-Ponndorf reduction)
Derivatives:
chloramphenicol; cinnamyl acetate; cinnarizine; flunarizine; naftifine
Uses: fragrance ingredient/fixative

cinnarizine
[298-57-7]

$C_{26}H_{28}N_2$. M: 368.52.
Production:
• piperazine + benzhydrol + cinnamyl alcohol (amine formation/amine formation)
Uses: vasodilator drug

cinoxate
2-ethoxyethyl *p*-methoxycinnamate; [104-28-9]

$C_{14}H_{18}O_4$. M: 250.28. Pale yellow liquid. FP: <-25°C. Insoluble in water. Soluble in oxygenated solvents.
Production:
• *p*-anisaldehyde + acetic anhydride + ethylene glycol monoethyl ether (Perkin condensation/esterification)
Uses: sunscreening agent

CIPC *See:* chlorpropham

citral
3,7-dimethyl-2,6-octadien-1-al; [5392-40-5]

$C_{10}H_{16}O_1$. M: 152.24. Pale yellow liquid with a strong, lemon odour. BP: 229°C. d: 0.89 kg/l (20°C). Insoluble in water. Soluble in oxygenated solvents. Both natural and synthetic products are a mixture of *cis*- and *trans*-isomers.
Production:
• *Litsea cubeba* oil (extraction)
• lemongrass oil (extraction)
• geraniol-nerol, mixed (alcohol oxidation)
• dehydrolinalool (isomerisation)
• isobutylene + formaldehyde (condensation)
Derivatives:
citral dimethyl acetal; geranonitrile; α-isomethylionone; methylionone; pseudoionone
Uses: flavouring/fragrance ingredient

citral dimethyl acetal
3,7-dimethyl-2,6-octadien-1-al dimethyl acetal;
[7549-37-3]

$$(CH_3)_2C=CHCH_2CH_2\overset{\underset{\displaystyle CH_3}{|}}{C}=CHCH(OCH_3)_2$$

$C_{12}H_{22}O_2$. M: 198.31.
Production:
• citral + methanol (acetal formation)
Uses: fragrance ingredient (soap, detergents)

citrazinic acid
2,6-dihydroxyisonicotinic acid; [99-11-6]

$C_6H_5N_1O_4$. M: 155.12. Yellow powder. Decomposes on heating.
Production:
• citric acid + ammonia (condensation)
Uses: reprographic reagent

citric acid
2-hydroxypropane-1,2,3-tricarboxylic acid; E330 (EC);
[77-92-9]

$$\begin{array}{c} CH_2COOH \\ HO-\overset{\displaystyle |}{\underset{\displaystyle |}{C}}-COOH \\ CH_2COOH \end{array}$$

$C_6H_8O_7$. M: 192.12. Colourless crystals. MP: 153–154°C. d: 1.66 kg/l. Soluble in water and alcohol. Also available commercially as the monohydrate.
Production:
• molasses + *Aspergillus niger* mould + calcium hydroxide + sulphuric acid (fermentation)
Derivatives: ammonium citrate, dibasic; ammonium ferric citrate; calcium citrate; citrazinic acid; fatty acid glycerides, citrated; potassium citrate; sodium citrate; tri-*n*-butyl citrate; triethyl citrate
Uses: buffering agent (cosmetics, toiletries); efflorescent powders and tablets; acidulant (soft drinks, preserves, confectionery); mineral flotation agent (talc); industrial cleaning/electroplating/anodising reagent

(+)-citronellal
(+)-3,7-dimethyl-6-octen-1-al; [2385-77-5]

$$(CH_3)_2C=CHCH_2CH_2\overset{\underset{\displaystyle CH_3}{|}}{C}HCH_2CHO$$

$C_{10}H_{18}O_1$. M: 154.25.
Production:
• citronella oil, Java (fractionation; coproduced with geraniol/(±)-citronellol)
Derivatives:
(±)-citronellol; hydroxycitronellal; isopulegol

(±)-citronellal
3,7-dimethyl-6-octen-1-al; [106-23-0]

$$(CH_3)_2C=CHCH_2CH_2\overset{\underset{\displaystyle CH_3}{|}}{C}HCH_2CHO$$

$C_{10}H_{18}O_1$. M: 154.25. Colourless liquid with a herbal odour. BP: 207°C. d: 0.85 kg/l (20°C). Insoluble in water. Soluble in alcohol.
Production:
• *Eucalyptus citriodora* oil (extraction)
• geraniol-nerol, mixed (rearrangement)
Derivatives: (±)-citronellol; citronellonitrile; citronelloxyacetaldehyde; hydroprene; hydroxycitronellal
Uses: fragrance ingredient

citronella oil, Ceylon
[8000-29-1]
Yellow liquid with a characteristic odour. d: ~0.90 kg/l (20°C). Soluble in alcohol. Extracted from citronella grass (*Cymbopogon nardus*) by steam distillation.
Uses: fragrance ingredient (soap, technical products)

citronella oil, Java
[8000-29-1]
Pale yellow to brown liquid with a characteristic odour. d: ~0.89 kg/l (20°C). Soluble in alcohol. Obtained by steam distillation of citronella grass (*Cymbopogon nardus*). The main components of the oil are citronellal, geraniol and citronellol. The main producing countries are Indonesia, Taiwan and China.
Derivatives:
(+)-citronellal; (±)-citronellol; geraniol
Uses: fragrance ingredient

(−)-citronellol
rhodinol; [7540-51-4]

$$(CH_3)_2C=CHCH_2CH_2C-\overset{\underset{\displaystyle H}{|}}{\overset{\displaystyle CH_3}{|}}C-CH_2CH_2OH$$

$C_{10}H_{20}O_1$. M: 156.27.
Production:
• geranium oil (saponification/fractionation)
Uses: fragrance ingredient

(±)-citronellol
3,7-dimethyl-6-octen-1-ol; [26489-01-0]

$$(CH_3)_2C=CHCH_2CH_2\overset{\underset{\displaystyle CH_3}{|}}{C}HCH_2CH_2OH$$

$C_{10}H_{20}O_1$. M: 156.27. Colourless liquid with a rose-like odour. BP: 244°C. d: ~0.86 kg/l (20°C). Insoluble in water. Soluble in oxygenated solvents. Both the racemic mixture and the racemic enantiomers are available commercially. The (+)-enantiomer is the main component of Java citronella oil, the (−)-enantiomer that of geranium and rue oils.

Production:
- citronella oil, Java (fractionation; coproduced with geraniol/(+)-citronellal)
- (±)-citronellal/(+)-citronellal (hydrogenation)
- geraniol-nerol, mixed (hydrogenation)

Derivatives: citronellyl acetate; citronellyl formate; citronellyl isobutyrate; citronellyl isovalerate; citronellyl propionate; citronellyl tiglate; hydroxycitronellal; rose oxide; tetrahydrogeraniol

Uses: fragrance/flavouring ingredient

citronellonitrile

citronellic acid nitrile; citronellyl nitrile; [51566-62-2]

$$(CH_3)_2C=CHCH_2CH_2\overset{\underset{\displaystyle CH_3}{|}}{C}HCH_2CN$$

$C_{10}H_{17}N_1$. M: 151.26. Colourless liquid with a citrus odour.

Production:
- (±)-citronellal + hydroxylamine sulphate (imine formation/dehydration)

Uses: fragrance ingredient (soap, detergents)

citronelloxyacetaldehyde

[7492-67-3]

$$(CH_3)_2C=CHCH_2CH_2\overset{\underset{\displaystyle CH_3}{|}}{C}HCH_2CH_2OCH_2CHO$$

$C_{12}H_{22}O_2$. M: 198.31.

Production:
- (±)-citronellal + chloroacetaldehyde (ether formation/hydrolysis)

Uses: fragrance ingredient

citronellyl acetate

[150-84-5]; [67650-82-2]

$$(CH_3)_2C=CHCH_2CH_2\overset{\underset{\displaystyle CH_3}{|}}{C}HCH_2CH_2O\overset{\underset{\displaystyle}{\overset{\displaystyle O}{||}}}{C}CH_3$$

$C_{12}H_{22}O_2$. M: 198.31. Colourless liquid with a rose-like odour. BP: 240°C. d: 0.89 kg/l (20°C). Soluble in alcohol.

Production:
- (±)-citronellol + acetic acid (esterification)

Uses: flavouring/fragrance ingredient

citronellyl formate

[105-85-1]

$$(CH_3)_2C=CHCH_2CH_2\overset{\underset{\displaystyle CH_3}{|}}{C}HCH_2CH_2O\overset{\underset{\displaystyle}{\overset{\displaystyle O}{||}}}{C}H$$

$C_{11}H_{20}O_2$. M: 184.28. Colourless liquid with a floral odour. BP: 97°C (2.0 kPa). d: 0.89 kg/l (15°C). Soluble in alcohol.

Production:
- (±)-citronellol + formic acid (esterification)

Uses: fragrance ingredient

citronellyl isobutyrate

[97-89-2]

$$(CH_3)_2C=CHCH_2CH_2\overset{\underset{\displaystyle CH_3}{|}}{C}HCHCH_2O\overset{\underset{\displaystyle}{\overset{\displaystyle O}{||}}}{C}CH(CH_3)_2$$

$C_{14}H_{26}O_2$. M: 226.36. Colourless liquid with a floral odour.

Production:
- (±)-citronellol + isobutyric acid (esterification)

Uses: fragrance ingredient

citronellyl isovalerate

[68922-10-1]

$$(CH_3)_2C=CHCH_2CH_2\overset{\underset{\displaystyle CH_3}{|}}{C}HCHCH_2O\overset{\underset{\displaystyle}{\overset{\displaystyle O}{||}}}{C}CH_2CH(CH_3)_2$$

$C_{15}H_{28}O_2$. M: 240.38. Colourless liquid with a heavy, floral odour.

Production:
- (±)-citronellol + isovaleric acid (esterification)

Uses: fragrance ingredient

citronellyl propionate

[141-14-0]

$$(CH_3)_2C=CHCH_2CH_2\overset{\underset{\displaystyle CH_3}{|}}{C}HCHCH_2O\overset{\underset{\displaystyle}{\overset{\displaystyle O}{||}}}{C}C_2H_5$$

$C_{13}H_{24}O_2$. M: 212.33. Colourless liquid with a rose-like odour. BP: 122°C (2.0 kPa). d: 0.89 kg/l (15°C). Soluble in alcohol.

Production:
- (±)-citronellol + propionic acid (esterification)

Uses: flavouring/fragrance ingredient

citronellyl tiglate

[24717-85-9]

$$(CH_3)_2C=CHCH_2CH_2\overset{\underset{\displaystyle CH_3}{|}}{C}HCHCH_2O\overset{\underset{\underset{\displaystyle CH_3}{|}}{\overset{\displaystyle O}{||}}}{C}C=CHCH_3$$

$C_{15}H_{26}O_2$. M: 238.37. Liquid with a fruity-floral odour.

Production:
- (±)-citronellol + tiglic acid (esterification)

Uses: fragrance ingredient

clavulanic acid

[58001-44-8]

$C_8H_9N_1O_5$. M: 199.16.

Production:
- microbial fermentation medium + *Streptomyces clavuligerus* bacteria (fermentation)

Uses:
antibacterial drug adjunct

clay

Microscopic mixture of minerals and colloidal materials comprising mainly hydrous aluminium silicates. There are several different types of clay such as kaolin, illite, vermiculite and montmorillonite which differ from each other in their chemical structure. Many are used commercially under their own name.

Derivatives:
aluminium sulphate

Uses:
foundry sands; Portland cement raw material; bricks, ventilation blocks; tiles, pipes, conduit tiles, raw material (furnace linings, firebricks, shaped vessels); pottery/stoneware

CLD *See:* caprolactam disulphide

clemastine

[15686-51-8]; [14976-57-9] (fumarate)

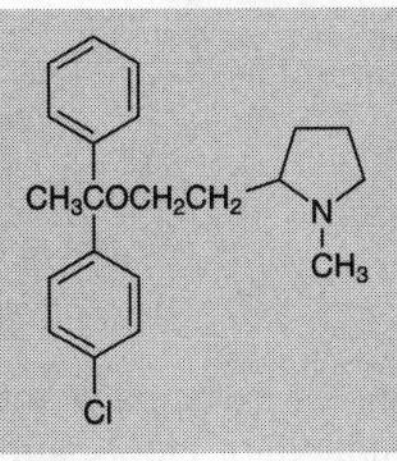

$C_{21}H_{26}Cl_1N_1O_1$. M: 343.90. Available commercially as the free base or hydrogen maleate salt.

Production:
• pyrrole + chloroacetyl chloride + dimethyl sulphate + *p*-chlorobenzophenone + methylmagnesium chloride (Friedel-Crafts acylation/hydrogenation/ether formation/Grignard reaction/methylation)

Uses:
antihistamine drug

clemizole

[442-52-4]

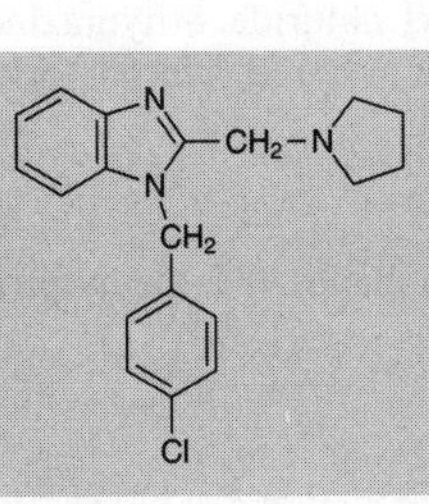

$C_{19}H_{20}Cl_1N_3$. M: 325.84.

Production:
• *o*-chloronitrobenzene + *p*-chlorobenzylamine + chloroacetyl chloride + pyrrolidine (amine formation/nitro reduction/amine formation/condensation)

Uses:
antihistamine drug; penicillin adjunct

clenbuterol

[37148-27-9]

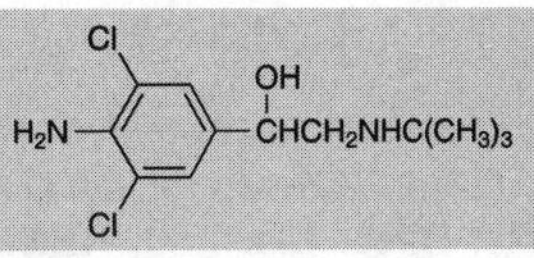

$C_{12}H_{18}Cl_2N_2O_1$. M: 277.19. Available commercially as the hydrochloride.

Production:
• *p*-aminoacetophenone + *t*-butylamine (alpha bromination/amine formation/ring chlorination/carbonyl reduction)

Uses: bronchodilator drug

1,6-Cleve's acid

1-aminonaphthalene-6-sulphonic acid; 5-aminonaphthalene-2-sulphonic acid; Cleve's acid; 1-naphthylamine-6-sulphonic acid

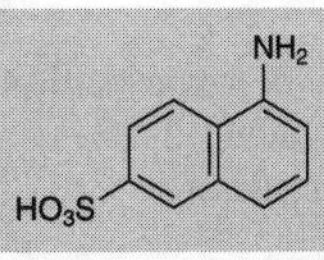

$C_{10}H_9N_1O_3S_1$. M: 223.25. White, crystalline solid.

Production:
• naphthalene-2-sulphonic acid (nitration/nitro reduction/separation; coproduced with Cleve's acid, mixed)

Derivatives: Direct Blue 75; Direct Blue 120

1,7-Cleve's acid

1-aminonaphthalene-7-sulphonic acid; 8-aminonaphthalene-2-sulphonic acid; 1-naphthylamine-7-sulphonic acid

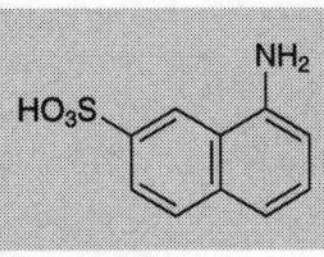

$C_{10}H_9N_1O_3S_1$. M: 223.25. Crystalline solid. Slightly soluble in water and alcohol.

Production:
• Cleve's acid, mixed (isomerisation/separation)

Derivatives:
Acid Black 60; Acid Blue 118; 8-amino-2-naphthol; Direct Blue 71; Direct Blue 78; Food Black 1

Cleve's acid, mixed

1-naphthylamine-6/7-sulphonic acid

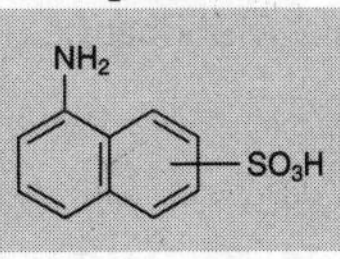

$C_{10}H_9N_1O_3S_1$. M: 223.25. Mixed product containing 1,6-Cleve's acid and 1,7-Cleve's acid.

Production:
- naphthalene-2-sulphonic acid (nitration/nitro reduction/separation; coproduced with 1,6-Cleve's acid)

Derivatives:
Acid Orange 51; 1,7-Cleve's acid; Direct Black 9; Direct Black 78; Direct Black 80; Reactive Brown 1

clidinium bromide
[3485-62-9]

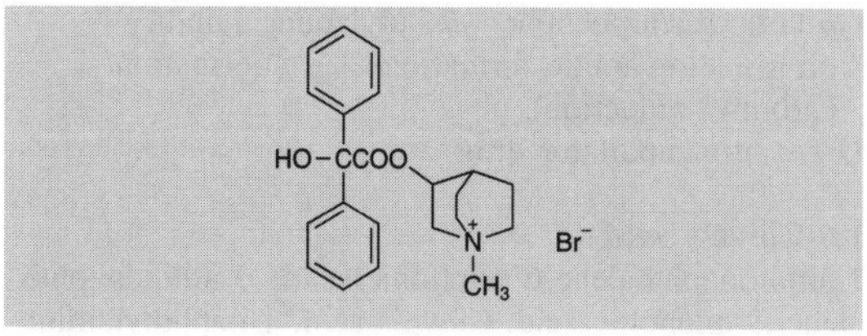

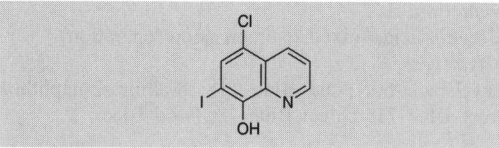

$C_{22}H_{26}Br_1N_1O_3$. M: 432.36.
Production:
- quinuclidin-3-ol + benzilic acid + methyl bromide (amide formation/quaternisation)

Uses: anticholinergic drug

clindamycin
[18323-44-9]

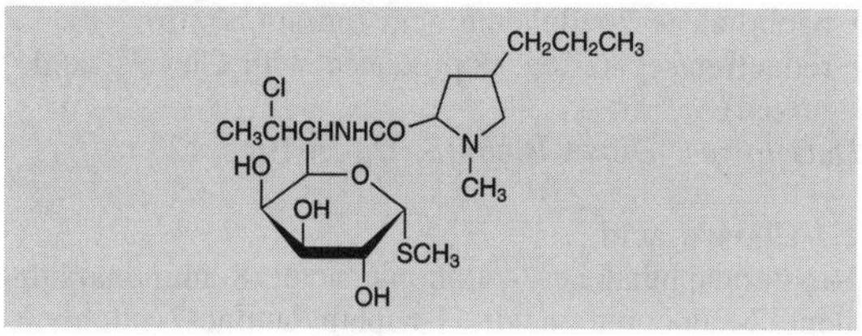

$C_8H_{33}Cl_1N_2O_5S_1$. M: 304.86.
Production:
- lincomycin (chlorination)

Uses: antibacterial drug

clioquinol
5-chloro-7-iodo-8-quinolinol; iodochlorhydroxyquin; [130-26-7]

$C_9H_5Cl_1I_1N_1O_1$. M: 305.50.
Production:
- 8-hydroxyquinoline (chlorination/ring iodination)

Uses:
intestinal antiseptic

clobazam
[22316-47-8]
$C_{16}H_{13}Cl_1N_2O_2$. M: 300.74.

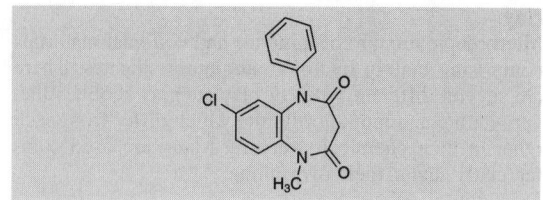

Production:
- 4-chloro-2-nitroaniline + ethyl cyanoacetate + methyl bromide + bromobenzene (amide formation/methylation/nitrile hydrolysis/nitro reduction/amine formation/amide formation)

Uses: anxiolytic drug

cloethocarb
2-(2-chloro-1-methoxyethoxy)phenyl methylcarbamate; [51487-69-5]

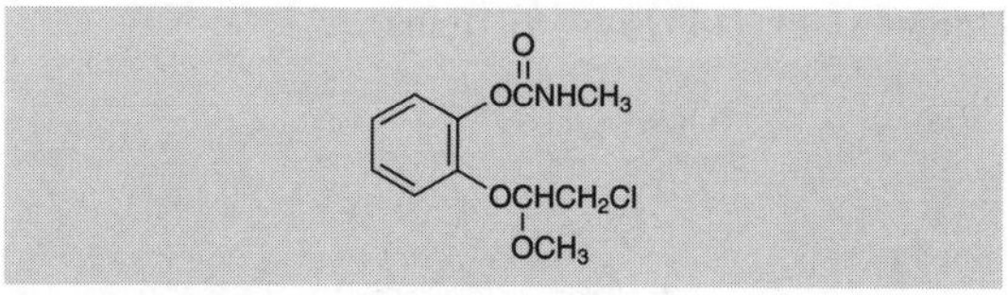

$C_{11}H_{14}Cl_1N_1O_4$. M: 259.69.
Production:
- chloral + methanol + catechol + methyl isocyanate (acetal formation/alcohol chlorination/ether formation/isocyanate addition)

Uses: insecticide/nematicide

clofentezine
3,6-bis(2-chlorophenyl)-1,2,4,5-tetrazine; [74115-24-5]

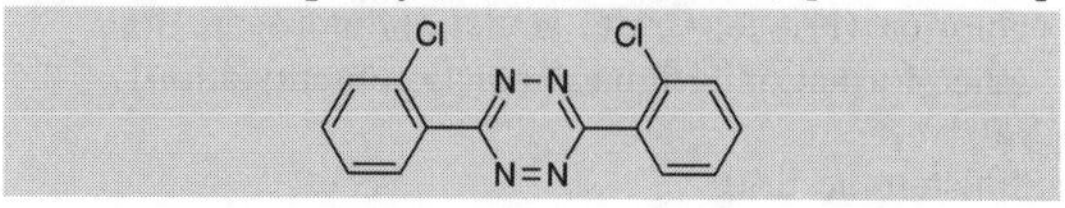

$C_{14}H_8Cl_2N_4$. M: 303.15.
Production:
- o-chlorobenzoyl chloride + hydrazine (amide formation/chlorination/dehydrochlorination)

Uses: acaricide

clofibrate
ethyl 2-(4-chlorophenoxy)-2-methylpropionate; [637-07-0]

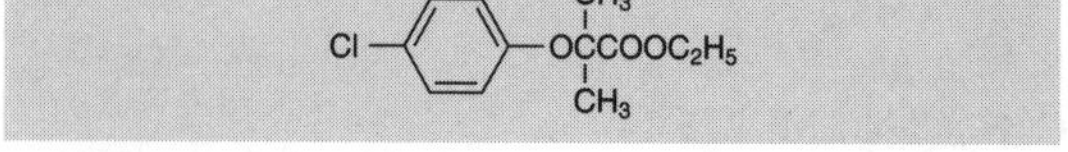

$C_{12}H_{15}Cl_1O_3$. M: 242.70.
Production:
- p-chlorophenol + acetone + chloroform + ethanol (condensation/dehydrochlorination/esterification)

Derivatives:
etofibrate

Uses: lipid reduction drug

cloflucarban
4,4'-dichloro-3-(trifluoromethyl)-*N,N*'-diphenylurea

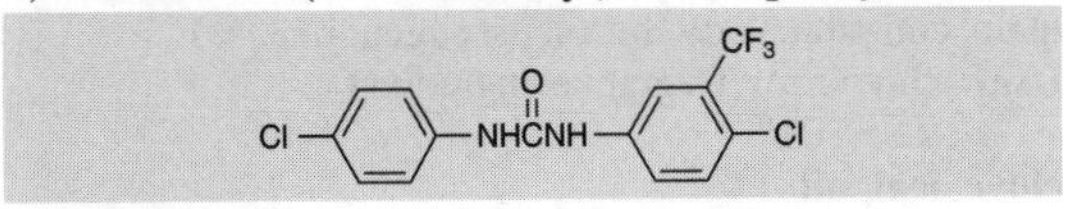

$C_{14}H_9Cl_2F_3N_2O_1$. M: 349.13.
Production:
• 5-amino-2-chlorobenzotrifluoride + *p*-chlorophenyl isocyanate (isocyanate addition)
Uses:
insect resist agent (wool treatment)

clomazone
2-(2-chlorobenzyl)-4,4-dimethyl-1,2-oxazolidin-3-one; dimethazone; fenoxam; [81777-89-1]

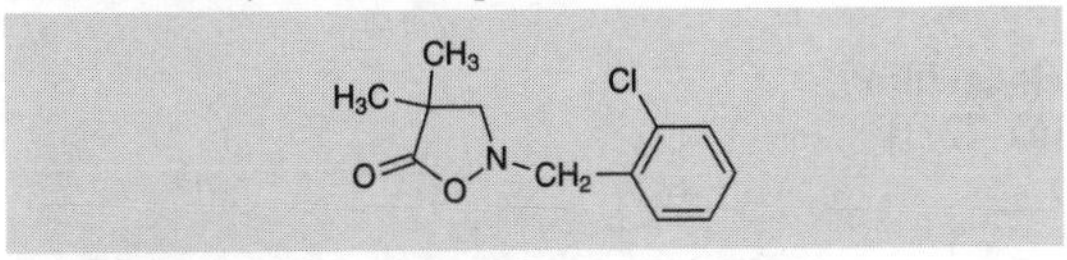

$C_{12}H_{14}Cl_1N_1O_2$. M: 239.70.
Production:
• *o*-chlorobenzaldehyde + hydroxylamine sulphate + monochloropivaloyl chloride (reductive amination/ condensation)
Uses: herbicide

clomethiazole
5-(2-chloroethyl)-4-methylthiazole; [533-45-9]

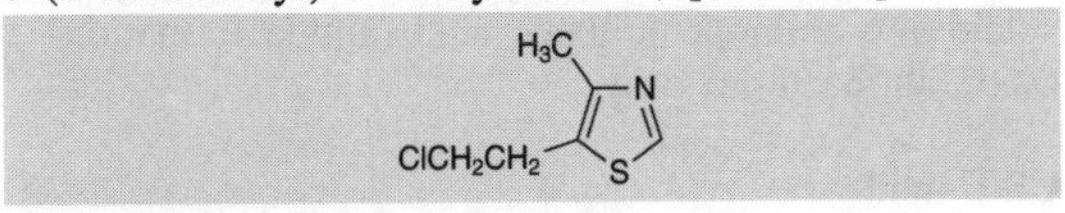

$C_6H_8Cl_1N_1S_1$. M: 161.65.
Production:
• 5-(2-hydroxyethyl)-4-methylthiazole (alcohol chlorination)
Uses:
anticonvulsant/hypnotic/sedative drug

clonazepam
[1622-61-3]

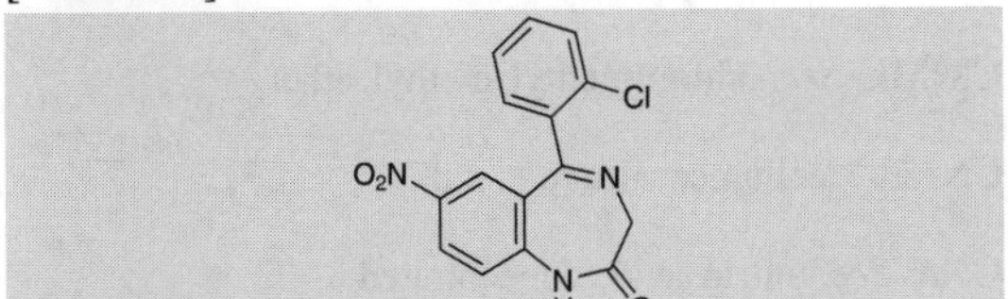

$C_{15}H_{10}Cl_1N_3O_3$. M: 315.71.
Production:
• 2-amino-5-chloro-2'-fluorobenzophenone + chloro-acetyl chloride + ammonia (dechlorination/amide formation/condensation/nitration)
Uses:
anticonvulsant drug

clonidine
[4205-90-7]

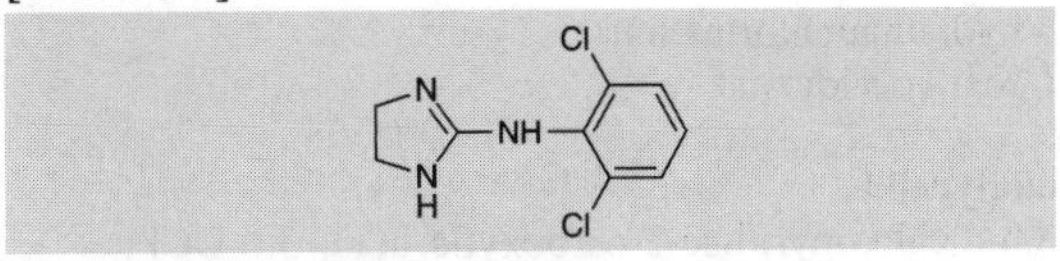

$C_9H_9Cl_2N_3$. M: 230.10. Available as the hydrochloride.
Production:
• ethylenethiourea + dimethyl sulphate + 2,6-di-chloroaniline (methylation/amidine formation)
Uses: antihypertensive drug

clopamide
[636-54-4]

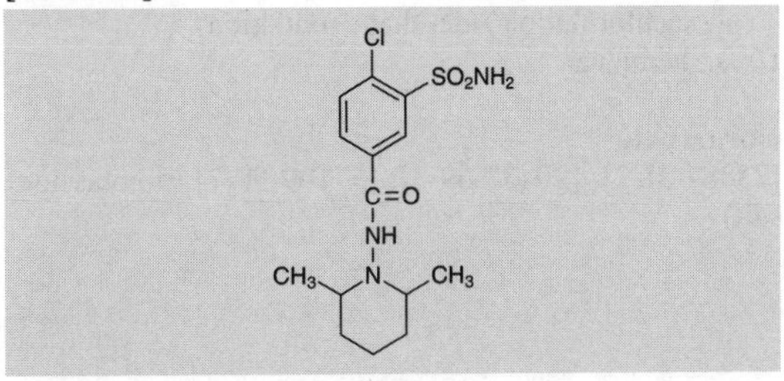

$C_{14}H_{20}Cl_1N_3O_3S_1$. M: 345.84.
Production:
• 2,6-dimethylpiperidine + *p*-chlorobenzoyl chloride + chlorosulphonic acid + ammonia (diazotisation/ hydrogenation/chlorosulphonation/sulphonamide formation/amide formation)
Uses: diuretic drug

clopenthixol
[982-24-1]

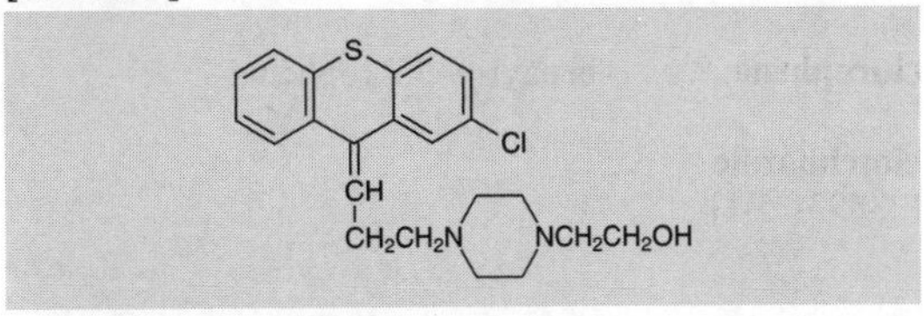

$C_{22}H_{25}Cl_1N_2O_1S_1$. M: 400.97.
Production:
• allyl bromide + 2-chlorothioxanthone + *N*-hydroxy-ethylpiperazine (Grignard reagent formation/ Grignard reaction/dehydration/amine formation)
Uses: neuroleptic drug

clopidol
[2971-90-6]

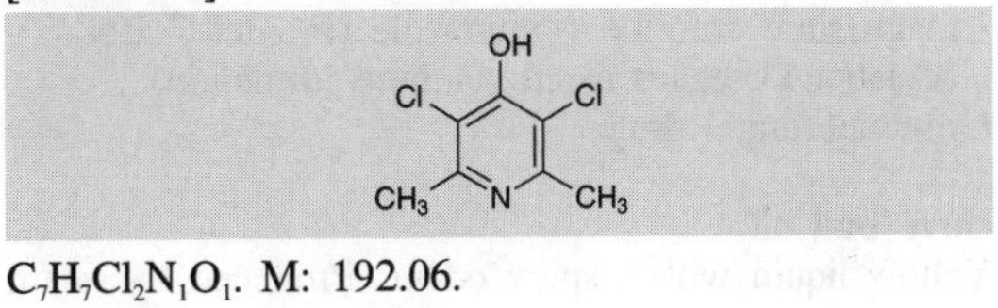

$C_7H_7Cl_2N_1O_1$. M: 192.06.

Production:
- 2,6-lutidine (amine formation/diazotisation/ hydration/chlorination)

Uses: coccidiostat

clopyralid
3,6-dichloropyridine-2-carboxylic acid; 3,6-DCP; [1702-17-6]

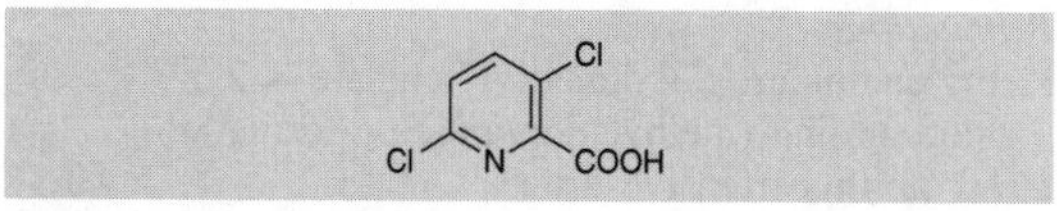

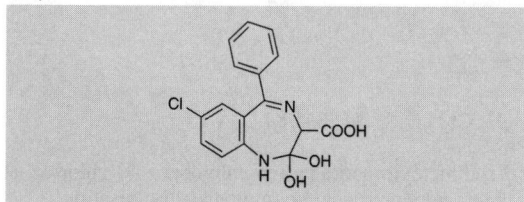

$C_6H_3Cl_2N_1O_2$. M: 192.01.
Production:
- α-picoline + chlorine + nitric acid, concentrated (photochlorination/side-chain oxidation)

Uses: herbicide

clorazepate
[23887-31-2]; [20432-69-3]; [57109-90-7] (dipotassium salt)

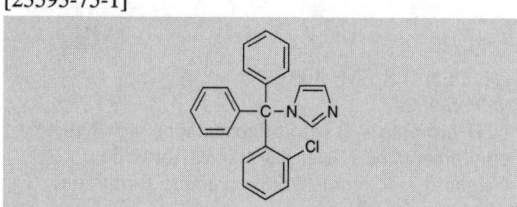

$C_{16}H_{13}Cl_1N_2O_4$. M: 332.74. Available commercially as the dipotassium salt.
Production:
- 2-amino-5-chlorobenzophenone + diethyl 2-amino-malonate hydrochloride (condensation)

Uses: anxiolytic/sedative drug

clorophene See: o-benzyl-p-chlorophenol

clotrimazole
[23593-75-1]

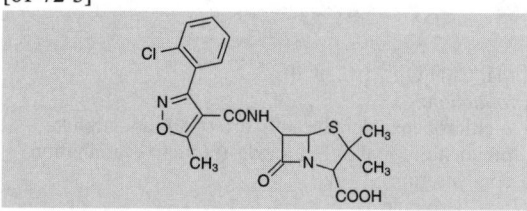

$C_{22}H_{17}Cl_1N_2$. M: 344.84.
Production:
- o-chlorobenzoyl chloride + benzene + phenyl-magnesium chloride + imidazole (Friedel-Crafts acylation/Grignard reaction/amine formation)

Uses: antifungal drug

clove bud oil
Yellow liquid with a spicy odour. Produced by steam distillation of cloves (Syzigium aromaticum flower buds). d: 1.05 kg/l (25°C). Soluble in ethanol. The main constituent of the oil is eugenol (85%).
Uses: flavouring/fragrance ingredient

clove leaf oil
clove oil; [8000-34-8]
Liquid. Produced by steam distillation of clove tree (Syzigium aromaticum) leaves. d: 1.04 kg/l (20°C). Soluble in alcohol. The main constituent is eugenol (80%). Produced primarily in Indonesia, Madagascar and Tanzania.
Derivatives: eugenol
Uses: dental antiseptic; fragrance/flavouring ingredient

clove oil See: clove leaf oil

cloxacillin
[61-72-3]

$C_{19}H_{18}Cl_1N_3O_5S_1$. M: 435.87.
Production:
- 3-(2-chlorophenyl)-5-methylisoxazole-4-carboxylic acid + 6-aminopenicillanic acid (amide formation)

Uses: antibacterial drug

CLT acid
See: 5-amino-2-chlorotoluene-4-sulphonic acid

CM See: polyethylene, chlorinated

CMC See: sodium carboxymethyl cellulose

CMD See: manganese dioxide

CME See: N-cetyl ethylmorpholinium ethosulphate

CMME See: chloromethyl methyl ether

CN See: cellulose nitrate

CNA See: nitric acid, concentrated

CNSL See: cashew nutshell oil

coal
Carboniferous ore. Coal ranges in type from lignite and brown coals, through sub-bituminous and bituminous coals to anthracite. Various classification systems are used, most of which are based on the

different calorific values and volatile matter content of the different types of coal. The moisture, ash and sulphur content is also important. The hardest coals, with the highest carbon content, are the anthracites (*qv*). These are characterised by their jet-black colour, their smokeless flame, low sulphur content and high calorific value. Bulk density: 0.80–0.93 kg/l. Calorific value: ~30 MJ/kg. Bitumen coals have a slightly lower carbon content and although banded in structure, cleave into blocks. They ignite easily, giving a smoky flame, and have a high calorific value. Bulk density: 0.67–0.90 kg/l. Calorific value: 28–35 MJ/kg. Sub-bituminous coals differ from bituminous coals by the fact that it tends to cleave along the grain of the rock. They also have a relatively low heating value. Calorific value: 21–25 MJ/kg. Further down the scale are brown coals which are characterised by the appearance of woody matter embedded in their structure. They generally have a high moisture content and tend to disintegrate as they dry out. Calorific value: 16–23 MJ/kg. Coal is mined worldwide using both open cast and underground methods.
Derivatives: activated carbon; barium sulphide; cobalt; metallurgical coke; semicoke; sodium sulphide; synthesis gas; zinc oxide
Uses: domestic/industrial heating fuel; steam generation (electrical, industrial applications)

coal gas *See:* coke oven gas

coal tar, crude
Black, viscous liquid or solid with an aromatic odour. Mixture of mainly aromatic chemicals with a typical distillation range: 1% <180°C, 8% 180–230°C, 10% 230–270°C, 4% 270–300°C, 20% >300°C. The remainder is pitch (55%), water and ash. d: 1.18 kg/l. The majority of the constituents are soluble in toluene.
Production:
• coal (high-temperature carbonisation; byproduct of metallurgical coke production)
• coal (low-temperature carbonisation; byproduct of semicoke production)
• coal/lignite (coal gasification; byproduct of synthesis gas production)
Derivatives:
anthracene oil; carbolic oil; coal tar pitch; creosote oil; fluorene oil; light oil; naphthalene fraction; tar acid liquor

coal tar pitch
pitch, coal tar
Involatile coal-tar fraction with BP: >350°C. Several grades are available depending on the hardness of the pitch and its intended use.
Production:
• coal tar, crude (alkali extraction/fractionation; coproduced with light oil/carbolic oil/creosote oil/

naphthalene fraction/fluorene oil/anthracene oil/tar acid liquor)
Derivatives:
carbon, moulded; carbon black; carbon fibre; gas oil, heavy; gas oil, light; naphtha, heavy; needle coke; refinery gas
Uses: binder (coal briquettes); pipe coatings; road tars; roofing/flooring/damp-proof course membranes; submarine telephone cables

cobalt
[7440-48-4]

Co

Co_1. M: 58.93. Hard, grey, ductile metal. d: 8.9 kg/l. MP: 1,493°C. Ferromagnetic.
Production:
• copper-cobalt sulphide ores (ore roasting/acid leaching/electrolysis; byproduct of copper production)
• cobalt sulphide ores + limestone + coal (smelting)
• nickel-copper matte/nickel matte + hydrogen (pressure leaching/reduction; coproduced with nickel)
• lateritic ore (pressure leaching/solvent extraction/ electrolysis; coproduced with nickel)
Derivatives: cobalt oxide
Uses: cobalt-chromium-tungsten alloys (cemented carbide cutting tools); stellite alloys (extrusion dies, turbine blades, valve seats); super alloy ingredient; magnetic cobalt-rare earth alloys

cobalt acetate
cobaltous acetate; [71-48-7]

$[CH_3COO]_2Co$

$C_4H_6Co_1O_4$. M: 177.02. Available commercially as the tetrahydrate. Red crystals. Loses water of crystallisation when heated above 140°C. d: 1.71 kg/l. Soluble in water.
Production:
• cobalt carbonate, basic + acetic acid (salt formation)
Uses: esterification/oxidation catalyst; anodising reagent; mineral supplement

cobalt acetylacetonate
cobaltic acetylacetonate; [14024-48-7]

$$\left[CH_3\overset{\overset{O}{\|}}{C}CH=\underset{\underset{CH_3}{|}}{C}O \right]_3 Co$$

$C_{15}H_{21}Co_1O_6$. M: 356.25. Dark green crystals. MP: 214°C. Decomposes on heating above melting point. Soluble in organic solvents.
Production:
• cobalt hydroxide + acetylacetone (complex formation/oxidation)

Uses: Ziegler catalyst component; cobalt vacuum deposition agent

cobalt blue

cobalt aluminate blue; Thenard's Blue; Pigment Blue 28 (CI); 77346 (CI); [1345-16-0]

$$CoAl_2O_4$$

$Al_2Co_1O_4$. M: 176.89. Reddish-blue to greenish-blue solid.
Production:
• cobalt oxide + alumina trihydrate (calcination)
Uses: pigment (speciality paints, plastics)

cobalt carbonate, basic

cobaltous carbonate, basic; [7542-09-8]

$$mCoCO_3.Co(OH)_2$$

m = ~2.0. $C_2H_2Co_3O_8$. M: 330.83. Pale mauve powder. Insoluble in water. Soluble in acids and ammonia.
Production:
• cobalt sulphate + sodium carbonate (salt formation)
Derivatives: cobalt acetate; cobalt chloride

cobalt chloride

cobaltous chloride; [7646-79-9]; [7791-13-1]

$$CoCl_2$$

Cl_2Co_1. M: 129.84. Red crystals. MP: 86°C. Loses water of crystallisation on heating to 100°C. d: 1.92 kg/l (20°C). Solubility in water: 1.16 kg/l water (0°C).
Production:
• cobalt carbonate, basic/cobalt oxide + hydrochloric acid (salt formation)
Derivatives: cobalt phosphate
Uses:
electroplating reagent; Ziegler catalyst component; animal feed/fertiliser additive; textile mordant

cobalt 2-ethylhexoate *See:* cobalt octoate

cobalt green

cobalt titanate; Pigment Green 19 (CI); 77335 (CI); [8011-87-8]

$$(Co,Ni,Zn)_2(Ti,Al)O_4$$

Production:
• cobalt oxide + nickel carbonate, basic + zinc oxide + titanium dioxide, hydrate + alumina trihydrate (calcination)
Uses: plastics colorant

cobalt hydroxide

cobaltous hydroxide; [1307-86-4]

$$Co(OH)_2$$

$H_2Co_1O_2$. M: 92.95. Red powder. Decomposes with release of water when heated above 160°C. d: 3.60 kg/l (15°C). Insoluble in water.
Production:
• cobalt sulphate + sodium hydroxide (salt formation)
Derivatives:
cobalt acetylacetonate; cobalt naphthenate; cobalt octoate; cobalt tallate; ferrite
Uses: storage battery electrode raw material

cobalt naphthenate

cobaltous naphthenate; [61789-51-3]
Bluish-red powder. Insoluble in water. Soluble in oxygenated solvents.
Production:
• cobalt hydroxide + naphthenic acid (salt formation)
Uses: unsaturated polyester resin catalyst accelerator; adhesion promotion agent (rubber-steel bonding); paint drier

cobalt octoate

cobalt 2-ethylhexanoate; cobalt 2-ethylhexoate; [1588-79-0]

$$[C_7H_{15}COO]_2Co$$

$C_{16}H_{30}Co_1O_4$. M: 345.34.
Production:
• cobalt hydroxide + isooctanoic acid/2-ethylhexanoic acid (salt formation)
Uses: unsaturated polyester resin catalyst accelerator; adhesion promotion agent (rubber-steel bonding); paint drier

cobalt oxide

cobaltous oxide; [1307-96-6]

$$CoO$$

Co_1O_1. M: 74.93. Grey powder. MP: 1,935°C. d: 5.7–6.7 kg/l. Insoluble in water. Soluble in acid.
Production:
• cobalt (air oxidation)
Derivatives: cobalt blue; cobalt chloride; cobalt green; cobalt sulphate
Uses: catalyst raw material

cobalt phosphate

cobaltous phosphate; Pigment Violet 14 (CI); 77360 (CI); [10294-50-5]

$$Co_3(PO_4)_2$$

$Co_3O_8P_2$. M: 366.74. Available as the octahydrate. Bluish-pink powder. Loses water of crystallisation when heated above 200°C. d: 2.77 kg/l (25°C).
Production:
• cobalt chloride + disodium phosphate (salt formation)
Uses:
ceramic colorant; glaze/ceramics ingredient; steel phosphating reagent

cobalt sulphate
cobaltous sulphate; [10026-24-1]; [10124-43-3] (anhydrous)

$$CoSO_4$$

$Co_1O_4S_1$. M: 154.99. The main commercially product is the hexahydrate which is a light red, crystalline solid which loses water of crystallisation when heated above 42°C, producing the monohydrate at 100°C and the anhydrous salt above 250°C. d: 2.01 kg/l (25°C). Solubility in water: 330 g/l water (20°C). The monohydrate is also available commercially.
Production:
• cobalt oxide + sulphuric acid (salt formation)
Derivatives:
Acid Red 308; cobalt carbonate, basic; cobalt hydroxide
Uses: nickel/cobalt plating brightening agent; electroplating reagent; animal feed additive; glaze/ceramics ingredient

cobalt tallate
Production:
• cobalt hydroxide + tall oil, distilled (salt formation)
Uses: paint drier

cobalt titanate *See:* cobalt green

cocamine *See:* cocoamine

cochineal *See:* carmine

coco alcohol *See:* n-alkanol(C_{12}-C_{18})

cocoamido betaine *See:* cocoamidopropyl betaine

cocoamidopropyl betaine
cocamidopropyl betaine (CTFA); cocoamido betaine; [61789-40-0]

$$\underset{\underset{R\overset{O}{\overset{\|}{C}}NHCH_2CH_2CH_2\overset{+}{N}CH_2COO^-}{CH_3}}{CH_3}$$

R = coco-. $C_{19}H_{38}N_2O_3$. M: 342.52. Available commercially as a 30–35% solution in water.
Production:
• cocoamidopropyldimethylamine + sodium chloroacetate (dehydrochlorination)
Uses:
dispersant (alkaline degreasers); foam boosters (shampoos, bubble baths, liquid soaps)

cocoamidopropyldimethylamine

$$R\overset{O}{\overset{\|}{C}}NHCH_2CH_2CH_2N(CH_3)_2$$

R = coco-.

Production:
• coconut acid + 3-dimethylaminopropylamine (amide formation)
Derivatives: cocoamidopropyl betaine; cocoamidopropyldimethylamine oxide; cocoamidopropyldimethylamine propionate; cocoamidopropyldimethylammonium-3-sulphopropyl betaine; cocoamidopropyl sulphobetaine
Uses: cationic emulsifier (cosmetics, toiletries)

cocoamidopropyldimethylamine oxide
cocamidopropylamine oxide (CTFA)

$$\underset{\underset{R\overset{O}{\overset{\|}{C}}NHCH_2CH_2CH_2N \rightarrow O}{CH_3}}{CH_3}$$

R = coco-.
Production:
• cocoamidopropyldimethylamine + hydrogen peroxide (oxidation)
Uses: wetting agent/foam booster/conditioner (hair/bath products)

cocoamidopropyldimethylamine propionate
cocamidopropyl dimethylamine propionate

$$R\overset{O}{\overset{\|}{C}}NHCH_2CH_2CH_2NH(CH_3)_2^+ \quad C_2H_5COO^-$$

R = coco-.
Production:
• cocoamidopropyldimethylamine + propionic acid (salt formation)
Uses: antistatic agent (hair products)

cocoamidopropyldimethylammonium-3-sulphopropyl betaine

$$\underset{\underset{R\overset{O}{\overset{\|}{C}}CH_2CH_2CH_2\overset{+}{N}CH_2CH_2CH_2SO_3^-}{CH_3}}{CH_3}$$

R = coco-.
Production:
• cocoamidopropyldimethylamine + propane sultone (quaternisation)
Uses:
surfactant (detergents, industrial cleaners, shampoos)

cocoamidopropyl sulphobetaine
cocamidopropyl hydroxysultaine (CTFA)

$$\underset{\underset{R\overset{O}{\overset{\|}{C}}NHCH_2CH_2CH_2\overset{+}{N}CH_2\overset{OH}{C}HCH_2SO_3^-}{CH_3}}{}$$

R = coco-. Available as a 50% solution in water.
Production:
• cocoamidopropyldimethylamine + sodium 3-chloro-2-hydroxypropylsulphonate (ether formation)
Uses: mild surfactant (soaps, shampoos)

cocoamine
cocamine

$$RNH_2$$

R = coco-. Solid or liquid. MP: 14–18°C. A typical chain-length distribution is: 5% C_8, 5% C_{10}, 50% C_{12}, 20% C_{14}, 10% C_{16}, 10% C_{18}.
Production:
• coconut acid + ammonia (nitrile formation/ hydrogenation)
Derivatives: bis(2-hydroxyethyl)cocoamine; cocoamine acetate; cocoamine ethoxylates; *N*-coco-3-aminobutyric acid; cocoaminopropionic acid; *N*-coco-1,3-propane-diamine; dimethylcocoamine; disodium *N*-cocoylsulpho-succinamate
Uses: cationic flotation agent; anticaking agent (pot-assium fertilisers)

cocoamine acetate

$$RNH_3^+ \quad CH_3COO^-$$

R = coco-. Paste. The composition varies with the source of the cocoamine, but typically contains 50–60% C_{12} and 18–21% C_{14}.
Production:
• cocoamine + acetic acid (salt formation)
Uses: corrosion inhibitor; froth flotation agent; anti-caking agent (fertilisers)

cocoamine ethoxylates
PEG cocamine (CTFA)

$$RN\begin{array}{c}(CH_2CH_2O)_mH\\(CH_2CH_2O)_nH\end{array}$$

R = coco-, m+n = 5–15. Cocoamine ethoxylates are liquids containing 5–15 moles EO. HLB: 17.9–19.3 (5–15 moles EO).
Production:
• cocoamine + ethylene oxide (epoxidation)
Uses: corrosion inhibitor; emulsifier (wax, soluble oils, pesticides, cleaners, bitumen, silicone oils); antistatic agent (textile spin finishes, paper processing, plastics); wetting/dispersing agent (electrostatic paints, inks, dyes, pigments)

N-coco-3-aminobutyric acid
cocaminobutyric acid

$$R\overset{+}{-}NH_2\overset{CH_3}{\underset{|}{CH}}CH_2COO^-$$

R = coco-. Available as a 45–55% solution or paste in water. HLB: 13.6. Also available as the sodium salt.
Production:
• cocoamine + crotonic acid (esterification/carboxy-ethylation/hydrolysis)
Uses: dispersant/wetting agent (minerals, pigments)

cocoaminopropionic acid

$$R\overset{+}{-}NH_2CH_2CH_2COO^-$$

R = coco-.
Production:
• cocoamine + methyl acrylate (carboxyethylation/ hydrolysis)
Uses: dispersant/wetting agent (minerals, pigments)

cocoamphocarboxyglycinate
[68650-39-5]

$$Na^+ \quad {}^-OOCCH_2\overset{R}{\underset{CH_2CH_2OCH_2COO^-}{\overset{N}{\underset{N^+}{\bigcirc}}}}$$

R = coco-. Available as a solution containing 35–50% active matter. The product reduces the skin irritancy of other surfactants in blends.
Production:
• cocoyl imidazoline + sodium chloroacetate (ether formation/quaternisation)
Uses: surfactant (shampoos, hand cleaners)

cocoamphocarboxypropionate

$$Na^+ \quad {}^-OOCCH_2CH_2\overset{R}{\underset{CH_2CH_2OCH_2CH_2COO^-}{\overset{N}{\underset{N^+}{\bigcirc}}}}$$

R = coco-. Available as solutions containing 35–100% active matter.
Production:
• cocoyl imidazoline + methyl acrylate (carboxy-ethylation/ester hydrolysis)
Uses: electroplating bath additive; surfactant (industrial laundry detergents, industrial cleaners, paint strippers, non-aqueous cleaners, shampoos, skin cleansers)

cocoamphopropionate

$$HOCH_2CH_2\overset{R}{\underset{CH_2CH_2COO^-}{\overset{N}{\underset{N^+}{\bigcirc}}}}$$

R = coco-. Available as a 37% solution in water.
Production:
• cocoyl imidazoline + methyl acrylate (addition)
Uses: mild surfactant (shampoos); surfactant/solubilis-ing agent (heavy-duty cleaners)

coco betaine
cocoamino betaine; cocodimethylamino betaine; di-methylcocoamino betaine

$$R\overset{+}{-}\overset{CH_3}{\underset{CH_3}{\underset{|}{N}}}CH_2COO^-$$

R = coco-. Available commercially as a 35% solution in water.

Production:
• dimethylcocoamine + sodium chloroacetate
  (dehydrochlorination)
Uses: biocide/conditioner (toiletries, hand cleaners)

cocodimethylamine *See:* dimethylcocoamine

cocodimethylammonium-3-sulphopropylbetaine
Ralufon DCH (Raschig)

$$CH_3$$
$$R-\overset{+}{N}CH_2CH_2CH_2SO_3^-$$
$$CH_3$$

R = coco-.
Production:
• dimethylcocoamine + propane sultone (quaternisation)
Uses: electroplating bath additive; amphoteric surfactant (shampoos/industrial detergents)

cocoimidazoline betaine
cocoamphoglycinate (CTFA)

$$R \overset{N}{\underset{\underset{CH_2COO^-}{N^+}}{\text{}}} \quad HOCH_2CH_2$$

R = coco-. Available as a 43% solution in water. Reduces the irritability of other surfactants to skin.
Production:
• cocoyl imidazoline + sodium chloroacetate
  (dehydrochlorination)
Uses:
antistatic agent (textile spin finishes); mild surfactant (shampoos); solubiliser (hard-surface cleaners)

cocoimidazoline sulphobetaine
cocoamphopropylsulphonate (CTFA)

$$R \overset{N}{\underset{\underset{CH_2CHCH_2SO_3^-}{\underset{OH}{N^+}}}{\text{}}} \quad HOCH_2CH_2$$

R = coco-. Available as a 40% solution in water.
Production:
• cocoyl imidazoline + sodium 3-chloro-2-hydroxy-
  propylsulphonate (dehydrochlorination)
Uses: foam stabiliser/solubiliser (alkaline laundry detergents, cleaners); mild surfactant (toiletries)

coconut acid
coconut fatty acid; [61788-47-4]

$$RCOOH$$

R = coco-. $C_{12}H_{24}O_2$. M: 200.32. Pale yellow solid. MP: 22–29°C. Acid value: 255–275 mg KOH/g. Insoluble in water. A typical chain-length distribution is: 3% C_8, 5% C_{10}, 50% C_{12}, 20% C_{14}, 10% C_{16}, 10% $C_{18:1}$.

Production:
• coconut oil (hydrolysis)
Derivatives: aminoethyl cocoyl imidazoline; cocoamidopropyldimethylamine; cocoamine; coconut acid diethanolamide; coconut acid monoethanolamide; cocoyl imidazoline; cocoyl sarcosine; dicocoamine; C_8-C_{10} fatty acids; lauric acid, broad cut; neopentyl glycol dicocoate; oleic acid; sodium cocoyl isethionate; sodium *N*-cocoyl-*N*-methyltaurate
Uses: soap/cosmetics ingredient; soap raw material

coconut acid amide ethoxylates
PEG cocamide

$$\overset{O}{\overset{\|}{RCNH(CH_2CH_2O)_nH}}$$

R = coco-, n = 3–8.
Production:
• coconut acid monoethanolamide + ethylene oxide
  (epoxidation)
Uses: emulsifier (liquid detergents, textile auxiliaries, cosmetics, pesticides)

coconut acid diethanolamide
cocamide DEA (CTFA); coconut acid polydiethanolamide (2:1 type); coconut acid superamide (1:1 type)

$$\overset{O}{\overset{\|}{RCNH(CH_2CH_2OH)_2}}$$

R = coco-. Available as 1:1 or 2:1 types. The former is made from the methyl ester using an equimolar quantity of diethanolamine. It is a clear, amber liquid containing 80–90% amide and 10% free diethanolamine, together with secondary reaction products. The 2:1 type is made by reacting the acid with an excess of diethanolamine. It is a light amber liquid containing 60% fatty diethanolamide and 25% diethanolamine.
Production:
• coconut acid + diethanolamine (Kritchevsky reaction)
• methyl cocoate + diethanolamine (amide formation)
Uses: foam boosters/stabilisers (bath, shaving soaps); foam stabiliser/emulsifier (household, industrial cleaners); thickening agents/conditioners/stabilisers (shampoos)

coconut acid methyl ester *See:* methyl cocoate

coconut acid monoethanolamide
cocamide MEA (CTFA); coconut fatty acid monoethanolamide

$$\overset{O}{\overset{\|}{RCNHCH_2CH_2OH}}$$

R = coco-. Yellowish, waxy solid.
Production:
• coconut acid + monoethanolamine (amide formation)

Derivatives:
coconut acid amide ethoxylates; disodium coconut monoethanolamide sulphosuccinate
Uses: foam boosters/stabilisers (powder, liquid detergents, cleaners); foam boosters/stabilisers (shampoos, bubble bath)

coconut acid polydiethanolamide
See: coconut acid diethanolamide

coconut acid superamide
See: coconut acid diethanolamide

coconut alcohol *See:* n-alkanol(C_{12}-C_{18})

coconut oil
[8001-31-8]
White, greasy solid. MP: 24°C. d: 0.90 kg/l (0°C). Saponification value: 255–260 mg KOH/g. Insoluble in water. Soluble in oxygenated and chlorinated solvents.
Production:
• copra (expression/alkali refining)
Derivatives: alkyd resins, non-drying; coconut acid; methyl cocoate
Uses: soap/cosmetics/shortening/margarine/processed food ingredient

N-coco-1,3-propanediamine
cocoaminopropylamine; N-coco-1,3-diaminopropane; N-coco-1,3-propylenediamine

$$RNHCH_2CH_2CH_2NH_2$$

R = coco-. Liquid/paste. MP: 20°C. A typical chain-length distribution is: 6% C_8, 7% C_{10}, 50% C_{12}, 20% C_{14}, 10% C_{16}, 7% C_{18}.
Production:
• cocoamine + acrylonitrile (cyanoethylation/nitrile reduction)
Uses: flotation collector (sulphide ores); biocide (water treatment)

cocoyl imidazoline
2-cocoyl-1-(hydroxyethyl)imidazoline

R = coco-.
Production:
• coconut acid + aminoethylethanolamine (condensation)
Derivatives:
cocoamphocarboxyglycinate; cocoamphocarboxypropionate; cocoamphopropionate; cocoimidazoline betaine; cocoimidazoline sulphobetaine
Uses: emulsifier (industrial detergents, cleaners)

cocoyl sarcosine
[68411-97-2]

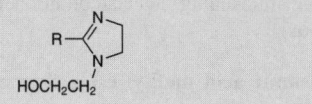

R = coco-. Available as the free acid or as the sodium or ammonium salts. The product is characterised by its good foaming and wetting properties, its hard water tolerance and its corrosion and enzyme inhibition.
Production:
• coconut acid + sarcosine (amide formation)
Uses: emulsifier (emulsion polymerisation); surfactant (carpet shampoos, fabric detergents, dishwashing liquids, cosmetics, toiletries, toothpaste)

COD *See:* 1,5-cyclooctadiene

codeine
methylmorphine; [76-57-3]; [125-25-7] (hydrobromide); [1422-07-7] (hydrochloride)

$C_{18}H_{21}N_1O_3$. M: 299.38. Available commercially as the free base monohydrate or as the hydrobromide or hydrochloride salts.
Production:
• morphine (methylation)
• opium (extraction; coproduced with morphine/thebaine)
Derivatives: dihydrocodeine; hydrocodone; oxycodone
Uses: analgesic/antitussive drug

cod liver oil
[8001-69-2]
Pale yellow liquid with a slight, fishy odour. Produced by expression of cod (*Gadus morrhua*) livers. d: 0.92 kg/l (20°C). Insoluble in water. Soluble in oxygenated and chlorinated solvents.
Uses: dietary supplement ingredient

COE *See:* cyclooctene

colmanite *See:* calcium borate, natural

complex ester oils
ester oils, complex

A = primary alcohol, B = dicarboxylic acid, C = poly-

alkylene glycol, D = monocarboxylic acid. Polymeric esters terminated with monohydric alcohols or monocarboxylic acids.
Production:
• dimethyl adipate/adipic acid/sebacic acid/azelaic acid + polyethylene glycol + tridecanol/isodecanol + pelargonic acid/2-ethylhexanoic acid/isooctanoic acid/isononanoic acid/isodecanoic acid (esterification)
Uses:
synthetic lubricant base oils

condensate *See:* gasoline, natural

COPE *See:* copolyester, thermoplastic elastomers

copoloid *See:* copper tallate

copolyester, thermoplastic elastomers
COPE; TPE-E; Arnitel (Akzo); Hytrel (Du Pont)

n = about 14. Thermoplastic elastomers characterised by their good elastic, abrasion and solvent resistance properties. d: 1.15–1.22 kg/l. MP: 165–210°C. Tensile strength: 40–50 MPa. Elongation at break: 500–850%. The elastomers are processed by injection moulding or extrusion.
Production:
• dimethyl terephthalate + poly(tetramethylene ether) glycol + 1,4-butanediol (esterification)
Uses: gaiters/bellows/covers/diaphragms; seals/belting/water hoses; sports shoes

copper
[7440-50-8]

Cu

Cu_1. M: 63.55. Red, malleable, ductile metal with high electrical and thermal conductivity. Available commercially as ingots, bars, wire, sheet, foil, tubing, shot and powder. MP: 1,083°C. BP: 2,595°C. d: 8.96 kg/l.
Production:
• copper, blister (electrolysis)
• copper oxide ores + iron (acid leaching/cementation)
• copper oxide ores + sulphuric acid (acid leaching/electrolysis)
• copper sulphide ores (heap leaching/cementation)
• copper sulphide ores (heap leaching/electrolysis)
• copper-cobalt sulphide ores (ore roasting/acid leaching/electrolysis)
• lead bullion (pyrometallurgical refining/Parkes process/Betterton-Kroll process; byproduct of lead production)
Derivatives: brass; copper hydroxide; copper oxychl-

oride; copper phthalocyanine; copper sulphate; cupric chloride; cupric oxide; cuprous chloride; cuprous oxide
Uses: nickel-silver alloys; copper-cadmium alloys (electrical conductors); copper-chromium alloys; copper-manganese-aluminium alloys (resistance wire, heating wire); copper-nickel alloys (chemical equipment); electrical conductors/components (wire, motors, generators, switchgear); beryllium-copper alloys (electrical contacts, springs, dies, bellows, welding disks); aluminium bronze ingredient (ship propellers, fittings, automobile engine components, plastic moulding dies); bronze ingredient (coins, bells, statues, pigment); leaded bronze ingredient (bearings); manganese bronze ingredient; phosphor bronze ingredient (bearings); reagent (Ullmann reactions); water piping

copper, blister
black copper

Cu

Impure form of copper produced by smelting copper ore concentrates in a reverbatory furnace to form copper matte (impure copper sulphides), followed by air oxidation in a convertor. Blister copper contains 96–98% copper and has a characteristic surface appearance produced by gas erupting from the melt during roasting.
Production:
• copper oxide ores (smelting/air conversion)
• copper sulphide ore concentrates (smelting/air conversion)
Derivatives: copper

copper arsenate, chromated
CCA; copper chrome arsenate
Production:
• chromic acid + copper sulphate/copper carbonate, basic + arsenic pentoxide (salt formation)
Uses: wood preservative

copperas red *See:* iron oxide red

copper carbonate, basic
Bremen Blue; malacite; [12069-69-1]

$CuCO_3.Cu(OH)_2$

$C_1H_2Cu_2O_5$. M: 221.11. Green powder. Decomposes when heated above 200°C. d: 3.7–4.0 kg/l. Insoluble in water.
Production:
• copper sulphate + sodium carbonate (salt formation)
Derivatives: ammoniacal copper arsenate; copper arsenate, chromated; copper fluoborate; copper gluconate; copper naphthenate; copper nitrate; copper oleate; cupric chloride
Uses: electroplating bath ingredient; animal feed additive

copper chloride, basic *See:* copper oxychloride

copper chrome arsenate *See:* copper arsenate, chromated

copper cyanide
cuprous cyanide; [544-92-3]

Cu₂(CN)₂

$C_2Cu_2N_2$. M: 179.12. Pale cream powder. Insoluble in water. Extremely toxic. Liberates hydrogen cyanide on contact with acid.
Production:
• copper sulphate + sodium cyanide (precipitation)
Derivatives:
Fluorescent Brightener 179; probenecid
Uses: copper-tin alloy plating process reagent; reagent (Sandmeyer reactions); brass/copper plating reagent

copper dimethyldithiocarbamate
CuDC; CuDD; [137-29-1]

$$[(CH_3)_2NC\overset{S}{\overset{\|}{}}S]_2Cu$$

$C_6H_{12}Cu_1N_2S_4$. M: 303.99. Brown powder. Decomposes on heating above 200°C. d: 1.6 kg/l. Insoluble in water and hydrocarbon solvents.
Production:
• sodium dimethyldithiocarbamate + copper sulphate (salt formation)
Uses: vulcanisation accelerator

copper fluoborate
copper bis(tetrafluoroborate); [38465-60-0]

Cu(BF₄)₂

$B_2Cu_1F_8$. M: 237.15.
Production:
• copper hydroxide/copper carbonate, basic + fluoboric acid (salt formation)
Uses: copper plating reagent (printed circuit boards)

copper gluconate
copper digluconate; cupric gluconate; [527-09-3]

$[HOCH(CHOH)_4COO]_2Cu$

$C_{12}H_{22}Cu_1O_{14}$. M: 453.85. Available as the monohydrate. Light blue, crystalline powder. Soluble in water.
Production:
• copper carbonate, basic/copper hydroxide + gluconic acid (salt formation)
Uses: dietary supplement ingredient; mouth deodorant ingredient

copper hydroxide
cupric hydroxide; [20427-59-2]
$H_2Cu_1O_2$. M: 97.57. Bluish-green powder. Decomposes

when heated above 100°C producing cupric oxide. d: 3.37 kg/l. Insoluble in water.

Cu(OH)₂

Production:
• copper + ammonia + sodium hydroxide (complex formation/air oxidation)
Derivatives: copper fluoborate; copper gluconate; copper naphthenate; copper nitrate; copper oleate; cupric chloride
Uses: mordant; cuprammonium rayon process reagent

copper 8-hydroxyquinoline *See:* oxine-copper

copper linoleate *See:* copper tallate

copper naphthenate
[1338-02-9]
Production:
• copper hydroxide/copper carbonate, basic + naphthenic acid (salt formation)
Uses:
wood preservative

copper nitrate
cupric nitrate; [10031-43-3] (trihydrate)

Cu(NO₃)₂

$Cu_1N_2O_6$. M: 187.55. Available commercially as the trihydrate. Blue, hydroscopic crystals. MP: 114°C. d: 2.32 kg/l (25°C). Soluble in water.
Production:
• copper hydroxide/cupric oxide/copper carbonate, basic + nitric acid (salt formation)
Uses: glaze/ceramics ingredient; pyrotechnic/rocket fuel ingredient; mordant/oxidising agent (textile dyeing); metal surface treatments agent

copper oleate
[1120-44-1]

$[CH_3(CH_2)_7CH=CH(CH_2)_7COO]_2Cu$

$C_{36}H_{33}Cu_1O_4$. M: 593.21. Bluish-green solid. Insoluble in water. Soluble in oxygenated solvents.
Production:
• copper hydroxide/copper carbonate, basic + oleic acid (salt formation)
• copper sulphate + sodium oleate (salt formation)
Uses:
fuel oil combustion improvement additive; biocide (marine antifouling paints)

copper oxide, black *See:* cupric oxide

copper oxide, red *See:* cuprous oxide

copper oxide, yellow *See:* cuprous oxide

copper oxinate *See:* oxine-copper

copper oxychloride
copper chloride, basic; copper oxychloride, basic; di-
copper chloride trihydroxide; [1332-40-7]

$Cu_2Cl(OH)_3$

$H_3Cl_1Cu_2O_3$. M: 213.56.
Production:
• cuprous chloride + copper (air oxidation)
• copper oxide ores + sodium chloride, natural (ore
  roasting/water leaching)
Uses: fungicide

copper phthalocyanine
phthalocyanine blue; Pigment Blue 15 (CI, α-form);
Pigment Blue 15:1 (CI, α-form); Pigment Blue 15:2
(CI, α-form); Pigment Blue 15:3 (CI, β-form); Pigment Blue 15:4 (CI, β-form); 74160 (CI); [147-14-8]

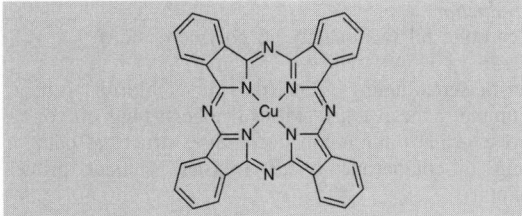

$C_{32}H_{16}Cu_1N_8$. M: 576.09. Available in the α- or β-
crystal modification.
Production:
• phthalic anhydride + urea + cuprous chloride
  (solvent process)
• phthalodinitrile + cuprous chloride + copper (fusion
  process)
Derivatives: Direct Blue 86; Pigment Green 7; Pigment
Green 36; Reactive Blue 7; Vat Blue 29
Uses: chrome green pigment component; pigment
(paints, printing inks, plastics)

copper sulphate
blue vitriol (pentahydrate); cupric sulphate;
[7758-98-7]; [7758-99-8] (pentahydrate)

$CuSO_4$

$Cu_1O_4S_1$. M: 159.61. Available commercially as the
pentaahydrate or monohydrate. The pentahydrate is a
blue, crystalline solid which converts to the monohydrate when heated above 110°C and to the anhydrous salt above 250°C. d: 2.29 kg/l (15°C). Solubility in water: 243 g/l water (0°C). The monohydrate is
a white, hygroscopic powder. Copper sulphate is also
produced as a byproduct of copper electrolysis and
etching processes. In this case the product is generally
only suitable for agricultural purposes.
Production:
• copper + sulphuric acid (salt formation)

Derivatives:
ammoniacal copper arsenate; Bordeaux mixture; copper
arsenate, chromated; copper carbonate, basic; copper
cyanide; copper dimethyldithiocarbamate; copper oleate;
copper tallate; Direct Blue 80; Direct Blue 84; Direct
Blue 93; Direct Blue 98; Direct Red 83; Direct Red
180; Direct Violet 66; oxine-copper; Reactive Blue 13;
Reactive Red 6; Reactive Violet 5; Sulphur Green 1
Uses:
flotation activator (lead, zinc, cobalt mineral processing); algicide; animal feed additive; preservative
(leather); copper plating reagent; soil nutrient

copper tallate
copoloid; copper linoleate
Production:
• copper sulphate + tall oil, distilled + calcium
  hydroxide (salt formation)
Uses: fungicide

copra
Dried meat of coconuts (*Cocus nucifera* fruit kernels).
The Philippines is the main producing country.
Derivatives: coconut oil

coriander oil
[8008-52-4]
Pale yellow liquid with a characteristic odour. Produced by steam distillation of coriander (*Coriandrum
sativum*) seed. d: 0.87 kg/l (20°C). Soluble in alcohol.
The major constituent of the oil is linalool (70%).
Poland, Hungary and Russia are the main producing
countries.
Uses: food/drink flavouring ingredient

corn oil *See:* maize oil

corn steep liquor
Liquor containing about 55% solids formed by concentration of the liquid in which maize is soaked prior
to milling.
Production:
• maize (milling/separation; byproduct of starch/
  maize gluten/maize bran production)
Derivatives: phenoxymethylpenicillin; phytic acid; thienamycin
Uses: animal feed ingredient; microbial fermentation
nutrient

corn syrup *See:* glucose syrup

cortisone
17α,21-dihydroxy-4-pregnene-3,11,20-trione; [53-06-5]
$C_{21}H_{28}O_5$. M: 360.44.
Production:
• androstadienedione (multistep synthesis)
• deoxycholic acid (multistep synthesis)

- 11-α-hydroxyprogesterone (multistep synthesis)
- hecogenin (multistep synthesis)

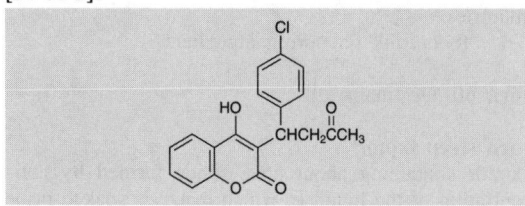

Derivatives: flunisolide; fluocinonide; hydrocortisone
Uses: antiinflammatory drug

corundum
alumina, natural
A hard, natural alumina mined in Canada, South Africa, USA, India, Madagascar and Russia.
Uses: metal/wood/glass abrasive (grinding wheels, papers, cloths)

cotton linters
α-cellulose
Short fibres separated from longer cotton fibres and seed during ginning. Linters are too short for textile fibre use. The product consists of 95% α-cellulose.
Derivatives: alkali cellulose; cellulose acetate; cellulose acetobutyrate; cellulose nitrate; cellulose propionate; cellulose triacetate

cotton oil *See:* cottonseed oil

coumachlor
3-[1-(4-chlorophenyl)-3-oxobutyl]-4-hydroxycoumarin; [81-82-3]

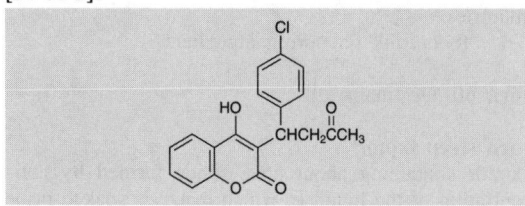

$C_{19}H_{15}Cl_1O_4$. M: 342.78.
Production:
- *p*-chlorobenzaldehyde + acetone + 4-hydroxy-coumarin (condensation/condensation)
Uses: rodenticide

o-coumaric acid *See:* *o*-hydroxycinnamic acid

coumarin
1,2-benzopyrone; benzopyrone; cumarin; [91-64-5]

$C_9H_6O_2$. M: 146.15. White crystals with a pleasant odour. MP: 68–70°C. BP: 298°C. d: 0.94 kg/l (20°C). Slightly soluble in hot water. Soluble in aqueous alkali, oxygenated and chlorinated solvents.

Production:
- salicylaldehyde + acetic anhydride (Perkin condensation)
Derivatives: dihydrocoumarin; *o*-hydroxycinnamic acid
Uses: nickel plating brightening agent; fragrance/flavouring ingredient

coumarone-indene resin
coumarone resin; indene-coumarone resin

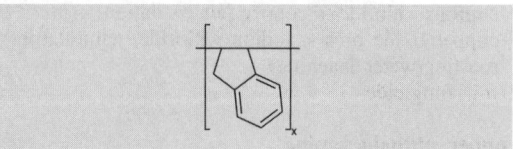

Brown solid. Softening point: 100°C. Consists mainly of polymerised indene with a degree of polymerisation of 20–25. The resins are compatible with a wide range of plastics, rubbers, waxes, bitumens and oils.
Production:
- carbolic oil (acid-catalysed polymerisation)
Uses:
plasticiser/softening agent (polyvinyl chloride, rubber, bitumen, adhesives); tackifier (rubber); tung oil-coumarone resins (aluminium decorative, structural paints); tung oil-coumarone resins (plaster, cement primer paints)

coumatetralyl
4-hydroxy-3-(1,2,3,4-tetrahydro-1-naphthyl)coumarin; [5836-29-3]

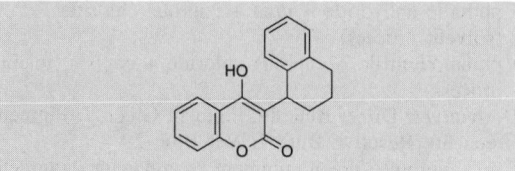

$C_{19}H_{16}O_3$. M: 292.34.
Production:
- tetralin + 4-hydroxycoumarin (oxidation/condensation)
Uses: rodenticide

CP *See:* cellulose propionate

4-CPAN *See:* 4-chlorophthalic anhydride

CPC *See:* cetylpyridinium chloride

CPH
See: 2,2′-methylenebis(4-methyl-6-cyclohexylphenol)

CPU *See:* polyurethane, cast elastomers

CPVC *See:* polyvinyl chloride, chlorinated

CR *See:* polychloroprene

cream of tartar *See:* potassium bitartrate

creosote *See:* tar oil, wood

creosote oil
wash oil
Wide-cut coal-tar fraction with a boiling range: 200–270°C containing naphthalene and tar acid fractions.
Production:
• coal tar, crude (alkali extraction/fractionation; coproduced with light oil/carbolic oil/naphthalene fraction/fluorene oil/anthracene oil/coal tar pitch/tar acid liquor)
Uses: road tar fluxing solvent; fuel oil; wash oil (coal gas purification); wood preservative

p-cresidine
3-amino-4-methoxytoluene; 2-methoxy-5-methylaniline; 5-methyl-*o*-anisidine; [120-71-8]

$C_8H_{11}N_1O_1$. M: 137.19. White, crystalline solid. MP: 48–51°C. BP: 235°C. Slightly soluble in water. Soluble in oxygenated and aromatic solvents.
Production:
• *m*-nitro-*p*-cresol (methylation/nitro reduction)
Derivatives:
N-(4-amino-5-methoxy-2-methylphenyl)benzamide; 5-amino-4-methoxytoluene-2-sulphonic acid; *N,N'*-bis-(2-methoxy-5-methylphenyl) urea; Direct Blue 67; Direct Green 26; Direct Violet 9; Disperse Black 2

m-cresol
m-cresylic acid; 3-methylphenol; [108-39-4]

$C_7H_8O_1$. M: 108.14. Colourless liquid with a phenolic odour. BP: 202–204°C. MP: 10–12°C. d: 1.03 kg/l (20°C). Slightly soluble in water. Miscible with oxygenated and chlorinated solvents.
Production:
• *o*-chlorotoluene (base-catalysed hydrolysis; coproduced with *o*-cresol)
• *m/p*-cresol (fractionation; coproduced with *p*-cresol)
Derivatives: Acid Orange 67; *p*-chloro-*m*-cresol; *m*-cresotic acid; 3-methyl-4-(methylmercapto)phenol; metolcarb; 4-nitro-*m*-cresol; 6-nitro-*m*-cresol; promecarb; thymol; toliprolol

m/p-cresol
$C_7H_8O_1$. M: 108.14. Amber liquid. BR: 197–205°C. d:

1.03–1.04 kg/l (20°C). Sparingly soluble in water. Soluble in aqueous alkali, oxygenated and aromatic solvents. The composition varies somewhat depending on the source of the product. From tar acids, the ratio of *m*-cresol:*p*-cresol is, typically, 1.3:1; from toluene it is 1.5:1. Tar acid fractions containing *m/p*-cresol with a high proportion of xylenols are also available.
Production:
• *o/p*-chlorotoluene (hydrolysis/fractionation; coproduced with *o*-cresol)
• toluene + propylene (Friedel-Crafts alkylation/oxidation/acid-catalysed hydrolysis; coproduced with acetone)
• cresylic acid (fractionation; coproduced with phenol/*o*-cresol/xylenol, mixed)
Derivatives:
2-*t*-butyl-*p*-cresol; 6-*t*-butyl-*m*-cresol; *m*-cresol; *p*-cresol; methylcyclohexanol; novolac resins; resol resins; tricresyl phosphate
Uses: phenolic resin comonomer

o-cresol
o-cresylic acid; 2-methylphenol; [95-48-7]

$C_7H_8O_1$. M: 108.14. Colourless liquid or solid with a phenolic odour. Discoloured by light and air. MP: 30–32°C. BP: 190–192°C. d: 1.05 kg/l (20°C). Soluble in hot water. Miscible with oxygenated and chlorinated solvents.
Production:
• *o/p*-chlorotoluene (hydrolysis/fractionation; coproduced with *m/p*-cresol)
• phenol + methanol (orthoalkylation; coproduced with 2,6-xylenol)
• *p*-toluenesulphonic acid (alkali fusion; byproduct of *p*-cresol production)
• *o*-chlorotoluene (base-catalysed hydrolysis; coproduced with *m*-cresol)
• cresylic acid (fractionation; coproduced with phenol/*m/p*-cresol/xylenol, mixed)
Derivatives:
Acid Orange 51; Acid Yellow 65; carvacrol; *p*-chloro-*o*-cresol; *o*-cresotic acid; *o*-cresyl glycidyl ether; 4,6-dinitro-*o*-cresol; 2-methylcyclohexanol; novolac resins; resol resins; tetrabromo-*o*-cresol; triethylene glycol bis[3-(3-*t*-butyl-4-hydroxy-5-methylphenyl)propionate]
Uses: disinfectant

p-cresol

p-cresylic acid; 4-methylphenol; [106-44-5]

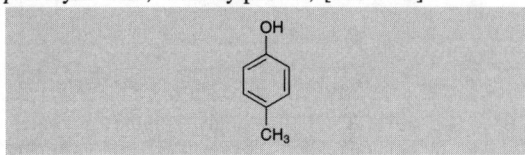

$C_7H_8O_1$. M: 108.14. White, crystalline solid with a phenolic odour. MP: 32–34°C. BP: 201–202°C. d: 1.03 kg/l (20°C). Slightly soluble in water. Soluble in aqueous alcohol and most organic solvents. Also available as a liquid containing 70–90% *p*-cresol.

Production:
• *p*-toluenesulphonic acid (alkali fusion)
• *m/p*-cresol (fractionation; coproduced with *m*-cresol)

Derivatives:
Acid Blue 118; *o*-amino-*p*-cresol; 2-*t*-butyl-*p*-cresol; *p*-cresyl phenylacetate; 2,6-di-*t*-butyl-*p*-cresol; 2,6-di-nitro-*p*-cresol; Disperse Yellow 3; 2-(2-hydroxy-5-methylphenyl)benzotriazole; *p*-methoxytoluene; 2,2′-methylenebis(4-methyl-6-cyclohexylphenol); 2,2′-methylenebis[4-methyl-6-(α-methylcyclohexyl)phenol]; 2,2′-methylenebis(4-methyl-6-nonylphenol); *m*-nitro-*p*-cresol; Solvent Green 4; tolclofos-methyl; 4-tolyl-2,1,5-diazoester

Uses: disinfectant

m-cresotic acid

m-cresotinic acid; 2-hydroxy-4-methylbenzoic acid; 4-methyl-2-hydroxybenzoic acid; 4-methylsalicylic acid

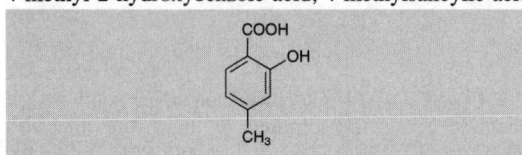

$C_8H_8O_3$. M: 152.15. Crystalline solid. MP: 175°C. Soluble in oxygenated solvents. Slightly soluble in water.

Production:
• *m*-cresol + carbon dioxide (Kolbe-Schmitt reaction)

Derivatives: proquazone

Uses:
dyestuffs intermediate

o-cresotic acid

2,3-cresotic acid; cresotinic acid; *o*-homosalicylic acid; 2-hydroxy-3-methylbenzoic acid; [83-40-9]

$C_8H_8O_3$. M: 152.15. White, crystalline solid. MP: 167°C. Slightly soluble in water. Soluble in oxygenated and chlorinated solvents.

Production:
• *o*-cresol + carbon dioxide (Kolbe-Schmitt reaction)

Derivatives:
Direct Orange 6; Mordant Blue 1; Mordant Blue 3; Mordant Violet 15; tolycaine

cresyldiphenyl phosphate

See: diphenyl cresyl phosphate

o-cresyl glycidyl ether

2,3-epoxypropyl α-tolyl ether; [2210-79-9]

$C_{10}H_{12}O_2$. M: 164.21. Colourless liquid. d: 1.08 kg/l (25°C). Viscosity: 50–200 centipoise (25°C).

Production:
• *o*-cresol + epichlorohydrin (dehydrochlorination)

Uses: reactive diluent (amino/epoxy resins)

cresylic acid

Amber liquid comprising mixed phenols, cresols and xylenols, the relative proportions of which depend on the source and distillation cut. BR: 205–230°C. d: ~1.02 kg/l (20°C). Slightly soluble in hot and cold water. Soluble in aqueous alkali, aromatic and oxygenated solvents.

Production:
• tar acids, crude (fractionation; coproduced with tar acids, high-boiling/cresylic pitch)
• gasoline, catalytic-cracker (alkali extraction/acidification; coproduced with sodium sulphide)

Derivatives:
ammonium *O,O*-dicresyl dithiophosphate; *m/p*-cresol; *o*-cresol; diphenyl cresyl phosphate; phenol; xylenol, mixed

Uses: epoxy-pitch coatings (marine paints); froth flotation agent (copper extraction); engine cleaner ingredient; polyurethane pitch coatings; solvent (wire enamels)

_m_-cresylic acid *See:* *m*-cresol

_o_-cresylic acid *See:* *o*-cresol

_p_-cresylic acid *See:* *p*-cresol

cresylic pitch

Residue of tar-acid distillation.

Production:
• tar acids, crude (fractionation; coproduced with tar acids, high-boiling/cresylic acid)

Uses:
binder (clay pigeons, coal briquettes)

_p_-cresyl methyl ether *See:* *p*-methoxytoluene

p-cresyl phenylacetate
4-methylphenyl phenylacetate; [101-94-0]

$C_{15}H_{14}O_2$. M: 226.27. Crystalline solid with floral odour. MP: 75–76°C.
Production:
• *p*-cresol + phenylacetic acid (esterification)
Uses: fragrance ingredient

crimson toner *See:* Pigment Red 57

crocein acid
[132-57-0]

$C_{10}H_8O_4S_1$. M: 224.23. Available commercially as the acid or sodium salt.
Production:
• β-naphthol (sulphonation)
Uses:
dyestuffs intermediate

cromolyn
chromoglycic acid; [16110-51-3]

$C_{23}H_{16}O_{11}$. M: 468.37. Available commercially as the disodium salt.
Production:
• 2,6-dihydroxyacetophenone + epichlorohydrin + diethyl oxalate (epoxidation/ether formation/ condensation/saponification)
Uses:
antiasthma/antiallergy drug

crotonaldehyde
2-butenal; crotonic aldehyde; [123-73-9]

$C_4H_6O_1$. M: 70.09. Colourless liquid with a pungent odour. MP: 69°C. BP: 102°C. Soluble in water. Miscible with most organic solvents. The commercial product is mainly the *trans*-isomer. It contains hydroquinone as a polymerisation inhibitor.
Production:
• acetaldehyde (aldol condensation/dehydration)
Derivatives:
n-butanol; chlorquinaldol; crotonic acid; 3,4-epoxy-6-

methylcyclohexylmethyl 3,4-epoxy-6-methylcyclohexane carboxylate; 3-methoxybutanol; sethoxydim; sorbic acid; tilidine; tricrotonylidenetetramine; 1,1,3-triethoxybutane; trimethyl 3-cyclohexenecarboxaldehyde; 1,1,3-tris(5-*t*-butyl-4-hydroxy-2-methylphenyl)butane

crotonic acid
2-butenoic acid; [3724-65-0]

$C_4H_6O_2$. M: 86.09. White crystals. MP: 72°C. BP: 185°C. d: 0.96 kg/l (80°C). Solubility in water: 555 g/l water (20°C). The commercial product is a mixture of the *cis* and *trans*-isomers.
Production:
• crotonaldehyde (air oxidation)
Derivatives:
t-butyl peroxycrotonate; *N*-coco-3-aminobutyric acid; dinocap; ethyl crotonate; trimedlure; vinyl acetatecrotonic acid copolymers
Uses:
carboxylated comonomer (polyvinyl acetate latex)

crotonylidene urea

$C_6H_{12}N_4O_2$. M: 172.20.
Production:
• acetaldehyde + urea (carbonyl condensation)
Uses:
controlled-release fertiliser

crude oil
Black, oily liquid found in sedimentary deposits in many countries. It consists of mixed hydrocarbons from methane to wax and is generally classified by its API gravity into light, medium or heavy oil. Light oils have a high API gravity, typically 45.0 (equivalent to d: 0.80 kg/l), and contain a higher proportion of lowerboiling hydrocarbons than heavy crude oils (typically, API: 18.0, equivalent to d: 0.95 kg/l). Crude oils are also classified according to their chemical type. 'Paraffinic' crude oils have a high proportion of aliphatic hydrocarbons, 'naphthenic' crudes a high proportion of cycloaliphatics. 'Aromatic' crude oils are also known. Several oils are of a mixed type and not easily classified according to this system. In addition to these classifications, crude oils are commonly referred to as either 'sweet' or 'sour'. The latter indicates the presence of hydrogen sulphide on the oil.
Derivatives:
gas oil, heavy; gas oil, light; kerosene; long residue; naphtha, heavy; naphtha, light; refinery gas

cryolite
sodium aluminium hexafluoride

$$Na_3AlF_6$$

$Al_1F_6Na_3$. M: 209.94. Although cryolite is a natural mineral, all commercial product is made synthetically.
Production:
• ammonium bifluoride + sodium aluminate (salt formation)
Uses:
aluminium production electrolyte; flux (light metal casting, porcelain enamel production); abrasive manufacturing additive

Crystal Violet *See:* Basic Violet 3

Crystal Violet Lactone

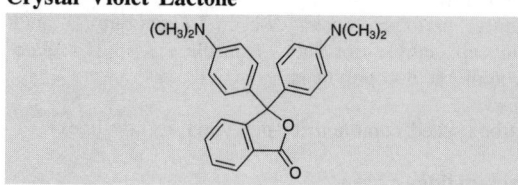

$C_{24}H_{24}N_2O_2$. M: 372.46.
Production:
• 4,4′-bis(dimethylamino)benzophenone + benzoic acid (carbonyl addition)
Uses:
colour-former (carbonless copying systems)

CS *See:* o-chlorobenzalmalononitrile

CSM *See:* polyethylene, chlorosulphonated

CSPE *See:* polyethylene, chlorosulphonated

C₄-stream, refinery
refinery B-B
Refinery C_4 stream before the separation of any C_4 chemicals. Contains, typically, 30–35% n-butene, 15–20% isobutene, 40% isobutane and 10% n-butane where the prime source of the C_4 is catalytic cracking. Thermal cracking produces a higher proportion of butanes.
Production:
• refinery gas (fractionation; coproduced with propylene/liquified petroleum gas)
Derivatives:
butadiene; gasoline, alkylate; gasoline, mixed ether; isobutane; raffinate I

C₄-stream, steam-cracked
Typical composition: 20–30% isobutylene, 15–20% 1-butene, 10% 2-butene, 35–50% butadiene, 5% butanes plus some C_3 and C_5 hydrocarbons. Boiling range of components: -48–+27°C.

Production:
• gasoline, dearomatised/gasoline, natural/naphtha, heavy (steam cracking; coproduced with gasoline, pyrolysis/ethylene/propylene/pyrolysis tar)
• gas oil, light (steam cracking; coproduced with gasoline, pyrolysis/ethylene/propylene/pyrolysis tar)
• liquified petroleum gas (steam cracking; coproduced with ethylene/propylene/gasoline, pyrolysis/pyrolysis tar)
Derivatives: butadiene; chloroprene; 1,5,9-cyclododeca-triene; 1,5-cyclooctadiene; raffinate I

C₅-stream, refinery
isoamylene concentrate
Product stream from a refinery catalytic cracker containing, typically, 35–40% isoamylenes and 20–25% n-amylenes. The diene content of the stream is close to zero.
Production:
• gasoline, catalytic-cracker (fractionation)
Derivatives: t-amyl alcohol; t-amyl methyl ether; hexanol, mixed; isoamylene

C₅-stream, steam-cracked
Product stream from steam cracking containing, typically, 7% cyclopentadiene, 13% isoprene, 10% piperylene and 20% monoolefins.
Production:
• gasoline, pyrolysis (fractionation)
Derivatives: dicyclopentadiene; hexachlorocyclopentadiene; hydrocarbon resins, C_5 aliphatic types; isoprene

CTAB *See:* cetyltrimethylammonium bromide

CTBN *See:* acrylonitrile-butadiene copolymers, carboxyl-terminated

CTC *See:* carbon tetrachloride

CTFE *See:* chlorotrifluoroethylene

CTO *See:* tall oil, crude

CTP *See:* N-(cyclohexylthio)phthalimide

CuDC *See:* copper dimethyldithiocarbamate

CuDD *See:* copper dimethyldithiocarbamate

cumaldehyde *See:* p-isopropylbenzaldehyde

cumarin *See:* coumarin

cumene
isopropylbenzene; [98-82-8]
C_9H_{12}. M: 120.20. Colourless liquid. BP: 152°C. FP: -96°C. d: 0.86 kg/l (25°C). Insoluble in water. Miscible

with oxygenated and chlorinated solvents. Flash point: 39°C (TCC).

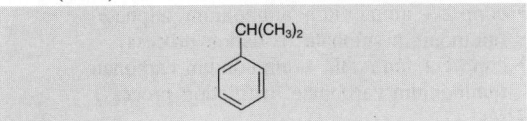

Production:
• propylene + benzene (Friedel-Crafts alkylation)
Derivatives:
cumene hydroperoxide; cumenesulphonic acid; cumidine; *p*-isopropylbenzaldehyde; α-methylstyrene

cumene hydroperoxide
CHP; [80-15-9]

$(CH_3)_2C-OOH$

$C_9H_{12}O_2$. M: 152.20. Colourless liquid comprising an aqueous solution containing 78–84% peroxide. The product has a 10-hour half-life at 158°C. Slightly soluble in water. Soluble in most organic solvents.
Production:
• cumene + oxygen (oxidation)
Derivatives: acetone; cumyl peroxyneodecanoate; cumyl peroxyneoheptanoate; dicumyl peroxide; phenol
Uses: unsaturated polyester resin crosslinking agent; polymerisation inhibitor

cumenesulphonic acid

$CH(CH_3)_2$

SO_3H

$C_9H_{12}O_3S_1$. M: 200.26. Brown, viscous liquid. d: 1.25 kg/l. Soluble in water. Also available as a 65% aqueous solution.
Production:
• cumene (sulphonation)
Derivatives: ammonium cumene sulphonate; *p*-isopropylphenol; sodium cumene sulphonate
Uses: esterification catalyst; foundry resin curing agent; phenolic/amino resin curing agent; electroplating bath additive

o-**cumenol** *See:* *o*-isopropylphenol

cumidine
4-aminocumene; 4-isopropylaniline; [643-28-7]
$C_9H_{13}N_1$. M: 135.21. Liquid. BP: 226–228°C. d: 0.95 kg/l (20°C). Insoluble in water.
Production:
• cumene (nitration/nitro reduction)

NH_2

$CH(CH_3)_2$

Derivatives: 2-isopropylthioxanthone; isoproturon

cuminic aldehyde *See:* *p*-isopropylbenzaldehyde

cuminyl alcohol *See:* *p*-isopropylbenzyl alcohol

cumyl peroxyneodecanoate

$C_6H_{13}C-CO-OC$ H_3C O CH_3 H_3C CH_3

$C_{19}H_{30}O_3$. M: 306.45.
Production:
• cumene hydroperoxide + neodecanoyl chloride (esterification)
Uses: polymerisation initiator

cumyl peroxyneoheptanoate
Esperox 740M (Witco)

$C_3H_7C-CO-OC$ H_3C O CH_3 H_3C CH_3

$C_{16}H_{24}O_3$. M: 264.37. Available as a solution containing 75% peroxide with a 10-hour half-life at 40°C.
Production:
• cumene hydroperoxide + neoheptanoyl chloride (dehydrochlorination)
Uses: polymerisation initiator

cupric bromide
copper dibromide; [7789-45-9]

$CuBr_2$

Br_2Cu_1. M: 223.36. Black, deliquescent crystals. MP: 498°C. d: 4.77 kg/l (25°C). Soluble in water.
Production:
• cupric oxide + hydrogen bromide, anhydrous (salt formation)
Uses: photographic image intensifying agent; bromination reagent

cupric chloride
copper(II) chloride; [1344-67-8]

$CuCl_2$

Cl_2Cu_1. M: 134.46. The anhydrous grade is a hygroscopic, yellowish-brown powder. d: 3.39 kg/l (25°C). MP: 620°C. Solubility in water: 710 g/l water (0°C). The dihydrate is green, hygroscopic needles. d: 2.54 kg/l. Releases water of crystallisation when heated to

100°C. Solubility in water: 1.10 kg/l water (0°C).
Production:
- copper + chlorine (reaction)
- copper hydroxide/cupric oxide/copper carbonate, basic + hydrochloric acid (salt formation)

Derivatives: cuprous chloride
Uses:
petroleum isomerisation/cracking catalyst; glass/ceramics ingredient; fireworks/flares ingredient; mordant (textile dyeing); photographic fixer ingredient; wet mercury production process reagent; copper plating reagent; reagent (precious metal refining)

cupric oxide
copper oxide, black; [1317-38-0]

CuO

Cu_1O_1. M: 79.55. Black powder. MP: 1,326°C. d: 6.3 kg/l. Insoluble in water.
Production:
- copper (air oxidation)
- copper + ammonia + ammonium carbonate (leaching/steam stripping)

Derivatives:
copper nitrate; cupric bromide; cupric chloride
Uses: catalyst; glass/enamel/ceramics/porcelain ingredient

cuprous chloride
copper(I) chloride

CuCl

Cl_1Cu_1. M: 99.00. Greenish-white crystalline powder. MP: 430°C. d: 4.14 kg/l (25°C). Slightly soluble in water with decomposition. Solutions are oxidised by air. The solid is stored in an oxygen-free atmosphere to avoid oxidation.
Production:
- cupric chloride + sulphur dioxide, pure (reduction)
- cupric chloride + copper + hydrochloric acid (reduction)

Derivatives: 5-chloro-2,4,6-trifluoropyrimidine; copper oxychloride; copper phthalocyanine; 2,4,5,6-tetrachloropyrimidine; trifluperidol
Uses: CFA pigment formation reagent; reagent (Sandmeyer reactions)

cuprous oxide
77402 (CI); copper oxide, red; copper oxide, yellow; cuprous oxide, red; cuprous oxide, yellow; red copper oxide; yellow copper oxide; [1317-39-1]

Cu₂O

Cu_2O_1. M: 143.09. Yellow, orange or red crystals. MP: 1,235°C. d: 6.0 kg/l (25°C). Insoluble in water. The yellow and orange isomorphs are the most reactive and therefore used as fungicides.

Production:
- copper (thermal oxidation)
- copper + ammonia + ammonium sulphate (ammonium sulphate oxidation process)
- copper + ammonia + ammonium carbonate (ammonium carbonate distillation process)

Uses:
biocide (marine antifouling paints); pigment (ceramics, glass)

curcumin
E100 (EC); turmeric; turmeric yellow; [458-37-7]

$C_{21}H_{20}O_6$. M: 368.38. Commercial products are extracted from a flour of turmeric (*Curcuma longa*) rhizomes which is grown in India and China. It is sold either as an oleoresin or as the pure product emulsified into a food-grade solvent. Insoluble in water.
Production:
- turmeric roots (solvent extraction/crystallisation)

Uses:
food colorant

cyanamide
carbodiimide; [420-04-2]

H₂NC≡N

$C_1H_2N_2$. M: 42.04. Colourless crystals. MP: 45–46°C. BP: 140°C. d: 1.28 kg/l. Soluble in water. Also available commercially as a 50% solution in water.
Production:
- calcium cyanamide + carbon dioxide (neutralisation)

Derivatives:
aminoguanidine bicarbonate; azathioprine; carbendazim; cyanamide-formaldehyde resins; N-cyanoimido-S,S-dimethyldithiocarbamate; dicyandiamide; N,N-dimethylguanidine; dodine; ethirimol; guanidine hydrochloride; guazatine acetate; lead cyanamide; O-methylisourea sulphate; pirimiphos-ethyl; pirimiphos-methyl; sodium dicyanamide; sulfaguanole; sulfamoxole; thiourea

cyanamide-formaldehyde resins
Production:
- cyanamide/dicyandiamide + formaldehyde (condensation)

Uses:
dyeing/tanning auxiliary; amino resin modifier; permanent-press textile finishing agent

cyanate ester resins
triazine resins
Low viscosity solid or liquid prepolymers. The cured resin has T_g: 200–300°C and is characterised by its excellent mechanical and electrical properties.

Production:
• bisphenol A + cyanuric chloride (ether formation)
Uses:
electrical/electronic encapsulation

cyanazine
2-chloro-4-(1-cyano-1-methylethylamino)-6-ethylamino-1,3,5-triazine; [21725-46-2]

$C_9H_{13}Cl_1N_6$. M: 240.69.
Production:
• acetone cyanohydrin + ammonia + cyanuric chloride + ethylamine (amine formation/amine formation/amine formation)
Uses: herbicide

cyanoacetamide
malonamide nitrile; [107-91-5]

$C_3H_4N_2O_1$. M: 84.07. White, crystalline solid. MP: 119°C. Soluble in water. Slightly soluble in alcohol.
Production:
• cyanoacetic acid + ammonia (amide formation)
Derivatives:
4-amino-5-aminomethyl-2-methylpyrimidine; cymoxanil; ethionamide; prothionamide

cyanoacetic acid
malonic nitrile; [372-09-8]

$C_3H_3N_1O_2$. M: 85.06.
Production:
• chloroacetic acid + sodium cyanide (cyanidation)
• chloroacetonitrile + carbon monoxide (carbonylation)
Derivatives: allyl cyanoacrylate; 3-amino-1-phenyl-5-pyrazolone; *n*-butyl cyanoacetate; butyl 2-cyano-3-methyl-*p*-methoxycinnamate; cefacetrile; cyanoacetamide; 2-ethoxyethyl cyanoacrylate; ethyl cyanoacetate; malonic acid; 1-(4-methoxybenzyl)-1,2,3,4,5,6,7,8-octahydroisoquinoline; β-methoxyethyl cyanoacrylate; methyl cyanoacetate; oxantel; 5-phenyl-3-methyl-2-pentenonitrile; pyrantel; pyrazophos; sulfadicramide; sulindac

2-cyanoethyl acrylate
[106-71-8]

$C_6H_7N_1O_2$. M: 125.14.
Production:
• sodium cyanide + ethylene oxide + acrylic acid (epoxidation/esterification)
Uses:
reactive comonomer (acrylate resins, adhesives, rubber)

N-(2-cyanoethyl)-N-ethylaniline
N-ethyl-N-(2-cyanoethyl)aniline; 3-(N-ethylphenylamino)propionitrile; [148-87-8]

$C_{11}H_{14}N_2$. M: 174.24. Liquid. BP: 156°C (0.8 kPa).
Production:
• N-ethylaniline + acrylonitrile (cyanoethylation)
Derivatives:
Disperse Orange 25; Disperse Red 73

1-(2-cyanoethyl)-2-ethyl-4-methylimidazole

$C_9H_{13}N_3$. M: 163.22.
Production:
• 2-ethyl-4-methylimidazole + acrylonitrile (cyanoethylation)
Uses:
epoxy resin curing agent

N-(2-cyanoethyl)-N-ethyl-m-toluidine
N-ethyl-N-(2-cyanoethyl)-*m*-toluidine; 3-[ethyl(3-methylphenyl)imino]propionitrile; [148-69-6]

$C_{12}H_{16}N_2$. M: 188.27. Liquid. BP: 152–158°C (0.8 kPa).
Production:
• N-ethyl-*m*-toluidine + acrylonitrile (cyanoethylation)
Derivatives:
Disperse Red 65; Disperse Yellow 99

2-cyanoethyl methacrylate

$C_7H_9N_1O_2$. M: 139.16.

Production:
- sodium cyanide + ethylene oxide + methyl methacrylate (epoxidation/transesterification)

Uses: reactive comonomer (acrylate resins/rubber)

N-(2-cyanoethyl)-*N*-methylaniline
[94-34-8]

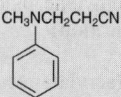

$C_{10}H_{12}N_2$. M: 160.22. Liquid. BP: 150–155°C (1.0 kPa).
Production:
- *N*-methylaniline + acrylonitrile (cyanoethylation)

Derivatives: Basic Red 14

cyanogen bromide
bromine cyanide; [506-68-3]

BrCN

$C_1Br_1N_1$. M: 105.92. Volatile, crystalline solid. MP: 52°C. BP: 61°C. d: 2.02 kg/l (20°C). Soluble in water and oxygenated solvents.
Production:
- sodium cyanide + bromine (addition)

Uses: von Braun degradation reagent

cyanogen chloride
[506-77-4]

ClC≡N

$C_1Cl_1N_1$. M: 61.47. Gas or liquid. BP: 13°C. FP: -6°C. d: 1.19 kg/l. Soluble in water and oxygenated solvents.
Production:
- chlorine + hydrogen cyanide (reaction)

Derivatives: Acid Yellow 127; *n*-butyl cyanoacetate; chlorosulphonyl isocyanate; cyanuric chloride; diethyl methylmalonate; diphenylguanidine; 2-ethoxyethyl cyanoacrylate; ethyl cyanoacetate; malononitrile; mephosfolan; β-methoxyethyl cyanoacrylate; methyl cyanoacetate; phosfolan; robenidine; sodium dicyanamide; tetramethylguanidine

N-cyanoguanidine See: dicyandiamide

N-cyanoimido-*S,S*-dimethyldithiocarbamate
cyanoimidodithiocarbonic acid, dimethyl ester; [10191-60-3]

$(CH_3S)_2C=NCN$

$C_4H_6N_2S_2$. M: 146.23.
Production:
- cyanamide + carbon disulphide + potassium hydroxide + dimethyl sulphate (thiocarbonylation/methylation)

Derivatives: cimetidine; pinacidil

cyanoimidodithiocarbonic acid, dimethyl ester
See: *N*-cyanoimido-*S,S*-dimethyldithiocarbamate

3-cyano-4-methyl-6-hydroxy-2-pyridone
3-cyano-6-hydroxy-4-methyl-2-pyridone; 6-hydroxy-3-cyano-4-methyl-2-pyridone

$C_7H_6N_2O_2$. M: 150.14.
Production:
- methyl acetoacetate + malononitrile (condensation)

Uses:
azoic dye coupling component (polyester dyeing)

2-cyano-4-nitroaniline *See:* 2-amino-5-nitrobenzonitrile

4-cyanophenol *See:* *p*-hydroxybenzonitrile

cyanophos
O-4-cyanophenyl *O,O*-dimethyl phosphorothioate; [2636-26-2]

$C_9H_{10}N_1O_3P_1S_1$. M: 243.22.
Production:
- *p*-hydroxybenzonitrile + *O,O*-dimethyl phosphorochlorothioate (dehydrochlorination)

Uses: insecticide

cyanopinacolone
1-cyano-3,3-dimethyl-2-oxobutane; pivaloacetonitrile; [59997-51-2]

$(CH_3)_3CCCH_2CN$

$C_7H_{11}N_1O_1$. M: 125.18. Solid.
Production:
- α-chloropinacolone + sodium cyanide (cyanidation)

Derivatives:
3-amino-5-*t*-butylisoxazole; ethyl pivaloacetate

cyanuric acid
isocyanuric acid (*keto*-form); *sym*-triazine-2,4,6-trione; 2,4,6-trihydroxy-1,3,5-triazine; 2,4,6-trihydroxy-*sym*-triazine; [108-80-5]

$C_3H_3N_3O_3$. M: 129.07. White crystals which decompose on heating without melting. d: 1.77 kg/l (0°C). Slightly soluble in cold water. Soluble in hot water.

Production:
• urea (thermal deammoniation)
Derivatives:
melamine cyanurate; sodium dichloroisocyanurate; thia-fensulfuron-methyl; trichloroisocyanuric acid; triglycidyl isocyanurate; 1,3,5-tris(4-*t*-butyl-3-hydroxy-2,6-dimeth-ylbenzyl)isocyanurate; 1,3,5-tris(3,5-di-*t*-butyl-4-hydr-oxybenzyl)isocyanurate
Uses: swimming pool chlorine stabiliser

cyanuric chloride
2,4,6-trichloro-1,3,5-triazine; 2,4,6-trichloro-*sym*-triazine; [108-77-0]

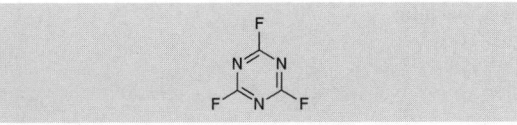

$C_3Cl_3N_3$. M: 184.41. White, crystalline powder with a pungent odour. MP: 146–148°C. d: 1.32 kg/l. Insoluble in water. Soluble in oxygenated solvents.
Production:
• cyanogen chloride (cyclisation)
Derivatives: 7-(4-amino-6-diethylaminotriazin-2-yl)am-ino-3-phenylcoumarin; anilazine; atrazine; 2,4-bis(*n*-octylthio)-6-(4-hydroxy-3,5-di-*t*-butylanilino)-1,3,5-tri-azine; 7-(4-chloro-6-diethylaminotriazin-2-yl)amino-3-phenylcoumarin; cyanate ester resins; cyanazine; cyan-uric fluoride; cyromazine; Direct Green 26; Direct Gre-en 28; eglinazine-ethyl; Fluorescent Brightener 9; Flu-orescent Brightener 24; Fluorescent Brightener 28; Flu-orescent Brightener 32; Fluorescent Brightener 86; Flu-orescent Brightener 103; Fluorescent Brightener 104; Fluorescent Brightener 119; Fluorescent Brightener 136; Fluorescent Brightener 142; Fluorescent Brightener 182; Fluorescent Brightener 193; Fluorescent Brightener 204; Fluorescent Brightener DM; Fluorescent Brightener DMDDEA; Fluorescent Brightener DMEA; hindered-amine cyanurates, polymeric; 2-methylmercapto-4,6-di-chlorotriazine; proglinazine-ethyl; propazine; Reactive Blue 2; Reactive Blue 4; Reactive Blue 7; Reactive Blue 13; Reactive Brown 1; Reactive Orange 1; Reactive Orange 13; Reactive Orange 4; Reactive Red 1; Reactive Red 2; Reactive Red 3; Reactive Red 4; Reactive Red 6; Reactive Red 12; Reactive Yellow 1; Reactive Yellow 3; Reactive Yellow 4; simazine; ter-buthylazine; trietazine; triethylenemelamine; trihydr-azinotriazine; Vat Red 28
Uses:
starch crosslinking agent

cyanuric fluoride
2,4,6-trifluoro-1,3,5-triazine; [675-14-9]
$C_3F_3N_3$. M: 135.04.
Production:
• cyanuric chloride + hydrogen fluoride (halogen exchange)

Uses:
Cibacron F reactive dyestuffs intermediate

cyclacillin
See: ciclacillin

cyclamen aldehyde
2-methyl-3-(*p*-isopropylphenyl)propanal; methyl-*p*-iso-propylphenylpropionaldehyde; [103-95-7]

$C_{13}H_{18}O_1$. M: 190.28. Pale yellow liquid with a strong, floral odour. d: 0.95 kg/l (20°C). Insoluble in water.
Production:
• *p*-isopropylbenzaldehyde + propionaldehyde (aldol condensation/dehydration/hydrogenation)
• α-methylcinnamaldehyde + propylene (hydrogenation/Friedel-Crafts alkylation/alcohol oxidation)
Uses:
fragrance ingredient

cyclandelate
[456-59-7]

$C_{17}H_{24}O_3$. M: 276.38.
Production:
• trimethylcyclohexanol + DL-mandelic acid (esterification)
Uses:
vasodilator drug

cycloate
S-ethyl *N*-cyclohexyl-*N*-ethyl(thiocarbamate); [1134-23-2]

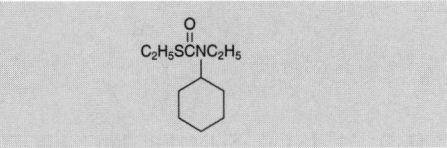

$C_{11}H_{21}N_1O_1S_1$. M: 215.36.
Production:
• *N*-ethylcyclohexylamine + ethyl chlorothioformate (dehydrochlorination)
Uses: herbicide

cyclobarbital
[52-31-3]

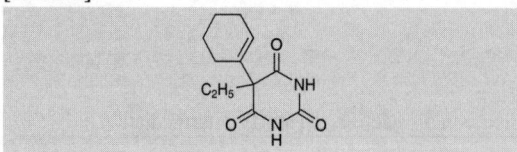

$C_{12}H_{16}N_2O_3$. M: 236.27.
Production:
• ethyl cyanoacetate + cyclohexanone + ethyl
  bromide + dicyandiamide (Cope reaction/
  dehydrobromination/cyclisation/nitrile hydrolysis/
  decarboxylation)
Uses: sedative/hypnotic drug

cyclobenzaprine
[303-53-7]

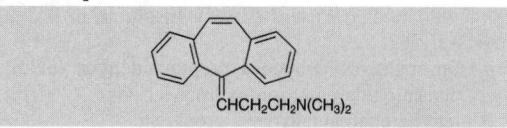

$C_{20}H_{21}N_1$. M: 275.40. Available as the free amine and
as the hydrochloride salt.
Production:
• 3-dimethylaminopropyl chloride hydrochloride +
  dibenzosuberenone-5 (Grignard reagent formation/
  Grignard reaction/dehydration)
Uses: muscle relaxant drug

cyclododecane
CDA

$C_{12}H_{24}$. M: 168.32.
Production:
• 1,5,9-cyclododecatriene (hydrogenation)
Derivatives:
cyclododecanol-cyclododecanone, mixed

cyclododecanol
CDOL; [1724-39-6]

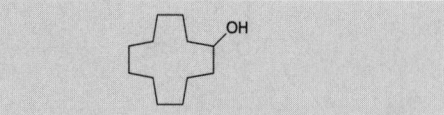

$C_{12}H_{24}O_1$. M: 184.32. Solid. FP: 75°C. BP: 273°C. d:
0.91 kg/l (81°C). Insoluble in water. Flash point:
138°C.
Production:
• cyclododecanol-cyclododecanone, mixed (separation)
Uses: levelling agent; speciality solvent

cyclododecanol-cyclododecanone, mixed

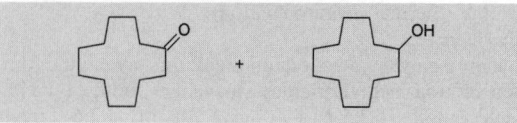

Intermediate stream. Not a commercially traded product.
Production:
• cyclododecane (air oxidation)
Derivatives:
cyclododecanol; cyclododecanone; 1,12-dodecanedioic
acid; dodemorph acetate

cyclododecanone
CDON; [830-13-7]

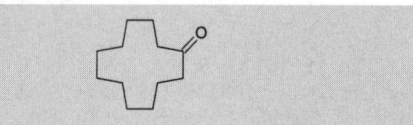

$C_{12}H_{22}O_1$. M: 182.31.
Production:
• cyclododecanol-cyclododecanone, mixed (oxidation)
Derivatives: 5-cyclohexadecen-1-one; lauryllactam; 15-
pentadecanolide
Uses: fragrance ingredient

1,5,9-cyclododecatriene
CDT; cyclododecatriene; [4904-61-4]

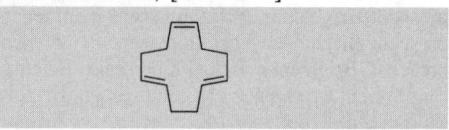

$C_{12}H_{18}$. M: 162.27. Liquid. MP: 10°C. BP: 222–244°C.
d: 0.88 kg/l (20°C). Insoluble in water. Mixed isomer
product containing 60% of the *trans,trans,trans*-isomer.
Production:
• C_4-stream, steam-cracked (cycloaddition;
  coproduced with raffinate I/1,5-cyclooctadiene)
Derivatives:
cyclododecane; hexabromocyclododecane; lauryllactam

cycloheptanone
suberone; [502-42-1]

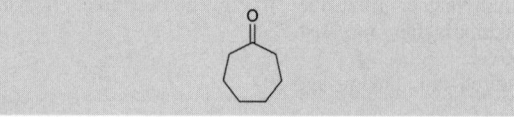

$C_7H_{12}O_1$. M: 112.18. Liquid. BP: 180°C. d: 0.95 kg/l
(20°C). Insoluble in water. Miscible with most organic
solvents.
Production:
• suberic acid (decarboxylation)
Derivatives: heptabarbital

5-cyclohexadecen-1-one
[37609-25-9]

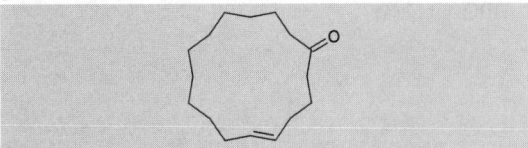

$C_{16}H_{28}O_1$. M: 236.40. Colourless liquid with a strong musk odour.
Production:
• cyclododecanone + acetylene (chlorination/ethynylation/Cope rearrangement)
Uses: fragrance ingredient

cyclohexane
[110-82-7]

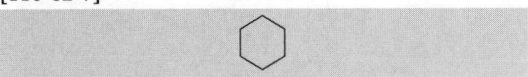

C_6H_{12}. M: 84.17. Colourless liquid. BP: 81°C. d: 0.78 kg/l (15°C). FP: 6°C. Insoluble in water. Soluble in alcohol, ether, chlorinated and aromatic solvents.
Production:
• benzene (hydrogenation)
Derivatives: cyclohexanol-cyclohexanone, mixed; cyclohexanone oxime
Uses: solvent (paint strippers, resins, wax, inks)

cyclohexanecarboxylic acid
hexahydrobenzoic acid; [98-89-5]

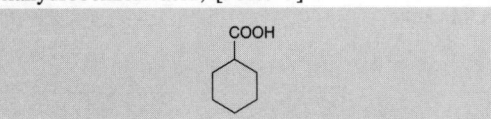

$C_7H_{12}O_2$. M: 128.18. Solid or liquid. MP: 29–31°C. BP: 232–233°C. d: 1.04 kg/l (20°C). Very slightly soluble in water. Soluble in most organic solvents.
Production:
• benzoic acid (hydrogenation)
Derivatives: praziquantel

cyclohexane-1,2-dicarboxylic anhydride
See: hexahydrophthalic anhydride

cyclohexane-1,4-diisocyanate
1,4-cyclohexyl diisocyanate

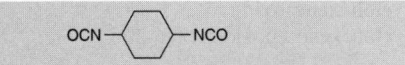

$C_8H_{10}N_2O_2$. M: 166.18. Solid. MP: 58–62°C. The commercial product is the *trans*-isomer.
Production:
• dimethyl cyclohexane-1,4-dicarboxylate + ammonia (amide formation/Hofmann degradation)
Uses: polyurethane elastomers

1,4-cyclohexanedimethanol
1,4-bis(hydroxymethyl)cyclohexane; cyclohexanedimethanol; 1,4-cyclohexylene glycol; 1,4-dimethylolcyclohexane; CHDM

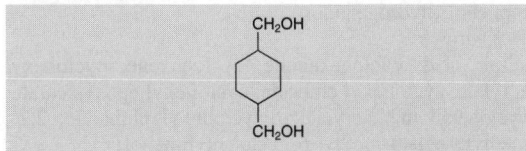

$C_8H_{16}O_2$. M: 144.22. White, waxy solid. MP: 45–50°C. BP: 286°C. d: 1.15 kg/l (20°C). Miscible with water and alcohol. Mixed *cis* and *trans*-isomer product.
Production:
• dimethyl terephthalate (hydrogenation)
Derivatives:
alkyd resins, water-soluble; 1,4-cyclohexanedimethanol diglycidyl ether; poly(1,4-cyclohexylenedimethylene terephthalate); poly(1,4-cyclohexylenedimethylene terephthalate-isophthalate); polyester resins, linear, medium molecular weight; poly(ethylene-1,4-cyclohexanedimethylene-terephthalate)

1,4-cyclohexanedimethanol diglycidyl ether

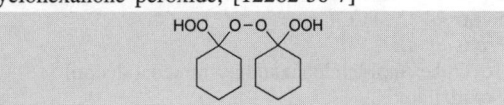

$C_{14}H_{24}O_4$. M: 256.34. Liquid. d: 1.11 kg/l (25°C).
Production:
• 1,4-cyclohexanedimethanol + epichlorohydrin (dehydrochlorination)
Uses: reactive diluent (epoxy resins)

cyclohexane peroxide
cyclohexanone peroxide; [12262-58-7]

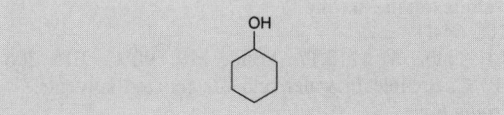

Mixed product containing monomeric, dimeric and trimeric peroxy and hydroperoxy compounds.
Production:
• cyclohexanone + hydrogen peroxide (peroxidation)
Uses:
unsaturated polyester resin crosslinking agent

cyclohexanethiol *See:* cyclohexyl mercaptan

cyclohexanol
hexalin; [108-93-0]

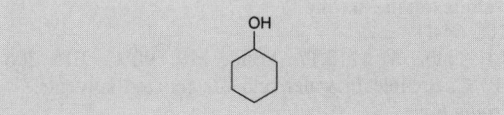

$C_6H_{12}O_1$. M: 100.17. Colourless liquid or solid. MP: 20°C. BP: 159–162°C. d: 0.96 kg/l (20°C). Solubility

in water: 36 g/l water (20°C). Miscible with oxygenated and chlorinated solvents.
Production:
• cyclohexanol-cyclohexanone, mixed (separation)
• phenol (hydrogenation)
Derivatives:
adipic acid; cyclohexanone; cyclohexene; cyclohexyl acrylate; cyclohexyl chloride; cyclohexyl epoxystearate; cyclohexyl methacrylate; dicyclohexyl phthalate; 2,2′-methylenebis(4-methyl-6-cyclohexylphenol)
Uses: solvent (resins, printing inks)

cyclohexanol-cyclohexanone, mixed
KA oil; ketone-alcohol oil

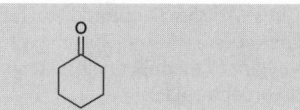

Intermediate stream. Not a commercially traded product.
Production:
• cyclohexane (oxidation)
Derivatives: adipic acid; cyclohexanol; cyclohexanone

cyclohexanone
[108-94-1]

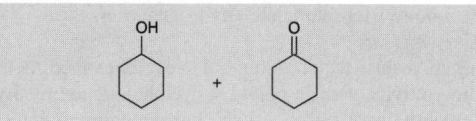

$C_6H_{10}O_1$. M: 98.15. Colourless liquid. BP: 150–158°C. FP: -31°C. d: 0.95 kg/l (20°C). Solubility in water: 23 g/l (20°C). Miscible with most organic solvents. Flash point: 44°C (TCC).
Production:
• cyclohexanol-cyclohexanone, mixed (alcohol oxidation)
• cyclohexanol (alcohol oxidation)
Derivatives:
caprolactone; ciclacillin; cyclobarbital; cyclohexane peroxide; cyclohexanone oxime; cyclohexanone resin; cyclohexylamine; 1,1-di(t-amylperoxy)cyclohexane; 1,1-di-(t-butylperoxy)cyclohexane; dicyclohexylamine; ethynyl cyclohexanol; hexobarbital; 1-hydroxycyclohexyl phenyl ketone; 1-(4-methoxybenzyl)-1,2,3,4,5,6,7,8-octahydro-isoquinoline; pyrogallol
Uses: solvent (resins, lacquers, printing inks)

cyclohexanone oxime
[100-64-1]
$C_6H_{11}N_1O_1$. M: 113.17. Solid. MP: 90°C. BP: 206–210°C. Soluble in water and oxygenated solvents.
Production:
• cyclohexanone + hydroxylamine sulphate (oxime formation)

• cyclohexane + nitrosyl chloride (photonitrosation)
• cyclohexanone + hydroxylamine phosphate (DSM HPO process)

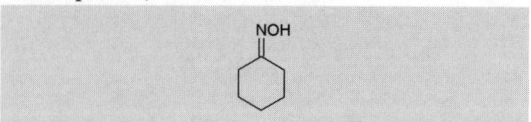

Derivatives: caprolactam
Uses: antioxidant

cyclohexanone peroxide *See:* cyclohexane peroxide

cyclohexanone resin
ketone resin

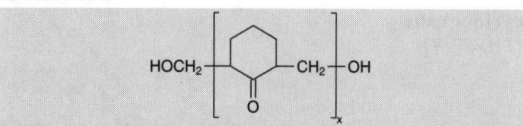

Colourless or pale yellow solid. Acid value: 0 mg KOH/g. Hydroxyl value: 0 mg KOH/g. Soluble in oxygenated solvents. Insoluble in aliphatic solvents and water.
Production:
• cyclohexanone + formaldehyde (carbonyl condensation)
Uses: adhesion promotion agent (printing inks); clear metal cellulose lacquer modifier; tackifier (polyamide hot melt adhesives)

cyclohexene
[110-83-8]

C_6H_{10}. M: 82.15.
Production:
• cyclohexanol (dehydration)
Derivatives:
cyclohexene oxide; cyclohexyl mercaptan; L-lysine

4-cyclohexene-1,2-dicarboximide
See: tetrahydrophthalimide

4-cyclohexene-1,2-dicarboxylic acid
See: tetrahydrophthalic anhydride

cyclohexene oxide
cyclohexene epoxide; [286-20-4]

$C_6H_{10}O_1$. M: 98.15. Liquid. BP: 130°C. MP: -30°C.
Production:
• cyclohexene (hypochlorination/dehydrochlorination)
Derivatives: propargite

cycloheximide
[66-81-9]

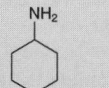

$C_{15}H_{23}N_1O_4$. M: 281.35.
Production:
• microbial fermentation medium + *Streptomyces griseus* bacteria (fermentation/extraction; byproduct of streptomycin production)
Uses:
fungicide/plant growth regulator

cyclohexyl acrylate

$CH_2=CHCO-$ (with O double bond) cyclohexyl

$C_9H_{14}O_2$. M: 154.21.
Production:
• cyclohexanol + acrylic acid (esterification)
Uses: acrylic resin comonomer

cyclohexylamine
CHA; [108-91-8]

NH_2 cyclohexyl

$C_6H_{13}N_1$. M: 99.18. Liquid with a strong, amine odour. BP: 133–134°C. FP: -17°C. d: 0.87 kg/l (4°C). Miscible with water and most organic solvents. Flash point: 28°C (CC).
Production:
• aniline (reduction; coproduced with dicyclohexylamine)
• cyclohexanone + ammonia (reductive ammoniation; coproduced with dicyclohexylamine)
Derivatives:
Acid Blue 62; calcium cyclamate; N-cyclohexyl-2-benzothiazolesulphenamide; cyclohexyl isocyanate; N-cyclohexylmaleimide; N-cyclohexyl-p-toluenesulphonamide; dicyclohexylcarbodiimide; N,N-diethylcyclohexylamine; N,N-dimethylcyclohexylamine; N-ethylcyclohexylamine; N-methylcyclohexylamine; sodium cyclamate
Uses: corrosion inhibitor (boiler water); process solvent

N-cyclohexyl-2-benzothiazolesulphenamide
benzothiazyl-2-cyclohexylsulphenamide; CBS; [95-33-0]

benzothiazole-SNH-cyclohexyl structure

$C_{13}H_{16}N_2S_2$. M: 264.41. Off-white powder. MP: 95–100°C. d: 1.27 kg/l. Insoluble in water. Soluble in aromatic solvents.

Production:
• 2-mercaptobenzothiazole + cyclohexylamine (oxidative coupling)
Uses:
vulcanisation accelerator

cyclohexyl chloride
chlorocyclohexane; [542-18-7]

$C_6H_{11}Cl_1$. M: 118.61. Liquid. BP: 141–143°C. MP: -44°C. d: 1.00 kg/l (20°C). Insoluble in water. Miscible with oxygenated and aromatic solvents.
Production:
• cyclohexanol (chlorination)
Derivatives:
azocyclotin; cyclomethycaine; cyhexatin

cyclohexyldiethylamine
See: N,N-diethylcyclohexylamine

1,4-cyclohexylene glycol
See: 1,4-cyclohexanedimethanol

cyclohexyl epoxystearate

$CH_3(CH_2)_7CH-CH(CH_2)_7CO-$ cyclohexyl (with epoxide and O double bond)

$C_{24}H_{44}O_3$. M: 380.61.
Production:
• oleic acid + peracetic acid + cyclohexanol (epoxidation/esterification)
Uses:
polyvinyl chloride costabiliser/plasticiser

cyclohexylethylamine *See:* N-ethylcyclohexylamine

cyclohexyl isocyanate
[3173-53-3]

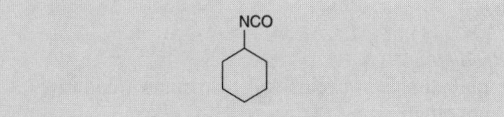

$C_7H_{11}N_1O_1$. M: 125.18.
Production:
• cyclohexylamine + phosgene (phosgenation)
Derivatives: glibenclamide; glipizide; hexazinone; hexythiazox; lenacil

N-cyclohexylmaleimide
$C_{10}H_{13}N_1O_2$. M: 179.22.
Production:
• maleic acid + cyclohexylamine (amide formation)

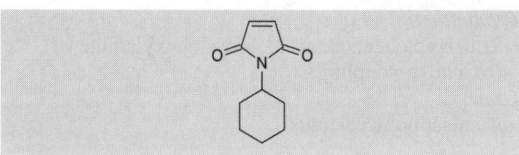

Derivatives:
vinyl chloride-cyclohexylmaleimide copolymers

cyclohexyl mercaptan
cyclohexanethiol; [1569-69-3]

$C_6H_{12}S_1$. M: 116.23. Liquid. BP: 155–161°C. d: 1.00 kg/l (15°C). Insoluble in water. Soluble in oxygenated and chlorinated solvents.
Production:
• cyclohexene + hydrogen sulphide (thiolation)
Derivatives:
N-(cyclohexylthio)phthalimide

cyclohexyl methacrylate
[101-43-9]

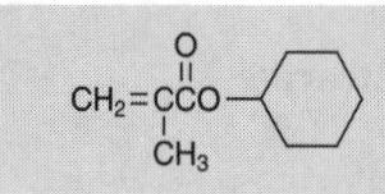

$CH_2=C$ CO CH_3

$C_{10}H_{16}O_2$. M: 168.24.
Production:
• cyclohexanol + methyl methacrylate (transesterification)
Uses: acrylic resin comonomer

N-(cyclohexylthio)phthalimide
CTP; Santogard PVI (Monsanto); [17796-82-6]

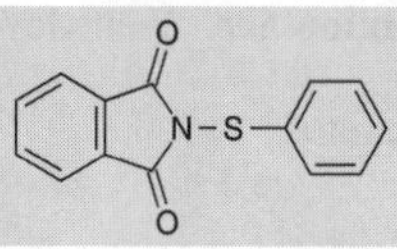

$C_{14}H_{15}N_1O_2S_1$. M: 261.34.
Production:
• phthalimide + cyclohexyl mercaptan (oxidative coupling)
Uses: vulcanisation retarder

N-cyclohexyl-p-toluenesulphonamide
[80-30-8]

CH_3 SO_2NH

$C_{13}H_{19}N_1O_2S_1$. M: 253.36. Brown solid. MP: 86°C. BP: 350°C. d: 1.13 kg/l (25°C). Insoluble in water. Soluble in oxygenated and aromatic solvents.

Production:
• p-toluenesulphonyl chloride + cyclohexylamine (sulphonamide formation)
Uses: plasticiser (polyamide hot melt adhesives)

cyclomethycaine
[139-62-8]; [6202-05-7] (sulphate)

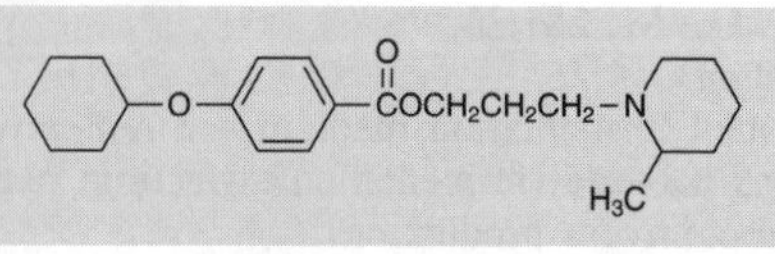

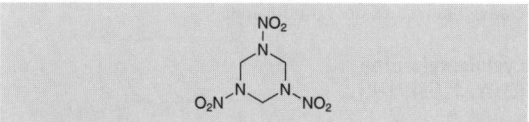

$C_{22}H_{33}N_1O_3$. M: 359.51.
Production:
• 1-bromo-3-chloropropane + 2-methylpiperidine + p-hydroxybenzoic acid + cyclohexyl chloride (amine formation/esterification/ether formation)
Uses: topical anaesthetic drug

cyclonite
cyclotrimethylenetrinitramine; hexogen; 1,3,5-trinitro-1,3,5-hexahydrotriazine; RDX; [121-82-4]

$C_3H_6N_6O_6$. M: 222.11.
Production:
• hexamethylenetetramine + ammonium nitrate + paraformaldehyde + nitric acid, concentrated (Bachmann process)
• hexamethylenetetramine (direct nitrolysis process)
Uses: military explosive

1,5-cyclooctadiene
cyclooctadiene; *cis,cis*-1,5-cyclooctadiene; COD; [111-78-4]

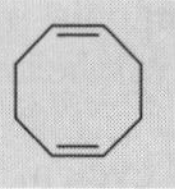

C_8H_{12}. M: 108.19.
Production:
• C₄-stream, steam-cracked (cycloaddition; coproduced with raffinate I/1,5,9-cyclododecatriene)
Derivatives: cyclooctene; hexachlorocyclopentadiene-cyclooctadiene adduct; 1,5-hexadiene
Uses: hydroformylation catalyst intermediate

cyclooctene
COE; [931-88-4]

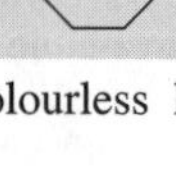

C_8H_{14}. M: 110.20. Colourless liquid. *cis*-isomer: MP:

-12°C. BP: 138°C. d: 0.85 kg/l (25°C). Soluble in oxygenated solvents.
Production:
• 1,5-cyclooctadiene (hydrogenation)
Derivatives:
1,9-decadiene; polyoctenylene, rubber; suberic acid

cyclopentadienised oils
Production:
• linseed oil/castor oil, dehydrated/tung oil/soyabean
  oil + dicyclopentadiene (Diels-Alder cycloaddition)
Uses:
rapid-drying oils (paints)

cyclopentanone
[120-92-3]

$C_5H_8O_1$. M: 84.11. Colourless liquid. BP: 130–131°C.
d: 0.94 kg/l (20°C). Insoluble in alcohol. Soluble in
ketone and ester solvents.
Production:
• adipic acid (Dieckmann condensation/decarboxylation)
Derivatives:
cyclopenthiazide; cyclopentylamine; 2-heptylcyclopent-
anone; methyl dihydrojasmonate

cyclopentene
[142-29-0]

C_5H_8. M: 68.11. Colourless liquid with a penetrating
odour. BP: 44°C. MP: -135°C. d: 0.77 kg/l (18°C). Almost insoluble in water. Soluble in hydrocarbons. Flash
point: -37°C.
Production:
• C_5-stream, steam-cracked (NMP solvent separation
  process; byproduct of dicyclopentadiene/isoprene
  production)
Derivatives:
cyclopentobarbital; cyclopentylamine

cyclopenthiazide
[742-20-1]

$C_{13}H_{18}Cl_1N_3O_4S_2$. M: 379.88.
Production:
• cyclopentanone + ethyl cyanoacetate + 5-chloro-
  aniline-2,4-disulphonamide (Cope reaction/
  hydrogenation/decarboxylation/condensation)

Uses: diuretic/antihypertensive drug

cyclopentobarbital
[76-68-6]

$C_{12}H_{14}N_2O_3$. M: 234.25.
Production:
• cyclopentene + diethyl malonate + allyl bromide +
  urea (alpha bromination/dehydrobromination/
  dehydrobromination/cyclisation)
Uses:
sedative/hypnotic drug

cyclopentylamine
[1003-03-8]

$C_5H_{11}N_1$. M: 85.15. Liquid. BP: 108°C.
Production:
• cyclopentanone + ammonia (reductive
  ammoniation)
• cyclopentene + ammonia (amine formation)
Derivatives: pencycuron

cyclophosphamide
[50-18-0]

$C_7H_{15}Cl_2N_2O_2P_1$. M: 261.09.
Production:
• diethanolamine + phosphorus oxychloride +
  3-aminopropanol (alcohol chlorination/
  dehydrochlorination/dehydrochlorination)
Uses:
antineoplastic drug

cyclopropane carboxylic acid
[1759-53-1]

$C_4H_6O_2$. M: 86.09. Liquid or solid. MP: 18–19°C. BP:
182–184°C. d: 1.09 kg/l (20°C). Soluble in hot water
and oxygenated solvents.
Production:
• ethylene + ethyl diazoacetate (addition)
Derivatives:
ancymidol; 4,4-bis(*p*-fluorophenyl)butyl chloride; cyclopropylamine; cyclopropylmethyl bromide

cyclopropylamine
aminocyclopropane; [765-30-0]

$C_3H_7N_1$. M: 57.10.
Production:
• cyclopropane carboxylic acid + ammonia (nitrile formation/Hofmann degradation)
Derivatives: cyromazine

cyclopropyl bromide
bromocyclopropane; [4333-56-6]

$C_3H_5Br_1$. M: 120.97. Liquid. BP: 68–70°C.
Production:
• allyl bromide + bromine + zinc (addition/debromination)
Derivatives: biotin; nortriptyline

cyclopropylmethyl bromide
bromomethylcyclopropane; [7051-34-5]

$C_4H_7Br_1$. M: 135.00. Colourless or pale yellow liquid with a characteristic odour. BP: 105–110°C. d: 1.40 kg/l. Insoluble in water.
Production:
• cyclopropane carboxylic acid (esterification/ester reduction/alcohol bromination)
Derivatives:
buprenorphine; cimetropium bromide; naltrexone; prazepam; profluralin

cyclotetramethylenetetranitramine *See:* octogen

cyclotrimethylenetrinitramine *See:* cyclonite

cycloxydim
2-[1-(ethoxyimino)butyl]-3-hydroxy-5-thian-3-ylcyclohex-2-enone; [99434-58-9]

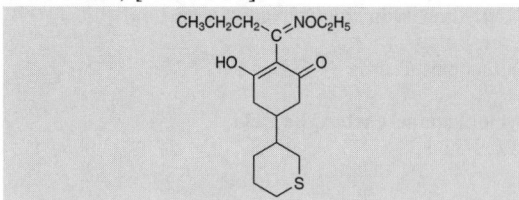

$C_{17}H_{27}N_1O_3S_1$. M: 325.48.
Production:
• allyl mercaptan + acrolein + acetone + dimethyl malonate + *n*-butyryl chloride + hydroxylamine sulphate + diethyl sulphate (carbonylethylation/cyclisation/condensation/decarboxylation/dehydrochlorination/oxime formation/ethylation)
Uses: herbicide

cyfluthrin
[68359-37-5]

$C_{22}H_{18}Cl_2F_1N_1O_3$. M: 434.30. The commercial product is a mixture of isomers.
Production:
• 4-fluoro-3-phenoxybenzaldehyde cyanohydrin + (*1RS*)-*cis/trans*-3-(2,2-dichlorovinyl)-2,2-dimethyl-cyclopropanecarboxylic acid (esterification)
Uses: insecticide

cyhalothrin
[68085-85-8]; [91465-08-6]

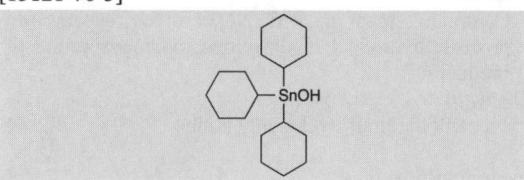

$C_{23}H_{19}Cl_1F_3N_1O_3$. M: 449.85. Available commercially as a mixed isomer product formed from the racemic α-cyanoalcohol with an (*RS*)-*cis* configuration of the cyclopropane ring. Selective crystallisation produces a mixture of two esters formed from the (*S*)-alcohol with the (*1R*)-*cis*-acid, and the (*R*)-alcohol with the (*1S*)-*cis*-acid.
Production:
• 3-phenoxybenzaldehyde cyanohydrin + 3-(2-chloro-3,3,3-trifluoropropenyl)-2,2-dimethylcyclopropane-carboxylic acid (esterification)
Uses: insecticide

cyhexatin
tricyclohexyltin hydroxide; Plictran (Dow Chemical); [13121-70-5]

$C_{18}H_{34}O_1Sn_1$. M: 385.16.
Production:
• cyclohexyl chloride + stannic chloride (dechlorination/hydration)
Uses: acaricide

***p*-cymene**
4-isopropyltoluene; [99-87-6]
$C_{10}H_{14}$. M: 134.22. Liquid. BP: 177°C. MP: -68°C. d: 0.86 kg/l (20°C). Insoluble in water. Soluble in aromatic and oxygenated solvents.

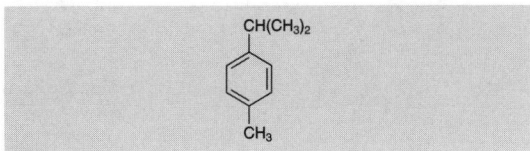

Production:
• dipentene (pyrolysis)
Derivatives: 6-acetyl-1,1,2,3,3,5-hexamethylindane; 6-acetyl-1,1,2,4,4,7-hexamethyltetralin; 4,6-dinitro-1,1,3,3,5-pentamethylindane; *p*-isopropylbenzaldehyde; γ-terpinene

cymoxanil
1-(2-cyano-2-methoxyiminoacetyl)-3-ethylurea; [57966-95-7]

$$CH_3CH_2NHCNHCC=NOCH_3$$
$$\underset{O}{\overset{O}{\parallel}}\;\underset{CN}{\overset{O}{\parallel}}$$

$C_7H_{10}N_4O_3$. M: 198.19.
Production:
• cyanoacetamide + ethyl isocyanate + sodium nitrite (isocyanate addition/nitrosation/methylation)
Uses: fungicide

cypermethrin
[67375-30-8]

$C_{22}H_{19}Cl_2N_1O_3$. M: 416.31. Mixed enantiomer product formed from the racemic α-cyano alcohol with a (*RS*)-*cis* configuration of the cyclopropane ring. Selective crystallisation produces a mixture of two esters: the (*S*)-alcohol with the (*1R*)-*cis*-acid, and the (*R*)-alcohol with the (*1S*)-*cis*-acid.
Production:
• 3-phenoxybenzaldehyde cyanohydrin + (*1RS*)-*cis*-3-(2,2-dichlorovinyl)-2,2-dimethylcyclopropane-carboxylic acid (esterification)
Uses: insecticide

cyproheptadine
[129-03-3]

$C_{21}H_{21}N_1$. M: 287.41. Available commercially as the free base and as the hydrochloride sesquihydrate salt.

Production:
• dibenzosuberenone-5 + isonipecotic acid (condensation/decarboxylation)
Uses: antihistamine/appetite stimulant drug

cyromazine
N-cyclopropyl-1,3,5-triazine-2,4,6-triamine; [66215-27-8]

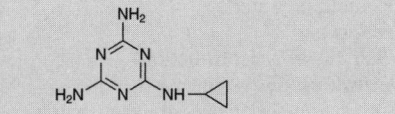

$C_6H_{10}N_6$. M: 166.19.
Production:
• cyanuric chloride + cyclopropylamine + ammonia (amine formation/amine formation)
Uses: insecticide

cysteamine hydrochloride
See: 2-mercaptoethylamine hydrochloride

L-cysteine
L-2-amino-3-thiopropionic acid; Cys; L-β-mercapto-alanine; [52-90-4]

$$HSCH_2-\underset{H}{\overset{NH_2}{C}}-COOH$$

$C_3H_7N_1O_2S_1$. M: 121.16. White crystals. Soluble in water. Oxidised by air to cystine in neutral and alkali solutions. Insoluble in organic solvents. Available commercially as the free base or hydrochloride salt.
Production:
• L-cystine (electrolytic reduction)
• 2-aminothiazoline-4-carboxylic acid (enzymatic hydrolysis)
• chloroacetaldehyde + hydrogen cyanide + ammonium bicarbonate + sodium sulphide (Bucherer-Bergs reaction/enzymatic thiolation)
Derivatives:
acetylcysteine; carbocysteine; cilastatin; mecysteine hydrochloride; oxytocin; timonacic
Uses: flavour enhancer/dough conditioner

DL-cysteine hydrochloride
[10318-18-0] (hydrate)

$$HSCH_2\overset{NH_3^+}{\underset{|}{C}HCOOH}\;\;Cl^-$$

$C_3H_8Cl_1N_1O_2S_1$. M: 157.61. Available as the monohydrate.
Production:
• mercaptoacetaldehyde + hydrogen cyanide + ammonia (Strecker synthesis)
Derivatives:
timonacic
Uses: animal feed supplement; cosmetics ingredient

L-cystine

3,3′-dithiobis(2-aminopropionic acid); [56-89-3]

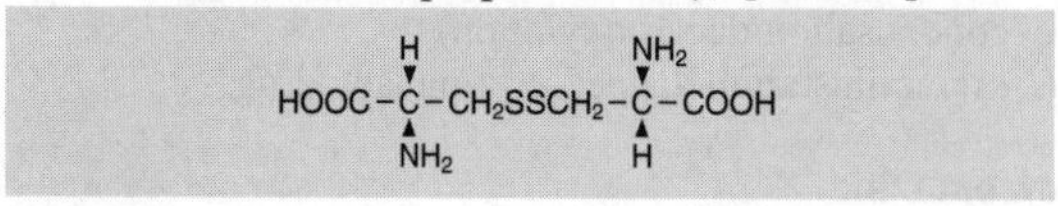

$$\underset{\underset{\text{NH}_2}{\uparrow}}{\text{HOOC}-\overset{\overset{\text{H}}{\downarrow}}{\text{C}}-\text{CH}_2\text{SSCH}_2-\overset{\overset{\text{NH}_2}{\downarrow}}{\underset{\underset{\text{H}}{\uparrow}}{\text{C}}}-\text{COOH}}$$

$C_6H_{12}N_2O_4S_2$. M: 240.31. White crystals. MP: 260°C. Insoluble in water.

Production:
• hair (hydrolysis/extraction)

Derivatives: L-cysteine

Uses: hair/nail damage adjuvant; parenteral nutrient ingredient

2,4-D
2,4-dichlorophenoxyacetic acid; [94-75-7]; [5742-19-8] (diethanolamine salt); [2008-39-1] (dimethylamine salt)

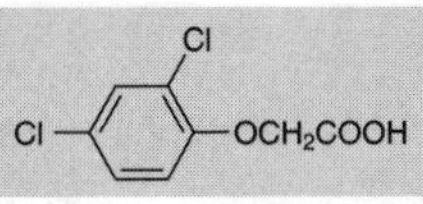

$C_8H_6Cl_2O_3$. M: 221.05. Available commercially as the acid, sodium, dimethylamine, diethanolamine or triethanolamine salts.
Production:
• 2,4-dichlorophenol + chloroacetic acid (ether formation)
Derivatives: 2,4-D-2-butoxyethyl; 2,4-D-butyl; 2,4-D-2-hydroxybutyl; 2,4-D-isooctyl
Uses: herbicide

DAA *See:* diacetone alcohol

2,4-DAA *See:* 2,4-diaminoanisole

DAB *See:* dialkylbenzene

DABCO *See:* triethylenediamine

DADMAC *See:* diallyldimethylammonium chloride

DADPM *See:* 4,4'-diaminodiphenylmethane, crude

daimuron
N-(4-methylphenyl)-N'-(1-methyl-1-phenylethyl)urea; dymron; [42609-52-9]

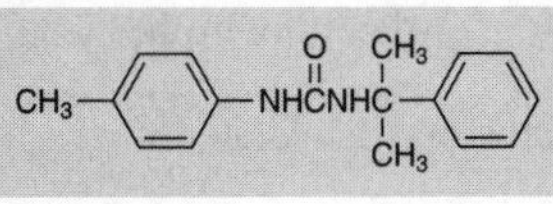

$C_{17}H_{20}N_2O_1$. M: 268.36.
Production:
• 2-phenyl-2-propylamine + phosgene + p-toluidine (phosgenation)
Uses: herbicide

DAIP *See:* diallyl isophthalate

dalapon *See:* α,α-dichloropropionic acid

DAM *See:* diallyl maleate

damar
dammar; [9000-16-2]
Exuded oleoresin from *Shorea* trees which grow in Malaysia and Indonesia. White to dark brown solid. MP: ~110°C. d: ~1.08 kg/l. Acid value 20–35 mg

KOH/g. Soluble in esters and aromatic solvents. Available commercially as standard or dewaxed grades.
Uses: gloss/adhesion promoter (cellulose nitrate lacquers); binder (paper varnishes)

daminozide
succinic acid mono(2,2-dimethylhydrazide); SADH; [1596-84-5]

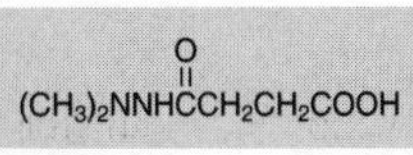

$C_6H_{12}N_2O_3$. M: 160.18.
Production:
• succinic anhydride + 1,1-dimethylhydrazine (amide formation)
Uses: plant growth regulator

danthron *See:* 1,8-dihydroxyanthraquinone

DAO *See:* deasphalted oil

DAP *See:* diallyl phthalate; diammonium phosphate

DAPI *See:* diaminophenylindane

dapsone *See:* 4,4'-diaminodiphenyl sulphone

darvon *See:* dextropropoxyphene

dazomet
tetrahydro-3,5-dimethyl-2H-1,3,5-thiadiazine-2-thione; DMTT; Basamid (BASF); [533-74-4]

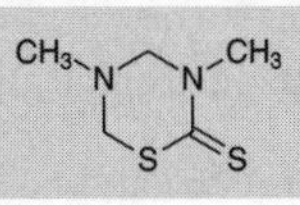

$C_5H_{10}N_2S_2$. M: 162.27.
Production:
• metam-sodium + formaldehyde + methylamine (carbonyl condensation)
Uses: slimicide (water treatment, surface coatings, adhesives); soil fumigant

2,4-DB
4-(2,4-dichlorophenoxy)butyric acid; [94-82-6]; [2758-42-1] (dimethylamine salt); [19480-40-1] (potassium salt); [10433-59-7] (sodium salt)

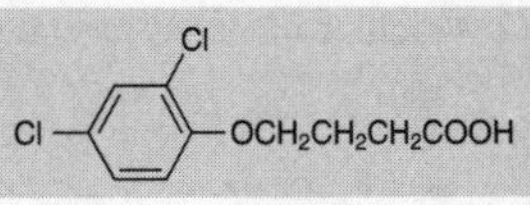

$C_{10}H_{10}Cl_2O_3$. M: 249.10. Available commercially as the acid, sodium, potassium or dimethylamine salts.

Production:
• 2,4-dichlorophenol + γ-butyrolactone (esterification)
Derivatives:
2,4-DB-butyl
Uses: herbicide

DBA *See:* di-*n*-butylamine

DBA acid *See:* alkylene(C₄-C₆)dicarboxylic acids

DBBP *See:* di-*n*-butyl butylphosphonate

2,4-DB-butyl
butyl 4-(2,4-dichlorophenoxy)butyrate

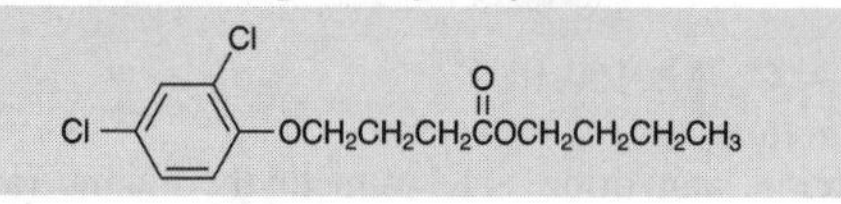

$C_{14}H_{18}Cl_2O_3$. M: 305.20.
Production:
• *n*-butanol + 2,4-DB (esterification)
Uses:
herbicide

DBDMH *See:* 1,3-dibromo-5,5-dimethylhydantoin

DBDPO *See:* decabromodiphenyl oxide

DBE *See:* ethylene dibromide; dimethyl alkylene(C₄-C₆)dicarboxylates

DBED *See:* benzathine

DBM *See:* methylene bromide; di-*n*-butyl maleate

DBNPA *See:* 2,2-dibromo-3-nitrilopropionamide

DBNPG *See:* dibromoneopentyl glycol

DBP *See:* di-*n*-butyl phthalate

DBPH *See:* 2,2′-dicyclopentadienylbis(6-*t*-butyl-4-methylphenol)

DBS *See:* di-*n*-butyl sebacate

DBTU *See:* di-*n*-butylthiourea

DBU *See:* 1,5-diazabicyclo[5.4.0]undec-5-ene

2,4-D-2-butoxyethyl
2-butoxyethyl (2,4-dichlorophenoxy)acetate; [1929-73-3]

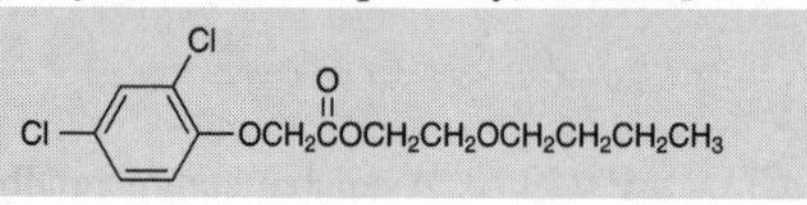

$C_{14}H_{18}Cl_2O_4$. M: 321.20.

Production:
• ethylene glycol monobutyl ether + 2,4-D
  (esterification)
Uses: herbicide

2,4-D-butyl
butyl (2,4-dichlorophenoxy)acetate; [94-80-4]

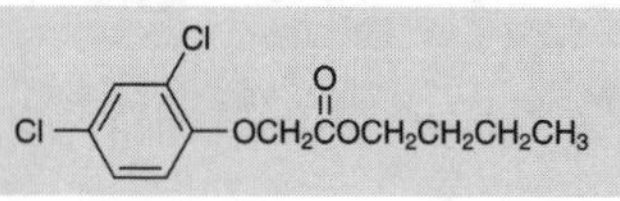

$C_{12}H_{14}Cl_2O_3$. M: 277.15.
Production:
• *n*-butanol + 2,4-D (esterification)
Uses: herbicide

DCB *See:* 1,4-dichlorobutane

DCBS
See: N,N-dicyclohexyl-2-benzothiazolesulphenamide

DCC *See:* dicyclohexylcarbodiimide

DCCD *See:* dicyclohexylcarbodiimide

DCD *See:* dicyandiamide

DCEE *See:* di-(2-chloroethyl)ether

DCHA *See:* dicyclohexylamine

DCHP *See:* dicyclohexyl phthalate

DCIMC acid *See:* 3-(2,6-dichlorophenyl)-5-methyl-isoxazole-4-carboxylic acid

3,4-DCNB *See:* 3,4-dichloronitrobenzene

DCO *See:* castor oil, dehydrated

2,4-DCP *See:* 2,4-dichlorophenol

3,6-DCP *See:* clopyralid

DCPD *See:* dicyclopentadiene

DDA *See:* epoxy-acrylate resins

DDBSA
See: dodecylbenzenesulphonic acid, linear; dodecylbenzenesulphonic acid, branched

DDDA *See:* 1,12-dodecanedioic acid

DDDM *See:* dichlorophen

DDEA *See:* Fluorescent Brightener 28

DDH *See:* 1,3-dichloro-5,5-dimethylhydantoin

DDM *See:* 4,4′-diaminodiphenylmethane, crude; *n*-dodecyl mercaptan

DDNP *See:* diazodinitrophenol

DDPM *See:* 4,4′-diaminodiphenylmethane, crude

DDPS *See:* 4,4′-diaminodiphenyl sulphone

DDS *See:* 4,4′-diaminodiphenyl sulphone; dodecenylsuccinic anhydride

DDSA *See:* dodecenylsuccinic anhydride

DDT
4,4′-dichlorodiphenyltrichloroethane; dichlorodiphenyltrichloroethane; [50-29-3]

$C_{14}H_9Cl_5$. M: 354.49. Mixed isomer product consisting of 70% *p,p′*-DDT and 30% *o,p′*-DDT.
Production:
• chloral + chlorobenzene (carbonyl condensation)
Derivatives: dicofol
Uses: insecticide

DDVP *See:* dichlorvos

DEA *See:* 2,6-diethylaniline; diethanolamine; *N,N*-diethylaniline

DEAC *See:* diethylaluminium chloride

DEAE *See:* diethylaminoethanol

DEAP *See:* 3-diethylaminopropylamine; 2,2-diethoxyacetophenone

deasphalted oil
DAO
Production:
• short residue (solvent deasphalting; coproduced with bitumen)
Derivatives: brightstock; gasoline, catalytic-cracker; heavy cycle oil; light cycle oil; lubricant oils, refined; refinery gas
Uses: raw material (petroleum coke production)

DEC *See:* 2-diethylaminoethyl chloride hydrochloride

decabromodiphenyl oxide
bis(pentabromophenyl) ether; decabrom; decabromodiphenyl ether; DBDPO; Saytex 102 (Ethyl); [1163-19-5]

$C_{12}Br_{10}O_1$. M: 959.17. Solid. MP: 300–315°C. d: 3.3 kg/l. Insoluble in water, oxygenated and aromatic solvents.
Production:
• diphenyl oxide + bromine (ring bromination)
Uses: fire-retardant additive (polyester, elastomers, polystyrene copolymers, polypropylene, crosslinked polyethylene)

1,9-decadiene
[1647-16-1]

$CH_2=CH(CH_2)_6CH=CH_2$

$C_{10}H_{18}$. M: 138.25.
Production:
• cyclooctene + ethylene (metathesis)
Uses: crosslinking comonomer

decahydronaphthalene
DHN; Decalin (Du Pont); [91-17-8]

$C_{10}H_{18}$. M: 138.25. Liquid. BP: 182–184°C. d: 0.88 kg/l (15°C). Insoluble in water. Commercial products contain mainly the *trans*-isomer.
Production:
• naphthalene (hydrogenation)
Uses: solvent

decahydro-β-naphthyl acetate
[10519-11-6]

$C_{12}H_{20}O_2$. M: 196.29. Colourless liquid with a fruity odour.
Production:
• β-naphthol + acetic anhydride (hydrogenation/esterification)
Uses:
perfume ingredient (technical/household products)

γ-decalactone
4-hydroxydecanoic acid lactone; [706-14-9]

$C_{10}H_{18}O_2$. M: 170.25. Colourless liquid with a fruity odour. BP: 156°C (2.3 kPa). d: 0.95 kg/l (21°C).

Production:
• *n*-heptanol + acrylic acid (free-radical addition)
Uses: fragrance/flavouring ingredient

n-decaldehyde

aldehyde C-10; capraldehyde; capric aldehyde; *n*-decan-al; *n*-decyl aldehyde; [112-31-2]

$$CH_3(CH_2)_8CHO$$

$C_{10}H_{20}O_1$. M: 156.27. Colourless liquid with a citrus odour. BP: 208°C. MP: -4°C. d: 0.83 kg/l (15°C). Insoluble in water. Soluble in alcohol.
Production:
• *n*-decanol (alcohol oxidation)
Uses: fragrance ingredient

n-decanoic acid *See:* capric acid

n-decanol

alcohol C-10; 1-decanol; *n*-decyl alcohol; [112-30-1]

$$CH_3(CH_2)_9OH$$

$C_{10}H_{22}O_1$. M: 158.29. Colourless liquid with a floral odour. BP: 226–230°C. MP: 6°C. d: 0.82 kg/l (25°C). Insoluble in water. Soluble in oxygenated solvents.
Production:
• ethylene (Alfol/Epal processes; coproduced with *n*-hexanol/*n*-octanol/*n*-alkanol(C_8-C_{10})/lauryl alcohol, narrow-cut/myristyl alcohol/*n*-alkanol(C_{12}-C_{14})/cetyl alcohol/stearyl alcohol/cetylstearyl alcohol/ *n*-alkanol(C_{12}-C_{18})/*n*-alkanol(C_{20+}))
Derivatives: *n*-decaldehyde; *n*-decyl chloride; *n*-decyl oleate; methyldidecylamine
Uses: fragrance ingredient

decant oil *See:* heavy cycle oil

1-decene

decene-1; decylene; [872-05-9]

$$CH_3(CH_2)_7CH=CH_2$$

$C_{10}H_{20}$. M: 140.27. Colourless liquid. BP: 170–171°C. Pour point: -66°C. d: 0.73 kg/l (25°C). Insoluble in water. Soluble in most organic solvents. Flash point: 45°C (CC).
Production:
• ethylene (Ziegler oligomerisation; coproduced with 1-butene/1-hexene/1-octene/1-dodecene/ α-olefins(C_{12}-C_{14})/α-olefins(C_{14}-C_{16})/α-olefins(C_{16}-C_{18})/α-olefins(C_{18+}))
Derivatives: *n*-alkanol(C_9-C_{11}); polyalphaolefins

DECHA *See:* N,N-diethylcyclohexylamine

DECTP *See:* O,O-diethyl phosphorochlorothioate

n-decyl alcohol *See:* *n*-decanol

n-decyl chloride

[1002-69-3]

$$CH_3(CH_2)_9Cl$$

$C_{10}H_{21}Cl_1$. M: 176.73. Liquid. BP: 222°C. d: 0.87 kg/l (20°C). Insoluble in water.
Production:
• *n*-decanol (chlorination)
Derivatives:
didecyldimethylammonium chloride

n-decyl oleate

$$CH_3(CH_2)_7CH=CH(CH_2)_7\overset{\overset{O}{\|}}{C}O(CH_2)_9CH_3$$

$C_{28}H_{54}O_2$. M: 422.74. Yellow liquid. MP: 3–6°C. Insoluble in water.
Production:
• *n*-decanol + oleic acid (esterification)
Uses: superfatting agent (hand cleaners, cosmetics, pharmaceuticals)

decyltetradecanol

2-decyl-1-tetradecanol; [58670-89-6]

$$\underset{CH_3(CH_2)_{11}CHCH_2OH}{\overset{(CH_2)_9CH_3}{|}}$$

$C_{24}H_{50}O_1$. M: 354.66. Liquid. d: 0.84 kg/l (17°C). Insoluble in water.
Production:
• lauryl alcohol, narrow-cut (Guerbet reaction)
Uses: solvent (cosmetics, toiletries)

DEDMA *See:* diethylene glycol dimethacrylate

DEET *See:* N,N-diethyl-*m*-toluamide

DEG *See:* diethylene glycol

DEGN *See:* diethylene glycol dinitrate

degras *See:* wool grease

DEHA *See:* diethylhydroxylamine

DEHM *See:* di-(2-ethylhexyl) maleate

DEHP *See:* di-(2-ethylhexyl) phthalate

DEHPA *See:* bis(2-ethylhexyl) hydrogen phosphate

dehydrated castor oil *See:* castor oil, dehydrated

dehydroacetic acid

DHA; [520-45-6]; [4418-26-2] (sodium salt)
$C_8H_8O_4$. M: 168.15. Off-white, crystalline powder. MP: 110°C. Insoluble in water. Soluble in oxygenated and

aromatic solvents. Available as free acid or as the sodium salt.

O

COCH₃

CH₃ O

Production:
• diketene (addition)
Uses: preservative; speciality plasticiser

7-dehydrocholesterol
provitamin D₃; [434-16-2]

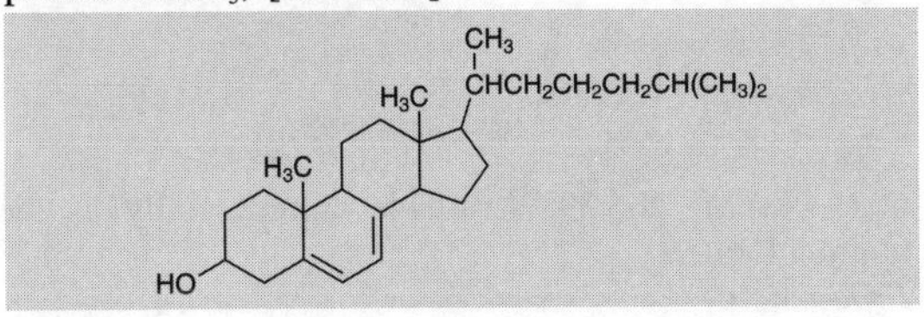

CH₃
CHCH₂CH₂CH₂CH(CH₃)₂
H₃C
H₃C
HO

$C_{27}H_{44}O_1$. M: 384.65. Solid. MP: 150°C (anhydrous). Insoluble in water. Soluble in oxygenated solvents.
Production:
• cholesterol (bromination/dehydrobromination/photo-chemical conversion)
Derivatives: vitamin D₃

dehydroepiandrosterone *See:* prasterone

dehydrolinalool
3,7-dimethyloct-6-en-1-yn-3-ol; [29171-20-8]

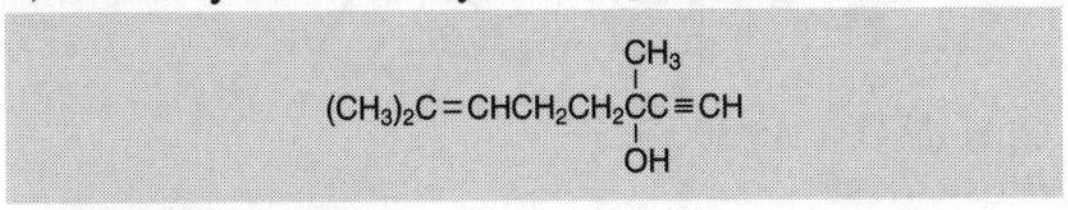

CH₃
(CH₃)₂C=CHCH₂CH₂CC≡CH
OH

$C_{10}H_{16}O_1$. M: 152.24.
Production:
• β-methylheptenone + acetylene (ethynylation)
Derivatives: citral; linalool; pseudoionone

dehydropregnenolone acetate

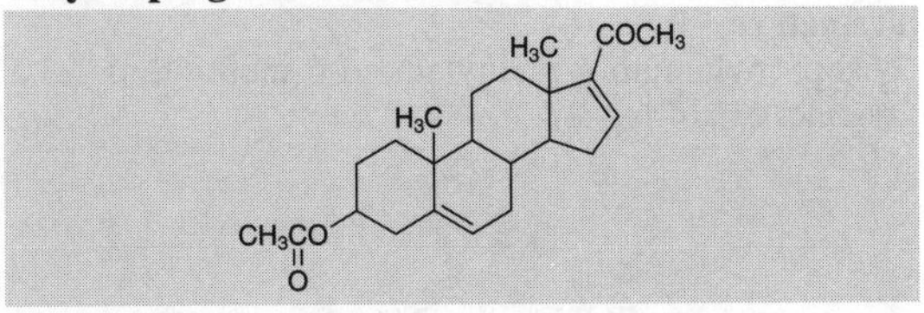

H₃C COCH₃
H₃C
CH₃CO O
O

$C_{23}H_{32}O_3$. M: 356.51.
Production:
• diosgenin/solasodine (multistep synthesis)
Derivatives: prasterone; progesterone

dehydrothio-*p*-toluidinesulphonic acid
$C_{14}H_{12}N_2O_3S_2$. M: 320.39.
Production:
• *p*-toluidine + sulphur (bake process/sulphonation)

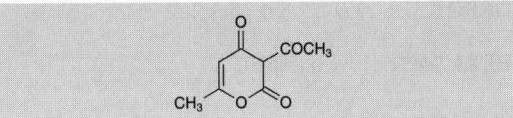

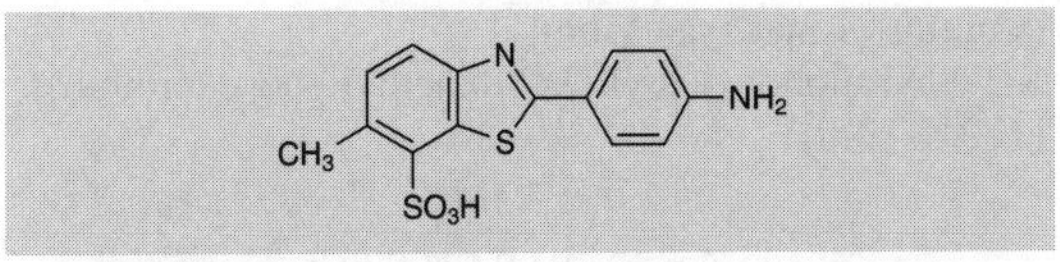

N
NH₂
CH₃ S
SO₃H

Derivatives: Direct Orange 18; Direct Yellow 28
Uses: dyestuffs intermediate

deltamethrin
[52918-63-5]

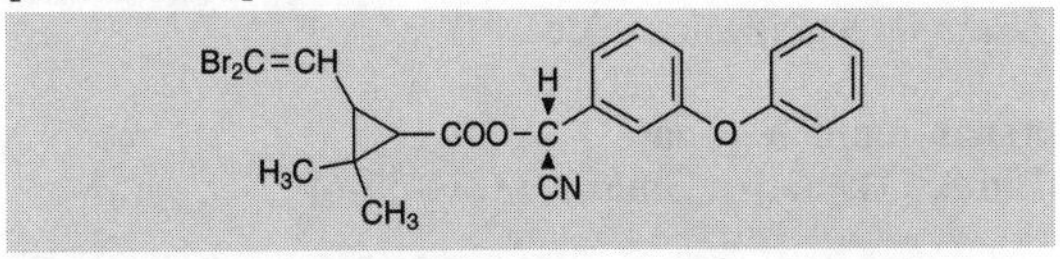

H
Br₂C=CH COO–C
H₃C CN
CH₃

$C_{22}H_{19}Br_2N_1O_3$. M: 505.21.
Production:
• 3-phenoxybenzaldehyde cyanohydrin + (*1R*)-*cis*-3-(2,2-dibromovinyl)-2,2-dimethylcyclopropanecarb-oxylic acid (esterification/racemate separation)
Derivatives:
tralomethrin
Uses: insecticide

DEM *See:* diethyl malonate

demeclocycline
[127-33-3]; [64-73-3] (hydrochloride)

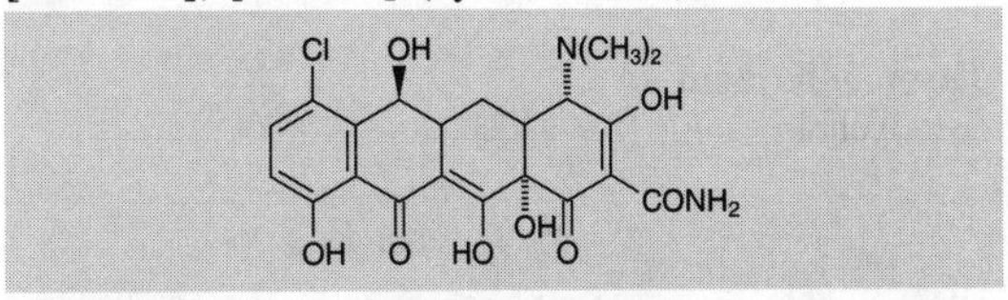

Cl OH N(CH₃)₂
OH
CONH₂
OH O HO OH O

$C_{21}H_{21}Cl_1N_2O_8$. M: 464.85. Available commercially as the free base or hydrochloride.
Production:
• microbial fermentation medium + *Streptomyces aureofaciens* bacteria (fermentation)
Derivatives:
sancycline
Uses: antibacterial drug

demeton-S-methyl
S-2-ethylthioethyl *O,O*-dimethylphosphorothioate; Meta-systox I (Bayer); [919-86-8]

O
(CH₃O)₂PSCH₂CH₂SC₂H₅

$C_6H_{15}O_3P_1S_2$. M: 230.29.
Production:
• 2-ethylthioethanol + *O,O*-dimethyl phosphorochloro-thioate (alcohol chlorination/hydrolysis/dehydro-chlorination)
Derivatives:
demeton-S-methylsulphon
Uses: acaricide/insecticide

demeton-S-methylsulphon

S-2-ethylsulphonylethyl O,O-dimethyl phosphorothioate; [17040-19-6]

$$C_2H_5SO_2CH_2CH_2SP(OCH_3)_2$$

$C_6H_{15}O_5P_1S_2$. M: 262.29.
Production:
• demeton-S-methyl + potassium permanganate (oxidation)
Uses: insecticide/acaricide

denatonium benzoate

Bitrex (Macfarlan Smith); [3734-33-6]

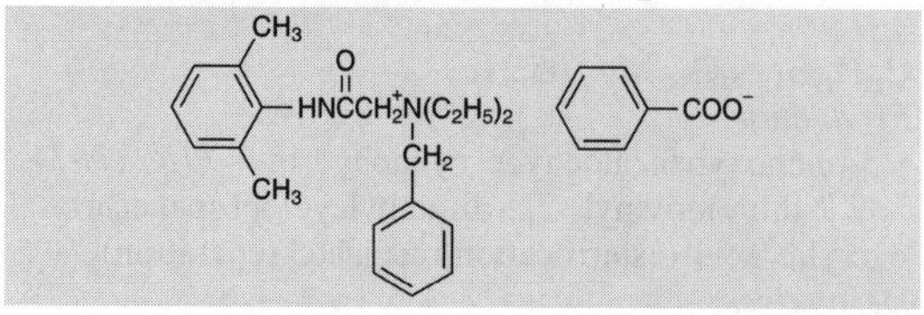

$C_{28}H_{34}N_2O_3$. M: 446.59. Very bitter-tasting white crystals. MP: 165°C. Soluble in water and alcohol.
Production:
• 2,6-xylidine + chloroacetyl chloride + diethylamine + benzyl chloride + benzoic acid (amide formation/ amine formation/amine formation/salt formation)
Uses: alcohol/household product denaturant

deoxycholic acid

desoxycholic acid; [83-44-3]

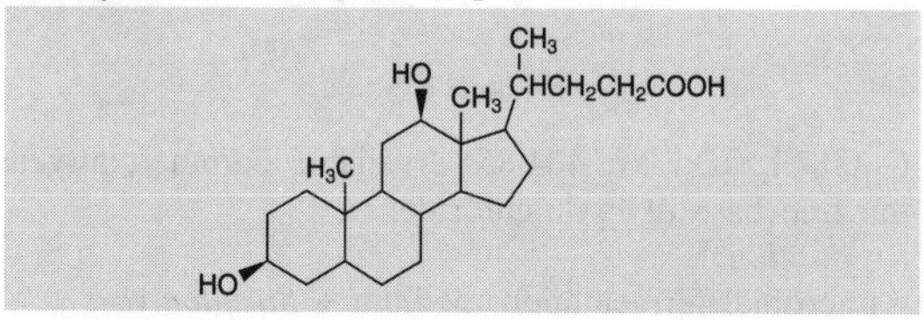

$C_{24}H_{40}O_4$. M: 392.58.
Production:
• animal bile extract (extraction)
Derivatives: cortisone
Uses: choleretic drug

D-2-deoxyribose

[533-67-5]

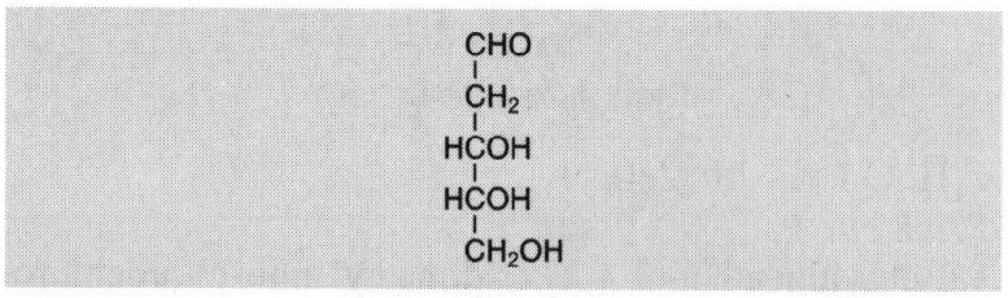

$C_5H_{10}O_4$. M: 134.13. Crystalline solid. MP: 91°C. Soluble in water. Slightly soluble in pyridine.
Production:
• nucleic acids (hydrolysis; coproduced with D-ribose)
Derivatives: idoxuridine

DEP *See:* diethyl phthalate

DEPCT *See:* O,O-diethyl phosphorochlorothioate

DEPI *See:* diethyl phosphite

derris *See:* rotenone

DES *See:* diethylstilbestrol; diethyl sulphate

desipramine

[50-47-5]; [58-28-6] (hydrochloride)

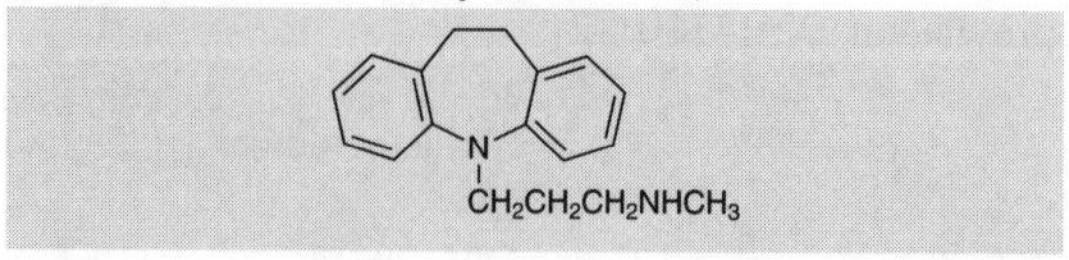

$C_{18}H_{22}N_2$. M: 266.39. Available commercially as the hydrochloride.
Production:
• imipramine + ethyl chloroformate (demethylation)
Derivatives:
lofepramine
Uses: antidepressant drug

desmedipham

3-ethoxycarbonylaminophenyl phenylcarbamate; [13684-56-5]

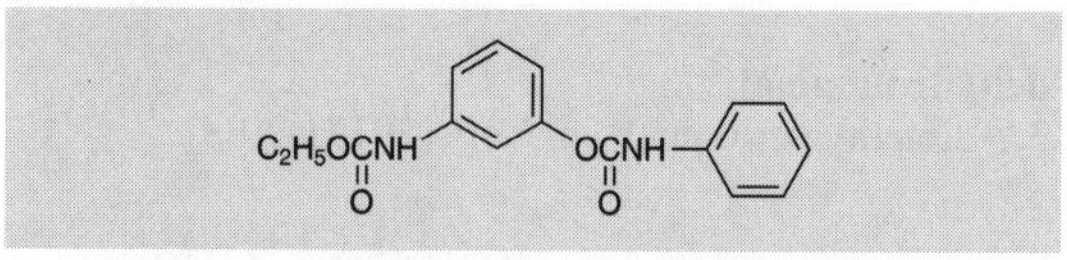

$C_{16}H_{16}N_2O_4$. M: 300.32.
Production:
• m-aminophenol + ethyl chloroformate + phenyl isocyanate (dehydrochlorination/isocyanate addition)
Uses: herbicide

desmethyldiazepam *See:* nordazepam

desmetryn

2-isopropylamino-4-methylamino-6-methylthio-1,3,5-triazine; [1014-69-3]

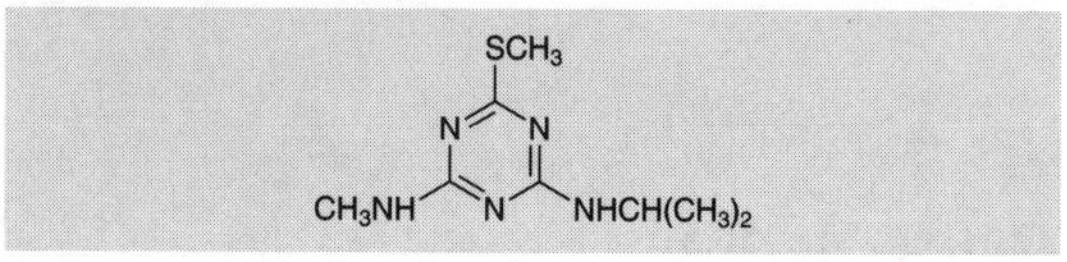

$C_8H_{15}N_5S_1$. M: 213.31.
Production:
• 2-methylmercapto-4,6-dichlorotriazine + methylamine + isopropylamine (amine formation/amine formation)
Uses: herbicide

desoxycholic acid *See:* deoxycholic acid

desoxyephedrine *See:* methamphetamine

2,4-DES-sodium *See:* disul-sodium

DETA *See:* diethylenetriamine

DETDA *See:* 3,5-diethyltoluenediamine

detergent alkylate *See:* dodecylbenzene, linear

detergent enzyme *See:* protease, bacterial, alkaline

DETPMPA *See:* diethylenetriaminepenta-(methylene phosphonic acid)

DETU *See:* diethylthiourea

dexamethasone
[50-02-2]

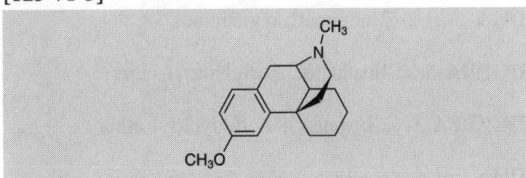

$C_{22}H_{29}F_1O_5$. M: 392.46. Available commercially as the 21-phosphate, disodium salt, the 21-isonicotinate and as other derivatives.
Production:
• androstadienedione (multistep synthesis; coproduced with betamethasone)
Uses: antiinflammatory drug

dexbrompheniramine *See:* brompheniramine

dexchlorpheniramine *See:* chlorphenamine

dextran
[9004-54-0]
Polysaccharides made up of D-glucose units linked predominantly α-D($1\rightarrow6$). M: 40,000–100,000, depending on the source.
Production:
• sucrose + *Leuconostoc dextranicum* bacteria/*Leuconostoc mesenteroides* bacteria (fermentation)
Uses: food ingredient; blood plasma additive

dextrin
British gum; white dextrin; yellow dextrin; [9004-53-9]
White dextrin is a white gum, soluble in hot water, produced by acid hydrolysis at low temperature. Yellow dextrin is a yellow or tan gum with a relatively low viscosity, soluble in cold water, and produced by hydrolysis with a small quantity of acid at higher temperatures. British gum is a brown, viscous gum which is very soluble in water and produced by thermal hydrolysis without the use of acid.

Production:
• starch (hydrolysis)
Uses: fabric back-coatings; flotation depressant (haematite ores); adhesives (case and carton sealing, tube winding, paper bag and envelope seams, stamps, gummed sheets, paper-board laminates); binder (match heads); textile finishing agent

dextromethorphan
[125-71-3]

$C_{18}H_{25}N_1O_1$. M: 271.41. Available commercially as the hydrobromide.
Production:
• 1-(4-methoxybenzyl)-1,2,3,4,5,6,7,8-octahydroiso-quinoline (methylation/cyclisation/racemate separation; coproduced with levorphanol)
Uses: antitussive drug

dextromoramide

$C_{25}H_{32}N_2O_2$. M: 392.54.
Production:
• diphenylacetic acid + pyrrolidine + morpholine + propylene oxide (amide formation/epoxidation/alcohol chlorination/racemate separation/dehydrochlorination)
Uses: analgesic drug

dextronic acid *See:* gluconic acid

dextropropoxyphene
1-benzyl-3-dimethylamino-2-methyl-1-phenylpropyl propionate; darvon; propoxyphene; [469-62-5]

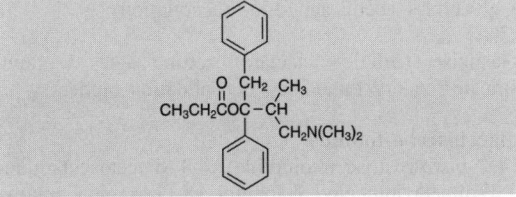

$C_{22}H_{29}N_1O_2$. M: 339.48. Available commercially as the free base or as the hydrochloride.

Production:
- propiophenone + formaldehyde + dimethylamine + benzyl chloride + propionyl chloride (Mannich reaction/Grignard reaction/racemate separation/ esterification)

Uses:
analgesic drug

dextrose *See:* D-glucose

DGA *See:* 2-(2-aminoethoxy)ethanol

DGEBA *See:* bisphenol A diglycidyl ether

DGEBPA *See:* bisphenol A diglycidyl ether

DHA
See: prasterone; dihydroxyacetone; dehydroacetic acid

DHBP *See:* 2,4-dihydroxybenzophenone

DHEG *See:* sodium dihydroxyethylglycine

2,4-D-2-hydroxybutyl
2-hydroxybutyl (2,4-dichlorophenoxy)acetate

$C_{12}H_{14}Cl_2O_4$. M: 293.15. Commonly sold in mixtures with MCPA-2-hydroxybutyl.
Production:
- 2,4-D + 1,2-butylene oxide (epoxidation)

Uses:
herbicide

diacetin
glycerol diacetate; glyceryl diacetate; [25395-31-7]
$C_7H_{12}O_5$. M: 176.17. Colourless, hygroscopic liquid. d: 1.19 kg/l (20°C). Saponification value: 540–600 mg KOH/g. Soluble in water, oxygenated and aromatic solvents.

Production:
- glycerol + acetic anhydride (acetylation)

Uses:
plasticiser (cellulose acetate); setting agent (sodium silicate foundry mould/soil consolidation binders)

diacetoacet-*o*-tolidide
4,4'-bis(*o*-acetoacetotoludiide); 4,4'-diacetoacetamido-3,3'-dimethylbiphenyl; Naphthol AS-G; Azoic Coupling Component 5 (CI); 37610 (CI); [91-96-3]
$C_{22}H_{24}N_2O_4$. M: 380.44.

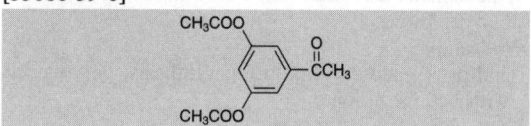

Production:
- methyl acetoacetate + *o*-tolidine (amide formation)

Uses: azoic dye coupling component

diacetone alcohol
4-hydroxy-4-methylpentan-2-one; DAA; [123-42-2]

$C_6H_{12}O_2$. M: 116.17. Colourless liquid with a pleasant odour. FP: -44°C. BP: 168°C. d: 0.94 kg/l (20°C). Completely miscible with water.
Production:
- acetone (aldol condensation)

Derivatives:
alloxydim-sodium; hexylene glycol; mesityl oxide
Uses: solvent (lacquers, paints, printing inks)

diacetonitrile *See:* β-aminocrotononitrile

3,5-diacetoxyacetophenone
[35086-59-0]

$C_{12}H_{12}O_5$. M: 236.22.
Production:
- 3,5-dihydroxyacetophenone + acetic anhydride (acetylation)

Derivatives: fenoterol; orciprenaline; reproterol

diacetyl
2,3-butanedione; [431-03-8]

$C_4H_6O_2$. M: 86.09. Yellow liquid with a strong odour. BP: 87–88°C. d: 0.99 kg/l (15°C). Soluble in water and oxygenated solvents.
Production:
- acetoin (alcohol oxidation)

Derivatives: dimethylglyoxime
Uses: flavouring ingredient (margarine, foodstuffs); gelatine hardening agent

diacetyl fatty acid monoglyceride tartrate
A(1) 6.24 (FAO/WHO); E472(e) (EC)
Sticky, amber paste or ivory flakes. MP: 15–43°C. Mixed product containing diacetyl tartrate esters of fatty acid monoglycerides.

Production:
• fatty acid monoglyceride + tartaric acid + acetic acid (esterification)
Uses: food emulsifier

C_{10} dialdehyde

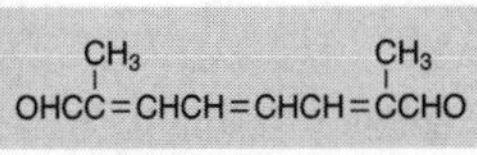

$$\underset{OHCC}{\overset{CH_3}{|}}=CHCH=CHCH=\underset{CCHO}{\overset{CH_3}{|}}$$

$C_{10}H_{12}O_2$. M: 164.21. Not a traded product.
Production:
• acetylene + acrolein + synthesis gas (ethynylation/ hydroformylation/hydrogenation)
Derivatives: β-carotene

dialkylaryl sulphonates, alkali-earth salts
Production:
• dialkylbenzene/dinonylnaphthalene/heavy alkylate, branched + sulphuric acid + calcium hydroxide/ magnesia, caustic-calcined/barium oxide/barium hydroxide (sulphonation/salt formation)
Uses: detergent/corrosion inhibitor (lubricants)

dialkylbenzene
DAB

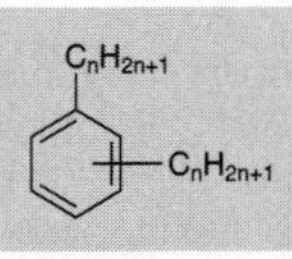

n = 10–14. $C_{30}H_{54}$. M: 414.76.
Production:
• dodecylbenzene, linear + n-olefins(C_{10}-C_{13})/ α-olefins(C_{12}-C_{14}) (Friedel-Crafts alkylation)
Derivatives:
dialkylaryl sulphonates, alkali-earth salts
Uses: synthetic lubricant base oils

di-*n*-alkyl(C_7-C_9) phthalate
di-*n*-octyl phthalate

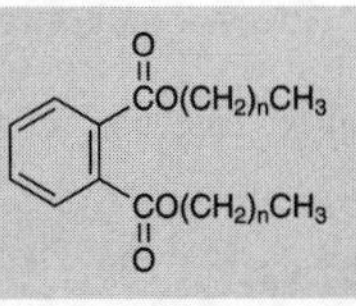

n = 6–8. Colourless liquid. BP: 226°C (0.65 kPa). d: 0.98 kg/l (20°C). Viscosity: 42 mPa.s (20°C). Insoluble in water.
Production:
• n-alkanol(C_7-C_9)/n-octanol + phthalic anhydride (esterification)
Uses: polyvinyl chloride plasticiser

di-*n*-alkyl(C_8-C_{10}) phthalate
Colourless liquid. d: 0.97 kg/l (20°C). Viscosity: 51 mPa.s (20°C). Insoluble in water.

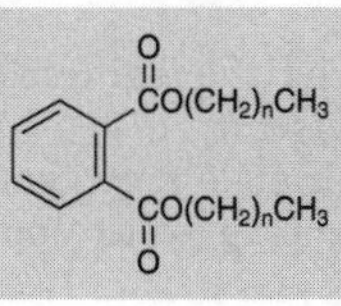

n = 7–9.
Production:
• n-alkanol(C_8-C_{10}) + phthalic anhydride (esterification)
Uses: polyvinyl chloride plasticiser

di-*n*-alkyl(C_9-C_{11}) phthalate

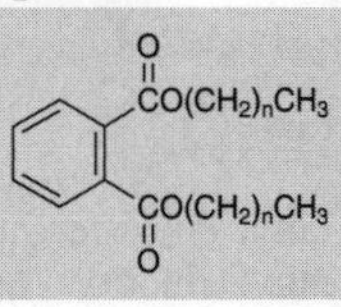

n = 8–10. Colourless, involatile liquid. d: 0.96 kg/l (20°C). Viscosity: 57 mPa.s (20°C). Insoluble in water.
Production:
• n-alkanol(C_9-C_{11}) + phthalic anhydride (esterification)
Uses:
polyvinyl chloride plasticiser

diallyl adipate
[2998-04-1]

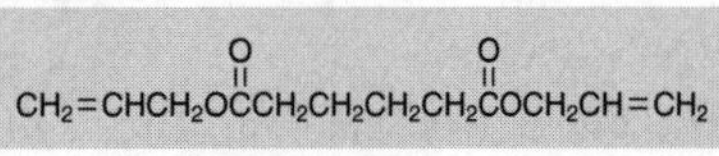

$$CH_2=CHCH_2O\overset{O}{\overset{\|}{C}}CH_2CH_2CH_2CH_2\overset{O}{\overset{\|}{C}}OCH_2CH=CH_2$$

$C_{12}H_{18}O_4$. M: 226.27. Colourless liquid. BP: 140°C (0.53 kPa). d: 1.02 kg/l (20°C). Insoluble in water. Soluble in oxygenated solvents.
Production:
• allyl alcohol + adipic acid (esterification)
Uses:
crosslinking comonomer

diallylamine
di-2-propenylamine; [124-02-7]

$$(CH_2=CHCH_2)_2NH$$

$C_6H_{11}N_1$. M: 97.17. Liquid with an unpleasant odour. BP: 111–112°C. d: 0.79 kg/l (20°C). Soluble in water.
Production:
• allyl chloride + ammonia (amine formation; coproduced with allylamine/triallylamine)
Derivatives:
diallyldimethylammonium chloride; dichlormid

2,2'-diallylbisphenol A

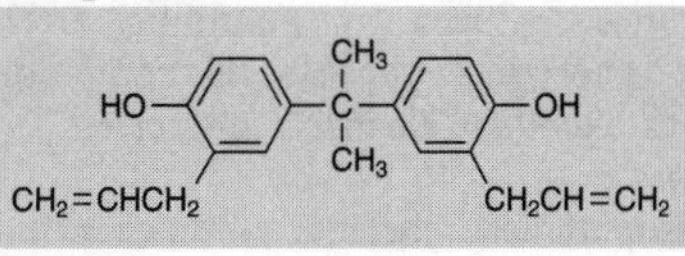

$C_{21}H_{22}O_2$. M: 306.41.

Production:
- bisphenol A + allyl chloride (ether formation/ Claisen rearrangement)

Derivatives: bismaleimide prepolymers

Uses: bismaleimide prepolymer comonomer

N,N-diallyldichloroacetamide *See:* dichlormid

diallyldimethylammonium chloride
dimethyldiallylammonium chloride; DADMAC; DIM-DAC; DMDAAC (National Starch & Chemical); [7398-69-8]

$$(CH_2=CHCH_2)_2^+N(CH_3)_2 \quad Cl^-$$

$C_8H_{16}Cl_1N_1$. M: 161.68.

Production:
- dimethylamine + allyl chloride (quaternisation)
- diallylamine + methyl chloride (quaternisation)

Derivatives:
acrylamide-diallyldimethylammonium chloride copolymers; poly(diallyldimethylammonium chloride)

diallyl fumarate
[2807-54-7]

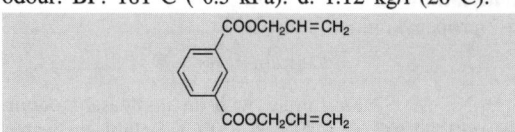

$C_{10}H_{12}O_4$. M: 196.21. Colourless liquid with a pungent odour. BP: 140°C (0.4 kPa). d: 1.05 kg/l (25°C). Insoluble in water. Soluble in oxygenated solvents.

Production:
- allyl alcohol + fumaric acid (esterification)

Uses: crosslinking comonomer

diallyl isophthalate
DAIP

$C_{14}H_{14}O_4$. M: 246.26. Liquid with a mild, characteristic odour. BP: 181°C (0.5 kPa). d: 1.12 kg/l (20°C).

Production:
- allyl alcohol + isophthalic acid (esterification)

Derivatives: diallyl isophthalate resins

diallyl isophthalate resins
Prepolymer moulding compounds in the form of white powders blended with peroxide catalyst, fillers and other additives. Cured by moulding at 150–160°C producing a product capable of continuous use at 220°C with excellent electrical properties.

Production:
- diallyl isophthalate (thermal polymerisation)

Uses: moulding compounds (electrical components)

diallyl maleate
DAM; Sipomer (Rhone-Poulenc); [999-21-3]

$C_{10}H_{12}O_4$. M: 196.21. Colourless liquid with a pungent odour. BP: 112°C (0.53 kPa). d: 1.07 kg/l (25°C). Polymerises on heating. Insoluble in water.

Production:
- allyl alcohol + maleic anhydride (esterification)

Uses: vinyl resin crosslinking agent

diallyl phthalate
DAP; [131-17-9]

$C_{14}H_{14}O_4$. M: 246.26. Colourless liquid. BP: 161°C (0.53 kPa). Pour point: -70°C. d: 1.12 kg/l (25°C). Insoluble in water. Soluble in oxygenated and chlorinated solvents.

Production:
- allyl alcohol + phthalic anhydride (esterification)

Derivatives:
diallyl phthalate resins

Uses: peroxide crosslinking coactivator; plasticiser/tackifying agent (polyvinyl chloride compounds); reactive diluent (polyester laminating resins)

diallyl phthalate resins
Prepolymer moulding compounds in the form of white powders blended with peroxide catalyst, fillers and other additives. Cured by moulding at 150–160°C producing a product with good temperature and electrical properties.

Production:
- diallyl phthalate (thermal polymerisation)

Uses:
moulding compounds (electrical components)

diallyl sulphide
allyl sulphide; [592-88-1]

$$CH_2=CHCH_2SCH_2CH=CH_2$$

$C_6H_{10}S_1$. M: 114.21. Liquid with a garlic-like odour. BP: 139°C. Insoluble in water.

Production:
- allyl chloride + sulphur (sulphurisation)

Uses: flavouring ingredient

2,4-diaminoanisole
4-methoxy-*m*-phenylenediamine; 2,4-DAA; Oxidative Base 12; 76050 (CI); [615-05-4]

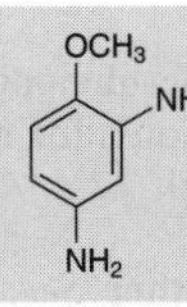

$C_7H_{10}N_2O_1$. M: 138.17. Crystalline solid. MP: 67°C. Darkened by light. Available commercially as the free base or as the sulphate salt.
Production:
• 2,4-dinitroanisole (nitro reduction)
Uses:
hair colorant

1,4-diaminoanthraquinone
Disperse Violet 1 (CI); Solvent Violet 11 (CI); 61100 (CI); [128-95-0]

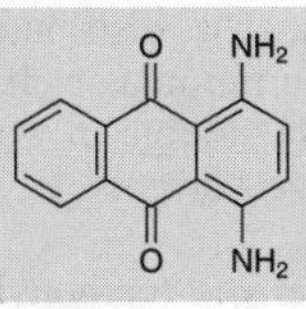

$C_{14}H_{10}N_2O_2$. M: 238.24. Violet needles. MP: 245–251°C. Soluble in hot water and aromatic solvents.
Production:
• 1-chloro-4-hydroxyanthraquinone + ammonia (amine formation)
• 1-aminoanthraquinone (nitration/nitro reduction)
Derivatives:
Acid Violet 41; Disperse Violet 28; Reactive Blue 6; Vat Brown 1; Vat Brown 44

1,5-diaminoanthraquinone
[129-44-2]

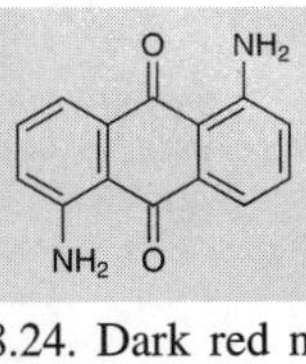

$C_{14}H_{10}N_2O_2$. M: 238.24. Dark red needles. Sublimes at 319°C. Insoluble in water.
Production:
• anthraquinone-1,5-disulphonic acid (nitration/nitro reduction)
Derivatives: Solvent Violet 14; 1,4,5,8-tetraaminoanthraquinone; Vat Yellow 3

p-diaminoanthrarufin
See: 1,5-diamino-4,8-dihydroxyanthraquinone

m-diaminobenzene *See:* m-phenylenediamine

o-diaminobenzene *See:* o-phenylenediamine

p-diaminobenzene *See:* p-phenylenediamine

2,4-diaminobenzenesulphonic acid
1,3-phenylenediamine-4-sulphonic acid; [88-63-1]

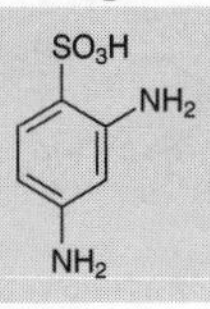

$C_6H_8N_2O_3S_1$. M: 188.20.
Production:
• m-phenylenediamine (sulphonation)
Derivatives:
Acid Yellow 127; Direct Orange 6; Mordant Brown 33; Reactive Blue 4; Reactive Blue 7; Reactive Red 4; Reactive Yellow 1

3,3'-diaminobenzidine
3,3',4,4'-tetraaminobiphenyl; TAB; [91-95-2]

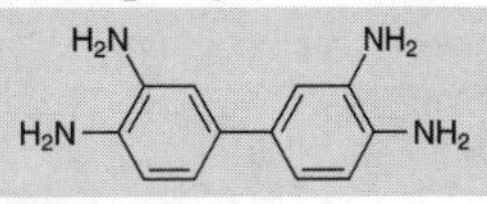

$C_{12}H_{14}N_4$. M: 214.27.
Production:
• 3,3'-dichlorobenzidine dihydrochloride/ammonia (ammoniation)
Derivatives: polybenzimidazole

3,5-diaminobenzoic acid
[535-87-5]

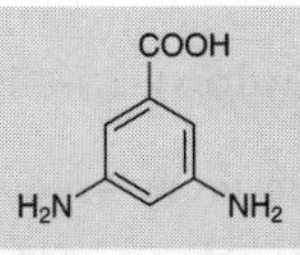

$C_7H_8N_2O_2$. M: 152.15. Available as the monohydrate. Yellow, crystalline solid. Loses water of crystallisation at 110°C. MP: 235–238°C with decomposition. Slightly soluble in water. Soluble in oxygenated solvents.
Production:
• 3,5-dinitrobenzoic acid (nitro reduction)
Derivatives: amidotrizoic acid
Uses: analytical reagent (nitrite)

4,4'-diaminobiphenyl-2,2'-disulphonic acid
See: benzidine-2,2'-disulphonic acid

1,4-diaminobutane
putrescine; tetramethylenediamine; [110-60-1]

$H_2NCH_2CH_2CH_2CH_2NH_2$

$C_4H_{12}N_2$. M: 88.15. Crystalline solid with an unpleasant odour. MP: 27–28°C. BP: 158–159°C. d: 0.88 kg/l (25°C). Soluble in water.
Production:
• succinonitrile (nitrile reduction)
Derivatives: polyamide 46

1,2-diaminocyclohexane
1,2DCH; Ancamine 1770 (Air Products and Chemical)

$C_6H_{14}N_2$. M: 114.19.
Production:
- adiponitrile (nitrile reduction; byproduct of hexa-methylenediamine production)
Uses: epoxy resin curing agent

4,4'-diamino-3,3'-dichlorobiphenyl dihydrochloride
See: 3,3'-dichlorobenzidine dihydrochloride

1,5-diamino-4,8-dihydroxyanthraquinone
p-diaminoanthrarufin; 4,8-diamino-1,5-dihydroxyanthra-quinone

$C_{14}H_{10}N_2O_4$. M: 270.24.
Production:
- 1,5-dihydroxy-4,8-dinitroanthraquinone (nitro reduction)
Derivatives: Disperse Blue 26; Disperse Blue 56; Vat Violet 15; Vat Violet 17

4,5-diamino-1,8-dihydroxy-2,7-diisobutylanthra-quinone
2,7-diisobutyl-1,8-dihydroxy-4,5-diaminoanthraquinone

$C_{22}H_{26}N_2O_4$. M: 382.46.
Production:
- 1,8-dihydroxyanthraquinone + isobutyl bromide (nitration/Friedel-Crafts alkylation/nitro reduction)
Uses: dye (liquid crystal displays)

4,4'-diamino-3,3'-dimethoxybiphenyl *See:* o-dianisidine

4,4'-diamino-3,3'-dimethylbiphenyl *See:* o-tolidine

4,4'-diaminodiphenylamine-2-sulphonic acid
[119-70-0]

$C_{12}H_{13}N_3O_3S_1$. M: 279.31.

Production:
- 2-chloro-5-nitrobenzenesulphonic acid + p-nitro-aniline (amine formation/nitro reduction)
Derivatives: Direct Black 22

4,4'-diaminodiphenyl ether *See:* 4,4'-oxydianiline

4,4'-diaminodiphenylmethane, crude
bis(p-aminophenyl)methane; 4,4'-methylenedianiline; DADPM; DDM; DDPM; MDA;

n = 0–3. Mixed product containing, principally, 4,4'-di-aminodiphenylmethane, but also higher aniline-form-aldehyde oligomers. The distribution depends on the aniline:formaldehyde ration as well as the reaction con-ditions. Very slightly soluble in water. Soluble in oxy-genated and aromatic solvents.
Production:
- aniline + formaldehyde (carbonyl condensation)
Derivatives:
bis(p-aminocyclohexyl)methane; bismaleimide prepoly-mers; bismethylenedianiline maleimide; 4,4'-diamino-diphenylmethane, pure; 4,4'-diphenylmethane diisocyan-ate, polymeric; polyether polyols, rigid; tetraglycidyl methylenedianiline
Uses:
cast polyurethane elastomer curing agent; epoxy resin curing agent

4,4'-diaminodiphenylmethane, polymeric
MDA, polymeric

n = 1–3.
Production:
- 4,4'-diaminodiphenylmethane, crude (fractionation; byproduct of 4,4'-diaminodiphenylmethane, pure production)
Derivatives: 4,4'-diphenylmethane diisocyanate, poly-meric

4,4'-diaminodiphenylmethane, pure
p,p'-diaminodiphenylmethane, pure; methylenedianiline; MDA; [101-77-9]

$C_{13}H_{14}N_2$. M: 198.26. Granules. MP: 89–91°C. BP: 220–230°C (0.4 kPa). Slightly soluble in water. Soluble in oxygenated and aromatic solvents.

Production:
- 4,4′-diaminodiphenylmethane, crude (fractionation)
Derivatives: 4,4′-difluorobenzophenone; 4,4′-dihydroxybenzophenone; 4,4′-diphenylmethane diisocyanate, pure

3,3′-diaminodiphenyl sulphone

$C_{12}H_{12}N_2O_2S_1$. M: 248.30. Crystals. MP: 168°C. Soluble in hot water and alcohol.
Production:
- nitrobenzene + sulphuryl chloride (chlorosulphonation/nitro reduction)
Uses: epoxy resin curing agent

4,4′-diaminodiphenyl sulphone
dapsone; sulphonyldianiline; DDPS; DDS

$C_{12}H_{12}N_2O_2S_1$. M: 248.30. Crystals. MP: 175–177°C. Insoluble in water. Soluble in aqueous acid and oxygenated solvents.
Production:
- aniline + sulphuryl chloride (chlorosulphonation)
Derivatives:
acediasulfone; poly(imide-sulphone)
Uses: epoxy resin curing agent (composite aircraft bodies/components); antileprosy drug

1,12-diaminododecane
dodecamethylenediamine; [2783-17-7]

$H_2N(CH_2)_{12}NH_2$

$C_{12}H_{28}N_2$. M: 200.36.
Production:
- 1,12-dodecanediol + ammonia (ammoniation)
Derivatives: polyamide 1212

1,2-diaminoethane *See:* ethylenediamine

1,6-diaminohexane *See:* hexamethylenediamine

1,5-diaminonaphthalene
1,5-naphthalenediamine; [2243-62-1]

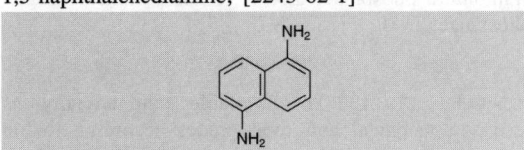

$C_{10}H_{10}N_2$. M: 158.20. Solid. MP: 190°C. Sublimes on further heating. d: 1.40 kg/l. Insoluble in water. Soluble in chlorinated and oxygenated solvents.

Production:
- 1,5/1,8-dinitronaphthalene (separation/nitro reduction)
Derivatives:
Disperse Blue 20; 1,5-naphthalene diisocyanate

1,8-diaminonaphthalene
1,8-naphthalenediamine; [479-27-6]

$C_{10}H_{10}N_2$. M: 158.20. Crystalline solid. Discoloured by light and air. MP: 66–67°C. Slightly soluble in water. Soluble in oxygenated solvents.
Production:
- 1,5/1,8-dinitronaphthalene (separation/nitro reduction)
Uses:
dyestuffs intermediate

2,4-diaminophenol dihydrochloride
amidol; 4-hydroxy-*m*-phenylenediamine dihydrochloride

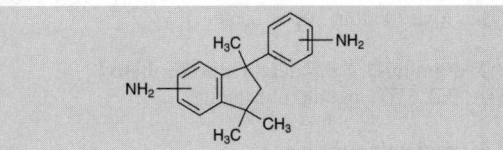

$C_6H_{10}Cl_2N_2O_1$. M: 197.07. White crystals. MP: 205°C. Soluble in water.
Production:
- 2,4-dinitrophenol (nitro reduction/salt formation)
Uses: photographic developing agent; hair dyeing/tinting ingredient;

diaminophenylindane
DAPI

$C_{18}H_{22}N_2$. M: 266.39.
Production:
- α-methylstyrene (condensation/nitration/nitro reduction)
Uses:
polyimide comonomer

1,2-diaminopropane
See: 1,2-propanediamine

1,3-diaminopropane
See: 1,3-propanediamine

2,6-diaminopyridine
[141-86-6]

$C_5H_7N_3$. M: 109.13. Light brown flakes. MP: 115–123°C. BP: 285°C. Soluble in water and oxygenated solvents.
Production:
- 2-aminopyridine + sodamide (Chichibabin reaction)
- glutaric acid + ammonia (nitrile formation/condensation)

Derivatives: flupirtine; phenazopyridine

4,4′-diaminostilbene-2,2′-disulphonic acid
amsonic acid; DAS; Direct Orange 15 (CI); 40002 (CI); 40003 (CI); [81-11-8]

$C_{14}H_{14}N_2O_6S_2$. M: 370.39. Yellow needles. Insoluble in water. Soluble in oxygenated solvents.
Production:
- 4,4′-dinitrostilbene-2,2′-disulphonic acid (nitro reduction)

Derivatives: Direct Yellow 4; Fluorescent Brightener 9; Fluorescent Brightener 24; Fluorescent Brightener 28; Fluorescent Brightener 32; Fluorescent Brightener 86; Fluorescent Brightener 103; Fluorescent Brightener 104; Fluorescent Brightener 119; Fluorescent Brightener 136; Fluorescent Brightener 142; Fluorescent Brightener 182; Fluorescent Brightener 193; Fluorescent Brightener 204; Fluorescent Brightener DM; Fluorescent Brightener DMDDEA; Fluorescent Brightener DMEA; sodium 4,4′-bis(4-phenyl-1,2,3-triazol-2-yl)stilbene-2,2′-disulphonate
Uses: dye (cotton, paper, leather)

4,4′-diamino-2,2′,5,5′-tetrachlorobiphenyl
See: 2,2′,5,5′-tetrachlorobenzidine

2,4/2,6-diaminotoluene
2,4-diaminotoluene; toluene-2,4-diamine; *m*-toluenediamine; *m*-tolylenediamine; MTD; TDA

$C_7H_{10}N_2$. M: 122.17. White crystals. MP: 90°C. BP: 283°C. d: 1.05 kg/l. Soluble in water and oxygenated solvents. Grades containing 65:35 and 80:20 of the 2,4- and 2,6-isomers are produced commercially.

Production:
- dinitrotoluene (nitro reduction)

Derivatives:
Basic Orange 1; *t*-butyltoluenediamine; 2,4-diaminotoluene-5-sulphonic acid; 3,5-diethyltoluenediamine; 3,5-di-(methylthio)toluenediamine; polyether polyols, rigid; Solvent Brown 12; Sulphur Brown 10; Sulphur Orange 1; toluene diisocyanate
Uses:
polyamide comonomer

3,4-diaminotoluene
toluene-3,4-diamine; *o*-toluenediamine; OTD; [496-72-0]

$C_7H_{10}N_2$. M: 122.17. Crystalline solid. MP: 88°C. Soluble in water.
Production:
- dinitrotoluene (nitro reduction; byproduct of 2,4/2,6-diaminotoluene production)

Derivatives:
chinomethionat; 2,3-dichloroquinoxaline-6-carboxyl chloride; 2-mercaptomethylbenzimidazole; tolyltriazole
Uses: epoxy resin curing agent; polyurethane polyol comonomer

2,4-diaminotoluene-5-sulphonic acid
4,6-diaminotoluene-3-sulphonic acid; *m*-tolylenediaminesulphonic acid

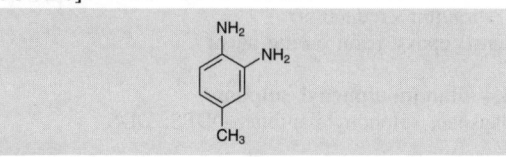

$C_7H_{10}N_2O_3S_1$. M: 202.23.
Production:
- 2,4/2,6-diaminotoluene (sulphonation)

Derivatives:
Direct Orange 6

diammonium phosphate
ammonium phosphate, dibasic; diammonium hydrogen phosphate; DAP; [7783-28-0]

$(NH_4)_2HPO_4$

$H_9N_2O_4P_1$. M: 132.05. Available commercially as fertiliser, technical and food grades according to the source and purity of the phosphoric acid. Pure product: White crystals. d: 1.62 kg/l. Solubility in water: 569 g/l water (20°C). The fertiliser grade typically contains 18% N and 46% P_2O_5.

Production:
- ammonia + phosphoric acid, crude (salt formation)
- ammonia + phosphoric acid, pure (salt formation)

Derivatives:
ammonium polyphosphate, solid

Uses:
binder (refractory bricks, tiles); fire-retardant (paper, textiles, cellulosics, wood); leavening agent/dough conditioner; yeast/microbial fermentation nutrient; fertiliser ingredient

diamond

Strong, hard, crystalline solid with good electrical insulation and chemical resistance properties. Pure, colourless, natural stones are cut and used for jewellery. Other natural stones, together with synthetic diamonds, are used by industry. d: 3.51 kg/l.

Production:
- graphite, natural (high-pressure rearrangement)

Uses: drilling/cutting/grinding material; grinding wheel abrasive; jewellery; wire-drawing dies

diamylamine

$$(C_4H_9CH_2)_2NH$$

$C_{10}H_{23}N_1$. M: 157.30.

Production:
- amyl alcohol, primary + ammonia (reductive ammoniation)

Derivatives:
antimony diamyldithiocarbamate; lead diamyldithiocarbamate; zinc diamyldithiocarbamate

2,5-di-*t*-amylhydroquinone

Santovar A (Monsanto); [79-74-3]

$C_{16}H_{26}O_2$. M: 250.39.

Production:
- hydroquinone + isoamylene (Friedel-Crafts alkylation)

Uses:
antioxidant (rubber)

1,1-di-(*t*-amylperoxy)cyclohexane

USP-90MD (Witco)

$C_{16}H_{32}O_4$. M: 288.44. Available as a solution containing 80% active matter. The product has a 10-hour half-life at 90°C.

Production:
- cyclohexanone + *t*-amyl hydroperoxide (ketal formation)

Uses: polymerisation catalyst; unsaturated polyester resin crosslinking agent

2,2-di-(*t*-amylperoxy)propane

$C_{13}H_{28}O_4$. M: 248.36. Decomposes on heating with a 10-hour half-life at 108°C.

Production:
- acetone + *t*-amyl hydroperoxide (ketal formation)

Uses: polymerisation initiator

o-dianisidine

4,4'-diamino-3,3'-dimethoxybiphenyl; dianisidine; 3,3'-dimethoxybenzidine; Fast Blue B base; Azoic Diazo Component 48 (CI); 37235 (CI); [119-90-4]

$C_{14}H_{16}N_2O_2$. M: 244.29. Crystalline solid. MP: 136–137°C. Insoluble in water. Soluble in oxygenated, chlorinated and aromatic solvents.

Production:
- *o*-nitroanisole (benzidine rearrangement)

Derivatives: N,N'-bis(3-hydroxy-2-naphthoyl)dianisidine; Direct Black 91; Direct Blue 1; Direct Blue 8; Direct Blue 15; Direct Blue 80; Direct Blue 84; Direct Blue 98; Pigment Orange 14; Pigment Orange 16; Pigment Red 37; Pigment Red 41; Pigment Red 42

Uses: polyurethane chain-extender

dian resins *See:* bisphenol A diglycidyl ether

N,N'-diaryl-*p*-phenylenediamine

Wingstay 100 (Goodyear Tire & Rubber)

$C_{20}H_{20}N_2$. M: 288.39. Mixed product consisting of N,N'-ditolyl-*p*-phenylenediamine, N,N'-diphenyl-*p*-phenylenediamine and N-phenyl-N'-tolyl-*p*-phenylenediamine.

Production:
- *o*-toluidine + aniline + hydroquinone (reductive amination/reductive amination)

Uses: antioxidant/antiozonant (rubber)

diatomaceous earth

diatomite; kieselguhr; [7631-86-9]
Friable, porous silica ore. High surface area. d: 0.45

kg/l (dry). Insoluble in water. Mined in USA, France, Germany and Italy.
Uses:
water/effluent/oil clarifying agent; filler (paper, plastics, cosmetics); filter medium (chemicals, oils, food, drinks, medicines); flattening agent (paints, printing inks); toothpaste abrasive; polishing compounds; absorbent/carrier (drugs, extracts, catalysts, explosives); heat/sound insulating material; raw material (high temperature/chemically-resistant bricks)

1,5-diazabicyclo[5.4.0]undec-5-ene
1,8-diazabicyclo[5.4.0]undec-7-ene; DBU; Polycat DBU (Air Products and Chemical); [6674-22-2]

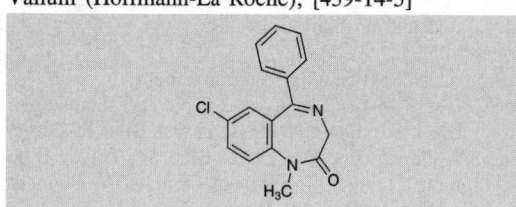

$C_9H_{16}N_2$. M: 152.24.
Production:
• caprolactam + acrylonitrile (cyanoethylation/nitrile reduction/imine formation)
Uses: polyurethane foam catalyst

diazepam
Valium (Hoffmann-La Roche); [439-14-5]

$C_{16}H_{13}Cl_1N_2O_1$. M: 284.74.
Production:
• nordazepam + dimethyl sulphate (methylation)
• 2-amino-5-chlorobenzophenone + dimethyl sulphate + ethyl glycinate hydrochloride (methylation/condensation)
• p-chloroaniline + benzyl chloride + ethyl acetoacetate + dimethyl sulphate + ammonia (Sumitomo process)
Derivatives:
medazepam; temazepam
Uses: anxiolytic/muscle relaxant drug

diazinon
O,O-diethyl O-2-isopropyl-6-methylpyrimidin-4-yl phosphorothioate; [333-41-5]

$C_{12}H_{21}N_2O_3P_1S_1$. M: 304.34.

Production:
• isobutyronitrile + ammonia + ethyl acetoacetate + O,O-diethyl phosphorochlorothioate (amidine formation/condensation/dehydrochlorination)
Uses:
acaricide/insecticide

2,1,4-diazo acid
See: 2-diazo-1-naphthol-4-sulphonic acid chloride

2,1,5-diazo acid
See: 2-diazo-1-naphthol-5-sulphonic acid chloride

1,4-diazobicyclo[2.2.2]octane
See: triethylenediamine

Diazo Brilliant Scarlet ROD
17845 (CI)

$C_{31}H_{24}N_5Na_1O_7S_1$. M: 633.60.
Production:
• N-m-aminobenzoyl-J acid + m-nitrobenzoyl chloride + o-anisidine (amide formation/nitro reduction/diazotisation/azo coupling)
Uses: dye (cotton)

diazodinitrophenol
DDNP; [28655-69-8]

$C_6H_2N_4O_5$. M: 210.11.
Production:
• sodium picramate + sodium nitrite (diazotisation)
Uses: explosive primers

2-diazo-1-naphthol-4-sulphonic acid chloride
2,1,4-diazo acid

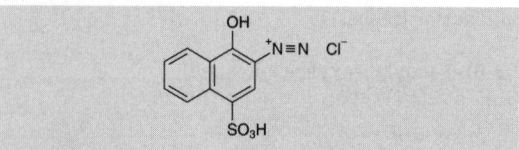

$C_{10}H_7Cl_1N_2O_4S_1$. M: 286.69.
Production:
• Nevile-Winther acid (nitration/nitro reduction/diazotisation)
Uses:
dyestuffs intermediate

2-diazo-1-naphthol-5-sulphonic acid chloride
2,1,5-diazo acid

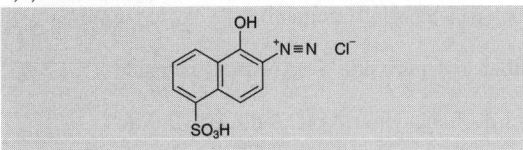

$C_{10}H_7Cl_1N_2O_4S_1$. M: 286.69.
Production:
• 5-hydroxynaphthalene-1-sulphonic acid (nitration/
nitro reduction/diazotisation)
Derivatives:
2,4-dihydroxybenzophenone 2,1,5-diazoester; 4-tolyl-
2,1,5-diazoester; 2,3,4-trihydroxybenzophenone mono-
2,1,5-diazoester

diazoxide
[364-98-7]

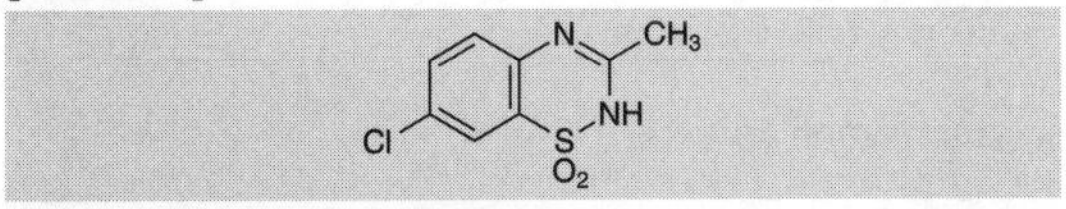

$C_8H_7Cl_1N_2O_2S_1$. M: 230.67.
Production:
• *p*-chloroaniline + chlorosulphonic acid + ammonia
+ triethyl orthoacetate (chlorosulphonation/sulphon-
amide formation/condensation)
Uses: antihypertensive/hyperglycemial drug

DIB *See:* 2,4,4-trimethylpentene

DIBA *See:* diisobutylamine

N,N'-dibenzaloxalyldihydrazide

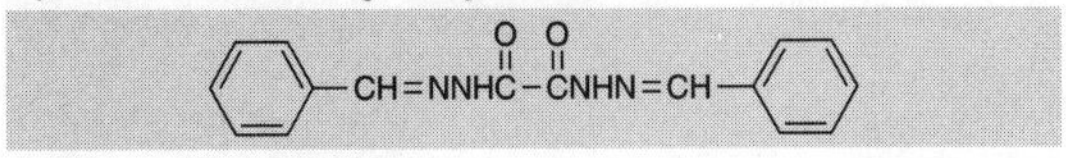

$C_{16}H_{14}N_4O_2$. M: 294.32.
Production:
• oxalic acid + hydrazine + benzaldehyde (amide
formation/imine formation)
Uses: metal deactivator (plastics)

dibenzanthrone
violanthrone; Vat Blue 20 (CI); 59800 (CI); [116-71-2]

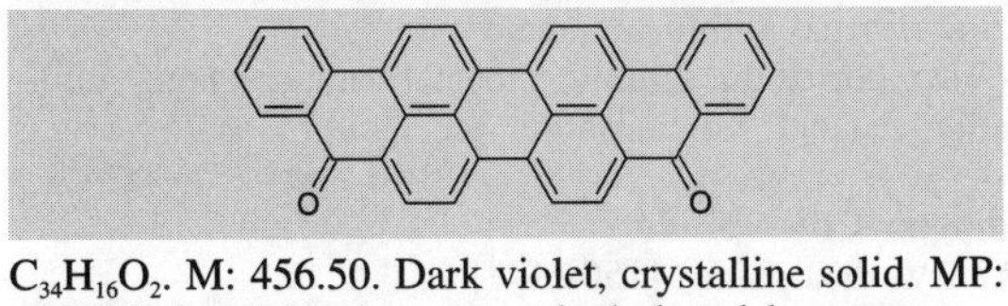

$C_{34}H_{16}O_2$. M: 456.50. Dark violet, crystalline solid. MP:
>380°C. Insoluble in water, alcohol and benzene.
Production:
• benzanthrone (oxidative coupling)
Derivatives:
Vat Blue 18; Vat Blue 19; Vat Green 9

5H-dibenzazepine *See:* iminostilbene

dibenzepin
[4498-32-2]

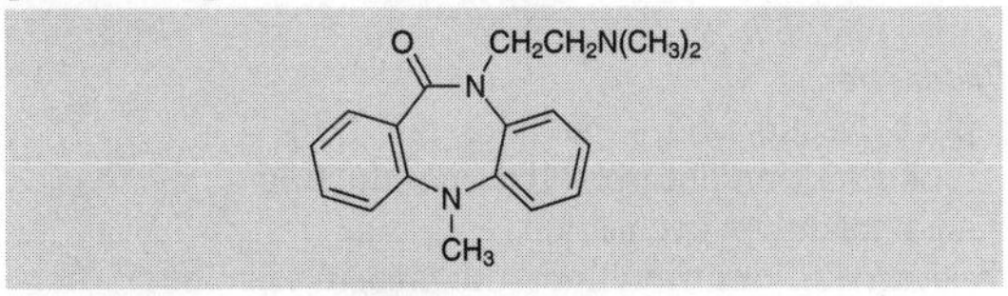

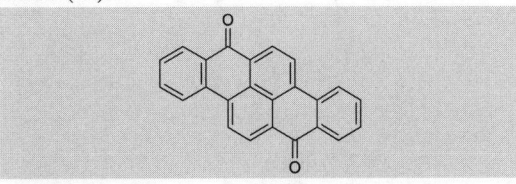

$C_{18}H_{21}N_3O_1$. M: 295.39.
Production:
• methyl *N*-methylanthranilate + *o*-chloronitrobenzene
+ 2-dimethylaminoethyl chloride hydrochloride
(amine formation/nitro reduction/amide formation/
amine formation)
Uses: antidepressant drug

dibenzo(b,f)cycloheptenone *See:* dibenzosuberenone-5

dibenzofuran *See:* diphenylene oxide

dibenzopyrenequinone
Indanthrene Golden Yellow GK; Vat Yellow 4 (CI);
59100 (CI)

$C_{24}H_{12}O_2$. M: 332.36.
Production:
• naphthalene + benzoyl chloride (Friedel-Crafts
acylation/condensation)
Derivatives:
Vat Orange 1
Uses: dye (cotton)

dibenzosuberenone-5
dibenzo(b,f)cycloheptenone; ENON; [2222-33-5]

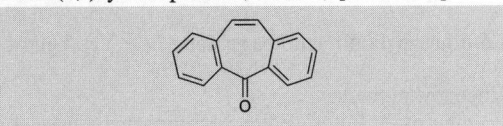

$C_{15}H_{10}O_1$. M: 206.24.
Production:
• dibenzosuberone + hydrogen bromide, anhydrous
(bromination/dehydrobromination)
Derivatives:
cyclobenzaprine; cyproheptadine; protriptyline

dibenzosuberone
dibenzo(b,f)cycloheptan-1-one; BRON; [1210-35-1]
$C_{15}H_{12}O_1$. M: 208.26.

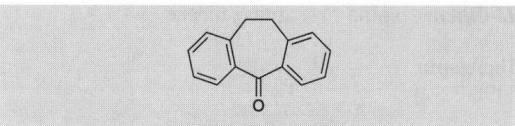

Production:
- phenylacetic acid + phthalic anhydride (condensation/decarboxylation/reduction/acid-catalysed cyclisation)

Derivatives: amitriptyline; dibenzosuberenone-5; nortriptyline; noxiptiline hydrochloride

2,2′-dibenzothiazyl disulphide
benzothiazolyl disulphide; 2,2′-dithiobis(benzothiazole); MBTS; [120-78-5]

$C_{14}H_8N_2S_4$. M: 332.48. Crystals. MP: 180°C. d: 1.50 kg/l. Insoluble in water.
Production:
- 2-mercaptobenzothiazole (oxidative coupling)

Uses: vulcanisation accelerator

3,5-dibenzoxyacetophenone
[28924-21-2]

$C_{22}H_{20}O_3$. M: 332.40. White or pale yellow powder. MP: 62–64°C. Slightly soluble in water. Soluble in alcohol and chlorinated solvents.
Production:
- 3,5-dihydroxyacetophenone + benzyl chloride (ether formation)

Derivatives: terbutaline

dibenzoyl *See:* benzil

1,5-dibenzoylaminoanthraquinone *See:* Vat Yellow 3

dibenzoylmethane
1,3-diphenyl-1,3-propanedione; 1,3-diphenylpropane-1,3-dione; [120-46-7]

$C_{15}H_{12}O_2$. M: 224.26. Crystalline solid. MP: 77–79°C. Soluble in oxygenated and chlorinated solvents. The *enol* form predominates at equilibrium.
Production:
- benzaldehyde + acetophenone (condensation/alcohol oxidation)

Derivatives: difenzoquat methosulphate
Uses:
analytical reagent (uranium)

dibenzoyl peroxide *See:* benzoyl peroxide

2,5-di-(benzoylperoxy)-2,5-dimethylhexane
2,5-dimethyl-2,5-bis(benzoylperoxy)hexane

$C_{22}H_{26}O_6$. M: 386.44. Decomposes on heating with a 10-hour half-life of 100°C.
Production:
- 2,5-dimethylhexane-2,5-dihydroperoxide + benzoyl chloride (esterification)

Uses:
polymerisation initiator

dibenzoyl-*p*-quinonedioxime
p-benzoquinone bis(*o*-benzoyloxime); [120-52-5]

$C_{20}H_{14}N_2O_4$. M: 346.34.
Production:
- *p*-quinonedioxime + benzoyl chloride (esterification)

Uses: crosslinking agent (rubber)

dibenzylamine
N,N-dibenzylamine; [103-49-1]

$C_{14}H_{15}N_1$. M: 197.28. Colourless to pale yellow liquid with an ammoniacal odour. BP: 160–163°C (1.3 kPa). MP: <-24°C. d: 1.03 kg/l (20°C). Insoluble in water. Soluble in oxygenated solvents.
Production:
- benzaldehyde + ammonia (reductive ammoniation; coproduced with benzylamine/tribenzylamine)

Derivatives:
zinc dibenzyldithiocarbamate
Uses: corrosion inhibitor; bacteriostatic agent; amination reagent; vulcanisation accelerator

dibenzyl disulphide
benzyl disulphide; [150-60-7]

$C_{14}H_{14}S_2$. M: 246.39. Pink flakes. MP: 71–72°C. Insoluble in water. Soluble in hydrocarbon solvents.

275 2,6-DIBROMO-4-NITROANILINE

Production:
- benzyl chloride + sodium sulphide (oxidation/
  dehydrochlorination)
Uses: antioxidant/antiwear additive (lubricants)

N,N′-dibenzylethylenediamine *See:* benzathine

DIBP *See:* diisobutyl phthalate

1,4-di-(bromoacetoxy)butenediol
See: 1,4-bis(bromoacetoxy)-2-butene

dibromoanthranthrone
See: Vat Orange 3

3,9-dibromobenzanthrone
[81-98-1]

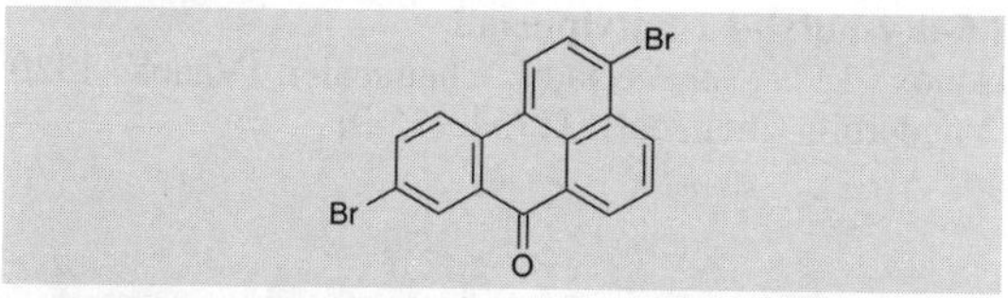

$C_{17}H_8Br_2O_1$. M: 388.06. Solid. MP: 225–230°C.
Production:
- benzanthrone (ring bromination)
Derivatives: Vat Black 8; Vat Black 25

1,4-dibromobutane
tetramethylene dibromide; [110-52-1]

$BrCH_2CH_2CH_2CH_2Br$

$C_4H_8Br_2$. M: 215.91. Liquid. BP: 194–196°C. MP:
-26°C. d: 1.81 kg/l (20°C). Insoluble in water.
Production:
- 1,4-butanediol (alcohol bromination)
Derivatives: pentoxyverine

dibromobutanediol-epichlorohydrin adduct
Ixol (Solvay)

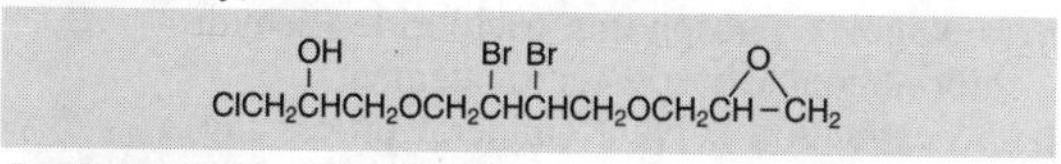

$C_{10}H_{17}Br_2Cl_1O_4$. M: 396.51.
Production:
- 1,4-butynediol + epichlorohydrin + bromine
  (epoxidation/addition)
Uses: fire-retardant rigid polyurethane polyol

1,2-dibromo-2,2-dichloroethyl dimethyl phosphate
See: naled

1,3-dibromo-5,5-dimethylhydantoin
DBDMH; [77-48-5]
$C_5H_6Br_2N_2O_2$. M: 285.92. Cream powder. MP: 187–
191°C with decomposition. Slightly soluble in water.
Contains 55% active bromine.

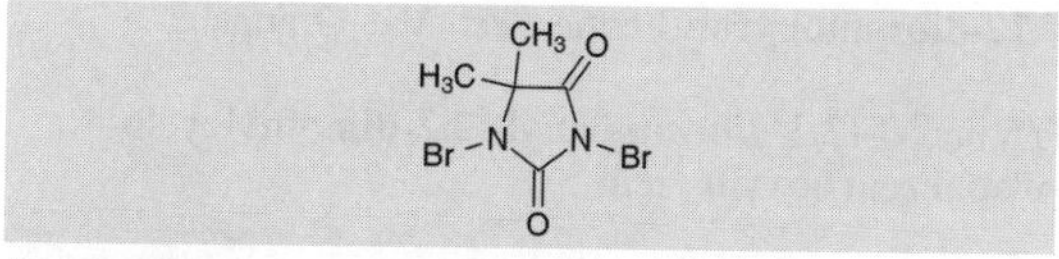

Production:
- 5,5-dimethylhydantoin + bromine (bromination)
Uses: biocide (cooling water systems, swimming
pools); bromination/oxidation reagent

1,2-dibromoethane *See:* ethylene dibromide

dibromoethyldibromocyclohexane
Saytex BCL-462 (Ethyl)

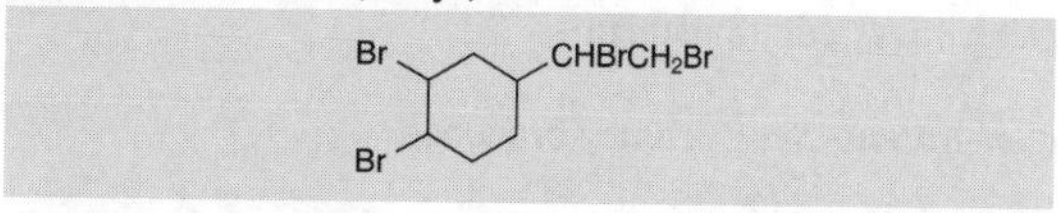

$C_8H_{12}Br_4$. M: 427.81. White powder. MP: 70–76°C. d:
2.38 kg/l. Insoluble in water. Soluble in oxygenated
and aromatic solvents.
Production:
- 4-vinylcyclohexene + bromine (addition)
Uses: fire-retardant additive (polystyrene, polyurethane,
polyvinyl chloride)

3,5-dibromo-4-hydroxybenzonitrile *See:* bromoxynil

dibromoneopentyl glycol
2,2-di-(bromomethyl)-1,3-propanediol; DBNPG

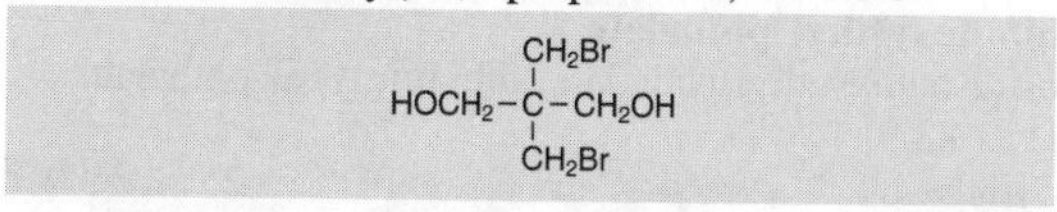

$C_5H_{10}Br_2O_2$. M: 261.94. White powder. MP: 85–105°C.
d: 2.0 kg/l. Insoluble in water. Soluble in oxygenated
and aromatic solvents.
Production:
- pentaerythritol + hydrobromic acid (alcohol
  bromination)
Uses: fire-retarded rigid polyurethane foam/unsaturated
polyester resin

2,6-dibromo-4-nitroaniline
4-nitro-2,6-dibromoaniline; [827-94-1]

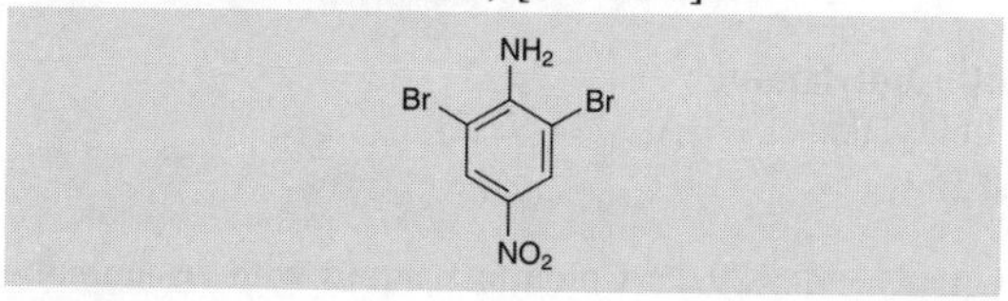

$C_6H_4Br_2N_2O_2$. M: 295.92. Yellow crystals. MP: 207°C.
Slightly soluble in water.
Production:
- p-nitroaniline (ring bromination)
Derivatives:
Disperse Blue 165

4,12-dibromopyranthrone *See:* Vat Orange 2

**(1R)-*cis*-3-(2,2-dibromovinyl)-2,2-dimethylcyclo-
propanecarboxylic acid**

$C_8H_{10}Br_2O_2$. M: 297.98.
Production:
• (1R)-*cis*-caronaldehyde + bromoform (condensation/
  dehydrobromination)
Derivatives: deltamethrin

di-*n*-butene *See:* octene, branched

dibutoxyethyl adipate
bis(2-butoxyethyl) adipate; [141-18-4]

$C_{18}H_{34}O_6$. M: 346.47. Colourless, viscous liquid. MP:
-34°C. d: 0.99 kg/l (20°C). Insoluble in water.
Production:
• ethylene glycol monobutyl ether + adipic acid/
  dimethyl adipate (esterification)
Uses: plasticiser

dibutoxyethyl phthalate
bis(2-butoxyethyl)phthalate; dibutylglycol phthalate;
[117-83-9]

$C_{20}H_{30}O_6$. M: 366.45. Involatile liquid. d: 1.06 kg/l
(25°C). Viscosity: 42 mPa.s (20°C). Insoluble in water.
Production:
• ethylene glycol monobutyl ether + phthalic
  anhydride (esterification)
Uses: polyvinyl chloride plasticiser

di-*n*-butylamine
dibutylamine; DBA; [111-92-2]

$C_8H_{19}N_1$. M: 129.25. Colourless liquid with an ammoniacal odour. BP: 160°C. FP: -62°C. d: 0.76 kg/l (4°C).
Slightly soluble in water. Soluble in oxygenated and
hydrocarbon solvents.
Production:
• *n*-butanol + ammonia (ammoniation; coproduced
  with *n*-butylamine/tri-*n*-butylamine)

Derivatives: carbosulphan; nickel di-*n*-butyldithio-
carbamate; zinc di-*n*-butyldithiocarbamate
Uses: corrosion inhibitor (textile lubricants, metalworking fluids); vulcanisation accelerator

di-*s*-butylamine
[626-23-3]

$C_8H_{19}N_1$. M: 129.25. Liquid. BP: 133–135°C. MP:
<-70°C. Soluble in water and most organic solvents.
Production:
• *s*-butanol + ammonia (amine formation; coproduced
  with *s*-butylamine)
Derivatives: tiocarbazil

2,6-di-*t*-butyl-4-*s*-butylphenol
Isonox 132 (Schenectady Chemicals); Vanox 1320
(Vanderbilt Chemical); [17540-75-9]

$C_{18}H_{30}O_1$. M: 262.44.
Production:
• 2,6-di-*t*-butylphenol + raffinate II (Friedel-Crafts
  alkylation)
Uses: antioxidant (plastics)

di-*n*-butyl butylphosphonate
DBBP; [78-46-6]

$C_{12}H_{27}O_3P_1$. M: 250.32. Liquid. d: 0.94 kg/l. Insoluble
in water.
Production:
• *n*-butanol + phosphorus trichloride (dehydro-
  chlorination/Arbusov rearrangement)
Uses: extraction solvent (mineral processing)

2,6-di-*t*-butyl-*p*-cresol
2,6-di-*t*-butyl-4-methylphenol; hydroxytoluene, butylated; BHT; Topanol O (ICI); E321 (EC); [128-37-0]

$C_{15}H_{24}O_1$. M: 220.35. White, crystalline solid. MP:
69°C. BP: 265°C. d: 1.05 kg/l (20°C). Bulk density:
0.51 kg/l. Insoluble in water. Soluble in ketones, esters
and hydrocarbon solvents. Flash point: 127°C (PMCC).

Production:
- *p*-cresol + isobutylene (Friedel-Crafts alkylation)
- 2-*t*-butyl-*p*-cresol + isobutylene (Friedel-Crafts alkylation)

Uses: antioxidant (fats, oils, soap, animal feed, solvents, lubricants, rubber, plastics, hot-melt adhesives); oxidation/gum inhibitor (gasoline)

2,6-di-*t*-butyldimethylamino-*p*-cresol
Ethanox 703 (Ethyl); [88-27-7]

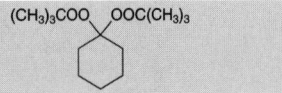

$C_{17}H_{29}N_1O_1$. M: 263.43.
Production:
- 2,6-di-*t*-butylphenol + formaldehyde + dimethylamine (Mannich reaction)

Uses: antioxidant (lubricants)

di-*n*-butyl ether
n-butyl ether; [142-96-1]

$$CH_3CH_2CH_2CH_2OCH_2CH_2CH_2CH_3$$

$C_8H_{18}O_1$. M: 130.23. Colourless liquid. BP: 142°C. MP: -98°C. d: 0.77 kg/l (20°C). Insoluble in water. Miscible with oxygenated solvents.
Production:
- *n*-butanol (dehydration)

Uses:
metal extraction solvent; Grignard reaction solvent

di-*n*-butyl fumarate
dibutyl fumarate; [105-75-9]

$$\underset{CH_3CH_2CH_2CH_2OOC}{\overset{H}{\diagdown}}C=C\underset{H}{\overset{COOCH_2CH_2CH_2CH_3}{\diagup}}$$

$C_{12}H_{20}O_4$. M: 228.29. Colourless liquid. BP: 285°C. FP: -16°C. Insoluble in water.
Production:
- *n*-butanol + fumaric acid (esterification)

Uses: vinyl resin comonomer

di-*n*-butyl maleate
dibutyl maleate; DBM; [105-76-0]

$$\underset{H}{\overset{H}{\diagdown}}C=C\underset{COOCH_2CH_2CH_2CH_3}{\overset{COOCH_2CH_2CH_2CH_3}{\diagup}}$$

$C_{12}H_{20}O_4$. M: 228.29. Colourless liquid. BP: 281°C. Insoluble in water.
Production:
- *n*-butanol + maleic anhydride (esterification)

Uses: vinyl resin comonomer

2,6-di-*t*-butyl-4-methoxymethylphenol

$$\underset{CH_2OCH_3}{\overset{OH}{(CH_3)_3C\diagup\diagdown C(CH_3)_3}}$$

$C_{16}H_{26}O_2$. M: 250.39.
Production:
- 2,6-di-*t*-butylphenol + formaldehyde + methanol (chloromethylation/ether formation)

Uses:
antioxidant (rubber)

di-*t*-butyl peroxide
t-butyl peroxide; DTBP; Trigonox B (Akzo); [110-05-4]

$$(CH_3)_3CO-OC(CH_3)_3$$

$C_8H_{18}O_2$. M: 146.23. Liquid. MP: -40°C. d: 0.79 kg/l (25°C). Decomposes at 190°C.
Production:
- *t*-butyl hydroperoxide + isobutylene (peroxidation)

Uses:
crosslinking agent (rubber, resins)

2,2-di-(*t*-butylperoxy)butane
Luperox 220 (Elf-Atochem); Trigonox DB50 (Akzo); [2167-23-9]

$$\left[(CH_3)_3COO\right]_2\overset{CH_3}{\underset{|}{C}}C_2H_5$$

$C_{12}H_{26}O_4$. M: 234.34.
Production:
- methyl ethyl ketone + *t*-butyl hydroperoxide (ketal formation)

Uses:
crosslinking agent (resins)

1,1-di-(*t*-butylperoxy)cyclohexane
Luperco 331 (Elf-Atochem); Trigonox 22-B-50 (Akzo); USP-400P (Witco)

$$(CH_3)_3COO\quad OOC(CH_3)_3$$

$C_{14}H_{28}O_4$. M: 260.37.
Production:
- cyclohexanone + *t*-butyl hydroperoxide (ketal formation)

Uses:
crosslinking agent (resins)

2,5-di-(*t*-butylperoxy)-2,5-dimethylhexane
2,5-dimethyl-2,5-di-(*t*-butylperoxy)hexane; Luperco 130 (Elf-Atochem); Interox DHBP (Interox); Trigonox 101 (Akzo); USP-711 (Witco)

$C_{16}H_{34}O_4$. M: 290.45. Liquid. MP: 8°C. d: 0.86 kg/l (25°C).
Production:
• 2,5-dimethylhexane-2,5-dihydroperoxide + isobutylene (peroxidation)
Uses:
crosslinking agent (plastics, rubber)

2,5-di-(*t*-butylperoxy)-2,5-dimethylhex-3-yne
2,5-dimethyl-2,5-di-(*t*-butylperoxy)hex-3-yne; Luperox 130 (Elf-Atochem); Trigonox 145 (Akzo)

$C_{16}H_{30}O_4$. M: 286.42.
Production:
• *t*-butyl hydroperoxide + dimethyl hexynediol (peroxidation)
Uses: crosslinking agent (resins)

1,1-di-(*t*-butylperoxy)-3,3,5-trimethylcyclohexane
Interox TMCH (Interox); Luperco 237 (Elf-Atochem); Trigonox 29/40 (Akzo)

$C_{17}H_{34}O_4$. M: 302.46. Liquid. Decomposes at 150°C.
Production:
• 3,3,5-trimethylcyclohexanone + *t*-butyl hydroperoxide (ketal formation)
Uses:
crosslinking agent (resins)

2,4-di-*t*-butylphenol
[96-76-4]

$C_{14}H_{22}O_1$. M: 206.33. Brown crystals. MP: 52°C. BP: 263°C. d: 0.92 kg/l.
Production:
• phenol + isobutylene (Friedel-Crafts alkylation; coproduced with *p*-*t*-butylphenol)
Derivatives:
bis(2,4-di-*t*-butylphenyl)pentaerythrityl diphosphite; 2,2′-ethylidene bis(4,6-di-*t*-butylphenol); 2-(2-hydroxy-3,5-di-*t*-butylphenyl)-5-chlorobenzotriazole; tetrakis(2,4-di-

t-butylphenyl)-4,4′-biphenyl diphosphonite; tris(2,4-di-*t*-butylphenyl) phosphite

2,6-di-*t*-butylphenol
Ionox 75 (Shell); Isonox 103 (Schenectady Chemicals); [128-39-2]

$C_{14}H_{22}O_1$. M: 206.33. Clear yellow solid. MP: 37°C. BP: 253°C. d: 0.91 kg/l (20°C). Insoluble in water. Soluble in aromatic solvents.
Production:
• isobutylene + phenol (orthoalkylation; coproduced with *o*-*t*-butylphenol)
Derivatives:
bis[*O*-ethyl-(3,5-di-*t*-butyl-4-hydroxybenzyl)phosphonic acid], calcium salt; 2,4-bis(*n*-octylthio)-6-(4-hydroxy-3,5-di-*t*-butylanilino)-1,3,5-triazine; 2,6-di-*t*-butyl-4-*s*-butylphenol; 2,6-di-*t*-butyldimethylamino-*p*-cresol; 2,6-di-*t*-butyl-4-methoxymethylphenol; dibutylphenol disulphide; di-(pentamethylhydroxypiperidyl) butyl-(di-3,5-*t*-butyl-4-hydroxybenzyl)malonate; 2-(2-hydroxy-3,5-*t*-butylphenyl)benzotriazole; methyl 3,5-di-*t*-butyl-4-hydroxyphenylpropionate; 4,4′-methylenebis(2,6-di-*t*-butylphenol); 1,3,5-tris(3,5-di-*t*-butyl-4-hydroxybenzyl)isocyanurate; 2,4,6-tris(3,5-di-*t*-butyl-4-hydroxybenzyl)mesitylene
Uses: antioxidant (oils, petrol, aviation fuels)

dibutylphenol disulphide

$C_{28}H_{42}O_2S_2$. M: 474.78.
Production:
• 2,6-di-*t*-butylphenol + sulphur monochloride (chlorosulphurisation)
Uses:
extreme-pressure additive (lubricants)

N,N′-di-*s*-butyl-*p*-phenylenediamine
[101-96-2]

$C_{14}H_{24}N_2$. M: 220.35. Reddish-brown liquid. MP: 18°C. d: 0.94 kg/l (20°C). Insoluble in water. Soluble in hydrocarbon solvents.
Production:
• *s*-butylamine + hydroquinone (reductive amination)
Uses:
antioxidant (motor fuels)

1,5-di-(p-t-butylphenylthio)anthraquinone

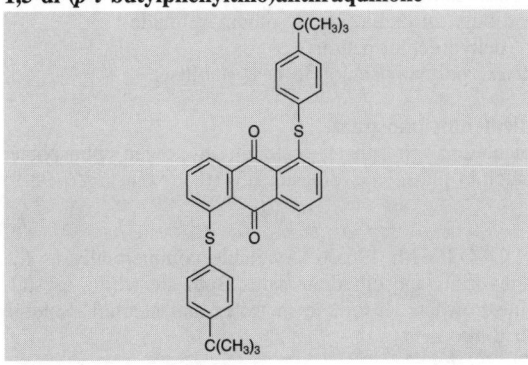

C$_{34}$H$_{32}$O$_2$S$_2$. M: 536.76.
Production:
• 1,5-dichloroanthraquinone + thiophenol +
  isobutylene (Friedel-Crafts alkylation/
  dehydrochlorination)
Uses: dye (liquid crystal displays)

di-n-butyl phthalate
DBP; [84-74-2]

C$_{16}$H$_{22}$O$_4$. M: 278.36. Pale yellow liquid. BP: 192–
198°C (1.3 kPa). d: 1.04 kg/l (20°C). Insoluble in
water.
Production:
• n-butanol + phthalic anhydride (esterification)
Uses: non-reactive epoxy resin diluent; plasticiser (adhesives, sealants); plasticiser (rubber, cellulosic, vinyl
chloride, vinyl acetate resins)

di-n-butyl sebacate
DBS; [109-43-3]

C$_{18}$H$_{34}$O$_4$. M: 314.47. Colourless, involatile liquid. BP:
345°C. d: 0.93 kg/l (25°C). Viscosity: 25 mPa.s
(20°C). Insoluble in water.
Production:
• n-butanol + sebacic acid (esterification)
Uses: plasticiser (polyvinyl butyral)

di-n-butyl succinate
dibutyl succinate; [141-03-7]

C$_{12}$H$_{22}$O$_4$. M: 230.31. Colourless liquid. BP: 274°C.

MP: -29°C. d: 0.98 kg/l (20°C). Insoluble in water.
Soluble in oxygenated solvents.
Production:
• n-butanol + succinic acid (esterification)
Uses: insect repellant

di-n-butylthiourea
N,N'-dibutylthiourea; DBTU; [109-46-6]

(CH$_3$CH$_2$CH$_2$CH$_2$NH)$_2$C=S

C$_9$H$_{20}$N$_2$S$_1$. M: 188.33. Off-white, odourless powder.
MP: 65°C. d: 1.0 kg/l. Insoluble in water and aliphatic
solvents. Soluble in oxygenated solvents.
Production:
• n-butylamine + carbon disulphide (thiocarbonylation)
Uses: corrosion inhibitor (metal pickling); vulcanisation
accelerator

dibutyltin bis(isooctylmaleate)
diisooctyl dibutyltindimaleate

(CH$_3$CH$_2$CH$_2$CH$_2$)$_2$Sn[OCCH=CHCOC$_8$H$_{17}$]$_2$

C$_{32}$H$_{56}$O$_8$Sn$_1$. M: 687.48.
Production:
• dibutyltin dichloride + isooctanol + maleic
  anhydride (esterification/dehydrochlorination)
Uses: polyvinyl chloride heat stabiliser

dibutyltin bis(isooctylmercaptoacetate)
See: dibutyltin diisooctylthioglycollate

dibutyltin bis(laurylmercaptide)

(CH$_3$CH$_2$CH$_2$CH$_2$)$_2$Sn[S(CH$_2$)$_{11}$CH$_3$]$_2$

C$_{32}$H$_{68}$S$_2$Sn$_1$. M: 635.71.
Production:
• dibutyltin dichloride + n-dodecyl mercaptan
  (dehydrochlorination)
Uses: polyurethane catalyst (2-pack coatings); polyvinyl
chloride heat stabiliser

dibutyltin bis(2-mercaptoethyl oleate)

(CH$_3$CH$_2$CH$_2$CH$_2$)$_2$Sn[SCH$_2$CH$_2$OC(CH$_2$)$_7$CH=CH(CH$_2$)$_7$CH$_3$]$_2$

C$_{48}$H$_{92}$O$_4$S$_2$Sn$_1$. M: 916.09.
Production:
• 2-mercaptoethanol + oleic acid + dibutyltin
  dichloride (esterification/dehydrochlorination)
Uses: polyvinyl chloride heat stabiliser

dibutyltin dichloride
di-n-butyltin dichloride; [683-18-1]

(CH$_3$CH$_2$CH$_2$CH$_2$)$_2$SnCl$_2$

C$_8$H$_{18}$Cl$_2$Sn$_1$. M: 303.83. White needles. MP: 41–42°C.

BP: 140–143°C (1.3 kPa). Soluble in oxygenated and aromatic solvents. Decomposed by hot water.
Production:
• tetra-*n*-butyltin + stannic chloride (Kocheshkov redistribution)
Derivatives: dibutyltin bis(isooctylmaleate); dibutyltin bis(laurylmercaptide); dibutyltin bis(2-mercaptoethyl oleate); dibutyltin diisooctylthioglycollate; dibutyltin dilaurate; dibutyltin maleate; dibutyltin sulphide

dibutyltin diisooctylthioglycollate
dibutyltin bis(isooctylmercaptoacetate)

$$(CH_3CH_2CH_2CH_2)_2Sn\left[SCH_2\overset{O}{\overset{\|}{C}}OC_8H_{17}\right]_2$$

$C_{28}H_{56}O_4S_2Sn_1$. M: 639.58.
Production:
• dibutyltin dichloride + isooctyl thioglycollate (dehydrochlorination)
Uses: polyurethane catalyst (reaction-injection moulding, high-resilience flexible foam); polyvinyl chloride heat stabiliser

dibutyltin dilaurate
di-*n*-butyltin dilaurate; [77-58-7]

$$(CH_3CH_2CH_2CH_2)_2Sn\left[O\overset{O}{\overset{\|}{C}}(CH_2)_{10}CH_3\right]_2$$

$C_{32}H_{64}O_4Sn_1$. M: 631.55. Yellow liquid or solid. MP: 22°C. Insoluble in water and alcohol. Soluble in ketones, esters and aromatic solvents.
Production:
• dibutyltin dichloride + lauric acid, broad cut (esterification)
Uses: polyurethane foam/silicone elastomers catalyst; polyvinyl chloride heat stabiliser

dibutyltin maleate
di-*n*-butyltin maleate; [78-04-6]

$$\left[\begin{matrix}(CH_2)_3CH_3\\ |\\ Sn-OOCCH=CHCOO\\ |\\ (CH_2)_3CH_3\end{matrix}\right]_n$$

$C_{12}H_{20}O_4Sn_1$. M: 346.98.
Production:
• dibutyltin dichloride + maleic acid (esterification)
Uses:
polyvinyl chloride heat stabiliser

dibutyltin sulphide
[4253-22-9]

$$\begin{matrix}CH_3CH_2CH_2CH_2 & & CH_2CH_2CH_2CH_3\\ & Sn & S & Sn \\ CH_3CH_2CH_2CH_2-Sn & & S & Sn-CH_2CH_2CH_2CH_3\\ & S & Sn & S\\ CH_3CH_2CH_2CH_2 & & CH_2CH_2CH_2CH_3\end{matrix}$$

$C_{24}H_{54}S_3Sn_3$. M: 794.95.

Production:
• dibutyltin dichloride + sodium sulphide (dehydrochlorination)
Uses: polyvinyl chloride heat stabiliser

dicalcium phosphate
bicalcium phosphate; calcium hydrogen phosphate; calcium phosphate, dibasic; E341(b) (EC); [7757-93-9]

$$CaHPO_4$$

$H_1Ca_1O_4P_1$. M: 136.06. Available commercially as the anhydrous and dihydrate salts. Both are white, crystalline powders. Insoluble in water and alcohol. Soluble in dilute acid.
Production:
• calcium hydroxide + phosphoric acid, pure (salt formation)
• bone, degreased (acid extraction; coproduced with ossein)
Derivatives: calcium pyrophosphate
Uses: toothpaste abrasive; mineral supplement (animal feed, foods, cereals, pharmaceuticals)

dicalcium pyrophosphate *See:* calcium pyrophosphate

dicamba
3,6-dichloro-2-methoxybenzoic acid; [1918-00-9]

$C_8H_6Cl_2O_3$. M: 221.05. Available commercially as the acid, sodium, potassium, dimethylamine and triethanolamine salts.
Production:
• 1,2,4-trichlorobenzene + carbon dioxide + dimethyl sulphate (hydrolysis/Kolbe-Schmitt reaction/methylation)
Uses: herbicide

dichlobenil *See:* 2,6-dichlorobenzonitrile

dichlofluanid
N-dichlorofluoromethylthio-*N'*,*N'*-dimethyl-*N*-phenyl-sulphamide; [1085-98-9]

$C_9H_{11}Cl_2F_1N_2O_2S_2$. M: 333.24.
Production:
• dimethylsulphamyl chloride + aniline + dichlorofluoromethanesulphenyl chloride (sulphonamide formation/dehydrochlorination)
Uses: fungicide

dichlone

2,3-dichloro-1,4-naphthoquinone; [117-80-6]

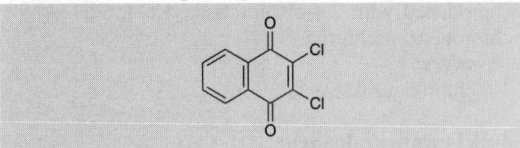

$C_{10}H_4Cl_2O_2$. M: 227.05.
Production:
• naphthionic acid + chlorine (chlorination)
Derivatives: dithianon
Uses: algicide/fungicide

dichlormid

N,N-diallyldichloroacetamide; 2,2-dichloro-*N,N*-di-2-propenylacetamide; [37764-25-3]

$$Cl_2CHCN(CH_2CH=CH_2)_2$$
(with O double bond on carbonyl)

$C_8H_{11}Cl_1N_1O_1$. M: 172.64.
Production:
• dichloroacetic acid + diallylamine (amide formation)
Uses: herbicide adjunct

dichloroacetic acid

2,2-dichloroacetic acid; [79-43-6]

$$Cl_2CHCOOH$$

$C_2H_2Cl_2O_2$. M: 128.95. Colourless liquid with a pungent odour. MP: 10–13°C. BP: 193–194°C. d: 1.56 kg/l (20°C). Miscible with water and alcohol.
Production:
• acetic acid + chlorine (alpha chlorination; byproduct of chloroacetic acid production)
Derivatives: dichlormid

1,3-dichloroacetone

1,3-dichloro-2-propanone; [534-07-6]

$$ClCH_2CCH_2Cl$$
(with O on carbonyl)

$C_3H_4Cl_2O_1$. M: 126.97. Crystalline solid. MP: 43–45°C. BP: 173°C. d: 1.38 kg/l (46°C). Soluble in water and oxygenated solvents.
Production:
• methyl γ-chloroacetoacetate (alpha chlorination/decarboxylation; coproduced with 1,1,3-trichloroacetone)
Uses: organic intermediate

α,4-dichloroacetophenone

2,4′-dichloroacetophenone; [937-20-2]

$C_8H_6Cl_2O_1$. M: 189.05.

Production:
• acetophenone (ring chlorination/alpha chlorination)
Derivatives: lofepramine; myclobutanil

2,4-dichloroacetophenone

[2234-16-4]

$C_8H_6Cl_2O_1$. M: 189.05. Solid. MP: 33–34°C. Insoluble in water.
Production:
• acetophenone + chlorine (ring chlorination; coproduced with 2,4,5-trichloroacetophenone)
Derivatives: α,α,2,4-tetrachloroacetophenone; α,2,4-trichloroacetophenone

2,5-dichloroaniline

Fast Scarlet GG base; Azoic Diazo Component 3 (CI); 37010 (CI); [95-82-9]

$C_6H_5Cl_2N_1$. M: 162.03. Needles. MP: 49–51°C. BP: 245°C. Slightly soluble in water. Soluble in oxygenated and aromatic solvents.
Production:
• 2,5-dichloronitrobenzene (nitration/nitro reduction)
Derivatives:
Acid Green 19; chloramben; 2,5-dichloro-*p*-phenylenediamine; 1-(2′,5′-dichloro-4′-sulphophenyl)-3-methylpyrazolone; 2,5-diethoxyaniline; Pigment Brown 25; Pigment Red 2; Pigment Red 9; Pigment Red 10; Pigment Red 88; Pigment Red 188; Pigment Red 214; Pigment Yellow 10; sulcofenuron

2,6-dichloroaniline

2-amino-*m*-dichlorobenzene; [608-31-1]

$C_6H_5Cl_2N_1$. M: 162.03. Crystalline solid. MP: 38–41°C. Slightly soluble in water. Soluble in oxygenated solvents.
Production:
• 2,6-dichlorobenzonitrile (Hofmann degradation)
Derivatives: clonidine

3,4-dichloroaniline

[95-76-1]
$C_6H_5Cl_2N_1$. M: 162.03. Crystalline solid. MP: 71–73°C.

BP: 272°C. Insoluble in water. Soluble in oxygenated solvents.

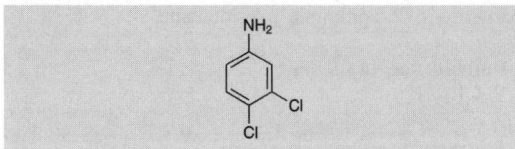

Production:
• 3,4-dichloronitrobenzene (nitro reduction)
Derivatives:
benzoylprop-ethyl; 3,4-dichlorophenyl isocyanate; propanil; triclocarban

3,5-dichloroaniline
[626-43-7]

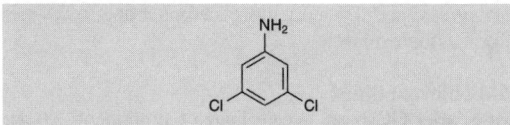

$C_6H_5Cl_2N_1$. M: 162.03. Needles. MP: 51–53°C. BP: 260°C. Insoluble in water. Soluble in oxygenated solvents.
Production:
• *m*-dichlorobenzene + ammonia (ring bromination/isomerisation/ammoniation)
Derivatives:
chlozolinate; iprodione; procymidone; vinclozolin

1,5-dichloroanthraquinone
[82-46-2]

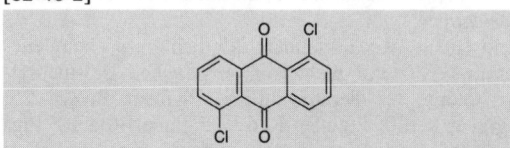

$C_{14}H_6Cl_2O_2$. M: 277.11. Pale yellow, crystalline solid. MP: 252°C. Insoluble in water. Slightly soluble in oxygenated and aromatic solvents.
Production:
• anthraquinone-1,5-disulphonic acid (sulphonate displacement)
Derivatives: 1,5-di-(*p-t*-butylphenylthio)anthraquinone; Vat Violet 13

2,4-dichlorobenzal chloride
α,α,2,4-tetrachlorotoluene

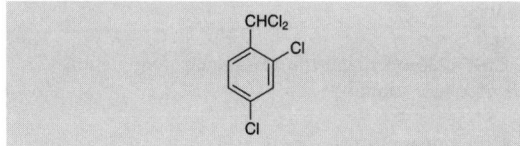

$C_7H_4Cl_4$. M: 229.92. Not a commercially traded product.

Production:
• 2,4-dichlorotoluene (side-chain chlorination; coproduced with 2,4-dichlorobenzyl chloride/2,4-dichlorobenzotrichloride)
Derivatives:
2,4-dichlorobenzaldehyde

2,4-dichlorobenzaldehyde
[874-42-0]

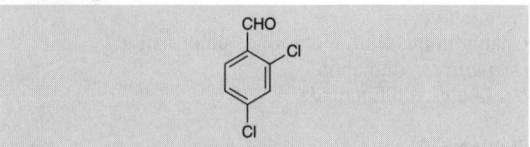

$C_7H_4Cl_2O_1$. M: 175.02.
Production:
• 2,4-dichlorobenzal chloride (hydrolysis)
Derivatives: diniconazole

2,6-dichlorobenzaldehyde
[83-38-5]

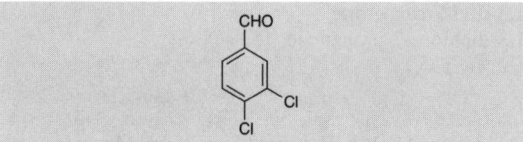

$C_7H_4Cl_2O_1$. M: 175.02. Crystalline solid. MP: 70–71°C. Insoluble in water. Soluble in hot alcohol.
Production:
• 2,6-dichlorotoluene (side-chain oxidation)
Derivatives:
2,6-dichlorobenzonitrile; 3-(2,6-dichlorophenyl)-5-methylisoxazole-4-carboxylic acid; Mordant Blue 1

3,4-dichlorobenzaldehyde
[6287-38-3]

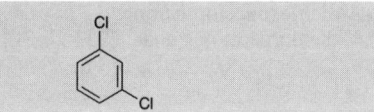

$C_7H_4Cl_2O_1$. M: 175.02.
Production:
• 3,4-dichlorotoluene (side-chain oxidation)
Derivatives:
4-fluoro-3-phenoxybenzaldehyde cyanohydrin

m-dichlorobenzene
1,3-dichlorobenzene; [541-73-1]

$C_6H_4Cl_2$. M: 147.01. Colourless liquid. BP: 172–173°C.

MP: -25°C. d: 1.29 kg/l (20°C). Insoluble in water. Soluble in oxygenated, chlorinated and aromatic solvents.

Production:
• *p*-dichlorobenzene (isomerisation)
Derivatives:
3,5-dichloroaniline; 2,4-dichloronitrobenzene

o-dichlorobenzene
1,2-dichlorobenzene; ODCB; [95-50-1]

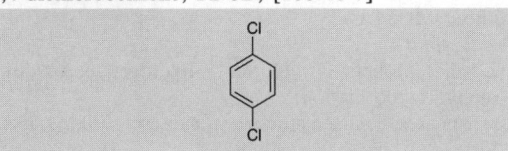

$C_6H_4Cl_2$. M: 147.01. Colourless to pale brown liquid with a pungent, aromatic odour. Available as a standard 72% 1,2-dichlorobenzene, 18% 1,4-dichlorobenzene mixture or as pure, 99% grade. Pure grade: BP: 179–180°C. FP: -17°C. Insoluble in water. Miscible with most organic solvents. Flash point: 72°C (CC).

Production:
• benzene + hydrogen chloride, anhydrous (Gulf oxy-chlorination process; coproduced with chlorobenzene/*p*-dichlorobenzene)
Derivatives: 3,4-dichloronitrobenzene
Uses: heat-transfer fluid; aircraft/vehicle/industrial engine cleaner ingredient; industrial deodorants, insecticides; solvent (dyestuff intermediates, toluene diisocyanate production)

p-dichlorobenzene
1,4-dichlorobenzene; PDCB; [106-46-7]

$C_6H_4Cl_2$. M: 147.01. Crystals with a strong, characteristic odour. MP: 54–56°C. BP: 173°C. Insoluble in water. Soluble in oxygenated, chlorinated and aromatic solvents.

Production:
• benzene + hydrogen chloride, anhydrous (Gulf oxy-chlorination process; coproduced with chlorobenzene/*o*-dichlorobenzene)
Derivatives: 4-chloro-2-nitrophenol; *m*-dichlorobenzene; 2,5-dichloronitrobenzene; poly(phenylene sulphide); 1,2,4,5-tetrachlorobenzene; 1,2,4-trichlorobenzene
Uses: disinfectant; moth balls

3,3'-dichlorobenzidine dihydrochloride
4,4'-diamino-3,3'-dichlorobiphenyl dihydrochloride; [5742-07-4] (dihydrochloride); [91-94-1] (free base)
$C_{12}H_{12}Cl_4N_2$. M: 326.05.

Production:
• *o*-chloronitrobenzene (reductive coupling/acid-catalysed rearrangement)
Derivatives:
3,3'-diaminobenzidine; Pigment Orange 13; Pigment Orange 34; Pigment Red 38; Pigment Yellow 12; Pigment Yellow 13; Pigment Yellow 14; Pigment Yellow 17; Pigment Yellow 55; Pigment Yellow 63; Pigment Yellow 83; Pigment Yellow 124; Pigment Yellow 127; Pigment Yellow 152; Pigment Yellow 170; Pigment Yellow 171
Uses: polyurethane chain-extender

2,6-dichlorobenzonitrile
dichlobenil; [1194-65-6]

$C_7H_3Cl_2N_1$. M: 172.02. White, crystalline solid with an aromatic odour. MP: 139–145°C. BP: 270°C. Insoluble in water. Soluble in oxygenated and chlorinated solvents.

Production:
• 2,6-dichlorotoluene + ammonia (ammoxidation)
• 2,6-dichlorobenzaldehyde + hydroxylamine sulphate (imine formation/dehydration)
Derivatives:
2,6-dichloroaniline; 2,6-difluorobenzamide
Uses: herbicide

2,4'-dichlorobenzophenone
[85-29-0]

$C_{13}H_8Cl_2O_1$. M: 251.11. Crystalline solid. MP: 67°C. BP: 214–215°C (2.9 kPa). Soluble in hot alcohol.
Production:
• *p*-chlorobenzoyl chloride + chlorobenzene (Friedel-Crafts acylation; coproduced with 4,4'-dichlorobenzophenone)
Derivatives: fenarimol

4,4'-dichlorobenzophenone
di-(4-chlorophenyl)ketone; [90-98-2]

$C_{13}H_8Cl_2O_1$. M: 251.11. Crystalline solid. MP: 144–

146°C. BP: 353°C. Insoluble in water. Soluble in hot alcohol, oxygenated and chlorinated solvents.
Production:
- *p*-chlorobenzoyl chloride + chlorobenzene (Friedel-Crafts acylation; coproduced with 2,4'-dichloro-benzophenone)

Derivatives: Acid Blue 213

2,4-dichlorobenzotrichloride

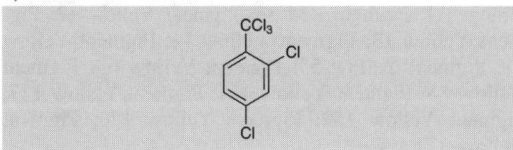

$C_7H_3Cl_5$. M: 264.37.
Production:
- 2,4-dichlorotoluene (side-chain chlorination; coproduced with 2,4-dichlorobenzyl chloride/2,4-dichlorobenzal chloride)

Derivatives: 2,4-dichlorobenzotrifluoride; 2,4-dichloro-benzoyl chloride

2,4-dichlorobenzotrifluoride
[320-60-5]

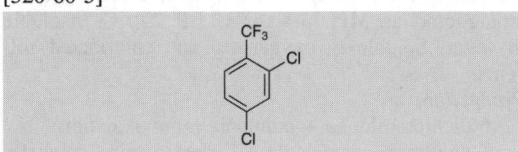

$C_7H_3Cl_2F_3$. M: 215.00. Liquid. BP: 117–118°C. d: 1.38 kg/l (20°C). Insoluble in water.
Production:
- 2,4-dichlorobenzotrichloride + hydrogen fluoride (halogen exchange)

Derivatives: dinitramine; prodiamine

3,4-dichlorobenzotrifluoride
[328-84-7]

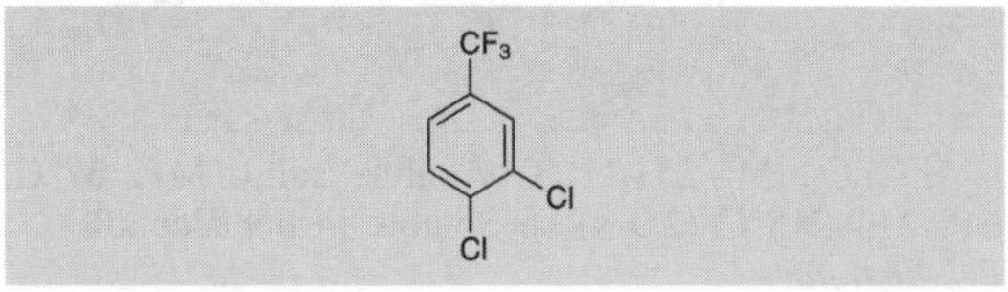

$C_7H_3Cl_2F_3$. M: 215.00.
Production:
- 3,4-dichlorotoluene + hydrogen fluoride (side-chain chlorination/halogen exchange)

Derivatives:
acifluorfen; D-fluvalinate; oxyfluorfen

2,4-dichlorobenzoyl chloride
[89-75-8]
$C_7H_3Cl_3O_1$. M: 209.46. Colourless liquid. Hydrolysed by hot water and hot alcohol.

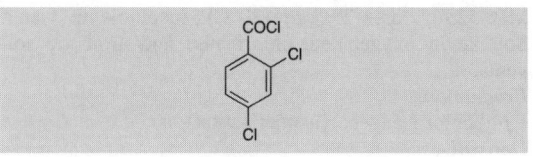

Production:
- 2,4-dichlorobenzotrichloride (hydrolysis)

Derivatives: Acid Red 107; 2,4-dichlorobenzoyl peroxide; 2,4-dichloro-5-sulphamoylbenzoic acid; mepacrine

3,5-dichlorobenzoyl chloride

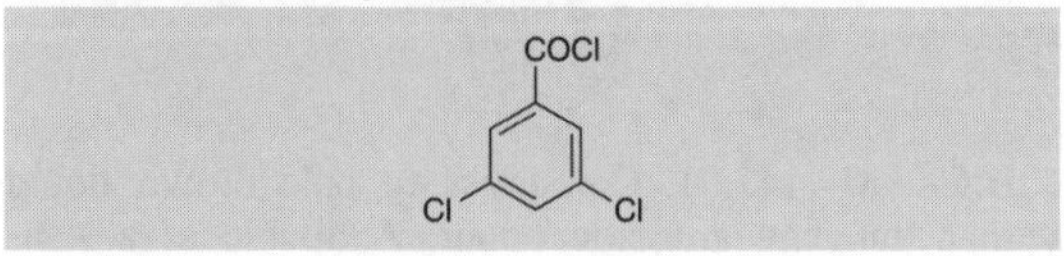

$C_7H_3Cl_3O_1$. M: 209.46. Needles. MP: 185–187°C. Sublimes on further heating. Slightly soluble in water. Soluble in oxygenated solvents.
Production:
- benzoic acid (ring chlorination)

Derivatives: propyzamide

2,4-dichlorobenzoyl peroxide
bis(2,4-dichlorobenzoyl) peroxide; Cadox TS-50 (Akzo); [133-14-2]

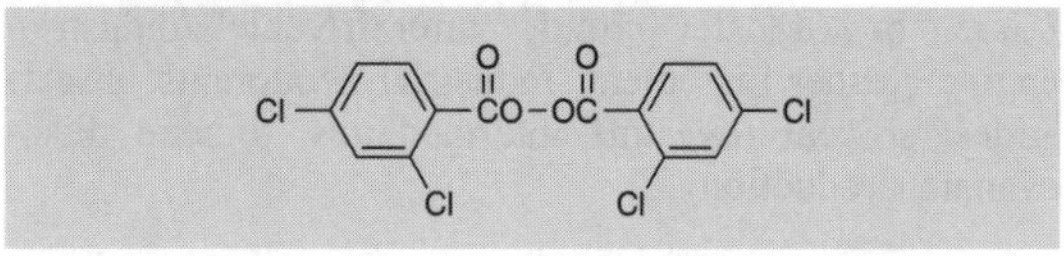

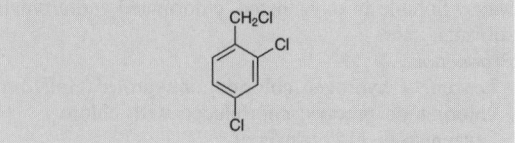

$C_{14}H_6Cl_4O_4$. M: 380.01. Available commercially as a 50% solution in silicone oil. It has a half-life of 10-hours at 54°C.
Production:
- 2,4-dichlorobenzoyl chloride + hydrogen peroxide (dehydrochlorination)

Uses: heat-vulcanised silicone rubber crosslinking agent

2,4-dichlorobenzyl chloride
α,2,4-trichlorotoluene; [94-99-5]

$C_7H_5Cl_3$. M: 195.48. Colourless liquid. BP: 250–252°C. d: 1.42 kg/l (25°C). Insoluble in water. Soluble in oxygenated solvents.
Production:
- 2,4-dichlorotoluene (side-chain chlorination; coproduced with 2,4-dichlorobenzotrichloride/2,4-dichlorobenzal chloride)

Derivatives:
chlorphonium chloride; diclobutrazol; miconazole

2,6-dichlorobenzyl chloride
α,2,6-trichlorotoluene; [2014-83-7]

$C_7H_5Cl_3$. M: 195.48. Solid. MP: 36–39°C. Insoluble in water. Soluble in oxygenated solvents.
Production:
• 2,6-dichlorotoluene (side-chain chlorination)
Derivatives:
isoconazole

1,4-dichlorobutane
1,4-butane dichloride; tetramethylene dichloride; DCB; [110-56-5]

$ClCH_2CH_2CH_2CH_2Cl$

$C_4H_8Cl_2$. M: 127.01. Colourless liquid. BP: 153–155°C. MP: -34°C. d: 1.16 kg/l (20°C). Insoluble in water. Miscible with chlorinated solvents.
Production:
• 1,4-butanediol (chlorination)
Derivatives:
3,3-tetramethyleneglutaric acid

1,1-dichloro-2,2-difluoroethylene
[79-35-6]

$CCl_2=CF_2$

$C_2Cl_2F_2$. M: 132.93.
Production:
• 1,1,2-trichloro-1,2,2-trifluoroethane (dechlorination; byproduct of chlorotrifluoroethylene production)
Derivatives:
methoxyflurane

dichlorodifluoromethane
CFC-12; Freon 12 (Du Pont); R12; [75-71-8]

CF_2Cl_2

$C_1Cl_2F_2$. M: 120.92. Colourless, odourless, non-flammable gas. BP: -30°C.
Production:
• carbon tetrachloride + hydrogen fluoride (halogen exchange; coproduced with trichlorofluoromethane)
• natural gas + hydrogen fluoride + chlorine (Montedison single-step process; coproduced with trichlorofluoromethane)
Uses:
blowing agent (polyvinyl chloride/polyurethane foams); R-500 refrigerant gas component; aerosol propellant; refrigerant/air conditioning gas

1,4-dichloro-2,5-dimethoxybenzene
See: chloroneb

1,3-dichloro-5,5-dimethylhydantoin
DDH; [118-52-5]

$C_4H_6Cl_2N_2O_2$. M: 185.01. White powder. Slightly soluble in water.
Production:
• 5,5-dimethylhydantoin + chlorine (chlorination)
Uses: bleaching agent (laundry detergents)

dichlorodimethylsilane
dimethyldichlorosilane; [75-78-5]

$(CH_3)_2SiCl_2$

$C_2H_6Cl_2Si_1$. M: 129.07. Colourless liquid. BP: 70°C. d: 1.07 kg/l (25°C). Hydrolysed by water producing hydrogen chloride.
Production:
• silicon, metallurgical grade + methyl chloride (Direct process; coproduced with chlorotrimethylsilane/trichloromethylsilane/dichloromethylsilane)
Derivatives: dimethylsiloxane oligomers; silicone-polyol block copolymers
Uses: surface treatment agent (silica)

dichlorodiphenylsilane
diphenyldichlorosilane; [80-10-4]

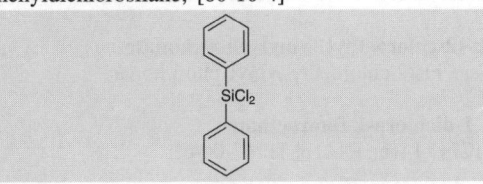

$C_{12}H_{10}Cl_2Si_1$. M: 253.21. Colourless liquid. BP: 304°C. Hydrolysed by water producing hydrogen chloride.
Production:
• silicon, metallurgical grade + chlorobenzene (Direct process; coproduced with trichlorophenylsilane)
Derivatives: dimethylsiloxane oligomers

4,4′-dichlorodiphenyl sulphone
p,p′-dichlorodiphenyl sulphone; di-(4-chlorophenyl) sulphone; di-(*p*-chlorophenyl) sulphone

$C_{12}H_8Cl_2O_2S_1$. M: 287.16.
Production:
• chlorobenzene + chlorosulphonic acid (sulphonation)
Derivatives:
poly(4,4′-phenoxybiphenyl sulphone); polysulphone

4,4′-dichlorodiphenyltrichloroethane *See:* DDT

1,1-dichloroethane
ethylidene chloride; [75-34-3]

$$CH_3CHCl_2$$

$C_2H_4Cl_2$. M: 98.96. Colourless liquid. BP: 57°C. FP: -97°C. d: 1.17 kg/l (25°C). Insoluble in water. Miscible with oxygenated and chlorinated solvents. Flash point: -12°C (TCC).
Production:
• vinyl chloride + hydrogen chloride, anhydrous (addition)
Derivatives: 1,1,1-trichloroethane; 1,1,2-trichloroethane

1,2-dichloroethane *See:* ethylene dichloride

1,1-dichloroethylene *See:* vinylidene chloride

di-(2-chloroethyl)ether
bis(2-chloroethyl)ether; chlorex; β,β′-dichlorodiethyl ether; *sym*-dichloroethyl ether; DCEE; [111-44-4]

$$ClCH_2CH_2OCH_2CH_2Cl$$

$C_4H_8Cl_2O_1$. M: 143.01. Colourless liquid. BP: 178°C. MP: -24°C. d: 1.22 kg/l (20°C). Insoluble in water. Soluble in oxygenated and aromatic solvents.
Production:
• diethylene glycol (chlorination)
Derivatives:
polysulphide, rubber
Uses: selective solvent (lubricating oil dearomatisation)

di-(2-chloroethyl) vinyl phosphonate
See: bis(2-chloroethyl)vinyl phosphonate

1,1-dichloro-1-fluoroethane
HCFC-141b; R141b; [1717-00-6]

$$CH_3CFCl_2$$

$C_2H_3Cl_2F_1$. M: 116.95. Colourless liquid. BP: 32°C. MP: -103°C. d: 1.25 kg/l (10°C). Insoluble in water.
Production:
• 1,1,1-trichloroethane + hydrogen fluoride (halogen exchange; coproduced with 1-chloro-1,1-difluoro-ethane)
Uses: refrigerant gas

dichlorofluoromethane
fluorodichloromethane; HFC-21; R21; Freon 21 (Du Pont); [75-43-4]

$$CHFCl_2$$

$C_1H_1Cl_2F_1$. M: 102.93. Colourless, odourless, non-flammable liquid. BP: 9°C.
Production:
• chloroform + hydrogen fluoride (halogen exchange; coproduced with chlorodifluoromethane)
Uses: refrigerant gas

dichlorofluoromethanesulphenyl chloride
fluorodichloromethylsulphenyl chloride

$$CFCl_2SCl$$

$C_1Cl_3F_1S_1$. M: 169.43.
Production:
• trichloromethanesulphenyl chloride + hydrogen fluoride (halogen exchange)
Derivatives:
dichlofluanid; *N*-(dichlorofluoromethylthio)phthalimide; tolylfluanid

N-(dichlorofluoromethylthio)phthalimide
Preventol (Bayer)

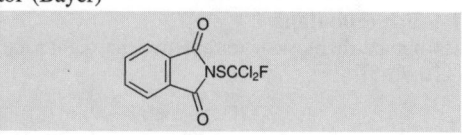

$C_9H_4Cl_2F_1N_1O_2S_1$. M: 280.11.
Production:
• phthalimide + dichlorofluoromethanesulphenyl chloride (amine formation)
Uses:
preservative (plastics, paints)

α-dichlorohydrin *See:* glycerol-1,3-dichlorohydrin

dichloromethane *See:* methylene chloride

3,6-dichloro-2-methoxybenzoic acid *See:* dicamba

dichloromethyl-3-(2-hydroperfluoroalkoxy)propyl-silane

$$\underset{\displaystyle F(CF_2)_nCHFCF_2OCH_2CH_2CH_2SiCl_2}{\overset{\displaystyle CH_3}{|}}$$

n = 0–1.
Production:
• 2-hydroperfluoroethyl allyl ether/2-hydroperfluoro-propyl allyl ether + dichloromethylsilane (hydrosilation)
Derivatives: fluorosilicone elastomers

dichloromethyl-2-(perfluoroalkyl)ethylsilane

$$\underset{\displaystyle CF_3(CF_2)_nCH_2CH_2SiCl_2}{\overset{\displaystyle CH_3}{|}}$$

n = 5–7.
Production:
• perfluorooctylethylene/perfluorohexylethylene + dichloromethylsilane (hydrosilation)
Derivatives: fluorosilicone elastomers

dichloromethylphenylsilane
[149-74-6]
$C_7H_8Cl_2Si_1$. M: 191.14.

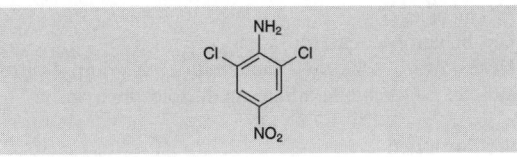

Production:
- phenylmagnesium chloride + trichloromethylsilane (Grignard reaction)

Derivatives: dimethylsiloxane oligomers; poly(dimethylsiloxane), vinylated

Uses: silicone oil/silicone rubber comonomer

dichloromethylsilane

methyldichlorosilane; [75-54-7]

$$CH_3SiHCl_2$$

$C_1H_4Cl_2Si_1$. M: 115.04. Colourless liquid. BP: 41°C. d: 1.11 kg/l (25°C). Hydrolysed by water releasing hydrogen chloride.

Production:
- silicon, metallurgical grade + methyl chloride (Direct process; coproduced with chlorotrimethylsilane/dichlorodimethylsilane/trichloromethylsilane)

Derivatives: dichloromethyl-3-(2-hydroperfluoroalkoxy)propylsilane; dichloromethyl-2-(perfluoroalkyl)ethylsilane; dichloromethyl-3,3,3-trifluoropropylsilane; dichloromethylvinylsilane; flusilazole; poly(dimethylsiloxane), crosslinking; silicone-polyol block copolymers

dichloromethyl-3,3,3-trifluoropropylsilane

$$CF_3CH_2CH_2SiCl_2 \quad (CH_3)$$

$C_4H_7Cl_2F_3Si_1$. M: 211.09.

Production:
- dichloromethylsilane + 3,3,3-trifluoropropylene (hydrosilation)

Derivatives: fluorosilicone elastomers; poly(trifluoropropylmethylsiloxane)

Uses: silicone oil comonomer

dichloromethylvinylsilane

methylvinyldichlorosilane

$$CH_2=CHSiCl_2 \quad (CH_3)$$

$C_3H_6Cl_2Si_1$. M: 141.08. Colourless liquid. BP: 93°C. d: 1.08 kg/l (25°C).

Production:
- dichloromethylsilane + acetylene (hydrosilation)

Derivatives: poly(dimethylsiloxane), vinylated

2,3-dichloro-1,4-naphthoquinone *See:* dichlone

2,6-dichloro-4-nitroaniline

dicloran; Allisan (Schering); [99-30-9]

$C_6H_4Cl_2N_2O_2$. M: 207.02. Brownish-yellow, crystalline solid. MP: 195°C. Insoluble in water. Soluble in oxygenated solvents.

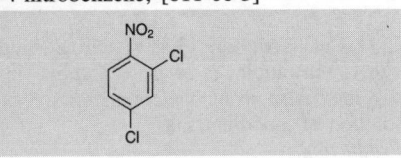

Production:
- *p*-nitroaniline (ring chlorination)

Derivatives: Basic Orange 30:1; Disperse Brown 1; Disperse Orange 30

Uses: fungicide

2,4-dichloronitrobenzene

1,3-dichloro-4-nitrobenzene; [611-06-3]

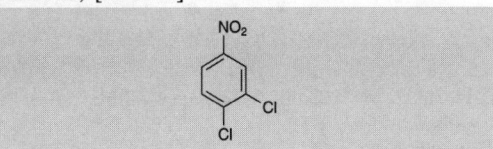

$C_6H_3Cl_2N_1O_2$. M: 192.01. Solid. MP: 32°C. BP: 258–259°C. Insoluble in water. Soluble in alcohol.

Production:
- *m*-dichlorobenzene (nitration)

Derivatives:
chlomethoxyfen; 2,4-difluoroaniline

2,5-dichloronitrobenzene

1,4-dichloro-2-nitrobenzene; [89-61-2]

$C_6H_3Cl_2N_1O_2$. M: 192.01. Crystalline solid. MP: 54–56°C. BP: 266°C. d: 1.67 kg/l (22°C). Insoluble in water. Soluble in hot alcohol and chlorinated solvents.

Production:
- *p*-dichlorobenzene (nitration)

Derivatives:
Acid Red 249; 4-chloro-2-nitroaniline; 4-chloro-2-nitroanisole; 2,5-dichloroaniline; 2,5-dimethoxyaniline; domperidone; 2,2′,5,5′-tetrachlorobenzidine; 2,4,5-trichloroaniline; triclosan

3,4-dichloronitrobenzene

1,2-dichloro-4-nitrobenzene; 1-nitro-3,4-dichlorobenzene; 3,4-DCNB; [99-54-7]

$C_6H_3Cl_2N_1O_2$. M: 192.01. Needles. MP: 41–42°C. BP: 255–256°C. Insoluble in water. Soluble in oxygenated solvents.

Production:
• *o*-dichlorobenzene (nitration)
Derivatives: 3-chloro-4-fluoroaniline; 2-chloro-4-nitro-aniline; 3,4-dichloroaniline; methazole; metoxuron

dichlorophen

5,5'-dichloro-2,2'-dihydroxydiphenylmethane; 4,4'-di-chloro-2,2'-methylenediphenol; dichlorophene; 2,2'-methylenebis(4-chlorophenol); DDDM; [97-23-4]

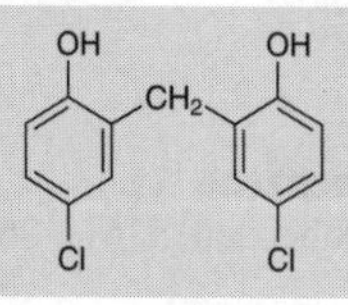

$C_{13}H_{10}Cl_2O_2$. M: 269.13. Crystalline solid. MP: 177–178°C. Insoluble in water. Soluble in oxygenated solvents. Also available commercially as an aqueous solution of a sodium salt.
Production:
• *p*-chlorophenol + formaldehyde (carbonyl addition)
Uses: anthelmintic drug; bactericide (soap, toiletries); biostabiliser (textiles, rubber, wood); moss control agent (turf treatment)

2,4-dichlorophenol

2,4-DCP; [120-83-2]

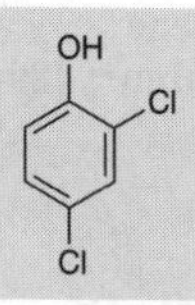

$C_6H_4Cl_2O_1$. M: 163.01. Pale yellow solid. MP: 42°C. BP: 210°C. Sparingly soluble in water. Soluble in aqueous alkali, oxygenated and chlorinated solvents.
Production:
• phenol + chlorine (ring chlorination; coproduced with 2,4,6-trichlorophenol)
Derivatives: bifenox; bithionol; chlomethoxyfen; 2,4-D; 2,4-DB; dichlorprop; diclofop-methyl; disul-sodium; phosdiphen; prothiofos; triclosan
Uses: dyestuffs intermediate

2,6-dichlorophenol

[87-65-0]

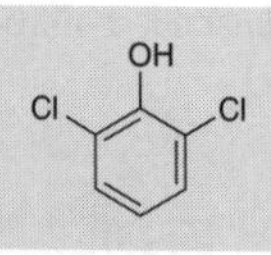

$C_6H_4Cl_2O_1$. M: 163.00. White, crystalline solid. MP: 65–66°C.
Production:
• phenol + chlorine (ring chlorination; byproduct of 2,4-dichlorophenol/2,4,6-trichlorophenol production)
Derivatives: diclofenac; guanoclor

2,4-dichlorophenoxyacetic acid *See:* 2,4-D

4-(2,4-dichlorophenoxy)butyric acid *See:* 2,4-DB

2-(2,4-dichlorophenoxy)propionic acid
See: dichlorprop

2,5-dichloro-*p*-phenylenediamine

2,5-diamino-*p*-dichlorobenzene

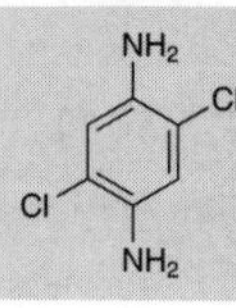

$C_6H_6Cl_2N_2$. M: 177.04.
Production:
• 2,5-dichloroaniline (nitration/nitro reduction)
Derivatives:
Pigment Red 214; Pigment Red 221; Pigment Red 242

3,4-dichlorophenyl isocyanate

[102-36-3]

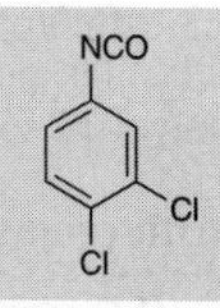

$C_7H_3Cl_2N_1O_1$. M: 188.02.
Production:
• 3,4-dichloroaniline + phosgene (phosgenation)
Derivatives: diuron; linuron; neburon; sulcofenuron

3-(2,6-dichlorophenyl)-5-methylisoxazole-4-carb-oxylic acid

DCIMC acid (Shell); [3919-76-4]

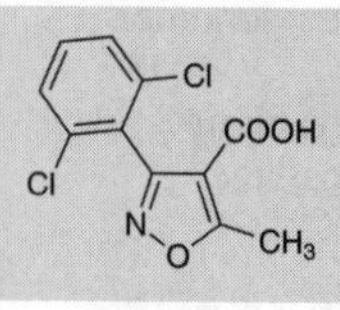

$C_{11}H_7Cl_2N_1O_3$. M: 272.10. Solid.
Production:
• 2,6-dichlorobenzaldehyde + methyl acetoacetate + hydroxylamine hydrochloride (Knoevenagel condensation/chlorination/cyclisation)
Derivatives:
dicloxacillin

1,4-dichlorophthalazine-6-carboxyl chloride

$C_9H_3Cl_3N_2O_1$. M: 261.49.
Production:
• trimellitic anhydride + hydrazine (amide formation/chlorination)
Derivatives: Reactive Red 96

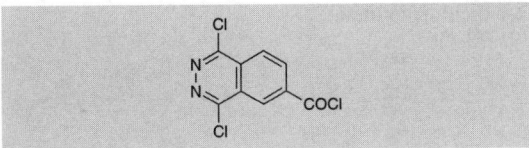

Uses: reactive dyestuffs intermediate

1,2-dichloropropane *See:* propylene dichloride

1,3-dichloro-2-propanol
See: glycerol-1,3-dichlorohydrin

1,3-dichloro-2-propanone *See:* 1,3-dichloroacetone

1,3-dichloropropene
1,3-dichloropropylene; Telone II (Dow Chemical);
[542-75-6]

ClCH=CHCH₂Cl

$C_3H_4Cl_2$. M: 110.97. Amber liquid with pungent odour.
BP: 104–114°C. FP: <-50°C. d: 1.22 kg/l (25°C).
Slightly soluble in water. Soluble in oxygenated and
chlorinated solvents.
Production:
• propylene + chlorine (high-temperature chlorination;
  byproduct of allyl chloride production)
Derivatives: 1,2,3-trichloropropane
Uses: soil fumigant

α,α-dichloropropionic acid
dalapon; 2,2-dichloropropionic acid; [75-99-0];
[127-20-8] (sodium salt)

$C_3H_4Cl_2O_2$. M: 142.97. Available commercially as the
acid, sodium, or magnesium salts.
Production:
• propionic acid + chlorine (alpha chlorination)
Uses: herbicide

1,3-dichloropropylene *See:* 1,3-dichloropropene

3,6-dichloropyridazine
[141-30-0]

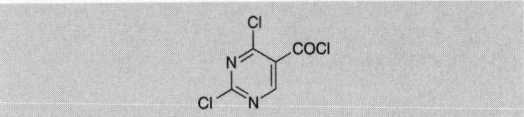

$C_4H_2Cl_2N_2$. M: 148.98. Solid. MP: 67–69°C.
Production:
• maleic hydrazide (chlorination)
Derivatives: sulfamethoxypyridazine

3,6-dichloropyridine-2-carboxylic acid *See:* clopyralid

2,4-dichloropyrimidine-5-carboxyl chloride

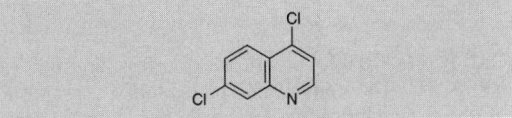

$C_4H_1Cl_3N_2O_1$. M: 199.42.
Production:
• diethyl ethoxymethylenemalonate + urea
  (condensation/chlorination)
Uses:
reactive dyestuffs intermediate

2,9-dichloroquinacridone
Quinacridone Magenta B; Pigment Red 202 (CI)

$C_{20}H_{10}Cl_2N_2O_2$. M: 381.22.
Production:
• dimethyl succinylosuccinate + p-chloroaniline
  (amine formation/condensation)
Uses:
pigment (printing inks, lacquers)

3,10-dichloroquinacridone
Fast Red EG; Pigment Red 209 (CI); 73905 (CI)

$C_{20}H_{10}Cl_2N_2O_2$. M: 381.22. Yellowish-red solid.
Production:
• dimethyl succinylosuccinate + m-chloroaniline
  (amine formation/condensation)
Uses: plastics colorant

4,7-dichloroquinoline
[86-98-6]

$C_9H_5Cl_2N_1$. M: 198.06. Solid. MP: 87°C.
Production:
• diethyl ethoxymethylenemalonate + m-chloroaniline
  (Shraup synthesis/decarboxylation/chlorination)
Derivatives:
chloroquine; glafenine

2,3-dichloroquinoxaline-6-carboxyl chloride

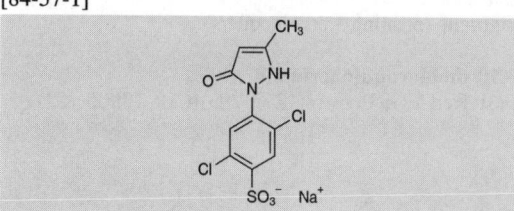

$C_9H_3Cl_3N_2O_1$. M: 261.49.
Production:
- 3,4-diaminotoluene + oxalyl chloride (amide formation/alcohol chlorination/side-chain oxidation)

Uses: reactive dyestuffs intermediate

2,4-dichloro-5-sulphamoylbenzoic acid
dichlorsulphonamide; [2736-23-4]

$C_7H_5Cl_2N_1O_4S_1$. M: 270.10.
Production:
- 2,4-dichlorobenzoyl chloride + chlorosulphonic acid + ammonia (chlorosulphonation/sulphonamide formation)

Derivatives: furosemide

1-(2′,5′-dichloro-4′-sulphophenyl)-3-methylpyrazolone
[84-57-1]

$C_{10}H_8Cl_2N_2Na_1O_4S_1$. M: 346.14.
Production:
- 2,5-dichloroaniline + diketene (sulphonation/diazotisation/reduction/condensation)

Derivatives: Acid Yellow 17; Acid Yellow 19; Acid Yellow 29; Reactive Yellow 1

1,2-dichloro-1,1,2,2-tetrafluoroethane
sym-dichlorotetrafluoroethane; CFC-114; R114; Freon 114 (Du Pont); [76-14-2]

CF₂ClCF₂Cl

$C_2Cl_2F_4$. M: 170.92. Colourless, odourless, liquified gas. BP: 3.5°C. The commercial product has a proportion of the 1,1-dichloro-isomer which has a very similar boiling point and refrigeration characteristics.
Production:
- perchloroethylene + hydrogen fluoride (fluorination; coproduced with 1,1,2-trichloro-1,2,2-trifluoroethane /chloropentafluoroethane/tetrachlorodifluoroethane)

Uses: aerosol propellant; refrigerant/air conditioning gas

2,4-dichlorotoluene
[95-73-8]

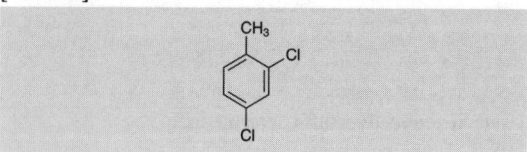

$C_7H_6Cl_2$. M: 161.04. Liquid. BP: 196–197°C. d: 1.24 kg/l (20°C). Insoluble in water.
Production:
- *o*-chlorotoluene (ring chlorination; coproduced with 2,6-dichlorotoluene)
- *p*-chlorotoluene (ring chlorination; coproduced with 3,4-dichlorotoluene)

Derivatives:
2,4-dichlorobenzal chloride; 2,4-dichlorobenzotrichloride; 2,4-dichlorobenzyl chloride

2,6-dichlorotoluene

$C_7H_6Cl_2$. M: 161.04. Liquid. BP: 200°C. d: 1.27 kg/l. Insoluble in water.
Production:
- *o*-chlorotoluene (ring chlorination; coproduced with 2,4-dichlorotoluene)

Derivatives:
2-chloro-6-fluorotoluene; 2,6-dichlorobenzaldehyde; 2,6-dichlorobenzonitrile; 2,6-dichlorobenzyl chloride; 2,3,6-TBA-sodium

3,4-dichlorotoluene
[95-75-0]

$C_7H_6Cl_2$. M: 161.04. Liquid. BP: 200–202°C. d: 1.25 kg/l (20°C). Insoluble in water.
Production:
- *p*-chlorotoluene (ring chlorination; coproduced with 2,4-dichlorotoluene)

Derivatives:
3,4-dichlorobenzaldehyde; 3,4-dichlorobenzotrifluoride

1,1-dichloro-2,2,2-trifluoroethane
dichlorotrifluoroethane; HCFC-123; R123; [306-83-2]

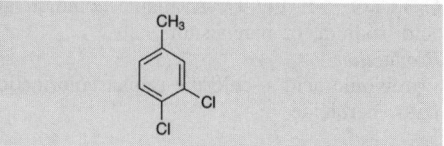

$C_2H_1Cl_2F_3$. M: 152.93. Liquid/gas. BP: 29°C. MP: -107°C. d: 1.47 kg/l (15°C).

Production:
- perchloroethylene + hydrogen fluoride (halogen exchange)

Derivatives: 1-chloro-1,2,2,2-tetrafluoroethane; pentafluoroethane

Uses: refrigerant gas

(*1RS*)-*cis*-3-(2,2-dichlorovinyl)-2,2-dimethylcyclopropanecarboxylic acid

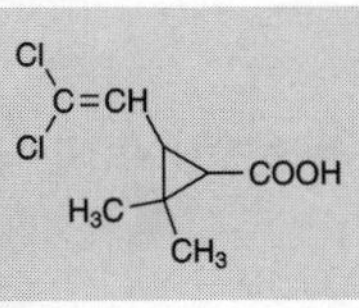

$C_8H_{10}Cl_2O_2$. M: 209.08. Mixed enantiomer product with a (*1RS*)-*cis* configuration to the propane ring.

Production:
- methyl 3,3-dimethyl-4-pentenoate + carbon tetrachloride (addition/dehydrochlorination/dehydrochlorination)
- (*1RS*)-*cis/trans*-3-(2,2-dichlorovinyl)-2,2-dimethylcyclopropanecarboxylic acid (racemate separation)

Derivatives: cypermethrin

(*1RS*)-*cis/trans*-3-(2,2-dichlorovinyl)-2,2-dimethylcyclopropanecarboxylic acid

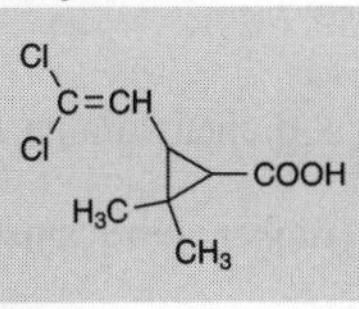

$C_8H_{10}Cl_2O_2$. M: 209.08.

Production:
- 2-methyl-3-buten-2-ol + trichloroacetic acid + ethyl diazoacetate (ether formation/rearrangement/decarboxylation/addition)

Derivatives:
cyfluthrin; (*1RS*)-*cis*-3-(2,2-dichlorovinyl)-2,2-dimethylcyclopropanecarboxylic acid; permethrin

dichlorprop

2-(2,4-dichlorophenoxy)propionic acid; 2,4-DP; [120-36-5]

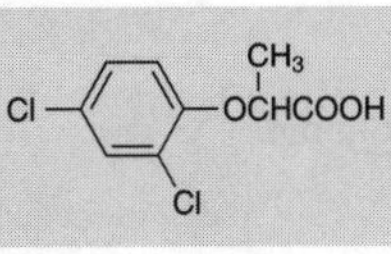

$C_9H_8Cl_2O_3$. M: 235.07. Available commercially as the potassium or ethylamine salts.

Production:
- α-chloropropionic acid + 2,4-dichlorophenol (ether formation)

Derivatives: dichlorprop-isooctyl

Uses: herbicide

dichlorprop-isooctyl

isooctyl 2-(2,4-dichlorophenoxy)propionate

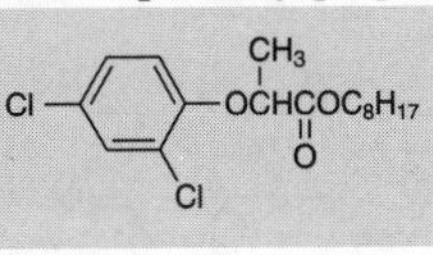

$C_{17}H_{24}Cl_2O_3$. M: 347.29.

Production:
- isooctanol + dichlorprop (esterification)

Uses: herbicide

dichlorvos

O,O-dimethyl-*O*-(2,2-dichlorovinyl)phosphate; DDVP; [62-73-7]

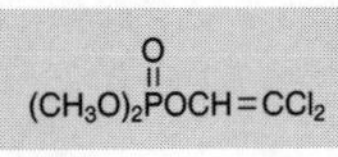

$C_4H_7Cl_2O_4P_1$. M: 220.98.

Production:
- trimethyl phosphite + chloral (Perkow reaction)
- trichlorfon (dehydrochlorination/rearrangement)

Derivatives: naled

Uses: acaricide/insecticide

diclobutrazol

1-(2,4-dichlorophenyl)-4,4-dimethyl-2-(1H-1,2,4-triazol-1-yl)pentan-3-ol; [66345-62-8]

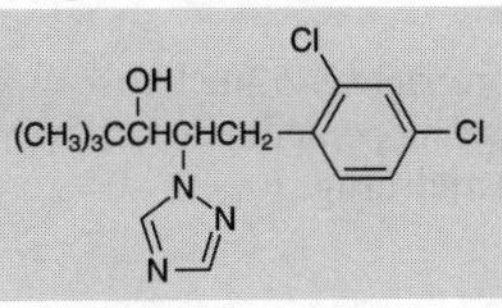

$C_{15}H_{19}Cl_2N_3O_1$. M: 328.24.

Production:
- α-chloropinacolone + 1,2,4-triazole + 2,4-dichlorobenzyl chloride (amine formation/dehydrochlorination/carbonyl reduction)

Uses: fungicide

diclofenac

[15307-86-5]; [15307-79-6] (sodium salt)

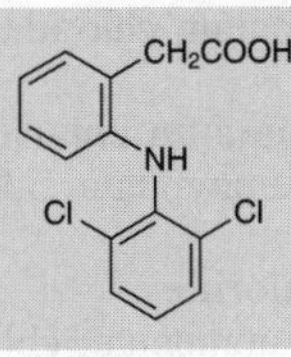

$C_{14}H_{11}Cl_2N_1O_2$. M: 296.16. Available commercially as the sodium salt.

Production:
- 2,6-dichlorophenol + aniline + oxalyl chloride (amine formation/amide formation/Friedel-Crafts acylation/Wolff-Kishner reduction/hydrolysis)

Uses: antiinflammatory drug

diclofop-methyl

methyl 2-[4-(2,4-dichlorophenoxy)phenoxy]propionate; [51338-27-3]

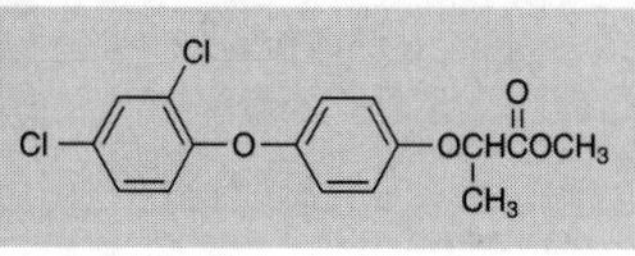

$C_{16}H_{14}Cl_2O_4$. M: 341.20.
Production:
• 2,4-dichlorophenol + 2-(4-chlorophenoxy)propionic acid + methanol (ether formation/esterification)
Uses: herbicide

dicloran *See:* 2,6-dichloro-4-nitroaniline

dicloxacillin

[3116-76-5]

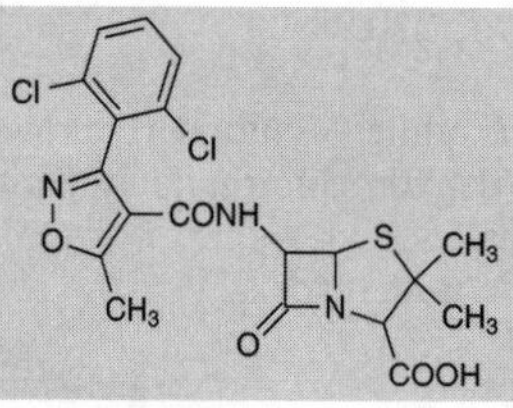

$C_{19}H_{17}Cl_2N_3O_5S_1$. M: 470.33. Available commercially as the sodium monohydrate salt.
Production:
• 3-(2,6-dichlorophenyl)-5-methylisoxazole-4-carboxylic acid + 6-aminopenicillanic acid (amide formation)
Uses: antibacterial drug

dicocoamine

dicocamine (CTFA); dilauramine; dilaurylamine

R_2NH

R = coco-. Solid. MP: 40–47°C. A typical chain-length distribution is: 58% C_{12}, 23% C_{14}, 10% C_{16}.
Production:
• coconut acid + ammonia (nitrile formation/ hydrogenation/deammoniation)
Derivatives:
dimethyldicocoammonium chloride

dicocodimethylammonium chloride

See: dimethyldicocoammonium chloride

dicocodimonium chloride

See: dimethyldicocoammonium chloride

dicofol

2,2,2-trichloro-1,1-di-(4-chlorophenyl)ethanol; Kelthane (Rohm and Haas); [115-32-2]
$C_{14}H_9Cl_5O_1$. M: 370.49.
Production:
• DDT + chlorine (chlorination/hydrolysis)

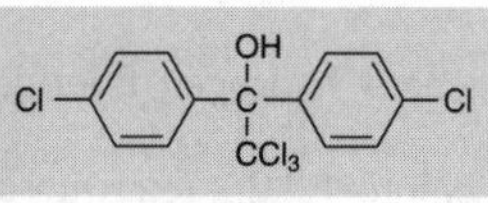

Derivatives: chlorobenzilate
Uses: acaricide

dicrotophos

3-dimethoxyphosphinoyloxy-*N,N*-dimethylisocrotonamide; [141-66-2]

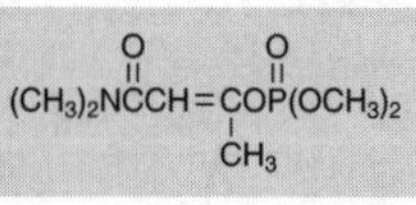

$C_8H_{16}N_1O_5P_1$. M: 237.19.
Production:
• *N,N*-dimethylacetoacetamide + trimethyl phosphite (Perkow reaction)
Uses:
insecticide/acaricide

p-dicumyldiphenylamine

diphenylamine, α-methylstyrenated

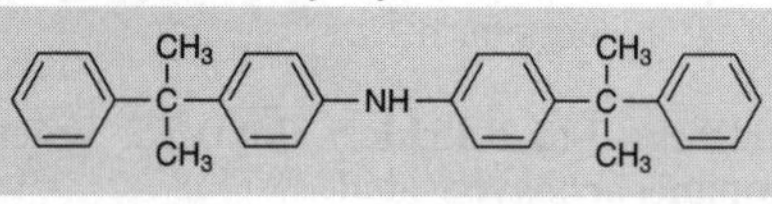

$C_{30}H_{31}N_1$. M: 405.59.
Production:
• α-methylstyrene + diphenylamine (Friedel-Crafts alkylation)
Uses: antioxidant (rubber, lubricants)

dicumyl peroxide

Esperal 115RG (Witco); [80-43-3]

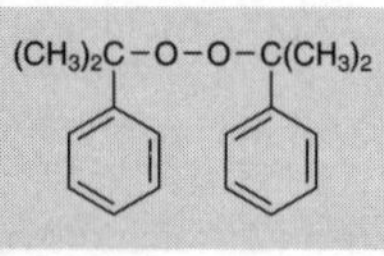

$C_{18}H_{11}O_2$. M: 259.29. Granules. The product has a 10-hour half-life at 115°C.
Production:
• cumene hydroperoxide + α-methylstyrene (addition)
Uses: polyethylene/polyester/silicone rubber crosslinking agent

dicy *See:* dicyandiamide

dicyandiamide

N-cyanoguanidine; dicy; dicyanodiamide; DCD; [461-58-5]

$(H_2N)_2C=NCN$

$C_2H_4N_4$. M: 84.08. White, crystalline solid. MP: 208–211°C. Slightly soluble in water and alcohol. Soluble in liquid ammonia.

Production:
• cyanamide (dimerisation)
Derivatives: acetoguanamine; benzoguanamine; cyanamide-formaldehyde resins; cyclobarbital; Fluorescent Brightener 179; guanidine nitrate; guanylurea sulphate; heptabarbital; hexobarbital; melamine; metformin; moroxydine; pentobarbital; poly(hexamethylenebiguanide) hydrochloride; *o*-tolylbiguanide
Uses:
heat-cured epoxy resin curing agent; flotation depressant (copper ores); intumescent paint ingredient; electrostatic powder coating ingredient; plasticiser (starch adhesives)

m-dicyanobenzene *See:* isophthalodinitrile

o-dicyanobenzene *See:* phthalodinitrile

1,4-dicyanobutane *See:* adiponitrile

dicyanodiamide *See:* dicyandiamide

dicyanodiamidine sulphate *See:* guanylurea sulphate

1,2-dicyanoethane *See:* succinonitrile

dicyanomethane *See:* malononitrile

dicyclohexylamine
DCHA; [101-83-7]

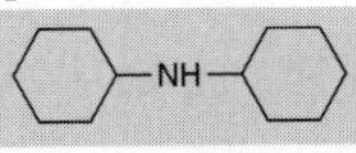

$C_{12}H_{23}N_1$. M: 181.32. Liquid with an amine odour. BP: 256°C. MP: -1°C. d: 0.91 kg/l (4°C). Slightly soluble in water. Soluble in oxygenated solvents.
Production:
• aniline (reduction; coproduced with cyclohexylamine)
• cyclohexanone + ammonia (reductive ammoniation; coproduced with cyclohexylamine)
Derivatives: dicyclohexylammonium nitrite; *N,N*-dicyclohexyl-2-benzothiazolesulphenamide; *N*-methyldicyclohexylamine
Uses: corrosion inhibitor (lubricants); solvent (antibiotic production)

dicyclohexylammonium nitrite
VPI 260 (Shell); [3129-91-7]

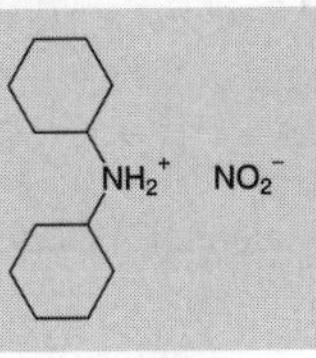

$C_{12}H_{24}N_2O_2$. M: 228.33. Solid.

Production:
• dicyclohexylamine + sodium nitrite (nitrosation)
Uses:
vapour-phase corrosion inhibitor

N,N-dicyclohexyl-2-benzothiazolesulphenamide
benzothiazyl-2-dicyclohexylsulphenamide; DCBS; [4979-32-2]

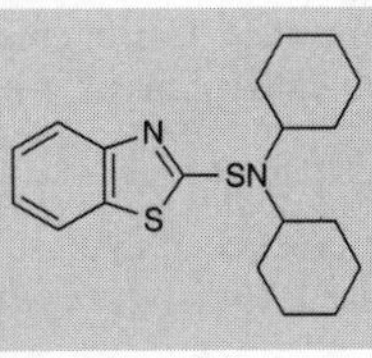

$C_{19}H_{26}N_2S_2$. M: 346.56.
Production:
• 2-mercaptobenzothiazole + dicyclohexylamine (oxidative coupling)
Uses: vulcanisation accelerator

dicyclohexylcarbodiimide
N,N-dicyclohexylcarbodiimide; DCC; DCCD; [538-75-0]

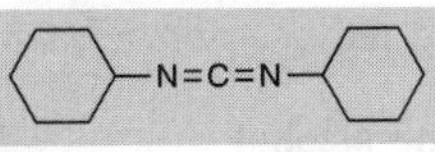

$C_{13}H_{22}N_2$. M: 206.33.
Production:
• cyclohexylamine + carbon disulphide (thiocarbonylation/dehydrosulphurisation)
Uses:
amide formation/esterification reagent

dicyclohexylmethane-4,4′-diisocyanate
See: 4,4′-diisocyanatodicyclohexylmethane

N,N-dicyclohexylmethylamine
See: *N*-methyldicyclohexylamine

dicyclohexyl phthalate
DCHP; [84-61-7]

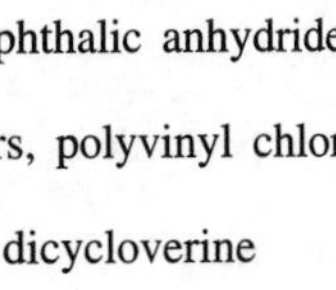

$C_{20}H_{26}O_4$. M: 330.43. White, crystalline solid. MP: 63–65°C. BP: 245–246°C (1.3 kPa). d: 1.15 kg/l (20°C). Insoluble in water.
Production:
• cyclohexanol + phthalic anhydride (esterification)
Uses:
plasticiser (lacquers, polyvinyl chloride)

dicyclomine *See:* dicycloverine

dicyclopentadiene
DCPD; [77-73-6]

$C_{10}H_{12}$. M: 132.21. Yellow liquid or solid. MP: 32°C. Decomposes to cyclopentadiene (BP: 41°C) on heating. d: 0.97 kg/l (20°C). Insoluble in water. Miscible with most organic solvents. Commercial products are stabilised with 100–200 ppm of *t*-butylcatechol or a similar inhibitor.
Production:
• C_5-stream, steam-cracked (NMP solvent separation process; coproduced with isoprene)
Derivatives:
adamantane; bis(aminomethyl)norbornane; chlordane; cyclopentadienised oils; dicyclopentadiene alcohol; dicyclopentadiene dioxide; 2,2'-dicyclopentadienylbis-(6-*t*-butyl-4-methylphenol); dicyclopentadienyl titanium dichloride; dicyclopentenyl acetate; ethylene-propylene-diene terpolymer, rubber; ethylidene norbornene; ferrocene; heptachlor; heptenophos; hydrocarbon resins, dicyclopentadiene types; nadic anhydride; norbornene; poly(dicyclopentadiene)
Uses: unsaturated polyester resin comonomer

dicyclopentadiene alcohol

$C_{10}H_{14}O_1$. M: 150.22.
Production:
• dicyclopentadiene (hydration)
Derivatives:
dicyclopentadiene alcohol epoxide; dicyclopentenyl acrylate; dicyclopentenyl methacrylate

dicyclopentadiene alcohol epoxide

$C_{10}H_{14}O_2$. M: 166.22.
Production:
• dicyclopentadiene alcohol + peracetic acid (epoxidation)
Uses: cycloaliphatic epoxy resins

dicyclopentadiene dioxide
Unox Epoxide 207 (Union Carbide); [81-21-0]

$C_{10}H_{12}O_2$. M: 164.21.
Production:
• dicyclopentadiene + peracetic acid (epoxidation)
Uses:
cycloaliphatic epoxy resins

dicyclopentadiene resins
See: hydrocarbon resins, dicyclopentadiene types

2,2'-dicyclopentadienylbis(6-*t*-butyl-4-methylphenol)
DBPH

$C_{32}H_{44}O_2$. M: 460.70.
Production:
• 2-*t*-butyl-*p*-cresol + dicyclopentadiene (Friedel-Crafts alkylation)
Uses:
antioxidant (plastics, rubber)

dicyclopentadienyl iron *See:* ferrocene

dicyclopentadienyl titanium dichloride
titanocene dichloride; [1271-19-8]

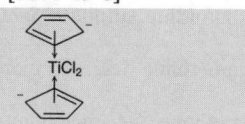

$C_{10}H_{10}Cl_2Ti_1$. M: 249.00.
Production:
• dicyclopentadiene + titanium tetrachloride (complex formation)
Uses: Ziegler catalyst component

dicyclopentenyl acetate
[2500-83-6] (5-ene isomer); [5413-60-5] (6-ene isomer)

$C_{12}H_{26}O_2$. M: 202.34. Colourless liquid with a herbal odour. Mixed isomer product.
Production:
• dicyclopentadiene + acetic acid (acetylation)
Uses:
fragrance ingredient (soap, household products)

dicyclopentenyl acrylate

$C_{13}H_{16}O_2$. M: 204.27.
Production:
• dicyclopentadiene alcohol + acrylic acid (esterification)
Uses:
acrylic resin functional comonomer

dicyclopentenyl methacrylate

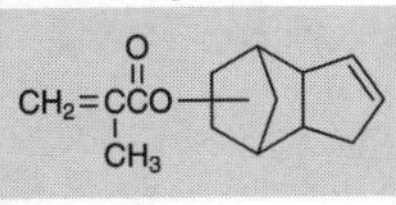

$C_{14}H_{18}O_2$. M: 218.29.
Production:
• dicyclopentadiene alcohol + methyl methacrylate (transesterification)
Uses: acrylic resin functional comonomer

dicycloverine
dicyclomine; [77-19-0]

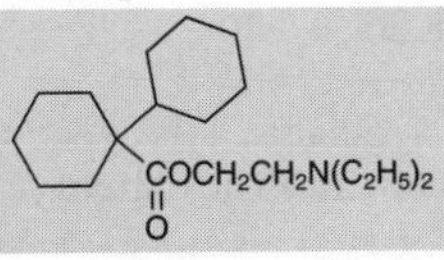

$C_{19}H_{35}N_1O_2$. M: 309.50. Available as the free amine or hydrochloride salt.
Production:
• 1,5-pentanediol + benzyl cyanide + diethylaminoethanol (alcohol bromination/condensation/nitrile hydrolysis/esterification/hydrogenation)
Uses: anticholinergic drug

DIDA *See:* diisodecyl adipate

didecanoyl peroxide

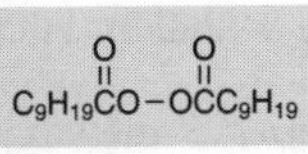

$C_{20}H_{38}O_4$. M: 342.52. Flakes. The product has a 10-hour half-life at 62°C.
Production:
• neodecanoyl chloride + hydrogen peroxide (dehydrochlorination)
Uses: polymerisation initiator

didecyl adipate *See:* diisodecyl adipate

didecyldimethylammonium chloride
didecyldimonium chloride (CTFA); dimethyldidecylammonium chloride; *N,N*-dimethyldidecylammonium chloride; [771-61-9]

$C_{22}H_{48}Cl_1N_1$. M: 362.08. Liquid. Commercial products usually contain 97% C_{10} or 10% C_8, 90% C_{10}. The product is usually sold as a 50% solution in isopropanol/water.
Production:
• methyldidecylamine + methyl chloride (quaternisation)
• dimethylamine + *n*-decyl chloride (amine formation/quaternisation)
Uses: biocide (disinfectant/laundry formulations)

didecyldimonium chloride
See: didecyldimethylammonium chloride

didecylmethylamine *See:* methyldidecylamine

didecyl phenyl phosphite
phenyl didecyl phosphite

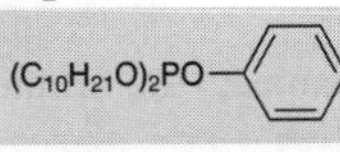

$C_{26}H_{47}O_3P_1$. M: 438.64. Clear liquid. MP: 0°C. d: 0.94 kg/l (25°C).
Production:
• isodecanol + phosphorus trichloride + phenol (dehydrochlorination/dehydrochlorination)
Uses:
polyvinyl chloride heat costabilisers

DIDP *See:* diisodecyl phthalate

didymium
Mixed praseodymium-neodymium metal.
Production:
• didymium oxide + hydrochloric acid (salt formation/calcination/electrolysis)
Uses: magnesium alloy additive

didymium oxide
Mixed praseodymium-neodymium oxide concentrate.
Production:
• lanthanum-praseodymium-neodymium oxide concentrate (solvent extraction; coproduced with lanthanum oxide)
• rare earth oxide, hydrate (solvent extraction; coproduced with cerium oxide/lanthanum oxide/ /samarium oxide)
Derivatives:
didymium; neodymium oxide; praseodymium oxide
Uses: coloured glass

dienochlor
perchloro-1,1′-bicyclopenta-2,4-diene; [2227-17-0]

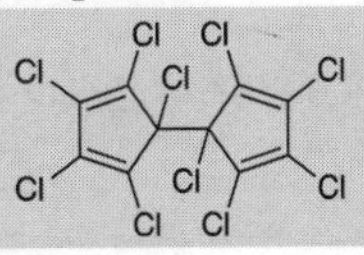

$C_{10}Cl_{10}$. M: 474.64.
Production:
• hexachlorocyclopentadiene (reductive coupling)
Uses: acaricide

diester oils
oils, diester

A = primary alcohol, B = dicarboxylic acid.

Production:
- isodecanol/*n*-alkanol(C_9-C_{11})/tridecanol + adipic acid/dimethyl adipate/sebacic acid/azelaic acid/ trimethyladipic acid/1,12-dodecanedioic acid (esterification)

Uses: synthetic lubricant base oils

diethanolamine

di-(2-hydroxyethyl)amine; 2,2'-iminodiethanol; DEA; DELA; [111-42-2]

$$HN(CH_2CH_2OH)_2$$

$C_4H_{11}N_1O_2$. M: 105.14. Colourless, hygroscopic liquid or solid. MP: 28°C. BP: >270°C. d: 1.09 kg/l (30°C). Miscible with water, alcohol and acetone. Insoluble in hydrocarbon solvents.

Production:
- ammonia + ethylene oxide (epoxidation; coproduced with monoethanolamine/triethanolamine)

Derivatives:
buspirone; 1-(3-chlorophenyl)piperazine hydrochloride; coconut acid diethanolamide; cyclophosphamide; diethanolamine 2-[perfluoroalkyl(C_6-C_{12})]ethyl phosphate; *O,O*-diethyl bis(2-hydroxyethyl)aminomethyl-phosphonate; diphenoxylate; dipyridamole; Fluorescent Brightener 24; Fluorescent Brightener 28; Fluorescent Brightener 104; Fluorescent Brightener 119; Fluorescent Brightener DMDDEA; lauric acid diethanolamide; linoleic acid diethanolamide; 1-(2-methoxyphenyl)-piperazine hydrochloride; morpholine; oleic acid diethanolamide; polyols, polyisocyanate polyaddition; sodium dihydroxyethylglycine; stearic acid diethanol-amide; tall oil fatty acid diethanolamide; trofosfamide; urea-formaldehyde resins, cationic

Uses:
hydrogen sulphide extraction solvent (gas processing); solubilising agent (metalworking fluids, printing inks, textile auxiliaries, rubber chemicals)

diethanolamine 2-[perfluoroalkyl(C_6-C_{12})]ethyl phosphate

Zonyl (Du Pont)

$$\left[CF_3(CF_2)_mCH_2CH_2O\right]_n \overset{O}{\underset{\|}{P}} O^- \; {}^+HN(CH_2CH_2OH)_2\Big]_{3-n}$$

m = 5–11, n = 1–2.

Production:
- 2-[perfluoroalkyl(C_6-C_{12})]ethanol + phosphorus pentoxide + diethanolamine (esterification)

Uses: waterproofing agent (paper)

diethatyl-ethyl

[38727-55-8]
$C_{16}H_{22}Cl_1N_1O_3$. M: 311.82.

Production:
- 2,6-diethylaniline + ethyl chloroacetate + chloro-acetyl chloride (amine formation/amide formation)

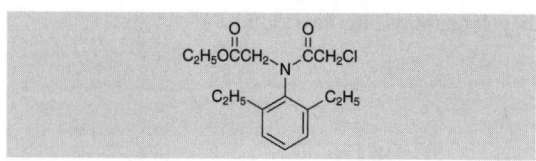

Uses: herbicide

2,2-diethoxyacetophenone

α,α-diethoxyacetophenone; DEAP

$C_{12}H_{16}O_3$. M: 208.26.

Production:
- glyoxylic acid + ethanol + benzene (acetal formation/Friedel-Crafts acylation)

Uses:
photoinitiator (radiation-cured lacquers, inks)

2,5-diethoxyaniline

[94-85-9]

$C_{10}H_{15}N_1O_2$. M: 181.24.

Production:
- 2,5-dichloroaniline + sodium ethoxide (ether formation)

Derivatives: 4'-amino-2',5'-diethoxybenzanilide

1,2-diethoxyethane

See: ethylene glycol diethyl ether

2,2-diethoxy-2-phenylacetophenone

See: benzil diethyl acetal

diethyl 2-(acetamido)malonate

diethyl acetylaminomalonate; [1068-90-2]

$C_9H_{15}N_1O_5$. M: 217.22. Solid. MP: 95°C. Slightly soluble in hot water and oxygenated solvents.

Production:
- acetic anhydride + diethyl 2-aminomalonate hydrochloride (acetylation)

Derivatives: L-tryptophan

N,N-diethylacetoacetamide

acetoacet-*N,N*-diethylamide; [2235-46-3]

$C_8H_{15}N_1O_2$. M: 157.22.

Production:
• diketene + diethylamine (condensation)
Derivatives:
phosphamidon

diethylaluminium chloride
DEAC; [96-10-6]

$(C_2H_5)_2AlCl$

$C_4H_{10}Al_1Cl_1$. M: 120.55. Colourless liquid. Spontaneously flammable in air, emitting dense smoke. BP: 214°C. FP: -74°C. d: 0.97 kg/l (25°C). Reacts violently with water.
Production:
• aluminium + ethyl chloride (reaction; coproduced with ethylaluminium dichloride)
Uses: Ziegler catalyst component (ethylene-propylene rubber production)

diethylamine
[109-89-7]

$(C_2H_5)_2NH$

$C_4H_{11}N_1$. M: 73.14. Liquid. BP: 56°C. MP: -50°C. d: 0.71 kg/l (4°C). Miscible with water forming alkaline solutions. Miscible with oxygenated solvents.
Production:
• ethanol + ammonia (amine formation; coproduced with ethylamine/triethylamine)
Derivatives:
amfepramone; 7-(4-amino-6-diethylaminotriazin-2-yl)-amino-3-phenylcoumarin; 7-(4-chloro-6-diethylamino-triazin-2-yl)amino-3-phenylcoumarin; denatonium benzoate; *N,N*-diethylacetoacetamide; diethylamine borane; diethylaminoethanol; *N,N*-diethyl-3-amino-4-methoxy-benzenesulphonamide; 3-diethylaminopropylamine; diethylcarbamoyl chloride; *N,N*-diethylethylenediamine; diethylhydroxylamine; *N,N*-diethyl-*m*-toluamide; dinitramine; lidocaine; napropamide; nikethamide; pirimiphos-ethyl; pirimiphos-methyl; propanidid; sodium diethyldithiocarbamate; thiobencarb; tolycaine; trietazine

diethylamine borane

$(C_2H_5)_2NH.BH_3$

$C_4H_{14}B_1N_1$. M: 86.97.
Production:
• diethylamine + sodium borohydride + boron trifluoride (complex formation)
Uses: reducing agent (electrodeless coatings)

1-diethylamino-4-aminopentane
See: 4-amino-1-diethylaminopentane

p-diethylaminobenzaldehyde
N,N-diethyl-4-aminobenzaldehyde; [120-21-8]
$C_{11}H_{15}N_1O_1$. M: 177.25. Solid. MP: 37–40°C. BP:

174°C (2.3 kPa). Soluble in water, oxygenated and aromatic solvents.

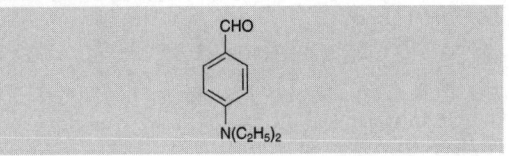

Production:
• *N,N*-diethylaniline + dimethylformamide (Vilsmeier reaction)
Derivatives: Acid Blue 104; Acid Violet 17; Basic Violet 16

diethylaminoethanol
2-diethylaminoethanol; *N,N*-diethyl-2-aminoethanol; *N,N*-diethylethanolamine; DEAE; [100-37-8]

$(C_2H_5)_2NCH_2CH_2OH$

$C_6H_{15}N_1O_1$. M: 117.20. Liquid. BP: 161–163°C. MP: -70°C. Soluble in water. Miscible with most organic solvents.
Production:
• diethylamine + ethylene oxide (epoxidation)
Derivatives:
dicycloverine; 2-diethylaminoethyl acrylate; 2-diethyl-aminoethyl chloride hydrochloride; 2-diethylaminoethyl methacrylate; *N,N*-diethylethylenediamine; nicametate; oxybuprocaine; pentoxyverine; procaine
Uses:
pigment dispersant (paints); solvent (gas sweetening processes); textile/leather/paper auxiliary; corrosion inhibitor (boiler water treatment)

2-diethylaminoethyl acrylate

$CH_2=CHCOOCH_2CH_2N(C_2H_5)_2$

$C_9H_{17}N_1O_2$. M: 171.25.
Production:
• diethylaminoethanol + acrylic acid (esterification)
Uses:
acrylic resin comonomer

2-(diethylamino)ethyl 4-aminobenzoate
See: procaine

diethylaminoethyl cellulose

$R-CH_2CH_2N(C_2H_5)_2$

R = cellulose-.
Production:
• alkali cellulose + 2-diethylaminoethyl chloride hydrochloride (ether formation)
Uses:
weakly basic ion-exchange resins (food, chemical, pharmaceutical purification)

2-diethylaminoethyl chloride hydrochloride
β-chloroethyldiethylamine hydrochloride; DEC;
[869-24-9]

$$(C_2H_5)_2\overset{+}{N}HCH_2CH_2Cl \quad Cl^-$$

$C_6H_{15}Cl_2N_1$. M: 172.11. Needles. MP: 208–212°C.
Soluble in water and alcohol.
Production:
• diethylaminoethanol (alcohol chlorination)
Derivatives:
carbocromen; diethylaminoethyl cellulose; 5-diethyl-amino-2-pentanone; doxylamine; flurazepam; lucanthone; naftidrofuryl; starch, cationic

2-diethylaminoethyl methacrylate

$$CH_2=CCOCH_2CH_2N(C_2H_5)_2$$
$$\underset{CH_3}{|}$$

$C_{10}H_{19}N_1O_2$. M: 185.27.
Production:
• diethylaminoethanol + methyl methacrylate (trans-esterification)
Derivatives: polymethacrylates, oil-soluble dispersants

diethyl 2-aminomalonate hydrochloride

$$H_2^+NCH(COOC_2H_5)_2 \quad Cl^-$$

$C_7H_{13}Cl_1N_1O_4$. M: 210.64. Solid. MP: 166°C with decomposition. Soluble in water and oxygenated solvents.
Production:
• diethyl malonate (nitration/nitro reduction)
Derivatives: clorazepate; diethyl 2-(acetamido)malonate

N,N-diethyl-3-amino-4-methoxybenzenesulphonamide
2-amino-4-diethylaminosulphonylanisole; 3-amino-4-methoxybenzenesulphon-N,N-diethylamide; 2-methoxy-5-(diethylaminosulphonyl)aniline; Azoic Diazo Component 42 (CI); 37150 (CI); [97-35-8]

$C_{11}H_{18}N_2O_3S_1$. M: 258.33.
Production:
• 2-aminoanisole-4-sulphonic acid + diethylamine (sulphonamide formation)
Derivatives:
Pigment Red 5
Uses: azoic dye diazo component

7-diethylamino-4-methylcoumarin
4-methyl-7-diethylaminocoumarin; MDAC; Fluorescent Brightener 140 (CI);
$C_{14}H_{17}N_1O_2$. M: 231.30.

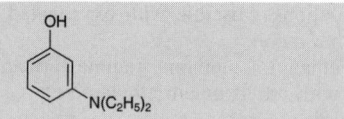

Production:
• m-diethylaminophenol + ethyl acetoacetate (Pechmann reaction)
Uses:
fluorescent brightening agent (polyamide, acetate, polyester); fluorescent brightening agent (paper, detergents)

5-diethylamino-2-pentanone
[105-14-6]

$$(C_2H_5)_2NCH_2CH_2CH_2\overset{O}{\overset{||}{C}}CH_3$$

$C_9H_{19}N_1O_1$. M: 157.26.
Production:
• 2-diethylaminoethyl chloride hydrochloride + ethyl acetoacetate (dehydrochlorination/decarboxylation)
Derivatives: 4-amino-1-diethylaminopentane; pamaquine

m-diethylaminophenol
N,N-diethyl-3-aminophenol; [91-68-9]

$C_{10}H_{15}N_1O_1$. M: 165.24. Needles. MP: 87°C. BP: 267°C. Slightly soluble in hot water. Soluble in oxygenated and aromatic solvents.
Production:
• metanilic acid + ethanol (amine formation/alkali fusion)
Derivatives: Acid Red 52; Basic Blue 3; Basic Violet 10; 7-diethylamino-4-methylcoumarin; N,N-diethyl-m-anisidine; Mordant Red 15

3-diethylaminopropylamine
3-aminopropyldiethylamine; N,N-diethylamino-1,3-propanediamine; N,N-diethylaminopropylamine; DEAP;
[104-78-9]

$$(C_2H_5)_2NCH_2CH_2CH_2NH_2$$

$C_7H_{18}N_2$. M: 130.23. Colourless liquid with an ammoniacal odour. BP: 168–173°C. MP: <-60°C. Soluble in water and oxygenated solvents.
Production:
• diethylamine + acrylonitrile (cyanoethylation/nitrile reduction)
Uses: epoxy resin curing agent

2,6-diethylaniline
DEA; [579-66-8]
$C_{10}H_{15}N_1$. M: 149.24. Yellow liquid. BP: 243°C. MP:

3°C. d: 0.96 kg/l (20°C). Insoluble in water. Soluble in oxygenated solvents.

Production:
- aniline + ethylene (orthoalkylation)

Derivatives: alachlor; butachlor; diethatyl-ethyl; 4,4'-methylenebis(3-chloro-2,6-diethylaniline); pretilachlor

N,N-diethylaniline
DEA; [91-66-7]

$C_{10}H_{15}N_1$. M: 149.24. Yellow liquid. MP: -39°C. BP: 216°C. d: 0.94 kg/l (20°C). Insoluble in water. Soluble in oxygenated and chlorinated solvents.

Production:
- aniline + ethanol (amine formation; coproduced with N-ethylaniline)

Derivatives:
Acid Blue 1; Acid Blue 3; Basic Green 1; Basic Violet 4; Basic Yellow 37; 4,4'-bis(diethylamino)benzophenone; p-diethylaminobenzaldehyde; N,N-diethyl-p-phenylenediamine; naphtholactam blue; Solvent Yellow 56

Uses: unsaturated polyester resin curing accelerator

N,N-diethyl-m-anisidine
3-(diethylamino)anisole; N,N-diethyl-3-methoxyaniline; [92-18-2]

$C_{11}H_{17}N_1O_1$. M: 179.27. Liquid. BP: 150°C. Insoluble in water. Soluble in oxygenated solvents.

Production:
- m-diethylaminophenol + dimethyl sulphate (methylation)

Derivatives: Basic Blue 3

diethylbenzene, mixed
polyethylbenzene

$C_{10}H_{14}$. M: 134.22. Byproduct stream from ethylbenzene production containing disubstituted and higher benzene derivatives.

Production:
- benzene + ethylene (Friedel-Crafts alkylation; byproduct of ethylbenzene production)

Derivatives: divinylbenzene

Uses: fuel (steam generation)

O,O-diethyl bis(2-hydroxyethyl)aminomethylphosphonate

$C_9H_{22}N_1O_5P_1$. M: 255.25.

Production:
- diethyl phosphite + diethanolamine + formaldehyde (Mannich reaction)

Uses:
fire-retardant rigid polyurethane polyol

diethyl n-butylmalonate
[133-08-4]

$C_{11}H_{20}O_4$. M: 216.28. Liquid. BP: 235–240°C. Soluble in oxygenated solvents.

Production:
- n-butyl chloride + diethyl malonate (dehydrochlorination)

Derivatives: di-(pentamethylhydroxypiperidyl) butyl-(di-3,5-t-butyl-4-hydroxybenzyl)malonate; oxyphenbutazone; phenylbutazone

diethylcarbamazine
[90-89-1]; [1642-54-2] (dihydrogen citrate)

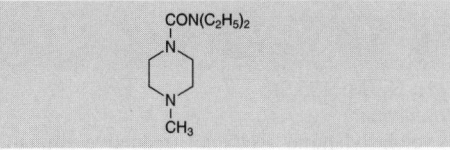

$C_{10}H_{21}N_3O_1$. M: 199.30. Available commercially as the free base or as the citrate salt.

Production:
- N-methylpiperazine + diethylcarbamoyl chloride (dehydrochlorination)

Uses: anthelmintic drug

diethylcarbamoyl chloride
[88-10-8]

$C_5H_{10}Cl_1N_1O_1$. M: 135.59. Liquid. BP: 187–190°C. MP: -32°C. Decomposed by hot water and hot alcohol.

Production:
- diethylamine + phosgene (phosgenation)

Derivatives:
celiprolol; diethylcarbamazine

diethyl carbonate
ethyl carbonate; [105-58-8]

$$(C_2H_5O)_2CO$$

$C_5H_{10}O_3$. M: 118.13. Colourless liquid with a mild odour. BP: 126–128°C. d: 0.98 kg/l (20°C). Insoluble in water. Miscible with most organic solvents.
Production:
• ethanol + ethyl chloroformate (dehydrochlorination)
Derivatives:
3-(2-chloroethyl)aminopropanol hydrochloride; 4-hydroxycoumarin; ketoprofen; nifuratel; phenylmalonic acid
Uses:
carboethoxylation reagent; solvent (resins, lacquers)

diethyl chlorophosphate
O,O-diethyl phosphorochloridate; [814-49-3]

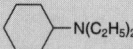

$C_4H_{10}Cl_1O_3P_1$. M: 172.54. Colourless liquid. Hydrolysed by water and alcohol.
Production:
• ethanol + phosphorus oxychloride (dehydrochlorination)
Derivatives:
fosamine-ammonium; mephosfolan; phosfolan

diethyl chlorothiophosphate
See: O,O-diethyl phosphorochlorothioate

N,N-diethylcyclohexylamine
cyclohexyldiethylamine; DECHA; [91-65-6]

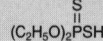

$C_{10}H_{21}N_1$. M: 155.29.
Production:
• cyclohexylamine + ethanol (reductive amination; coproduced with *N*-ethylcyclohexylamine)
Uses: polyurethane catalyst

O,O-diethyl dithiophosphoric acid
O,O-diethyl phosphorodithioic acid; [298-06-6]

$$\overset{S}{\underset{\|}{(C_2H_5O)_2PSH}}$$

$C_4H_{11}O_2P_1S_2$. M: 186.23.
Production:
• ethanol + phosphorus pentasulphide (addition)
Derivatives:
azinphos-ethyl; chlormephos; *O,O*-diethyl phosphorochlorothioate; disulfoton; ethion; fonofos; mecarbam; phorate; phosalone; prothoate; sodium *O,O*-diethyl dithiophosphate; terbufos

diethylenediamine *See:* piperazine

diethylene glycol
diglycol; digol; DEG; [111-46-6]

$$HOCH_2CH_2OCH_2CH_2OH$$

$C_4H_{10}O_3$. M: 106.12. Colourless, hygroscopic liquid. BP: 245–252°C. d: 1.12 kg/l (20°C). Miscible with water, alcohol and ketones.
Production:
• ethylene oxide (hydration; coproduced with ethylene glycol/triethylene glycol)
Derivatives: 2,2-bis(β-dimethylaminoethyl) ether; bis-(2-morpholinoethyl)ether; di-(2-chloroethyl)ether; diethylene glycol bis(chloroformate); diethylene glycol dibenzoate; diethylene glycol diethyl ether; diethylene glycol dimethacrylate; diethylene glycol dimethyl ether; diethylene glycol dinitrate; diethylene glycol monolaurate; diethylene glycol monooleate; diethylene glycol monostearate; dioxane; *N*-ethylmorpholine; *N*-formylmorpholine; iotroxic acid; *N*-methylmorpholine; morpholine; polyester polyols, aromatic; polyester polyols, slightly-branched; tetrabromophthalate diol; tetraethylene glycol; triethylene glycol; unsaturated polyester resins, coating grades; unsaturated polyester resins, isophthalate grades
Uses: alkyd/unsaturated polyester resin comonomer; dehydration/hydrate suppression agent (natural gas processing); extraction solvent (Udex process); antifreeze blending component; polyurethane chain-extender; softening agent/lubricant (textile processing); solvent (printing inks)

diethylene glycol bis(allyl carbonate)
diallyl diglycol carbonate; diallyl 2,2′-oxydiethyl dicarbonate; CR39 monomer; optical monomer; Nouryset 200 (Akzo); [142-22-3]

$$\overset{O}{\underset{\|}{CH_2=CHCH_2OCOCH_2CH_2OCH_2CH_2}}\overset{O}{\underset{\|}{OCOCH_2CH=CH_2}}$$

$C_{12}H_{18}O_7$. M: 274.26. Colourless liquid with a mild odour. BP: 160°C. d: 1.14 kg/l (20°C). Insoluble in water. Soluble in ketones, esters and hydrocarbon solvents.
Production:
• allyl alcohol + diethylene glycol bis(chloroformate) (esterification)
Uses: allyl resin transparent castings (spectacle lenses)

diethylene glycol bis(chloroformate)
[106-75-2]

$$\overset{O}{\underset{\|}{ClCOCH_2CH_2OCH_2CH_2}}\overset{O}{\underset{\|}{OCCl}}$$

$C_6H_8Cl_2O_5$. M: 231.03. Liquid. MP: 5–6°C. BP: 125–127°C (0.65 kPa).
Production:
• diethylene glycol + phosgene (phosgenation)
Derivatives: diethylene glycol bis(allyl carbonate)

diethylene glycol dibenzoate
Benzoflex 2-45 (Velsicol Chemical); [120-55-8]

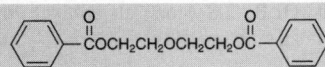

$C_{18}H_{18}O_5$. M: 314.33. High-boiling liquid or solid with a mild, ester odour. FP: 16°C. d: 1.17 kg/l (25°C). Insoluble in water. Soluble in aliphatic and aromatic solvents.
Production:
• diethylene glycol + benzoic acid (esterification)
Uses: plasticiser (vinyl acetate resins)

diethylene glycol dibutyl ether

$$CH_3(CH_2)_3OCH_2CH_2OCH_2CH_2O(CH_3)_3CH_3$$

$C_{12}H_{26}O_3$. M: 218.34.
Production:
• diethylene glycol monobutyl ether + *n*-butyl chloride (ether formation)
Uses: coupling solvent

diethylene glycol diethyl ether
[112-36-7]

$$C_2H_5OCH_2CH_2OCH_2CH_2OC_2H_5$$

$C_8H_{18}O_3$. M: 162.23. Colourless liquid. BP: 189°C. d: 0.81 kg/l (20°C). Soluble in water and most organic solvents.
Production:
• diethylene glycol + diethyl sulphate (ether formation)
Uses: solubiliser

diethylene glycol dimethacrylate
DEDMA

$$CH_2=CCOCH_2CH_2OCH_2CH_2OCC=CH_2$$
$$||$$
$$CH_3CH_3$$

$C_{12}H_{18}O_5$. M: 242.26. Colourless liquid with ester-like odour.
Production:
• diethylene glycol + methyl methacrylate (transesterification)
Uses: crosslinked acrylic/vinyl resin comonomer

diethylene glycol dimethyl ether
bis(2-methoxyethyl) ether; diglyme; [111-96-6]

$$CH_3OCH_2CH_2OCH_2CH_2OCH_3$$

$C_6H_{14}O_3$. M: 134.18. Colourless liquid. BP: 162°C. FP: -68°C. d: 0.94 kg/l (20°C). Soluble in water and most organic solvents.
Production:
• diethylene glycol + dimethyl sulphate (ether formation)
Uses: solubiliser

diethylene glycol dinitrate
DEGN; [693-21-0]

$$O_2NOCH_2CH_2OCH_2CH_2ONO_2$$

$C_4H_8N_2O_7$. M: 196.10.
Production:
• diethylene glycol (nitration)
Uses:
alcohol-based diesel fuel cetane improver; plasticiser (nitrocellulose explosives)

diethylene glycol monobutyl ether
butoxydiglycol; (2-(2-*n*-butoxyethoxy)ethanol; butyl diglycol; Butyl Carbitol (Union Carbide); Butyl Diethoxol (ICI); Butyl Dioxitol (Shell); [112-34-5]

$$CH_3CH_2CH_2CH_2OCH_2CH_2OCH_2CH_2OH$$

$C_8H_{18}O_3$. M: 162.23. Colourless liquid. BP: 224–235°C. d: 0.95 kg/l (20°C). Miscible with water and most organic solvents. Flash point: 78°C (CC).
Production:
• *n*-butanol + ethylene oxide (epoxidation; coproduced with ethylene glycol monobutyl ether/ triethylene glycol monobutyl ether)
Derivatives: diethylene glycol dibutyl ether; diethylene glycol monobutyl ether acetate; piperonyl butoxide
Uses:
coupling solvent (liquid cleaners, cutting fluids, textile auxiliaries); solvent (lacquers, paints, printing inks)

diethylene glycol monobutyl ether acetate
[124-17-4]

$$CH_3CH_2CH_2CH_2OCH_2CH_2OCH_2CH_2OCCH_3$$

$C_{10}H_{20}O_4$. M: 204.27. Colourless liquid with a mild odour. BP: 235–250°C. d: 0.98 kg/l (20°C). Miscible with water and most organic solvents.
Production:
• diethylene glycol monobutyl ether + acetic acid (esterification)
Uses:
coalescing solvent (water-based paints)

diethylene glycol monoethyl ether
ethoxydiglycol; 2-(2-ethoxyethoxy)ethanol; ethyl diglycol; ethyl digol; Carbitol (Union Carbide); Diethoxol (ICI); [111-90-0]

$$C_2H_5OCH_2CH_2OCH_2CH_2OH$$

$C_6H_{14}O_3$. M: 134.18. Colourless liquid. BP: 200–204°C. d: 0.99 kg/l (20°C). The product is being replaced in many applications because of its toxicity.
Production:
• ethanol + ethylene oxide (epoxidation; coproduced with ethylene glycol monoethyl ether/triethylene glycol monoethyl ether)

Derivatives:
2-(2-ethoxyethoxy)ethyl acrylate
Uses: solvent (paints, inks, wood stains, textile printing, dyeing)

diethylene glycol monoethyl ether acrylate
See: 2-(2-ethoxyethoxy)ethyl acrylate

diethylene glycol monolaurate
2-(2-hydroxyethoxy)ethyl laurate; [141-20-8]

$$CH_3(CH_2)_{10}\overset{\overset{\textstyle O}{\|}}{C}OCH_2CH_2OCH_2CH_2OH$$

$C_{16}H_{32}O_4$. M: 288.44. Pale yellow liquid. MP: 16–19°C. HLB: 6.2 (non self-emulsifying grades).
Production:
• diethylene glycol + lauric acid, broad cut (esterification)
Uses: antifoam/dispersant (paints)

diethylene glycol monomethyl ether
methoxydiglycol; (2-(2-methoxyethoxy)ethanol; methyldigol; Methyl Carbitol (Union Carbide); Methyl Diethoxol (ICI); Methyl Dioxitol (Shell); [111-77-3]

$$CH_3OCH_2CH_2OCH_2CH_2OH$$

$C_5H_{12}O_3$. M: 120.15. Colourless liquid with ether-like odour. BP: 188–198°C. d: 1.02 kg/l (20°C). Flash point: 93°C (TOC). Miscible with water and most organic solvents.
Production:
• methanol + ethylene oxide (epoxidation)
Uses:
brake fluid component; aviation fuel antiicing additive; solvent (paints, printing inks, resins, waxes, dyes)

diethylene glycol monooleate
2-(2-hydroxyethoxy)ethyl oleate; PEG-2 oleate; [106-12-7]

$$CH_3(CH_2)_7CH=CH(CH_2)_7\overset{\overset{\textstyle O}{\|}}{C}OCH_2CH_2OCH_2CH_2OH$$

$C_{22}H_{42}O_4$. M: 370.58. Amber liquid. MP: <0°C. HLB: 5.2 (non self-emulsifying grades).
Production:
• diethylene glycol + oleic acid (esterification)
Uses:
low-foaming emulsifier (pesticides, textile lubricants, emulsion paints, polishes)

diethylene glycol monostearate
2-(2-hydroxyethoxy)ethyl stearate; PEG-2 stearate; [106-11-6]

$$CH_3(CH_2)_{16}\overset{\overset{\textstyle O}{\|}}{C}OCH_2CH_2OCH_2CH_2OH$$

$C_{22}H_{44}O_4$. M: 372.59. Cream coloured wax. MP:

45–55°C. Available commercially as self-emulsifying and non self-emulsifying grades, depending on the free acid content. HLB: 2.8 (non self-emulsifying grades), 5.4 (self-emulsifying grades).
Production:
• diethylene glycol + stearic acid (esterification)
Uses: emulsifier/pearlising agent (cosmetics, pharmaceuticals); metal drawing lubricants

diethylenetriamine
N-(2-aminoethyl)-1,2-ethanediamine; bis(2-aminoethyl)-amine; DETA; [111-40-0]

$$H_2NCH_2CH_2NHCH_2CH_2NH_2$$

$C_4H_{13}N_3$. M: 103.16. Colourless, hygroscopic liquid with a strong, ammoniacal odour. BP: 207°C. MP: -39°C. d: 0.95 kg/l (20°C). Miscible with water, oxygenated and aromatic solvents. Immiscible with aliphatic solvents. Flash point: 99°C (TOC).
Production:
• ethylene dichloride + ammonia (amine formation; coproduced with triethylenetetramine/ethylenediamine/piperazine/tetraethylenepentamine/aminoethylpiperazine/polyethylenepolyamine)
• monoethanolamine + ammonia (ammoniation; coproduced with ethylenediamine/piperazine/*N*-hydroxyethylpiperazine/aminoethylpiperazine/aminoethylethanolamine)
• ethylenediamine + monoethanolamine (reductive amination; coproduced with triethylenetetramine/tetraethylenepentamine/polyethylenepolyamine)
Derivatives: adipic acid-dimethylaminohydroxypropyl-diethylenetriamine copolymers; amine-cyanoethylation adducts; aminoethyl behenyl imidazoline; aminoethyl cocoyl imidazoline; aminoethyl oleyl imidazoline; aminoethyl tallow imidazoline; diethylenetriamine ethoxylate; diethylenetriaminepentaacetic acid, pentasodium salt; diethylenetriaminepenta-(methylene phosphonic acid); pentamethyldiethylenetriamine; polyamide resins, non-reactive; polyamide resins, reactive; polyether polyols, rigid; urea-formaldehyde resins, cationic
Uses: epoxy resin curing agent

diethylenetriamine ethoxylate

$$HOCH_2CH_2NHCH_2CH_2NHCH_2CH_2NHCH_2CH_2OH$$

$C_8H_{21}N_3O_2$. M: 191.27. Colourless liquid. d: 1.04 kg/l (25°C). Viscosity: 1.5–3.5 poise (25°C). Amine value: 1,100–1,200 mg KOH/g.
Production:
• diethylenetriamine + ethylene oxide (epoxidation)
Uses: epoxy resin curing agent

diethylenetriaminepentaacetic acid, pentasodium salt
pentasodium diethylenetriaminepentaacetate; pentasodium pentetate (CTFA); sodium DTPA; [140-01-2]
$C_{14}H_{18}N_3Na_5O_{10}$. M: 503.25.

$$CH_2COO^-$$
$$(^-OOCCH_2)_2NCH_2CH_2NCH_2CH_2N(CH_2COO^-)_2 \quad 5Na^+$$

Production:
• diethylenetriamine + formaldehyde + hydrogen cyanide + sodium hydroxide (cyanomethylation/nitrile hydrolysis/salt formation)

Uses: reagent (wood pulp pretreatment); sequestrant (paper deinking, industrial/household cleaners)

diethylenetriaminepenta-(methylene phosphonic acid) DETPMPA

$$\left[(HO)_2\overset{O}{\underset{\parallel}{P}}CH_2\right]_2NCH_2CH_2NCH_2CH_2N\left[CH_2\overset{O}{\underset{\parallel}{P}}(OH)_2\right]_2$$
$$CH_2P(OH)_2$$
$$\overset{\parallel}{O}$$

$C_9H_{28}N_3O_{15}P_5$. M: 573.19. Available commercially as an aqueous solution containing 50% active matter. d: 1.14 kg/l. Soluble in water.

Production:
• diethylenetriamine + formaldehyde + phosphorous acid (Mannich reaction)

Uses: peroxide stabiliser (pulp/paper bleaching); scale inhibitor/chelant (boilers, cooling towers, oilfield water systems); sequestrant (powder laundry, industrial detergents)

N,N-diethyl-1,2-ethanediamine
See: N,N-diethylethylenediamine

diethyl ether
ether; ethyl ether; [60-29-7]

$$C_2H_5OC_2H_5$$

$C_4H_{10}O_1$. M: 74.12. Colourless, volatile liquid with an ethereal odour. BP: 34°C. d: 0.72 kg/l (15°C). Solubility in water: 85 g/l water (15°C). Miscible with most organic solvents. Flash point: -45°C (COC). Highly flammable.

Production:
• ethylene (catalytic hydration; byproduct of ethanol production)

Derivatives: boron trifluoride etherate

Uses: diesel fuel ignition primer; extraction solvent; ethylation reagent; solvent (Grignard/Wurtz reactions)

diethyl ethoxymethylenemalonate
ethyl ethoxymethylenemalonate; EEMM; [87-13-8]

$$C_2H_5OCH=C(COOC_2H_5)_2$$

$C_{10}H_{16}O_5$. M: 216.23. Liquid. BP: 280°C with decomposition. Insoluble in water. Soluble in oxygenated solvents.

Production:
• diethyl malonate + triethyl orthoformate (Knoevenagel condensation)

Derivatives: 2,4-dichloropyrimidine-5-carboxyl chloride; 4,7-dichloroquinoline; nalidixic acid; norfloxacin; oxolinic acid; pipemidic acid; piromidic acid

N,N-diethylethylenediamine
N,N-diethyl-1,2-ethanediamine; [100-36-7]

$$(C_2H_5)_2NCH_2CH_2NH_2$$

$C_6H_{16}N_2$. M: 116.21. Liquid. BP: 145–148°C. MP: <-70°C. d: 0.82 kg/l (20°C). Miscible with water. Soluble in oxygenated solvents.

Production:
• diethylaminoethanol + ammonia (amine formation)
• diethylamine + acrylamide (Micheal addition/Hofmann degradation)

Derivatives:
bromopride; metoclopramide; procainamide; tiapride

diethyl ethylmalonate
[133-13-1]

$$C_2H_5CH(COOC_2H_5)_2$$

$C_9H_{16}O_4$. M: 188.23. Liquid. BP: 207–209°C. d: 1.00 kg/l (20°C). Slightly soluble in water. Soluble in oxygenated solvents.

Production:
• ethyl chloride + diethyl malonate (dehydrochlorination)

Uses: pharmeceutical intermediate

di-(2-ethylhexyl) adipate
dioctyl adipate; DOA; [103-23-1]

$$CH_3(CH_2)_3CHCH_2O\overset{O}{\underset{\parallel}{C}}CH_2CH_2CH_2CH_2\overset{O}{\underset{\parallel}{C}}OCH_2CH(CH_2)_3CH_3$$
$$C_2H_5 \qquad\qquad\qquad\qquad\qquad C_2H_5$$

$C_{22}H_{42}O_4$. M: 370.58. Colourless liquid. BP: 224°C (1.3 kPa). d: 0.92 kg/l (20°C). Insoluble in water.

Production:
• 2-ethylhexanol + adipic acid (esterification)

Uses:
industrial lubricants; textile spin finishes; plasticiser (polyvinyl chloride, rubber)

di-(2-ethylhexyl)amine
bis(2-ethylhexyl)amine; dioctylamine; [106-20-7]

$$\left[CH_3(CH_2)_3\overset{C_2H_5}{\underset{}{CH}}CH_2\right]_2NH$$

$C_{16}H_{35}N_1$. M: 241.47. Liquid. BP: 157–159°C (2.7 kPa). MP: <-70°C. Insoluble in water. Soluble in oxygenated solvents.

Production:
• 2-ethylhexanol + ammonia (ammoniation; coproduced with 2-ethylhexylamine)

Uses:
dyestuffs intermediate

di-(2-ethylhexyl) azelate
dioctyl azelate; DOZ; [103-24-2]

$$CH_3(CH_2)_3CHCH_2OC(CH_2)_7COCH_2C(CH_2)_3CH_3$$
$$C_2H_5 \quad O \quad\quad O \quad C_2H_5$$

$C_{25}H_{48}O_4$. M: 412.65. Colourless, involatile liquid. d: 0.92 kg/l (25°C). Viscosity: 16–18 mPa.s (20°C). Insoluble in water.
Production:
• 2-ethylhexanol + azelaic acid (esterification)
Uses:
polyvinyl chloride plasticiser

di-(2-ethylhexyl) maleate
dioctyl maleate; DEHM; DOM; [142-16-5]

$$H\overset{\displaystyle C}{\underset{\displaystyle C}{\|}}COOCH_2C(CH_2)_3CH_3$$
$$COOCH_2C(CH_2)_3CH_3$$
$$C_2H_5$$

$C_{20}H_{36}O_4$. M: 340.51.
Production:
• 2-ethylhexanol + maleic anhydride (esterification)
Derivatives:
sodium di-(2-ethylhexyl)sulphosuccinate

di-(2-ethylhexyl) phthalate
dioctyl phthalate; DEHP; DOP; [117-81-7]

$$COOCH_2CH(CH_2)_3CH_3$$
$$COOCH_2CH(CH_2)_3CH_3$$

$C_{24}H_{38}O_4$. M: 390.56. Colourless liquid. d: 0.98 kg/l (20°C). BP: 220°C (0.65 kPa). Viscosity: 78 mPa.s (20°C). Insoluble in water.
Production:
• 2-ethylhexanol + phthalic anhydride (esterification)
Uses:
plasticiser (polyvinyl chloride, rubber, adhesives, PVA emulsion paints, lacquers); non-reactive epoxy resin diluent

di-(2-ethylhexyl) sebacate
dioctyl sebacate; DOS; [122-62-3]

$$CH_3(CH_2)_3CHCH_2OC(CH_2)_8COCH_2C(CH_2)_3CH_3$$
$$C_2H_5 \quad O \quad\quad O \quad C_2H_5$$

$C_{22}H_{42}O_4$. M: 370.58. Pale yellow, involatile liquid. d: 0.91 kg/l (25°C). Viscosity: 21 mPa.s (20°C). Insoluble in water.
Production:
• 2-ethylhexanol + sebacic acid (esterification)
Uses:
polyvinyl chloride plasticiser; synthetic lubricants

diethylhydroxylamine
DEHA; [3710-84-7]

$$(C_2H_5)_2NOH$$

$C_4H_{11}N_1O_1$. M: 89.14. Liquid. BP: 130°C. FP: -26–-25°C. d: 0.87 kg/l (20°C). Soluble in water. Flash point: 45°C.
Production:
• diethylamine + hydrogen peroxide (oxidation)
Uses:
oxygen scavenger (boiler water treatment)

diethyl 2-hydroxy-2-methylmalonate
See: diethyl α-isomalate

diethyl α-isomalate
diethyl 2-hydroxy-2-methylmalonate; diethyl methyl-tartronate

$$CH_3C(COOC_2H_5)_2$$
$$OH$$

$C_8H_{14}O_5$. M: 190.19.
Production:
• acetaldehyde + hydrogen cyanide + isopropenyl acetate + ethanol (cyanohydrin formation/alcohol oxidation/cyanohydrin formation/acetylation/nitrile hydrolysis/esterification/deacetylation)
Derivatives: chlozolinate

diethyl ketone
3-pentanone; [96-22-0]

$$(C_2H_5)_2C{=}O$$

$C_5H_{10}O_1$. M: 86.13. Colourless liquid with an acetone-like odour. BP: 100–102°C. MP: -45°C. Slightly soluble in water. Miscible with oxygenated solvents.
Production:
• ethylene + synthesis gas (hydroformylation)
• propionic acid (decarboxylative coupling)
Derivatives: pendimethalin

diethyl maleate
ethyl maleate; [141-05-9]

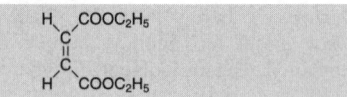

$$H\overset{\displaystyle C}{\underset{\displaystyle C}{\|}}COOC_2H_5$$
$$HCOOC_2H_5$$

$C_8H_{12}O_4$. M: 172.19. Colourless liquid. BP: 221–224°C. d: 1.07 kg/l (20°C). Insoluble in water. Soluble in oxygenated solvents.
Production:
• ethanol + maleic anhydride (esterification)
Derivatives:
2-ethylcyclopentane-1,3-dione; malathion; 2-methyl-cyclopentane-1,3-dione
Uses: nickel plating brightening agent; polyvinyl acetate latex comonomer

diethyl malonate

ethyl malonate; DEM; [105-53-3]

$$C_2H_5OCCH_2COC_2H_5$$

with the two O's above the C's (diethyl malonate structure)

$C_7H_{12}O_4$. M: 160.18. Liquid with a pleasant odour. BP: 198–200°C. MP: -50°C. d: 1.06 kg/l (20°C). Slightly soluble in water. Soluble in oxygenated solvents.

Production:
• ethanol + malonic acid (esterification)
• chloroacetic acid + carbon monoxide + ethanol (carbonylation/esterification)

Derivatives:
barbital; barbituric acid; biotin; butalbital; cyclopentobarbital; diethyl 2-aminomalonate hydrochloride; diethyl *n*-butylmalonate; diethyl ethoxymethylenemalonate; diethyl ethylmalonate; difenacoum; dimethindene; etrimfos; flocoumafen; methohexital; methyl dihydrojasmonate; naftidrofuryl; phenprocoumone; sulfinpyrazone; 3,3-tetramethyleneglutaric acid; thiopental sodium

Uses: isocyanate blocking agent

N,N-diethyl-3-methoxyaniline
See: N,N-diethyl-*m*-anisidine

N,N-diethyl-3-methylbenzamide
See: N,N-diethyl-*m*-toluamide

diethyl methylmalonate

$$CH_3CH(COOC_2H_5)_2$$

$C_8H_{14}O_4$. M: 174.20. Liquid. BP: 201°C. d: 1.02 kg/l (20°C). Slightly soluble in water. Soluble in oxygenated solvents.

Production:
• propionitrile + cyanogen chloride + ethanol (dehydrochlorination/nitrile hydrolysis/esterification)

Derivatives: sulfaperin; sulindac

diethyl methyltartronate *See:* diethyl α-isomalate

diethyl oxalacetate

diethyl 2-oxosuccinate; [108-56-5]

$$C_2H_5OOCCCH_2COOC_2H_5$$

with O above the third C (diethyl oxalacetate structure)

$C_8H_{12}O_5$. M: 188.19.

Production:
• diethyl oxalate + ethyl acetate (Claisen condensation)

Derivatives: ethyl 1-phenylpyrazolone-3-carboxylate; ethyl 1-(4-sulphophenyl)-5-pyrazolone-3-carboxylate

diethyl oxalate

ethyl oxalate; [95-92-1]

$C_6H_{10}O_4$. M: 146.15. Colourless liquid. BP: 184–186°C. FP: -41°C. d: 1.08 kg/l (20°C). Slightly soluble in water with gradual hydrolysis. Miscible with most organic solvents.

$$\begin{array}{l} COOC_2H_5 \\ | \\ COOC_2H_5 \end{array}$$

Production:
• ethanol + oxalic acid (esterification)

Derivatives: cefoperazone; cromolyn; diethyl oxalacetate; ethionamide; piperacillin; prothionamide

N,N-diethyl-p-phenylenediamine

p-aminodiethylaniline; Developer CD1 (Kodak)

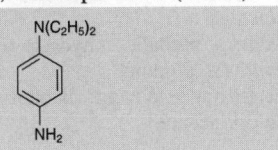

$C_{10}H_{16}N_2$. M: 164.25. Liquid. BP: 260–262°C. Insoluble in water. Available commercially as the free base and as the bisulphate or hydrochloride salts.

Production:
• *N,N*-diethylaniline + sodium nitrite (nitrosation/nitro reduction)

Uses: photographic developing agent

diethyl phosphite

DEPI; [762-04-9]

$$\left[C_2H_5O \right]_2 \overset{O}{\underset{}{P}} - H$$

$C_4H_{11}O_3P_1$. M: 138.10. Colourless liquid. BP: 138°C. d: 1.07 kg/l (25°C). Soluble in water.

Production:
• ethanol + phosphorus trichloride (dehydrochlorination)

Derivatives: O,O-diethyl bis(2-hydroxyethyl)aminomethylphosphonate

O,O-diethyl phosphorochloridate

See: diethyl chlorophosphate

O,O-diethyl phosphorochlorothioate

diethyl chlorothiophosphate; *O,O*-diethyl phosphorochloridothioate; *O,O*-diethyl phosphorothiochloridate; diethyl thiophosphoryl chloride; DECTP; DEPCT; [2524-04-1]

$$(C_2H_5O)_2 \overset{S}{\underset{}{P}} Cl$$

$C_4H_{10}Cl_1O_2P_1S_1$. M: 188.60.

Production:
• *O,O*-diethyl dithiophosphoric acid + chlorine (chlorination)

Derivatives:
chlorpyrifos; diazinon; fensulfothion; isazofos; isoxathion; parathion; phoxim; pirimiphos-ethyl; pyrazophos; quinalphos; sulfotep; triazophos

O,O-diethyl phosphorodithioic acid
See: O,O-diethyl dithiophosphoric acid

diethyl phthalate
DEP; [84-66-2]

$C_{12}H_{14}O_4$. M: 222.24. Colourless liquid. BP: 294°C. MP: -3°C. d: 1.12 kg/l (20°C). Insoluble in water. Miscible with oxygenated and aromatic solvents.
Production:
• ethanol + phthalic anhydride (esterification)
Derivatives: pindone
Uses: fragrance diluent; alcohol denaturant; plasticiser (cellulose acetate)

diethylpropion *See:* amfepramone

diethylstilbestrol
DES; [56-53-1]

$C_{18}H_{20}O_2$. M: 268.36.
Production:
• *p*-hydroxypropiophenone (carbonyl reduction/alcohol bromination/Grignard reagent formation/Grignard reaction/dehydration)
Uses: oestrogenic hormone drug

diethyl succinate
ethyl succinate

$C_8H_{14}O_4$. M: 174.20. Colourless liquid. MP: -22°C. BP: 128°C. d: 1.04 kg/l (20°C). Insoluble in water. Soluble in oxygenated solvents.
Production:
• ethanol + succinic acid (esterification)
Uses:
flavouring ingredient

diethyl sulphate
ethyl sulphate; DES; [64-67-5]

$C_4H_{10}O_4S_1$. M: 154.18. Colourless liquid with a mint-like odour. BP: 208°C with decomposition. MP: -24°C.

d: 1.18 kg/l (20°C). Insoluble in water. Hydrolysed by hot water. Miscible with oxygenated solvents.
Production:
• ethanol + oleum (sulphation)
Derivatives: Acid Brown 20; benzoin ethyl ether; benzoximate; *N*-cetyl ethylmorpholinium ethosulphate; chlorobenzilate; 2-chloro-3-hexyne; cycloxydim; diethylene glycol diethyl ether; Disperse Blue 183; ethenzamide; ethidimuron; ethylene glycol diethyl ether; ethyl vanillin; 3-hexenol; β-naphthyl ethyl ether; oxyfluorfen; piprozolin; propenylguethol; sethoxydim; Vat Red 13; viloxazine

diethyl sulphide *See:* ethyl sulphide

diethyl thiophosphoryl chloride
See: O,O-diethyl phosphorochlorothioate

diethylthiourea
1,3-diethylthiourea; *N,N'*-diethylthiourea; DETU; [105-55-5]

$C_5H_{12}N_2S_1$. M: 132.22. Pale yellow flakes or powder with a characteristic odour. MP: 75°C. d: 1.1 kg/l. Soluble in water, oxygenated and aromatic solvents.
Production:
• ethylamine + carbon disulphide (thiocarbonylation)
Uses: corrosion inhibitor (metal pickling); vulcanisation accelerator

N,N-diethyl-*m*-toluamide
N,N-diethyl-3-methylbenzamide; *N,N*-diethyltoluamide; DEET; [134-62-3]

$C_{12}H_{17}N_1O_1$. M: 191.28. Colourless liquid. BP: 160°C (2.5 kPa). d: 1.00 kg/l (20°C). Slightly soluble in water. Soluble in oxygenated and aromatic solvents.
Production:
• *m*-toluic acid + diethylamine (amide formation)
Uses: insect repellant

3,5-diethyltoluenediamine
2,4-diamino-3,5-diethyltoluene; DETDA

$C_{12}H_{20}N_2$. M: 192.30. Mixed product containing 75% 3,5-diethyl-2,4-toluenediamine, 20% 3,5-diethyl-2,6-toluenediamine and 5% other amines.

Production:
- 2,4/2,6-diaminotoluene + ethylene (Friedel-Crafts alkylation)

Uses: reaction-injection moulding polyurethane/polyurea curing agent

N,N-diethyl-*m*-toluidine
[91-67-8]

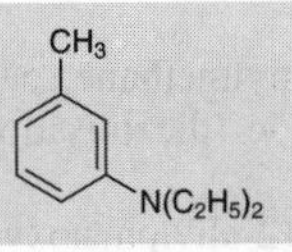

$C_{11}H_{17}N_2$. M: 177.27. Yellow liquid. BP: 110–112°C (0.13 kPa). Insoluble in water.
Production:
- *m*-toluidine + ethanol (amine formation; coproduced with *N*-ethyl-*m*-toluidine)

Derivatives:
Acid Blue 15; 2-amino-5-diethylaminotoluene; Disperse Blue 339

diethyl zinc
zinc diethyl; [557-20-0]

$C_4H_{10}Zn_1$. M: 123.49. Liquid. BP: 118°C. MP: -28°C. Spontaneously ignites in air. Miscible with ether and hydrocarbon solvents.
Production:
- zinc chloride + ethyl chloride + triethylaluminium (reaction)

Uses: polymerisation/epoxidation catalyst

difenacoum
3-[3-biphenyl-4-yl-1,2,3,4-tetrahydro-1-naphthyl]-4-hydroxycoumarin; [56073-07-5]

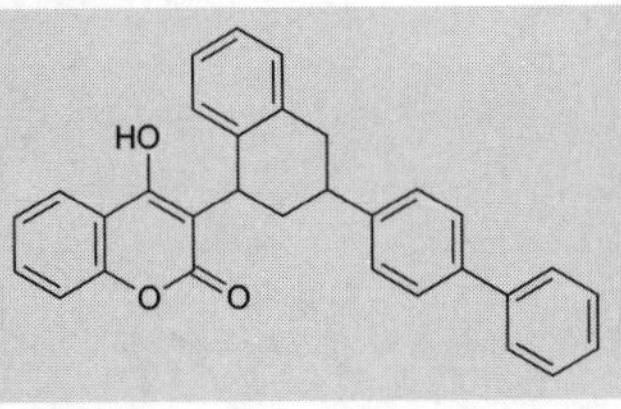

$C_{31}H_{24}O_3$. M: 444.53.
Production:
- phenylacetyl chloride + biphenyl + diethyl malonate + 4-hydroxycoumarin (Friedel-Crafts acylation/carbonyl condensation/cyclisation/ hydrogenation/decarboxylation/condensation)

Derivatives: brodifacoum
Uses: rodenticide

difenoxuron
3-[4-(4-methoxyphenoxy)phenyl]-1,1-dimethylurea; [14214-32-5]

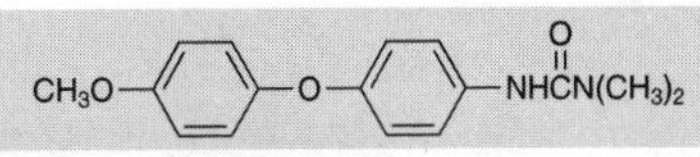

$C_{16}H_{18}N_2O_3$. M: 286.33.
Production:
- hydroquinone monomethyl ether + *p*-chloronitrobenzene + dimethylcarbamoyl chloride (ether formation/nitro reduction/isocyanate addition)

Uses:
herbicide

difenzoquat methosulphate
1,2-dimethyl-3,5-diphenylpyrazolium methylsulphate; [43222-48-6]

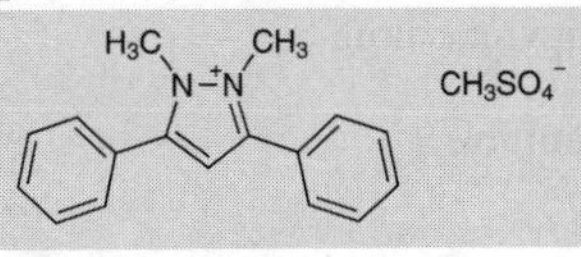

$C_{18}H_{20}N_2O_4S_1$. M: 360.43.
Production:
- dibenzoylmethane + methyl hydrazine + dimethyl sulphate (condensation/methylation)

Uses: herbicide

diflubenzuron
1-(4-chlorophenyl)-3-(2,6-difluorobenzoyl)urea; [35367-38-5]

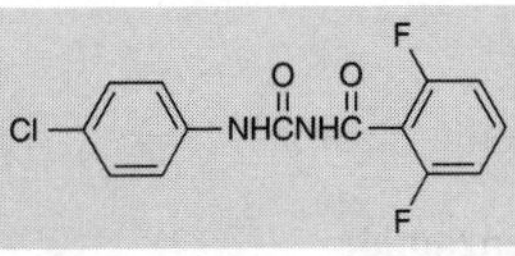

$C_{14}H_9Cl_1F_2N_2O_2$. M: 310.68.
Production:
- *p*-chlorophenyl isocyanate + 2,6-difluorobenzamide (isocyanate addition)

Uses:
insecticide

diflufenican
2′,4′-difluoro-2-(3-trifluoromethylphenoxy)-3-nicotinanilide; [83164-33-4]

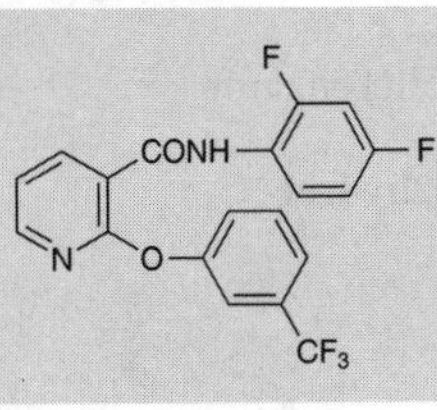

$C_{19}H_{11}F_5N_2O_2$. M: 394.30.
Production:
- 2-chloronicotinic acid + *m*-hydroxybenzotrifluoride + 2,4-difluoroaniline (ether formation/amide formation)

Uses: herbicide

diflunisal
[22494-42-4]

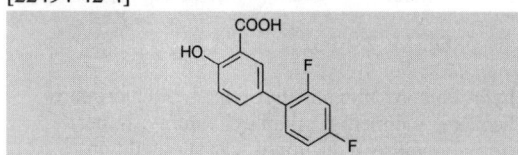

$C_{13}H_8F_2O_3$. M: 250.20.
Production:
• biphenyl + carbon dioxide (nitration/partial nitro reduction/Balz-Schiemann reaction/nitro reduction/ diazotisation/hydration/Kolbe-Schmitt reaction)
Uses:
analgesic/antipyretic drug

2,4-difluoroaniline
[367-25-9]

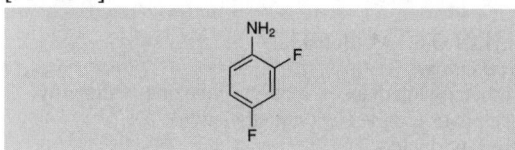

$C_6H_5F_2N_1$. M: 129.12. Liquid. BP: 168–170°C. MP: -8°C.
Production:
• 2,4-dichloronitrobenzene (halogen exchange/nitro reduction)
Derivatives:
diflufenican; teflubenzuron

2,6-difluorobenzamide
[18063-03-1]

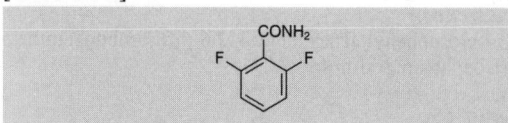

$C_7H_5F_2N_1O_1$. M: 157.13. Solid.
Production:
• 2,6-dichlorobenzonitrile (halogen exchange/nitrile hydration)
Derivatives:
diflubenzuron; teflubenzuron

4,4'-difluorobenzhydrol
[365-24-2]

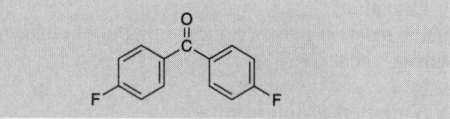

$C_{13}H_{10}F_2O_1$. M: 220.22.
Production:
• 4,4'-difluorobenzophenone (carbonyl reduction)
Derivatives: flunarizine

4,4'-difluorobenzophenone
[345-92-6]

$C_{13}H_8F_2O_1$. M: 218.20.
Production:
• 4,4'-diaminodiphenylmethane, pure + sodium nitrite + hydrogen fluoride (diazotisation/azo fluorination/ oxidation)
Derivatives: 4,4'-bis(2-allylphenoxy)benzophenone; 4,4'-difluorobenzhydrol; polyether ether ketone; polyether ketone; polyether ketone ether ketone ketone

difluoroethane
1,1-difluoroethane; HFC-152a; R152a; [75-37-6]

CH_3CHF_2

$C_2H_4F_2$. M: 66.05. Colourless, odourless, liquified gas. R-500 is an azeotropic mixture of R-12 with R-152a with BP: -33.3°C.
Production:
• vinylidene fluoride (hydrogenation)
Uses: R-500 refrigerant gas component

1,1-difluoroethylene *See:* vinylidene fluoride

1,2-difluoro-1,1,2,2-tetrachloroethane
See: tetrachlorodifluoroethane

Diglycolamine *See:* 2-(2-aminoethoxy)ethanol

diglyme *See:* diethylene glycol dimethyl ether

digoxin
[20830-75-5]

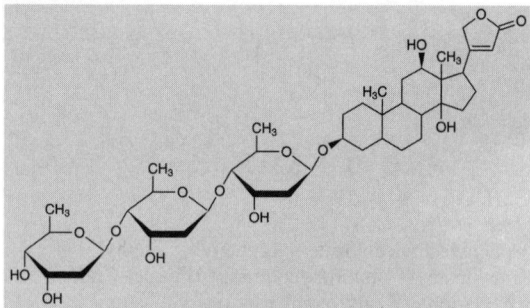

$C_{41}H_{64}O_{14}$. M: 780.95. Available commercially as the α-acetyl, the β-acetyl and the β-methyl derivatives.
Production:
• *Digitalis lanata* leaves (extraction)
Uses: cardiotonic drug

diheptadecyl ketone *See:* distearyl ketone

diheptyl-*p*-phenylenediamine
See: N,N′-bis(1,4-dimethylpentyl)-*p*-phenylenediamine

dihydralazine
[484-23-1]; [7327-87-9] (sulphate)

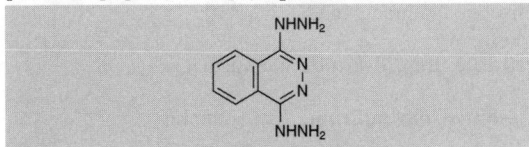

$C_8H_{10}N_6$. M: 190.21. Available commercially as the free base and as the hydrogen sulphate salt.
Production:
• phthalic anhydride + hydrazine (amide formation/ chlorination/amine formation)
Uses: antihypertensive drug

dihydrocinnamaldehyde
See: 3-phenylpropionaldehyde

dihydrocinnamic alcohol
See: 3-phenylpropanol

dihydrocodeine
[125-28-0]

$C_{18}H_{23}N_1O_3$. M: 301.39. Available commercially as the free base or as the bitartrate salt.
Production:
• codeine (hydrogenation)
Uses: analgesic/antitussive drug

dihydrocoumarin
benzodihydropyrone; 3,4-dihydrocoumarin; [119-84-6]

$C_9H_8O_2$. M: 148.16. Colourless crystals with a herbal odour. MP: 25°C. BP: 272°C. d: 1.17 kg/l (18°C). Insoluble in water. Soluble in chlorinated solvents.
Production:
• coumarin (hydrogenation)
Uses: flavouring ingredient

di-(hydrogenated tallow)dimethylammonium chloride
See: dimethyldistearylammonium chloride

dihydrojasmone
3-methyl-2-pentyl-2-cyclopenten-1-one; [1128-08-1]
$C_{11}H_{18}O_1$. M: 166.26. Colourless liquid with a jasmine-like odour.

Production:
• *n*-heptaldehyde + methyl vinyl ketone (addition/ aldol condensation)
Uses:
fragrance ingredient

dihydromyrcenol
2,6-dimethyl-7-octen-2-ol; [18479-58-8]

$C_{10}H_{20}O_1$. M: 156.27. Colourless liquid with a citrus odour. BP: 78°C (1.3 kPa). d: 0.84 kg/l (20°C). Insoluble in water.
Production:
• pinane (pyrolysis/hydrochlorination/hydration)
Derivatives:
hydroxycitronellal
Uses: perfume ingredient (soap, toiletries)

9,10-dihydro-9-oxoanthracene
See: anthrone

2,5-dihydroperoxy-2,5-dimethylhexane
See: 2,5-dimethylhexane-2,5-dihydroperoxide

dihydroxyacetone
DHA; [96-26-4]

$C_3H_6O_3$. M: 90.08. Colourless, hygroscopic, crystalline powder. MP: 78–80°C. Soluble in water and alcohol.
Production:
• glycerol + *Acetobacter suboxydans* bacteria (fermentation)
Uses: tanning agent

2,4-dihydroxyacetophenone
4-acetylresorcinol; resacetophenone; [89-84-9]

$C_8H_8O_3$. M: 152.15. Solid. MP: 143–145°C. Insoluble in water. Soluble in hot alcohol.
Production:
• resorcinol + acetonitrile (Hoeben-Hoesch reaction; coproduced with 2,6-dihydroxyacetophenone)
Uses:
analytical reagent

2,6-dihydroxyacetophenone
2-acetylresorcinol; [699-83-2]

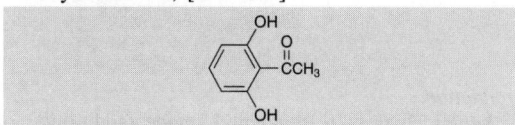

$C_8H_8O_3$. M: 152.15.
Production:
• resorcinol + acetonitrile (Hoeben-Hoesch reaction; coproduced with 2,4-dihydroxyacetophenone)
Derivatives: cromolyn

3,5-dihydroxyacetophenone

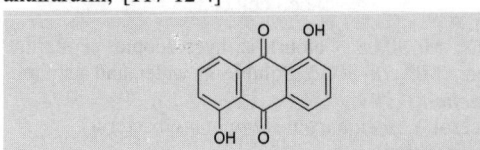

$C_8H_8O_3$. M: 152.15. Solid. MP: 147–148°C. Soluble in water and oxygenated solvents.
Production:
• acetophenone (sulphonation/alkali fusion)
Derivatives:
3,5-diacetoxyacetophenone; 3,5-dibenzoxyacetophenone

dihydroxyaluminium monostearate
See: aluminium monostearate

1,2-dihydroxyanthraquinone *See:* alizarin

1,4-dihydroxyanthraquinone *See:* quinizarin

1,5-dihydroxyanthraquinone
anthrarufin; [117-12-4]

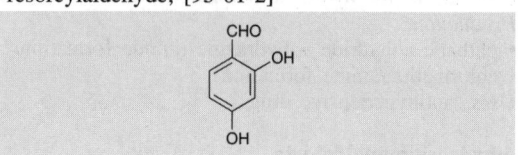

$C_{14}H_8O_4$. M: 240.21. Yellow flakes. MP: 280°C. Sublimes. Insoluble in water. Soluble in aromatic solvents.
Production:
• anthraquinone-1,5-disulphonic acid (alkali fusion)
Derivatives:
Acid Blue 45; 1,5-dihydroxy-4,8-dinitroanthraquinone

1,8-dihydroxyanthraquinone
chrysazine; danthron; [117-10-2]

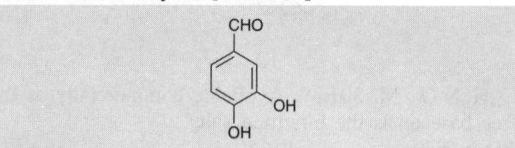

$C_{14}H_8O_4$. M: 240.21. Reddish-yellow needles. MP: 191–

193°C. Sublimes. Insoluble in water. Soluble in oxygenated solvents.
Production:
• anthraquinone-1,8-disulphonic acid (alkali fusion)
Derivatives: anthralin; 4,5-diamino-1,8-dihydroxy-2,7-diisobutylanthraquinone
Uses:
cathartic drug; dyestuffs intermediate

1,8-dihydroxyanthrone *See:* anthralin

2,4-dihydroxybenzaldehyde
β-resorcylaldehyde; [95-01-2]

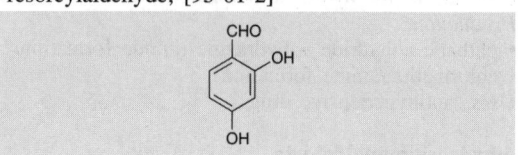

$C_7H_6O_3$. M: 138.13. White needles. MP: 135–137°C. Soluble in water and oxygenated solvents.
Production:
• resorcinol + hydrogen cyanide (Gattermann reaction)
Derivatives:
Food Brown 3; 7-hydroxycoumarin
Uses: dyestuffs intermediate

3,4-dihydroxybenzaldehyde
protocatechualdehyde; [139-85-5]

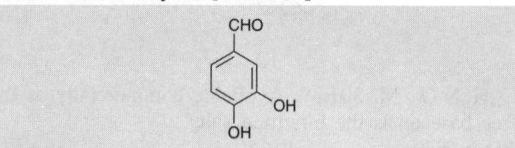

$C_7H_6O_3$. M: 138.13.
Production:
• vanillin (demethylation)
Derivatives: levodopa

m-dihydroxybenzene *See:* resorcinol

o-dihydroxybenzene *See:* catechol

p-dihydroxybenzene *See:* hydroquinone

2,4-dihydroxybenzoic acid
β-resorcylic acid; BRA; [89-86-1]

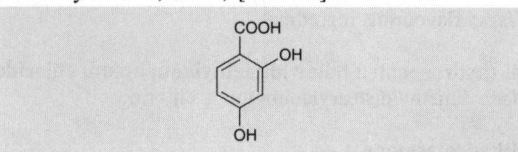

$C_7H_6O_4$. M: 154.13. Solid. MP: 225–227°C with decomposition. Soluble in oxygenated solvents and hot water.

Production:
• resorcinol + potassium bicarbonate (salt formation/
  Kolbe-Schmitt reaction/acidification; coproduced
  with 2,6-dihydroxybenzoic acid)
Derivatives:
Mordant Red 15

2,6-dihydroxybenzoic acid
γ-resorcylic acid; [303-07-1]

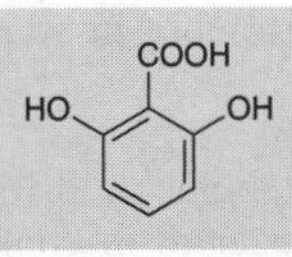

$C_7H_6O_4$. M: 154.13. Needles. MP: 157–159°C with
decomposition. Soluble in hot water and oxygenated
solvents.
Production:
• resorcinol + potassium bicarbonate (salt formation/
  Kolbe-Schmitt reaction/acidification; coproduced
  with 2,4-dihydroxybenzoic acid)
Derivatives:
2,6-dimethoxybenzoic acid; resorantel

3,5-dihydroxybenzoic acid
resorcinic acid; α-resorcylic acid; [99-10-5]

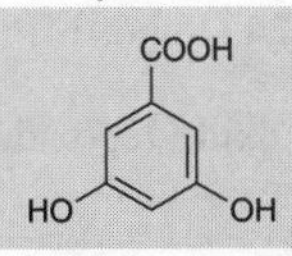

$C_7H_6O_4$. M: 154.13. White crystalline solid. MP:
236–238°C with decomposition. Soluble in water and
oxygenated solvents.
Production:
• benzoic acid (sulphonation/alkali fusion)
Uses:
chemical intermediate

2,4-dihydroxybenzophenone
benzophenone-1 (CTFA); DHBP; [131-56-6]

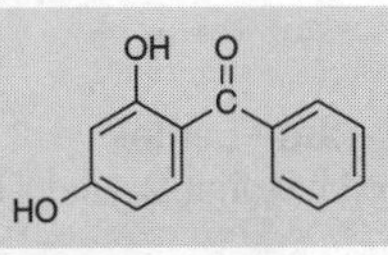

$C_{13}H_{10}O_3$. M: 214.22.
Off-white powder. MP: 136–147°C.
Production:
• resorcinol + benzoyl chloride (Friedel-Crafts
  acylation)
Derivatives:
4-(2-acryloyloxyethoxy)-2-hydroxybenzophenone; 2,4-
dihydroxybenzophenone 2,1,5-diazoester; 2-hydroxy-4-
dodecoxybenzophenone; 2-hydroxy-4-methoxybenzophe-
none; 2-hydroxy-4-octoxybenzophenone
Uses: light stabiliser (plastics)

4,4'-dihydroxybenzophenone

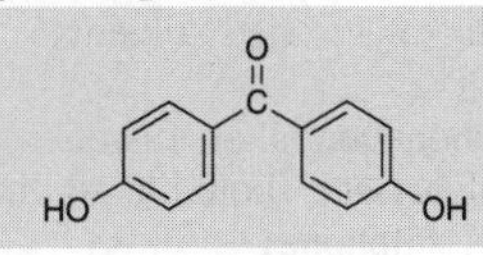

$C_{13}H_{10}O_3$. M: 214.22. Solid. MP: 212°C. Soluble in hot
water and oxygenated solvents.
Production:
• 4,4'-diaminodiphenylmethane, pure + sodium nitrite
  (oxidation/diazotisation/hydration)
Derivatives: 4,4'-dimethoxytriphenylmethyl chloride;
polyether ketone

2,4-dihydroxybenzophenone 2,1,5-diazoester
[31001-73-7]

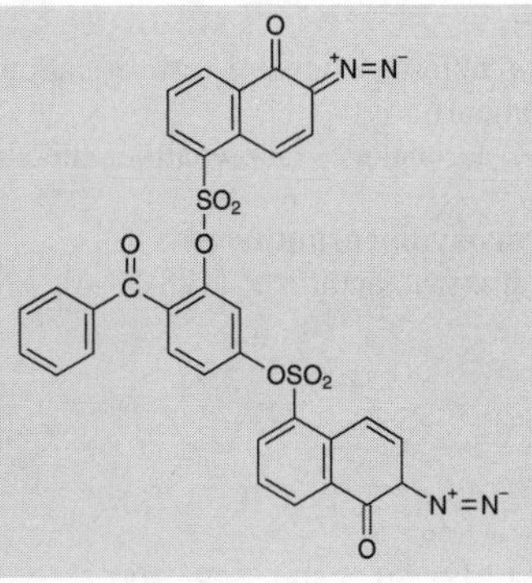

$C_{33}H_{18}N_4O_9S_2$. M: 678.65.
Production:
• 2,4-dihydroxybenzophenone + 2-diazo-1-naphthol-
  5-sulphonic acid chloride (esterification)
Uses:
positive photoreprographic plate light sensitive agent

2,2'-dihydroxybiphenyl
2,2'-biphenol; *o,o'*-biphenol; biphenyl-2,2'-diol; 2,2'-bis-
(hydroxyphenyl); [1806-29-7]

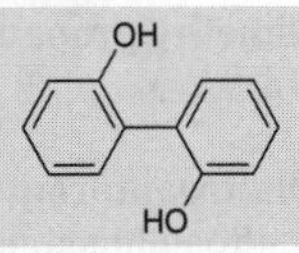

$C_{12}H_{10}O_2$. M: 186.21.
Production:
• diphenylene oxide (ether hydrolysis)
Uses: disinfectant

4,4'-dihydroxybiphenyl
4,4'-biphenol; *p,p'*-biphenol; biphenyl-4,4'-diol; *p,p'*-di-
hydroxybiphenyl; 4,4'-dihydroxydiphenyl; [92-88-6]

$C_{12}H_{10}O_2$. M: 186.21. White, crystalline solid. MP:

269°C. Sublimes on further heating. Slightly soluble in water. Soluble in oxygenated solvents.
Production:
• biphenyl (sulphonation/alkali fusion)
Derivatives: polyarylate, liquid-crystalline; poly(4,4′-phenoxybiphenyl sulphone)

dihydroxybutanedioic acid *See:* tartaric acid

3,4-dihydroxy-ω-chloroacetophenone
2-chloro-3′,4-dihydroxyacetophenone; [99-40-1]

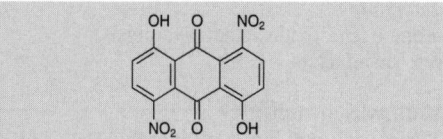

$C_8H_7Cl_1O_3$. M: 186.60.
Production:
• catechol + chloroacetic acid (esterification/Fries rearrangement)
Derivatives: adrenalone; isoprenaline; theodrenaline

16,17-dihydroxydibenzanthrone
16,17-dihydroxyviolanthrone; [128-59-6]

$C_{34}H_{16}O_4$. M: 488.50. Solid. MP: 300°C.
Production:
• benzanthrone (oxidative coupling/quinone reduction)
Derivatives: Vat Blue 16; Vat Green 1

2,5-dihydroxy-2,5-dimethylhexane
See: dimethyl hexanediol

2,5-dihydroxy-2,5-dimethyl-3-hexyne
See: dimethyl hexynediol

1,3-dihydroxy-2,2-dimethylpropane
See: neopentyl glycol

1,5-dihydroxy-4,8-dinitroanthraquinone
4,8-dihydroxy-1,5-dinitroanthraquinone;4,8-dinitroanth-rarufin; [128-91-6]

$C_{14}H_6N_2O_8$. M: 330.20.
Production:
• 1,5-dihydroxyanthraquinone (nitration)
Derivatives:
1,5-diamino-4,8-dihydroxyanthraquinone

4,4′-dihydroxydiphenyl sulphide *See:* 4,4′-thiodiphenol

4,4′-dihydroxydiphenyl sulphone
bisphenol S; di-(*p*-hydroxyphenyl) sulphone; sulphonyl bisphenol; [80-09-1]

$C_{12}H_{10}O_4S_1$. M: 250.27. White crystals. MP: 240°C. d: 1.37 kg/l (15°C). Insoluble in water. Soluble in oxygenated solvents.
Production:
• phenol + chlorosulphonic acid (chlorosulphonation)
Uses: phenolic/polyester resin comonomer

***m*-di-(2-hydroxyethoxy)benzene**
See: resorcinol di-(2-hydroxyethyl) ether

***p*-di-(2-hydroxyethoxy)benzene**
See: hydroquinone di-(β-hydroxyethyl) ether

***N,N*-di-(2-hydroxyethyl)aniline**
2,2′-(phenylimino)bisethanol; [120-07-0]

$C_{10}H_{15}N_1O_2$. M: 181.24. Solid. MP: 52°C.
Production:
• aniline + ethylene oxide (epoxidation)
Uses: dyestuffs intermediate

di-(2-hydroxyethyl)bisphenol A
2,2-bis(*p*-β-hydroxyethoxyphenyl)propane; di-(β-hydroxyethyl)bisphenol A; [901-44-0]

$C_{19}H_{24}O_4$. M: 316.40.
Production:
• bisphenol A + ethylene oxide (epoxidation)
Derivatives: vinyl ester resins

di-(2-hydroxyethyl)butynediol
1,4-di-(2-hydroxyethoxy)but-2-yne; [1606-85-5]

$C_8H_{14}O_4$. M: 174.20.
Production:
• 1,4-butynediol + ethylene oxide (epoxidation)
Uses: electroplating brightening agent

***N,N*-di-(2-hydroxyethyl)-*m*-chloroaniline**
2,2′-[(3-chlorophenyl)imino]bisethanol; 2,2′-(*m*-chlorophenylimino)diethanol; [92-00-2]
$C_{10}H_{14}Cl_1N_1O_2$. M: 215.68. Solid. MP: 83–87°C. BP: 230–246°C (2.3 kPa).

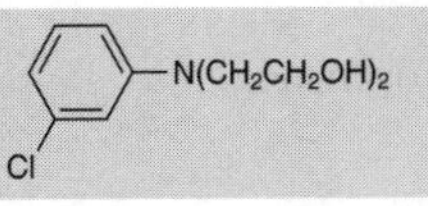

Production:
• *m*-chloroaniline + ethylene oxide (epoxidation)
Derivatives:
Disperse Brown 1

di-(2-hydroxyethyl)dimethylhydantoin dilaurate

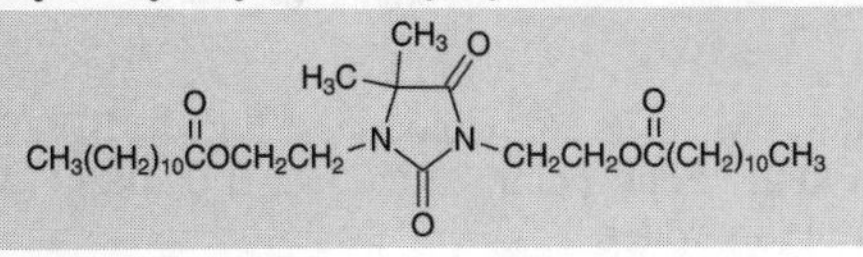

$C_{29}H_{60}N_2O_6$. M: 532.80.
Production:
• 5,5-dimethylhydantoin + ethylene oxide + lauric acid, broad cut (epoxidation/esterification)
Uses: textile auxiliaries

dihydroxyethyl sulphide
See: thiodiglycol

N,N′-di-(2-hydroxyethyl)-m-toluidine
2,2′-[(3-methylphenyl)imino]bisethanol; 2,2′-(*m*-tolyl-imino)diethanol; [91-99-6]

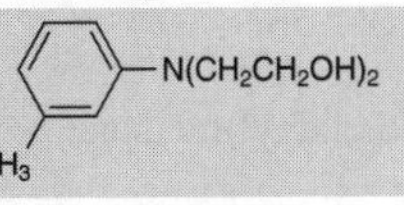

$C_{11}H_{17}N_1O_2$. M: 195.27. Solid. MP: 65–68°C. BP: 210–225°C (0.7 kPa).
Production:
• *m*-toluidine + ethylene oxide (epoxidation)
Derivatives:
Disperse Red 5; Disperse Red 17

2,4-dihydroxy-n-hexylbenzene *See:* hexylresorcinol

2,6-dihydroxyisonicotinic acid *See:* citrazinic acid

2,2′-dihydroxy-4-methoxybenzophenone
Cyasorb UV-24 (American Cyanamid)

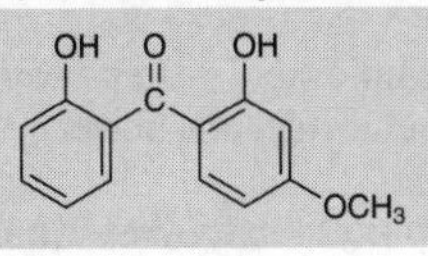

$C_{14}H_{12}O_4$. M: 244.25.
Production:
• resorcinol + salicylic acid (Friedel-Crafts acylation/methylation)
Uses: light stabiliser (oil-based products)

3,4-dihydroxy-ω-(methylamino)acetophenone
See: adrenalone

di-(hydroxymethyl) oleyloxazoline
2-(heptadecenyl)-4,4-bis(hydroxymethyl)oxazoline

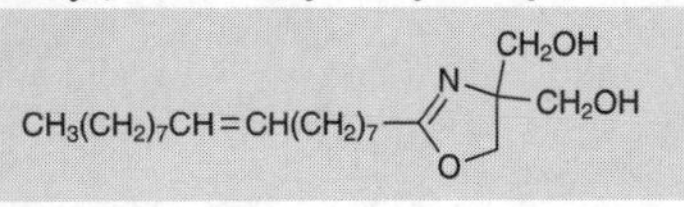

$C_{22}H_{41}N_1O_3$. M: 367.58.
Production:
• oleic acid + tris(hydroxymethyl)aminomethane (condensation)
Derivatives:
di-(hydroxymethyl) oleyloxazoline ethoxylates
Uses: corrosion inhibitor; emulsifier; pigment dispersant

di-(hydroxymethyl) oleyloxazoline ethoxylates

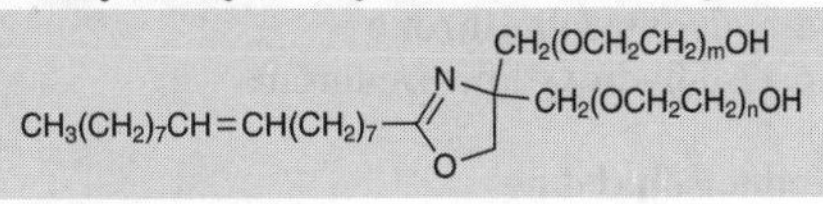

m+n = 4. $C_{30}H_{57}N_1O_7$. M: 543.79.
Production:
• di-(hydroxymethyl) oleyloxazoline + ethylene oxide (epoxidation)
Uses: emulsifier/corrosion inhibitor (cutting fluids)

N,N′-di-(hydroxymethyl)urea *See:* dimethylolurea

1,5-dihydroxynaphthalene *See:* 1,5-naphthalenediol

4,5-dihydroxynaphthalene-2,7-disulphonic acid
See: chromotropic acid

3,4-dihydroxyphenylethylamine
See: dopamine

17α,21-dihydroxy-4-pregnene-3,11,20-trione
See: cortisone

di-(2-hydroxypropyl)bisphenol A
Dow Resin 565 (Dow Chemical)

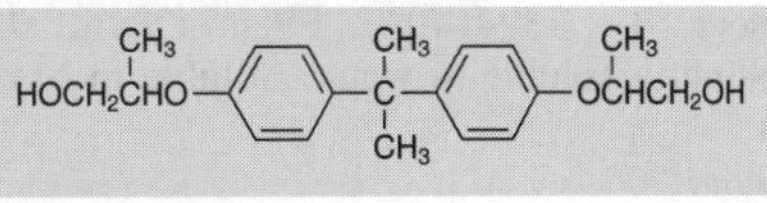

$C_{21}H_{14}O_4$. M: 330.34.
Production:
• bisphenol A + propylene oxide (epoxidation)
Uses:
chemically-resistant unsaturated polyester resin comonomer; polyurethane chain-extender

7-(2,3-dihydroxypropyl)theophylline
See: diprophylline

2,4-dihydroxypteridine *See:* lumazine

2,4-dihydroxypyrimidine *See:* uracil

2,4-dihydroxyquinoline
quinoline-2,4-diol; [52851-41-9]

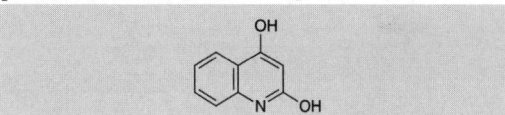

$C_9H_7N_1O_2$. M: 161.17. Solid. MP: >340°C.
Production:
• isatin + chloroacetic acid (oxidation)
Derivatives:
Acid Red 179; Pigment Green 10

dihydroxysuccinic acid *See:* tartaric acid

16,17-dihydroxyviolanthrone
See: 16,17-dihydroxydibenzanthrone

1,3-diiminoisoindoline

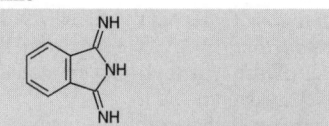

$C_8H_7N_3$. M: 145.17.
Production:
• phthalodinitrile + ammonia (imine formation)
Derivatives:
Pigment Yellow 139
Uses: pigment raw material

5,7-diiodo-8-hydroxyquinoline *See:* iodoquinol

diiodomethane *See:* methylene iodide

diisobutylamine
DIBA; [110-96-3]

$$[(CH_3)_2CHCH_2]_2NH$$

$C_8H_{19}N_1$. M: 129.25. Colourless liquid with an ammoniacal odour. BP: 139–140°C. FP: -74°C. d: 0.74 kg/l (4°C). Slightly soluble in water. Soluble in oxygenated solvents.
Production:
• isobutanol + ammonia (ammoniation)
Derivatives: butylate

diisobutylene *See:* 2,4,4-trimethylpentene

diisobutyl ketone
2,4-dimethyl-4-heptanone; [108-83-8]

$$(CH_3)_2CHCH_2\overset{O}{\overset{\|}{C}}CH_2CH(CH_3)_2$$

$C_9H_{18}O_1$. M: 142.24. Colourless liquid. BP: 169°C. FP: -46°C. d: 0.81 kg/l (20°C). Insoluble in water. Flash point: 49°C (TCC).

Production:
• phorone (hydrogenation)
Uses: solvent

diisobutyl phthalate
DIBP; [84-69-5]

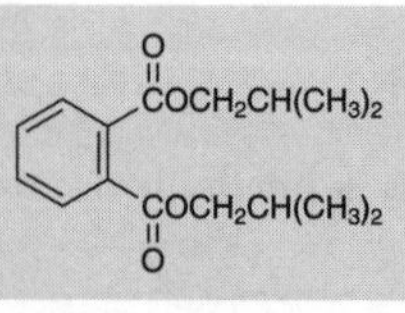

$C_{16}H_{22}O_4$. M: 278.36. Colourless liquid. BP: 165°C (0.67 kPa). Pour point: -37°C. d: 1.04 kg/l (20°C). Insoluble in water.
Production:
• isobutanol + phthalic anhydride (esterification)
Uses:
plasticiser (polyvinyl chloride, polyvinyl acetate)

4,4'-diisocyanatodicyclohexylmethane
dicyclohexylmethane-4,4'-diisocyanate; methylenebis-(4-cyclohexylisocyanate); HMDI; RMDI; Desmodur W (Bayer)

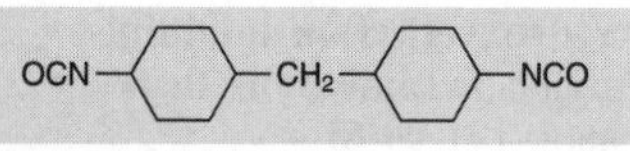

$C_{15}H_{22}N_2O_2$. M: 262.35.
Production:
• bis(*p*-aminocyclohexyl)methane + phosgene (phosgenation)
Derivatives: elastane
Uses: polyurethane elastomer comonomer

4,4'-diisocyanatodiphenylmethane
See: 4,4'-diphenylmethane diisocyanate, pure grade

diisodecyl adipate
DIDA; didecyl adipate; [27178-16-1]

$C_{26}H_{50}O_4$. M: 426.69. Colourless liquid. d: 0.92 kg/l (20°C). Viscosity: 30 mPa.s (20°C). Insoluble in water.
Production:
• isodecanol + adipic acid (esterification)
Uses: polyvinyl chloride plasticiser

diisodecyl 4,5-epoxytetrahydrophthalate
Flexol PEP (Union Carbide)

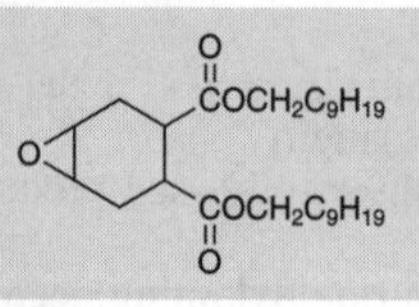

$C_{28}H_{50}O_5$. M: 466.70.

Production:
- tetrahydrophthalic anhydride + isodecanol +
  performic acid/peracetic acid (esterification/
  peroxidation)

Uses: plasticiser

diisodecyl phthalate
DIDP

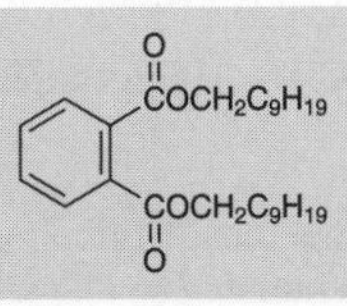

$$\text{COCH}_2\text{C}_9\text{H}_{19}$$

$C_{28}H_{46}O_4$. M: 446.68. Colourless, involatile liquid. d: 0.97 kg/l (20°C). Viscosity: 145 mPa.s (20°C). Insoluble in water.

Production:
- isodecanol + phthalic anhydride (esterification)

Uses:
polyvinyl chloride plasticiser

diisononanoyl peroxide *See:* isononanoyl peroxide

diisononyl adipate
dinonyl adipate; DINA

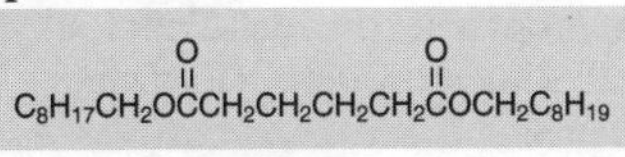

$$C_8H_{17}CH_2OCCH_2CH_2CH_2CH_2COCH_2C_8H_{19}$$

$C_{24}H_{46}O_4$. M: 398.63. Colourless liquid. BP: 250–260°C (1.3 kPa). d: 0.92 kg/l (20°C). Viscosity: 25 mPa.s (20°C). Insoluble in water.

Production:
- isononanol + adipic acid (esterification)

Uses: polyvinyl chloride plasticiser

diisononyl phthalate
DINP; [28553-12-0]

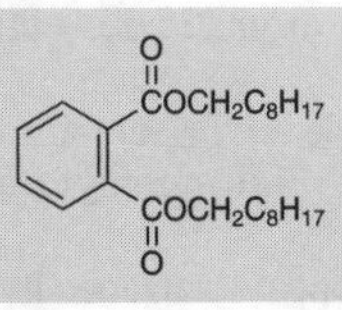

$$\text{COCH}_2\text{C}_8\text{H}_{17}$$
$$\text{COCH}_2\text{C}_8\text{H}_{17}$$

$C_{26}H_{44}O_4$. M: 420.64.

Production:
- isononanol + phthalic anhydride (esterification)

Uses: plasticiser (polyvinyl chloride cable compounds/ plastisols)

diisooctyl adipate
dioctyl adipate; DIOA

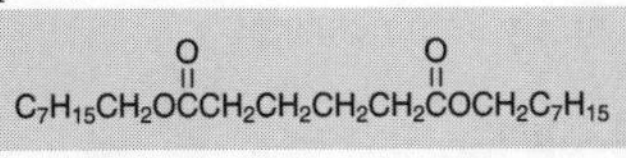

$$C_7H_{15}CH_2OCCH_2CH_2CH_2CH_2COCH_2C_7H_{15}$$

$C_{22}H_{42}O_4$. M: 370.58. Pale yellow liquid. d: 0.92 kg/l (25°C). Insoluble in water.

Production:
- isooctanol + adipic acid (esterification)

Uses:
industrial lubricants; textile spin finishes; plasticiser (polyvinyl chloride, rubber)

diisooctyl azelate
DIOZ

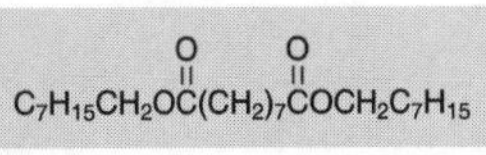

$$C_7H_{15}CH_2OC(CH_2)_7COCH_2C_7H_{15}$$

$C_{25}H_{48}O_4$. M: 412.65. Colourless liquid. MP: -68°C. d: 0.92 kg/l (25°C).

Production:
- isooctanol + azelaic acid (esterification)

Uses:
polyvinyl chloride plasticiser; synthetic lubricant base oils

diisooctyl dibutyltindimaleate
See: dibutyltin bis(isooctylmaleate)

diisooctyl phthalate
DIOP; [27554-26-3]

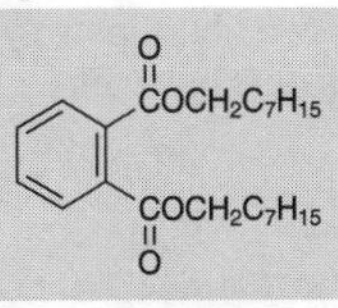

$$\text{COCH}_2\text{C}_7\text{H}_{15}$$
$$\text{COCH}_2\text{C}_7\text{H}_{15}$$

$C_{26}H_{38}O_4$. M: 414.59. Colourless, involatile liquid. d: 0.99 kg/l (20°C). Viscosity: 78 mPa.s (20°C). Insoluble in water.

Production:
- isooctanol + phthalic anhydride (esterification)

Uses:
plasticiser (polyvinyl chloride, rubber, adhesives, sealants, emulsion paints)

diisopropanolamine
DIPA; 1,1'-iminodipropan-2-ol; [110-97-4]

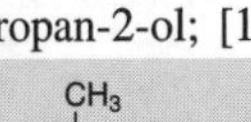

$$\text{CH}_3$$
$$\text{HN(CHCH}_2\text{OH)}_2$$

$C_6H_{15}N_1O_2$. M: 133.20. White solid with a mils ammoniacal odour. MP: 44°C. BP: 249°C. d: 0.99 kg/l (25°C). Soluble in water and alcohol.

Production:
- ammonia + propylene oxide (epoxidation; coproduced with monoisopropanolamine/ triisopropanolamine)

Derivatives:
2,6-dimethylmorpholine

Uses: cosolvent (Sulfinol gas-desulphurisation process); solubiliser/corrosion inhibitor (metalworking fluids); solvent (Shell Adip desulphurisation/Claus offgas treatment processes)

m-diisopropenylbenzene
m-DIPEB; [3748-13-8]

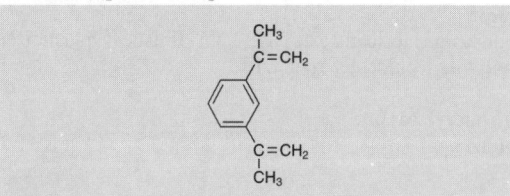

$C_{12}H_{14}$. M: 158.24.
Production:
• *m*-diisopropylbenzene (dehydrogenation)
Derivatives: isopropenyldimethylbenzyl isocyanate; tetramethyl-*m*-xylene diisocyanate

p-diisopropenylbenzene
p-DIPEB; [1605-18-1]

$$CH_2=C-\bigcirc-C=CH_2$$
$$\quad CH_3 \qquad\qquad CH_3$$

$C_{12}H_{14}$. M: 158.24.
Production:
• *p*-diisopropylbenzene (dehydrogenation)
Derivatives: 1,4-bis(*t*-butylperoxyisopropyl)benzene; tetramethyl-*p*-xylene diisocyanate

diisopropyl adipate
[6938-94-9]

$$(CH_3)_2CHO\overset{O}{\overset{\|}{C}}(CH_2)_4\overset{O}{\overset{\|}{C}}OCH(CH_3)_2$$

$C_{12}H_{22}O_4$. M: 230.31. Colourless to pale yellow liquid.
Production:
• adipic acid + isopropanol (esterification)
Uses: emollient/cosolvent (cosmetics)

diisopropylamine
[108-18-9]

$$\left[(CH_3)_2CH\right]_2NH$$

$C_6H_{15}N_1$. M: 101.20. Colourless liquid with an ammoniacal odour. BP: 83–84°C. MP: -96°C. d: 0.72 kg/l (4°C). Slightly soluble in water. Soluble in oxygenated solvents.
Production:
• isopropanol + ammonia (amine formation; coproduced with isopropylamine)
Derivatives: 2-diisopropylaminoethanol; tri-allate

2-diisopropylaminoethanol
diisopropylethanolamine; *N,N*-diisopropylethanolamine; [96-80-0]

$$\left[(CH_3)_2CH\right]_2NCH_2CH_2OH$$

$C_8H_{19}N_1O_1$. M: 145.25. Colourless liquid. BP: 191°C. FP: -39°C. Slightly soluble in water.

Production:
• diisopropylamine + ethylene oxide (epoxidation)
Derivatives: 2-diisopropylaminoethyl chloride hydrochloride; propantheline bromide

2-diisopropylaminoethyl chloride hydrochloride
[4261-68-1]

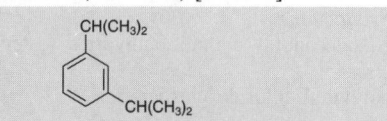

$C_8H_{19}Cl_2N_1$. M: 200.16. Hygroscopic solid. MP: 133–134°C.
Production:
• 2-diisopropylaminoethanol (alcohol chlorination)
Derivatives: disopyramide

m-diisopropylbenzene
1,3-diisopropylbenzene; *m*-DIPB; [99-62-7]

$$\bigcirc\overset{CH(CH_3)_2}{\underset{CH(CH_3)_2}{}}$$

$C_{12}H_{18}$. M: 162.27. Colourless liquid. BP: 203°C. MP: -63°C. d: 0.86 kg/l (20°C). Insoluble in water. Miscible with most organic solvents.
Production:
• benzene + propylene (Friedel-Crafts alkylation; coproduced with *p*-diisopropylbenzene)
Derivatives:
acetone; *m*-diisopropenylbenzene; resorcinol

p-diisopropylbenzene
1,4-diisopropylbenzene; *p*-DIPB

$$(CH_3)_2CH-\bigcirc-CH(CH_3)_2$$

$C_{12}H_{18}$. M: 162.27. Colourless liquid. BP: 210°C. MP: -17°C. d: 0.86 kg/l (20°C). Insoluble in water. Soluble in oxygenated and aromatic solvents.
Production:
• benzene + propylene (Friedel-Crafts alkylation; coproduced with *m*-diisopropylbenzene)
Derivatives:
acetone; *p*-diisopropenylbenzene; hydroquinone

diisopropyl bis(triethanolaminotitanate)
See: triethanolamine titanate

O,O-diisopropyl dithiophosphoric acid
See: *O,O*-diisopropyl phosphorodithioic acid

diisopropylethanolamine
See: 2-diisopropylaminoethanol

diisopropyl ether
isopropyl ether; [108-20-3]
$C_6H_{14}O_1$. M: 102.18. Colourless liquid with ether-like

odour. MP: -86°C. BP: 69°C. d: 0.72 kg/l (20°C). Slightly soluble in water. Soluble in oxygenated solvents.

$$(CH_3)_2CHOCH(CH_3)_2$$

Production:
• propylene (hydration; byproduct of isopropanol production)
Uses:
extraction agent (phosphoric acid, phenol purification); solvent (paints, stain removers)

diisopropylidene acetone *See:* phorone

diisopropyl ketone
2,4-dimethylpentan-3-one; [565-80-0]

$$(CH_3)_2CHCCH(CH_3)_2 \quad (O)$$

$C_7H_{14}O_1$. M: 114.19. Colourless liquid. BP: 122–126°C. d: 0.81 kg/l (20°C). Insoluble in water. Miscible with oxygenated solvents.
Production:
• isobutyric acid (decarboxylative coupling)
Uses: solvent

diisopropyl malonate
[13195-64-7]

$$CH_2\left[COOCH(CH_3)_2\right]_2$$

$C_9H_{16}O_4$. M: 188.23.
Production:
• chloroacetic acid + carbon monoxide + isopropanol (carbonylation/esterification)
Derivatives: isoprothiolane

diisopropylnaphthalene
KMC

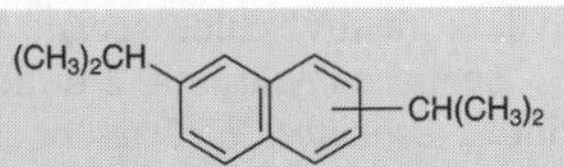

$$(CH_3)_2CH \cdots CH(CH_3)_2$$

$C_{16}H_{20}$. M: 212.34. Mixed isomer product.
Production:
• naphthalene + propylene (Friedel-Crafts alkylation)
Derivatives:
sodium diisopropylnaphthalene sulphonate
Uses: solvent (carbonless copying paper)

diisopropyl 5-nitroisophthalate *See:* nitrothal-isopropyl

diisopropyl peroxydicarbonate
diisopropyl percarbonate; IPP; [105-64-6]

$$(CH_3)_2CHOCO-OCOCH(CH_3)_2 \quad (O \quad O)$$

$C_8H_{14}O_6$. M: 206.19. Solid or liquid. MP: 8–10°C. d: 1.08 kg/l (15°C). Available commercially as 100%

paste or as a 50% solution in toluene. The product has a 10-hour half-life at 45°C.
Production:
• hydrogen peroxide + isopropyl chloroformate (dehydrochlorination)
Uses: polymerisation initiator

N,N′-diisopropyl-p-phenylenediamine

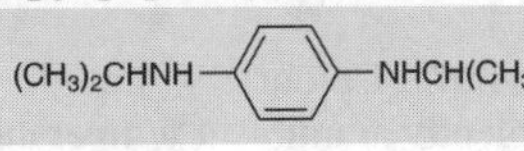

$$(CH_3)_2CHNH \cdots NHCH(CH_3)_2$$

$C_{12}H_{20}N_2$. M: 192.30.
Production:
• hydroquinone + isopropylamine (reductive amination)
Uses: antioxidant (motor fuels)

O,O-diisopropyl phosphorodithioic acid
O,O-diisopropyl dithiophosphoric acid; [107-56-2]

$$\left[(CH_3)_2CHO\right]_2PSH \quad (S)$$

$C_6H_{15}O_2P_1S_2$. M: 214.29.
Production:
• isopropanol + phosphorus pentasulphide (addition)
Derivatives: bensulide; iprobenfos

diisotridecyl adipate

$$C_{12}H_{25}CH_2OC(CH_2)_4COCH_2C_{12}H_{25} \quad (O \quad O)$$

$C_{32}H_{62}O_4$. M: 510.85. Liquid. Pour point: -52°C.
Production:
• tridecanol + adipic acid (esterification)
Uses: textile spin finishes/rolling oils

diisotridecyl phthalate
ditridecyl phthalate; DITP; DTDP; [119-06-2]

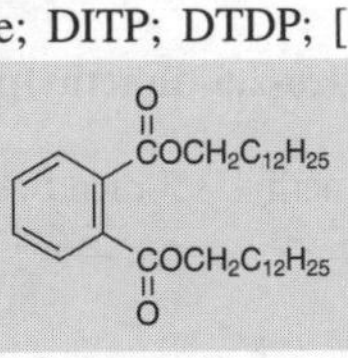

$$COCH_2C_{12}H_{25} \quad (O) \quad COCH_2C_{12}H_{25} \quad (O)$$

$C_{34}H_{58}O_4$. M: 530.83. Colourless, involatile liquid. d: 0.95 kg/l (20°C). Viscosity: 310 mPa.s (20°C). Insoluble in water.
Production:
• tridecanol + phthalic anhydride (esterification)
Uses: polyvinyl chloride plasticiser

dikegulac-sodium
[52508-35-7]

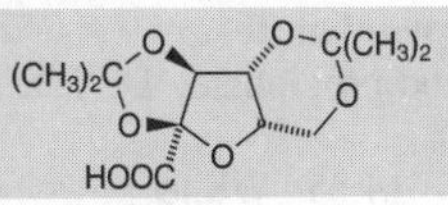

$$(CH_3)_2C \cdots C(CH_3)_2 \quad HOOC$$

$C_{12}H_{17}Na_1O_7$. M: 296.25.

Production:
• L-sorbose + acetone (acetal formation/oxidation)
Uses: plant growth regulator

diketene
[674-82-8]

$$CH_2=C-O$$
$$H_2C-C=O$$

$C_4H_4O_2$. M: 84.07. Colourless liquid. BP: 127°C. Polymerises violently at ambient temperatures. Handled under refrigeration. Not a commercially traded product.
Production:
• ketene (dimerisation)
Derivatives: 5-acetoacetamidobenzimidazolone; acetoacetanilide; acetoacet-*o*-anisidide; acetoacet-*o*-chloroanilide; acetoacet-4-chloro-2,5-dimethoxyanilide; acetoacet-4-chloro-2-methylanilide; acetoacet-*p*-phenetidide; acetoacet-*o*-toluidide; acetoacet-*p*-toluidide; acetoacet-2,4-xylidide; *t*-butyl acetoacetate; 1-(6'-chloro-2'-methylphenyl)-3-methylpyrazolone; 1-(6'-chloro-2'-methyl-4'-sulphophenyl)-4-methylpyrazolone; 1-(2'-chloro-5'-sulphophenyl)-3-methylpyrazolone; 1-(4'-chloro-2'-sulphophenyl)-3-methylpyrazolone; dehydroacetic acid; 1-(2',5'-dichloro-4'-sulphophenyl)-3-methylpyrazolone; *N,N*-diethylacetoacetamide; *N,N*-dimethylacetoacetamide; ethyl acetoacetate; ethyl γ-chloroacetoacetate; isopropyl acetoacetate; *N*-methylacetoacetamide; methyl acetoacetate; methyl γ-chloroacetoacetate; 1-(4'-methylphenyl)-3-methylpyrazolone; 3-methyl-1-phenyl-5-pyrazolone; Pigment Yellow 124; Pigment Yellow 152; Pigment Yellow 170; 1-(4'-sulpho-2'-methylphenyl)-3-methylpyrazolone; 1-(3'-sulphophenyl)-3-methylpyrazolone; 1-(4'-sulphophenyl)-3-methylpyrazolone

dilaurylamine *See:* dicocoamine

dilauryl 1,4-dihydro-2,6-dimethylpyridine-3,5-dicarboxylate
1,4-dihydro-2,6-dimethyl-3,5-dicarbododecyloxypyridine

$CH_3(CH_2)_{11}OOC$, $COO(CH_2)_{11}CH_3$
CH_3 N CH_3
H

$C_{33}H_{59}N_1O_4$. M: 533.84.
Production:
• methyl acetoacetate + *n*-alkanol(C_{12}-C_{13})/ *n*-alkanol(C_{12}-C_{14}) + formaldehyde + ammonia (transesterification/Hantzsch synthesis)
Uses:
polyvinyl chloride heat stabiliser

dilauryl thiodipropionate
dilauryl 3,3'-thiodipropionate; DLTDP; DLTP; LTDP; [123-28-4]
$C_{30}H_{58}O_4S_1$. M: 514.85. White powder. MP: 38°C. d: 0.90 kg/l.

$$S[CH_2CH_2CO(CH_2)_{11}CH_3]_2$$

Production:
• thiodipropionic acid + *n*-alkanol(C_{12}-C_{13})/ *n*-alkanol(C_{12}-C_{14}) (esterification)
Uses:
antioxidant (plastics, rubber, oils, grease)

dilazep
[35898-87-4]

$C_{31}H_{44}N_2O_{10}$. M: 604.69. Available commercially as the dihydrochloride salt.
Production:
• ethylenediamine + acrylonitrile + 3,4,5-trimethoxybenzoic acid (cyanoethylation/reductive amination/ cyanoethylation/nitrile hydrolysis/esterification)
Uses: vasodilator drug

diltiazem
[42399-41-7]

$C_{22}H_{26}N_2O_4S_1$. M: 414.52. Available commercially as the (+)-*cis*-isomer hydrochloride salt.
Production:
• *p*-anisaldehyde + methyl chloroacetate + 2-aminothiophenol + acetic anhydride + 2-dimethylaminoethyl chloride hydrochloride (Darzens reaction/ epoxidation/saponification/racemate separation/ condensation/amine formation)
Uses: antianginal drug

DIMDAC *See:* diallyldimethylammonium chloride

dimefuron
[34205-21-5]

$C_{15}H_{19}Cl_1N_4O_3$. M: 338.79.
Production:
• 2-chloro-4-nitroaniline + sodium nitrite + dimethylcarbamoyl chloride + pivalic acid + phosgene

(diazotisation/nitro reduction/dehydrochlorination/ reduction/amide formation/phosgenation)
Uses: herbicide

dimelamine phosphate

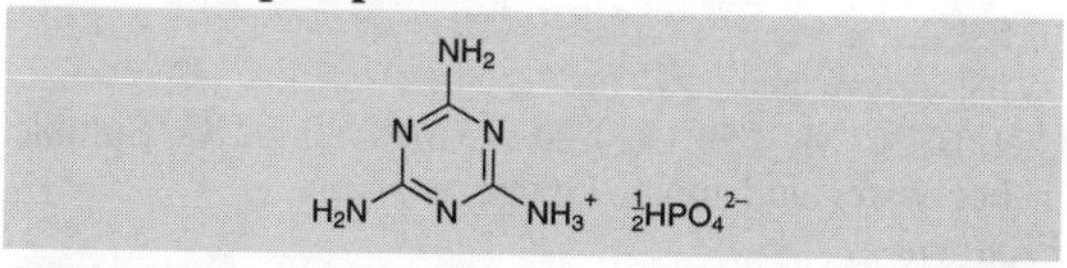

$C_6H_{15}N_{12}O_4P_1$. M: 350.24. White powder. d: 1.66 kg/l. Solubility in water: 2 g/l water. Starts to decompose at 300°C.
Production:
• melamine + phosphoric acid, pure (salt formation)
Uses: fire-retardant (paper, plastics); intumescent paint/ mastic ingredient

dimepranol
See: dimethylisopropanolamine

dimer acid
[61788-89-4]; [6144-28-1]
Viscous liquid. d: 0.98 kg/l (25°C). Acid value: 192–198 mg KOH/g. Saponification value: 195–200 mg KOH/g. Mixed product produced by cycloaddition of unsaturated fatty acids. Different grades are available with dimer contents varying from 75% to 98%.
Production:
• tall oil fatty acid/castor oil, dehydrated (dimerisation/hydrogenation; coproduced with trimer acid/isostearic acid)
Derivatives: polyamide resins, non-reactive; polyamide resins, reactive
Uses: alkyd/epoxy ester/polyurethane resin comonomer; corrosion inhibitor

1,2-dimercaptoethane *See:* 1,2-ethanedithiol

1,3-dimercaptoisopropyldimethylamine
2-(dimethylamino)propane-1,3-dithiol

$$(CH_3)_2NCH(CH_2SH)_2$$

$C_5H_{13}N_1S_2$. M: 151.29.
Production:
• 2-aminopropane-1,3-diol + dimethyl sulphate + sodium hydrosulphide (amine methylation/alcohol chlorination/thiolation)
Derivatives:
bensultap; cartap; thiocyclam hydrogen oxalate

2,5-dimercapto-1,3,4-thiadiazole
DMTD; [1072-71-5]

$C_2H_2N_2S_3$. M: 150.24.

Production:
• hydrazine + carbon disulphide (condensation)
Uses:
corrosion inhibitor

dimethachlor
2-chloro-*N*-(2,6-dimethylphenyl)-*N*-(2-methoxyethyl)-acetamide; [50563-36-5]

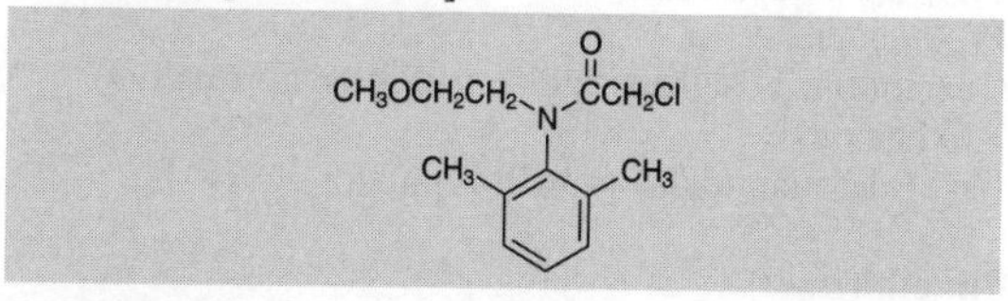

$C_{13}H_{18}Cl_1N_1O_2$. M: 255.74.
Production:
• ethylene glycol monomethyl ether + 2,6-xylidine + chloroacetyl chloride (amine formation/dehydro-chlorination)
Uses:
herbicide

dimethametryn
2-(1,2-dimethylpropylamino)-4-ethylamino-6-methyl-thio-1,3,5-triazine; [22936-75-0]

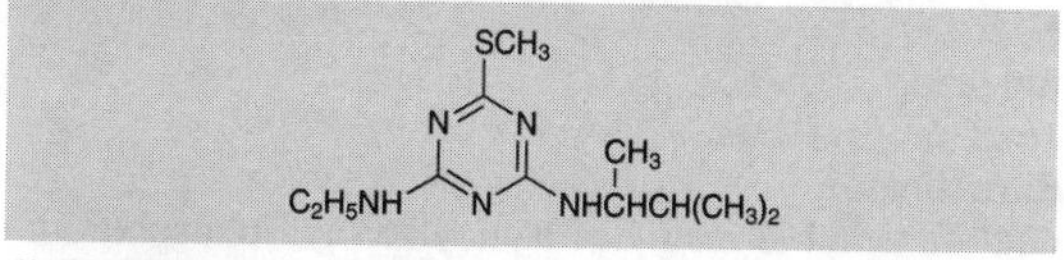

$C_{11}H_{21}N_5S_1$. M: 255.38.
Production:
• 2-methylmercapto-4,6-dichlorotriazine + ethylamine + 3-methyl-2-butylamine (amine formation/amine formation)
Uses: herbicide

dimethazone *See:* clomazone

dimethindene
[5636-83-9]; [3614-69-5] (hydrogen maleate)

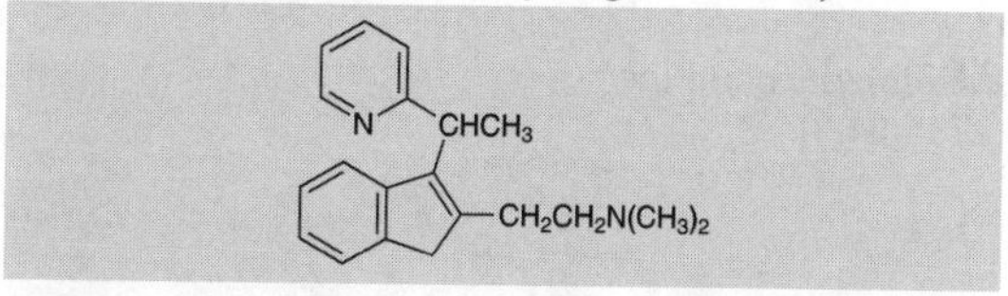

$C_{20}H_{24}N_2$. M: 292.42. Available commercially as the hydrogen maleate.
Production:
• benzyl chloride + diethyl malonate + 2-dimethyl-aminoethyl chloride hydrochloride + 2-ethylpyridine (dehydrochlorination/dehydrochlorination/ cyclisation/Grignard reagent formation/Grignard reaction/dehydration)
Uses:
antihistamine drug

dimethipin
2,3-dihydro-5,6-dimethyl-1,4-dithiine 1,1,4,4-tetroxide;
Harvade (Uniroyal Chemical); [55290-64-7]

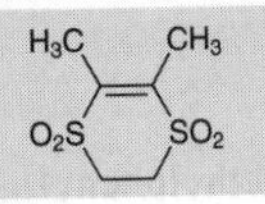

$C_6H_{10}O_4S_2$. M: 210.28.
Production:
• acetoin + 1,2-ethanedithiol (sulphide formation/
  oxidation)
Uses: defoliant/plant growth regulator

dimethirimol
5-butyl-2-dimethylamino-6-methylpyrimidin-4-ol;
[5221-53-4]

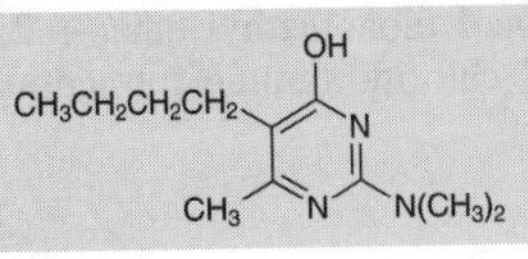

$C_{11}H_{19}N_3O_1$. M: 209.29.
Production:
• ethyl acetoacetate + *n*-butyl chloride + *N,N*-di-
  methylguanidine (dehydrochlorination/condensation)
Uses:
fungicide

dimethoate
O,O-dimethyl *S*-methylcarbamoylmethyl phosphorodithioate; [60-51-5]

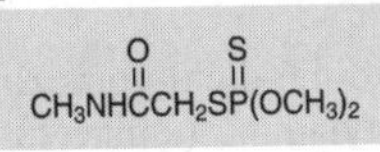

$C_5H_{12}N_1O_3P_1S_2$. M: 229.26.
Production:
• methyl chloroacetate + *O,O*-dimethyl
  dithiophosphoric acid + methylamine
  (dehydrochlorination/amide formation)
Uses:
acaricide/insecticide

2,4-dimethoxyaniline
[2735-04-8]

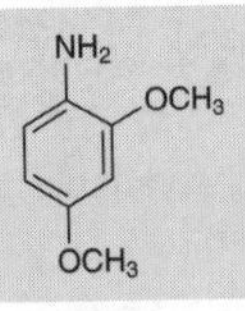

$C_8H_{11}N_1O_2$. M: 153.19. White, crystalline solid. MP:
80–82°C. Soluble in hot water and oxygenated solvents.
Production:
• resorcinol dimethyl ether (nitration/nitro reduction)
Derivatives:
Basic Yellow 11; Pigment Yellow 124

2,5-dimethoxyaniline
[102-56-7]

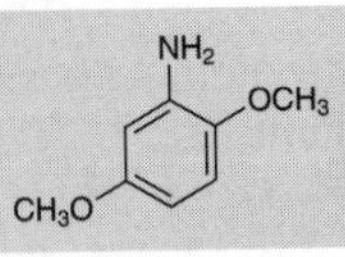

$C_8H_{11}N_1O_2$. M: 153.19. Flakes. MP: 80–82°C. Soluble
in hot water and most organic solvents.
Production:
• 2,5-dichloronitrobenzene + methanol (ether formation)
Derivatives:
4-amino-2,5-dimethoxybenzenesulphonic acid; 4-chloro-
2,5-dimethoxyaniline; 4-(*p*-nitrophenyl)azo-2,5-dimeth-
oxyaniline; Pigment Red 184; Solvent Red 80

2,5-dimethoxyaniline-4-(β-hydroxyethyl)sulphone
See: 2,5-dimethoxy-5-(β-hydroxyethylsulphonyl)aniline

3,4-dimethoxybenzaldehyde *See:* veratraldehyde

1,3-dimethoxybenzene *See:* resorcinol dimethyl ether

1,4-dimethoxybenzene
See: hydroquinone dimethyl ether

3,4-dimethoxybenzeneacetonitrile
See: veratryl cyanide

3,3′-dimethoxybenzidine *See:* *o*-dianisidine

2,6-dimethoxybenzoic acid
[1466-76-8]

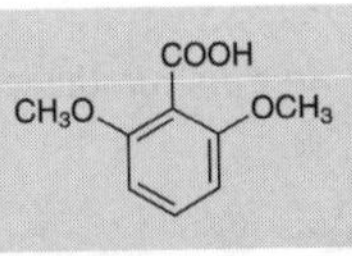

$C_9H_{10}O_4$. M: 182.18. Solid. MP: 188–189°C. Insoluble
in water. Soluble in oxygenated solvents.
Production:
• 2,6-dihydroxybenzoic acid + dimethyl sulphate
  (methylation)
Derivatives: benzoximate; isoxaben; meticillin

3,4-dimethoxybenzoic acid *See:* veratric acid

4,4′-dimethoxybenzoin *See:* anisoin

3,4-dimethoxybenzyl cyanide
See: veratryl cyanide

2,4-dimethoxy-5-chloroaniline
See: 5-chloro-2,4-dimethoxyaniline

1,2-dimethoxyethane
See: ethylene glycol dimethyl ether

2,2-dimethoxyethylethylamine
See: N-methylaminoacetaldehyde dimethyl acetal

di-(2-methoxyethyl) phthalate
dimethyl glycol phthalate; DMEP; DMGP; [117-82-8]

$C_{14}H_{18}O_6$. M: 282.28. Colourless liquid. BP: 190–210°C (45 kPa). d: 1.17 kg/l (20°C). Insoluble in water.
Production:
• ethylene glycol monomethyl ether + phthalic anhydride (esterification)
Uses:
plasticiser (cellulose acetate)

2,5-dimethoxy-5-(β-hydroxyethylsulphonyl)aniline
2-(4-amino-2,5-dimethoxyphenylsulphonyl)ethanol;
2,5-dimethoxyaniline-4-(β-hydroxyethyl)sulphone

$C_{10}H_{15}N_1O_5S_1$. M: 261.29.
Production:
• 4-amino-2,5-dimethoxybenzenesulphonic acid + ethylene oxide (sulphonyl reduction/epoxidation)
Derivatives: Reactive Yellow 17

3,4-dimethoxyphenylacetic acid
See: homoveratric acid

2,2-dimethoxy-2-phenylacetophenone
See: benzil dimethyl acetal

3,4-dimethoxyphenylethylamine
See: homoveratrylamine

3-(3,4-dimethoxyphenyl)propene
See: methyl eugenol

1,1-dimethoxypropan-2-one
See: methylglyoxal dimethyl acetal

dimethoxystrychine *See:* brucine

4,4′-dimethoxytriphenylmethyl chloride
4,4′-dimethoxytrityl chloride
$C_{21}H_{19}Cl_1O_2$. M: 338.83. Solid. MP: 119–123°C.
Production:
• 4,4′-dihydroxybenzophenone + phenylmagnesium bromide (methylation/Grignard reaction/chlorination)

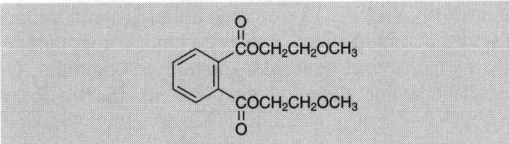

Uses: amino group protection reagent

16,17-dimethoxyviolanthrone *See:* Vat Green 1

dimethylacetamide
N,N-dimethylacetamide; DMA; DMAC; [127-19-5]

$C_4H_9N_1O_1$. M: 87.12. Colourless liquid. MP: -20°C. BP: 160°C. d: 0.95 kg/l (15°C). Miscible with water, oxygenated solvents and aromatics.
Production:
• acetic acid + dimethylamine (amide formation)
Uses: selective solvent (butadiene extraction); solvent (vinyl, acrylic, cellulose, polyimide processing)

N,N-dimethylacetoacetamide
acetoacet-N,N-dimethylamide; [2044-64-6]

$C_6H_{11}N_1O_2$. M: 129.17.
Production:
• diketene + dimethylamine (condensation)
Derivatives: dicrotophos

dimethyl acetonedicarboxylate
dimethyl 3-oxoglutarate; [1830-54-2]

$C_7H_{10}O_5$. M: 174.16. Liquid. BP: 128–130°C (1.2 kPa).
Production:
• methyl γ-chloroacetoacetate + sodium cyanide + methanol (cyanidation/alcoholysis)
Derivatives: zomepirac

dimethyl adipate
[627-93-0]

$C_8H_{14}O_4$. M: 174.20. Liquid. MP: 10°C. d: 1.06 kg/l (20°C). Insoluble in water. Soluble in oxygenated solvents.
Production:
• methanol + adipic acid (esterification)
• dimethyl alkylene(C_4-C_6)dicarboxylates (fractionation; coproduced with dimethyl succinate/ dimethyl glutarate)

Derivatives: complex ester oils; dibutoxyethyl adipate; diester oils; 1,6-hexanediol; lenacil; polyester polyols, slightly-branched; polyester resins, carboxylated; polyester resins, hydroxylated; polyester resins, linear, medium molecular weight

dimethyl alkylene(C_4-C_6)dicarboxylates

DBE solvent (Du Pont); RPDE solvent (Rhône-Poulenc)

$$CH_3OC(CH_2)_nCOCH_3$$

n = 2–4. Colourless liquid. BP: 299–230°C. d: 1.09 kg/l (20°C). Solubility in water: 5.6 g/l solution (20°C). Flash point: 108°C (TOC). A typical composition is: 65% dimethyl glutarate, 25% dimethyl succinate and 10% dimethyl adipate.

Production:
- methanol + alkylene(C_4-C_6)dicarboxylic acids (esterification)

Derivatives: dimethyl adipate; dimethyl glutarate; dimethyl succinate; dinonyl alkylene(C_4-C_6)dicarboxylate

Uses:
solvent (coil, can, automotive resin coatings)

dimethylalkyl(C_{13}-C_{15})amine

Synprolam 35DM (ICI)

$$C_nH_{2n+1}CH_2N(CH_3)_2$$

n = 12–14. $C_{16}H_{35}N_1$. M: 241.47. Liquid.

Production:
- n-alkanol(C_{13}-C_{15}) + dimethylamine (reductive amination)

Derivatives: alkyl(C_{13}-C_{15})dimethylamine oxide; alkyl-(C_{13}-C_{15})dimethylbenzylammonium chloride; alkyl(C_{13}-C_{15})trimethylammonium chloride

Uses:
mineral flotation agent

3,3-dimethylallyl alcohol *See:* 3-methyl-2-buten-1-ol

dimethylamine

DMA; [124-40-3]

$$(CH_3)_2NH$$

$C_2H_7N_1$. M: 45.09. Colourless liquified gas with an ammoniacal odour. BP: 7°C. MP: -92°C. d: 0.66 kg/l (4°C). Soluble in water forming alkaline solutions. Soluble in oxygenated solvents. Also available as 40% or 60% aqueous solutions.

Production:
- methanol + ammonia (amine formation; coproduced with methylamine/trimethylamine)

Derivatives:
adipic acid-dimethylaminohydroxypropyldiethylenetriamine copolymers; benzyldimethylamine; 2,2-bis(β-dimethylaminoethyl) ether; dextropropoxyphene; diallyl-

dimethylammonium chloride; 2,6-di-*t*-butyldimethylamino-*p*-cresol; didecyldimethylammonium chloride; dimethylacetamide; *N,N*-dimethylacetoacetamide; dimethylalkyl(C_{13}-C_{15})amine; dimethylamine borane; 6-dimethylamino-1,2-dimethylquinolinium iodide; dimethylaminomethylphenol; 3-dimethylamino-2-methylpropyl chloride hydrochloride; 3-dimethylaminopropylamine; dimethylcarbamoyl chloride; dimethylcetylamine; dimethylcocoamine; dimethylethanolamine; dimethylformamide; *N,N*-dimethylguanidine; 1,1-dimethylhydrazine; dimethylisopropanolamine; dimethyllaurylamine; dimethylmyristylamine; dimethyloctylamine; dimethylstearylamine; dimethylsulphamyl chloride; diphenamid; diuron; famphur; fenothiocarb; fenuron; hexamethylphosphoramide; hexazinone; metformin; oxamyl; phenolic resins, amino-substituted; polyacrylamide, aminomethylated; poly(2-hydroxypropyl dimethylammonium chloride); polystyrene, crosslinked, aminated; ranitidine; sodium dimethyldithiocarbamate; tetramethylguanidine; tetramethylurea; tilidine; tiotixene; 2,4,6-tris(dimethylaminomethyl)phenol

Uses:
unsaturated polyester resin catalyst accelerator

dimethylamine borane

$$(CH_3)_2NH.BH_3$$

$C_2H_{10}B_1N_1$. M: 58.92.

Production:
- dimethylamine + sodium borohydride + boron trifluoride (complex formation)

Uses:
reducing agent (electrodeless coatings)

4-(dimethylamino)aniline

See: *N,N*-dimethyl-*p*-phenylenediamine

1,4-di-(methylamino)anthraquinone

See: Disperse Blue 14

p-dimethylaminobenzaldehyde

N,N-dimethyl-4-aminobenzaldehyde; Ehrlich's reagent; [100-10-7]

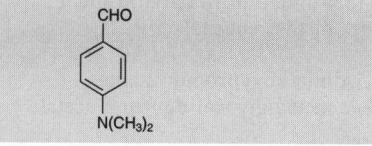

$C_9H_{11}N_1O_1$. M: 149.20. Yellow, crystalline solid. MP: 68–69°C. BP: 166°C (20 kPa). Soluble in oxygenated solvents.

Production:
- *N,N*-dimethylaniline + dimethylformamide (Vilsmeier reaction)

Derivatives: Acid Violet 49; *p*-dimethylaminobenzoic acid; Mordant Violet 15

p-dimethylaminobenzoic acid
4-dimethylaminobenzoic acid; [619-84-1]

$(CH_3)_2N$—⬡—COOH

$C_9H_{11}N_1O_2$. M: 165.20. Solid. MP: 235–239°C. Soluble in alcohol.
Production:
• p-dimethylaminobenzaldehyde (carbonyl oxidation)
Derivatives:
butoxyethyl p-dimethylaminobenzoate; ethyl p-dimethylaminobenzoate; 2-ethylhexyl p-dimethylaminobenzoate

6-dimethylamino-1,2-dimethylquinolinium iodide

$(CH_3)_2N$—⬡⬡—CH₃ I⁻
N⁺
CH₃

$C_{13}H_{17}I_1N_2$. M: 328.19.
Production:
• p-chloroaniline + methyl vinyl ketone + dimethylamine + methyl iodide (Skraup synthesis/amine formation/quaternisation)
Derivatives:
pyrvinium pamoate

2-dimethylaminoethanol *See:* dimethylethanolamine

2-(2-dimethylaminoethoxy)ethanol
ZR-70 (Texaco Chemical); [1704-62-7]

$(CH_3)_2NCH_2CH_2OCH_2CH_2OH$

$C_6H_{15}N_1O_2$. M: 133.20. Liquid. BP: 204°C. FP: <-70°C. d: 0.95 kg/l (20°C). Soluble in water.
Production:
• 2-(2-aminoethoxy)ethanol (methylation)
Uses:
polyurethane foam catalyst

2-dimethylaminoethyl acrylate

O
‖
$CH_2=CHCOCH_2CH_2N(CH_3)_2$

$C_7H_{13}N_1O_2$. M: 143.19.
Production:
• dimethylethanolamine + acrylic acid (esterification)
Derivatives:
acrylamide copolymers, cationic; polyacrylate resins, aminated

2-dimethylaminoethyl 4-n-butylaminobenzoate
See: tetracaine

2-dimethylaminoethyl chloride hydrochloride
2-chloroethyldimethylammonium chloride; DMC; [4584-46-7]

$(CH_3)_2^+NHCH_2CH_2Cl$ Cl⁻

$C_4H_{11}Cl_2N_1$. M: 144.05. Solid. MP: 205–208°C. Soluble in water and alcohol.
Production:
• dimethylethanolamine + hydrochloric acid (alcohol chlorination/salt formation)
Derivatives:
bephenium hydroxynaphthoate; brompheniramine; carbinoxamine; chloropyramine; chlorphenamine; chlorphenoxamine; dibenzepin; diltiazem; dimethindene; diphenhydramine; doxylamine; meclofenoxate; mepyramine; noxiptiline hydrochloride; pheniramine; phenyltoloxamine; starch, cationic; tamoxifen; 5-thio-1-(β-dimethylaminoethyl)tetrazole; tripelennamine

2-dimethylaminoethyl methacrylate
DMAEMA; [2867-47-2]

O
‖
$CH_2=CCOCH_2CH_2N(CH_3)_2$
|
CH₃

$C_8H_{16}N_1O_2$. M: 158.23. Clear liquid. BP: 182–190°C. d: 0.93 kg/l (25°C). Soluble in water. Flash point: 74°C (TOC). Commercial products contain hydroquinone methyl ether or similar polymerisation inhibitors.
Production:
• dimethylethanolamine + methyl methacrylate (transesterification)
Derivatives: acrylamide copolymers, cationic; dimethylaminoethyl methacrylate-acrylamide copolymers; polymethacrylates, oil-soluble dispersants; trimethylammoniumethyl methacrylate chloride
Uses: cationic comonomer (polyacrylamide; thermosetting acrylic resins)

dimethylaminoethyl methacrylate-acrylamide copolymers

COOCH₂CH₂N(CH₃)₂
|
+[CH₂–C]ₓ+[CH₂–CH]ᵧ+
| |
CH₃   CONH₂

Production:
• acrylamide + 2-dimethylaminoethyl methacrylate (aqueous polymerisation)
Uses: cationic flocculants (water treatment)

dimethylaminomethylphenol
DMAMP; [120-65-0]

OH
|
⬡—CH₂N(CH₃)₂

$C_9H_{13}N_1O_1$. M: 151.21. Mixed product containing the o- and p-isomers. Dark-red liquid. Soluble in hot water and oxygenated solvents.

Production:
- dimethylamine + formaldehyde + phenol (Mannich reaction)

Uses: epoxy resin curing agent

2-dimethylamino-2-methyl-1-propanol
DMAMP; [7005-47-2]

$$(CH_3)_2NCCH_2OH \quad \text{with } CH_3 \text{ above and } CH_3 \text{ below}$$

$C_6H_{15}N_1O_1$. M: 117.20. Liquid/solid. MP: 19°C. BP: 160°C. d: 0.90 kg/l (25°C). Miscible with water forming alkaline solutions.

Production:
- 2-amino-2-methyl-1-propanol + formaldehyde (methylation)

Uses: polyurethane foam catalyst; corrosion inhibitor (steam distribution systems); emulsifier (creams, lotions, oils, waxes)

3-dimethylamino-2-methylpropyl chloride hydrochloride
3-chloro-2-methylpropyldimethylamine

$$(CH_3)_2^+NHCH_2CHCH_2Cl \quad Cl^- \quad \text{with } CH_3 \text{ above}$$

$C_6H_{14}Cl_1N_1$. M: 135.64. Hygroscopic solid. MP: 167–170°C.

Production:
- methallyl chloride + dimethylamine + hydrogen chloride, anhydrous (amine formation/anti-Markownikoff addition)

Derivatives:
levomepromazine; trimipramine

2-(dimethylamino)propane-1,3-dithiol
See: 1,3-dimercaptoisopropyldimethylamine

1-dimethylamino-2-propanol
See: dimethylisopropanolamine

3-dimethylaminopropanol
[3179-63-3]

$$(CH_3)_2NCH_2CH_2CH_2OH$$

$C_5H_{13}N_1O_1$. M: 103.16. Liquid. BP: 162–163°C. MP: -35°C. Soluble in water.

Production:
- 3-aminopropanol (methylation)

Derivatives:
3-dimethylaminopropyl chloride hydrochloride

3-dimethylaminopropylamine
3-aminopropyldimethylamine; *N,N*-dimethylaminopropylamine; *N,N*-dimethyl-1,3-propanediamine; DMAP; DMAPA; [109-55-7]

$$(CH_3)_2NCH_2CH_2CH_2NH_2$$

$C_5H_{14}N_2$. M: 102.17. Colourless liquid with an ammoniacal odour. BP: 132–140°C. MP: <-50°C. Soluble in water and oxygenated solvents.

Production:
- dimethylamine + acrylonitrile (cyanoethylation/ nitrile reduction)

Derivatives:
Basic Blue 22; behenamidopropyldimethylamine; cocoamidopropyldimethylamine; dimethylaminopropyl methacrylamide; isostearamidopropyldimethylamine; lauramidopropyldimethylamine; myristylamidopropyldimethylamine; oleamidopropyldimethylamine; propamocarb; stearamidopropyldimethylamine; tallowamidopropyldimethylammonium-3-sulphopropyl betaine; *N,N',N'''*-tris-(dimethylaminopropyl)hexahydro-1,3,5-triazine

Uses: corrosion inhibitor (aviation gasoline); cold-cured epoxy resin curing agent

3-dimethylaminopropyl chloride hydrochloride
3-chloropropyldimethylammonium chloride; γ-dimethylaminopropyl chloride hydrochloride; 1-dimethylamino-3-propyl chloride hydrochloride; DMPC; [5407-04-5]

$$(CH_3)_2^+NCH_2CH_2CH_2Cl \quad Cl^-$$

$C_5H_{13}Cl_2N_1$. M: 158.07.

Production:
- 3-dimethylaminopropanol (acid chloride formation)

Derivatives: amitriptyline; chlorpromazine; chlorprothixene; cyclobenzaprine; doxepin; imipramine; maprotiline; melitracen; *N,N,N',N'',N''*-pentamethyldipropylenetriamine; promazine; prothipendyl; protriptyline; starch, cationic; triflupromazine

dimethylaminopropyl methacrylamide
N-(3-dimethylaminopropyl) methacrylamide; DMAPMA

$$CH_2=CCNHCH_2CH_2CH_2N(CH_3)_2 \quad \text{with } O \text{ (double bond) above C and } CH_3 \text{ below}$$

$C_9H_{18}N_2O_1$. M: 170.25. Pale yellow liquid. d: 0.94 kg/l.

Production:
- methacrylyl chloride + 3-dimethylaminopropylamine (amide formation)

Derivatives: acrylamide copolymers, cationic; 3-(methacrylamidopropyl)trimethylammonium chloride; polymethacrylates, oil-soluble dispersants

4-dimethylaminopyridine
4-DMAP

$$\text{pyridine ring with } N(CH_3)_2 \text{ substituent}$$

$C_7H_{10}N_2$. M: 122.17.

Production:
• 4-aminopyridine (methylation)
Uses: alkylation/acylation catalyst

N,N-dimethylaminosulphonyl chloride
See: dimethylsulphamyl chloride

N,N-dimethylaniline
DMA; [121-69-7]

$C_8H_{11}N_1$. M: 121.19. Liquid. BP: 194–195°C. MP: 2°C. d: 0.96 kg/l (20°C). Insoluble in water. Soluble in oxygenated and chlorinated solvents.
Production:
• aniline + methanol (amine formation; coproduced with *N*-methylaniline)
Derivatives: Basic Blue 1; Basic Blue 9; Basic Blue 54; Basic Green 4; Basic Red 22; Basic Violet 1; Basic Violet 3; 4,4′-bis(dimethylamino)benzophenone; bis-(p-dimethylaminophenyl)methane; p-dimethylaminobenzaldehyde; *N,N*-dimethyl-*p*-nitrosoaniline; tetryl
Uses:
unsaturated polyester resin curing accelerator; extraction solvent (sulphur dioxide refining); acylation reagent

2,3-dimethylaniline *See:* 2,3-xylidine

2,4-dimethylaniline *See:* 2,4-xylidine

2,5-dimethylaniline *See:* 2,5-xylidine

2,6-dimethylaniline *See:* 2,6-xylidine

3,4-dimethylaniline *See:* 3,4-xylidine

3,5-dimethylaniline *See:* 3,5-xylidine

dimethyl anisylidenemalonate
See: methyl 2-carbomethoxy-4′-methoxycinnamate

dimethyl anthranilate
See: methyl *N*-methylanthranilate

dimethylbehenylamine
dimethyl behenamine (CTFA)

$$CH_3(CH_2)_{21}N(CH_3)_2$$

$C_{24}H_{51}N_1$. M: 353.68.
Production:
• erucamide (hydrogenation/methylation)
Derivatives: behenyldimethylbenzylammonium chloride; behenyltrimethylammonium chloride; dimethylbehenylamine oxide

dimethylbehenylamine oxide
behenamine oxide (CTFA)

$$CH_3(CH_2)_{21}\overset{\overset{\displaystyle CH_3}{|}}{\underset{\underset{\displaystyle CH_3}{|}}{N}}{\rightarrow}O$$

$C_{24}H_{51}N_1O_1$. M: 369.68. Paste containing 30% active material.
Production:
• dimethylbehenylamine + hydrogen peroxide (peroxidation)
Uses:
foam stabiliser/softener (cosmetics, hair products)

N,N-dimethylbenzylamine
See: benzyldimethylamine

dimethyl benzyl carbinol
α,α-dimethylphenethyl alcohol; 1-phenyl-2-methyl-2-propanol; [100-86-7]

$$\underset{}{\overset{OH}{\underset{|}{CH_2C(CH_3)_2}}}$$

$C_{10}H_{14}O_1$. M: 150.22. Liquid or solid with a mild, floral odour. MP: 24°C. BP: 215°C. d: 0.98 kg/l (20°C). Insoluble in water. Soluble in oxygenated and aromatic solvents.
Production:
• benzyl chloride + acetone (Grignard reagent formation/Grignard reaction)
Derivatives:
dimethyl benzyl carbinyl acetate; dimethyl benzyl carbinyl butyrate
Uses: fragrance ingredient

dimethyl benzyl carbinyl acetate
α,α-dimethylphenethyl acetate; [151-05-3]

$$CH_3\overset{\overset{\displaystyle O}{\|}}{C}O\underset{\underset{\displaystyle CH_3}{|}}{\overset{\overset{\displaystyle CH_3}{|}}{C}}CH_2$$

$C_{12}H_{16}O_2$. M: 192.26. Colourless liquid or solid with a floral odour. MP: 30°C.
Production:
• dimethyl benzyl carbinol + acetic anhydride (esterification)
Uses:
fragrance ingredient

dimethyl benzyl carbinyl butyrate
α,α-dimethylphenethyl butyrate; [10094-34-5]

$$(CH_3)_2CH\overset{\overset{\displaystyle O}{\|}}{C}O\underset{\underset{\displaystyle CH_3}{|}}{\overset{\overset{\displaystyle CH_3}{|}}{C}}CH_2$$

$C_{14}H_{20}O_2$. M: 220.31. Colourless liquid with a fruity odour.

Production:
- dimethyl benzyl carbinol + *n*-butyric acid (esterification)

Uses: fragrance ingredient

1,1-dimethylbiguanide *See:* metformin

1,1′-dimethyl-4,4′-bipyridinium chloride
See: paraquat dichloride

3,3-dimethylbutan-2-one *See:* pinacolone

2,3-dimethyl-1-butene
2,3-dimethylbutene-1; DMB-1; [563-78-0]

$$CH_3$$
$$(CH_3)_2CHC=CH_2$$

C_6H_{13}. M: 85.17. Colourless liquid. BP: 56°C. FP: -73°C. d: 0.71 kg/l (20°C). Insoluble in water. Soluble in oxygenated solvents.
Production:
- 2,3-dimethyl-2-butene (isomerisation)

Derivatives: 6-acetyl-1,1,2,4,4,7-hexamethyltetralin

2,3-dimethyl-2-butene
2,3-dimethylbutene-2; tetramethylethylene; DMB-2; [563-79-1]

$$(CH_3)_2C=C(CH_3)_2$$

C_6H_{12}. M: 84.17. Colourless liquid. BP: 72–73°C. FP: -74°C. d: 0.71 kg/l (20°C). Soluble in oxygenated and hydrocarbon solvents.
Production:
- propylene (dimerisation/isomerisation/separation)

Derivatives: 2,3-dimethyl-1-butene; fenpropathrin

N-(1,3-dimethylbutyl)-N′-phenyl-p-phenylenediamine
See: N-hexyl-N′-phenyl-p-phenylenediamine

dimethylcarbamoyl chloride
[79-44-7]

$$O$$
$$(CH_3)_2N\overset{||}{C}Cl$$

$C_3H_6Cl_1N_1O_1$. M: 107.54. Colourless liquid. BP: 101–103°C (13.3 kPa). MP: -33°C. Hydrolysed by water and alcohol.
Production:
- dimethylamine + phosgene (phosgenation)

Derivatives:
chlorotoluron; chloroxuron; difenoxuron; dimefuron; fluometuron; isoproturon; isouron; karbutilate; metoxuron; pirimicarb; pyridostigmine bromide

dimethyl carbonate
methyl carbonate; DMC; [616-38-6]
$C_3H_6O_3$. M: 90.08. Liquid. MP: 1°C. BP: 90–91°C. d:

1.07 kg/l (20°C). Insoluble in water. Soluble in oxygenated solvents.

$$O$$
$$CH_3O\overset{||}{C}OCH_3$$

Production:
- methanol + carbon monoxide (oxidative carbonylation)

Derivatives:
3-thienylmalonic acid
Uses: methylation/phosgenation reagent

dimethylcetylamine
cetyldimethylamine; *N,N*-dimethylcetylamine; dimethylhexadecylamine; dimethyl palmitamine (CTFA); hexadecyldimethylamine

$$CH_3(CH_2)_{15}N(CH_3)_2$$

$C_{18}H_{39}N_1$. M: 269.52. Liquid. BP: 100–136°C (0.4 kPa). The product typically contains 92% C_{16}.
Production:
- *n*-hexadecylamine (methylation)
- cetyl alcohol + dimethylamine (reductive amination)
- cetyl chloride + dimethylamine (amine formation)

Derivatives:
cetyldimethylbenzylammonium chloride; cetyltrimethylammonium bromide; palmityldimethylammonium-3-sulphopropylbetaine
Uses: polyurethane catalyst

dimethyl chlorothiophosphate
See: O,O-dimethyl phosphorochlorothioate

dimethylcocoamine
cocodimethylamine; dimethyl cocamine (CTFA); *N,N*-dimethylcocoamine

$$RN(CH_3)_2$$

R = coco-. $C_{14}H_{31}N_1$. M: 213.41.
Production:
- cocoamine (methylation)
- *n*-alkanol(C_{12}-C_{18}) + dimethylamine (direct amination)

Derivatives:
coco betaine; cocodimethylammonium-3-sulphopropylbetaine; dimethylcocobenzylammonium chloride
Uses: corrosion inhibitor (process plant streams); flotation collector (sulphide ores); polymerisation inhibitor (butadiene)

dimethylcocoamino betaine *See:* coco betaine

dimethylcocobenzylammonium chloride
benzalkonium chloride (CTFA); cocodimethylbenzylammonium chloride
Liquid. A typical chain-length distribution is: 5% C_8, 5% C_{10}, 50% C_{12}, 20% C_{14}, 10% C_{16}, 10% C_{18}. The

product is often sold as a 50% solution in water. 90% active material is also produced.

R = coco-.
Production:
• dimethylcocoamine + benzyl chloride (quaternisation)
Uses: disinfectant (detergent sanitisers); emulsifier (metalworking fluids)

dimethyl cyclohexane-1,4-dicarboxylate
DMCD

$C_{10}H_{16}O_4$. M: 200.24. The commercial product is the *trans*-isomer.
Production:
• dimethyl terephthalate (hydrogenation)
Derivatives: cyclohexane-1,4-diisocyanate; polyester resins, linear, medium molecular weight

dimethyl-3-cyclohexenecarboxaldehyde
Cyclal C (Kao); [68737-61-1]

$C_9H_{14}O_1$. M: 138.21. Mixed isomer product containing mainly the 2,4- and 3,5-dimethyl isomers.
Production:
• 2-methylpentadiene + acrolein (Diels-Alder cycloaddition)
Uses: fragrance ingredient (household products)

N,N-dimethylcyclohexylamine
DMCHA; Catalyst SFC (ICI); [98-94-2]

$C_8H_{18}N_1$. M: 128.24. Colourless to pale yellow liquid. BP: 160°C. d: 0.85 kg/l (4°C). Soluble in water.
Production:
• cyclohexylamine + methanol (amine formation; coproduced with *N*-methylcyclohexylamine)
Uses: polyurethane foam catalyst; fuel oil additive

di-(methylcyclohexyl) phthalate
$C_{22}H_{30}O_4$. M: 358.48. Involatile liquid. d: 1.07 kg/l (25°C). Viscosity: 145–155 mPa.s (20°C). Insoluble in water.

Production:
• methylcyclohexanol + phthalic anhydride (esterification)
Uses: plasticiser (lacquers, polyvinyl chloride)

dimethyldiallylammonium chloride
See: diallyldimethylammonium chloride

dimethyldichlorosilane
See: dichlorodimethylsilane

O,O-dimethyl-*O*-(2,2-dichlorovinyl)phosphate
See: dichlorvos

dimethyldicocoammonium chloride
dicocodimethylammonium chloride; dicocodimonium chloride

R = coco-. $C_{26}H_{56}Cl_1N_1$. M: 418.20. Available commercially as a solution containing 75% active matter in water.
Production:
• dicocoamine + methyl chloride (quaternisation)
Uses: fabric softener; biocide (oilfield applications)

dimethyldidecylammonium chloride
See: didecyldimethylammonium chloride

dimethyldi-(hydrogenated tallow)ammonium chloride
See: dimethyldistearylammonium chloride

dimethyldihydroxyethylene urea
1,3-dimethyl-4,5-dihydroxyethylene urea

$C_5H_{10}N_2O_3$. M: 146.14.
Production:
• glyoxal + *N,N'*-dimethylurea (condensation)
Uses:
permanent-press textile finishing agent

dimethyldioctylammonium chloride
di-*n*-octyldimethylammonium chloride; dioctyldimethylammonium chloride

$C_{18}H_{40}Cl_1N_1$. M: 305.98.

Production:
- dimethyloctylamine + *n*-octyl chloride (quaternisation)

Uses: biocide (cooling water systems)

N,N-dimethyl-2,2-diphenylacetamide
See: diphenamid

1,2-dimethyl-3,5-diphenylpyrazolium methylsulphate
See: difenzoquat methosulphate

N,N'-dimethyldiphenylthiuram disulphide
MPTD; [10591-84-1]

$$\text{NCS-SCN}$$

$C_{16}H_{16}N_2S_4$. M: 364.58.
Production:
- *N*-methylaniline + carbon disulphide (condensation/ oxidation)

Uses: vulcanisation accelerator

dimethyldistearylammonium chloride
di-(hydrogenated tallow)dimethylammonium chloride; dimethyldi-(hydrogenated tallow)ammonium chloride; N,N-dimethyldistearylammonium chloride; N,N-distearyldimethylammonium chloride; distearyldimonium chloride (CTFA); quaternium-18 (CTFA); [61789-80-8]

$$\left[CH_3(CH_2)_{17}\right]_2 N(CH_3)_2^+ \quad Cl^-$$

$C_{38}H_{80}Cl_1N_1$. M: 586.52. Paste. MP: 36–44°C. A typical chain-length distribution is: 5% C_{14}, 30% C_{16}, 65% C_{18}. HLB: 9.7.
Production:
- distearylamine + methyl chloride (methylation)

Uses:
conductivity regulator (electrostatic paints); debonding aid (absorbent cellulose fluff production); organophilic surface treatment agent (bentonite); self-sizing/softening agent (paper tissue); softening/antistatic agent (hair conditioners, shampoos, textiles)

dimethyldistearylammonium methosulphate
[61789-81-9]

$$\left[CH_3(CH_2)_{17}\right]_2 N(CH_3)_2^+ \quad CH_3SO_4^-$$

$C_{39}H_{83}N_1O_4S_1$. M: 662.16. Pale brown powder.
Production:
- distearylamine + dimethyl sulphate (methylation)

Uses: fabric softener

dimethylditallowammonium chloride
ditallowdimethylammonium chloride; ditallowdimonium chloride (CTFA)

$$R_2N(CH_3)_2^+ \quad Cl^-$$

R = tallow-.

Production:
- ditallowamine + methyl chloride (quaternisation)

Uses:
surfactant (cationic cleaners, antistatic agents)

O,O-dimethyl dithiophosphoric acid
O,O-dimethyl phosphorodithioic acid; [32534-66-0]

$$\underset{\|}{\overset{S}{(CH_3O)_2PSH}}$$

$C_2H_7O_2P_1S_2$. M: 158.18.
Production:
- methanol + phosphorus pentasulphide (addition)

Derivatives:
anilofos; azamethiphos; azinphos-methyl; dimethoate; O,O-dimethyl phosphorochlorothioate; formothion; malathion; methidathion; phenthoate; phosmet; thiometon; vamidothion

dimethyldodecylamine *See:* dimethyllaurylamine

dimethyldodecylbenzylammonium chloride
See: dimethyllaurylbenzylammonium chloride

dimethylethanolamine
deanol; 2-dimethylaminoethanol; N,N-dimethylethanolamine; DMAE; DMEA; [108-01-0]

$$(CH_3)_2NCH_2CH_2OH$$

$C_4H_{11}N_1O_1$. M: 89.14. Colourless liquid with an amine-like odour. BP: 133–136°C. MP: <-70°C. d: 0.89 kg/l (20°C). Miscible with water, oxygenated and aromatic solvents.
Production:
- dimethylamine + ethylene oxide (epoxidation)

Derivatives:
alkyd resins, water-soluble; 2-dimethylaminoethyl acrylate; 2-dimethylaminoethyl chloride hydrochloride; 2-dimethylaminoethyl methacrylate; orphenadrine; polystyrene, crosslinked, hydroxyethyldimethylbenzylammoniated; suxamethonium chloride; tetracaine; tromantadine
Uses: polyurethane foam catalyst; corrosion inhibitor/ solubiliser (metalworking fluids); antidepressant drug; solubiliser (radiation-cured coatings, inks); process solvent (Shell Claus offgas treatment)

dimethyl ether
DME; methyl ether; [115-10-6]

$$CH_3OCH_3$$

$C_2H_6O_1$. M: 46.07. Colourless gas with ether-like odour. BP: -25°C. Soluble in water and oxygenated solvents.
Production:
- synthesis gas (high/medium/low-pressure processes; byproduct of methanol production)

Uses: aerosol propellant; refrigerant gas

N,N-dimethylethylamine
ethyldimethylamine; [598-56-1]

$$C_2H_5N(CH_3)_2$$

$C_4H_{11}N_1$. M: 73.14. Liquid. BP: 36°C.
Production:
• ethylamine (methylation)
Uses: polyurethane catalyst

dimethylformamide
N,N-dimethylformamide; DMF; [68-12-2]

$$\underset{HCN(CH_3)_2}{\overset{O}{\overset{\|}{}}}$$

$C_3H_7N_1O_1$. M: 73.10. Colourless liquid with a mild, characteristic odour. BP: 153°C. FP: -61°C. d: 0.96 kg/l (4°C). Miscible with water and oxygenated solvents. Insoluble in aliphatic hydrocarbons. Flash point: 58°C (CC).
Production:
• methyl formate + dimethylamine (amide formation)
• carbon monoxide + dimethylamine (direct amide synthesis)
Derivatives:
p-diethylaminobenzaldehyde; p-dimethylaminobenzaldehyde; Disperse Yellow 99; etretinate; formetanate hydrochloride; p-methylbenzaldehyde; pyrantel; rifampin; Vat Yellow 20
Uses: aromatics extraction solvent; petrol antiicing additive; process solvent; reagent (Vilsmeier reactions); solvent (paint strippers, cleaners, acetylene extraction/storage, polyurethane/polyamide/vinyl coatings, zinc electroplating, acrylic/elastane fibre spinning)

dimethyl glutarate

$$\underset{CH_3OC(CH_2)_3COCH_3}{\overset{O\quad\ O}{\overset{\|\quad\ \|}{}}}$$

$C_7H_{12}O_4$. M: 160.18. Colourless liquid. BP: 230°C. MP: -42°C. d: 1.09 kg/l (20°C). Soluble in oxygenated solvents.
Production:
• dimethyl alkylene(C_4-C_6)dicarboxylates (fractionation; coproduced with dimethyl succinate/dimethyl adipate)
Derivatives: glutaric acid; 3,5,6-trichloro-2-pyridone
Uses: solvent

dimethylglyoxime
butanedione dioxime; butane dioxime; [95-45-4]

$$CH_3C=NOH$$
$$CH_3C=NOH$$

$C_4H_8N_2O_2$. M: 116.11. White crystals. MP: 238°C. Insoluble in water. Soluble in oxygenated solvents.
Production:
• diacetyl + hydroxylamine sulphate (oxime formation)

Uses: complexing agent (nickel ore processing); analytical reagent

N,N-dimethylguanidine
[6145-42-2]; [22583-29-5] (chloride); [1186-46-5] (sulphate)

$$\underset{(CH_3)_2N-C=NH}{\overset{NH_2}{\overset{|}{}}}$$

$C_2H_9N_3$. M: 75.11.
Production:
• cyanamide + dimethylamine (addition)
Derivatives: dimethirimol; pirimicarb

2,6-dimethyl-2-heptanol
[13254-34-7]

$$\underset{(CH_3)_2CHCH_2CH_2CH_2C(CH_3)_2}{\overset{OH}{\overset{|}{}}}$$

$C_9H_{20}O_1$. M: 144.26. Colourless liquid with a floral odour. BP: 171°C. d: 0.82 kg/l (20°C). Insoluble in water. Soluble in oxygenated solvents.
Production:
• β-methylheptenone + methylmagnesium chloride (Grignard reaction/hydrogenation)
Uses: fragrance ingredient

2,4-dimethyl-4-heptanone *See:* diisobutyl ketone

dimethylhexadecylamine *See:* dimethylcetylamine

dimethylhexadecylbenzylammonium chloride
See: cetyldimethylbenzylammonium chloride

2,5-dimethylhexane-2,5-dihydroperoxide
2,5-dihydroperoxy-2,5-dimethylhexane; [3025-88-5]

$$\underset{(CH_3)_2CCH_2CH_2C(CH_3)_2}{\overset{OOH\quad\ OOH}{\overset{|\qquad\ \ |}{}}}$$

$C_8H_{18}O_4$. M: 178.23. White powder. Decomposes on heating with a 10-hour half-life at 154°C. Slightly soluble in water. Soluble in oxygenated and hydrocarbon solvents.
Production:
• dimethyl hexanediol + hydrogen peroxide (peroxidation)
Derivatives: 2,5-bis(2-ethylhexanoylperoxy)-2,5-dimethylhexane; 2,5-di-(benzoylperoxy)-2,5-dimethylhexane; 2,5-di-(t-butylperoxy)-2,5-dimethylhexane

dimethyl hexanediol
2,5-dihydroxy-2,5-dimethylhexane; 2,5-dimethylhexane-2,5-diol; [110-03-2]

$$\underset{OH\qquad\ OH}{\underset{|\qquad\quad |}{(CH_3)_2CCH_2CH_2C(CH_3)_2}}$$

$C_8H_{18}O_2$. M: 146.23. Crystalline solid. MP: 92°C. BP:

214°C. d: 0.90 kg/l (20°C). Soluble in water and oxygenated solvents.
Production:
• dimethyl hexynediol (hydrogenation)
Derivatives: (*1R*)-*trans*-chrysanthemic acid; (*1RS*)-*cis/trans*-chrysanthemic acid; 2,5-dimethylhexane-2,5-dihydroperoxide

1,5-dimethylhexylamine *See:* octodrine

dimethyl hexynediol
2,5-dihydroxy-2,5-dimethyl-3-hexyne; 2,5-dimethyl-2,5-dihydroxy-3-hexyne; [142-30-3]

$$(CH_3)_2CC \equiv CC(CH_3)_2$$
$$\qquad\ OH\ \quad\ OH$$

$C_8H_{14}O_2$. M: 142.20. Needles. MP: 95°C. BP: 205°C. d: 0.95 kg/l (20°C). Slightly soluble in water. Soluble in oxygenated solvents.
Production:
• acetone + acetylene (ethynylation)
Derivatives:
2,5-di-(*t*-butylperoxy)-2,5-dimethylhex-3-yne; dimethyl hexanediol

dimethyl hexynol
3,5-dimethyl-1-hexyn-3-ol; Surfynol 61 (Air Products and Chemical); [107-54-0]

$$(CH_3)_2CHCH_2 \overset{\overset{\displaystyle CH_3}{|}}{\underset{\underset{\displaystyle OH}{|}}{C}} C \equiv CH$$

$C_8H_{15}O_1$. M: 127.21.
Production:
• methyl isobutyl ketone + acetylene (ethynylation)
Uses: volatile surfactant (printing inks, electroplating, glass cleaning)

5,5-dimethylhydantoin
dimethylhydantoin; DMH; DM hydantoin; [77-71-4]

$C_5H_8N_2O_2$. M: 128.12. White, crystalline solid. MP: 176–178°C. Soluble in water and oxygenated solvents.
Production:
• acetone + hydrogen cyanide + ammonium bicarbonate (Bucherer-Bergs reaction)
Derivatives:
1-bromo-3-chloro-5,5-dimethylhydantoin; 1,3-dibromo-5,5-dimethylhydantoin; 1,3-dichloro-5,5-dimethylhydantoin; di-(2-hydroxyethyl)dimethylhydantoin dilaurate; dimethylhydantoin ether monooleate; dimethylhydantoin-glycidyl adducts; dimethylol dimethylhydantoin; monomethylol dimethylhydantoin

dimethylhydantoin ether monooleate

m+n = 5–20.
Production:
• 5,5-dimethylhydantoin + ethylene oxide + oleic acid (epoxidation/esterification)
Uses: textile auxiliaries

dimethylhydantoin-glycidyl adducts

Production:
• 5,5-dimethylhydantoin + epichlorohydrin (dehydrochlorination)
Uses: epoxy resins

1,1-dimethylhydrazine
dimethylhydrazine, unsymmetrical; UDMH; [57-14-7]

$$(CH_3)_2NNH_2$$

$C_2H_8N_2$. M: 60.09. Colourless, hygroscopic, fuming liquid with a characteristic, ammoniacal odour. BP: 63°C. MP: -57°C. d: 0.78 kg/l (25°C). Miscible with water and alcohol.
Production:
• dimethylamine + ammonia + sodium hypochlorite (chloramine process)
• hydrazine + acetic anhydride + formaldehyde + hydrogen (amide formation/reductive methylation/amide hydrolysis)
Derivatives:
daminozide
Uses: rocket fuel

N,N-dimethyl(hydrogenated tallow)amine
See: dimethylstearylamine

N,N-dimethyl(hydrogenated tallow)benzylammonium chloride *See:* dimethylstearylbenzylammonium chloride

dimethyl hydroquinone
See: hydroquinone dimethyl ether

α,α-dimethyl-α-hydroxyacetophenone
2-hydroxy-2,2-dimethylacetophenone; Darocur 1173 (Merck)

$C_{10}H_{12}O_2$. M: 164.21.

Production:
- acetone cyanohydrin + benzene (nitrile hydrolysis/ Friedel-Crafts acylation)

Uses:
photoinitiator (radiation-cured lacquers, inks)

1,1-dimethyl-3-hydroxybutyl peroxy-2-ethylhexanoate

$$CH_3CHCH_2CO-OCC(CH_2)_3CH_3$$

with substituents OH, CH_3, O, CH_3, C_2H_5

$C_{14}H_{28}O_4$. M: 260.37.
Production:
- hexylene glycol + hydrogen peroxide + 2-ethylhexanoyl chloride (peroxidation/ dehydrochlorination)

Uses:
vinyl polymerisation catalyst

1,1-dimethyl-3-hydroxybutyl peroxyneoheptanoate

$$CH_3CHCH_2CO-OC-CC_3H_7$$

with substituents OH, CH_3, O, CH_3, CH_3, CH_3

$C_{13}H_{26}O_4$. M: 246.35.
Production:
- hexylene glycol + hydrogen peroxide + neoheptanoyl chloride (peroxidation/ dehydrochlorination)

Uses:
vinyl polymerisation catalyst

2,5-dimethyl-4-hydroxy-3-furanone
[3658-77-3]

$C_6H_8O_3$. M: 128.13. Colourless crystals with a pine-apple-like odour. MP: 77–79°C.
Production:
- 2,5-hexynediol + ozone (oxidation/acid-catalysed cyclisation)

Uses: flavouring ingredient

N,O-dimethylhydroxylamine
methoxymethylamine; [5725-96-2]

$$CH_3NHOCH_3$$

$C_2H_7N_1O_1$. M: 61.09.
Production:
- hydroxylamine sulphate (methylation)

Derivatives:
chlorbromuron; linuron; metobromuron; monolinuron

2,4-dimethyl-3'-hydroxy-2'-naphthanilide
See: 3-hydroxy-2-naphth-2',4'-xylidide

dimethyl isophthalate
[1459-93-4]

$C_{10}H_{10}O_4$. M: 194.19. Solid. MP: 103–104°C. Slightly soluble in alcohol.
Production:
- methanol + isophthalic acid (esterification)

Derivatives:
polyamide 6I; polyamide TR55; poly(1,4-cyclohexyl-enedimethylene terephthalate-isophthalate); polyester resins, linear, medium molecular weight
Uses: polyarylate resin comonomer; perfume fixative

dimethylisopropanolamine
dimepranol; 1-dimethylamino-2-propanol; DMIPA; [108-16-7]

$$(CH_3)_2NCHCH_2OH$$

with substituent CH_3

$C_5H_{13}N_1O_1$. M: 103.16. Liquid. BP: 123–126°C. Pour point: -85°C. d: 0.85 kg/l (20°C). Soluble in water and oxygenated solvents.
Production:
- dimethylamine + propylene oxide (epoxidation)

Derivatives:
isothipendyl; methadone; promethazine; N,N,N-trimeth-yl-2-hydroxypropylammonium 2-ethylhexanoate

dimethyl ketone *See:* acetone

dimethyllaurylamine
dimethyldodecylamine; N,N-dimethyllaurylamine; do-decyldimethylamine; lauryldimethylamine; [112-18-5]

$$CH_3(CH_2)_{11}N(CH_3)_2$$

$C_{14}H_{31}N_1$. M: 213.41. Liquid. Commercial product varies with source and chain-length distribution of the lauryl group. A narrow cut product typically contains 98% C_{12}, a broad cut product 70% C_{12}, 30% C_{14}. MP: -10°C.
Production:
- laurylamine (methylation)
- lauryl alcohol, narrow-cut/n-alkanol(C_{12}-C_{13})/ n-alkanol(C_{12}-C_{14}) + dimethylamine (reductive amination)
- lauryl chloride + dimethylamine (amine formation)
Derivatives: dimethyllaurylamine oxide; dimethyllaur-ylbenzylammonium chloride; lauryl betaine; lauryldi-methylammonium-3-sulphopropylbetaine

dimethyllaurylamine oxide
dimethyllauramine oxide; N,N-dimethyllaurylamine oxide

R = lauryl-. $C_{14}H_{31}N_1O_1$. M: 229.41. Liquid. A typical chain-length distribution is: 70% C_{12}, 30% C_{14}. The product is often sold as a 30% solution in water.
Production:
• dimethyllaurylamine + hydrogen peroxide (oxidation)
Uses:
foam boosters/stabilisers (liquid, powder detergents, shampoos); antistatic agent (textile spin finishes)

dimethyllaurylbenzylammonium chloride
dimethyldodecylbenzylammonium chloride; lauralkonium chloride

$C_{21}H_{38}Cl_1N_1$. M: 339.99. Available as a 50% or 80% solution in water. The chain-length distribution is, typically: 40% C_{12}, 50% C_{14} and 10% C_{16}.
Production:
• dimethyllaurylamine + benzyl chloride
  (quaternisation)
Uses: disinfectant (detergent sanitisers); emulsifier (metalworking fluids); algicide (swimming pools)

dimethyl maleate
[624-48-6]

$C_6H_8O_4$. M: 144.13. Colourless liquid. MP: -19°C. BP: 205°C. d: 1.16 kg/l (20°C). Insoluble in water.
Production:
• maleic anhydride + methanol (esterification)
Derivatives:
methyl glyoxylate methyl hemiacetal
Uses: carboxylated comonomer (polyvinyl acetate latex)

dimethyl malonate
DMM; [108-59-8]

$C_5H_8O_4$. M: 132.11. Colourless liquid. BP: 180–181°C. d: 1.15 kg/l (25°C). Slightly soluble in water. Soluble in oxygenated solvents.
Production:
• methanol + malonic acid (esterification)
• chloroacetic acid + carbon monoxide + methanol
  (carbonylation/esterification)

Derivatives: alloxydim-sodium; cycloxydim; methyl 2-carbomethoxy-4'-methoxycinnamate; methyl 3-methyl-orsellinate; sethoxydim

3,7-dimethyl-7-methoxyoctan-1-al
See: methoxycitronellal

2,4-dimethyl-6-(α-methylcyclohexyl)phenol
2-(α-methylcyclohexyl)-4,6-dimethylphenol

$C_{15}H_{23}O_1$. M: 219.34.
Production:
• 2,4-xylenol + 2-methylcyclohexanol (Friedel-Crafts
  alkylation)
Uses: antioxidant (rubber)

dimethyl methylphosphonate
DMMP; [756-79-6]

$C_3H_9O_3P_1$. M: 124.07. Clear, hygroscopic liquid. BP: 180°C. FP: <-50°C. d: 1.16 kg/l (25°C). Miscible with water and most organic solvents.
Production:
• trimethyl phosphite (Arbusov rearrangement)
Uses: fire-retardant additive (polyurethane foam, unsaturated polyester resin)

2,6-dimethylmorpholine
[141-91-3]

$C_6H_{12}N_1O_1$. M: 114.18. Liquid. BP: 147°C. FP: -85°C. d: 0.93 kg/l (20°C). Miscible with water, oxygenated and aromatic solvents.
Production:
• diisopropanolamine (ether formation)
Derivatives:
dodemorph acetate; fenpropimorph; tridemorph

dimethylmyristylamine
dimethylmyristamine; *N,N*-dimethylmyristylamine; dimethyltetradecylamine; *N,N*-dimethyltetradecylamine; myristyldimethylamine; tetradecyldimethylamine; [112-75-4]

$C_{16}H_{35}N_1$. M: 241.47. Liquid. Commercial products vary

with source and chain-length distribution of the myristyl group. A narrow cut product typically contains 96% C_{14}. Broader cut products typically contain 40% C_{12}, 50% C_{14}, 10% C_{16}. MP: -8°C.
Production:
• *n*-tetradecylamine (methylation)
• myristyl alcohol + dimethylamine (reductive amination)
Derivatives: myristyldimethylamine oxide; myristyldimethylammonium-3-sulphopropylbetaine; myristyldimethylbenzylammonium chloride; myristyltrimethylammonium bromide

dimethylmyristylbenzylammonium chloride
See: myristyldimethylbenzylammonium chloride

dimethyl naphthalene-2,6-dicarboxylate
dimethyl 2,6-naphthalenedicarboxylate; DM-2,6-NDC

$C_{14}H_{12}O_4$. M: 244.25.
Production:
• naphthalene-2,6-dicarboxylic acid + methanol (esterification)
Derivatives: polyarylate, liquid-crystalline; poly(ethylene naphthalate)

dimethylnaphthalene fraction
Production:
• C_{10+} aromatics (fractionation; coproduced with naphthalene fraction/methylnaphthalene fraction)
Derivatives: indole; naphthalene-2,6-dicarboxylic acid

dimethyl 5-nitroisophthalate

$C_{10}H_9N_1O_6$. M: 239.18. Crystalline solid. MP: 121–123°C.
Production:
• methanol + 5-nitroisophthalic acid (esterification)
Derivatives: iohexol

N,N-dimethyl-p-nitrosoaniline
4-nitroso-*N,N*-dimethylaniline; [138-89-6]

$C_8H_{10}N_2O_1$. M: 150.18. Green crystals. MP: 93°C. d: 1.15 kg/l (20°C). Slightly soluble in water. Soluble in oxygenated solvents.

Production:
• *N,N*-dimethylaniline + sodium nitrite (nitrosation)
Derivatives:
Basic Blue 6; *N,N*-dimethyl-*p*-phenylenediamine

3,7-dimethyl-2,6-octadien-1-al *See:* citral

3,7-dimethyl-2,6-octadien-1-al dimethyl acetal
See: citral dimethyl acetal

3,7-dimethyl-1,6-octadien-3-ol *See:* linalool

3,7-dimethyl-2,6-octadien-1-ol
See: geraniol-nerol, mixed

3,7-dimethyl-*cis*-2,6-octadien-1-ol *See:* nerol

3,7-dimethyl-*trans*-2,6-octadien-1-ol *See:* geraniol

3,7-dimethyl-2,6-octadien-1-yl phenylacetate
See: geranyl phenylacetate

3,7-dimethyloctan-1-ol *See:* tetrahydrogeraniol

3,7-dimethyloctan-3-ol *See:* tetrahydrolinalool

3,7-dimethyl-6-octen-1-al *See:* (±)-citronellal

2,6-dimethyl-7-octen-2-ol *See:* dihydromyrcenol

3,7-dimethyl-6-octen-1-ol *See:* (±)-citronellol

dimethyloctylamine
n-octyldimethylamine; [7378-99-6]

$CH_3(CH_2)_7N(CH_3)_2$

$C_{10}H_{23}N_1$. M: 157.30. Liquid. MP: <-10°C. d: 0.77 kg/l (25°C). Flash point: 70°C. Commercial products are generally >95% C_8.
Production:
• *n*-octanol + dimethylamine (reductive amination)
Derivatives:
dimethyldioctylammonium chloride

dimethyl octynediol
3,6-dimethyl-4-octyne-3,6-diol; Surfynol 82 (Air Products and Chemical); [1321-87-5]

$C_{10}H_{18}O_2$. M: 170.25.
Production:
• acetylene + methyl ethyl ketone (ethynylation)
Uses:
defoaming agent (electroplating baths); defoaming/wetting agent (pesticides); solubiliser (shampoos)

1,3-dimethylol-4,5-dihydroxyethylene urea
DMDHEU

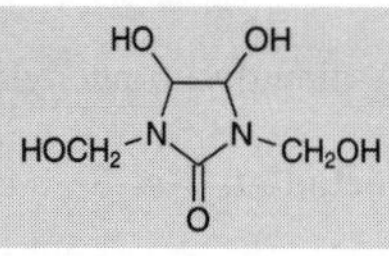

$C_5H_{10}N_2O_5$. M: 178.14.
Production:
• glyoxal + formaldehyde + urea (condensation)
Uses:
permanent-press textile finishing agent

dimethylol dimethylhydantoin
1,3-dimethylol-5,5-dimethylhydantoin; DMDH

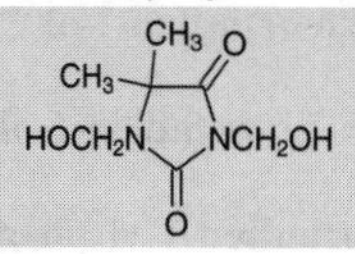

$C_7H_{12}N_2O_4$. M: 188.19.
Production:
• 5,5-dimethylhydantoin + formaldehyde (condensation)
Uses:
preservative (cosmetics)

N,N'-dimethylolethylene urea
DMEU; [28906-87-8]

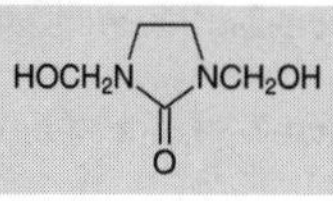

$C_5H_{10}N_2O_3$. M: 146.14.
Production:
• ethylene urea + formaldehyde (carbonyl condensation)
Uses: leather tanning auxiliary; amino resin modifier; textile auxiliary (permanent press finishes)

N,N-dimethyloleylamine *See:* oleyldimethylamine

1,3-dimethylolhexahydro-2-pyrimidone
See: dimethylolpropylene urea

4,5-dimethylol-3-hydroxy-2-methylpyridine
See: pyridoxine

dimethylolpropylene urea
1,3-bis(hydroxymethyl)tetrahydro-2-(1H)-pyrimidinone; 1,3-dimethylolhexahydro-2-pyrimidone; DMPU; [65405-39-2]

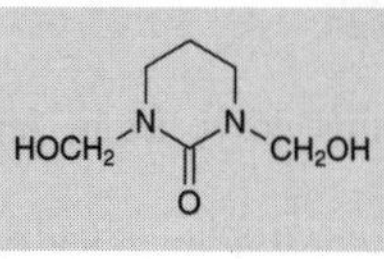

$C_6H_{12}N_2O_3$. M: 160.18.

Production:
• propylene urea + formaldehyde (condensation/hydroxymethylation)
Uses: permanent-press textile finishing agent

dimethylolurea
N,N'-di-(hydroxymethyl)urea; DMU; [140-95-4]

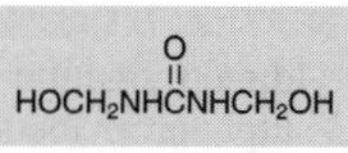

$C_3H_8N_2O_3$. M: 120.10. Powder. MP: 120–123°C. Soluble in water.
Production:
• urea + formaldehyde (carbonyl condensation)
Uses: textile/leather/paper finishes

4,4-dimethyl oxazolidine
Bioban CS-1135 (Angus Chemical); [51200-87-4]

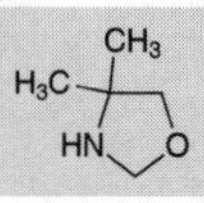

$C_5H_{11}N_1O_1$. M: 101.15. The commercial product contains a small proportion of the *N*-methyl derivative which also has biocidal activity.
Production:
• 2-amino-2-methyl-1-propanol + formaldehyde (condensation)
Uses: biocide (metalworking fluids, paints, oilfield chemicals)

dimethyl 3-oxoglutarate
See: dimethyl acetonedicarboxylate

2,2-dimethylpentanoic acid
[1185-39-3]

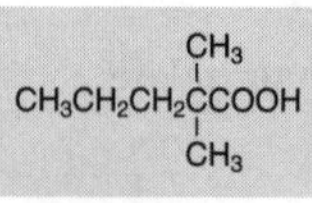

$C_7H_{14}O_2$. M: 130.19. Liquid.
Production:
• methylpentene, mixed + carbon monoxide (Koch carbonylation; coproduced with 2-ethyl-2-methylbutanoic acid)
Derivatives: monalide

2,4-dimethylpentan-3-one *See:* diisopropyl ketone

α,α-dimethylphenethyl acetate
See: dimethyl benzyl carbinyl acetate

α,α-dimethylphenethyl alcohol
See: dimethyl benzyl carbinol

α,α-dimethylphenethyl butyrate
See: dimethyl benzyl carbinyl butyrate

dimethyl phenethyl carbinol
4-phenyl-2-methyl-2-butanol; [103-05-9]

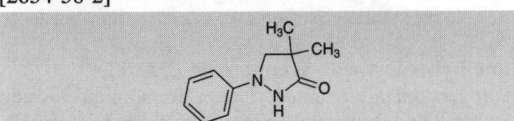

$C_{11}H_{16}O_1$. M: 164.25. Colourless liquid with a floral odour. BP: 124°C (1.9 kPa). d: 0.96 kg/l (20°C). Insoluble in water. Soluble in oxygenated solvents.
Production:
• benzylacetone + methylmagnesium chloride (Grignard reaction)
Uses: fragrance ingredient

dimethylphenol *See:* xylenol, mixed

2,4-dimethylphenol *See:* 2,4-xylenol

2,6-dimethylphenol *See:* 2,6-xylenol

3,4-dimethylphenol *See:* 3,4-xylenol

3,5-dimethylphenol *See:* 3,5-xylenol

N,N-dimethyl-p-phenylenediamine
p-aminodimethylaniline; 4-(dimethylamino)aniline; ADMA; [99-98-9]

$C_8H_{12}N_2$. M: 136.20. Red-violet crystals. Degraded by light and air. MP: 37°C. BP: 257–262°C. Slightly soluble in water. Soluble in oxygenated and chlorinated solvents. Available commercially as the free base, hydrochloride or bisulphate.
Production:
• N,N-dimethyl-p-nitrosoaniline (nitro reduction)
Derivatives: Basic Blue 9
Uses: photographic developing agent

4,4-dimethyl-1-phenyl-3-pyrazolidinone
[2654-58-2]

$C_{11}H_{14}N_2O_1$. M: 190.24. Solid.
Production:
• monochloropivaloyl chloride + phenylhydrazine (dehydrochlorination)
Uses: photographic coupling agent intermediate

2,3-dimethyl-1-phenyl-3-pyrazolin-5-one
See: phenazone

1,1-dimethyl-3-phenylurea *See:* fenuron

dimethyl phosphite
O,O-dimethyl phosphorous acid; DMPI

$C_2H_7O_3P_1$. M: 110.05. Liquid. BP: 170–171°C. d: 1.20 kg/l (20°C). Soluble in alcohol.
Production:
• methanol + phosphorus trichloride (dehydrochlorination)
Derivatives: trichlorfon

O,S-dimethyl phosphoroamidothioate
See: methamidophos

O,O-dimethyl phosphorochlorothioate
dimethyl chlorothiophosphate; O,O-dimethyl phosphorochloridothioate; O,O-dimethyl phosphorothiochloridate; dimethyl thiophosphoryl chloride; DMCTP; DMPCT; methyl PCT; [2524-03-0]

$C_2H_6Cl_1O_2P_1S_1$. M: 160.55.
Production:
• O,O-dimethyl dithiophosphoric acid + chlorine (chlorination)
Derivatives: chlorpyrifos-methyl; cyanophos; demeton-S-methyl; etrimfos; famphur; fenitrothion; fenthion; iodofenphos; methacrifos; methamidophos; omethoate; oxydemeton-methyl; parathion-methyl; pirimiphos-methyl; temephos; tolclofos-methyl

O,O-dimethyl phosphorodithioic acid
See: O,O-dimethyl dithiophosphoric acid

O,O-dimethyl phosphorous acid
See: dimethyl phosphite

dimethyl phthalate
DMP; [131-11-3]

$C_{10}H_{10}O_4$. M: 194.19. Colourless liquid. BP: 284°C. MP: -1°C. d: 1.19 kg/l (20°C). Insoluble in water. Miscible with oxygenated and chlorinated solvents.
Production:
• methanol + phthalic anhydride (esterification)
Derivatives: chlorophacinone; diphacinone
Uses: insect repellant; peroxide phlegmatising agent; plasticiser (cellulose acetate)

N,N′-dimethylpiperazine
1,4-dimethylpiperazine; DMP; [106-58-1]

$C_6H_{14}N_2$. M: 114.19. Colourless, mobile liquid. BP: 133°C. FP: -1°C. d: 0.85 kg/l (20°C).
Production:
• piperazine + formaldehyde (methylation; coproduced with *N*-methylpiperazine)
Uses: polyurethane foam catalyst; raw material (cationic surfactants)

2,6-dimethylpiperidine
2,6-lupetidine; Nanofin (INN); [504-03-0]

$C_7H_{15}N_1$. M: 113.21. Liquid. BP: 128°C. d: 0.85 kg/l (0°C). Miscible with water and alcohol.
Production:
• 2,6-lutidine (hydrogenation)
Derivatives:
clopamide

1,1-dimethylpiperidinium chloride
See: mepiquat chloride

N,N-dimethyl-1,3-propanediamine
See: 3-dimethylaminopropylamine

2,2-dimethyl-1,3-propanediol *See:* neopentyl glycol

2,2-dimethylpropanoic acid *See:* pivalic acid

1,2-dimethylpropylamine *See:* 3-methyl-2-butylamine

2,6-dimethylpyridine *See:* 2,6-lutidine

3,4-dimethylpyridine *See:* 3,4-lutidine

2,9-dimethylquinacridone
Quinacridone Magenta Y; Pigment Red 122 (CI); 73915 (CI)

$C_{22}H_{16}N_2O_2$. M: 340.38.
Production:
• dimethyl succinylosuccinate + *p*-toluidine (amine formation/condensation)
Uses:
pigment (plastics, enamels, lacquers, inks)

dimethylsiloxane oligomers
Mixture of low molecular weight cyclic and linear silicones which forms the primary intermediate in silicone production.
Production:
• dichlorodimethylsilane/dichloromethylphenylsilane/ dichlorodiphenylsilane (hydrolysis)
Derivatives: octamethylcyclotetrasiloxane; poly(dimethylsiloxane), crosslinking; poly(dimethylsiloxane), hydroxyl-terminated; silicone oils; silicone resin

dimethylstearylamine
dimantine (INN); dimethyl hydrogenated tallow amine (CTFA); dimethylstearamine; dymanthine; hydrogenated tallowdimethylamine; octadecyldimethylamine; stearyldimethylamine; [124-28-7]

$C_{20}H_{43}N_1$. M: 297.57. Liquid/paste. Commercial product varies with source and chain-length distribution of the stearyl group. A typical grade from hydrogenated tallow has a chain-length distribution of: 5% C_{14}, 30% C_{16}, 65% C_{18}. Purer grades from stearylamine or stearyl alcohol contain 95% C_{18}.
Production:
• stearylamine (methylation)
• stearyl alcohol + dimethylamine (reductive amination)
Derivatives: dimethylstearylamine oxide; dimethylstearylbenzylammonium chloride; stearyldimethylammonium-3-sulphopropylbetaine; 3-(trimethoxysilyl)propyldimethyloctadecylammonium chloride
Uses: cationic flotation agent (quartz, feldspar); electrophoretic paint additive; oiliness additive (lubricants)

dimethylstearylamine oxide
stearamine oxide (CTFA); stearyl DMO

$C_{20}H_{43}N_1O_1$. M: 313.57. White paste containing 25% active matter in water.
Production:
• dimethylstearylamine + hydrogen peroxide (oxidation)
Uses: foam stabiliser/softener (cosmetics, hair products)

dimethylstearylbenzylammonium chloride
hydrogenated tallowdimethylbenzylammonium chloride; octadecyldimethylbenzylammonium chloride; stearalkonium chloride

$C_{27}H_{50}Cl_1N_1$. M : 764.54. Paste. MP: 35–40°C. A typical chain-length distribution is: 30% C_{14}, 65% C_{16}. Usually sold as a 76% solution in isopropanol/water.

Production:
- dimethylstearylamine + benzyl chloride (quaternisation)

Uses: dye levelling agent; antistatic agent/disinfectant (paper); organophilic surface treatment agent (bentonite); softening/antistatic agent (hair conditioners)

dimethyl succinate
methyl succinate

$$CH_2COOCH_3$$
$$|$$
$$CH_2COOCH_3$$

$C_6H_{10}O_4$. M: 146.15. Colourless liquid. MP: 19°C. BP: 195°C. d: 1.12 kg/l (20°C). Solubility in water: 8 g/l water (25°C).
Production:
- succinic acid + methanol (esterification)
- dimethyl alkylene(C_4-C_6)dicarboxylates (fractionation; coproduced with dimethyl adipate/ dimethyl glutarate)

Derivatives: dimethyl succinylosuccinate; poly(N-β-hydroxyethyl-2,2,6,6-tetramethyl-4-hydroxypiperidyl succinate); succinic acid

dimethyl succinylosuccinate
DMSS

$C_{10}H_{12}O_6$. M: 228.20.
Production:
- dimethyl succinate (condensation)
Derivatives:
2,9-dichloroquinacridone;   3,10-dichloroquinacridone; 2,9-dimethylquinacridone; Pigment Violet 19

dimethylsulphamyl chloride
N,N-dimethylaminosulphonyl chloride; [13360-57-1]

$$(CH_3)_2NSO_2Cl$$

$C_2H_6Cl_1O_2S_1$. M: 129.58. Not a commercially traded product.
Production:
- dimethylamine + chlorosulphonic acid (sulphonamide formation)
Derivatives: bupirimate; dichlofluanid; tolylfluanid

dimethyl sulphate
[77-78-1]

$$(CH_3O)_2SO_2$$

$C_2H_6O_4S_1$. M: 126.13. Colourless liquid. BP: 189°C with decomposition. MP: -27°C. d: 1.33 kg/l (20°C). Hydrolysed by water. Soluble in organic solvents.

Production:
- methanol + oleum (esterification)
Derivatives:
Acid Blue 41; anisole; Basic Blue 22; Basic Blue 41; Basic Blue 54; Basic Red 22; Basic Yellow 28; benzyldimethylamine; 1,4-bis(methoxymethyl)benzene; 1-bromo-4-methylaminoanthraquinone; caffeine; clemastine; clonidine; N-cyanoimido-S,S-dimethyldithiocarbamate; diazepam; dicamba; N,N-diethyl-m-anisidine; diethylene glycol dimethyl ether; difenzoquat methosulphate; 1,3-dimercaptoisopropyldimethylamine; 2,6-dimethoxybenzoic acid; dimethyldistearylammonium methosulphate; dipyrone; Direct Yellow 12; Disperse Blue 26; N,N-ditallowamidoethyl-N-methylammonium ethoxylate methosulphate; ethyl 2-(2-aminothiazolyl)-methoxyiminoacetate; ethylene glycol dimethyl ether; etozolin; flunitrazepam; Fluorescent Brightener 179; glibenclamide; guaiacol; homoveratric acid; hydroquinone dimethyl ether; hydroquinone monomethyl ether; 2-hydroxy-4-methoxybenzophenone; isoflurane; mephenytoin; 4-methoxyacetophenone; methoxycitronellal; 2-methoxyphenylacetic acid; 6-methoxy-1-tetralone; p-methoxytoluene; 1-methylamino-1-methylthio-2-nitroethylene;   methylenebis(dimethylcyclohexylamine); methyl eugenol; methyl isoeugenol; 1-methyl-1-(oleamidoethyl) oleylimidazoline methosulphate; methylphenobarbital; N-methylpyrrole; 1-methyl-1-(tallowamidoethyl)tallowimidazoline methosulphate; N-methyl-2-p-tolylindole; metrizoic acid; β-naphthyl methyl ether; neburon; phenazone; Pigment Yellow 18; propyphenazone; pyrifenox; resorcinol dimethyl ether; sulfadimethoxine; sulpiride; tetraethylene glycol dimethyl ether; theobromine; tiapride; trimethadione; 3,4,5-trimethoxybenzaldehyde; trimethylphenylammonium hydroxide; Vat Green 1; veratraldehyde
Uses: methylation reagent

dimethyl sulphide
DMS; [75-18-3]

$$(CH_3)_2S$$

$C_2H_6S_1$. M: 62.13. Colourless liquid with an unpleasant odour. BP: 37°C. FP: -83°C. d: 0.85 kg/l (20°C). Insoluble in water. Soluble in oxygenated solvents.
Production:
- methanol + hydrogen sulphide (thiolation)
- sulphate pulp black liquor + sulphur + sodium sulphide (demethylation)
Derivatives:
dimethyl sulphoxide
Uses: catalyst preactivator; gas odorant

dimethyl sulphoxide
DMSO; [67-68-5]

$$(CH_3)_2S=O$$

$C_2H_6O_1S_1$. M: 78.13. Hygroscopic liquid. BP: 189°C.

FP: 18.5°C. d: 1.10 kg/l (20°C). Soluble in water and oxygenated solvents. Flash point: 95°C (TOC).
Production:
• dimethyl sulphide (oxidation)
Uses:
aprotic process solvent (chemical synthesis); solvent (paint strippers, polyacrylonitrile/polysulphone production); topical antiinflammatory drug

dimethyl terephthalate
DMT; [120-61-6]

$COOCH_3$ — benzene ring — $COOCH_3$

$C_{10}H_{10}O_4$. M: 194.19. Available commercially in molten or flake form. MP: 141°C. Sublimes at 290°C. Slightly soluble in hot water. Soluble in oxygenated solvents.
Production:
• p-xylene + methanol (side-chain oxidation/esterification)
Derivatives:
N,N'-bis(5-chloro-2,4-dimethoxyphenyl)terephthalodiacetamide; 1,4-bis(methoxymethyl)benzene; chlorthaldimethyl; copolyester, thermoplastic elastomers; 1,4-cyclohexanedimethanol; dimethyl cyclohexane-1,4-dicarboxylate; p-phenylene diisocyanate; Pigment Red 188; polyamide 6-(3)T; polyarylate, liquid-crystalline; poly(butylene terephthalate); poly(1,4-cyclohexylenedimethylene terephthalate); poly(1,4-cyclohexylenedimethylene terephthalate-isophthalate); polyester carbonate; polyester resins, linear, medium molecular weight; poly(ethylene-1,4-cyclohexanedimethylene-terephthalate); poly(ethylene terephthalate); polynorbornamide; terephthalic acid

dimethyl tetrachloroterephthalate
See: chlorthal-dimethyl

dimethyltetradecylamine
See: dimethylmyristylamine

dimethyl thiophosphoryl chloride
See: O,O-dimethyl phosphorochlorothioate

3,5-di-(methylthio)toluenediamine
Ethacure 300 (Ethyl)

$C_9H_{14}N_2S_2$. M: 214.35. Liquid. Pour point: 4°C. d: 1.21 kg/l (20°C).

Production:
• 2,4/2,6-diaminotoluene + methyl sulphenyl chloride (dehydrochlorination)
Uses: polyurea foam crosslinking agent; cast polyurethane elastomer curing agent

dimethyltin bis(isooctylthioglycollate)
dimethyltin bis(isooctylmercaptoacetate)

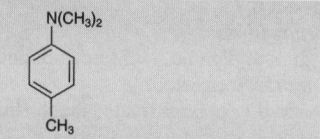
$(CH_3)_2Sn\left[SCH_2\overset{O}{\overset{\|}{C}}OC_8H_{17}\right]_2$

$C_{22}H_{44}O_4S_2Sn_1$. M: 555.41.
Production:
• dimethyltin dichloride + isooctyl thioglycollate (dehydrochlorination)
Uses:
polyvinyl chloride heat stabiliser

dimethyltin bis(2-mercaptoethyl oleate)

$(CH_3)_2Sn\left[SCH_2CH_2O\overset{O}{\overset{\|}{C}}(CH_2)_7CH=CH(CH_2)_7CH_3\right]_2$

$C_{42}H_{80}O_4S_2Sn_1$. M: 831.92.
Production:
• 2-mercaptoethanol + oleic acid + dimethyltin dichloride (esterification/dehydrochlorination)
Uses:
polyvinyl chloride heat stabiliser

dimethyltin dichloride
[753-73-1]

$(CH_3)_2SnCl_2$

$C_2H_6Cl_2Sn_1$. M: 219.67. Colourless crystals. MP: 107°C. BP: 185–190°C. Soluble in water.
Production:
• stannic chloride + tetramethyltin (Kocheshkov redistribution)
Derivatives:
dimethyltin bis(isooctylthioglycollate); dimethyltin bis(2-mercaptoethyl oleate)

N,N-dimethyl-p-toluidine
DMPT; [99-97-8]

$N(CH_3)_2$ — benzene ring — CH_3

$C_9H_{13}N_1$. M: 135.21. Liquid. BP: 211°C. d: 0.94 kg/l (20°C). Insoluble in water. Soluble in oxygenated solvents.
Production:
• p-toluidine + methanol (amine formation)
Uses:
epoxy resin curing agent

6,10-dimethyl-5,9-undecadien-2-one
See: geranylacetone

6,10-dimethyl-3,5,9-undecatrien-2-one
See: pseudoionone

N,N′-dimethylurea
1,3-dimethylurea; dimethylurea; dimethylurea, symmetrical; DMU; [96-31-1]

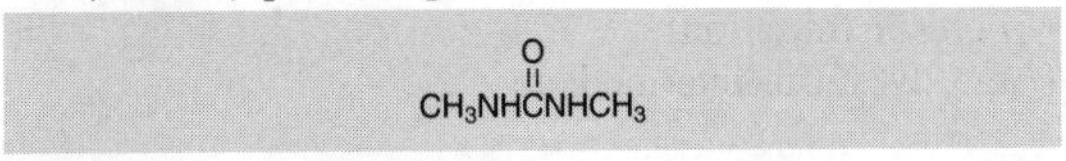

$$CH_3NHCNHCH_3$$
(O double bond on C)

$C_3H_8N_2O_1$. M: 88.10. White, crystalline solid. MP: 104°C. Decomposes on heating to 260°C. d: 1.14 kg/l. Soluble in water and alcohol.
Production:
• methylamine + carbon dioxide (addition)
Derivatives: 6-amino-1,3-dimethyluracil; dimethyldihydroxyethylene urea

1,3-dimethylxanthine *See:* theophylline

3,7-dimethylxanthine *See:* theobromine

dimorpholine disulphide *See:* 4,4′-dithiodimorpholine

2,2′-dimorpholinodiethyl ether *See:* bis(2-morpholinoethyl)ether

dimyristyl thiodipropionate
dimyristyl 3,3′-thiodipropionate; DMTDP; [16545-54-3]

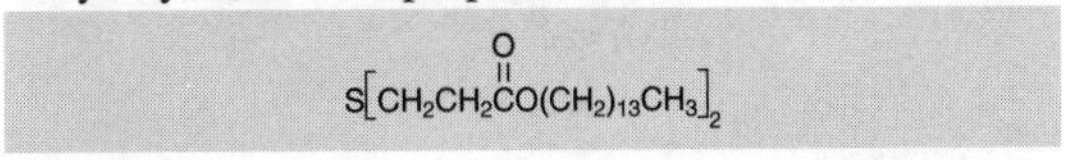

$$S[CH_2CH_2CO(CH_2)_{13}CH_3]_2$$
(O double bond on C)

$C_{34}H_{66}O_4S_1$. M: 570.96. White powder. MP: 49°C. d: 0.90 kg/l (20°C).
Production:
• myristyl alcohol + methyl acrylate + hydrogen sulphide (transesterification/addition)
Uses: antioxidant (plastics, rubber, grease)

DINA *See:* diisononyl adipate

dinaphthalenemethane sulphonate *See:* sodium dinaphthalenemethane sulphonate

N,N′-di-β-naphthyl-p-phenylenediamine
DNPD; [93-46-9]

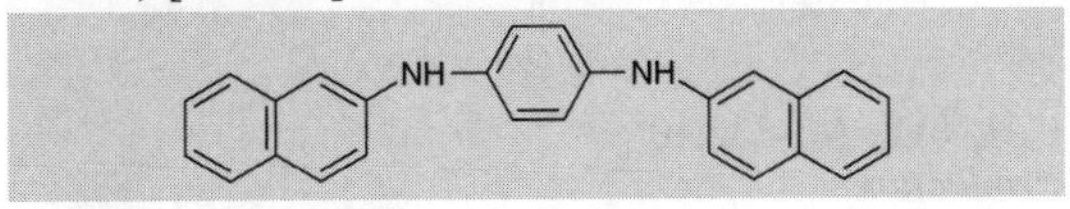

$C_{26}H_{20}N_2$. M: 360.46.
Production:
• p-phenylenediamine + β-naphthol (amine formation)
Uses:
antioxidant/antiozonant (plastics, rubber)

DINGU *See:* dinitroglycoluril

diniconazole
[83657-24-3]

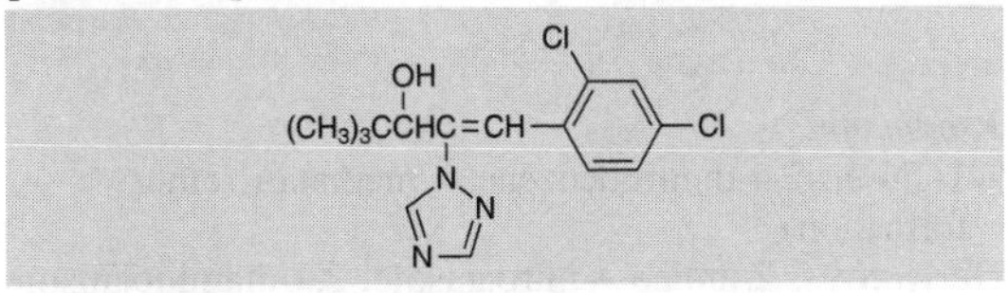

$(CH_3)_3CCHC=CH$— with OH group; dichlorophenyl; triazole ring

$C_{15}H_{17}Cl_2N_3O_1$. M: 326.23.
Production:
• α-chloropinacolone + 1,2,4-triazole + 2,4-dichlorobenzaldehyde (amine formation/carbonyl condensation/carbonyl reduction)
Uses: fungicide

dinitramine
2-amino-4-diethylamino-3,5-dinitrobenzotrifluoride; [29091-05-2]

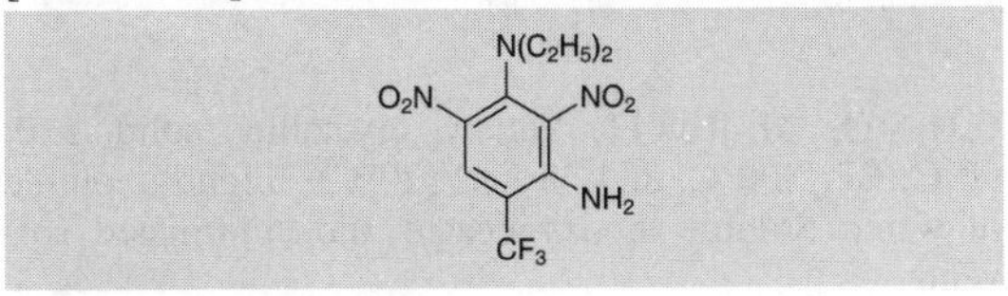

$N(C_2H_5)_2$; O_2N; NO_2; NH_2; CF_3

$C_{11}H_{13}F_3N_4O_4$. M: 322.24.
Production:
• 2,4-dichlorobenzotrifluoride + diethylamine + ammonia (nitration/amine formation/amine formation)
Uses:
herbicide

2,4-dinitroaniline
[97-02-9]

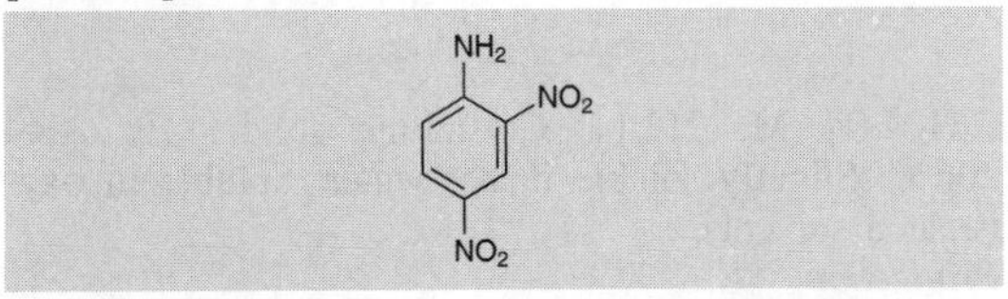

NH_2; NO_2; NO_2

$C_6H_5N_3O_4$. M: 183.13. Yellow, crystalline solid. MP: 188°C. d: 1.61 kg/l (15°C). Insoluble in cold water. Slightly soluble in hot water and alcohol.
Production:
• 1-chloro-2,4-dinitrobenzene + ammonia (amine formation)
Derivatives: 6-bromo-2,4-dinitroaniline; 6-chloro-2,4-dinitroaniline; Pigment Orange 5; Sulphur Blue 11; Sulphur Yellow 9

2,4-dinitroanisole
[119-27-7]
$C_7H_6N_2O_5$. M: 198.13. Yellow needles. MP: 94–95°C. Sublimes. Slightly soluble in water. Soluble in oxygenated solvents.

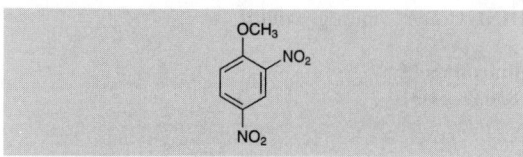

Production:
• 1-chloro-2,4-dinitrobenzene + methanol (ether formation)
Derivatives: 2-amino-4-nitroanisole; 2,4-diaminoanisole
Uses: dyestuffs intermediate

4,8-dinitroanthrarufin
See: 1,5-dihydroxy-4,8-dinitroanthraquinone

m-dinitrobenzene
1,3-dinitrobenzene; [99-65-0]

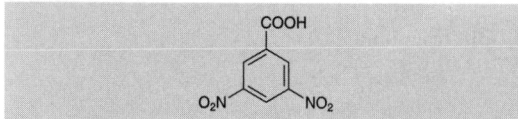

$C_6H_4N_2O_4$. M: 168.11. Yellow, crystalline solid. MP: 90°C. BP: 300°C. d: 1.58 kg/l (20°C). Slightly soluble in water. Soluble in oxygenated and chlorinated solvents.
Production:
• nitrobenzene (nitration/separation)
Derivatives:
m-nitroaniline; *m*-phenylenediamine; Sulphur Green 9

3,5-dinitrobenzoic acid
[99-34-3]

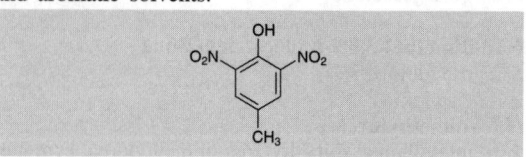

$C_7H_4N_2O_6$. M: 212.11. Crystalline solid. MP: 204–206°C. Slightly soluble in hot water. Soluble in oxygenated solvents.
Production:
• benzoic acid (nitration)
Derivatives:
3,5-diaminobenzoic acid
Uses: analytical reagent (alcohols, alkyl halides); photographic coupling agent intermediate

2,4-dinitro-6-chloroaniline
See: 6-chloro-2,4-dinitroaniline

2,4-dinitrochlorobenzene
See: 1-chloro-2,4-dinitrobenzene

2,6-dinitro-*p*-cresol
2,6-dinitro-4-methylphenol; DNPC; [609-93-8]
$C_7H_6N_2O_5$. M: 198.13. Yellow aqueous paste. MP:

80–85°C. Insoluble in water. Soluble in oxygenated and aromatic solvents.

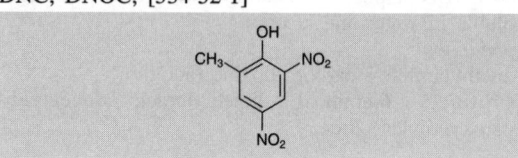

Production:
• *p*-cresol (nitration)
Uses: dyestuffs intermediate

4,6-dinitro-*o*-cresol
DNC; DNOC; [534-52-1]

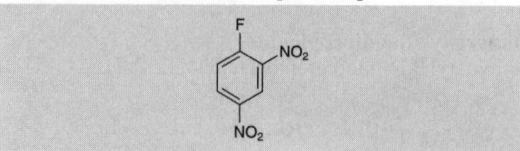

$C_7H_6N_2O_5$. M: 198.13.
Production:
• *o*-cresol (nitration)
Uses:
insecticide/acaricide/herbicide

2,4-dinitrofluorobenzene
1-fluoro-2,4-dinitrobenzene; [70-34-8]

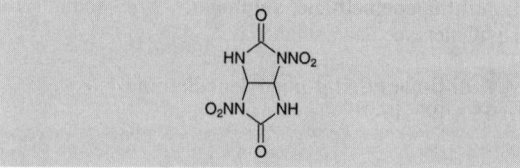

$C_6H_3F_1N_2O_4$. M: 186.10.
Production:
• 1-chloro-2,4-dinitrobenzene + hydrogen fluoride (halogen exchange)
Uses:
amino acid characterisation reagent

dinitroglycoluril
DNGU; DINGU (SNPE Chimie); [55510-04-8]

$C_4H_4N_6O_6$. M: 232.10.
Production:
• glycoluril + nitric acid, concentrated (nitration)
Uses: explosives

2,6-dinitro-4-methylphenol
See: 2,6-dinitro-*p*-cresol

1,5/1,8-dinitronaphthalene
[605-71-0] (1,5-isomer); [602-38-0] (1,8-isomer)

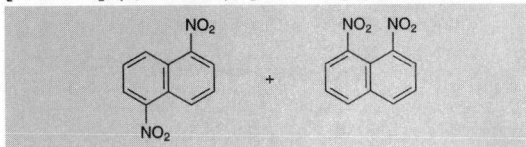

$C_{10}H_6N_2O_4$. M: 218.17. Mixed isomer product. Greyish-yellow powder. MP: >140°C. Insoluble in water. Soluble in acetone and aromatic solvents.
Production:
• naphthalene (nitration)
Derivatives:
1,5-diaminonaphthalene; 1,8-diaminonaphthalene; Sulphur Brown 7
Uses: explosives

4,6-dinitro-1,1,3,3,5-pentamethylindane
moskene

$C_{14}H_{18}N_2O_4$. M: 278.30.
Production:
• *p*-cymene + isobutylene (cycloaddition/nitration)
Uses: fragrance ingredient

2,4-dinitrophenol
[51-28-5]

$C_6H_4N_2O_5$. M: 184.10. Yellow crystals containing about 15% water. MP: 106–108°C (anhydrous). Soluble in hot water, oxygenated and chlorinated solvents.
Production:
• 1-chloro-2,4-dinitrobenzene (hydrolysis)
Derivatives:
2-amino-4-nitrophenol; 2-amino-4-nitrophenol-6-sulphonic acid; 2,4-diaminophenol dihydrochloride; picric acid; Sulphur Black 1

N,N'-dinitroso-N,N'-dimethylterephthalamide
NTA; [133-55-1]

$C_{10}H_{10}N_4O_4$. M: 250.22. Decomposes on heating above 100°C.

Production:
• terephthaloyl chloride + methylamine + sodium nitrite (amide formation/nitrosation)
Uses: blowing agent

N,N'-dinitrosopentamethylenetetramine
3,7-dinitroso-1,3,5,7-tetraazabicyclo[3.3.1]nonane; DNPT; [101-25-7]

$C_5H_{10}N_6O_2$. M: 186.17. Pale yellow, crystalline powder. Starts to decompose at 120–125°C releasing 260 ml/g of gas. Soluble in *N,N*-dimethylformamide and other polar solvents.
Production:
• hexamethylenetetramine + sodium nitrite (nitrosation)
Uses:
blowing agent (foamed rubber)

3,7-dinitroso-1,3,5,7-tetraazabicyclo[3.3.1]nonane
See: N,N'-dinitrosopentamethylenetetramine

4,4'-dinitrostilbene-2,2'-disulphonic acid
DNSDSA; Direct Yellow 11 (CI); 40000 (CI); [128-42-7]

$C_{14}H_{14}N_2O_{10}S_2$. M: 434.39.
Production:
• 4-nitrotoluene-2-sulphonic acid + sodium hypochlorite (oxidative coupling)
Derivatives:
4,4'-diaminostilbene-2,2'-disulphonic acid; Direct Yellow 6; Direct Yellow 106

dinitrotoluene
DNT

$C_7H_6N_2O_4$. M: 182.14. Mixed product consisting of the 2,4- and 2,6-dinitro isomers. The standard route, using toluene as a raw material, produces a 2,4:2,6-isomer ratio of 80:20. The route from *o*-nitrotoluene produces a 65:35 ratio. With *p*-nitrotoluene, 100% 2,4-isomer is produced.
Production:
• toluene (nitration)
• *o*-nitrotoluene (nitration)
• *p*-nitrotoluene (nitration)

Derivatives:
2-amino-4-nitrotoluene; 2,4/2,6-diaminotoluene
Uses: explosives; rocket propellant

dinocap
Karathane (Rohm and Haas); [39300-45-3]

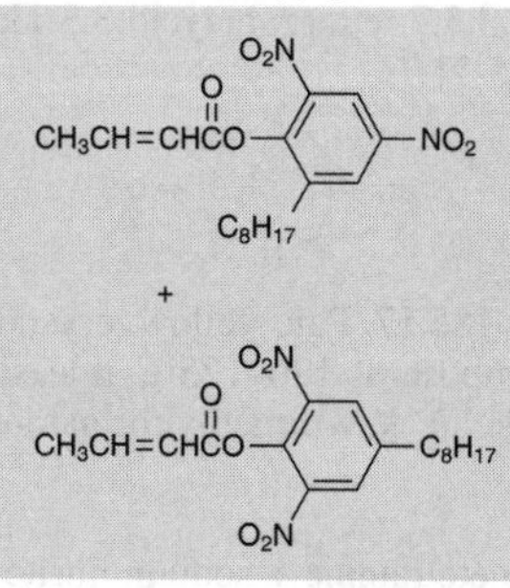

$C_{18}H_{24}N_2O_6$. M: 364.39. Mixed product. The octyl group is linear, but attached at the 2, 3 or 4 position on the chain. In addition, the octyl group can be at either the ortho or para position on the phenyl ring.
Production:
• phenol + 1-octene + crotonic acid (Friedel-Crafts alkylation/nitration/esterification)
Uses: acaricide/fungicide

dinonyl adipate *See:* diisononyl adipate

dinonyl alkylene(C₄-C₆)dicarboxylate

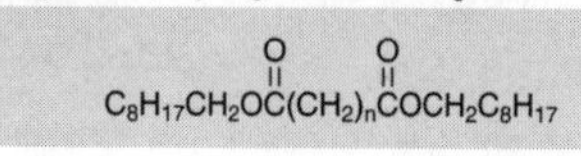

n = 2–4. Colourless, involatile liquid. d: 0.93 kg/l (20°C). Pour point: -47°C. Insoluble in water. Flash point: 198°C.
Production:
• isononanol + dimethyl alkylene(C₄-C₆)dicarboxylates (transesterification)
Uses: plasticiser (polyvinyl chloride/chlorosulphonated polyethylene sealants)

dinonylnaphthalene

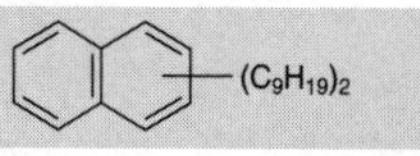

$C_{28}H_{44}$. M: 380.66. Mixed isomer product.
Production:
• nonene, branched + naphthalene (Friedel-Crafts alkylation)
Derivatives:
dialkylaryl sulphonates, alkali-earth salts

dinonylphenol
2,4-dinonylphenol; [1323-65-5]; [137-99-5] (2,4-isomer)
$C_{24}H_{42}O_1$. M: 346.60. Amber liquid with a slightly phenolic odour. BP: 305–380°C. d: 0.92 kg/l (20°C).

Mixed product with the 2,4-isomer as the major component.

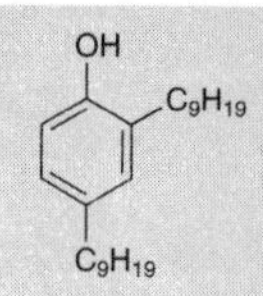

Production:
• nonene, branched + phenol (Friedel-Crafts alkylation; coproduced with nonylphenol)
Derivatives: dinonylphenol ethoxylates; phenolic resins, oil-soluble, oil-reactive

dinonylphenol ethoxylates
nonyl nonoxynol (CTFA)

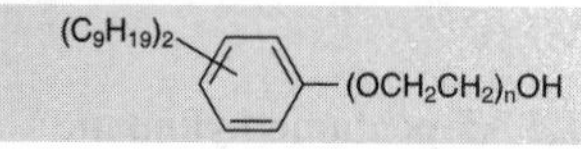

n = 5–30. Liquid or paste, depending on the molecular weight.
Production:
• dinonylphenol + ethylene oxide (epoxidation)
Uses: crude oil/lubricant demulsifier component; emulsifier (pesticides); low-foaming surfactant (household/industrial detergents); textile/paper processing aids

dinonyl phthalate
DNP

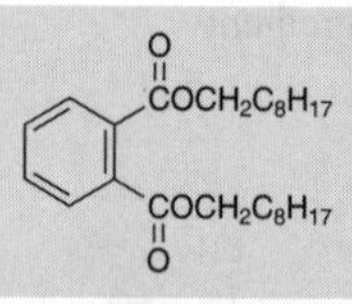

$C_{26}H_{42}O_4$. M: 418.63. Colourless liquid. Pour point: -32°C. d: 0.97 kg/l. Viscosity: 110 cP (20°C). Insoluble in water. Flash point: 221°C.
Production:
• nonanol + phthalic anhydride (esterification)
Uses: plasticiser (polyvinyl chloride/nitrile rubber/chloroprene rubber)

dinoseb
2-*s*-butyl-4,6-dinitrophenol; 2-(1-methylpropyl)-4,6-dinitrophenol; Premerge (Dow Chemical); [88-85-7]

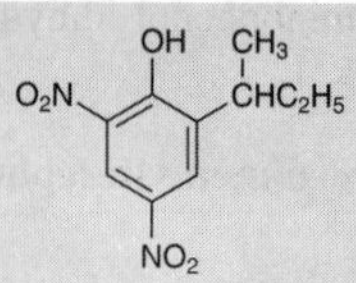

$C_{10}H_{12}N_2O_5$. M: 240.22.
Production:
• o-*s*-butylphenol (nitration)
Derivatives: dinoseb acetate
Uses: herbicide/insecticide

dinoseb acetate
2-s-butyl-4,6-dinitrophenyl acetate; [2813-95-8]

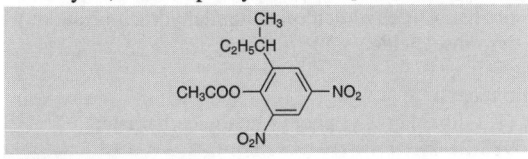

$C_{12}H_{14}N_2O_6$. M: 282.24.
Production:
• acetic anhydride + dinoseb (acetylation)
Uses: herbicide

dinoterb
2-t-butyl-4,6-dinitrophenol; [1420-07-1]

$C_{10}H_{12}N_2O_5$. M: 240.22. Available commercially as the ammonium or diethanolamine salts.
Production:
• o-t-butylphenol (nitration)
Uses: herbicide

DINP *See:* diisononyl phthalate

DIOA *See:* diisooctyl adipate

dioctyl adipate
See: di-(2-ethylhexyl) adipate; diisooctyl adipate

dioctylamine *See:* di-(2-ethylhexyl)amine

dioctyl azelate *See:* di-(2-ethylhexyl) azelate

dioctyldimethylammonium chloride
See: dimethyldioctylammonium chloride

dioctyl maleate *See:* di-(2-ethylhexyl) maleate

dioctyl octylphosphonate
bis(2-ethylhexyl) 2-ethylhexylphosphonate; [10143-60-9]

$$\left[CH_3(CH_2)_3\overset{\displaystyle C_2H_5}{\overset{|}{CH}}CH_2O\right]_2 \overset{\displaystyle O}{\overset{||}{P}}CH_2\overset{\displaystyle C_2H_5}{\overset{|}{CH}}(CH_2)_3CH_3$$

$C_{24}H_{51}O_3P_1$. M: 418.64.
Production:
• 2-ethylhexanol + phosphorus trichloride (dehydrochlorination/Arbusov rearrangement)
Uses:
extraction solvent (mineral processing)

4,4'-di-t-octylphenylamine
See: diphenylamine, octylated

dioctyl phosphoric acid
See: bis(2-ethylhexyl) hydrogen phosphate

dioctyl phthalate *See:* di-(2-ethylhexyl) phthalate

di-n-octyl phthalate *See:* di-n-alkyl(C_7-C_9) phthalate

dioctyl sebacate *See:* di-(2-ethylhexyl) sebacate

di-n-octyltin dichloride
dioctyltin dichloride

$$\left[CH_3(CH_2)_7\right]_2 SnCl_2$$

$C_{16}H_{34}Cl_2Sn_1$. M: 416.05.
Production:
• tetra-n-octyltin + stannic chloride (Kocheshkov redistribution)
Derivatives:
dioctyltin diisooctylthioglycollate; dioctyltin dilaurate; dioctyltin maleate; dioctyltin β-mercaptopropionate

dioctyltin diisooctylthioglycollate
dioctyltin bis(isooctylmercaptoacetate); [26401-97-8]

$$\left[CH_3(CH_2)_7\right]_2 Sn\left[SCH_2\overset{\displaystyle O}{\overset{||}{C}}OCH_2C_7H_{15}\right]_2$$

$C_{36}H_{72}O_4S_2Sn_1$. M: 751.80.
Production:
• isooctyl thioglycollate + di-n-octyltin dichloride (dehydrochlorination)
Uses: polyurethane catalyst (reaction-injection moulding, high-resilience flexible foam); polyvinyl chloride heat stabiliser

dioctyltin dilaurate
di-n-octyltin dilaurate; [3648-18-8]

$$\left[CH_3(CH_2)_7\right]_2 Sn\left[\overset{\displaystyle O}{\overset{||}{O}}C(CH_2)_{10}CH_3\right]_2$$

$C_{40}H_{80}O_4Sn_1$. M: 743.77.
Production:
• lauric acid, broad cut + di-n-octyltin dichloride (esterification)
Uses:
polyvinyl chloride heat stabiliser

dioctyltin maleate
di-n-octyltin maleate

$$\left[\begin{matrix}(CH_2)_7CH_3\\ | \\ Sn-OOCCH=CHCOO \\ | \\ (CH_2)_7CH_3\end{matrix}\right]_n$$

$C_{20}H_{36}O_4Sn_1$. M: 459.20.
Production:
• maleic acid + di-n-octyltin dichloride (esterification)
Uses:
polyvinyl chloride heat stabiliser

dioctyltin β-mercaptopropionate

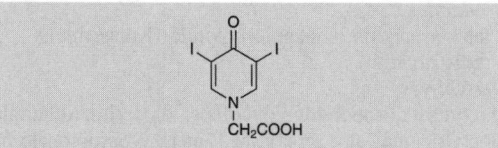

$[CH_3(CH_2)_7]_2Sn(SCH_2CH_2COOH)_2$

$C_{19}H_{38}O_2S_1Sn_1$. M: 449.26.
Production:
• 3-mercaptopropionic acid + di-*n*-octyltin dichloride (reduction/dehydrochlorination)
Uses:
polyvinyl chloride heat stabiliser

diodone

3,5-diiodo-4-pyridone-1-acetic acid; iodopyracet (diethanolamine salt); [101-29-1]; [300-37-8] (diethanolamine salt)

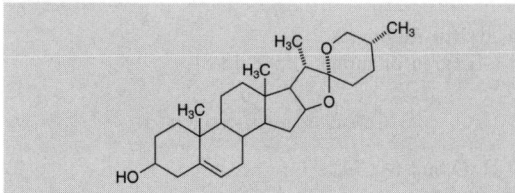

$C_7H_5I_2N_1O_3$. M: 404.94.
Production:
• pyridine + thionyl chloride + chloroacetic acid (ring chlorination/hydration/ring iodination/amine formation)
Derivatives:
propyliodone
Uses: x-ray diagnostic aid

DIOP *See:* diisooctyl phthalate

diosgenin
[512-04-9]

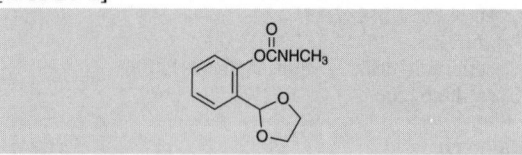

$C_{27}H_{42}O_3$. M: 414.64. Crystalline solid. MP: 205°C. Insoluble in water. Soluble in oxygenated and chlorinated solvents.
Production:
• *Dioscorea* root (extraction)
Derivatives:
dehydropregnenolone acetate

dioxabenzofos

2-methoxy-4H-benzo-1,3,2-dioxaphosphorine 2-sulphide; [3811-49-2]

$C_8H_9O_3P_1S_1$. M: 216.19.

Production:
• salicyl alcohol + thiophosphoryl chloride + methanol (dehydrochlorination/dehydrochlorination)
Uses: insecticide

dioxacarb

2-(1,3-dioxolan-2-yl)phenyl methylcarbamate; [6988-21-2]

$C_{11}H_{13}N_1O_4$. M: 223.23.
Production:
• salicylaldehyde + ethylene glycol + methyl isocyanate (acetal formation/isocyanate addition)
Uses: insecticide

dioxane

1,4-dioxane; [123-91-1]

$C_4H_8O_2$. M: 88.10. Colourless liquid. BP: 101°C. FP: 12°C. Completely miscible with water.
Production:
• diethylene glycol (dehydration)
Uses: extraction agent; polar solvent; stabiliser (1,1,1-trichloroethane)

9,10-dioxoanthracene-1,8-disulphonic acid
See: anthraquinone-1,8-disulphonic acid

9,10-dioxoanthracene-2,7-disulphonic acid
See: anthraquinone-2,7-disulphonic acid

dioxolane

1,3-dioxolane; ethylene glycol formal; [646-06-0]

$C_3H_6O_2$. M: 74.08.
Production:
• formaldehyde + ethylene glycol (ketal formation)
Derivatives: polyacetal, copolymers
Uses: solvent

DIOZ *See:* diisooctyl azelate

DIPA *See:* diisopropanolamine

DIPAN *See:* diphenylacetonitrile

m-DIPB *See:* m-diisopropylbenzene

***p*-DIPB** *See:* *p*-diisopropylbenzene

***m*-DIPEB** *See:* *m*-diisopropenylbenzene

***p*-DIPEB** *See:* *p*-diisopropenylbenzene

dipentaerythritol
[126-58-9]

$$HOH_2C \qquad CH_2OH$$
$$HOCH_2CCH_2-O-CH_2CCH_2OH$$
$$HOH_2C \qquad CH_2OH$$

$C_{10}H_{22}O_7$. M: 254.28. White solid. MP: 221°C. d: 1.36 kg/l (25°C). Soluble in water. Slightly soluble in oxygenated solvents. Mixed product containing, typically, 85% dipentaerythritol, together with pentaerythritol and tripentaerythritol.
Production:
• acetaldehyde + formaldehyde (aldol condensation/ Cannizzaro reaction; byproduct of pentaerythritol production)
Derivatives: dipentaerythritol hexapelargonate; tetrabromodipentaerythritol
Uses: alkyd/unsaturated polyester resin comonomer; polyvinyl chloride heat costabilisers

dipentaerythritol hexapelargonate

$$\left[CH_3(CH_2)_7\overset{O}{\overset{\|}{C}}OCH_2\right]_3CCH_2OCH_2C\left[CH_2O\overset{O}{\overset{\|}{C}}(CH_2)_7CH_3\right]_3$$

$C_{64}H_{118}O_{13}$. M: 1095.63.
Production:
• dipentaerythritol + pelargonic acid (esterification)
Uses: synthetic lubricant base oils

dipentamethylenethiuram tetrasulphide
bis(*N*,*N*'-pentamethylene)thiuram tetrasulphide; DPTT; P25 (Robinson Brothers)

$$\underset{NCS-S-S-SCN}{\overset{S \qquad\qquad S}{\overset{\|}{} \qquad \overset{\|}{}}}$$

$C_{12}H_{20}N_2S_6$. M: 384.68. Creamy yellow powder. MP: 114°C. d: 1.5 kg/l. Insoluble in water and hydrocarbons.
Production:
• piperidine + carbon disulphide + sulphur monochloride (thiocarbonylation/chlorosulphurisation)
Uses:
vulcanisation accelerator

di-(pentamethylhydroxypiperidyl) butyl-(di-3,5-*t*-butyl-4-hydroxybenzyl)malonate
$C_{42}H_{70}N_2O_5$. M: 683.02.
Production:
• diethyl *n*-butylmalonate + 2,6-di-*t*-butylphenol + 1,2,2,6,6-pentamethyl-4-hydroxypiperidine + formaldehyde (chloromethylation/

dehydrochlorination/esterification)
Uses:
light stabiliser (plastics)

di-(1,2,2,6,6-pentamethyl-4-piperidyl) sebacate

$C_{30}H_{56}N_2O_4$. M: 508.79.
Production:
• 1,2,2,6,6-pentamethyl-4-hydroxypiperidine + sebacoyl chloride (esterification)
Uses:
light stabiliser (plastics)

dipentene
DL-limonene; (±)-1,8-*p*-menthadiene; 1-methyl-4-isopropenylcyclohexene; [138-86-3]

$C_{10}H_{16}$. M: 136.24. Colourless liquid with a lemon-like odour. BP: 175–195°C. d: 0.85 kg/l (20°C). Insoluble in water. Miscible with alcohol. Mixed product, the main constituents of which are (+) and (−)-limonene (>80%). See also limonene.
Production:
• pinewood stumps (steam distillation; coproduced with turpentine oil, wood/pine oil/rosin, wood)
• pine gum (fractionation; coproduced with pine oil/ rosin, gum/turpentine oil, gum)
• pine oil (fractionation; coproduced with anethole/ 3-carene)
Derivatives:
p-cymene; terpene resins; terpenes, sulphurised
Uses: antiskinning agent/solvent (paints); cosolvent (mineral extraction); fragrance ingredient (household products); pine oil cleaning formulations; solvent (phenolic resins); swelling/softening agent (rubber); wetting agent (pigments)

dipentene glycol *See:* terpin hydrate

diphacinone
2-(diphenylacetyl)indan-1,3-dione; [82-66-6]

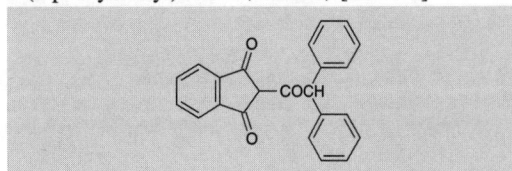

$C_{23}H_{16}O_3$. M: 340.38.
Production:
• diphenylacetonitrile + methyl acetate + dimethyl phthalate (condensation/condensation)
Uses: rodenticide

diphenamid
N,N-dimethyl-2,2-diphenylacetamide; [957-51-7]

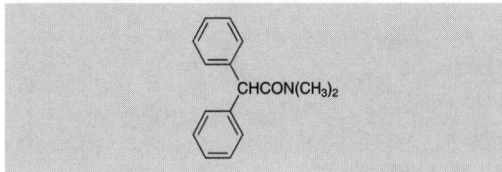

$C_{16}H_{17}N_1O_1$. M: 239.33.
Production:
• diphenylacetic acid + dimethylamine (amide formation/methylation)
Derivatives:
loperamide
Uses: herbicide

diphenhydramine
Benadryl (Warner-Lambert); [58-73-1]; [147-24-0] (hydrochloride)

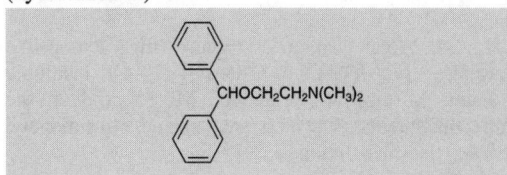

$C_{17}H_{21}N_1O_1$. M: 255.37. Available commercially as the free base or as the hydrochloride salt.
Production:
• benzhydrol + 2-dimethylaminoethyl chloride hydrochloride (ether formation)
Uses: antihistamine drug

diphenic acid
2,2′-biphenyldicarboxylic acid; biphenyl-2,2′-dicarboxylic acid; 2,2′-diphenic acid; [482-05-3]
$C_{14}H_{10}O_4$. M: 242.23. Crystalline solid. MP: 228–229°C. Insoluble in water. Soluble in oxygenated and aromatic solvents.

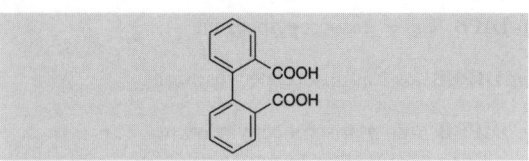

Production:
• phenanthrene (oxidative cleavage)
Uses: alkyd/unsaturated polyester resin comonomer

diphenoxylate
[915-30-0]

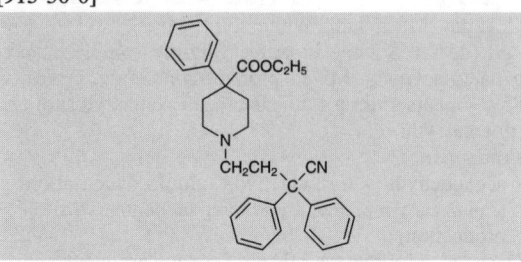

$C_{30}H_{32}N_2O_2$. M: 452.60.
Production:
• benzyl cyanide + diethanolamine + ethanol + ethylene oxide + diphenylacetonitrile (alcohol chlorination/dehydrochlorination/nitrile hydrolysis/ esterification/epoxidation/chlorination/dehydrochlorination)
Uses: antidiarrheal drug

diphenyl *See:* biphenyl

diphenylacetic acid
[117-34-0]

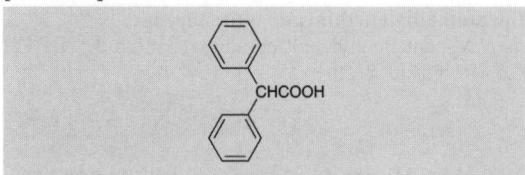

$C_{14}H_{12}O_2$. M: 212.25. Crystalline solid. MP: 146–148°C. Sublimes on further heating. d: 1.26 kg/l (15°C). Soluble in hot water and hot alcohol.
Production:
• benzilic acid (alcohol reduction)
• diphenylacetonitrile (nitrile hydrolysis)
Derivatives: dextromoramide; diphenamid

diphenylacetonitrile
benzhydryl cyanide; diphenylmethyl cyanide; DIPAN; [86-29-3]

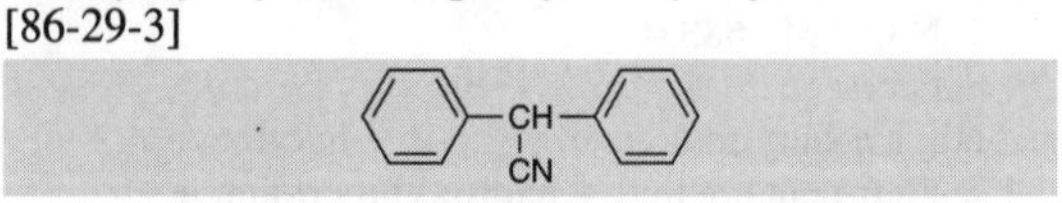

$C_{14}H_{11}N_1$. M: 193.25. yellow, crystalline powder. MP:

72–74°C. Insoluble in water. Soluble in oxygenated solvents.
Production:
• benzophenone + sodium cyanide (cyanohydrin formation/alcohol reduction)
Derivatives: diphacinone; diphenoxylate; diphenylacetic acid; fenpiverinium bromide; methadone

diphenylamine
DPA; [122-39-4]

$C_{12}H_{11}N_1$. M: 169.23. Grey, crystalline solid. MP: 52–54°C. BP: 302°C. Insoluble in water. Soluble in oxygenated and aromatic solvents.
Production:
• phenol + ammonia (amine formation; byproduct of aniline production)
Derivatives:
acetone-diphenylamine condensates; Acid Yellow 36; *p*-dicumyldiphenylamine; diphenylamine, octylated; diphenylamine, styrenated; phenothiazine
Uses: antioxidant (lubricants)

diphenylamine, octylated
4,4′-di-*t*-octylphenylamine; ODPA

$C_{28}H_{43}N_1$. M: 393.66.
Production:
• diphenylamine + 2,4,4-trimethylpentene (Friedel-Crafts alkylation)
Uses: antioxidant (plastics, rubber, lubricants)

diphenylamine, styrenated
SDPA

$C_{28}H_{27}N_1$. M: 377.54. Liquid.
Production:
• diphenylamine + styrene (Friedel-Crafts alkylation)
Uses: antioxidant (rubber, latex)

diphenylantimony 2-ethylhexanoate
diphenylstilbene-2-ethylhexanoate

$C_{20}H_{25}O_2Sb_1$. M: 419.17.

Production:
• benzene + 2-ethylhexanoic acid + antimony trichloride (dehydrochlorination/dehydrochlorination)
Uses: plastics biostabiliser

diphenyl carbonate
[102-09-0]

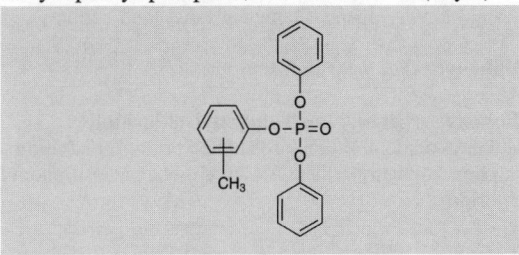

$C_{13}H_{10}O_3$. M: 214.22. White, crystalline solid. MP: 80°C. BP: 302°C. d: 1.12 kg/l (90°C). Insoluble in water. Soluble in oxygenated solvents.
Production:
• phenol + phosgene (phosgenation)
Derivatives:
polycarbonate; polycarbonate diols

diphenyl cresyl phosphate
cresyldiphenyl phosphate; Disflamoll DPK (Bayer)

$C_{19}H_{17}O_4P_1$. M: 340.32. Colourless liquid. BP: 235–261°C (1.3 kPa). d: 1.18 kg/l (20°C). Not miscible with benzene or water.
Production:
• phosphorus oxychloride + cresylic acid (esterification)
Uses:
petrol anti-surface ignition agents; plasticiser (polyvinyl chloride, rubber, cellulose esters)

diphenyl decyl phosphite

$C_{22}H_{31}O_3P_1$. M: 374.46.
Production:
• phosphorus trichloride + isodecanol + phenol (dehydrochlorination/dehydrochlorination)
Uses: polyvinyl chloride heat costabilisers

diphenyldichlorosilane *See:* dichlorodiphenylsilane

diphenylene oxide
dibenzofuran; [38178-38-0]
$C_{12}H_8O_1$. M: 168.19. Crystalline solid. MP: 86–87°C.

BP: 287°C. Insoluble in water. Soluble in oxygenated and aromatic solvents.

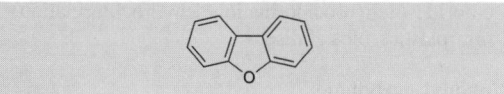

Production:
• fluorene oil (fractionation; coproduced with acenaphthene/fluorene)
Derivatives: 2,2'-dihydroxybiphenyl; diphenylene oxide-3,6-disulphohydrazide

diphenylene oxide-3,6-disulphohydrazide

$C_{12}H_{12}N_4O_5S_2$. M: 356.38.
Production:
• diphenylene oxide + chlorosulphonic acid + hydrazine (chlorosulphonation/sulphonamide formation)
Uses: blowing agent (foamed plastics and rubber)

diphenyl ether *See:* diphenyl oxide

diphenyl ether 4,4'-bis(sulphonyl chloride)
biphenyl oxide-4,4'-dichlorosulphonate; 4,4'-bis(chlorosulphono)diphenyl ether; 4,4'-oxybis(benzenesulphonyl chloride)

$C_{12}H_8Cl_2O_5S_2$. M: 367.22.
Production:
• diphenyl oxide + chlorosulphonic acid (chlorosulphonation)
Derivatives: 4,4'-oxybis(benzenesulphohydrazide); polyether sulphone

diphenyl 2-ethylhexyl phosphate
2-ethylhexyl diphenylphosphate; Disflamoll DPO (Bayer)

$C_{20}H_{27}O_4P_1$. M: 362.41. Colourless, involatile liquid. d: 1.08 kg/l (20°C). Viscosity: 25 mPa.s (20°C). Insoluble in water.
Production:
• phenol + 2-ethylhexanol + phosphorus oxychloride (dehydrochlorination/dehydrochlorination)
Uses:
fire-resistant polyvinyl chloride plasticiser

diphenylglycollic acid *See:* benzilic acid

diphenylguanidine
N,N'-diphenylguanidine; melaniline; DPG; [102-06-7]

$C_{13}H_{13}N_3$. M: 211.26. Crystalline solid. MP: 147–148°C. d: 1.13 kg/l. Decomposes on heating above 170°C. Very slightly soluble in water. Soluble in oxygenated and chlorinated solvents.
Production:
• aniline + cyanogen chloride (dehydrochlorination/ nitrile addition)
Uses:
vulcanisation accelerator

diphenylhydantoin *See:* phenytoin

diphenyl isophthalate
DPIP; [744-45-6]

$C_{20}H_{14}O_4$. M: 318.33. White solid. MP: 136–138°C. Insoluble in water. Soluble in acetone.
Production:
• phenol + isophthalic acid (esterification)
Derivatives: polybenzimidazole

diphenyl isopropylphenyl phosphate
See: isopropylphenyl diphenyl phosphate

diphenyl ketone
See: benzophenone

di-(phenylmercury) dodecenylsuccinate
PMDS

$C_{28}H_{36}Hg_2O_4$. M: 837.78.
Production:
• benzene + mercuric chloride + dodecenylsuccinic anhydride (salt formation)
Uses:
preservative (water-based paints)

diphenylmethane
benzylbenzene; [101-81-5]
$C_{13}H_{12}$. M: 168.24. Needles with a floral odour. MP: 26°C. BP: 264°C. d: 1.00 kg/l (25°C). Insoluble in

water. Soluble in oxygenated, chlorinated and hydro-carbon solvents.

Production:
- benzene + methylene chloride (Friedel-Crafts alkylation)

Uses: fragrance ingredient

4,4′-diphenylmethane diisocyanate, polymeric
diphenylmethane-4,4′-diisocyanate, polymeric; methyl-enebis(*p*-phenyl isocyanate), polymeric; MDI; PAPI; PMDI

n = 0–3. Fawn or brown liquid with aromatic odour. MP: ~0°C. d: 1.24 kg/l (25°C). Viscosity: 130–2,700 mPa.s (25°C). Reacts with water releasing carbon dioxide. The average NCO functionality of commercial grades is in the range 2.5–3.1.

Production:
- 4,4′-diaminodiphenylmethane, crude/4,4′-diamino-diphenylmethane, polymeric + phosgene (phosgenation)

Derivatives:
poly(amide-imide); polyhydantoin resins; polyisocyan-urate, rigid foam; polyols, polyisocyanate polyaddition; polyurethane, flexible foam, cold-moulded; polyureth-ane, integral-skin foam; polyurethane, rigid foam; poly-urethane, semi-rigid foam; polyurethane, latex; ureth-ane-acrylate resins

4,4′-diphenylmethane diisocyanate, pure
4,4′-diisocyanatodiphenylmethane;diisocyanatodiphenyl-methane; diphenylmethane diisocyanate; diphenylmeth-ane-4,4′-diisocyanate; MDI; [101-68-8]

$C_{15}H_{10}N_2O_2$. M: 250.25. Pale yellow solid. MP: 38–43°C. BP: 314°C. d: 1.23 kg/l (25°C). Hydrolysed by water. MDI blocked with, for example, phenol is pre-ferred in some applications.

Production:
- 4,4′-diaminodiphenylmethane, pure + phosgene (phosgenation)

Derivatives: 4,4′-diphenylmethane diisocyanate poly-ether prepolymers; 4,4′-diphenylmethane diisocyanate trimer; elastane; polyester polyurethane prepolymers, hydroxyl-terminated; polyester polyurethane prepoly-mers, isocyanate-terminated; polyurethane, thermoplastic elastomers

Uses: elastomeric fabric coatings

4,4′-diphenylmethane diisocyanate polyether prepoly-mers

R = short chain diol. Liquid isocyanate containing urethane linkages. The isocyanate functionality is 2.0.

Production:
- dipropylene glycol/1,4-butanediol + 4,4′-diphenyl-methane diisocyanate, pure (isocyanate addition)

Derivatives: polyurethane, cast elastomers; polyureth-ane, integral-skin foam; polyurethane, microcellular foam; polyurethane-polyurea, reaction injection-moulded elastomers

Uses: 2-pack elastomeric polyurethane coatings (fabric coatings, impact-resistant floor coatings)

4,4′-diphenylmethane diisocyanate trimer
Stable, low viscosity liquid isocyanate based on ureton-imine structure. The isocyanate functionality is up to 2.2.

Production:
- 4,4′-diphenylmethane diisocyanate, pure (isocyanate addition)

Derivatives:
polyurethane, flexible foam, cold-moulded

diphenylmethyl cyanide *See:* diphenylacetonitrile

diphenylolpropane *See:* bisphenol A

diphenyl oxide
diphenyl ether; phenyl ether; [101-84-8]

$C_{12}H_{10}O_1$. M: 170.21. Colourless liquid. MP: 27°C. BP: 257°C. d: 1.07 kg/l (27°C). Insoluble in water. Mis-cible with oxygenated solvents.

Production:
- phenol (ether formation)
- chlorobenzene (hydration; byproduct of phenol production)

Derivatives:
decabromodiphenyl oxide; diphenyl ether 4,4′-bis(sul-phonyl chloride); octabromodiphenyl oxide; 10,10′-oxybisphenoxyarsine; pentabromodiphenyl oxide; poly-ether ketone ketone; polyether sulphone

Uses:
heat-transfer oil; perfume ingredient (soap, detergents)

N,N′-diphenyl-*p*-phenylenediamine
DPPD; [74-31-7]

$C_{18}H_{16}N_2$. M: 260.34.

Production:
- hydroquinone + aniline (reductive amination/ reductive amination)
- *p*-phenylenediamine + phenol (amine formation)

Uses: antioxidant/antiozonant (rubber, lubricants)

diphenyl phthalate
DPP; [84-62-8]

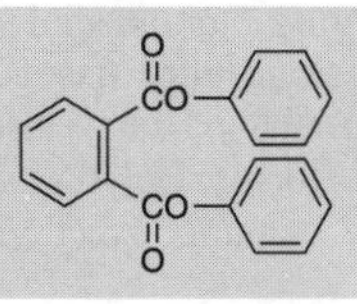

$C_{20}H_{14}O_4$. M: 318.33. Crystalline solid. MP: 69°C. d: 1.28 kg/l (25°C). Insoluble in water.
Production:
- phenol + phthalic anhydride (esterification)

Uses: polyvinyl chloride plasticiser

1,3-diphenyl-1,3-propanedione *See:* dibenzoylmethane

diphenylpyraline
[147-20-6]; [132-18-3] (hydrochloride)

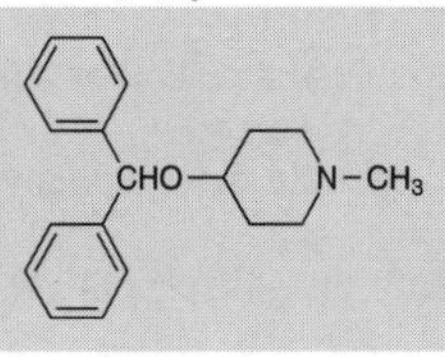

$C_{19}H_{23}N_1O_1$. M: 281.40. Available commercially as the free base or as the hydrochloride salt.
Production:
- 4-hydroxy-1-methylpiperidine + benzhydrol (alcohol chlorination/ether formation)

Uses: antihistamine drug

diphenylstilbene-2-ethylhexanoate
See: diphenylantimony 2-ethylhexanoate

diphenyl sulphone
[127-63-9]

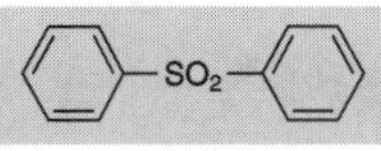

$C_{12}H_{10}O_2S_1$. M: 218.27. White crystals. MP: 128°C. BP: 378°C. Insoluble in water. Soluble in aromatic solvents.
Production:
- benzene + chlorosulphonic acid (chloro-sulphonation; byproduct of benzenesulphonyl chloride production)
- benzene (sulphonation; byproduct of benzene-sulphonic acid production)

Derivatives:
diphenylsulphone-3,3'-disulphohydrazide

diphenylsulphone-3,3'-disulphohydrazide
bis(3-hydrazinosulphonylphenyl)sulphone; 3,3'-sulphon-yldi-(benzenesulphonyl hydrazine); [3375-11-9]

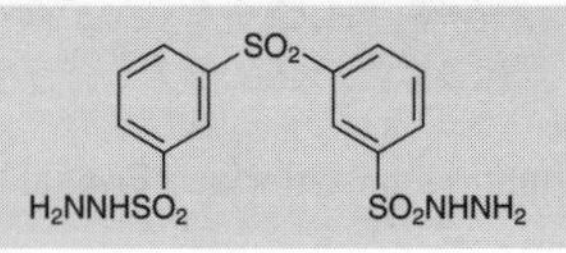

$C_{12}H_{14}N_4O_6S_3$. M: 406.45.
Production:
- diphenyl sulphone + hydrazine + chlorosulphonic acid (chlorosulphonation/sulphonamide formation)

Uses: blowing agent (foamed plastics)

N,N'-**diphenylthiourea** *See:* thiocarbanilide

dyphylline *See:* diprophylline

dipicolinic acid
pyridine-2,6-dicarboxylic acid; [499-83-2]

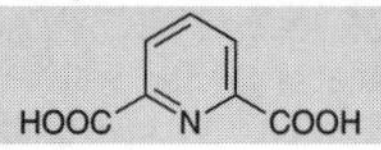

$C_7H_5N_1O_4$. M: 167.13.
Production:
- 2,6-lutidine (side-chain oxidation)

Derivatives: pyricarbate
Uses: metal complexing agent; stabiliser (hydrogen peroxide)

dipropetryn
2-ethylthio-4,6-di-(isopropylamino)-1,3,5-triazine; [4147-51-7]

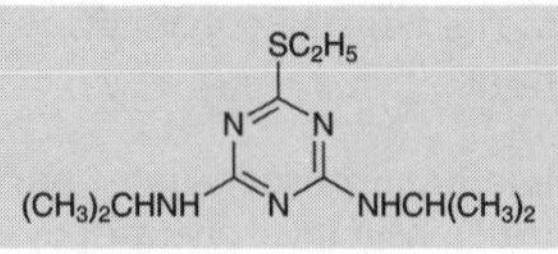

$C_{11}H_{21}N_5S_1$. M: 255.38.
Production:
- propazine + ethyl mercaptan (sulphide formation)

Uses: herbicide

diprophylline
7-(2,3-dihydroxypropyl)theophylline; dyphylline; [479-18-5]

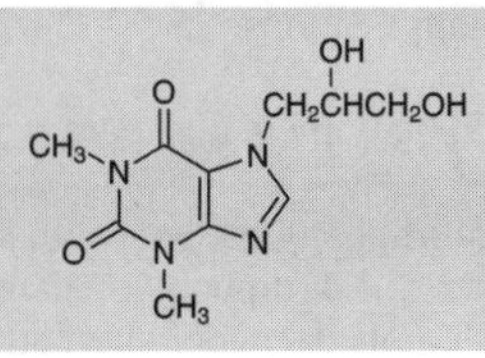

$C_{10}H_{14}N_4O_4$. M: 254.25.
Production:
- theophylline + chlorohydrin (amine formation)

Uses: bronchodilator drug

di-*n*-propylamine
[142-84-7]

$$(CH_3CH_2CH_2)_2NH$$

$C_6H_{15}N_1$. M: 101.20. Colourless liquid with an ammoniacal odour. BP: 109–110°C. MP: -63°C. d: 0.74 kg/l (4°C). Soluble in water and oxygenated solvents.
Production:
• propionaldehyde + ammonia (reductive ammoniation; coproduced with *n*-propylamine)
Derivatives:
EPTC; isopropalin; oryzalin; probenecid; prodiamine; trifluralin; vernolate

O,O-di-*n*-propyl dithiophosphoric acid
O,O-di-*n*-propyl phosphorodithioic acid

$$(CH_3CH_2CH_2O)_2\overset{\overset{\displaystyle S}{\|}}{P}SH$$

$C_6H_{15}O_2P_1S_2$. M: 214.28.
Production:
• *n*-propanol + phosphorus pentasulphide (addition)
Derivatives: piperophos

dipropylene glycol
DPG; [110-98-5]

$$\underset{HOCHCH_2OCHCH_2OH}{\overset{CH_3 \quad CH_3}{|\qquad\ |}}$$

$C_6H_{14}O_3$. M: 134.18. Colourless liquid. BP: 228–232°C. d: 1.02 kg/l (20°C). Miscible with water and oxygenated solvents.
Production:
• propylene oxide (hydration; coproduced with propylene glycol/tripropylene glycol)
Derivatives:
4,4'-diphenylmethane diisocyanate polyether prepolymers; dipropylene glycol diacrylate; dipropylene glycol dibenzoate; dipropylene glycol monosalicylate; polymeric plasticisers
Uses:
alkyd/unsaturated polyester resin comonomer; hydraulic fluid component; aromatics extraction solvent; fragrance diluent; petrol antiicing additive; polyurethane chain-extender; solvent (printing inks)

dipropylene glycol diacrylate
DPBDA

$$CH_2{=}CHCOCH_2\overset{\overset{\displaystyle CH_3}{|}}{C}HOCH_2\overset{\overset{\displaystyle CH_3}{|}}{C}HOCCH{=}CH_2$$

$C_{12}H_{18}O_5$. M: 242.26.
Production:
• dipropylene glycol + acrylic acid (esterification)
Uses:
crosslinked acrylic resin comonomer; reactive diluent (lacquers, printing inks)

dipropylene glycol dibenzoate
PPG-2 dibenzoate; Benzoflex 9-88 (Velsicol Chemical); [94-51-9]

$$\text{(benzene ring)}{-}\overset{\overset{\displaystyle O}{\|}}{C}OCH\overset{\overset{\displaystyle CH_3}{|}}{C}H_2O\overset{\overset{\displaystyle CH_3}{|}}{C}HCH_2O\overset{\overset{\displaystyle O}{\|}}{C}{-}\text{(benzene ring)}$$

$C_{20}H_{22}O_5$. M: 342.39. High-boiling liquid with a mild, ester odour. Pour point: -19°C. d: 1.12 kg/l (25°C). Insoluble in water. Soluble in aliphatic and aromatic solvents.
Production:
• dipropylene glycol + benzoic acid (esterification)
Uses:
plasticiser (castable polyurethanes, polyvinyl chloride plastisols, polyvinyl acetate adhesives)

dipropylene glycol monohexyl ether

$$\underset{CH_3(CH_2)_5OCHCH_2OCHCH_2OH}{\overset{CH_3 \qquad CH_3}{|\qquad\quad |}}$$

$C_{12}H_{26}O_3$. M: 218.34.
Production:
• *n*-hexanol + propylene oxide (epoxidation)
Uses:
flotation frothing agent

dipropylene glycol monoisobutyl ether
isobutoxypropoxypropanol

$$\underset{(CH_3)_2CHCH_2OCHCH_2OCHCH_2OH}{\overset{CH_3 \qquad CH_3}{|\qquad\quad |}}$$

$C_{10}H_{22}O_3$. M: 190.29. Liquid. BP: 220°C. d: 0.91 kg/l. Soluble in water and most organic solvents. Flash point: 110°C (PMCC).
Production:
• isobutanol + propylene oxide (epoxidation)
Uses: solvent (paints)

dipropylene glycol monomethyl ether
methoxypropoxypropanol; DPM; DPMG; Propasol DM (Union Carbide); [34590-94-8]

$$\underset{CH_3OCHCH_2OCHCH_2OH}{\overset{CH_3 \quad CH_3}{|\qquad\ |}}$$

$C_7H_{16}O_3$. M: 148.21. Colourless liquid. BP: 187°C. FP: -80°C. d: 0.95 kg/l (20°C). Miscible with water and most organic solvents. Flash point: 79°C (TCC). The product is a mixture of isomers.
Production:
• methanol + propylene oxide (epoxidation)
Uses: solvent (paints, resins)

dipropylene glycol monosalicylate
[68683-31-8]
$C_{11}H_{14}O_5$. M: 226.22. Pale yellow liquid with a pleasant odour. d: 1.16 kg/l. Insoluble in water. Soluble in alcohol.

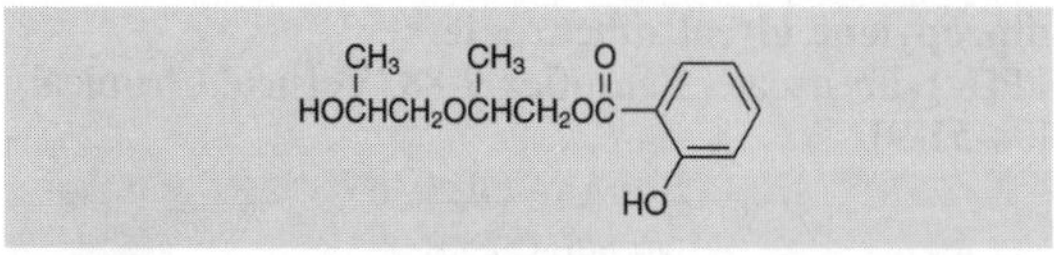

Production:
• dipropylene glycol + salicylic acid (esterification)
Uses: sunscreening agent (cosmetics); light stabiliser (plastics)

dipropylenetriamine

N-(3-aminopropyl)-1,3-propanediamine; di-(3-amino-propyl)amine; 3,3′-iminobispropylamine; [56-18-8]

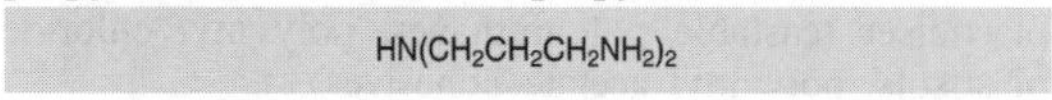

$C_6H_{17}N_3$. M: 131.23. Liquid. BP: 110–120°C (1.3 kPa). MP: -16°C.
Production:
• ammonia + acrylonitrile (cyanoethylation/nitrile reduction; coproduced with 1,3-propanediamine)
Uses:
epoxy resin curing agent; raw material (disinfectants, preservatives)

di-*n*-propyl ketone

heptan-4-one; [123-19-3]

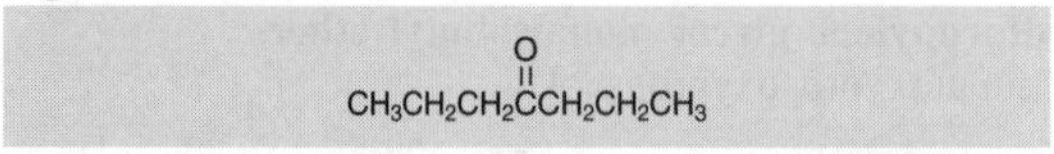

$C_7H_{14}O_1$. M: 114.19. Colourless liquid with penetrating odour. BP: 143–146°C. MP: -36°C. d: 0.82 kg/l (15°C). Insoluble in water.
Production:
• *n*-butyric acid (decarboxylative coupling)
Uses:
pharmaceutical raw material

di-(*n*-propyl) peroxydicarbonate

Lupersol 211 (Elf-Atochem); Triganox NPP (Akzo)

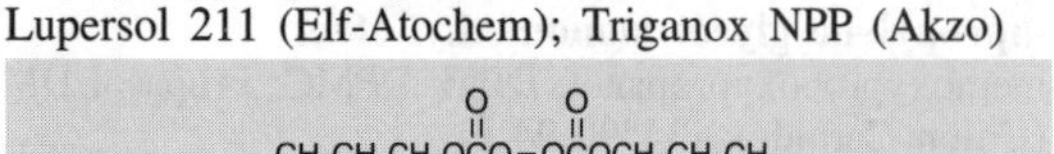

$C_8H_{14}O_6$. M: 206.19. Available commercially as a pure liquid or as a solution in white spirit with a 85% peroxide content. Decomposes on heating with a 10-hour half-life at 45°C.
Production:
• *n*-propyl chloroformate + hydrogen peroxide (dehydrochlorination)
Uses: polymerisation initiator

di-*n*-propyl phosphorodithioic acid

See: *O,O*-di-*n*-propyl dithiophosphoric acid

dipyridamole

[58-32-2]
$C_{24}H_{40}N_8O_4$. M: 504.64.

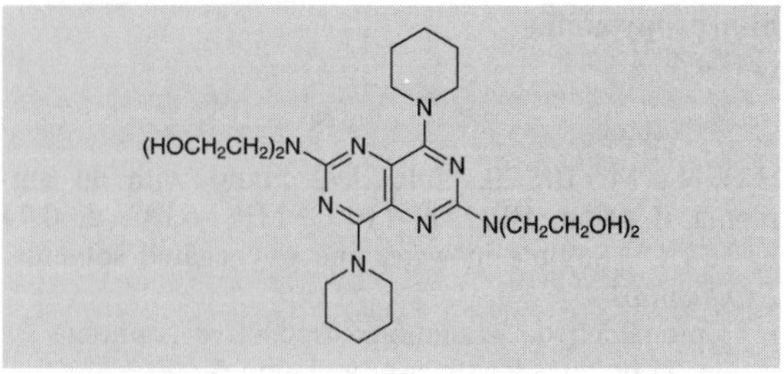

Production:
• 5-aminoorotic acid + sodium cyanate + sodium iodide + piperidine + diethanolamine (cyanate addition/chlorination/amine formation/amine formation)
Uses:
vasodilator drug

2,2′-dipyridyl *See:* 2,2′-bipyridine

dipyrone

metamizol; [5907-38-0]

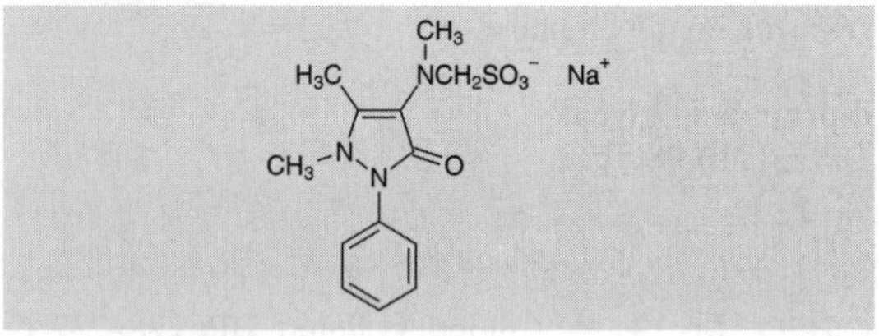

$C_{13}H_{16}N_3Na_1O_4S_1$. M: 333.34.
Production:
• 4-aminoantipyrine + dimethyl sulphate + formaldehyde + sodium bisulphite (amine protection/methylation/hydrolysis/sulphomethylation)
Uses:
antipyretic/antirheumatic drug

diquat dibromide

[85-00-7]

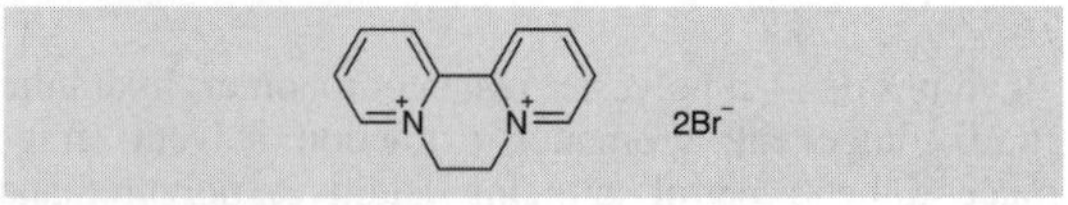

$C_{12}H_{12}Br_2N_2$. M: 344.05.
Production:
• 2,2′-bipyridine + ethylene dibromide (quaternisation)
Uses: herbicide

Direct Black 3

Neutral Grey G; 27710 (CI)

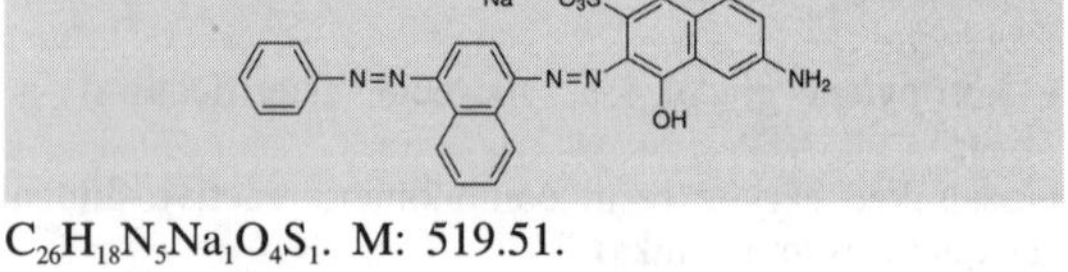

$C_{26}H_{18}N_5Na_1O_4S_1$. M: 519.51.

Production:
- benzenediazonium chloride + gamma acid +
  1-naphthylamine (diazotisation/azo coupling/
  azo coupling)

Uses:
dye (cotton, silk)

Direct Black 9
31560 (CI)

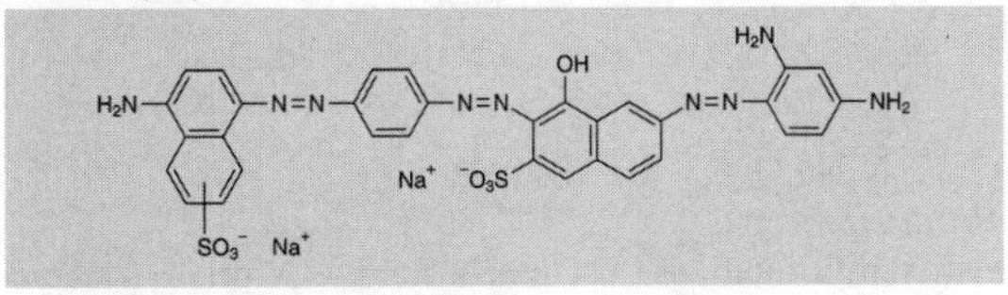

$C_{32}H_{23}N_9Na_2O_7S_2$. M: 755.69.

Production:
- *p*-nitroaniline + Cleve's acid, mixed +
  gamma acid + *m*-phenylenediamine (diazotisation/
  azo coupling/diazotisation/azo coupling/amide
  hydrolysis/diazotisation/azo coupling)

Uses:
dye (cotton)

Direct Black 19
35255 (CI)

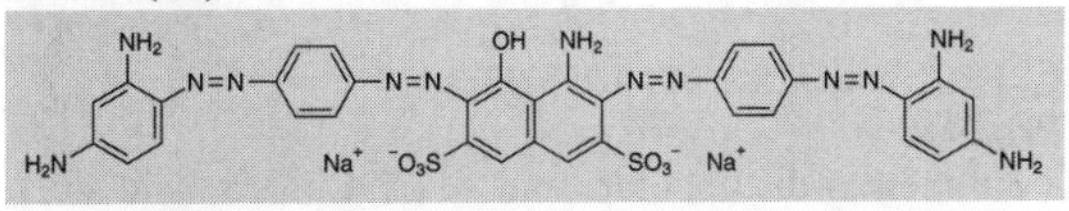

$C_{34}H_{27}N_{13}Na_2O_7S_2$. M: 839.78.

Production:
- *m*-phenylenediamine + *p*-nitroaniline + H acid
  (diazotisation/azo coupling/nitro reduction/
  diazotisation/azo coupling)

Uses:
dye (cotton, leather, paper, viscose)

Direct Black 22
35435 (CI)

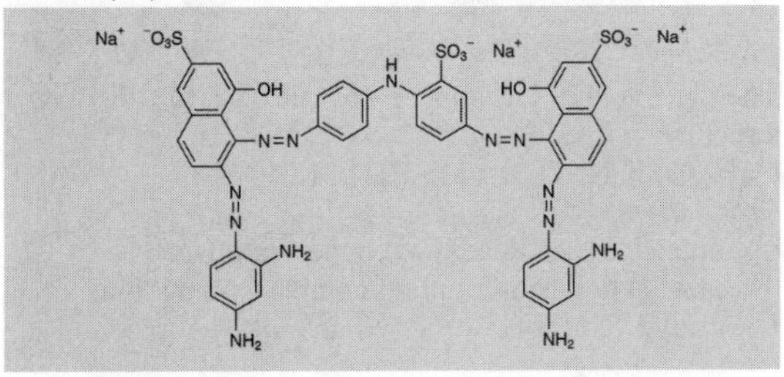

$C_{44}H_{32}N_{13}Na_3O_{11}S_3$. M: 1083.98.

Production:
- 4,4'-diaminodiphenylamine-2-sulphonic acid +
  gamma acid + *m*-phenylenediamine (diazotisation/
  azo coupling/diazotisation/azo coupling)

Uses:
dye (cotton, bast fibres, leather)

Direct Black 78
30015 (CI)

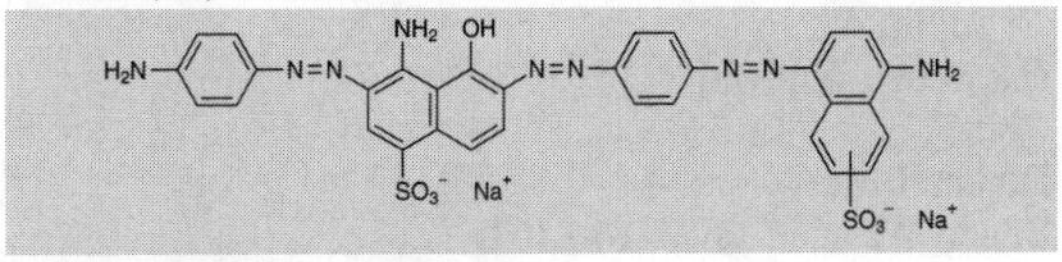

$C_{32}H_{23}N_9Na_2O_7S_2$. M: 755.69.

Production:
- *p*-nitroaniline + Cleve's acid, mixed + S acid
  (diazotisation/azo coupling/diazotisation/azo
  coupling/nitro reduction/diazotisation/azo coupling/
  nitro reduction)

Uses: dye (cotton, wool, silk, polyamide, leather)

Direct Black 80
31600 (CI)

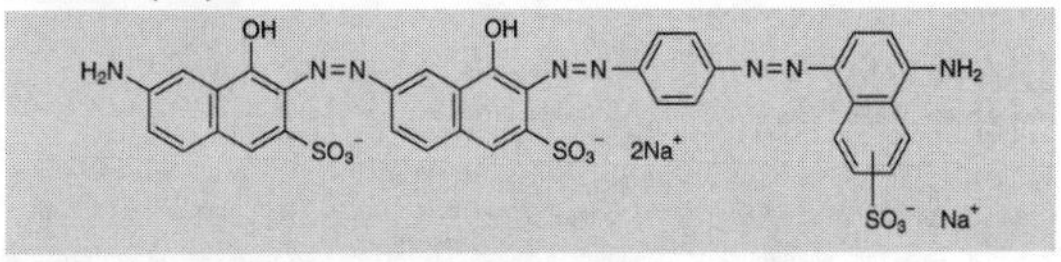

$C_{36}H_{23}N_8Na_3O_{11}S_3$. M: 908.79.

Production:
- *p*-aminoacetanilide + gamma acid + Cleve's acid,
  mixed (diazotisation/azo coupling/amide
  hydrolysis/diazotisation/azo coupling/diazotisation/
  azo coupling)

Uses: dye (cotton, viscose)

Direct Black 91
30400 (CI)

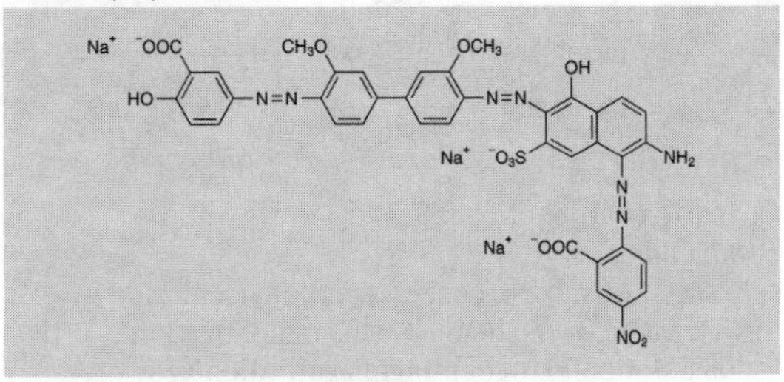

$C_{38}H_{25}N_8Na_3O_{13}S_1$. M: 902.70.

Production:
- *o*-dianisidine + salicylic acid + J acid + 5-nitro-
  anthranilic acid (diazotisation/azo coupling/
  diazotisation/azo coupling/diazotisation/azo coupling)

Uses: dye (cotton)

Direct Blue 1
24410 (CI)

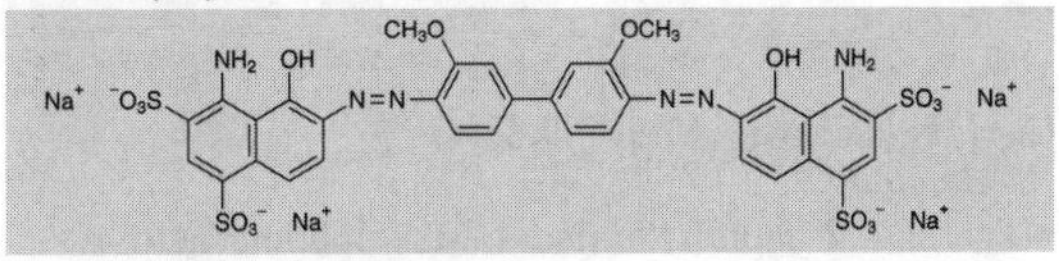

$C_{34}H_{24}N_6Na_4O_{16}S_4$. M: 992.80.

Production:
- *o*-dianisidine + Chicago acid (diazotisation/azo coupling)

Uses: dye (cotton)

Direct Blue 8
Benzo Azurine G; 24140 (CI)

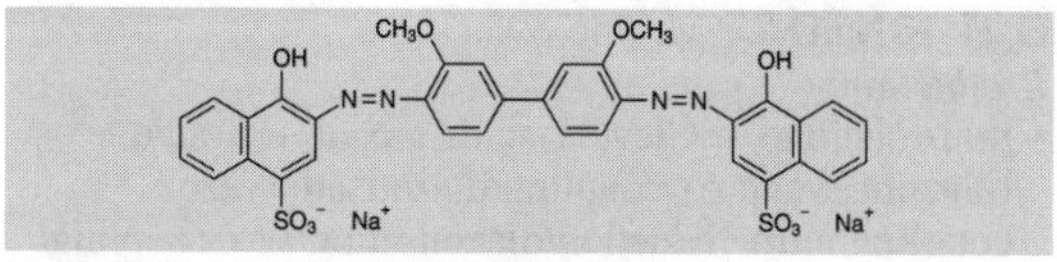

$C_{34}H_{24}N_4Na_2O_{10}S_2$. M: 758.69.
Production:
- *o*-dianisidine + Nevile-Winther acid (diazotisation/azo coupling)

Uses: dye (cotton, paper)

Direct Blue 15
24400 (CI); [2429-74-5]

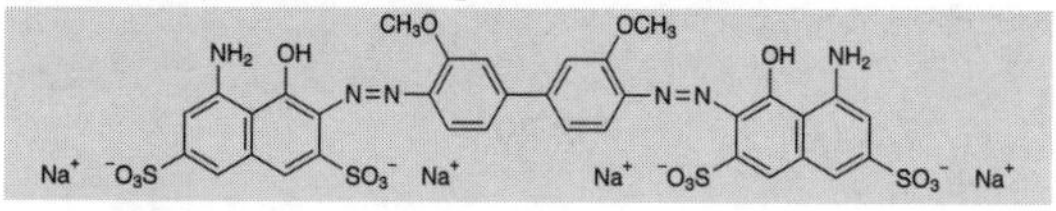

$C_{34}H_{24}N_6Na_4O_{16}S_4$. M: 992.80.
Production:
- *o*-dianisidine + H acid (diazotisation/azo coupling)

Uses: dye (cotton)

Direct Blue 67
Sirius Supra Blue F3R; 27925 (CI)

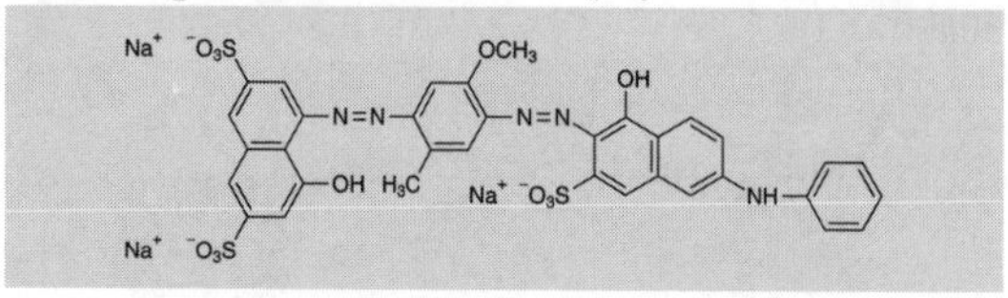

$C_{34}H_{24}N_5Na_3O_{12}S_3$. M: 859.74.
Production:
- *N*-acetyl-H acid + benzenesulphonyl chloride + *p*-cresidine + *N*-phenyl-J acid (sulphonation/ diazotisation/azo coupling/diazotisation/azo coupling/hydrolysis)

Uses: dye (cotton)

Direct Blue 71
34140 (CI)

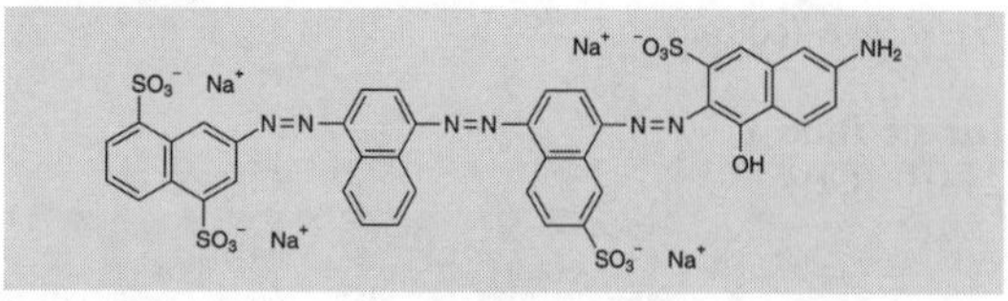

$C_{40}H_{23}N_7Na_4O_{13}S_4$. M: 1029.88.
Production:
- J acid + 2-naphthylamine-4,8-disulphonic acid + 1-naphthylamine + 1,7-Cleve's acid (diazotisation/

azo coupling/diazotisation/azo coupling/diazotisation/azo coupling)

Uses: dye (cotton, silk, paper)

Direct Blue 75
34220 (CI)

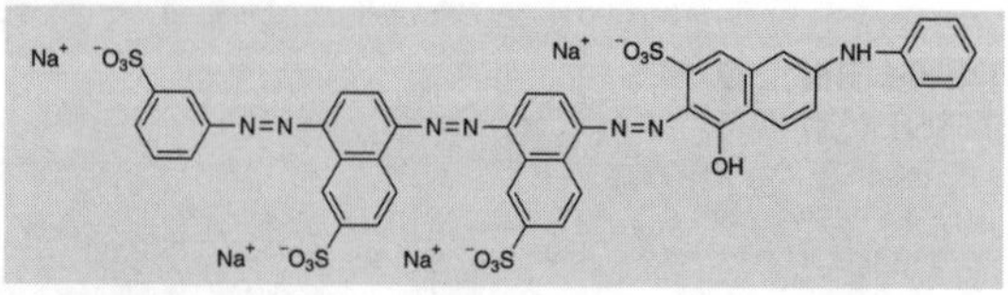

$C_{42}H_{25}N_7Na_4O_{13}S_4$. M: 1055.92.
Production:
- metanilic acid + 1,6-Cleve's acid + *N*-phenyl-J acid (diazotisation/azo coupling/diazotisation/azo coupling/diazotisation/azo coupling)

Uses: dye (cotton)

Direct Blue 78
34200 (CI)

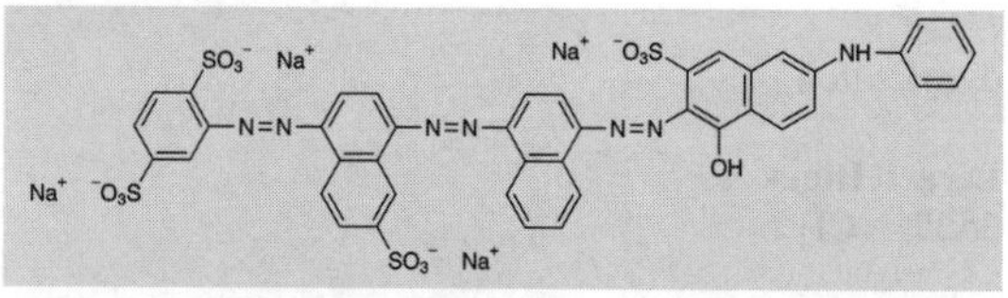

$C_{42}H_{25}N_7Na_4O_{13}S_4$. M: 1055.92.
Production:
- aniline-2,5-disulphonic acid + 1,7-Cleve's acid + 1-naphthylamine + *N*-phenyl-J acid (diazotisation/ azo coupling/diazotisation/azo coupling/ diazotisation/azo coupling)

Uses: dye (cotton)

Direct Blue 80

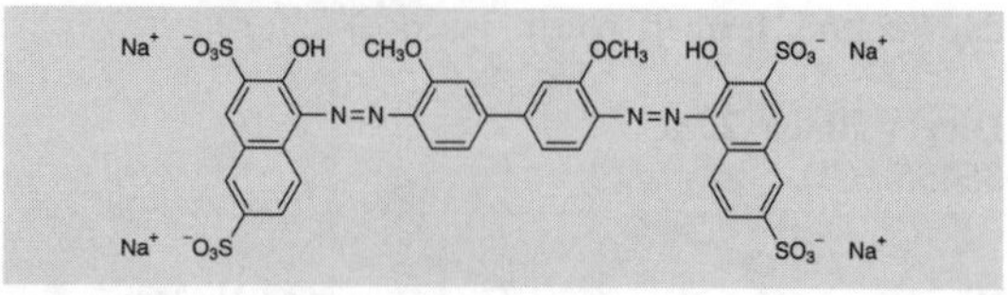

The dye is the 1:1 copper complex of the displayed structure.
$C_{34}H_{20}Cu_1N_4Na_4O_{16}S_4$. M: 1024.31.
Production:
- *o*-dianisidine + R acid + copper sulphate (diazotisation/azo coupling/complex formation)

Uses: dye (cotton)

Direct Blue 84
23160 (CI); [13569-92-1]

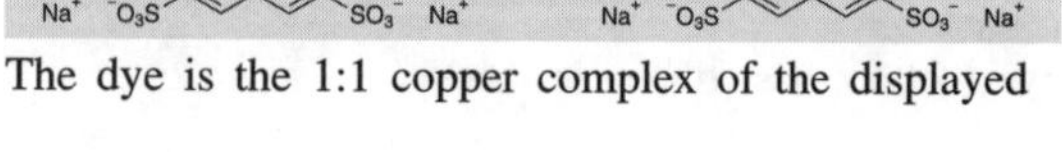

The dye is the 1:1 copper complex of the displayed

structure. $C_{32}H_{16}Cu_1N_4Na_4O_{18}S_4$. M: 1028.25.
Production:
- *o*-dianisidine + chromotropic acid + copper
  sulphate (diazotisation/azo coupling/complex
  formation)

Uses: dye (cotton)

Direct Blue 86
Pigment Blue 17 (CI, barium salt); Solvent Blue 38
(CI, amine salt); 74180 (CI); 74180:1 (CI, barium salt)

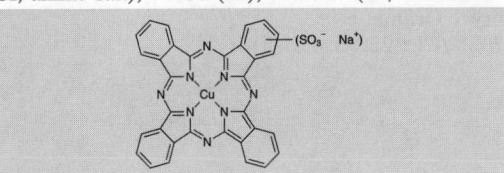

The chemical is mixture of copper phthalocyanine
sulphonates.
Production:
- copper phthalocyanine (sulphonation)

Uses:
direct dye (cotton, paper, leather); solvent dye (lacquers, ballpen inks)

Direct Blue 93
Sirius Supra Blue 3RL; 22810 (CI)

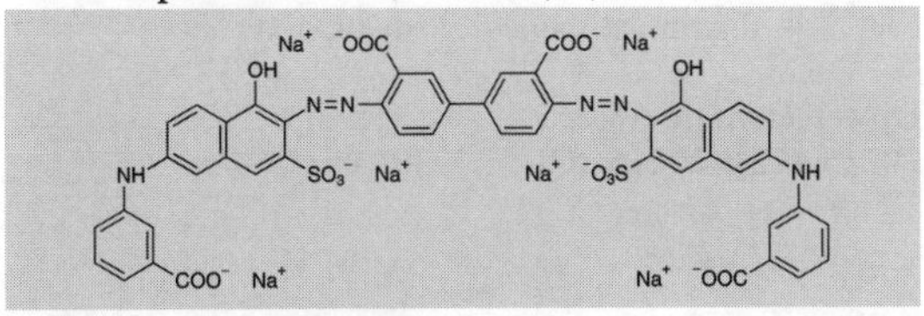

$C_{48}H_{26}N_6Na_6O_{16}$. M: 1080.70.
Production:
- J acid + *m*-aminobenzoic acid + benzidine-
  3,3′-dicarboxylic acid + copper sulphate (amine
  formation/diazotisation/azo coupling/
  complex formation)

Uses: dye (cotton)

Direct Blue 98
23155 (CI); [6656-03-7]

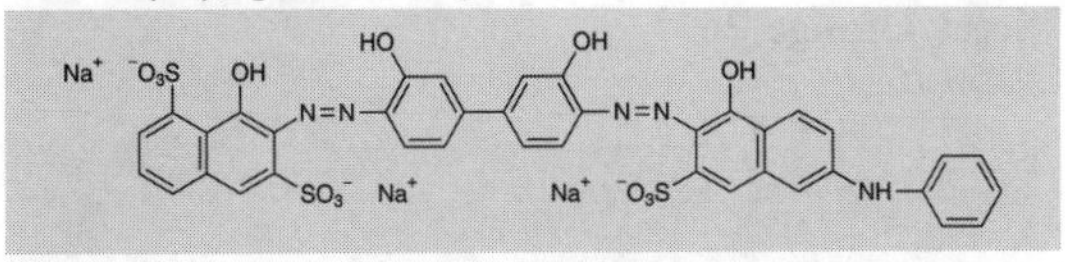

The dye is the copper complex of the displayed
structure. $C_{76}H_{48}Cu_1N_{10}Na_6O_{26}S_6$. M: 1911.13.
Production:
- *o*-dianisidine + *N*-phenyl-J acid + copper sulphate
  + 1-naphthol-3,8-disulphonic acid (diazotisation/azo
  coupling/diazotisation/azo coupling/complex
  formation)

Uses: dye (cotton, leather, paper)

Direct Blue 106
51300 (CI)

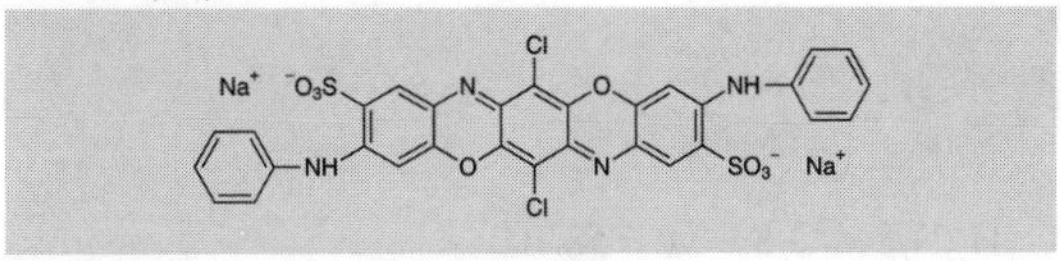

$C_{30}H_{16}Cl_2N_4Na_2O_8S_2$. M: 741.50.
Production:
- 4-aminodiphenylamine-2-sulphonic acid + chloranil
  (condensation/ether formation)

Uses:
dye (cotton, polyamide fibres)

Direct Blue 108
Sirius Light Blue FFGL; Sirius Light Blue FFRL;
51320 (CI)

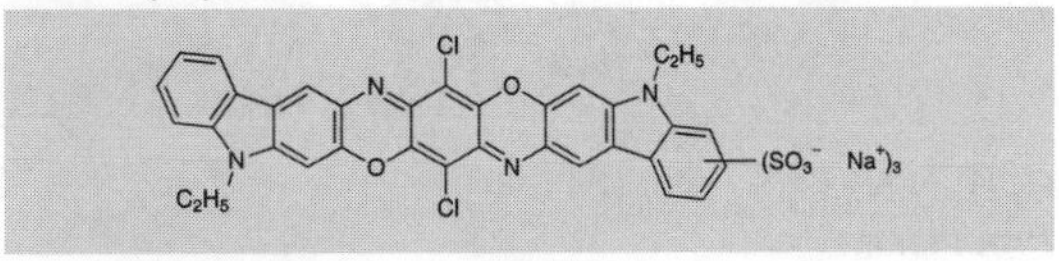

$C_{34}H_{22}Cl_2N_4Na_3O_{11}S_3$. M: 898.64.
Production:
- 3-amino-*N*-ethylcarbazole + chloranil (carbonyl
  condensation/sulphonation)

Uses:
dye (cotton)

Direct Blue 109
51310 (CI)

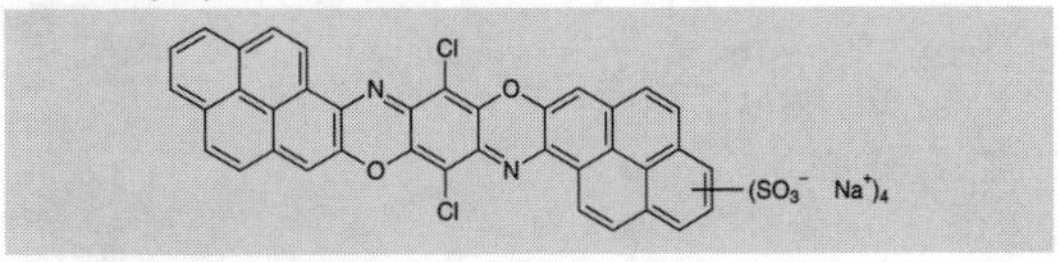

$C_{38}H_{12}Cl_2N_2Na_4O_{14}S_4$. M: 1011.65.
Production:
- pyrene + chloranil (nitration/nitro reduction/
  condensation)

Uses:
dye (cotton)

Direct Blue 120
34085 (CI)

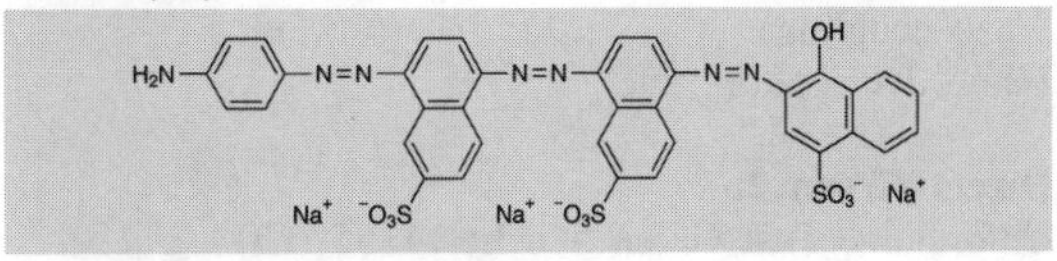

$C_{36}H_{22}N_7Na_3O_{10}S_3$. M: 877.78.
Production:
- *p*-nitroaniline + 1,6-Cleve's acid + Nevile-Winther
  acid (diazotisation/azo coupling/diazotisation/azo
  coupling/nitro reduction)

Uses:
dye (cotton)

Direct Brown 44
35005 (CI)

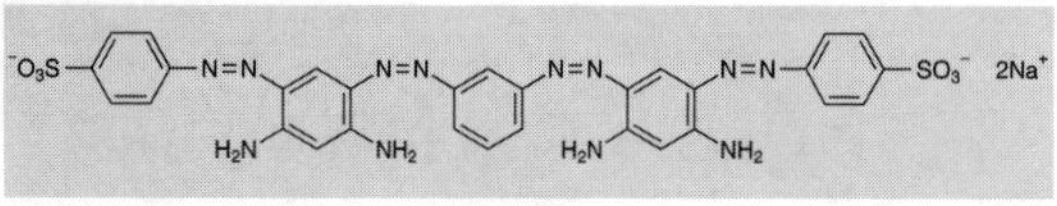

$C_{30}H_{24}N_{12}Na_2O_6S_2$. M: 758.70.
Production:
- Basic Brown 1 + sulphanilic acid (diazotisation/ azo coupling)

Uses: dye (cotton, leather)

Direct Green 13
Brilliant Benzo Fast Green GL; 28470 (CI)

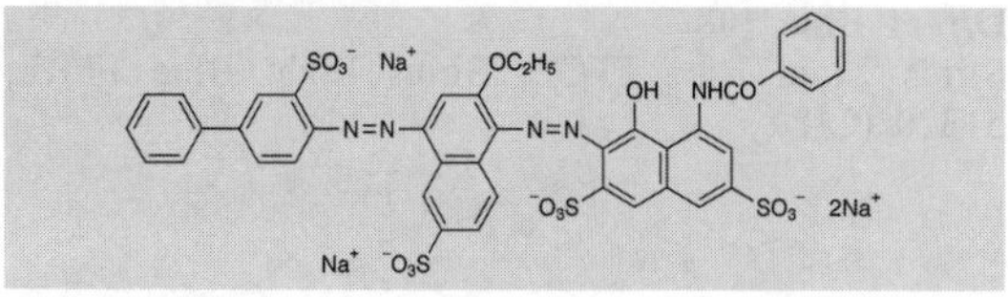

$C_{41}H_{27}N_5Na_4O_{15}S_4$. M: 1049.90.
Production:
- 4-aminobiphenyl-3-sulphonic acid + 2-ethoxy-1-naphthylamine-6-sulphonic acid + benzoyl chloride + H acid (diazotisation/azo coupling/amide formation/diazotisation/azo coupling)

Uses: dye (cotton)

Direct Green 26
Chlorantine Fast Green BLL; 34045 (CI)

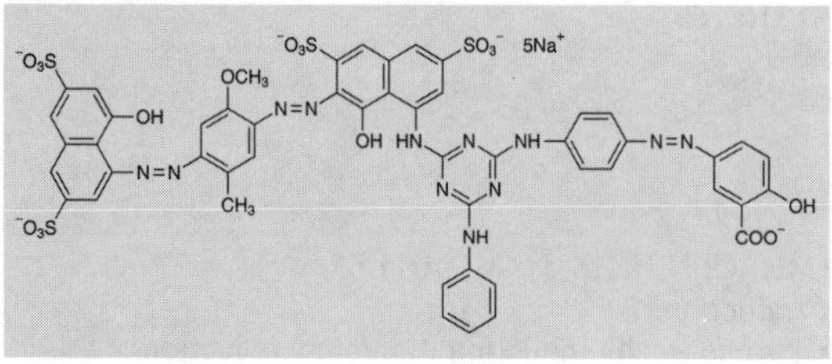

$C_{50}H_{33}N_{12}Na_5O_{18}S_4$. M: 1333.08.
Production:
- cyanuric chloride + H acid + *p*-nitroaniline + salicylic acid + *p*-cresidine (amine formation/amine formation/nitro reduction/diazotisation/azo coupling/diazotisation/azo coupling/diazotisation/ azo coupling)

Uses: dye (cotton, jute)

Direct Green 28
Chlorantine Fast Green 5GLL; 14155 (CI)
$C_{42}H_{27}N_{10}Na_3O_{11}S_2$. M: 980.84.
Production:
- cyanuric chloride + aniline + 4-nitroaniline-2-sulphonic acid + bromamine acid + 5-amino-salicylic acid (amine formation/amine formation/ nitro reduction/amine formation/diazotisation/azo coupling/amine formation)

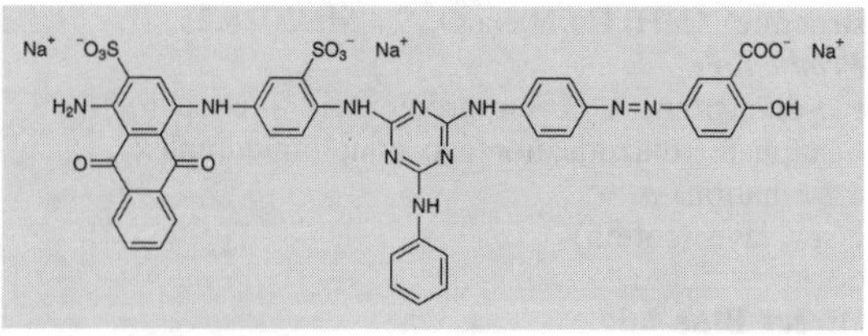

Uses: dye (cotton)

Direct Orange 6
23365 (CI); 23375 (CI)

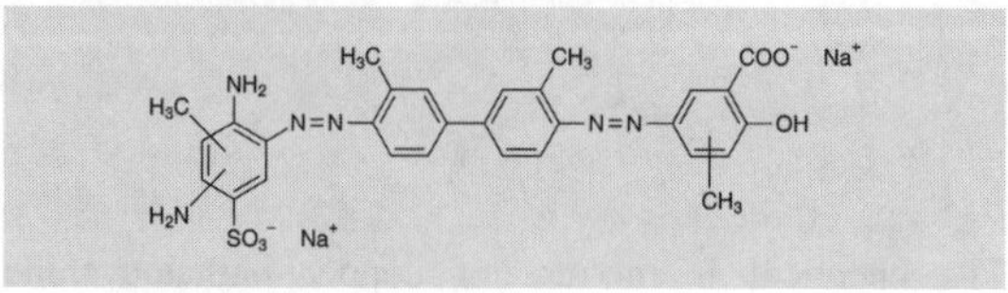

$C_{28}H_{24}N_6Na_2O_6S_1$. M: 618.57.
Production:
- *o*-tolidine + 2,4-diaminobenzenesulphonic acid/ 2,4-diaminotoluene-5-sulphonic acid + *o*-cresotic acid/salicylic acid (diazotisation/azo coupling/ diazotisation/azo coupling)

Uses: dye (cotton, polyamide fibres)

Direct Orange 15
See: 4,4′-diaminostilbene-2,2′-disulphonic acid

Direct Orange 18
20215 (CI); 20216 (CI); 20230 (CI)

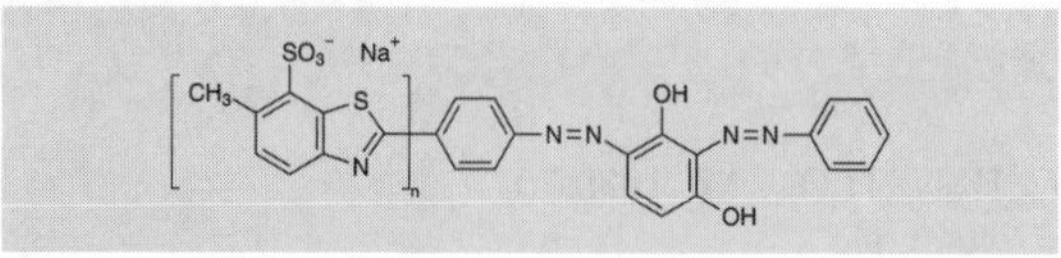

n = 1–2.
Production:
- dehydrothio-*p*-toluidinesulphonic acid/Direct Yellow 59 + benzenediazonium chloride + resorcinol (azo coupling/diazotisation/azo coupling)

Uses:
dye (cotton)

Direct Orange 26
29150 (CI)

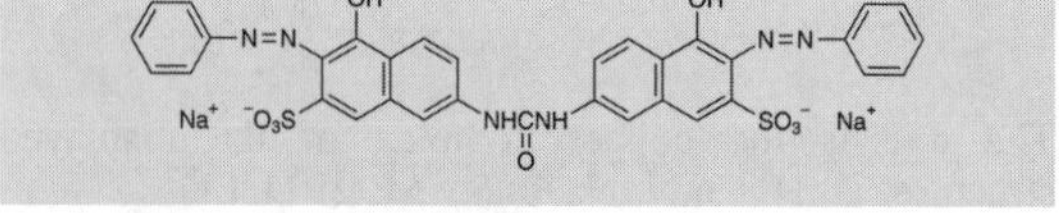

$C_{33}H_{22}N_6Na_2O_9S_2$. M: 756.68.
Production:
- benzenediazonium chloride + J acid urea (azo coupling)

Uses:
dye (cotton, wool, polyamide)

Direct Orange 29
29155 (CI)

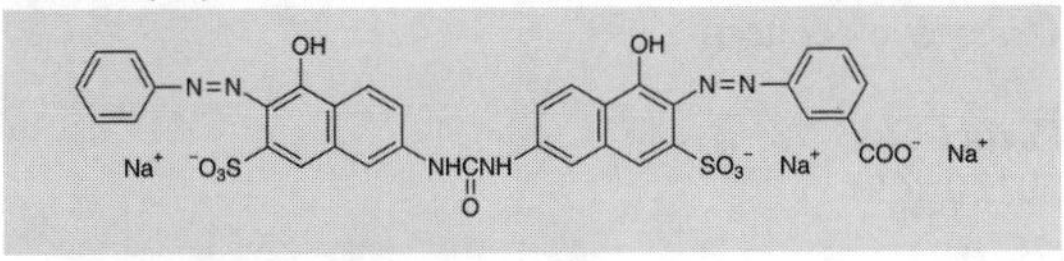

$C_{34}H_{21}N_6Na_3O_{11}S_2$. M: 822.67.
Production:
• aniline + *m*-aminobenzoic acid + J acid urea
(diazotisation/azo coupling/diazotisation/azo coupling)
Uses:
dye (cotton, silk, wool, polyamide)

Direct Orange 34
Direct Orange 39 (CI); 40215 (CI)

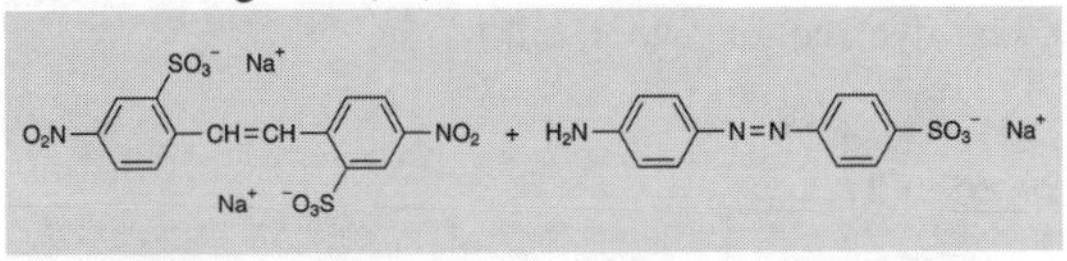

Production:
• aniline + sulphanilic acid + 4-nitrotoluene-
2-sulphonic acid (diazotisation/azo coupling/base-
catalysed condensation)
Uses: dye (cotton)

Direct Orange 39 *See:* Direct Orange 34

Direct Orange 72
29058 (CI)

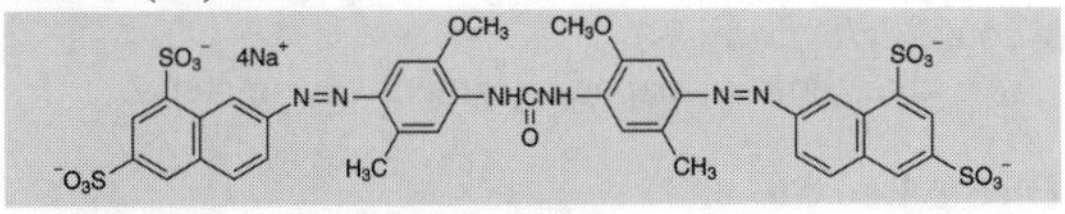

$C_{37}H_{28}N_6Na_4O_{15}S_4$. M: 1016.88.
Production:
• *N,N'*-bis(2-methoxy-5-methylphenyl) urea + amino-
G acid (diazotisation/azo coupling)
Uses: dye (cotton, silk, leather, paper)

Direct Orange 75
Diazo Brilliant Orange GR; 17840 (CI)

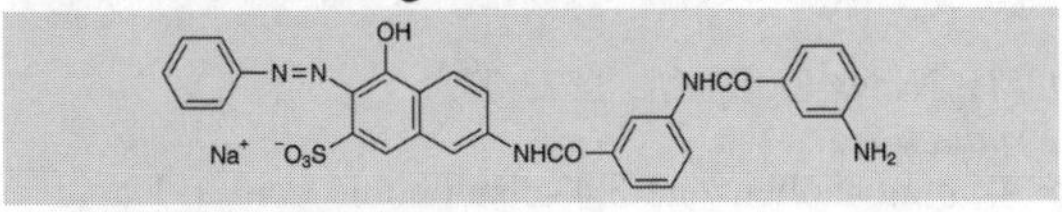

$C_{30}H_{22}N_5Na_1O_6S_1$. M: 603.59.
Production:
• *N-m*-aminobenzoyl-J acid + *m*-nitrobenzoyl chloride
+ benzenediazonium chloride (amide formation/
nitro reduction/azo coupling)
Uses: dye (cotton)

Direct Orange 102
29156 (CI)
$C_{32}H_{21}N_6Na_3O_{11}S_2$. M: 798.65.

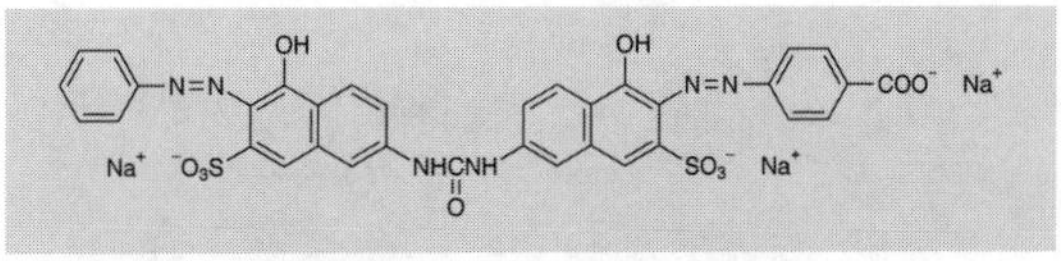

Production:
• aniline + *p*-aminobenzoic acid + J acid urea
(diazotisation/azo coupling/diazotisation/azo coupling)
Uses: dye (cotton)

Direct Red 2
23500 (CI)

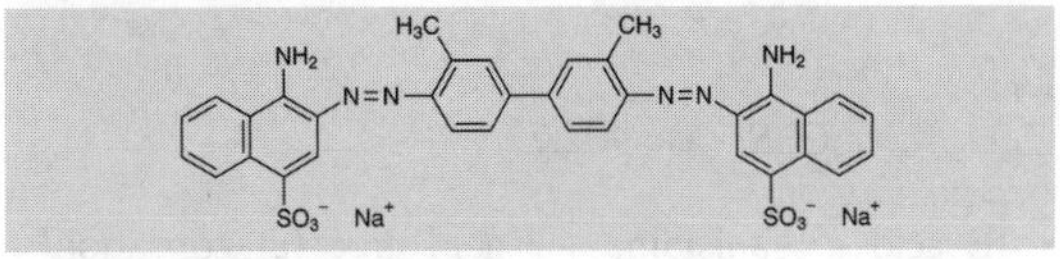

$C_{23}H_{26}N_6Na_2O_6S_2$. M: 592.60.
Production:
• *o*-tolidine + naphthionic acid (diazotisation/azo
coupling)
Uses: dye (cotton, wool, silk, polyamide, linen, jute,
leather, paper)

Direct Red 4
29165 (CI)

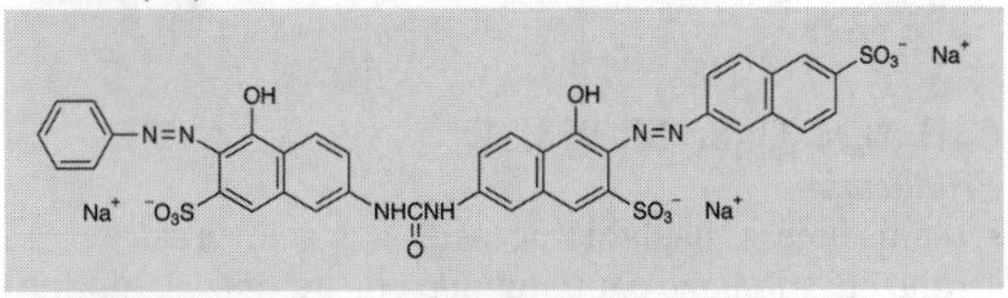

$C_{37}H_{23}N_6Na_3O_{12}S_3$. M: 908.78.
Production:
• aniline + Broenner's acid + J acid urea
(diazotisation/azo coupling/diazotisation/azo coupling)
Uses: dye (cotton, silk, polyamide, leather, paper)

Direct Red 16
27680 (CI)

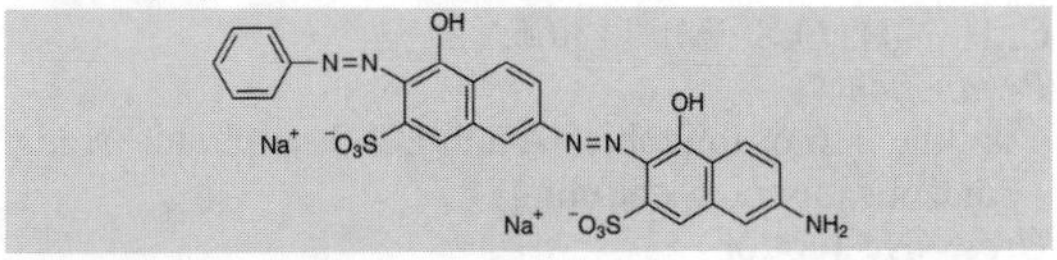

$C_{26}H_{17}N_5Na_2O_8S_2$. M: 637.56.
Production:
• aniline + J acid (diazotisation/azo coupling/
diazotisation/azo coupling)
Uses: dye (cotton)

Direct Red 23
29160 (CI); [3441-14-3]
$C_{35}H_{24}N_7Na_2O_{10}S_2$. M: 812.72.
Production:
• benzenediazonium chloride + *p*-aminoacetanilide +
J acid urea (diazotisation/azo coupling/azo coupling)

Uses: dye (cotton, paper); pigment raw material

Direct Red 24
29185 (CI)

$C_{35}H_{25}N_6Na_3O_{13}S_3$. M: 902.77.
Production:
- 4B acid + *o*-anisidine + J acid urea (diazotisation/azo coupling/diazotisation/azo coupling)

Uses: dye (cotton, paper); pigment raw material

Direct Red 26
29190 (CI)

$C_{38}H_{25}N_6Na_3O_{13}S_3$. M: 938.81.
Production:
- *o*-anisidine + naphthionic acid + J acid urea (diazotisation/azo coupling/diazotisation/azo coupling)

Uses: dye (cotton, wool, polyamide, leather, paper)

Direct Red 31
29100 (CI)

$C_{32}H_{21}N_5Na_2O_8S_2$. M: 713.66.
Production:
- aniline + 6,6'-iminobis(1-naphthol-3-sulphonic acid) (diazotisation/azo coupling)

Uses: dye (cotton)

Direct Red 72
29200 (CI)

R = methyl, methoxy-.
Production:
- *o*-toluidine/*o*-anisidine + Broenner's acid + J acid

urea (diazotisation/azo coupling/diazotisation/azo coupling)
Uses: dye (cotton)

Direct Red 73
29180 (CI)

$C_{38}H_{25}N_6Na_3O_{12}S_3$. M: 922.81.
Production:
- *o*-toluidine + Broenner's acid + J acid urea (diazotisation/azo coupling/diazotisation/azo coupling)

Uses: dye (cotton, wool, silk)

Direct Red 79
29065 (CI)

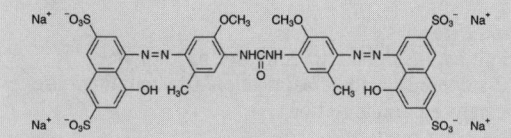

$C_{37}H_{28}N_6Na_2O_{17}S_2$. M: 938.76.
Production:
- *N*-acetyl-H acid + *p*-toluenesulphonyl chloride + *N,N'*-bis(2-methoxy-5-methylphenyl) urea (sulphonation/amide hydrolysis/diazotisation/azo coupling/hydrolysis)

Uses: dye (cotton, paper); pigment raw material

Direct Red 80
35780 (CI); [2610-10-8]

$C_{45}H_{26}N_{10}Na_6O_{21}S_6$. M: 1373.07.
Production:
- 4-aminoazobenzene-3,4'-disulphonic acid + J acid urea (diazotisation/azo coupling)

Uses: dye (cotton, leather, paper)

Direct Red 81
28160 (CI); [2610-11-9]
$C_{29}H_{20}N_5Na_1O_8S_1$. M: 621.56.
Production:
- J acid + benzoyl chloride + 4'-aminoazobenzene-4-sulphonic acid (amide formation/diazotisation/azo coupling)

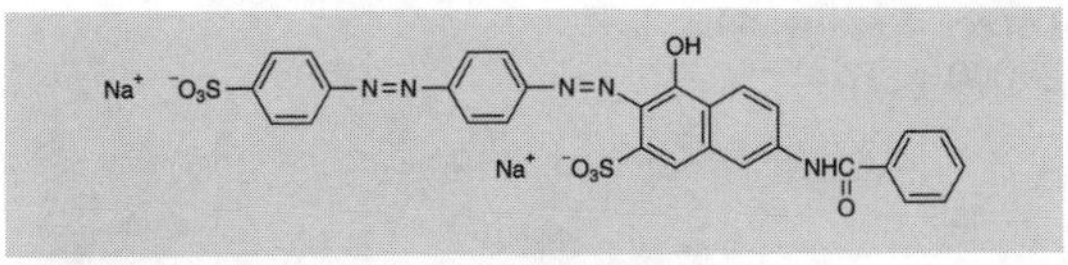

Uses: dye (cotton, silk, leather, paper)

Direct Red 83
29225 (CI)

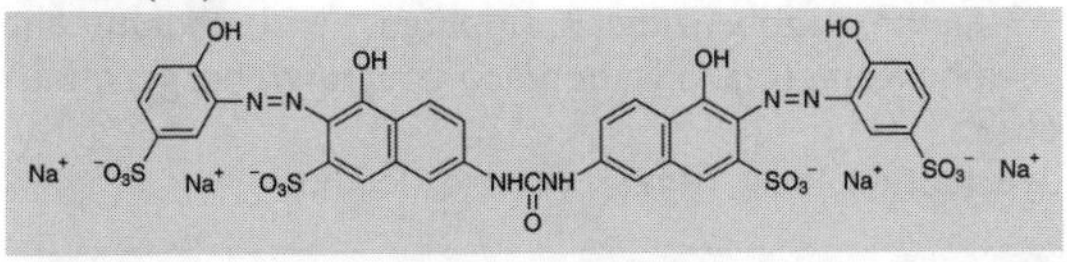

The dye is the 1:2 copper complex of the displayed structure. $C_{33}H_{18}Cu_1N_6Na_4O_{17}S_2$. M: 990.17.
Production:
• 2-aminoanisole-4-sulphonic acid + J acid urea + copper sulphate (diazotisation/azo coupling/complex formation/demethylation)
Uses:
dye (cotton, leather, paper); pigment raw material

Direct Red 118
Rosanthrene O; 17780 (CI)

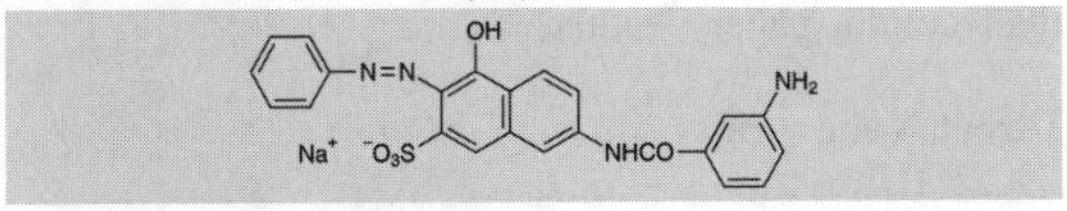

$C_{23}H_{17}N_4Na_1O_5S_1$. M: 484.46.
Production:
• N-m-aminobenzoyl-J acid + benzenediazonium chloride (azo coupling)
Uses:
dye (cotton, wool, silk)

Direct Red 149
29110 (CI)

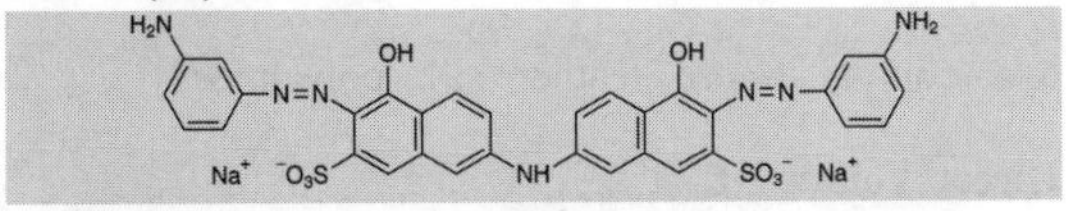

$C_{32}H_{23}N_7Na_2O_8S_2$. M: 743.68.
Production:
• m-nitroaniline + methyl formate + 6,6'-iminobis-(1-naphthol-3-sulphonic acid) (amide formation/nitro reduction/diazotisation/azo coupling/amide hydrolysis)
Uses: dye (cotton)

Direct Red 153
28210 (CI)

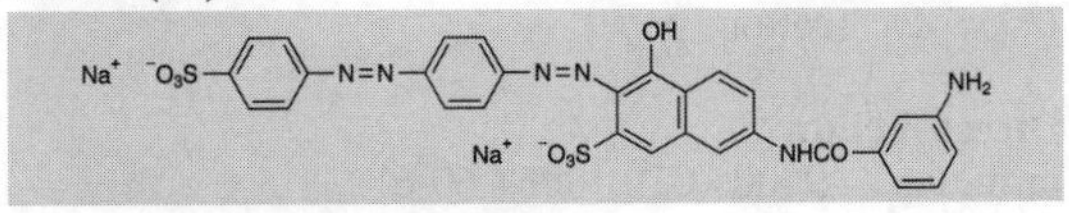

$C_{29}H_{20}N_6Na_2O_8S_2$. M: 690.62.

Production:
• 4'-aminoazobenzene-4-sulphonic acid + N-m-aminobenzoyl-J acid (diazotisation/azo coupling)
Uses: dye (cotton)

Direct Red 180
24565 (CI)

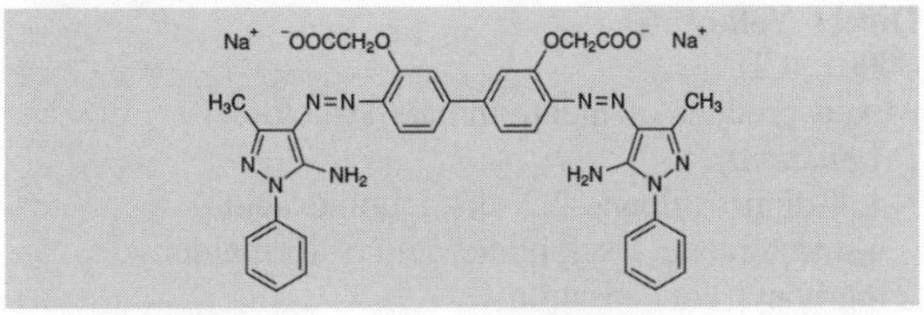

The dye is the 1:2 copper complex of the displayed structure. $C_{36}H_{30}Cu_1N_{10}O_6$. M: 762.25.
Production:
• o-nitrophenol + chloroacetic acid + 5-amino-3-methyl-1-phenylpyrazole + copper sulphate (ether formation/benzidine rearrangement/diazotisation/azo coupling/complex formation)
Uses: dye (cotton)

Direct Violet 9
27885 (CI)

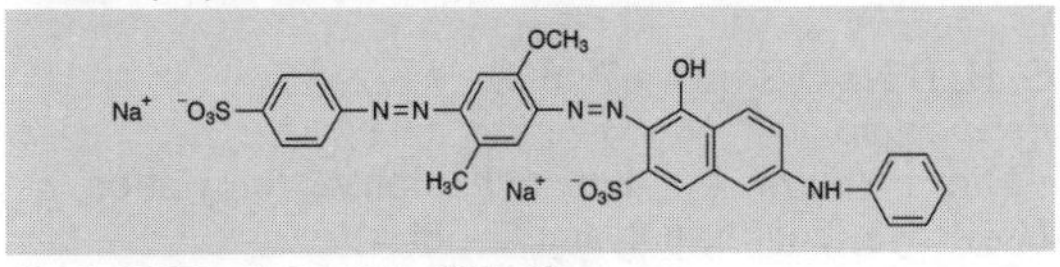

$C_{30}H_{23}N_5Na_2O_8S_2$. M: 691.65.
Production:
• sulphanilic acid + p-cresidine + N-phenyl-J acid (diazotisation/azo coupling/diazotisation/azo coupling)
Uses: dye (cotton, wool, silk)

Direct Violet 66
29120 (CI)

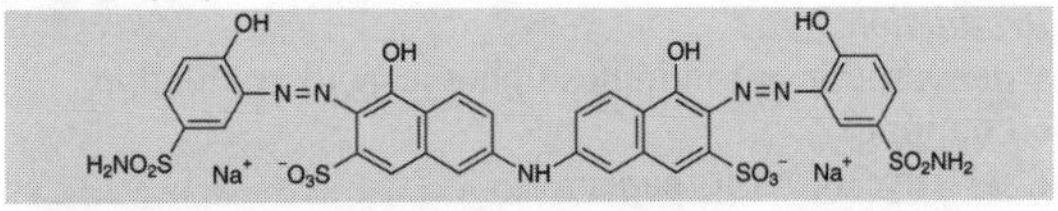

The dye is the 1:2 copper complex of the displayed structure. $C_{32}H_{23}Cu_1N_7O_{14}S_4$. M: 921.38.
Production:
• 2-aminophenol-4-sulphonamide + 6,6'-iminobis-(1-naphthol-3-sulphonic acid) + copper sulphate (diazotisation/azo coupling/complex formation)
Uses: dye (cotton)

Direct Yellow 4
Brilliant Yellow; 24890 (CI)
$C_{26}H_{18}N_4Na_2O_8S_2$. M: 624.56.
Production:
• 4,4'-diaminostilbene-2,2'-disulphonic acid + phenol (diazotisation/azo coupling)

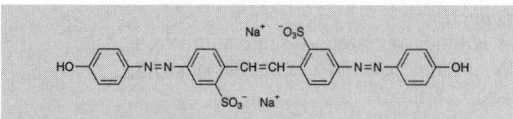

Derivatives: Direct Yellow 12
Uses: dye (cotton, paper)

Direct Yellow 6
40001 (CI)
Mixed product of indeterminate structure.
Production:
- 4,4'-dinitrostilbene-2,2'-disulphonic acid/
  4-nitrotoluene-2-sulphonic acid + formaldehyde
  (carbonyl condensation)
Uses: dye (cotton, paper, leather); pigment intermediate

Direct Yellow 11
See: 4,4'-dinitrostilbene-2,2'-disulphonic acid

Direct Yellow 12
Chrysophenine G; 24895 (CI); [2870-32-8]

$C_{30}H_{24}N_4Na_2O_8S_2$. M: 678.65.
Production:
- Direct Yellow 4 + dimethyl sulphate (ethylation)
Uses: dye (cotton, polyamide fibres)

Direct Yellow 28
19555 (CI)

$C_{28}H_{18}N_2Na_2O_6S_4$. M: 652.69.
Production:
- dehydrothio-*p*-toluidinesulphonic acid (oxidative
  coupling)
Uses: dye (cotton, paper)

Direct Yellow 34
29060 (CI)

$C_{36}H_{28}N_6Na_4O_{15}S_4$. M: 1004.86.
Production:
- *N,N'*-bis(2-methoxy-5-methylphenyl) urea +
  2-naphthylamine-4,8-disulphonic acid
  (diazotisation/azo coupling)
Uses: dye (cotton, paper)

Direct Yellow 44
29000 (CI)

$C_{27}H_{20}N_6Na_2O_8S_1$. M: 634.53.
Production:
- *p*-nitroaniline + salicylic acid + 4-amino-
  3-methoxyazobenzene-3'-sulphonic acid, sodium salt
  + phosgene (diazotisation/azo coupling/phosgenation)
Uses:
dye (cotton, bast fibres, viscose, leather)

Direct Yellow 49
29035 (CI)

$C_{29}H_{22}N_6Na_2O_7$. M: 612.51.
Production:
- *m*-aminobenzoic acid + *o*-anisidine + phosgene
  (diazotisation/azo coupling/phosgenation)
Uses:
dye (cotton, paper, leather)

Direct Yellow 50
29025 (CI)

$C_{34}H_{24}N_6Na_4O_{13}S_4$. M: 944.81.
Production:
- 2-naphthylamine-4,8-disulphonic acid + *m*-toluidine
  + phosgene (diazotisation/azo coupling/phosgenation)
Uses:
dye (cotton, viscose, leather, silk, polyamide)

Direct Yellow 51
29030 (CI)

$C_{34}H_{24}N_6Na_4O_{13}S_4$. M: 944.80.
Production:
- 2-naphthylamine-4,8-disulphonic acid + 2,5-xylidine
  + phosgene (diazotisation/azo coupling/phosgenation)
Uses: dye (cotton, paper)

Direct Yellow 59
primuline; 49000 (CI); [8064-60-6]
$C_{21}H_{14}N_3Na_1O_3S_3$. M: 475.54.

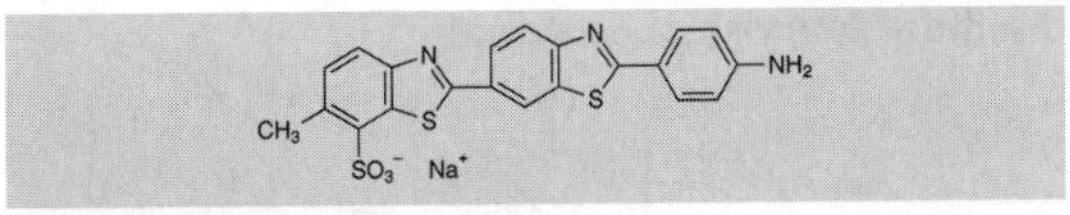

Production:
- p-toluidine + sulphur (thiolation/oxidative coupling/sulphonation)

Derivatives: Direct Orange 18

Uses: dye (cotton)

Direct Yellow 106
40300 (CI)

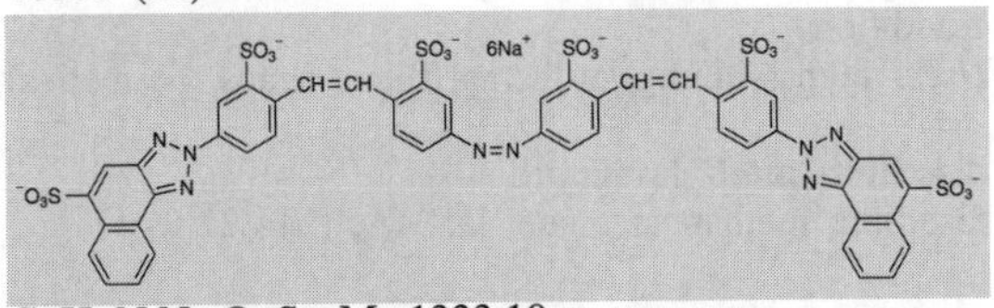

$C_{48}H_{26}N_8Na_6O_{18}S_6$. M: 1333.10.

Production:
- 4,4'-dinitrostilbene-2,2'-disulphonic acid + naphthionic acid (partial nitro reduction/diazotisation/condensation/oxidation/oxidative coupling)

Uses: dye (cotton)

Direct Yellow 118
29042 (CI)

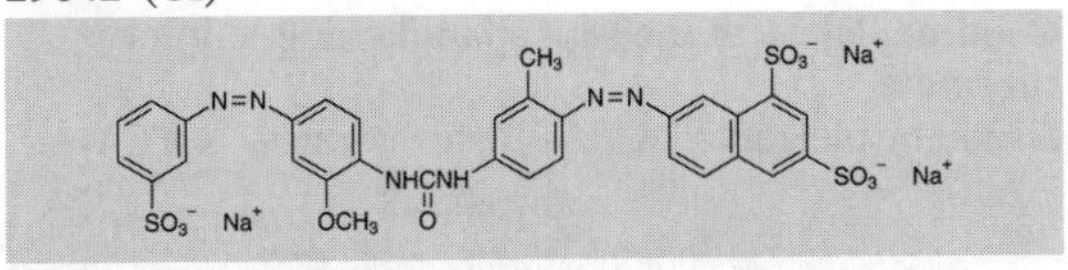

$C_{31}H_{23}N_6Na_3O_{11}S_3$. M: 820.71.

Production:
- 4-amino-3-methoxyazobenzene-3'-sulphonic acid, sodium salt + amino-G acid + m-toluidine + phosgene (diazotisation/azo coupling/phosgenation)

Uses: dye (paper)

N,N'-disalicylhydrazide

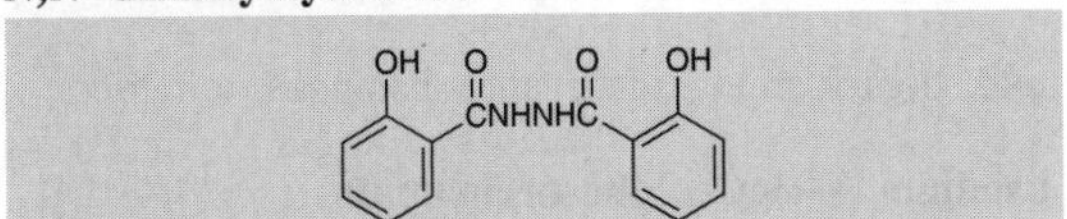

$C_{14}H_{12}N_2O_4$. M: 272.26.

Production:
- salicylic acid + hydrazine (amide formation)

Uses: metal deactivator (plastics)

N,N'-disalicylideneethylenediamine

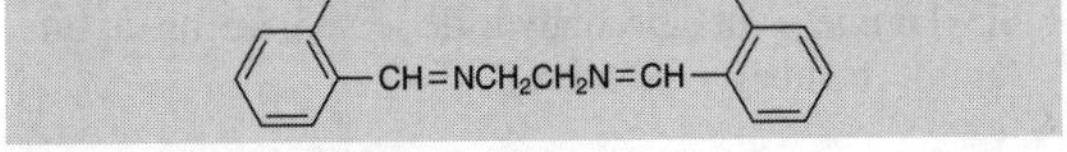

$C_{16}H_{18}N_2O_2$. M: 270.33.

Production:
- salicylaldehyde + ethylenediamine (imine formation)

Uses: metal deactivator (lubricants)

N,N'-disalicylidene-1,2-propanediamine
N,N'-disalicylidene-1,2-diaminopropane; [94-91-7]

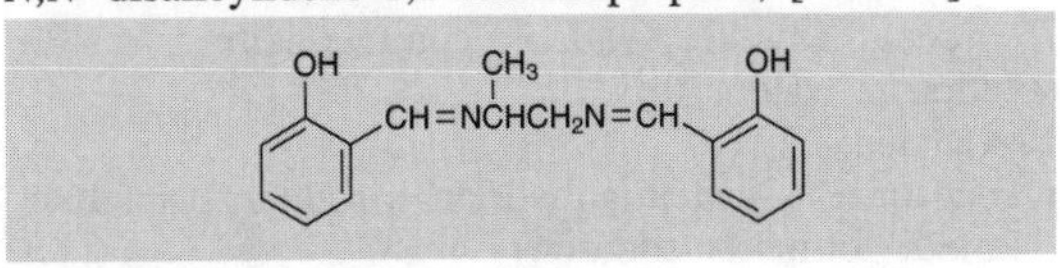

$C_{17}H_{18}N_2O_2$. M: 282.34.

Production:
- salicylaldehyde + 1,2-propanediamine (imine formation)

Uses: metal deactivator (jet/motor fuels)

disodium acid pyrophosphate
disodium dihydrogen diphosphate; disodium diphosphate; disodium pyrophosphate; SAPP; [7758-16-9]

$H_2Na_2O_7P_2$. M: 221.94. White chips or powder. Soluble in water producing acidic solutions.

Production:
- sodium carbonate/sodium hydroxide + phosphoric acid, pure (salt formation/thermal dehydration)

Uses: potato antidarkening agent; leavening agent

disodium benzaldehyde-2,4-disulphonate
disodium formylbenzene-2,4-disulphonate; [88-39-1]

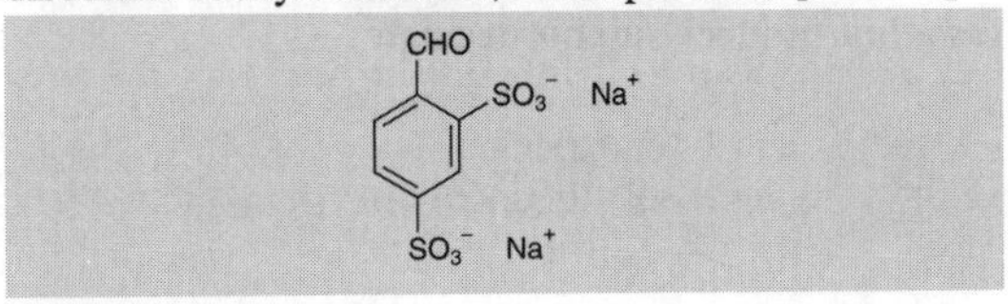

$C_7H_6O_7S_2$. M: 266.25.

Production:
- toluene (sulphonation/side-chain oxidation)

Derivatives: Acid Blue 1; Acid Blue 7; Acid Red 52

Uses: photographic coupling agent intermediate

disodium coconut monoethanolamide sulphosuccinate
disodium cocamido MEA-sulphosuccinate (CTFA)

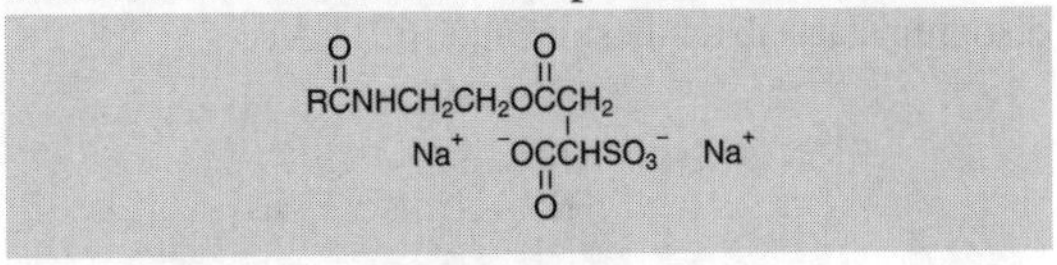

R = coco-. Clear, yellow liquid. Available commercially as a 40% solution in water.

Production:
- coconut acid monoethanolamide + maleic anhydride + sodium bisulphite (esterification/addition)

Uses: mild surfactant (shampoos, bath products, rug cleaners, dishwashing liquids)

disodium *N*-cocoylsulphosuccinamate

$$\begin{array}{c} O \\ \parallel \\ RNHCCH_2 \\ | \\ Na^+ \quad {}^-OCCHSO_3^- \quad Na^+ \\ \parallel \\ O \end{array}$$

R = coco-. Liquid. Available commercially as a 40% solution in water.
Production:
• cocoamine + maleic anhydride + sodium bisulphite (amide formation/addition)
Uses:
foaming agent (foamed rubber/carpetbacking latex)

disodium ethylenebis(dithiocarbamate) *See:* nabam

disodium ethylenediaminetetraacetate
See: ethylenediaminetetraacetic acid, disodium salt

disodium fluorophosphate
See: sodium fluorophosphate

disodium formylbenzene-2,4-disulphonate
See: disodium benzaldehyde-2,4-disulphonate

disodium guanosine-5′-monophosphate
See: sodium 5′-guanylate

disodium inosine-5′-monophosphate
See: sodium 5′-inosate

disodium isodecylsulphosuccinate

$$\begin{array}{c} O \\ \parallel \\ C_{10}H_{21}OCCH_2 \\ | \\ Na^+ \quad {}^-OCCHSO_3^- \quad Na^+ \\ \parallel \\ O \end{array}$$

$C_{14}H_{24}Na_2O_7S_1$. M: 382.37.
Production:
• isodecanol + maleic anhydride + sodium bisulphite (esterification/addition)
Uses: emulsifier (polyvinyl chloride suspension polymerisation); foaming agent (coatings)

disodium lauryl ether sulphosuccinate
disodium laurethsulphosuccinate (CTFA)

$$\begin{array}{c} O \\ \parallel \\ CH_3(CH_2)_{11}(OCH_2CH_2)_nOCCH_2 \\ | \\ Na^+ \quad {}^-OCCHSO_3^- \quad Na^+ \\ \parallel \\ O \end{array}$$

Clear, pale yellow liquid. Available commercially as a 30–40% solution in water.
Production:
• *n*-alkanol(C_{12}-C_{14}) ethoxylates + maleic anhydride + sodium bisulphite (esterification/addition)
Uses: surfactant (baby shampoos)

disodium laurylsulphosuccinate

$$\begin{array}{c} O \\ \parallel \\ CH_3(CH_2)_{11}OCCH_2 \\ | \\ Na^+ \quad {}^-OCCHSO_3^- \quad Na^+ \\ \parallel \\ O \end{array}$$

$C_{16}H_{28}Na_2O_7S_1$. M: 410.43. White liquid or solid. Most commonly available commercially as a 30–40% solution in water.
Production:
• *n*-alkanol(C_{12}-C_{14})/*n*-alkanol(C_{12}-C_{13}) + maleic anhydride + sodium bisulphite (esterification/addition)
Uses: high-foaming surfactant (hand soaps, cosmetics)

disodium methylarsonate
disodium methanearsonate; DSMA; [144-21-8]

$$\begin{array}{c} O \\ \parallel \\ CH_3AsO^- \quad Na^+ \\ | \\ O^- \quad Na^+ \end{array}$$

$C_1H_3As_1Na_2O_3$. M: 183.93. The commercial product is the hexahydrate.
Production:
• methyl chloride + arsenic trioxide + sodium hydroxide (reaction/salt formation)
Uses: herbicide

disodium oleic monoisopropanolamide sulphosuccinate
disodium oleamido MIPA-sulphosuccinate (CTFA)

$$\begin{array}{c} O \quad\quad CH_3 \quad O \\ \parallel \quad\quad | \quad\quad \parallel \\ CH_3(CH_2)_7CH=CH(CH_2)_7CNHCHCH_2OCCH_2 \\ | \\ Na^+ \quad {}^-OCCHSO_3^- \quad Na^+ \\ \parallel \\ O \end{array}$$

$C_{25}H_{43}Na_2O_8S_1$. M: 549.65. Amber liquid. Available commercially as a 35% solution in water.
Production:
• oleic acid monoisopropanolamide + maleic anhydride + sodium bisulphite (esterification/addition)
Uses:
mild, high-foaming surfactant (shampoos, toiletries)

disodium *N*-oleylsulphosuccinamate

$$\begin{array}{c} O \\ \parallel \\ CH_3(CH_2)_7CH=CH(CH_2)_8NHCCH_2 \\ | \\ Na^+ \quad {}^-OCCHSO_3^- \quad Na^+ \\ \parallel \\ O \end{array}$$

$C_{22}H_{39}N_1Na_2O_6S_1$. M: 491.59. Liquid. Available commercially as a 40% solution in water.
Production:
• oleylamine + maleic anhydride + sodium bisulphite (amide formation/addition)
Uses:
foaming agent (foamed rubber/carpetbacking latex)

disodium phosphate

disodium hydrogen orthophosphate; disodium hydrogen phosphate; disodium orthophosphate; sodium phosphate, dibasic; DSP; E339 (EC); [7558-79-4]

$$Na_2HPO_4$$

$H_1Na_2O_4P_1$. M: 141.96. Available commercially as the anhydrous or dihydrate salts. Both are white, hygroscopic powders. Soluble in water.

Production:
• sodium carbonate/sodium hydroxide + phosphoric acid, pure (salt formation)

Derivatives:
chromium phosphate; cobalt phosphate; starch, sodium phosphate

Uses: emulsifier (processed cheese, quick-cook cereals, pharmaceuticals); metal phosphatising/electroplating reagent; pottery glazes/porcelain/enamels; scale inhibitor (boiler water treatment); textile/leather auxiliary

disodium *N*-stearylsulphosuccinamate

disodium stearylsulphosuccinamate

$$CH_3(CH_2)_{17}NHCCH_2$$
$$Na^+ \; ^-OCCHSO_3^- \; Na^+$$

$C_{22}H_{41}N_1Na_2O_6S_1$. M: 493.61. Liquid. Available commercially as a 40% solution in water.

Production:
• tallowamine + maleic anhydride + sodium bisulphite (amide formation/sulphonation)

Uses:
foaming agent (foamed rubber/carpetbacking latex)

2,4-D-isooctyl

isooctyl (2,4-dichlorophenoxy)acetate; [25168-26-7]

$$Cl$$
$$Cl \quad OCH_2COC_8H_{17}$$

$C_{16}H_{22}Cl_2O_3$. M: 333.27.
Production:
• isooctanol + 2,4-D (esterification)
Uses:
herbicide

disopyramide

[3737-09-5]; [22059-60-5] (phosphate)

$$(CH_3)_2CH$$
$$NCH_2CH_2 \quad CONH_2$$
$$(CH_3)_2CH \quad C$$

$C_{21}H_{29}N_3O_1$. M: 339.48. Available commercially as the free base and as the phosphate salt.

Production:
• benzyl cyanide + 2-chloropyridine + 2-diisopropylaminoethyl chloride hydrochloride (dehydrochlorination/alcohol chlorination/dehydrochlorination/nitrile hydration)
Uses: antiarrhythmic drug

Disperse Black 1

11365 (CI)

$$H_2N- \bigcirc -N=N- \bigcirc -NH_2$$

$C_{16}H_{14}N_4$. M: 262.32.
Production:
• *p*-nitroaniline + 1-naphthylamine (diazotisation/azo coupling/nitro reduction)
Uses: dye (polyamide, acetate fibres)

Disperse Black 2

11255 (CI); 37185 (CI)

$$H_3C$$
$$H_2N- \bigcirc -N=N- \bigcirc -NH_2$$
$$OCH_3$$

$C_{14}H_{16}N_4O_1$. M: 256.31.
Production:
• *p*-nitroaniline + *p*-cresidine (diazotisation/azo coupling/nitro reduction)
Uses: dye (polyamide, acetate fibres)

Disperse Blue 1

See: 1,4,5,8-tetraaminoanthraquinone

Disperse Blue 3

61505 (CI); [2475-46-9]

$$O \quad NHCH_3$$
$$O \quad NHCH_2CH_2OH$$

$C_{17}H_{16}N_2O_3$. M: 296.33.
Production:
• quinizarin + methylamine + monoethanolamine (amine formation/oxidation)
Uses:
dye (acetate, polyamide, polyacrylonitrile)

Disperse Blue 7

Solvent Blue 69 (CI); 62500 (CI)
$C_{18}H_{18}N_2O_6$. M: 358.35.
Production:
• quinizarin + monoethanolamine (amine formation/oxidation)

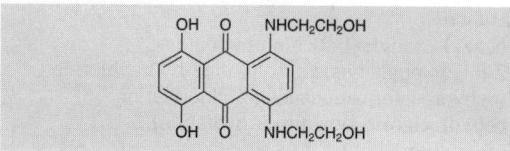

Uses:
dye (acetate, polyamide, polyester, polyacrylonitrile)

Disperse Blue 14
1,4-di-(methylamino)anthraquinone; 61500 (CI)

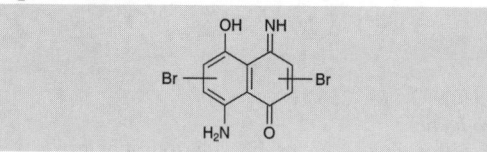

$C_{16}H_{14}N_2O_2$. M: 266.30.
Production:
• quinizarin + methylamine (amine formation)
Uses:
dye (polyamide, acetate fibres)

Disperse Blue 20

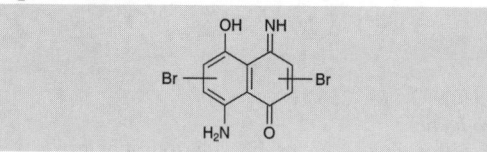

$C_{10}H_6Br_2N_2O_2$. M: 345.98.
Production:
• 1,5-diaminonaphthalene (sulphonation/oxidation/
ring bromination)
Uses: dye (acetate, polyester)

Disperse Blue 26
63305 (CI); [3860-63-7]

$C_{16}H_{14}N_2O_4$. M: 298.30.
Production:
• 1,5-diamino-4,8-dihydroxyanthraquinone + dimethyl
sulphate (methylation)
Uses:
dye (acetate, polyamide, polyester, polyacrylonitrile)

Disperse Blue 31
64505 (CI)
R = H, methyl-. Mixed product of methylated 1,4,5,8-
tetraminoanthraquinone adducts.
Production:
• 1,4,5,8-tetraaminoanthraquinone (methylation)

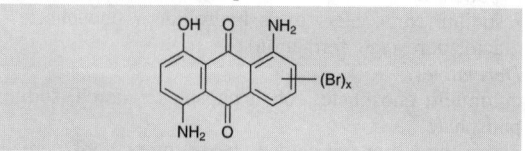

Uses: dye (acetate, polyamide, polyacrylonitrile)

Disperse Blue 56
63285 (CI); [12217-79-7]

Production:
• 1,5-diamino-4,8-dihydroxyanthraquinone (ring
bromination)
Uses:
dye (polyester, acrylic, acetate)

Disperse Blue 72
D&C Violet No. 2 (FDC); Solvent Violet 13 (CI);
60725 (CI); [81-48-1]

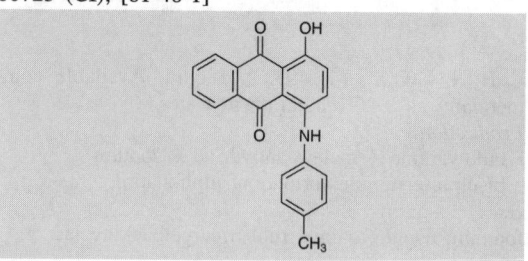

$C_{21}H_{15}N_1O_3$. M: 329.36.
Production:
• 1-chloro-4-hydroxyanthraquinone + *p*-toluidine
(amine formation)
Uses:
dye (triacetate, polyester)

Disperse Blue 73
63265 (CI); [12222-75-2]

$C_{20}H_{14}N_2O_5$. M: 362.33.
Production:
• Acid Blue 45 + anisole (sulphonate displacement/
reduction)
Uses:
dye (acetate, polyester)

Disperse Blue 79

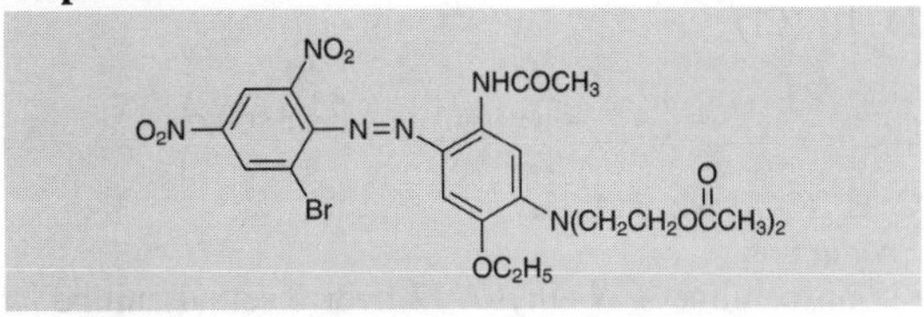

$C_{24}H_{27}Br_1N_6O_{10}$. M: 639.41.
Production:
- phenacetin + ethylene oxide + acetic anhydride + 6-bromo-2,4-dinitroaniline (nitration/nitro reduction/epoxidation/acetylation/diazotisation/azo coupling)

Uses: dye (polyester)

Disperse Blue 102
Eastone Blue GFD

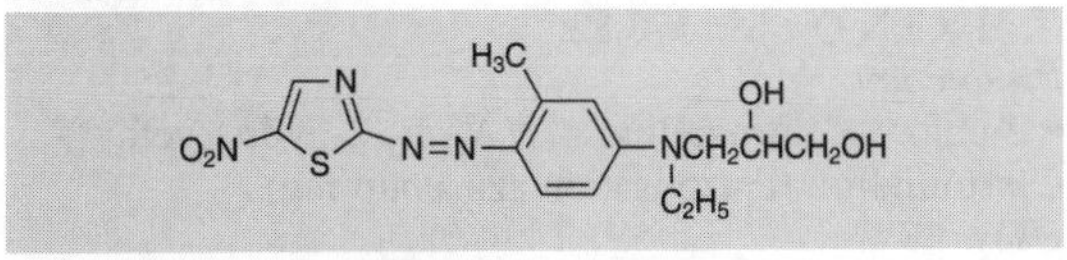

$C_{15}H_{19}N_5O_4S_1$. M: 365.40.
Production:
- *N*-ethyl-*m*-toluidine + epichlorohydrin + 2-amino-5-nitrothiazole (amine formation/diazotisation/azo coupling)

Uses: dye (acetate fibres)

Disperse Blue 125

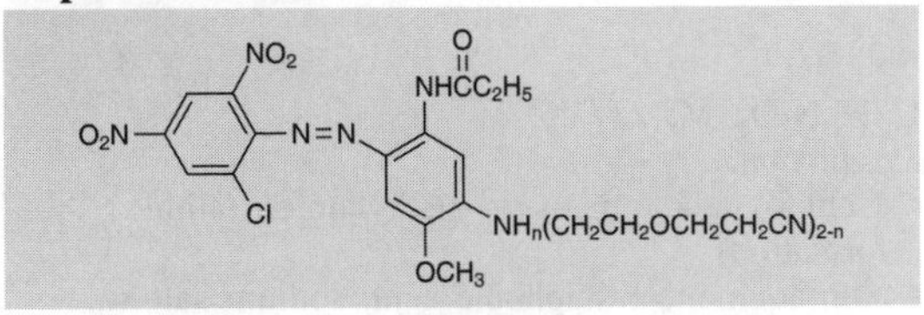

n = 0–1. Mixture containing 40% of the mono-2-cyan-oethoxyethylamine derivative and 60% of the di-2-cy-anoethoxyethylamine derivative.
Production:
- *p*-anisidine + ethylene oxide + acrylonitrile + propionyl chloride + 6-chloro-2,4-dinitroaniline (amide formation/nitration/nitro reduction/epoxidation/cyanoethylation/diazotisation/azo coupling)

Uses:
dye (acetate, polyester)

Disperse Blue 134 *See:* Solvent Blue 36

Disperse Blue 165
$C_{21}H_{21}N_7O_4$. M: 435.45.
Production:
- *p*-anisidine + acetic anhydride + ethanol + 2,6-dibromo-4-nitroaniline + sodium cyanide

(acetylation/nitration/nitro reduction/amine formation/diazotisation/azo coupling/cyanidation)

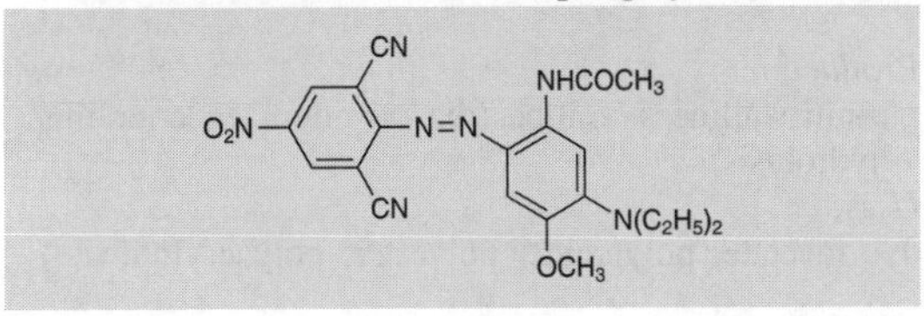

Uses:
dye (acetate, polyamide, polyester, polyacrylonitrile)

Disperse Blue 183

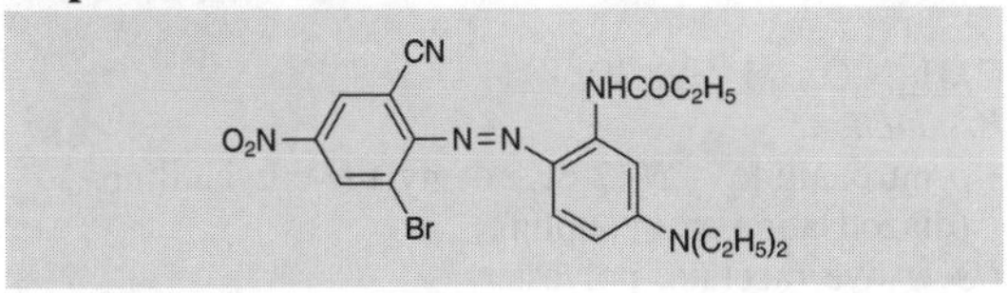

$C_{20}H_{21}Br_1N_6O_3$. M: 473.33.
Production:
- *m*-nitroaniline + diethyl sulphate + propionyl chloride + 2-amino-3-bromo-5-nitrobenzonitrile (ethylation/nitro reduction/amide formation/diazotisation/azo coupling)

Uses: dye (acetate)

Disperse Blue 339
HTP Violet 310 (Kodak)

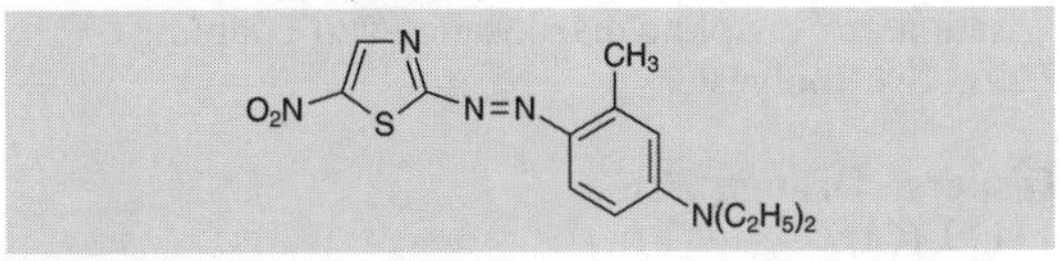

$C_{14}H_{17}N_5O_2S_1$. M: 319.39.
Production:
- 2-amino-5-nitrothiazole + *N,N*-diethyl-*m*-toluidine (diazotisation/azo coupling)

Uses: dye (acetate, polyester)

Disperse Brown 1
11152 (CI)

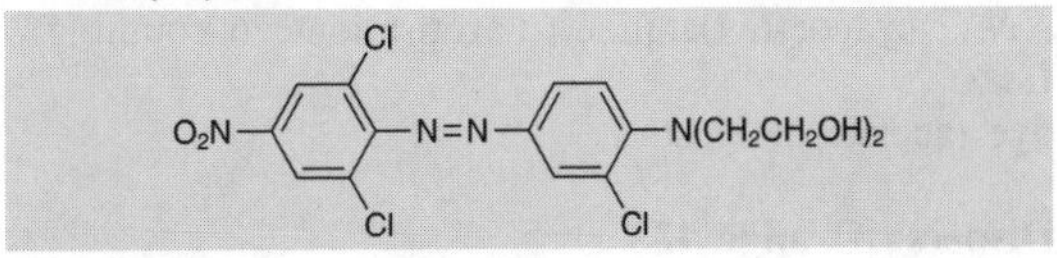

$C_{16}H_{15}Cl_3N_4O_4$. M: 433.69.
Production:
- 2,6-dichloro-4-nitroaniline + *N,N*-di-(2-hydroxy-ethyl)-*m*-chloroaniline (diazotisation/azo coupling)

Uses:
dye (acetate, polyamide, polyester)

Disperse Orange 3
Solvent Orange 9 (CI); 11005 (CI)
$C_{12}H_{10}N_4O_2$. M: 242.24.

O_2N—⟨benzene⟩—N=N—⟨benzene⟩—NH_2

Production:
• *p*-nitroaniline + aniline (diazotisation/azo coupling/ hydrolysis)
Uses:
dye (acetate, polyamide, polyester, polyacrylonitrile)

Disperse Orange 25
11227 (CI)

O_2N—⟨benzene⟩—N=N—⟨benzene⟩—NCH_2CH_2CN (C_2H_5)

$C_{17}H_{17}N_5O_2$. M: 323.37.
Production:
• *p*-nitroaniline + *N*-(2-cyanoethyl)-*N*-ethylaniline (diazotisation/azo coupling)
Uses: dye (acetate, polyester)

Disperse Orange 29
26077 (CI)

O_2N—⟨benzene⟩—N=N—⟨benzene⟩—N=N—⟨benzene⟩—OH (OCH_3)

$C_{19}H_{15}N_5O_4$. M: 377.37.
Production:
• *p*-nitroaniline + *o*-anisidine + phenol (diazotisation/azo coupling/diazotisation/azo coupling)
Uses: dye (polyester)

Disperse Orange 30
11119 (CI)

O_2N—⟨benzene(Cl,Cl)⟩—N=N—⟨benzene⟩—N(CH_2CH_2CN)($CH_2CH_2OCCH_3$, O)

$C_{19}H_{17}Cl_2N_5O_4$. M: 450.30.
Production:
• 2,6-dichloro-4-nitroaniline + *N*-(2-acetoxyethyl)-*N*-(2-cyanoethyl)aniline (diazotisation/azo coupling)
Uses:
dye (acetate, polyester)

Disperse Orange 138
11145 (CI)

O_2N—⟨benzene⟩—N=N—⟨benzene(Cl)⟩—$NHCH_2CH_2OH$

$C_{14}H_{13}Cl_1N_4O_3$. M: 320.73.
Production:
• *o*-chloroaniline + ethylene oxide + *p*-nitroaniline (epoxidation/diazotisation/azo coupling)
Uses: dye (acetate, polyamide)

Disperse Red 1
11110 (CI)

O_2N—⟨benzene⟩—N=N—⟨benzene⟩—NCH_2CH_2OH (C_2H_5)

$C_{16}H_{18}N_4O_3$. M: 314.35.
Production:
• *p*-nitroaniline + *N*-ethyl-*N*-(2-hydroxyethyl)aniline (diazotisation/azo coupling)
Uses:
dye (acetate, polyamide, polyacrylonitrile)

Disperse Red 5
Solvent Red 117 (CI); 11215 (CI)

O_2N—⟨benzene(Cl)⟩—N=N—⟨benzene(H_3C)⟩—$N(CH_2CH_2OH)_2$

$C_{17}H_{19}Cl_1N_4O_4$. M: 378.82.
Production:
• 2-chloro-4-nitroaniline + *N,N'*-di-(2-hydroxyethyl)-*m*-toluidine (diazotisation/azo coupling)
Uses:
dye (acetate, polyamide, polyester, polyacrylonitrile)

Disperse Red 9
Solvent Red 111 (CI); 60505 (CI); [82-38-2]

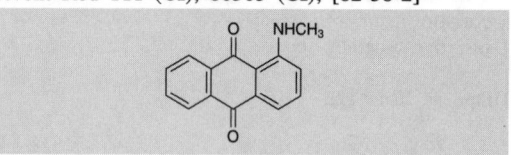

$C_{15}H_{11}N_1O_2$. M: 237.26.
Production:
• 1-chloroanthraquinone + methylamine (amine formation)
• anthraquinone-1-sulphonic acid, sodium salt + methylamine (sulphonate displacement)
Uses:
dye (acetate, polyamide, polyacrylonitrile)

Disperse Red 13
11115 (CI)

O_2N—⟨benzene(Cl)⟩—N=N—⟨benzene⟩—NCH_2CH_2OH (C_2H_5)

$C_{16}H_{17}Cl_1N_4O_3$. M: 348.80.
Production:
• 2-chloro-4-nitroaniline + *N*-ethyl-*N*-(2-hydroxyethyl)aniline (diazotisation/azo coupling)
Uses:
dye (acetate, polyamide, polyester, polyacrylonitrile)

Disperse Red 15
See: 1-amino-4-hydroxyanthraquinone

Disperse Red 17
11210 (CI)

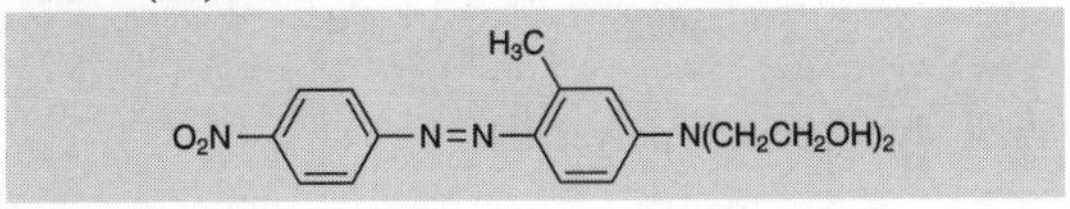

$C_{17}H_{20}N_4O_4$. M: 344.38.
Production:
• *p*-nitroaniline + *N,N'*-di-(2-hydroxyethyl)-
  m-toluidine (diazotisation/azo coupling)
Uses: dye (acetate, polyamide, polyacrylonitrile)

Disperse Red 22
60510 (CI)

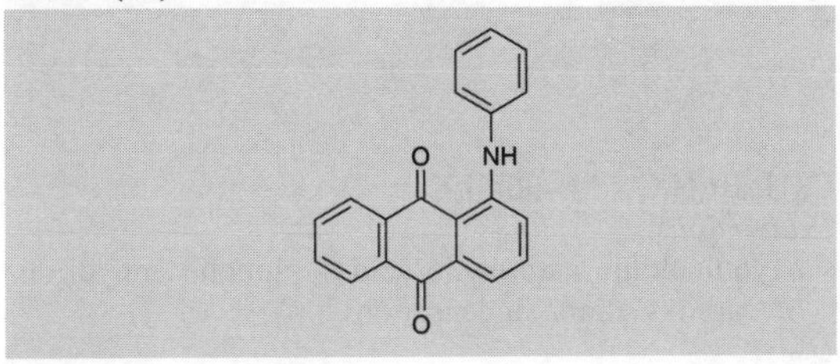

$C_{20}H_{13}N_1O_2$. M: 299.33.
Production:
• 1-chloroanthraquinone + aniline (amine formation)
• anthraquinone-1-sulphonic acid, sodium salt +
  aniline (sulphonate displacement)
Uses: dye (acetate)

Disperse Red 60
1-amino-4-hydroxy-2-phenoxyanthraquinone; 60756 (CI)

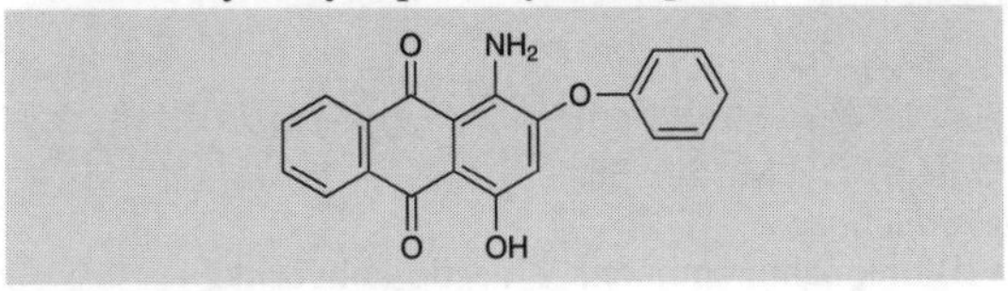

$C_{20}H_{12}N_1O_4$. M: 330.33.
Production:
• 1-amino-2-bromo-4-hydroxyanthraquinone + phenol
  (ether formation)
Uses:
dye (acetate, polyamide, polyester)

Disperse Red 65
11228 (CI)

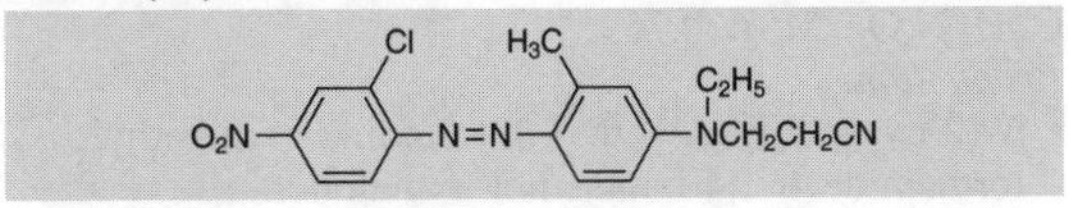

$C_{18}H_{18}Cl_1N_5O_2$. M: 371.82.
Production:
• 2-chloro-4-nitroaniline + *N*-(2-cyanoethyl)-*N*-ethyl-
  m-toluidine (diazotisation/azo coupling)
Uses:
dye (acetate, polyester)

Disperse Red 73
11116 (CI)

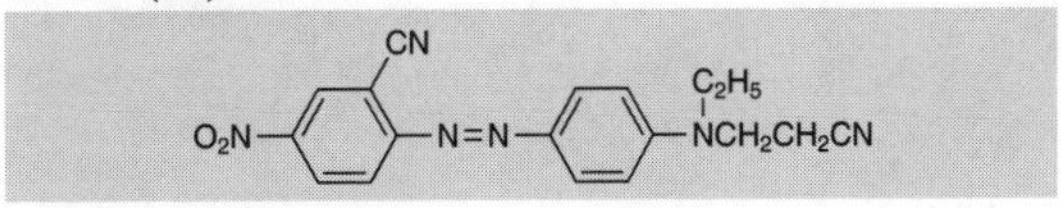

$C_{18}H_{16}N_6O_2$. M: 348.37.
Production:
• 2-amino-5-nitrobenzonitrile + *N*-(2-cyanoethyl)-
  N-ethylaniline (diazotisation/azo coupling)
Uses:
dye (acetate, polyester)

Disperse Violet 1
See: 1,4-diaminoanthraquinone

Disperse Violet 28
61102 (CI); [81-42-5]

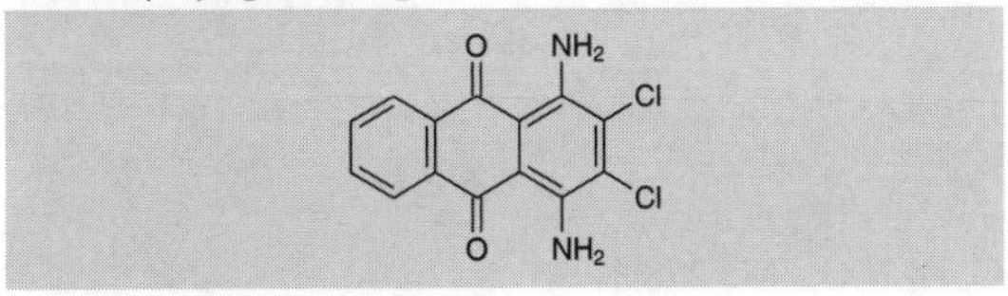

$C_{14}H_8Cl_2N_2O_2$. M: 307.13.
Production:
• 1,4-diaminoanthraquinone (ring chlorination)
Uses:
dye (acetate, polyamide)

Disperse Yellow 3
Solvent Yellow 77 (CI); 11855 (CI)

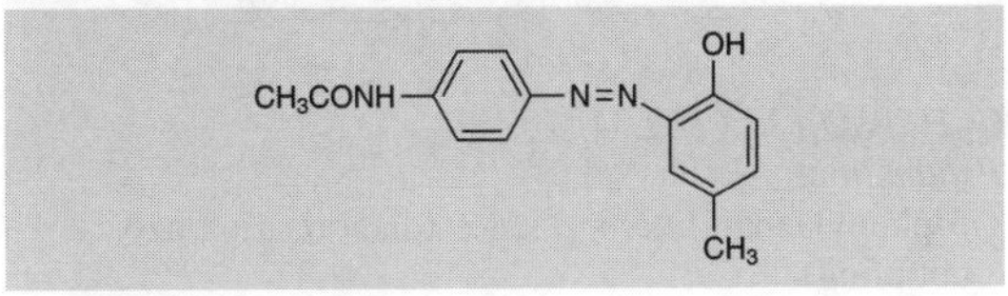

$C_{15}H_{15}N_3O_2$. M: 269.30.
Production:
• *p*-aminoacetanilide + *p*-cresol (diazotisation/azo
  coupling)
Uses:
dye (acetate, polyamide, polyester, polyacrylonitrile)

Disperse Yellow 9
Solvent Orange 53 (CI); 10375 (CI)

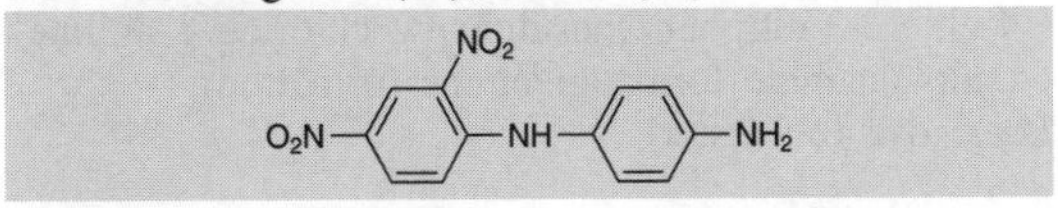

$C_{12}H_{10}N_4O_4$. M: 274.24.
Production:
• 1-chloro-2,4-dinitrobenzene + *p*-phenylenediamine
  (amine formation)
Uses:
dye (acetate, polyester, polyacrylonitrile)

Disperse Yellow 14
10340 (CI)

$C_{12}H_9N_3O_4$. M: 259.22.
Production:
• aniline + 1-chloro-2,4-dinitrobenzene (amine formation)
Uses: dye (acetate)

Disperse Yellow 16
12700 (CI); Pyrazolone Yellow 3G; Solvent Yellow 16 (CI); Sudan Yellow 3G (BASF); [4314-14-1]

$C_{16}H_{14}N_4O_1$. M: 278.31.
Production:
• aniline + 3-methyl-1-phenyl-5-pyrazolone (diazotisation/azo coupling)
Uses: plastics colorant

Disperse Yellow 23
26070 (CI)

$C_{18}H_{14}N_4O_1$. M: 302.34.
Production:
• p-phenylazoaniline + phenol (diazotisation/azo coupling)
Uses: dye (acetate, polyamide, polyester)

Disperse Yellow 33

$C_{18}H_{15}N_3O_4S_1$. M: 369.40.
Production:
• 4-chloro-3-nitrobenzenesulphonyl chloride + aniline (sulphonamide formation/amine formation)
Uses: dye (polyester)

Disperse Yellow 42
10338 (CI)
$C_{18}H_{15}N_3O_4S_1$. M: 369.40.
Production:
• 4-chloro-3-nitrobenzenesulphonyl chloride + aniline (sulphonamide formation/amine formation)

Uses: dye (acetate, polyester)

Disperse Yellow 54
See: quinophthalone

Disperse Yellow 64
Foron Yellow SE-3GL; 47023 (CI)

$C_{18}H_{10}Br_1N_1O_3$. M: 368.19.
Production:
• oxyquinaldine carboxylic acid + phthalic anhydride (decarboxylation/condensation)
Uses:
dye (acetate, polyamide, polyester)

Disperse Yellow 77

$C_{23}H_{12}N_2O_2$. M: 348.36.
Production:
• 1-aminoanthraquinone + acetic anhydride + anthranilic acid (amide formation/condensation)
Uses: dye (polyester)

Disperse Yellow 99
48420 (CI)

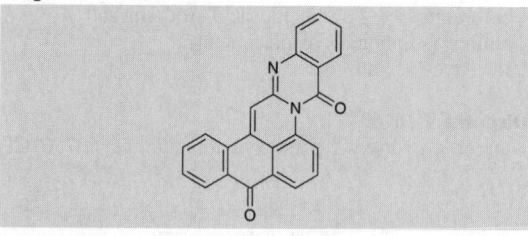

$C_{36}H_{40}N_6O_4$. M: 620.76.
Production:
• N-(2-cyanoethyl)-N-ethyl-m-toluidine + dimethyl-formamide + 1,4-butanediol + malononitrile (Vilsmeier reaction/nitrile hydrolysis/condensation/esterification)
Uses: dye (triacetate, polyester)

distearoylhexamethylenediamine
See: hexamethylenebis(stearamide)

distearylamine
hydrogenated ditallow amine (CTFA)

$$[CH_3(CH_2)_{17}]_2 NH$$

$C_{36}H_{75}N_1$. M: 522.00.
Production:
• stearylamine (deammoniation)
Derivatives:
dimethyldistearylammonium chloride; dimethyldistearylammonium methosulphate

distearyldimonium chloride
See: dimethyldistearylammonium chloride

distearyl disulphide
dioctadecyl disulphide; Hostanox SE10 (Hoechst)

$$CH_3(CH_2)_{17}S - S(CH_2)_{17}CH_3$$

$C_{36}H_{74}S_2$. M: 571.12.
Production:
• stearyl mercaptan (oxidation)
Uses: antioxidant (plastics)

distearyl ketone
diheptadecyl ketone; pentatriacontan-18-one; stearone (CTFA); [504-53-0]

$$CH_3(CH_2)_{16}\overset{O}{\overset{\|}{C}}(CH_2)_{16}CH_3$$

$C_{35}H_{70}O_1$. M: 506.94.
Production:
• alkylketene dimer (hydration/decarboxylation)
Uses: plastics processing lubricant

distearylpentaerythrityl diphosphite

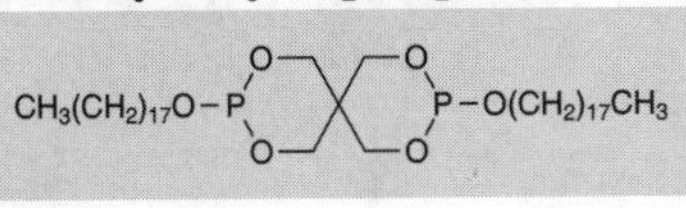

$$CH_3(CH_2)_{17}O - P \overset{O}{\underset{O}{\diagdown}} \overset{O}{\underset{O}{\diagup}} P - O(CH_2)_{17}CH_3$$

$C_{41}H_{82}P_2O_6$. M: 733.05.
Production:
• pentaerythritol + phosphorus trichloride + stearyl alcohol (dehydrochlorination/dehydrochlorination)
Uses: antioxidant (plastics)

distearyl thiodipropionate
di-*n*-octadecyl 3,3′-thiodipropionate; distearyl 3,3′-thiodipropionate; DSTDP; DSTP; [693-36-7]

$$S\left[CH_2CH_2\overset{O}{\overset{\|}{C}}O(CH_2)_{17}CH_3\right]_2$$

$C_{42}H_{82}O_4S_1$. M: 683.18. White powder. MP: 63°C. d: 0.90 kg/l.
Production:
• stearyl alcohol + thiodipropionic acid (esterification)
Uses:
antioxidant (plastics, rubber, grease)

distigmine bromide
[15876-67-2]

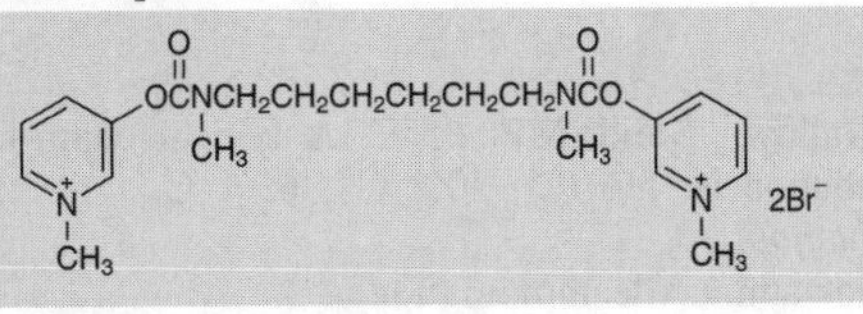

$$\underset{CH_3}{OCNCH_2CH_2CH_2CH_2CH_2CH_2N\overset{O}{\overset{\|}{C}}O} \quad 2Br^-$$

$C_{22}H_{32}Br_2N_4O_4$. M: 576.34.
Production:
• 3-hydroxypyridine + hexamethylene diisocyanate + methyl bromide (isocyanate addition/quaternisation)
Uses:
parasympathomimetic drug

disulfoton
S-2-ethylthioethyl *O,O*-diethyl phosphorodithionate; [298-04-4]

$$C_2H_5SCH_2CH_2S\overset{S}{\overset{\|}{P}}(OC_2H_5)_2$$

$C_8H_{19}O_2P_1S_3$. M: 274.40.
Production:
• 2-ethylthioethanol + *O,O*-diethyl dithiophosphoric acid (sulphide formation)
Uses: insecticide/acaricide

disulphur dichloride
See: sulphur monochloride

disul-sodium
2,4-DES-sodium; sodium 2-(2,4-dichlorophenoxy)ethyl sulphate; [149-26-8]

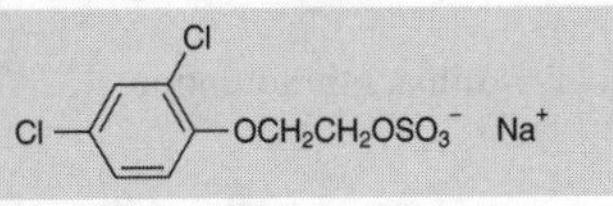

$$Cl - \bigcirc\hspace{-0.5em}\langle \overset{Cl}{}\rangle - OCH_2CH_2OSO_3^- \quad Na^+$$

$C_8H_7Cl_2Na_1O_5S_1$. M: 309.10.
Production:
• 2,4-dichlorophenol + ethylene oxide + chlorosulphonic acid (epoxidation/sulphonation/sodium salt formation)
Uses: herbicide

N,N-ditallowamidoethyl-*N*-methylammonium ethoxylate methosulphate
quaternium-53

$$\underset{}{(RCNHCH_2CH_2)_2^+N(CH_2CH_2O)_nH} \quad \overset{CH_3}{} \quad CH_3SO_4^-$$

n = about 3.0.
Production:
• tallow acid + ethylenediamine + ethylene oxide + dimethyl sulphate (amide formation/epoxidation/methylation)
Uses:
fabric softener

ditallowamine

N,N-ditallowamine

$$R_2NH$$

R = tallow-. Solid. MP: 65°C. A typical chain-length distribution is: 5% C_{14}, 30% C_{16}, 65% C_{18}.
Production:
• tallowamine (deammoniation)
Derivatives:
dimethylditallowammonium chloride

ditallowdimethylammonium chloride
See: dimethylditallowammonium chloride

ditallowdimonium chloride
See: dimethylditallowammonium chloride

di-(2,2,6,6-tetramethyl-4-piperidyl) sebacate
bis(2,2,6,6-tetramethyl-4-piperidyl) decanedioate; Tinuvin 770 (Ciba-Geigy); [52829-07-9]

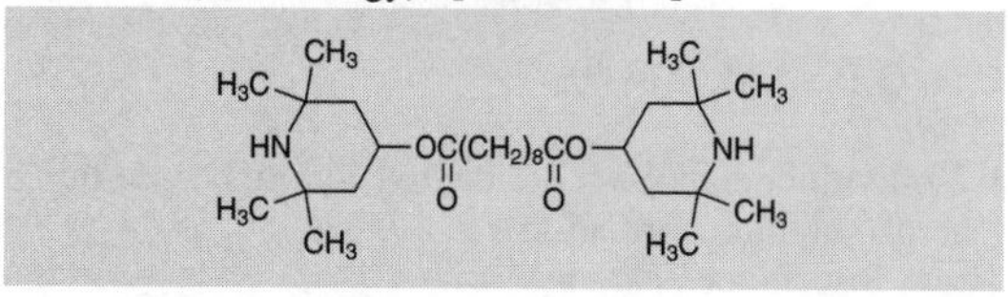

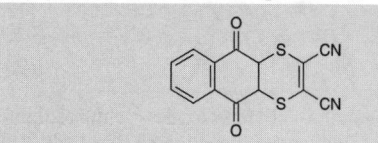

$C_{28}H_{52}N_2O_4$. M: 480.74.
Production:
• 4-hydroxy-2,2,6,6-tetramethylpiperidine + sebacoyl chloride (esterification)
Uses:
light stabiliser (plastics)

dithianon
2,3-dicyano-1,4-dithiaanthraquinone; [3347-22-6]

$C_{14}H_4N_2O_2S_2$. M: 296.32.
Production:
• carbon disulphide + hydrogen cyanide + dichlone (condensation/sulphide formation)
Uses: fungicide

3,3′-dithiobis(2-aminopropionic acid) *See:* L-cystine

2,2′-dithiodibenzoic acid
[119-80-2]

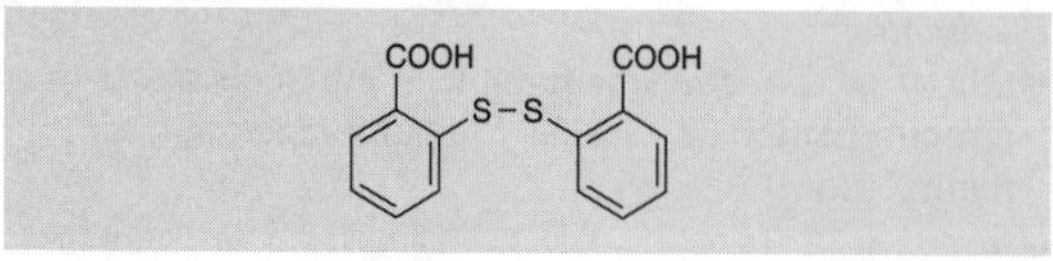

$C_{14}H_{10}O_4S_2$. M: 306.36.

Production:
• anthranilic acid + sodium hydrosulphide (diazotisation/oxidative coupling)
Derivatives:
benzoisothiazolin-3-one; carbomethoxybenzenesulphonyl isocyanate; sodium saccharin

4,4′-dithiodimorpholine
dimorpholine disulphide; DTDM; [103-34-4]

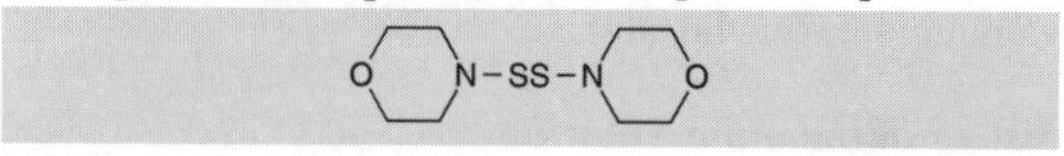

$C_8H_{16}N_2O_2S_2$. M: 236.36. Crystalline solid. MP: 124°C.
Production:
• morpholine + sulphur monochloride (chlorosulphurisation)
Uses: vulcanisation agent

di-*o*-tolylguanidine
DOTG; [97-39-2]

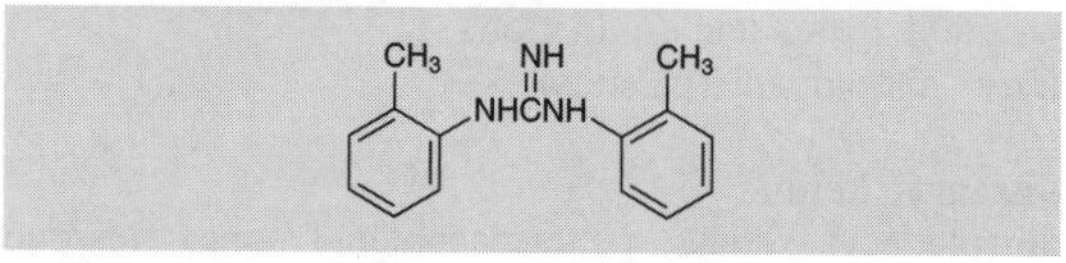

$C_{15}H_{17}N_3$. M: 239.32. White powder. MP: 179°C. Slightly soluble in water and alcohol.
Production:
• *o*-toluidine + carbon disulphide + ammonia (condensation/imine formation)
Uses: vulcanisation accelerator

di-*o*-tolylthiourea
DOTT

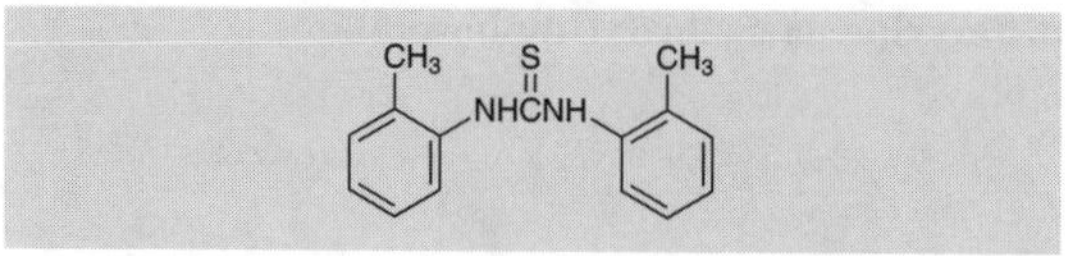

$C_{15}H_{16}N_2S_1$. M: 256.36. Colourless crystals with an unpleasant odour. MP: 144–148°C. Insoluble in water. Soluble in oxygenated and aromatic solvents.
Production:
• *o*-toluidine + carbon disulphide (reaction)
Uses: acid corrosion inhibitor

DITP *See:* diisotridecyl phthalate

ditridecyl phthalate *See:* diisotridecyl phthalate

ditridecyl thiodipropionate
ditridecyl 3,3′-thiodipropionate; DTDTP; Cyanox 711 (American Cyanamid); [10595-72-9]

$$S(CH_2CH_2COCH_2C_{12}H_{25})_2$$

$C_{32}H_{62}O_4S_1$. M: 542.91. Mobile liquid. MP: <-24°C. d:

0.94 kg/l (20°C). Insoluble in water. Soluble in oxygenated solvents.
Production:
• tridecanol + methyl acrylate + hydrogen sulphide (transesterification/addition)
Uses:
antioxidant (polyolefins, rubber)

3,5-di-(trifluoromethyl)aniline
3,5-bis(trifluoromethyl)aniline; Fast Orange GGD base; Azoic Diazo Component 16 (CI); 37045 (CI); [328-74-5]

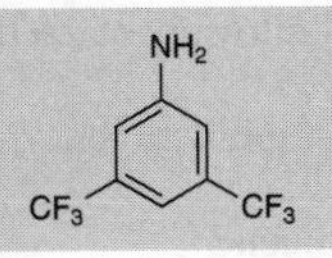

$C_8H_5F_6N_1$. M: 229.13.
Production:
• *m*-xylene (side-chain chlorination/ammoniation/halogen exchange/nitration/nitro reduction)
Uses: azoic dye diazo component

di-(trimethylsilyl)amine
hexamethyldisilazane; HMDS; [999-97-3]

$[(CH_3)_3Si]_2NH$

$C_6H_{19}N_1Si_2$. M: 161.40.
Production:
• chlorotrimethylsilane + ammonia (dehydrochlorination)
Uses: silylating agent

diuron
3-(3,4-dichlorophenyl)-1,1-dimethylurea; [330-54-1]

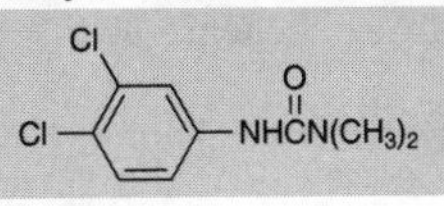

$C_9H_{10}Cl_2N_2O_1$. M: 233.10.
Production:
• 3,4-dichlorophenyl isocyanate + dimethylamine (isocyanate addition)
Uses: herbicide

divinylbenzene
DVB; [108-57-6]

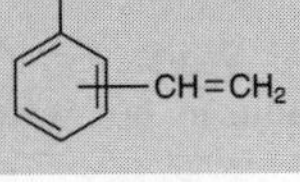

$C_{10}H_{10}$. M: 130.19. Available as inhibited 22% or 55% solutions in styrene. BP: 180°C (calculated). d: 0.90 kg/l (22% solution, 20°C). Insoluble in water. Solutions containing higher divinylbenzene concentrations polymerise explosively.

Production:
• diethylbenzene, mixed (fractionation/dehydrogenation)
Derivatives: poly(4-vinylpyridine); styrene-divinylbenzene copolymers
Uses: nitrile/butadiene rubber comonomer; reactive diluent (unsaturated polyester resins)

DLTP *See:* dilauryl thiodipropionate

DMA *See:* dimethylamine; 2,6-xylidine; *N,N*-dimethylaniline; dimethylacetamide

DMAC *See:* dimethylacetamide

DMAE *See:* dimethylethanolamine

DMAEMA *See:* 2-dimethylaminoethyl methacrylate

DMAMP
See: 2-dimethylamino-2-methyl-1-propanol; dimethylaminomethylphenol

DMAP *See:* 3-dimethylaminopropylamine

4-DMAP *See:* 4-dimethylaminopyridine

DMAPA *See:* 3-dimethylaminopropylamine

DMAPMA *See:* dimethylaminopropyl methacrylamide

DMB *See:* hydroquinone dimethyl ether

DMB-1 *See:* 2,3-dimethyl-1-butene

DMB-2 *See:* 2,3-dimethyl-2-butene

DMC *See:* 2-dimethylaminoethyl chloride hydrochloride; dimethyl carbonate

DMCD *See:* dimethyl cyclohexane-1,4-dicarboxylate

DMCHA *See:* *N,N*-dimethylcyclohexylamine

DMCTP *See:* *O,O*-dimethyl phosphorochlorothioate

DMDAAC *See:* diallyldimethylammonium chloride

DMDEE *See:* bis(2-morpholinoethyl)ether

DMDH *See:* dimethylol dimethylhydantoin

DMDHEU
See: 1,3-dimethylol-4,5-dihydroxyethylene urea

DMDZ *See:* nordazepam

DME *See:* dimethyl ether

DMEA *See:* dimethylethanolamine

DMEP *See:* di-(2-methoxyethyl) phthalate

DMEU *See:* *N,N'*-dimethylolethylene urea

DMF *See:* dimethylformamide

DMGP *See:* di-(2-methoxyethyl) phthalate

DMH *See:* 5,5-dimethylhydantoin

DM hydantoin *See:* 5,5-dimethylhydantoin

DMIPA *See:* dimethylisopropanolamine

DMK *See:* acetone

DMM *See:* dimethyl malonate

DMMP *See:* dimethyl methylphosphonate

DM-2,6-NDC
See: dimethyl naphthalene-2,6-dicarboxylate

DMP *See:* dimethyl phthalate; *N,N'*-dimethylpiperazine

2,4-DMP *See:* 2,4-xylenol

DMPC *See:* 3-dimethylaminopropyl chloride hydrochloride

DMPCT *See:* *O,O*-dimethyl phosphorochlorothioate

DMPI *See:* dimethyl phosphite

DMPT *See:* *N,N*-dimethyl-*p*-toluidine

DMPU *See:* dimethylolpropylene urea

DMS *See:* dimethyl sulphide

DMSO *See:* dimethyl sulphoxide

DMSS *See:* dimethyl succinylosuccinate

DMT *See:* dimethyl terephthalate

DMTD *See:* 2,5-dimercapto-1,3,4-thiadiazole

DMTDP *See:* dimyristyl thiodipropionate

DMTT *See:* dazomet

DMU *See:* *N,N'*-dimethylurea; dimethylolurea

DNB *See:* octene, branched

DNC *See:* 4,6-dinitro-*o*-cresol

DNGU *See:* dinitroglycoluril

DNOC *See:* 4,6-dinitro-*o*-cresol

DNP *See:* dinonyl phthalate

DNPC *See:* 2,6-dinitro-*p*-cresol

DNPD *See:* *N,N'*-di-β-naphthyl-*p*-phenylenediamine

DNPT *See:* *N,N'*-dinitrosopentamethylenetetramine

DNSDSA *See:* 4,4'-dinitrostilbene-2,2'-disulphonic acid

DNT *See:* dinitrotoluene

DOA *See:* di-(2-ethylhexyl) adipate

dobutamine
[34368-04-2]

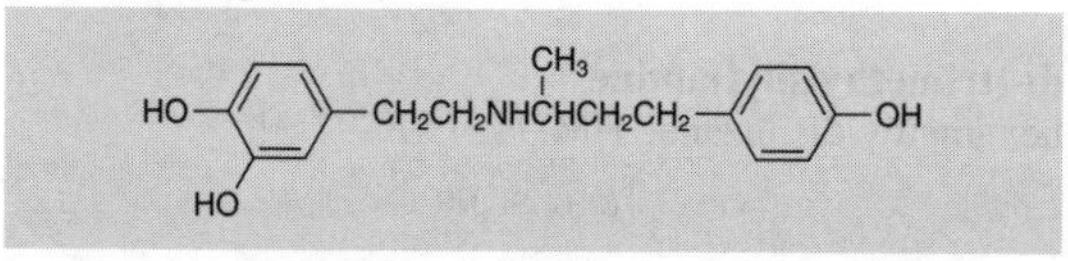

$C_{18}H_{23}N_1O_3$. M: 301.39.
Production:
• *p*-anisaldehyde + acetone + homoveratrylamine (aldol condensation/hydrogenation/reductive amination/hydrolysis)
Uses:
cardiotonic drug

docosanoic acid *See:* behenic acid

1-docosanol *See:* behenyl alcohol

docosenamide *See:* erucamide

14-docosenoic acid *See:* erucic acid

dodecamethylenediamine *See:* 1,12-diaminododecane

1,12-dodecanedioic acid
dodecanedioic acid; DDDA; [693-23-2]

$$HOOC(CH_2)_{10}COOH$$

$C_{12}H_{22}O_4$. M: 230.31. White, crystalline powder. MP: 129°C. Slightly soluble in hot water.
Production:
• cyclododecanol-cyclododecanone, mixed (oxidation)
Derivatives: diester oils; 1,12-dodecanediol; ethylene glycol dodecane-1,12-dioate; polyamide 6 terpolymers; polyamide 612; polyamide 1212; poly(ether-amide) elastomers

1,12-dodecanediol
dodecane-1,12-diol; [5675-51-4]

$$HO(CH_2)_{12}OH$$

$C_{12}H_{26}O_2$. M: 202.34. Solid. MP: 81°C. BP: 183°C (1.2 kPa).
Production:
• 1,12-dodecanedioic acid (hydrogenation)
Derivatives: 1,12-diaminododecane; 1,12-dodecanediyl dimethacrylate; 15-pentadecanolide
Uses: polyurethane polyol comonomer

1,12-dodecanediyl dimethacrylate

$$CH_2=\overset{O}{\overset{\|}{C}}CO(CH_2)_{12}O\overset{O}{\overset{\|}{C}}C=CH_2$$
$$\underset{CH_3}{|} \qquad \underset{CH_3}{|}$$

$C_{20}H_{34}O_4$. M: 338.49.
Production:
• 1,12-dodecanediol + methyl methacrylate (transesterification)
Uses: crosslinked acrylic resin comonomer

dodecane-12-lactam *See:* lauryllactam

n-dodecanethiol *See:* *n*-dodecyl mercaptan

n-dodecanoic acid *See:* lauric acid, narrow cut

n-dodecanol *See:* lauryl alcohol, narrow-cut

dodecanoyl peroxide *See:* lauroyl peroxide

dodecene, branched
propylene tetramer; tetrapropylene; triisobutylene; TIB; TNB; [6842-15-5]

$$\underset{CH_3}{\overset{CH_3}{C_9H_{19}\overset{|}{C}=CH_2}}$$

$C_{12}H_{24}$. M: 168.32. Mixed product, the composition of which depends on the raw materials and manufacturing process. Dodecenes produced from raffinate II are the most linear with an average of 1.1–1.3 side-chains per molecule.
Production:
• raffinate I (acid-catalysed alkylation; coproduced with 2,4,4-trimethylpentene/raffinate II)
• propylene (phosphoric acid-catalysed oligomerisation; coproduced with nonene, branched)
• gasoline, polymer (fractionation; coproduced with hexene, branched/heptene, branched/octene, branched/nonene, branched)
• raffinate II (Dimersol X/Octol processes; coproduced with octene, branched)
Derivatives: dodecenylsuccinic anhydride; dodecylbenzene, branched; *t*-dodecyl mercaptan; dodecylphenol; isoparaffin solvents; tridecanol

1-dodecene
dodec-1-ene; [112-41-4]

$$CH_3(CH_2)_9CH=CH_2$$

$C_{12}H_{24}$. M: 168.32. Colourless liquid. BP: 213–216°C. Pour point: -37°C. d: 0.75 kg/l (25°C).
Production:
• ethylene (Ziegler oligomerisation; coproduced with 1-butene/1-hexene/1-octene/1-decene/α-olefins(C_{12}-C_{14})/α-olefins(C_{14}-C_{16})/α-olefins(C_{16}-C_{18})/α-olefins(C_{18+}))
Derivatives: *n*-dodecyl mercaptan; *n*-tridecaldehyde

dodecenylsuccinic anhydride
alkenyl(C_{10}-C_{14})succinic anhydride; ASA; DDS; DDSA; [25377-73-5]

$C_{16}H_{26}O_3$. M: 266.39.
Production:
• dodecene, branched + maleic anhydride (ene reaction)
Derivatives: di-(phenylmercury) dodecenylsuccinate; dodecyl succinate propoxylates; manganese dodecenylsuccinate; sodium starch dodecenylsuccinate
Uses: epoxy resin curing agent; paper sizing ingredient

n-dodecyl alcohol *See:* lauryl alcohol, narrow-cut

n-dodecyl aldehyde *See:* lauraldehyde

p-dodecylaniline

$C_{18}H_{31}N_1$. M: 261.46. Colourless liquid. BP: 340–350°C. d: 0.91 kg/l (25°C). Insoluble in water. Soluble in most organic solvents.
Production:
• dodecylphenol + ammonia (ammoniation)
Derivatives: Acid Blue 138; Acid Red 138

dodecylbenzene, branched
detergent alkylate, hard; [123-01-3]

$C_{18}H_{30}$. M: 246.44. Alkylbenzene with a branched sidechain averaging 12 carbon atoms. BP: 267–304°C. d: 0.87 kg/l (10°C). Non-biodegradable.
Production:
• dodecene, branched + benzene (HF alkylation)

Derivatives: dodecylbenzenesulphonic acid, branched
Uses:
industrial lubricating oil; rubber secondary plasticiser

dodecylbenzene, linear
detergent alkylate; linear alkylbenzene; LAB

CH$_3$(CH$_2$)$_{11}$—⬡

C$_{18}$H$_{30}$. M: 246.44. Colourless to pale yellow, high-boiling liquid. d: 0.86 kg/l (15°C). Insoluble in water. Three different alkyl chain-length distributions are commonly available: C$_{12}$-C$_{15}$, C$_{12}$-C$_{13}$ and C$_{10}$-C$_{13}$. A typical product from the hydrofluoric acid alkylation process contains: 93% w/w *n*-alkylbenzene and 15% w/w 2-phenylalkane.
Production:
• *n*-olefins(C$_{10}$-C$_{13}$)/α-olefins(C$_{12}$-C$_{14}$)/gas oil, light, Arge + benzene (HF alkylation)
• *n*-monochloroparaffins (C$_{10}$-C$_{13}$) + benzene (Friedel-Crafts alkylation)
Derivatives:
dialkylbenzene; dodecylbenzenesulphonic acid, linear

dodecylbenzenesulphonic acid, branched
alkylbenzenesulphonic acid; ABS; DDBSA

C$_{12}$H$_{25}$—⬡—SO$_3$H

C$_{18}$H$_{30}$O$_3$S$_1$. M: 326.50. Brown liquid.
Production:
• dodecylbenzene, branched + sulphuric acid (sulphonation)
Derivatives:
sodium dodecylbenzenesulphonate
Uses: emulsifier (metalworking fluids, pesticides, emulsion polymerisation); surfactant (industrial detergents, cleaners)

dodecylbenzenesulphonic acid, linear
alkylbenzene sulphonic acid; ABS; DDBSA; LABS

CH$_3$(CH$_2$)$_n$—⬡—SO$_3$H

n = 10–13. C$_{18}$H$_{30}$O$_3$S$_1$. M: 326.50. Pale yellow to dark brown, viscous liquid. A typical chain-length distribution is: 13% C$_{10}$, 34% C$_{11}$, 31% C$_{12}$, 22% C$_{13}$ for broad-cut grades. Narrow-cut grades are also available.
Production:
• dodecylbenzene, linear + sulphuric acid (sulphonation)
Derivatives: calcium alkylbenzenesulphonate; monoisopropanolamine alkylbenzenesulphonate; sodium alkylbenzenesulphonate, linear; triethanolamine alkylbenzenesulphonate

n-dodecyl chloride *See:* lauryl chloride

dodecyldimethylamine *See:* dimethyllaurylamine

dodecyl gallate
E312 (EC); [1166-52-5]

HO—, HO—, HO—⬡—CO(CH$_2$)$_{11}$CH$_3$

C$_{19}$H$_{30}$O$_5$. M: 338.44. White, crystalline solid. MP: 96–97°C. Insoluble in water. Soluble in oxygenated solvents. Not approved for food use in the USA.
Production:
• lauryl alcohol, narrow-cut + gallic acid (esterification)
Uses: antioxidant (oils, fats, cereals)

n-dodecyl mercaptan
n-dodecanethiol; lauryl mercaptan; DDM; [112-55-0]

CH$_3$(CH$_2$)$_{11}$SH

C$_{12}$H$_{26}$S$_1$. M: 202.40. Colourless liquid. BP: 274–278°C. d: 0.85 kg/l (15°C). Insoluble in water.
Production:
• 1-dodecene + hydrogen sulphide (anti-Markownikoff addition)
Derivatives: dibutyltin bis(laurylmercaptide)
Uses: unsaturated polyester resin catalyst accelerator; chain-transfer agent (styrene-butadiene/chloroprene rubber production)

t-dodecyl mercaptan
dodecyl mercaptan; TDM

CH$_3$
|
C$_9$H$_{19}$CSH
|
CH$_3$

C$_{12}$H$_{26}$S$_1$. M: 202.40. Colourless liquid. BP: 230–247°C. d: 0.86 kg/l (15°C). Insoluble in water.
Production:
• dodecene, branched + hydrogen sulphide (thiolation)
Uses: chain transfer agent (styrene-butadiene, nitrile rubber production)

n-dodecyl methacrylate *See:* lauryl methacrylate

dodecylphenol
[27193-86-8]

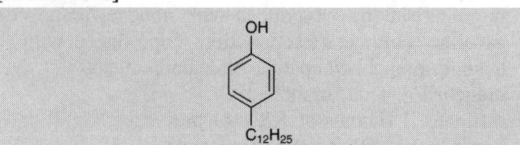

C$_{18}$H$_{30}$O$_1$. M: 262.44. Pale yellow liquid with a slight, phenolic odour. BP: 307–330°C. d: 0.93 kg/l (20°C). Insoluble in water. Mixed isomer product.

Production:
• dodecene, branched + phenol (Friedel-Crafts alkylation)
Derivatives: alkylphenol-polyamine adducts; barium-zinc heat stabilisers; cadmium-barium heat stabilisers; cadmium-zinc heat stabilisers; calcium alkyl salicylates; *p*-dodecylaniline; dodecylphenol ethoxylates; dodecyl-salicylaldoxime; phenates, alkali-earth salts; phenates, sulphurised, alkali-earth salts
Uses: phenolic resin comonomer

dodecylphenol ethoxylates
dodoxynol (CTFA)

$$C_{12}H_{25}\text{—}\bigcirc\text{—}O(CH_2CH_2O)_nH$$

n = 4–12. Commercial products contain 6–12 moles EO. Liquid. d: 1.01–1.06 kg/l. Soluble in water when n > 8. HLB: 9–13.5 (6–12 moles EO).
Production:
• dodecylphenol + ethylene oxide (epoxidation)
Uses: dispersant; surfactant/wetting agent (household/industrial cleaners)

1-dodecylpyridinium chloride
See: laurylpyridinium chloride

dodecylsalicylaldoxime
2-hydroxy-5-dodecylbenzaldoxime; LIX 622 (Henkel); LIX 6022 (Henkel)

$$\begin{array}{c} OH \\ \bigcirc CH=NOH \\ C_{12}H_{25} \end{array}$$

$C_{19}H_{31}N_1O_2$. M: 305.47.
Production:
• chloroform + dodecylphenol + hydroxylamine sulphate (Reimer-Tiemann reaction/oxime formation)
Uses: copper extraction reagent

dodecyl succinate propoxylates

$$\begin{array}{c} O \quad CH_3 \\ CH_3(CH_2)_8CH=CHCH_2CHCO(CHCH_2O)_nH \\ CH_2COOH \end{array}$$

The product is a mixture of the dicarboxylic acid and the monoester.
Production:
• dodecenylsuccinic anhydride + polypropylene glycol (esterification)
Uses: corrosion inhibitor (turbine oils, hydraulic fluids)

dodecyltrimethylammonium chloride
laurtrimonium chloride; lauryltrimethylammonium chloride; LTAC; [112-00-5]

$$CH_3(CH_2)_{11}N(CH_3)_3{}^+ \quad Cl^-$$

$C_{15}H_{34}Cl_1N_1$. M: 263.89.
Production:
• laurylamine + methyl chloride (quaternisation)
Uses:
cationic emulsifier (cosmetics)

dodemorph acetate
4-cyclododecyl-2,6-dimethylmorpholine; [31717-87-0]

$$\begin{array}{c} CH_3 \\ N\text{—}O \quad CH_3COOH \\ CH_3 \end{array}$$

$C_{20}H_{39}N_1O_3$. M: 341.54.
Production:
• cyclododecanol-cyclododecanone, mixed + 2,6-dimethylmorpholine + acetic acid (reductive amination/salt formation)
Uses: fungicide

dodine
1-dodecylguanidinium acetate; [2439-10-3]

$$\begin{array}{c} NH_2 \\ CH_3(CH_2)_{11}NHC=NH_2{}^+ \quad CH_3COO^- \end{array}$$

$C_{15}H_{33}N_3O_2$. M: 287.44.
Production:
• laurylamine + cyanamide + acetic acid (addition/salt formation)
Uses: fungicide

dolomite

$$CaCO_3.MgCO_3$$

Natural dolomite is mined in many parts of the world.
Derivatives:
dolomite, calcined
Uses:
filler/extender (plastics, sealants, coatings); raw material (sulphite pulp process); water treatment chemical

dolomite, calcined
dolime

$$CaO.nMgO$$

Production:
• dolomite (calcination)
Derivatives:
magnesia, caustic-calcined; magnesium; magnesium carbonate, basic; magnesium hydroxide
Uses: raw material (sulphite pulp process); water treatment chemical

DOM *See:* di-(2-ethylhexyl) maleate

domperidone
[57808-66-9]

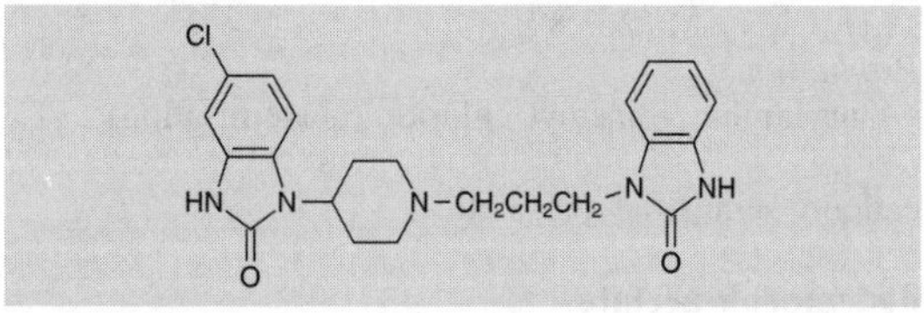

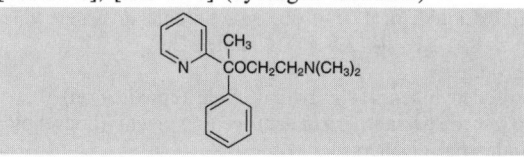

$C_{22}H_{22}Cl_1N_5O_2$. M: 423.90.
Production:
- *o*-chloronitrobenzene + 3-aminopropanol +
  potassium cyanate + 2,5-dichloronitrobenzene +
  4-amino-*N*-benzylpiperidine (amine formation/nitro
  reduction/cyanate addition/amine formation/nitro
  reduction/debenzylation/amine formation/cyanate
  addition)
Uses:
antiemetic drug

DOP *See:* di-(2-ethylhexyl) phthalate

dopamine
3,4-dihydroxyphenylethylamine; [51-61-6]

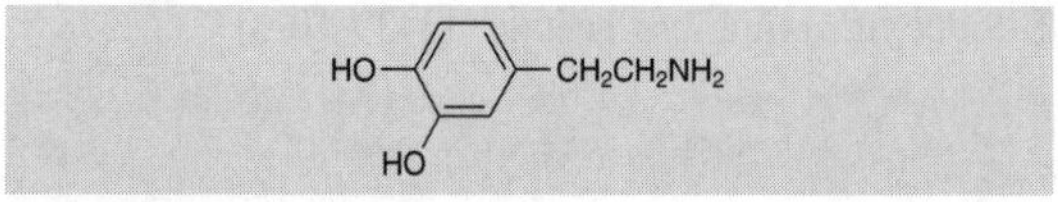

$C_8H_{11}N_1O_2$. M: 153.19. Available commercially as the
free base or hydrochloride.
Production:
- homoveratrylamine (hydrolysis)
Uses:
cardiotonic drug

DOS *See:* di-(2-ethylhexyl) sebacate

DOTG *See:* di-*o*-tolylguanidine

DOTT *See:* di-*o*-tolylthiourea

doxepin
[1668-19-5]

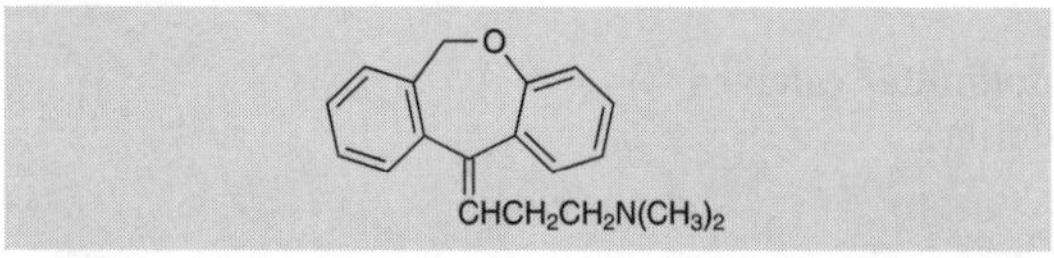

$C_{19}H_{21}N_1O_1$. M: 279.39. Available commercially as the
hydrochloride salt of the *cis,trans*-isomer mixture.
Production:
- methyl salicylate + benzyl chloride + 3-dimethyl-
  aminopropyl chloride hydrochloride (ether
  formation/cyclisation/Grignard reagent formation/
  Grignard reaction/dehydration)
Uses:
antidepressant drug

doxycycline
[17086-28-1]

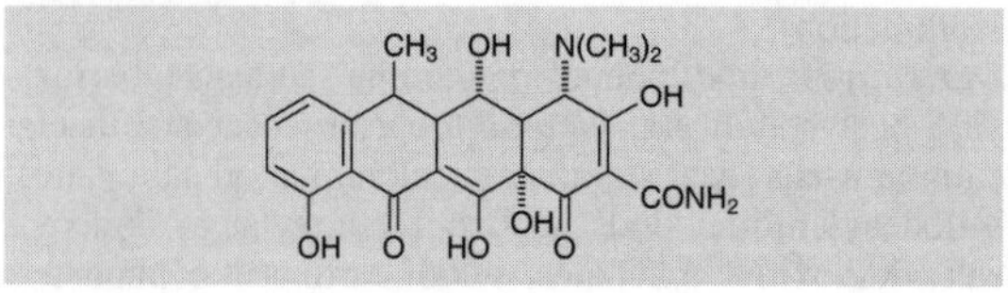

$C_{22}H_{24}N_2O_8$. M: 444.43. Available commercially as the
free base or hydrochloride.
Production:
- oxytetracycline (hydrogenation)
Uses:
antibacterial drug

doxylamine
[469-21-6]; [562-10-7] (hydrogen succinate)

$C_{17}H_{22}N_2O_1$. M: 270.38. Available commercially as the
hydrogen succinate.
Production:
- 2-acetylpyridine + phenylmagnesium bromide +
  2-dimethylaminoethyl chloride hydrochloride
  (Grignard reaction/ether formation)
- pyridine + acetophenone + 2-diethylaminoethyl
  chloride hydrochloride (Grignard reagent
  formation/Grignard reaction/ether formation)
Uses: antihistamine drug

DOZ *See:* di-(2-ethylhexyl) azelate

2,4-DP *See:* dichlorprop

DPA *See:* diphenylamine

DPBDA *See:* dipropylene glycol diacrylate

DPG *See:* dipropylene glycol; diphenylguanidine

DPIP *See:* diphenyl isophthalate

DPM *See:* dipropylene glycol monomethyl ether

DPMG *See:* dipropylene glycol monomethyl ether

DPP *See:* bisphenol A; diphenyl phthalate

DPPD *See:* *N,N′*-diphenyl-*p*-phenylenediamine

DPTT *See:* dipentamethylenethiuram tetrasulphide

DPTU *See:* thiocarbanilide

drazoxolon
4-(2-chlorophenylhydrazono)-3-methylisoxazol-5-one;
[5707-69-7]

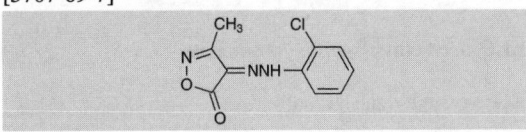

$C_{10}H_8Cl_1N_3O_2$. M: 237.64.
Production:
- *o*-chloroaniline + sodium nitrite + ethyl acetoacetate + hydroxylamine sulphate (diazotisation/
  imine formation/cyclisation/azo coupling/
  condensation)

Uses: fungicide

droperidol
[548-73-2]

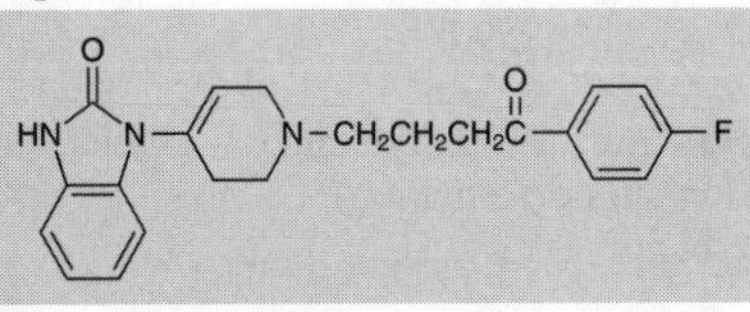

$C_{22}H_{22}F_1N_3O_2$. M: 379.44.
Production:
- *o*-phenylenediamine + 1-benzyl-3-carb-
  ethoxy-4-piperidone hydrochloride +
  4-chloro-4′-fluorobutyrophenone
  (condensation/debenzylation/amine formation)

Uses: neuroleptic drug

DSMA *See:* disodium methylarsonate

DSP *See:* disodium phosphate

DSS *See:* sodium di-(2-ethylhexyl)sulphosuccinate

DSTDP *See:* distearyl thiodipropionate

DSTP *See:* distearyl thiodipropionate

DTBP *See:* di-*t*-butyl peroxide

DTDM *See:* 4,4′-dithiodimorpholine

DTDP *See:* diisotridecyl phthalate

durene
1,2,4,5-tetramethylbenzene; [95-93-2]

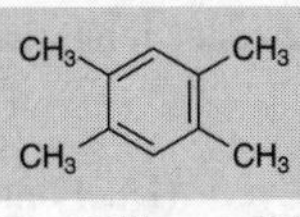

$C_{10}H_{14}$. M: 134.22. Crystalline solid. MP: 80–82°C. BP:
193–195°C. Insoluble in water. Miscible with oxygenated solvents.

Production:
- trimethylbenzene fraction (fractionation; coproduced
  with pseudocumene/mesitylene)

Derivatives: pyromellitic dianhydride

E

econazole
[27220-47-9]

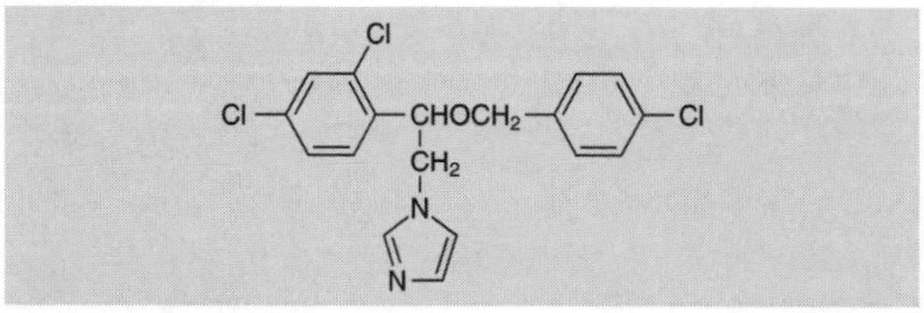

$C_{18}H_{15}Cl_3N_2O_1$. M: 381.69. Available commercially as the nitrate.
Production:
• α,2,4-trichloroacetophenone + imidazole + *p*-chlorobenzyl chloride (amine formation/carbonyl reduction/ether formation)
Uses: antifungal drug

ECTFE *See:* poly(ethylene-chlorotrifluoroethylene)

EDA *See:* ethylenediamine

EDB *See:* ethylene dibromide

EDC *See:* ethylene dichloride

EDDI *See:* ethylenediamine dihydroiodide

edetic acid *See:* ethylenediaminetetraacetic acid

edifenphos
O-ethyl *S,S*-diphenyl phosphorodithioate; [17109-49-8]

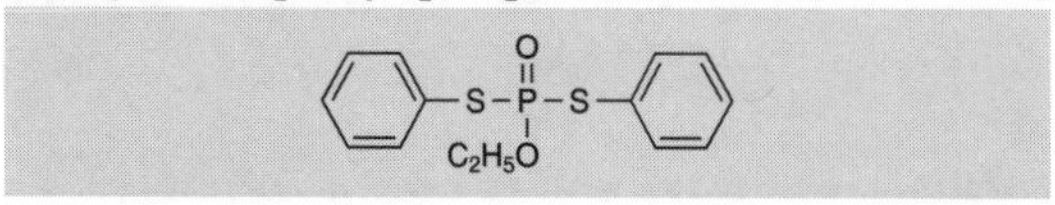

$C_{14}H_{15}O_2P_1S_2$. M: 310.37.
Production:
• phosphorus oxychloride + ethanol + thiophenol (dehydrochlorination/dehydrochlorination)
Uses: fungicide

EDMA *See:* ethylene glycol dimethacrylate

EDTA *See:* ethylenediaminetetraacetic acid

EDTMPA
See: ethylenediaminetetra-(methylene phosphonic acid)

EEA *See:* ethylene-ethyl acrylate copolymers

2-EEA *See:* ethylene glycol monoethyl ether acetate

EEMM *See:* diethyl ethoxymethylenemalonate

EEP *See:* ethyl 3-ethoxypropionate

EG *See:* ethylene glycol

EGA *See:* ethylene glycol monoethyl ether acetate

eglinazine-ethyl
ethyl *N*-[4-chloro-6-(ethylamino)-1,3,5-triazin-2-yl]-glycinate; [6616-80-4]

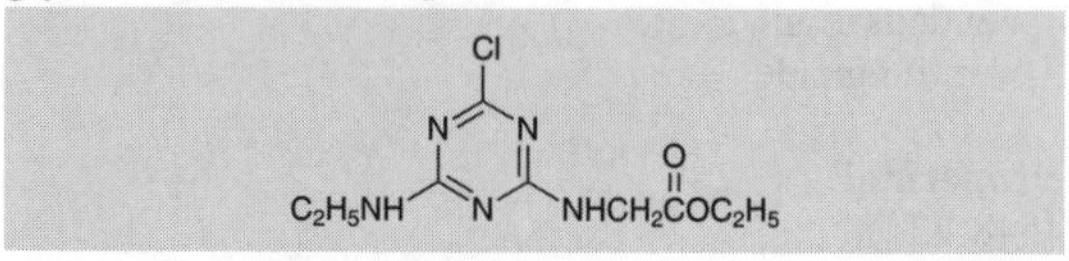

$C_9H_{14}Cl_1N_5O_2$. M: 259.69.
Production:
• cyanuric chloride + ethylamine + glycine (amine formation/amine formation)
Uses: herbicide

EGSSIPA
See: sodium bis(2-hydroxyethyl)-5-sulphoisophthalate

2EH *See:* 2-ethylhexanol

EHA *See:* 2-ethylhexyl acrylate

EHEC *See:* ethyl hydroxyethyl cellulose

2EHMA *See:* 2-ethylhexyl methacrylate

2EHN *See:* 2-ethylhexyl nitrate

Ehrlich's reagent *See:* *p*-dimethylaminobenzaldehyde

2-EHT *See:* 2-ethylhexyl titanate

EIAK *See:* ethyl amyl ketone

eicosanol

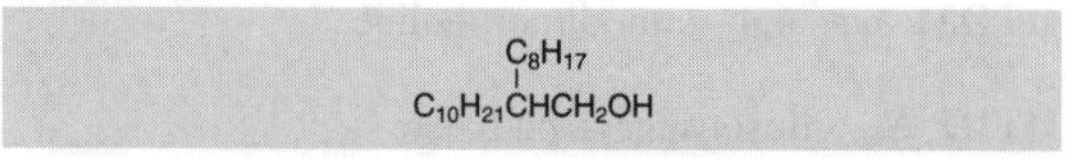

$C_{20}H_{42}O_1$. M: 298.56. Branched-chain primary alcohol.
Production:
• isodecanol (Guerbet reaction)
Derivatives: alkylbenzene, long-chain

elastane
Durlastan (Bayer); Lycra (Du Pont); spandex;
Elastomeric fibre made of alternating hard and soft segments of polyurea and polyether. d: 1.2 kg/l. Fibres stretch to 500–600% without breaking. Tenacity: 6.0–

9.0 g/tex. Sold as filament and as staple blends with non-elastic fibres.
Production:
- 4,4′-diisocyanatodicyclohexylmethane/4,4′-diphenyl-methane diisocyanate, pure + ethylenediamine/hydrazine + poly(tetramethylene ether) glycol (isocyanate addition)

Uses:
elastomeric textile fibres (undergarments, stockings, swimwear, sportswear)

electrocorundum *See:* alumina, fused

ELO *See:* linseed oil, epoxidised

EMA *See:* ethylene-methyl acrylate copolymers; ethylene-maleic anhydride copolymers

EMAA *See:* ethylene-methacrylic acid copolymers

embonic acid *See:* pamoic acid

EMD *See:* manganese dioxide

emery
Emery is a natural mixture of corundum with magnetite.
Uses: metal/wood/glass abrasive (grinding wheels, papers, cloths)

EMP *See:* polypropylene, elastomer-modified

empenthrin
[54406-48-3]

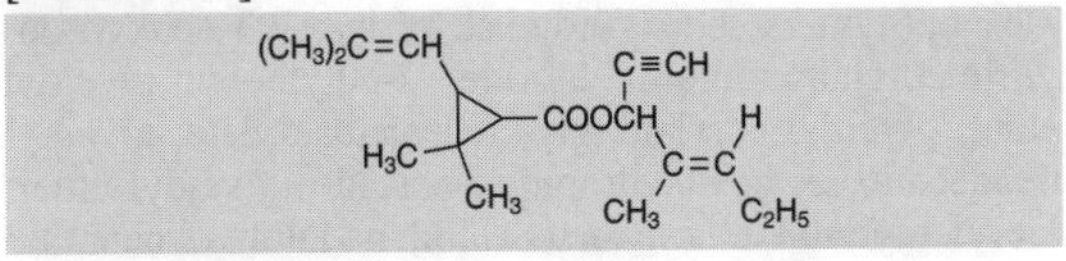

$C_{18}H_{26}O_2$. M: 274.41.
Production:
- propionaldehyde + acetylene + (*1RS*)-*trans*-chrysanthemic acid (aldol condensation/dehydration/ethynylation/esterification)

Uses: insecticide

EMPP *See:* polypropylene, elastomer-modified

EN *See:* ethylidene norbornene

enalapril
[75847-73-3]; [76095-16-4] (maleate)
$C_{20}H_{28}N_2O_5$. M: 376.44. Available commercially as the free base and as the maleate salt.
Production:
- 3-phenylpropionaldehyde + L-alanine + L-proline (cyanohydrin formation/nitrile hydrolysis/esterification/amide formation/amine formation)

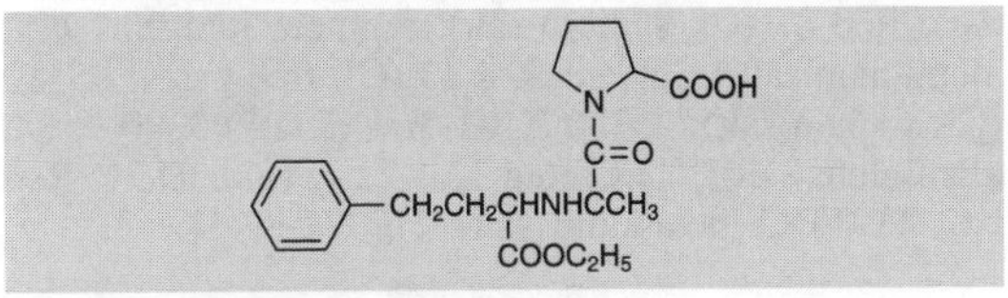

Uses: antihypertensive drug

enanthaldehyde *See:* *n*-heptaldehyde

enanthic acid *See:* *n*-heptanoic acid

ENB *See:* ethylidene norbornene

endosulphan
[115-29-7]

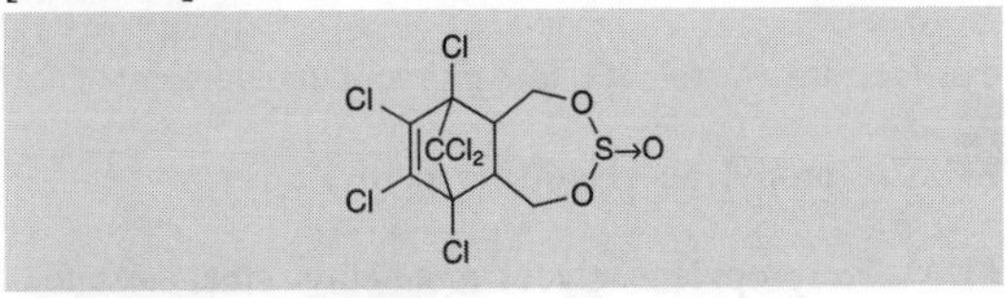

$C_9H_6Cl_6O_3S_1$. M: 406.93.
Production:
- hexachlorocyclopentadiene + 1,4-butenediol + thionyl chloride (Diels-Alder cycloaddition/sulphonation)

Uses: acaricide/insecticide

endothal-sodium
[145-73-3]

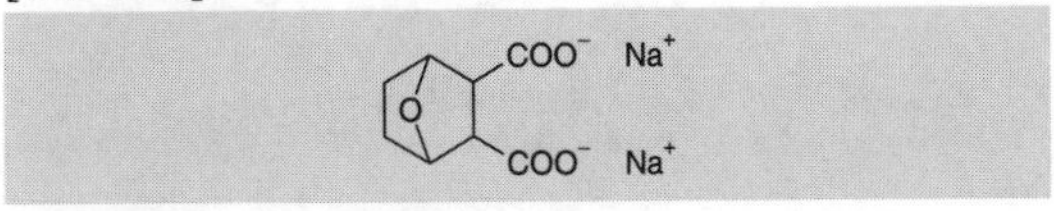

$C_8H_8Na_2O_5$. M: 230.12.
Production:
- furan + maleic anhydride + sodium hydroxide (Diels-Alder cycloaddition/salt formation)

Uses: defoliant/herbicide/algicide

enflurane
[13838-16-9]

CHF_2OCF_2CHFCl

$C_3H_2Cl_1F_5O_1$. M: 184.49.
Production:
- chlorotrifluoroethylene + methanol + hydrogen fluoride (addition/photochlorination/fluorination)

Uses: inhalation anaesthetic drug

enilconazole *See:* imazalil

ENON *See:* dibenzosuberenone-5

EO *See:* ethylene oxide

eosine

Acid Red 87 (CI, sodium salt); Pigment Red 90:1 (CI, aluminium salt); Solvent Red 43 (CI, free base); 45380 (CI, sodium salt); 45380:2 (CI, free acid); 45380:3 (CI, aluminium salt); D&C Red No. 22 (FDC); D&C Red No. 23 (FDC, potassium salt); [17372-87-1]

$C_{20}H_6Br_4Na_2O_5$. M: 691.86.
Production:
• fluorescein (ring bromination)
Uses:
dye (red ink, wool, stains); pigment (cosmetics)

EP *See:* propylene glycol monoethyl ether

EPA *See:* propylene glycol monoethyl ether acetate

EPDM

See: ethylene-propylene-diene terpolymer, rubber

EPDM/PP

See: polypropylene, elastomer-modified

DL-ephedrine

[299-42-3]; [50-98-6] (hydrochloride)

$C_{10}H_{15}N_1O_1$. M: 165.24. Available commercially as the racemic free base or as the hydrochloride or sulphate salt. Also available as the L(–)-free base or hydrochloride salt. The *threo* isomer, called pseudoephedrine, also has pharmacological properties.
Production:
• norephedrine (methylation)
• propiophenone + isoamyl nitrite + methylamine (alpha carbonylation/reductive amination)
Uses: sympathicomimetic drug

L-ephedrine

L-*erythro*-2-methylamino-1-phenylpropan-1-ol; [299-42-3]; [50-98-6] (hydrochloride); [134-72-5] (sulphate)

$C_{10}H_{15}N_1O_1$. M: 165.24. Available as the free base, the hydrochloride and the sulphate salts.

Production:
• microbial fermentation medium + benzaldehyde + methylamine (microbial conversion/reductive amination)
Uses: sympathicomimetic drug

epichlorohydrin

ECH; [106-89-8]

$C_3H_5Cl_1O_1$. M: 92.52. Colourless liquid. BP: 114–118°C. FP: -57°C. d: 1.17 kg/l (25°C). Solubility in water: 60 g/l water (25°C). Miscible with oxygenated solvents. Flash point: 33°C (TOC).
Production:
• glycerol-1,3-dichlorohydrin + calcium hydroxide (dehydrochlorination)
• allyl alcohol + chlorine (chlorination/dehydrochlorination)
Derivatives:
acebutolol; adipic acid-dimethylaminohydroxypropyldiethylenetriamine copolymers; allyl glycidyl ether; atenolol; bisphenol A diglycidyl ether; bisphenol A glycidyl ether prepolymers; bisphenol F diglycidyl ether; bisphenol H diglycidyl ether; 1,4-butanediol diglycidyl ether; *n*-butyl glycidyl ether; *t*-butyl glycidyl ether; carazolol; cashew nutshell glycidyl ether; cashew nutshellphenol condensate diglycidyl ether; celiprolol; chlorohydrin; 3-chloro-2-hydroxypropyltrimethylammonium chloride; *o*-cresyl glycidyl ether; cromolyn; 1,4-cyclohexanedimethanol diglycidyl ether; dibromobutanediol-epichlorohydrin adduct; dimethylhydantoin-glycidyl adducts; Disperse Blue 102; epichlorohydrin-ethylene oxide copolymers; epoxy-novolac resins; 2,3-epoxypropyltrimethylammonium chloride; 2-ethylhexyl glycidyl ether; glycidyl acrylate; glycidyl methacrylate; glycidyl neodecanoate; hexahydrophthalic acid diglycidyl ether; lauryl glycidyl ether; metoprolol; nadolol; α-naphthyl glycidyl ether; nifuratel; ornidazole; oxprenolol; phenyl glycidyl ether; polyepichlorohydrin; poly(2-hydroxypropyl dimethylammonium chloride); polypropylene glycol diglycidyl ether; Reactive Blue 6; sodium 3-chloro-2-hydroxypropylsulphonate; starch, crosslinked; tetrabromobisphenol A diglycidyl ether; 1,1,2,2-tetra-[*p*-(2,3-epoxypropoxy)phenyl]ethane; tetraglycidyl methylenedianiline; thioglycerol; timolol; toliprolol; *p*,*p′*,*p″*-tri-(2,3-epoxypropoxy)triphenylmethane; triglycidyl-*p*-aminophenol; triglycidyl isocyanurate; tris(1,3-dichloro-2-propyl) phosphate; tris(hydroxyphenyl)methane triglycidyl ether; viloxazine; xanthinol nicotinate
Uses:
starch crosslinking agent

epichlorohydrin-ethylene oxide copolymers

Rubber. The vulcanisate is characterised by good solvent resistance and reasonable low temperature flexibility. The upper working temperature is about 150°C. Vulcanisation is by means of ethylenethiourea.

Production:
• epichlorohydrin + ethylene oxide (epoxidation)
Uses: paper/printing/copier roller coverings; vehicle seals, hoses, membranes

epicillin
[26774-90-3]

$C_{16}H_{21}N_3O_4S_1$. M: 351.43.
Production:
• D-α-phenylglycine + 6-aminopenicillanic acid (Birch reduction/Dane salt formation/amide formation/hydrolysis)
Uses: antibacterial drug

epinephrine
adrenaline; [51-43-4]

$C_9H_{13}N_1O_3$. M: 183.21. Available commercially as the L(−)-enantiomer.
Production:
• adrenalone (carbonyl reduction/racemate separation)
• catechol + N-methylaminoacetaldehyde dimethyl acetal (carbonyl addition/racemate separation)
• veratraldehyde/piperonal + nitromethane (condensation/demethylation/nitro reduction/ methylation/racemate separation)
Uses: adrenergic/bronchodilator drug

epirizole
[18694-40-1]

$C_{11}H_{14}N_4O_2$. M: 234.26.
Production:
• methyl acetoacetate + aminoguanidine bicarbonate (condensation)
Uses: analgesic drug

EPM *See:* ethylene-propylene copolymers, rubber

EPN *See:* O-ethyl O-(4-nitrophenyl) phenylphosphono-thioate

epoxide resins *See:* bisphenol A diglycidyl ether; bis-phenol A glycidyl ether prepolymers

epoxy-acrylate resins
bisphenol A epoxy acrylate; DDA; Dianol diacrylate (Akzo)

Production:
• bisphenol A diglycidyl ether/bisphenol A glycidyl ether prepolymers + acrylic acid (esterification)
Uses: binder (radiation-cured printing inks, paper-foil lacquers)

1,2-epoxybutane *See:* 1,2-butylene oxide

β-(3,4-epoxycyclohexyl)ethyltrimethoxysilane
[3388-04-3]

$C_{11}H_{22}O_4Si_1$. M: 246.39. Liquid. BP: 310°C. d: 1.06 kg/l (25°C). Flash point: 93°C (PMCC).
Production:
• 4-vinylcyclohexene + trichlorosilane + methanol + peracetic acid (hydrosilation/dehydrochlorination/ epoxidation)
Uses: plastics coupling agent

3,4-epoxycyclohexylmethyl 3,4-epoxycyclohexylcarb-oxylate
Araldite CY179 (Ciba-Geigy); [2386-87-0]

$C_{14}H_{20}O_4$. M: 252.31.
Production:
• butadiene + acrolein + peracetic acid (Diels-Alder cycloaddition/Tishchenko reaction/epoxidation)
Uses:
cycloaliphatic epoxy resins

epoxy ester resins
Production:
• linseed fatty acids/fatty acids, polyunsaturated, conjugated/castor oil fatty acids, dehydrated + bisphenol A glycidyl ether prepolymers/bisphenol A diglycidyl ether (esterification)

Uses: chemical/abrasion resistant industrial paints (machinery/floors); long oil alkyd resin modifier

3,4-epoxy-6-methylcyclohexylmethyl 3,4-epoxy-6-methylcyclohexane carboxylate
Unox Epoxide 201 (Union Carbide)

$C_{16}H_{24}O_4$. M: 280.37.
Production:
• butadiene + crotonaldehyde + peracetic acid (cycloaddition/Tishchenko reaction/epoxidation)
Uses: epoxy resins

epoxy-novolac resins
epoxy-phenolic resins

Semi-solid resin. Both phenol and cresol-based products are available commercially.
Production:
• novolac resins + epichlorohydrin (ether formation)
Derivatives: vinyl ester resins
Uses: electrical/electronic encapsulation; composite aircraft bodies/components; epoxy resin adhesion modifier; heat-resistant laminated paper sheet

epoxy-phenolic resins *See:* epoxy-novolac resins

1,2-epoxypropane *See:* propylene oxide

2,3-epoxypropyl acrylate *See:* glycidyl acrylate

2,3-epoxypropyltrimethylammonium chloride
glycidyltrimethylammonium chloride; [3033-77-0]

$C_6H_{15}Cl_1N_1O_1$. M: 152.65.
Production:
• epichlorohydrin + trimethylamine (quaternisation)
Derivatives: acrylamide copolymers, cationic; poly(glycidyltrimethylammonium chloride); starch, cationic

epoxy resins *See:* bisphenol A diglycidyl ether; bisphenol A glycidyl ether prepolymers

eprazinone
[10402-90-1]
$C_{24}H_{32}N_2O_2$. M: 380.53.

Production:
• styrene + ethanol + piperazine + formaldehyde + propiophenone (alkoxychlorination/ethylation/amine formation/Mannich reaction)
Uses: antitussive drug

EPS *See:* polystyrene, expandable

Epsom salts *See:* magnesium sulphate

EPTC
S-ethyl dipropylthiocarbamate; [759-94-4]

$C_9H_{19}N_1O_1S_1$. M: 189.32.
Production:
• ethyl chlorothioformate + di-*n*-propylamine (dehydrochlorination)
Uses: herbicide

ergocalciferol *See:* calciferol

ergosterol
provitamin D_2; [57-87-4]

$C_{28}H_{44}O_1$. M: 396.66. Solid. MP: 166–183°C. Insoluble in water.
Production:
• yeast (extraction)
Derivatives: androstadienedione; calciferol

erucamide
docosenamide; erucic acid amide; [112-84-5]

$CH_3(CH_2)_7CH=CH(CH_2)_{11}CONH_2$

$C_{22}H_{43}N_1O_1$. M: 337.59. White, waxy beads. MP: 79–85°C. Iodine value: 72–80 g I_2/100 g. Insoluble in water. Slightly soluble in oxygenated solvents.
Production:
• erucic acid + ammonia (amide formation)
Derivatives: dimethylbehenylamine
Uses: plastics processing lubricant; polyethylene slip agents (bottle cap liners); slip improvement additive (printing ink)

erucic acid
14-docosenoic acid; [8047-28-7]

$$CH_3(CH_2)_7CH=CH(CH_2)_{11}COOH$$

$C_{22}H_{42}O_2$. M: 338.58. Pale yellow solid. Titre: 28–32°C. Acid value: 165–170 mg KOH/g. Iodine value: 75–85 g I_2/100 g. Commercial products contain, typically, 90–92% $C_{22:1}$.
Production:
• rapeseed fatty acids (fractionation; coproduced with oleic acid)
Derivatives:
behenic acid; behenyl alcohol; erucamide; erucic acid stearylamide; ethylene brassylate
Uses: alkyd resin comonomer

erucic acid stearylamide
stearylerucamide

$$CH_3(CH_2)_7CH=CH(CH_2)_{11}\overset{O}{\overset{||}{C}}NH(CH_2)_{17}CH_3$$

$C_{40}H_{79}N_1O_1$. M: 590.08. Solid. MP: 163–171°C.
Production:
• erucic acid + stearylamine (amide formation)
Uses: internal plastics processing lubricant

erythorbic acid *See:* isoascorbic acid

erythromycin
[114-07-8]

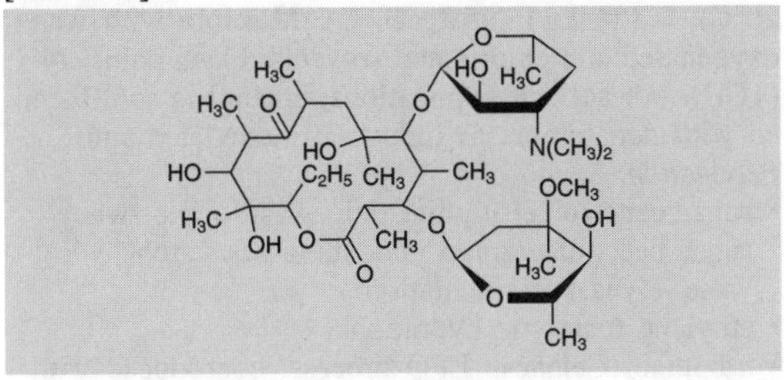

$C_{37}H_{67}N_1O_{13}$. M: 733.95. Mixed product comprising erythromycin A, erythromycin B and erythromycin C, with erythromycin A as the major component.
Production:
• microbial fermentation medium + *Streptomyces erythreus* bacteria (fermentation/esterification)
Uses: antibacterial drug

erythrosine *See:* Acid Red 51

ESBO *See:* soyabean oil, epoxidised

esfenvalerate
[66230-04-4]
$C_{25}H_{22}Cl_1N_1O_3$. M: 419.91.
Production:
• (S)-α-(4-chlorophenyl)isovaleric acid + 3-phenoxy-

benzaldehyde cyanohydrin (racemate separation/esterification) 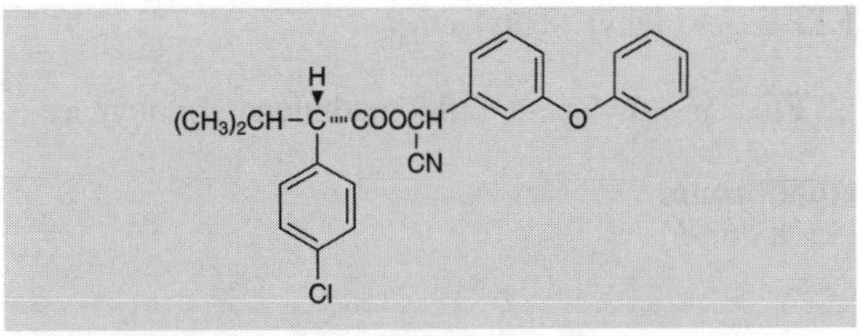
Uses: insecticide

ESO *See:* soyabean oil, epoxidised

ester oils, complex *See:* complex ester oils

estradiol
[50-28-2]

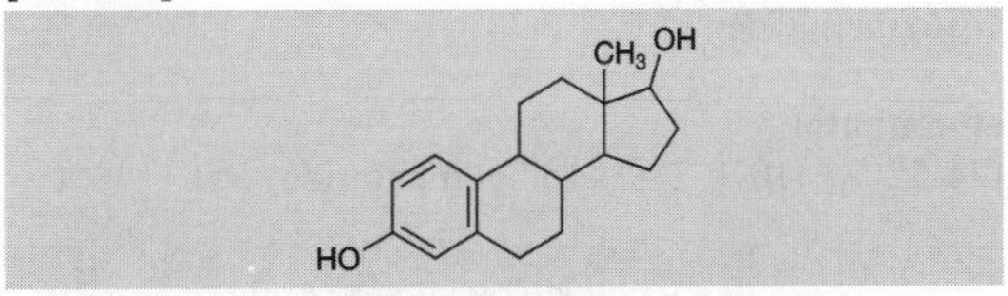

$C_{18}H_{24}O_2$. M: 272.39. Available commercially as the 17-propionate and other derivatives.
Production:
• estrone (carbonyl reduction)
• 3-methoxyestra-2,5-diene-17-ol (demethylation/reduction)
Uses: female hormone therapy

estrone
[53-16-7]

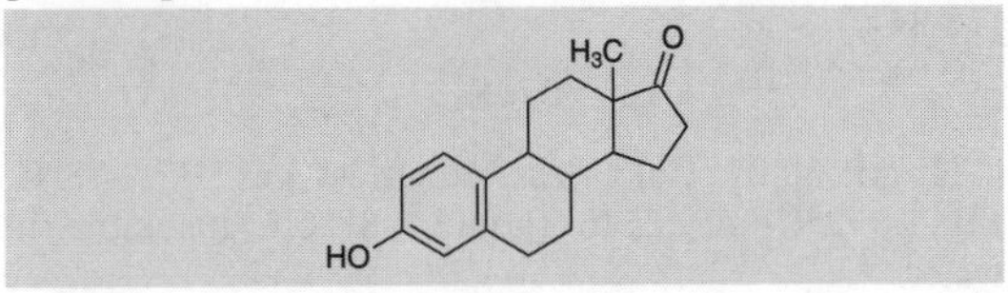

$C_{18}H_{22}O_2$. M: 270.38. Available commercially as the pipirazinium sulphate and other derivatives.
Production:
• androstadienedione (pyrolysis)
Derivatives: estradiol; ethynylestradiol; mestranol; 3-methoxyestra-2,5-diene-17-ol
Uses: female hormone therapy

etacelasil
2-chloroethyltris(2-methoxyethoxy)silane; [37894-46-5]

$$(CH_3OCH_2CH_2O)_3SiCH_2CH_2Cl$$

$C_{11}H_{25}Cl_1O_6Si_1$. M: 316.85.
Production:
• silicon tetrachloride + ethylene + ethylene glycol monomethyl ether (addition/dehydrochlorination)
Uses: abscission agent (olives)

ETBE *See:* ethyl *t*-butyl ether

ETFE *See:* ethylene-tetrafluoroethylene copolymers

ethalfluralin
[55283-68-6]

$C_{13}H_{14}F_3N_3O_4$. M: 333.26.
Production:
• 4-chloro-3,5-dinitrobenzotrifluoride + ethylamine +
  methallyl chloride (amine formation/amine formation)
Uses: herbicide

ethambutol
[74-55-5]; [1070-11-7] (dihydrochloride)

$$\underset{\text{HOCH}_2\text{CHNHCH}_2\text{CH}_2\text{NHCHCH}_2\text{OH}}{\overset{\text{C}_2\text{H}_5 \qquad\quad \text{C}_2\text{H}_5}{|\qquad\qquad\qquad |}}$$

$C_{10}H_{24}N_2O_2$. M: 204.31. Available commercially as the free base or hydrochloride.
Production:
• 2-aminobutanol + glyoxal (racemate separation/
  reductive amination)
Uses:
tuberculostatic drug

ethane
[74-84-0]

$$CH_3CH_3$$

C_2H_6. M: 30.07. Colourless, odourless gas. BP: -88°C. MP: -172°C. d: 0.546 (liquid, -88°C). Insoluble in water.
Production:
• natural gas, wet (fractionation; coproduced with
  natural gas/liquified petroleum gas/gasoline, natural)
Derivatives:
carbon tetrachloride; ethyl chloride; ethylene; perchloroethylene

1,2-ethanediamine *See:* ethylenediamine

1,2-ethanediol *See:* ethylene glycol

1,2-ethanedithiol
1,2-dimercaptoethane; ethylene dimercaptan; [540-63-6]

$$HSCH_2CH_2SH$$

$C_2H_6S_2$. M: 94.20. Liquid. BP: 146–149°C. d: 1.12 kg/l (15°C). Soluble in oxygenated solvents.

Production:
• 2-mercaptoethanol + hydrogen sulphide
  (acetylation/thiolation)
Derivatives:
1,2-bis(2-aminophenylthio)ethane; dimethipin; isoprothiolane; phosfolan

ethanesulphonyl chloride
[594-44-5]

$$CH_3CH_2SO_2Cl$$

$C_2H_5Cl_1O_2S_1$. M: 128.57. Pale yellow liquid. BP: 171°C. d: 1.36 kg/l (20°C). Hydrolysed by water and alcohol. Flash point: 86°C.
Production:
• ethyl mercaptan + sodium hypochlorite (oxidation/
  chlorination)
Derivatives:
2-ethylsulphonyl-5-trifluoromethylaniline

ethanethiol *See:* ethyl mercaptan

ethanol
alcohol; ethyl alcohol; industrial methylated spirit; IMS; [64-17-5]

$$C_2H_5OH$$

$C_2H_6O_1$. M: 46.07. Colourless, hygroscopic liquid with a pleasant odour. Available as absolute or 95% grades. BP 78°C. FP: -114°C (100%). d: 0.790 kg/l (100%, 20°C), 0.804 kg/l (95%, 20°C). Miscible with water, oxygenated and chlorinated solvents. Flash point: 14°C (TCC). For solvent applications, ethanol is sold blended with denaturants as industrial methylated spirit.
Production:
• sugar cane juice/sulphite pulp waste liquor/whey/
  sugar beet juice/grape juice/molasses/starch hydrolysate + yeast (fermentation)
• ethylene (catalytic hydration)
• *n*-butane (Celanese LPO process; coproduced with
  methanol/acetone/methyl ethyl ketone/formic acid/
  acetic acid/propionic acid/*n*-butyric acid/methyl
  formate)
• oxygenates, Fischer-Tropsch, mixed (fractionation;
  coproduced with methanol/isopropanol/*n*-butanol/
  isobutanol/amyl alcohol, primary/acetaldehyde/
  acetone/methyl ethyl ketone)
Derivatives:
acetaldehyde; acetochlor; γ-aminopropyltriethoxysilane; Basic Red 1; benazolin-ethyl; bis[*O*-ethyl-(3,5-di-*t*-butyl-4-hydroxybenzyl)phosphonic acid], calcium salt; 4,4-bis(*p*-fluorophenyl)butyl chloride; butamifos; *n*-butylethylamine; cadusafos; chloral; clofibrate; 2,2-diethoxyacetophenone; diethylamine; *m*-diethylaminophenol; *N,N*-diethylaniline; diethyl carbonate; diethyl chlorophosphate; *N,N*-diethylcyclohexylamine; *O,O*-diethyl dithiophosphoric acid; diethylene glycol monoethyl

ether; diethyl α-isomalate; diethyl maleate; diethyl malonate; diethyl methylmalonate; diethyl oxalate; diethyl phosphite; diethyl phthalate; diethyl succinate; diethyl sulphate; *N,N*-diethyl-*m*-toluidine; diphenoxylate; Disperse Blue 165; edifenphos; eprazinone; ethofumesate; ethoprophos; ethyl acetate; ethyl acetoacetate; ethyl acrylate; ethylamine; *N*-ethylaniline; ethyl benzoate; ethyl biscoumacetate; ethyl bromide; ethyl bromoacetate; ethyl *t*-butyl ether; ethyl butyrate; ethyl caprate; ethyl caproate; ethyl caprylate; ethyl chloride; ethyl chloroacetate; ethyl γ-chloroacetoacetate; ethyl chloroformate; ethyl α-chloropropionate; ethyl crotonate; ethyl cyanoacetate; *N*-ethylcyclohexylamine; ethyl *p*-dimethylaminobenzoate; ethylene; ethylene glycol monoethyl ether; ethyl 3-ethoxypropionate; ethyl formate; ethyl glycinate hydrochloride; ethyl heptanoate; ethyl 4-hydroxybenzoate; ethyl iodide; ethyl isonipecotinate; ethyl lactate; ethyl levulinate; ethyl methacrylate; ethyl 1-naphthylacetate; ethyl *p*-nitrobenzoate; *O*-ethyl *O*-(4-nitrophenyl) phenylphosphonothioate; ethyl phenylacetate; ethyl propionate; ethyl silicate; ethyl stearate; ethyl succinyl chloride; ethyl tiglate; ethyl *p*-toluenesulphonate; *N*-ethyl-*m*-toluidine; ethyl trifluoroacetate; ethyl valerate; ethyl vanillate; ethyl vinyl ether; etretinate; etridiazole; fenamiphos; fenoxaprop-ethyl; fluoroglycofen-ethyl; flurbiprofen; fosetyl-aluminium; iodoform; isofenphos; leucinocaine; mercury fulminate; monoethyl 5-nitroisophthalate; pethidine; *o*-phenetidine; *p*-phenetidine; phosdiphen; polyvinyl alcohol; potassium ethyl xanthate; profenofos; propylene glycol monoethyl ether; prothiofos; quizalofop-ethyl; single cell protein; sodium ethoxide; sulprofos; tetraethylammonium hydroxide; tilidine; 1,1,3-triethoxybutane; triethoxyvinylsilane; triethylamine; triethyl citrate; triethylene glycol monoethyl ether; triethyl orthoacetate; triethyl orthoformate; triethyl phosphate; triethyl phosphite
Uses: alcoholic drinks; petrol octane booster; solvent/cosolvent (paints, lacquer thinners, printing inks, dyes); solvent (pharmaceuticals, toiletries); solvent/coupling agent/wetting agent (cleaners, polishes, coatings); disinfectant

ethanolamine *See:* monoethanolamine

ethanolamine thioglycollate
[126-97-6]

HSCH$_2$COO$^-$ $^+$NH$_3$CH$_2$CH$_2$OH

C$_4$H$_{11}$N$_1$O$_3$S$_1$. M: 153.20. Colourless to pale pink viscous liquid containing 40% active matter in water. d: 1.23 kg/l (20°C). pH: 9.8.
Production:
• monoethanolamine + thioglycollic acid (salt formation)
Uses: cold permanent hair waving solutions

ethene *See:* ethylene

ethenzamide
2-ethoxybenzamide; [938-73-8]

C$_9$H$_{11}$N$_1$O$_2$. M: 165.20.
Production:
• salicylamide + diethyl sulphate (ethylation)
Uses:
analgesic drug

ethephon
chlorethephon; 2-chloroethylphosphonic acid; CEPA; [16672-87-0]

C$_2$H$_6$Cl$_1$O$_3$P$_1$. M: 144.49.
Production:
• tris(2-chloroethyl) phosphite (rearrangement/acid catalysed hydrolysis)
Derivatives:
polystyrene, crosslinked, phosphonated
Uses: defoliant (cotton); flow stimulant (natural rubber, pine gum); ripening aid (fruit, nuts)

ether *See:* diethyl ether

ethidimuron
1-(5-ethylsulphonyl-1,3,4-thiadiazol-2-yl)-1,3-dimethylurea; [30043-49-3]

C$_7$H$_{12}$N$_4$O$_3$S$_2$. M: 264.34.
Production:
• 4-methyl thiosemicarbazide + carbon disulphide + diethyl sulphate + methyl isocyanate (condensation/ethylation/sulphide oxidation/isocyanate addition)
Uses: herbicide

ethiofencarb
2-ethylthiomethylphenyl methylcarbamate; [29973-13-5]

C$_{11}$H$_{15}$N$_1$O$_2$S$_1$. M: 225.31.
Production:
• salicyl alcohol + ethyl mercaptan + methyl isocyanate (alcohol chlorination/sulphide formation/isocyanate addition)
Uses: insecticide

ethion
S,S'-methylene bis(O,O-diethyl phosphorodithionate);
[563-12-2]

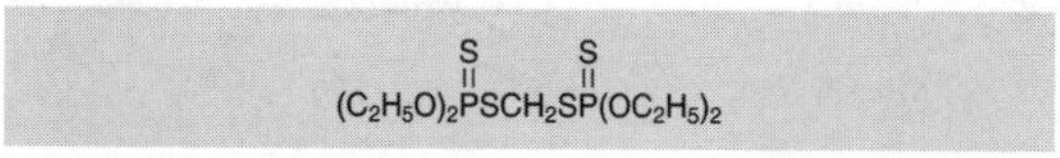

$$(C_2H_5O)_2PSCH_2SP(OC_2H_5)_2$$

$C_9H_{22}O_4P_2S_4$. M: 384.49.
Production:
• O,O-diethyl dithiophosphoric acid + formaldehyde
(carbonyl addition)
Uses: insecticide/acaricide

ethionamide
[536-33-4]

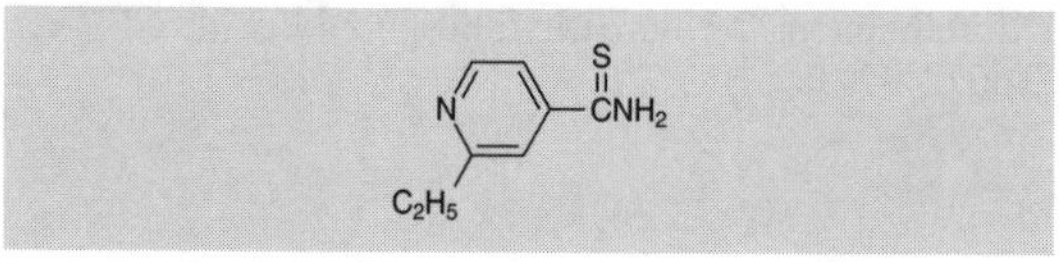

$C_8H_{10}N_2S_1$. M: 166.24.
Production:
• methyl ethyl ketone + diethyl oxalate + cyanoacetamide + ammonia + hydrogen sulphide (carbonyl
condensation/cyclisation/nitrile hydrolysis/
decarboxylation/nitrile formation/nitrile addition)
Uses: tuberculostatic drug

ethirimol
5-n-butyl-2-(ethylamino)-4-hydroxy-6-methylpyrimidine;
5-n-butyl-2-(ethylamino)-6-methyl-4-pyrimidol;
[23947-60-6]

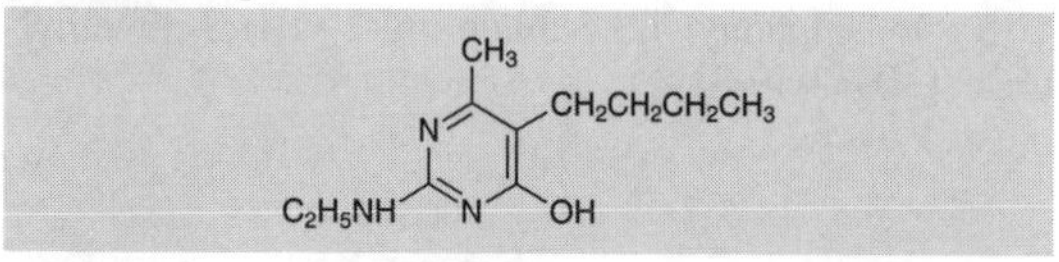

$C_{11}H_{19}N_3O_1$. M: 209.29.
Production:
• n-butyl chloride + ethyl acetoacetate + ethylamine
+ cyanamide (dehydrochlorination/addition/
condensation)
Derivatives: bupirimate
Uses: fungicide

ethofumesate
2-ethoxy-2,3-dihydro-3,3-dimethylbenzofuran-5-yl meth-
anesulphonate; [26225-79-6]

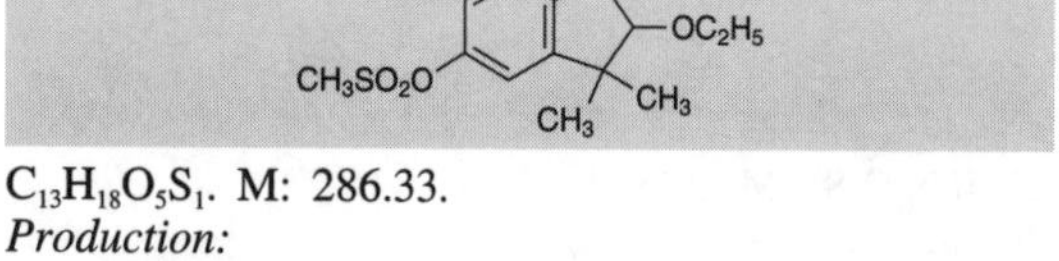

$C_{13}H_{18}O_5S_1$. M: 286.33.
Production:
• p-benzoquinone + isobutyraldehyde + ethanol +
methanesulphonyl chloride (condensation/
sulphonation)
Uses: herbicide

ethoprophos
O-ethyl S,S-dipropyl phosphorodithioate; [13194-48-4]

$$CH_3CH_2OP(SCH_2CH_2CH_3)_2$$

$C_8H_{19}O_2P_1S_2$. M: 242.34.
Production:
• n-propyl mercaptan + phosphorus trichloride +
ethanol + hydrogen peroxide (dehydrochlorination/
dehydrochlorination/oxidation)
Uses:
insecticide/nematicide

ethosuximide
[77-67-8]

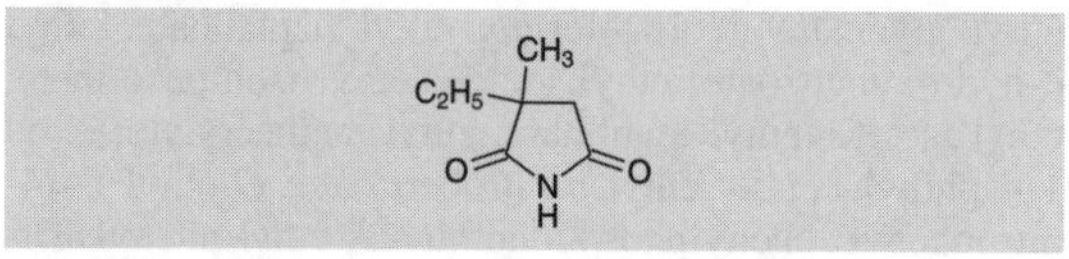

$C_7H_{11}N_1O_2$. M: 141.18.
Production:
• methyl ethyl ketone + ethyl cyanoacetate +
hydrogen cyanide + ammonia (Cope reaction/
addition/nitrile hydrolysis/decarboxylation/ester
hydrolysis/amide formation)
Uses: antiepileptic drug

2-ethoxyaniline *See:* o-phenetidine

2-ethoxybenzamide *See:* ethenzamide

**N-(p-ethoxycarbonylphenyl)-N'-ethyl-N'-phenyl-
formamidine**
Givsorb UV-2 (Givaudan-Roure); [65416-20-8]

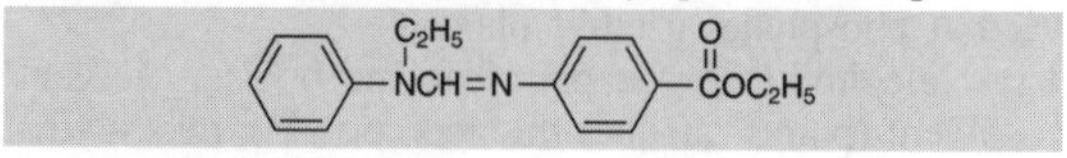

$C_{18}H_{20}N_2O_2$. M: 296.37.
Production:
• ethyl p-aminobenzoate + triethyl orthoformate +
N-ethylaniline (imine formation/amide formation)
Uses:
light stabiliser (plastics)

**N-(p-ethoxycarbonylphenyl)-N'-methyl-N'-phenyl-
formamidine**
Givsorb UV-1 (Givaudan-Roure); [57834-33-0]

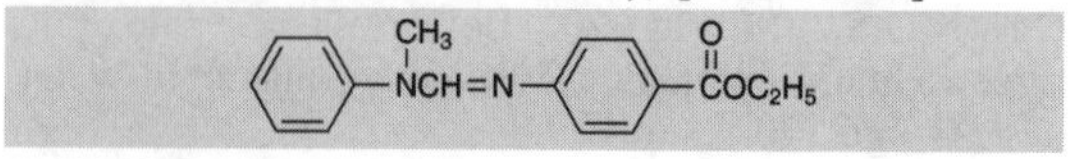

$C_{17}H_{18}N_2O_2$. M: 282.34.
Production:
• ethyl p-aminobenzoate + triethyl orthoformate +
N-methylaniline (imide formation/amide formation)
Uses:
light stabiliser (plastics)

6-ethoxy-1,2-dihydro-2,2,4-trimethylquinoline
See: 6-ethoxy-2,2,4-trimethyl-1,2-dihydroquinoline

2-ethoxyethanol
See: ethylene glycol monoethyl ether

2-(2-ethoxyethoxy)ethanol
See: diethylene glycol monoethyl ether

2-(2-ethoxyethoxy)ethyl acrylate
diethylene glycol monoethyl ether acrylate

$$C_2H_5OCH_2CH_2OCH_2CH_2O\overset{\overset{O}{\|}}{C}CH=CH_2$$

$C_9H_{16}O_4$. M: 188.23.
Production:
• diethylene glycol monoethyl ether + acrylic acid
  (esterification)
Uses: acrylic rubber comonomer

2-ethoxyethyl acetate
See: ethylene glycol monoethyl ether acetate

2-ethoxyethyl cyanoacrylate

$$CH_2=\underset{\underset{CN}{|}}{\overset{\overset{O}{\|}}{C}}COCH_2CH_2OCH_2CH_3$$

$C_8H_{11}N_1O_3$. M: 169.19.
Production:
• ethylene glycol monoethyl ether + cyanoacetic acid
  + formaldehyde (esterification/aldol condensation/
  thermal depolymerisation)
• ethylene glycol monoethyl ether acetate + cyanogen
  chloride + formaldehyde (dehydrochlorination/aldol
  condensation/thermal depolymerisation)
Uses: low-odour cyanoacrylate adhesives

2-ethoxyethyl *p*-methoxycinnamate *See:* cinoxate

3-ethoxy-4-hydroxybenzaldehyde *See:* ethyl vanillin

2-ethoxy-3′-hydroxy-2′-naphthanilide
See: 3-hydroxy-2-naphth-*o*-phenetidide

4-ethoxy-3′-hydroxy-2′-naphthanilide
See: 3-hydroxy-2-naphth-*p*-phenethidide

β-ethoxynaphthalene *See:* β-naphthyl ethyl ether

2-ethoxy-1-naphthylamine-6-sulphonic acid

$C_{12}H_{13}N_1O_4S_1$. M: 267.30.

Production:
• Schaeffer's acid (nitrosation/nitro reduction)
Derivatives: Direct Green 13

2-ethoxy-2-phenylacetophenone
See: benzoin ethyl ether

ethoxypropanol
See: propylene glycol monoethyl ether

ethoxypropyl acetate
See: propylene glycol monoethyl ether acetate

ethoxyquin
See: 6-ethoxy-2,2,4-trimethyl-1,2-dihydroquinoline

ethoxysilane
See: ethyl silicate

6-ethoxy-2,2,4-trimethyl-1,2-dihydroquinoline
6-ethoxy-1,2-dihydro-2,2,4-trimethylquinoline; ethoxyquin; ETMQ; Santoquin (Monsanto); [91-53-2]

$C_{14}H_{19}N_1O_1$. M: 217.31.
Production:
• *p*-phenetidine + acetone (carbonyl condensation/
  Skraup synthesis)
Uses:
rubber antioxidant/antiozonant; preservative (animal
feed, fruit)

ethyl acetate
[141-78-6]

$C_4H_8O_2$. M: 88.10. Colourless liquid with a fruity
odour. BP: 76–78°C. d: 0.90 kg/l (20°C). Solubility in
water: 77 g/l solution (20°C). Miscible with oxygenated and chlorinated solvents.
Production:
• acetaldehyde (Tishchenko reaction)
• ethanol + acetic acid (esterification)
• polyvinyl acetate + ethanol (transesterification;
  byproduct of polyvinyl alcohol production)
Derivatives:
2-acetobutyrolactone; acetone-1,3-dicarboxylic acid; allethrolone; *N,N′*-bis(5-chloro-2,4-dimethoxyphenyl)tere-
phthalodiacetamide; diethyl oxalacetate; ethyl benzoylacetate; ethyl cyanoacetate; ethyl pivaloacetate; rimantidine; sulfafurazole; uracil
Uses: flavouring/fragrance ingredient; solvent (lacquers,
printing inks); spotting solvent (dry cleaning)

ethyl acetoacetate
[141-97-9]

$$CH_3CCH_2COC_2H_5$$
(O, O)

$C_6H_{10}O_3$. M: 130.15. Liquid with a pleasant odour. BP: 177–183°C. MP: -47°C. d: 1.02 kg/l (25°C). Slightly soluble in water. Miscible with oxygenated, chlorinated and aromatic solvents.
Production:
• ethanol + diketene (addition)
Derivatives:
bromacil; carbocromen; ceftazidime; diazepam; diazinon; 7-diethylamino-4-methylcoumarin; 5-diethylamino-2-pentanone; dimethirimol; drazoxolon; ethirimol; ethyl 3,3-bis(*t*-amylperoxy)butyrate; ethyl 3,3-bis(*t*-butylperoxy)butyrate; ethylene glycol bis[3,3-bis(3-*t*-butyl-4-hydroxyphenyl)butyrate]; geranylacetone; haloxon; 4-hydroxymethyl-5-methylimidazole hydrochloride; hymexazol; 6-methyluracil; methyprylon; nifedipine; nitrendipine; pentoxifylline; phytol; pirimicarb; pirimiphos-ethyl; pirimiphos-methyl; propentofylline; pyrazophos; terbacil

ethyl acrylate
[140-88-5]

$$CH_2=CHCOC_2H_5$$
(O)

$C_5H_8O_2$. M: 100.11. Liquid with a pungent odour. BP: 99°C. FP: <-70°C. d: 0.94 kg/l (20°C). Slightly soluble in water. Soluble in oxygenated solvents.
Production:
• ethanol + acrylic acid (esterification)
Derivatives:
acrylic resins, amidated; acrylic resins, latex; acrylic rubber; benfuracarb; 1-benzyl-3-carbethoxy-4-piperidone hydrochloride; ethylene-ethyl acrylate copolymers, <8% ethyl acrylate; ethylene-ethyl acrylate copolymers, 18-23% ethyl acrylate; ethylene-ethyl acrylate copolymers, latex; ethyl 3-ethoxypropionate; methyl methacrylate copolymers, high molecular weight; 1-methyl-4-piperidone; vinylidene chloride copolymers, latex
Uses:
acrylic resin comonomer (paint, adhesives, textile, leather, paper coatings); nitrile rubber comonomer

ethyl alcohol *See:* ethanol

ethylaluminium dichloride
EADC

$$C_2H_5AlCl_2$$

$C_2H_5Al_1Cl_2$. M: 126.95. Colourless liquid. Spontaneously flammable in air, emitting dense smoke. BP: 194°C. FP: 31°C. d: 1.23 kg/l (25°C). Reacts violently with water.

Production:
• aluminium + ethyl chloride (reaction; coproduced with diethylaluminium chloride)
Uses: rubber catalyst component

ethylaluminium sesquichloride
triethyldialuminium trichloride; EASC; [12075-68-2]

$$(C_2H_5)_3Al_2Cl_3$$

$C_6H_{15}Al_2Cl_3$. M: 247.51. Colourless liquid. Spontaneously flammable in air, emitting dense smoke. BP: 210°C. FP: -21°C. d: 1.09 kg/l (25°C). Reacts violently with water.
Production:
• aluminium + ethyl chloride (reaction)
Uses: Ziegler catalyst component (ethylene-propylene rubber production)

ethylamine
aminoethane; monoethylamine; MEA; [75-04-7]

$$C_2H_5NH_2$$

$C_2H_7N_1$. M: 45.09. Liquid/gas with an ammoniacal odour. BP: 17°C. MP: -81°C. d: 0.68 kg/l (4°C). Miscible with water forming alkaline solutions. Miscible with oxygenated solvents. Also available commercially as 50% or 70% aqueous solutions.
Production:
• ethanol + ammonia (amine formation; coproduced with diethylamine/triethylamine)
Derivatives:
ametryn; atrazine; boron trifluoride monoethylamine; carbetamide; cyanazine; diethylthiourea; dimethametryn; *N,N*-dimethylethylamine; eglinazine- ethyl; ethalfluralin; ethirimol; *N*-ethylethanolamine; ethyl isocyanate; *N*-ethyl *O*-isopropyl thionocarbamate; *N*-ethyl-1-naphthylamine; *N*-ethyl-*p*-toluenesulphonamide; etilefrine; fenfluramine; flumetralin; Fluorescent Brightener 72; Fluorescent Brightener 182; mebeverine; propetamphos; *N*-salicylideneethylamine; simazine; Solvent Blue 59; Solvent Red 19; terbuthylazine; trietazine; *N,N',N''*-triethylhexahydrotriazine

ethyl *p*-aminobenzoate
benzocaine; ethyl 4-aminobenzoate; [94-09-7]

$$H_2N-\langle\rangle-COC_2H_5$$
(O)

$C_9H_{11}N_1O_2$. M: 165.20. Crystalline solid. MP: 88–90°C. Insoluble in water. Soluble in oxygenated and chlorinated solvents.
Production:
• ethyl *p*-nitrobenzoate (nitro reduction)
Derivatives: *N*-(p-ethoxycarbonylphenyl)-*N'*-ethyl-*N'*-phenylformamidine; *N*-(p-ethoxycarbonylphenyl)-*N'*-methyl-*N'*-phenylformamidine; procaine
Uses: photographic coupling agent intermediate

2-ethyl-2-aminopropan-1,3-diol
aminoamylene glycol; 2-amino-2-ethyl-1,3-propanediol;
AEPD; [115-70-8]

$$CH_3CH_2C(CH_2OH)_2 \overset{\displaystyle NH_2}{|}$$

$C_5H_{13}N_1O_2$. M: 119.16. Crystalline solid. MP: 37–39°C.
BP: 152–153°C (1.3 kPa). d: 1.10 kg/l (20°C). Miscible with water forming alkaline solutions.
Production:
• 2-ethyl-2-nitro-1,3-propanediol (nitro reduction)
Derivatives:
ethyl hydroxymethyl oleyloxazoline
Uses: emulsifier (creams, lotions, oils, waxes)

ethyl 2-(2-aminothiazolyl)methoxyiminoacetate

$C_8H_{11}N_3O_3S_1$. M: 229.26.
Production:
• ethyl γ-chloroacetoacetate + sodium nitrite +
dimethyl sulphate + thiourea (imine formation/methylation/condensation)
Derivatives:
cefmenoxime; cefotaxime; ceftizoxime; ceftriaxone

ethyl amyl ketone
ethyl isoamyl ketone; 5-methyl-3-heptanone; EIAK

$$CH_3CH_2CHCH_2CCH_2CH_3 \overset{\displaystyle CH_3\ \ \ O}{|\ \ \ \ \ \ ||}$$

$C_8H_{16}O_1$. M: 128.22. Colourless liquid. BP: 168°C. Insoluble in water.
Production:
• methyl ethyl ketone (aldol condensation/dehydration/hydrogenation)
Uses: high-boiling lacquer solvent

ethyl *n*-amyl ketone
3-octanone; [106-68-3]

$$C_2H_5CCH_2CH_2CH_2CH_2CH_3 \overset{\displaystyle O}{||}$$

$C_8H_{16}O_1$. M: 128.22. Liquid with a fruity odour. BP: 157–162°C. d: 0.82 kg/l (20°C). Slightly soluble in water. Miscible with oxygenated solvents.
Production:
• 1-octen-3-ol (hydrogenation/alcohol oxidation)
Derivatives: 3-octanol
Uses: fragrance ingredient

N-ethylaniline
MEA; [103-69-5]
$C_8H_{11}N_1$. M: 121.19. Colourless liquid. BP: 204–205°C.

FP: -63°C. d: 0.96 kg/l. Insoluble in water. Soluble in oxygenated solvents.

Production:
• aniline + ethanol (amine formation; coproduced with *N,N*-diethylaniline)
Derivatives:
Acid Red 32; Acid Red 57; Acid Red 68; *N*-(2-cyanoethyl)-*N*-ethylaniline; *N*-(*p*-ethoxycarbonylphenyl)-*N′*-ethyl-*N′*-phenylformamidine; ethylbenzylaniline; *N*-ethyl-*N*-(2-hydroxyethyl)aniline; *N*-ethyl-*N*-phenylbenzylamine-3-sulphonic acid; zinc ethylphenyldithiocarbamate
Uses: unsaturated polyester resin curing accelerator

2-ethylanthraquinone
[84-51-5]

$C_{16}H_{12}O_2$. M: 236.28. Crystalline solid. MP: 105°C. Insoluble in water.
Production:
• phthalic anhydride + ethylbenzene (Friedel-Crafts acylation)
Derivatives: hydrogen peroxide

ethylbenzene
phenylethane; [100-41-4]

C_8H_{10}. M: 106.17. Colourless liquid. BP: 136°C. MP: -95°C. d: 0.86 kg/l (25°C). Insoluble in water. Miscible with most organic solvents. Flash point: 15°C (TCC).
Production:
• benzene + ethylene (Friedel-Crafts alkylation)
• xylene, mixed (superfractionation)
Derivatives:
5-amino-2-chloroethylbenzene-4-sulphonic acid; 2-ethylanthraquinone; propylene oxide; styrene

ethyl benzoate
[93-89-0]

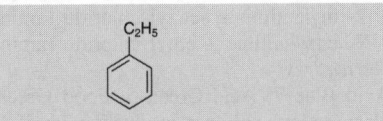

$C_9H_{10}O_2$. M: 150.18. Colourless liquid with a fruity

odour. BP: 211–212°C. MP: -35°C. d: 1.05 kg/l (25°C). Insoluble in water. Miscible with oxygenated and chlorinated solvents.
Production:
• ethanol + benzoic acid (transesterification)
Derivatives: ethyl benzoylacetate
Uses: fragrance/flavouring ingredient

ethyl benzoin ether *See:* benzoin ethyl ether

ethyl benzoylacetate
[94-02-0]

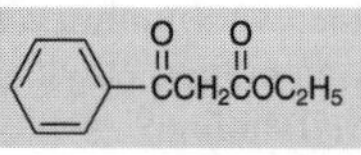

$C_{11}H_{12}O_3$. M: 192.22. Liquid with pleasant odour. MP: <0°C. BP: 265–270°C with decomposition. d: 1.12 kg/l (20°C). Insoluble in water. Soluble in alcohol.
Production:
• ethyl benzoate + ethyl acetate (Claisen condensation)
Derivatives: isoxathion
Uses: photographic coupling agent intermediate

ethylbenzylaniline
N,N-benzylethylaniline; *N*-benzyl-*N*-ethylaniline; [92-59-1]

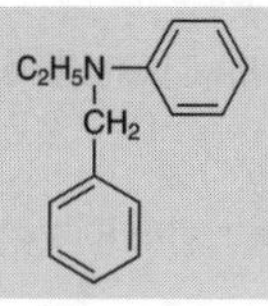

$C_{15}H_{17}N_1$. M: 211.31. Pale yellow liquid. BP: 285°C (95 kPa). d: 1.03 kg/l (20°C). Insoluble in water. Soluble in oxygenated solvents.
Production:
• *N*-ethylaniline + benzyl chloride (amine formation)
• *N*-benzylaniline + ethyl chloride (amine formation)
Derivatives:
Acid Blue 7; Acid Green 5; Food Green 3
Uses: casein polymer production clarifying agent

ethyl 3,3-bis(*t*-amylperoxy)butyrate

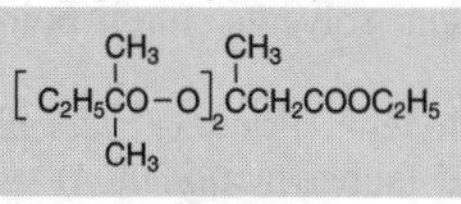

$C_{16}H_{32}O_6$. M: 320.43. Decomposes on heating with a 10-hour half-life at 112°C.
Production:
• ethyl acetoacetate + *t*-amyl hydroperoxide (ketal formation)
Uses: polymerisation initiator

ethyl 3,3-bis(*t*-butylperoxy)butyrate
Luperco 233 (Elf-Atochem); USP-333P (Witco)
$C_{14}H_{28}O_6$. M: 292.36.

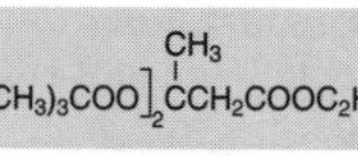

Production:
• ethyl acetoacetate + *t*-butyl hydroperoxide (ketal formation)
Uses:
crosslinking agent (resins)

ethyl biscoumacetate
ethyl bis(4-hydroxycoumarinyl)acetate; [548-00-5]

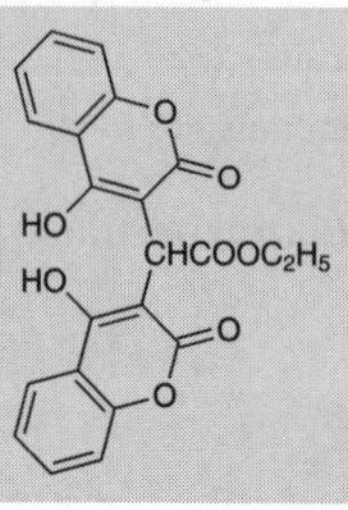

$C_{22}H_{16}O_8$. M: 408.36.
Production:
• 4-hydroxycoumarin + glyoxylic acid + ethanol (carbonyl addition/esterification)
Uses:
anticoagulant drug

ethyl bromide
bromoethane; [74-96-4]

$C_2H_5Br_1$. M: 108.96. Colourless liquid with an ethereal odour. BP: 38°C. FP: -119°C. d: 1.45 kg/l (25°C). Slightly soluble in water. Miscible with most organic solvents.
Production:
• ethanol + hydrobromic acid (alcohol bromination)
Derivatives:
cyclobarbital; ethylmagnesium bromide; heptabarbital; methyprylon; norfloxacin; pentobarbital; phenobarbital; tetraethylammonium bromide; thiopental sodium; valdetamide
Uses: ethylation reagent

ethyl bromoacetate
[105-36-2]

$C_4H_7Br_1O_2$. M: 167.00. Colourless liquid with a pungent odour. BP: 157–159°C. FP: -14°C. d: 1.50 kg/l (20°C). Insoluble in water. Miscible in oxygenated and aromatic solvents.
Production:
• ethanol + bromoacetic acid (esterification)
Derivatives:
carbocromen; hydroprene; quinuclidin-3-ol

ethyl *t*-butyl ether
ETBE

$$(CH_3)_3COC_2H_5$$

$C_6H_{14}O_1$. M: 102.18.
Production:
• isobutylene + ethanol (ether formation)
Uses: petrol blending component

ethyl butyrate
ethyl butanoate; [105-54-4]

$$CH_3CH_2CH_2\overset{\overset{\displaystyle O}{\|}}{C}OC_2H_5$$

$C_6H_{12}O_2$. M: 116.17. Colourless liquid with a pine-apple-like odour. BP: 121°C. d: 0.88 kg/l (20°C). Slightly soluble in water. Soluble in most organic solvents.
Production:
• ethanol + *n*-butyric acid (esterification)
Derivatives: iopanoic acid
Uses: flavouring ingredient

ethyl caprate
ethyl decanoate; [110-38-3]

$$CH_3(CH_2)_8\overset{\overset{\displaystyle O}{\|}}{C}OC_2H_5$$

$C_{12}H_{24}O_2$. M: 200.32. Colourless liquid with a pleasant odour. BP: 244°C. Insoluble in water.
Production:
• ethanol + capric acid (esterification)
Uses: flavouring ingredient

ethyl caproate
ethyl hexanoate; ethyl hexoate; [123-66-0]

$$CH_3(CH_2)_4\overset{\overset{\displaystyle O}{\|}}{C}OC_2H_5$$

$C_8H_{16}O_2$. M: 144.22. Colourless liquid with a pine-apple-like odour. BP: 167°C. d: 0.87 kg/l (20°C). Insoluble in water. Soluble in most organic solvents.
Production:
• ethanol + caproic acid (esterification)
Uses: flavouring ingredient

ethyl caprylate
ethyl octanoate; ethyl octoate; [106-32-1]

$$CH_3(CH_2)_6\overset{\overset{\displaystyle O}{\|}}{C}OC_2H_5$$

$C_{10}H_{20}O_2$. M: 172.27. Colourless liquid with a fruity odour. BP: 208°C. d: 0.87 kg/l (20°C). Insoluble in water.
Production:
• ethanol + caprylic acid (esterification)
Uses: flavouring ingredient

N-ethylcarbazole
9-ethylcarbazole; *N*-ethyldibenzopyrrole; [86-28-2]

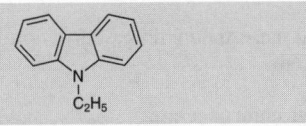

$C_{14}H_{13}N_1$. M: 195.26. Flakes. MP: 68°C. d: 1.06 kg/l (80°C). Insoluble in water. Soluble in oxygenated solvents.
Production:
• carbazole + ethyl chloride (ethylation)
Derivatives:
3-amino-*N*-ethylcarbazole; Vat Blue 42

Ethyl Cellosolve *See:* ethylene glycol monoethyl ether

ethyl cellulose
EC; Ethocel (Dow Chemical); [9004-57-3]
White granules. Different grades vary in their molecular weight and degree of substitution. Commercial products contain 72–87% ethyl substitution. The polymers are characterised by their toughness, flexibility, good thermal and low temperature properties. Soluble in alcohol and aromatic solvents.

R = H, ethyl-.
Production:
• alkali cellulose + ethyl chloride (ether formation)
Uses:
lacquer resin (fabric, paper, leather, electrical insulation coatings); strippable hot melt coatings; binder/viscosity modifier (paints, printing inks, varnishes, lacquers)

ethyl chloride
chloroethane; [75-00-3]

$$CH_3CH_2Cl$$

$C_2H_5Cl_1$. M: 64.51. Colourless, liquified gas. BP: 12°C. FP: -139°C. d: 0.90 kg/l (20°C). Insoluble in water. Miscible with oxygenated, chlorinated and aromatic solvents.
Production:
• ethylene + hydrogen chloride, anhydrous (addition)
• ethane + chlorine (chlorination)
• ethanol + hydrochloric acid (alcohol chlorination)
Derivatives:
barbital; diethylaluminium chloride; diethyl ethylmalonate; diethyl zinc; ethylaluminium dichloride; ethylaluminium sesquichloride; ethylbenzylaniline; *N*-ethyl-

carbazole; ethyl cellulose; ethyl hydroxyethyl cellulose; tetraethylammonium chloride; tetraethyl lead
Uses:
local anaesthetic drug; ethylation reagent; extraction solvent

ethyl chloroacetate
[105-39-5]

$$ClCH_2COC_2H_5$$

$C_4H_7Cl_1O_2$. M: 122.55. Liquid with a pungent odour. BP: 142–144°C. MP: -26°C. d: 1.15 kg/l (20°C). Insoluble in water. Miscible with oxygenated solvents.
Production:
• ethanol + chloroacetic acid (esterification)
Derivatives:
β-C_{14} aldehyde; benazolin; diethatyl-ethyl; ethyl methylphenylglycidate; ethyl 3-phenylglycidate; etomidate; piracetam; polyhydantoin resins; 3-pyridino-4-methyl-6-hydroxy-2-pyridone chloride; 2,6,10-trimethylundecenal

ethyl γ-chloroacetoacetate
ethyl 4-chloroacetoacetate; [638-07-3]

$$ClCH_2CCH_2COOC_2H_5$$

$C_6H_9Cl_1O_3$. M: 164.59. Liquid with a pungent odour. BP: 220°C with decomposition. FP: -8°C. d: 1.22 kg/l (15°C). Slightly soluble in water. Soluble in oxygenated and aromatic solvents.
Production:
• diketene + hydrogen chloride, anhydrous + ethanol (reaction)
Derivatives: aztreonam; cefotiam; ethyl 2-(2-aminothiazolyl)methoxyiminoacetate

ethyl 2-[4-(6-chlorobenzoxazol-2-yloxy)phenoxy]-propionate *See:* fenoxaprop-ethyl

ethyl chloroformate
ethyl chlorocarbonate; [541-41-3]

$$C_2H_5OCCl$$

$C_3H_5Cl_1O_2$. M: 108.52. Liquid. BP: 93–95°C. MP: ~-80°C. d: 1.14 kg/l (20°C). Insoluble in water. Miscible with most organic solvents.
Production:
• ethanol + phosgene (phosgenation)
Derivatives: Acid Black 58; azlocillin; cefoperazone; 1-chloroethyl ethyl carbonate; chlorpropamide; desipramine; desmedipham; diethyl carbonate; fenoxycarb; flupirtine; glisoxepide; maprotiline; mecarbam; mezlocillin; molsidomine; piperacillin; protriptyline
Uses: acylation reagent

ethyl α-chloropropionate
ethyl 2-chloropropionate; [535-13-7]

$$CH_3CHCOC_2H_5 \atop Cl$$

$C_5H_9Cl_1O_2$. M: 136.57. Liquid with a pleasant odour. BP: 147–148°C. d: 1.09 kg/l (20°C). Insoluble in water. Miscible with oxygenated solvents. The commercial product is a racemic mixture.
Production:
• ethanol + α-chloropropionic acid (esterification)
Derivatives:
benzoylprop-ethyl; vamidothion

ethyl chlorothioformate
ethyl chlorothiolformate; S-ethylmercaptocarbonyl chloride; [2941-64-2]

$$C_2H_5SCCl$$

$C_3H_5Cl_1O_1S_1$. M: 124.58.
Production:
• ethyl mercaptan + phosgene (phosgenation)
Derivatives:
butylate; cycloate; EPTC; molinate

ethyl citrate
See: triethyl citrate

ethyl crotonate
[623-70-1]

$$CH_3CH=CHCOC_2H_5$$

$C_6H_{10}O_2$. M: 114.15. Colourless solid. MP: 45°C. BP: 126°C (*cis*-isomer), 145°C (*trans*-isomer). d: 0.92 kg/l (20°C). Soluble in oxygenated solvents. Commercial products are a mixture of isomers.
Production:
• crotonic acid + ethanol (esterification)
Uses: fragrance ingredient

ethyl cyanide *See:* propionitrile

ethyl cyanoacetate
[105-56-6]

$$NCCH_2COOC_2H_5$$

$C_5H_7N_1O_2$. M: 113.12. Colourless liquid with a pleasant odour. BP: 208–210°C. MP: -23°C. d: 1.06 kg/l (25°C). Insoluble in water. Miscible with oxygenated solvents.
Production:
• ethanol + cyanoacetic acid (esterification)
• ethyl acetate + cyanogen chloride (dehydrochlorination)

Derivatives:
allopurinol; 6-amino-1,3-dimethyluracil; 6-amino-1-methyluracil; clobazam; cyclobarbital; cyclopenthiazide; ethosuximide; ethyl 2-cyanoacrylate; ethyl 2-cyano-3-phenylcinnamate; etozolin; fendiline; heptabarbital; hexobarbital; 6-hydroxy-2,4,5-triaminopyrimidine; hypoxanthine; mesuximide; pentobarbital; piprozolin; prenylamine; valdetamide; valproic acid

ethyl 2-cyanoacrylate

$C_6H_7N_1O_2$. M: 125.14. Colourless liquid with a sharp odour. Lachrymatory. BP: 54–56 (0.25 kPa). d: 1.05 kg/l. Polymerised by water.
Production:
• ethyl cyanoacetate + formaldehyde (aldol condensation/thermal depolymerisation)
Uses: cyanoacrylate adhesives

N-ethyl-N-(2-cyanoethyl)aniline
See: N-(2-cyanoethyl)-N-ethylaniline

N-ethyl-N-(2-cyanoethyl)-m-toluidine
See: N-(2-cyanoethyl)-N-ethyl-m-toluidine

ethyl 2-cyano-3-phenylcinnamate
ethyl 2-cyano-3,3-diphenylacrylate; etocrilene (INN); [5232-99-5]

$C_{18}H_{15}N_1O_2$. M: 277.33.
Production:
• benzophenone + ethyl cyanoacetate (Cope reaction)
Uses: UV absorber (plastics)

N-ethylcyclohexylamine
cyclohexylethylamine; CEA; [5459-93-8]

$C_8H_{17}N_1$. M: 127.24. Colourless to amber liquid. BP: 170°C. FP: <-50°C. d: 0.85 kg/l (4°C). Soluble in water and oxygenated solvents.
Production:
• cyclohexylamine + ethanol (reductive amination; coproduced with N,N-diethylcyclohexylamine)
Derivatives:
cycloate
Uses: vulcanisation accelerator

2-ethylcyclopentane-1,3-dione
1-ethyl-2,5-cyclopentadione

$C_7H_{10}O_2$. M: 126.16.
Production:
• diethyl maleate + ethyl propionate (Claisen condensation/decarboxylation/hydrogenation)
Derivatives: norgestrel

3-ethyl-2-cyclopenten-2-ol-1-one

$C_7H_{10}O_2$. M: 126.16.
Production:
• 2-propionylfuran (rearrangement/oxidation)
Uses: flavouring ingredient

ethyl decanoate *See:* ethyl caprate

ethyl diazoacetate
[623-73-4]

$C_4H_6N_2O_2$. M: 114.10. Yellow liquid with a pungent odour. MP: -22°C. Explosive. Slightly soluble in water. Miscible with oxygenated and aromatic solvents. Not a commercially traded product.
Production:
• ethyl glycinate hydrochloride + sodium nitrite (diazotisation)
Derivatives:
(1R)-trans-chrysanthemic acid; (1RS)-cis/trans-chrysanthemic acid; cilastatin; cyclopropane carboxylic acid; (1RS)-cis/trans-3-(2,2-dichlorovinyl)-2,2-dimethylcyclopropanecarboxylic acid; fenpropathrin; tranylcypromine

ethyldimethylamine *See:* N,N-dimethylethylamine

ethyl p-dimethylaminobenzoate
Quantacure EPD (Shell); [10287-53-3]

$C_{11}H_{15}N_1O_2$. M: 193.25.
Production:
• p-dimethylaminobenzoic acid + ethanol (esterification)
Uses: photoactivator (printing inks, lacquers)

ethyl enantate *See:* ethyl heptanoate

ethylene
ethene; [74-85-1]

$$CH_2{=}CH_2$$

C_2H_4. M: 28.05. Colourless gas with a mild, pleasant odour. BP: -104°C. FP: -169°C. Relative density: 0.978 (gas, air=1). Slightly soluble in water. Soluble in acetone and benzene.

Production:
- ethane (steam cracking)
- propane (steam cracking; coproduced with propylene)
- liquified petroleum gas (steam cracking; coproduced with propylene/C₄-stream, steam-cracked/gasoline, pyrolysis/pyrolysis tar)
- naphtha, heavy/gasoline, natural/gasoline, dearomatised (steam cracking; coproduced with propylene/C₄-stream, steam-cracked/gasoline, pyrolysis/pyrolysis tar)
- gas oil, light (steam cracking; coproduced with propylene/C₄-stream, steam-cracked/gasoline, pyrolysis/pyrolysis tar)
- natural gas + *n*-butane (Hüls electric arc process; coproduced with acetylene)
- ethanol (dehydration)

Derivatives: acetaldehyde; *n*-alkanol(C₈-C₁₀); *n*-alkanol(C₁₂-C₁₄); *n*-alkanol(C₁₂-C₁₈); *n*-alkanol(C₂₀₊); benzoctamine; 1-butene; cetyl alcohol; cetylstearyl alcohol; cyclopropane carboxylic acid; 1,9-decadiene; *n*-decanol; 1-decene; 2,6-diethylaniline; diethyl ketone; 3,5-diethyltoluenediamine; 1-dodecene; etacelasil; ethanol; ethylbenzene; ethyl chloride; ethylene-acrylic acid copolymers; ethylene-acrylic acid copolymers, ionomeric; ethylene chlorohydrin; ethylene dibromide; ethylene dichloride; ethylene-ethyl acrylate copolymers, <8% ethyl acrylate; ethylene-ethyl acrylate copolymers, 18-23% ethyl acrylate; ethylene-ethyl acrylate copolymers, latex; ethylene-maleic anhydride copolymers; ethylene-methacrylic acid copolymers; ethylene-methyl acrylate copolymers; ethylene-methyl acrylate terpolymer, ionomeric; ethylene oxide; ethylene-propylene copolymers; ethylene-propylene copolymers, rubber; ethylene-propylene-diene terpolymer, rubber; ethylene-tetrafluoroethylene copolymers; ethylene-vinyl acetate copolymers, <10% vinyl acetate; ethylene-vinyl acetate copolymers, 15% vinyl acetate; ethylene-vinyl acetate copolymers, 18-50% vinyl acetate; ethylene-vinyl acetate copolymers, 40-50% vinyl acetate; ethylene-vinyl alcohol copolymers; ethyl mercaptan; 2-ethyl-6-methylaniline; ethyl sulphide; 1,4-hexadiene; 1,5-hexadiene; *n*-hexanol; 1-hexene; *m*-(β-hydroxyethylsulphonyl)aniline; *p*-(β-hydroxyethylsulphonyl)aniline; 5-(β-hydroxyethylsulphonyl)-2-methoxyaniline; lauryl alcohol, narrow-cut; maprotiline; 2,2′-methylenebis-(4-ethyl-6-*t*-butylphenol); methyl propyl ketone; myristyl alcohol; neohexene; norbornene; *n*-octanol; 1-octene; α-olefins, mixed; α-olefins(C₁₂-C₁₄); α-olefins-(C₁₄-C₁₆); α-olefins(C₁₆-C₁₈); α-olefins(C₁₈₊); 2-[perfluoroalkyl(C₆-C₁₂)]ethanol; perfluorohexylethylene; 2-(perfluorooctyl)ethanol; perfluorooctylethylene; polyethylene, high-density; polyethylene, high-density, high molecular weight; polyethylene, high-density, ultra-high molecular weight; polyethylene, linear low-density; polyethylene, low-density; polyethylene, very low-density; poly(ethylene-chlorotrifluoroethylene); polyethylene wax, high-density; polyethylene wax, low-density; propionaldehyde; propionic acid; propylene; sodium 2-chloroethanesulphonate; stearyl alcohol; thioctic acid; triethylaluminium; 3,3,3-trifluoropropylene; vinyl acetate; vinyl acetate-ethylene-vinyl chloride copolymers; vinyl chloride-ethylene copolymers; vinyltoluene

Uses: fruit ripening agent

ethylene-acrylic acid copolymers
EAA

$$-\!\left[CH_2{-}CH_2\right]_x\!\!-\!\left[CH_2{-}\underset{\displaystyle COOH}{CH}\right]_y\!-$$

Production:
- ethylene + acrylic acid (polymerisation)

Uses:
adhesive film (carpet underlay); laminating adhesives (aluminium/plastic film)

ethylene-acrylic acid copolymers, ionomeric
Surlyn A (Du Pont)

$$-\!\left[CH_2{-}CH_2\right]_x\!\!-\!\left[CH_2{-}\underset{\displaystyle COO^-\ Na^+}{CH}\right]_y\!\!-\!\left[CH_2{-}\underset{\displaystyle COOH}{CH}\right]_z\!-$$

Thermoplastic with thermosetting characteristics at low temperature due to ionic crosslinking between molecules. At high temperature the crosslinks break allowing the polymer to be processed as a thermoplastic. d: 0.93 kg/l. Tensile strength: 14 MPa. Tensile modulus: 200–250 MPa. Excellent stress cracking and solvent resistance.

Production:
- ethylene + acrylic acid (high-pressure bulk polymerisation)

Uses: packaging film bonding layers; golf ball covers; blow-moulded oil/fat containers; ski boots/shoe heels; transparent films (food packaging)

ethylene bis(acrylamide)

$$CH_2{=}CHCNHCH_2CH_2NHCCH{=}CH_2$$
(with two $\overset{O}{\|}$ groups on the carbonyls)

$C_8H_{12}N_2O_2$. M: 168.20.
Production:
- acrylic acid + ethylenediamine (amide formation)
Derivatives:
sodium polyacrylate, crosslinked
Uses: acrylic resin crosslinking agent

ethylene bis(5,6-dibromonorbornane-2,3-dicarbox-imide)

Saytex BN-451 (Ethyl)

$C_{20}H_{20}Br_4N_2O_4$. M: 672.02. Off-white powder. MP: 310°C. d: 2.05 kg/l. Insoluble in water, alcohol and aromatic solvents. Slightly soluble in acetone.

Production:
• nadic anhydride + bromine + ethylenediamine (addition/imide formation)

Uses: plastics fire-retardant additive

ethylene bis(stearamide)

[110-30-5]

$CH_3(CH_2)_{16}CNHCH_2CH_2NHC(CH_2)_{16}CH_3$

$C_{38}H_{76}N_2O_2$. M: 593.04. Solid. MP: 143°C. Bulk density: 0.6 g/ml. Flash point: 290°C (COC). Insoluble in water.

Production:
• ethylenediamine + stearic acid (amide formation)

Uses: defoaming agent; plastics mould release agent/ processing lubricant

ethylene bis(tetrabromophthalimide)

Saytex BT-93 (Ethyl)

$C_{18}H_4Br_8N_2O_4$. M: 951.47. Pale yellow powder. MP: >450°C. d: 2.77 kg/l. Insoluble in water and most organic solvents.

Production:
• tetrabromophthalic anhydride + ethylenediamine (imide formation)

Uses: fire-retardant additive (thermoplastics)

ethylene brassylate

ethylene glycol brassylate; 1,13-tridecanedioic acid ethylene ester; [105-95-3]

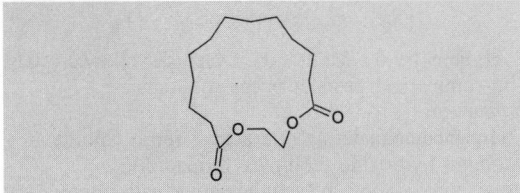

$C_{15}H_{26}O_4$. M: 270.37. Liquid with musk-like odour. BP:

140°C (1.3 kPa). d: 1.02 kg/l (60°C).

Production:
• erucic acid + ethylene glycol (ozonolysis/ esterification)

Uses: fragrance ingredient/fixative

ethylene carbonate

[96-49-1]

$C_3H_4O_3$. M: 88.06. White solid with a mild odour. FP: 36°C. BP: 248°C. d: 1.32 kg/l (39°C). Soluble in water.

Production:
• ethylene oxide + carbon dioxide (epoxidation)

Uses: aprotic extraction/process solvent; hydraulic fluid additive; hydroxyethylation reagent; solvent (polyacrylonitrile polymerisation/spinning, chemical synthesis)

ethylene chlorohydrin

2-chloroethanol; 2-chloroethyl alcohol; [107-07-3]

CH_2Cl
CH_2OH

$C_2H_5Cl_1O_1$. M: 80.51. Colourless liquid. BP: 127–136°C. MP: -67°C. Miscible with water and alcohol.

Production:
• ethylene + sodium hypochlorite (addition)

Uses: hydroxyethylation reagent

ethylenediamine

1,2-diaminoethane; 1,2-ethanediamine; EDA; [107-15-3]

$H_2NCH_2CH_2NH_2$

$C_2H_8N_2$. M: 60.09. Colourless, hygroscopic liquid with a strong, ammoniacal odour. BP: 117°C. MP: 11°C. d: 0.90 kg/l (20°C). Absorbs carbon dioxide from the air. Miscible with water, oxygenated and aromatic solvents. Flash point: 42°C (CC).

Production:
• ethylene dichloride + ammonia (amine formation; coproduced with diethylenetriamine/triethylenetetramine/piperazine/tetraethylenepentamine/aminoethylpiperazine/polyethylenepolyamine)
• ethylene glycol + ammonia (ammoniation)
• monoethanolamine + ammonia (ammoniation; coproduced with diethylenetriamine/piperazine/ N-hydroxyethylpiperazine/aminoethylpiperazine/ aminoethylethanolamine)

Derivatives: N-(2-aminoethyl)-γ-aminopropyltrimethoxysilane; aminoethylethanolamine; antazoline; benzathine; N,N′-bis(2-hydroxypropyl)-2-methylpiperazine; diethylenetriamine; dilazep; N,N′-disalicylideneethylenediamine; N,N-ditallowamidoethyl-N-methylammonium ethoxylate methosulphate; elastane; ethylene bis(acrylamide); ethylene bis(5,6-dibromonorbornane-2,3-dicarboximide); ethylene bis(stearamide); ethylene bis(tetra-bromophthalimide); ethylenediamine dihydroiodide; ethylenediamine propoxylate/ethoxylates; ethylenediaminetetraacetic acid; ethylenediaminetetra-(methylene phosphonic acid); ethylenethiourea; ethylene urea; fenoxazoline; glycidyl-amine adducts; mazindol; metiram; nabam; naphazoline; oxymetazoline; polyamide resins, non-reactive; polyamide resins, reactive; polyether polyols, rigid; polyethylenepolyamine; polyols, epoxy dispersion; tetraethylenepentamine; tetrahydroxypropyl ethylenediamine; tetramethylethylenediamine; tetryzoline; tolazoline; tramazoline; triethylenetetramine; urea-formaldehyde resins, cationic; xylometazoline

Uses:

polyurethane chain-extender; electrodeless nickel coating reagent

ethylenediamine dihydroiodide
EDDI

$$H_2NCH_2CH_2NH_2 \quad 2HI$$

$C_2H_{10}I_2N_2$. M: 315.92.
Production:
• ethylenediamine + hydriodic acid (salt formation)
Uses: animal feed additive

ethylenediamine propoxylate/ethoxylates
poloxamine (CTFA); Soprofor ED (Rhone-Poulenc); Tetronic (BASF)

$$H(OCH_2CH_2)_y(OCHCH_2)_x \overset{CH_3}{|} \quad \overset{CH_3}{|} (CH_2CHO)_x(CH_2CH_2O)_yH$$
$$NCH_2CH_2N$$
$$H(OCH_2CH_2)_y(OCHCH_2)_x \underset{CH_3}{|} \quad \underset{CH_3}{|} (CH_2CHO)_x(CH_2CH_2O)_yH$$

Liquid or flakes. M: 1,650–26,000 depending on PO and EO content. These are usually block copolymers with the PO blocks adjacent to the amine group. Products with the EO block in this position are also available. See also tetrahydroxypropyl ethylenediamine.
Production:
• ethylenediamine + propylene oxide + ethylene oxide (epoxidation)
Uses: crude oil demulsifier component; low-foaming surfactant (domestic, industrial cleaners); dispersant/thickening agent (paints, printing inks, cosmetics, rubber production); solubiliser/wetting agent (textile, paper auxiliaries);

ethylenediaminetetraacetic acid
edetic acid (INN); EDTA; [60-00-4]

$$(HOOCCH_2)_2NCH_2CH_2N(CH_2COOH)_2$$

$C_{10}H_{16}N_2O_8$. M: 292.24.
Production:
• ethylenediamine + formaldehyde + hydrogen cyanide (cyanomethylation/nitrile hydrolysis)

Derivatives: ethylenediaminetetraacetic acid, ammonium ferric salt; ethylenediaminetetraacetic acid, calcium disodium salt; ethylenediaminetetraacetic acid, disodium salt; ethylenediaminetetraacetic acid, sodium ferric salt; ethylenediaminetetraacetic acid, tetrasodium salt
Uses: chelation agent (detergents, disinfectants, rare earth separation); antioxidant (cosmetics); metal deactivator (lubricants); scale inhibitor (boiler water treatment); textile/leather processing auxiliary

ethylenediaminetetraacetic acid, ammonium ferric salt

$$(^-OOCCH_2)_2NCH_2CH_2N(CH_2COO^-)_2 \quad NH_4^+.Fe^{3+}$$

$C_{10}H_{16}Fe_1N_3O_8$. M: 362.10. Available as a 50% solution in water.
Production:
• ethylenediaminetetraacetic acid + ammonia + ferric chloride (complex formation)
Uses: dietary supplement ingredient

ethylenediaminetetraacetic acid, calcium disodium salt
calcium disodium EDTA; sodium calcium edetate (INN); [62-33-9]

$$(^-OOCCH_2)_2NCH_2CH_2N(CH_2COO^-)_2 \quad Ca^{2+}.2Na^+$$

$C_{10}H_{12}Ca_1N_2Na_2O_8$. M: 374.27. White powder. Bulk density: 0.67. Soluble in water.
Production:
• ethylenediaminetetraacetic acid + calcium hydroxide + sodium hydroxide (salt formation)
Uses: food additive

ethylenediaminetetraacetic acid, disodium salt
disodium EDTA; [139-33-3]

$$(^-OOCCH_2)_2NCH_2CH_2N(CH_2COO^-)_2 \quad 2H^+.2Na^+$$

$C_{10}H_{14}N_2Na_2O_8$. M: 336.20.
Production:
• ethylenediaminetetraacetic acid + sodium hydroxide (salt formation)
Uses: chelation agent (detergents, disinfectants); antioxidant (cosmetics); scale inhibitor (boiler water treatment); textile/leather processing auxiliary

ethylenediaminetetraacetic acid, sodium ferric salt
sodium ferric EDTA

$$(^-OOCCH_2)_2NCH_2CH_2N(CH_2COO^-)_2 \quad Na^+.Fe^{3+}$$

$C_{10}H_{12}Fe_1N_2Na_1O_8$. M: 367.05. Greenish-yellow crystals. The commercial product is the trihydrate.
Production:
• ethylenediaminetetraacetic acid + ferric chloride + sodium hydroxide (complex formation)
Uses: photographic bleach/developer bath component; fertiliser trace element additive

ethylenediaminetetraacetic acid, tetrasodium salt
tetrasodium EDTA; [64-02-8]

$$(^-OOCCH_2)_2NCH_2CH_2N(CH_2COO^-)_2 \quad 4Na^+$$

$C_{10}H_{12}N_2Na_4O_8$. M: 380.17.
Production:
• ethylenediaminetetraacetic acid + sodium hydroxide (salt formation)
Uses:
chelation agent (detergents, disinfectants); descaling agent (industrial metal cleaners); antioxidant (cosmetics); sequesterant (metal coating/plating baths); redox activator (styrene-butadiene rubber production); scale inhibitor (boiler water treatment); textile/leather processing auxiliary

ethylenediaminetetra(methylene phosphonic acid)
EDTMPA

$$[(HO)_2\overset{O}{\overset{\|}{P}}CH_2]_2NCH_2CH_2N[CH_2\overset{O}{\overset{\|}{P}}(OH)_2]_2$$

$C_6H_{20}N_2O_{12}P_4$. M: 436.13. White, crystalline solid with a 90% active acid content. Also available as a 25% active acid solution of the hexasodium salt.
Production:
• ethylenediamine + formaldehyde + phosphorous acid (Mannich reaction)
Uses:
electroplating bath additive; scale inhibitor/chelant (boilers, cooling towers, oilfield water systems); sequestrant (laundry/industrial detergent powders)

ethylene dibromide
1,2-dibromoethane; DBE; EDB; [106-93-4]

$$CH_2BrCH_2Br$$

$C_2H_4Br_2$. M: 187.86. Colourless liquid with a chloroform-like odour. BP: 131°C. FP: 10°C. d: 2.17 kg/l (20°C). Insoluble in water. Soluble in oxygenated solvents.
Production:
• ethylene + bromine (addition)
Derivatives: diquat dibromide; tetramisole; theodrenaline; Vat Blue 16
Uses:
petrol antiknock additive; soil/grain fumigant

ethylene dichloride
1,2-dichloroethane; dichloroethane; ethylene chloride; EDC; [107-06-2]

$$CH_2ClCH_2Cl$$

$C_2H_4Cl_2$. M: 98.96. Colourless liquid with a chloroform-like odour. BP: 84°C. FP: -36°C. d: 1.26 kg/l (20°C). Very slightly soluble in water. Miscible with oxygenated and chlorinated solvents. Flash point: 16°C (TOC).

Production:
• ethylene + hydrogen chloride, anhydrous + oxygen (oxychlorination)
• ethylene + chlorine (chlorination)
Derivatives: aminoethylpiperazine; chlormequat chloride; diethylenetriamine; ethylenediamine; perchloroethylene; piperazine; polyethylenepolyamine; polysulphide; rubber; tetraethylenepentamine; trichloroethylene; triethylenetetramine; vinyl chloride
Uses: scavenging component (petrol antiknock packages); solvent (Di-Me oil dewaxing process); solvent (paint strippers, adhesives); storage fumigant

ethylene-ethyl acrylate copolymers, <8% ethyl acrylate
EEA

$$\left[CH_2-CH_2\right]_x\left[CH_2-\overset{COOC_2H_5}{\underset{|}{CH}}\right]_y$$

Thermoplastic with better low-temperature impact strength the polyethylene. Food approved in many countries.
Production:
• ethylene + ethyl acrylate (polymerisation)
Uses: stretch film (food packaging)

ethylene-ethyl acrylate copolymers, 18-23% ethyl acrylate

$$\left[CH_2-CH_2\right]_x\left[CH_2-\overset{COOC_2H_5}{\underset{|}{CH}}\right]_y$$

Thermoplastics. d: 0.93 kg/l. Low molecular weight grades are flexible resins. High molecular weight grades are used for injection moulding/extrusion.
Production:
• ethylene + ethyl acrylate (polymerisation)
Uses: extruded/injection moulded components; hot melt adhesives

ethylene-ethyl acrylate copolymers, latex

$$\left[CH_2-CH_2\right]_x\left[CH_2-\overset{COOC_2H_5}{\underset{|}{CH}}\right]_y$$

Production:
• ethylene + ethyl acrylate (emulsion polymerisation)
Uses: gaskets/gloves; heat-seal coatings

ethylene glycol
1,2-ethanediol; glycol; monoethylene glycol; MEG; EG; [107-21-1]

$$HOCH_2CH_2OH$$

$C_2H_6O_2$. M: 62.07. Colourless, hygroscopic liquid. BR: 196–200°C. FP: -13°C. d: 1.11 kg/l (20°C). Soluble in water and most organic solvents. Flash point: 11°C (CC). Available commercially as fibre or antifreeze grades.

Production:
- ethylene oxide (hydration; coproduced with diethylene glycol/triethylene glycol)

Derivatives:
dioxacarb; dioxolane; ethylene brassylate; ethylenediamine; ethylene glycol bis[3,3-bis(3-*t*-butyl-4-hydroxyphenyl)butyrate]; ethylene glycol diethyl ether; ethylene glycol dimethacrylate; ethylene glycol dinitrate; ethylene glycol distearate; ethylene glycol dodecane-1,12-dioate; ethylene glycol monostearate; glyoxal; montan ester waxes; oxabetrinil; oxalic acid; polyester polyols, linear; polyester resins, linear, medium molecular weight; poly(ethylene-adipate); poly-(ethylene-1,4-cyclohexanedimethylene-terephthalate); poly(ethylene naphthalate); poly(ethylene terephthalate); polymeric plasticisers; unsaturated polyester resins, isophthalate grades

Uses: antifreeze component; heat-transfer fluid; humectant (starch adhesives); plasticiser (regenerated cellulose film); solvent (surface coatings, printing inks); polyurethane chain-extender

ethylene glycol bis[3,3-bis(3-*t*-butyl-4-hydroxyphenyl)butyrate]
bis[3,3-bis(4′-hydroxy-3′-*t*-butylphenyl)butanoic acid] glycol ester; Hostanox O3 (Hoechst)

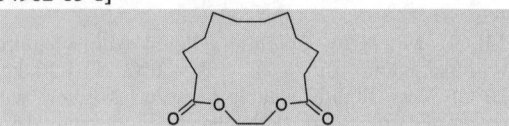

$C_{50}H_{66}O_8$. M: 795.07.
Production:
- ethylene glycol + *o*-*t*-butylphenol + ethyl acetoacetate (transesterification/carbonyl condensation)

Uses: antioxidant (plastics)

ethylene glycol diethyl ether
1,2-diethoxyethane; [629-14-1]

$C_2H_5OCH_2CH_2OC_2H_5$

$C_6H_{14}O_2$. M: 118.18. Colourless liquid. BP: 123°C. d: 0.85 kg/l (20°C). Soluble in water and most organic solvents.
Production:
- ethylene glycol + diethyl sulphate (ether formation)

Uses: solubiliser

ethylene glycol dimethacrylate
EDMA; [97-90-5]
$C_{10}H_{14}O_4$. M: 198.22. Pale yellow liquid. BP: 97°C (0.53 kPa). d: 1.05 kg/l (25°C). Insoluble in water.

Flash point: 113°C (COC). Commercial products contain hydroquinone methyl ether or similar polymerisation inhibitors.

$$CH_2{=}CCOCH_2CH_2OCC{=}CH_2$$

Production:
- ethylene glycol + methyl methacrylate (transesterification)

Uses:
crosslinked acrylic/vinyl resin comonomer; engineering adhesives; peroxide crosslinking agent (rubber)

ethylene glycol dimethyl ether
1,2-dimethoxyethane; glyme; [110-71-4]

$CH_3OCH_2CH_2OCH_3$

$C_4H_{10}O_2$. M: 90.12. Colourless liquid. BP: 85°C. MP: -58°C. d: 0.87 kg/l (20°C). Soluble in water and most organic solvents.
Production:
- ethylene glycol monomethyl ether + dimethyl sulphate (ether formation)

Uses: process solvent/solubiliser

ethylene glycol dinitrate
nitroglycol; [628-96-6]

$$CH_2ONO_2$$
$$CH_2ONO_2$$

$C_2H_4N_2O_6$. M: 152.05.
Production:
- ethylene glycol (nitration)

Uses: plasticiser (nitrocellulose explosives)

ethylene glycol distearate
glycol distearate; [627-83-8]

$$CH_3(CH_2)_{16}COCH_2CH_2OC(CH_2)_{16}CH_3$$

$C_{38}H_{74}O_4$. M: 595.01. White to yellow powder. MP: 60–65°C. HLB: 2.5 (self-emulsifying grades), 1.6 (non self-emulsifying grades).
Production:
- ethylene glycol + stearic acid (esterification)

Uses: emulsifier/opacifier/viscosity modifier (cosmetics)

ethylene glycol dodecane-1,12-dioate
α,ω-dodecanedioic acid ethylene glycol diester; [54982-83-1]

$C_{14}H_{24}O_4$. M: 256.34. Liquid with a musk-like odour.

MP: 18°C. BP: 139–141°C (2.7 kPa). d: 1.03 kg/l (60°C).
Production:
• 1,12-dodecanedioic acid + ethylene glycol (esterification)
Uses: fragrance ingredient (synthetic musk)

ethylene glycol formal *See:* dioxolane

ethylene glycol monobutyl ether
2-*n*-butoxyethanol; ethylene glycol mono-*n*-butyl ether; *n*-butyl glycol; Butyl Cellosolve (Union Carbide); Butyl Ethoxol (ICI); Butyl Oxitol (Shell); [111-76-2]

CH₃CH₂CH₂CH₂OCH₂CH₂OH

$C_6H_{14}O_2$. M: 118.18. Colourless liquid with a slight, rancid odour. BP: 168–173°C. d: 0.90 kg/l (20°C). Miscible with water and most organic solvents.
Production:
• *n*-butanol + ethylene oxide (epoxidation; coproduced with diethylene glycol monobutyl ether/ triethylene glycol monobutyl ether)
Derivatives:
2,4,5-T-(2-butoxyethyl); butoxyethyl *p*-dimethylamino-benzoate; 2,4-D-2-butoxyethyl; dibutoxyethyl adipate; dibutoxyethyl phthalate; ethylene glycol monobutyl ether acetate; tributoxyethyl phosphate; triclopyr-2-butoxyethyl
Uses: crude oil/water coupling solvent (oil-well workovers); solvent (surface coatings, adhesives, organosol production)

ethylene glycol monobutyl ether acetate
Butyl Cellosolve Acetate (Union Carbide)

$$CH_3CH_2CH_2CH_2OCH_2CH_2O\overset{\overset{\displaystyle O}{\|}}{C}CH_3$$

$C_8H_{16}O_3$. M: 160.22. Colourless liquid. BP: 192°C. FP: <-63°C. d: 0.94 kg/l (20°C). Solubility in water: 15 g/l solution (20°C). Flash point: 74°C (TOC).
Production:
• ethylene glycol monobutyl ether + acetic acid (esterification)
Uses: solvent (paints, resins)

ethylene glycol monoethyl ether
2-ethoxyethanol; ethoxyethanol; Ethoxol (ICI); Ethyl Cellosolve (Union Carbide); Ethyl Oxitol (Shell); [110-80-5]

C₂H₅OCH₂CH₂OH

$C_4H_{10}O_2$. M: 90.12. Colourless, mobile liquid with an ether-like odour. BP: 133–137°C. d: 0.93 kg/l (20°C).
Production:
• ethanol + ethylene oxide (epoxidation; coproduced with diethylene glycol monoethyl ether/triethylene glycol monoethyl ether)

Derivatives:
cinoxate; 2-ethoxyethyl cyanoacrylate; ethylene glycol monoethyl ether acetate; haloxyfop-ethoxyethyl
Uses:
coupling solvent (soluble oils, agrochemicals); solvent (surface coatings, lacquers)

ethylene glycol monoethyl ether acetate
ethoxyethanol acetate; 2-ethoxyethyl acetate; ethyl glycol acetate; 2-EEA; EGA; Cellosolve Acetate (Union Carbide); Ethoxol Acetate (ICI); Oxitol Acetate (Shell); [111-15-9]

$$C_2H_5OCH_2CH_2O\overset{\overset{\displaystyle O}{\|}}{C}CH_3$$

$C_6H_{12}O_3$. M: 132.17. Colourless liquid. BP: 150–160°C. d: 0.97 kg/l (20°C). Flash point: 53°C (PMCC). Partially miscible with water. Miscible with most organic solvents.
Production:
• ethylene glycol monoethyl ether + acetic acid (esterification)
Derivatives: 2-ethoxyethyl cyanoacrylate
Uses: solvent (paints, printing inks)

ethylene glycol monomethyl ether
2-methoxyethanol; 2-ME; Methyl Cellosolve (Union Carbide); Methyl Ethoxol (ICI); Methyl Oxitol (Shell); [109-86-4]

CH₃OCH₂CH₂OH

$C_3H_8O_2$. M: 76.09. Colourless liquid. BR: 123–125°C. FP: -86°C. d: 0.96 kg/l (20°C). Miscible with water and organic solvents. Flash point: 41°C (TCC).
Production:
• methanol + ethylene oxide (epoxidation)
Derivatives: 2-amino-5-[*N*-ethyl-*N*-(2-methoxyethyl)amino]toluene; dimethachlor; di-(2-methoxyethyl) phthalate; etacelasil; ethylene glycol dimethyl ether; ethylene glycol monomethyl ether acetate; 2-methoxyethyl acrylate; 2-methoxyethyl chloroformate; β-methoxyethyl cyanoacrylate; metoprolol; nimodipine; tris(β-methoxyethoxy)vinylsilane
Uses: jet fuel antiicing additive; solvent (lacquers, printing inks); textile auxiliary

ethylene glycol monomethyl ether acetate
2-methoxyethyl acetate; 2-MEA; Methyl Cellosolve Acetate (Union Carbide); Methyl Ethoxol Acetate (ICI); Methyl Oxitol Acetate (Shell); [110-49-6]

$$CH_3OCH_2CH_2O\overset{\overset{\displaystyle O}{\|}}{C}CH_3$$

$C_5H_{10}O_3$. M: 118.13. Colourless liquid with ester-like odour. BP: 140–150°C. d: 1.00 kg/l (20°C). Flash point: 57°C (TOC). Miscible with water and most organic solvents.

Production:
- ethylene glycol monomethyl ether + acetic acid (esterification)

Derivatives: β-methoxyethyl cyanoacrylate

Uses: solvent (printing inks)

ethylene glycol monophenyl ether

ethylene glycol phenyl ether; β-phenoxyethanol; 2-phenoxyethanol; phenoxyethanol; Phenyl Cellosolve (Union Carbide); Dalpad A (Dow Chemical); [122-99-6]

$C_8H_{10}O_2$. M: 138.17. Colourless liquid with mild, aromatic odour. BP: 245°C. Solubility in water: 27 g/l water. Soluble in alcohol. The product is also sold in a mixture with 30% diethylene glycol monophenyl ether. BP: 251°C.

Production:
- phenol + ethylene oxide (epoxidation)

Derivatives:
2-phenoxyethyl acrylate; 2-phenoxyethyl isobutyrate

Uses: coalescing solvent (water-based paints); perfume solvent/fixative; solvent (bactericide/germicide formulations)

ethylene glycol monostearate

glycol monostearate; glycol stearate; [111-60-4]

$C_{20}H_{40}O_3$. M: 328.54. White or yellow flakes. MP: 56–60°C. Sold as self-emulsifying (SE) or non-self-emulsifying (NSE) grades for cosmetic use. HLB: 3.0–3.9 (SE grades), 0.9–2.1 (NSE grades).

Production:
- ethylene glycol + stearic acid (esterification)

Uses: auxiliary emulsifier/opacifier/viscosity modifier (cream shampoo; lotions); polyvinyl chloride processing lubricant

ethylene glycol-propylene glycol block copolymers

Pluronic (BASF); poloxamer (CTFA)

Liquid, powder or flake. EO-PO-EO copolymers with an EO content ranging from 10% to 80%. M: 1,100–10,000.

Production:
- polypropylene glycol + ethylene oxide (epoxidation)

Uses: defoaming agent (metal cleaners, antifreeze, cutting fluids, water treatment); drilling mud/crude oil processing demulsifier component; emulsifier/dispersant (pesticides, paint, emulsion polymerisation); leather tanning auxiliary; wetting agent (pesticides, foundry resins, paper additives, rinse aids); wetting/defoaming agent (dish/bottle washing detergents)

ethyleneimine

aziridine; [151-56-4]

$C_2H_5N_1$. M: 43.07. Liquid with a strong ammonia-like odour. BP: 56°C. MP: -74°C. d: 0.83 kg/l (25°C). Miscible with water forming alkaline solutions. Miscible with most organic solvents.

Production:
- monoethanolamine (sulphonation/dehydration)

Derivatives: polyethyleneimine; triethylenemelamine; triethylenephosphoramide; trimethylolpropane tri-(3-aziridinopropionate)

Uses: aminoethylation reagent; raw material (cationic polyelectrolytes);

ethylene-maleic anhydride copolymers

EMA (Monsanto)

Production:
- ethylene + maleic anhydride (polymerisation)

Uses: dispersant (detergents, oil-well drilling mud); thickening agent (textile printing pastes, cosmetics); water-soluble films (pharmaceutical capsules)

ethylene-methacrylic acid copolymers

EMAA; Elvax II (Du Pont)

Production:
- ethylene + methacrylic acid (polymerisation)

Uses: hot melt adhesives

ethylene-methyl acrylate copolymers

EMA

Acceptable for use in contact with food in many countries.

Production:
- ethylene + methyl acrylate (polymerisation)

Uses: extrusion coatings; polyolefin impact modifier; stretch film (food packaging)

ethylene-methyl acrylate terpolymer, ionomeric

EAM; Vamac (Du Pont)

Elastomer made of ethylene, methyl acrylate and a third, unspecified, carboxylate monomer. Crosslinked by diamines. The vulcanised product has good low temperature and elongation properties as well as good oil, heat and weather resistance.

X = carboxylic monomer.
Production:
• ethylene + methyl acrylate (polymerisation)
Uses: fire-resistant cable insulation; automotive seals, hoses, vibration damping devices

ethylene norbornene *See:* ethylidene norbornene

ethylene oxide
EO; [75-21-8]

$C_2H_4O_1$. M: 44.05. Colourless gas or liquid. BP: 10°C. MP: -112°C. d: 0.89 kg/l (4°C). Miscible with water and oxygenated solvents. Explosive and highly flammable product which, although it can be transported, is generally used *in situ.*
Production:
• ethylene + oxygen (oxidation)
Derivatives: aciclovir; alfentanil; *n*-alkanol(C$_9$-C$_{11}$) ethoxylates; *n*-alkanol(C$_{12}$-C$_{13}$) ethoxylates; *n*-alkanol(C$_{12}$-C$_{14}$) ethoxylates; *n*-alkanol(C$_{12}$-C$_{15}$) ethoxylates; *n*-alkanol(C$_{12}$-C$_{18}$) ethoxylates; *n*-alkanol(C$_{13}$-C$_{15}$) ethoxylates; *n*-alkanol(C$_{14}$-C$_{15}$) ethoxylates; alkanol (C$_{30}$-C$_{50}$) ethoxylates; aminoethylethanolamine; bamifylline; bis-(2-hydroxyethyl)alkyl(C$_{13}$-C$_{15}$)amine; bis(2-hydroxyethyl)-γ-aminopropyltriethoxysilane; bis(2-hydroxyethyl)-cocoamine; bis(2-hydroxyethyl)isotridecyl-3-oxypropylamine; bis(2-hydroxyethyl)oleylamine; bis(2-hydroxyethyl)tallowamine; *N-n*-butylaminoethanol; *t*-butylaminoethanol; *N-n*-butyldiethanolamine; castor oil ethoxylates; cetyl alcohol ethoxylates; cetyloleyl alcohol ethoxylates; cetylstearyl alcohol ethoxylates; 3-(2-chloroethyl)aminopropanol hydrochloride; choline chloride; cocoamine ethoxylates; coconut acid amide ethoxylates; 2-cyanoethyl acrylate; 2-cyanoethyl methacrylate; diethanolamine; diethylaminoethanol; diethylene glycol; diethylene glycol monobutyl ether; diethylene glycol monoethyl ether; diethylene glycol monomethyl ether; diethylenetriamine ethoxylate; *N,N*-di-(2-hydroxyethyl)aniline; di-(2-hydroxyethyl)bisphenol A; di-(2-hydroxyethyl)butynediol; *N,N*-di-(2-hydroxyethyl)-*m*-chloroaniline; di-(2-hydroxyethyl)dimethylhydantoin dilaurate; *N,N'*-di-(2-hydroxyethyl)-*m*-toluidine; di-(hydroxymethyl) oleyloxazoline ethoxylates; 2-diisopropylaminoethanol; 2,5-dimethoxy-5-(β-hydroxyethylsulphonyl)aniline; dimethylethanolamine; dimethylhydantoin ether monooleate; dinonylphenol ethoxylates; diphenoxylate; Disperse Blue 79; Disperse Blue 125; Disperse Orange 138; disul-sodium; *N,N*-ditallowam-

idoethyl-*N*-methylammonium ethoxylate methosulphate; dodecylphenol ethoxylates; epichlorohydrin-ethylene oxide copolymers; ethylene carbonate; ethylenediamine propoxylate/ ethoxylates; ethylene glycol; ethylene glycol monobutyl ether; ethylene glycol monoethyl ether; ethylene glycol monomethyl ether; ethylene glycol monophenyl ether; ethylene glycol-propylene glycol block copolymers; *N*-ethylethanolamine; *N*-ethyl-*N*-(2-hydroxyethyl)aniline; *N*-ethyl-*N*-(2-hydroxyethyl)-*m*-toluidine; 2-ethylthioethanol; etofibrate; etofylline; fenpiverinium bromide; glycerol monolaurate ethoxylates; glycerol monostearate ethoxylates; guanoclor; haloxon; 3-hexenol; hydroquinone di-(β-hydroxyethyl) ether; 2-hydroxyethyl acrylate; hydroxyethylaniline; hydroxyethyl cellulose; 2-hydroxyethyl methacrylate; 4-(2-hydroxyethyl)morpholine; hydroxyethyl starch; hydroxyzine; isodecyl ethoxylates; isodecyl-3-oxypropylamine ethoxylates; isotridecanol ethoxylates; lanolin ethoxylates; lauryl alcohol ethoxylate/propoxylates; lauryl alcohol ethoxylates; loperamide; 2-mercaptoethanol; methyldiethanolamine; methylethanolamine; methyl glucoside ethoxylates; metronidazole; monoethanolamine; nonylphenol ethoxylates; octylphenol ethoxylates; oleamide ethoxylates; oleyl alcohol ethoxylates; oleylamine ethoxylates; oxadixyl; pentoxyverine; 2-(perfluorooctyl)ethyl ethoxylates; phenethyl alcohol; phenol-formaldehyde alkoxylates; pipazetate; polyacetal, copolymers; polyalkylene glycol; polyepichlorohydrin; polyether polyols, flexible; polyether polyols, flexible, amine-terminated; polyethylene glycol; polyethylene glycol monolaurate; polyethylene glycol monomethyl ether; polyethylene glycol monooleate; polyethylene glycol monostearate; polyethylene glycol monotallate; poly(ethylene oxide) resins; pretilachlor; *n*-propylethanolamine; resorcinol di-(2-hydroxyethyl) ether; silicone-polyol block copolymers; sodium bis-(2-hydroxyethyl)-5-sulphoisophthalate; sodium isethionate; sorbitan monolaurate ethoxylates; sorbitan monooleate ethoxylates; sorbitan monopalmitate ethoxylates; sorbitan monostearate ethoxylates; sorbitan trioleate ethoxylates; sorbitan tristearate ethoxylates; soya amine ethoxylates; stearyl alcohol ethoxylates; stearylamine ethoxylates; sulfinpyrazone; tallow alcohol ethoxylates; tallowamine ethoxylates; *N*-tallow-1,3-propanediamine ethoxylates; tetrabromobisphenol A bis(2-hydroxyethyl ether); tetraethylene glycol; tetrakis(2-chloroethyl)ethylene diphosphate; tetramethyl decynediol ethoxylates; thiodiglycol; triethanolamine; triethylene glycol; triethylene glycol monobutyl ether; triethylene glycol monoethyl ether; triethylene glycol monomethyl ether; tris(2-chloroethyl) phosphate; tris(2-chloroethyl) phosphite
Uses: fumigant; sterilising agent

ethylene-propylene copolymers
olefin copolymers; OCP;
Random copolymers containing 40–60% w/w ethylene.

M: 50,000–200,000.

$$-\!\!\left[CH_2\!-\!CH_2\right]_x\!\!\left[CH_2\!-\!\underset{\underset{CH_3}{|}}{CH}\right]_y\!\!-$$

Production:
• ethylene + propylene + ethylidene norbornene (Ziegler polymerisation)
Uses: viscosity modifier (lubricating oils)

ethylene-propylene copolymers, rubber
EPM

$$-\!\!\left[CH_2\!-\!CH_2\right]_x\!\!\left[CH_2\!-\!\underset{\underset{CH_3}{|}}{CH}\right]_y\!\!-$$

Elastomer vulcanised by peroxide crosslinking. The vulcanisates are characterised by their excellent elastic properties and their good age and weather resistance. The product is a random copolymer of ethylene and propylene.
Production:
• ethylene + propylene (Ziegler polymerisation)
Derivatives: polypropylene, elastomer-modified
Uses: cable insulation/jacketing; construction profiles/ sealing strips; automotive extrusions (hoses, bumper strips, window, door and boot seals); polyethylene film (general packaging, sacks); washing machine hoses; white-wall tyre compounds

ethylene-propylene-diene terpolymer, rubber
EPDM

$$-\!\!\left[CH_2\!-\!CH_2\right]_x\!\!\left[CH_2\!-\!\underset{\underset{CH_3}{|}}{CH}\right]_y\!\!X\!-$$

X = curing site. Elastomer vulcanised by sulphur or peroxide crosslinking. Vulcanisates are characterised by their excellent elastic properties and their good age and weather resistance. The product is a random co-polymer of ethylene and propylene.
Production:
• ethylene + propylene + dicyclopentadiene/ ethylidene norbornene/1,4-hexadiene (Ziegler polymerisation)
Derivatives:
acrylonitrile-(ethylene-propylene-diene)-styrene copoly-mers; polypropylene, elastomer-modified; polystyrene, high-impact
Uses: cable insulation/jacketing; construction profiles/ sealing strips; automotive window, door/boot mould-ings; short-chain reactive plasticisers; white-wall tyre compounds

ethylene-tetrafluoroethylene copolymers
ETFE; Halon ET (Ausimont); poly(ethylene-tetrafluoro-ethylene); Tefzel (Du Pont)

$$-\!\!\left[CH_2\!-\!CH_2\right]_x\!\!\left[CF_2\!-\!CF_2\right]_y\!\!-$$

Thermoplastic. d: 1.70 kg/l. Tensile strength: 45 MPa.

Elongation at break: 150%. The polymer has a higher impact strength than polytetrafluoroethylene.
Production:
• ethylene + tetrafluoroethylene (polymerisation)
Uses: electrical wire insulation; industrial fibres; weather-resistant films (pneumatic buildings)

ethylenethiourea
2-mercaptoimidazoline; ETU; [96-45-7]

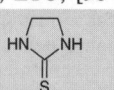

$C_3H_6N_2S_1$. M: 102.15. White, odourless powder. MP: 185°C. Soluble in water. Insoluble in hydrocarbon solvents.
Production:
• ethylenediamine + carbon disulphide (amidine formation)
Derivatives: clonidine
Uses: vulcanisation accelerator

ethylene urea
2-imidazolinone; [120-93-4]

$C_3H_6N_2O_1$. M: 86.09. White, crystalline solid. MP: 131°C. Soluble in water.
Production:
• ethylenediamine + urea (condensation)
Derivatives:
azlocillin; *N,N'*-dimethylolethylene urea; mezlocillin

ethylene-vinyl acetate copolymers, <10% vinyl acetate
EVA; EVM

$$-\!\!\left[CH_2\!-\!CH_2\right]_x\!\!\left[CH_2\!-\!\underset{\underset{\underset{CH_3}{|}}{\underset{C=O}{|}}}{CH}\right]_y\!\!-$$

Thermoplastic with better flexibility, softness and surface gloss than polyethylene. Many grades are food approved.
Production:
• ethylene + vinyl acetate (high-pressure bulk polymerisation)
Uses:
cable insulation/jacketing; heavy sacking film; shrink/ heat-sealing film; stretch film (food packaging)

ethylene-vinyl acetate copolymers, 15% vinyl acetate
VA; VAE
Available as solid rubber or as latex containing 50–60% solids.

$$\begin{matrix} & & O \\ & & \| \\ & & OCCH_3 \\ & & | \\ -[CH_2-CH_2]_x-[CH_2-CH]_y- \end{matrix}$$

Production:
• vinyl acetate + ethylene (emulsion polymerisation)
Uses: latex adhesives (paper, plastics, packaging, book-binding, construction, leather); textile auxiliaries/dressings/coatings; binder (interior/exterior emulsion paints); rubber shoesoling, flexible gaskets, tubing, toys

ethylene-vinyl acetate copolymers, 18-50% vinyl acetate
EVA; EVM
Flexible resins. These polymers often include a small percentage of a carboxylic acid monomer to improve adhesion.

$$\begin{matrix} & & O \\ & & \| \\ & & OCCH_3 \\ & & | \\ -[CH_2-CH_2]_x-[CH_2-CH]_y- \end{matrix}$$

Production:
• ethylene + vinyl acetate (solution polymerisation)
Uses: hot melt/packaging adhesives; pour point depressant (lubricants); wax additive

ethylene-vinyl acetate copolymers, 40-50% vinyl acetate
EVA; EVM

$$\begin{matrix} & & O \\ & & \| \\ & & OCCH_3 \\ & & | \\ -[CH_2-CH_2]_x-[CH_2-CH]_y- \end{matrix}$$

Elastomers used as such (for hot melt adhesives) or vulcanised by peroxide crosslinking. The vulcanisate is characterised by its excellent heat, age and weather resistance. Its mechanical properties are relatively poor, however.
Production:
• ethylene + vinyl acetate (solution polymerisation)
Derivatives: (ethylene-vinyl acetate)-vinyl chloride graft copolymers; polyvinyl chloride, high-impact
Uses: heat-resistant cable insulation, profiles, seals; hot melt adhesives; roof covering membranes

(ethylene-vinyl acetate)-vinyl chloride graft copolymers
EVA/VC
Thermoplastic blend produced by suspension polymerisation of vinyl chloride containing dissolved ethylene-vinyl acetate copolymer. The concentration of the latter is about 6% of the final product.
Production:
• vinyl chloride + ethylene-vinyl acetate copolymers, 40-50% vinyl acetate (polymerisation)
Uses:
processing aid/impact modifier (polyvinyl chloride)

ethylene-vinyl alcohol copolymers
EVOH; Eval (Kuraray); Exceed (Okura Industrial); [25067-34-9]

$$\begin{matrix} & & OH \\ & & | \\ -[CH_2-CH_2]_x-[CH_2-CH]_y- \end{matrix}$$

Partially crystalline thermoplastic available as biaxially-oriented laminated film which is characterised by its low gas permeability.
Production:
• ethylene + vinyl acetate (polymerisation/hydrolysis)
Uses: barrier resins (food packaging film)

N-ethylethanolamine
[110-73-6]

$$C_2H_5NHCH_2CH_2OH$$

$C_4H_{11}N_1O_1$. M: 89.14. Colourless liquid with an ammoniacal odour. BP: 168–170°C. d: 0.91 kg/l (20°C). Soluble in water and oxygenated solvents.
Production:
• ethylamine + ethylene oxide (epoxidation)
Derivatives: bamifylline; N-ethylethylenediamine; 2-(N-ethylperfluorooctylsulphonamido)ethanol

ethyl 3-ethoxypropionate
EEP; [763-69-9]

$$\begin{matrix} & O \\ & \| \\ C_2H_5OCH_2CH_2COC_2H_5 \end{matrix}$$

$C_7H_{14}O_3$. M: 146.19. Liquid. BP: 170°C. Slightly soluble in water.
Production:
• ethanol + ethyl acrylate (Michael addition)
Derivatives: 4-amino-5-bromomethyl-2-methylpyrimidine hydrobromide

N-ethylethylenediamine
2-aminoethyl(ethyl)amine; [110-72-5]

$$C_2H_5NHCH_2CH_2NH_2$$

$C_4H_{12}N_2$. M: 88.15. Liquid. BP: 128–130°C. Soluble in water and oxygenated solvents.
Production:
• N-ethylethanolamine + ammonia (ammoniation)
Derivatives:
cefoperazone; piperacillin

ethyl formate
[109-94-4]

$$\begin{matrix} & O \\ & \| \\ HCOC_2H_5 \end{matrix}$$

$C_3H_6O_2$. M: 74.08. Colourless liquid with a spicy odour. BP: 52–56°C. MP: -80°C. Slightly soluble in water with gradual decomposition. Miscible with oxygenated and aromatic solvents.

Production:
• carbon monoxide + ethanol (base-catalysed alcoholysis)
Derivatives:
7-amino-3-phenylcoumarin; 5-benzyl-3-furylmethyl alcohol; etomidate; fluridone; methyprylon; uracil
Uses: disinfectant/preservative; flavouring ingredient

ethyl glycinate hydrochloride
ethyl ammoniumacetate hydrochloride; ethyl glycine hydrochloride; [623-33-6]

$$H_3^+NCH_2COOC_2H_5 \quad Cl^-$$

$C_4H_{10}Cl_1N_1O_2$. M: 139.58. Crystalline solid. Sublimes at 145°C. Soluble in water and alcohol.
Production:
• ethanol + glycine (esterification)
Derivatives:
bromazepam; diazepam; ethyl diazoacetate; nordazepam; proglinazine-ethyl

ethyl heptanoate
ethyl enantate; [106-30-9]

$$CH_3(CH_2)_5\overset{\overset{O}{\|}}{C}OC_2H_5$$

$C_9H_{18}O_2$. M: 158.24. Liquid with a fruity odour. BP: 189°C. d: 0.86 kg/l (25°C). Insoluble in water. Soluble in oxygenated solvents.
Production:
• ethanol + *n*-heptanoic acid (esterification)
Uses: flavouring ingredient

2-ethylhexaldehyde
2-ethylhexanal; [123-05-7]

$$CH_3(CH_2)_3\overset{\overset{C_2H_5}{|}}{C}HCHO$$

$C_8H_{16}O_1$. M: 128.22. Colourless liquid. BP: 163–164°C. d: 0.82 kg/l (20°C). Slightly soluble in water. Miscible with most organic solvents.
Production:
• *n*-butyraldehyde (aldol condenation/dehydration/hydrogenation)
Derivatives: 2-ethylhexanoic acid; 2-ethylhexoin oxime; ethyl octynol

ethyl hexanoate *See:* ethyl caproate

2-ethylhexanoic acid
2-ethylhexoic acid; [149-57-5]

$$CH_3(CH_2)_3\overset{\overset{C_2H_5}{|}}{C}HCOOH$$

$C_8H_{16}O_2$. M: 144.22. Clear liquid. BP: 215–224°C. d: 0.91 kg/l (20°C). Solubility in water: 1.4 g/l water (25°C).

Production:
• 2-ethylhexaldehyde (carbonyl oxidation)
Derivatives:
aluminium octoate; barium-zinc heat stabilisers; cadmium-barium heat stabilisers; cadmium-zinc heat stabilisers; cobalt octoate; complex ester oils; diphenyl-antimony 2-ethylhexanoate; 2-ethylhexanoyl chloride; lead octoate; stannous octoate; *N,N,N*-trimethyl-2-hydroxypropylammonium 2-ethylhexanoate; zinc 2-ethylhexanoate; zirconium octoate

2-ethylhexanol
2-ethylhexyl alcohol; octanol; 2-EH; 2EH; [104-76-7]

$$CH_3(CH_2)_3\overset{\overset{C_2H_5}{|}}{C}HCH_2OH$$

$C_8H_{18}O_1$. M: 130.23. Colourless liquid. BP: 184–185°C. d: 0.83 kg/l (20°C). Solubility in water: 10 g/l (20°C). Miscible with most organic solvents. Flash point: 75°C (TCC). Competes with isooctanol.
Production:
• *n*-butyraldehyde (aldol condensation/hydrogenation)
• propylene + synthesis gas (Shell hydroformylation process; coproduced with *n*-butanol/isobutanol)
Derivatives:
bis(2-ethylhexyl) hydrogen phosphate; *n*-butyl octyl phthalate; di-(2-ethylhexyl) adipate; di-(2-ethylhexyl)-amine; di-(2-ethylhexyl) azelate; di-(2-ethylhexyl) maleate; di-(2-ethylhexyl) phthalate; di-(2-ethylhexyl) sebacate; dioctyl octylphosphonate; diphenyl 2-ethylhexyl phosphate; 2-ethylhexyl acrylate; 2-ethylhexylamine; 2-ethylhexyl chloroformate; 2-ethylhexyl glycidyl ether; 2-ethylhexyl methacrylate; 2-ethylhexyl nitrate; 2-ethylhexyl oleate; 2-ethylhexyl palmitate; 2-ethylhexyl *p*-methylaminobenzoate; 2-ethylhexyl *p*-methoxycinnamate; 2-ethylhexyl salicylate; 2-ethylhexyl stearate; 2-ethylhexyl titanate; isooctyl epoxytallate; molybdenum di-(2-ethylhexyl) dithiophosphate; polymeric plasticisers; sodium 2-ethylhexyl sulphate; tri-(2-ethylhexyl) phosphate; tri-(2-ethylhexyl) trimellitate; zinc dioctyl dithiophosphate
Uses:
disinfectant; flotation frothing agent; solvent

2-ethylhexanoyl chloride
[760-67-8]

$$CH_3(CH_2)_3\overset{\overset{C_2H_5}{|}}{C}HCOCl$$

$C_8H_{15}Cl_1O_1$. M: 162.66. Liquid. BP: 180°C. MP: -60°C. d: 0.95 kg/l (20°C). Flash point: 79°C (TOC).
Production:
• 2-ethylhexanoic acid (acid chloride formation)
Derivatives: *t*-amyl peroxy-2-ethylhexanoate; 2,5-bis-(2-ethylhexanoylperoxy)-2,5-dimethylhexane; *t*-butyl peroxy-2-ethylhexanoate; 1,1-dimethyl-3-hydroxybutyl peroxy-2-ethylhexanoate

2-ethylhexoin oxime
LIX 63 (Henkel)

$$CH_3(CH_2)_3\overset{\overset{\displaystyle OH}{|}}{C}H\overset{}{C}H-\overset{\overset{\displaystyle NOH}{\|}}{C}CH(CH_3)_2CH_3$$
$$\underset{C_2H_5}{|} \quad \underset{C_2H_5}{|}$$

$C_{16}H_{33}N_1O_2$. M: 271.45.
Production:
• 2-ethylhexaldehyde + hydroxylamine sulphate (condensation/oxime formation)
Uses: copper extraction reagent

2-ethylhexyl acrylate
octyl acrylate; EHA; [103-11-7]

$$CH_2=CH\overset{\overset{\displaystyle O}{\|}}{C}OCH_2\overset{\overset{\displaystyle C_2H_5}{|}}{C}H(CH_2)_3CH_3$$

$C_{11}H_{20}O_2$. M: 184.28. Liquid with pleasant odour. BP: 214–218°C with polymerisation. d: 0.88 kg/l (20°C).
Production:
• 2-ethylhexanol + acrylic acid (esterification)
Derivatives:
acrylic resins, carboxylated; acrylic resins, hydroxylated; acrylic resins, latex; acrylic resins, solvent-based; styrene-acrylic copolymers; vinyl chloride-acrylic ester copolymers; vinyltoluene-acrylic copolymers, latex
Uses: acrylic/vinyl resin comonomer

2-ethylhexylamine
2-ethyl-1-hexaneamine; [104-75-6]

$$CH_3CH_2CH_2CH_2\overset{\overset{\displaystyle C_2H_5}{|}}{C}HCH_2NH_2$$

$C_8H_{19}N_1$. M: 129.25. Liquid. BP: 168–171°C. MP: <-70°C. Insoluble in water. Soluble in oxygenated solvents.
Production:
• 2-ethylhexanol + ammonia (ammoniation; coproduced with di-(2-ethylhexyl)amine)
Derivatives: 2-ethylhexyliminobis(methylenephosphonic acid); hexetidine

2-ethylhexyl chloroformate
[24468-13-1]

$$CH_3(CH_2)_3\overset{}{C}HCH_2\overset{\overset{\displaystyle O}{\|}}{O}CCl$$
$$\underset{C_2H_5}{|}$$

$C_9H_{17}Cl_1O_2$. M: 192.69. Liquid. MP: <-55°C.
Production:
• 2-ethylhexanol + phosgene (phosgenation)
Derivatives:
t-amyl peroxy-2-ethylhexylcarbonate; bis(2-ethylhexyl) peroxydicarbonate; t-butyl peroxy-2-ethylhexylcarbonate

2-ethylhexyl p-dimethylaminobenzoate
Escalol 507 (Mallinckrodt)

$$(CH_3)_2N-\underset{}{\bigcirc}-\overset{\overset{\displaystyle O}{\|}}{C}OCH_2\overset{\overset{\displaystyle C_2H_5}{|}}{C}H(CH_2)_3CH_3$$

$C_{17}H_{27}N_1O_2$. M: 277.42.
Production:
• p-dimethylaminobenzoic acid + 2-ethylhexanol (esterification)
Uses: photoactivator (printing inks, lacquers); sunscreening agent

2-ethylhexyl epoxystearate
octyl epoxystearate

$$CH_3(CH_2)_7\overset{}{C}H-CH(CH_2)_7\overset{\overset{\displaystyle O}{\|}}{C}OCH_2\overset{\overset{\displaystyle C_2H_5}{|}}{C}H(CH_2)_3CH_3$$

$C_{26}H_{50}O_3$. M: 410.69.
Production:
• 2-ethylhexyl oleate + peracetic acid (peroxidation)
Derivatives: barium-zinc heat stabilisers
Uses: polyvinyl chloride costabiliser/plasticiser

2-ethylhexyl epoxytallate *See:* isooctyl epoxytallate

2-ethylhexyl glycidyl ether
[2461-15-6]

$$CH_3(CH_2)_3\overset{\overset{\displaystyle C_2H_5}{|}}{C}HCH_2OCH_2\overset{\overset{\displaystyle O}{}}{C}H-CH_2$$

$C_{11}H_{22}O_2$. M: 186.30. Liquid.
Production:
• 2-ethylhexanol + epichlorohydrin (ether formation)
Uses: reactive diluent (epoxy resins)

2-ethylhexyliminobis(methylenephosphonic acid)
Briquest 281 (Albright and Wilson)

$$CH_3(CH_2)_3\overset{\overset{\displaystyle C_2H_5}{|}}{C}HCH_2N\left[CH_2\overset{\overset{\displaystyle O}{\|}}{P}(OH)_2\right]_2$$

$C_{10}H_{25}N_1O_6P_2$. M: 317.26.
Production:
• 2-ethylhexylamine + formaldehyde + phosphorous acid (Mannich reaction)
Uses: flotation collector (oxide ores)

2-ethylhexyl methacrylate
octyl methacrylate; 2EHMA

$$CH_2=\overset{}{C}\overset{\overset{\displaystyle O}{\|}}{C}OCH_2\overset{\overset{\displaystyle C_2H_5}{|}}{C}H(CH_2)_3CH_3$$
$$\underset{CH_3}{|}$$

$C_{12}H_{22}O_2$. M: 198.31.
Production:
• 2-ethylhexanol + methyl methacrylate (transesterification)
Derivatives: polymethacrylates, oil-soluble; polymethacrylates, oil-soluble dispersants
Uses: acrylic resin comonomer

2-ethylhexyl *p*-methoxycinnamate
Givsorb 101 (Givaudan-Roure); [5466-77-3]

$$CH_3O-\!\!\!\!\!\!\langle\ \rangle\!\!\!\!\!\!-CH=CHCOCH_2CH(CH_2)_3CH_3$$

with $\overset{O}{\overset{\|}{}}$ and C_2H_5 substituent shown

$C_{18}H_{26}O_3$. M: 290.41.
Production:
• *p*-anisaldehyde + sodium acetate + 2-ethylhexanol
(Perkin condensation/esterification)
Uses: light stabiliser (plastics)

2-ethylhexyl nitrate
octyl nitrate; 2EHN; EHN

$$\overset{C_2H_5}{\underset{|}{CH_3(CH_2)_3CHCH_2ONO_2}}$$

$C_8H_{17}N_1O_3$. M: 175.24.
Production:
• 2-ethylhexanol (nitration)
Uses: diesel fuel ignition improver

2-ethylhexyl oleate
[26399-02-0]

$$CH_3(CH_2)_7CH=CH(CH_2)_7\overset{O}{\overset{\|}{C}}OCH_2\overset{C_2H_5}{\underset{|}{CH}}(CH_2)_3CH_3$$

$C_{26}H_{50}O_2$. M: 394.69. Liquid. Cloud point: -28°C.
Insoluble in water.
Production:
• 2-ethylhexanol + methyl oleate (esterification)
Derivatives:
2-ethylhexyl epoxystearate
Uses: lubricant (metalworking fluids)

2-ethylhexyl palmitate
octyl palmitate; [29806-73-3]

$$CH_3(CH_2)_{14}\overset{O}{\overset{\|}{C}}OCH_2\overset{C_2H_5}{\underset{|}{CH}}(CH_2)_3CH_3$$

$C_{24}H_{48}O_2$. M: 368.64. Colourless or pale yellow liquid.
MP: 2–6°C. Insoluble in water.
Production:
• 2-ethylhexanol + palmitic acid (esterification)
Uses: emollient (cosmetics)

2-ethylhexyl salicylate
octyl salicylate; [118-60-5]

$$\overset{C_2H_5}{\underset{|}{CH_3(CH_2)_3CHCH_2O}}\overset{O}{\overset{\|}{C}}-\!\!\!\!\!\!\langle\ \rangle$$
HO

$C_{15}H_{22}O_3$. M: 250.34.
Production:
• 2-ethylhexanol + salicylic acid (esterification)
Uses:
fragrance ingredient

2-ethylhexyl stearate
octyl stearate (CTFA); [22047-49-0]

$$CH_3(CH_2)_{16}\overset{O}{\overset{\|}{C}}OCH_2\overset{C_2H_5}{\underset{|}{C}}(CH_2)_3CH_3$$

$C_{26}H_{52}O_2$. M: 396.71. Liquid. Cloud point: 10–15°C.
Production:
• 2-ethylhexanol + stearic acid (esterification)
Uses: lubricant (textile spin finishes); plasticiser/solvent
(paper coating, metalworking fluids)

2-ethylhexyl titanate
tetra-2-ethylhexyl orthotitanate; titanium 2-ethylhexyl-
ate; titanium tetraoctoxide; 2-EHT

$$\left[\overset{C_2H_5}{\underset{|}{CH_3(CH_2)_3CCH_2O}}\right]_4 Ti$$

$C_{32}H_{68}O_4Ti_1$. **M**: 564.79. Pale yellow liquid. BP: 245°C
(1.7 kPa). Pour point: -4°C. d: 0.94 kg/l (20°C).
Soluble in oxygenated, chlorinated and hydrocarbon
solvents.
Production:
• 2-ethylhexanol + isopropyl titanate (transesterification)
Uses: esterification catalyst; crosslinking agent (paints,
printing inks)

ethyl 4-hydroxybenzoate
ethyl *p*-hydroxybenzoate; ethylparaben; E214 (EC);
[120-47-8]

$$HO-\!\!\!\!\!\!\langle\ \rangle\!\!\!\!\!\!-\overset{O}{\overset{\|}{C}}OC_2H_5$$

$C_9H_{10}O_3$. M: 166.18. White, crystalline solid. MP:
116–118°C. BP: 298°C with decomposition. Insoluble
in water. Soluble in oxygenated solvents. Also available as the sodium salt. Not approved for food use in
the USA.
Production:
• ethanol + *p*-hydroxybenzoic acid (esterification)
Uses: biocide (latices, emulsions); preservative (fruit,
preserves, soft drinks)

N-ethyl-*N*-(2-hydroxyethyl)aniline
2-(ethylphenylamino)ethanol; *N*-ethyl-*N*-phenylethanol-
amine; *N*-(2-hydroxyethyl)-*N*-ethylaniline; [92-50-2]

$$\overset{C_2H_5}{\underset{|}{\langle\ \rangle-NCH_2CH_2OH}}$$

$C_{10}H_{15}N_1O_1$. M: 165.24. Solid. MP: 36°C. BP: 130–
134°C (0.7 kPa).
Production:
• *N*-ethylaniline + ethylene oxide (epoxidation)
Derivatives:
Basic Blue 41; Basic Orange 30:1; Basic Red 18; Bas-
ic Red 18:1; Disperse Red 1; Disperse Red 13; *N*-eth-
yl-*N*-(2-hydroxyethyl)-*p*-phenylenediamine

ethyl hydroxyethyl cellulose
hydroxyethyl ethyl cellulose; EHEC

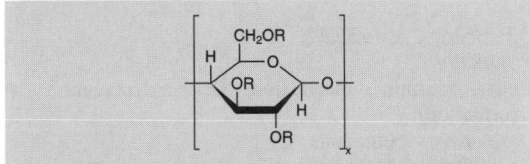

R = ethyl, poly(oxyethyl)-.
Production:
• hydroxyethyl cellulose + ethyl chloride (ether
  formation)
Uses:
binder (printing inks); protective colloid (acrylic/vinyl
latex); thickening agent/protective colloid (emulsion
paints, liquid cleaner formulations)

N-ethyl-*N*-(2-hydroxyethyl)-*p*-phenylenediamine
4-amino-*N*-ethyl-*N*-(β-hydroxyethyl)aniline

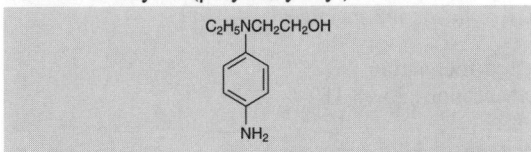

$C_{10}H_{16}N_2O_1$. M: 180.25. Available commercially as the
bisulphate.
Production:
• *N*-ethyl-*N*-(2-hydroxyethyl)aniline + sodium nitrite
  (nitrosation/nitro reduction)
Uses: photographic developing agent

N-ethyl-*N*-(2-hydroxyethyl)-*m*-toluidine
2-(*N*-ethyl-*m*-toluidino)ethanol; [91-88-3]

$C_{11}H_{17}N_1O_1$. M: 179.27. Solid or liquid. MP: 23°C. BP:
237°C.
Production:
• *N*-ethyl-*m*-toluidine + ethylene oxide (epoxidation)
Derivatives: 2-amino-5-[*N*-ethyl-*N*-(2-hydroxyethyl)ami-
no]toluene; Basic Blue 119; Serisol Blue RD

ethyl 4-hydroxy-3-methoxybenzoate
See: ethyl vanillate

ethyl hydroxymethyl oleyloxazoline
Alkaterge-E (Angus Chemical); [68140-98-7]

$C_{23}H_{43}N_1O_2$. M: 365.60. Clear, yellow liquid. FP:

-31°C. d: 0.93 kg/l (25°C). Almost insoluble in water.
Soluble in most organic solvents and oils.
Production:
• oleic acid + 2-ethyl-2-aminopropan-1,3-diol
  (condensation)
Uses:
emulsifier/corrosion inhibitor (soluble cutting oils);
antifoam (antibiotic production); pigment grinding aid;
wetting agent (paper, textiles, metal cleaners)

4-ethyl-3-hydroxy-1-octyne *See:* ethyl octynol

2-ethyl-3-hydroxy-4H-pyran-4-one *See:* ethyl maltol

2,2'-ethylidene bis(4,6-di-*t*-butylphenol)
6,6-ethylidenebis(2,4-di-*t*-butylphenol); Isonox 129
(Schenectady Chemicals); Vanox 1290 (Vanderbilt
Chemical); [35958-30-6]

$C_{30}H_{46}O_2$. M: 438.70.
Production:
• 2,4-di-*t*-butylphenol + acetaldehyde (carbonyl
  condensation)
Uses: antioxidant (plastics)

ethylidene norbornene
ethylene norbornene; 5-ethylidene-2-norbornene; EN;
ENB; [16219-75-3]

C_9H_{12}. M: 120.20.
Production:
• dicyclopentadiene + butadiene (Diels-Alder cyclo-
  addition/rearrangement)
Derivatives: ethylene-propylene copolymers; ethylene-
propylene-diene terpolymer, rubber

ethyl iodide
[75-03-6]

C_2H_5I

$C_2H_5I_1$. M: 155.96. Colourless or red liquid with an
ethereal odour. BP: 72°C. MP: -108°C. d: 1.95 kg/l
(20°C). Insoluble in water. Soluble in most organic
solvents.
Production:
• ethanol + iodine (alcohol iodination)
Derivatives: nalidixic acid; oxolinic acid

ethyl isoamyl ketone *See:* ethyl amyl ketone

ethyl isocyanate
[109-90-0]

C2H5NCO

C3H5N1O1. M: 71.08.
Production:
• ethylamine + phosgene (phosgenation)
Derivatives:
alfentanil; cymoxanil

ethyl isonipecotinate
ethyl piperidine-4-carboxylate; [1126-09-6]

HN—COC2H5 (O)

C8H15N1O2. M: 157.22. Liquid. Soluble in water, oxygenated and aromatic solvents.
Production:
• ethanol + isonipecotic acid (esterification)
Derivatives: azacyclonol

N-ethyl *O*-isopropyl thionocarbamate
O-isopropyl *N*-ethyl thionocarbamate; IPETC; Z-200 (Dow Chemical)

(CH3)2CHOCNHC2H5 (S)

C6H13N1O1S1. M: 147.24.
Production:
• sodium isopropyl xanthate + ethylamine (dethiolation)
Uses:
flotation collector (sulphide ores)

ethyl lactate
[97-64-3]

OH
CH3CHCOOC2H5

C5H10O3. M: 118.13. Colourless liquid. BP: 154°C. d: 1.04 kg/l (15°C). Miscible with water and oxygenated solvents. The commercial product is a racemic mixture.
Production:
• ethanol + DL-lactic acid (esterification)
Uses:
solvent (lacquers, cellulose acetate)

ethyl levulinate
ethyl 4-oxopentanoate; ethyl 4-oxovalerate; [539-88-8]

O   O
CH3CCH2CH2COC2H5

C7H12O3. M: 144.18. Colourless liquid. BP: 206°C. Soluble in water. Miscible with oxygenated solvents.
Production:
• ethanol + levulinic acid (esterification)
Derivatives:
indomethacin; mefruside

ethylmagnesium bromide

C2H5MgBr

C2H5Br1Mg1. M: 133.27.
Production:
• ethyl bromide + magnesium (Grignard reagent formation)
Derivatives: methadone
Uses: Grignard reagent

ethyl maltol
2-ethyl-3-hydroxy-4H-pyran-4-one; [4940-11-8]

OH
C2H5 (O)

C7H8O3. M: 140.14.
Production:
• 2-propionylfuran (rearrangement/oxidation)
Uses: flavouring ingredient

ethyl mercaptan
ethanethiol; [75-08-1]

C2H5SH

C2H6S1. M: 62.13. Colourless liquid with a strong, unpleasant odour. BP: 34–36°C. MP: -144°C. d: 0.84 kg/l (15°C). Slightly soluble in water. Soluble in oxygenated solvents.
Production:
• ethylene + hydrogen sulphide (addition)
Derivatives: dipropetryn; ethanesulphonyl chloride; ethiofencarb; ethyl chlorothioformate; 2-ethylthioethanol; MCPA-thioethyl; phorate; sethoxydim

2-ethylmercaptoethanol *See:* 2-ethylthioethanol

ethyl methacrylate
[97-63-2]

O
CH2=CCOC2H5
CH3

C6H10O2. M: 114.15. Colourless liquid. BP: 118–119°C. d: 0.91 kg/l (20°C). Insoluble in water. Soluble in oxygenated solvents. Flash point: 21°C (TOC). Commercial products contain hydroquinone methyl ether or similar polymerisation inhibitors.
Production:
• methyl methacrylate + ethanol (transesterification)
Uses: acrylic resin comonomer

2-ethyl-6-methylaniline
6-ethyl-2-methylaniline
C9H13N1. M: 135.21. Orange liquid. BP: 231°C. MP: -25°C. d: 0.97 kg/l (20°C). Insoluble in water.

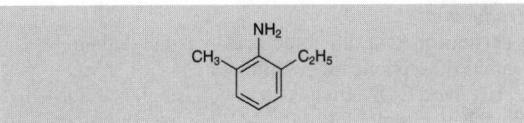

Production:
• *o*-toluidine + ethylene (orthoalkylation)
Derivatives:
acetochlor; metolachlor

N-ethyl-3-methylaniline *See:* N-ethyl-*m*-toluidine

2-ethyl-2-methylbutanoic acid
[19889-37-3]

$$(CH_3CH_2)_2CCOOH$$

with CH_3 on the central carbon.

$C_7H_{14}O_2$. M: 130.19. Liquid.
Production:
• methylpentene, mixed + carbon monoxide (Koch carbonylation; coproduced with 2,2-dimethyl-pentanoic acid)
Derivatives: isoxaben

2-ethyl-4-methylimidazole
[931-36-2]

$C_6H_{10}N_2$. M: 110.16.
Production:
• propionitrile + ammonia + hydroxyacetone (amidine formation/condensation)
Derivatives: 1-(2-cyanoethyl)-2-ethyl-4-methylimidazole
Uses: epoxy resin curing agent

ethyl methylphenylglycidate
aldehyde C-16; ethyl 3-methyl-3-phenylglycidate; strawberry aldehyde; [77-83-8]

$C_{12}H_{14}O_3$. M: 206.24. Liquid with strawberry-like odour. BP: 153–155°C (2.4 kPa). d: 1.51 kg/l (25°C). The commercial products consist of a mixture of the *cis*- and *trans*-isomers.
Production:
• acetophenone + ethyl chloroacetate (Darzens reaction)
Uses: fragrance ingredient (technical products)

5-ethyl-3-methyl-5-phenylhydantoin *See:* mephenytoin

3-[ethyl(3-methylphenyl)imino]propionitrile
See: N-(2-cyanoethyl)-N-ethyl-*m*-toluidine

5-ethyl-2-methylpyridine
See: 2-methyl-5-ethylpyridine

N-ethylmorpholine
4-ethylmorpholine; NEM; [100-74-3]

$C_6H_{13}N_1O_1$. M: 115.18. Liquid with characteristic odour. BP: 138°C. FP: -63°C. d: 0.91 kg/l.
Production:
• diethylene glycol + ammonia (amine formation)
Uses:
polyurethane foam catalyst

ethyl 1-naphthylacetate
[2122-70-5]

$C_{14}H_{14}O_2$. M: 214.26.
Production:
• ethanol + 1-naphthylacetic acid (esterification)
Uses: plant growth regulator

N-ethyl-1-naphthylamine
N-ethyl-α-naphthylamine; [118-44-5]

$C_{12}H_{13}N_1$. M: 171.24. Colourless liquid. BP: 305°C. Insoluble in water. Soluble in oxygenated solvents.
Production:
• α-naphthol + ethylamine (amine formation)
Derivatives: Basic Blue 7

ethyl p-nitrobenzoate
ethyl 4-nitrobenzoate

$C_9H_9N_1O_4$. M: 195.18. Colourless crystalline solid. MP: 57°C. Insoluble in water. Soluble in oxygenated solvents.
Production:
• *p*-nitrobenzoic acid + ethanol (esterification)
Derivatives:
ethyl *p*-aminobenzoate
Uses: sunscreening agent

ethyl 5-nitroisophthalate
See: monoethyl 5-nitroisophthalate

O-ethyl *O*-(4-nitrophenyl) phenylphosphonothioate
EPN; [2104-64-5]

$$O_2N \text{---} \langle \rangle \text{---} OPOC_2H_5 \quad (S, phenyl)$$

$C_{14}H_{14}N_1O_4P_1S_1$. M: 323.30.
Production:
• phosphenyl chloride + ethanol + *p*-nitrophenol + sulphur (dehydrochlorination/dehydrochlorination/thionation)
Uses: insecticide/acaricide

2-ethyl-2-nitro-1,3-propanediol
2-ethyl-2-nitropropan-1,3-diol; 2-nitro-2-ethyl-1,3-propanediol; NEPD; [597-09-1]

$$CH_2OH$$
$$C_2H_5CNO_2$$
$$CH_2OH$$

$C_5H_{11}N_1O_4$. M: 149.15. Solid. MP: 56°C with decomposition. Solubility in water: 400 g/l water (20°C).
Production:
• formaldehyde + 1-nitropropane (hydroxymethylation)
Derivatives: 2-ethyl-2-aminopropan-1,3-diol

ethyl octoate *See:* ethyl caprylate

ethyl octynol
4-ethyl-3-hydroxy-1-octyne; 3-hydroxy-4-ethyl-1-octyne

$$C_2H_5$$
$$CH_3(CH_2)_3CHCHC \equiv CH$$
$$OH$$

$C_{10}H_{18}O_1$. M: 154.25.
Production:
• 2-ethylhexaldehyde + acetylene (ethynylation)
Uses: electroplating bath additive; acid corrosion inhibitor (steel pickling, oil-well acidising)

ethyl orthoacetate *See:* triethyl orthoacetate

ethyl orthoformate *See:* triethyl orthoformate

ethyl 4-oxovalerate *See:* ethyl levulinate

ethylparaben *See:* ethyl 4-hydroxybenzoate

ethyl parathion *See:* parathion

2-(*N*-ethylperfluorooctylsulphonamido)ethanol

$$C_2H_5$$
$$CF_3(CF_2)_7SO_2NCH_2CH_2OH$$

$C_{12}H_{10}F_{17}N_1O_3S_1$. M: 571.25.

Production:
• perfluorooctanesulphonic acid + *N*-ethylethanolamine (sulphonamide formation)
Derivatives: 2-(*N*-ethylperfluorooctylsulphonamido)ethyl phosphate, ammonium salt; 2-(*N*-ethylperfluorooctylsulphonamido)ethyl acrylate

2-(*N*-ethylperfluorooctylsulphonamido)ethyl acrylate

$$\underset{\text{CH}_2=\text{CHCOCH}_2\text{CH}_2\text{NSO}_2(\text{CF}_2)_7\text{CF}_3}{\overset{O \quad\quad C_2H_5}{}}$$

$C_{15}H_{12}F_{17}N_1O_4S_1$. M: 625.30.
Production:
• 2-(*N*-ethylperfluorooctylsulphonamido)ethanol + acryloyl chloride (esterification)
Uses: acrylic resin comonomer (textile finishes); comonomer (water-resistant paper coatings)

2-(*N*-ethylperfluorooctylsulphonamido)ethyl phosphate, ammonium salt

$$\left[CF_3(CF_2)_7SO_2NCH_2CH_2O \right]_n \overset{O}{\underset{}{P}}(O^- \ NH_4^+)_{3-n} \quad (C_2H_5)$$

n = 1–2.
Production:
• 2-(*N*-ethylperfluorooctylsulphonamido)ethanol + phosphorus pentoxide + ammonia (esterification/salt formation)
Uses: water/oil-resistant coatings (paper)

ethyl phenylacetate
[101-97-3]

$$\langle \rangle \text{---} CH_2COC_2H_5 \quad (O)$$

$C_{10}H_{12}O_2$. M: 164.21. Colourless liquid with a pleasant odour. BP: 226–227°C. d: 1.03 kg/l (20°C). Insoluble in water. Soluble in oxygenated solvents.
Production:
• ethanol + phenylacetic acid (esterification)
Derivatives: phenthoate; phenylmalonic acid
Uses: flavouring/fragrance ingredient

N-ethyl-*N*-phenylbenzylamine-3-sulphonic acid
α-(*N*-ethylanilino)toluene-3-sulphonic acid; *N*-ethyl-*N*-(3-sulphobenzyl)aniline; [101-11-1]

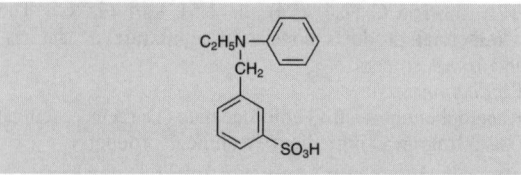

$C_{15}H_{17}N_1O_3S_1$. M: 291.37.
Production:
• *N*-ethylaniline + benzaldehyde-3-sulphonic acid (reductive amination)

Derivatives:
Acid Blue 9; Acid Blue 15; Acid Green 3; Acid Green 9; Acid Red 119; Acid Violet 17; Acid Violet 49

ethyl 3-phenylglycidate
[121-39-1]

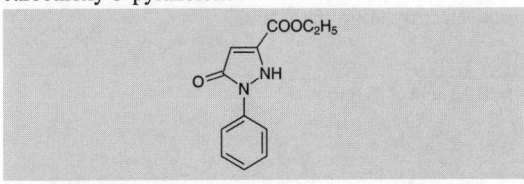

$C_{11}H_{12}O_3$. M: 192.22. Colourless liquid with a strawberry-like odour. BP: 104°C (0.04 kPa). d: 1.10 kg/l (20°C).
Production:
• benzaldehyde + ethyl chloroacetate (Darzens reaction)
Uses: fragrance ingredient

ethyl phenyl ketone *See:* propiophenone

ethyl 1-phenylpyrazolone-3-carboxylate
ethyl 1-phenyl-5-pyrazolone-3-carboxylate; 1-phenyl-3-carbethoxy-5-pyrazolone

$C_{12}H_{12}N_2O_3$. M: 232.24.
Production:
• diethyl oxalacetate + phenylhydrazine (condensation)
Derivatives:
Pigment Red 38; Pigment Red 42

ethyl piperidine-4-carboxylate
See: ethyl isonipecotinate

ethyl pivaloacetate
[17094-34-7]

$(CH_3)_3CCCH_2COC_2H_5$

$C_9H_{16}O_3$. M: 172.23. Liquid.
Production:
• cyanopinacolone (nitrile hydrolysis)
• methyl pivalate + ethyl acetate (Claisen condensation)
Uses: photographic coupling agent intermediate

ethyl propionate
[105-37-3]

$CH_3CH_2COC_2H_5$

$C_5H_{10}O_2$. M: 102.13. Colourless liquid with a rum-like odour. BP: 99°C. FP: -73°C. d: 0.89 kg/l (20°C).

Slightly soluble in water. Miscible with most organic solvents.
Production:
• ethanol + propionic acid (esterification)
Derivatives:
2-ethylcyclopentane-1,3-dione; 2-methylcyclopentane-1,3-dione
Uses: flavouring ingredient

2-ethylpyridine
[100-71-0]

$C_7H_9N_1$. M: 107.16. Liquid. BP: 149°C. d: 0.95 kg/l (0°C). Slightly soluble in water. Soluble in oxygenated solvents.
Production:
• 2-vinylpyridine (hydrogenation)
Derivatives: dimethindene

5-ethylpyridine-2,3-dicarboxylic acid
See: 5-ethylquinolinic acid

5-ethylquinolinic acid
5-ethylpyridine-2,3-dicarboxylic acid

$C_9H_9N_1O_4$. M: 195.18.
Production:
• 2-methyl-5-ethylpyridine + potassium cyanide (sulphonation/cyanidation/side-chain oxidation)
Derivatives: imazethapyr

N-ethylsalicylimide
See: *N*-salicylideneethylamine

ethyl silicate
ethoxysilane; tetraethoxysilane; tetraethyl orthosilicate; tetraethyl silicate; TEOS; [78-10-4]

$Si(OC_2H_5)_4$

$C_8H_{20}O_4Si_1$. M: 208.34. Colourless liquid. BP: 165–166°C. d: 0.93 kg/l (20°C). Insoluble in water.
Production:
• ethanol + silicon tetrachloride (dehydrochlorination)
Derivatives:
silicone rubber, cold-cured, 2-component, polycondensation-types
Uses: sandstone solidification reagent; ceramic paste binder; anticorrosion zinc primer paints; Sol-gel glass process raw material; polyethyl silicate fire-resistant paints; glass surface treatment agent; waterproofing/acidproofing agent (mortars, cements)

ethyl stearate
[111-61-5]

$$CH_3(CH_2)_{16}COC_2H_5$$

$C_{20}H_{40}O_2$. M: 312.54.
Production:
• ethanol + stearic acid (esterification)
Uses:
plastics processing lubricant

ethyl succinyl chloride

$$C_2H_5OCCH_2CH_2CCl$$

$C_6H_9Cl_1O_3$. M: 164.59.
Production:
• ethanol + succinic anhydride (esterification)
Derivatives:
5-benzyl-3-furylmethyl alcohol; fenbufen; mebeverine

ethyl sulphate *See:* diethyl sulphate

ethyl sulphide
diethyl sulphide; [352-93-2]

$$(C_2H_5)_2S$$

$C_4H_{10}S_1$. M: 90.18. Liquid. BP: 91–101°C. MP: -103°C. d: 0.84 kg/l (15°C). Slightly soluble in water. Soluble in oxygenated solvents.
Production:
• ethylene + hydrogen sulphide (addition)
Uses: gas odorant

2-ethylsulphonyl-5-trifluoromethylaniline
3-amino-4-ethylsulphonylbenzotrifluoride; Azoic Diazo Component 19 (CI); 37065 (CI)

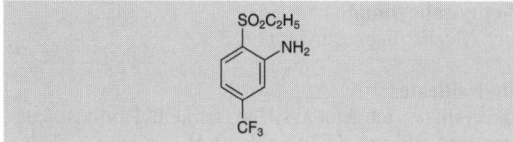

$C_9H_{10}F_3N_1O_2S_1$. M: 253.24.
Production:
• *m*-aminobenzotrifluoride + ethanesulphonyl chloride (chlorosulphonation)
Uses:
azoic dye diazo component

ethyl 1-(4-sulphophenyl)-5-pyrazolone-3-carboxylate
[20514-27-6]
$C_{12}H_{11}N_2Na_1O_6S_1$. M: 334.27.
Production:
• sulphanilic acid + diethyl oxalacetate (diazotisation/reduction/condensation/sodium salt formation)

Derivatives: tartrazine
Uses: photographic coupling agent intermediate

2-ethylthioethanol
2-ethylmercaptoethanol; β-ethylthioethanol; 2-hydroxyethyl ethyl sulphide; 3-thiapentanol; [110-77-0]

$$C_2H_5SCH_2CH_2OH$$

$C_4H_{10}O_1S_1$. M: 106.18. Pale yellow liquid with an unpleasant odour. BP: 181–184°C. d: 1.02 kg/l (15°C). Soluble in oxygenated solvents.
Production:
• ethyl mercaptan + ethylene oxide (epoxidation)
Derivatives: demeton-S-methyl; disulfoton; oxydemeton-methyl; thiometon; tinidazole
Uses: electroplating bath additive

ethyl tiglate
ethyl 2-methyl-2-butenate

$C_7H_{12}O_2$. M: 128.18. Colourless liquid with a floral odour. BP: 156°C. d: 0.92 kg/l (20°C). Insoluble in water.
Production:
• ethanol + tiglic acid (esterification)
Uses: fragrance/flavouring ingredient

N-ethyl-*p*-toluenesulphonamide
[80-39-7]

$C_9H_{13}N_1O_2S_1$. M: 199.27. Pale yellow, viscous liquid. d: 1.19 kg/l. Flash point: 175°C (COC).
Production:
• *p*-toluenesulphonic acid + ethylamine (sulphonamide formation)
Uses: plasticiser (polyamide hot melt adhesives)

ethyl *p*-toluenesulphonate
ethyl toluene-4-sulphonate; [80-40-0]
$C_9H_{12}O_3S_1$. M: 200.26. Crystalline solid. MP: 34°C. d: 1.17 kg/l. Insoluble in water. Soluble in oxygenated solvents.

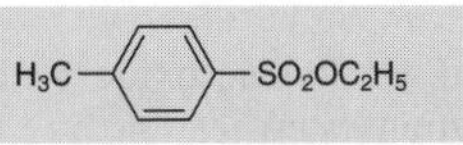

Production:
- *p*-toluenesulphonyl chloride + ethanol (dehydrochlorination)

Uses: ethylation reagent

N-ethyl-*m*-toluidine

3-ethylaminotoluene; *N*-ethyl-3-methylaniline; [102-27-2]

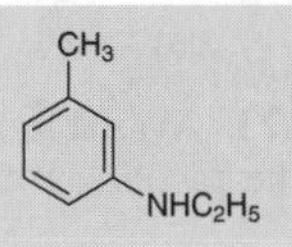

$C_9H_{13}N_1$. M: 135.21. Yellow liquid. BP: 215°C. Soluble in alcohol.
Production:
- *m*-toluidine + ethanol (amine formation; coproduced with *N,N*-diethyl-*m*-toluidine)

Derivatives:
2-amino-5-[*N*-ethyl-*N*-(2-methoxyethyl)amino]toluene; 2-amino-5-[*N*-ethyl-*N*-(2-methylsulphonaminoethyl)-amino]toluene; *N*-(2-cyanoethyl)-*N*-ethyl-*m*-toluidine; Disperse Blue 102; *N*-ethyl-*N*-(2-hydroxyethyl)-*m*-toluidine; *N*-ethyl-*N*-*m*-tolylbenzylamine-3-sulphonic acid

N-ethyl-N-*m*-tolylbenzylamine-3-sulphonic acid

N-ethyl-*N*-(3-sulphobenzyl)-*m*-toluidine

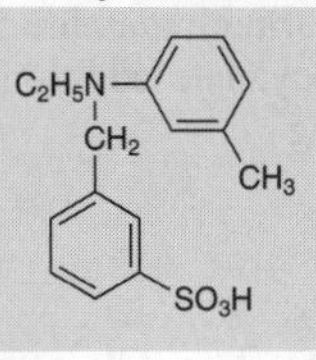

$C_{16}H_{19}N_1O_3S_1$. M: 305.40.
Production:
- *N*-ethyl-*m*-toluidine + benzaldehyde-3-sulphonic acid (reductive amination)

Derivatives:
Acid Blue 104; Acid Green 22

ethyl trifluoroacetate

[383-63-1]

$C_4H_5F_3O_2$. M: 142.07. Liquid. BP: 60–62°C.
Production:
- trifluoroacetic acid + ethanol (esterification)

Uses: amino group protection reagent

ethyl valerate

[539-82-2]
$C_7H_{14}O_2$. M: 130.19. Colourless liquid with a fruity odour. BP: 144–146°C. d: 0.88 kg/l (20°C). Insoluble in water. Miscible with oxygenated solvents.

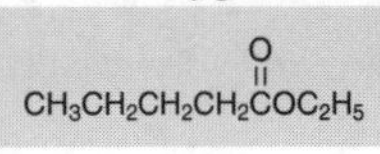

Production:
- ethanol + valeric acid (esterification)

Uses: flavouring ingredient

ethyl vanillate

ethyl 4-hydroxy-3-methoxybenzoate; ethyl 3-methoxy-4-hydroxybenzoate

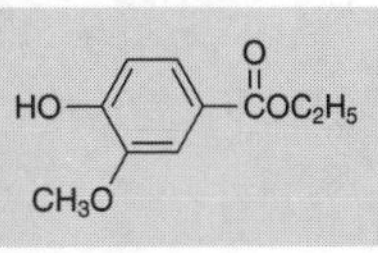

$C_{10}H_{12}O_4$. M: 196.21.
Production:
- ethanol + vanillic acid (esterification)

Uses: preservative (food, cosmetics)

ethyl vanillin

bourbonal; 3-ethoxy-4-hydroxybenzaldehyde; 4-hydroxy-3-ethoxybenzaldehyde; [121-32-4]

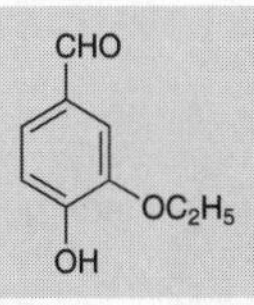

$C_9H_{10}O_3$. M: 166.18. White crystals with vanilla-like odour. MP: 77–78°C. Slightly soluble in water. Soluble in most organic solvents.
Production:
- catechol + diethyl sulphate + glyoxylic acid (ethylation/carbonyl addition/oxidation/decarboxylation)

Uses: fragrance/flavouring ingredient (chocolate)

ethyl vinyl ether

vinyl ethyl ether; EVE; [109-92-2]

$C_4H_8O_1$. M: 72.10. Colourless liquid. BP: 36°C. FP: -115°C. d: 0.75 kg/l (20°C). Slightly soluble in water. Soluble in oxygenated solvents.
Production:
- acetylene + ethanol (ethynylation)

Derivatives: β-carotene; 2-hexenal

ethyne *See:* acetylene

ethynyl cyclohexanol

1-ethynylcyclohexanol; [78-27-3]
$C_8H_{12}O_1$. M: 124.19. White, crystalline solid. MP: 22°C. BP: 73°C (1.6 kPa). Insoluble in water. Soluble in oxygenated and aromatic solvents.

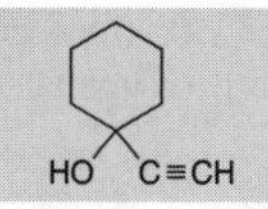

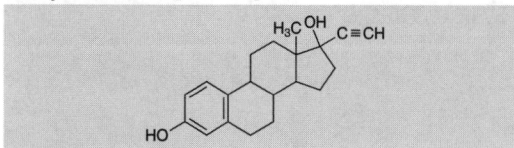

Production:
• cyclohexanone + acetylene (ethynylation)
Uses:
acid corrosion inhibitor (steel pickling, electroplating)

ethynylestradiol
ethinyl estradiol; [57-63-6]

$C_{20}H_{24}O_2$. M: 296.41.
Production:
• estrone + acetylene (ethynylation)
Uses: contraceptive drug

etidronic acid
See: hydroxyethylidene(diphosphonic acid)

etilefrine
[709-55-7]

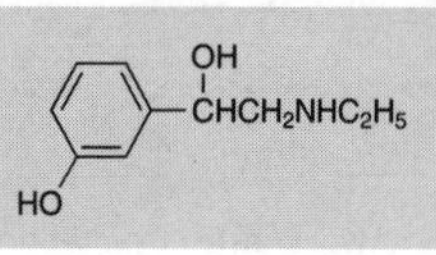

$C_{10}H_{15}N_1O_2$. M: 181.24. Available commercially as the racemic hydrochloride.
Production:
• *m*-hydroxyacetophenone + ethylamine (alpha bromination/amine formation/carbonyl reduction)
Uses:
antihypotensive drug

ETMQ
See: 6-ethoxy-2,2,4-trimethyl-1,2-dihydroquinoline

etocrilene
See: ethyl 2-cyano-3-phenylcinnamate

etofibrate
[31637-97-5]

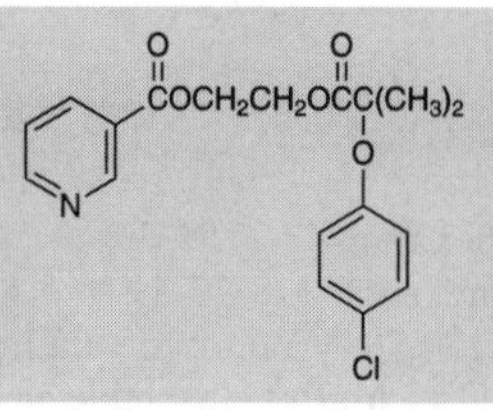

$C_{18}H_{18}Cl_1N_1O_5$. M: 363.79.

Production:
• nicotinic acid + ethylene oxide + clofibrate (epoxidation/transesterification)
Uses: antiarteriosclerotic drug

etofylline
[519-37-9]

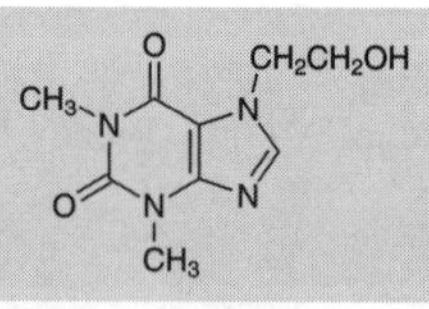

$C_9H_{12}N_4O_3$. M: 224.23. Available commercially as the free alcohol or as the nicotinate ester.
Production:
• theophylline + ethylene oxide (epoxidation)
Uses: bronchodilator/vasodilator drug

etomidate
[33125-97-2]

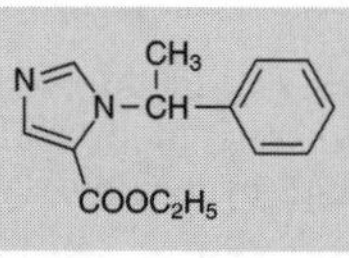

$C_{14}H_{16}N_2O_2$. M: 244.29.
Production:
• D-α-phenylethylamine + ethyl chloroacetate + formic acid + ethyl formate + potassium thiocyanate (amine formation/amide formation/Claisen condensation/thiocyanate addition/dethiolation)
Uses: hypnotic drug

etozolin
[73-09-6]

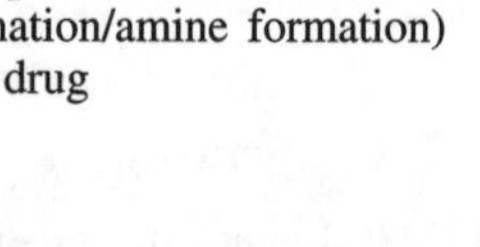

$C_{13}H_{20}N_2O_3S_1$. M: 284.37.
Production:
• ethyl cyanoacetate + thioglycollic acid + dimethyl sulphate + piperidine (condensation/methylation/alpha bromination/amine formation)
Uses: diuretic drug

etretinate
[54350-48-0]

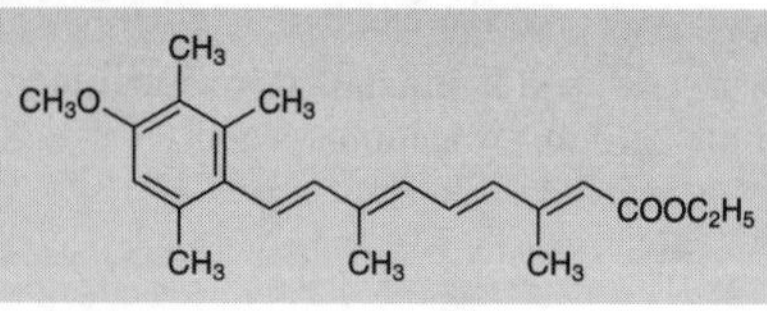

$C_{23}H_{30}O_3$. M: 354.49.

Production:
- 2,3,5-trimethylphenol + dimethylformamide + acetone + methyl chloroacetate + propionaldehyde + glyoxylic acid + ethanol (methylation/Vilsmeier reaction/carbonyl condensation/ethynylation/ esterification/aldol condensation/Wittig reaction)

Uses: antipsoriatic drug

etridiazole
5-ethoxy-3-trichloromethyl-1,2,4-thiadiazole; [2593-15-9]

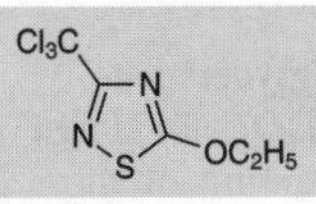

$C_5H_5Cl_3N_2O_1S_1$. M: 247.52.
Production:
- trichloroacetic acid + ammonium chloride + trichloromethanesulphenyl chloride + ethanol (amide formation/amidine formation/condensation/ ether formation)

Uses: fungicide

etrimfos
O-6-ethoxy-2-ethylprimidin-4-yl O,O-dimethyl phosphorothioate; [38260-54-7]

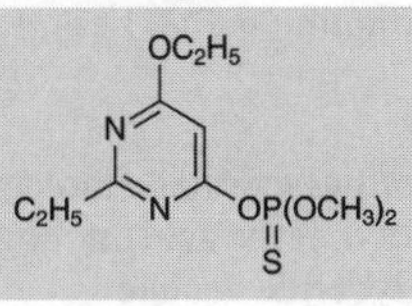

$C_{10}H_{17}N_2O_4P_1S_1$. M: 292.29.
Production:
- propionitrile + ammonia + diethyl malonate + O,O-dimethyl phosphorochlorothioate (amidine formation/condensation/dehydrochlorination)

Uses:
insecticide/acaricide

ETU *See:* ethylenethiourea

eucalyptol
cineol; cineole; 1,8-epoxy-p-menthane; [470-82-6]

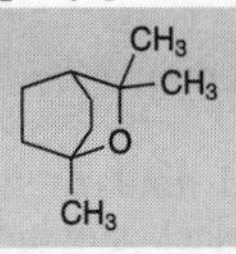

$C_{10}H_{18}O_1$. M: 154.25. Yellowish liquid with camphor-like odour. MP: 1°C. BP: 176°C. d: 0.93 kg/l (20°C). Insoluble in water. Soluble in alcohol and ether.
Production:
- *Eucalyptus globulus* oil (fractionation)

Uses:
flavouring ingredient (mouth-care products); fragrance ingredient

eugenol
4-allyl-2-methoxyphenol; 2-methoxy-4-allylphenol; [97-53-0]

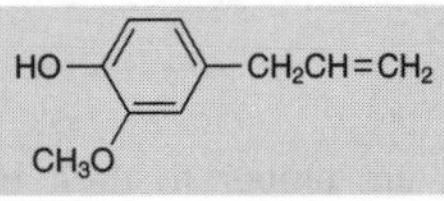

$C_{10}H_{12}O_2$. M: 164.21. Colourless or yellowish liquid with clove-like odour. MP: 9°C. BP: 255°C. d: 1.07 kg/l (20°C). Insoluble in water. Soluble in most organic solvents.
Production:
- clove leaf oil/cinnamon leaf oil (alkali extraction)

Derivatives: benzyl isoeugenol; eugenyl acetate; iso-eugenol; methyl eugenol
Uses:
dental analgesic; disinfectant; fragrance ingredient

eugenol methyl ether *See:* methyl eugenol

eugenyl acetate
3-(4-acetoxy-3-methoxyphenyl)propene; 4-allyl-2-methoxyphenyl acetate; [93-28-7]

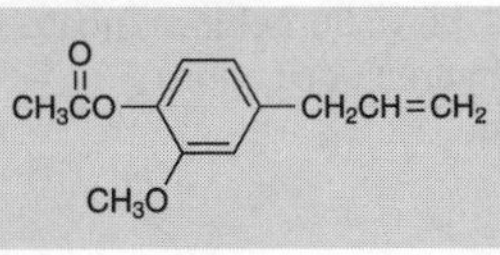

$C_{12}H_{14}O_3$. M: 206.24. White crystals with slight clove-like odour. MP: 27°C. BP: 120–121°C (0.4 kPa). d: 1.08 kg/l (25°C). Slightly soluble in water. Soluble in alcohol.
Production:
- eugenol + acetic anhydride (esterification)

Uses: fragrance ingredient

EVA *See:* ethylene-vinyl acetate copolymers

EVA/VC *See:* (ethylene-vinyl acetate)-vinyl chloride graft copolymers

EVE *See:* ethyl vinyl ether

EVM *See:* ethylene-vinyl acetate copolymers

EVOH *See:* ethylene-vinyl alcohol copolymers

F

factice
oil, vulcanised
Sulphur factices are amber to dark brown solids. d: 1.01–1.04 kg/l. Sulphur monochloride factices are white solids. d: 1.02–1.07 kg/l.
Production:
• rapeseed oil/castor oil/fish oil + sulphur/sulphur monochloride (sulphurisation)
Uses: processing aid (rubber)

famphur
O-4-dimethylsulphamoylphenyl *O,O*-dimethyl phosphorothioate; famophos; [52-85-7]

$$(CH_3)_2NSO_2 \longrightarrow \overset{S}{\underset{||}{OP(OCH_3)_2}}$$

$C_{10}H_{16}N_1O_5P_1S_2$. M: 325.35.
Production:
• *p*-phenolsulphonic acid + dimethylamine + *O,O*-dimethyl phosphorochlorothioate (sulphonamide formation/dehydrochlorination)
Uses: insecticide

farnesol
3,7,11-trimethyl-2,6,10-dodecatrien-1-ol; [4602-84-0]

$$(CH_3)_2C=CHCH_2CH_2\overset{CH_3}{\underset{|}{C}}=CHCH_2CH_2\overset{CH_3}{\underset{|}{C}}=CHCH_2OH$$

$C_{15}H_{26}O_1$. M: 222.37. Colourless liquid with a floral odour.
Production:
• nerolidol (isomerisation)
Uses: fragrance ingredient

fatty acid glycerides, acetylated
Pale yellow liquid or waxy solid. MP: 10–45°C depending on grade.
Production:
• fatty acid mono/diglycerides + acetic acid (acetylation)
Uses:
fat plasticising agent

fatty acid glycerides, citrated
A(1) 6.23 (FAO/WHO); citroglycerides; E472(c) (EC)
Mixed product containing different citrate esters of fatty acid glycerides. Ivory powder or flakes. Available as self-emulsifying or nonself-emulsifying grades.
Production:
• fatty acid mono/diglycerides + citric acid (esterification)
Uses:
food emulsifier

fatty acid imidazoline polyamines
Production:
• isostearic acid/tallow acid/tall oil fatty acid/tall oil, distilled/fatty acid pitch + triethylenetetramine/ tetraethylenepentamine/polyethylenepolyamine/ aminoethylpiperazine (amide formation)
Uses: corrosion inhibitor (oilfield chemicals)

fatty acid mono/diglycerides
A(1) 6.20 (FAO/WHO); E471 (EC)
Mixed product consisting of the 1,2- and 1,3-glyceryl esters of fatty acids.
Production:
• lard/soyabean oil/sunflower oil + glycerol (transesterification)
Derivatives:
fatty acid glycerides, acetylated; fatty acid glycerides, citrated; fatty acid monoglyceride
Uses: food emulsifier; softening agent (textile finishes)

fatty acid monoglyceride
A(1) 6.20 (FAO/WHO); E471 (EC)
Mixed product containing the 1- and 2-glyceryl esters of fatty acids.
Production:
• fatty acid mono/diglycerides (molecular distillation)
Derivatives: diacetyl fatty acid monoglyceride tartrate; fatty acid monoglyceride lactate
Uses: food emulsifier

fatty acid monoglyceride lactate
lactoglycerides; A(1) 6.25 (FAO/WHO); E472(b) (EC)
Mixed product containing different lactate esters of fatty acid glycerides. Ivory powder or flakes.
Production:
• fatty acid monoglyceride + DL-lactic acid (esterification)
Uses: food emulsifier

fatty acid pitch
stearine pitch
Pitch produced by decomposition of fatty acids during distillation.
Derivatives: fatty acid imidazoline polyamines
Uses: raw material (black stoving enamels)

C_8-C_{10} fatty acids
capric/caprylic acids; caprylic/capric acids

$$CH_3(CH_2)_nCOOH$$

n = 6–8. Liquid. Cloud point: 5°C. A typical chain-length distribution is: 1% C_6, 53% C_8, 40% C_{10}, 6% C_{12}.

Production:
- coconut acid/palm kernel fatty acids (fractionation; coproduced with lauric acid, broad cut/oleic acid)

Derivatives:
n-alkanol(C_8-C_{10}); barium-zinc heat stabilisers; cadmium-barium heat stabilisers; cadmium-zinc heat stabilisers; capric acid; caprylic acid; glycerol dicaprylate/caprate; propylene glycol dicaprylate/caprate; trialkyl(C_8-C_{10})amine; trimethylolpropane tri-(caprylate/caprate)

C_8-C_{10} fatty acids, methyl ester

$$CH_3(CH_2)_n\overset{\overset{O}{\|}}{C}OCH_3$$

n = 6–8. Overhead from first distillation of coconut or palm kernel acid methyl ester. A typical chain-length distribution is: 2% C_6, 58% C_8, 40% C_{10}.

Production:
- methyl cocoate (fractionation; coproduced with methyl cocoate, topped)
- palm kernel methyl ester (fractionation; coproduced with palm kernel methyl ester, topped)

Derivatives:
methyl caprate; methyl caproate; methyl caprylate

C_{14}-C_{18} fatty acids, methyl ester

$$CH_3(CH_2)_n\overset{\overset{O}{\|}}{C}OCH_3$$

n = 12–16. Residual fraction of coconut and palm kernel oil methyl ester distillation. The chain-length distribution is, typically: 5% C_{14}, 25% C_{16}, 70% C_{18}.

Production:
- methyl cocoate, topped/palm kernel methyl ester, topped (fractionation; coproduced with methyl laurate)

Derivatives: cetyloleyl alcohol; cetylstearyl alcohol

fatty acids, polyunsaturated, conjugated

Yellow liquid. Titre: 16°C. Chain-length distribution is, typically: 35–50% conjugated $C_{18:2}$, 10–25% unconjugated $C_{18:2}$, 24% $C_{18:1}$ and 16% saturated $\leq C_{18}$.

Production:
- sunflower acid/soyabean acid (rearrangement)

Derivatives:
alkyd resins, long-oil; alkyd resins, medium-oil; alkyd resins, short-oil; epoxy ester resins

fatty oils, sulphurised

Fatty oils containing S_2 or S_5 linkages. Disulphides do not react with copper below 100°C and are therefore referred to as 'inactive'. Pentasulphides react with copper at low temperature and are used where higher product performance is needed.

Production:
- rapeseed oil/lard oil/cottonseed oil/soyabean oil/ fish oil/palm oil/methyl oleate + sulphur (sulphurisation)

Uses: extreme-pressure additive (lubricants)

FCIMC acid *See:* 3-(2-chloro-6-fluorophenyl)-5-methylisoxazole-4-carboxylic acid

feldspar

Generic name for a group of aluminosilicate minerals containing potassium, sodium or calcium as the cations. The product usually consists of a concentrate containing 5–20% of other minerals, usually quartz. Mined worldwide.

Uses: abrasive; roofing compounds; ceramic glazes/ enamels (household products, sanitaryware); glass raw material; pottery

fenamiphos

ethyl 3-methyl-4-(methylthio)phenyl isopropylphosphoramidate; [22224-92-6]

$$CH_3S-\bigcirc\hspace{-1.2em}\bigcirc-\overset{\overset{O}{\|}}{O}\!POC_2H_5$$
$$\underset{CH_3}{}\quad NHCH(CH_3)_2$$

$C_{13}H_{22}N_1O_3P_1S_1$. M: 303.36.

Production:
- 3-methyl-4-(methylmercapto)phenol + phosphorus oxychloride + ethanol + isopropylamine (dehydrochlorination/dehydrochlorination/dehydrochlorination)

Uses: nematicide

fenarimol

2,4′-dichloro-α-(pyrimidin-5-yl)benzhydryl alcohol; [60168-88-9]

$C_{17}H_{12}Cl_2N_2O_1$. M: 331.21.

Production:
- 2,4′-dichlorobenzophenone + 5-bromopyrimidine (Grignard reagent formation/Grignard reaction)

Uses: fungicide

fenbufen

[36330-85-5]

$$\bigcirc\!\!-\!\!\bigcirc-\overset{\overset{O}{\|}}{C}CH_2CH_2COOH$$

$C_{16}H_{14}O_3$. M: 254.29.

Production:
- biphenyl + ethyl succinyl chloride (Friedel-Crafts acylation)

Uses: antiinflammatory drug

fenbutatin oxide

bis[tris(2-methyl-2-phenylpropyl)tin] oxide;
[13356-08-6]

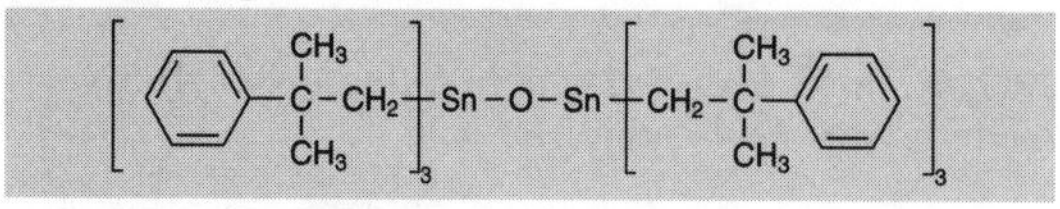

$C_{60}H_{78}O_1Sn_2$. M: 1052.66.
Production:
• benzene + methallyl chloride + stannic chloride
(Friedel-Crafts alkylation/dechlorination/base-
catalysed hydrolysis)
Uses:
acaricide

fenchone

1,3,3-trimethylbicyclo[2,2,1]heptan-2-one; [1195-79-5]

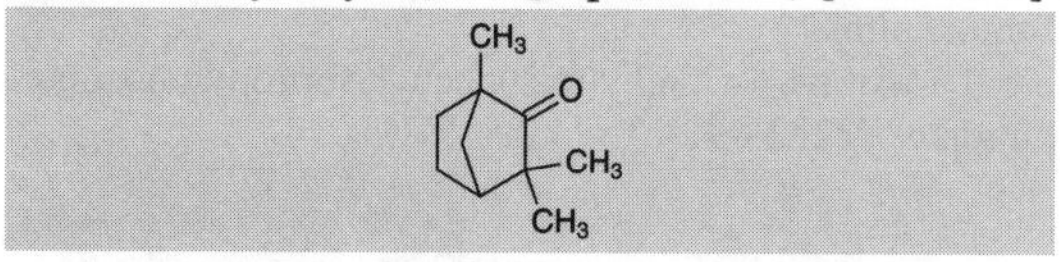

$C_{10}H_{16}O_1$. M: 152.24.
Production:
• α-pinene (hydration/dehydrogenation)
Uses:
perfume ingredient (technical products)

fendiline

[13042-18-7]

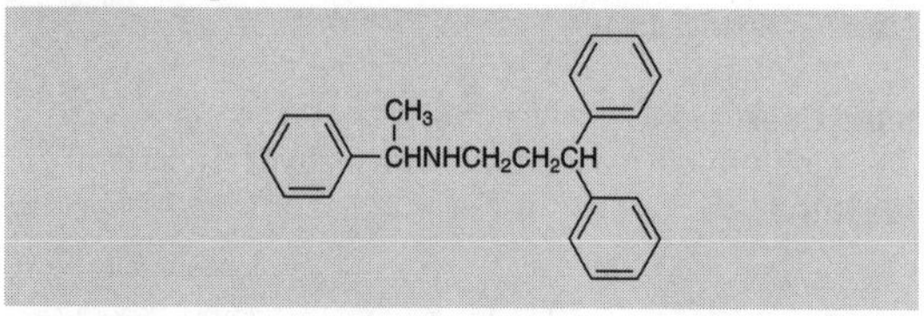

$C_{23}H_{25}N_1$. M: 315.46. Available commercially as the
hydrochloride.
Production:
• benzaldehyde + ethyl cyanoacetate + phenylmagnesium bromide + acetophenone (Cope
reaction/Grignard reaction/decarboxylation/nitrile
reduction/reductive amination)
Uses:
vasodilator drug

fenetylline

fenethylline; [3736-08-1]; [1892-80-4] (hydrochloride)

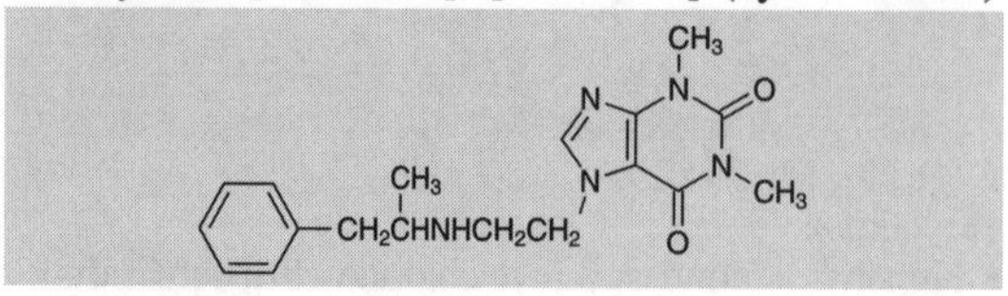

$C_{18}H_{23}N_5O_2$. M: 341.42. Available commercially as the
hydrochloride.

Production:
• monoethanolamine + phenylacetone + theophylline
(amine formation/amine formation)
Uses: nerve stimulant drug

fenfluramine

[458-24-2]; [404-82-0] (hydrochloride)

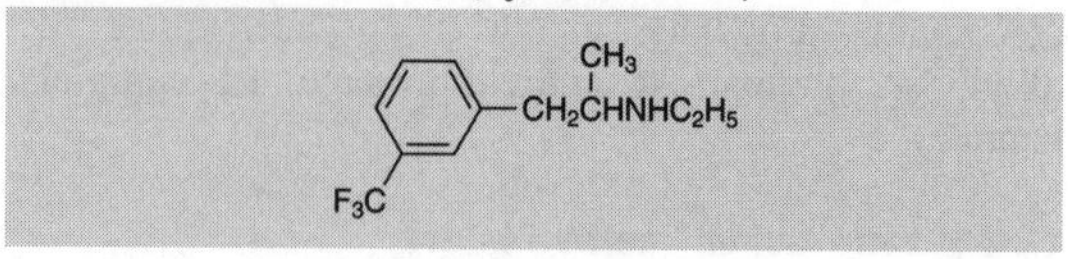

$C_{12}H_{16}F_3N_1$. M: 231.26. Available commercially as the
racemic hydrochloride and as the (+)-enantiomer free
base.
Production:
• benzotrifluoride + acetyl chloride + methyl acetate
+ ethylamine (Friedel-Crafts acylation/Willgerodt
reaction/condensation/reductive amination)
Uses: anorexic drug

fenfuram

2-methylfuran-3-carboxanilide; [24691-80-3]

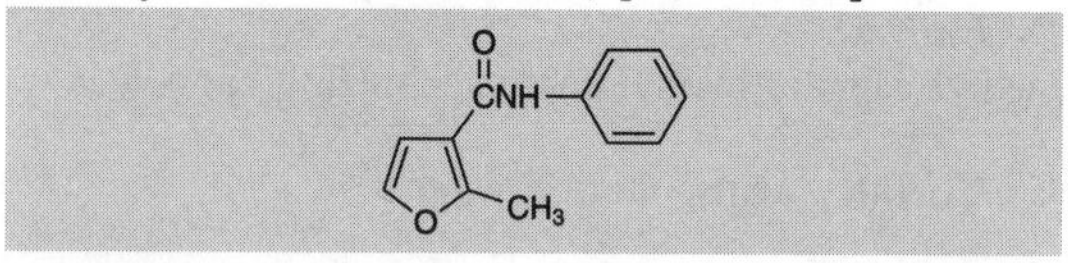

$C_{12}H_{11}N_1O_2$. M: 201.23.
Production:
• methyl acetoacetate + chloroacetaldehyde + aniline
(carbonyl condensation/dehydrochlorination/amide
formation)
Uses: fungicide

fenitrothion

O,O-dimethyl *O*-(3-methyl-4-nitrophenyl)phosphoro-
thioate; [122-14-5]

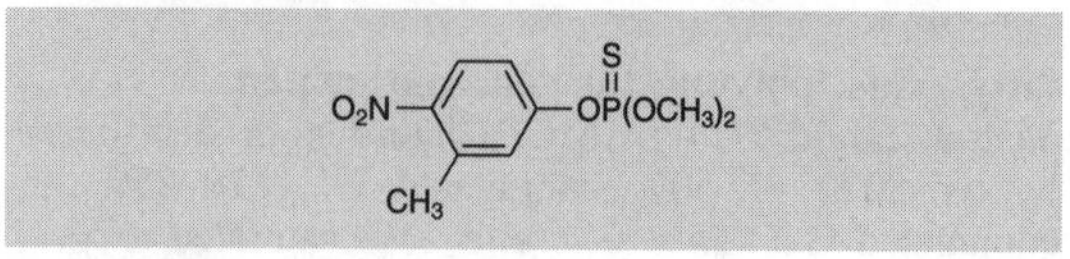

$C_9H_{12}N_1O_5P_1S_1$. M: 277.23.
Production:
• 4-nitro-*m*-cresol + *O,O*-dimethyl phosphorochlorothioate (dehydrochlorination)
Uses: insecticide

fennel oil

Pale yellow liquid with a fennel odour. Produced by
steam distillation of fennel seeds (*Foeniculum vulgare*).
Sweet grades of oil are produced from the *dulce*, bitter
grades from the *vulgare* varieties. d: 0.96 kg/l (25°C).
Slightly soluble in water. Soluble in alcohol. The main
constituents are anethole (55–80%) and fenchone.
Uses: food/pharmaceutical flavouring ingredient

fenobucarb
2-s-butylphenyl methylcarbamate; BPMC; [3766-81-2]

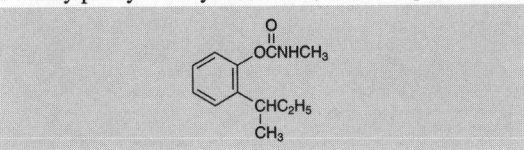

$C_{12}H_{17}N_1O_2$. M: 207.28.
Production:
• o-s-butylphenol + methyl isocyanate (isocyanate addition)
Uses: insecticide

fenoprofen
[31879-05-7]

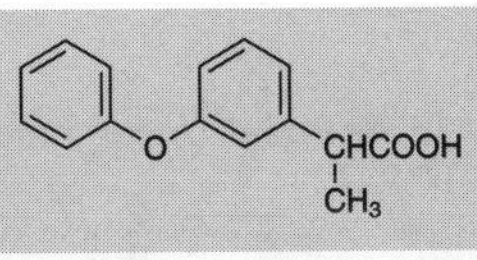

$C_{15}H_{14}O_3$. M: 242.27. Available commercially as the calcium dihydrate salt.
Production:
• bromobenzene + m-hydroxyacetophenone + sodium cyanide (ether formation/carbonyl reduction/alcohol bromination/cyanidation/nitrile hydrolysis)
Uses:
antiinflammatory drug

fenoterol
[13392-18-2]

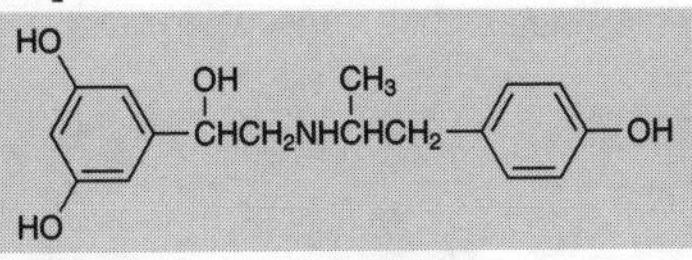

$C_{17}H_{21}N_1O_4$. M: 303.37. Available commercially as the hydrobromide.
Production:
• p-methoxyphenylacetone + benzylamine + 3,5-diacetoxyacetophenone (reductive amination/alpha bromination/amine formation/hydrolysis/carbonyl reduction)
Uses: bronchodilator drug

fenothiocarb
S-4-phenoxybutyl dimethylthiocarbamate; [62850-32-2]

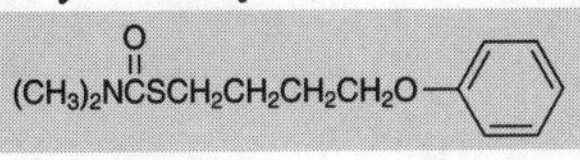

$C_{13}H_{19}N_1O_2S_1$. M: 253.36.
Production:
• phenol + tetrahydrofuran + carbonyl sulphide + dimethylamine (ether formation/alcohol chlorination/thiocarbonylation/dehydrochlorination)
Uses: acaricide

fenoxam *See:* clomazone

fenoxaprop-ethyl
ethyl 2-[4-(6-chlorobenzoxazol-2-yloxy)phenoxy]propionate; [66441-23-4]

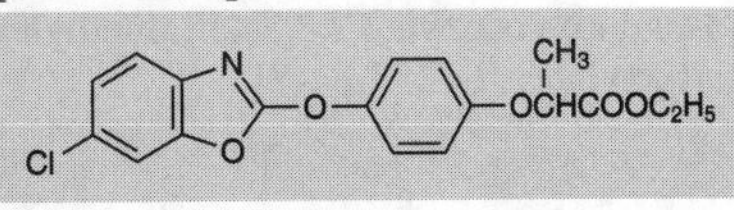

$C_{18}H_{16}Cl_1N_1O_5$. M: 361.78.
Production:
• benzoxazolone + 2-(4-chlorophenoxy)propionic acid + ethanol (ring chlorination/ether formation/esterification)
Uses:
herbicide

fenoxazoline
[4846-91-7]

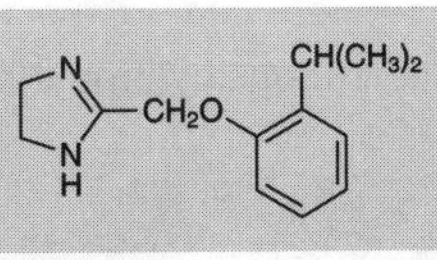

$C_{13}H_{18}N_2O_1$. M: 218.29.
Production:
• chloroacetonitrile + ethylenediamine + o-isopropylphenol (condensation/ether formation)
Uses:
vasoconstrictor drug

fenoxycarb
ethyl 2-(4-phenoxyphenoxy)ethylcarbamate;
[79127-80-3]

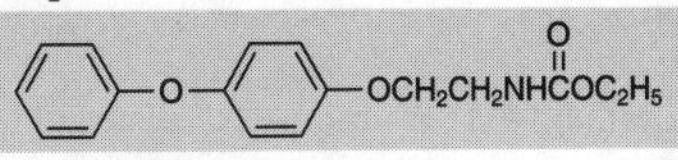

$C_{17}H_{19}N_1O_4$. M: 301.35.
Production:
• phenol + p-chlorophenol + monoethanolamine + ethyl chloroformate (ether formation/dehydrochlorination/ether formation)
Uses: insecticide

fenpiverinium bromide
[125-60-0]

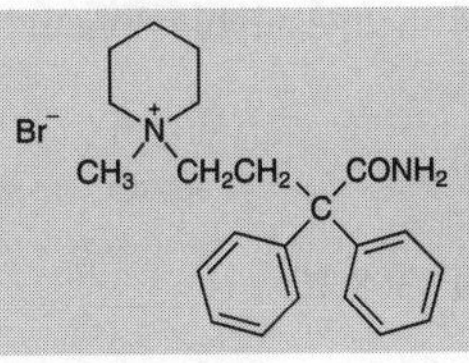

$C_{22}H_{29}Br_1N_2O_1$. M: 417.38.
Production:
• piperidine + ethylene oxide + diphenylacetonitrile + methyl bromide (epoxidation/alcohol chlorin-

ation/dehydrochlorination/nitrile hydrolysis/
methylation)
Uses: antispasmodic drug

fenpropathrin

α-cyano-3-phenoxybenzyl 2,2,3,3-tetramethylcyclo-
propanecarboxylate; [64257-84-7]

$C_{22}H_{23}N_1O_3$. M: 349.43.
Production:
• 2,3-dimethyl-2-butene + ethyl diazoacetate +
3-phenoxybenzaldehyde cyanohydrin (addition/
esterification)
Uses: acaricide/insecticide

fenpropidin

1-[3-(4-*t*-butylphenyl)-2-methylpropyl]piperidine;
[67306-00-7]

$C_{19}H_{31}N_1$. M: 273.47.
Production:
• 4-*t*-butyl-α-methylhydrocinnamaldehyde +
piperidine (reductive amination)
Uses: fungicide

fenpropimorph

4-[3-(4-*t*-butylphenyl)-2-methylpropyl]-2,6-dimethyl-
morpholine; [67306-03-0]

$C_{20}H_{33}N_1O_1$. M: 303.49.
Production:
• 4-*t*-butyl-α-methylhydrocinnamaldehyde + 2,6-di-
methylmorpholine (reductive amination)
Uses: fungicide

fensulfothion

O,O-diethyl *O*-4-methylsulphinylphenyl phosphorothioate; [115-90-2]

$C_{11}H_{17}O_4P_1S_2$. M: 308.36.
Production:
• *p*-methylmercaptophenol + *O,O*-diethyl phosphorochlorothioate + hydrogen peroxide (dehydro-
chlorination/oxidation)
Uses: insecticide/nematicide

fentanyl

N-(1-phenylethyl-4-piperidyl)propionanilide; [437-38-7]

$C_{22}H_{28}N_2O_1$. M: 336.47. Available commercially as the
free base or citrate.
Production:
• 1-benzyl-4-piperidone + aniline + propionyl
chloride + phenethyl alcohol (reductive
amination/amide formation/amine dealkylation/
amine formation)
Uses: analgesic drug

fenthion

O,O-dimethyl *O*-[3-methyl-4-(methylthio)phenyl] phosphorothioate; [55-38-9]

$C_{10}H_{15}O_3P_1S_2$. M: 278.33.
Production:
• 3-methyl-4-(methylmercapto)phenol + *O,O*-dimethyl
phosphorochlorothioate (dehydrochlorination)
Uses: insecticide

fentin acetate

triphenyltin acetate; TPT; [900-95-8]

$C_{20}H_{18}O_2Sn_1$. M: 409.05.
Production:
• fentin hydroxide + sodium acetate (esterification)
Uses:
fungicide/algicide

fentin fluoride

fluorotriphenylstannane; triphenyltin fluoride; [379-52-2]

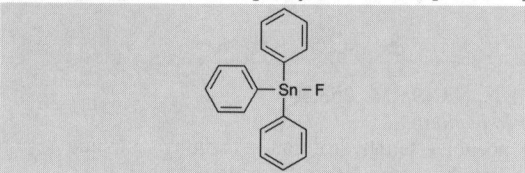

$C_{18}H_{15}F_1Sn_1$. M: 369.01. Powder. MP: 357°C. Slightly
soluble in water. Soluble in organic solvents.

Production:
- tetraphenyltin + stannic chloride + sodium fluoride (disproportionation/halogen exchange)

Uses: biocide (marine antifouling paints)

fentin hydroxide
triphenyltin hydroxide; TPT; [76-87-9]

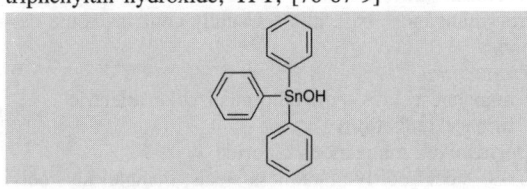

$C_{18}H_{16}O_1Sn_1$. M: 367.02.

Production:
- tetraphenyltin + stannic chloride (disproportionation/hydrolysis)

Derivatives: fentin acetate

Uses: fungicide

fenuron
1,1-dimethyl-3-phenylurea; [101-42-8]

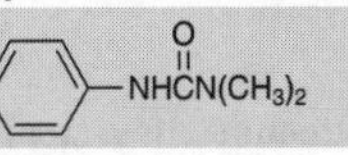

$C_9H_{12}N_2O_1$. M: 164.21. Available commercially as the free base or as the trichloroacetate salt.

Production:
- dimethylamine + phenyl isocyanate (isocyanate addition)

Uses: herbicide

fenvalerate
2-α-cyano-3-phenoxybenzyl 2-(4-chlorophenyl)-3-methylbutyrate; [51630-58-1]

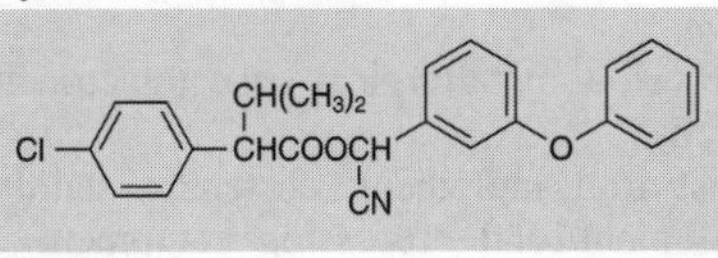

$C_{25}H_{22}Cl_1N_1O_3$. M: 419.91.

Production:
- (RS)-α-(4-chlorophenyl)isovaleric acid + 3-phenoxybenzaldehyde cyanohydrin (esterification)

Uses:
insecticide

fenyramidol
phenyramidol; [553-69-5]

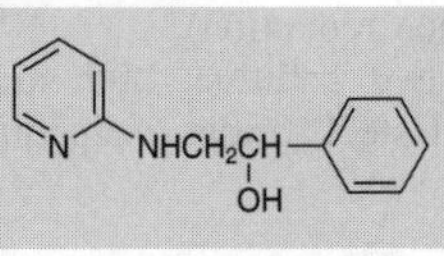

$C_{13}H_{14}N_2O_1$. M: 214.26. Available commercially as the free base or as the hydrochloride salt.

Production:
- 2-aminopyridine + styrene oxide (epoxidation)

Uses:
muscle relaxant drug

FEP
See: tetrafluoroethylene-hexafluoropropylene copolymers

ferbam
ferric dimethyldithiocarbamate; [14484-64-1]

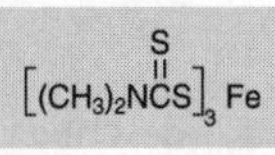

$C_9H_{18}Fe_1N_3S_6$. M: 416.49

Production:
- sodium dimethyldithiocarbamate + ferric chloride (salt formation)

Uses: fungicide

ferric acetylacetonate

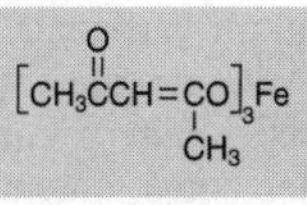

$C_{15}H_{21}Fe_1O_6$. M: 353.17. Ruby-red, crystalline solid. MP: 181°C with decomposition. d: 1.33 kg/l. Slightly soluble in water.

Production:
- ferric chloride + acetylacetone (complex formation)

Uses:
polyurethane catalyst (elastomers)

ferric ammonium citrate
See: ammonium ferric citrate

ferric chloride
[7705-08-0]

$FeCl_3$

Cl_3Fe_1. M: 162.21. Yellowish-brown aqueous solution containing, typically, 60% w/v $FeCl_3$.

Production:
- iron + hydrochloric acid + chlorine (salt formation)

Derivatives:
ammonium ferric citrate; ethylenediaminetetraacetic acid, ammonium ferric salt; ethylenediaminetetraacetic acid, sodium ferric salt; ferbam; ferric acetylacetonate; hydroxyethylethylenediaminetriacetic acid, sodium ferric salt; Prussian Blue

Uses:
dyeing auxiliary; etchant (printed circuit boards, photoengraving); flocculant (effluent, sewage treatment); analytical reagent; leaching agent (chalcopyrite ores)

ferric dimethyldithiocarbamate *See:* ferbam

ferric ferrocyanide *See:* Prussian Blue

ferric sulphate
iron sulphate; [10028-22-5]

$$Fe_2(SO_4)_3$$

$Fe_2O_{12}S_3$. M: 399.87. Yellowish-white, hydroscopic powder. d: 3.1 kg/l. Slightly soluble in cold water.
Production:
• ferrous sulphate + chlorine (oxidation)
Uses: flocculant (water treatment); aluminium etchant ingredient; copper/stainless steel pickling agent

ferrite
General term used to describe magnetic ceramics. Cubic ferrites have a spinel crystal structure and are used where temporary magnetic properties are required. Hexagonal ferrites are used for permanent magnets. See also zinc ferrite.
Production:
• iron oxide red + zinc oxide + manganese dioxide
  + nickel oxide, black + cobalt hydroxide + barium
  hydroxide + strontium carbonate (calcination)
Uses: hexagonal ferrite magnets (motors, alternators, loudspeakers, magnetic items); cubic ferrite magneto-ceramics (transformer cores, antennae)

ferrite yellow *See:* iron oxide yellow

ferroboron
[11108-67-1]
Iron-boron alloy containing 15–18% boron.
Production:
• boron oxide/boric acid + iron ore + aluminium
  (aluminothermal reduction)
• boron oxide/boric acid + metallurgical coke/metal-
  lurgical coke + iron (electric furnace reduction)
Uses: alloy steel hardening additive

ferrocene
dicyclopentadienyl iron; [102-54-5]

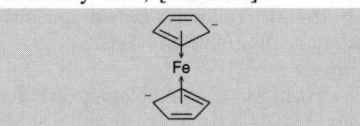

$C_{10}H_{10}Fe_1$. M: 186.04. Yellow needles. MP: 172–174°C. BP: 249°C. Stable to 460°C. Insoluble in water.
Production:
• dicyclopentadiene + iron (complex formation)
Uses: catalyst (rocket propellants, petroleum fuels)

ferrochrome
ferrochromium
Metal lumps. Ferrochrome is an iron-chromium alloy containing 70% chromium.
Production:
• chromite + metallurgical coke (electric furnace
  reduction)

Derivatives: chrome lignosulphonate; chromium; chromium sulphate
Uses: cast iron/stainless steel/high-chromium tool steels; low-alloy steels (turbine blades, generator parts); steel chromising reagent

ferromanganese
Iron-manganese base alloy. Usually contains some carbon.
Production:
• manganese ores + metallurgical coke (electric
  furnace reduction)
Derivatives: manganous chloride
Uses: steel additive (stainless steels, manganese steels)

ferromolybdenum
[11121-95-2]
Molybdenum-iron base alloy containing 62–70% molybdenum.
Production:
• iron ore + molybdenum trioxide + aluminium
  (aluminothermal reduction)
• molybdenum trioxide + ferrosilicon (silicothermal
  reduction)
Uses:
chromium-molybdenum alloy steels; dual phase steels; high-speed steels (machine tools); high-strength, low-alloy steels (structural steel, bridges, pipelines); nickel-chromium-molybdenum alloy steels (pipelines); stainless steels (curtain walling, window frames, chemical, food equipment); stainless steels (cutlery, household utensils, sinks, tubes, barrels)

ferronickel
Nickel-iron base alloy sometimes containing a proportion of cobalt.
Production:
• lateritic ore + metallurgical coke (electric furnace
  reduction)
Uses: cast iron ingredient; austenitic stainless steels (chemical plant/food processing equipment); stainless steel ingredient; maraging steels (diecasting tools, aircraft undercarriage); nickel-resist irons (corrosion-resistant seawater handling equipment); nickel steels; cryogenic steels

ferroniobium
Base alloy of iron and niobium.
Production:
• niobium-tantalum ores + metallurgical coke
  (electric furnace reduction)
Uses: carbon steel additive; high-strength, low-alloy steels (structural steel, bridges, pipelines)

ferrophosphorus
iron phosphide
Granules or briquettes containing, typically, 22–23%

phosphorus and 69–70% iron. Ferrophosphorus from phosphate ore originating on the US west coast contains recoverable (10%) quantities of vanadium.
Production:
• apatite + metallurgical coke + quartz (electric furnace reduction; byproduct of phosphorus production)
Derivatives: vanadium tetrachloride
Uses: steel additive

ferrosilicon

Ferrosilicon is an alloy of iron and silicon. The Fe:Si ratio ranges from 93:7 to 10:90.
Production:
• iron + quartz + metallurgical coke (electric furnace reduction)
Derivatives:
ferromolybdenum; ferrovanadium; magnesium
Uses: corrosion-resistant casting steels; deoxiding agent (steel production); aluminium alloy ingredient; steel alloys (springs, motor, transformer cores, machine tools)

ferrotungsten
[12604-57-8]
Tungsten-iron base alloy containing 70–85% tungsten.
Production:
• tungsten ore concentrates + metallurgical coke (electric furnace reduction)
Uses: high speed steels (cutting tools/hard surface machinery); stellite alloys (extrusion dies, turbine blades, valve seats); alloy steels

ferrous chloride
[7758-94-3]; [13478-10-9] (tetrahydrate)

$$FeCl_2$$

Cl_2Fe_1. M: 126.76. Available as the tetrahydrate. Green, deliquescent crystals. Loses water of crystallisation above 110°C. d: 1.93 kg/l. Soluble in water and alcohol. Oxidised readily in solution. The applications of ferrous chloride depend on its purity. Byproduct material is generally only suitable for conversion to iron oxide for steel production.
Production:
• iron + hydrochloric acid (salt formation)
• steel pickling effluent (separation)
• rutile/anatase/titanium slag + chlorine + sponge coke, calcined (chloride process; byproduct of titanium tetrachloride production)
Uses: ferrite ceramics raw material; reducing agent; reducing/flocculating agent (effluent treatment)

ferrous fluoborate
[15283-51-9]
$B_2F_8Fe_1$. M: 229.45. Available commercially as a 41% solution in water.

$$Fe(BF_4)_2$$

Production:
• ferrous sulphate + fluoboric acid (salt formation)
Uses:
electroplating bath ingredient

ferrous fumarate
[141-01-5]

$C_4H_2Fe_1O_4$. M: 169.91. Reddish-brown powder. d: 2.44 kg/l. Slightly insoluble in water.
Production:
• ferrous sulphate + fumaric acid (salt formation)
Uses: animal feed additive

ferrous gluconate
iron gluconate; [299-29-6]

$$[HOCH_2(CHOH)_4COO^-]_2 Fe^{2+}$$

$C_{12}H_{22}Fe_1O_{14}$. M: 446.15. Available as the dihydrate. Yellow powder. Soluble in water forming acidic solutions.
Production:
• gluconic acid + ferrous sulphate (salt formation)
Uses: food additive; animal feed supplement

ferrous oxalate
iron oxalate; [516-03-0]

$$\begin{matrix} COO^- \\ | \\ COO^- \end{matrix} \quad Fe^{2+}$$

$C_2Fe_1O_4$. M: 143.87. Pale yellow, crystalline powder. d: 2.28 kg/l. Decomposes on heating to 160°C releasing carbon monoxide. Slightly soluble in water.
Production:
• ferrous sulphate + sodium oxalate (salt formation)
Uses: photographic developer ingredient; tinted glass additive

ferrous sulphate
iron sulphate; [7720-78-7]

$$FeSO_4$$

$Fe_1O_4S_1$. M: 151.91. Available commercially as the monohydrate (30% Fe), heptahydrate (20% Fe) and 'moist' (18% Fe) grades, as well as in solution (5% Fe) form. The heptahydrate is a blue-green crystalline solid which loses its water of crystallisation when heated above 65°C, forming the monohydrate. d: 1.87 kg/l. The monohydrate is a yellowish crystalline solid which loses its water of crystallisation at 300°C. Soluble in water. Solutions are oxidised slowly by air to the ferric salt.

Production:
- ilmenite/titanium slag + oleum (sulphate process; byproduct of titanium dioxide, hydrate production)

Derivatives:
Acid Green 1; calcium ferrocyanide; ferric sulphate; ferrous fluoborate; ferrous fumarate; ferrous gluconate; ferrous oxalate; iron oxide, transparent; iron oxide black; iron oxide red; iron oxide yellow; Pigment Green 8; potassium ferrocyanide; Prussian Blue; sodium ferrocyanide; Solvent Black 5

Uses: redox polymerisation initiator component

ferrovanadium
[12604-58-9]
Production:
- iron-vanadium ore/vanadium pentoxide/vanadium-bearing slag + ferrosilicon (silicothermal reduction)
- vanadium pentoxide/iron-vanadium ore/vanadium-bearing slag + aluminium (aluminothermal reduction)
- vanadium pentoxide + iron + aluminium (electric furnace reduction)

Derivatives: vanadium tetrachloride

Uses: high-strength, low alloy steel additive (bridges, buildings, pipelines); high-speed steels (engine, vehicle, machinery parts)

Fischer's aldehyde
1,3,3-trimethylindoline-Δ^2,α-aldehyde; Tribase aldehyde F (BASF); [84-83-3]

$C_{13}H_{15}N_1O_1$. M: 201.27. Solid. MP: 103–110°C.
Production:
- Fischer's base + N-methylformamide (Vilsmeier reaction)

Derivatives:
Basic Orange 21; Basic Red 12; Basic Yellow 11
Uses: dyestuffs intermediate

Fischer's base
1,3,3-trimethyl-2-methyleneindoline; [118-12-7]

$C_{12}H_{15}N_1$. M: 173.26. Liquid. BP: 106–110°C (0.5 kPa). MP: -9°C.
Production:
- N-methylaniline + methylbutynol (condensation)

Derivatives:
Basic Red 14; Basic Violet 16; Basic Yellow 28; Fischer's aldehyde
Uses: dyestuffs intermediate

fish acid
The chain-length distribution varies markedly with the type of fish but always contains a high proportion (45%) of highly unsaturated C_{20}–C_{22} fatty acids. The remainder is mainly $C_{18:1}$, $C_{16:1}$ and $C_{16:0}$ fatty acids.
Production:
- fish oil (hydrolysis)

Derivatives:
fish acid fish amide; fish acid stearylamide; fish amine

fish acid, hydrogenated
A typical chain-length distribution is: 15% $\leq C_{16}$, 30% C_{18}, 30% C_{20}, 25% C_{22}.
Production:
- fish oil, hydrogenated (hydrolysis)

Derivatives: fish amine, hydrogenated
Uses: toilet soap raw material

fish acid fish amide

R,R' = fish-.
Production:
- fish acid + fish amine (amide formation)

Uses: internal plastics processing lubricant

fish acid stearylamide

R = fish-.
Production:
- fish acid + stearylamine (amide formation)

Uses: internal plastics processing lubricant

fish amine

R = fish-. Solid/flake. MP: 34–39°C.
Production:
- fish acid + ammonia (nitrile formation/hydrogenation)

Derivatives:
fish acid fish amide; stearic acid fish amide
Uses: fertiliser anticaking agent; mineral flotation agent

fish amine, hydrogenated

n = 15–21. A typical chain-length distribution is: 15% $\leq C_{16}$, 30% C_{18}, 30% C_{20}, 25% C_{22}.
Production:
- fish acid, hydrogenated + ammonia (nitrile formation/hydrogenation)

Derivatives:
N-alkyl(C_{16}-C_{22})-1,3-propanediamine
Uses: fertiliser anticaking agent; mineral flotation agent

fish meal

White powder containing, typically, 70% protein.
Production:
• pilchard fish/menhaden fish/herring fish/sardine fish
  (extraction; byproduct of fish oil production)
Uses: animal feed ingredient

fish oil

[8002-50-4]
Mixed fatty acid triglycerides from sardine, pilchard, herring and menhaden fish. Titre: 27–32°C (herring oil). Fish oils are characterised by their highly unsaturated C_{20}–C_{22} fatty acid content (2–6 double bonds). A typical chain-length distribution is: 25% C_{20}, 20% C_{22}. The remainder is mainly $C_{18:1}$, $C_{16:1}$ and $C_{16:0}$ fatty acid triglycerides. Mackerel and herring have a higher C_{22} content; pilchard, anchovy and menhaden, a higher C_{16} content. Bodied and blown grades of fish oil are also available commercially. They are produced by boiling or by blowing air through the oil.
Production:
• pilchard fish/menhaden fish/herring fish/sardine fish
  (extraction)
Derivatives: factice; fatty oils, sulphurised; fish acid; fish oil, hydrogenated
Uses:
drying oil (alkyd resins); leather tanning auxiliary; margarine, cooking oils

fish oil, hydrogenated

Production:
• fish oil (hydrogenation)
Derivatives: fish acid, hydrogenated
Uses: margarine, shortening, soap, greases

flake white *See:* lead carbonate, basic

flamprop-methyl

methyl *N*-benzoyl-*N*-(3-chloro-4-fluorophenyl)-DL-alaninate; [52756-25-9]

$C_{17}H_{15}Cl_1F_1N_1O_3$. M: 307.71.
Production:
• methyl α-chloropropionate + 3-chloro-4-fluoro-
  aniline + benzoyl chloride (amine formation/amide
  formation)
Uses: herbicide

flamprop-M-isopropyl

isopropyl *N*-benzoyl-*N*-(3-chloro-4-fluorophenyl)-D-alaninate; [63782-90-1]

$C_{19}H_{19}Cl_1F_1N_1O_3$. M: 363.82.
Production:
• (*S*)-α-chloropropionic acid + isopropanol +
  3-chloro-4-fluoroaniline + benzoyl chloride
  (esterification/amine formation/amide formation)
Uses: herbicide

flavanthrone

Flavanthrone Yellow; Indanthrene Yellow G; Pigment Yellow 24 (CI); Vat Yellow 1 (CI); 70600 (CI); Paliogen Yellow L1870 (BASF); Chromophtal Yellow A2R (Ciba-Geigy); [475-71-8]

$C_{28}H_{12}N_2O_2$. M: 408.42.
Production:
• 2-amino-1-chloroanthraquinone (condensation)
Derivatives: Solubilised Vat Yellow 1
Uses: dye (cotton); pigment (paints, plastics)

Flavanthrone Yellow *See:* flavanthrone

flexicoke

petroleum coke
Small black particles (80% <200 mesh) containing high levels of metal impurities. Available either as wet cake or as dry grains.
Production:
• gas oil, vacuum (Flexicoke process; byproduct of
  naphtha, heavy/refinery gas/coke oven gas/gas oil,
  heavy production)
Uses: fuel (cement/lime production)

flocoumafen

[90035-08-8]

$C_{33}H_{25}F_3O_4$. M: 542.55.

Production:
- phenylacetyl chloride + phenol + 4-(trifluoro-methyl)benzyl alcohol + diethyl malonate + 4-hydroxycoumarin (Friedel-Crafts acylation/ether formation/carbonyl condensation/cyclisation/hydrogenation/decarboxylation/condensation)

Uses:
rodenticide

floxacillin *See:* flucloxacillin

fluazifop-butyl

butyl 2-[4-(5-trifluoromethyl-2-pyridinyloxy)phenoxy]-propionate; [69806-50-4]

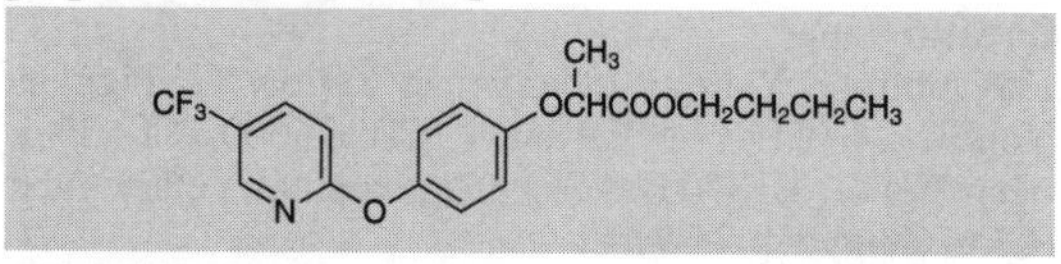

$C_{19}H_{20}F_3N_1O_4$. M: 383.37.
Production:
- *n*-butanol + 2-(4-chlorophenoxy)propionic acid + 2-hydroxy-5-(trifluoromethyl)pyridine (esterification/ether formation)

Uses: herbicide

fluazifop-P-butyl

butyl (*R*)-2-[4-(5-trifluoromethyl-2-pyridinyloxy)phen-oxy]propionate; [79241-46-6]

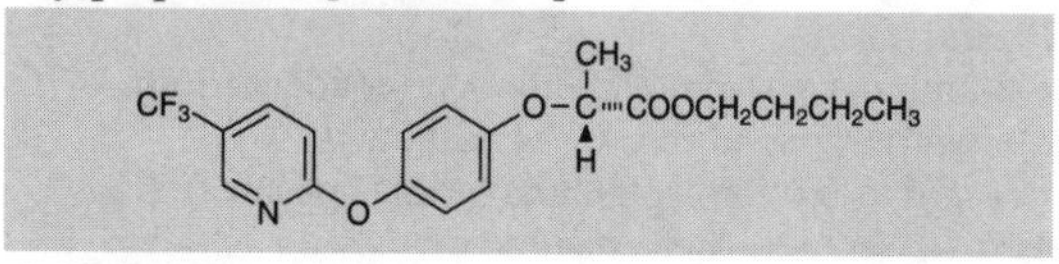

$C_{19}H_{20}F_3N_1O_4$. M: 383.37.
Production:
- *n*-butanol + (*S*)-α-chloropropionic acid + *p*-chloro-phenol + 2-hydroxy-5-(trifluoromethyl)pyridine (esterification/ether formation/ether formation)

Uses: herbicide

flubendazole

[31430-15-6]

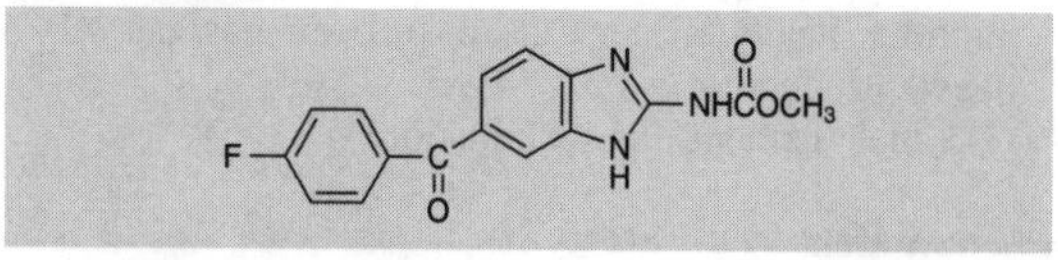

$C_{16}H_{12}F_1N_3O_3$. M: 313.30.
Production:
- 4-chloro-3-nitrobenzoic acid + fluorobenzene + ammonia + *O*-methylisourea sulphate + methyl chloroformate (Friedel-Crafts acylation/ammoniation/nitro reduction/condensation/dehydrochlorination)

Uses:
anthelmintic drug

fluchloralin

N-(2-chloroethyl)-2,6-dinitro-*N*-propyl-4-(trifluoro-methyl)aniline; [33245-39-5]

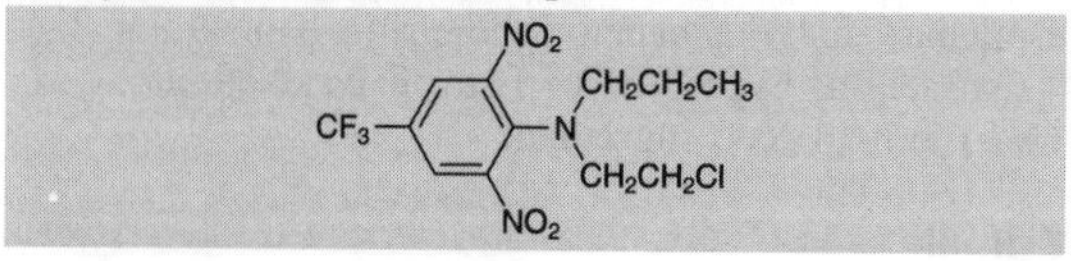

$C_{12}H_{13}Cl_1F_3N_3O_4$. M: 355.69.
Production:
- *n*-propylethanolamine + 4-chloro-3,5-dinitrobenzotri-fluoride (amine formation/chlorination)

Uses:
herbicide

flucloxacillin

floxacillin; [5250-39-5]; [1847-24-1] (sodium salt)

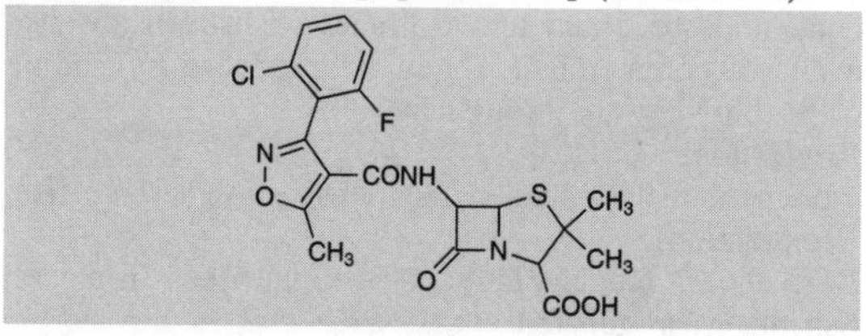

$C_{19}H_{17}Cl_1F_1N_3O_5S_1$. M: 453.87. Available commercially as the acid or sodium monohydrate salts.
Production:
- 3-(2-chloro-6-fluorophenyl)-5-methylisoxazole-4-carboxylic acid + 6-aminopenicillanic acid (amide formation)

Uses:
antibacterial drug

flucofenuron

N,N'-bis(4-chloro-3-trifluoromethylphenyl)urea

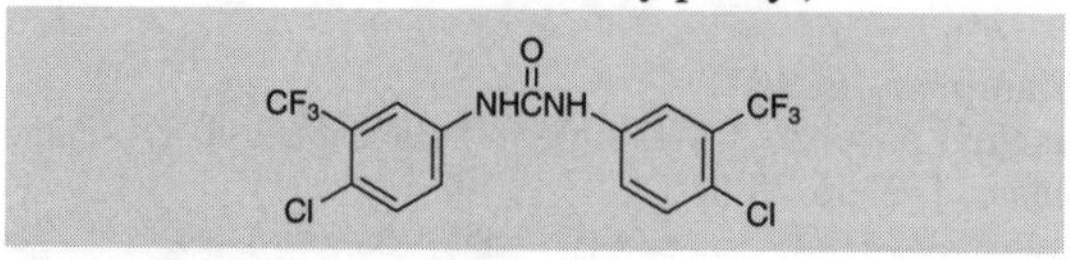

$C_{15}H_8Cl_2F_6N_2O_1$. M: 417.13.
Production:
- 5-amino-2-chlorobenzotrifluoride + phosgene (phosgenation)

Uses:
insect resist agent (wool treatment)

flucythrinate

α-cyano-3-phenoxybenzyl (*S*)-2-(4-difluoromethoxy-phenyl)-3-methylbutyrate; [70124-77-5]
$C_{26}H_{23}F_2N_1O_4$. M: 451.48.
Production:
- *p*-hydroxybenzaldehyde + chlorodifluoromethane + sodium cyanide + isopropyl bromide + 3-phenoxy-benzaldehyde cyanohydrin (ether formation/Grignard reagent formation/Grignard reaction/

racemate separation/alcohol chlorination/
cyanidation/nitrile hydrolysis/esterification)

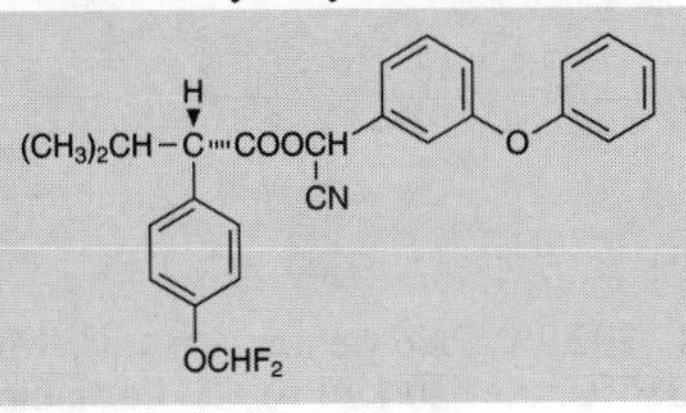

Uses: insecticide

flucytosine
[2022-85-7]

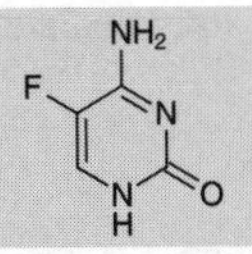

$C_4H_4F_1N_3O_1$. M: 129.09.
Production:
• fluorouracil + ammonia (chlorination/amine
  formation/hydrolysis)
Uses: antifungal drug

flufenamic acid

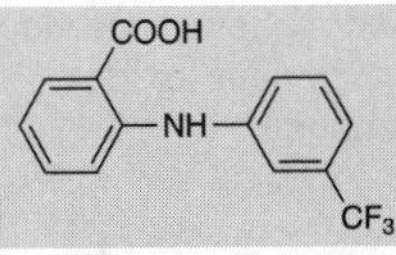

$C_{14}H_{10}F_3N_1O_2$. M: 281.23. The product is available as
the acid, butyl ester or aluminium salt.
Production:
• *m*-aminobenzotrifluoride + *o*-chlorobenzoic acid
  (amine formation)
Uses:
antiinflammatory/analgesic drug

fluid coke
petroleum coke
Spherically-shaped black particles normally ≤5 mm in
diameter. Low volatiles contents.
Production:
• gas oil, vacuum (fluid coking; coproduced with
  naphtha, heavy/refinery gas/gas oil, heavy)
Uses:
fuel (electricity generation, cement/lime production)

flumetralin
N-(2-chloro-6-fluorobenzyl)-*N*-ethyl-α,α,α-trifluoro-
2,6-dinitro-*p*-toluidine; [62924-70-3]
$C_{16}H_{12}Cl_1F_4N_3O_4$. M: 421.74.
Production:
• 2-chloro-6-fluorobenzaldehyde + ethylamine +
  4-chloro-3,5-dinitrobenzotrifluoride (reductive
  amination/amine formation)

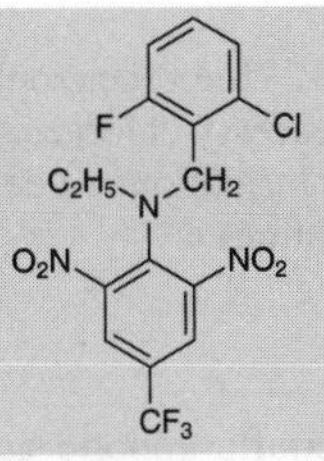

Uses: plant growth regulator

flunarizine
[52468-60-7]

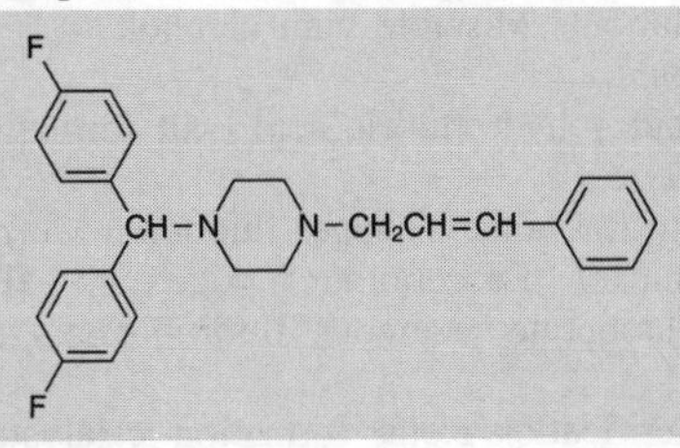

$C_{26}H_{26}F_2N_2$. M: 404.51. Available commercially as the
hydrochloride.
Production:
• 4,4′-difluorobenzhydrol + piperazine + cinnamyl
  alcohol (amine formation/amine formation)
Uses:
vasodilator drug

flunisolide
[3385-03-3]

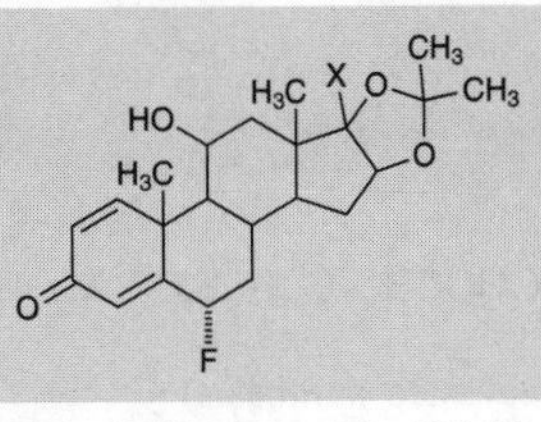

X = -COCH$_2$OH. $C_{24}H_{31}F_1O_6$. M: 434.50.
Production:
• cortisone (multistep synthesis)
Uses:
antiasthmatic drug

flunitrazepam
[1622-62-4]

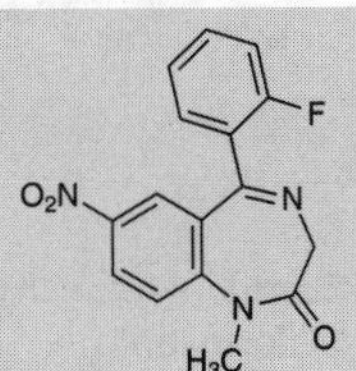

$C_{16}H_{12}F_1N_3O_3$. M: 313.30.

Production:
- 2-amino-5-chloro-2′-fluorobenzophenone + dimethyl sulphate + chloroacetyl chloride + ammonia (methylation/dechlorination/amide formation/ condensation/nitration)

Uses: hypnotic drug

fluoboric acid

fluoroboric acid; tetrafluoroboric acid; [16872-11-0]

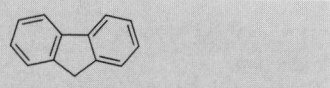

HBF$_4$

$H_1B_1F_4$. M: 87.81. Colourless liquid. BP: 130°C with decomposition. Miscible with water forming strongly acidic solutions. Miscible with alcohol.
Production:
- boric acid + hydrofluoric acid (salt formation)

Derivatives:
ammonium fluoborate; copper fluoborate; ferrous fluoborate; nickel fluoborate; potassium fluoborate; sodium fluoborate; stannous fluoroborate; zinc fluoborate

Uses: esterification/acetal formation catalyst; electroplating bath additive; etchant (semiconductor manufacture); hot-rolled steel pickling agent; azoic dye diazo component salts; aluminium surface treatment reagent

fluocinonide

[356-12-7]

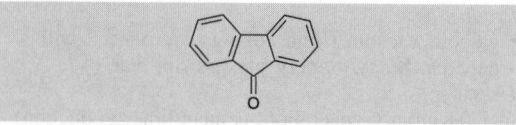

X = -COCH$_2$COOCH$_3$. C$_{26}$H$_{32}$F$_2$O$_7$. M: 494.54.
Production:
- cortisone (multistep synthesis)

Uses:
antiinflammatory drug

fluometuron

N-(3-trifluoromethylphenyl)-N′,N′-dimethylurea; Cotoran (FMC); [2164-17-2]

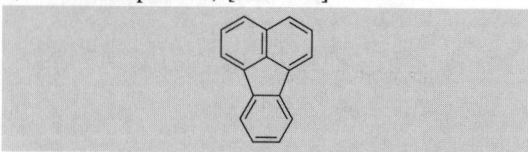

C$_{10}$H$_{11}$F$_3$N$_2$O$_1$. M: 232.20.
Production:
- m-aminobenzotrifluoride + dimethylcarbamoyl chloride (dehydrochlorination)

Uses:
herbicide

fluoranthene

1,2-benzacenaphthene; [206-44-0]

C$_{16}$H$_{10}$. M: 202.26. Pale yellow crystals. MP: 111°C. BP: 375–385°C. d: 1.20 kg/l (0°C). Insoluble in water.
Production:
- anthracene oil (fractionation; byproduct of anthracene production)

Uses:
fluorescent dyestuffs intermediate

fluorene

[86-73-7]

C$_{13}$H$_{10}$. M: 166.22. White flakes. MP: 112–115°C. BP: 295°C. Insoluble in water. Soluble in oxygenated and aromatic solvents.
Production:
- fluorene oil (fractionation; coproduced with acenaphthene/diphenylene oxide)

Derivatives: fluorenone

fluorene oil

Narrow-cut, coal-tar fraction with a boiling range: 290–305°C.
Production:
- coal tar, crude (alkali extraction/fractionation; coproduced with tar acid liquor/naphthalene fraction/anthracene oil/coal tar pitch/light oil/ carbolic oil/creosote oil)

Derivatives:
acenaphthene; diphenylene oxide; fluorene

fluorenone

9-fluorenone; [486-25-9]

C$_{13}$H$_8$O$_1$. M: 180.20. Solid. MP: 83°C. BP: 342°C. d: 1.13 kg/l (100°C). Insoluble in water. Soluble in oxygenated and aromatic solvents.
Production:
- fluorene (oxidation)

Derivatives: 2-methyl-3-phenylbenzyl alcohol; 2,4,7-trinitrofluorenone

Uses:
reagent (Oppenauer oxidation)

fluorescein

uranine (disodium salt); uranine yellow (disodium salt); Acid Yellow 73 (CI, sodium salt); Solvent Yellow 94 (CI, free acid); 45350 (CI, sodium salt); 45350:1 (CI, free acid); D&C Yellow No. 7 (FDC); D&C Yellow No. 8 (FDC, sodium salt); [2321-07-5]; [518-47-8] (sodium salt)

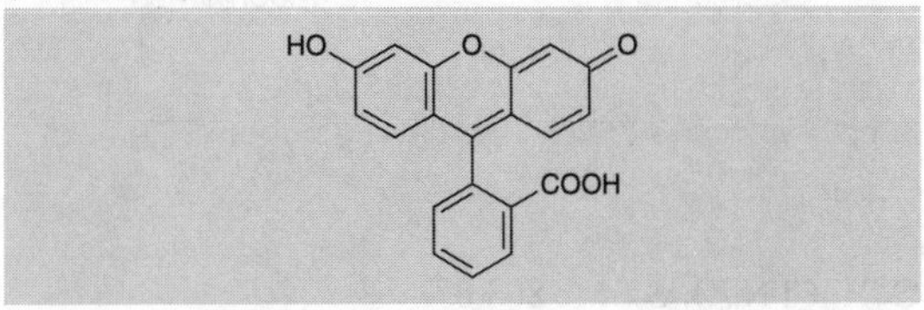

$C_{20}H_{12}O_5$. M: 332.31. Yellowish-red powder. Decomposes when heated above 290°C. Soluble in water and ethanol. Soluble in dilute alkali forming fluorescent solutions.

Production:
• resorcinol + phthalic anhydride (carbonyl condensation/ether formation)

Derivatives: Acid Orange 11; Acid Red 51; eosine; Solvent Violet 10

Uses: acid dye (fluorescent water marker); solvent dye (cosmetics, medicine)

Fluorescent Brightener 9

4,4'-bis(4,6-dianilinotriazin-2-ylamino)stilbene-2,2'-disulphonic acid; Blankophor CA (Bayer); Photine D (Hickson and Welch); [17863-51-3] (*cis*-isomer)

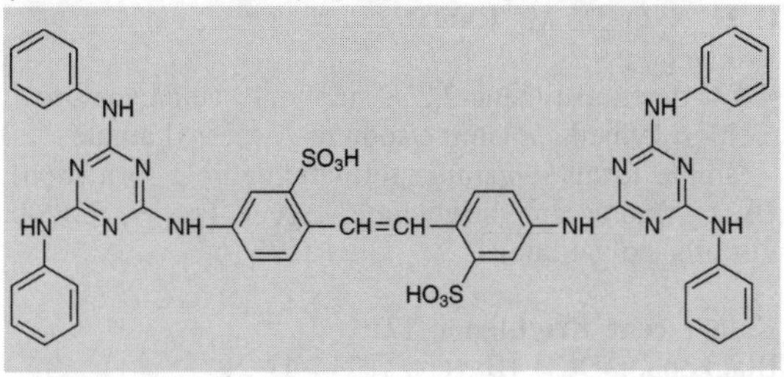

$C_{44}H_{36}N_{12}O_6S_2$. M: 892.97.

Production:
• 4,4'-diaminostilbene-2,2'-disulphonic acid + cyanuric chloride + aniline (amine formation/amine formation)

Uses: fluorescent brightening agent (detergents)

Fluorescent Brightener 24

Tinopal 2B (Ciba-Geigy); Tinopal 2BF (Ciba-Geigy); [17118-40-0] (*cis*-isomer)

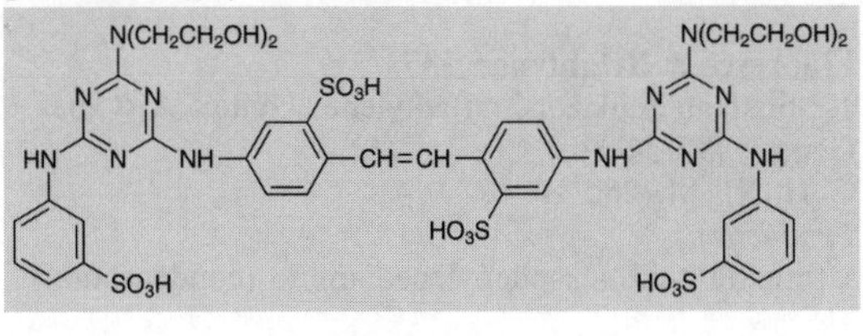

$C_{40}H_{44}N_{12}O_{16}S_4$. M: 1077.11.

Production:
• 4,4'-diaminostilbene-2,2'-disulphonic acid + cyanuric chloride + diethanolamine + metanilic acid (amine formation/amine formation/amine formation)

Uses: fluorescent brightening agent (detergents)

Fluorescent Brightener 28

DDEA; Blankophor BA (Bayer); [17118-44-4] (*cis*-isomer)

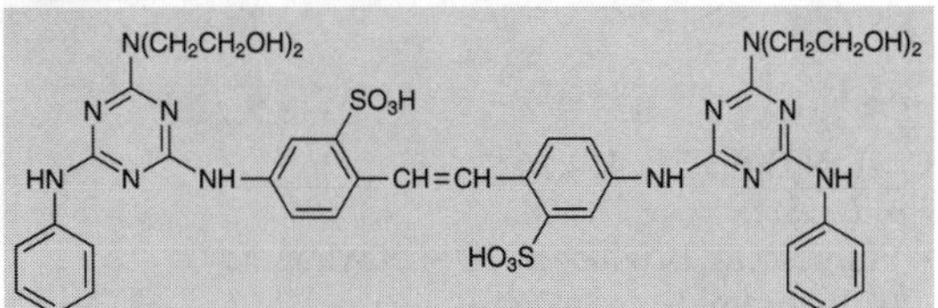

$C_{40}H_{44}N_{12}O_{10}S_2$. M: 916.99.

Production:
• 4,4'-diaminostilbene-2,2'-disulphonic acid + cyanuric chloride + diethanolamine + aniline (amine formation/amine formation/amine formation)

Uses:
fluorescent brightening agent (cotton, polyamide)

Fluorescent Brightener 32

4,4'-bis(4-anilino-6-hydroxytriazin-2-ylamino)stilbene-2,2'-disulphonic acid; 40620 (CI); Uvitex RBS (Ciba-Geigy); Blankophor B (Bayer)

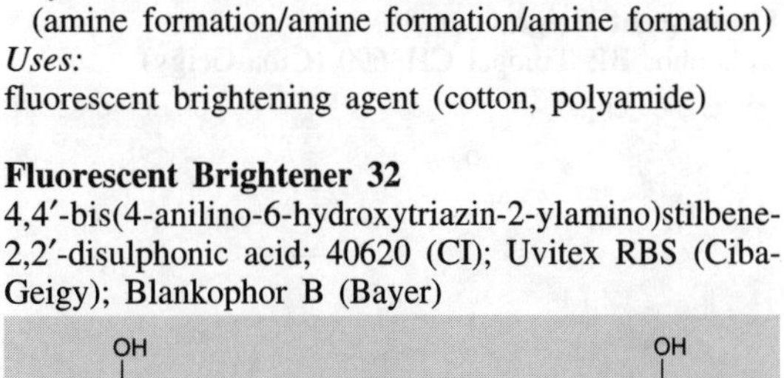

$C_{32}H_{26}N_{10}O_8S_2$. M: 742.75.

Production:
• 4,4'-diaminostilbene-2,2'-disulphonic acid + cyanuric chloride + aniline (amine formation/amine formation/hydration)

Uses: fluorescent brightening agent (cotton, polyamide); fluorescent brightening agent (detergents); fluorescent brightening agent (paper)

Fluorescent Brightener 46

40645 (CI); Tinopal RBS (Ciba-Geigy); [4434-38-2]

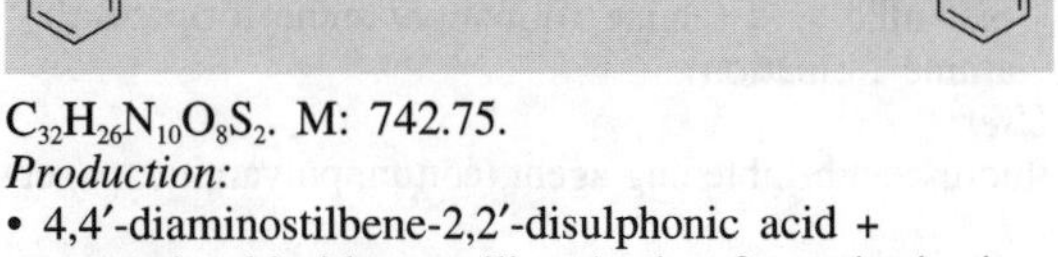

$C_{24}H_{17}N_3O_3S_1$. M: 427.48.

Production:
- 4-aminostilbene-2-sulphonic acid + 1-naphthylamine (diazotisation/azo coupling/oxidative coupling)

Derivatives: Fluorescent Brightener 72

Uses: fluorescent brightening agent (detergents)

Fluorescent Brightener 72
Tinopal E (Ciba-Geigy)

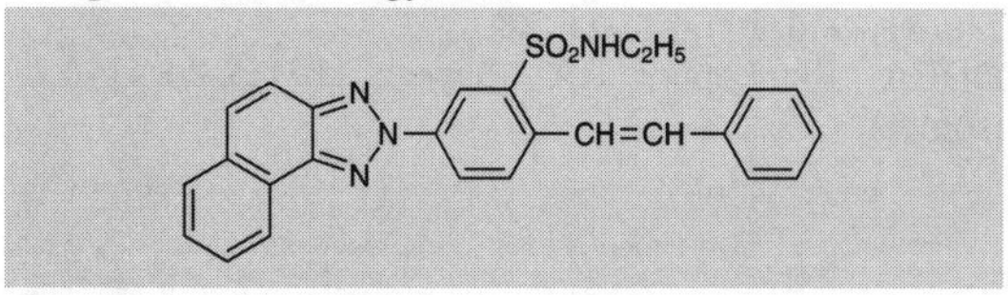

$C_{26}H_{22}N_4O_2S_1$. M: 454.56.

Production:
- Fluroescent Brightener 46 + ethylamine (sulphonamide formation)

Uses:
fluorescent brightening agent (polyester)

Fluorescent Brightener 74 *See:* Solvent Green 4

Fluorescent Brightener 86
Mikephor BI; Tinopal CH3690 (Ciba-Geigy)

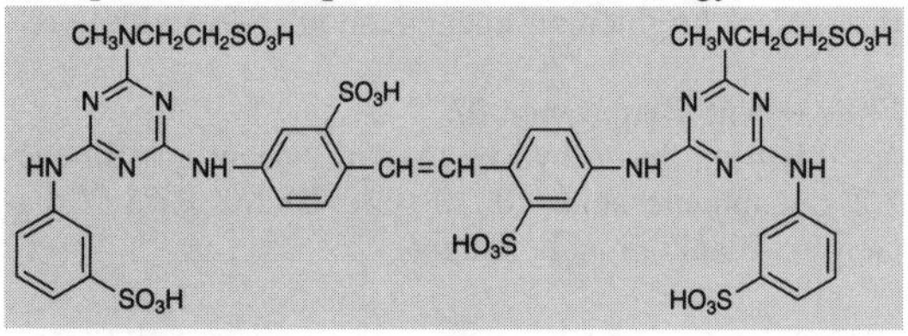

$C_{38}H_{40}N_{12}O_{18}S_6$. M: 1145.18.

Production:
- 4,4'-diaminostilbene-2,2'-disulphonic acid + cyanuric chloride + sodium *N*-methyltaurate + metanilic acid (amine formation/amine formation/ amine formation)

Uses:
fluorescent brightening agent (cotton, polyamide, paper)

Fluorescent Brightener 103
Tinopal BST (Ciba-Geigy)

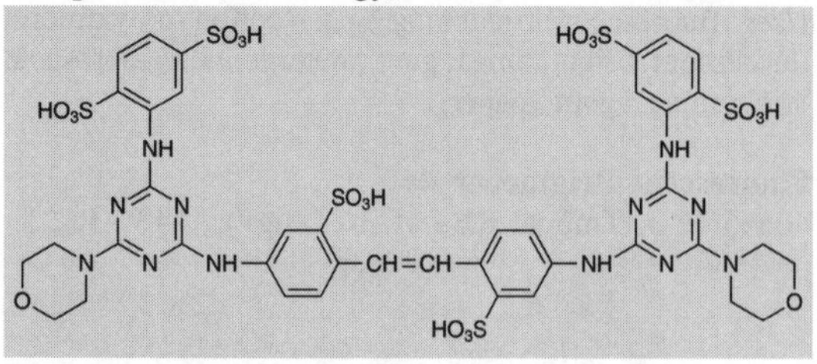

$C_{40}H_{40}N_{12}O_{20}S_6$. M: 1201.20.

Production:
- 4,4'-diaminostilbene-2,2'-disulphonic acid + morpholine + aniline-2,5-disulphonic acid +

cyanuric chloride (amine formation/amine formation/amine formation)

Uses: fluorescent brightening agent (detergents)

Fluorescent Brightener 104
Tinopal RP (Ciba-Geigy)

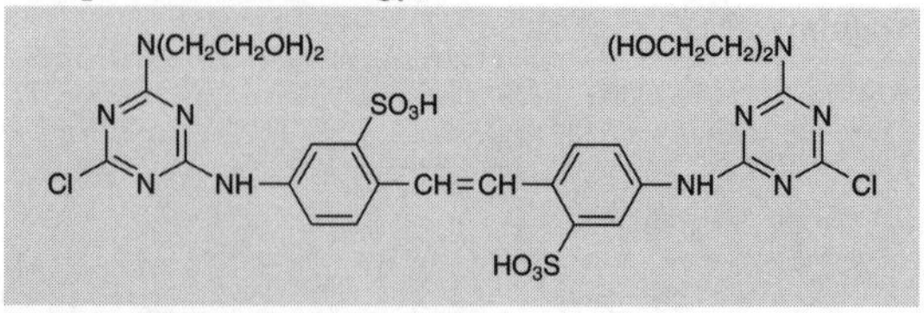

$C_{28}H_{32}Cl_2N_{10}O_{10}S_2$. M: 803.67.

Production:
- 4,4'-diaminostilbene-2,2'-disulphonic acid/ diethanolamine/cyanuric chloride (amine formation/ amine formation)

Uses: fluorescent brightening agent (wool, polyamide, polyester)

Fluorescent Brightener 119
Blankophor REU (Bayer); Uvitex CK (Ciba-Geigy)

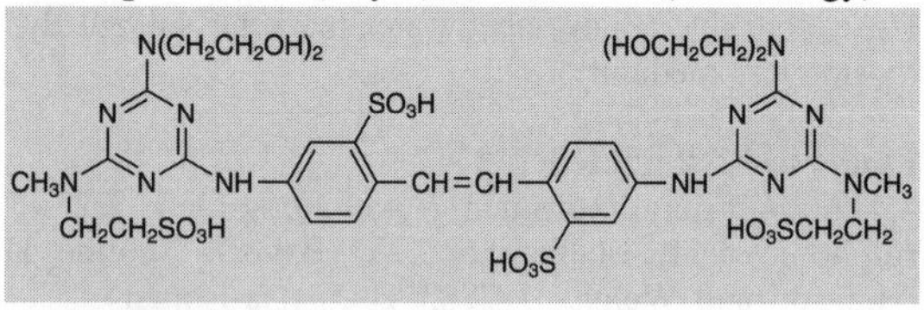

$C_{34}H_{48}N_{12}O_{16}S_4$. M: 1009.07.

Production:
- 4,4'-diaminostilbene-2,2'-disulphonic acid/cyanuric chloride/diethanolamine/sodium *N*-methyltaurate (amine formation/amine formation/amine formation)

Uses: fluorescent brightening agent (paper, cotton, viscose, polyamide)

Fluorescent Brightener 121
Blankophor DCB (Bayer); [2744-49-2]

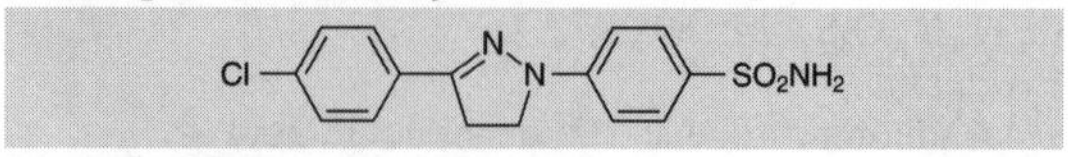

$C_{15}H_{14}Cl_1N_3O_2S_1$. M: 335.80.

Production:
- chlorobenzene + 3-chloropropionyl chloride + sulphanilamide (Friedel-Crafts acylation/ diazotisation/azo reduction/condensation)

Uses: fluorescent brightening agent (wool, polyamide, cellulose acetate)

Fluorescent Brightener 133
1,2-bis(benzimidazol-2-yl)ethylene; Uvitex A (Ciba-Geigy); [95-34-1]
$C_{16}H_{12}N_4$. M: 260.31.

Production:
- fumaric acid + *o*-phenylenediamine (condensation)

Uses: fluorescent brightening agent (synthetic fibres)

Fluorescent Brightener 135
1,2-bis(5-methylbenzoxazol-2-yl)ethylene; Uvitex ERN (Ciba-Geigy); [1041-00-5]

$C_{18}H_{14}N_2O_2$. M: 290.32.
Production:
• fumaric acid + *o*-amino-*p*-cresol (condensation)
Uses:
fluorescent brightening agent (synthetic fibres, plastics)

Fluorescent Brightener 136
4,4′-bis(4-anilino-6-methoxytriazin-2-ylamino)stilbene-2,2′-disulphonic acid; Uvitex PRS (Ciba-Geigy)

$C_{34}H_{30}N_{10}O_8S_2$. M: 770.80.
Production:
• 4,4′-diaminostilbene-2,2′-disulphonic acid + aniline + sodium methoxide + cyanuric chloride (amine formation/amine formation/ether formation)
Uses: fluorescent brightening agent (paper)

Fluorescent Brightener 140
See: 7-diethylamino-4-methylcoumarin

Fluorescent Brightener 142
Mikephor BX (Mitsui); Uvitex VR (Ciba-Geigy)

$C_{36}H_{36}N_{12}O_8S_2$. M: 828.89.
Production:
• 4,4′-diaminostilbene-2,2′-disulphonic acid + aniline + monoethanolamine + cyanuric chloride (amine formation/amine formation/amine formation)
Uses:
fluorescent brightening agent (polyamide fibres)

Fluorescent Brightener 162
N-methyl-4-methoxynaphthalimide; Mikowhite AT; [3271-05-4]

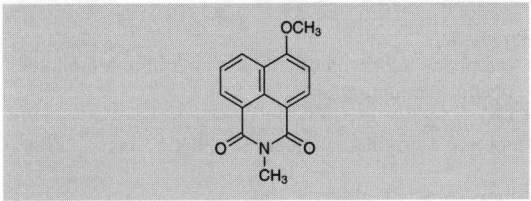

$C_{14}H_{11}N_1O_3$. M: 241.25.
Production:
• sodium methoxide + naphthalic anhydride + methylamine (sulphonation/imine formation/amine formation)
Uses:
fluorescent brightening agent (synthetic fibres)

Fluorescent Brightener 179
Fluorlite XMF (ICI); [3271-22-5]

$C_{21}H_{15}N_3O_2$. M: 341.37.
Production:
• pyrene + copper cyanide + dicyandiamide + dimethyl sulphate (nitration/nitro reduction/diazotisation/Sandmeyer reaction/condensation/hydrolysis/methylation)
Uses: fluorescent brightening agent (polyester)

Fluorescent Brightener 182

$C_{36}H_{36}N_{12}O_6S_2$. M: 796.89.
Production:
• 4,4′-diaminostilbene-2,2′-disulphonic acid + aniline + ethylamine + cyanuric chloride (amine formation/amine formation/amine formation)
Uses: fluorescent brightening agent (cotton)

Fluorescent Brightener 184
2,5-bis(5-*t*-butylbenzoxazol-2-yl)thiophene; Uvitex OB (Ciba-Geigy)
$C_{26}H_{26}N_2O_2S_1$. M: 430.57.

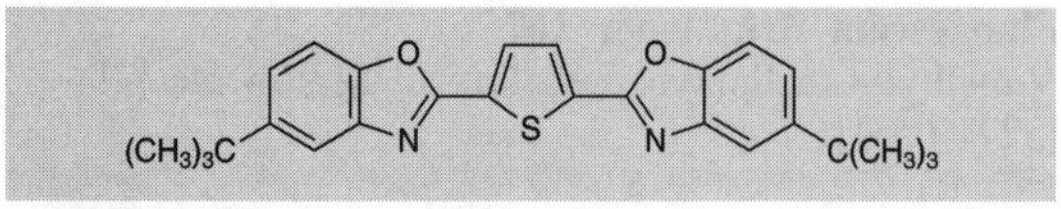

Production:

- thiophene-2,5-dicarboxylic acid + 2-amino-4-*t*-butyl-phenol (condensation)

Uses:

fluorescent brightening agent (synthetic fibres, plastics)

Fluorescent Brightener 190

2,5-bis(benzoxazol-2-yl)thiophene; Uvitex SOF (Ciba-Geigy); [2866-43-5]

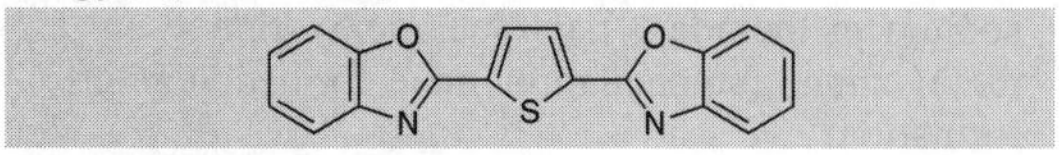

$C_{18}H_{10}N_2O_2S_1$. M: 318.35.

Production:

- thiophene-2,5-dicarboxylic acid + *o*-aminophenol (condensation)

Uses: fluorescent brightening agent (detergents, synthetic fibres, plastics)

Fluorescent Brightener 193

Blankophor PSL (Bayer)

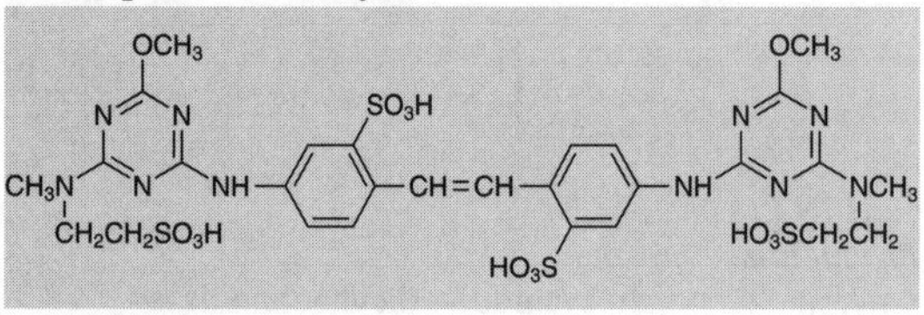

$C_{28}H_{34}N_{10}O_{14}S_4$. M: 862.90.

Production:

- 4,4'-diaminostilbene-2,2'-disulphonic acid + sodium *N*-methyltaurate + sodium methoxide + cyanuric chloride (amine formation/amine formation/ether formation)

Uses: fluorescent brightening agent (paper)

Fluorescent Brightener 199

Palanil Brilliant White R (BASF); [13001-39-3]

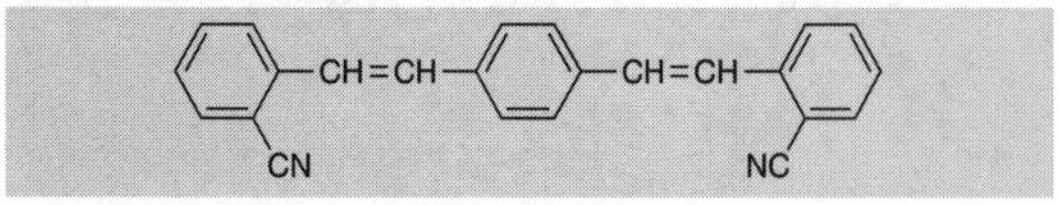

$C_{24}H_{16}N_2$. M: 332.40.

Production:

- *o*-nitrobenzaldehyde + sodium cyanide + 1,4-bis-(chloromethyl)benzene + triethyl phosphite (nitro reduction/Sandmeyer reaction/Wittig reaction)

Uses:

fluorescent brightening agent (polyester)

Fluorescent Brightener 204

Albaton ZN; Blankophor RA (Bayer)

$C_{32}H_{28}N_{12}O_6S_2$. M: 740.77.

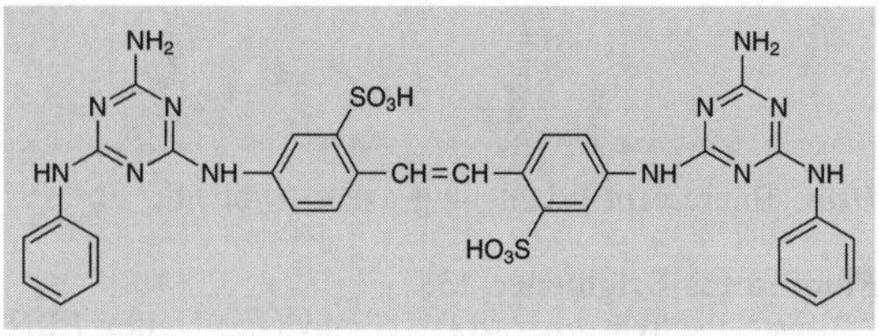

Production:

- 4,4'-diaminostilbene-2,2'-disulphonic acid + ammonia + aniline + cyanuric chloride (amine formation/amine formation/amine formation)

Uses: fluorescent brightening agent (cotton, polyamide)

Fluorescent Brightener 312

Hostalux PR (Hoechst)

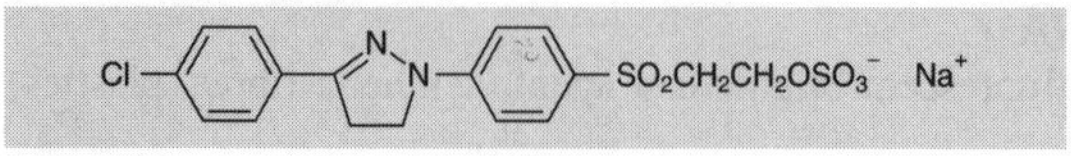

$C_{17}H_{16}Cl_1N_2Na_1O_6S_2$. M: 466.89.

Production:

- chlorobenzene + 3-chloropropionyl chloride + *p*-(β-hydroxyethylsulphonyl)aniline (Friedel-Crafts acylation/diazotisation/azo reduction/condensation)

Uses: fluorescent brightening agent (polyamide, acetate, polyacrylonitrile)

Fluorescent Brightener 354

4-(5-*t*-butylbenzoxazol-2-yl)-4'-phenylstilbene; Uvitex EFT (Ciba-Geigy)

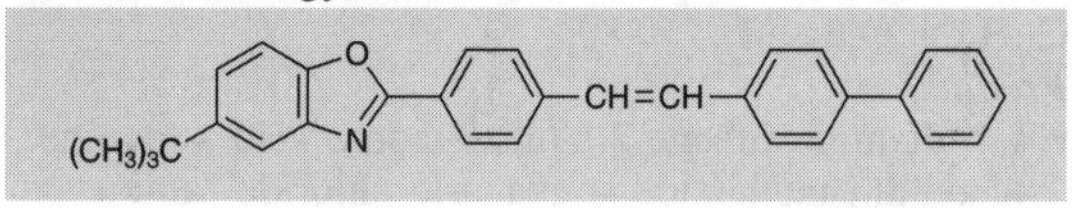

$C_{31}H_{27}N_1O_1$. M: 429.57.

Production:

- 2-amino-4-*t*-butylphenol + *p*-toluoyl chloride + biphenyl-4-carboxylic acid (condensation/anil synthesis)

Uses:

fluorescent brightening agent (melt-spun polyester)

Fluorescent Brightener DM

Tinopal DMS (Ciba-Geigy); [32466-46-9] (*cis*-isomer)

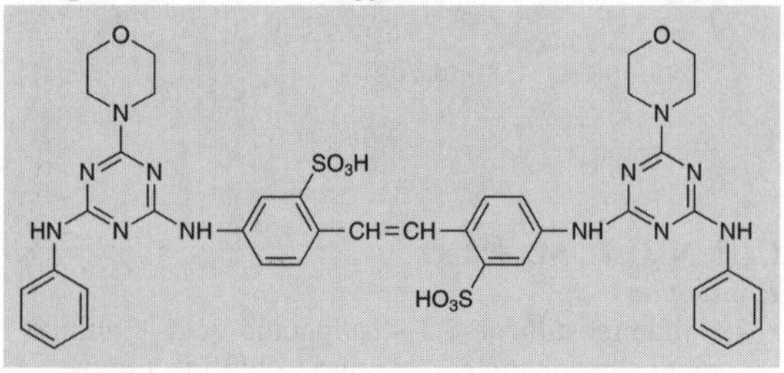

$C_{40}H_{40}N_{12}O_8S_2$. M: 880.96.

Production:

- 4,4'-diaminostilbene-2,2'-disulphonic acid +

morpholine + aniline + cyanuric chloride (amine formation/amine formation/amine formation)
Uses: fluorescent brightening agent (detergents)

Fluorescent Brightener DMDDEA
[16470-24-9] (acid)

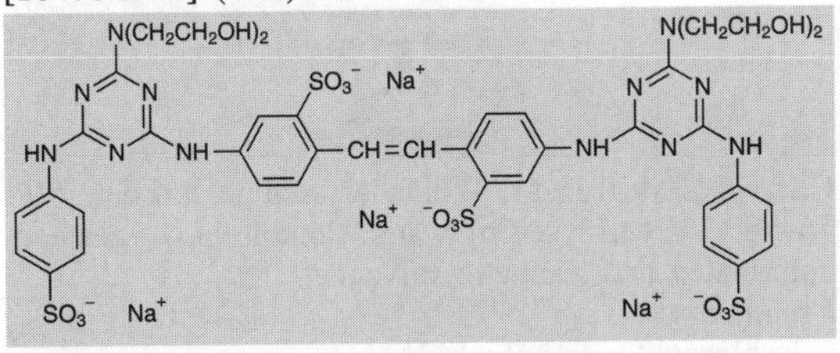

C₄₀H₄₀N₁₂Na₄O₁₆S₄. M: 1165.04. Not bleach-stable.
Production:
• 4,4′-diaminostilbene-2,2′-disulphonic acid + cyanuric chloride + diethanolamine + sulphanilic acid (amine formation/amine formation/amine formation)
Uses: fluorescent brightening agent (detergents)

Fluorescent Brightener DMEA
[17118-46-6] (*trans*-isomer)

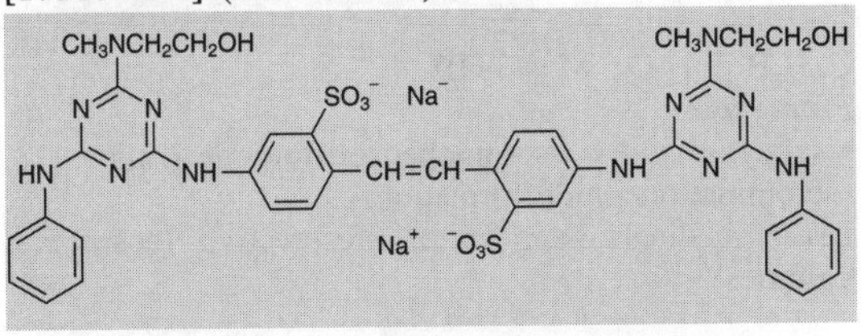

C₃₈H₃₈N₁₂Na₂O₈S₂. M: 900.90. Not bleach-stable.
Production:
• 4,4′-diaminostilbene-2,2′-disulphonic acid + cyanuric chloride + methylethanolamine + aniline (amine formation/amine formation/amine formation)
Uses: fluorescent brightening agent (detergents)

fluorine
[7782-41-4]

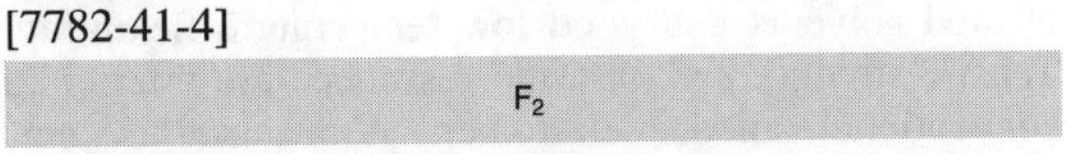

F₂

F₂. M: 38.00. Pale yellow gas. BP: -188°C. Soluble in water with decomposition, forming hydrofluoric acid. Highly reactive. Strong oxidising agent.
Production:
• hydrofluoric acid (electrolysis)
Derivatives:
carbon tetrafluoride; fluorouracil; iodine pentafluoride; perfluorodecalin; perfluorodimethylcyclohexane; perfluoro-*n*-hexane; perfluoromethylcyclohexane; perfluoromethyldecalin; perfluoro(methyl vinyl ether); perfluoro-*n*-pentane; sulphur hexafluoride; uranium hexafluoride
Uses:
gaseous surface treatment agent (polyethylene bottles)

fluoristan *See:* stannous fluoride

fluorite *See:* fluorspar

fluoroacetamide
[640-19-7]

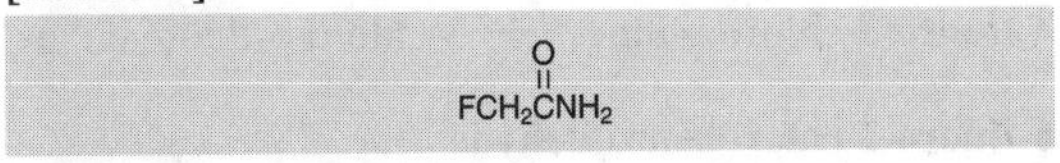

FCH₂CNH₂

C₂H₄F₁N₁O₁. M: 77.06.
Production:
• sodium fluoroacetate + ammonia (amide formation)
Uses: rodenticide

2-fluoro-2′-amino-5′-chlorobenzophenone
See: 2-amino-5-chloro-2′-fluorobenzophenone

p-fluoroaniline
4-fluoroaniline; [371-40-4]

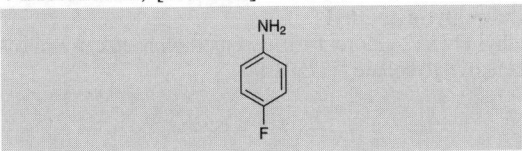

C₆H₆F₁N₁. M: 111.13. Liquid. BP: 186–187°C. d: 1.17 kg/l (20°C). Slightly soluble in water.
Production:
• *p*-chloronitrobenzene + hydrogen fluoride (halogen exchange/nitro reduction)
Derivatives:
fluoromide

fluorobenzene
phenyl fluoride; [462-06-6]

C₆H₅F₁. M: 96.11. Liquid with an aromatic odour. BP: 85°C. d: 1.08 kg/l (25°C). Insoluble in water. Miscible with oxygenated solvents.
Production:
• aniline + sodium nitrite + hydrogen fluoride (diazotisation/azo fluorination)
Derivatives:
p-bromofluorobenzene; 4-chloro-4′-fluorobutyrophenone; flubendazole; nuarimol

4-fluorobenzyl chloride
[456-42-8]

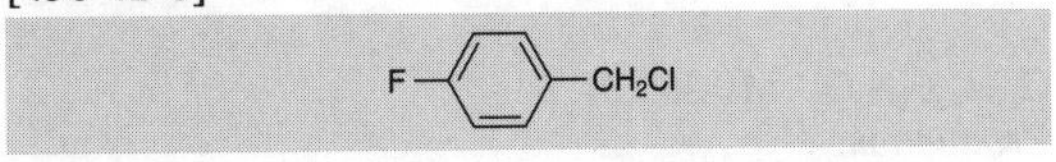

C₇H₆Cl₁F₁. M: 144.58. Liquid with a pungent odour. BP: 83°C (3.5 kPa). Insoluble in water.

Production:
- *p*-fluorotoluene (side-chain chlorination)
Derivatives: astemizole; flupirtine; sulindac

fluoroboric acid *See:* fluoboric acid

4-fluoro-3-chloroaniline *See:* 3-chloro-4-fluoroaniline

6-fluoro-2-chlorobenzaldehyde
See: 2-chloro-6-fluorobenzaldehyde

2-fluoro-6-chlorotoluene
See: 2-chloro-6-fluorotoluene

1-fluoro-2,4-dinitrobenzene
See: 2,4-dinitrofluorobenzene

fluoroform *See:* trifluoromethane

fluoroglycofen-ethyl
ethyl *O*-[5-(2-chloro-4-trifluoromethylphenoxy)-2-nitro-benzoyl]glycollate; [77501-90-7]

$C_{18}H_{13}Cl_1F_3N_1O_7$. M: 447.74.
Production:
- ethanol + glycollic acid + acifluorfen
  (esterification/esterification)
Uses: herbicide

fluoromide
2,3-dichloro-*N*-4-fluorophenylmaleimide; [41205-21-4]

$C_{10}H_4Cl_2F_1N_1O_2$. M: 260.06.
Production:
- acetylenedicarboxylic acid + *p*-fluoroaniline
  (chlorination/amide formation)
Uses: fungicide

4-fluoro-3-phenoxybenzaldehyde cyanohydrin

$C_{14}H_{10}F_1N_1O_2$. M: 243.24.
Production:
- 3,4-dichlorobenzaldehyde + hydrogen fluoride +
  phenol + sodium cyanide (halogen exchange/ether

formation/cyanohydrin formation)
Derivatives: cyfluthrin

4-fluorophthalic anhydride
4-FPAN; [319-03-9]

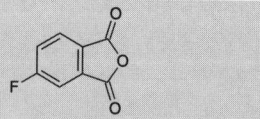

$C_8H_3F_1O_3$. M: 166.11. White, crystalline powder. MP: 76–78°C. Hydrolysed by water. Soluble in oxygenated, chlorinated and aromatic solvents.
Production:
- 4-chlorophthalic anhydride (halogen exchange)
Derivatives: poly(ether-imide)

fluorosalan
3,5-dibromo-2-hydroxy-*N*-(3-trifluoromethylphenyl)-benzamide; [4776-06-1]

$C_{14}H_8Br_2F_3N_1O_2$. M: 439.02.
Production:
- salicylic acid + *m*-aminobenzotrifluoride (ring
  bromination/amide formation)
Uses: medical disinfectant; preservative (cosmetics,
toiletries)

fluorosilicone elastomers
FSI

R = fluoroalkyl-. The polymers are characterised by their good ozone and weather resistance, inertness to oil and solvents and good low temperature flexibility. Tensile strength and abrasion resistance are inferior to conventional silicone elastomers. Vulcanised by per-oxide.
Production:
- dichloromethyl-2-(perfluoroalkyl)ethylsilane/
  dichloromethyl-3-(2-hydroperfluoroalkoxy)propyl-
  silane/dichloromethyl-3,3,3-trifluoropropylsilane
  (base-catalysed polymerisation)
Uses: aerospace components; low-temperature seals

fluorosulphonic acid
fluosulphuric acid; [7789-21-1]

HSO₃F

$H_1F_1O_3S_1$. M: 100.07. Colourless liquid. BP: 163°C.

MP: -89°C. d: 1.73 kg/l (25°C). Reacts violently with water. Highly toxic.
Production:
• sulphur trioxide + hydrofluoric acid (reaction)
Uses:
alkylation/acylation/condensation catalyst; fluorination reagent

p-fluorotoluene
4-fluorotoluene; [352-32-9]

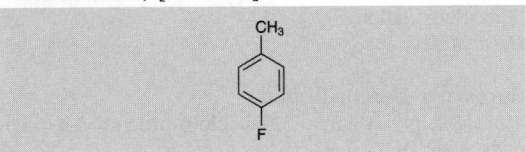

$C_7H_7F_1$. M: 110.14. Liquid with a bitter almond-like odour. BP: 116°C. d: 0.99 kg/l (25°C).
Production:
• *p*-toluidine + sodium nitrite + hydrogen fluoride (diazotisation/thermal rearrangement)
Derivatives: 4-fluorobenzyl chloride

fluorouracil
5-fluorouracil; [51-21-8]

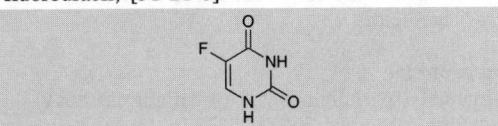

$C_4H_3F_1N_2O_2$. M: 130.07.
Production:
• uracil + fluorine (fluorination)
Derivatives: flucytosine; tegafur
Uses: antineoplastic drug

fluorspar
calcium fluoride; fluorite
Mined in many different countries within North America, Europe, Africa and Asia.
Derivatives: boron trifluoride; hydrogen fluoride
Uses:
aluminium electrolysis adjunct; Portland cement ingredient; glass/enamel/ceramics ingredient; slagging additive (steel production); smelting/refining agent (lead, copper, brass, ferroalloys, nickel alloys)

fluosilicic acid *See:* hexafluorosilicic acid

fluosulphuric acid *See:* fluorosulphonic acid

flupenthixol
[2709-56-0]
$C_{23}H_{25}F_3N_2O_1S_1$. M: 434.51.
Production:
• *p*-chlorobenzotrifluoride + thiosalicylic acid + allyl bromide + N-hydroxyethylpiperazine (sulphide

formation/condensation/Grignard reagent formation/Grignard reaction/dehydration/amine formation)

Uses: neuroleptic drug

fluphenazine
[69-23-8]; [5002-47-1] (decanoate ester); [146-56-5] (dihydrochloride); [2746-81-8] (heptanoate ester)

$C_{22}H_{26}F_3N_3O_1S_1$. M: 437.52. Available commercially as the free base, the dihydrochloride salt or as the heptanoate or decanoate esters.
Production:
• 2-(trifluoromethyl)phenothiazine + 1-bromo-3-chloropropane + N-hydroxyethylpiperazine (amine formation/amine formation)
Uses:
neuroleptic drug

flupirtine
[56995-20-1]

$C_{15}H_{17}F_1N_4O_2$. M: 304.33.
Production:
• 2,6-diaminopyridine + 4-fluorobenzyl chloride + ethyl chloroformate (nitration/amine formation/nitro reduction/dehydrochlorination)
Uses: analgesic drug

flurazepam
[17617-23-1]; [1172-18-5] (hydrochloride)

$C_{21}H_{23}Cl_1F_1N_3O_1$. M: 387.88. Available commercially as the dihydrochloride salt.

Production:

- 2-amino-5-chloro-2'-fluorobenzophenone + 2-diethylaminoethyl chloride hydrochloride + chloroacetyl chloride + ammonia (amine formation/amide formation/condensation)

Uses: hypnotic/sedative drug

flurbiprofen
[5104-49-4]

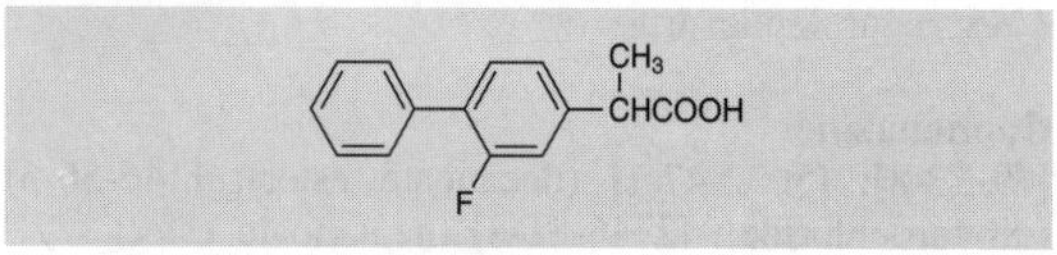

$C_{15}H_{13}F_1O_2$. M: 244.26.
Production:

- bromobenzene + acetyl chloride + ethanol (Friedel-Crafts acylation/nitration/Ullmann reaction/nitro reduction/Balz-Schiemann reaction/Willgerodt reaction/esterification)

Uses: antiinflammatory drug

flurenol-butyl
butyl 9-hydroxyfluorene-9-carboxylate; flurecol-butyl; [2314-09-2]

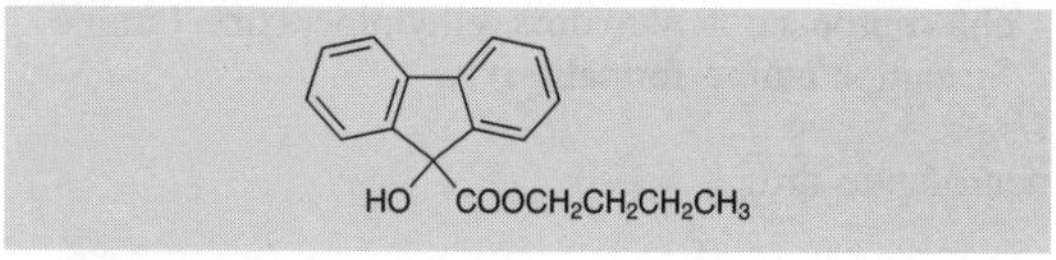

$C_{18}H_{18}O_3$. M: 282.34.
Production:

- 9,10-phenanthrenequinone + *n*-butanol (rearrangement/esterification)

Uses: herbicide

fluridone
1-methyl-3-phenyl-5-(3-trifluoromethylphenyl)-4-pyrid-one; [59756-60-4]

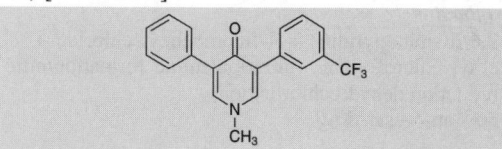

$C_{19}H_{14}F_3N_1O_1$. M: 329.32.
Production:

- benzotrifluoride + benzyl cyanide + acetyl chloride + ethyl formate + methylamine (Friedel-Crafts acylation/Willgerodt reaction/condensation/decarboxylation/carbonyl condensation/amine formation)

Uses: herbicide

flurochloridone
3-chloro-4-(chloromethyl)-1-[3-(trifluoromethyl)phenyl-]-2-pyrrolidinone; [61213-25-0]

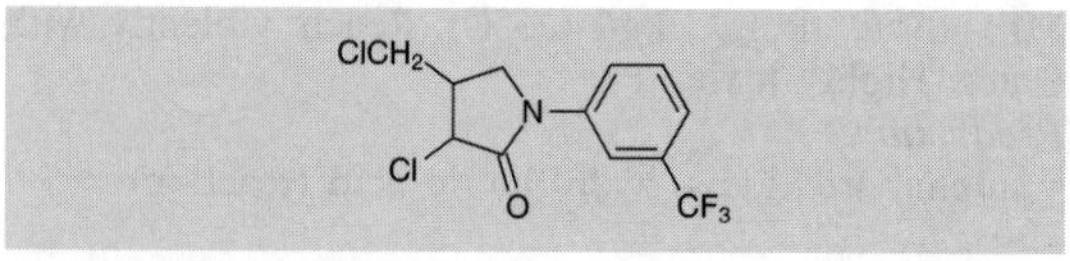

$C_{12}H_{10}Cl_2F_3N_1O_1$. M: 312.12.
Production:

- methyl γ-chloroacetoacetate + *m*-aminobenzotrifluoride + chloroacetyl chloride (amine formation/amide formation/Reformatsky reaction/chlorination/decarboxylation)

Uses: herbicide

fluroxypyr-1-methylheptyl
1-methylheptyl 4-amino-3,5-dichloro-6-fluoro-2-pyridyloxyacetate; [69377-81-7]

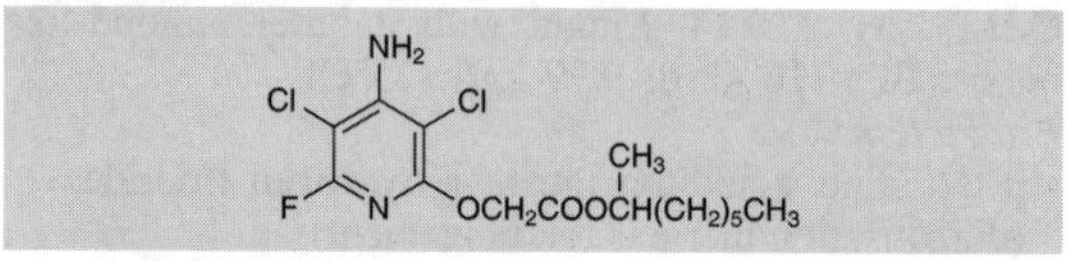

$C_{15}H_{21}Cl_2F_1N_2O_3$. M: 367.25.
Production:

- triclopyr + sodium fluoride + 2-octanol (halogen exchange/nitration/nitro reduction/esterification)

Uses: herbicide

flurprimidol
2-(methyl-1-pyrimidin-5-yl)-1-(4-trifluoromethoxy)-phenylpropan-2-ol; [56425-91-3]

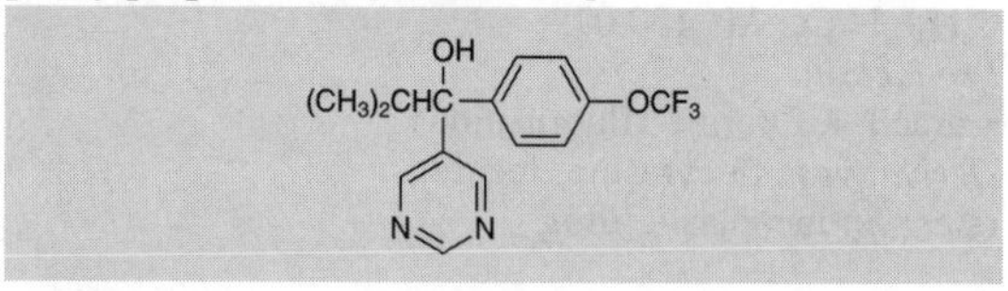

$C_{15}H_{15}F_3N_2O_2$. M: 312.28.
Production:

- phenol + isobutyroyl chloride + bromotrifluoromethane + 5-bromopyrimidine (esterification/Fries rearrangement/ether formation/Grignard reagent formation/Grignard reaction)

Uses:
plant growth regulator

flusilazole
di-(4-fluorophenyl)methyl(1H-1,2,4-triazol-1-ylmethyl)-silane; [85509-19-9]

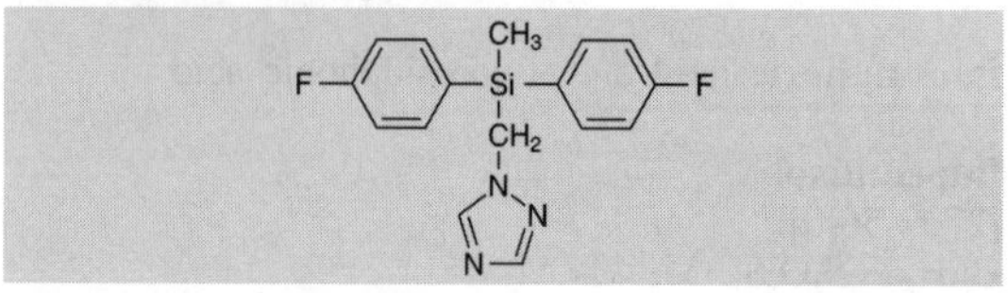

$C_{16}H_{15}F_2N_3Si_1$. M: 315.41.
Production:

- *p*-bromofluorobenzene + dichloromethylsilane +

formaldehyde + 1,2,4-triazole (Grignard reagent formation/Grignard reaction/Mannich reaction)
Uses:
fungicide

fluspirilene
[1841-19-6]

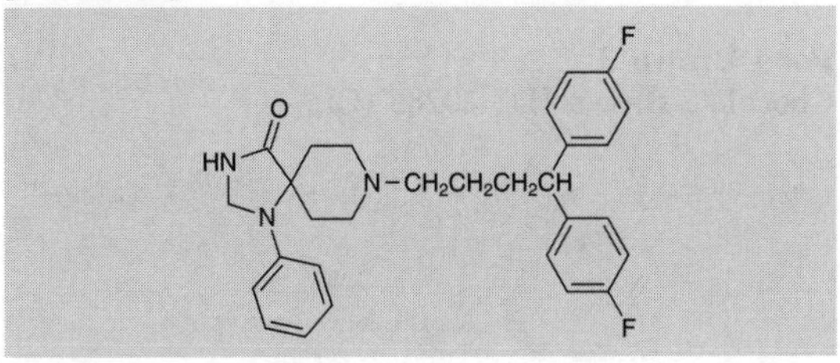

$C_{29}H_{31}F_2N_3O_1$. M: 475.59.
Production:
• 1-benzyl-4-piperidone + aniline + hydrogen cyanide + formaldehyde + 4,4-bis(*p*-fluorophenyl)butyl chloride (imine formation/addition/nitrile hydration/Mannich reaction/amine formation)
Uses:
neuroleptic drug

flutolanil
α,α,α-trifluoro-3′-isopropoxy-*o*-toluanilide; [66332-96-5]

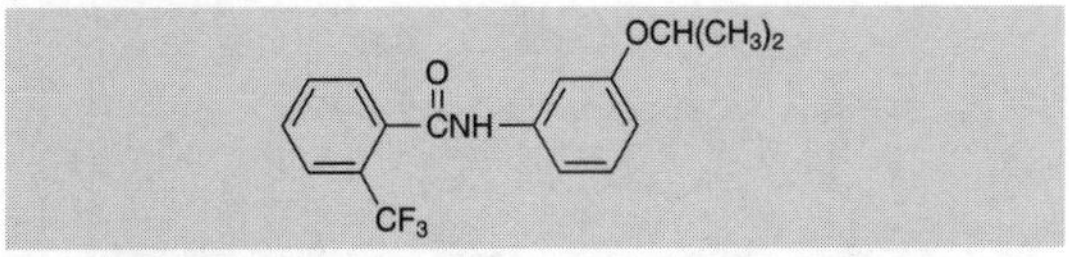

$C_{17}H_{16}F_3N_1O_2$. M: 323.32.
Production:
• 2-(trifluoromethyl)benzoyl fluoride + *m*-aminophenol + isopropanol (amide formation/ether formation)
Uses: fungicide

flutriafol
2,4′-difluoro-α-(1H-1,2,4-triazol-1-ylmethyl)benzhydryl alcohol; [76674-21-0]

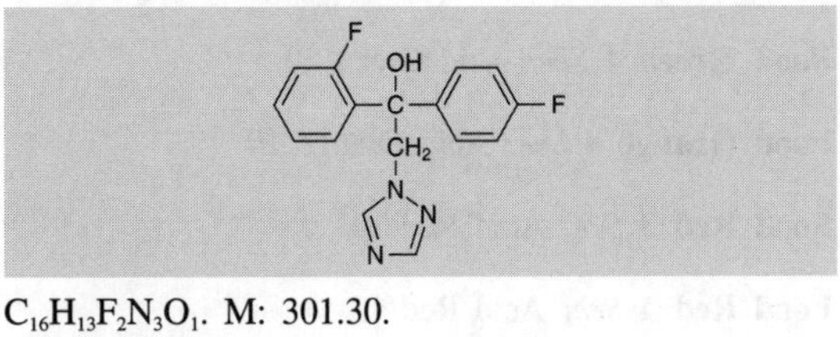

$C_{16}H_{13}F_2N_3O_1$. M: 301.30.
Production:
• *o*-aminoacetophenone + *p*-bromofluorobenzene + 1,2,4-triazole (diazotisation/azo fluorination/alpha chlorination/Grignard reagent formation/Grignard reaction/amine formation)
Uses: fungicide

D-fluvalinate
α-cyano-3-phenoxybenzyl *N*-(2-2-chloro-4-trifluoromethylphenyl)-D-valinate; [69409-94-5]

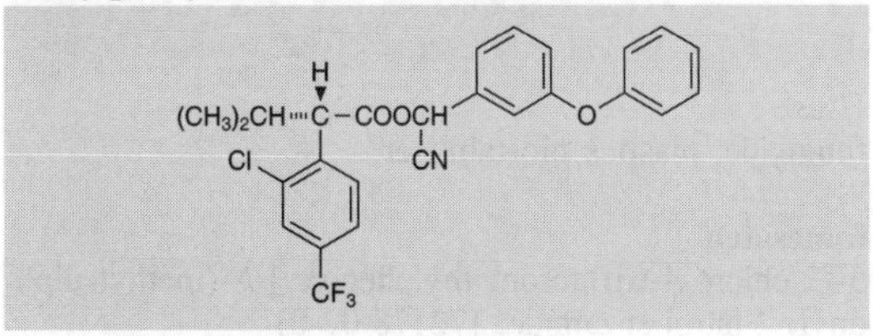

$C_{26}H_{22}Cl_1F_3N_2O_3$. M: 502.92.
Production:
• D-valine + 3,4-dichlorobenzotrifluoride + 3-phenoxybenzaldehyde cyanohydrin (esterification/amine formation)
Uses: insecticide/acaricide

FMVE *See:* perfluoro(methyl vinyl ether)

folic acid
pteroylglutamic acid; PGA; [59-30-3]

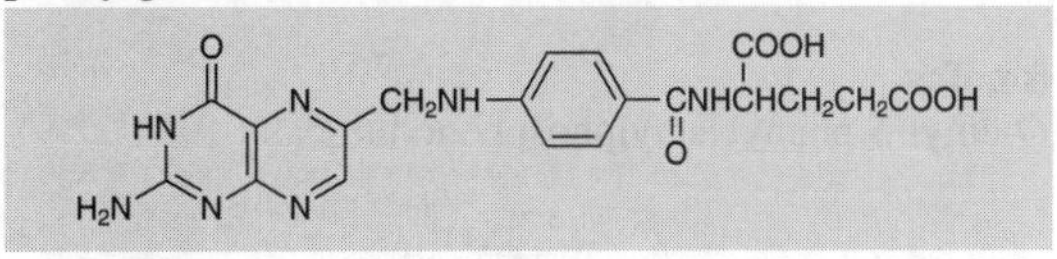

$C_{19}H_{19}N_7O_6$. M: 441.40.
Production:
• 6-hydroxy-2,4,5-triaminopyrimidine + 1,1,3-trichloroacetone + *p*-nitrobenzoyl chloride + L-glutamic acid (condensation/amide formation/nitro reduction/amine formation)
Derivatives: folinic acid
Uses: dietary supplement ingredient; antianemic drug

folinic acid
5-formyltetrahydrofolic acid; 5-formyl-5,6,7,8-tetrahydropteroyl-L-glutamic acid; [58-05-9]

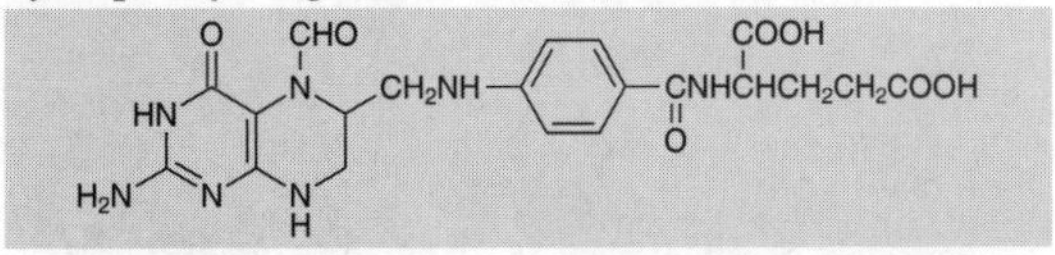

$C_{20}H_{23}N_7O_7$. M: 473.44. Available commercially as the calcium pentahydrate salt.
Production:
• folic acid (amide formation/hydrogenation)
Uses:
antianemic/methotrexate antidote drug

folpet
N-(trichloromethylthio)phthalimide; [133-07-3]
$C_9H_4Cl_3N_1O_2S_1$. M: 296.56.
Production:
• phthalimide + trichloromethanesulphenyl chloride (dehydrochlorination)

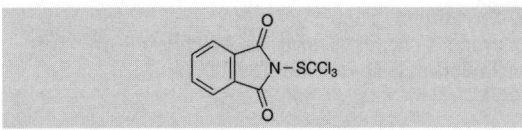

Uses:
fungicide; plastics biostabiliser

fomesafen
5-[2-chloro-4-trifluoromethylphenoxy]-*N*-(methylsulph-onyl)-2-nitrobenzamide; [72178-02-0]

$C_{15}H_{10}Cl_1F_3N_2O_6S_1$. M: 438.74.
Production:
• acifluorfen + ammonia + methanesulphonyl chloride (amide formation/sulphonamide formation)
Uses: herbicide

fonofos
O-ethyl *S*-phenyl ethylphosphonodithioate; [944-22-9]

$C_{10}H_{15}O_1P_1S_2$. M: 246.33.
Production:
• *O,O*-diethyl dithiophosphoric acid + chlorine + thiophenol (rearrangement/chlorination/dehydrochlorination)
Uses:
insecticide

Food Black 1
Black PN; 28440 (CI); E151 (EC)

$C_{28}H_{17}N_5Na_4O_{14}S_4$. M: 867.70.
Production:
• acetic anhydride + K acid + sulphanilic acid + 1,7-Cleve's acid (amide formation/diazotisation/azo coupling/diazotisation/azo coupling)
Uses:
food colorant

Food Blue 1 *See:* Acid Blue 74

Food Blue 2 *See:* Acid Blue 9

Food Blue 3 *See:* Acid Blue 1

Food Blue 4 *See:* indanthrone

Food Blue 5 *See:* Acid Blue 3

Food Brown 3
Chocolate Brown HT; 20285 (CI)

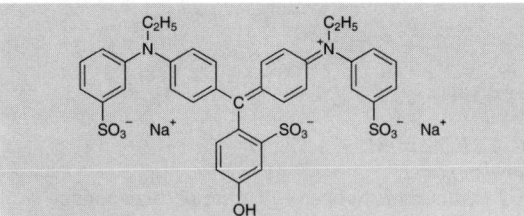

$C_{27}H_{18}N_4Na_2O_9S_2$. M: 652.57.
Production:
• 2,4-dihydroxybenzaldehyde + naphthionic acid (carbonyl reduction/diazotisation/azo coupling)
Uses:
food colorant

Food Green 1 *See:* Acid Green 3

Food Green 3
Fast Green FCF; 42053 (CI); FD&C Green No. 3 (FDC); [2353-45-9]

$C_{35}H_{30}N_2Na_2O_{10}S_3$. M: 780.79. Water-soluble.
Production:
• *p*-hydroxybenzaldehyde + ethylbenzylaniline (carbonyl addition/sulphonation/oxidation/sodium salt formation)
Uses: food colorant

Food Green 4 *See:* Acid Green 50

Food Orange 4 *See:* Acid Orange 10

Food Red 3 *See:* Acid Red 14

Food Red 4 *See:* Acid Red 13

Food Red 5 *See:* Acid Red 26

Food Red 7 *See:* Acid Red 18

Food Red 9 *See:* Acid Red 27

Food Red 10 *See:* Acid Red 1

Food Red 11 *See:* Acid Violet 7

Food Red 14 *See:* Acid Red 51

Food Red 17
Allura Red AC; Curry Red; 16035 (CI); FD&C Red
No. 40 (FDC); E129 (EC); [25956-17-6]

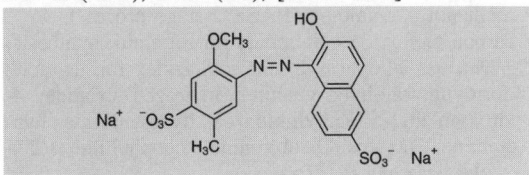

$C_{18}H_{14}N_2Na_2O_8S_2$. M: 496.42.
Production:
• 5-amino-4-methoxytoluene-2-sulphonic acid +
  Schaeffer's acid (diazotisation/azo coupling)
Uses: water-soluble food colorant

Food Violet 1 *See:* Acid Violet 17

Food Violet 2 *See:* Acid Violet 49

Food Yellow 2
See: 4-aminoazobenzene-3,4'-disulphonic acid

Food Yellow 3
Sunset Yellow FCF; Orange Yellow S; Pigment Yellow 104 (CI, aluminium salt); 15985 (CI); 15985:1 (CI,
aluminium salt); FD&C Yellow No. 6 (FDC); E110
(EC); [2783-94-0]

$C_{16}H_{10}N_2Na_2O_7S_2$. M: 452.37.
Production:
• sulphanilic acid + Schaeffer's acid (diazotisation/
  azo coupling)
Uses:
pigment (printing inks); water-soluble food colorant

Food Yellow 4 *See:* tartrazine

Food Yellow 13 *See:* Acid Yellow 3

formaldehyde
formalin (aqueous solution); methanal; [50-00-0]

$$H_2C=O$$

$C_1H_2O_1$. M: 30.03. Available as, typically, a 37% sol-

ution in water with 0–15% methanol and a polymerisation inhibitor. Colourless liquid with an unpleasant
odour. BP: 96°C. d: 1.08 kg/l (25°C). Miscible with
water and oxygenated solvents.
Production:
• methanol (catalytic dehydrogenation)
Derivatives:
acetochlor; Acid Blue 15; acrylic resins, amidated;
alkylphenol-polyamine adducts; allyl cyanoacrylate;
2-aminobutanol; 2-amino-2-methyl-1,3-propanediol;
2-aminopropane-1,3-diol; aminotris(methylene phosphonic acid); azamethiphos; azinphos-ethyl; azinphos-
methyl; Basic Red 14; Basic Yellow 37; betahistine;
bis(4-amino-3-methylcyclohexyl)methane; bis(*p*-dimeth-
ylaminophenyl)methane; bis[*O*-ethyl-(3,5-di-*t*-butyl-4-
hydroxybenzyl)phosphonic acid], calcium salt; *N,N*'-
bis(methoxymethyl)urone; bisphenol F diglycidyl ether;
bisthiosemi; 5-bromo-5-nitro-1,3-dioxane; 2-bromo-2-
nitropropane-1,3-diol; buprofezin; butachlor; 1,4-but-
ynediol; casein plastics; cefazolin; chloromethyl methyl
ether; chloromethyl pivalate; citral; cyanamide-formaldehyde resins; cyclohexanone resin; dazomet; dextropropoxyphene; 4,4'-diaminodiphenylmethane, crude;
2,6-di-*t*-butyldimethylamino-*p*-cresol; 2,6-di-*t*-butyl-4-
methoxymethylphenol; *O,O*-diethyl bis-
(2-hydroxyethyl)aminomethylphosphonate; diethylenetriaminepentaacetic acid, pentasodium salt; diethylene-
triaminepenta(methylene phosphonic acid); dilauryl 1,4-
dihydro-2,6-dimethylpyridine-3,5-dicarboxylate; dimethylaminomethylphenol; 2-dimethylamino-2-methyl-1-pro-
panol; 1,1-dimethylhydrazine; 1,3-dimethylol-4,5-dihyd-
roxyethylene urea; dimethylol dimethylhydantoin; *N,N*'-
dimethylolethylene urea; dimethylolpropylene urea; dimethylolurea; 4,4-dimethyl oxazolidine; *N,N*'-dimethyl-
piperazine; dioxolane; di-(pentamethylhydroxypiperidyl)
butyl-(di-3,5-*t*-butyl-4-hydroxybenzyl)malonate; dipyrone; Direct Yellow 6; eprazinone; ethion; 2-ethoxy-
ethyl cyanoacrylate; ethyl 2-cyanoacrylate; ethylenediaminetetraacetic acid; ethylenediaminetetra(methylene
phosphonic acid); 2-ethylhexyliminobis(methylenephosphonic acid); 2-ethyl-2-nitro-1,3-propanediol; flusilazole; fluspirilene; glycine; glycollic acid; glyphosate;
hexamethoxymethylmelamine; hexamethylenediamine-
tetra(methylenephosphonic acid); hexamethylenetetramine; 4,5,5,6,7,7-hexamethylindanopyran; hexetidine;
hydrochlorothiazide; hydroflumethiazide; hydroxyethylethylenediaminetriacetic acid, trisodium salt; 2-[(hydroxymethyl)amino]ethanol; 2-[(hydroxymethyl)amino]-2-
methylpropanol; 4-hydroxymethyl-5-methylimidazole
hydrochloride; *N*-hydroxymethyl-3,4,5,6-tetrahydroph-
thalimide; imidazole; iminodiacetic acid; isoprene;
melamine-formaldehyde resins; melamine-formaldehyde
resins, butylated; meprobamate; metazachlor; methacrifos; methacrolein; methidathion; methotrexate; β-
methoxyethyl cyanoacrylate; 3-methyl-2-buten-1-ol;
N,N'-methylenebisacrylamide; 4,4'-methylenebis(2-chl-
oroaniline); 4,4'-methylenebis(3-chloro-2,6-diethylanil-

ine); 4,4′-methylenebis(2,6-di-*t*-butylphenol); 2,2′-methylenebis(4-ethyl-6-*t*-butylphenol); methylenebis(maleimide); 2,2′-methylenebis(4-methyl-6-*t*-butylphenol); 2,2′-methylenebis(4-methyl-6-cyclohexylphenol); 2,2′-methylenebis[4-methyl-6-(α-methylcyclohexyl)phenol]; 2,2′-methylenebis(4-methyl-6-nonylphenol); α-methylheptenone; methyl isopropenyl ketone; 2-methyl-2-nitropropanol; methylnonylacetaldehyde; *N*-methylolacrylamide; 5-methylol 1-aza-3,7-dioxabicyclo[3,3,0]octane; methylol carbamate resins; *N*-methylol methacrylamide; 2-methyl-3-phenylbenzyl alcohol; *N*-methylpiperazine; methyl vinyl ketone; molsidomine; monomethylol dimethylhydantoin; morpholinomethyl-nitropropane adduct; neopentyl glycol; neopentyl glycol monohydroxypivalate; nifurtoinol; nitrilotriacetic acid; novolac resins; oxymetazoline; pamoic acid; pantolactone; paraformaldehyde; pentaerythritol; phenol-formaldehyde sulphonates; phenolic resins, oil-soluble, non oil-reactive; phenolic resins, oil-soluble, oil-reactive; *N*-phenylglycine; phorate; phosalone; phosmet; α-picoline; β-picoline; γ-picoline; piperonyl butoxide; polyacetal, homopolymers; polyacrylamide, aminomethylated; polyacrylamide, methylolated; polyacrylamide, sulphomethylated; poly(methylene-thiodiethyl ether); polyvinyl formal; propantheline bromide; pyridine; ranitidine; resol resins; resorcinol-formaldehyde resins; sarcosine; sodium dihydroxyethylglycine; sodium dinaphthalenemethane sulphonate; sodium formaldehyde sulphoxylate; sodium *N*-hydroxyethylglycine; sodium polynaphthalenemethane sulphonate; stearamidomethylpyridinium chloride; terbufos; tetrakis(hydroxymethyl)phosphonium chloride; tetrakis(hydroxymethyl)phosphonium sulphate; thenalidine; 2-(thiocyanomethylthio)benzothiazole; thioridazine; thiourea-urea-formaldehyde resins; timonacic; tolmetin; 1,2,4-triazole; *N,N′,N″*-triethylhexahydrotriazine; trimethylolethane; trimethylolglycoluril; trimethylolpropane; 2,3,5-trimethylphenol; trioxane; 1,3,5-tris(4-*t*-butyl-3-hydroxy-2,6-dimethylbenzyl)isocyanurate; 1,3,5-tris(3,5-di-*t*-butyl-4-hydroxybenzyl)isocyanurate; 2,4,6-tris(3,5-di-*t*-butyl-4-hydroxybenzyl)mesitylene; 2,4,6-tris(dimethylaminomethyl)phenol; *N,N′,N″*-tris(dimethylaminopropyl)hexahydro-1,3,5-triazine; *N,N′,N″*-tris(2-hydroxyethyl)hexahydrotriazine; tris(hydroxymethyl)nitromethane; tris(hydroxyphenyl)methane triglycidyl ether; urea-formaldehyde-furfuryl alcohol resins; urea-formaldehyde resins; urea-formaldehyde resins, anionic; urea-formaldehyde resins, butylated; urea-formaldehyde resins, cationic; 2-vinylpyridine; 4-vinylpyridine; xylometazoline
Uses:
nickelplating brightening agent; reagent (Eschweiler-Clarke amine methylation reaction, chloromethylation); latex coagulant; creaseproof textile finishing agent; disinfectant; embalming fluids; photographic gelatine hardening agent; preservative (hides, skins); reagent (casein plastic formalisation); crosslinking agent (paper waterproofing)

formamide
[75-12-7]

$C_1H_3N_1O_1$. M: 45.04. Colourless, hygroscopic liquid with a mild, ammonia-like odour. BP: 210°C. FP: 2°C. Soluble in water and alcohol.
Production:
• methanol + ammonia (BASF 2-stage process)
• carbon monoxide + ammonia (direct amide synthesis)
Derivatives: allopurinol; chlorothiazide; formic acid; *N*-formylmorpholine; guanine; hydrogen cyanide; 4-hydroxymethyl-5-methylimidazole hydrochloride; hypoxanthine; isazofos; theobromine; theophylline; 1,2,4-triazole; triazophos; triforine
Uses: aromatics, acetylene, butadiene extraction solvent; process solvent

formetanate hydrochloride
3-dimethylaminomethyleneaminophenyl methylcarbamate hydrochloride; [23422-53-9]

$$(CH_3)_2^+NHCH=N-\underset{}{\bigcirc}-OCNHCH_3 \qquad Cl^-$$

$C_{11}H_{16}Cl_1N_3O_2$. M: 257.72.
Production:
• dimethylformamide + *m*-aminophenol + methyl isocyanate (imine formation/isocyanate addition)
Uses: insecticide/acaricide

formic acid
E236 (EC); [64-18-6]

HCOOH

$C_1H_2O_2$. M: 46.03. Colourless liquid with a pungent odour. BP: 101°C MP: 7°C. d: 1.22 kg/l (20°C). Miscible with water. Flash point: 48°C (TCC). Also available as 85% or 90% aqueous solutions.
Production:
• carbon monoxide + methanol (two-stage formate process; coproduced with methyl formate)
• formamide (amide hydrolysis)
• sodium formate/calcium formate (acidification)
• naphtha, heavy (liquid-phase oxidation; coproduced with acetone/methyl ethyl ketone/acetic acid/propionic acid)
• *n*-butane (Celanese LPO process; coproduced with methanol/ethanol/acetone/methyl ethyl ketone/acetic acid/propionic acid/*n*-butyric acid/methyl formate)
Derivatives:
aluminium formate, basic; 3-amino-1,2,4-triazole; ammonium formate; anisyl formate; chlorzoxazone; citronellyl formate; etomidate; geranyl formate; isoamyl formate; linalyl formate; mecillinam; nickel formate; per-

formic acid; phenethyl formate; pyridoxine; sulfaphenazole; tricyclazole
Uses:
latex coagulant; disinfectant; food preservative; pH control/reducing agent (dyeing, electroplating, pickling baths); reagent (Leuckart-Wallach reactions, Eschweiler-Clarke reactions); silage fermentation additive; textile/leather/paper auxiliary

formothion
S-(*N*-formyl-*N*-methylcarbamoylmethyl) *O,O*-dimethyl phosphorodithioate; [2540-82-1]

$$CH_3NCCH_2SP(OCH_3)_2$$

with $\overset{O}{\underset{}{\|}}$, $\overset{S}{\underset{}{\|}}$, and CHO substituent

$C_6H_{12}N_1O_4P_1S_2$. M: 257.28.
Production:
• chloroacetyl chloride + *N*-methylformamide + *O,O*-dimethyl dithiophosphoric acid (amide formation/dehydrochlorination)
Uses:
insecticide/acaricide

2-formylbenzenesulphonic acid
See: benzaldehyde-2-sulphonic acid

3-formylbenzenesulphonic acid
See: benzaldehyde-3-sulphonic acid

3-formylcrotonyl acetate

$$CHO$$
$$CH_3C=CHCH_2OCCH_3$$
with $\overset{O}{\underset{}{\|}}$

$C_7H_{10}O_3$. M: 142.16. Not commercially traded.
Production:
• 1,4-butenediol + acetic acid + synthesis gas (acetylation/hydroformylation)
Derivatives:
vitamin A

_N_-formylmorpholine
[4394-85-8]

$$HCN \bigcirc O$$
with $\overset{O}{\underset{}{\|}}$

$C_5H_9N_1O_2$. M: 115.13. Solid or liquid. MP: 20°C. BP: 244°C.
Production:
• formamide + diethylene glycol (amine formation)
Uses: selective solvent (Morphylex aromatics extraction process)

fosamine-ammonium
ammonium ethyl carbamoylphosphonate; [25954-13-6]
$C_3H_{11}N_2O_4P_1$. M: 170.10.

$$NH_2COPOC_2H_5$$
with $\overset{O}{\underset{O^-}{\|}}$ and NH_4^+

Production:
• methyl formate + diethyl chlorophosphate + ammonia (dehydrochlorination/amine formation)
Uses: herbicide

fosetyl-aluminium
ethyl hydrogen phosphonate; [39148-24-8]

$$\left[C_2H_5OPO\right]_3Al$$
with $\overset{O}{\underset{H}{\|}}$

$C_6H_{18}Al_1O_9P_3$. M: 354.10.
Production:
• ethanol + phosphorus trichloride + aluminium sulphate (dehydrochlorination/Arbusov rearrangement/salt formation)
Uses: fungicide

4-FPAN *See:* 4-fluorophthalic anhydride

French chalk *See:* talc

fructose
D-fructose; [57-48-7]

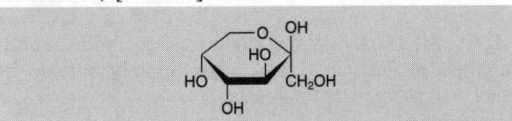

$C_6H_{12}O_6$. M: 180.16. White, crystalline powder. MP: 103–105°C with decomposition. Soluble in water. Slightly soluble in alcohol. Occurs in both puranose and furanose forms with the pyranose form predominating in aqueous solutions at room temperature.
Production:
• high-fructose syrup (separation)
Uses: food additive; parenteral nutrient ingredient

6FTA *See:* hexafluoropropane-2,2-bis(phenyl-3′,4′-dicarboxylic acid anhydride)

fthalide *See:* phthalide

fuberidazole
2-(2-furyl)benzimidazole; [3878-19-1]

$C_{11}H_8N_2O_1$. M: 184.19.
Production:
• furfural + *o*-phenylenediamine (condensation)
Uses: fungicide

fuchsine *See:* Basic Violet 14

fuel gas
Fuel gas is a term used to describe a petrochemical or refinery gas stream used as fuel in boilers or other equipment. Natural gas is often referred to as fuel gas when used for this purpose. The composition of fuel gas varies considerably from one source to another but often includes hydrogen, lower hydrocarbons, carbon monoxide, carbon dioxide, nitrogen and water. It is usually characterised by its heating value. Coke oven gas is a type of fuel gas produced by the carbonisation of coal.
Uses: electricity/steam generation

fuller's earth
attapulgite; palygorskite
Clay composed mainly of montmorillonites or bentonites. Grades used in drilling muds are composed mainly of palygorskite, but called 'attapulgite'.
Uses: vegetable/mineral oil decolouring agent; filter medium; viscosifier (saltwater drilling muds)

fumaric acid
[110-17-8]

$C_4H_4O_4$. M: 116.07. White, odourless, crystalline solid. Sublimes at 200°C. d: 1.62 kg/l. Slightly soluble in water and oxygenated solvents.
Production:
• maleic anhydride (hydration/isomerisation; coproduced with DL-malic acid)
Derivatives:
L-aspartic acid; biotin; diallyl fumarate; di-*n*-butyl fumarate; ferrous fumarate; Fluorescent Brightener 133; Fluorescent Brightener 135; maleic resins; L-malic acid; styrene-fumarate copolymers
Uses:
alkyd/unsaturated polyester resin comonomer; acidulant (soft drinks, fruit juice, pie fillings, wine, sour doughs)

fumaric resins *See:* maleic resins

funori
Extract of *Gloiopeltis furcata* seaweed produced in Japan.
Uses: textile sizing/finishing agent

furalaxyl
N-(2-furoyl)-*N*-(2,6-xylyl)-DL-alaninate; [57646-30-7]
$C_{17}H_{19}N_1O_4$. M: 301.35.
Production:
• 2-furoic acid + 2,6-xylidine + methyl α-chloropropionate (amide formation/amine formation)

Uses: fungicide

furan
furane; [110-00-9]

$C_4H_4O_1$. M: 68.07. Volatile liquid with a strong, ethereal odour. BP: 32–33°C. FP: -86°C. d: 0.94 kg/l (20°C). Slightly soluble in water. Miscible with most organic solvents. Flash point: -35°C (TCC).
Production:
• furfural (decarbonylation)
Derivatives: 2-acetylfuran; endothal-sodium; 2-propionylfuran; pyrrole; tegafur; tetrahydrofuran

2-furanmethanethiol *See:* furfuryl mercaptan

furan resins
furane resins

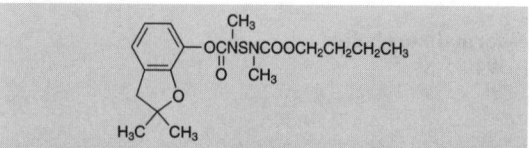

Dark brown, liquid thermosetting resin cured by acid, commonly *p*-toluenesulphonic acid. The cured resins are characterised by their good heat, fire and chemical resistance properties.
Production:
• furfural + furfuryl alcohol (polycondensation)
Uses: grinding wheels; laminating resins (chemical plant components/handling equipment)

furathiocarb
[65907-30-4]

$C_{18}H_{26}N_2O_5S_1$. M: 382.47.
Production:
• carbofuran + sulphur dichloride + methylamine + *n*-butyl chloroformate (dehydrochlorination/dehydrochlorination/dehydrochlorination)
Uses: insecticide

furfural
furfuraldehyde; [98-01-1]
$C_5H_4O_2$. M: 96.08. Colourless liquid with a character-

istic odour. Discoloured by light and air. BP: 162°C. FP: -37°C. Solubility in water: 83 g/kg solution (20°C). Flash point: 62°C (TCC).

Production:
• bagasse/corncobs/quebracho wood, extracted/sulphite pulp waste liquor/chestnut wood, extracted/cereal waste (extraction)
Derivatives: fuberidazole; furan; furan resins; furfuryl alcohol; furfurylamine; 2-furoic acid; 2-methyltetrahydrofuran; 5-nitrofurfural diacetate; urea-formaldehyde-furfuryl alcohol resins
Uses: novolac resin comonomer (moulding powders); selective solvent (butadiene/aromatics extraction); solvent (fatty acid/wood rosin separation)

furfuryl alcohol
[98-00-0]

$C_5H_6O_2$. M: 98.10. Colourless liquid with a mild odour. BP: 170°C. d: 1.13 kg/l (20°C). Miscible with water and oxygenated solvents.
Production:
• furfural (hydrogenation)
Derivatives: furan resins; furfuryl mercaptan; levulinic acid; naftidrofuryl; ranitidine; tetrahydrofurfuryl alcohol; urea-formaldehyde-furfuryl alcohol resins
Uses: gel retarder (casein/protein glues); non-reactive epoxy resin diluent

furfurylamine
2-aminomethylfuran; [617-89-0]

$C_5H_7N_1O_1$. M: 97.12. Colourless liquid. BP: 145°C. d: 1.10 kg/l (20°C). Miscible with water. Soluble in oxygenated solvents.
Production:
• furfural + ammonia (reductive ammoniation)
Derivatives: furosemide

furfuryl mercaptan
2-furanmethanethiol; 2-furfuryl mercaptan; [98-02-2]

$C_5H_6O_1S_1$. M: 114.16. Liquid with unpleasant odour. BP: 160°C. d: 1.13 kg/l (20°C).
Production:
• furfuryl alcohol + thiourea (thiolation)
Uses:
flavouring ingredient (coffee aromas)

furnace black *See:* carbon black

furnace coke *See:* metallurgical coke

2-furoic acid
furan-2-carboxylic acid; [88-14-2]

$C_5H_4O_3$. M: 112.08. Crystalline solid. MP: 129–130°C. BP: 230–232°C. Soluble in water and oxygenated solvents.
Production:
• furfural (carbonyl oxidation)
Derivatives: furalaxyl; prazosin

furonazide
4-pyridinecarboxylic acid 1-(2-furanyl)ethylidene hydrazide; [3460-67-1]

$C_{12}H_{11}N_3O_2$. M: 229.24.
Production:
• 2-acetylfuran + isoniazid (imine formation)
Uses: tuberculostatic drug

furosemide
[54-31-9]

$C_{12}H_{11}Cl_1N_2O_5S_1$. M: 330.73.
Production:
• 2,4-dichloro-5-sulphamoylbenzoic acid + chlorosulphonic acid + ammonia + furfurylamine (amide formation)
Uses: diuretic drug

2-furyl methyl ketone *See:* 2-acetylfuran

fusel oil
Oily liquid with an unpleasant odour. Boiling range: 120–140°C. The major constituents are isoamyl alcohol, 2-methyl-1-butanol and isobutanol.
Production:
• molasses/starch hydrolysate/whey/sugar cane juice/sulphite pulp waste liquor/sugar beet juice + yeast (fermentation; byproduct of ethanol production)
Derivatives: amyl alcohol, primary
Uses: solvent

G

G acid

G salt (potassium salt); 2-hydroxynaphthalene-6,8-disulphonic acid; 2-naphthol-6,8-disulphonic acid; 7-naphthol-1,3-disulphonic acid; [118-32-1]

$C_{10}H_8O_7S_2$. M: 304.29. Available commercially as the free acid or as the potassium salt.

Production:
- β-naphthol (sulphonation; coproduced with R acid)

Derivatives: Acid Orange 10; Acid Red 18; Acid Red 73; Acid Red 114; Acid Violet 58; amino-G acid

galactaric acid *See:* mucic acid

galena *See:* zinc-lead sulphide ores

gallic acid

3,4,5-trihydroxybenzoic acid; [149-91-7]

$C_7H_6O_5$. M: 170.12. Available as the monohydrate. White needles. Sublimes at 210°C. d: 1.69 kg/l (20°C). Soluble in water and oxygenated solvents.

Production:
- *p*-hydroxybenzoic acid (sulphonation/alkali fusion)

Derivatives: bismuth subgallate; dodecyl gallate; *n*-octyl gallate; *n*-propyl gallate; pyrogallol

gamma acid

6-amino-4-hydroxynaphthalene-2-sulphonic acid; 7-amino-1-hydroxynaphthalene-3-sulphonic acid; 2-amino-8-naphthol-6-sulphonic acid; 6-amino-4-naphthol-2-sulphonic acid; γ acid; [90-51-7]

$C_{10}H_9N_1O_4S_1$. M: 239.25.

Production:
- amino-G acid (alkali fusion)

Derivatives:
Acid Brown 20; Acid Red 32; Acid Red 37; Acid Red 42; Acid Red 57; Acid Red 68; Acid Red 266; Acid Red 337; Acid Violet 1; Acid Violet 14; Direct Black 3; Direct Black 9; Direct Black 22; Direct Black 80; *N*-phenylgamma acid; Reactive Orange 16

garlic oil

Orange oil with a garlic-like odour. Produced by steam distillation of garlic (*Allium sativum*) bulbs. d: 1.05 kg/l (15°C).

Uses: flavouring ingredient

gas oil, heavy

Brownish distillate. BP: 300–350°C. d: ~0.86 kg/l. The term is not used precisely in the industry and often refers to vacuum gas oil which has a boiling range of 350–500°C. The product is desulphurised by hydrotreatment before sale as a fuel.

Production:
- crude oil (atmospheric distillation; coproduced with naphtha, light/naphtha, heavy/kerosene/gas oil, light/long residue/refinery gas)
- long residue (visbreaking; coproduced with naphtha, heavy/refinery gas)
- long residue (thermal cracking; coproduced with naphtha, heavy/gas oil, light/refinery gas)
- gas oil, vacuum (hydrocracking; coproduced with naphtha, light/naphtha, heavy/kerosene/gas oil, light/refinery gas)
- lubricant oils, distillates (hydrocracking; byproduct of lubricant oils, hydrocracked/brightstock production)
- heavy cycle oil/pyrolysis tar/coal tar pitch (delayed coking process; coproduced with naphtha, heavy/gas oil, light/needle coke/refinery gas)
- short residue (delayed coking process; coproduced with naphtha, heavy/gas oil, light/sponge coke, green/shot coke/refinery gas)
- gas oil, vacuum (fluid coking; coproduced with naphtha, heavy/fluid coke/refinery gas)
- gas oil, vacuum (Flexicoke process; coproduced with naphtha, heavy/refinery gas/coke oven gas)

Derivatives: naphthenic acid

Uses: diesel fuel (stationary and marine engines); boiler/industrial/marine/locomotive fuel oil blending component; industrial/commercial heating oil

gas oil, light

Brownish distillate. BP: 235–300°C. d: ~0.84 kg/l. The term is not used precisely and generally refers to the lighter of two gas oil streams in a refinery. The product is usually desulphurised by hydrotreatment before use.

Production:
- crude oil (atmospheric distillation; coproduced with naphtha, light/naphtha, heavy/kerosene/gas oil,

heavy/long residue/refinery gas)
- long residue (thermal cracking; coproduced with naphtha, heavy/gas oil, heavy/refinery gas)
- gas oil, vacuum (hydrocracking; coproduced with naphtha, light/naphtha, heavy/kerosene/gas oil, heavy/refinery gas)
- heavy cycle oil/pyrolysis tar/coal tar pitch (delayed coking process; coproduced with naphtha, heavy/gas oil, heavy/needle coke/refinery gas)
- short residue (delayed coking process; coproduced with naphtha, heavy/gas oil, heavy/sponge coke, green/shot coke/refinery gas)
- synthesis gas (Synthol Fischer-Tropsch process; coproduced with naphtha, light, Synthol/naphtha, heavy/wax, Fischer-Tropsch/oxygenates, Fischer-Tropsch, mixed/refinery gas)
- methanol (Mobil MTG process; coproduced with naphtha, light/naphtha, heavy/refinery gas)
- synthesis gas (Shell MDS process; coproduced with naphtha, heavy/kerosene/wax, Fischer-Tropsch/refinery gas)
- lubricant oils, distillates (hydrocracking; byproduct of lubricant oils, hydrocracked/brightstock production)

Derivatives:
C_4-stream, steam-cracked; ethylene; gasoline, pyrolysis; high-boiling aliphatic solvents; high-boiling aliphatic solvents, dearomatised; naphthenic acid; *n*-paraffins (C_{14}-C_{18}); propylene; pyrolysis tar
Uses:
diesel fuel; domestic/industrial heating fuel; mineral flotation agent; solvent (cutback bitumens); wash oil (ethylene purification)

gas oil, light, Arge
Highly linear, olefinic gas oil stream.
Production:
- synthesis gas (Arge Fischer-Tropsch process; coproduced with naphtha, heavy/wax, Fischer-Tropsch/oxygenates, Fischer-Tropsch, mixed/refinery gas)
Derivatives: dodecylbenzene, linear

gas oil, vacuum
VGO
Oily hydrocarbon fraction boiling in the range 350–510°C, with decomposition at normal pressures.
Production:
- long residue (vacuum distillation; coproduced with short residue/bitumen/lubricant oils, distillates)
Derivatives: coke oven gas; fluid coke; gas oil, heavy; gas oil, light; gasoline, catalytic-cracker; heavy cycle oil; kerosene; light cycle oil; naphtha, heavy; naphtha, light; refinery gas

gasoline, alkylate
Mixed stream consisting of branched C_5–C_{10} hydrocarbons with a high average octane rating.

Production:
- raffinate II/propylene/C_4-stream, refinery + isobutane (HF alkylation)
Uses:
petrol blending component

gasoline, catalytic-cracker
gasoline, FCC; gasoline, high-octane
Production:
- deasphalted oil/long residue/gas oil, vacuum (fluidised-bed catalytic cracking; coproduced with light cycle oil/heavy cycle oil/refinery gas)
Derivatives: cresylic acid; C_5-stream, refinery; gasoline, mixed ether; sodium sulphide
Uses: aviation gasoline blending component; petrol blending component

gasoline, dearomatised
Production:
- reformate/gasoline, pyrolysis (solvent extraction; coproduced with aromatics, mixed)
Derivatives:
C_4-stream, steam-cracked; ethylene; gasoline, pyrolysis; propylene; pyrolysis tar
Uses: petrol blending component

gasoline, mixed ether
Gasoline blending stream enriched with mixed C_4–C_6 methyl ethers.
Production:
- methanol + gasoline, catalytic-cracker + C_4-stream, refinery (BP Etherol process)
Uses: petrol blending component

gasoline, natural
condensate; natural gas liquids; NGL
Mixed product consisting of pentanes and higher hydrocarbons which separate from wet natural gas at normal temperatures and pressures. When the wet gas is associated with oil, the natural gasoline is often blended into the crude oil for transport to the treatment plant. In pure gas fields it is processed and handled separately.
Production:
- natural gas, wet (fractionation; coproduced with natural gas/ethane/liquified petroleum gas)
Derivatives: C_4-stream, steam-cracked; ethylene; gasoline, pyrolysis; propylene; pyrolysis tar
Uses: petrol blending component

gasoline, polymer
Mixed stream containing unsaturated C_2–C_4 dimers, trimers and tetramers.
Production:
- refinery gas (phosphoric acid-catalysed oligomerisation)
- refinery gas (UOP solid-bed catalyst process)

Derivatives: dodecene, branched; heptane; heptene, branched; hexane, mixed; *n*-hexane; hexene, branched; isohexane; isopentane; nonene, branched; octene, branched; *n*-pentane
Uses: aviation gasoline blending component

gasoline, pyrolysis
Mixed hydrocarbon stream from steam cracking containing 60–75% aromatics and 12–15% dienes. BR: 45– 190°C.
Production:
• liquified petroleum gas (steam cracking; coproduced with ethylene/propylene/C_4-stream, steam-cracked/pyrolysis tar)
• naphtha, heavy/gasoline, natural/gasoline, dearomatised (steam cracking; coproduced with ethylene-/propylene/C_4-stream, steam-cracked/pyrolysis tar)
• gas oil, light (steam cracking; coproduced with ethylene/propylene/C_4-stream, steam-cracked/ pyrolysis tar)
Derivatives: C_5-stream, steam-cracked; gasoline, dearomatised; gasoline, pyrolysis, hydrogenated

gasoline, pyrolysis, hydrogenated
Stabilised feedstocks suitable for aromatics extraction. Hydrogenated removes the unsaturated aliphatic and sulphur compounds from the pyrolysis gasoline. Typical properties: BR: 40–180°C. Benzene content: 40%. Toluene content: 20%.
Production:
• gasoline, pyrolysis (hydrorefining)
Derivatives:
aromatics, mixed

gasoline, reformate *See:* reformate

gasoline, straight-run *See:* naphtha, light

gauno phosphate
Natural phosphate ore produced mainly on the island of Nauru and exported to Australia.
Uses:
fertiliser

GBL *See:* γ-butyrolactone

GDO *See:* glycerol dioleate

gelatine
[9000-70-8]
Colourless or yellowish sheet, flakes or powder. Gelatine is classified commercially as being edible, technical, photographic or pharmaceutical quality, depending on its physical and chemical properties. The poorer grades of technical gelatine are similar to animal glue (*qv*). Product obtained by acid extraction is referred to as 'Type A', that by alkali extraction as 'Type B'. The two differ slightly in their isoelectric points and pH but have similar physical properties.
Production:
• ossein/limed calfhide splits (alkali extraction)
• pigskin + hydrochloric acid (acid extraction)
• chrome-tanned hides (magnesia extraction process)
Uses:
drug capsules; food ingredient (jellies, ice cream, confectionery, meat products); microencapsulation coacervate ingredient (carbonless copying paper); pharmaceutical tablet binder; photographic emulsion

geraniol
3,7-dimethyl-*trans*-2,6-octadien-1-ol; [106-24-1]

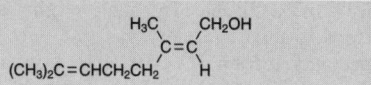

$C_{10}H_{18}O_1$. M: 154.25. Colourless liquid with a rose-like odour. BP: 230°C. d: 0.89 kg/l (20°C). Insoluble in water. Miscible with water. The corresponding *cis*-isomer is nerol.
Production:
• palmarosa oil (fractionation)
• citronella oil, Java (fractionation; coproduced with (±)-citronellol/(+)-citronellal)
• geraniol-nerol, mixed (isomer separation; coproduced with nerol)
Derivatives: geranyl acetate; geranyl butyrate; geranyl formate; geranyl isobutyrate; geranyl isovalerate; geranyl phenylacetate; geranyl propionate; geranyl tiglate; tetrahydrogeraniol
Uses: fragrance ingredient (soap, cosmetics)

geraniol-nerol, mixed
3,7-dimethyl-2,6-octadien-1-ol

$$(CH_3)_2C=CHCH_2CH_2\overset{\overset{\displaystyle CH_3}{|}}{C}=CHCH_2OH$$

$C_{10}H_{18}O_1$. M: 154.25. Mixed product comprising the *cis* and *trans*-isomers of 3,7-dimethyl-2,6-octadien-1-ol.
Production:
• linalool (isomerisation)
• myrcene (hydrochlorination/hydration/esterification/ separation/ester hydrolysis)
Derivatives:
citral; (±)-citronellal; (±)-citronellol; geraniol; nerol
Uses: fragrance ingredient

geranium oil
Greenish-yellow to brown liquid. d: ~0.90 kg/l (15°C). Slightly soluble in water. Soluble in oxygenated and chlorinated solvents. Extracted from various *Pelargonium* species and hybrids. The main producing countries are Reunion, India, Kenya, Russia, Egypt and the north African countries. The main component of the oil is (−)-citronellol.

Derivatives: (–)-citronellol
Uses: fragrance ingredient

geranonitrile
geranic acid nitrile; geranyl nitrile; [5146-66-7]

$$(CH_3)_2C=CHCH_2CH_2\overset{CH_3}{\underset{|}{C}}=CHCN$$

$C_{10}H_{15}N_1$. M: 149.24. Colourless liquid. Citrus odour.
Production:
• citral + hydroxylamine sulphate (imine formation/
  dehydration)
• β-methylheptenone + acetonitrile (condensation)
Uses: fragrance ingredient (soap, detergents)

geranyl acetate
geraniol acetate; [105-87-3]

$$(CH_3)_2C=CHCH_2CH_2\overset{CH_3}{\underset{|}{C}}=CHCH_2O\overset{O}{\overset{||}{C}}CH_3$$

$C_{12}H_{20}O_2$. M: 196.29. Colourless liquid with a lavender-like odour. BP: 242°C. d: 0.91 kg/l (20°C). Insoluble in water. Soluble in oxygenated solvents.
Production:
• geraniol + acetic acid (esterification)
Uses: fragrance ingredient

geranylacetone
6,10-dimethyl-5,9-undecadien-2-one; [689-67-8]

$$(CH_3)_2C=CHCH_2CH_2\overset{CH_3}{\underset{|}{C}}=CHCH_2CH_2\overset{O}{\overset{||}{C}}CH_3$$

$C_{13}H_{22}O_1$. M: 194.32. Colourless liquid with a rose-like odour.
Production:
• linalool + ethyl acetoacetate (condensation/
  decarboxylation)
Derivatives:
nerolidol; squalane
Uses: fragrance ingredient

geranyl butyrate
geraniol butyrate; [106-29-6]

$$(CH_3)_2C=CHCH_2CH_2\overset{CH_3}{\underset{|}{C}}=CHCH_2O\overset{O}{\overset{||}{C}}CH_2CH_2CH_3$$

$C_{14}H_{24}O_2$. M: 224.34. Colourless liquid with a floral odour. BP: 113°C (1.5 kPa). d: 0.93 kg/l (20°C). Insoluble in water. Soluble in alcohol and ether.
Production:
• geraniol + *n*-butyric acid (esterification)
Uses: flavouring/fragrance ingredient

geranyl formate
geraniol formate; [105-86-2]
$C_{11}H_{18}O_2$. M: 182.26. Colourless liquid with a rose-like odour.

$$(CH_3)_2C=CHCH_2CH_2\overset{CH_3}{\underset{|}{C}}=CHCH_2O\overset{O}{\overset{||}{C}}H$$

Production:
• geraniol + formic acid (esterification)
Uses: fragrance ingredient

geranyl isobutyrate
geraniol isobutyrate; [2345-26-8]

$$(CH_3)_2C=CHCH_2CH_2\overset{CH_3}{\underset{|}{C}}=CHCH_2O\overset{O}{\overset{||}{C}}CH(CH_3)_2$$

$C_{14}H_{24}O_2$. M: 224.34. Colourless liquid with a rose-like odour. BP: 265°C. d: 0.90 kg/l (20°C). Insoluble in water. Soluble in alcohol.
Production:
• geraniol + isobutyric acid (esterification)
Uses: fragrance/flavouring ingredient

geranyl isovalerate
geraniol isovalerate; [109-20-6]

$$(CH_3)_2C=CHCH_2CH_2\overset{CH_3}{\underset{|}{C}}=CHCH_2O\overset{O}{\overset{||}{C}}CH_2CH(CH_3)_2$$

$C_{15}H_{26}O_2$. M: 238.37. Colourless liquid with a rose-like odour. BP: 277°C. d: 0.89 kg/l (20°C). Insoluble in water. Soluble in alcohol.
Production:
• geraniol + isovaleric acid (esterification)
Uses: fragrance/flavouring ingredient

geranyl phenylacetate
3,7-dimethyl-2,6-octadien-1-yl phenylacetate; [102-22-7]

$$(CH_3)_2C=CHCH_2CH_2\overset{CH_3}{\underset{|}{C}}=CHCH_2O\overset{O}{\overset{||}{C}}CH_2-\langle\rangle$$

$C_{18}H_{24}O_2$. M: 272.39. Viscous, yellow liquid with mild, sweet odour.
Production:
• phenylacetic acid + geraniol (esterification)
Uses: perfume fixative

geranyl propionate
geraniol propionate; [105-90-8]

$$(CH_3)_2C=CHCH_2CH_2\overset{CH_3}{\underset{|}{C}}=CHCH_2O\overset{O}{\overset{||}{C}}CH_2CH_3$$

$C_{13}H_{22}O_2$. M: 210.32. Colourless liquid with a rose-like odour. BP: 257°C. d: 0.90 kg/l (20°C). Insoluble in water. Soluble in alcohol.
Production:
• geraniol + propionic acid (esterification)
Uses: fragrance ingredient

geranyl tiglate
$C_{15}H_{24}O_2$. M: 236.35. Colourless liquid with a floral odour. d: 0.93 kg/l (15°C). Insoluble in water.

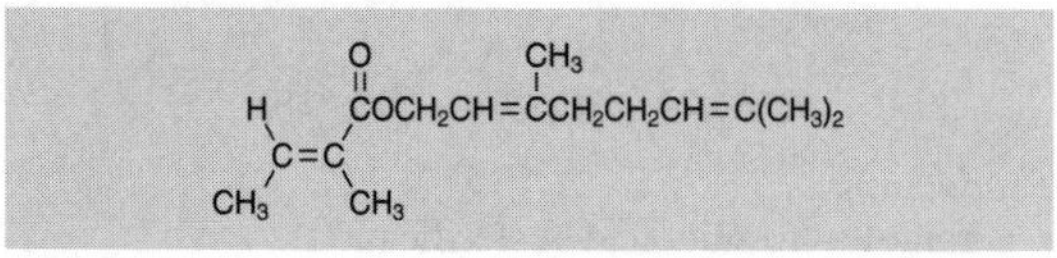

Production:
• geraniol + tiglic acid (esterification)
Uses: fragrance/flavouring ingredient

germanium
[7440-56-4]

Ge

Ge_1. M: 72.59. Grey, shiny, brittle semi-metal. MP: 937°C. d: 5.32 kg/l (25°C). Semiconductor. Stable in air and water at ambient temperatures.
Production:
• germanium oxide (hydrogenation/zone refining)
Uses: infra-red optical devices; semiconductor devices

germanium oxide
germanium dioxide; [1310-53-8]

GeO_2

Ge_1O_2. M: 104.59. White powder. MP: 1,115°C. d: 4.23 kg/l (25°C). Slightly soluble in water.
Production:
• germanium concentrates + hydrochloric acid (salt formation/hydration)
Derivatives: germanium

gibberellic acid
[77-06-5]

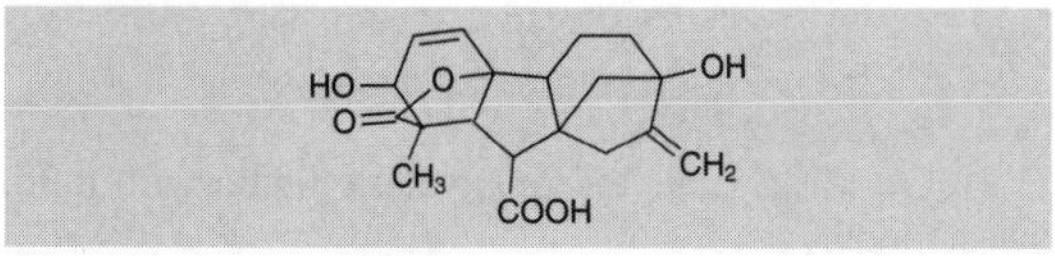

$C_{19}H_{22}O_6$. M: 346.38.
Production:
• *Gibberella fujikuroi* fungus (extraction)
Uses: brewing enzyme activator; plant growth regulator

gilsonite *See:* asphaltite

ginger oil
[8007-08-7]
Yellow liquid. Produced by steam distillation of ginger root (*Zingiber officinale* rhizomes). d: 0.88 kg/l (15°C). Slightly soluble in alcohol. The main producing areas are West Africa and South-East Asia.
Uses:
food/drink flavouring ingredient

glafenine
[3820-67-5]
$C_{19}H_{17}Cl_1N_2O_4$. M: 372.81.

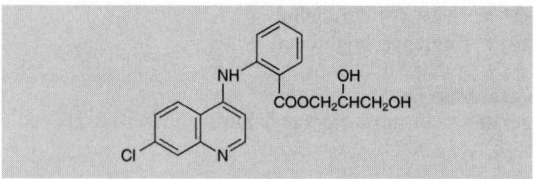

Production:
• glycerol + acetone + *o*-nitrobenzoyl chloride + 4,7-dichloroquinoline (diacetal formation/ esterification/nitro reduction/amine formation/ hydrolysis)
Uses:
analgesic/antiphlogistic drug

Glauber's salt *See:* sodium sulphate

glibenclamide
gliburide; glyburide; [10238-21-8]

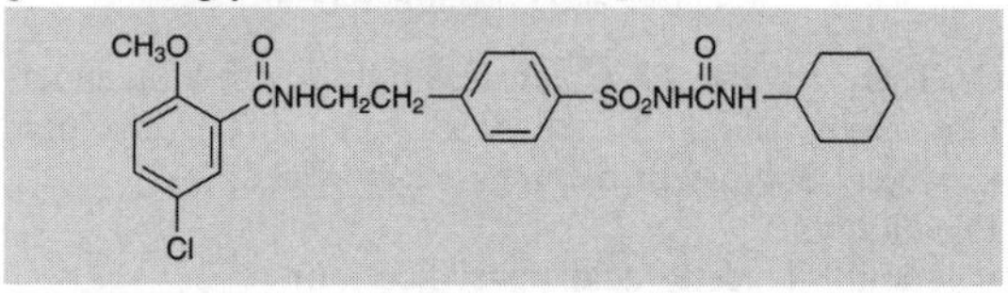

$C_{23}H_{28}Cl_1N_3O_5S_1$. M: 494.00.
Production:
• 5-chlorosalicylic acid + dimethyl sulphate + 2-phenylethylamine + chlorosulphonic acid + ammonia + cyclohexyl isocyanate (methylation/ amide formation/chlorosulphonation/sulphonamide formation/isocyanate addition)
Uses: antidiabetic drug

glibornuride
[26944-48-9]

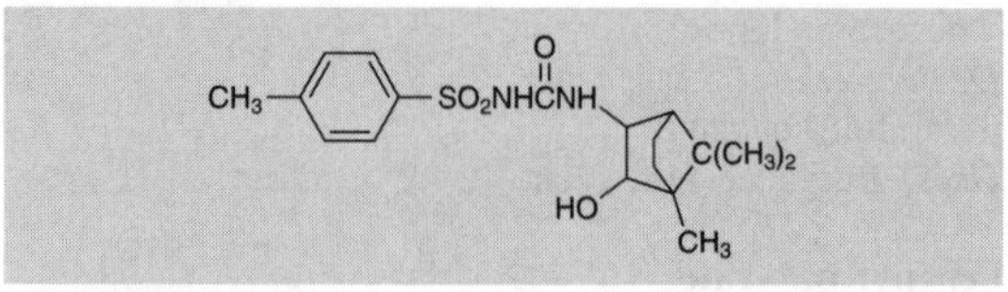

$C_{18}H_{24}N_2O_4S_1$. M: 364.46.
Production:
• camphor + *n*-butyl nitrite + *p*-toluenesulphonyl isocyanate (nitrosation/hydrogenation/isocyanate addition)
Uses: antidiabetic drug

glipizide
[29094-61-9]

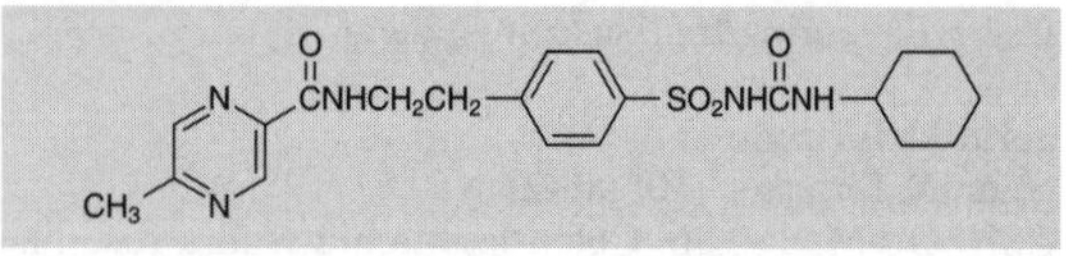

$C_{21}H_{27}N_5O_4S_1$. M: 445.55.

Production:
- 5-methylpyrazine-2-carboxylic acid + 2-phenyl-ethylamine + chlorosulphonic acid + ammonia + cyclohexyl isocyanate (amide formation/chlorosulphonation/sulphonamide formation/isocyanate addition)

Uses: antidiabetic drug

glisoxepide
[25046-79-1]

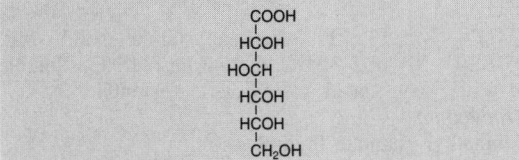

$C_{20}H_{27}N_5O_5S_1$. M: 449.53.
Production:
- acetonylacetone + sodium nitrite + 2-phenylethylamine + chlorosulphonic acid + ammonia + ethyl chloroformate + hexamethyleneimine (nitrosation/cyclisation/side-chain oxidation/amide formation/chlorosulphonation/sulphonamide formation/dehydrochlorination/diazotisation/hydrogenation/urea formation)

Uses: antidiabetic drug

Gln *See:* L-glutamine

Glu *See:* L-glutamic acid

glucoamylase
amyloglucosidase; E.C.3.2.1.3 (Enzyme Commission); [9032-08-0]
Exoamylase enzyme which hydrolyses α-1,4-glucoside bonds. α-1,3- and α-1,6-bonds are also cleaved, but at a slower rate.
Production:
- mould fermentation medium + *Aspergillus niger* mould/*Rhizopus niveus* mould (fermentation)

Derivatives: starch hydrolysate

gluconic acid
dextronic acid; glyconic acid; [526-95-4]

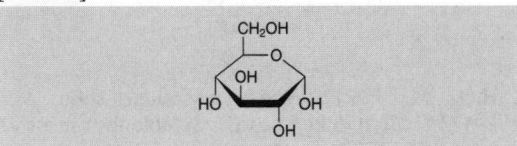

$C_6H_{12}O_7$. M: 196.16. Available commercially as a light amber liquid containing 50% active matter in water.
Production:
- sodium gluconate (acidification)

Derivatives:
copper gluconate; ferrous gluconate
Uses: sequestrant (alkaline dairy, brewery cleaners)

gluconolactone
gluconic acid δ-lactone; glucono delta lactone; [90-80-2]

$C_6H_{10}O_6$. M: 178.14. White crystals. Decompose on heating above 153°C. Soluble in water with hydrolysis forming acidic solutions.
Production:
- sodium gluconate (esterification)

Uses: acidulant (baking powder, processed meat, prepared foods)

D-glucose
corn sugar; dextrose; α-dextrose; grape sugar; [50-99-7]

$C_6H_{12}O_6$. M: 180.16. White, crystalline powder. MP: 156–158°C. Soluble in water. Slightly soluble in alcohol. The commercial product is the natural D(+)-enantiomer monohydrate.
Production:
- starch hydrolysate (drying)

Derivatives: chloralose
Uses: food ingredient; humectant (starch adhesives); raw material (caramel production)

glucose isomerase
E.C.5.3.1.18 (Enzyme Commission); Maxazyme; Sweetzyme; [9055-00-9]
Immobilised enzyme used to convert glucose to fructose.
Production:
- microbial fermentation medium + *Bacillus actinoplanes* bacteria (fermentation/extraction)

Derivatives:
high-fructose syrup

glucose syrup
corn syrup; [8029-43-4]
Clear, colourless, viscous liquid containing dextrose, maltose and higher di- and polysaccharides. Different grades are characterised by their reduced sugar content expressed in terms of dextrose equivalents (DE). By convention, grades with DE<20 are termed 'maltodextrin' (*qv*), while those with DE>80 are called 'starch hydrolysate' (*qv*). Acid conversion produces syrups with DE: 30–47 of which 'confectionery syrups' with

DE: ~40 are the most popular. Acid-enzyme conversion gives DE: 60–70 while enzyme converted syrups usually have a high maltose content.
Production:
• starch + α-amylase, bacterial/α-amylase, fungal (acid-enzyme conversion)
• starch + hydrochloric acid (acid conversion)
• starch + α-amylase, bacterial (enzyme conversion)
Derivatives:
chromium sulphate, basic; high-maltose syrup; DL-lactic acid; maltose; starch hydrolysate
Uses: food sweetener (confectionery, fruit processing, alcoholic drinks, baked produce, prepared foods, soft drinks); microbial fermentation nutrient

D-glucuronolactone
D-glucurono-6,3-lactone; [32449-92-6]

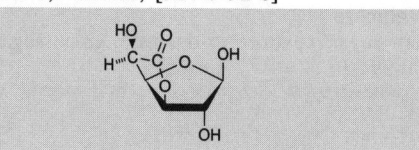

$C_6H_8O_6$. M: 176.12. White, crystalline solid. MP: 172–173°C. d: 1.76 kg/l (20°C). Soluble in water with gradual reversion to the free acid.
Production:
• starch hydrolysate (aldehyde protection/oxidation/ hydrolysis/dehydration)
Derivatives: glyconiazide

glufosinate-ammonium
ammonium 2-amino-4-(hydroxymethylphosphinyl)-butanoate; [77182-82-2]

$$CH_3PCH_2CH_2CHCOO^- \quad NH_4^+$$

$C_5H_{15}N_2O_4P_1$. M: 198.15.
Production:
• phosphorus trichloride + methyl chloride + acrolein + hydrogen cyanide + ammonia (Kinnear-Perrin reaction/hydrolysis/Michael addition/Strecker synthesis)
Uses: herbicide

L-glutamic acid
L-2-aminopentanedioic acid; Glu; [56-86-0]

$$HOOCCH_2CH_2-\overset{NH_2}{\underset{H}{C}}-COOH$$

$C_5H_9N_1O_4$. M: 147.13. Available commercially as the naturally-occurring L(+)-enantiomer in the form of the free base or hydrochloride salt. Crystalline solid. Sublimes when heated to 200°C. d: 1.54 kg/l (20°C). Soluble in water.

Production:
• microbial fermentation medium + *Corynebacterium glutamicum* bacteria (fermentation/separation)
Derivatives: folic acid; methotrexate; monopotassium glutamate; monosodium glutamate; oxytocin
Uses:
gastric medicines; infusion solutions/diagnostic aids; raw material (peptide drugs)

L-glutamine
L-2-amino-4-carbamoylbutanoic acid; Gln; levoglutamide; [56-85-9]

$$H_2NCCH_2CH_2-\overset{NH_2}{\underset{H}{C}}-COOH$$

$C_5H_{10}N_2O_3$. M: 146.14. Available commercially as the naturally-occurring L(+)-enantiomer. Decomposes on heating above 185°C. Soluble in water.
Production:
• microbial fermentation medium + *Corynebacterium glutamicum* bacteria (fermentation/separation; byproduct of L-glutamic acid production)
Uses: infusion solutions/diagnostic aids; raw material (peptide drugs)

glutaraldehyde
glutaral; pentane-1,5-dial; [111-30-8]

$$OHCCH_2CH_2CH_2CHO$$

$C_5H_8O_2$. M: 100.11. Colourless liquid. BP: 187–189°C. Soluble in water. Usually sold as a 50% or 25% solution in water.
Production:
• 2-methoxydihydropyran (hydrolysis)
Derivatives: 1,5-pentanediol
Uses:
gelatine hardening agent; biocide (cosmetics, water treatment, oilfield applications); leather tanning auxiliary

glutaric acid
pentane-1,5-dioic acid; [110-94-1]

$$HOOCCH_2CH_2CH_2COOH$$

$C_5H_8O_4$. M: 132.11. White, crystalline solid. MP: 95–98°C. BP: 302–304°C. d: 1.43 kg/l (15°C). Soluble in water, oxygenated and aromatic solvents.
Production:
• dimethyl glutarate (hydrolysis)
Derivatives:
2,6-diaminopyridine

Gly *See:* glycine

glyburide *See:* glibenclamide

glycerine *See:* glycerol

glycerol

glycerin; glycerine; 1,2,3-propanetriol; E422 (EC); [56-81-5]

$$CH_2OH$$
$$CHOH$$
$$CH_2OH$$

$C_3H_8O_3$. M: 92.09. Colourless, hygroscopic liquid. BP: 290°C. FP: 18°C. d: 1.26 kg/l (25°C). Miscible with water and alcohol. Flash point: 176°C (TOC). Grades containing 80–99.5% glycerol in water are available commercially.

Production:
• glycerol-1,3-dichlorohydrin + sodium hydroxide (reaction)
• tallow (hydrolysis; byproduct of tallow acid production)
• tallow, hydrogenated (hydrolysis; byproduct of stearic acid production)
• coconut oil (hydrolysis; byproduct of coconut acid production)
• coconut oil + methanol (transesterification; byproduct of methyl cocoate production)
• palm kernel oil (hydrolysis; byproduct of palm kernel fatty acids production)
• palm kernel oil + methanol (alcoholysis; byproduct of palm kernel methyl ester production)
• castor oil (hydrolysis; byproduct of ricinoleic acid production)
• castor oil + methanol (transesterification; byproduct of methyl ricinoleate production)
• castor oil, dehydrated (hydrolysis; byproduct of castor oil fatty acids, dehydrated production)
• rapeseed oil (hydrolysis; byproduct of rapeseed fatty acids production)
• palm oil (hydrolysis; byproduct of palm acid production)
• fish oil (hydrolysis; byproduct of fish acid production)
• fish oil, hydrogenated (hydrolysis; byproduct of fish acid, hydrogenated production)
• tobacco seed oil (hydrolysis; byproduct of tobacco seed fatty acids production)

Derivatives:
alkyd resins, long-oil; alkyd resins, medium-oil; alkyd resins, non-drying; alkyd resins, short-oil; alkyd resins, water-soluble; benzanthrone; diacetin; dihydroxyacetone; fatty acid mono/diglycerides; glafenine; glycerol, iodinated; glycerol dicaprylate/caprate; glycerol dioleate; glycerol mono-4-aminobenzoate; glycerol monoisostearate; glycerol monolaurate; glycerol monooleate; glycerol monoricinoleate; glycerol monostearate; glycerol propoxylate triacrylate; glycerol tribehenate; glycerol trimontanate; maleic resins; maleinised oils; nitroglycerine; pamaquine; phenolic resins, rosin-modified; polyester resins, carboxylated; polyester resins, hydroxylated; polyether polyols, flexible; polyether polyols, flexible, amine-terminated; polyether polyols, rigid; polyglycerol; primaquine; rosin ester gum; triacetin; triolein; tristearin; urethane-alkyd resins

Uses:
humectant (tobacco, starch adhesives, textile sizes); solvent/humectant (food, cosmetics, pharmaceuticals); plasticiser (regenerated cellulose film, sodium silicate foundry resins); polyurethane crosslinking agent; solvent (printing inks); polyvinyl chloride heat costabilisers

glycerol, iodinated

[5634-39-9]

$$ICH_2CH_2 \quad O \quad CH_2OH$$

$C_6H_{11}I_1O_3$. M: 258.06. Mixed product containing 70% 1-iodoethyl and 30% 2-iodoethyl-isomers.

Production:
• glycerol + iodine (reaction)

Uses: cough medicine ingredient

glycerol α-allyl ether

allyl glyceryl ether; [123-34-2]

$$OH \qquad O$$
$$HOCH_2CHCH_2OCH_2CH-CH_2$$

$C_6H_{12}O_4$. M: 148.17. Liquid.

Production:
• allyl alcohol + chlorohydrin (ether formation/hydration)

Derivatives:
unsaturated polyester resins, coating grades

glycerol diacetate *See:* diacetin

glycerol dicaprylate/caprate

$$O$$
$$CH_2OC(CH_2)_nCH_3$$
$$CHOOC(CH_2)_nCH_3$$
$$CH_2OH$$

n = 8–10. Liquid. Pour point: -5°C. d: 0.95 kg/l (25°C). Flash point: 240°C (COC).

Production:
• glycerol + C_8-C_{10} fatty acids (esterification)

Uses:
emollient/cosolvent (toiletries)

glycerol-1,3-dichlorohydrin

α-dichlorohydrin; 1,3-dichloro-2-propanol; 1,3-dichloropropan-2-ol; [96-23-1]

$$OH$$
$$ClCH_2CHCH_2Cl$$

$C_3H_6Cl_2O_1$. M: 128.99. Liquid. BP: 176°C. d: 1.36 kg/l (25°C). Soluble in water and oxygenated solvents.

Production:
• allyl chloride + chlorine (hypochlorination)
Derivatives:
epichlorohydrin; glycerol

glycerol dioleate
GDO

$$CH_2OC(CH_2)_7CH=CH(CH_2)_7CH_3$$
$$CHOOC(CH_2)_7CH=CH(CH_2)_7CH_3$$
$$CH_2OH$$

Pale yellow liquid. HLB: 2.8. The product is a mixture of mono-, di- and tri-oleates.
Production:
• oleic acid + glycerol (esterification)
Uses: defoaming agent (paints); emulsifier/lubricant (textile spin finishes, metalworking fluids); internal polyvinyl chloride processing lubricant; superfatting agent (soaps, hand cleaners)

glycerol mono-4-aminobenzoate
glyceryl *p*-aminobenzoate; [136-44-7]

$$H_2N-C_6H_4-COCH_2CHCH_2OH$$

$C_{10}H_{13}N_1O_4$. M: 211.22. Solid or liquid. Slightly soluble in water. Soluble in oxygenated solvents.
Production:
• glycerol + *p*-aminobenzoic acid (esterification)
Uses: sunscreening agent (cosmetics)

glycerol monoisostearate
glyceryl isostearate (CTFA)

$$CH_2OCC_{17}H_{35}$$
$$CHOH$$
$$CH_2OH$$

$C_{21}H_{42}O_4$. M: 358.57. Clear liquid/soft solid. HLB: 3.0.
Production:
• glycerol + isostearic acid (esterification)
Uses:
emollient/emulsifier (cosmetics)

glycerol monolaurate
glyceryl laurate (CTFA)

$$CH_3(CH_2)_{10}COCH_2CHCH_2OH$$

$C_{15}H_{30}O_4$. M: 274.40. White paste sold as self-emulsifying (SE) or non self-emulsifying (NSE) grades. MP: 21–26°C (SE grades), 42–43°C (NSE grades). HLB: 6.8 (SE grades), 4.0 (NSE grades). Also commonly sold as a 38–50% solution in water.
Production:
• glycerol + lauric acid, narrow cut (esterification)

Derivatives: glycerol monolaurate ethoxylates
Uses: stabiliser/thickening agent/opacifier (skin creams, lotions, shampoos)

glycerol monolaurate ethoxylates

$$CH_2OC(CH_2)_{10}CH_3$$
$$CH(OCH_2CH_2)_mOH$$
$$CH(OCH_2CH_2)_nOH$$

m+n = 8–40. Liquid/waxy solids depending on the molecular weight. HLB: 11.0–17.0 (8–40 moles EO).
Production:
• glycerol monolaurate + ethylene oxide (epoxidation)
Uses: stabiliser/solubiliser (cosmetics, toiletries)

glycerol monooleate
glyceryl oleate; [111-03-5]

$$CH_3(CH_2)_7CH=CH(CH_2)_7COCH_2CHCH_2OH$$

$C_{21}H_{40}O_4$. M: 356.55. Pale yellow liquid. Sold as self-emulsifying (SE) or non-self-emulsifying (NSE) grades for cosmetic use. HLB: 5.1 (SE grades), 2.7–3.3 (NSE grades).
Production:
• glycerol + oleic acid (esterification)
Uses:
emollient/thickener, opacifier (skin creams, lotions, shampoos); emulsifier (hydrocarbon oils, textile spin finishes); plastics mould release agent; plastics processing lubricant; softening agent (textile finishes); viscosity stabiliser (alkyd paints)

glycerol monoricinoleate
glyceryl ricinoleate; GMRO

$$CH_3(CH_2)_5CHCH_2CH=CH(CH_2)_7COCH_2CHCH_2OH$$

$C_{21}H_{40}O_5$. M: 372.54. Yellow liquid. HLB: 2.1. Cloud point: -10°C.
Production:
• castor oil + glycerol (transesterification)
Uses: plastics processing lubricant

glycerol monostearate
glyceryl stearate (CTFA); hydrogenated tallow glyceride (CTFA); GMS; [31566-31-1]; [11099-07-3] (crude grade); [123-94-4] (pure grade)

$$CH_3(CH_2)_{16}COCH_2CHCH_2OH$$

$C_{21}H_{42}O_4$. M: 358.57. White, waxy beads or flakes. Drop point: 54–60°C. Saponification value: 162–172 mg KOH/g. Available as non-self-emulsifying and self-emulsifying grades, depending on the free acid content. HLB: 3.5–6.0.

Production:
• glycerol + stearic acid (esterification)
Derivatives: glycerol monostearate ethoxylates
Uses: emulsifier (food, pharmaceuticals, cosmetics, toiletries); internal polyvinyl chloride processing lubricant; oil-well drilling mud lubricant; softening agent (textile finishes); stabiliser/thickener/opacifier (skin cream, lotions, shampoos)

glycerol monostearate ethoxylates

$$CH_2OC(CH_2)_{16}CH_3$$
$$CH(OCH_2CH_2)_mOH$$
$$CH(OCH_2CH_2)_nOH$$

m+n = 20–30. Liquid/waxy solids depending on the molecular weight. HLB: 15.0–16.4 (20–30 moles EO).
Production:
• glycerol monostearate + ethylene oxide (epoxidation)
Uses: food emulsifier/dough conditioner; solubiliser (perfumes)

glycerol propoxylate triacrylate
polyether acrylate; GPTA

$$CH_2=CHC(OCH_2CH_2)_nOCH \quad CH_2O(CH_2CHO)_mCH=CH_2$$
$$CH_2O(CH_2CHO)_nCH=CH_2$$

Production:
• glycerol + propylene oxide + acrylic acid (epoxidation/esterification)
Uses:
radiation-cured lacquers/printing ink prepolymers

glycerol triacetate *See:* triacetin

glycerol tribehenate

$$CH_2OC(CH_2)_{20}CH_3$$
$$CHOOC(CH_2)_{20}CH_3$$
$$CH_2OC(CH_2)_{20}CH_3$$

$C_{69}H_{134}O_6$. M: 1059.82. Solid. MP: 78°C.
Production:
• glycerol + behenic acid (esterification)
Uses: plastics processing lubricant

glycerol trimontanate
glyceryl trimontanate
Solid. MP: 70°C.
Production:
• glycerol + montanic acid (esterification)
Uses: plastics processing lubricant

glycerol trinitrate *See:* nitroglycerine

glycerol trioleate *See:* triolein

γ-glycidoxypropyltrimethoxysilane

$$CH_2-CHCH_2OCH_2CH_2CH_2Si(OCH_3)_3$$

$C_9H_{20}O_5Si_1$. M: 236.34.
Production:
• trichlorosilane + allyl glycidyl ether + methanol (hydrosilation/dehydrochlorination)
Uses: plastics coupling agent

glycidyl acrylate
2,3-epoxypropyl acrylate; [106-90-1]

$$CH_2=CHCOCH_2CH-CH_2$$

$C_6H_8O_3$. M: 128.13. Liquid. Polymerises on heating. FP: -41°C. d: 1.11 kg/l (20°C). Insoluble in water.
Production:
• epichlorohydrin + acrylic acid (esterification)
Uses:
reactive comonomer (acrylate resins, rubber)

glycidyl-amine adducts

$$RCH_2CHCH_2-O \quad C \quad OCH_2CHCH_2O-R$$

R = 2-aminoethylamino-. n = 1–16.
Production:
• bisphenol A glycidyl ether prepolymers + ethylenediamine (epoxidation)
Uses: epoxy resin curing agent

glycidyl methacrylate
2,3-epoxypropyl methacrylate; [106-91-2]

$$CH_2=CCOCH_2CH-CH_2$$
$$CH_3$$

$C_7H_{10}O_3$. M: 142.16. Liquid. d: 1.07 kg/l (25°C). Commercial products contain hydroquinone methyl ether or similar polymerisation inhibitors.
Production:
• epichlorohydrin + methacrylic acid (esterification)
Uses:
adhesion promotion/crosslinking comonomer (acrylic/vinyl resins)

glycidyl neodecanoate
Cardura E10 (Shell); neodecanoic acid glycidyl ester

$$C_6H_{13}CCOOCH_2CH-CH_2$$
$$CH_3$$

$C_{13}H_{24}O_3$. M: 228.33. BP: 249°C.

Production:
- neodecanoic acid + epichlorohydrin (esterification)

Uses: alkyd/acrylic resin comonomer; reactive diluent (epoxy resins)

glycidyltrimethylammonium chloride
See: 2,3-epoxypropyltrimethylammonium chloride

glycine
aminoacetic acid; Gly; [56-40-6]

$$H_2NCH_2COOH$$

$C_2H_5N_1O_2$. M: 75.07. White crystals. MP: 232–236°C. Decomposes on further heating. d: 1.60 kg/l. Soluble in water. Insoluble in alcohol and ether.
Production:
- formaldehyde + ammonia + hydrogen cyanide (cyanomethylation/nitrile hydrolysis; coproduced with iminodiacetic acid/nitrilotriacetic acid)

Derivatives: 2-acetamidocinnamic acid; cefazolin; chloramphenicol; eglinazine-ethyl; ethyl glycinate hydrochloride; iprodione; levodopa; orotic acid; oxytocin; L-serine; sulfalene; thiamphenicol
Uses: food sweetening agent; infusion solutions

glycollic acid
hydroxyacetic acid; [79-14-1]

$$HOCH_2C\overset{O}{\overset{\|}{C}}H$$

$C_2H_4O_3$. M: 76.05. Colourless solid. MP: 79°C. BP: 100°C with decomposition. d: 1.49 kg/l (25°C). Soluble in water and oxygenated solvents.
Production:
- formaldehyde + carbon monoxide (carbonylation)
- chloroacetic acid (hydration)

Derivatives: *n*-butyl glycollate; fluoroglycofen-ethyl; mefenacet; starch, acrylamidoglycollic acid-modified; sulphaquinoxaline
Uses:
copperplating brightening agent; aluminium anodising reagent; dairy cleaner ingredient; electrodeless nickel-hydrazine coating reagent; leather tanning auxiliary

glycoluril
acetylene urea; [496-46-8]

$C_4H_6N_4O_2$. M: 142.12. Crystalline solid. MP: 300°C with decomposition. Slightly soluble in hot water.
Production:
- glyoxal + urea (carbonyl condensation)

Derivatives: dinitroglycoluril; tetranitroglycoluril; trimethylolglycoluril

glyconiazide
[3691-74-5]

$C_{12}H_{13}N_3O_6$. M: 295.24.
Production:
- isoniazid + D-glucuronolactone (imine formation)

Uses: tuberculostatic drug

glyconic acid *See:* gluconic acid

glycyrrhizinic acid
glycyrrhizic acid; glycyrrhizin; [1405-86-3]
$C_{42}H_{62}O_{16}$. M: 822.94. Crystalline solid with an intense sweet taste. Soluble in water and alcohol. Available commercially as the acid, ammonium and dipotassium salts.
Production:
- liquorice extract (extraction)

Uses: foam stabiliser; sweetening agent (confectionery)

glyme *See:* ethylene glycol dimethyl ether

glyoxal
[107-22-2]

$$O{=}CHCH{=}O$$

$C_2H_2O_2$. M: 58.04. Available commercially as a 40% solution of the polymeric hydrate in water. Chemically, the product behaves as the monomer.
Production:
- acetaldehyde + nitric acid, concentrated (oxidation)
- ethylene glycol (oxidation)

Derivatives: dimethyldihydroxyethylene urea; 1,3-dimethylol-4,5-dihydroxyethylene urea; ethambutol; glycoluril; glyoxylic acid; D-α-(4-hydroxyphenyl)glycine; imidazole; lumazine; 2-methylimidazole; quinoxaline; sulfalene; 1,1, 2,2-tetra[*p*-(2,3-epoxypropoxy)phenyl]ethane
Uses: vinyl acetate/acrylic resin crosslinking agent; disinfectant; gelatine hardening agent; textile finishing agent (permanent-press cotton, rayon fabrics); wet-resistance additive (paper coatings)

glyoxylic acid
[298-12-4]

$$HC\overset{O}{\overset{\|}{C}}OOH$$

$C_2H_2O_3$. M: 74.04. Available commercially as an aqueous solution containing 50% active matter. d: 1.34

kg/l (20°C). Soluble in water and alcohol. Insoluble in ether and most organic solvents.
Production:
- glyoxal + nitric acid (carbonyl oxidation)
- methyl glyoxylate methyl hemiacetal (ester hydrolysis)

Derivatives:
allantoin; 2,2-diethoxyacetophenone; ethyl biscoumacetate; ethyl vanillin; etretinate; hydantoin; *p*-hydroxybenzaldehyde; methyl glyoxylate methyl hemiacetal; orotic acid; piperonal; polyacrylamide, glyoxylic acid-modified; quinalphos; quizalofop-ethyl; vanillin

glyphosate
N-(phosphonomethyl)glycine; [1071-83-6]

$$(HO)_2PCH_2NHCH_2COOH$$

$C_3H_8N_1O_5P_1$. M: 169.06.
Production:
- phosphorus trichloride + formaldehyde + iminodiacetic acid (Perkow reaction/hydrolysis/amine formation/amine dealkylation)

Uses: herbicide

GMP *See:* sodium 5'-guanylate

GMRO *See:* glycerol monoricinoleate

GMS *See:* glycerol monostearate

gold
[7440-57-5]

Au

Au_1. M: 196.97. Yellow, soft, ductile, malleable metal. Relatively unreactive. MP: 1,063°C. BP: 2,966°C. d: 19.3 kg/l. Gold is generally alloyed with other metals such as copper, silver or zinc in jewellery applications. Palladium and nickel are used to produce 'white gold', also used in jewellery. The gold content of alloys is expressed in 24th parts called carats. A 50% gold alloy is therefore 12 carat and pure gold, 24 carat.
Production:
- gold ores, free-milling (cyanidation/reduction)
- gold ores, refractory (ore roasting/cyanidation/reduction)
- gold-telluride ores (froth flotation/ore roasting/cyanidation/reduction)
- copper anodic slimes (sulphating roast process/hydrometallurgical refining; coproduced with platinum/silver/palladium/selenium/tellurium)
- lead bullion (pyrometallurgical refining/Parkes process/Betterton-Kroll process; byproduct of lead production)
- lead bullion (electrochemical refining; byproduct of lead production)

Derivatives: chloroauric acid
Uses: dental fixatives; jewellery/medals/coins; rolled gold/gold leaf (lettering, ornamental decoration)

GPTA *See:* glycerol propoxylate triacrylate

grape sugar *See:* D-glucose

graphite, manufactured
[7782-42-5]

C_1. M: 12.01. Soft, grey solid with slippery surface. d: 2.1–2.3 kg/l. Good electrical and heat conductor.
Production:
- carbon, moulded (Acheson/Castner processes)

Uses: chemical handling equipment/components; electrical brushes, contact rods, sliding rings; electrodes (arc/carbide/alloy smelting furnaces); electrodes (electrolysis); furnace/mould lining material; anticorrosion/conductive paints; bearings, seals and guides; moulds/crucibles (metal, glass, ceramic industries); nuclear reactor moderators/reflectors/fuel elements

graphite, natural
Graphite occurs naturally either in veins or disseminated in other rocks. Vein graphite is hand cobbled and screened to produce lump graphite. Disseminated graphite is concentrated to produce flake graphite of 80–85% or 95% purity. Sri Lanka, Mexico, Canada, USA and Russia are the major producing countries.
Derivatives: carbon, moulded; diamond
Uses: brake linings; electric motor/generator brushes; chemical handling equipment; crucibles/retorts/sleeves/nozzles; dry batteries; filler (rubber); iron/steel foundry facing material; anticorrosion/conductive paints; bearings; steel ingredient; lubricity additive (lubricants, greases); nuclear fuel rod matrix material; pencil lead; polishing/grinding pastes

graphite fibre *See:* carbon fibre

green coke *See:* needle coke; sponge coke, green

Grilamid TR55 *See:* polyamide TR55

groundnut oil *See:* peanut oil

G salt *See:* G acid

GTBA *See:* *t*-butanol

guaiacol
2-hydroxyanisole; *o*-hydroxyanisole; *o*-methoxyphenol; methylcatechol; [90-05-1]
$C_7H_8O_2$. M: 124.14. White or yellow liquid or solid. Discoloured by light and air. MP: 28–29°C. BP: 204–206°C. Slightly soluble in water. Miscible with oxygenated and chlorinated solvents.

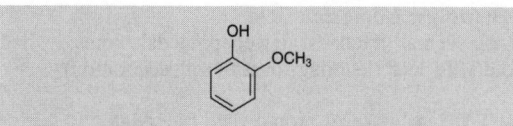

Production:
• catechol + dimethyl sulphate (methylation)
Derivatives: guaifenesin; isocamphylcyclohexanol; iso-eugenol; vanillin
Uses: antioxidant

guaiacol α-glyceryl ether *See:* guaifenesin

guaiacwood oil
Liquid. d: ~0.97 kg/l (25°C). Soluble in alcohol. The main constituent of the oil is guaiol. It is extracted from wood of the guaiac (*Bulnesia sarmienti*) tree which grows wild in Paraguay and Argentina.
Derivatives: guaiyl acetate
Uses: fragrance ingredient/fixative

guaifenesin
guaiacol α-glyceryl ether; [93-14-1]

$C_{10}H_{14}O_4$. M: 198.22.
Production:
• guaiacol + chlorohydrin (epoxidation)
Derivatives: methocarbamol
Uses: muscle relaxant/expectorant drug

guaiyl acetate
[134-28-1]

$C_{17}H_{28}O_2$. M: 264.41. Pale yellow liquid with a woody odour.
Production:
• guaiacwood oil + acetic anhydride (esterification)
Uses: fragrance ingredient

guanethidine
2-(1-heptamethyleneimino)ethylguanidine;
[55-65-2]; [60-02-6] (sulphate)

$C_{10}H_{22}N_4$. M: 198.32.

Production:
• 6-aminocaproic acid + sodium cyanide + chloro-acetonitrile + *O*-methylisourea sulphate (cyanidation/nitrile hydrolysis/amide formation/amine formation/carbonyl reduction/condensation)
Uses: antihypertensive drug

guanidine carbonate
[593-85-1]

$C_3H_{12}N_6O_3$. M: 180.17. Pale yellow, crystalline powder. MP: 197°C. d: 1.24 kg/l. Solubility in water: 430 g/l water (20°C). Insoluble in alcohol.
Production:
• urea + ammonia (low-pressure catalytic process; byproduct of melamine production)
• guanidine nitrate + sodium carbonate (salt formation)
• ammonium thiocyanate + ammonia (reaction)
Derivatives:
2-amino-4,6-dimethylpyrimidine; guanidine phosphate, dibasic; guanidine phosphate, monobasic; guanidine stearate; guanidine sulphamate; sulfaguanidine; urea-formaldehyde resins, cationic
Uses: melamine-formaldehyde resin comonomer; soft-ening/antistatic agent (hair products)

guanidine hydrochloride
guanidinium chloride; [50-01-1]

$C_1H_6Cl_1N_3$. M: 95.53. Crystalline powder. Soluble in water and alcohol.
Production:
• cyanamide + ammonium chloride (deammoniation)
• guanidine nitrate (ion-exchange)
Derivatives:
amiloride; 2-aminopyrimidine; 6-hydroxy-2,4,5-triam-inopyrimidine; 5-nitroso-2,4,6-triaminopyrimidine; sulfa-merazine; sulfamethazine; sulfaperin; trimethoprim
Uses: antistatic agent (textile finishing); microbial pro-tein extraction agent

guanidine nitrate
guanidinium nitrate; [506-93-4]

$C_1H_6N_4O_3$. M: 122.09. Crystalline powder. MP: 214–216°C. Soluble in water and alcohol.
Production:
• dicyandiamide + ammonium nitrate (deammoniation)
Derivatives: chloroazodin; guanidine carbonate; guan-idine hydrochloride; guanidine phosphate, dibasic;

guanidine phosphate, monobasic; guanidine sulphamate; nitroguanidine; sulfaguanidine; *N,N',N''*-triaminoguanidine nitrate
Uses: flotation depressant (copper ores)

guanidine phosphate, dibasic
guanidine hydrogen phosphate; [5423-23-4]

$$\left[H_2N-\overset{\overset{NH_2}{|}}{C}=NH_2^+\right]_2 \quad HPO_4^{2-}$$

$C_2H_{13}N_6O_4P_1$. M: 216.13. Solid. MP: 246°C. d: 1.48 kg/l (25°C). Soluble in water.
Production:
• guanidine nitrate/guanidine carbonate + phosphoric acid, pure (salt formation)
Uses: fire-retardant (wood, paper, textiles)

guanidine phosphate, monobasic
guanidine dihydrogen phosphate; [5423-22-3]

$$H_2N-\overset{\overset{NH_2}{|}}{C}=NH_2^+ \quad H_2PO_4^-$$

$C_1H_8N_3O_4P_1$. M: 157.06. Solid. MP: 130°C. d: 1.68 kg/l (25°C). Soluble in water forming acidic solutions.
Production:
• guanidine nitrate/guanidine carbonate + phosphoric acid, pure (salt formation)
Uses: fire-retardant additive (phenolic resins)

guanidine stearate

$$H_2N-\overset{\overset{NH_2}{|}}{C}=NH_2^+ \quad CH_3(CH_2)_{16}COO^-$$

$C_{19}H_{41}N_3O_2$. M: 343.56.
Production:
• guanidine carbonate + stearic acid (salt formation)
Uses: emulsifier/wetting agent (surface coatings, paper production)

guanidine sulphamate

$$H_2N-\overset{\overset{NH_2}{|}}{C}=NH_2^+ \quad NH_2SO_3^-$$

$C_1H_8N_4O_3S_1$. M: 156.16.
Production:
• guanidine nitrate/guanidine carbonate + sulphamic acid (salt formation)
Uses: fire-retardant (Japanese paper screens)

guanine
2-amino-6-oxypurine; [73-40-5]

$C_5H_5N_5O_1$. M: 151.12. Off-white odourless powder.

MP: >300°C. Practically insoluble in water. Soluble in alkaline solutions.
Production:
• 6-hydroxy-2,4,5-triaminopyrimidine + formamide (condensation)
Derivatives: aciclovir; thioguanine
Uses: pearling pigment/sunscreening agent (cosmetics)

guanoclor
[5001-32-1]

$C_9H_{12}Cl_2N_4O_1$. M: 263.14.
Production:
• 2,6-dichlorophenol + ethylene oxide + hydrazine + *O*-methylisourea sulphate (epoxidation/amine formation/amine formation)
Uses: antihypertensive drug

guanylurea sulphate
carbamylguanidine sulphate; dicyanodiamidine sulphate

$$\left[H_2N\overset{\overset{NH}{||}}{C}NHCONH_2\right]_2 \quad H_2SO_4$$

$C_4H_{14}N_8O_6S_1$. M: 302.26. White, crystalline solid. Loses water when heated to 110°C. Soluble in water.
Production:
• dicyandiamide + sulphuric acid (nitrile hydration/salt formation)
Derivatives:
urea-formaldehyde resins, cationic

guar gum
guar flour; jaguar gum; E412 (EC); [9000-30-0]
Powder comprising the endosperm of guar plant (*Cyamopsis tetragonolobus* or *C. psoraloides*) seeds which is grown in the USA, India and Pakistan. The product is principally a polysaccharide gum. Soluble in water forming viscous solutions.
Derivatives:
hydroxypropyl guar
Uses: filtration aid; paper dry-strength additive; thickening/stabilising agent (salad dressing, dairy products, sauces); viscosifier (oil-well workover fluids, slurry explosives); water clarification aid/flocculant/flotation depressant (mineral dressing)

guazatine acetate
[13516-27-3]

$$H_2N\overset{\overset{NH}{||}}{C}NH(CH_2)_8NH(CH_2)_8NHCNH_2 \quad .3CH_3COOH$$

Partially substituted, mixed product based mainly on the octamethylenediamine monomer, dimer and trimer.

Production:
- suberic acid + ammonia + cyanamide + acetic acid (nitrile formation/hydrogenation/addition)

Uses: fungicide

Guignet's Green *See:* Pigment Green 18

gum arabic
gum acacia; E414 (EC); [9000-01-5]
Dried exudate from the *Acacia senegal* tree, which grows in North and Central Africa. Available as 'tears' or powder. The prime product is grown in Kordofan province (Sudan). The product is principally a polysaccharide gum. Soluble in water forming viscous solutions. Insoluble in alcohol.
Uses:
flotation depressant; lithographic reagent; thickening/stabilising agent (soft drinks, cake mixes, glazes, confectionery)

gum ghatti
Exudate of the *Anogeissus latifolia* tree which is grown in southern India and Sri Lanka.
Uses:
thickening/stabilising agent (soft drinks, cake mixes, glazes, confectionery); emulsifier (pharmaceuticals)

gum karaya
India tragacanth; kadaya gum; karaya gum; sterculia gum; E416 (EC); [9000-36-6]
Dried exudate of the *Sterculia urens* tree which grows in central India. White powder. The product is principally a polysaccharide gum. Soluble in water forming viscous solutions.
Uses: dental fixatives; emulsifier/stabiliser (salad dressing, sauces, cosmetics, pharmaceuticals); paper dry-strength additive

gum tragacanth
tragacanth gum; E413 (EC); [9000-65-1]
Exudate from white gavan shrubs (*Astragalus*) which grow in Turkey, Iran, Iraq and Syria. The product is principally a polysaccharide gum. M: ~840,000. Soluble in water forming viscous solutions.
Uses: emulsifier/stabiliser (salad dressing, sauces, cosmetics, pharmaceuticals)

guncotton *See:* cellulose nitrate

gypsum
calcium sulphate dihydrate; [7778-18-9]

$$CaSO_4.2H_2O$$

$H_2Ca_1O_5S_1$. M: 154.16. White powder. Loses water of crystallisation when heated to 128°C, forming hemihydrate. d: 2.32 kg/l. Solubility in water: 2.4 g/l (20°C).

Production:
- gypsum, natural (mining)
- apatite + sulphuric acid (wet phosphoric acid dihydrate process; coproduced with phosphoric acid, crude)
- sulphur dioxide, raw + calcium hydroxide (flue-gas desulphurisation)
- molasses + *Aspergillus niger* mould + calcium hydroxide + sulphuric acid (fermentation; byproduct of citric acid production)
- calcium tartrate + sulphuric acid (acidification; byproduct of tartaric acid production)

Derivatives: anhydrite; calcium oxide; calcium sulphate hemihydrate; sulphur dioxide, raw
Uses:
metal polishing compounds; portland cement ingredient; pigment/extender (paints, paper, pharmaceuticals)

gypsum, dead-burned *See:* anhydrite

H acid
1-amino-8-hydroxynaphthalene-3,6-disulphonic acid;
5-amino-4-hydroxynaphthalene-2,7-disulphonic acid;
8-amino-1-naphthol-3,6-disulphonic acid; 17200 (CI);
[90-20-0]

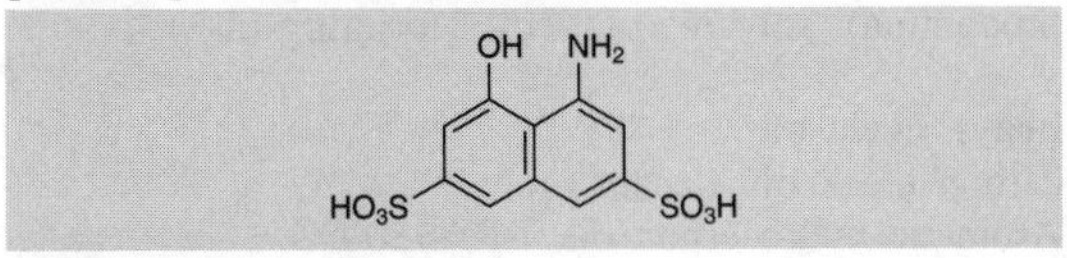

$C_{10}H_9N_1O_7S_2$. M: 319.31.
Production:
• Koch acid (alkali fusion)
Derivatives:
N-acetyl-H acid; Acid Black 1; Acid Blue 29; Acid
Blue 92; Acid Green 19; Acid Red 249; chromotropic
acid; Direct Black 19; Direct Blue 15; Direct Green
13; Direct Green 26; Reactive Black 5; Reactive Red
1; Reactive Red 2; Reactive Red 3; Reactive Red 4;
Reactive Red 12; Reactive Red 17; Reactive Red 96

Halar *See:* poly(ethylene-chlorotrifluoroethylene)

Halon 1211 *See:* bromochlorodifluoromethane

Halon 1301 *See:* bromotrifluoromethane

haloperidol
[52-86-8]

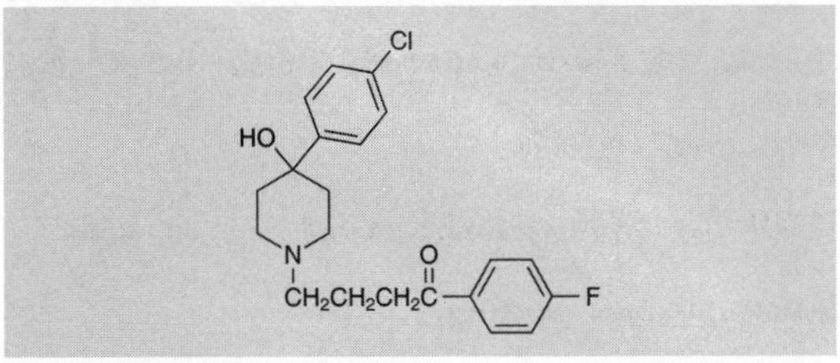

$C_{21}H_{23}Cl_1F_1N_1O_2$. M: 375.87.
Production:
• 4-(4-chlorophenyl)-4-hydroxypiperidine + 4-chloro-
4′-fluorobutyrophenone (dehydrochlorination)
Uses: neuroleptic drug

halothane
2-bromo-2-chloro-1,1,1-trifluoroethane; [151-67-7]

$CF_3CHClBr$

$C_2H_1Br_1Cl_1F_3$. M: 197.37.
Production:
• 1-chloro-2,2,2-trifluoroethane + bromine (photo-
bromination)
Uses: inhalation anaesthetic drug

haloxon
[321-55-1]

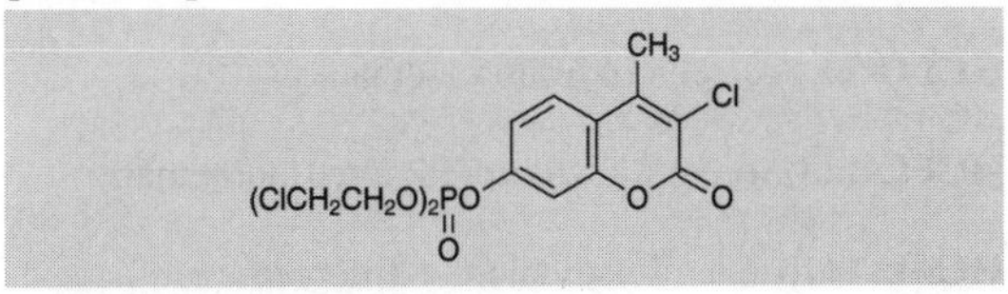

$C_{14}H_{14}Cl_3O_6P_1$. M: 415.58.
Production:
• resorcinol + ethyl acetoacetate + phosphorus
trichloride + ethylene oxide (Skraup synthesis/
alpha chlorination/dehydrochlorination/epoxidation)
Uses: anthelmintic drug

haloxyfop-ethoxyethyl
[87237-48-7]

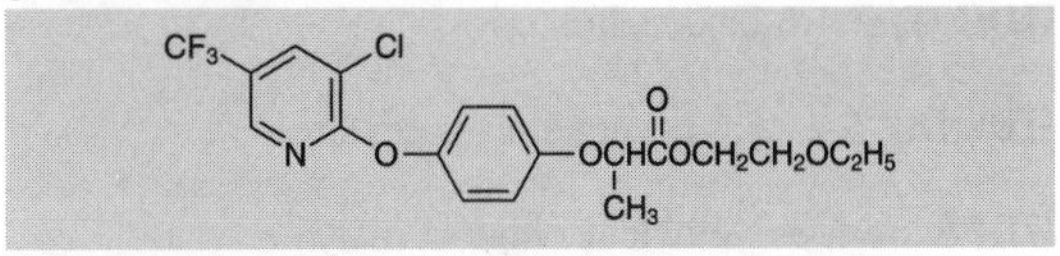

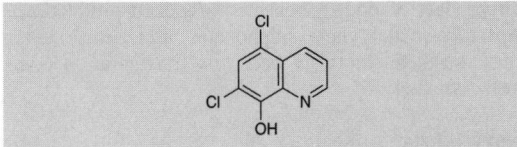

$C_{19}H_{19}Cl_1F_3N_1O_5$. M: 433.80.
Production:
• ethylene glycol monoethyl ether + 2-(4-chloro-
phenoxy)propionic acid + 3-chloro-2-hydroxy-5-tri-
fluoromethylpyridine (esterification/ether formation)
Uses: herbicide

halquinol
5,7-dichloro-8-quinolinol; [8067-69-4]

$C_9H_5Cl_2N_1O_1$. M: 214.06. The commercial product contains about 70% dichloroquinolinol and 30% monochl-
oroquinolinol.
Production:
• 8-hydroxyquinoline (chlorination)
Uses: intestinal antiseptic

HAN *See:* C_{10+} aromatics

2-HAP *See:* *o*-hydroxyacetophenone

4-HAP *See:* *p*-hydroxyacetophenone

HBCD *See:* hexabromocyclododecane

HBN *See:* *p*-hydroxybenzonitrile

HBPA *See:* 4,4′-methylenebiscyclohexanol

HCB *See:* 5-chloro-2-hydroxybenzophenone; hexachlorobenzene

HCCPD *See:* hexachlorocyclopentadiene

HCFC-22 *See:* chlorodifluoromethane

HCFC-123 *See:* 1,1-dichloro-2,2,2-trifluoroethane

HCFC-141b *See:* 1,1-dichloro-1-fluoroethane

HCFC-142b *See:* 1-chloro-1,1-difluoroethane

γ-HCH *See:* lindane

HDDA *See:* 1,6-hexanediol diacrylate

HDI *See:* hexamethylene diisocyanate

HDO *See:* 1,6-hexanediol

HDODA *See:* 1,6-hexanediol diacrylate

HDPE *See:* polyethylene, high-density

HEA *See:* 2-hydroxyethyl acrylate

heavy alkylate, branched
polydodecylbenzene
Mixed stream comprising the heavy byproducts of detergent alkylate production.
Production:
• dodecene, branched + benzene (HF alkylation; byproduct of dodecylbenzene, branched production)
Derivatives: dialkylaryl sulphonates, alkali-earth salts
Uses: synthetic lubricant base oils (refrigeration compressors); fuel

heavy alkylate, linear
Mixed stream comprising isomerised byproducts of detergent alkylate production.
Production:
• n-olefins(C_{10}-C_{13})/α-olefins(C_{12}-C_{14})/gas oil, light, Arge + benzene (HF alkylation; byproduct of dodecylbenzene, linear production)
• n-monochloroparaffins (C_{10}-C_{13}) + benzene (Friedel-Crafts alkylation; byproduct of dodecylbenzene, linear production)
Uses: fuel

heavy aromatic naphtha *See:* C_{10+} aromatics

heavy aromatic oils
Dutrex (Shell)
Liquid. d: 0.98–1.03 kg/l (15°C). Aromatic fraction of lubricant base oils extracted during refining. The composition and properties of the oil vary with the origin and type of crude oil being processed.
Production:
• lubricant oils, distillates/lubricant oils, hydrocracked/deasphalted oil (solvent refining; byproduct of lubricant oils, refined production)
Uses: fuel oil blending component; plasticiser/extender (rubber); raw material (carbon black, petroleum coke production); solvent (pesticides, printing inks)

heavy cycle oil
carbon black oil; decant oil
Aromatic hydrocarbon oil. BR: >300°C.
Production:
• long residue/gas oil, vacuum/deasphalted oil (fluidised-bed catalytic cracking; coproduced with gasoline, catalytic-cracker/light cycle oil/refinery gas)
Derivatives:
carbon black; gas oil, heavy; gas oil, light; naphtha, heavy; needle coke; refinery gas

HEC *See:* hydroxyethyl cellulose

hecogenin
[467-55-0]

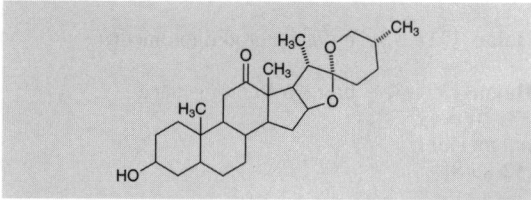

$C_{27}H_{42}O_4$. M: 430.64. Extracted from the sisal (*Agave*) plant.
Derivatives: cortisone

HEDP *See:* hydroxyethylidene(diphosphonic acid)

heliotropin *See:* piperonal

helium
[7440-59-7]

He

He_1. M: 4.00. Colourless, odourless, inert gas. BP: -269°C. d: 0.178 g/l (gas, 0°C). Slightly soluble in water.
Production:
• natural gas (cryogenic separation)
Uses: cryogenic gas; diving gas; balloon/airship gas; lasers; shielding gas (metal refining, welding)

HEMA *See:* 2-hydroxyethyl methacrylate

HEMPA *See:* hexamethylphosphoramide

henna
Orange-red powder comprising the dried leaves of *Lawsonia inermis* and related species. The main producing regions are North Africa and India.
Uses: hair colorant

HEP *See: N*-hydroxyethylpiperazine

heparin sodium
[9005-49-6]
Mixed product containing sulphated polysaccharides made up of D-glucosamine, D-glucuronic acid and L-iduronic acid units. Available commercially usually in the form of the sodium salt. The calcium and magnesium salts are also sold, however.
Production:
• cattle/pig intestinal mucosa (extraction)
Uses: anticoagulant drug

heptabarbital
[509-86-4]

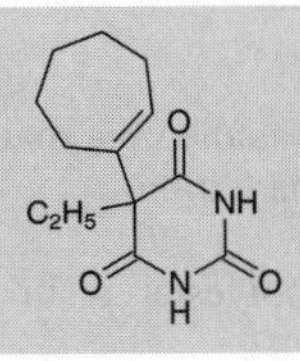

$C_{13}H_{18}N_2O_3$. M: 250.29.
Production:
• ethyl cyanoacetate + cycloheptanone + ethyl bromide + dicyandiamide (Cope reaction/dehydrobromination/cyclisation/nitrile hydrolysis/decarboxylation)
Uses:
sedative/hypnotic drug

heptachlor
1,4,5,6,7,8,8-heptachloro-3a,4,7,7a-tetrahydro-4,7-methanoindene; [76-44-8]

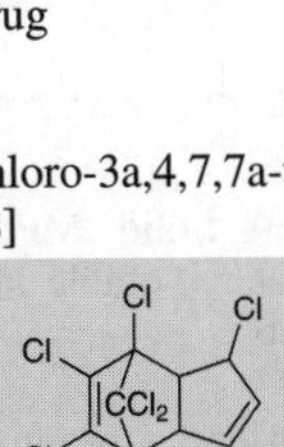

$C_{10}H_5Cl_7$. M: 373.32.
Production:
• hexachlorocyclopentadiene + dicyclopentadiene + chlorine (Diels-Alder cycloaddition/alpha chlorination)
Uses: insecticide

γ-heptalactone

$C_7H_{12}O_2$. M: 128.18.

Production:
• *n*-butanol + acrylic acid (free-radical addition)
Uses:
food sequestrant/acidifier

n-heptaldehyde
enanthaldehyde; *n*-heptanal; [111-71-7]

$$CH_3(CH_2)_5CHO$$

$C_7H_{14}O_1$. M: 114.19. Colourless liquid with a strong, fruity odour. BP: 152–154°C. d: 0.82 kg/l (20°C). Slightly soluble in water. Miscible with most organic solvents.
Production:
• methyl ricinoleate (catalytic dehydrogenation; coproduced with methyl undecylenate)
• *n*-heptanol (alcohol oxidation)
Derivatives: α-amylcinnamaldehyde; dihydrojasmone; 2-heptylcyclopentanone

heptane
[142-82-5]

$$C_7H_{16}$$

C_7H_{16}. M: 100.21. Colourless liquid. BP: 94–99°C. d: 0.71 kg/l (15°C). Insoluble in water. Miscible with oxygenated, chlorinated and hydrocarbon solvents. Flash point: <0°C (TOC).
Production:
• gasoline, polymer (fractionation/hydrogenation; coproduced with hexane, mixed)
Uses: polyolefin production reaction diluent; solvent (fast-drying adhesives, lacquers); extraction solvent (vegetable/essential/animal oil processing)

n-heptanoic acid
enanthic acid; [111-14-8]

$$CH_3(CH_2)_5COOH$$

$C_7H_{14}O_2$. M: 130.19. Colourless liquid with a rancid odour. BP: 249–271°C. d: 0.90 kg/l (20°C). Solubility in water: 0.25 g/l water (25°C).
Production:
• 1-hexene (hydroformylation/carbonyl oxidation)
Derivatives:
allyl enanthate; ethyl heptanoate; trimethylolpropane triheptanoate
Uses: butter marker; alkyd resin comonomer

n-heptanol
1-heptanol; heptyl alcohol; *n*-heptyl alcohol; [111-70-6]

$$CH_3(CH_2)_6OH$$

$C_7H_{16}O_1$. M: 116.21. Colourless liquid with a pleasant odour. BP: 175°C. d: 0.82 kg/l (20°C). Solubility in water: 1.8 g/l water (25°C). Soluble in oxygenated solvents.

Production:
- 1-hexene + synthesis gas (hydroformylation/ hydrogenation)

Derivatives: γ-decalactone; *n*-heptaldehyde
Uses: extraction agent (phosphoric acid purification)

2-heptanone *See:* methyl *n*-amyl ketone

4-heptanone *See:* di-*n*-propyl ketone

heptene, branched

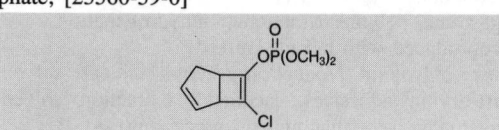

C_7H_{14}. M: 98.19. Liquid. Mixture of branched heptene isomers, the relative proportions of which vary with the feedstock and the fractionation. By removing the lighter isoheptenes, a heptene fraction with enhanced (55%) linearity is obtained.
Production:
- gasoline, polymer (fractionation; coproduced with hexene, branched/octene, branched/nonene, branched/dodecene, branched)

Derivatives:
isooctanol; isooctanoic acid; isoparaffin solvents
Uses: lubricant additive raw material

heptenophos
7-chlorobicyclo[3.2.0]hepta-2,6-dien-6-yl dimethyl phosphate; [23560-59-0]

$C_9H_{12}Cl_1O_4P_1$. M: 250.62.
Production:
- dicyclopentadiene + chloral + trimethyl phosphite (cycloaddition/Michaelis-Arbuzov reaction)

Uses: insecticide

heptopargil
bornan-2-one *O*-prop-2-ynyloxime; [73886-28-9]

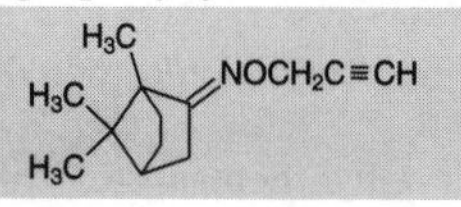

$C_{13}H_{19}N_1O_1$. M: 205.30.
Production:
- camphor + hydroxylamine hydrochloride + propargyl alcohol (oxime formation/ether formation)

Uses: plant growth regulator

***n*-heptyl alcohol** *See:* *n*-heptanol

2-heptylcyclopentanone
[137-03-1]
$C_{12}H_{22}O_1$. M: 182.31. Colourless, viscous liquid with a

jasmine-like odour. BP: 130°C (1.3 kPa). d: 0.89 kg/l (20°C).

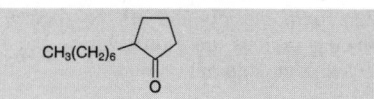

Production:
- cyclopentanone + *n*-heptaldehyde (carbonyl condensation/hydrogenation)

Uses: fragrance ingredient

HET anhydride
chlorendic anhydride

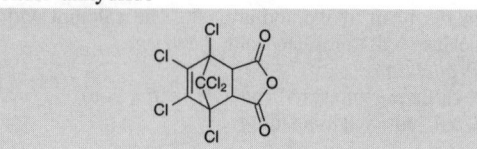

$C_9H_2Cl_6O_3$. M: 370.84. White, crystalline powder. MP: 239°C. d: 1.73 kg/l. Soluble in oxygenated and aromatic solvents.
Production:
- hexachlorocyclopentadiene + maleic anhydride (Diels-Alder cycloaddition)

Uses:
fire-retarded alkyd/polyester resin comonomer; epoxy resin curing agent

hexa *See:* hexamethylenetetramine

hexabromocyclododecane
HBCD; [74398-41-7]

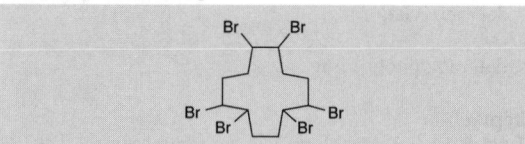

$C_{12}H_{18}Br_6$. M: 641.69. Solid. MP: 185–195°C. d: 2.1 kg/l. Insoluble in water. Soluble in ketone, chlorinated and aromatic solvents.
Production:
- 1,5,9-cyclododecatriene + bromine (addition)

Uses: fire-retardant additive (polystyrene)

hexabutyldistannoxane *See:* tri-*n*-butyltin oxide

hexachlorobenzene
HCB; perchlorobenzene; [118-74-1]

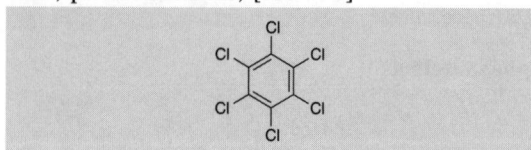

C_6Cl_6. M: 284.79. Colourless crystals. MP: 224–228°C.

BP: 319°C. d: 2.04 kg/l (25°C). Insoluble in water and ethanol.
Production:
• benzene (ring chlorination)
Derivatives: pentachlorophenol; pentachlorothiophenol
Uses: fungicide

hexachlorocyclopentadiene
HCCPD; perchlorocyclopentadiene; [77-47-4]

C_5Cl_6. M: 272.77. Yellowish-green liquid. BP: 240°C. MP: -10°C. d: 1.70 kg/l (25°C). Insoluble in water.
Production:
• C_5-stream, steam-cracked + chlorine (chlorination)
Derivatives:
chlordane; dienochlor; endosulphan; heptachlor; HET anhydride; hexachlorocyclopentadiene-cyclooctadiene adduct
Uses:
fire-retardant unsaturated polyester resin comonomer

hexachlorocyclopentadiene-cyclooctadiene adduct
Dechlorane Plus (Occidental Chemical)

$C_{18}H_{12}Cl_{12}$. M: 653.74.
Production:
• hexachlorocyclopentadiene + 1,5-cyclooctadiene (Diels-Alder cycloaddition)
Uses: fire-retardant additive (plastics)

hexachloroethane
perchloroethane; [67-72-1]

$$CCl_3CCl_3$$

C_2Cl_6. M: 236.74. White crystals with a camphor-like odour. d: 2.09 kg/l. Sublimes on heating to 187°C. Insoluble in water. Soluble in most organic solvents.
Production:
• ethylene dichloride + chlorine (chlorination; byproduct of trichloroethylene/perchloroethylene production)
• ethane/propane + chlorine (chlorinolysis; byproduct of perchloroethylene/carbon tetrachloride production)
Uses:
aluminium/magnesium alloy degassing agent; anthelmintic drug; moth repellant; smoke screen formulations

3,3,4,5,6,7-hexachloroisoindolinone
$C_8H_1Cl_6N_1O_1$. M: 339.83.

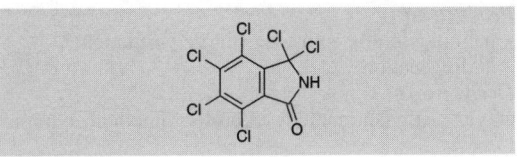

Production:
• phthalodinitrile (chlorination)
Derivatives: Pigment Yellow 110
Uses:
pigment raw material

hexachlorophene
2,2'-methylenebis(3,4,6-trichlorophenol); [70-30-4]

$C_{13}H_6Cl_6O_2$. M: 406.91. White, crystalline solid. MP: 164–165°C. Insoluble in water. Soluble in oxygenated solvents.
Production:
• paraformaldehyde + 2,4,5-trichlorophenol (carbonyl addition)
Uses: biocide

hexaconazole
2-(2,4-dichlorophenyl)-1-(1H-1,2,4-triazol-1-yl)hexan-2-ol; [79983-71-4]

$C_{14}H_{17}Cl_2N_3O_1$. M: 314.22.
Production:
• α,2,4-trichloroacetophenone + 1,2,4-triazole + *n*-butyl chloride (amine formation/Grignard reagent formation/Grignard reaction)
Uses:
fungicide

hexadecanoic acid *See:* palmitic acid

1-hexadecanol *See:* cetyl alcohol

n-hexadecylamine
hexadecylamine; palmitamine (CTFA); palmitylamine; [143-27-1]

$$CH_3(CH_2)_{15}NH_2$$

$C_{16}H_{35}N_1$. M: 241.47. White solid with a characteristic amine odour. MP: 39°C. A typical chain-length distribution is: 4% C_{14}, 92% C_{16}, 4% C_{18}.

Production:
• palmitic acid + ammonia (nitrile formation/
  hydrogenation)
Derivatives:
cetyltrimethylammonium chloride; dimethylcetylamine

1,4-hexadiene
hexadiene; HX; [592-45-0] (*trans*-isomer)

$$CH_2=CHCH_2CH=CHCH_3$$

C_6H_{10}. M: 82.15. Liquid. BP: 66°C. d: 0.71 kg/l
(15°C). Insoluble in water. Soluble in oxygenated
solvents.
Production:
• butadiene + ethylene (catalytic addition)
Derivatives:
ethylene-propylene-diene terpolymer, rubber

1,5-hexadiene
[592-42-7]

$$CH_2=CHCH_2CH_2CH=CH_2$$

C_6H_{10}. M: 82.15. Liquid.
Production:
• 1,5-cyclooctadiene + ethylene (metathesis)
Uses: crosslinking comonomer

2,4-hexadienoic acid *See:* sorbic acid

hexafluoroacetone
1,1,1,3,3,3-hexafluoro-2-propanone; [684-16-2]

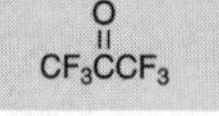

$$\overset{O}{\underset{\|}{CF_3CCF_3}}$$

$C_3F_6O_1$. M: 166.02. Colourless gas. BP: -27°C. d: 1.32
kg/l (25°C). Non-flammable. Reacts with water.
Production:
• hexafluoropropylene oxide (rearrangement)
Derivatives: bisphenol AF; hexafluoroisopropanol;
hexafluoropropane-2,2-bis(phenyl-3′,4′-dicarboxylic acid
anhydride)

2,2,3,4,4,4-hexafluorobutanol

$$CF_3CHFCF_2CH_2OH$$

$C_4H_4F_6O_1$. M: 182.06.
Production:
• hexafluoropropylene + methanol (telomerisation)
Derivatives:
perfluoroalkyl acrylates; perfluoroalkyl methacrylates

hexafluoroisobutylene
3,3,3-trifluoro-1-(trifluoromethyl)prop-1-ene; HFIB;
[382-10-5]

$$(CF_3)_2C=CH_2$$

$C_4H_2F_6$. M: 164.05. Colourless gas. BP: 14°C.

Production:
• hexafluoropropylene (pyrolysis/defluorination)
Derivatives:
hexafluoroisobutylene-vinylidene fluoride copolymers

hexafluoroisobutylene-vinylidene fluoride copolymers
poly(hexafluoroisobutylene-vinylidene fluoride); CM-1
(Allied-Signal); CM-X (Ausimont); [34149-71-8]

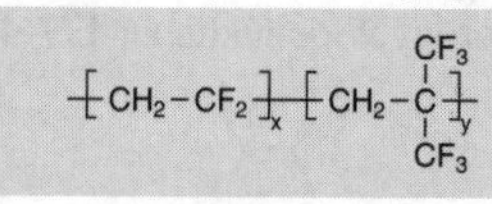

$$-[CH_2-CF_2]_x-[CH_2-\underset{CF_3}{\overset{CF_3}{C}}]_y-$$

Thermoplastic. d: 1.88 kg/l. The polymer has excellent
chemical resistance and electrical insulation properties.
It can be processed by injection moulding.
Production:
• vinylidene fluoride + hexafluoroisobutylene
  (polymerisation)
Uses:
antistick/chemically-resistant mouldings/linings; electrical insulation

hexafluoroisopropanol
1,1,1,3,3,3-hexafluoropropan-2-ol; HFIP; [920-66-1]

$$(CF_3)_2CHOH$$

$C_3H_2F_6O_1$. M: 168.04. Liquid. BP: 58°C.
Production:
• hexafluoroacetone (carbonyl reduction)
Derivatives: acrinathrin; perfluoroalkyl acrylates; perfluoroalkyl methacrylates

4,4′-hexafluoroisopropylidenediphenol
See: bisphenol AF

hexafluoropropane-2,2-bis(phenyl-3′,4′-dicarboxylic acid anhydride)
2,2-bis(3′,4′-anhydrodicarboxyphenyl)hexafluoropropane;
6FTA

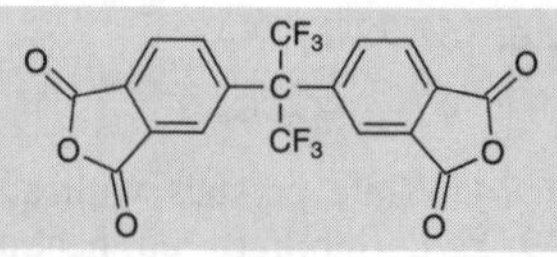

$C_{19}H_6F_6O_6$. M: 444.24.
Production:
• *o*-xylene + hexafluoroacetone (carbonyl
  condensation/side-chain oxidation)
Uses:
polyimide resin monomer

hexafluoropropylene
hexafluoropropene; HFP; [116-15-4]

$$CF_3CF=CF_2$$

C_3F_6. M: 150.02. Colourless gas. BP: -29°C. Insoluble in water.

Production:
- chlorodifluoromethane (pyrolysis; byproduct of tetrafluoroethylene production)

Derivatives: 2,2,3,4,4,4-hexafluorobutanol; hexafluoro-isobutylene; hexafluoropropylene oxide; 2-hydroperfluoropropyl allyl ether; poly(perfluoropropyl ether); tetrafluoroethylene-hexafluoropropylene copolymers; vinylidene fluoride-hexafluoropropylene copolymers; vinylidene fluoride-hexafluoropropylene-tetrafluoroethylene terpolymers

hexafluoropropylene oxide
hexafluoropropene oxide; HFPO; [428-59-1]

$C_3F_6O_1$. M: 166.02. Colourless gas. BP: -27°C.
Production:
- hexafluoropropylene + hydrogen peroxide (peroxidation)

Derivatives:
hexafluoroacetone; perfluoroethercarboxylic acid oligomers; perfluoro(methyl vinyl ether); perfluoro(propyl vinyl ether); poly(hexafluoropropylene oxide); tetrafluoroethylene-perfluoro(vinyl ether carboxylate) copolymers; tetrafluoroethylene-perfluoro(vinyl ether sulphonate) copolymers

hexafluorosilicic acid
fluosilicic acid; hydrofluorosilicic acid; [16961-83-4]

$H_2F_6Si_1$. M: 144.10. Available as a solution in water which is strongly acidic and has a pungent odour.
Production:
- apatite + sulphuric acid (wet phosphoric acid dihydrate process; byproduct of phosphoric acid, crude/gypsum production)
- apatite + sulphuric acid (wet phosphoric acid hemihydrate process; byproduct of phosphoric acid, crude/calcium sulphate hemihydrate production)
- silicon tetrafluoride + hydrofluoric acid (reaction)

Derivatives: aluminium fluoride; ammonium fluosilicate; magnesium fluorosilicate; potassium hexafluorosilicate; sodium fluoride; sodium hexafluorosilicate; zinc hexafluorosilicate
Uses: curing agent (bricks, tiles); lead refining electrolyte; electroplating bath ingredient; mineral flotation agent (phosphate ores); sterilising agent (glass bottles); tanning auxiliary; wood preservative

hexahydrobenzoic acid
See: cyclohexanecarboxylic acid

hexahydrophthalic acid diglycidyl ether
$C_{14}H_{20}O_6$. M: 284.30.

Production:
- hexahydrophthalic anhydride + epichlorohydrin (condensation)

Uses: epoxy resin prepolymer (electrical applications)

hexahydrophthalic anhydride
cyclohexane-1,2-dicarboxylic anhydride; HHPA; [85-42-7]

$C_8H_{10}O_3$. M: 154.17. Colourless liquid. MP: 35°C. d: 1.19 kg/l (40°C). Soluble in epoxy resins and most organic solvents.
Production:
- tetrahydrophthalic anhydride (hydrogenation)

Derivatives:
hexahydrophthalic acid diglycidyl ether
Uses: epoxy resin curing agent (electrical castings)

n-hexaldehyde
aldehyde C-6; caproaldehyde; caproic aldehyde; *n*-hexanal; *n*-hexyl aldehyde; [66-25-1]

$C_6H_{12}O_1$. M: 100.17. Colourless liquid with a strong, fruity odour. BP: 128°C. MP: <-20°C. d: 0.83 kg/l (20°C). Slightly soluble in water. Soluble in oxygenated solvents.
Production:
- *n*-hexanol (catalytic dehydrogenation)

Derivatives: caproic acid; 1-octen-3-ol
Uses: flavouring ingredient

hexalin *See:* cyclohexanol

hexamethoxymethylmelamine
hexakis(methoxymethyl)melamine; HMMM; [3089-11-0]

$C_{15}H_{30}N_6O_6$. M: 390.43.
Production:
- melamine + formaldehyde + methanol (condensation)

Derivatives:
melamine-epoxy resins

Uses: saturated polyester resin crosslinking agent (high-solids stoving finishes); hydroxyl-terminated thermosetting acrylic resin crosslinking agent; alkyd-amino acid-cured resins (industrial and clear wood finishes); alkyd-amino stoving resins (domestic equipment, vehicle finishes)

hexamethyldisilazane *See:* di-(trimethylsilyl)amine

hexamethyldisiloxane
[107-46-0]

$$(CH_3)_3SiOSi(CH_3)_3$$

$C_6H_{18}O_1Si_2$. M: 162.38.
Production:
• chlorotrimethylsilane (hydrolysis/ether formation)
Derivatives:
O,N-bis(trimethylsilyl)acetamide; silicone oils
Uses: silicone chain termination reagent

N,N′-hexamethylenebis[3-(3,5-di-*t*-butyl-4-hydroxyphenyl)propionamide]
N,N′-hexamethylenebis(3,5-di-*t*-butyl-4-hydroxy)hydrocinnamamide; Irganox 1098 (Ciba-Geigy)

$C_{40}H_{64}N_2O_4$. M: 636.96. White crystals. MP: 159°C. d: 1.05 kg/l. Soluble in oxygenated solvents.
Production:
• hexamethylenediamine + methyl 3,5-di-*t*-butyl-4-hydroxyphenylpropionate (amide formation)
Uses: antioxidant (polyamides)

hexamethylenebis(stearamide)
distearoylhexamethylenediamine

$$CH_3(CH_2)_{16}CNH(CH_2)_6NHC(CH_2)_{16}CH_3$$

$C_{42}H_{84}N_2O_2$. M: 649.14.
Production:
• hexamethylenediamine + stearic acid (amide formation)
Uses:
corrosion inhibitor (oil-well drilling fluids)

hexamethylenediamine
1,6-diaminohexane; 1,6-hexanediamine; hexane-1,6-diamine; HMD; HMDA; [124-09-4]

$$H_2NCH_2CH_2CH_2CH_2CH_2CH_2NH_2$$

$C_6H_{16}N_2$. M: 116.21. White flakes. MP: 42°C. BP: 205°C. Soluble in water. Slightly soluble in alcohol.
Production:
• adiponitrile (nitrile reduction)

Derivatives: *N,N′*-bis(2,2,6,6-tetramethyl-4-piperidyl)-1,6-hexamethylenediamine; chlorhexidine; *N,N′*-hexamethylenebis[3-(3,5-di-*t*-butyl-4-hydroxyphenyl)propionamide]; hexamethylenebis(stearamide); hexamethylenediaminetetra-(methylenephosphonic acid); hexamethylene diisocyanate; polyamide 6 terpolymers; polyamide 6I; polyamide 66; polyamide 66/610; polyamide 69; polyamide 610; polyamide 612; polyamide resins, nonreactive; poly(ether-amide) elastomers; poly(hexamethylenebiguanide) hydrochloride

hexamethylenediaminetetra-(methylenephosphonic acid)
HMDTMP

$C_{10}H_{28}N_2O_{12}P_4$. M: 492.23. White powder. Also available as aqueous solutions of the hexapotassium or hexasodium salts.
Production:
• hexamethylenediamine + formaldehyde + phosphorous acid (Mannich reaction)
Uses:
scale/corrosion inhibitor (industrial water systems)

hexamethylene diisocyanate
HDI; [822-06-0]

$$OCNCH_2CH_2CH_2CH_2CH_2CH_2NCO$$

$C_8H_{12}N_2O_2$. M: 168.20. Liquid. BP: 127°C (1.3 kPa). MP: -67°C. d: 1.05 kg/l (20°C). Hydrolysed by water. Flash point: 140°C (OC). The product is used in a 'blocked' form in many applications.
Production:
• hexamethylenediamine + phosgene (phosgenation)
Derivatives: distigmine bromide; hexamethylene diisocyanate trimer; hexamethylene diisocyanate-trimethylolpropane adduct; urethane-acrylate resins

hexamethylene diisocyanate trimer

$C_{23}H_{38}N_6O_5$. M: 478.58. The biuret of hexamethylene diisocyanate usually sold as a 75% solution in solvent.
Production:
• hexamethylene diisocyanate (isocyanate addition)
Uses: isocyanate component (polyurethane coatings)

hexamethylene diisocyanate-trimethylolpropane adduct
$C_{30}H_{50}N_6O_9$. M: 638.76. Mixed product. Prepolymer formed by partial reaction of 3 moles of hexamethyl-

ene diisocyanate with 1 mole of trimethylolpropane.

$$CH_3CH_2C\left[CH_2O\overset{O}{\overset{\|}{C}}NH(CH_2)_6NCO\right]_3$$

Production:
• trimethylolpropane + hexamethylene diisocyanate
  (isocyanate addition)
Uses: isocyanate component (polyurethane coatings)

hexamethylene glycol *See:* 1,6-hexanediol

hexamethyleneimine
[111-49-9]

$C_6H_{13}N_1$. M: 99.18. Colourless liquid with an ammonia-cal odour. BP: 138–140°C. FP: -37°C. d: 0.88 kg/l (15°C). Soluble in water and oxygenated solvents.
Production:
• adiponitrile (nitrile reduction; byproduct of
  hexamethylenediamine production)
Derivatives:
glisoxepide; mecillinam; molinate; tolazamide

hexamethylenetetramine
methenamine; hexa; hexamine; HMT; HMTA; E239
(EC); [100-97-0]

$C_6H_{12}N_4$. M: 140.20. White crystalline powder with a weak, amine odour. Sublimes at 263°C with some de-composition. Solubility in water: 87 g/l water (20°C).
Production:
• formaldehyde + ammonia (condensation)
Derivatives: cyclonite; *N,N'*-dinitrosopentamethylene-tetramine; norfenefrine; octogen
Uses: phenolic resin curing agent; camping stove fuel tablets; nitrile rubber hardness/strength additive; anal-ytical reagent; reagent (Delepine reaction); silage fer-mentation additive; stabiliser (photography); vulcanis-ation accelerator

4,5,5,6,7,7-hexamethylindanopyran
4,5,5,6,7,7-hexamethyl-1H-indano[2,3:c]pyran; Galaxol-ide; [1222-05-5]

$C_{18}H_{26}O_1$. M: 258.41. Viscous liquid with a musk-like odour. BP: 129°C (1.1 kPa). d: 1.00 kg/l (20°C).

Production:
• α-methylstyrene + 2-methyl-2-butene + propylene
  oxide + formaldehyde (cycloaddition/epoxidation/
  condensation)
Uses: fragrance ingredient (soap, detergents, cosmetics)

hexamethylphosphoramide
hexamethylphosphoric triamide; HEMPA; HMPA;
[680-31-9]

$$\left[(CH_3)_2N\right]_3P=O$$

$C_6H_{18}N_3O_1P_1$. M: 179.20. Colourless liquid. MP: 7.2°C. BP: 235°C. d: 1.03 kg/l. Miscible with water.
Production:
• dimethylamine + phosphorus oxychloride
  (dehydrochlorination)
Uses: jet fuel antiicing additive; aprotic process solvent (chemical synthesis)

hexamine *See:* hexamethylenetetramine

hexane, mixed

$$C_6H_{14}$$

C_6H_{14}. M: 86.18. Colourless liquid. BP: 65–70°C. d: 0.67 kg/l (15°C). Insoluble in water. Miscible with oxygenated, chlorinated and hydrocarbon solvents. Flash point: <0°C (TOC).
Production:
• gasoline, polymer (fractionation/hydrogenation;
  coproduced with heptane)
Uses: polyolefin production reaction diluent; solvent (fast-drying adhesives, lacquers); extraction solvent (vegetable/essential/animal oil processing)

***n*-hexane**
[110-54-3]

$$CH_3CH_2CH_2CH_2CH_2CH_3$$

C_6H_{14}. M: 86.18. Colourless liquid. BP: 67–70°C. d: 0.66 kg/l (15°C). Insoluble in water. Miscible with oxygenated, chlorinated and hydrogenated solvents. Flash point: <0°C (TCC).
Production:
• gasoline, polymer (molecular sieve separation;
  coproduced with *n*-pentane/isopentane/isohexane)
Derivatives: perfluoro-*n*-hexane
Uses: Molex/Isosiv *n*-paraffin processing desorbent

hexane-1,6-diamine *See:* hexamethylenediamine

1,6-hexanediol
hexamethylene glycol; hexane-1,6-diol; HDO;
[629-11-8]

$$HOCH_2CH_2CH_2CH_2CH_2CH_2OH$$

$C_6H_{14}O_2$. M: 118.18. White crystals. MP: 40–42°C. BP:

250°C. Soluble in water and oxygenated solvents.
Production:
• dimethyl adipate (ester reduction)
Derivatives: 1,6-hexanediol diacrylate; 1,6-hexanediol dimethacrylate; 1,6-hexanediyl bis[3-(3,5-di-*t*-butyl-4-hydroxyphenyl)propionate]; polycarbonate diols; polyester polyols, linear; polyester resins, linear, medium molecular weight
Uses: polyurethane chain-extender

1,6-hexanediol diacrylate
hexamethylene glycol diacrylate; HDDA; HDODA

$$CH_2=CHCO(CH_2)_6OCCH=CH_2$$

$C_{12}H_{18}O_4$. M: 226.27.
Production:
• 1,6-hexanediol + acrylic acid (esterification)
Uses:
reactive diluent (radiation-cured inks, lacquers)

1,6-hexanediol dimethacrylate
hexamethylene glycol dimethacrylate

$$CH_2=CCO(CH_2)_6OCC=CH_2$$
$$CH_3 \quad\quad CH_3$$

$C_{14}H_{22}O_4$. M: 254.33.
Production:
• 1,6-hexanediol + methyl methacrylate (transesterification)
Uses: crosslinked acrylic resin comonomer; reactive diluent (radiation-cured inks, lacquers)

hexane-2,5-dione *See:* acetonylacetone

1,6-hexanediyl bis[3-(3,5-di-*t*-butyl-4-hydroxyphenyl)-propionate]
Irganox 259 (Ciba-Geigy); [35074-77-2]

$C_{40}H_{62}O_6$. M: 638.93. Off-white powder. MP: 101°C.
d: 1.08 kg/l.
Production:
• 1,6-hexanediol + methyl 3,5-di-*t*-butyl-4-hydroxyphenylpropionate (transesterification)
Uses: antioxidant (plastics)

1,2,6-hexanetriol
1,2,6-trihydroxyhexane; [106-69-4]

$$OH$$
$$HOCH_2CHCH_2CH_2CH_2CH_2OH$$

$C_6H_{14}O_3$. M: 134.18. Pale yellow, hygroscopic liquid.

Pour point: -20°C. d: 1.11 kg/l. Miscible with water and oxygenated solvents.
Production:
• acrolein (cycloaddition/hydrogenation)
Uses: alkyd/polyester/polyurethane resin comonomer; ointment base (pharmaceuticals); softening agent (technical papers, printing inks)

hexanitrostilbene
HNS; [20062-22-0]

$C_{14}H_6N_6O_{12}$. M: 450.23.
Production:
• 2,4,6-trinitrotoluene + sodium hypochlorite (oxidative coupling)
Uses: explosives

hexanoic acid *See:* caproic acid

n-hexanol
1-hexanol; hexyl alcohol; [111-27-3]

$$CH_3CH_2CH_2CH_2CH_2CH_2OH$$

$C_6H_{14}O_1$. M: 102.18. Colourless liquid. BP: 151–160°C.
FP: -52°C. d: 0.81 kg/l (20°C). Slightly soluble in water. Soluble in oxygenated solvents. Flash point: 61°C (CC).
Production:
• ethylene (Alfol/Epal processes; coproduced with *n*-octanol/*n*-decanol/*n*-alkanol(C_8-C_{10})/lauryl alcohol, narrow-cut/myristyl alcohol/*n*-alkanol(C_{12}-C_{14})/cetyl alcohol/cetylstearyl alcohol/stearyl alcohol/*n*-alkanol(C_{12}-C_{18})/*n*-alkanol(C_{20+}))
Derivatives:
dipropylene glycol monohexyl ether; *n*-hexaldehyde; *n*-hexyl benzoate; *n*-hexyl bromide; *n*-hexyl chloride; *n*-hexyl salicylate; γ-nonalactone
Uses: flotation frothing agent; fragrance ingredient

hexan-6-olide *See:* caprolactone

hexazinone
3-cyclohexyl-6-dimethylamino-1-methyl-1,3,5-triazine-2,4-dione; [51235-04-2]

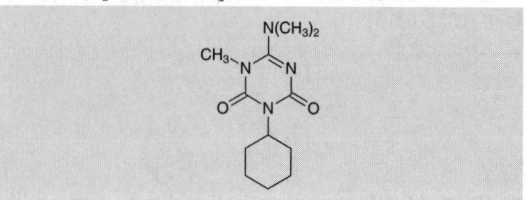

$C_{12}H_{20}N_4O_2$. M: 252.32.

Production:
- *O*-methylisourea sulphate + cyclohexyl isocyanate + methyl chloroformate + dimethylamine (isocyanate addition/condensation/amine formation)

Uses: herbicide

2-hexenal
leaf aldehyde; [6728-26-3]

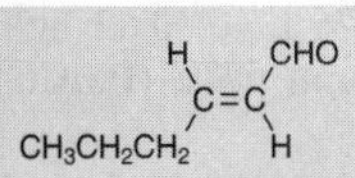

$C_6H_{10}O_1$. M: 98.15. Colourless liquid with a strong, herbal odour. The commercial product is the *trans*-isomer. BP: 146–147°C. d: 0.85 kg/l (20°C). Insoluble in water. Soluble in oxygenated solvents.

Production:
- *n*-butyraldehyde + ethyl vinyl ether (carbonyl condensation)

Derivatives: 2-hexenol
Uses: fragrance ingredient

1-hexene
hexene-1; [592-41-6]

$$CH_3(CH_2)_3CH=CH_2$$

C_6H_{12}. M: 84.17. Colourless liquid. BP: 63–64°C. d: 0.67 kg/l (25°C). Insoluble in water. Soluble in most organic solvents.

Production:
- ethylene (Ziegler oligomerisation; coproduced with 1-butene/1-octene/1-decene/1-dodecene/α-olefins $(C_{12}\text{-}C_{14})$/α-olefins$(C_{14}\text{-}C_{16})$/α-olefins$(C_{16}\text{-}C_{18})$/ α-olefins(C_{18+}))
- naphtha, light, Synthol (extraction; coproduced with 1-pentene)

Derivatives:
n-alkanol(C_7-C_9); *n*-heptanoic acid; *n*-heptanol; *n*-hexyl mercaptan; polyethylene, high-density; polyethylene, linear low-density

hexene, branched
Dimate; propylene dimer

$$(CH_3)_2CHCH=CHCH_3 \quad + \quad (CH_3)_2CHCH_2CH=CH_2$$

C_6H_{12}. M: 84.17. Colourless liquid. BP: 53–56°C. d: 0.67 kg/l. Mixed propylene dimers comprising mainly 4-methyl-1-pentene and 4-methyl-2-pentene. Flash point: -30°C.

Production:
- gasoline, polymer (fractionation; coproduced with heptene, branched/octene, branched/nonene, branched/dodecene, branched)
- propylene (Dimersol G process)

Derivatives: isoheptanol; neoheptanoic acid
Uses:
petrol blending component

2-hexenol
trans-2-hexene-1-ol; [928-95-0]

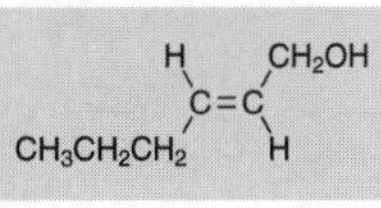

$C_6H_{12}O_1$. M: 100.17. The commercial product is the *trans*-isomer.
Production:
- 2-hexenal (carbonyl reduction)

Derivatives:
2-hexenyl acetate
Uses: fragrance ingredient

3-hexenol
cis-3-hexen-1-ol; leaf alcohol; [928-96-1]

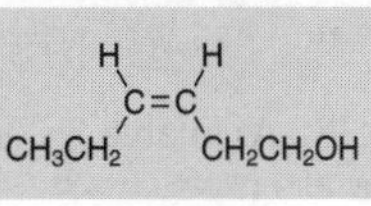

$C_6H_{12}O_1$. M: 100.17. Colourless liquid with a herbal odour. The commercial product is the *cis*-isomer. BP: 157°C. d: 0.85 kg/l (20°C). Soluble in oxygenated solvents.

Production:
- diethyl sulphate + acetylene + ethylene oxide (ethynylation/epoxidation/hydrogenation)

Derivatives:
3-hexenyl acetate; 3-hexenyl isobutyrate; violet leaf alcohol
Uses: fragrance ingredient

2-hexenyl acetate
[2497-18-9]

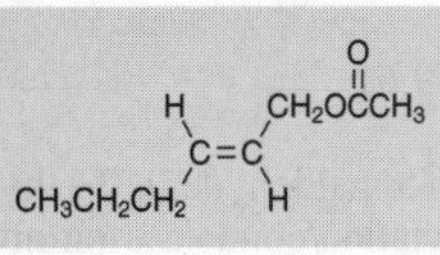

$C_8H_{14}O_2$. M: 142.20. Liquid with a fruity odour. The commercial product is the *trans*-isomer.
Production:
- 2-hexenol + acetic acid (esterification)

Uses: flavouring ingredient

3-hexenyl acetate
[3681-71-8]

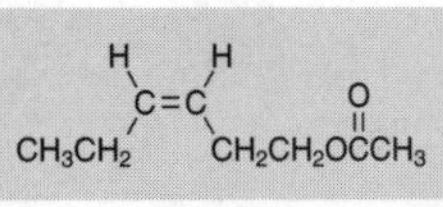

$C_8H_{14}O_2$. M: 142.20. Liquid with a fruity odour. The commercial product is the *cis*-isomer.
Production:
- 3-hexenol + acetic acid (esterification)

Uses:
fragrance ingredient

3-hexenyl isobutyrate
[41519-23-7]

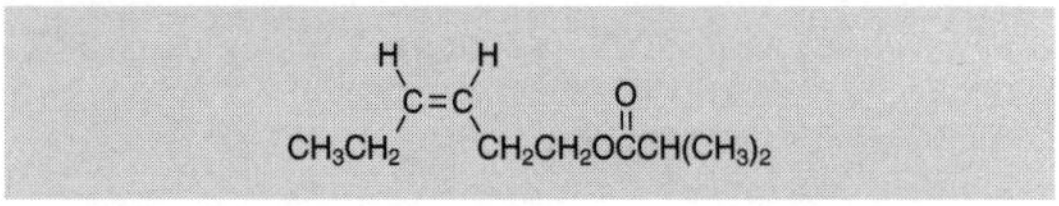

$C_{10}H_{18}O_2$. M: 170.25. Liquid with a fruity odour. The commercial product is the *cis*-isomer.
Production:
• 3-hexenol + isobutyric acid (esterification)
Uses: fragrance ingredient

hexestrol
[84-16-2]

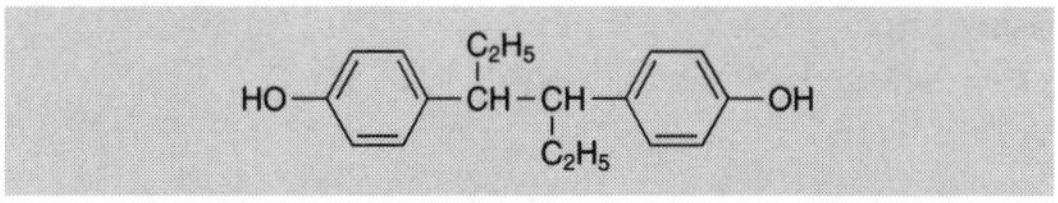

$C_{18}H_{22}O_2$. M: 270.38. Available as the free phenol or as the diphosphate ester.
Production:
• *p*-hydroxypropiophenone (carbonyl reduction/alcohol bromination/Grignard reagent formation/reductive coupling)
Uses: animal growth stimulant

hexetidine
[141-94-6]

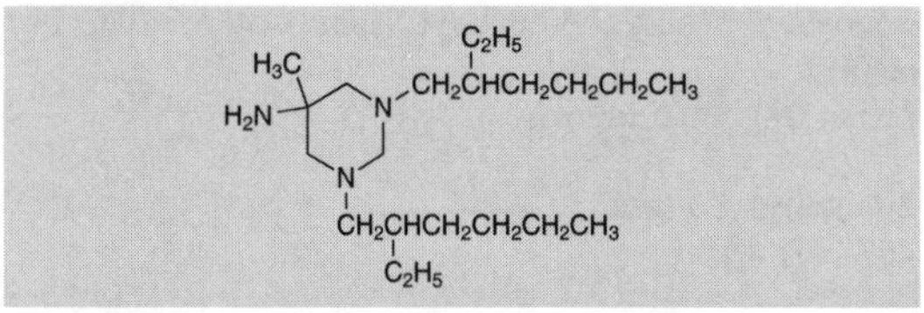

$C_{21}H_{45}N_3$. M: 339.61.
Production:
• nitroethane + formaldehyde + 2-ethylhexylamine (hydroxymethylation/condensation/nitro reduction)
Uses: antiseptic

hexobarbital
[56-29-1]

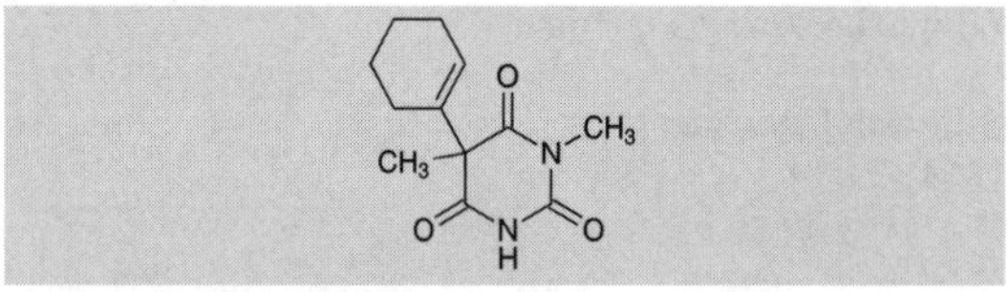

$C_{12}H_{16}N_2O_3$. M: 236.27.
Production:
• cyclohexanone + ethyl cyanoacetate + methyl bromide + dicyandiamide (Cope reaction/dehydro-bromination/cyclisation/methylation/nitrile hydrolysis/decarboxylation)
Uses:
sedative/hypnotic/anaesthetic drug

hexogen *See:* cyclonite

hexyl acetate
Exxate 600 (Exxon Chemical)

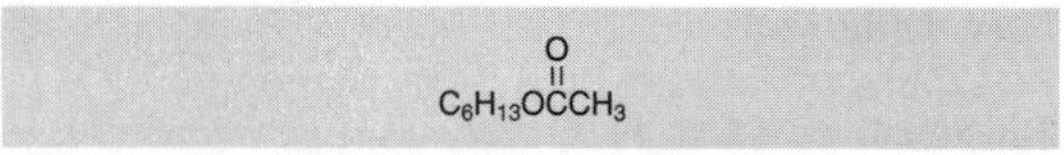

$C_8H_{16}O_2$. M: 144.22. Colourless liquid with a pleasant odour. BP: 164–176°C. d: 0.87 kg/l (20°C). Insoluble in water. Flash point: 57°C (PMCC).
Production:
• hexanol, mixed + acetic acid (esterification)
Uses: solvent (paints)

hexyl alcohol *See:* n-hexanol

n-hexyl benzoate
hexyl benzoate; [6789-88-4]

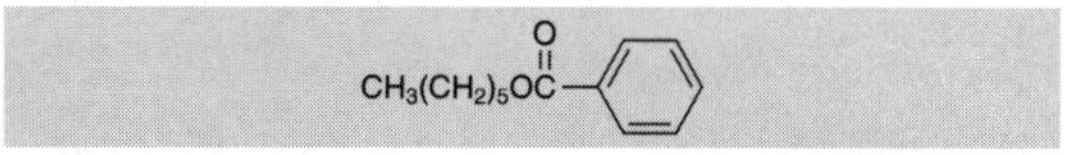

$C_{13}H_{18}O_2$. M: 206.28. Colourless liquid with a fruity odour. BP: 272°C.
Production:
• *n*-hexanol + benzoic acid (transesterification)
Uses: perfume fixative

n-hexyl bromide
1-bromohexane; [111-25-1]

$C_6H_{13}Br_1$. M: 165.07. Pale yellow liquid. BP: 154–158°C. MP: -85°C. d: 1.18 kg/l (20°C). Insoluble in water. Soluble in oxygenated solvents.
Production:
• *n*-hexanol + hydrogen bromide, anhydrous (alcohol bromination)
Derivatives:
methyl 2-nonynoate

n-hexyl chloride
1-chlorohexane; [544-10-5]

$C_6H_{13}Cl_1$. M: 120.62. Liquid. BP: 132–134°C. d: 0.88 kg/l (20°C). Insoluble in water.
Production:
• *n*-hexanol + hydrochloric acid (alcohol chlorination)
Derivatives:
pentifylline; tri-*n*-hexylamine

α-hexylcinnamaldehyde
hexylcinnamaldehyde; [101-86-0]

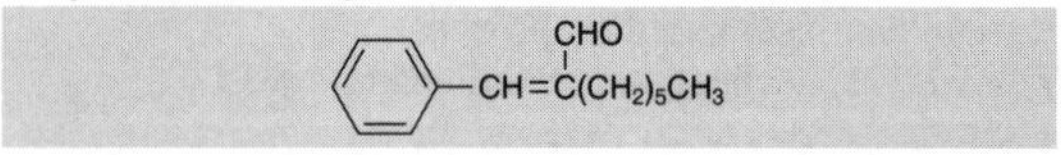

$C_{15}H_{20}O_1$. M: 216.32. Yellow liquid with a floral odour.

Production:
• benzaldehyde + *n*-octaldehyde (aldol condensation)
Uses: fragrance ingredient

hexylene glycol
2-methylpentane-2,4-diol; [107-41-5]

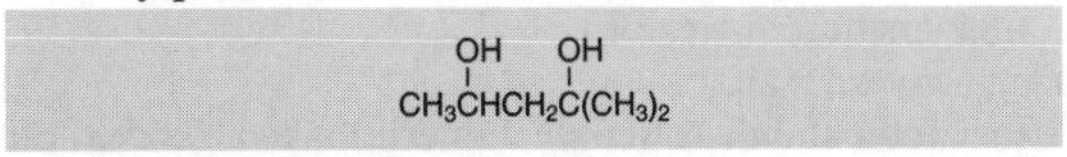

$$\underset{OH \quad\; OH}{CH_3CHCH_2C(CH_3)_2}$$

$C_6H_{14}O_2$. M: 118.18. Colourless liquid with mild, pleasant odour. FP: -50°C. BP: 197°C. d: 0.92 kg/l (20°C). Completely soluble in water.
Production:
• diacetone alcohol (hydrogenation)
Derivatives:
1,1-dimethyl-3-hydroxybutyl peroxy-2-ethylhexanoate; 1,1-dimethyl-3-hydroxybutyl peroxyneoheptanoate; 2-methylpentadiene; 2,2'-oxybis(4,4,6-trimethyl)-1,3,2-dioxaborinane
Uses: unsaturated polyester resin comonomer; solvent (hydraulic fluids, agrochemicals, water-based paints, printing inks, cosmetics)

n-hexyl mercaptan
hexane-1-thiol; [111-31-9]

$$CH_3(CH_2)_5SH$$

$C_6H_{14}S_1$. M: 118.24. Liquid. BP: 150–155°C. d: 0.85 kg/l (15°C). Insoluble in water. Soluble in oxygenated solvents.
Production:
• 1-hexene + hydrogen sulphide (addition)
Derivatives: perfluorohexanesulphonic acid

N-hexyl-*N'*-phenyl-*p*-phenylenediamine
N-(1,3-dimethylbutyl)-*N'*-phenyl-*p*-phenylenediamine; 6PPD; Santoflex 13 (Monsanto)

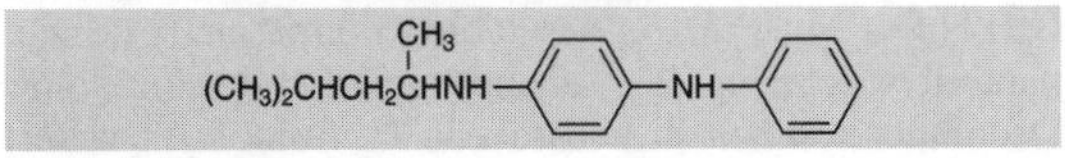

$C_{18}H_{24}N_2$. M: 268.40.
Production:
• methyl isobutyl ketone + *p*-aminodiphenylamine (reductive amination)
Uses: antioxidant/antiozonant (rubber)

hexylresorcinol
caprocol; 2,4-dihydroxy-*n*-hexylbenzene

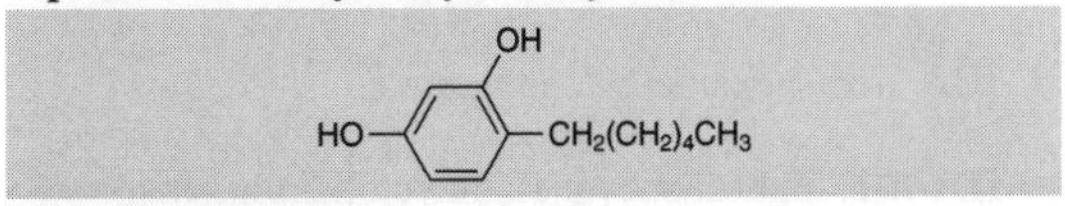

$C_{12}H_{18}O_2$. M: 194.27.
Production:
• resorcinol + caproic acid (esterification/Fries rearrangement/Wolff-Kishner reduction)
Uses: anthelmintic drug

n-hexyl salicylate
[6259-76-3]
$C_{13}H_{18}O_3$. M: 222.28. Colourless liquid with a floral odour. BP: 167–168°C (1.6 kPa). d: 1.03 kg/l (25°C). Insoluble in water. Soluble in oxygenated solvents.

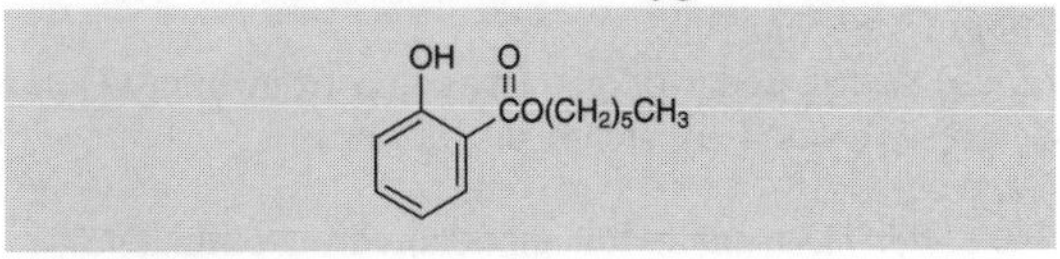

Production:
• *n*-hexanol + salicylic acid (esterification)
Uses: fragrance ingredient

2,5-hexynediol
3-hexyne-2,5-diol; [3031-66-1]

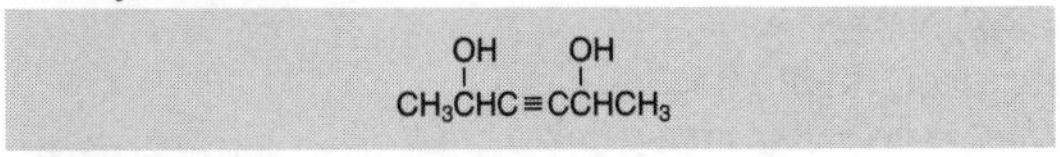

$$\underset{OH \qquad\;\; OH}{CH_3CHC \equiv CCHCH_3}$$

$C_6H_{10}O_2$. M: 114.15. Solid. MP: 72°C. BP: 93–106°C.
Production:
• acetylene + acetaldehyde (ethynylation)
Derivatives:
2,5-dimethyl-4-hydroxy-3-furanone
Uses: corrosion inhibitor (metalworking fluids)

hexythiazox
5-(4-chlorophenyl)-*N*-cyclohexyl-4-methyl-2-oxo-1,3-thiazolidine-3-carboxamide; [78587-05-0]

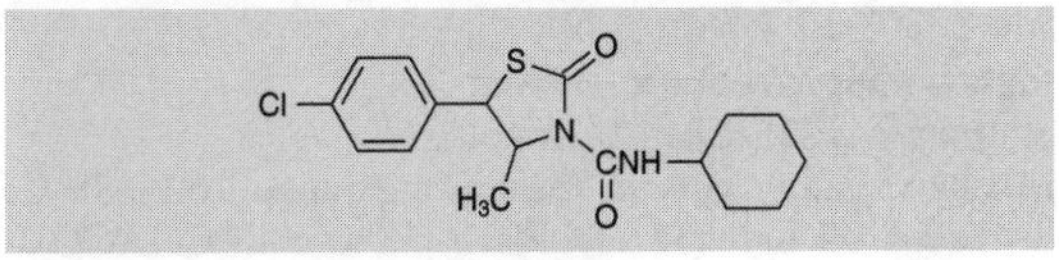

$C_{17}H_{21}Cl_1N_2O_2S_1$. M: 352.88.
Production:
• chlorobenzene + α-chloropropionic acid + ammonia + carbonyl sulphide + cyclohexyl isocyanate (Friedel-Crafts acylation/ammoniation/carbonyl reduction/condensation/isocyanate addition)
Uses: acaricide

HFC-21 *See:* dichlorofluoromethane

HFC-23 *See:* trifluoromethane

HFC-134a *See:* 1,1,1,2-tetrafluoroethane

HFC-152a *See:* difluoroethane

HFCS *See:* high-fructose syrup

HFIB *See:* hexafluoroisobutylene

HFIP *See:* hexafluoroisopropanol

HFP *See:* hexafluoropropylene

HFPO *See:* hexafluoropropylene oxide

HHPA *See:* hexahydrophthalic anhydride

hiba oil
Thuja dolabrata oil
Liquid with a cedar odour. Extracted from hiba (*Thuja dolabrata*) wood by steam distillation.
Derivatives:
4-acetyl-1,1,6-trimethylethanooctahydronaphthalene

high-boiling aliphatic solvents
Selected distillation fractions with BP: 210–330°C. The products are specifically intended for printing applications and have narrowly-defined boiling ranges. d: 0.76–0.92 kg/l (15°C). Aromatics content: 10–18% v/v.
Production:
• gas oil, light (fractionation)
Uses: solvent (printing inks)

high-boiling aliphatic solvents, dearomatised
Colourless or pale yellow narrow distillation cuts with boiling points in the range 210–320°C. Usually sold as branded products. d: 0.76–0.81 kg/l (15°C). Aromatics content: <1%.
Production:
• gas oil, light (hydrogenation/fractionation)
Uses:
solvent (letterpress, lithographic inks)

high-boiling aromatic solvents
Aromasol (ICI); Shellsol (Shell)
Mixed aromatic cuts in the boiling range 162–285°C. d: 0.87–0.99 kg/l (15°C). Flash point: >43°C (ACC).
Production:
• trimethylbenzene fraction (fractionation)
Uses:
cosolvent (mineral extraction); solvent (petroleum additives, oilfield chemical, tank cleaning, stoving/dipping/roller coating paint finishes, printing inks, pesticides, timber treatments)

high-fructose syrup
high-fructose corn syrup; HFCS; Cornsweet; Isomerose; Isosweet; Isosyrup
Available commercially as clear, colourless solutions in water containing 70–80% active matter. Grades are produced with 42% or 55% fructose on a dry weight basis. The remainder is mainly glucose. The syrup has about the same sweetness as sucrose.
Production:
• starch hydrolysate + glucose isomerase (enzymatic isomerisation)
Derivatives:
fructose
Uses: canned/baked/dairy product ingredient; sweetening agent (soft drinks)

high-maltose syrup
HMS
Colourless syrup containing 65-80% maltose. The remainder is mainly higher oligosaccharides.
Production:
• glucose syrup + pullulanase + β-amylase (enzymatic conversion)
Derivatives: maltitol
Uses: food stabiliser (confectionery, baked goods, soft drinks, brewing); microbial fermentation nutrient

hindered-amine cyanurates, polymeric
Chimassorb 947FL (Chimosa)

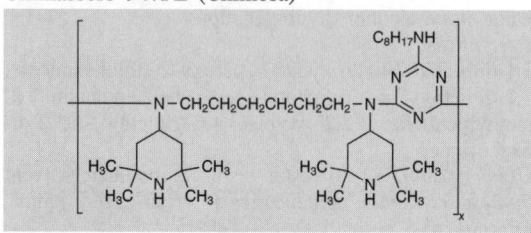

Production:
• *t*-octylamine + cyanuric chloride + *N,N'*-bis(2,2,6,6-tetramethyl-4-piperidyl)-1,6-hexamethylenediamine (amine formation/amine formation)
Uses: light stabiliser (plastics)

HIPS *See:* polystyrene, high-impact

L-histidine
L-α-amino-β-imidazolepropionic acid; His; [71-00-1]; [1007-42-7] (hydrochloride)

$C_6H_9N_3O_2$. M: 155.16. Available commercially as the naturally-occurring L(−)-enantiomer. Crystalline solid. Decomposes when heated to 280°C. Soluble in water.
Production:
• blood meal (hydrolysis/extraction)
Uses: infusion solutions/diagnostic aids; raw material (peptide drugs)

HMBP *See:* 2-methyl-3-phenylbenzyl alcohol

HMD *See:* hexamethylenediamine

HMDA *See:* hexamethylenediamine

HMDI *See:* 4,4′-diisocyanatodicyclohexylmethane

HMDS *See:* di-(trimethylsilyl)amine

HMDTMP *See:* hexamethylenediaminetetra-(methylenephosphonic acid)

HMMM *See:* hexamethoxymethylmelamine

HMP *See:* sodium hexametaphosphate

HMPA *See:* hexamethylphosphoramide

HMS *See:* high-maltose syrup

HMT *See:* hexamethylenetetramine

HMTA *See:* hexamethylenetetramine

HMWPE
See: polyethylene, high-density, high molecular weight

HMX *See:* octogen

HNBR *See:* nitrile rubber, hydrogenated

HNS *See:* hexanitrostilbene

homomenthol *See:* trimethylcyclohexanol

homomenthyl salicylate
3,3,5-trimethylcyclohexyl salicylate

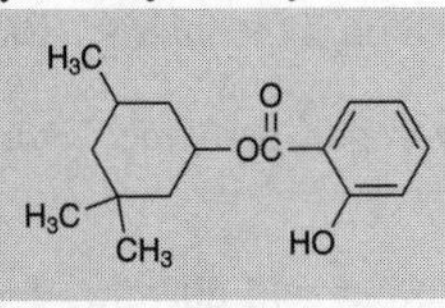

$C_{16}H_{22}O_3$. M: 262.36. Pale yellow liquid. Insoluble in water. Soluble in oxygenated solvents.
Production:
• trimethylcyclohexanol + salicylic acid (esterification)
Uses: sunscreening agent (cosmetics)

*o***-homosalicylic acid** *See: o*-cresotic acid

homovanillic acid
4-hydroxy-3-methoxyphenylacetic acid

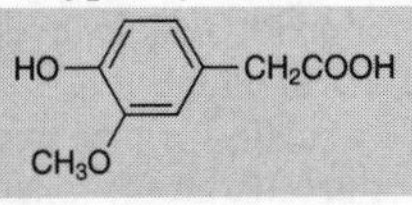

$C_9H_{10}O_3$. M: 166.18. White, crystalline solid. MP: 142–145°C. Soluble in water.
Production:
• vanillin + sodium cyanide (cyanohydrin formation/ hydrogenation)
Derivatives: propanidid

homoveratric acid
3,4-dimethoxyphenylacetic acid; [93-40-3]
$C_{10}H_{12}O_4$. M: 196.21. Crystalline solid. MP: 97–99°C. Slightly soluble in water. Soluble in oxygenated solvents.

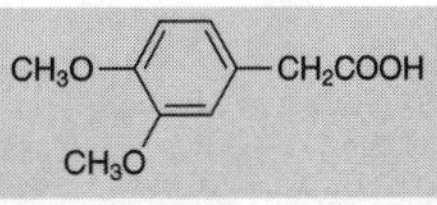

Production:
• catechol + acetic acid + dimethyl sulphate (esterification/Fries rearrangement/methylation/ Willgerodt reaction)
Derivatives: methyldopa; papaverine; veratryl cyanide

homoveratrylamine
3,4-dimethoxyphenylethylamine; [120-20-7]

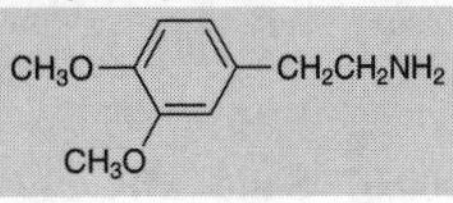

$C_{10}H_{15}N_1O_2$. M: 181.24. Pale-yellow liquid. BP: 118–123°C.
Production:
• veratryl cyanide (nitrile reduction)
Derivatives:
dobutamine; dopamine; papaverine; verapamil

HPA *See:* 2-hydroxypropyl acrylate

HPC *See:* hydroxypropyl cellulose

HPMA *See:* 2-hydroxypropyl methacrylate

HPN *See:* neopentyl glycol monohydroxypivalate

HPP *See:* allopurinol

HQ *See:* hydroquinone

HQDME *See:* hydroquinone dimethyl ether

HQMME *See:* hydroquinone monomethyl ether

HS *See:* hydroxylamine sulphate

HTAB *See:* cetyltrimethylammonium bromide

HTBD *See:* polybutadiene, hydroxyl-terminated

HTH *See:* calcium hypochlorite

HX *See:* 1,4-hexadiene

HXDI *See:* xylene diisocyanate, hydrogenated

hycanthone
[3105-97-3]
$C_{20}H_{24}N_2O_2S_1$. M: 356.48.
Production:
• lucanthone + *Aspergillus scleroticum* mould (microbial conversion)

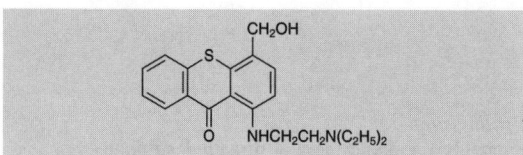

Uses: anthelmintic drug

hydantoin
[461-72-3]

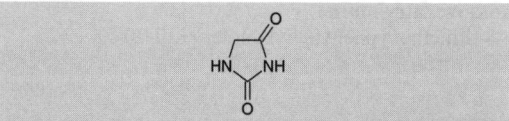

$C_3H_4N_2O_2$. M: 100.07. Solid. MP: 217–218°C. Soluble in water and hot alcohol.
Production:
• glyoxylic acid + urea (amide formation)
Derivatives: DL-phenylalanine
Uses: textile auxiliary

hydramethylnon
[67485-29-4]

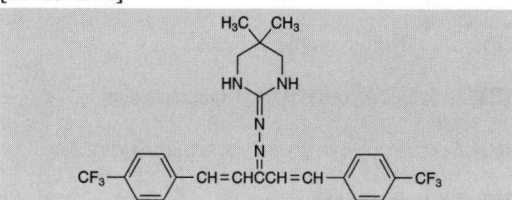

$C_{25}H_{24}F_6N_4$. M: 494.48.
Production:
• 4-(trifluoromethyl)benzaldehyde + acetone + hydrazine + neopentyl glycol + urea (carbonyl condensation/imine formation/condensation/imine formation)
Uses: insecticide

hydratropaldehyde
hydratropic aldehyde; 2-phenylpropionaldehyde;
[93-53-8]

$C_9H_{10}O_1$. M: 134.18. Colourless liquid with a hyacinth-like odour.
Production:
• styrene + synthesis gas (hydroformylation; coproduced with 3-phenylpropionaldehyde)
Derivatives: hydratropaldehyde dimethyl acetal
Uses: fragrance ingredient

hydratropaldehyde dimethyl acetal
2-phenylpropionaldehyde dimethyl acetal; [90-87-9]
$C_{11}H_{16}O_2$. M: 180.25.

Production:
• hydratropaldehyde + methanol (acetal formation)
Uses:
fragrance ingredient

hydrazine
hydrazine hydrate; [302-01-2]

H_4N_2. M: 32.04. Available commercially as anhydrous grade, hydrate or sulphate. Anhydrous hydrazine is a waxy solid. d: 1.00 kg/l (25°C). Hydrazine hydrate is a colourless liquid containing 63.4% hydrazine (1:1 N_2H_4:H_2O). BP: 120–121°C. Aqueous solutions with lower hydrazine contents are also available. A 35% aqueous solution is commonly used for boiler treatment applications. Hydrazine sulphate is a crystalline solid. MP: 254°C. Slightly soluble in water forming acidic solutions.
Production:
• ammonia + sodium hypochlorite (Raschig hydrazine process)
• ammonia + sodium hypochlorite (Bayer hydrazine process)
• ammonia + hydrogen peroxide (hydrogen peroxide process)
Derivatives:
acetazolamide; adipic acid dihydrazide; allopurinol; alprazolam; aminoguanidine bicarbonate; 2,2′-azobisisobutyronitrile; azodicarbonamide; benzene-1,3-disulphohydrazide; benzenesulphohydrazide; *t*-butylhydrazinium chloride; clofentezine; *N,N*′-dibenzaloxalyldihydrazide; 1,4-dichlorophthalazine-6-carboxyl chloride; dihydralazine; 2,5-dimercapto-1,3,4-thiadiazole; 1,1-dimethylhydrazine; diphenylene oxide-3,6-disulphohydrazide; diphenylsulphone-3,3′-disulphohydrazide; *N,N*′-disalicylhydrazide; elastane; guanoclor; hydramethylnon; hydrazinobis[3-(3,5-di-*t*-butyl-4-hydroxyphenyl)propionate]; hydriodic acid; isoniazid; maleic hydrazide; metamitron; metazachlor; methidathion; 2-methyl-5-mercapto-1,3,4-thiadiazole; 4-methyl thiosemicarbazide; metribuzin; nifuratel; nitrofurantoin; oxadiazon; 4,4′-oxybis(benzenesulphohydrazide); Pigment Yellow 101; poly(*p*-benzhydrazoterephthalamide); polyols, polyurea dispersion; pyrazophos; pyridate; robenidine; *N*-salicylidene-*N*′-salicoylhydrazine; semicarbazide hydrochloride; thiosemicarbazide; *p*-toluenesulphohydrazide; *N,N′,N″*-triaminoguanidine nitrate; triazolam; 1,2,4-triazole; tricyclazole; trihydrazinotriazine
Uses:
oxygen scavenger (boiler water treatment); electrodeless nickel coating reagent; rocket propellant

hydrazine hydrate *See:* hydrazine

hydrazinobis[3-(3,5-di-t-butyl-4-hydroxyphenyl)propionate]

$C_{34}H_{52}N_2O_4$. M: 552.80.
Production:
• hydrazine + methyl 3,5-di-*t*-butyl-4-hydroxyphenyl-propionate (amide formation)
Uses: metal deactivator (plastics)

hydrazobenzene
N,N'-diphenylhydrazine; [122-66-7]

$C_{12}H_{12}N_2$. M: 184.24. Solid. MP: 125–130°C. d: 1.16 kg/l (15°C). Soluble in alcohol.
Production:
• nitrobenzene (reductive coupling)
Derivatives: phenylbutazone; sulfinpyrazone

hydriodic acid
hydrogen iodide; [10034-85-2]

HI

H_1I_1. M: 127.91. Hydriodic acid is a solution of hydrogen iodide in water. Grades containing 55%, 47% and 10% hydrogen iodide are available commercially.
Production:
• hydrogen + iodine (reaction)
• hydrazine + iodine (reaction)
Derivatives:
ethylenediamine dihydroiodide; sodium iodide

hydroabietyl alcohol
Abitol (Hercules)

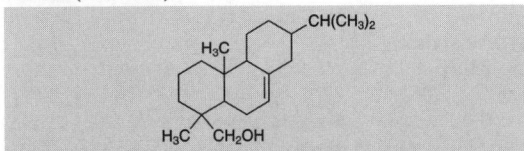

$C_{20}H_{34}O_1$. M: 290.49. Colourless, viscous liquid. Insoluble in water.
Production:
• methyl abietate (hydrogenation)
Derivatives:
hydroabietyl phthalate
Uses: tackifier (adhesives)

hydroabietyl phthalate
Cellolyn 21 (Hercules)
$C_{46}H_{70}O_4$. M: 687.07. Solid. MP: 63°C. d: 1.06 kg/l (20°C).

Production:
• hydroabietyl alcohol + phthalic anhydride (esterification)
Uses: polyvinyl chloride plasticiser

hydrobromic acid
[10035-10-6]

HBr

H_1Br_1. M: 80.91. Available commercially as an azeotropic, 48% solution. Pale yellow liquid. d: 1.48 kg/l (20°C). BP: 126°C. FP: -11°C. Miscible with water. Also available as a 60% solution. See also hydrogen bromide, anhydrous.
Production:
• hydrogen bromide, anhydrous (dissolution)
Derivatives: allyl bromide; ammonium bromide; 5-bromovaleric acid; *n*-butyl bromide; calcium bromide; dibromoneopentyl glycol; ethyl bromide; isopropyl bromide; lithium bromide; methyl bromide; potassium bromide; *n*-propyl bromide; sodium bromide; tetrabromodipentaerythritol; thiomalic acid; tribromoneopentyl alcohol; zinc bromide

hydrocarbon-maleic resins
Production:
• hydrocarbon resins, C₅ aliphatic types + maleic anhydride (cycloaddition)
Uses: paper sizing ingredient

hydrocarbon resins, C₅ aliphatic types
petroleum resins, C₅ aliphatic types
Production:
• C₅-stream, steam-cracked (polymerisation)
Derivatives:
hydrocarbon-maleic resins
Uses: tackifier (hot melt/pressure-sensitive adhesives); binder (printing inks)

hydrocarbon resins, C₉ aromatic types
petroleum resins, C₉ aromatic types
Resin formed by polymerisation of C₉ aromatics fractions (BP: 150–200°C) which contain indene, α-methylstyrene, vinyltoluene, styrene and dicyclopentadiene in addition to unpolymerisable components.
Production:
• C₉₊ aromatics (polymerisation)
Uses: binder (varnishes); tackifier (hot melt adhesives)

hydrocarbon resins, dicyclopentadiene types

dicyclopentadiene resins; petroleum resins, dicyclopentadiene types

Pale yellow solid. Softening point: 100–115°C (Ring and Ball Method). d: 1.11 kg/l.

Production:
• dicyclopentadiene (polymerisation)

Uses: hot melt carpet backing; rubber compounding ingredient; tackifier (hot melt/pressure-sensitive adhesives, coatings); thermoplastic road paints; binder (printing inks)

hydrochloric acid

muriatic acid; [7647-01-0]

HCl

H_1Cl_1. M: 36.46. Pale yellow liquid with a pungent odour. Available commercially as a 31% w/w (22° Baumé, d: 1.16 kg/l) or 35% w/w (22°Baumé, d: 1.18 kg/l) solution in water. Attacks most metals with the evolution of hydrogen. Hydrochloric acid is mainly produced as a byproduct of dehydrochlorination reactions. See also hydrogen chloride, anhydrous.

Production:
• hydrogen chloride, anhydrous (dissolution)

Derivatives: acetamidine hydrochloride; aluminium chloride, hexahydrate; ammonium paratungstate; animal glue; antimony trichloride; barium chloride; n-butyl chloride; cadmium chloride; calcium chloride; chlorine; chloroauric acid; 3-(2-chloroethyl)aminopropanol hydrochloride; 1-(3-chlorophenyl)piperazine hydrochloride; chloroplatinic acid; choline chloride; chromic chloride; cobalt chloride; cupric chloride; cuprous chloride; didymium; 2-dimethylaminoethyl chloride hydrochloride; ethyl chloride; ferric chloride; ferrous chloride; gelatine; germanium oxide; glucose syrup; n-hexyl chloride; hydrogen chloride, anhydrous; lithium chloride; magnesium chloride; maltodextrin; manganous chloride; mecysteine hydrochloride; 2-mercaptoethylamine hydrochloride; nickel chloride; polyaluminium chloride; rare earth chloride, hydrate; rutile; semicarbazide hydrochloride; stannous chloride; stearamidomethylpyridinium chloride; tetrakis(hydroxymethyl)phosphonium chloride; zinc ammonium chloride; zirconium oxychloride

Uses:
leather deliming/tanning agent; industrial cleaning agent; ion-exchange resin regeneration (water treatment, chemical purification); oil-well acidising reagent; pH control (water treatment); metal pickling agent; alcohol chlorination reagent; animal glue production; sugar/oils/fats/wax refining agent; starch hydrolysis reagent; textile scouring agent; water/industrial plant descaling chemical

hydrochlorothiazide

[58-93-5]

$C_7H_8Cl_1N_3O_4S_2$. M: 297.74.

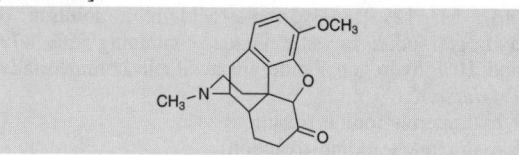

Production:
• formaldehyde + 5-chloroaniline-2,4-disulphonamide (carbonyl condensation)

Uses: diuretic drug

hydrocinnamic acid

3-phenylpropionic acid; [501-52-0]

$C_9H_{10}O_2$. M: 150.18. White crystals. MP: 48–49°C. Soluble in oxygenated, aromatic and chlorinated solvents. Also soluble in hot water.

Production:
• cinnamic acid (hydrogenation)

Uses: fragrance intermediate

hydrocinnamic alcohol *See:* 3-phenylpropanol

hydrocinnamic aldehyde *See:* 3-phenylpropionaldehyde

hydrocodone

[125-29-1]

$C_{18}H_{21}N_1O_3$. M: 299.38. Available commercially as the bitartrate hemipentahydrate salt.

Production:
• codeine (isomerisation)

Uses: analgesic/antitussive drug

hydrocortisone

[50-23-7]

$C_{21}H_{30}O_5$. M: 362.46. Available commercially as the free product and as a variety of 17- and 21-substituted derivatives.

Production:
• cortisone (carbonyl reduction)

Derivatives: prednisolone

Uses: antiinflammatory drug

hydrocyanic acid *See:* hydrogen cyanide

hydroflumethiazide
[135-09-1]

$C_8H_8F_3N_3O_4S_2$. M: 331.29.
Production:
• *m*-aminobenzotrifluoride + chlorosulphonic acid + ammonia + formaldehyde (chlorosulphonation/ sulphonamide formation/carbonyl condensation)
Uses: diuretic drug

hydrofluoric acid
white acid

HF

H_1F_1. M: 20.01. Colourless, fuming liquid. d: 1.16 kg/l. Soluble in water. Available commercially as a 70% solution in steel containers or as a 50% solution in plastic-lined containers. Attacks glass. When the HF concentration is <60% it also attacks steel. See also hydrogen fluoride.
Production:
• hydrogen fluoride (dissolution)
Derivatives: aluminium fluoride; antimony trifluoride; boron trifluoride; chromic fluoride; fluoboric acid; fluorine; fluorosulphonic acid; hexafluorosilicic acid; potassium bifluoride; potassium fluoride; potassium fluorozirconate; rare earth fluoride; sodium fluoride; stannous fluoride; zinc fluoride
Uses: building cleaning agent; etchant (semiconductor manufacture); flotation depressant; frosting/polishing agent (glass, enamel); aluminium brightening agent; metal cleaning/electropolishing bath ingredient; oil-well acidising reagent; stainless steel pickling agent

hydrogen
[1333-74-0]

H_2

H_2. M: 2.02. Colourless gas. BP: -253°C. FP: 259°C. d: 0.07 kg/l (-253°C). Relative density: 0.0695 (gas, air=1). Slightly soluble in water.
Production:
• synthesis gas + water (shift reaction/solvent extraction; coproduced with carbon dioxide)
• synthesis gas (cryogenic separation; coproduced with carbon monoxide)
• water (electrolysis; coproduced with oxygen)
• propane (dehydrogenation; byproduct of propylene production)
• isobutane (dehydrogenation; byproduct of isobutylene production)
• liquified petroleum gas (BP-UOP Cyclar process; byproduct of aromatics, mixed production)

• natural gas + *n*-butane (Hüls electric arc process; byproduct of ethylene/acetylene production)
• sodium chloride, natural (mercury cell electrolysis; byproduct of chlorine/sodium hydroxide production)
• sodium chloride, natural (diaphram cell electrolysis; byproduct of chlorine/sodium hydroxide production)
• sodium chloride, natural (membrane cell electrolysis; byproduct of chlorine/sodium hydroxide production)
• potassium chloride (mercury cell electrolysis; byproduct of chlorine/potassium hydroxide production)
• potassium chloride (membrane cell electrolysis; byproduct of chlorine/potassium hydroxide production)
• sodium chloride, natural (electrolytic oxidation; byproduct of sodium chlorate production)
• sodium chlorate (electrolysis; byproduct of sodium perchlorate production)
• chlorine (Merck process; byproduct of sodium perchlorate production)
• hydrochloric acid (electrolysis; byproduct of chlorine production)
• hydrofluoric acid (electrolysis; byproduct of fluorine production)
Derivatives:
1,4-butanediol; calcium hydride; caprolactam; cobalt; 1,1-dimethylhydrazine; hydriodic acid; hydrogen bromide, anhydrous; hydrogen chloride, anhydrous; hydrogen peroxide; hydrogen sulphide; hydroxylamine phosphate; hydroxylamine sulphate; lithium hydride; molybdenum; nickel; L-phenylalanine; silica, fumed; silicon, electronic grade; sodium borohydride; sodium hydride; tetrahydrofuran; titanium hydride; triethylaluminium; triisobutylaluminium; tri-*n*-octylaluminium; tungsten; uranium metal, U^{235} enriched; zirconium hydride
Uses: fuel gas; petroleum hydrotreating/hydrocracking/ hydroforming reagent; nitro reduction/hydrogenation reagent; vegetable oil hardening reagent; rocket fuel; welding gas

hydrogenated tallow *See:* tallow, hydrogenated

hydrogenated tallowamine acetate
See: stearylamine acetate

hydrogenated tallowamine ethoxylates
See: stearylamine ethoxylates

hydrogenated tallow-1,3-diaminopropane
See: stearyl-1,3-propanediamine

hydrogen bromide, anhydrous
[10035-10-6] (aqueous solution)

HBr

H_1Br_1. M: 80.91. Colourless, liquified gas with an acrid

odour. BP: -67°C. MP: -87°C. Soluble in water forming hydrobromic acid. See also hydrobromic acid.
Production:
• hydrogen + bromine (reaction)
Derivatives:
4-amino-5-bromomethyl-2-methylpyrimidine hydrobromide; ω-aminoundecanoic acid; 1-bromo-3-chloropropane; cetyl bromide; cupric bromide; dibenzosuberenone-5; *n*-hexyl bromide; hydrobromic acid; metolachlor; myristyl bromide; *n*-octyl bromide; vinyl bromide
Uses: alcohol bromination reagent

hydrogen chloride, anhydrous
[7647-01-0]

HCl

H_1Cl_1. M: 36.46. Colourless gas with a pungent odour. BP: -85°C. MP: -114°C. Relative density: 1.27 (gas, air=1). Soluble in water and alcohol. Hydrogen chloride is mainly produced as a byproduct of dehydrochlorination reactions. The production of chlorocarbons, chlorofluorocarbons, isocyanates, phosphate esters and fumed silica are important sources of this product. See also hydrochloric acid.
Production:
• hydrogen + chlorine (reaction)
• hydrochloric acid (distillation)
• sodium chloride, natural + sulphur dioxide, pure (Hargreaves process; byproduct of sodium sulphate production)
• sodium chloride, natural + sulphuric acid (Mannheim process; byproduct of sodium sulphate production)
• sodium chloride, natural + sulphuric acid (salt formation; byproduct of sodium bisulphate production)
• potassium chloride + sulphur dioxide, pure (Hargreaves process; byproduct of potassium sulphate production)
• potassium chloride + sulphuric acid (salt formation; byproduct of potassium sulphate production)
Derivatives: carbon tetrachloride; cetyl chloride; chlorobenzene; chloroform; chloromethyl methyl ether; chloroprene; chlorosulphonic acid; *o*-dichlorobenzene; *p*-dichlorobenzene; 1,1-dichloroethane; 3-dimethylamino-2-methylpropyl chloride hydrochloride; ethyl chloride; ethyl γ-chloroacetoacetate; ethylene dichloride; hydrochloric acid; manganous chloride; methyl chloride; methyl γ-chloroacetoacetate; methylene chloride; nitrosyl chloride; *n*-octyl chloride; rubber hydrochloride; silicon tetrachloride; 1,2,3-trichloropropane; trichlorosilane; vinyl chloride
Uses: alkylation/isomerisation/polymerisation catalyst; alcohol chlorination/chloromethylation reagent

hydrogen cyanide
hydrocyanic acid; prussic acid; [74-90-8]

HCN

$C_1H_1N_1$. M: 27.03. Colourless, highly-toxic liquid with an almond-like odour. BP: 26°C. MP: -14°C. d: 0.70 kg/l (20°C). Soluble in water and oxygenated solvents.
Production:
• natural gas + ammonia (Andrussow/BMA processes)
• raffinate II + ammonia (Shawinigan electrothermal process)
• formamide (BASF formamide process)
• propylene + ammonia (ammoxidation; byproduct of acrylonitrile production)
Derivatives:
acetone cyanohydrin; acetone-1,3-dicarboxylic acid; adiponitrile; adrenalone; D-alanine; DL-alanine; alfentanil; 2-amino-2-methylisopentamide; benzoyl cyanide; bis-(aminomethyl)norbornane; *t*-butylamine; calcium ferrocyanide; cyanogen chloride; L-cysteine; DL-cysteine hydrochloride; diethylenetriaminepentaacetic acid, pentasodium salt; diethyl α-isomalate; 2,4-dihydroxybenzaldehyde; 5,5-dimethylhydantoin; dithianon; ethosuximide; ethylenediaminetetraacetic acid; fluspirilene; glufosinate-ammonium; glycine; hydroxyethylethylenediaminetriacetic acid, trisodium salt; *p*-hydroxyphenylacetonitrile; D-α-(4-hydroxyphenyl)glycine; iminodiacetic acid; imipenem; isocyanic acid; isophoronediamine; DL-lactic acid; levodopa; mephenytoin; mesuximide; DL-methionine; methionine hydroxy analogue; methyldopa; molsidomine; myclobutanil; nitrilotriacetic acid; *t*-octylamine; oxamide; pantolactone; DL-phenylalanine; D-α-phenylglycine; *N*-phenylglycine; 2-phenyl-2-propylamine; phenytoin; potassium cyanide; sarcosine; sodium cyanide; sodium dihydroxyethylglycine; sodium *N*-hydroxyethylglycine; succinonitrile; triethyl orthoformate; trimethyl orthoformate; DL-valine; zinc cyanide

hydrogen fluoride
[7664-39-3]

HF

H_1F_1. M: 20.01. Colourless to pale brown, liquified gas. BP: 19–20°C. Fumes in air. Soluble in water forming hydrofluoric acid. See also hydrofluoric acid.
Production:
• fluorspar + sulphuric acid (acidification)
Derivatives:
aluminium fluoride; ammonium bifluoride; benzotrifluoride; beryllium; *o*-chlorobenzotrifluoride; *p*-chlorobenzotrifluoride; 1-chloro-1,1-difluoroethane; chlorodifluoromethane; 3-chloro-2-hydroxy-5-trifluoromethylpyridine; chloropentafluoroethane; 1-chloro-1,2,2,2-tetrafluoroethane; 1-chloro-2,2,2-trifluoroethane; 5-chloro-2,4,6-trifluoropyrimidine; cyanuric fluoride; 2,4-dichlorobenzotrifluoride; 3,4-dichlorobenzotrifluoride; dichlorodifluoromethane; 1,1-dichloro-1-fluoroethane; dichlorofluoro-

methane; dichlorofluoromethanesulphenyl chloride; 1,2-dichloro-1,1,2,2-tetrafluoroethane; 1,1-dichloro-2,2,2-trifluoroethane; 4,4′-difluorobenzophenone; 2,4-dinitrofluorobenzene; enflurane; *p*-fluoroaniline; fluorobenzene; 4-fluoro-3-phenoxybenzaldehyde cyanohydrin; *p*-fluorotoluene; hydrofluoric acid; 2-hydroxy-5-(trifluoromethyl)pyridine; isoflurane; pentafluoroethane; perfluorobutanesulphonic acid; perfluorohexanesulphonic acid; perfluorooctanesulphonic acid; perfluorooctanoic acid; perfluorotriamylamine; perfluorotributylamine; perfluorotrihexylamine; tetrachlorodifluoroethane; 1,1,1,2-tetrafluoroethane; trichlorofluoromethane; 1,1,2-trichloro-1,2,2-trifluoroethane; trifluoroacetic acid; trifluoromethane; trifluoromethanesulphonic acid; 4-(trifluoromethyl)benzaldehyde; 2-(trifluoromethyl)benzoyl fluoride; 3-(trifluoromethyl)benzoyl fluoride; 4-(trifluoromethyl)benzyl alcohol; uranium hexafluoride; vinyl fluoride
Uses: chemical/petroleum alkylation catalyst; semiconductor manufacturing reagent

hydrogen iodide *See:* hydriodic acid

hydrogen peroxide
[7722-84-1]

$$H_2O_2$$

H_2O_2. M: 34.02. Available commercially as a colourless, aqueous solution containing 30%, 35%, 50%, 70% or 85% H_2O_2 by weight. Miscible with water.
Production:
- hydrogen + oxygen + 2-ethylanthraquinone/amylanthraquinone (anthroquinone process)
- ammonium persulphate (hydrolysis)
Derivatives:
acetylacetone peroxide; alkyl(C_{13}-C_{15})dimethylamine oxide; *t*-amyl hydroperoxide; barium peroxide; benzoyl peroxide; bis(2-hydroxyethyl)alkyl(C_{13}-C_{15})amine oxide; bis(2-hydroxyethyl)cocoamine oxide; bis(2-hydroxyethyl)tallowamine oxide; *t*-butyl hydroperoxide; cadusafos; calcium peroxide; catechol; *p*-chlorobenzoyl peroxide; cocoamidopropyldimethylamine oxide; cyclohexane peroxide; 2,4-dichlorobenzoyl peroxide; didecanoyl peroxide; diethylhydroxylamine; diisopropyl peroxydicarbonate; dimethylbehenylamine oxide; 2,5-dimethylhexane-2,5-dihydroperoxide; 1,1-dimethyl-3-hydroxybutyl peroxy-2-ethylhexanoate; 1,1-dimethyl-3-hydroxybutyl peroxyneoheptanoate; dimethyllaurylamine oxide; dimethylstearylamine oxide; di-(*n*-propyl) peroxydicarbonate; ethoprophos; fensulfothion; hexafluoropropylene oxide; hydrazine; hydroquinone; isononanoyl peroxide; lauroyl peroxide; methyl ethyl ketone peroxide; methyl isobutyl ketone peroxide; myristyldimethylamine oxide; oleyldimethylamine oxide; oxycarboxin; oxydemetonmethyl; peracetic acid; performic acid; peroxysulphuric acid; pyridine-*N*-oxide; sodium chlorite; sodium perborate; sodium percarbonate; sodium 2-pyridinethiol-*N*-oxide; starch, oxidised; succinic acid peroxide; sulfin-

pyrazone; thiourea dioxide; tri-*n*-octylphosphine oxide; urea peroxide
Uses: redox polymerisation initiator component; disinfectant/deodorising agent (water effluent, food/beverage equipment/packaging); etchant; bleaching agent(deinked waste paper, groundwood pulp, hair, feathers, oil, wax, grease); oxidising agent (chemical synthesis, dyestuffs); textile bleach/desizing agent

hydrogen sulphide
[7783-06-4]

$$H_2S$$

H_2S_1. M: 34.08. Colourless gas with a characteristic, rotten-egg odour. BP: -61°C. FP: -86°C. d: 0.993 kg/l (-61°C). Relative density: 1.19 (gas, air=1). Solubility in water: 4 g/l solution (20°C) with decomposition. Toxic. Flammable.
Production:
- natural gas/synthesis gas/refinery gas/coke oven gas (solvent extraction)
- hydrogen + sulphur (reaction)
- natural gas (Lacq distillation process)
- natural gas + sulphur (reaction; byproduct of carbon disulphide production)
- metallurgical coke + sulphur (reaction; coproduced with carbon disulphide)
Derivatives: 2-aminothiophenol; ammonium sulphide; *n*-butyl mercaptan; *s*-butyl mercaptan; *t*-butyl mercaptan; cyclohexyl mercaptan; dimethyl sulphide; dimyristyl thiodipropionate; ditridecyl thiodipropionate; *n*-dodecyl mercaptan; *t*-dodecyl mercaptan; 1,2-ethanedithiol; ethionamide; ethyl mercaptan; ethyl sulphide; *n*-hexyl mercaptan; isopropyl mercaptan; 2-mercaptoethanol; 3-mercaptopropionic acid; methyl mercaptan; *n*-octyl mercaptan; pentachlorothiophenol; pentaerythritol tetrakis(3-mercaptopropionate); 1,2-propanedithiol; *n*-propyl mercaptan; prothionamide; sodium hydrosulphide; sulphur; tetrahydrothiophene; thidiazuron; thioacetic acid; thiodiglycol; thiodipropionic acid; 3,3′-thiodipropionitrile; thiourea
Uses: analytical reagent; raw material (Kraft paper production); heavy water enrichment reagent

hydromorphone
[466-99-9]

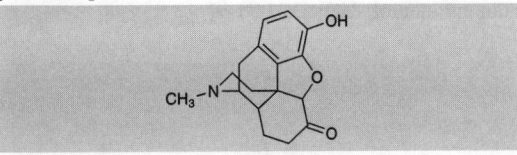

$C_{17}H_{19}N_1O_3$. M: 285.35. Available commercially as the hydrochloride.
Production:
- morphine (catalytic rearrangement)
Uses: analgesic drug

2-hydroperfluoroethyl allyl ether

HCF₂CF₂OCH₂CH=CH₂

$C_5H_6F_4O_1$. M: 158.09.
Production:
• tetrafluoroethylene + allyl alcohol (addition)
Derivatives:
dichloromethyl-3-(2-hydroperfluoroalkoxy)propylsilane

1,1-hydroperfluorooctanol
2,2,3,3,4,4,5,5,6,6,7,7,8,8,8-pentadecafluorooctan-1-ol;
[307-30-2]

CF₃(CF₂)₆CH₂OH

$C_8H_3F_{15}O_1$. M: 400.08.
Production:
• perfluorooctanoic acid (esterification/ester reduction)
Derivatives:
perfluoroalkyl acrylates; perfluoroalkyl methacrylates

2-hydroperfluoropropyl allyl ether

CF₃CHFCF₂OCH₂CH=CH₂

$C_6H_6F_6O_1$. M: 208.11.
Production:
• hexafluoropropylene + allyl alcohol (addition)
Derivatives:
dichloromethyl-3-(2-hydroperfluoroalkoxy)propylsilane

hydroprene
ethyl 3,7,11-trimethyldodeca-2,4-dienoate; [41096-46-2]

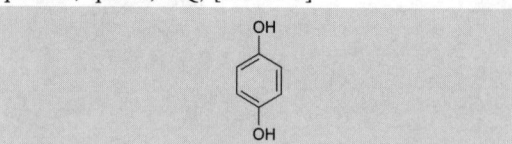

$C_{17}H_{30}O_2$. M: 266.43. The commercial product is the
trans,trans-isomer.
Production:
• chloroacetone + ethyl bromoacetate + (±)-citronellal
  (Reformatsky reaction/dehydration/hydrogenation/
  Wittig reaction)
Uses:
insect growth regulator

hydroquinone
1,4-dihydroxybenzene; *p*-dihydroxybenzene; hydroxy-
quinone; quinol; HQ; [123-31-9]

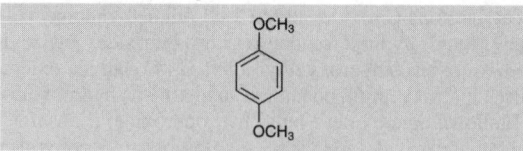

$C_6H_6O_2$. M: 110.12. Crystals. Discoloured by light and
air. MP: 172–173°C with decomposition. d: 1.33 kg/l
(15°C). Slightly soluble in water. Soluble in oxygenated solvents.

Production:
• *p*-benzoquinone (reduction)
• *p*-diisopropylbenzene (oxidation/acid-catalysed
  hydrolysis; coproduced with acetone)
• phenol + hydrogen peroxide (oxidation; coproduced
  with catechol)
Derivatives: chloranil; 2,5-di-*t*-amylhydroquinone; *N,N'*-
diaryl-*p*-phenylenediamine; *N,N'*-di-*s*-butyl-*p*-phenylene-
diamine; *N,N'*-diisopropyl-*p*-phenylenediamine; *N,N'*-
diphenyl-*p*-phenylenediamine; hydroquinone di-(β-hydroxyethyl) ether; hydroquinone dimethyl ether; hydroquinone monomethyl ether; polyether ether ketone; Sulphur Blue 11
Uses: polyarylate comonomer; photographic developing
agent; polymerisation inhibitor

hydroquinone di-(β-hydroxyethyl) ether
1,4-di-(2-hydroxyethoxy)benzene; *p*-di-(2-hydroxyeth-
oxy)benzene; hydroquinone di-(2-hydroxyethyl) ether

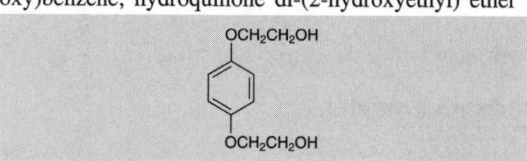

$C_{10}H_{14}O_4$. M: 198.22.
Production:
• hydroquinone + ethylene oxide (epoxidation)
Uses:
polyurethane elastomer crosslinking agent

hydroquinone dimethyl ether
1,4-dimethoxybenzene; dimethyl hydroquinone; DMB;
HQDME; [654-42-2]

$C_8H_{10}O_2$. M: 138.17. White crystals with a strong,
sweet odour. MP: 56°C. BP: 213°C. d: 1.04 kg/l
(55°C). Slightly soluble in water. Soluble in ether and
benzene.
Production:
• hydroquinone + dimethyl sulphate (methylation)
Uses:
perfume ingredient (soap)

hydroquinone monomethyl ether
4-hydroxyanisole; *p*-hydroxyanisole; *p*-methoxyphenol;
HA; HQMME; MEHQ; [150-76-5]
$C_7H_8O_2$. M: 124.14. White solid. MP: 53°C. BP:
243°C. d: 1.55 kg/l (20°C). Soluble in water, oxygenated solvents and benzene.
Production:
• hydroquinone + dimethyl sulphate (methylation)

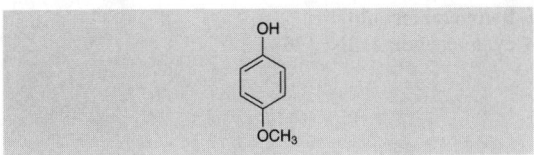

Derivatives:
Acid Brown 20; *t*-butylhydroxyanisole; difenoxuron
Uses: stabiliser (styrene monomer)

4-hydroxyacetanilide *See:* paracetamol

hydroxyacetic acid *See:* glycollic acid

hydroxyacetone
acetol; 1-hydroxy-2-propanone; [116-09-6]

$$CH_3\overset{O}{\underset{}{C}}CH_2OH$$

$C_3H_6O_2$. M: 74.08. Colourless liquid. BP 40°C (1.3 kPa). MP: -6°C. Soluble in water and oxygenated solvents.
Production:
• propylene glycol (gas-phase catalytic oxidation)
Derivatives:
2-ethyl-4-methylimidazole; 4-hydroxymethyl-5-methylimidazole hydrochloride; oxyquinaldine carboxylic acid
Uses: dyeing/printing auxiliary

m-hydroxyacetophenone
3-acetylphenol; *m*-acetylphenol; 3-hydroxyacetophenone; [121-71-1]

$C_8H_8O_2$. M: 136.15. Crystalline solid. BP: 296°C. MP: 94–95°C. Soluble in hot water, oxygenated, aromatic and chlorinated solvents.
Production:
• acetophenone (nitration/nitro reduction/diazotisation/hydrolysis)
Derivatives:
etilefrine; fenoprofen; norfenefrine; phenylephrine hydrochloride

o-hydroxyacetophenone
2-acetylphenol; *o*-acetylphenol; 2-hydroxyacetophenone; 2-HAP; [118-93-4]

$C_8H_8O_2$. M: 136.15. Liquid. BP: 102°C (1.9 kPa). d: 1.13 kg/l (20°C). Slight soluble in water. Soluble in oxygenated solvents.

Production:
• phenyl acetate (Fries rearrangement; coproduced with *p*-hydroxyacetophenone)
Derivatives: celiprolol; 4-hydroxycoumarin; 2-methoxyphenylacetic acid

p-hydroxyacetophenone
4-hydroxyacetophenone; 4-HAP; [99-93-4]

$C_8H_8O_2$. M: 136.15. Solid. MP: 107–110°C. Slightly soluble in water. Soluble in oxygenated solvents.
Production:
• phenyl acetate (Fries rearrangement; coproduced with *o*-hydroxyacetophenone)
Derivatives:
bufexamac; *p*-hydroxyphenylacetic acid; 4-methoxyacetophenone; paracetamol; synephrine

2-hydroxy-4-aminobenzoic acid
See: *p*-aminosalicylic acid

m-hydroxyaniline *See:* *m*-aminophenol

o-hydroxyaniline *See:* *o*-aminophenol

p-hydroxyaniline *See:* *p*-aminophenol

2-hydroxyaniline-5-sulphonic acid
See: 2-aminophenol-4-sulphonic acid

o-hydroxyanisole *See:* guaiacol

p-hydroxyanisole *See:* hydroquinone monomethyl ether

hydroxyanisole, butylated *See:* *t*-butylhydroxyanisole

1-hydroxyanthraquinone
[129-43-1]

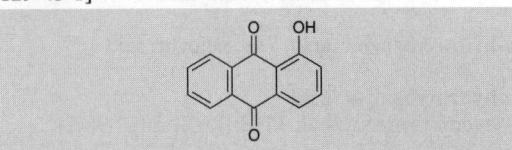

$C_{14}H_8O_3$. M: 224.21. Orange-red needles. MP: 193°C. Sublimes. Insoluble in water. Soluble in oxygenated and aromatic solvents.
Production:
• anthraquinone-1-sulphonic acid, sodium salt (alkali fusion)
Derivatives:
Mordant Black 13; quinizarin

3-hydroxy-1-azabicyclo[2,2,2]octane
See: quinuclidin-3-ol

m-hydroxybenzaldehyde
3-hydroxybenzaldehyde; [100-83-4]

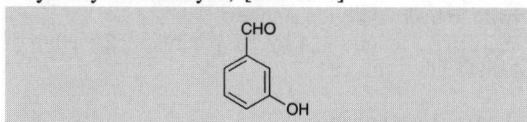

C$_7$H$_6$O$_2$. M: 122.13. Crystalline solid. MP: 117–119°C. Slightly soluble in water. Soluble in oxygenated and aromatic solvents.
Production:
• *m*-nitrobenzaldehyde (nitro reduction/diazotisation/ hydrolysis)
Derivatives: oxantel

o-hydroxybenzaldehyde *See:* salicylaldehyde

p-hydroxybenzaldehyde
4-hydroxybenzaldehyde; [123-08-0]

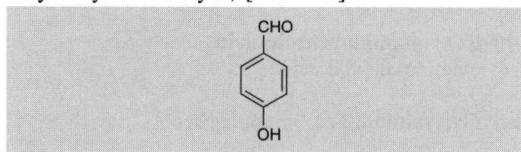

C$_7$H$_6$O$_2$. M: 122.13. Needles with a mild odour. MP: 117°C. Sublimes. Soluble in hot water, oxygenated and aromatic solvents.
Production:
• phenol + glyoxylic acid (carbonyl addition/ decarboxylation)
• phenol + chloroform (Reimer-Tiemann reaction; coproduced with salicylaldehyde)
Derivatives: *p*-anisaldehyde; bromofenoxim; flucythrinate; Food Green 3; *p*-hydroxybenzonitrile; *p*-hydroxybenzylacetone; D-α-(4-hydroxyphenyl)glycine; *p,p',p''*-tri-(2,3-epoxypropoxy)triphenylmethane; 3,4,5-trimethoxybenzaldehyde

o-hydroxybenzamide *See:* salicylamide

o-hydroxybenzoic acid *See:* salicylic acid

p-hydroxybenzoic acid
4-hydroxybenzoic acid; PHB; PHBA; [99-96-7]

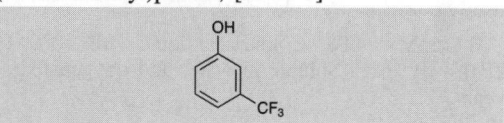

C$_7$H$_6$O$_3$. M: 138.13. White, crystalline solid. MP: 214–215°C. d: 1.49 kg/l (20°C). Very slightly soluble in water. Soluble in oxygenated solvents.
Production:
• phenol + carbon dioxide (Kolbe-Schmitt reaction)
Derivatives: *n*-butyl 4-hydroxybenzoate; cyclomethycaine; ethyl 4-hydroxybenzoate; gallic acid; methyl 4-hydroxybenzoate; phenyl *p*-hydroxybenzoate; polyarylate, liquid-crystalline; propyl 4-hydroxybenzoate

p-hydroxybenzonitrile
4-cyanophenol; HBN; [767-00-0]

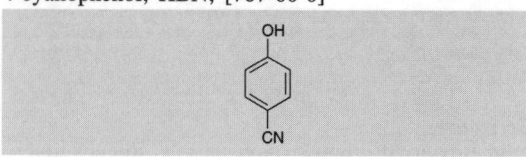

C$_7$H$_5$N$_1$O$_1$. M: 119.13. Crystalline solid. MP: 111–113°C. Soluble in hot water, oxygenated and chlorinated solvents.
Production:
• *p*-hydroxybenzaldehyde + hydroxylamine sulphate (imine formation/dehydration)
Derivatives: bromoxynil; cyanophos; ioxynil

m-hydroxybenzotrifluoride
3-(trifluoromethyl)phenol; [98-17-9]

C$_7$H$_5$F$_3$O$_1$. M: 162.11.
Production:
• *m*-aminobenzotrifluoride (diazotisation/hydrolysis)
Derivatives: diflufenican

p-hydroxybenzylacetone
4-hydroxybenzylacetone; 1-(*p*-hydroxyphenyl)-3-butanone; 4-(*p*-hydroxyphenyl)-2-butanone; 2-(4-hydroxyphenyl)ethyl methyl ketone; raspberry ketone; [5471-51-2]

C$_{10}$H$_{12}$O$_2$. M: 164.21. Colourless crystals with raspberry-like odour. MP: 82–83°C.
Production:
• *p*-hydroxybenzaldehyde + acetone (carbonyl condensation/hydrogenation)
Uses: flavouring ingredient

2-hydroxybenzyl alcohol *See:* salicyl alcohol

p-hydroxybenzyl cyanide
See: *p*-hydroxyphenylacetonitrile

2-hydroxybiphenyl *See:* *o*-phenylphenol

4-hydroxybiphenyl *See:* *p*-phenylphenol

2-[2'-hydroxy-3',5'-bis(1-methyl-1-phenylethyl)]benzotriazole
2-(benzotriazol-2-yl)-4,6-bis(1-methyl-1-phenylethyl)-phenol; Tinuvin 234 (Ciba-Geigy)
C$_{30}$H$_{29}$N$_3$O$_1$. M: 447.58.

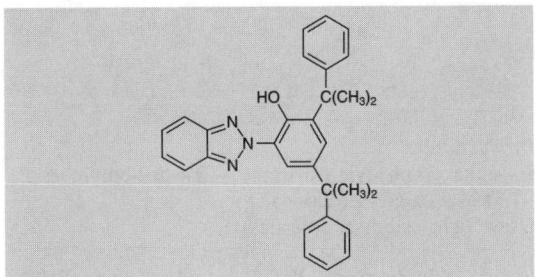

Production:
• phenol + α-methylstyrene + *o*-nitroaniline (Friedel-Crafts alkylation/diazotisation/azo coupling/nitro reduction/condensation)
Uses: light stabiliser (plastics)

3-hydroxybutan-2-one *See:* acetoin

2-(2-hydroxy-3-*t*-butyl-5-methylphenyl)-5-chloro-benzotriazole
Tinuvin 326 (Ciba-Geigy)

$C_{17}H_{18}Cl_1N_3O_1$. M: 315.80. Light yellow powder. MP: 140°C.
Production:
• 4-chloro-*o*-phenylenediamine + 2-*t*-butyl-*p*-cresol (nitrosation/condensation)
Uses: light stabiliser (plastics)

3-hydroxy-1-butyne *See:* 3-butyn-2-ol

4-hydroxybutyranilide
See: N-butyryl-*p*-aminophenol

2-hydroxy-5-chloroaniline-3-sulphonic acid
See: 2-amino-4-chlorophenol-6-sulphonic acid

2-hydroxy-5-chlorobenzophenone
See: 5-chloro-2-hydroxybenzophenone

4-hydroxy-4-(4-chlorophenyl)piperidine
See: 4-(4-chlorophenyl)-4-hydroxypiperidine

***o*-hydroxycinnamic acid**
o-coumaric acid; [583-17-5]

$C_9H_8O_3$. M: 164.16. Needles. MP: 214°C. Slightly soluble in water. Soluble in alcohol.

Production:
• coumarin (ester hydrolysis)
Uses: nickelplating brightening agent

hydroxycitronellal
3,7-dimethyl-7-hydroxyoctan-1-al; hydroxydihydrocitronellal; [107-75-5]

$C_{10}H_{20}O_2$. M: 172.27. Colourless liquid with a floral odour. BP: 90°C (1.3 kPa). d: 0.92 kg/l (15°C). Slightly soluble in water. Soluble in alcohol. The racemic mixture and the (+)-enantiomer (from (+)-citronellal) are available commercially.
Production:
• (±)-citronellal/(+)-citronellal (hydration)
• (±)-citronellol (hydration/alcohol oxidation)
• dihydromyrcenol + peracetic acid (epoxidation/hydrogenation/alcohol oxidation)
• α-methylheptenone + methylmagnesium chloride + synthesis gas (Grignard reaction/hydroformylation)
Derivatives:
hydroxycitronellal-anthranilate adduct; hydroxycitronellal dimethyl acetal; methoxycitronellal
Uses: fragrance/flavouring ingredient

hydroxycitronellal-anthranilate adduct

$C_{18}H_{27}N_1O_3$. M: 305.42.
Production:
• hydroxycitronellal + methyl anthranilate (imine formation)
Uses: fragrance ingredient

hydroxycitronellal dimethyl acetal
hydroxyacetal; hydroxydihydrocitronellal dimethyl acetal; [141-92-4]

$C_{12}H_{26}O_3$. M: 218.34. Colourless liquid with a floral odour. BP: 131 (1.6 kPa). d: 0.93 kg/l (25°C). Soluble in alcohol.
Production:
• hydroxycitronellal + methanol (acetal formation)
Uses:
fragrance ingredient (soap, detergents)

4-hydroxycoumarin
benzotetronic acid; [1076-38-6]
$C_9H_6O_3$. M: 162.15. Needles. MP: 212–213°C. Soluble in water and oxygenated solvents.

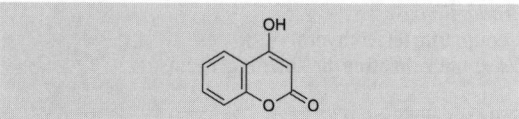

Production:
- *o*-hydroxyacetophenone + diethyl carbonate (Claisen condensation)

Derivatives: acenocoumarol; bromadiolone; coumachlor; coumatetralyl; difenacoum; ethyl biscoumacetate; flocoumafen; warfarin

7-hydroxycoumarin
umbelliferone; [93-35-6]

$C_9H_6O_3$. M: 162.15. Needles. MP: 226–229°C. Slightly soluble in water. Soluble in oxygenated solvents.
Production:
- 2,4-dihydroxybenzaldehyde + acetic anhydride (Perkin condensation)

Uses: sunscreening agent

1-hydroxycyclohexyl phenyl ketone
1-hydroxycyclohexylacetophenone; Irgacure 184 (Ciba-Geigy)

$C_{13}H_{16}O_2$. M: 204.27.
Production:
- cyclohexanone + sodium cyanide + benzene (cyanohydrin formation/nitrile hydrolysis/ Friedel-Crafts acylation)

Uses:
photoinitiator (radiation-cured lacquers, inks)

2-(2-hydroxy-3,5-di-*t*-butylphenyl)benzotriazole
Tinuvin 320 (Ciba-Geigy)

$C_{20}H_{25}N_3O_1$. M: 323.44. Off-white powder. MP: 152–154°C.
Production:
- *o*-nitroaniline + 2,6-di-*t*-butylphenol (diazotisation/ azo coupling/nitro reduction/condensation)

Uses: light stabiliser (plastics)

2-(2-hydroxy-3,5-di-*t*-butylphenyl)-5-chlorobenzotri-azole
Tinuvin 327 (Ciba-Geigy)
$C_{20}H_{24}Cl_1N_3O_1$. M: 357.88.

Production:
- 4-chloro-*o*-phenylenediamine + 2,4-di-*t*-butylphenol (nitrosation/condensation)

Uses: light stabiliser (plastics)

hydroxydihydrocitronellal *See:* hydroxycitronellal

2-hydroxy-2,2-dimethylacetophenone
See: α,α-dimethyl-α-hydroxyacetophenone

o-**hydroxydiphenyl** *See:* *o*-phenylphenol

p-**hydroxydiphenyl** *See:* *p*-phenylphenol

2-hydroxy-2,2-diphenylacetic acid *See:* benzilic acid

2-hydroxy-4-dodecoxybenzophenone
DOBP; UV-Chek AM 320 (Ferro); [2985-59-3]

$C_{25}H_{34}O_3$. M: 382.54.
Production:
- 2,4-dihydroxybenzophenone + lauryl chloride (ether formation)

Uses: UV absorber (plastics)

2-hydroxyethyl acrylate
HEA; [818-61-1]

$$CH_2=CHCOOCH_2CH_2OH$$

$C_5H_8O_3$. M: 116.11.
Production:
- acrylic acid + ethylene oxide (epoxidation)

Derivatives: acrylic resins, hydroxylated; 4-(2-acryloyloxyethoxy)-2-hydroxybenzophenone; polyester-acrylate resins; urethane-acrylate resins
Uses: reactive comonomer (acrylic, vinyl acetate, styrene-butadiene, nitrile resins); reactive diluent (radiation-cured coatings)

hydroxyethylaniline
N-(2-hydroxyethyl)aniline; 2-(phenylamino)ethanol; [122-98-5]

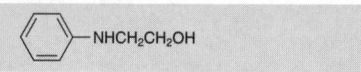

$C_8H_{11}N_1O_1$. M: 137.19. Liquid. BP: 282–287°C. Pour point: -30°C.

Production:
• aniline + ethylene oxide (epoxidation)
Derivatives:
N-(2-acetoxyethyl)-*N*-(2-cyanoethyl)aniline

hydroxyethyl cellulose
HEC; [9004-62-0]

R = H, 2-hydroxyethyl-. White powder. Bulk density: 0.7 kg/l. Soluble in water.
Production:
• alkali cellulose + ethylene oxide (epoxidation)
Derivatives: ethyl hydroxyethyl cellulose; methyl hydroxyethylcellulose
Uses: cast resins (water-soluble films); toothpaste/cosmetics ingredient; mineral flotation depressant; thickening agent/protective colloid (paints, adhesives, paper coatings, latex production); viscosifier (drilling muds, building products)

hydroxyethylethylenediaminetriacetic acid, sodium ferric salt
sodium ferric HEEDTA

Complex formed between the ferric ion and the trisodium hydroxyethylethylenediaminetriacetate salt.
Production:
• hydroxyethylethylenediaminetriacetic acid, trisodium salt + ferric chloride (salt formation)
Uses: slow-release fertiliser ingredient

hydroxyethylethylenediaminetriacetic acid, trisodium salt
trisodium hydroxyethylethylenediaminetriacetate; HEDTA, trisodium salt; HEEDTA, trisodium salt; [139-89-9]

$C_{10}H_{15}N_2Na_3O_7$. M: 344.20. Light yellow liquid. BP: 107°C. FP: <-20°C. d: 1.29 kg/l (25°C). Sold as a solution in water containing 40% active matter. Soluble in water forming alkaline solutions.
Production:
• aminoethylethanolamine + hydrogen cyanide + formaldehyde + sodium hydroxide (cyanomethylation/nitrile hydrolysis/salt formation)

Derivatives: hydroxyethylethylenediaminetriacetic acid, sodium ferric salt
Uses: chelating agent (alkaline industrial cleaners, latex production); complexing agent (rare earth separation)

hydroxyethylidene(diphosphonic acid)
etidronic acid (CTFA); hydroxyethane diphosphonic acid; ADPA; HEDP; [2809-21-4]

$C_2H_8O_7P_2$. M: 206.02. Available commercially as an aqueous solution with a 60% active acid content. Also available as the sodium salt.
Production:
• acetic anhydride + phosphorous acid (addition)
Uses:
dispersant (laundry detergents); scale inhibitor (boilers, cooling towers)

2-hydroxyethyl methacrylate
β-hydroxyethyl methacrylate; HEMA; [868-77-9]

$C_6H_{10}O_3$. M: 130.15. Liquid. BP: 95°C (1.3 kPa). FP: -12°C. d: 1.06 kg/l (25°C). Miscible with water. Flash point: 108°C (COC). Commercial products contain hydroquinone methyl ether or similar polymerisation inhibitors.
Production:
• ethylene oxide + methacrylic acid (epoxidation)
Derivatives: acrylic resins, hydroxylated; polyester-acrylate resins; poly(2-hydroxyethyl methacrylate); polymethacrylates, oil-soluble dispersants; urethane-acrylate resins
Uses: marine antifouling paint resin comonomer; reactive comonomer (acrylic, styrene-butadiene resins)

1-(2-hydroxyethyl)-2-methyl-5-nitroimidazole
See: metronidazole

5-(2-hydroxyethyl)-4-methylthiazole
4-methyl-5-β-hydroxyethylthiazole

$C_6H_9N_1O_1S_1$. M: 143.21.
Production:
• 2-acetobutyrolactone + carbon disulphide + ammonia (alpha chlorination/decarboxylation/condensation/oxidation)
Derivatives:
clomethiazole; thiamine

4-(2-hydroxyethyl)morpholine

N-hydroxyethylmorpholine; 2-(4-morpholino)ethanol;
[622-40-2]

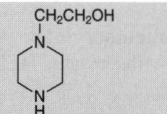

$C_6H_{13}N_1O_2$. M: 131.18. Colourless liquid. BP: 223–225°C. MP: 1–2°C. d: 1.07 kg/l. Soluble in water and alcohol.
Production:
• morpholine + ethylene oxide (epoxidation)
Derivatives: nimorazole

3-hydroxy-4-ethyl-1-octyne *See:* ethyl octynol

N-hydroxyethylpiperazine

N-(2-hydroxyethyl)piperazine; piperazineethanol; HEP;
[103-76-4]

$C_6H_{14}N_2O_1$. M: 130.19. Yellow, hygroscopic liquid with a mild, ammoniacal odour. BP: 246°C. MP: -21°C. d: 1.06 kg/l (20°C). Miscible with water, oxygenated and aromatic solvents. Flash point: 135°C (OC).
Production:
• monoethanolamine + ammonia (ammoniation;
  coproduced with ethylenediamine/diethylene-
  triamine/piperazine/aminoethylpiperazine/
  aminoethylethanolamine)
Derivatives:
clopenthixol; flupenthixol; fluphenazine; hydroxyzine; opipramol; perphenazine
Uses: polyurethane catalyst (elastomers, foam)

hydroxyethyl starch

Ten-o-film (CPC International)

R – OCH₂CH₂OH

R = starch-. Degrees of substitution of 0.05– 0.10 are typical.
Production:
• starch + ethylene oxide (epoxidation)
Uses: mineral filtration, clarification aid; protective colloid (emulsion paints); sizing agent (paper, textiles); textile backcoating

m-(β-hydroxyethylsulphonyl)aniline

2-(3-aminophenylsulphonyl)ethanol; aniline-3-(β-hydroxyethyl)sulphone
$C_8H_{11}N_1O_3S_1$. M: 201.25.
Production:
• metanilic acid + ethylene (chlorination/addition)

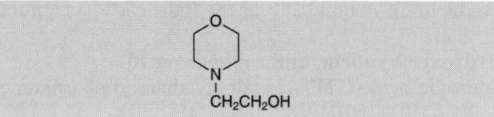

Derivatives: Reactive Blue 19

p-(β-hydroxyethylsulphonyl)aniline

2-(4-aminophenylsulphonyl)ethanol; aniline-4-(β-hydroxyethyl)sulphone

$C_8H_{11}N_1O_3S_1$. M: 201.25.
Production:
• sulphanilic acid + ethylene (chlorination/addition)
Derivatives: Fluorescent Brightener 312; Reactive Black 5; Reactive Orange 16

5-(β-hydroxyethylsulphonyl)-2-methoxyaniline

2-amino-5-(β-hydroxyethylsulphonyl)anisole; 2-(3-amino-4-methoxyphenylsulphonyl)ethanol; 2-methoxyaniline-4-(β-hydroxyethyl)sulphone

$C_9H_{13}N_1O_4S_1$. M: 231.27.
Production:
• 2-aminoanisole-4-sulphonic acid + ethylene
  (chlorination/addition)
Derivatives: Reactive Violet 5

α-hydroxyisobutyronitrile *See:* acetone cyanohydrin

hydroxylamine hydrochloride

hydroxylammonium chloride; [5470-11-1]

$HONH_3^+$ Cl^-

$H_4Cl_1N_1O_1$. M: 69.49. Solid. MP: 155–157°C with decomposition. Solubility in water: 830 g/l water (17°C). Soluble in alcohol.
Production:
• ammonium chloride (electrolytic reduction)
Derivatives:
cefuroxime; 3-(2-chloro-6-fluorophenyl)-5-methylisoxazole-4-carboxylic acid; 3-(2-chlorophenyl)-5-methylisoxazole-4-carboxylic acid; 3-(2,6-dichlorophenyl)-5-methylisoxazole-4-carboxylic acid; heptopargil; menadoxime; 5-methyl-3-phenylisoxazole-4-carboxylic acid; noxiptiline hydrochloride; prasterone
Uses: preservative (photographic developers); ammoniation reagent

hydroxylamine phosphate

hydroxylamine dihydrogen phosphate
$H_6N_1O_5P_1$. M: 131.02. Not a traded product. Formed as an intermediate in the DSM caprolactam process.

$$HONH_3^+ \quad H_2PO_4^-$$

Production:
• nitric oxide + hydrogen + phosphoric acid, pure (nitrate reduction process)
Derivatives: cyclohexanone oxime

hydroxylamine sulphate
HS; [10039-54-0]

$$(HONH_3^+)_2 \quad SO_4^{2-}$$

$H_8N_2O_6S_1$. M: 164.12. Colourless, hygroscopic crystals. MP: 170°C with decomposition. Solubility in water: 329 g/l water (0°C).
Production:
• nitric oxide + ammonium bicarbonate + sulphur dioxide, pure + ammonia (Raschig hydroxylamine process)
• nitric oxide + hydrogen + sulphuric acid (nitric oxide reduction process)
Derivatives: aldicarb; alloxydim-sodium; 3-amino-5-*t*-butylisoxazole; amphetamine; benzoximate; bromofenoxim; bufexamac; butocarboxim; butyraldoxime; *n*-butyronitrile; chlordiazepoxide; *p*-chlorobenzylamine; cinnamonitrile; citronellonitrile; clomazone; cyclohexanone oxime; cycloxydim; 2,6-dichlorobenzonitrile; dimethylglyoxime; *N,O*-dimethylhydroxylamine; dodecylsalicylaldoxime; drazoxolon; 2-ethylhexoin oxime; geranonitrile; *p*-hydroxybenzonitrile; 2-hydroxy-5-nonylacetophenoxime; 2-hydroxy-5-nonylbenzophenoxime; hymexazol; isobutyronitrile; isoxaben; isoxathion; lauryllactam; lorazepam; methomyl; 3-methyl-2-butylamine; methyl ethyl ketoxime; nonylsalicylaldoxime; nordazepam; paracetamol; propionitrile; pyrifenox; *p*-quinonedioxime; sethoxydim; sulfafurazole; sulfamethoxazole; thiodicarb; thiofanox; triazolam
Uses:
preservative (photographic developers)

p-**hydroxylauranilide** *See: N*-lauroyl-*p*-aminophenol

4-hydroxy-3-methoxybenzaldehyde *See:* vanillin

4-hydroxy-3-methoxybenzoic acid *See:* vanillic acid

2-hydroxy-4-methoxybenzophenone
benzophenone-3 (CTFA); oxybenzone; Cyasorb UV-9 (American Cyanamid); [131-57-7]

$C_{14}H_{12}O_3$. M: 228.25. Pale cream powder. MP: 62°C.
Production:
• 2,4-dihydroxybenzophenone + dimethyl sulphate (ether formation)

Derivatives:
2-hydroxy-4-methoxybenzophenone-5-sulphonic acid
Uses:
light stabiliser (plastics)

2-hydroxy-4-methoxybenzophenone-5-sulphonic acid
benzophenone-4; Cyasorb UV-284 (American Cyanamid); [4065-45-6]

$C_{14}H_{12}O_6S_1$. M: 308.30.
Production:
• 2-hydroxy-4-methoxybenzophenone (sulphonation)
Uses:
light stabiliser (plastics)

4-hydroxy-3-methoxyphenylacetic acid
See: homovanillic acid

N-(hydroxymethyl)acrylamide
See: N-methylolacrylamide

2-[(hydroxymethyl)amino]ethanol
Troysan 174 (Troy)

$$HOCH_2NHCH_2CH_2OH$$

$C_3H_9N_1O_2$. M: 91.11.
Production:
• monoethanolamine + formaldehyde (hydroxymethylation)
Uses:
biocide (paint, latices)

2-[(hydroxymethyl)amino]-2-methylpropanol
Troysan 192 (Troy)

$$HOCH_2NHCHCH_2OH$$

$C_5H_{13}N_1O_2$. M: 119.16.
Production:
• 2-amino-2-methyl-1-propanol + formaldehyde (hydroxymethylation)
Uses: biocide (paint, latices)

2-hydroxy-5-methylaniline *See: o*-amino-*p*-cresol

2-hydroxy-3-methylbenzoic acid *See: o*-cresotic acid

2-hydroxy-4-methylbenzoic acid *See: m*-cresotic acid

N-(hydroxymethyl)methacrylamide
See: N-methylol methacrylamide

4-hydroxymethyl-5-methylimidazole hydrochloride
5-hydroxymethyl-4-methylimidazole hydrochloride;
[38585-62-5]

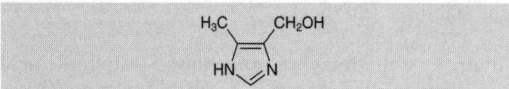

$C_5H_8N_2O_1$. M: 112.12.
Production:
• ethyl acetoacetate + formamide (alpha
chlorination/condensation/ester reduction)
• hydroxyacetone + formamide + formaldehyde
(condensation/hydroxymethylation)
Derivatives: cimetidine

4-hydroxy-4-methylpentan-2-one
See: diacetone alcohol

**3/4-(4-hydroxy-4-methylpentyl)-3-cyclohexenecarbox-
aldehyde**
Lyral; [31906-04-4]

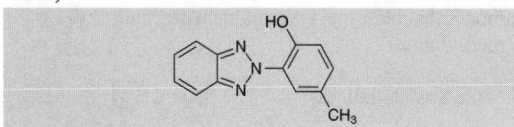

$C_{13}H_{22}O_2$. M: 210.32.
Production:
• myrcenol + acrolein (Diels-Alder cycloaddition)
Uses: fragrance ingredient/fixative (soap, detergents)

2-(2-hydroxy-5-methylphenyl)benzotriazole
Tinuvin P (Ciba-Geigy); Vanox UV-1 (Vanderbilt Chemical)

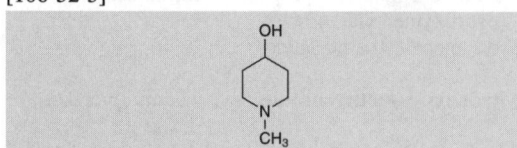

$C_{13}H_{11}N_3O_1$. M: 225.25.
Production:
• *o*-nitroaniline + *p*-cresol (diazotisation/azo
coupling/nitro reduction/condensation)
Uses: light stabiliser (plastics)

4-hydroxy-1-methylpiperidine
4-hydroxy-*N*-methylpiperidine; 1-methylpiperidin-4-ol;
[106-52-5]

$C_6H_{13}N_1O_1$. M: 115.18.
Production:
• 1-methyl-4-piperidone (carbonyl reduction)
Derivatives:
diphenylpyraline

2-hydroxy-2-methylpropanenitrile
See: acetone cyanohydrin

3-hydroxy-2-methyl-4-pyrone *See:* maltol

2-hydroxy-5-methylsulphonylaniline
See: 2-amino-4-methylsulphonylphenol

N-hydroxymethyl-3,4,5,6-tetrahydrophthalimide

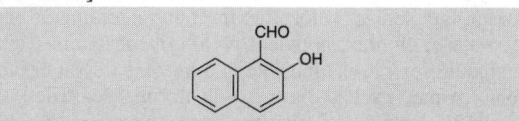

$C_9H_{11}N_1O_3$. M: 181.20.
Production:
• tetrahydrophthalic anhydride + urea + formaldehyde
(rearrangement/amide formation/hydroxymethylation)
Derivatives: tetramethrin

2-hydroxy-1-naphthaldehyde
[708-06-5]

$C_{11}H_8O_2$. M: 172.18. Solid. MP: 79–82°C.
Production:
• β-naphthol (Vilsmeier reaction)
Derivatives: Pigment Yellow 101
Uses:
dyestuffs intermediate

1-hydroxynaphthalene-2-carboxylic acid
See: α-hydroxynaphthoic acid

1-hydroxynaphthalene-3,8-disulphonic acid
See: 1-naphthol-3,8-disulphonic acid

2-hydroxynaphthalene-3,6-disulphonic acid
See: R acid

2-hydroxynaphthalene-6,8-disulphonic acid
See: G acid

8-hydroxynaphthalene-1,6-disulphonic acid
See: 1-naphthol-3,8-disulphonic acid

1-hydroxynaphthalene-5-sulphonic acid
See: 5-hydroxynaphthalene-1-sulphonic acid

2-hydroxynaphthalene-6-sulphonic acid
See: Schaeffer's acid

4-hydroxynaphthalene-1-sulphonic acid
See: Nevile-Winther acid

5-hydroxynaphthalene-1-sulphonic acid

1-hydroxynaphthalene-5-sulphonic acid; L Acid;
1-naphthol-5-sulphonic acid; [117-59-9]

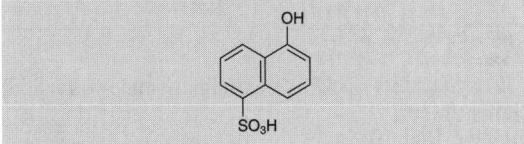

$C_{10}H_8O_4S_1$. M: 224.23.
Production:
• 1-naphthylamine-5-sulphonic acid (Bucherer reaction)
Derivatives:
2-diazo-1-naphthol-5-sulphonic acid chloride

8-hydroxynaphthalene-1-sulphonic acid

1-naphthol-8-sulphonic acid

$C_{10}H_8O_4S_1$. M: 224.23. Crystalline solid. MP: 106°C.
Soluble in water.
Production:
• peri acid (Bucherer reaction)
Derivatives: Acid Blue 158; Acid Blue 159

3-hydroxy-2-naphthanilide

2-hydroxy-3-naphthanilide; Naphthol AS; Azoic Coupling Component 2 (CI); 37505 (CI); [92-77-3]

$C_{17}H_{13}N_1O_2$. M: 263.30. Solid. MP: 243°C. Insoluble in water.
Production:
• β-oxynaphthoic acid + aniline (amide formation)
Derivatives: Pigment Red 2; Pigment Red 22
Uses: azoic dye coupling component

3-hydroxy-2-naphth-*o*-anisidide

2-methoxy-3'-hydroxy-2'-naphthanilide; Naphthol AS-OL; Azoic Coupling Component 20 (CI); Developer 22 (CI); 37530 (CI); [135-62-6]

$C_{18}H_{15}N_1O_3$. M: 293.33.
Production:
• β-oxynaphthoic acid + *o*-anisidine (amide formation)
Derivatives: Pigment Red 9; Pigment Red 188
Uses: azoic dye coupling component

3-hydroxy-2-naphth-*p*-anisidide

4-methoxy-3'-hydroxy-2'-naphthanilide; Naphthol AS-RL; Azoic Coupling Component 11 (CI); 37535 (CI); [92-79-5]

$C_{18}H_{15}N_1O_3$. M: 293.33.
Production:
• β-oxynaphthoic acid + *p*-anisidine (amide formation)
Uses: azoic dye coupling component

3-hydroxy-2-naphth-4'-chloro-2',5'-dimethoxyanilide

See: 4-chloro-2,5-dimethoxy-3'-hydroxy-2'-naphthanilide

3-hydroxy-2-naphth-5'-chloro-2',4'-dimethoxyanilide

See: 5-chloro-2,4-dimethoxy-3'-hydroxy-2'-naphthanilide

3-hydroxy-2-naphth-4'-chloro-2'-methylanilide

See: 4-chloro-3'-hydroxy-2'-naphth-*m*-toluidide

3-hydroxy-2-naphth-5'-chloro-2'-methylanilide

See: 5-chloro-3'-hydroxy-2'-naphth-*o*-toluidide

3-hydroxy-2-naphth-3'-nitroanilide

See: 3-nitro-3'-hydroxy-2'-naphthanilide

α-hydroxynaphthoic acid

1-hydroxynaphthalene-2-carboxylic acid; 1-hydroxy-2-naphthoic acid; 1-naphthol-2-carboxylic acid

$C_{11}H_8O_3$. M: 188.18.
Production:
• α-naphthol + carbon dioxide (Kolbe-Schmitt reaction)
Uses: photographic coupling agent intermediate

β-hydroxynaphthoic acid

See: β-oxynaphthoic acid

1-hydroxy-2-naphthoic acid

See: α-hydroxynaphthoic acid

3-hydroxy-2-naphthoic acid

See: β-oxynaphthoic acid

5-(2'-hydroxy-3'-naphthoyl)aminobenzimidazolone

$C_{18}H_{13}N_3O_3$. M: 319.32.

Production:
- β-oxynaphthoic acid + 5-aminobenzimidazolone (amide formation)

Derivatives: Pigment Brown 25; Pigment Red 171; Pigment Red 175; Pigment Red 176; Pigment Red 185; Pigment Red 208; Pigment Violet 32

3-hydroxy-2-naphth-*p*-phenethidide

4-ethoxy-3′-hydroxy-2′-naphthanilide; 3-hydroxy-2-naphth-4′-ethoxyanilide; Naphthol AS-BP (Hoechst); Naphthol AS-VL (Hoechst); Azoic Coupling Component 30 (CI); Azoic Coupling Component 46 (CI); 37559 (CI); [4711-68-6]

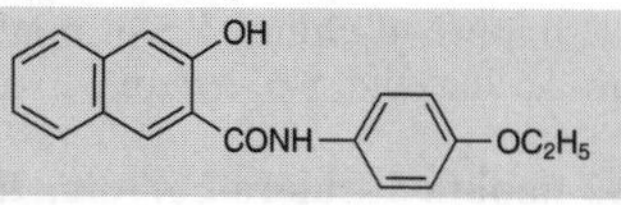

$C_{19}H_{17}N_1O_3$. M: 307.36.
Production:
- β-oxynaphthoic acid + *p*-phenetidine (amide formation)

Uses: azoic dye coupling component

3-hydroxy-2-naphth-*o*-phenetidide

2-ethoxy-3′-hydroxy-2′-naphthanilide; Azoic Coupling Component 14 (CI); 37558 (CI); [92-74-0]

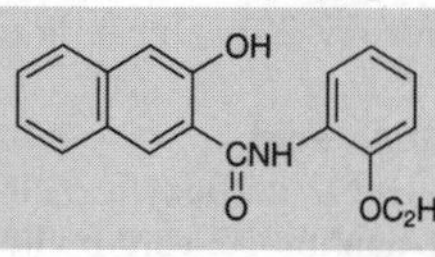

$C_{19}H_{17}N_1O_3$. M: 307.36.
Production:
- β-oxynaphthoic acid + *o*-phenetidine (amide formation)

Derivatives: Pigment Red 170

3-hydroxy-2-naphth-*o*-toluidide

2-methyl-3′-hydroxy-2′-naphthanilide; Naphthol AS-D; Azoic Coupling Component 18 (CI); Developer 21 (CI); 37520 (CI); [135-61-5]

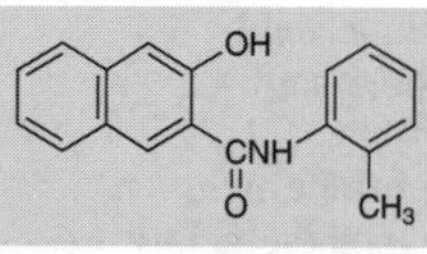

$C_{18}H_{15}N_1O_2$. M: 277.33.
Production:
- β-oxynaphthoic acid + *o*-toluidine (amide formation)

Derivatives: Pigment Red 12; Pigment Red 13; Pigment Red 14; Pigment Red 17; Pigment Red 112

Uses: azoic dye coupling component

3-hydroxy-2-naphth-*p*-toluidide

4-methyl-3′-hydroxy-2′-naphthanilide; Naphthol AS-RT; Azoic Coupling Component 31 (CI); 37521 (CI); [3651-62-5]

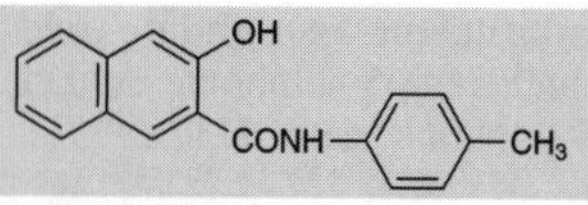

$C_{18}H_{15}N_1O_2$. M: 277.33.
Production:
- β-oxynaphthoic acid + *p*-toluidine (amide formation)

Derivatives:
Pigment Red 10

Uses: azoic dye coupling component

3-hydroxy-2-naphth-2′,4′-xylidide

2,4-dimethyl-3′-hydroxy-2′-naphthanilide; Naphthol AS-MX; Azoic Coupling Component 29 (CI); 37527 (CI); [92-75-1]

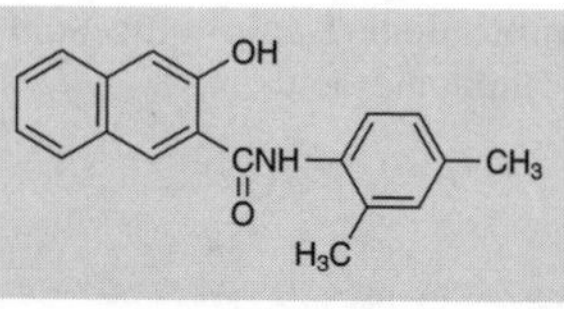

$C_{19}H_{17}N_1O_2$. M: 291.36. Solid. MP: 223–225°C.
Production:
- β-oxynaphthoic acid + 2,4-xylidine (amide formation)

Uses: azoic dye diazo component

2-hydroxy-4-nitroaniline
See: 2-amino-5-nitrophenol

2-hydroxy-5-nitroaniline-3-sulphonic acid
See: 2-amino-4-nitrophenol-6-sulphonic acid

3-hydroxy-4-nitrotoluene *See:* 6-nitro-*m*-cresol

4-hydroxy-3-nitrotoluene *See:* *m*-nitro-*p*-cresol

5-hydroxy-2-nitrotoluene *See:* 4-nitro-*m*-cresol

2-hydroxy-5-nonylacetophenoxime
SME529 (Shell); [59344-62-6]

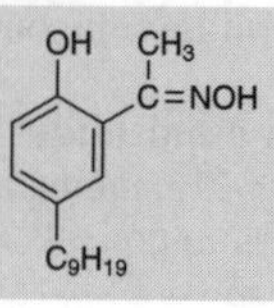

$C_{17}H_{27}N_1O_2$. M: 277.42.
Production:
- nonylphenol + acetic anhydride + hydroxylamine sulphate (esterification/Fries rearrangement/oxime formation)

Uses: copper extraction reagent

2-hydroxy-5-nonylbenzophenoxime
LIX 65N (Henkel)
$C_{22}H_{29}N_1O_2$. M: 339.48.

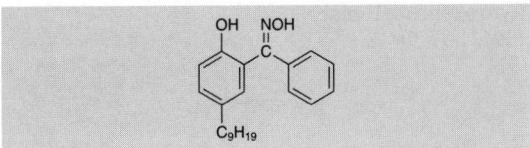

Production:
- nonylphenol + benzoyl chloride + hydroxylamine
  sulphate (Friedel-Crafts acylation/oxime formation)
Uses: copper extraction reagent

2-hydroxy-4-octoxybenzophenone
2-hydroxy-4-*n*-octoxybenzophenone; benzophenone-12
(CTFA); Carstab 700 (Carstab); Cyasorb UV 531 (American Cyanamid); [1843-05-6]

$C_{21}H_{26}O_3$. M: 326.44.
Production:
- 2,4-dihydroxybenzophenone + *n*-octyl bromide
  (ether formation)
Uses: light stabiliser (plastics)

2-(2-hydroxy-5-*t*-octylphenyl)benzotriazole
Cyasorb UV 5411 (American Cyanamid)

$C_{20}H_{25}N_3O_1$. M: 323.44.
Production:
- *o*-nitroaniline + *p*-*t*-octylphenol (diazotisation/azo
  coupling/nitro reduction/condensation)
Uses: light stabiliser (plastics)

D-α-hydroxyphenylacetic acid *See:* D-mandelic acid

p-hydroxyphenylacetic acid
[156-38-7]

$C_8H_8O_3$. M: 152.15. Needles. MP: 148–150°C. Sublimes. Soluble in hot water and oxygenated solvents.
Production:
- *p*-hydroxyacetophenone (Willgerodt reaction)
Derivatives:
p-hydroxyphenylacetonitrile

p-hydroxyphenylacetonitrile
4-hydroxybenzyl cyanide; *p*-hydroxybenzyl cyanide;
4-hydroxyphenylacetonitrile; [14191-95-8]
$C_8H_7N_1O_1$. M: 133.16.

Production:
- *p*-hydroxyphenylacetic acid + ammonia (nitrile
  formation)
- *p*-toluenesulphonic acid + hydrogen cyanide (side-
  chain chlorination/alkali fusion/cyanidation)
Derivatives: atenolol; benoxaprofen; tyramine

1-(*p*-hydroxyphenyl)-3-butanone
See: *p*-hydroxybenzylacetone

4-(*p*-hydroxyphenyl)-2-butanone
See: *p*-hydroxybenzylacetone

D-α-(4-hydroxyphenyl)glycine
[22818-40-2]

$C_8H_9N_1O_3$. M: 167.17. The commercial product is the
D(−)-enantiomer.
Production:
- phenol + glyoxal + urea (carbonyl condensation/
  hydrolysis/racemate separation)
- *p*-hydroxybenzaldehyde + hydrogen cyanide +
  ammonia (Strecker synthesis/racemate separation)
Derivatives: amoxicillin; cefadroxil; cefoperazone

N-(4-hydroxyphenyl)glycine
glycin; [122-87-2]

$C_8H_9N_1O_3$. M: 167.17.
Production:
- *p*-aminophenol + chloroacetic acid (amine
  formation)
Uses: photographic developing agent

11-α-hydroxyprogesterone
[68-96-2]

$C_{21}H_{30}O_3$. M: 330.47.
Production:
- progesterone (microbial conversion)
Derivatives: cortisone

2-hydroxypropane-1,2,3-tricarboxylic acid
See: citric acid

1-hydroxy-2-propanone
See: hydroxyacetone

α-hydroxypropionic acid
See: DL-lactic acid

p-hydroxypropiophenone
4-hydroxypropiophenone; paroxypropione; [70-70-2]

$C_9H_{10}O_2$. M: 150.18. Crystalline solid. MP: 148–151°C. Slightly soluble in hot water. Soluble in oxygenated solvents.
Production:
• phenol + propionic acid (esterification/Fries rearrangement)
Derivatives:
buphenine; diethylstilbestrol; hexestrol; isoxsuprine
Uses: hormone inhibitor drug

2-hydroxypropyl acrylate
HPA; hydroxypropyl acrylate; [999-61-1]

$C_6H_{10}O_3$. M: 130.15. Colourless liquid. FP: -30°C. BP: >210°C. d: 1.05 kg/l (25°C). Miscible with water and oxygenated solvents.
Production:
• acrylic acid + propylene oxide (epoxidation)
Derivatives:
polyester-acrylate resins; urethane-acrylate resins
Uses: reactive comonomer (acrylic, vinyl acetate, styrene-butadiene, nitrile resins)

hydroxypropyl cellulose
cellulose 2-hydroxypropyl ether; HPC; E463 (EC); [9004-64-2]

R = H, polyoxypropyl-. White, granular powder. Softening temperature: 100–150°C. Bulk density: 0.5 kg/l. Soluble in cold water and polar solvents. M: 80,000–1,150,000, varying with the source of the cellulose and the PO content.
Production:
• alkali cellulose + propylene oxide (epoxidation)
Uses: ceramics binder; mineral flotation depressant; protective colloid (suspension polymerisation); thickening agent/ protective colloid (emulsion paints, adhesives); thickening/filming agent (food, cosmetics)

hydroxypropyl guar
[39421-75-5]

R = guar gum-.
Production:
• guar gum + propylene oxide (epoxidation)
Uses: mineral flotation depressant; textile auxiliaries; viscosifier (oil-well workover/completion fluids)

1-(2-hydroxypropyl)imidazole

$C_6H_{10}N_2O_1$. M: 126.16.
Production:
• imidazole + propylene oxide (epoxidation)
Uses:
polyurethane foam catalyst

2-hydroxypropyl methacrylate
HPMA; [923-26-2]

$C_7H_{12}O_3$. M: 144.18. Colourless liquid. BP: 96°C (1.3 kPa). FP: <-70°C. d: 1.03 kg/l (25°C). Soluble in water. Flash point: 121°C. Commercial products contain hydroquinone methyl ether or similar polymerisation inhibitors.
Production:
• methacrylic acid + propylene oxide (epoxidation)
Derivatives:
polyester-acrylate resins; urethane-acrylate resins
Uses: engineering adhesives; reactive comonomer (acrylic, styrene-butadiene resins)

hydroxypropyl starch
Ten-o-film (CPC International)

R = starch-. Degrees of substitution of 0.05–0.10 are typical.
Production:
• starch + propylene oxide (epoxidation)
Uses: mineral filtration, clarification aid; protective colloid (emulsion paints); sizing agent (paper, textiles); textile backcoating

3-hydroxypyridine
3-pyridinol; 3-pyridol; [109-00-2]
$C_5H_5N_1O_1$. M: 95.10. Beige to brown, crystalline powder. MP: 125–130°C. Slightly soluble in water. Soluble in oxygenated solvents.

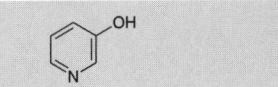

Production:
• 3-aminopyridine (diazotisation/hydration)
Derivatives:
distigmine bromide; pyridostigmine bromide

3-hydroxyquinaldine-4-carboxylic acid
See: oxyquinaldine carboxylic acid

8-hydroxyquinoline
oxine; oxyquinoline; 8-quinolinol; [148-24-3]

$C_9H_7N_1O_1$. M: 145.17. White, crystalline powder. MP: 72–74°C. BP: 267°C. Insoluble in water. Soluble in acetone, chlorinated and aromatic solvents. Available commercially as the free base or as the sulphate salt.
Production:
• quinoline (sulphonation/alkali fusion)
Derivatives:
clioquinol; halquinol; iodoquinol; Mordant Orange 26; oxine-copper
Uses: chelating agent/flotation collector (sulphide ore); analytical reagent (metal assay); topical antiseptic

4-hydroxystearanilide *See:* N-stearoyl-p-aminophenol

12-hydroxystearic acid
hydroxystearic acid; [106-14-9]

$$CH_3(CH_2)_5CH(CH_2)_{10}COOH$$
$$OH$$

$C_{18}H_{36}O_3$. M: 300.49. White solid. MP: 83°C. Insoluble in water. Soluble in alcohol.
Production:
• ricinoleic acid (hydrogenation)
Derivatives:
lithium 12-hydroxystearate
Uses: plastics processing lubricant

4-hydroxy-2,2,6,6-tetramethylpiperidine
[2226-96-2]

$C_9H_{19}N_1O_1$. M: 157.26.
Production:
• phorone + ammonia (imine formation/carbonyl reduction)

Derivatives: N,N′-bis(2,2,6,6-tetramethyl-4-piperidyl)-1,6-hexamethylenediamine; di-(2,2,6,6-tetramethyl-4-piperidyl) sebacate

4-hydroxy-2,2,6,6-tetramethyl-1-piperidine ethanol

$C_{11}H_{23}N_1O_2$. M: 201.31.
Production:
• phorone + monoethanolamine (amine formation)
Derivatives:
poly(N-β-hydroxyethyl-2,2,6,6-tetramethyl-4-hydroxy-piperidyl succinate)
Uses: light stabiliser (plastics)

hydroxytoluene, butylated *See:* 2,6-di-t-butyl-p-cresol

6-hydroxy-2,4,5-triaminopyrimidine

$C_4H_7N_5O_1$. M: 141.13.
Production:
• ethyl cyanoacetate + guanidine hydrochloride (condensation/nitrosation/nitro reduction)
Derivatives: folic acid; guanine

2-hydroxy-3,5,6-trichloropyridine
See: 3,5,6-trichloro-2-pyridone

2-hydroxy-5-(trifluoromethyl)pyridine
5-(trifluoromethyl)-2-hydroxypyridine

$C_6H_4F_3N_1O_1$. M: 163.10.
Production:
• β-picoline + chlorine + hydrogen fluoride (chlorination/halogen exchange/hydrolysis; coproduced with 3-chloro-2-hydroxy-5-trifluoromethylpyridine)
Derivatives: fluazifop-butyl; fluazifop-P-butyl

hydroxyzine
[68-88-2]; [2192-20-3] (dihydrochloride)
$C_{21}H_{27}Cl_1N_2O_2$. M: 374.91. Available commercially as the free base or the dihydrochloride salt.
Production:
• p-chlorobenzophenone + N-hydroxyethylpiperazine + ethylene oxide (reductive amination/epoxidation)

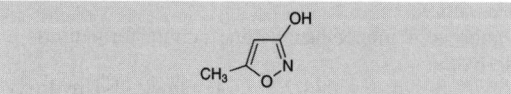

Uses: tranquilliser/antihistamine drug

hymexazol
5-methylisoxazol-3-ol; [10004-44-1]

$C_4H_5N_1O_2$. M: 99.09.
Production:
• ethyl acetoacetate + hydroxylamine sulphate (amide
  formation/cyclisation)
Uses: fungicide

hyoscine *See:* scopolamine

DL-hyoscyamine *See:* atropine

hypo *See:* sodium thiosulphate

hypoxanthine
[68-94-0]

$C_5H_4N_4O_1$. M: 136.11. White powder. MP: >250°C.
Practically insoluble in water. Soluble in strong acids
and alkalis.
Production:
• ethyl cyanoacetate + thiourea + sodium nitrite +
  formamide (condensation/nitrosation/hydrogenation/
  condensation)
Derivatives: 6-chloropurine
Uses: photographic chemical

ibuprofen
2-(*p*-isobutylphenyl)propionic acid; [15687-27-1]

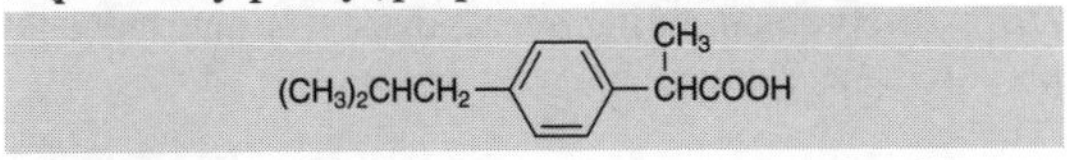

$(CH_3)_2CHCH_2$—⟨ ⟩—$\overset{\overset{CH_3}{|}}{CHCOOH}$

$C_{13}H_{18}O_2$. M: 206.28.
Production:
- isobutylbenzene + acetyl chloride + triethyl-aluminium + potassium cyanide (Friedel-Crafts acylation/cyanohydrin formation/hydrogenation/nitrile hydrolysis)
- isobutylbenzene + propionyl chloride + methanol (Friedel-Crafts acylation/ketal formation/alpha bromination/rearrangement)
- isobutylbenzene + acetyl chloride + carbon monoxide (Friedel-Crafts acylation/carbonyl reduction/carbonylation)
- isobutylbenzene + acetyl chloride + methyl chloro-acetate (Friedel-Crafts acylation/Darzens reaction/hydrolysis/decarboxylation/carbonyl oxidation)
Uses: antiinflammatory drug

IBVE *See:* isobutyl vinyl ether

IDA *See:* isodecyl acrylate

idoxuridine
[54-42-2]

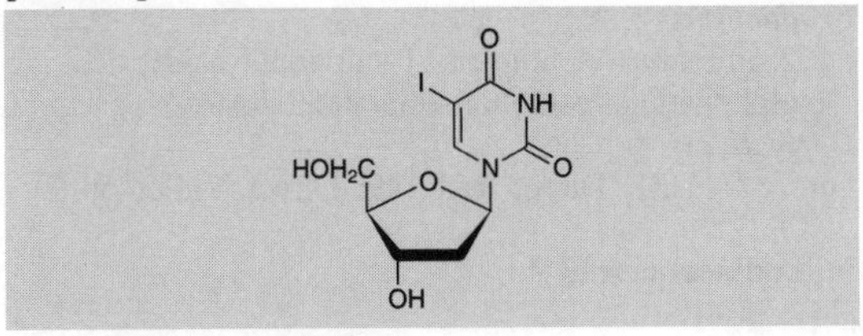

$C_9H_{11}I_1N_2O_5$. M: 354.09.
Production:
- uracil + iodine + D-2-deoxyribose (ring iodination/mercury-catalysed amination/amine formation/saponification)
Uses: antiviral drug

IEM *See:* isocyanatoethyl methacrylate

ifosfamide
[3778-73-2]

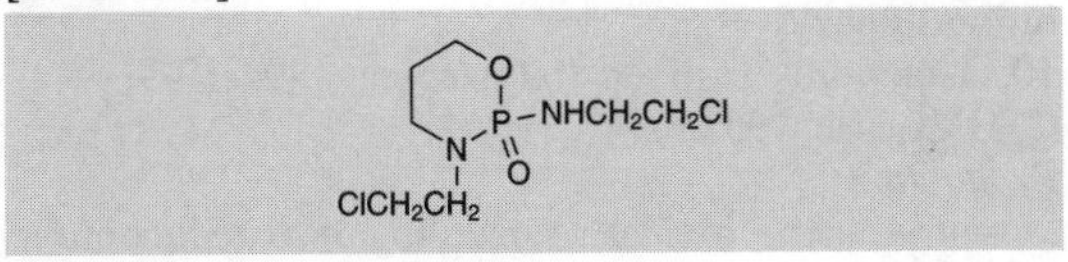

$C_7H_{15}Cl_2N_2O_2P_1$. M: 261.09.

Production:
- monoethanolamine + phosphorus oxychloride + 3-(2-chloroethyl)aminopropanol hydrochloride (alcohol chlorination/dehydrochlorination/dehydrochlorination)
Uses: antineoplastic drug

IIR *See:* butyl rubber

Ile *See:* L-isoleucine

ilmenite
Ilmenite is a mixed iron-titanium mineral concentrate with a TiO_2 content of 35–60%. Major producing countries are Australia, Canada, South Africa, Russia, Senegal, Norway and the USA.
Production:
- mineral sands (separation; coproduced with rutile/zircon/monazite)
Derivatives: iron; rutile; titanium dioxide, hydrate

imazalil
1-(β-allyloxy-2,4-dichlorophenethyl)imidazole; chloramizol; enilconazole; [35554-44-0]

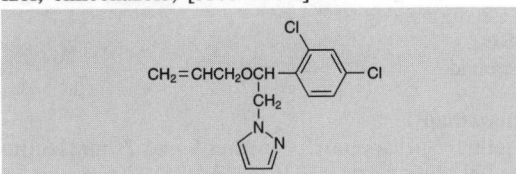

$C_{14}H_{14}Cl_2N_2O_1$. M: 297.18.
Production:
- α,2,4-trichloroacetophenone + imidazole + allyl chloride (amine formation/carbonyl reduction/ether formation)
Uses: fungicide

imazamethabenz-methyl
methyl 2/6-(4-isopropyl-4-methyl-5-oxo-2-imidazolin-2-yl)-*p/m*-toluate; [81334-34-1]

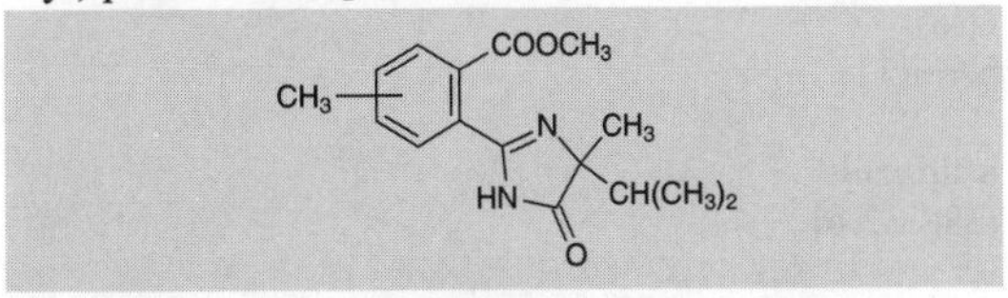

$C_{16}H_{20}N_2O_3$. M: 288.34. Mixed isomer product.
Production:
- methanol + 4-methylphthalic anhydride + 2-amino-2-methylisopentamide (esterification/amidine formation)
Uses: herbicide

imazapyr-isopropylammonium

isopropylammonium 2-(4-isopropyl-4-methyl-5-oxo-2-imidazolin-2-yl)nicotinate; [81335-37-7]

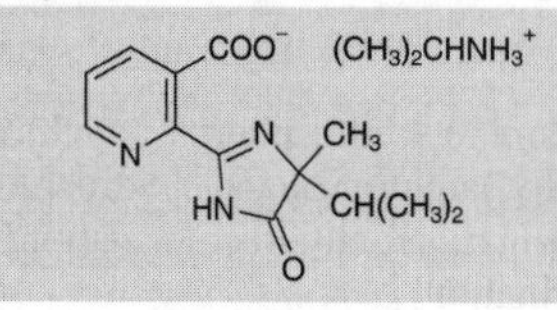

$C_{16}H_{24}N_4O_3$. M: 320.40.
Production:
• quinolinic acid + 2-amino-2-methylisopentamide + isopropylamine (condensation/salt formation)
Uses: herbicide

imazaquin-ammonium

ammonium 2-(4-isopropyl-4-methyl-5-oxo-2-imidazolin-2-yl)quinoline-3-carboxylate; [81335-47-9]

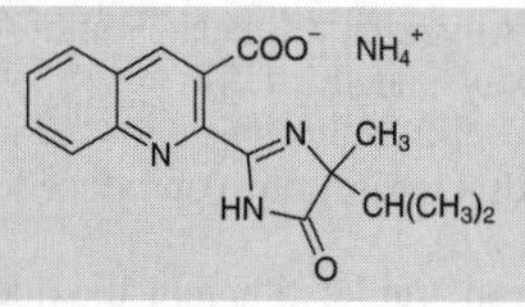

$C_{17}H_{20}N_4O_3$. M: 328.38.
Production:
• quinoline-2,3-dicarboxylic acid + 2-amino-2-methylisopentamide + ammonia (condensation/salt formation)
Uses:
herbicide

imazethapyr

5-ethyl-2-(4-isopropyl-4-methyl-5-oxo-2-imidazolin-2-yl)nicotinic acid; [81335-77-5]

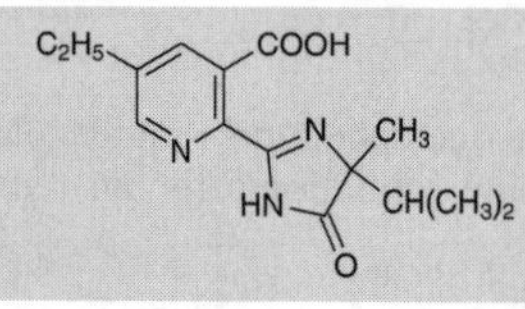

$C_{15}H_{19}N_3O_3$. M: 289.33.
Production:
• 5-ethylquinolinic acid + 2-amino-2-methyliso-pentamide (condensation)
Uses:
herbicide

imidazole

[288-32-4]

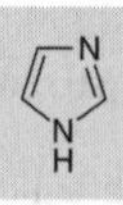

$C_3H_4N_2$. M: 68.07. Crystalline solid. MP: 88–90°C. BP: 257°C. Soluble in water, oxygenated and chlorinated solvents.

Production:
• glyoxal + formaldehyde + ammonia (Radziszewski reaction)
Derivatives: clotrimazole; econazole; 1-(2-hydroxypropyl)imidazole; imazalil; isoconazole; miconazole; 4-nitroimidazole; prochloraz; triflumizole; N-vinylimidazole
Uses: epoxy resin curing agent; dyestuffs intermediate; polyurethane catalyst

2-imidazolinone *See:* ethylene urea

2,2′-iminobis(naphthalene-1-sulphonic acid)

di-β-naphthylamine-1,1′-disulphonic acid

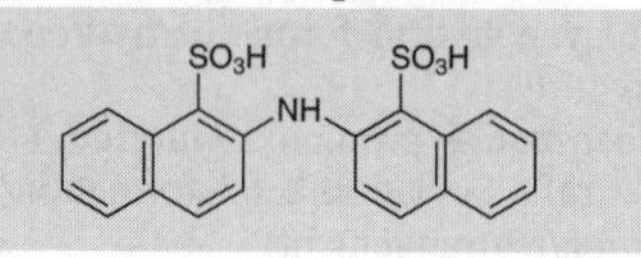

$C_{20}H_{15}N_1O_6S_2$. M: 429.47.
Production:
• β-naphthol + ammonia (sulphonation/ammoniation; byproduct of Tobias acid production)
Derivatives: 6,6′-iminobis(1-naphthol-3-sulphonic acid)

6,6′-iminobis(1-naphthol-3-sulphonic acid)

2,2′-iminobis(5-naphthol-7-sulphonic acid)

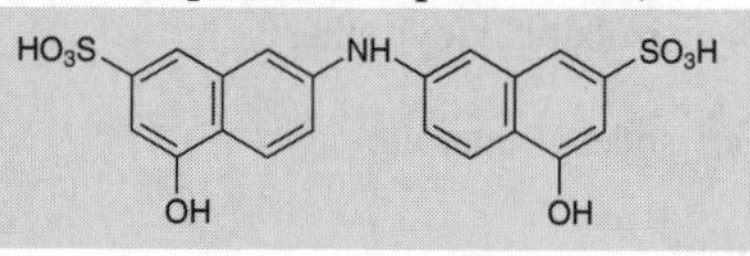

$C_{20}H_{15}N_1O_8S_2$. M: 461.47.
Production:
• 2,2′-iminobis(naphthalene-1-sulphonic acid) (sulphonation/desulphonation/alkali fusion)
Derivatives:
Direct Red 31; Direct Red 149; Direct Violet 66

iminodiacetic acid

[142-73-4]

$HN(CH_2COOH)_2$

$C_4H_7N_1O_4$. M: 133.11. Crystalline solid. MP: 248°C. Slightly soluble in water. Insoluble in alcohol, chlorinated and aromatic solvents.
Production:
• formaldehyde + ammonia + hydrogen cyanide (cyanomethylation/nitrile hydrolysis; coproduced with glycine/nitrilotriacetic acid)
Derivatives: glyphosate

iminodibenzyl

10,11-dihydro-5H-dibenz[b,f]azepine; [494-19-9]
$C_{14}H_{13}N_1$. M: 195.26.
Production:
• o-nitrotoluene (oxidative coupling/nitro reduction/deammoniation)

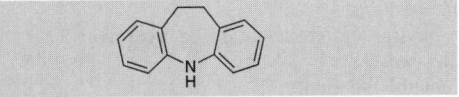

Derivatives:
iminostilbene; imipramine; trimipramine

iminostilbene
5H-dibenzazepine; [256-96-2]

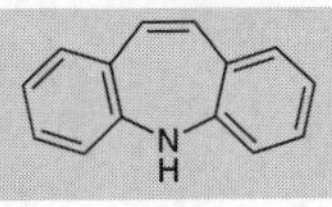

$C_{14}H_{11}N_1$. M: 193.25.
Production:
• iminodibenzyl + acetic anhydride (amide
   formation/bromination/dehydrobromination)
Derivatives: carbamazepine; opipramol

imipenem
[74431-23-5]

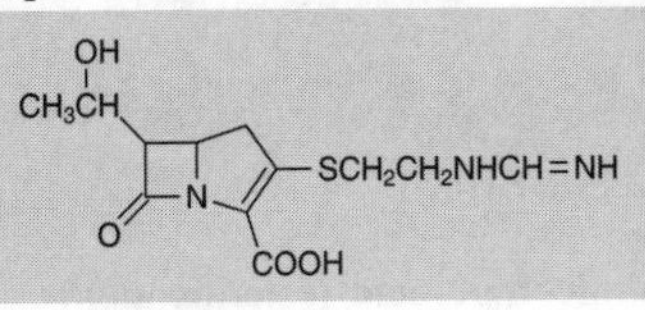

$C_{12}H_{17}N_3O_4S_1$. M: 299.35.
Production:
• hydrogen cyanide + methanol + thienamycin
   (nitrile addition/amine formation)
Uses: antibacterial drug

imipramine
[50-49-7]

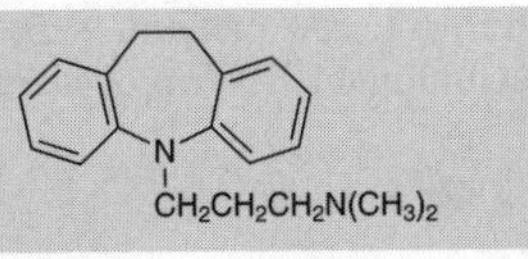

$C_{19}H_{24}N_2$. M: 280.41. Available commercially as the
free base or as the hydrochloride salt.
Production:
• iminodibenzyl + 3-dimethylaminopropyl chloride
   hydrochloride (amine formation)
Derivatives: desipramine
Uses: antidepressant drug

IMP *See:* sodium metaphosphate, insoluble; sodium
5′-inosate

IMS *See:* ethanol

indanthrone
indanthrene; Indanthrene Blue; Indanthrone Blue; Pigment Blue 60 (CI); Vat Blue 4 (CI); Food Blue 4
(CI); 69800 (CI); [81-77-6]

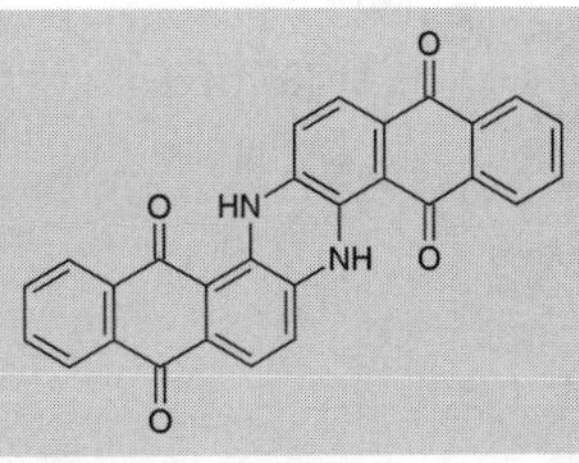

$C_{28}H_{14}N_2O_4$. M: 442.43. Blue needles. MP: 470–500°C
with decomposition. Insoluble in water and oxygenated
solvents.
Production:
• 2-aminoanthraquinone (base-catalysed condensation)
Derivatives: Vat Blue 6
Uses:
dye (cotton); pigment (paints, printing inks, plastics)

indene-coumarone resin *See:* coumarone-indene resin

indigo
Vat Blue 1 (CI); 73000 (CI); [482-89-3]

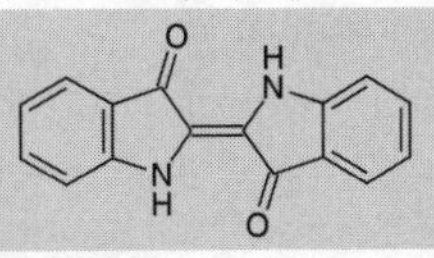

$C_{16}H_{10}N_2O_2$. M: 262.27. Dark blue, crystalline solid.
Insoluble in water. Soluble in chlorinated and aromatic
solvents.
Production:
• *N*-phenylglycine + sodamide (dehydrative
   coupling/oxidative coupling)
Derivatives: Acid Blue 74; isatin; Solubilised Vat Blue
1; Vat Blue 5
Uses:
dye (cotton)

indigo carmine *See:* Acid Blue 74

indigotine *See:* Acid Blue 74

indole
[120-72-9]

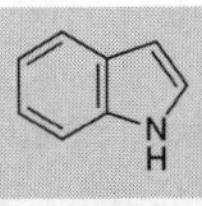

$C_8H_7N_1$. M: 117.16. Flakes with an unpleasant odour
when undiluted. MP: 52–54°C. BP: 254°C. Soluble in
hot water and oxygenated solvents.
Production:
• dimethylnaphthalene fraction (acid extraction)
Derivatives: indol-3-ylacetic acid; 4-indol-3-ylbutyric
acid; L-tryptophan
Uses:
perfume fixative

indol-3-ylacetic acid
3-indoleacetic acid; IAA; [87-51-4]

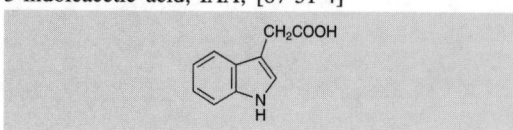

$C_{10}H_9N_1O_2$. M: 175.19.
Production:
• indole + chloroacetic acid (amine formation)
Uses: plant growth regulator

4-indol-3-ylbutyric acid
IBA; [133-32-4]

$C_{12}H_{13}N_1O_2$. M: 203.24.
Production:
• indole + γ-butyrolactone (condensation)
Uses: plant growth regulator

indomethacin
[53-86-1]

$C_{19}H_{16}Cl_1N_1O_4$. M: 357.80.
Production:
• *p*-anisidine + ethyl levulinate + *p*-chlorobenzoyl chloride (diazotisation/hydrogenation/Fischer indole synthesis/amide formation/saponification)
Uses: antiinflammatory/analgesic drug

industrial methylated spirit *See:* ethanol

inositol
hexahydroxycyclohexane; [87-89-8]

$C_6H_{12}O_6$. M: 180.16. Crystalline solid. MP: 224–225°C. d: 1.75 kg/l. Soluble in water. The commercial product is *cis*-1,2,3,5-*trans*-4,6-cyclohexanehexol, the main isomer found in nature.

Production:
• phytic acid (base-catalysed hydrolysis)
Derivatives:
inositol nicotinate
Uses: dietary supplement ingredient

inositolhexaphosphoric acid *See:* phytic acid

inositol nicotinate
inositol niacinate; [6556-11-2]

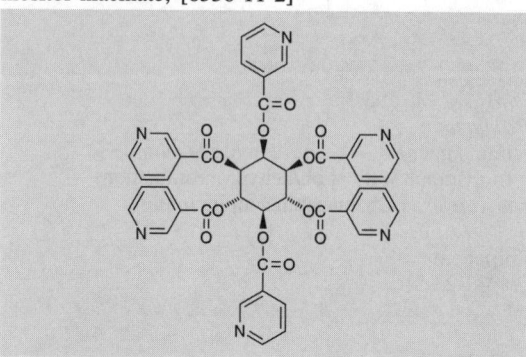

$C_{42}H_{30}N_6O_{12}$. M: 810.73.
Production:
• inositol + nicotinic acid (esterification)
Uses: vasodilator drug

insulin, human
[11061-68-0]
Polypeptide made up of 51 amino-acid units in two primary chains.
Production:
• pig pancreas (extraction/enzymatic substitution)
• microbial fermentation medium + *Escherichia coli* bacteria (recombinant DNA procedures/fermentation)
Uses:
antidiabetic drug

invert sugar
$C_6H_{12}O_6$. M: 180.16. Mixed product containing 50% glucose and 50% fructose.
Production:
• sugar cane juice/sugar beet juice (acid-catalysed hydrolysis)
Derivatives:
mannitol; sorbitol
Uses: food/confectionery/brewing ingredient; humectant (starch adhesives); parenteral nutrient ingredient

iobenzamic acid
[3115-05-7]
$C_{16}H_{13}I_3N_2O_3$. M: 662.00.
Production:
• aniline + acrylonitrile + 3-amino-2,4,6-triiodobenzoic acid (cyanoethylation/amide formation)

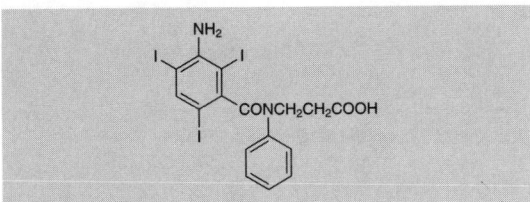

Uses: x-ray diagnostic aid

iocarmic acid
[10397-75-8]

C$_{24}$H$_{20}$I$_6$N$_4$O$_8$. M: 1253.86. Available commercially as the di-*N*-methylglucamine salt.
Production:
• monoethyl 5-nitroisophthalate + methylamine + adipic acid (amide formation/nitro reduction/amide formation/ring iodination)
Uses: x-ray diagnostic aid

iocetamic acid
[16034-77-8]

C$_{12}$H$_{13}$I$_3$N$_2$O$_3$. M: 613.95.
Production:
• *m*-nitroaniline + methacrylic acid + acetic anhydride (Michael addition/acetylation/nitro reduction/ring iodination)
Uses: x-ray diagnostic aid

iodine
[7553-56-2]

I$_2$

I$_2$. M: 253.81. Bluish-black flakes. MP: 114°C. BP: 185°C. d: 4.93 kg/l (25°C). Insoluble in water. Soluble in alkaline iodide solution, oxygenated and chlorinated solvents.
Production:
• sodium iodate liquor + sulphur dioxide, pure (reduction)
• natural brines + chlorine (halogen exchange)
Derivatives: ethyl iodide; glycerol, iodinated; hydriodic acid; idoxuridine; iodine monochloride; iodine pentafluoride; methyl 3-fluorocarbonylperfluoropropionate; potassium iodate; potassium iodide; povidone-iodine; sodium iodate
Uses:
sulphonation/chlorination/condensation/amine alkylation catalyst; disinfectant; Ziegler catalyst component; analytical reagent (fats, oils); ring iodination reagent

iodine monochloride
[7790-99-0]

ICl

Cl$_1$I$_1$. M: 162.36. Black crystals or reddish-brown liquid. MP: 27°C (α-form), 14°C (β-form). BP: 97–101°C with decomposition. Soluble in water and oxygenated solvents.
Production:
• iodine + chlorine (halogen exchange)
Uses: analytical reagent (fats, oils)

iodine pentafluoride
[7783-66-6]

IF$_5$

F$_5$I$_1$. M: 221.89. Liquid. MP: 9°C. BP: 101°C. d: 3.19 kg/l (25°C). Reacts violently with water, hydrocarbons and many inorganic compounds.
Production:
• iodine + fluorine (reaction)
Derivatives: perfluoroalkyl(C$_6$-C$_{12}$) iodide; perfluorohexyl iodide; perfluorooctyl iodide
Uses: iodine fluoride addition reagent

iodipamide *See:* adipiodone

iodochlorhydroxyquin *See:* clioquinol

iodofenphos
O-2,5-dichloro-4-iodophenyl *O,O*-dimethyl phosphorothioate; [18181-70-9]

C$_8$H$_8$Cl$_2$I$_1$O$_3$P$_1$S$_1$. M: 412.99.
Production:
• 1,2,4-trichlorobenzene + *O,O*-dimethyl phosphorochlorothioate (ring iodination/dehydrochlorination)
Uses: insecticide/acaricide

iodoform
[75-47-8]

CHI$_3$

C$_1$H$_1$I$_3$. M: 393.73. Yellow crystals with a characteristic odour. MP: 115°C. d: 4.08 kg/l. Insoluble in water. Soluble in oxygenated and chlorinated solvents.

Production:
- acetone + potassium iodide + sodium hydroxide (haloform reaction)
- ethanol + potassium iodide (electrolysis)

Derivatives:
methylene iodide

Uses: topical antiseptic

iodomethane *See:* methyl iodide

iodopyracet *See:* diodone

iodoquinol
5,7-diiodo-8-hydroxyquinoline

$C_9H_5I_2N_1O_1$. M: 396.96.
Production:
- 8-hydroxyquinoline (ring iodination)

Uses: antiseptic

iodoxamic acid
[31127-82-9]

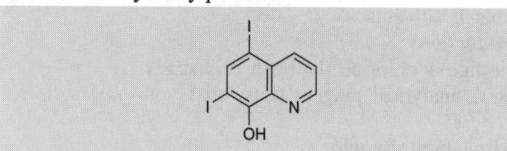

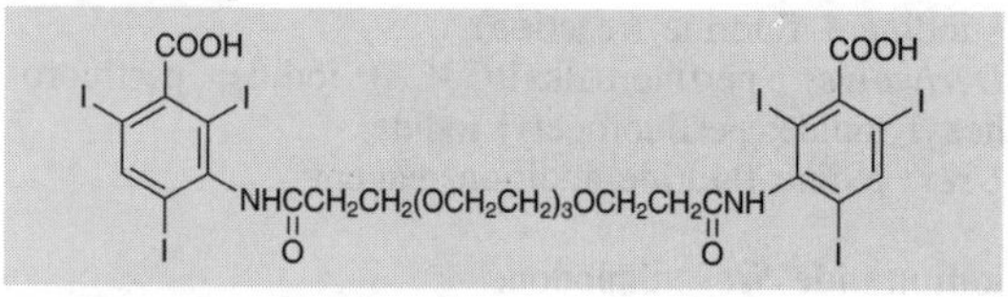

$C_{26}H_{26}I_6N_2O_{10}$. M: 1287.92.
Production:
- triethylene glycol + acrylonitrile + 3-amino-2,4,6-triiodobenzoic acid (cyanoethylation/amide formation)

Uses: x-ray diagnostic aid

ioglycamic acid
[2618-25-9]

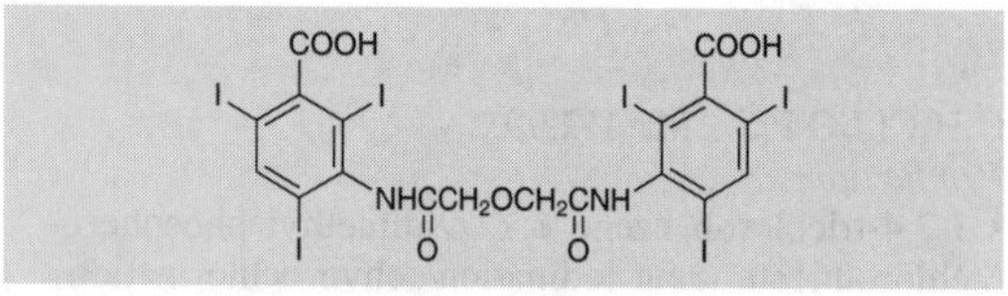

$C_{18}H_{10}I_6N_2O_7$. M: 1127.70.
Production:
- chloroacetic acid + 3-amino-2,4,6-triiodobenzoic acid (ether formation/amide formation)

Uses: x-ray diagnostic aid

iohexol
[66108-95-0]
$C_{19}H_{26}I_3N_3O_9$. M: 821.14.

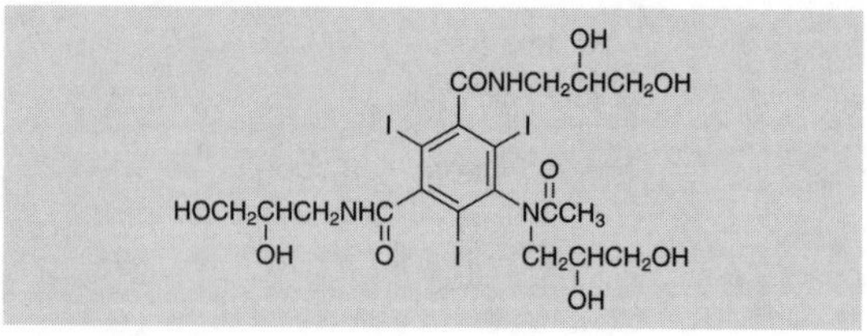

Production:
- dimethyl 5-nitroisophthalate + ammonia + acetic anhydride + chlorohydrin (ammoniation/nitro reduction/ring iodination/acetylation/amine formation)

Uses:
x-ray diagnostic aid

ION *See:* isooctyl nitrate

ionone
4-(2,6,6-trimethyl-2-cyclohexen-1-yl)-3-buten-2-one (α-isomer); 4-(2,6,6-trimethyl-1-cyclohexen-1-yl)-3-buten-2-one (β-isomer); 4-(2,2-dimethyl-6-methylenecyclohexenyl)-3-buten-2-one (γ-isomer); [127-41-3] (α-isomer); [79-76-5] (γ-isomer)

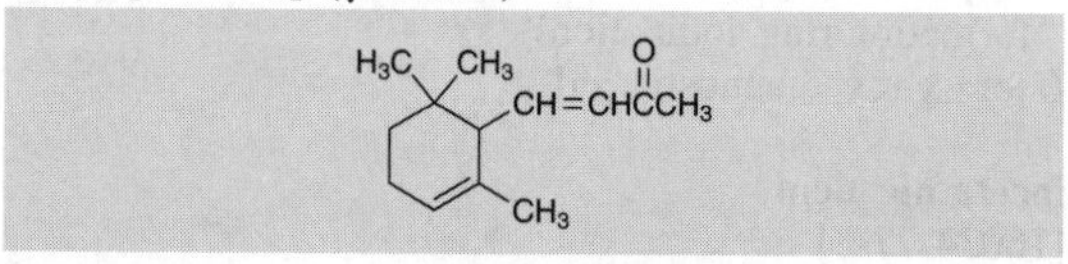

$C_{13}H_{20}O_1$. M: 192.30. Yellow liquid with a violet-like odour. BP: 121°C (1.3 kPa). d: 0.93 kg/l (20°C). Insoluble in water. Miscible with alcohol. Mixed product containing the α, β and γ-isomer. The displayed structure shows the α-isomer.
Production:
- pseudoionone (acid-catalysed rearrangement)

Uses: fragrance ingredient

β-ionone
4-(2,6,6-trimethyl-1-cyclohexen-1-yl)-3-buten-2-one; [14901-07-6]

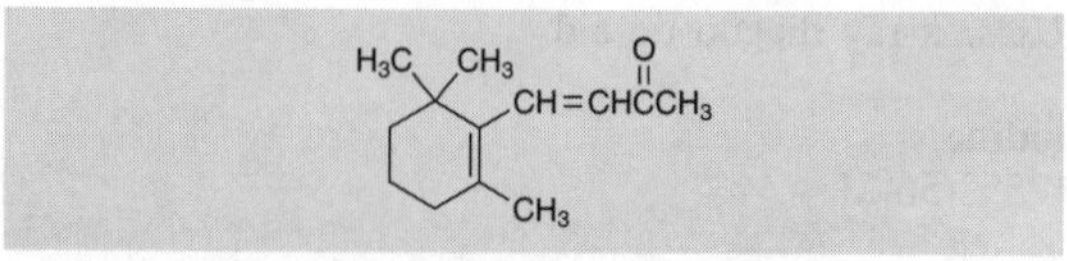

$C_{13}H_{20}O_1$. M: 192.30. Yellow liquid with a violet-like odour. BP: 122°C (1.0 kPa). d: 0.95 kg/l (20°C). Insoluble in water. Miscible with alcohol.
Production:
- pseudoionone (acid-catalysed rearrangement/isomerisation)

Derivatives:
β-C_{14} aldehyde; β-carotene; vitamin A

iopanoic acid
3-(3-amino-2,4,6-triiodophenyl)-2-ethylpropanoic acid; iodopanoic acid; [96-83-3]

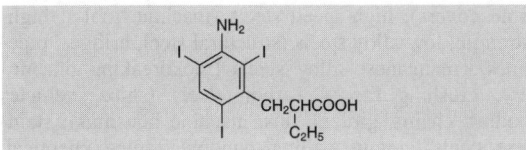

$C_{11}H_{12}I_3N_1O_2$. M: 570.94.
Production:
- *m*-nitrobenzaldehyde + ethyl butyrate (carbonyl condensation/hydrogenation/saponification/ring iodination)

Uses: x-ray diagnostic aid

iotalamic acid
5-acetamido-2,4,6-triiodo-*N*-methylisophthalamic acid; iothalamic acid; [2276-90-6]

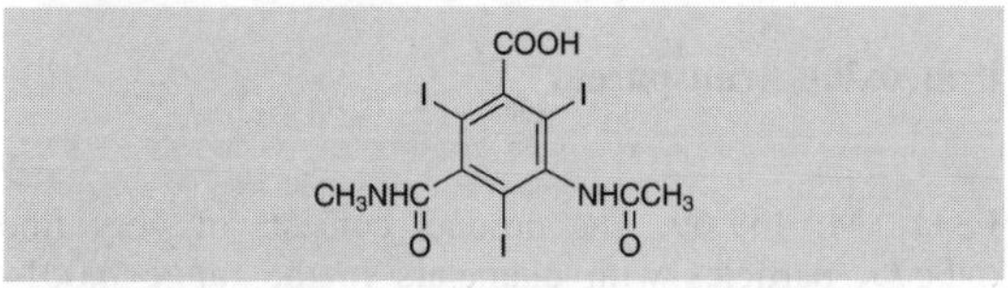

$C_{11}H_9I_3N_2O_4$. M: 613.91. Available commercially as the sodium or *N*-methylglucamine salt.
Production:
- monoethyl 5-nitroisophthalate + methylamine + acetic anhydride (amide formation/nitro reduction/ acetylation/ring iodination)

Uses: x-ray diagnostic aid

iotroxic acid
[51022-74-3]

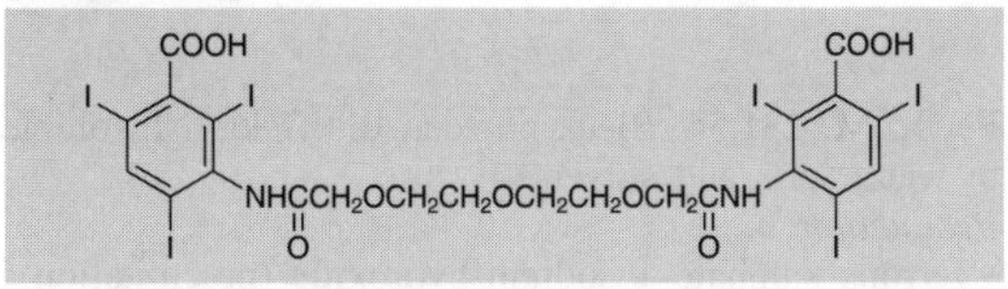

$C_{22}H_{18}I_6N_2O_9$. M: 1215.80.
Production:
- diethylene glycol + chloroacetic acid + 3-amino-2,4,6-triiodobenzoic acid (ether formation/amide formation)

Uses: x-ray diagnostic aid

ioxynil
[1689-83-4]

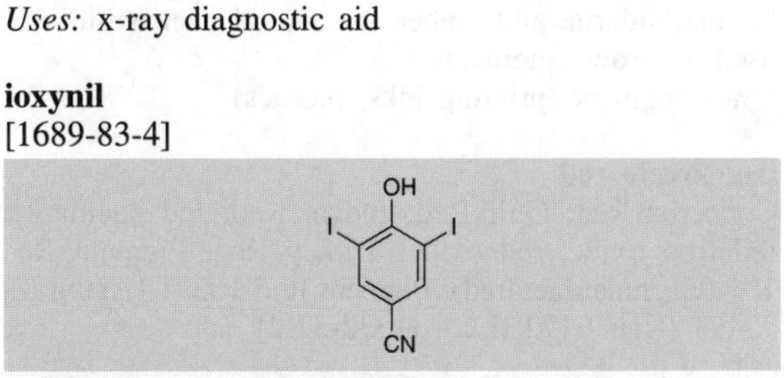

$C_7H_3I_2N_1O_1$. M: 370.92. Available commercially as the acid, sodium or potassium salts.
Production:
- *p*-hydroxybenzonitrile (ring iodination)

Derivatives: ioxynil octanoate
Uses: herbicide

ioxynil octanoate
4-cyano-2,6-diiodophenyl octanoate; [3861-47-0]

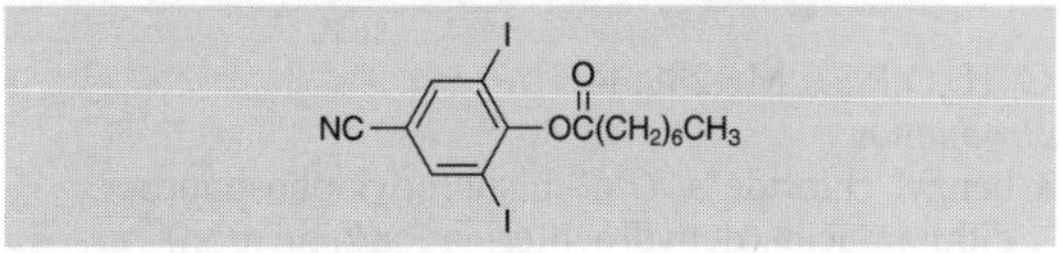

$C_{15}H_{17}I_2N_1O_2$. M: 497.12.
Production:
- ioxynil + caprylyl chloride (esterification)

Uses: herbicide

IPA *See:* isophthalic acid; isopropanol

IPC *See:* propham

IPD *See:* isophoronediamine

IPDI *See:* isophorone diisocyanate

ipecac extract
Produced by hot water extraction of ipecac (*Cephaelis ipecacuanha*) root.
Uses:
emetic medicines; expectorant drug; alkaloid products

IPETC *See:* *N*-ethyl *O*-isopropyl thionocarbamate

IPL *See:* isopropyl lanolate

IPM *See:* isopropyl myristate

IPN *See:* isophthalodinitrile

IPP
See: diisopropyl peroxydicarbonate; isopropyl palmitate

IPPD *See:* *N*-isopropyl-*N'*-phenyl-*p*-phenylenediamine

ipratropium bromide
[22254-24-6]

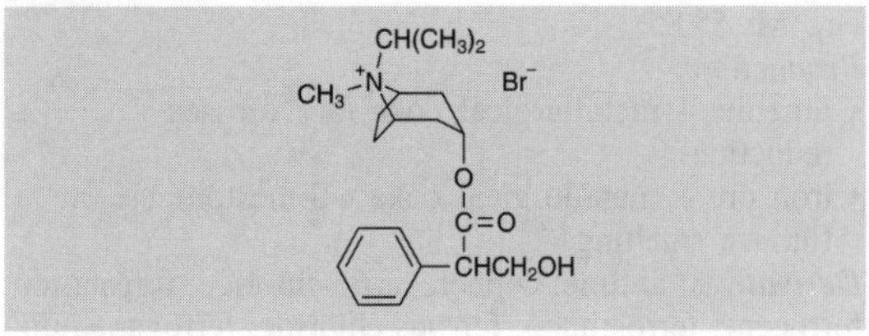

$C_{20}H_{30}Br_1N_1O_3$. M: 412.37.
Production:
- atropine + isopropyl bromide (quaternisation)

Uses:
bronchodilator drug

iprobenfos

S-benzyl *O,O*-diisopropyl phosphorothioate;
[26087-47-8]

$C_{13}H_{21}O_3P_1S_1$. M: 288.34.
Production:
• benzyl chloride + *O,O*-diisopropyl phosphorodithioic acid (dehydrochlorination/oxidation)
Uses: fungicide

iprodione

3-(3,5-dichlorophenyl)-*N*-isopropyl-2,4-dioxoimidazol-
idine-1-carboxamide; [36734-19-7]

$C_{13}H_{13}Cl_2N_3O_3$. M: 330.17.
Production:
• glycine + 3,5-dichloroaniline + phosgene +
isopropylamine (amide formation/phosgenation/
condensation/dehydrochlorination)
Uses: fungicide

iproniazid

[54-92-2]

$C_9H_{13}N_3O_1$. M: 179.22.
Production:
• isoniazid + acetone (imine formation/hydrogenation)
Uses: tuberculostatic drug

IPT *See:* isopropyl titanate

iron

[7439-89-6]

Fe

Fe_1. M: 55.85.
Production:
• ilmenite + metallurgical coke (arc furnace
reduction)
• iron ore + metallurgical coke + limestone (blast
furnace smelting)
Derivatives: aniline; copper; ferric chloride; ferroboron;
ferrocene; ferrosilicon; ferrous chloride; ferrovanadium;
iron pentacarbonyl
Uses: carbon steels (rails, tools, machine/engine parts,
guns); cast iron (pipes, fittings, gratings, stoves, fires,
baths, machine tools, electrical machinery); cast iron
(vehicle components, engine parts, ingot moulds, man-

hole covers); high-speed steels (machine tools); high-
strength, low-alloy steels (structural steel, bridges, pipelines); manganese alloy steels (rockbreaking machinery, crushing faces); carbon steels (ships, vehicles
bodies, chains, girders, tins, machine housings); stainless steels (curtain walling, window frames, chemical,
food equipment); stainless steels (cutlery, household
utensils, sinks, tubes, barrels)

iron blue *See:* Prussian Blue

iron oxide, micaceous

Natural iron oxide pigment consisting of metallic grey,
glistening flakes of diameter up to 70 μ. Mined in
Austria and France. d: 4.7 kg/l.
Uses: anticorrosion pigment (protective paints)

iron oxide, transparent

Fe_2O_3

Fe_2O_3. M: 159.69. The product consists of very fine
α-Fe_2O_3 particles with diameters in the range 0.001–
0.01 nm.
Production:
• iron pentacarbonyl (thermal conversion/calcination)
• ferrous sulphate + sodium hydroxide (precipitation)
Uses: magnetic ferrite cores (electronic components);
transparent pigments (paints)

iron oxide black

black magnetic oxide; black oxide, precipitated; magnetite; Pigment Black 11 (CI); 77499 (CI); E172 (EC)

Fe_3O_4

Fe_3O_4. M: 231.54. Black powder. d: 4.7 kg/l. Insoluble
in water, oils and solvents.
Production:
• ferrous sulphate + sodium hydroxide (precipitation)
Uses:
pigment (paints, plastics, caulks, sealants, printing inks)

iron oxide brown

burnt sienna; burnt umber; Pigment Brown 7 (CI)
Sienna, siderite and umber are natural iron oxide ores
used as brown pigments.
Uses: pigment (printing inks, plastics)

iron oxide red

Copperas Red; Gulf Red; Indian Red; red haematite;
red iron oxide; red oxide; Turkey Red; Pigment Red
101 (CI, manufactured); Pigment Red 102 (CI, natural);
77491 (CI); E172 (EC); [1332-37-2]

α-Fe_2O_3

Fe_2O_3. M: 159.69. Red powder. d: 4.5–5.0 kg/l.
Insoluble in water, oils and solvents. Sienna, siderite,
Persian red, Spanish red and red ochre are natural iron

oxide ores used as red pigments. The residue from bauxite conversion to aluminium is also a red iron oxide. It is used as an anticorrosion pigment.
Production:
• ferrous sulphate (calcination)
• ferrous sulphate + sodium hydroxide (precipitation)
Derivatives:
chrome iron brown; ferrite; zinc ferrite
Uses: ceramic tiles/sanitaryware colorant; food colorant; pigment (concrete, roofing tiles, paving slabs, plaster, bitumen, stoving finishes, primer paints, plastics, sealants, caulks, printing inks)

iron oxide yellow
ferrite yellow; ochre; sienna; yellow ochre; Pigment Yellow 42 (CI); 77492 (CI); E172 (EC)

FeOOH

$H_1Fe_1O_2$. M: 88.85. Yellow pigment. Converts to red iron oxide on heating. d: 4.0 kg/l. Insoluble in water, oils and or solvents. Limonite, yellow ochre and sienna are natural iron oxide minerals used as yellow pigments.
Production:
• ferrous sulphate + sodium hydroxide (precipitation)
Uses: pigment (concrete, roofing tiles, paving slabs, paints, plastics, caulks, sealants, printing inks)

iron pentacarbonyl
[13463-40-6]

Fe(CO)₅

$C_5Fe_1O_5$. M: 195.89. Viscous, yellow liquid. BP: 105°C. MP: -21°C. d: 1.46 kg/l (21°C). Insoluble in water.
Production:
• iron + carbon monoxide (complex formation)
Derivatives:
iron oxide, transparent
Uses: Reppe hydrocarbonylation catalyst

iron sulphate *See:* ferric sulphate; ferrous sulphate

isatin
indole-2,3-dione; [91-56-5]

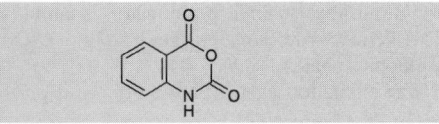

$C_8H_5N_1O_2$. M: 147.14. Orange crystals. MP: 198°C. Soluble in hot water and alcohol.
Production:
• indigo (oxidation)
Derivatives:
2,4-dihydroxyquinoline; oxyquinaldine carboxylic acid
Uses: analytical reagent

isatoic anhydride
[118-48-9]

$C_8H_5N_1O_3$. M: 163.14.
Production:
• phthalimide + sodium hypochlorite (Hofmann degradation)
Derivatives: anthranilic acid
Uses: blowing agent (foamed plastics)

isazofos
O-s-chloro-1-isopropyl-1H-1,2,4-triazol-3-yl *O,O*-diethyl phosphorothioate; [42509-80-8]

$C_9H_{17}Cl_1N_3O_3P_1S_1$. M: 313.74.
Production:
• semicarbazide hydrochloride + formamide + isopropanol + *O,O*-diethyl phosphorochlorothioate (amine formation/dehydrochlorination)
Uses:
insecticide/nematicide

ISDN *See:* isosorbide dinitrate

ISMN *See:* isosorbide-5-mononitrate

isoamyl acetate
banana oil; [123-92-2]

(CH₃)₂CHCH₂CH₂OCCH₃

$C_7H_{14}O_2$. M: 130.19. Colourless liquid with a strong, banana-like odour. BP: 142°C. d: 0.87 kg/l (25°C). Slightly soluble in water. Miscible with most organic solvents.
Production:
• isoamyl alcohol + acetic acid (esterification)
Uses: flavouring ingredient

isoamyl alcohol
isopentanol; isopentyl alcohol; 3-methylbutan-1-ol; 3-methylbutanol; primary isoamyl alcohol; [123-51-3]

(CH₃)₂CHCH₂CH₂OH

$C_5H_{12}O_1$. M: 88.15. Colourless liquid with an unpleasant odour. BP: 130–133°C. MP: -88°C. d: 0.81 kg/l (20°C). Solubility in water: 25 g/l water.
Production:
• isobutylene + synthesis gas (hydroformylation)

Derivatives: isoamyl acetate; isoamyl butyrate; isoamyl formate; isoamyl isobutyrate; isoamyl isovalerate; isoamyl nitrite; isoamyl propionate; isoamyl salicylate; isovaleraldehyde; isovaleric acid; sodium *O,O*-diisoamyl dithiophosphate

Uses: extraction agent (phosphoric acid purification)

isoamyl butyrate

isoamyl *n*-butyrate; [106-27-4]

$$CH_3CH_2CH_2COCH_2CH_2CH(CH_3)_2$$

$C_9H_{18}O_2$. M: 158.24. Colourless liquid with a strong, fruity odour. BP: 179°C. d: 0.90 kg/l (20°C). Insoluble in water. Soluble in most organic solvents.

Production:
• isoamyl alcohol + *n*-butyric acid (esterification)

Uses: flavouring ingredient

isoamylene

$$CH_3C=CHCH_3 \quad + \quad CH_2=CCH_2CH_3$$

C_5H_{10}. M: 70.13. Colourless liquid. BP: 20–38°C. d: ~0.65 kg/l (20°C). Isoamylene is a mixture of 2-methyl-2-butene and 2-methyl-1-butene.

Production:
• C_5-stream, refinery (hydration/separation/dehydration)

Derivatives: amylanthraquinone; *t*-amyl hydroperoxide; *p-t*-amylphenol; 2,5-di-*t*-amylhydroquinone; isoprene; 2-methyl-2-butene; 3-methylthiophene

isoamyl formate

[110-45-2]

$$(CH_3)_2CHCH_2CH_2OCH$$

$C_6H_{12}O_2$. M: 116.17. Colourless liquid with a fruity odour. BP: 124°C. d: 0.88 kg/l (20°C). Slightly soluble in water. Soluble in oxygenated solvents.

Production:
• isoamyl alcohol + formic acid (esterification)

Uses: flavouring ingredient

isoamyl isobutyrate

[2050-01-3]

$$(CH_3)_2CHCOCH_2CH_2CH(CH_3)_2$$

$C_9H_{18}O_2$. M: 158.24.

Production:
• isoamyl alcohol + isobutyric acid (esterification)

Uses: flavouring ingredient

isoamyl isovalerate

[659-70-1]

$C_{10}H_{20}O_2$. M: 172.27. Colourless liquid with an apple-like odour. BP: 192°C. d: 0.86 kg/l (20°C). Insoluble in water. Soluble in oxygenated solvents.

$$(CH_3)_2CHCH_2COCH_2CH_2CH(CH_3)_2$$

Production:
• isoamyl alcohol + isovaleric acid (esterification)

Uses: flavouring ingredient (confectionery)

isoamyl nitrite

amyl nitrite; [1002-16-0]

$$(CH_3)_2CHCH_2CH_2ON=O$$

$C_5H_{11}N_1O_2$. M: 117.15. Pale yellow liquid with a strong, fruity odour. BP: 97–98°C. Insoluble in water. Miscible with oxygenated and chlorinated solvents. Decomposes in air and light.

Production:
• isoamyl alcohol + sodium nitrite (nitrosation)

Derivatives:
DL-ephedrine; norephedrine; sodium 4,4'-bis(4-phenyl-1,2,3-triazol-2-yl)stilbene-2,2'-disulphonate

Uses: diazotisation/alpha carbonylation reagent

isoamyl propionate

$$CH_3CH_2COCH_2CH_2CH(CH_3)_2$$

$C_8H_{16}O_2$. M: 144.22.

Production:
• isoamyl alcohol + propionic acid (esterification)

Uses: flavouring ingredient

isoamyl salicylate

3-methylbutyl salicylate; [87-20-7]

$$COCH_2CH_2CH(CH_3)_2$$

$C_{12}H_{16}O_3$. M: 208.26. Colourless liquid with sweet odour. BP: 280°C. d: 1.04 kg/l (20°C). Insoluble in water. Soluble in alcohol and chlorinated solvents.

Production:
• isoamyl alcohol + salicylic acid (esterification)

Uses: fragrance ingredient (soap)

isoascorbic acid

D-*erythro*-ascorbic acid; D-2,3-didehydro-*erythro*-hexono-1,4-lactone; erythorbic acid; [89-65-6]

$$C-CH_2OH$$

$C_6H_8O_6$. M: 176.12. Crystalline solid. Soluble in water and oxygenated solvents.

Production:
- mould fermentation medium + *Penicillium notatum* mould (fermentation)

Derivatives: sodium erythorbate

Uses: antioxidant (food); oxygen scavenger (boiler water treatment)

isobornyl acetate
[125-12-2]

$C_{12}H_{20}O_2$. M: 196.29. Colourless liquid with a pine odour. BP: 102°C (1.6 kPa), d: 0.99 kg/l (20°C). The product is usually a mixture of optical isomers. It is the *exo*-isomer of bornyl acetate.

Production:
- camphene + acetic acid (rearrangement/addition)

Derivatives:
camphor; isobornyl acrylate; isobornyl methacrylate

Uses:
fragrance ingredient (soap, household products)

isobornyl acrylate

$C_{13}H_{20}O_2$. M: 208.30.

Production:
- isobornyl acetate + methyl acrylate (transesterification)

Uses: reactive diluent (radiation-cured coatings)

isobornyl methacrylate

$C_{14}H_{22}O_2$. M: 222.33.

Production:
- isobornyl acetate + methyl methacrylate (transesterification)

Uses: reactive diluent (radiation-cured coatings)

isobutane
[75-28-5]

C_4H_{10}. M: 58.12. Colourless liquified gas. BP: -12°C. d: 0.56 kg/l (20°C). Flash point: -83°C. Insoluble in water. Soluble in oxygenated and hydrocarbon solvents.

Production:
- butane, mixed (fractionation; coproduced with *n*-butane)
- butane, mixed/*n*-butane/C_4-stream, refinery (isomerisation)

Derivatives: *t*-butyl hydroperoxide; gasoline, alkylate; isobutylene

Uses:
aerosol propellant; solvent (Phillips HDPE process)

isobutanol
isobutyl alcohol; 2-methyl-1-propanol; IBA; [78-83-1]

$(CH_3)_2CHCH_2OH$

$C_4H_{10}O_1$. M: 74.12. Colourless liquid. BP: 107–109°C. FP: -108°C. d: 0.80 kg/l (20°C). Solubility in water: 100 g/l solution (25°C). Miscible with most organic solvents.

Production:
- isobutyraldehyde (hydrogenation)
- propylene + synthesis gas (Shell hydroformylation process; coproduced with *n*-butanol/2-ethylhexanol)
- oxygenates, Fischer-Tropsch, mixed (fractionation; coproduced with methanol/ethanol/isopropanol/ *n*-butanol/amyl alcohol, primary/acetaldehyde/ acetone/methyl ethyl ketone)

Derivatives: diisobutylamine; diisobutyl phthalate; dipropylene glycol monoisobutyl ether; isobutyl acetate; isobutyl acrylate; isobutyl bromide; isobutyl 4-chloro-3,5-diaminobenzoate; isobutyl chloroformate; isobutyl methacrylate; isobutyl nitrite; isobutyl oleate; isobutyl phenylacetate; isobutyl salicylate; isobutyl stearate; isobutyl vinyl ether; propylene glycol monoisobutyl ether; sodium *O,O*-diisobutyl dithiophosphate; sodium diisobutylsulphosuccinate; sodium isobutyl xanthate

Uses:
extraction agent (phosphoric acid purification)

isobutoxypropanol
See: propylene glycol monoisobutyl ether

isobutoxypropoxypropanol
See: dipropylene glycol monoisobutyl ether

isobutyl acetate
[110-19-0]

$C_6H_{12}O_2$. M: 116.17. Colourless liquid. BP: 115–118°C. d: 0.87 kg/l (20°C). Solubility in water: 700 g/l water (20°C). Flash point: 18°C (TCC).

Production:
- isobutanol + acetic acid (esterification)

Uses:
flavouring ingredient; solvent (lacquers, resins, adhesives, printing inks)

isobutyl acrylate
[106-63-8]

$$CH_2=CHCOCH_2CH(CH_3)_2$$

$C_7H_{12}O_2$. M: 128.18. Liquid. FP: -61°C. BP: 138°C. d: 0.89 kg/l (20°C).
Production:
- isobutanol + acrylic acid (esterification)
Uses: acrylic resin comonomer

isobutyl alcohol *See:* isobutanol

isobutylbenzene
IBB; [538-93-2]

$$(CH_3)_2CHCH_2-\text{(phenyl)}$$

$C_{10}H_{14}$. M: 134.22. Colourless liquid. BP: 173°C. MP: -51°C. d: 0.85 kg/l (20°C). Insoluble in water. Miscible with oxygenated and aromatic solvents. Flash point: 44°C (COC).
Production:
- toluene + propylene (potassium-catalysed alkylation; coproduced with *n*-butylbenzene)
Derivatives: ibuprofen

isobutyl bromide
[78-77-3]

$$(CH_3)_2CHCH_2Br$$

$C_4H_9Br_1$. M: 137.01. Colourless liquid. BP: 91°C. d: 1.27 kg/l (15°C). Slightly soluble in water. Soluble in oxygenated and chlorinated solvents.
Production:
- isobutanol (alcohol bromination)
Derivatives: butalbital; 4,5-diamino-1,8-dihydroxy-2,7-diisobutylanthraquinone; β-naphthyl isobutyl ether

isobutyl 4-chloro-3,5-diaminobenzoate
DD-1604 (Bayer)

$$\text{structure: benzene ring with } H_2N, Cl, H_2N \text{ substituents and } COCH_2CH(CH_3)_2$$

$C_{11}H_{15}Cl_1N_2O_2$. M: 242.70.
Production:
- *p*-chlorobenzoic acid + isobutanol (nitration/nitro reduction/esterification)
Uses: polyurethane elastomer curing agent

isobutyl chloroformate
isobutyl chlorocarbonate; [543-27-1]
$C_5H_9Cl_1O_2$. M: 136.57.
Production:
- isobutanol + phosgene (phosgenation)

$$(CH_3)_2CHCH_2OCCl \text{ (with O double bond)}$$

Derivatives:
methylol carbamate resins
Uses: amide formation reagent

isobutylene
isobutene; 2-methylpropene; [115-11-7]

$$(CH_3)_2C=CH_2$$

C_4H_8. M: 56.10. Colourless gas commercially available with 94% or 99% purity. BP: -7°C. FP: -139°C. Insoluble in water. Soluble in oxygenated solvents.
Production:
- raffinate I (sulphuric acid separation processes; coproduced with raffinate II)
- raffinate I (molecular sieve separation; coproduced with raffinate II)
- *t*-butanol (dehydration)
- isobutane (dehydrogenation)
- raffinate I (Exxon two-stage methanol process)
Derivatives:
bromobutide; *t*-butanol; *N*-*t*-butylacryl-amide; *t*-butyl-amine; *t*-butylbenzene; *t*-butylcatechol; *t*-butyl chloro-acetate; 2-*t*-butyl-*p*-cresol; 6-*t*-butyl-*m*-cresol; 6-*t*-butyl-2,4-dimethylphenol; *t*-butylhydraz-inium chloride; *t*-butyl hydroperoxide; *t*-butylhydroxyanisole; *t*-butyl mer-captan; 4-*t*-butyl-α-methylhydro-cinnamaldehyde; *o*-*t*-butylphenol; *p*-*t*-butylphenol; butyl rubber; *p*-*t*-butyl-toluene; *t*-butyltoluenediamine; 5-*t*-butyl-*m*-xylene; cil-astatin; citral; 2,6-di-*t*-butyl-*p*-cresol; di-*t*-butyl per-oxide; 2,5-di-(*t*-butylperoxy)-2,5-dimethylhexane; 2,4-di-*t*-butylphenol; 2,6-di-*t*-butylphenol; 1,5-di-(*p*-*t*-butyl-phenylthio)anthraquinone; 4,6-dinitro-1,1,3,3,5-penta-methylindane; ethyl *t*-butyl ether; isoamyl alcohol; isoprene; methacrolein; methacrylonitrile; methallyl chloride; 3-methyl-2-buten-1-ol; methyl *t*-butyl ether; β-methylepichlorohydrin; α-methylheptenone; methyl isoamyl ketone; pivalic acid; polyisobutylene, high molecular weight; polyisobutylene, low molecular weight; sodium methallyl sulphonate; triethylene glycol bis[3-(3-*t*-butyl-4-hydroxy-5-methylphenyl)propionate]; triisobutylaluminium; xylenol, butylated

2,2′-isobutylidenebis(4,6-dimethylphenol)
IBPH

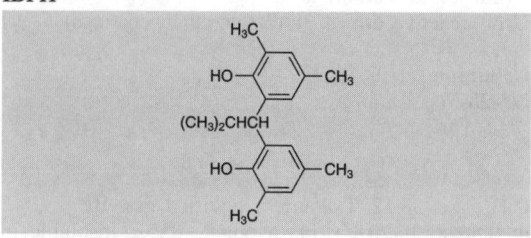

$C_{20}H_{26}O_2$. M: 298.43.

Production:
- 2,4-xylenol + isobutyraldehyde (carbonyl condensation)

Uses: antioxidant (rubber)

isobutylidene urea
isobutylidene diurea; IBDU

$$(CH_3)_2CHCH(NHCNH_2)_2$$

$C_6H_{14}N_4O_2$. M: 174.21.
Production:
- urea + isobutyraldehyde (carbonyl condensation)

Uses: controlled-release fertiliser

isobutyl methacrylate
IBMA; [97-86-9]

$$CH_2=CCOCH_2CH(CH_3)_2$$
$$CH_3$$

$C_8H_{14}O_2$. M: 142.20. Colourless liquid with ether-like odour. BP: 155°C. d: 0.88 kg/l (25°C). Insoluble in water. Flash point: 49°C (TOC). Commercial products contain hydroquinone methyl ether or similar polymerisation inhibitors.
Production:
- isobutanol + methyl methacrylate (transesterification)

Uses: acrylic resin comonomer

isobutyl nitrite
[542-56-3]

$$(CH_3)_2CHCH_2ONO$$

$C_4H_9N_1O_2$. M: 103.12. Colourless liquid. BP: 67°C. Slightly soluble in water with gradual hydrolysis. Soluble in oxygenated solvents.
Production:
- isobutanol + sodium nitrite (nitrosation)

Uses: diazotisation/alpha carbonylation reagent

isobutyl oleate

$$CH_3(CH_2)_7CH=CH(CH_2)_7COCH_2CH(CH_3)_2$$

$C_{22}H_{42}O_2$. M: 338.58. Yellow liquid. Pour point: -21°C. d: 0.86 kg/l (20°C). Flash point: 195°C (COC). Insoluble in water. Miscible with paraffin oil.
Production:
- isobutanol + oleic acid (esterification)

Uses: emulsifier/bodying agent/emollient (toiletries, cosmetics); lubricity additive (metalworking fluids)

isobutyl phenylacetate
[102-13-6]
$C_{12}H_{16}O_2$. M: 192.26. Colourless liquid with a sweet odour. BP: 247°C. d: 0.99 kg/l. Insoluble in water.

Soluble in oxygenated solvents.

$$CH_2COCH_2CH(CH_3)_2$$

Production:
- isobutanol + phenylacetic acid (esterification)

Uses: flavouring ingredient

isobutyl salicylate
[87-19-4]

$$COCH_2CH(CH_3)_2$$
$$OH$$

$C_{11}H_{14}O_3$. M: 194.23. Colourless liquid. BP: 259–260°C. MP: 6°C. Insoluble in water. Soluble in oxygenated solvents.
Production:
- isobutanol + salicylic acid (esterification)

Uses: flavouring/fragrance ingredient

isobutyl stearate
[646-13-9]

$$CH_3(CH_2)_{16}COCH_2CH(CH_3)_2$$

$C_{22}H_{44}O_2$. M: 340.59.
Production:
- stearic acid + isobutanol (esterification)

Uses:
emollient (cosmetics); plastics processing lubricant

isobutyl vinyl ether
vinyl isobutyl ether; IBVE; IVE; [109-53-5]

$$CH_2=CHOCH_2CH(CH_3)_2$$

$C_6H_{12}O_1$. M: 100.17. Colourless liquid. BP: 83°C. MP: -112°C. d: 0.77 kg/l (20°C). Slightly soluble in water. Soluble in most organic solvents.
Production:
- isobutanol + acetylene (ethynylation)

Derivatives: poly(isobutyl vinyl ether-vinyl chloride)
Uses: acrylic resin comonomer (adhesives, textiles, leather, paper coatings)

isobutyraldehyde
isobutanal; isobutyl aldehyde; [78-84-2]

$$(CH_3)_2CHCHO$$

$C_4H_8O_1$. M: 72.10. Colourless liquid with a pungent odour. BP: 63–65°C. MP: -66°C. d: 0.79 kg/l (20°C). Soluble in water. Miscible with oxygenated and aromatic solvents.
Production:
- propylene + synthesis gas (hydroformylation; coproduced with *n*-butyraldehyde)

Derivatives:
aldicarb; ethofumesate; isobutanol; 2,2′-isobutylidene-bis(4,6-dimethylphenol); isobutylidene urea; isobutyric acid; isobutyronitrile; neopentyl glycol; neopentyl glycol monohydroxypivalate; pantolactone; 2,2,4-trimethyl-1,3-pentanediol; 2,2,4-trimethyl-1,3-pentanediol mono-isobutyrate; DL-valine

isobutyric acid
isobutanoic acid; 2-methylpropanoic acid; 2-methyl-propionic acid; [79-31-2]

$$(CH_3)_2CHCOOH$$

$C_4H_8O_2$. M: 88.10. Colourless liquid with a disagreeable odour. BP: 153–156°C. MP: -46°C. d: 0.95 kg/l (20°C). Soluble in water. Miscible with oxygenated and chlorinated solvents.
Production:
• isobutyraldehyde (carbonyl oxidation)
Derivatives: citronellyl isobutyrate; diisopropyl ketone; geranyl isobutyrate; 3-hexenyl isobutyrate; isoamyl isobutyrate; isobutyroyl chloride; phenethyl isobutyrate; 2-phenoxyethyl isobutyrate; piperonyl isobutyrate; sucrose acetate isobutyrate; 2,2,4-trimethyl-1,3-pentanediol diisobutyrate
Uses: disinfectant/preservative; pharmaceutical derivatisation reagent

isobutyronitrile
isopropyl cyanide; 2-methylpropanenitrile; [78-82-0]

$$(CH_3)_2CHC \equiv N$$

$C_4H_7N_1$. M: 69.11. Colourless liquid. BP: 104°C. d: 0.76 kg/l (4°C). Slightly soluble in water. Soluble in oxygenated solvents.
Production:
• isobutyraldehyde + hydroxylamine sulphate (oxime formation/dehydration)
Derivatives: diazinon

isobutyroyl chloride
isobutyryl chloride; [79-30-1]

$$(CH_3)_2CHCOCl$$

$C_4H_7Cl_1O_1$. M: 106.55.
Production:
• isobutyric acid (chlorination)
Derivatives:
(RS)-α-(4-chlorophenyl)isovaleric acid; flurprimidol

isocamphylcyclohexanol
Sandela (Givaudan-Roure); Sandel H&R (Haarmann & Reimer); Santalex-T (Takasago International); [4105-12-8]
$C_{16}H_{28}O_1$. M: 236.40. Mixed product used as a substitute for sandalwood oil. The main odiferous component is 3-*trans*-isocamphylcyclohexanol.

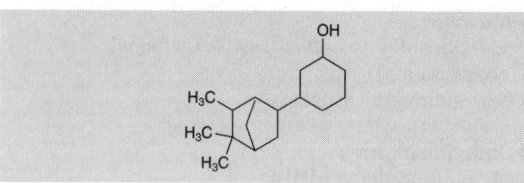

Production:
• camphene + guaiacol (addition/hydrogenation)
Uses:
fragrance ingredient (soaps, detergents)

isocinchomeronic acid
pyridine-2,5-dicarboxylic acid; [100-26-5]

$C_7H_5N_1O_4$. M: 167.13. Crystalline solid. MP: 236–237°C. Decomposes to nicotinic acid when heated further. Slightly soluble in hot water and alcohol.
Production:
• 2-methyl-5-ethylpyridine (side-chain oxidation)
Derivatives: nicotinic acid

isoconazole
[27523-40-6]

$C_{18}H_{14}Cl_4N_2O_1$. M: 416.13. Available commercially as the nitrate.
Production:
• α,2,4-trichloroacetophenone + imidazole + 2,6-dichlorobenzyl chloride (amine formation/carbonyl reduction/ether formation)
Uses: antifungal drug

isocyanatoethyl methacrylate
2-isocyanatoethyl methacrylate; IEM

$C_7H_9N_1O_3$. M: 155.16.
Production:
• methacrylic acid + monoethanolamine + phosgene (esterification/phosgenation)
Uses: crosslinked polymer polyol/styrene-acrylic resin comonomer

3-isocyanatomethyl-3,5,5-trimethylcyclohexyl isocyanate *See:* isophorone diisocyanate

isocyanic acid
[75-13-8]

HNCO

$C_1H_1N_1O_1$. M: 43.03. Intermediate material. Not a commercially traded product.
Production:
• hydrogen cyanide (air oxidation)
Derivatives:
isopropenyldimethylbenzyl isocyanate; tetramethyl-*m*-xylene diisocyanate; tetramethyl-*p*-xylene diisocyanate

isocyanuric acid *See:* cyanuric acid

isocyclocitral
See: trimethyl 3-cyclohexenecarboxaldehyde

isodecanoic acid
[26403-17-8]

$C_9H_{19}COOH$

$C_{10}H_{20}O_2$. M: 172.27. Liquid. BP: 250–280°C. Pour point: <-65°C. d: 0.91 kg/l (20°C). Slightly soluble in water.
Production:
• isodecanol (alcohol oxidation)
Derivatives: barium-zinc heat stabilisers; cadmium-barium heat stabilisers; cadmium-zinc heat stabilisers; complex ester oils
Uses: emulsifier/coupling solvent (metalworking fluids); alkyd resin modifier

isodecanol
decyl alcohol; isodecyl alcohol

$C_9H_{19}CH_2OH$

$C_{10}H_{22}O_1$. M: 158.29. Colourless liquid. BP: 214–224°C. d: 0.84 kg/l (20°C). Insoluble in water.
Production:
• nonene, branched + synthesis gas (hydroformylation)
Derivatives: *n*-butyl isodecyl phthalate; complex ester oils; didecyl phenyl phosphite; diester oils; diisodecyl adipate; diisodecyl 4,5-epoxytetrahydrophthalate; diisodecyl phthalate; diphenyl decyl phosphite; disodium isodecylsulphosuccinate; eicosanol; isodecanoic acid; isodecyl acrylate; isodecyl ethoxylates; isodecyl methacrylate; isodecyl-3-oxypropylamine ethoxylates; polymeric plasticisers; zinc didecyl dithiophosphate
Uses: froth flotation foam modifier; oiliness additive (lubricants); solvent

isodecyl acrylate
IDA

$CH_2=CHCOOCH_2C_9H_{19}$

$C_{13}H_{24}O_2$. M: 212.33.

Production:
• isodecanol + acrylic acid (esterification)
Uses:
acrylic resin comonomer (packaging adhesives); reactive diluent (radiation-cured inks, lacquers)

isodecyl alcohol *See:* isodecanol

isodecyl ether phosphoric acid

$$\left[C_9H_{19}CH_2(OCH_2CH_2)_6O\right]_n P(OH)_{3-n}$$

n = 1–2.
Production:
• isodecyl ethoxylates + phosphorus pentoxide (reaction)
Uses: emulsifier/extreme-pressure additive (metalworking fluids); wetting agent (industrial cleaners)

isodecyl ethoxylates

$C_9H_{19}CH_2O(CH_2CH_2O)_nH$

n = 3–8. Colourless liquids. HLB: 12.5 (6 moles EO).
Production:
• isodecanol + ethylene oxide (epoxidation)
Derivatives: isodecyl ether phosphoric acid
Uses:
emulsifier (solvent-based cold cleaners); leather tanning auxiliary; primary surfactant (cleaning agents, detergents)

isodecyl methacrylate
[29964-84-9]

$$CH_2=CCOOCH_2C_9H_{19}$$
$$CH_3$$

$C_{14}H_{26}O_2$. M: 226.36. Colourless liquid. d: 0.88 kg/l (25°C). Insoluble in water. Flash point: 121°C (COC). Commercial products contain hydroquinone or similar polymerisation inhibitors.
Production:
• isodecanol + methyl methacrylate (transesterification)
Derivatives:
polymethacrylates, oil-soluble; polymethacrylates, oil-soluble dispersants

isodecyl-3-oxypropylamine ethoxylates

$$C_9H_{19}CH_2OCH_2CH_2CH_2N \begin{matrix}(CH_2CH_2O)_mH\\(CH_2CH_2O)_nH\end{matrix}$$

m+n = 2–15.
Production:
• isodecanol + acrylonitrile + ethylene oxide (cyanoethylation/hydrogenation/epoxidation)
Uses: cationic emulsifier; corrosion inhibitor

isoeugenol

1-(4-hydroxy-3-methoxyphenyl)propylene; 2-hydroxy-5-propenylanisole; 2-methoxy-4-propenylphenol; [97-54-1]

$$HO-\text{(ring)}-CH=CHCH_3$$
$$CH_3O$$

$C_{10}H_{12}O_2$. M: 164.21. Viscous, yellow liquid with clove-like odour. Commercial grades are a mixture of *cis* and *trans*-isomers with BP: 269–271°C. d: 1.09 kg/l (20°C). Slowly soluble in water. Soluble in most organic solvents.
Production:
• eugenol (isomerisation)
• guaiacol + propionaldehyde (carbonyl condensation/base-catalysed cleavage)
Derivatives:
methyl isoeugenol; propenylguethol; vanillin
Uses: fragrance ingredient

isoeugenol methyl ether *See:* methyl isoeugenol

isofenphos

isopropyl *O*-[ethoxy(isopropylamino)phosphinothioyl]-salicylate; [25311-71-1]

$$\begin{array}{c} O \\ \| \\ COCH(CH_3)_2 \\ S \\ \| \\ OPOC_2H_5 \\ | \\ NHCH(CH_3)_2 \end{array}$$

$C_{15}H_{24}N_1O_4P_1S_1$. M: 345.39.
Production:
• isopropanol + salicylic acid + thiophosphoryl chloride + isopropylamine + ethanol (esterification/dehydrochlorination/dehydrochlorination/dehydrochlorination)
Uses: insecticide

isoflurane

1-chloro-2,2,2-trifluoroethyldifluoromethyl ether; [26675-46-7]

$$CF_3CHClOCHF_2$$

$C_3H_2Cl_1F_5O_1$. M: 184.49. Colourless liquid with an ethereal odour. BP: 48°C. Nonflammable.
Production:
• 2,2,2-trifluoroethanol + dimethyl sulphate + chlorine + hydrogen fluoride (methylation/photochlorination/halogen exchange)
Uses:
inhalation anaesthetic drug

isoheptanol

Alphanol 700 (ICI)
$C_7H_{16}O_1$. M: 116.21. Colourless liquid. BP: 164–174°C.

d: 0.82 kg/l (20°C). Insoluble in water. Miscible with oxygenated solvents.

$$C_6H_{13}CH_2OH$$

Production:
• hexene, branched (hydroformylation)
Derivatives:
isoheptyl acetate
Uses: solvent; lubricant antiwear additive raw material

isoheptyl acetate

Exxate 700 (Exxon Chemical)

$$\begin{array}{c} O \\ \| \\ CH_3COCH_2C_6H_{13} \end{array}$$

$C_9H_{18}O_2$. M: 158.24. Colourless liquid. BP: 176–200°C. Insoluble in water. d: 0.87 kg/l (20°C). Flash point: 60°C (TCC).
Production:
• isoheptanol + acetic acid (esterification)
Uses: solvent (paints)

isohexane

$$C_6H_{14}$$

C_6H_{14}. M: 86.18. Colourless liquid. BP: 55–62°C. d: 0.67 kg/l (15°C). Insoluble in water.
Production:
• gasoline, polymer (molecular sieve separation; coproduced with *n*-pentane/isopentane/*n*-hexane)
Uses: polyolefin production reaction diluent; solvent (fast-drying adhesives, lacquers); extraction solvent (vegetable/essential/animal oil processing)

L-isoleucine

L-2-amino-3-methylpentanoic acid; Ile; [73-32-5]

$$\begin{array}{c} NH_2 \\ | \\ C_2H_5CH-C-COOH \\ | \quad | \\ CH_3 \ H \end{array}$$

$C_6H_{13}N_1O_2$. M: 131.18. Available commercially in the naturally-occurring L(+)-enantiomer. Waxy solid. Sublimes on heating to 170°C. Soluble in water.
Production:
• microbial fermentation medium + *Serratia marcescens* bacteria (fermentation; coproduced with L-threonine)
Derivatives:
oxytocin
Uses: infusion solutions/diagnostic aids; raw material (peptide drugs)

α-isomethylionone

3-methyl-4-(2,6,6-trimethyl-2-cyclohex-1-yl)-1-buten-2-one; [127-51-5]
$C_{14}H_{22}O_1$. M: 206.33. Yellow liquid with a violet-like odour. d: 0.94 kg/l (20°C). Soluble in alcohol.

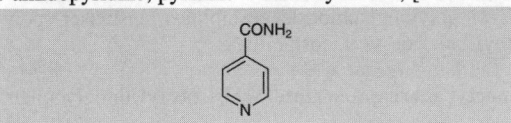

Production:
• citral + methyl ethyl ketone (carbonyl condensation/acid-catalysed rearrangement)
Uses: fragrance ingredient

isoniazid
[54-85-3]

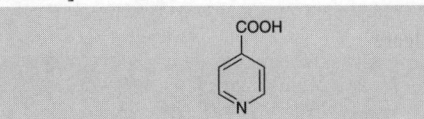

$C_6H_7N_3O_1$. M: 137.15.
Production:
• methyl isonicotinate + hydrazine (amide formation)
Derivatives: furonazide; glyconiazide; iproniazid
Uses: tuberculostatic drug

isonicotinamide
4-amidopyridine; pyridine-4-carbonylamide; [1453-82-3]

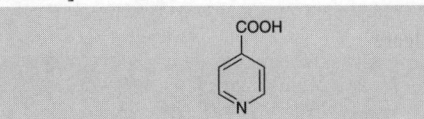

$C_6H_6N_2O_1$. M: 122.13.
Production:
• isonicotinic acid + ammonia (amide formation)
Derivatives: cefsulodin

isonicotinic acid
4-pyridinecarboxylic acid; pyridine-4-carboxylic acid; [55-22-1]

$C_6H_5N_1O_2$. M: 123.12. Flakes. Sublimes at 310°C. Slightly soluble in hot water forming acidic solutions. Insoluble in alcohol and aromatic solvents.
Production:
• γ-picoline (side-chain oxidation)
Derivatives:
isonicotinamide; isonipecotic acid; methyl isonicotinate

isonipecotic acid
piperidine-4-carboxylic acid; [498-94-2]

$C_6H_{11}N_1O_2$. M: 129.17. Off-white solid. MP: 310°C. Bulk density: 0.66 kg/l. Soluble in water. Insoluble in alcohol.

Production:
• isonicotinic acid (hydrogenation)
Derivatives: azatadine; cyproheptadine; ethyl isonipecotinate; ketotifen; pizotifen; quinuclidin-3-ol

isononanoic acid
3,5,5-trimethylhexanoic acid; [3302-10-1]

$$\underset{(CH_3)_3CCH_2CHCH_2COOH}{\overset{CH_3}{|}}$$

$C_9H_{18}O_2$. M: 158.24. Clear liquid. BP: 228–241°C. d: 0.90 kg/l (20°C). Insoluble in water. The product is predominantly 3,5,5-trimethylhexanoic acid.
Production:
• 2,4,4-trimethylpentene (hydroformylation/oxidation)
Derivatives:
complex ester oils; isononanoyl chloride

isononanol
isononyl alcohol

$$C_8H_{17}CH_2OH$$

$C_9H_{20}O_1$. M: 144.26. Colourless liquid. BR: 199–215°C. d: 0.84 kg/l (20°C). Insoluble in water. Flash point: 88°C (PMCC). See also nonanol.
Production:
• octene, branched + synthesis gas (hydroformylation)
Derivatives:
diisononyl adipate; diisononyl phthalate; dinonyl alkylene(C_4-C_6)dicarboxylate; trinonyl trimellitate
Uses: froth flotation foam modifier

isononanoyl chloride
3,5,5-trimethylhexanoyl chloride

$$\underset{(CH_3)_3CCH_2CHCH_2CCl}{\overset{CH_3 \quad O}{| \qquad ||}}$$

$C_9H_{17}Cl_1O_1$. M: 176.69. Liquid. BP: 189°C. MP: -80°C. d: 0.95 kg/l (20°C). Hydrolysed by water. Flash point: 97°C (COC).
Production:
• isononanoic acid (acid chloride formation)
Derivatives: isononanoyl peroxide

isononanoyl peroxide
diisononanoyl peroxide

$$\underset{C_8H_{17}CO-OCC_8H_{17}}{\overset{O \qquad O}{|| \qquad ||}}$$

$C_{18}H_{34}O_4$. M: 314.47. Solution containing 75% peroxide with a 10-hour half-life at 60°C.
Production:
• isononanoyl chloride + hydrogen peroxide (dehydrochlorination)
Uses: polymerisation initiator

isononene *See:* nonene, branched

isononyl acetate
3,5,5-trimethylhexyl acetate; [58430-94-7]

$$\underset{\underset{CH_3}{|}}{(CH_3)_3CCH_2CHCH_2CH_2}\overset{\overset{O}{||}}{O}CCH_3$$

$C_{11}H_{22}O_2$. M: 186.30. Colourless liquid with a fruity odour.
Production:
• nonanol + acetic acid (esterification)
Uses: fragrance ingredient (technical products)

isononyl alcohol *See:* isononanol

isooctane
2,2,4-trimethylpentane; [540-84-1]

$$(CH_3)_3CCH_2CH(CH_3)_2$$

C_8H_{18}. M: 114.23.
Production:
• 2,4,4-trimethylpentene (hydrogenation)
Uses: engine test fuel; petrol blending component

isooctanoic acid
[25103-52-0]

$$C_7H_{15}COOH$$

$C_8H_{16}O_2$. M: 144.22. Clear liquid. BP: 220–231°C. d: 0.91 kg/l (20°C). Mixture of branched chain carboxylic acids.
Production:
• heptene, branched (hydroformylation/alcohol oxidation)
Derivatives: cobalt octoate; complex ester oils; lead octoate; stannous octoate

isooctanol
isooctyl alcohol; [26952-21-6]

$$C_7H_{15}CH_2OH$$

$C_8H_{18}O_1$. M: 130.23. Colourless liquid. BP: 183–193°C. d: 0.83 kg/l (20°C). Insoluble in water. Flash point: 74°C (PMCC). Mixed isomer product. Competes with 2-ethylhexanol.
Production:
• heptene, branched (hydroformylation)
Derivatives:
2,4-D-isooctyl; dibutyltin bis(isooctylmaleate); dichlorprop-isooctyl; diisooctyl adipate; diisooctyl azelate; diisooctyl phthalate; isooctyl epoxytallate; isooctyl nitrate; isooctyl oleate; isooctyl phosphoric acid; isooctyl stearate; isooctyl thioglycollate; MCPA-isooctyl; polymeric plasticisers; sodium diisooctylsulphosuccinate; 2,4,5-T-isooctyl; triisooctylamine; triisooctyl phosphite; triisooctyl trimellitate; zinc dioctyl dithiophosphate
Uses: froth flotation foam modifier

isooctyl acid phosphate *See:* isooctyl phosphoric acid

isooctyl alcohol *See:* isooctanol

isooctyl epoxystearate
isooctyl 9,10-epoxystearate

$$CH_3(CH_2)_7CH\overset{\overset{O}{\triangle}}{-}CH(CH_2)_7\overset{\overset{O}{||}}{C}OCH_2C_7H_{15}$$

$C_{26}H_{50}O_3$. M: 410.69. Liquid. MP: -13°C. d: 0.94 kg/l. Decomposes on heating.
Production:
• isooctyl oleate + peracetic acid/performic acid (epoxidation)
Derivatives: barium-zinc heat stabilisers; cadmium-zinc heat stabilisers

isooctyl epoxytallate
2-ethylhexyl epoxytallate; octyl epoxytallate
$C_{26}H_{52}O_3$. M: 412.71.
Production:
• tall oil fatty acid + 2-ethylhexanol/isooctanol (esterification/peroxidation)
Derivatives: barium-zinc heat stabilisers; cadmium-zinc heat stabilisers
Uses: polyvinyl chloride costabiliser/plasticiser; polyvinyl chloride heat costabilisers

isooctyl mercaptoacetate *See:* isooctyl thioglycollate

isooctyl nitrate
ION

$$C_7H_{15}CH_2ONO_2$$

$C_8H_{17}N_1O_3$. M: 175.24.
Production:
• isooctanol (nitration)
Uses: diesel fuel ignition improver

isooctyl oleate

$$CH_3(CH_2)_7CH=CH(CH_2)_7\overset{\overset{O}{||}}{C}OCH_2C_7H_{15}$$

$C_{26}H_{50}O_2$. M: 394.69. Pale yellow, involatile liquid. Pour point: -27°C. d: 0.87 kg/l (20°C). Saponification value: 140–145 mg KOH/g. Iodine value: 65–70 g I_2/100 g. Insoluble in water. Soluble in hydrocarbon oils.
Production:
• isooctanol + oleic acid (esterification)
Derivatives:
isooctyl epoxystearate
Uses: lubricant (metalworking fluids)

isooctyl phosphoric acid
isooctyl acid phosphate

$$(C_7H_{15}CH_2O)_n\overset{\overset{O}{||}}{P}(OH)_{3-n}$$

n = 1–2.

Production:
- isooctanol + phosphorus pentoxide (reaction)

Uses: lubricity/detergent additive (textile lubricants, metalworking fluids)

isooctyl stearate

$$CH_3(CH_2)_{16}\overset{\overset{\textstyle O}{\|}}{C}OCH_2C_7H_{15}$$

$C_{26}H_{52}O_2$. M: 396.71. Colourless, involatile liquid. Saponification value: 145–150 mg KOH/g. d: 0.86 kg/l (20°C). Insoluble in water. Soluble in hydrocarbon oils.
Production:
- isooctanol + stearic acid (esterification)

Uses:
lubricant (metalworking fluids/textile spin finishes); plasticiser/flow improver (plastics, rubber, lacquers)

isooctyl thioglycollate
isooctyl mercaptoacetate

$$HSCH_2\overset{\overset{\textstyle O}{\|}}{C}OCH_2C_7H_{15}$$

$C_{10}H_{20}O_2S_1$. M: 204.33. Colourless or pale yellow liquid. BP: 80–88°C (6 kPa). d: 1.04 kg/l (20°C).
Production:
- isooctanol + thioglycollic acid (esterification)

Derivatives: antimony tris(isooctyl thioglycollate); dibutyltin diisooctylthioglycollate; dimethyltin bis(isooctylthioglycollate); dioctyltin diisooctylthioglycollate; monobutyltin tris(isooctylthioglycollate); monomethyltin tris(isooctylthioglycollate)

isoparaffin solvents
Isopar (Exxon Chemical)

$$C_nH_{2n+2}$$

n = 7–12. Series of aliphatic solvents in the boiling range 97–249°C. d: 0.70–0.78 kg/l (15°C). Low aromatics. Flash point: 5–78°C (TCC).
Production:
- heptene, branched/octene, branched/2,4,4-trimethylpentene/nonene, branched/dodecene, branched (hydrogenation)

Uses: catalyst carrier; electrostatic photocopying fluid; alkylene oxide entraining solvent; polyolefin production diluent; solvent (aerosols, paints, varnishes)

isopentane
[78-78-4]

$$(CH_3)_2CHCH_2CH_3$$

C_5H_{12}. M: 72.15. Colourless, volatile liquid. BP: 27–29°C. d: 0.62 kg/l (20°C). Insoluble in water.
Production:
- gasoline, polymer (molecular sieve separation; coproduced with *n*-pentane/*n*-hexane/isohexane)

Uses: blowing agent (expandable polystyrene); solvent (ethylene-propylene rubber production)

isopentanoic acid *See:* isovaleric acid

isopentanol *See:* isoamyl alcohol

isophorone
3,5,5-trimethyl-2-cyclohexen-1-one; [78-59-1]

$C_9H_{14}O_1$. M: 138.21. Colourless liquid. BR: 210–216°C. d: 0.92 kg/l (20°C). Slightly soluble in water. Soluble in oxygenated solvents. Flash point: 84°C (OC).
Production:
- acetone (carbonyl condensation)

Derivatives:
isophoronediamine; trimethylcyclohexanol; 3,3,5-trimethylcyclohexanone; 3,5-xylenol
Uses: levelling agent (textile printing); solvent (resins, lacquers, printing inks)

isophoronediamine
3-aminomethyl-3,5,5-trimethylcyclohexylamine; IPD

$C_{10}H_{22}N_2$. M: 170.30.
Production:
- isophorone + hydrogen cyanide + ammonia (addition/reductive ammoniation)

Derivatives: isophorone diisocyanate
Uses: epoxy resin curing agent

isophorone diisocyanate
3-isocyanatomethyl-3,5,5-trimethylcyclohexyl isocyanate; IPDI; [4098-71-9]

$C_{12}H_{18}N_2O_2$. M: 222.28. Colourless liquid. d: 1.06 kg/l (20°C). The product is often used with the isocyanate groups blocked.
Production:
- isophoronediamine + phosgene (phosgenation)

Derivatives:
urethane-acrylate resins
Uses: electrostatic powder coatings; 1-pack polyurethane enamels; isocyanate component (polyurethane elastomers)

isophthalic acid

benzene-1,3-dicarboxylic acid; *m*-phthalic acid; IPA; [121-91-5]

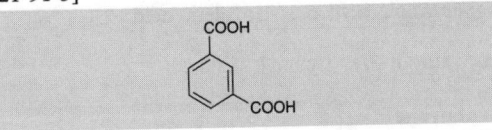

$C_8H_6O_4$. M: 166.14. Colourless, crystalline powder. MP: 342–343°C. Slightly soluble in hot water. Soluble in oxygenated solvents.
Production:
• *m*-xylene (oxidation)
Derivatives:
diallyl isophthalate; dimethyl isophthalate; diphenyl isophthalate; isophthaloyl chloride; 5-nitroisophthalic acid; sodium sulphoisophthalic acid; unsaturated polyester resins, isophthalate grades
Uses: alkyd resin comonomer

isophthalodinitrile

1,3-dicyanobenzene; *m*-dicyanobenzene; isophthalonitrile; IPN; [626-17-5]

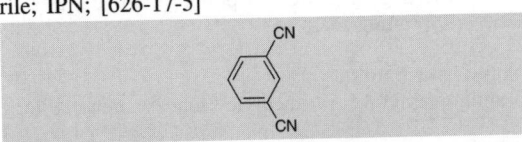

$C_8H_4N_2$. M: 128.13. White flakes. MP: 161–162°C. Slightly soluble in hot water. Soluble in hot alcohol, ether, chlorinated and aromatic solvents.
Production:
• *m*-xylene + ammonia (ammoxidation)
Derivatives:
chlorothalonil; *m*-xylylenediamine

isophthaloyl chloride

[99-63-8]

$C_8H_4Cl_2O_2$. M: 203.03. White, crystalline solid. MP: 42°C. BP: 276°C. d: 1.34 kg/l (15°C). Hydrolysed by water and alcohol.
Production:
• isophthalic acid (acid chloride formation)
Derivatives: polyarylate, amorphous; polyether ketone ketone; poly(*m*-phenyleneisophthalamide); Vat Orange 17; Vat Yellow 23; Vat Yellow 26

isoprenaline

isoproterenol; [7683-59-2]; [51-30-9] (hydrochloride); [299-95-6] (sulphate)
$C_{11}H_{17}N_1O_3$. M: 211.27. Available commercially as the racemic hydrochloride or sulphate dihydrate.

Production:
• 3,4-dihydroxy-ω-chloroacetophenone + isopropylamine (amine formation/carbonyl reduction)
Uses: bronchodilator drug

isoprene

2-methyl-1,3-butadiene; [78-79-5]

C_5H_8. M: 68.11. Colourless liquid. BP: 34°C. FP: -146°C. d: 0.67 kg/l (25°C). Insoluble in water. Soluble in most organic solvents.
Production:
• isoamylene (catalytic dehydrogenation)
• C_5-stream, steam-cracked (NMP solvent separation process; coproduced with dicyclopentadiene)
• isobutylene + formaldehyde (Kuraray 2-stage process)
Derivatives: 4-acetyl-1,1-dimethyl-6-*t*-butylindane; butyl rubber; β-methylheptenone; polyisoprene; polyisoprene, hydrogenated; styrene-isoprene block copolymers, hydrogenated; styrene-isoprene triblock copolymers

isoprene rubber *See:* polyisoprene

isoprocarb

[2631-40-5]

$C_{11}H_{15}N_1O_2$. M: 193.25.
Production:
• *o*-isopropylphenol + methyl isocyanate (isocyanate addition)
Uses: insecticide/nematicide

isopropalin

4-isopropyl-2,6-dinitro-*N*,*N*-dipropylaniline; [33820-53-0]

$C_{15}H_{23}N_3O_4$. M: 309.36.
Production:
• *p*-isopropylphenol + di-*n*-propylamine (nitration/chlorination/amine formation)
Uses: herbicide

isopropanol
isopropyl alcohol; 2-propanol; IPA; [67-63-0]

$$(CH_3)_2CHOH$$

$C_3H_8O_1$. M: 60.09. Colourless liquid with a pleasant odour. BP: 82–83°C. FP: -89°C. d: 0.78 kg/l (20°C). Miscible with water and most organic solvents. Flash point: 15°C (TCC).
Production:
• propylene (hydration)
• oxygenates, Fischer-Tropsch, mixed (fractionation; coproduced with methanol/ethanol/*n*-butanol/ isobutanol/amyl alcohol, primary/acetaldehyde/ acetone/methyl ethyl ketone)
Derivatives:
acetone; aluminium isopropoxide; anilofos; bromopropylate; diisopropyl adipate; diisopropylamine; diisopropyl malonate; *O,O*-diisopropyl phosphorodithioic acid; flamprop-M-isopropyl; flutolanil; isazofos; isofenphos; isopropyl acetate; isopropyl acetoacetate; isopropylamine; isopropyl bromide; *N*-isopropyl-*N′*-*t*-butylthiourea; isopropyl chloroformate; isopropyl lanolate; isopropyl myristate; isopropyl oleate; isopropyl palmitate; isopropyl stearate; isopropyl titanate; mepronil; methoprene; nitrothal-isopropyl; oxadiazon; potassium isopropyl xanthate; sodium *O,O*-diisopropyl dithiophosphate; sodium isopropyl xanthate
Uses: disinfectant; extraction agent (phosphoric acid purification); extraction solvent (vegetable oil refining); petrol antiicing additive; solvent (cleaners, polishes, resins, gums, paints, lacquer thinners, printing inks, cosmetics, drugs)

isopropanolamine *See:* monoisopropanolamine

isopropenyl acetate
[108-22-5]

$$CH_2=COCCH_3$$
$$CH_3$$

$C_5H_8O_2$. M: 100.11. Liquid. BP: 93–94°C. d: 0.91 kg/l (20°C).
Production:
• acetone + ketene (addition)
Derivatives: acetylacetone; diethyl α-isomalate
Uses: enol formation reagent

isopropenylbenzene *See:* α-methylstyrene

isopropenyldimethylbenzyl isocyanate
m-isopropenyldimethylbenzyl isocyanate; TMI
$C_{13}H_{15}N_1O_1$. M: 201.27. Colourless, fluid liquid.
Production:
• *m*-diisopropenylbenzene + isocyanic acid (hydrochlorination/dehydrochlorination; coproduced with tetramethyl-*m*-xylene diisocyanate)

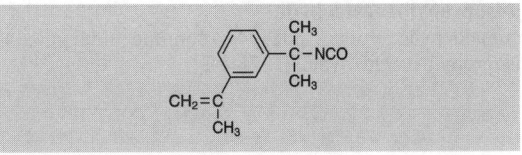

Uses: crosslinked acrylic/vinyl/styrene resin comonomer

isopropyl acetate
[108-21-4]

$$CH_3COCH(CH_3)_2$$

$C_5H_{10}O_2$. M: 102.13. Colourless liquid with a strong, fruity odour. BP: 88°C. FP: -73°C. d: 0.87 kg/l (20°C). Solubility in water: 29 g/l solution (20°C).
Production:
• isopropanol + acetic acid (esterification)
Uses: fragrance ingredient; solvent (cellulose derivatives, printing inks)

isopropyl acetoacetate
[542-08-5]

$$CH_3CCH_2COCH(CH_3)_2$$

$C_7H_{12}O_3$. M: 144.18. Liquid. BP: 185–187°C. MP: -27°C. d: 0.99 kg/l (20°C). Soluble in water. Miscible with most organic solvents.
Production:
• isopropanol + diketene (esterification)
Derivatives: nimodipine; propetamphos

isopropyl alcohol *See:* isopropanol

isopropylamine
2-aminopropane; monoisopropylamine; MIPA; [75-31-0]

$$(CH_3)_2CHNH_2$$

$C_3H_9N_1$. M: 59.11. Liquid. BP: 31–33°C. MP: -101°C. d: 0.69 kg/l (4°C). Miscible with water and oxygenated solvents. Also available commercially as a 70% solution in water.
Production:
• isopropanol + ammonia (amine formation; coproduced with diisopropylamine)
Derivatives:
acebutolol; ametryn; atenolol; atrazine; aziprotryne; benfuracarb; bentazone; desmetryn; *N,N′*-diisopropyl-*p*-phenylenediamine; fenamiphos; imazapyr-isopropylammonium; iprodione; isofenphos; isoprenaline; methoprotryne; metoprolol; orciprenaline; oxprenolol; procarbazine; proglinazine-ethyl; propazine; propranolol; proquazone; prothoate; Solvent Blue 36; sotalol; tebutam; toliprolol

4-isopropylaniline *See:* cumidine

p-isopropylbenzaldehyde

cumaldehyde; cumic aldehyde; cuminic aldehyde; 4-isopropylbenzaldehyde; [122-03-2]

$$(CH_3)_2CH - \langle\rangle - CHO$$

$C_{10}H_{12}O_1$. M: 148.21. Colourless liquid with a strong odour. BP: 235°C. d: 0.98 kg/l (20°C). Insoluble in water. Soluble in oxygenated solvents.
Production:
• *p*-cymene (side-chain oxidation)
• cumene + carbon monoxide (Gattermann-Koch reaction)
Derivatives:
cyclamen aldehyde; *p*-isopropylbenzyl alcohol
Uses: fragrance ingredient

isopropylbenzene *See:* cumene

isopropyl benzoin ether *See:* benzoin isopropyl ether

p-isopropylbenzyl alcohol

cumic alcohol; cuminyl alcohol; 4-isopropylbenzyl alcohol; [536-60-7]

$$(CH_3)_2CH - \langle\rangle - CH_2OH$$

$C_{10}H_{14}O_1$. M: 150.22. Liquid with a strong caraway-like odour. BP: 249°C. d: 0.98 kg/l (18°C). Soluble in oxygenated solvents. Slightly soluble in water.
Production:
• *p*-isopropylbenzaldehyde (carbonyl reduction)
Uses: flavouring ingredient

isopropyl bromide

2-bromopropane; [75-26-3]

$$(CH_3)_2CHBr$$

$C_3H_7Br_1$. M: 122.99. Colourless liquid. BP: 59°C. MP: -91°C. d: 1.31 kg/l (20°C). Slightly soluble in water. Soluble in oxygenated solvents.
Production:
• isopropanol + hydrobromic acid (alcohol bromination)
Derivatives:
flucythrinate; ipratropium bromide; verapamil

N-isopropyl-*N'*-*t*-butylthiourea

N-*t*-butyl-*N'*-isopropylthiourea; [52599-24-3]

$$\underset{\displaystyle (CH_3)_2CHNHCNHC(CH_3)_3}{\overset{\displaystyle S}{\overset{\displaystyle \|}{}}}$$

$C_8H_{18}N_2S_1$. M: 174.30.
Production:
• *t*-butylamine + ammonium thiocyanate + isopropanol (thiocyanate addition/amine formation)
Derivatives:
buprofezin

isopropyl chloroformate

isopropyl chlorocarbonate; [108-23-6]

$$\underset{\displaystyle (CH_3)_2CHOCCl}{\overset{\displaystyle O}{\overset{\displaystyle \|}{}}}$$

$C_4H_7Cl_1O_2$. M: 122.55. Colourless liquid. BP: 34°C (6.7 kPa). MP: <-70°C. Hydrolysed by water.
Production:
• isopropanol + phosgene (phosgenation)
Derivatives: *t*-butyl peroxyisopropylcarbonate; chlorpropham; diisopropyl peroxydicarbonate; methylol carbamate resins; propham

isopropyl cyanide *See:* isobutyronitrile

isopropyl ether *See:* diisopropyl ether

4,4'-isopropylidenediphenol

See: bisphenol A

4,4'-isopropylidenediphenyl dimethacrylate

See: bisphenol A dimethacrylate

isopropyl lanolate

IPL; [63393-93-1]
Pale yellow liquid or paste.
Production:
• isopropanol + lanolin acid (esterification)
Uses:
emollient (skin, hair care products)

isopropyl mercaptan

propane-2-thiol; [75-33-2]

$$(CH_3)_2CHSH$$

$C_3H_8S_1$. M: 76.15. Liquid with unpleasant odour. BR: 52–58°C. d: 0.82 kg/l (15°C).
Production:
• propylene + hydrogen sulphide (addition)
Uses: gas odorant

2-isopropyl-5-methylphenol *See:* thymol

5-isopropyl-2-methylphenol *See:* carvacrol

isopropyl myristate

IPM; [110-27-0]

$$\underset{\displaystyle CH_3(CH_2)_{12}COCH(CH_3)_2}{\overset{\displaystyle O}{\overset{\displaystyle \|}{}}}$$

$C_{17}H_{34}O_2$. M: 270.46. Liquid. Cloud point: -3–+5°C. d: 0.85 kg/l (20°C). Almost insoluble in water. Soluble in oils and oxygenated solvents.
Production:
• isopropanol + myristic acid (esterification)
Uses: emollient/lubricant (hand cleaners, toilet soaps, skin creams)

isopropyl oleate
[112-11-8]

$$CH_3(CH_2)_7CH=CH(CH_2)_7COCH(CH_3)_2$$

$C_{21}H_{40}O_2$. M: 324.55. Colourless, odourless liquid. Pour point: -21°C. d: 0.87 kg/l (20°C). Flash point: 185°C (COC). Insoluble in water. Miscible with paraffin oil.
Production:
• isopropanol + oleic acid (esterification)
Uses:
emulsifier/bodying agent/emollient (toiletries, cosmetics); lubricity additive (lubricants); plasticiser (rubber)

isopropyl palmitate
IPP; [142-91-6]

$$CH_3(CH_2)_{14}COCH(CH_3)_2$$

$C_{19}H_{38}O_2$. M: 298.51. Liquid. Cloud point: 12–14°C. Insoluble in water. Soluble in oils and oxygenated solvents.
Production:
• isopropanol + palmitic acid (esterification)
Uses:
emollient/lubricant (skin cream); metal stamping oils

isopropylphenol

$$\text{OH} \quad \text{CH(CH}_3)_2$$

$C_9H_{12}O_1$. M: 136.20. Mixed isomer product.
Production:
• phenol + propylene (Friedel-Crafts alkylation)
Derivatives: isopropylphenyl diphenyl phosphate; tris-(isopropylphenyl) phosphate

o-isopropylphenol
o-cumenol; 2-hydroxycumene; 2-isopropylphenol; OIP; [88-69-7]

$$\text{OH} \quad \text{CH(CH}_3)_2$$

$C_9H_{12}O_1$. M: 136.20. Amber liquid or solid. MP: 16°C. BP: 215°C. d: 0.99 kg/l (20°C). Slightly soluble in water. Soluble in oxygenated solvents.
Production:
• phenol + propylene (orthoalkylation)
Derivatives: fenoxazoline; isoprocarb

p-isopropylphenol
4-hydroxycumene; 4-isopropylphenol
$C_9H_{12}O_1$. M: 136.20. Solid. MP: 61–63°C. BP: 225°C.

Slightly soluble in water. Soluble in oxygenated solvents.

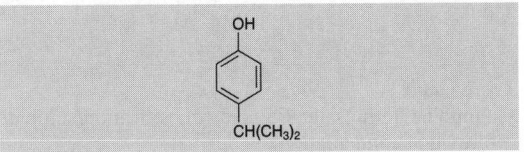

Production:
• cumenesulphonic acid (alkali fusion)
Derivatives: isopropalin

isopropylphenyl diphenyl phosphate
diphenyl isopropylphenyl phosphate; Reofos (FMC)

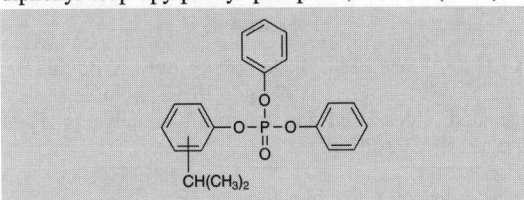

$C_{21}H_{21}O_4P_1$. M: 368.37.
Production:
• isopropylphenol + phenol + phosphorus oxychloride (dehydrochlorination)
Uses:
fire-resistant engineering plastic plasticiser

N-isopropyl-*N'*-phenyl-*p*-phenylenediamine
p-isopropylaminodiphenylamine; IPPD; Santoflex IP (Monsanto); [101-72-4]

$$(CH_3)_2CHNH-\!\!\!\bigcirc\!\!\!-NH-\!\!\!\bigcirc$$

$C_{15}H_{18}N_2$. M: 226.31. Black flakes. MP: 75°C. Insoluble in water. Soluble in aromatic solvents.
Production:
• acetone + *p*-aminodiphenylamine (reductive amination)
Uses: antioxidant/antiozonant (rubber)

isopropyl stearate
[112-10-7]

$$CH_3(CH_2)_{16}COCH(CH_3)_2$$

$C_{21}H_{42}O_2$. M: 326.57. Pale yellow liquid. MP: 16–20°C.
Production:
• isopropanol + stearic acid (esterification)
Uses:
emollient/lubricant (cosmetics, toiletries); textile processing lubricant

2-isopropylthioxanthone
isopropyl thioxanthone; Quantacure ITX (Shell)
$C_{16}H_{14}O_1S_1$. M: 254.35.

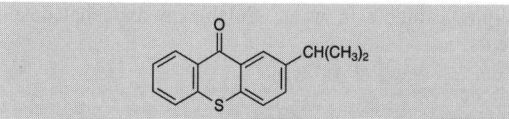

Production:
• cumidine + thiosalicylic acid (diazotisation/sulphide formation/condensation)
Uses:
photoinitiator (radiation-cured lacquers, inks)

isopropyl titanate
tetraisopropyl orthotitanate; titanium isopropylate; titanium tetraisopropoxide; IPT; TPT

$$\left[(CH_3)_2CHO\right]_4Ti$$

$C_{12}H_{28}O_4Ti_1$. M: 284.25. Almost colourless liquid. BP: 232°C. MP: 17°C. d: 0.97 kg/l (20°C). Soluble in oxygenated, chlorinated and hydrocarbon solvents. Flash point: 59°C (APCC).
Production:
• isopropanol + titanium tetrachloride (dehydrochlorination)
Derivatives:
2-ethylhexyl titanate; triethanolamine titanate
Uses:
transesterification catalyst

isoproterenol *See:* isoprenaline

isoprothiolane
diisopropyl 1,3-dithiolan-2-ylidenemalonate; [50512-35-1]

$C_{12}H_{18}O_4S_2$. M: 290.40.
Production:
• 1,2-ethanedithiol + phosgene + diisopropyl malonate (phosgenation/carbonyl condensation)
Uses: fungicide

isoproturon
3-(4-isopropylphenyl)-1,1-dimethylurea; [34123-59-6]

$C_{12}H_{18}N_2O_1$. M: 206.28.
Production:
• cumidine + dimethylcarbamoyl chloride (dehydrochlorination)
Uses: herbicide

isopulegol
8-*p*-menthen-3-ol; [89-79-2]
$C_{10}H_{18}O_1$. M: 154.25. Colourless liquid with a mint-like

odour. BP: 74°C (1.0 kPa). d: 0.91 kg/l (25°C). Mixed isomer product with (−)-isopulegol as the chief component.

Production:
• (+)-citronellal (acid-catalysed cyclisation)
Uses: perfume ingredient

isoquinoline
[119-65-3]

$C_9H_7N_1$. M: 129.17. Colourless liquid or solid with a pungent odour. MP: 26–28°C. BP: 241–243°C. Insoluble in water. Miscible with oxygenated solvents.
Production:
• methylnaphthalene fraction (acid extraction; coproduced with quinoline)
Derivatives: praziquantel

isosafrole
1,2-methylenedioxy-4-propenylbenzene; 3,4-methylenedioxy-1-propenylbenzene; [120-58-1]

$C_{10}H_{10}O_2$. M: 162.19. Colourless liquid with an anise-like odour. BP: 253°C. d: 1.12 kg/l (20°C). Insoluble in water. Miscible with oxygenated and aromatic solvents.
Production:
• safrole (base-catalysed rearrangement)
Derivatives: piperonal; propenylguethol
Uses: flavouring/fragrance ingredient

isosebacic acid

$C_{10}H_{18}O_4$. M: 202.25. Mixed product containing 2-ethylsuberic acid and 2,5-diethyladipic acid.
Production:
• butadiene (dimerisation/hydrogenation/hydroformylation; byproduct of sebacic acid production)
Derivatives: polymeric plasticisers

isosorbide
1,4:3,6-dianhydro-D-glucitol; [652-67-5]
$C_6H_{10}O_4$. M: 146.15. White, crystalline solid. MP: 61–64°C.

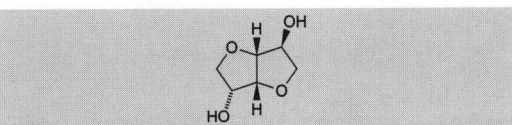

Production:
• sorbitol (dehydration)
Derivatives:
isosorbide dinitrate; isosorbide-5-mononitrate
Uses: diuretic drug

isosorbide dinitrate
ISDN; [87-33-2]

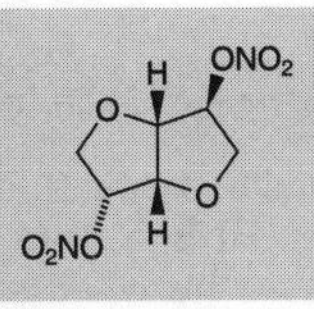

$C_6H_8N_2O_8$. M: 236.13.
Production:
• isosorbide (nitration)
Uses: antianginal drug

isosorbide-5-mononitrate
ISMN

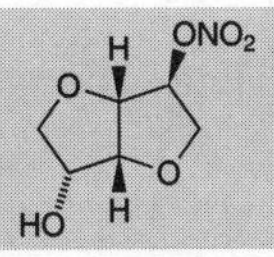

$C_6H_9N_1O_6$. M: 191.14.
Production:
• isosorbide (nitration)
Uses: antianginal drug

isostearamidopropyl betaine

$C_{17}H_{35}C(=O)NHCH_2CH_2CH_2N^+(CH_3)_2CH_2COO^-$

$C_{25}H_{50}N_2O_3$. M: 426.68. Available as a 30% solution in water.
Production:
• isostearamidopropyldimethylamine + sodium chloroacetate (quaternisation)
Uses: mild, high-foaming surfactant (shampoos, skin products)

isostearamidopropyldimethylamine

$C_{17}H_{35}C(=O)NHCH_2CH_2CH_2N(CH_3)_2$

$C_{23}H_{48}N_2O_1$. M: 368.64. Pale amber liquid.
Production:
• isostearic acid + 3-dimethylaminopropylamine (amide formation)
Derivatives:
isostearamidopropyl betaine; isostearamidopropyldimethylamine lactate
Uses: cationic emulsifier (cosmetics, toiletries)

isostearamidopropyldimethylamine lactate

$C_{17}H_{35}C(=O)NHCH_2CH_2CH_2NH(CH_3)_2^+ \quad CH_3CH(OH)COO^-$

$C_{26}H_{54}N_2O_4$. M: 458.73. Compatible with anionic surfactants.
Production:
• isostearamidopropyldimethylamine + DL-lactic acid (salt formation)
Uses: conditioning agent (hair products)

isostearic acid
[30399-84-9]; [2724-58-5]

$C_{17}H_{35}COOH$

$C_{18}H_{36}O_2$. M: 284.49. Yellow liquid. Cloud point: 2°C. d: 0.89 kg/l (25°C). Flash point: 175°C (COC). Mixture of branched C_{18} isomers. Insoluble in water.
Production:
• tall oil fatty acid/castor oil, dehydrated (dimerisation/hydrogenation; coproduced with dimer acid/trimer acid)
Derivatives:
fatty acid imidazoline polyamines; glycerol monoisostearate; isostearamidopropyldimethylamine; isostearyl alcohol; isostearyl imidazoline; isostearyl isostearate
Uses: deleafing inhibitor (aerosol metallic paints); soap/shampoo ingredient

isostearoamphopropionate

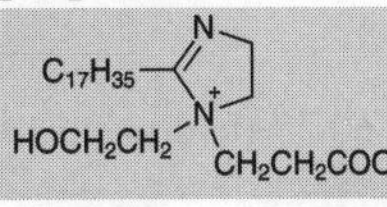

$C_{25}H_{48}N_2O_3$. M: 424.66. Amber liquid comprising a 35% solution in water.
Production:
• isostearyl imidazoline + methyl acrylate (Michael addition/ester hydrolysis)
Uses:
viscosifier (water-based lubricants)

isostearyl alcohol
[27458-93-1]; [41744-75-6]

$C_{18}H_{37}OH$

$C_{18}H_{38}O_1$. M: 270.50. Mixture of branched C_{18} isomers. Insoluble in water.
Production:
• isostearic acid (hydrogenation)
Derivatives:
isostearyl isostearate; isostearyl pivalate

isostearyl imidazoline
isostearyl hydroxyethylimidazoline (CTFA)

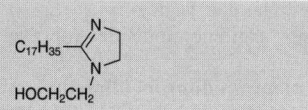

$C_{22}H_{44}N_2O_1$. M: 352.60.
Production:
• isostearic acid + aminoethylethanolamine
 (condensation)
Derivatives: isostearoamphopropionate
Uses: softening/antistatic agent

isostearyl isostearate
[41669-30-1]; [67166-49-8]

$$C_{17}H_{35}COC_{18}H_{37}$$

$C_{36}H_{72}O_2$. M: 536.98. Pale yellow liquid. Saponification value: 95–110 mg KOH/g.
Production:
• isostearyl alcohol + isostearic acid (esterification)
Uses: emollient (cosmetics, toiletries)

isostearyl pivalate
isostearyl neopentanoate

$$(CH_3)_3CCOC_{18}H_{37}$$

$C_{23}H_{46}O_2$. M: 354.62. Pale yellow liquid. Saponification value: 135–155 mg KOH/g.
Production:
• isostearyl alcohol + pivalic acid (esterification)
Uses: emollient (cosmetics, toiletries)

isothipendyl
[482-15-5]; [1225-60-1] (hydrochloride)

$$CH_2CHN(CH_3)_2$$
$$CH_3$$

$C_{16}H_{19}N_3S_1$. M: 285.41. Available commercially as the hydrochloride.
Production:
• 1-azaphenothiazine + dimethylisopropanolamine
 (amine formation)
Uses: antihistamine drug

isotridecanol *See:* tridecanol

isotridecanol ether phosphoric acid
trideceth phosphate (CTFA)
Commercial products contain 2–10 moles EO. Pale yellow or colourless liquid.

$$\left[C_{12}H_{25}CH_2O(CH_2CH_2O)_n\right]_x P(OH)_{3-x}$$

n = 2–10, x = 1–2.
Production:
• isotridecanol ethoxylates + phosphorus pentoxide
 (esterification)
Uses:
emulsifier/lubricant/antistatic additive (textile spin finishes); extreme-pressure/emulsifier/corrosion inhibitor additives (metalworking fluids); plastics antistatic agent

isotridecanol ethoxylates
trideceth (CTFA)

$$C_{12}H_{25}CH_2O(CH_2CH_2O)_nH$$

n = 3–20. Commercial products contain 3–20 moles EO. Liquid or pastes. HLB: 8.0–16.3 (3–20 moles EO).
Production:
• tridecanol + ethylene oxide (epoxidation)
Derivatives:
isotridecanol ether phosphoric acid
Uses: emulsifier (olein, oils, solvents, waxes); foam boosters/builders (detergents); low-temperature scouring/wetting agent (household/industrial cleaners); wetting agent (metal pickling baths)

isotridecyl methacrylate

$$CH_2=CCOCH_2C_{12}H_{25}$$
$$CH_3$$

$C_{17}H_{32}O_2$. M: 268.45.
Production:
• methyl methacrylate + tridecanol (transesterification)
Derivatives:
polymethacrylates, oil-soluble

isotridecyl-3-oxypropylamine
3-aminopropyl isotridecyl ether; 3-aminopropyl tridecyl ether; tridecyl 3-aminopropyl ether; tridecyl-3-oxypropylamine

$$C_{12}H_{25}CH_2OCH_2CH_2CH_2NH_2$$

$C_{16}H_{35}N_1O_1$. M: 257.47.
Production:
• tridecanol + acrylonitrile (addition/nitrile reduction)
Derivatives:
bis(2-hydroxyethyl)isotridecyl-3-oxypropylamine; isotridecyl oxypropyl-1,3-propylenediamine
Uses: corrosion inhibitor; bitumen emulsifier; mineral flotation agent

isotridecyl oxypropyl-1,3-propylenediamine

$$C_{12}H_{25}CH_2OCH_2CH_2CH_2NHCH_2CH_2CH_2NH_2$$

$C_{19}H_{42}N_2O_1$. M: 314.56. Light amber liquid.

Production:
- isotridecyl-3-oxypropylamine + acrylonitrile (addition/nitrile reduction)

Uses: corrosion inhibitor (oilfield chemicals); flotation collector (sulphide ores)

isotridecyl stearate
tridecyl stearate; TDS; [31556-45-3]

$$CH_3(CH_2)_{16}COCH_2C_{12}H_{25}$$

$C_{31}H_{62}O_2$. M: 466.84. Colourless liquid.
Production:
- tridecanol + stearic acid (esterification)

Uses: lubricant (textile spin finishes); plastics processing lubricant

isouron
3-(5-*t*-butylisoxazol-3-yl)-1,1-dimethylurea; [55861-78-4]

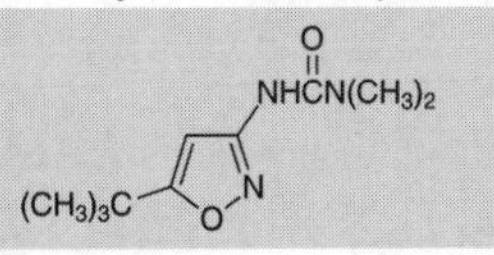

$C_{10}H_{17}N_3O_2$. M: 211.27.
Production:
- 3-amino-5-*t*-butylisoxazole + dimethylcarbamoyl chloride (dehydrochlorination)

Uses: herbicide

isovaleraldehyde
isovaleral; 3-methylbutyraldehyde; [590-86-3]

$$(CH_3)_2CHCH_2CHO$$

$C_5H_{10}O_1$. M: 86.13. Colourless liquid with a strong, apple-like odour. BP: 92°C. MP: -51°C. d: 0.79 kg/l (20°C). Slightly soluble in water. Miscible with oxygenated solvents.
Production:
- isoamyl alcohol (alcohol oxidation)

Derivatives: butizide
Uses: fragrance/flavouring ingredient

isovaleric acid
isopentanoic acid; 3-methylbutanoic acid; 3-methylbutyric acid; [503-74-2]

$$(CH_3)_2CHCH_2COOH$$

$C_5H_{10}O_2$. M: 102.13. Colourless liquid with a disagreeable odour. BP: 176–177°C. MP: -30°C. d: 0.93 kg/l (20°C). Slightly soluble in water. Soluble in oxygenated and chlorinated solvents.
Production:
- isoamyl alcohol (alcohol oxidation)

Derivatives:
benzyl isovalerate; citronellyl isovalerate; geranyl isovalerate; isoamyl isovalerate; phenethyl isovalerate

isoxaben
N-[3-(1-ethyl-1-methylpropyl)isoxazol-5-yl]-2,6-dimethoxybenzamide; [82558-50-7]

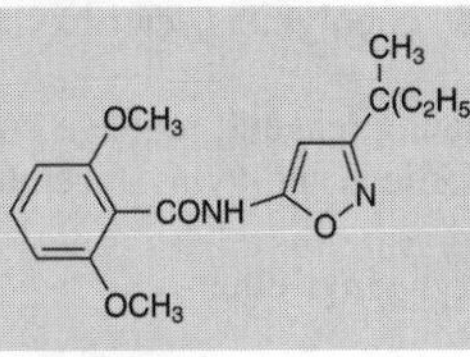

$C_{18}H_{24}N_2O_4$. M: 332.40.
Production:
- 2-ethyl-2-methylbutanoic acid + acetonitrile + hydroxylamine sulphate + 2,6-dimethoxybenzoic acid (condensation/oxime formation/cyclisation/amide formation)

Uses: herbicide

isoxathion
O,O-diethyl *O*-5-phenylisoxazol-3-yl phosphorothioate; [18854-01-8]

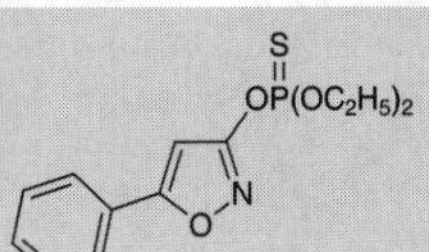

$C_{13}H_{16}N_1O_4P_1S_1$. M: 313.31.
Production:
- ethyl benzoylacetate + hydroxylamine sulphate + *O,O*-diethyl phosphorochlorothioate (amide formation/chlorination/cyclisation/dehydrochlorination)

Uses: insecticide

isoxsuprine
[395-28-8]

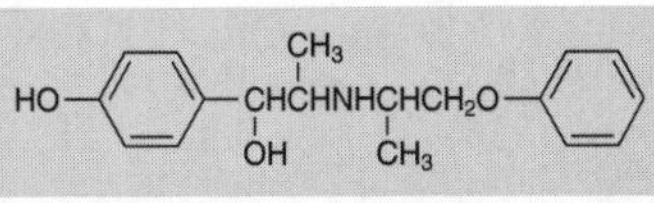

$C_{18}H_{23}N_1O_3$. M: 301.39. Available commercially as the hydrochloride.
Production:
- phenol + propylene oxide + ammonia + *p*-hydroxypropiophenone (epoxidation/ammoniation/alpha bromination/amine formation/hydrolysis/carbonyl reduction)

Uses: vasodilator drug

itaconic acid
methylene succinic acid; [97-65-4]

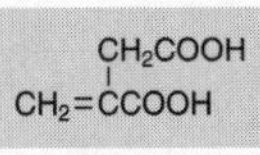

$$CH_2COOH$$
$$CH_2=CCOOH$$

$C_5H_6O_4$. M: 130.10. White, hygroscopic solid with a characteristic odour. MP: 166–167°C. d: 1.63 kg/l. Soluble in water and alcohol.

Production:
• molasses + *Aspergillus terreus* mould (fermentation)
Derivatives:
styrene-butadiene copolymers, carboxylated
Uses:
aluminium anodising reagent; reactive comonomer (acrylic, styrene-butadiene, polyvinyl acetate, nitrile latex)

IVE *See:* isobutyl vinyl ether

ivermectin
avermectin; [70288-86-7]

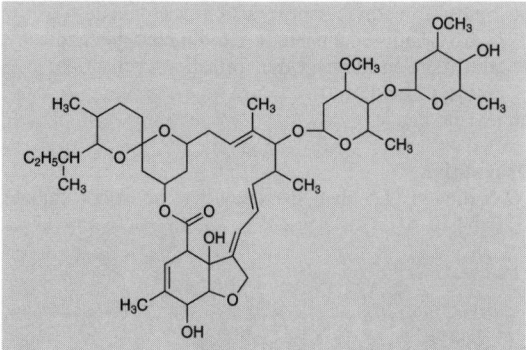

$C_{48}H_{74}O_{14}$. M: 815.05. Mixed product containing 80% 22,23-dihydroavermectin B_{1a}.
Production:
• microbial fermentation medium + *Streptomyces avermitilis* bacteria (fermentation/extraction)
Uses: anthelmintic drug

Ixef *See:* poly(*m*-xylyleneadipamide)

Ixol *See:* dibromobutanediol-epichlorohydrin adduct

J acid
2-amino-5-hydroxynaphthalene-7-sulphonic acid;
6-amino-1-hydroxynaphthalene-3-sulphonic acid;
7-amino-4-hydroxynaphthalene-2-sulphonic acid;
2-amino-5-naphthol-7-sulphonic acid; 7-amino-4-naphthol-2-sulphonic acid; [87-02-5]

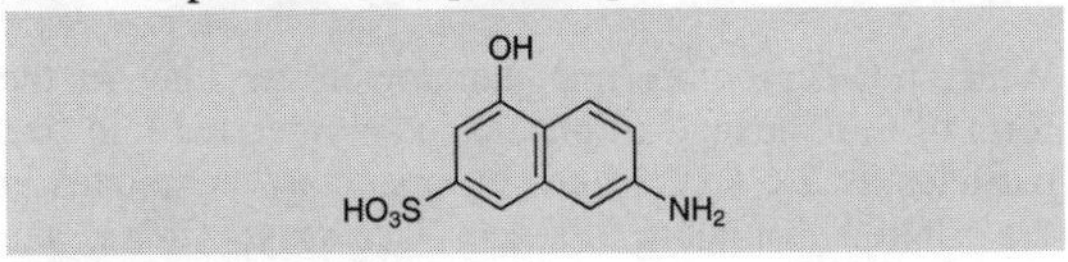

$C_{10}H_9N_1O_4S_1$. M: 239.25.
Production:
• 2-naphthylamine-1,5,7-trisulphonic acid (hydrolysis/alkali fusion)
Derivatives: Acid Red 137; *N-m*-aminobenzoyl-J acid; Direct Black 91; Direct Blue 71; Direct Blue 93; Direct Red 16; Direct Red 81; J acid urea; *N*-phenyl-J acid; Reactive Orange 1; Reactive Orange 13; Reactive Orange 4

J acid urea
carbonyl-J-acid; 5,5′-dihydroxy-2,2′-dinaphthylurea-7,7′-disulphonic acid

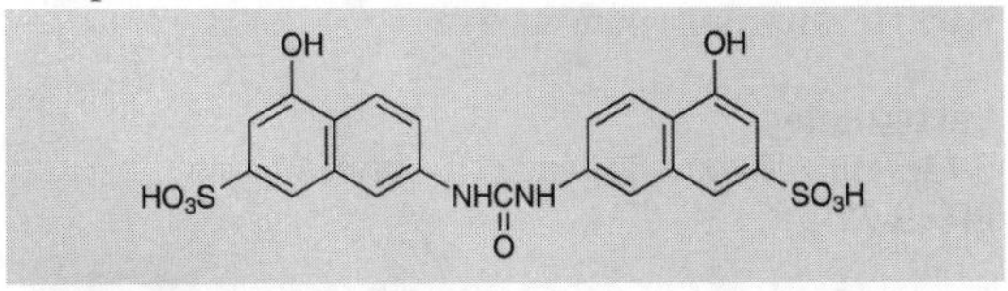

$C_{21}H_{16}N_2O_9S_2$. M: 504.49.
Production:
• J acid + phosgene (phosgenation)
Derivatives: Direct Orange 26; Direct Orange 29; Direct Orange 102; Direct Red 4; Direct Red 23; Direct Red 24; Direct Red 26; Direct Red 72; Direct Red 73; Direct Red 80; Direct Red 83

japan wax
[8001-39-6]
Yellow solid. MP: 52–55°C. Acid value: 20 mg KOH/g. Saponification value: 225 mg KOH/g. Insoluble in water and cold alcohol. The wax is obtained from the fruit of the *Rhus succedanea* trees. Its main constituent is tripalmitin and other triglycerides.
Uses: candles; polish ingredient; plastics processing lubricant; binder (Chinese lacquerware coatings)

jasmine aldehyde *See:* α-amylcinnamaldehyde

jojoba oil
Liquid. Cloud point: 4–9°C. BP: 400°C. d: 0.86 kg/l (25°C). The oil is extracted from the seeds of the jojoba shrub (*Simmondsia chinensis*) which is grown in USA and Central America. It is composed mainly of esters formed from C_{20}–C_{22} alcohols and carboxylic acids.
Uses: lubricant (shampoos, cosmetics)

juniperberry oil
Colourless to greenish-yellow liquid with a characteristic odour. Produced by steam distillation of juniper (*Juniper communis*) berries. d: 0.87 kg/l (25°C). Soluble in ethanol. The main producing countries are Czechoslovakia, Hungary, Yugoslavia and Italy.
Uses: flavouring ingredient (gin)

K

K acid

4-amino-5-hydroxynaphthalene-1,7-disulphonic acid;
5-amino-4-hydroxynaphthalene-2,8-disulphonic acid;
8-amino-1-naphthol-3,5-disulphonic acid; [130-23-4]

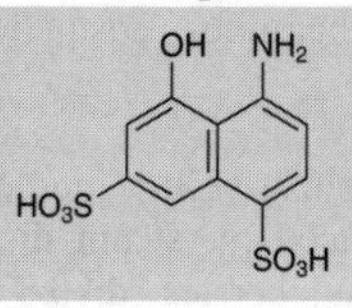

$C_{10}H_9N_1O_7S_2$. M: 319.31.
Production:
• 8-naphthylamine-1,3,5-trisulphonic acid (alkali fusion)
Derivatives:
Acid Red 107; Acid Red 108; Food Black 1

kadethrin

[58769-20-3]

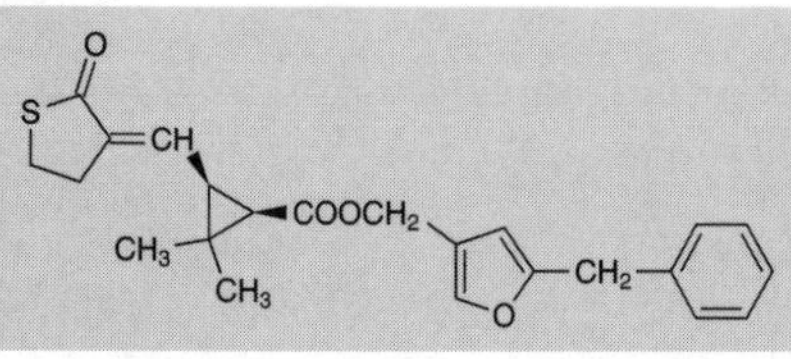

$C_{23}H_{24}O_4S_1$. M: 396.50. Yellow-brown solid. MP 31°C.
Soluble in acetone, aromatic and chlorinated solvents.
Production:
• 5-benzyl-3-furylmethyl alcohol + kadethrinic acid (esterification)
Uses: insecticide

kadethrinic acid

3-(2-oxothiolan-3-ylidenemethyl)-2,2-dimethylcyclo-propanecarboxylic acid

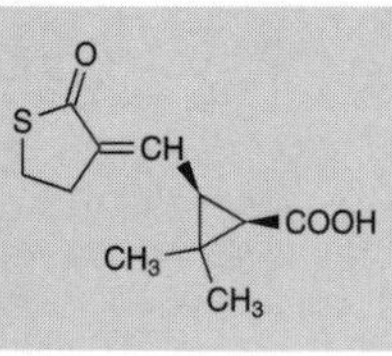

$C_{11}H_{14}O_3S_1$. M: 226.29. The product has a (*1R*)-*cis* configuration.
Production:
• 4-chlorobutyryl chloride + sodium hydrosulphide + (*1R*)-*cis*-caronaldehyde (mercaptan formation/condensation/condensation/dehydration)
Derivatives: kadethrin

Kalrez *See:* tetrafluoroethylene-perfluoro(methyl vinyl ether) copolymers

KA oil *See:* cyclohexanol-cyclohexanone, mixed

kaolin

china clay; sodium aluminosilicate; Pigment White 19 (CI); 77004 (CI); [1332-58-7]

Al_2O_3/SiO_2

White powder comprising aluminosilicate clay in the form of thin, hexagonal platelets agglomerated into fine particles. d: 2.6 kg/l. Mined by open cast techniques in the United Kingdom, France, Germany, China, the USA and elsewhere. Calcined kaolin is used as an extender in paint. The surface is treated with silanes when intended for use as a filler.
Derivatives:
mullite; Pigment Blue 29; zeolite A
Uses:
colour laking base; filler/extender/pigment (paint, thermosetting resins, paper sizing, coatings); pigment (lacquers, printing inks); porcelain/pottery/ceramics/refractories ingredient

Kapton *See:* polyimide resins

karaya gum *See:* gum karaya

karbutilate

3-(3,3-dimethylureido)phenyl *t*-butylcarbamate;
[4849-32-5]

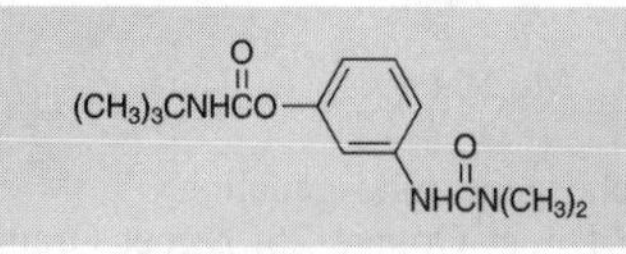

$C_{14}H_{21}N_3O_3$. M: 279.34.
Production:
• *m*-aminophenol + dimethylcarbamoyl chloride + phosgene + *t*-butylamine (dehydrochlorination/phosgenation/dehydrochlorination)
Uses: herbicide

kasugamycin

[6980-18-3]

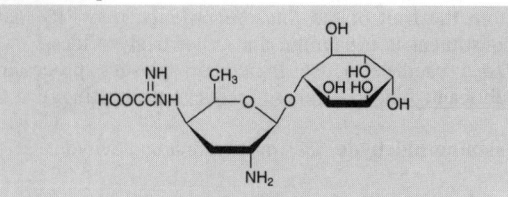

$C_{14}H_{25}N_3O_9$. M: 379.36. Available commercially as the free base or monohydrochloride salt.

Production:
- microbial fermentation medium + *Streptomyces kasugaensis* bacteria (fermentation/extraction)

Uses: fungicide

KAX *See:* potassium amyl xanthate

KDCC *See:* potassium dichloroisocyanurate

kerosene
kerosine; paraffin; paraffin oil; [8002-74-2]
Colourless liquid. BP: 150–235°C corresponding to a C_9–C_{14} cut. The product is usually desulphurised by hydrotreatment before blending and sale.
Production:
- crude oil (atmospheric distillation; coproduced with naphtha, light/naphtha, heavy/gas oil, light/gas oil, heavy/long residue/refinery gas)
- gas oil, vacuum (hydrocracking; coproduced with naphtha, light/naphtha, heavy/gas oil, light/gas oil, heavy/refinery gas)
- synthesis gas (Shell MDS process; coproduced with naphtha, heavy/gas oil, light/wax, Fischer-Tropsch/ refinery gas)

Derivatives:
kerosene, deodorised; naphthenic acid; *n*-paraffins (C_{10}-C_{13}); *n*-paraffins (C_{11}-C_{14}); *n*-paraffins (C_{14}-C_{18})
Uses: cooking fuel; jet fuel blending component; mineral flotation agent; plastics processing lubricant; solvent (cutback bitumens, printing inks)

kerosene, deodorised
[8008-20-6]
Production:
- kerosene (hydrogenation)

Uses:
domestic lamp oil; metal degreasing/cleaning solvents; solvent (paints, printing inks, floor polishes, coatings)

ketene
[463-51-4]

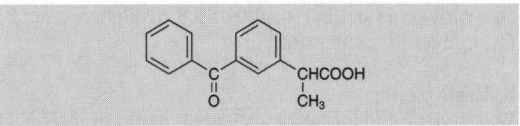

$C_2H_2O_1$. M: 42.04. Gas. MP: -56°C. Highly toxic. Used *in situ*. Not a commercially traded product.
Production:
- acetic acid (dehydration)

Derivatives: acetic anhydride; diketene; isopropenyl acetate; sorbic acid

4-ketobenztriazine *See:* benzazimide

ketone resin *See:* cyclohexanone resin

ketoprofen
[22071-15-4]
$C_{16}H_{14}O_3$. M: 254.29.

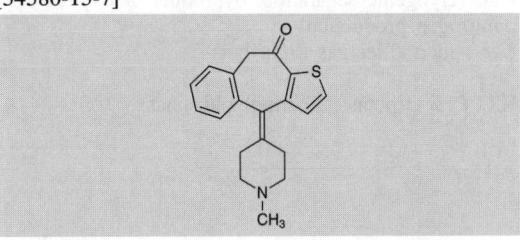

Production:
- 3-methylbenzophenone + sodium cyanide + diethyl carbonate + methyl iodide (side-chain bromination/ cyanidation/condensation/dehydroiodination/nitrile hydrolysis/decarboxylation)

Uses: antiinflammatory drug

ketotifen
[34580-13-7]

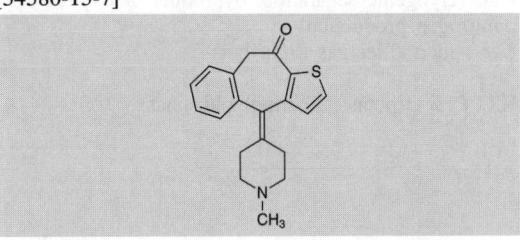

$C_{19}H_{19}N_1O_1S_1$. M: 309.43. Available commercially as the fumarate salt.
Production:
- benzothienocycloheptanone + isonipecotic acid (alpha bromination/dehydrobromination/ condensation/decarboxylation/isomer separation)

Uses: antiasthmatic drug

Kevlar *See:* poly(*p*-phenyleneterephthalamide)

KEX *See:* potassium ethyl xanthate

kieselguhr *See:* diatomaceous earth

KIPX *See:* potassium isopropyl xanthate

KMC *See:* diisopropylnaphthalene

KMS *See:* potassium metabisulphite

Koch acid
1-aminonaphthalene-3,6,8-trisulphonic acid; 8-amino-naphthalene-1,3,6-trisulphonic acid; 1-naphthylamine-3,6,8-trisulphonic acid; T acid; [117-42-0]

$C_{10}H_9N_1O_9S_3$. M: 383.37. White, crystalline solid. Slightly soluble in water.
Production:
- naphthalene-1,3,6-trisulphonic acid (nitration/nitro reduction)

Derivatives: H acid; 1-naphthol-3,8-disulphonic acid
Uses: dyestuffs intermediate

K-Resin
See: styrene-butadiene block copolymers, branched

krypton
[7439-90-9]

Kr

Kr$_1$. M: 83.80. Colourless, odourless gas. BP: -153°C.
d: 3.75 g/l (gas, 0°C). Slightly soluble in water.
Production:
• air (cryogenic separation; byproduct of oxygen-
  /nitrogen production)
Uses: inert filler gas (light bulbs)

KTPP *See:* potassium tripolyphosphate

L

LAB *See:* dodecylbenzene, linear

labetalol
[36894-69-6]

$C_{19}H_{24}N_2O_3$. M: 328.41. Available commercially as the hydrochloride.
Production:
• salicylamide + bromoacetyl bromide + benzylamine + benzylacetone (Friedel-Crafts acylation/carbonyl reduction/amine formation/carbonyl reduction)
Uses: antihypertensive drug

LABS *See:* sodium alkylbenzenesulphonate, linear; dodecylbenzenesulphonic acid, linear

L Acid *See:* 5-hydroxynaphthalene-1-sulphonic acid

D-lactic acid
(*R*)-lactic acid; [10326-41-7]

$C_3H_6O_3$. M: 90.08. White, crystalline powder. MP: 53°C. Soluble in water and alcohol. Insoluble in chlorinated and hydrocarbon solvents. This product is the 'unnatural' (*R*)-(−)-enantiomer.
Production:
• microbial fermentation medium + *Lactobacillus leichmannii* bacteria (fermentation)
Derivatives:
carbetamide; (*S*)-α-chloropropionic acid

DL-lactic acid
α-hydroxypropionic acid; 2-hydroxypropionic acid; E270 (EC); [50-21-5]

$C_3H_6O_3$. M: 90.08. White crystals. MP: 17°C. Soluble in water and alcohol.
Production:
• acetaldehyde + hydrogen cyanide (cyanohydrin formation/nitrile hydrolysis)
• glucose syrup/molasses + *Lactobacillus debrueckii* bacteria/*Lactobacillus leichmannii* bacteria (fermentation)

• whey + *Lactobacillus bulgaricus* bacteria (fermentation)
Derivatives: n-butyl lactate; calcium lactate; calcium stearoyl-2-lactylate; ethyl lactate; fatty acid monoglyceride lactate; isostearamidopropyldimethylamine lactate; lauryl lactate; myristyl lactate; pyruvic acid; sodium lactate; sodium stearoyl-2-lactylate; stearamidopropyldimethylamine lactate
Uses: electroplating bath additive; acidulant/flavouring ingredient (beer, soft drinks, bread, sauces, preserves); mordant; textile/leather auxiliary

L-lactic acid
[79-33-4]

$C_3H_6O_3$. M: 90.08. White, crystalline powder. MP: 53°C. Soluble in water and alcohol. Insoluble in chlorinated and hydrocarbon solvents. This product is the 'natural' (*S*)-(+)-enantiomer.
Production:
• microbial fermentation medium + *Lactobacillus debrueckii* bacteria/*Lactobacillus leichmannii* bacteria (fermentation)
Derivatives: lactophenetide

lactophenetide
p-lactophenetidide; [539-08-2]

$C_{11}H_{15}N_1O_3$. M: 209.25.
Production:
• *p*-phenetidine + L-lactic acid (amide formation)
Uses: analgesic/antirheumatic drug

lactose
milk sugar; [63-42-3]

$C_{12}H_{22}O_{11}$. M: 342.30. The commercial product is the monohydrate. White, odourless, crystalline powder. Loses water of crystallisation at 120°C. MP: 203°C with decomposition. Solubility in water: 200 g/l water (20°C).

Production:
• whey (acid-catalysed hydrolysis)
Derivatives: mucic acid
Uses: food/animal feed ingredient; microbial fermentation nutrient

LAH *See:* lithium aluminium hydride

lanolin
[8020-84-6]; [8006-54-0]
Pale yellow paste with slight odour containing 25–30% water. Anhydrous lanolin MP: 40°C. 'Liquid lanolin' is a solvent extracted form of lanolin used in cosmetics and pharmaceuticals. Lanolin is a mixture of esters based on steroid, triterpenoid and fatty alcohols, coupled with various fatty acids.
Production:
• wool grease (extraction/bleaching)
Derivatives:
lanolin, acetylated; lanolin, hydrogenated; lanolin acid; lanolin alcohol
Uses: corrosion inhibitor (lubricants); ointment base (pharmaceuticals, cosmetics); plasticiser (rubber); shampoo ingredient; tack reduction additive (printing inks)

lanolin, acetylated
[61788-48-5]
Yellow, soft solid. Anhydrous, highly lipophilic, mixed product. Saponification value: 95–120 mg KOH/g.
Production:
• lanolin + acetic anhydride (acetylation)
Uses: emollient (baby, suntan, cosmetic oils); superfatting agent (soaps, creams)

lanolin, hydrogenated
[8031-44-5]
Soft paste.
Production:
• lanolin (hydrogenation)
Uses: emollient (cosmetics, toiletries)

lanolin acid
[68424-43-1]
Pale yellow to brown, waxy solid. Available in crude or molecularly-distilled grades.
Production:
• lanolin (ester hydrolysis; coproduced with lanolin alcohol)
Derivatives:
isopropyl lanolate
Uses: corrosion inhibition/protective coatings; cosolvent/emollient (cosmetics, soap-based aerosols); wire drawing/metalforming oils

lanolin alcohol
wool alcohol; [8027-33-6]
Hard, yellow wax. The major constituents are cholesterol, lanosterol, dehydrolanosterol and various aliphatic alcohols. Available as standard, distilled or solvent-extracted grades.
Production:
• lanolin (ester hydrolysis; coproduced with lanolin acid)
Derivatives: cholesterol; lanolin alcohol, acetylated; lanolin ethoxylates; lanolin propoxylates; lanosterol
Uses: emulsifier (cosmetics)

lanolin alcohol, acetylated
[61788-49-6]
Pale yellow liquid. Saponification value: 180–200 mg KOH/g.
Production:
• lanolin alcohol + acetic anhydride (acetylation)
Uses: emollient/spreading agent (skin cleansers, soaps, baby products, shampoos)

lanolin ethoxylates
lanolin alcohol ethoxylates
Yellow to amber solid but usually sold as a 50–75% solution in water. Commercial grades contain 5 to 75 moles of ethylene oxide.
Production:
• lanolin alcohol + ethylene oxide (epoxidation)
Uses:
emollient (shampoos, soap, toiletries, pharmaceuticals)

lanolin propoxylates
polypropylene glycol monolanolin ether; PPG lanolin ether

$$R-O(CH_2\overset{\overset{\displaystyle CH_3}{|}}{C}HO)_nH$$

R = lanolin-, n = 2–20.
Production:
• lanolin alcohol + propylene oxide (epoxidation)
Uses: emollient/spreading agent (cosmetics)

lanosterol
[79-63-0]

$C_{30}H_{50}O_1$. M: 426.73. White, crystalline solid. MP: 138–140°C. Insoluble in water. Soluble in oxygenated and chlorinated solvents.
Production:
• lanolin alcohol (separation; coproduced with cholesterol)
Uses: emulsifier (cosmetics)

lanthanum oxide
lanthanum sesquioxide; lanthanum trioxide; [1312-81-8]

$$La_2O_3$$

La_2O_3. M: 325.82. White, amorphous, high-melting powder. d: 6.51 kg/l. Insoluble in water.
Production:
• lanthanum-praseodymium-neodymium oxide concentrate (solvent extraction; coproduced with didymium oxide)
• rare earth oxide, hydrate (solvent extraction; coproduced with didymium oxide/cerium oxide/samarium oxide)
Uses: barium titanate capacitors; optical glasses

larch gum
Stractan (St. Regis Paper); [37320-79-9]
Polysaccharide gum produced by aqueous extraction of Western larch wood (*Larix occidentalis*).
Uses:
thickening/emulsifying agent (food, cosmetics, pharmaceuticals)

lard
[61789-99-9]
Extract of pig fat produced by heating and separation. Soft, white solid with a mild, characteristic odour. MP: 36–42°C. Insoluble in water. Soluble in oxygenated, chlorinated and aromatic solvents.
Derivatives:
fatty acid mono/diglycerides; lard oil
Uses: food ingredient; pharmaceutical ingredient

lard oil
Pale yellow oil. Pour point: 0–15°C. Saponification value: 190–205 mg KOH/g. Iodine value: 65–80 g I_2/100 g. Insoluble in water. Soluble in mineral oil.
Production:
• lard (selective crystallisation)
Derivatives:
fatty oils, sulphurised; lard oil, chlorosulphurised
Uses: lubricity additive (metalworking fluids); wire-drawing, rolling oils

lard oil, chlorosulphurised
Production:
• lard oil + sulphur monochloride (chlorosulphurisation)
Uses: extreme-pressure additive (lubricants)

LAS *See:* sodium alkylbenzenesulphonate, linear

lauraldehyde
aldehyde C-12; *n*-dodecanal; *n*-dodecyl aldehyde; lauric aldehyde; lauryl aldehyde; [112-54-9]

$$CH_3(CH_2)_{10}CHO$$

$C_{12}H_{24}O_1$. M: 184.32. Colourless liquid or solid with a citrus odour. MP: 44°C. BP: 185°C (13.3 kPa). d: 0.83 kg/l (15°C). Insoluble in water. Soluble in alcohol.
Production:
• lauryl alcohol, narrow-cut (alcohol oxidation)
Uses: fragrance ingredient

lauralkonium chloride
See: dimethyllaurylbenzylammonium chloride

lauramidopropyldimethylamine
[3179-80-4]

$$CH_3(CH_2)_{10}\overset{\overset{\displaystyle O}{\|}}{C}NHCH_2CH_2CH_2N(CH_3)_2$$

$C_{17}H_{36}N_2O_1$. M: 284.49.
Production:
• lauroyl chloride + 3-dimethylaminopropylamine (amide formation)
Uses: cationic emulsifier (cosmetics/toiletries)

Laurent's acid *See:* 1-naphthylamine-5-sulphonic acid

lauric acid, broad cut

$$CH_3(CH_2)_nCOOH$$

n = 10–12. $C_{12}H_{24}O_2$. M: 200.32. White solid. Titre: 34–38°C. d: 0.87 kg/l (50°C). Insoluble in water. Soluble in oxygenated and aromatic solvents. Several grades are available commercially varying from 92% C_{12} to 55% C_{12}, 40% C_{14}.
Production:
• palm kernel fatty acids/coconut acid (fractionation; coproduced with C_8-C_{10} fatty acids/oleic acid)
Derivatives:
n-alkanol(C_{12}-C_{14}); alkyd resin, non-drying; barium-zinc heat stabilisers; cadmium-barium heat stabilisers; cadmium-zinc heat stabilisers; calcium laurate; dibutyltin dilaurate; diethylene glycol monolaurate; di-(2-hydroxyethyl)dimethylhydantoin dilaurate; dioctyltin dilaurate; lauric acid, narrow cut; lauric acid diethanolamide; lauric acid monoethanolamide; lauroyl chloride; laurylamine; lauryl imidazoline; methyl laurate; myristic acid; polyethylene glycol monolaurate; zinc laurate
Uses:
plasticising alkyd resin comonomer; plastics processing lubricant; superfatting agent (soap, lotions, creams)

lauric acid, narrow cut
dodecanoic acid; *n*-dodecanoic acid; [143-07-7]

$$CH_3(CH_2)_{10}COOH$$

$C_{12}H_{24}O_2$. M: 200.32. White solid. Titre: 39–42°C. d: 0.87 kg/l (50°C). Commercial products are available with 92–99% C_{12}.
Production:
• lauric acid, broad cut (fractionation; coproduced with myristic acid)

Derivatives: glycerol monolaurate; lauric acid diethanolamide; lauric acid monoethanolamide; lauric acid monoisopropanolamide; lauroyl sarcosine; lauryl alcohol, narrow-cut; laurylamine; polyethylene glycol dilaurate; polyethylene glycol monolaurate; propylene glycol monolaurate; sodium lauroyl sarcosinate; sorbitan monolaurate

Uses: superfatting agent (toilet soap)

lauric acid diethanolamide

lauramide DEA; lauric acid polydiethanolamide (2:1 type); lauric acid superamide (1:1 type)

$$CH_3(CH_2)_{10}\overset{\overset{O}{\|}}{C}N(CH_2CH_2OH)_2$$

$C_{16}H_{33}N_1O_3$. M: 287.44. Available as the 1:1 or 2:1 type. The former is produced from the methyl ester by reaction with an equimolar quantity of diethanolamine. It is a white, crystalline solid containing 87% amide and 10% free diethanolamine, together with secondary reaction products. The 2:1 type is made from the acid with an excess of diethanolamine. It contains 55% fatty diethanolamide, 25% diethanolamine, 5% fatty acid and 15% ester amines/amides.

Production:
• lauric acid, broad cut/lauric acid, narrow cut + diethanolamine (Kritchevsky reaction)
• methyl laurate + diethanolamine (amide formation)

Uses:
foam boosters/stabilisers (light-duty dishwashing liquids, industrial cleaners); foam boosters/stabilisers (shaving soaps, cosmetics, toiletries); thickening agents/conditioners/stabilisers (shampoos, lotions)

lauric acid monoethanolamide

$$CH_3(CH_2)_{10}\overset{\overset{O}{\|}}{C}NHCH_2CH_2OH$$

$C_{14}H_{29}N_1O_2$. M: 243.39. Cream wax. MP: 85°C. Bulk density: 0.4 kg/l.

Production:
• lauric acid, broad cut/lauric acid, narrow cut + monoethanolamine (amide formation)

Uses: foam boosters/stabilisers (liquid, powder detergents); thickening agent (dishwashing liquids, shampoos)

lauric acid monoisopropanolamide

lauramide MIPA

$$CH_3(CH_2)_{10}\overset{\overset{O}{\|}}{C}NHCH_2\overset{\overset{CH_3}{|}}{C}HOH$$

$C_{15}H_{31}N_1O_2$. M: 257.42. Flakes.

Production:
• lauric acid, narrow cut + monoisopropanolamine (amide formation)

Uses:
foam stabiliser/superfatting agent (soaps, toiletries)

lauric acid polydiethanolamide

See: lauric acid diethanolamide

lauric acid superamide

See: lauric acid diethanolamide

lauroamphocarboxyglycinate

$$CH_3(CH_2)_{10}\underset{Na^+ \quad {}^-OOCCH_2}{\overset{N}{\underset{N^+}{\fbox{}}}}CH_2CH_2OCH_2COO^-$$

$C_{20}H_{35}N_2Na_1O_5$. M: 406.50. Available as a 50% solution in water.

Production:
• lauryl imidazoline + sodium chloroacetate (ether formation/quaternisation)

Uses:
surfactant (shampoos, skin products)

lauroamphocarboxypropionate

$$CH_3(CH_2)_{10}\underset{Na^+ \quad {}^-OOCCH_2CH_2}{\overset{N}{\underset{N^+}{\fbox{}}}}CH_2CH_2OCH_2CH_2COO^-$$

$C_{22}H_{39}N_2Na_1O_5$. M: 434.54. Available as a 39% or 70% solution in water.

Production:
• lauryl imidazoline + methyl acrylate (Michael addition/ester hydrolysis)

Uses:
surfactant (shampoos, hard-surface cleaners)

lauroamphopropylsulphonate

See: laurylimidazoline sulphobetaine

lauroxy-2-hydroxypropyltrimethylammonium chloride

$$CH_3(CH_2)_{11}OCH_2\overset{\overset{OH}{|}}{C}HCH_2N(CH_3)_3^+ \quad Cl^-$$

$C_{18}H_{40}Cl_1N_1O_2$. M: 337.98.

Production:
• n-alkanol(C_{12}-C_{14}) + 3-chloro-2-hydroxypropyltrimethylammonium chloride (ether formation)

Uses:
cationic emulsifier (cosmetics)

N-lauroyl-p-aminophenol

p-hydroxylauranilide; lauric 4-hydroxyanilide; Suconox-12 (Hexcel); [103-98-0]

$$CH_3(CH_2)_{10}\overset{\overset{O}{\|}}{C}NH-\fbox{}-OH$$

$C_{18}H_{29}N_1O_2$. M: 291.44. Pale yellow solid. MP: 132°C.

Production:
• lauroyl chloride + p-aminophenol (amide formation)

Uses: antioxidant (plastics)

lauroyl chloride
n-dodecanoyl chloride

$$CH_3(CH_2)_{10}\overset{\overset{O}{\|}}{C}Cl$$

$C_{12}H_{23}Cl_1O_1$. M: 218.76. Liquid. BP: 258°C. MP: -17°C. d: 0.92 kg/l (20°C). Flash point: 147°C (TOC).
Production:
• lauric acid, broad cut (acid chloride formation)
Derivatives:
lauramidopropyldimethylamine; *N*-lauroyl-*p*-aminophenol; lauroyl peroxide

lauroyl peroxide
dodecanoyl peroxide; [105-74-8]

$$CH_3(CH_2)_{10}\overset{\overset{O}{\|}}{C}O-O\overset{\overset{O}{\|}}{C}(CH_2)_{10}CH_3$$

$C_{24}H_{46}O_4$. M: 398.63. White flakes. MP: 49°C. Decomposes on heating with release of oxygen. Half life is 10-hours at 62°C. Soluble in most organic solvents. Insoluble in water.
Production:
• lauroyl chloride + hydrogen peroxide
  (dehydrochlorination)
Uses: low-temperature, heat-cured polyester resin curing agent; polyvinyl chloride suspension polymerisation initiator

lauroyl sarcosine

$$CH_3(CH_2)_{10}\overset{\overset{O}{\|}}{C}N\underset{\underset{CH_3}{|}}{C}H_2COOH$$

$C_{15}H_{29}N_1O_3$. M: 271.40.
Production:
• lauric acid, narrow cut + sarcosine (amide formation)
Uses:
emulsifier (emulsion polymerisation); surfactant (carpet shampoos, dishwashing liquids, fabric detergents, cosmetics, toiletries, toothpaste)

laurtrimonium chloride
See: dodecyltrimethylammonium chloride

lauryl acrylate
alkyl(C_{12}-C_{14}) acrylate

$$CH_2=CH\overset{\overset{O}{\|}}{C}O(CH_2)_{11}CH_3$$

$C_{15}H_{28}O_2$. M: 240.39.
Production:
• *n*-alkanol(C_{12}-C_{14})/*n*-alkanol(C_{12}-C_{13}) + methyl
  acrylate (transesterification)
Uses: hydrophobic/flexible acrylic resin comonomer

lauryl alcohol, broad-cut *See:* *n*-alkanol(C_{12}-C_{14})

lauryl alcohol, narrow-cut
1-dodecanol; *n*-dodecanol; *n*-dodecyl alcohol; lauryl alcohol; [112-53-8]

$$CH_3(CH_2)_{11}OH$$

$C_{12}H_{26}O_1$. M: 186.34. White solid. MP: 24°C. BP: 258–264°C. d: 0.83 kg/l (25°C). Insoluble in water. Soluble in oxygenated solvents. Flash point: 270°C (CC).
Production:
• ethylene (Alfol/Epal processes; coproduced with
  n-hexanol/*n*-octanol/*n*-decanol/*n*-alkanol(C_8-C_{10})/
  myristyl alcohol/*n*-alkanol(C_{12}-C_{14})/cetyl alcohol/
  stearyl alcohol/cetylstearyl alcohol/ *n*-alkanol(C_{12}-
  C_{18})/*n*-alkanol(C_{20+}))
• lauric acid, narrow cut (hydrogenation)
• *n*-alkanol(C_{12}-C_{14}) (fractionation; coproduced with
  myristyl alcohol)
Derivatives:
decyltetradecanol; dimethyllaurylamine; dodecyl gallate; lauraldehyde; lauryl alcohol ethoxylates; lauryl chloride; lauryl lactate; sodium lauryl sulphate; triethanolamine lauryl sulphate

lauryl alcohol ethoxylate/propoxylates

$$CH_3(CH_2)_{11}(O\underset{\underset{CH_3}{|}}{C}HCH_2)_m(OCH_2CH_2)_nOH$$

Production:
• *n*-alkanol(C_{12}-C_{13})/*n*-alkanol(C_{12}-C_{14})/
  n-alkanol(C_{12}-C_{18}) + propylene oxide + ethylene
  oxide (epoxidation/epoxidation)
Uses: low-foaming surfactant/solubilisers (machine detergents, industrial cleaners)

lauryl alcohol ethoxylates
laureth (CTFA)

$$CH_3(CH_2)_{11}(OCH_2CH_2)_nOH$$

n = 2–23. Liquid or wax, depending on the ethylene oxide content. HLB: 9.5–17.0 (4–23 moles EO).
Production:
• lauryl alcohol, narrow-cut + ethylene oxide
  (epoxidation)
Uses: emulsifier (cosmetics)

laurylamine
alkyl(C_{12}-C_{14})amine; lauramine; [124-22-1]

$$CH_3(CH_2)_{11}NH_2$$

Production:
• lauric acid, broad cut/lauric acid, narrow cut +
  ammonia (nitrile formation/hydrogenation)
Derivatives:
dimethyllaurylamine; dodecyltrimethylammonium chloride; dodine
Uses: flotation collector

lauryl β-aminocrotonate

lauryl 3-aminocrotonate

$$NH_2$$
$$CH_3C=CHCOO(CH_2)_{11}CH_3$$

$C_{16}H_{31}N_1O_2$. M: 269.44.

Production:
- *n*-alkanol(C_{12}-C_{14})/*n*-alkanol(C_{12}-C_{13}) + β-amino-crotononitrile (nitrile hydrolysis/esterification)

Uses: polyvinyl chloride heat stabiliser

lauryl betaine

[683-10-3]

$$CH_3$$
$$CH_3(CH_2)_{11}NCH_2COO^- Na^+$$
$$CH_3$$

$C_{16}H_{33}N_1Na_1O_2$. M: 294.44. Liquid. A typical chain-length distribution is: 65% C_{12}, 35% C_{14}. The product is often sold as a 30% solution in water.

Production:
- dimethyllaurylamine + sodium chloroacetate (quaternisation)

Uses:
anticorrosion agent/emulsifier/softening agent (detergents); flow conditioner (heavy-duty detergent slurries); foam stabiliser (shampoos, bath formulations)

lauryl chloride

1-chlorododecane; *n*-dodecyl chloride

$$CH_3(CH_2)_{11}Cl$$

$C_{12}H_{25}Cl_1$. M: 204.78. Colourless liquid. d: 0.86 kg/l (20°C). Chain-length distribution varies with source of lauryl alcohol. Grades containing 95% C_{12} or 67% C_{12}, 28% C_{14} are available.

Production:
- lauryl alcohol, narrow-cut/*n*-alkanol(C_{12}-C_{14})/*n*-alkanol(C_{12}-C_{13}) (chlorination)

Derivatives:
dimethyllaurylamine; 2-hydroxy-4-dodecoxybenzophenone; laurylpyridinium chloride

lauryldimethylamine *See:* dimethyllaurylamine

lauryldimethylammonium-3-sulphopropylbetaine

Ralufon DL (Rashig)

$$CH_3$$
$$CH_3(CH_2)_{11}\overset{+}{N}CH_2CH_2CH_2SO_3^-$$
$$CH_3$$

$C_{17}H_{37}N_1O_3S_1$. M: 335.56.

Production:
- dimethyllaurylamine + propane su!tone (quaternisation)

Uses:
amphoteric surfactant (shampoos/industrial detergents)

lauryl glycidyl ether

alkyl(C_{12}-C_{14}) glycidyl ether

$$O$$
$$CH_3(CH_2)_{11}OCH_2CH-CH_2$$

$C_{15}H_{30}O_2$. M: 242.40.

Production:
- *n*-alkanol(C_{12}-C_{14})/*n*-alkanol(C_{12}-C_{13}) + epichlorohydrin (ether formation)

Uses: reactive diluent (epoxy resins)

lauryl imidazoline

2-lauryl-1-(hydroxyethyl)imidazoline (CTFA)

$$CH_3(CH_2)_{10}$$
HOCH_2CH_2

$C_{16}H_{32}N_2O_1$. M: 268.45. Solid. MP: 38°C.

Production:
- lauric acid, broad cut + aminoethylethanolamine (condensation)

Derivatives: lauroamphocarboxyglycinate; lauroamphocarboxypropionate; laurylimidazoline sulphobetaine

Uses: shampoo ingredient

laurylimidazoline sulphobetaine

lauroamphopropylsulphonate (CTFA)

$$CH_3(CH_2)_{10}$$
$$HOCH_2CH_2$$
$$CH_2CHCH_2SO_3^-$$
$$OH$$

$C_{19}H_{38}N_2O_5S_1$. M: 406.57. Available as a 45% solution in water.

Production:
- lauryl imidazoline + sodium 3-chloro-2-hydroxypropylsulphonate (dehydrochlorination)

Uses: mild surfactant (shampoos, skin-care products)

lauryllactam

12-aminododecanoic acid lactam; dodecane-12-lactam; [947-04-6]

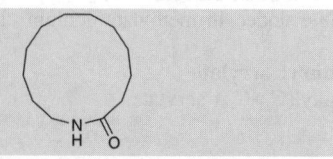

$C_{12}H_{23}N_1O_1$. M: 197.32. Colourless crystals. Insoluble in water. Soluble in most organic solvents.

Production:
- cyclododecanone + hydroxylamine sulphate (oxime formation/Beckmann rearrangement)
- 1,5,9-cyclododecatriene + nitrosyl chloride (addition/dehydrochlorination/hydrogenation/Beckmann rearrangement)

Derivatives: polyamide 6 terpolymers; polyamide 12; polyamide TR55; poly(ether-amide) elastomers

lauryl lactate
[6283-92-7]

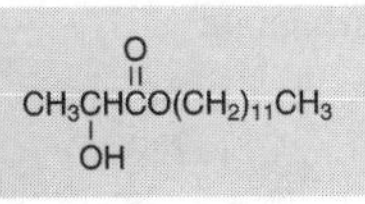

$C_{15}H_{30}O_3$. M: 258.40.
Production:
• lauryl alcohol, narrow-cut + DL-lactic acid (esterification)
Uses: wetting agent (toiletries)

lauryl mercaptan *See:* *n*-dodecyl mercaptan

lauryl methacrylate
n-dodecyl methacrylate; [142-90-5]

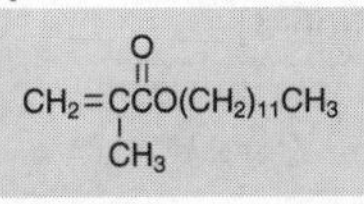

$C_{16}H_{30}O_2$. M: 254.42. Pale yellow liquid. BP: 272–343°C. FP: -22°C. d: 0.87 kg/l (25°C). Insoluble in water. Flash point: 132°C (COC). A typical chain-length distribution is: 3% C_{10}, 65% C_{12}, 25% C_{14}, 7% C_{16}. Commercial products contain hydroquinone or similar polymerisation inhibitors.
Production:
• *n*-alkanol(C_{12}-C_{14}) + methyl methacrylate (transesterification)
Derivatives:
polymethacrylates, oil-soluble; polymethacrylates, oil-soluble dispersants

laurylpyridinium chloride
1-dodecylpyridinium chloride; *N*-laurylpyridinium chloride; [104-74-5]

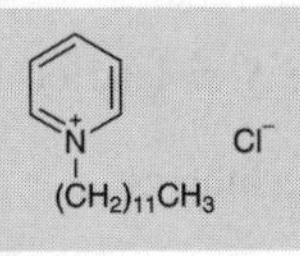

$C_{17}H_{30}Cl_1N_1$. M: 283.89.
Production:
• pyridine + lauryl chloride (quaternisation)
Uses:
biocide (cosmetics, toiletries)

lauryltrimethylammonium chloride
See: dodecyltrimethylammonium chloride

lavandin oil
Yellow liquid with a lavender-like odour. Produced by steam distillation of the flowers of *Lavandula augustifolia* x *L. latifolia* hybrids. d: 0.89 kg/l (20°C). Soluble in ethanol. Produced mainly in southern France, Bulgaria and Russia.
Uses: perfume ingredient

lavandulyl acetate
[25905-14-0]

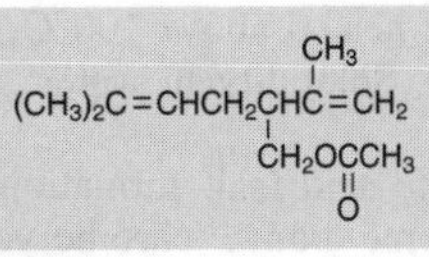

$C_{12}H_{20}O_2$. M: 196.29.
Production:
• 3-methyl-2-buten-1-ol + acetic acid (esterification/dimerisation)
Uses: fragrance ingredient

lavender oil
[8000-28-0]
Pale yellow liquid with a characteristic odour. Produced by steam distillation of lavender (*Lavendula vera*) flowers and stalks. d: 0.88 kg/l (20°C). Soluble in 70% ethanol. Its main constituent is linalyl acetate (35–60%). The oil is produced in several countries including France, Spain, Italy, Bulgaria and Russia.
Uses:
perfume ingredient

LDPE *See:* polyethylene, low-density

lead
[7439-92-1]

Pb

Pb_1. M: 207.19. Soft, grey metal which tarnishes readily in the atmosphere. MP: 327°C. BP: 1,770°C. d: 11.35 kg/l. Large quantities of lead and its alloys are recycled as scrap.
Production:
• lead bullion (pyrometallurgical refining/Parkes process/Betterton-Kroll process)
• lead bullion (electrochemical refining)
• zinc-lead sulphide ores + metallurgical coke (Imperial Smelting process; byproduct of zinc production)
Derivatives:
lead sulphate, monobasic; litharge; tetraethyl lead; tetramethyl lead
Uses:
anticorrosion pigment (primer paints); leaded bronze ingredient (bearings); phosphor bronze ingredient (bearings); lead-antimony alloys (battery plates, roofing, radiation protection, ammunition); lead-antimony-tin alloys (battery plates, casting applications); lead-calcium-tin alloys (electroplating anodes, radiation shielding); lead-tellurium alloys (nuclear shielding); lead-tin alloys (solder)

lead acetate

lead diacetate; [301-04-2]

(CH₃COO)₂Pb

$C_4H_6O_4Pb_1$. M: 325.28. Available as the trihydrate. White granules. d: 2.55 kg/l. Decomposes with loss of acetic acid when heated above 100°C. Absorbs carbon dioxide from air. Solubility in water: 443 g/l (20°C).
Production:
• litharge + acetic acid (salt formation)
Derivatives: chrome orange; chrome yellow; lead carbonate, basic; lead cyanamide; lead dimethyldithiocarbamate; lead trinitroresorcinate
Uses: esterification catalyst

lead azide

[13424-46-9]

Pb(N₃)₂

N_6Pb_1. M: 291.23. White powder. Insoluble in water. Explodes when struck.
Production:
• lead nitrate + sodium azide (salt formation)
Uses: military explosive primers

lead bis(dimethyl dithiocarbamate)

See: lead dimethyldithiocarbamate

lead bullion

Crude form of lead containing antimony, arsenic, tin, silver, gold, copper and bismuth as the main impurities.
Production:
• lead sulphide ore concentrates (smelting)
Derivatives: brass; lead

lead carbonate, basic

flake white; trilead bis(carbonate) dihydroxide; white lead; Pigment White 1 (CI); [1319-46-6]

Pb(OH)₂.2PbCO₃

$C_2H_2O_8Pb_3$. M: 775.60. White powder. d: 6.70 kg/l. Usage is controlled by national regulations because of the chemical's toxicity.
Production:
• lead acetate + carbon dioxide (salt formation)
Uses: pigment (wood primers, exterior paints)

lead chromate *See:* chrome yellow; chrome orange

lead cyanamide

[35112-70-0]

PbNC≡N

$C_1N_2Pb_1$. M: 247.21. Yellow pigment. d: 6.8 kg/l. Slightly soluble in water forming alkaline solutions. Its use in paint is controlled in many countries.

Production:
• lead acetate + cyanamide (salt formation)
Uses: anticorrosion pigment (primer paints)

lead diamyldithiocarbamate

amyl lead dithiocarbamate

[(C₅H₁₁)₂NĊS]₂Pb

$C_{22}H_{44}N_2Pb_1S_4$. M: 672.06. Sold as a solution in mineral oil containing about 16% Pb.
Production:
• diamylamine + carbon disulphide + litharge (condensation)
Uses: antiwear additive (gear oils, greases); vulcanisation accelerator

lead dimethyldithiocarbamate

lead bis(dimethyl dithiocarbamate); Ledate (Vanderbilt Chemical); [19010-66-3]

[(CH₃)₂NĊS]₂Pb

$C_6H_{12}N_2Pb_1S_4$. M: 447.63.
Production:
• sodium dimethyldithiocarbamate + lead acetate (salt formation)
Uses: vulcanisation accelerator

lead dioxide

lead oxide, brown; lead peroxide; [1309-60-0]
O_2Pb_1. M: 239.19. Brown-black powder. Decomposes on heating above 290°C with release of oxygen. d: 9.38 kg/l. Insoluble in water.
Production:
• red lead + chlorine (oxidation)
Uses:
polysulphide rubber curing agent; battery electrodes; match head ingredient; oxidising agent (dyestuffs)

lead 2-ethylhexoate *See:* lead octoate

lead monoxide *See:* litharge

lead naphthenate

[61790-14-5]
Production:
• litharge + naphthenic acid (salt formation)
Uses:
extreme-pressure additive (lubricants); paint drier

lead nitrate

[10099-74-8]

Pb(NO₃)₂

$N_2O_6Pb_1$. M: 331.19. White crystals. d: 4.53 kg/l. Soluble in water forming slightly acidic solutions.

Production:
• litharge + nitric acid (reaction)
Derivatives: chrome orange; chrome yellow; lead azide;
Pigment Red 104
Uses: match head ingredient; mordant; oxidising agent

lead octoate
lead 2-ethylhexoate

$(C_7H_{15}COO)_2Pb$

$C_{16}H_{30}O_4Pb_1$. M: 493.61.
Production:
• litharge + 2-ethylhexanoic acid/isooctanoic acid
  (salt formation)
Uses: polyurethane catalyst; antiwear/antirust additive
(lubricants); polyvinyl chloride heat stabiliser

lead oxide, brown *See:* lead dioxide

lead oxide, red *See:* red lead

lead oxide, yellow *See:* litharge

lead peroxide *See:* lead dioxide

lead phosphite, dibasic
[1344-40-7]

$2PbO.PbHPO_3$

$H_1O_5P_1Pb_3$. M: 733.55. Available commercially as the
hemihydrate.
Production:
• phosphorous acid + litharge (salt formation)
Uses: acid acceptor (rubber processing); polyvinyl chloride heat stabiliser

lead phthalate, dibasic

$C_8H_4O_6Pb_3$. M: 817.68. Available commercially as the
hemihydrate.
Production:
• litharge + phthalic anhydride (salt formation)
Uses: polyvinyl chloride heat stabiliser

lead silicochromate, basic
lead silicochromate; Oncor (Rheox)
Orange pigment consisting of lead chromate-coated
silica. d: 4.0 kg/l. Its use in paint is controlled in
many countries.
Production:
• chrome orange + sodium silicate (precipitation)
Uses: anticorrosion pigment (undercoat and finishing
paints); pigment (road marking paints)

lead stearate, dibasic

$[CH_3(CH_2)_{16}COO]_2Pb.2PbO$

$C_{36}H_{70}O_6Pb_3$. M: 1220.52.
Production:
• litharge + stearic acid (salt formation)
Uses: polyvinyl chloride heat stabiliser

lead stearate, normal
lead stearate; lead stearate, neutral; [1072-35-1]

$[CH_3(CH_2)_{16}COO]_2Pb$

$C_{36}H_{70}O_4Pb_1$. M: 774.15. White powder. MP: 125°C.
Insoluble in water.
Production:
• litharge + stearic acid (salt formation)
Uses: polyvinyl chloride heat stabiliser

lead styphnate *See:* lead trinitroresorcinate

lead sulphate, monobasic
Pigment White 2 (CI); [12036-76-9]

$PbO.PbSO_4$

$O_5Pb_2S_1$. M: 526.44. White powder. MP: 977°C. d:
6.92 kg/l. Insoluble in water.
Production:
• lead sulphide ore concentrates (air oxidation)
• litharge + lead + sulphuric acid (salt formation)
Uses:
pigment (marine primer paints)

lead sulphate, tribasic
[12397-06-7]

$3PbO.PbSO_4$

$O_7Pb_4S_1$. M: 972.82. Available as the monohydrate.
Fine, white powder. d: 6.90 kg/l. PbO content: 88–
90%. Insoluble in water.
Production:
• litharge + sulphuric acid (salt formation)
Uses:
polyvinyl chloride heat stabiliser

lead trinitroresorcinate
lead styphnate; [15245-44-0]

$C_6H_1N_3O_8Pb_1$. M: 450.28.
Production:
• resorcinol + nitric acid, concentrated + lead acetate
  (nitration/salt formation)
Uses: explosive primers

lead zirconate titanate
lead titanate zirconate; LZT

PbTiZrO₃

$O_3Pb_1Ti_1Zr_1$. M: 394.31.
Production:
- litharge + zirconia, high-purity + titanium dioxide, hydrate (calcination)

Uses: piezoceramics

leaf alcohol *See:* 3-hexenol

leaf aldehyde *See:* 2-hexenal

lecithin
E322 (EC); [8002-43-5]

OR   O⁻
ROCH₂CHCH₂OPOCH₂CH₂N(CH₃)₃
‖
O

R = mixed C_{16}-C_{22} fatty acids. Pale yellow to brown, viscous fluid or solid. d: 1.03 kg/l (25°C). Saponification value: 190–200 mg KOH/g. Iodine value: 95 g I₂/100 g. Acid value: 15–30 mg KOH/g. Dispersible in water. Soluble in hydrocarbon and chlorinated solvents. Insoluble in vegetable oils.
Production:
- soyabeans (solvent extraction/alkali refining; byproduct of soyabean oil/soyabean meal production)
- rapeseed, high erucic acid (solvent extraction; byproduct of rapeseed oil production)

Uses: pigments/fillers/clay dispersant (sealants, caulks, pesticides); emulsifier (margarine, confectionery, cosmetics, animal feed); emulsifier (oil-based drilling fluids); textile/leather auxiliary

lemongrass oil
verbena oil, Indian; [8007-02-1]
Reddish-yellow liquid. d: ~0.88 kg/l (20°C). Soluble in alcohol and chlorinated solvents. The main constituent of the oil is citral. The product is extracted from *Cymbopogon citrus* which is grown in Central and South America, and also from *C. flexuosus* which is grown in India and China.
Derivatives: citral

lemon oil
lemon peel oil; [8008-56-8]
Pale greenish-yellow liquid with a lemon odour. d: 0.85 kg/l (20°C). Extracted from lemon peel (*Citrus limon* fruit skin) as part of the juice production process. Produced in Italy, California (USA), Brazil and Argentina. The major constituents of the oil are (+)-limonene, β-pinene and γ-terpinene.
Derivatives: methoxsalen
Uses: flavouring/fragrance ingredient

lenacil
3-cyclohexyl-1,5,6,7-tetrahydrocyclopentapyrimidine-2,4-dione; [2164-08-1]

$C_{13}H_{18}N_2O_2$. M: 234.29.
Production:
- dimethyl adipate + cyclohexyl isocyanate + ammonia (Dieckmann condensation/isocyanate addition/condensation)

Uses: herbicide

L-leucine
L-α-aminoisocaproic acid; Leu; [61-90-5]

NH₂
(CH₃)₂CHCH₂–C–COOH
H

$C_6H_{13}N_1O_2$. M: 131.18. Available commercially as the naturally-occurring L(+)-enantiomer. Crystalline solid. Sublimes at 145°C. d: 1.29 kg/l (20°C). Soluble in water.
Production:
- animal glue (hydrolysis/extraction; coproduced with L-tyrosine/L-arginine/L-asparagine)

Derivatives: leucinocaine; oxytocin
Uses: infusion solutions/diagnostic aids; raw material (peptide drugs)

leucinocaine
[92-23-9]

O   N(C₂H₅)₂
H₂N–   –COCH₂CHCH₂CH(CH₃)₂

$C_{17}H_{28}N_2O_2$. M: 292.42.
Production:
- L-leucine + ethanol + *p*-nitrobenzoyl chloride (amine formation/ester reduction/esterification/nitro reduction)

Uses: local anaesthetic drug

levallorphan
[152-02-3]

CH₂=CHCH₂–N

OH

$C_{19}H_{25}N_1O_1$. M: 283.42.
Production:
- 1-(4-methoxybenzyl)-1,2,3,4,5,6,7,8-octahydroiso-quinoline + allyl bromide (demethylation/racemate

separation/amine formation/cyclisation)
Uses: morphine antagonist drug

levamisole *See:* tetramisole

levocarbinoxamine *See:* carbinoxamine

levodopa
[59-92-7]

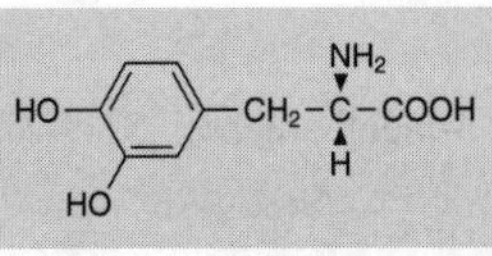

$C_9H_{11}N_1O_4$. M: 197.20. White, crystalline solid. MP: 276–278°C. Soluble in water. Practically insoluble in oxygenated, chlorinated and aromatic solvents.
Production:
• glycine + acetic anhydride + vanillin (amide formation/carbonyl condensation/chiral catalytic hydrogenation/hydrolysis)
• 3,4-dihydroxybenzaldehyde + hydrogen cyanide + ammonia (Strecker synthesis/racemate separation)
• catechol + pyruvic acid + ammonia (microbial conversion)
Uses: antiparkinsonian drug

levoglutamide *See:* L-glutamine

levomepromazine
methotrimeprazine; [60-99-1]; [1236-99-3] (hydrochloride); [7104-38-3] (maleate)

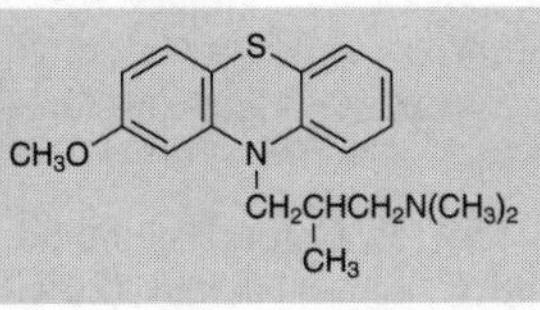

$C_{19}H_{24}N_2O_1S_1$. M: 328.47. Available commercially as the hydrochloride and maleate salts.
Production:
• 2-chlorophenothiazine + sodium methoxide + 3-dimethylamino-2-methylpropyl chloride hydrochloride (ether formation/amine formation/racemate separation)
Uses: neuroleptic drug

levomethadone
[125-58-6]

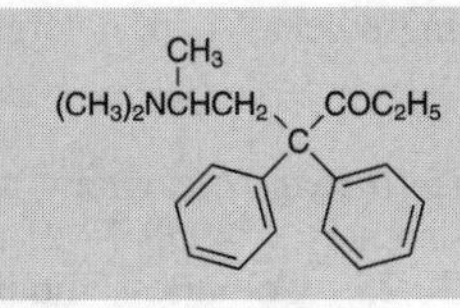

$C_{21}H_{27}N_1O_1$. M: 309.45. Available commercially as the L(−)-enantiomer hydrochloride.

Production:
• methadone (racemate separation)
Uses: analgesic drug

levorphanol
17-methylmorphinan-3-ol; [77-07-6]

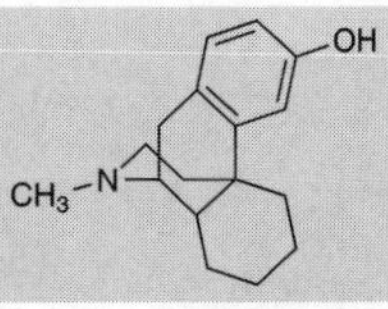

$C_{17}H_{23}N_1O_1$. M: 257.38. Available commercially as the (−)-tartrate dihydrate salt.
Production:
• 1-(4-methoxybenzyl)-1,2,3,4,5,6,7,8-octahydroisoquinoline (methylation/cyclisation/racemate separation; coproduced with dextromethorphan)
Uses: analgesic drug

levothyroxine sodium
[55-03-8]

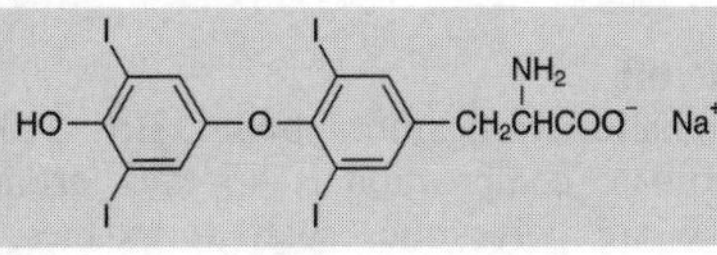

$C_{15}H_{10}I_4N_1Na_1O_4$. M: 798.86.
Production:
• L-tyrosine (ring iodination/oxidative coupling)
Uses: thyroid hormone drug

levulinic acid
4-ketopentanoic acid; laevulinic acid; 4-oxopentanoic acid; [123-76-2]

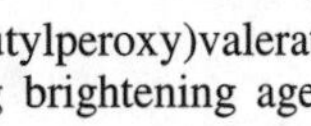

$C_5H_8O_3$. M: 116.11. Supercooled liquid. MP: 33–35°C. BP: 245–246°C. d: 1.14 kg/l (20°C). Soluble in water, oxygenated and aromatic solvents.
Production:
• natural rubber + ozone (ozonolysis)
• furfuryl alcohol (acid-catalysed rearrangement)
Derivatives:
n-butyl 4,4-di-(t-butylperoxy)valerate; ethyl levulinate
Uses: nickelplating brightening agent

lidocaine
[137-58-6]; [73-78-9] (hydrochloride)

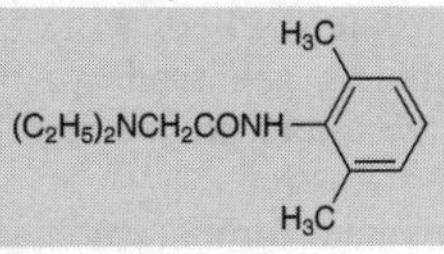

$C_{14}H_{22}N_2O_1$. M: 234.34. Available commercially as the free base and as the hydrochloride salt.

Production:
- chloroacetyl chloride + 2,6-xylidine + diethylamine (amide formation/amine formation)

Uses: local anaesthetic drug

lidoflazine
[3416-26-0]

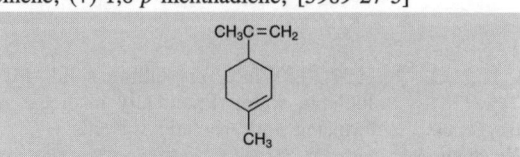

$C_{30}H_{35}F_2N_3O_1$. M: 491.63.
Production:
- chloroacetyl chloride + 2,6-xylidine + piperazine + 4,4-bis(*p*-fluorophenyl)butyl chloride (amide formation/amine formation/amine formation)

Uses: vasodilator drug

light cycle oil
Mixed aromatic hydrocarbon stream. BR: 210–300°C. Its approximate composition is 45–65% aromatics of which 75% are polycyclics such as indanes, naphthalene, methylnaphthalene, biphenyl and acenaphthene.
Production:
- long residue/gas oil, vacuum/deasphalted oil (fluidised-bed catalytic cracking; coproduced with gasoline, catalytic-cracker/heavy cycle oil/refinery gas)

Derivatives: naphthalene fraction
Uses: domestic/industrial heating fuel; diesel fuel blending component

light oil
Coal tar fraction. BR: <170°C.
Production:
- coal tar, crude (alkali extraction/fractionation; coproduced with tar acid liquor/carbolic oil/ naphthalene fraction/creosote oil/fluorene oil/ anthracene oil/coal tar pitch)

Derivatives: benzole
Uses: fuel oil

lignite
brown coal
Lignite and brown-coal are brownish-black low-grade coals consisting of decomposed wood and vegetable matter. Calorific value: 14–20 MJ/kg. The ore has a high moisture content and tends to disintegrate as it dries out. They are found predominantly in USA, Germany, Russia and Australia.
Derivatives: activated carbon; montan wax; Sulphur Brown 1; synthesis gas
Uses: domestic/industrial heating fuel

lignite wax *See:* montan wax

ligroin *See:* petroleum ether

lime *See:* calcium hydroxide; calcium oxide

lime, chlorinated *See:* bleaching powder

lime sulphur *See:* calcium polysulphide

(+)-limonene
cinene; (+)-1,8-*p*-menthadiene; [5989-27-5]

$C_{10}H_{16}$. M: 136.24. Colourless liquid with a lemon-like odour. BP: 176°C. d: 0.84 kg/l (20°C). Insoluble in water. Miscible with alcohol. This is the (+)-enantiomer.
Production:
- orange oil (fractionation)

Derivatives: (−)-carvone
Uses: fragrance ingredient (household products); pine oil cleaning formulations

(±)-limonene *See:* dipentene

linalool
3,7-dimethyl-1,6-octadien-3-ol; [78-70-6]

$C_{10}H_{18}O_1$. M: 154.25. Colourless liquid with a floral odour. BP: 198°C. d: ~0.86 kg/l (20°C). Insoluble in water. Soluble in alcohol. Available both as a racemic mixture and as separate enantiomers.
Production:
- pinane (oxidation/hydrogenation/thermal rearrangement)
- dehydrolinalool (hydrogenation)
- linalyl acetate (ester hydrolysis)

Derivatives:
geraniol-nerol, mixed; geranylacetone; linalool oxide; linalyl acetate; linalyl butyrate; linalyl formate; linalyl propionate; tetrahydrolinalool
Uses: fragrance ingredient (soap, detergents, toiletries)

linalool oxide
2-methyl-2-vinyl-5-(α-hydroxyisopropyl)tetrahydrofuran; [5989-33-3] (*cis*-isomer); [34995-77-2] (*trans*-isomer)
$C_{10}H_{18}O_2$. M: 170.25. Colourless liquid with floral odour. BP: 188°C. d: 0.94 kg/l (20°C). The commercial product is a mixture of the *cis* and *trans*-isomers.

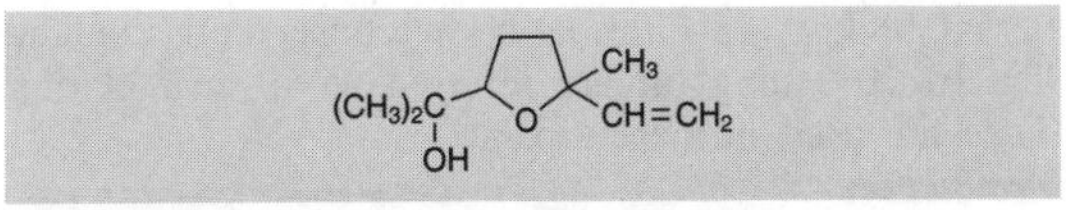

Production:
- linalool + peracetic acid (oxidation)

Uses: fragrance ingredient

linalyl acetate
[115-95-7]

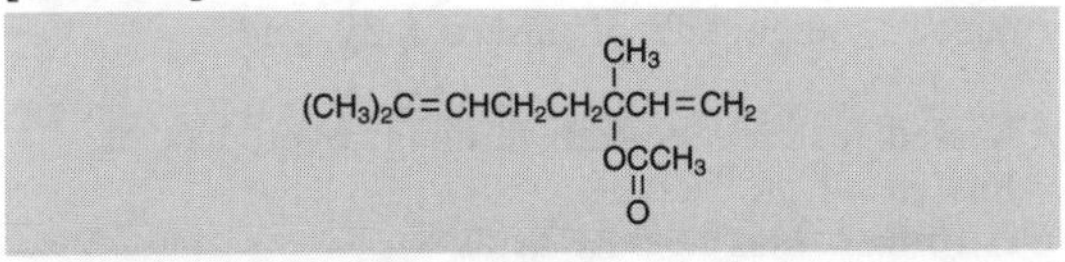

$C_{12}H_{20}O_2$. M: 196.29. Colourless liquid with a floral odour. BP: 220°C. d: 0.90 kg/l (20°C). Insoluble in water. Soluble in alcohol. Available commercially as a racemic mixture. The (−)-enantiomer is the main component in lavender and bergamot oils.

Production:
- linalool + acetic anhydride (esterification)
- myrcene (hydrochlorination/hydration/esterification/ separation/ester hydrolysis; byproduct of geraniol-nerol, mixed production)

Derivatives: linalool

Uses: fragrance ingredient

linalyl butyrate
[78-36-4]

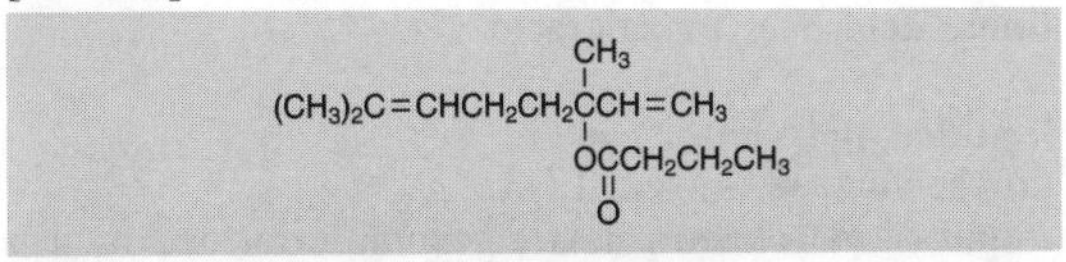

$C_{14}H_{24}O_2$. M: 224.34. Liquid with a floral odour. BP: 232°C. d: 0.90 kg/l (15°C). Insoluble in water.

Production:
- linalool + *n*-butyryl chloride (esterification)

Uses: fragrance ingredient

linalyl formate
[115-99-1]

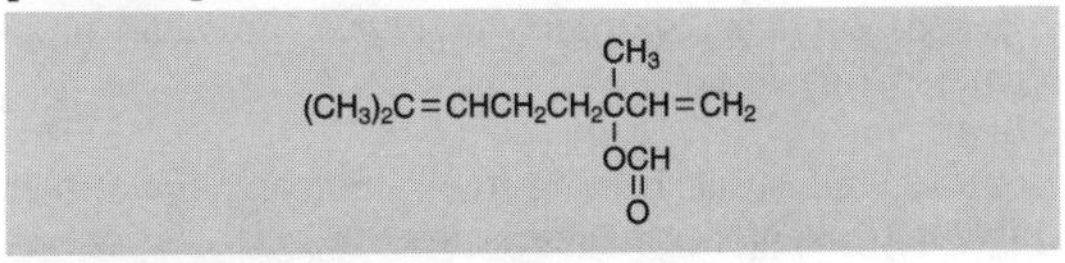

$C_{11}H_{18}O_2$. M: 182.26.

Production:
- linalool + formic acid (esterification)

Uses: lavender fragrances/eau de cologne

linalyl propionate
[144-39-8]

$C_{13}H_{22}O_2$. M: 210.32. Colourless liquid with a floral odour.

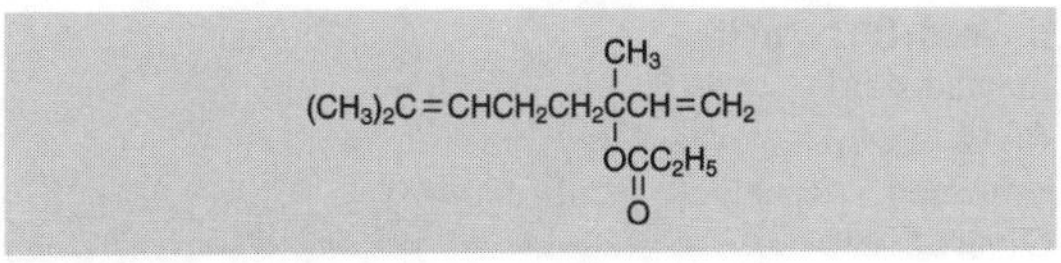

Production:
- linalool + propionic acid (esterification)

Uses: fragrance ingredient

lincomycin
[154-21-2]

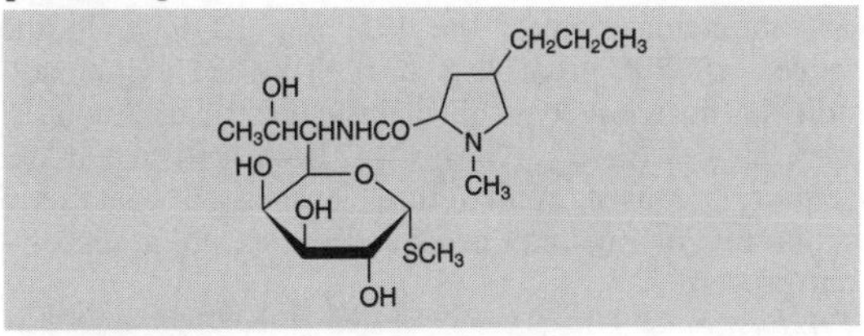

$C_{18}H_{34}N_2O_6S_1$. M: 406.53. Available as the free base and as the hydrochloride salt.

Production:
- microbial fermentation medium + *Streptomyces lincolnensis* bacteria (fermentation)

Derivatives: clindamycin

Uses: antibacterial drug

lindane
1α,2α,3β,4α,5α,6β-hexachlorocyclohexane; BHC; γ-HCH; [319-86-8]

$C_6H_6Cl_6$. M: 290.84. The commercial product contains >99% γ-isomer. Lower grade products are also available under the name of 'γ-HCH'.

Production:
- benzene + chlorine (photochlorination/isomer separation)

Uses: insecticide

linear alkylbenzene *See:* dodecylbenzene, linear

linoleic acid diethanolamide
linoleamide DEA (CTFA)

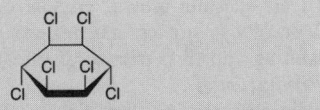

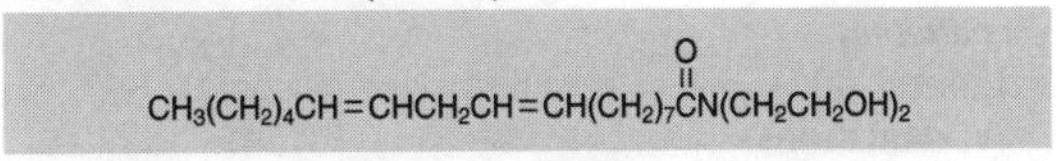

$C_{22}H_{41}N_1O_3$. M: 367.58. Yellow or brown liquid. Commercial products contain 85–100% amides.

Production:
- sunflower acid/soyabean acid + diethanolamine (amide formation)
- soyabean oil + diethanolamine (amide formation)

Uses: foam stabiliser/viscosifier (shampoos)

linseed fatty acids
linseed acid
Production:
• linseed soap stock (acidification)
Derivatives:
alkyd resins, long-oil; alkyd resins, medium-oil; alkyd resins, short-oil; epoxy ester resins

linseed oil
varnish linseed oil; VLO; [8001-26-1]
Yellow liquid with a distinctive odour. Titre: 19–21°C. Saponification value: 188–195 mg KOH/g. Iodine value: 160–200 g I_2/100 g. d: 0.93 kg/l (15°C). Insoluble in water. A typical chain-length distribution is: 20% $C_{18:1}$, 15% $C_{18:2}$, 55% $C_{18:3}$. Both acid and alkali refining are used. Acid refined linseed oil contains a proportion of free fatty acids and has excellent dispersant properties.
Production:
• linseed (extraction/alkali refining)
Derivatives: alkyd resins, long-oil; alkyd resins, medium-oil; alkyd resins, short-oil; cyclopentadienised oils; linseed oil, blown; linseed oil, boiled; linseed oil, epoxidised; linseed oil, heat-bodied; maleinised oils; urethane-alkyd resins
Uses:
drying oil (printing inks); glazing putty; binder (linoleum flooring); waterproofing agent (paper, fabrics)

linseed oil, blown
Clear, chestnut-brown, viscous oil. d: 0.96–1.00 kg/l. Viscosity is higher than linseed oil (>3 poise). Flow, wetting and dispersion properties are also better.
Production:
• linseed oil (oxidation)
Uses: drying oil (paints, printing inks)

linseed oil, boiled
Linseed oil of higher drying power, but of similar viscosity to untreated oil. Contains driers.
Production:
• linseed oil (thermal polymerisation)
Uses: drying oil (paints, printing inks)

linseed oil, epoxidised
ELO
Viscous liquid. d: 1.02 kg/l (25°C). Mixed product.
Production:
• linseed oil + peracetic acid/performic acid (epoxidation)
Uses:
styrene-butadiene block copolymer coupling agent; plasticiser/synergist (polyvinyl chloride heat stabilisers)

linseed oil, heat-bodied
enamel oil; lithographic varnish; stand oil
Pale to dark yellow, viscous, slow-drying oils. d:

0.95–0.98 kg/l (15°C). Heat-bodied linseed oils containing 10–20% tung oil are referred to as enamel oils. They are used in marine paints.
Production:
• linseed oil (thermal polymerisation)
Uses: binder (paint, printing inks)

linseed oil, maleinised *See:* maleinised oils

linseed soap stock
Aqueous sodium salt of linseed fatty acids.
Production:
• linseed (extraction/alkali refining; byproduct of linseed oil production)
Derivatives: linseed fatty acids

linuron
3-(3,4-dichlorophenyl)-1-methoxy-1-methylurea; [330-55-2]

$C_9H_{10}Cl_2N_2O_2$. M: 249.10.
Production:
• *N,O*-dimethylhydroxylamine + 3,4-dichlorophenyl isocyanate (isocyanate addition)
Uses: herbicide

lipoic acid *See:* thioctic acid

liquified petroleum gas
propane/butane, mixed; LPG
Liquified petroleum gas is a general term for commercial propane, butane or mixtures of the two.
Production:
• refinery gas (fractionation; coproduced with propylene/C_4-stream, refinery)
• natural gas, wet (fractionation; coproduced with natural gas/ethane/gasoline, natural)
Derivatives:
aromatics, mixed; butane, mixed; C_4-stream, steam-cracked; ethylene; gasoline, pyrolysis; propane; propylene; pyrolysis tar
Uses:
domestic/industrial heating fuel; motor vehicle fuel; solvent (solvent deasphalting processes)

liquorice extract
licorice extract
Produced by extraction from liquorice (*Glycyrrhiza glabra*) root.
Derivatives: glycyrrhizinic acid
Uses:
expectorant/antiinflammatory drug (cough medicines); flavouring ingredient (food, drinks)

lisinopril
[83915-83-7]; [76547-98-3]

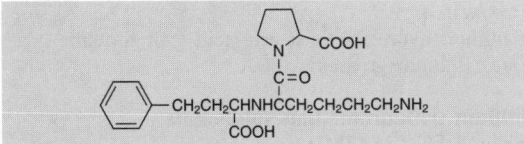

$C_{21}H_{31}N_3O_5$. M: 405.50.
Production:
• 3-phenylpropionaldehyde + L-lysine + L-proline
(cyanohydrin formation/nitrile hydrolysis/amide
formation/amine formation)
Uses: antihypertensive drug

litharge
lead monoxide; lead oxide, yellow; plumbous oxide;
[1317-36-8]

PbO

O_1Pb_1. M: 223.19. Yellow or orange powder. MP:
897°C. Sublimes. BP: 1472°C. d: 9.53 kg/l (α-form),
9.6 kg/l (β-form). Insoluble in water.
Production:
• lead (air oxidation)
Derivatives: calcium plumbate; lead acetate; lead
diamyldithiocarbamate; lead naphthenate; lead nitrate;
lead octoate; lead phosphite, dibasic; lead phthalate,
dibasic; lead stearate, dibasic; lead stearate, normal;
lead sulphate, monobasic; lead sulphate, tribasic; lead
zirconate titanate; red lead
Uses:
battery electrode paste; glaze/ceramics ingredient; vulcanisation agent

lithium
[7439-93-2]

Li

Li_1. M: 6.94. Silver-white metal. MP: 180°C. BP:
1,334°C. d: 0.53 kg/l. Reacts with water releasing
hydrogen. Soluble in liquid ammonia.
Production:
• lithium chloride (melt electrolysis)
Derivatives: n-butyllithium; lithium hydride
Uses: aluminium-lithium alloys; ethynylation reagent

lithium aluminium hydride
LAH; [16853-85-3]

LiAlH₄

$H_4Al_1Li_1$. M: 37.95. Greyish-white powder. Decomposes
on heating above 125°C releasing hydrogen. d: 0.92
kg/l. Hydrolysed by water and alcohols.
Production:
• lithium hydride + aluminium chloride, anhydrous
(dehydrochlorination)

Derivatives: silane
Uses: carbonyl/nitrile reduction reagent

lithium bromide
[7550-35-8]

LiBr

Br_1Li_1. M: 86.84. White, deliquescent powder. Anhydrous grade has MP: 547°C, d: 3.46 kg/l (25°C), solubility in water: 1.01 kg/l water (0°C). Sold commercially
as the anhydrous salt and as a solution in water.
Production:
• lithium carbonate + hydrobromic acid (salt formation)
Uses: heat-transfer fluids (air-conditioning/refrigeration)

lithium carbonate
[554-13-2]

Li₂CO₃

$C_1Li_2O_3$. M: 73.89.
Production:
• lithium-bearing ores + sulphuric acid + sodium
carbonate + calcium hydroxide (acid extraction
process)
• lithium-bearing ores + sodium carbonate (carbonate
extraction process)
• brine, residual + calcium oxide/dolomite, calcined
(precipitation; byproduct of magnesium hydroxide
production)
Derivatives: lithium bromide; lithium chloride; lithium
hydroxide; lithium silicate
Uses: flux (glass, enamel, ceramics production); aluminium melt electrolysis adjunct; psychiatric drug

lithium chloride
[7447-41-8]

LiCl

Cl_1Li_1. M: 42.39. White, deliquescent crystals. MP:
614°C. BP: 1,360°C. d: 2.07 kg/l (25°C). Solubility in
water: 770 g/l (20°C).
Production:
• lithium carbonate + hydrochloric acid (salt formation)
Derivatives: lithium; lithium hypochlorite; lithium trifluoromethanesulphonate
Uses:
drying agent (air dehumidification systems); battery
electrolyte

lithium hydride
[7580-67-8]

LiH

H_1Li_1. M: 7.95. White or grey crystals. MP: 680°C.
Decomposes in water releasing
Production:
• lithium + hydrogen (reaction)

Derivatives: lithium aluminium hydride
Uses:
raw material (hydrogen production); reducing agent

lithium hydroxide
[1310-65-2]

LiOH

$H_1Li_1O_1$. M: 23.95. White, deliquescent granules. MP:
470°C. Solubility in water: 64 g/l (20°C) forming
strongly alkaline solutions.
Production:
- lithium carbonate + calcium hydroxide (salt
  formation)
- lithium-bearing ores + limestone (lime fusion
  process)
Derivatives:
lithium 12-hydroxystearate; lithium stearate
Uses: esterification catalyst; alkaline storage batteries;
photographic developer ingredient

lithium 12-hydroxystearate
lithium hydroxystearate

OH
$CH_3(CH_2)_5CH(CH_2)_{10}COO^-$ Li^+

$C_{18}H_{35}Li_1O_3$. M: 306.42.
Production:
- lithium hydroxide + 12-hydroxystearic acid (salt
  formation)
Uses: lithium greases

lithium hypochlorite
[13840-33-0]

LiOCl

$Cl_1Li_1O_1$. M: 58.39. White, stable powder containing
about 12% available chlorine.
Production:
- lithium chloride + sodium hypochlorite (salt
  formation)
Uses: swimming pool disinfectant

lithium silicate
lithium metasilicate; [10102-24-6]

Li_2SiO_3

$Li_2O_3Si_1$. M: 89.97. White, crystalline powder. MP:
1,201°C. d: 2.52 kg/l (25°C). Insoluble in water.
Production:
- lithium carbonate + quartz (fusion)
Uses:
ceramic paste/welding electrode coating binder

lithium stearate
[4485-12-5]
$C_{18}H_{35}Li_1O_2$. M: 290.42.

$CH_3(CH_2)_{16}COO^-$ Li^+

Production:
- lithium hydroxide + stearic acid (salt formation)
Uses: lithium greases

lithium trifluoromethanesulphonate
Fluorad FC-124 (3M)

$F_3CSO_3^-$ Li^+

$C_1F_3Li_1O_3S_1$. M: 156.00.
Production:
- lithium chloride + trifluoromethanesulphonic acid
  (salt formation)
Uses:
battery electrolyte

Lithol Red *See:* Pigment Red 49

lithopone
zinc white; Pigment White 5 (CI); 77115 (CI);
[1345-05-7]

$BaSO_4.nZnS$

Production:
- zinc sulphate/zinc chloride + barium sulphide (salt
  formation)
Uses: pigment (printing inks)

LLDPE *See:* polyethylene, linear low-density

LNG *See:* natural gas

locust bean gum
carob gum; E410 (EC); [9000-40-2]
Yellow-green flour. Polysaccharide gum comprising the
endosperm of carob tree (*Ceratonia siliqua*) seeds. M:
~310,000. The tree is grown in southern Europe and
around the Mediterranean Sea.
Uses: paper dry-strength additive; food thickening/
stabilising agent

lofepramine
[23047-25-8]

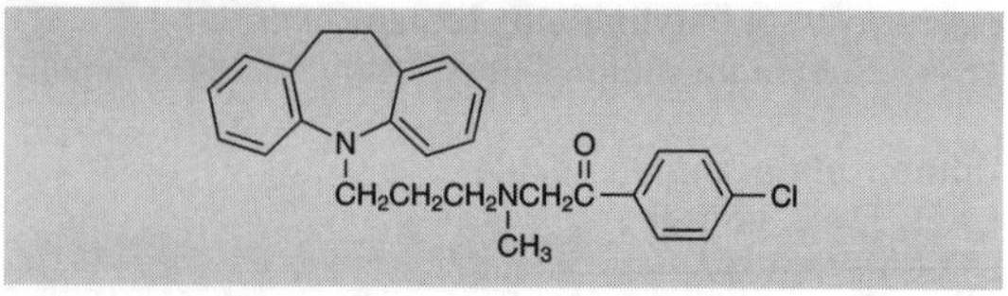

$C_{26}H_{27}Cl_1N_2O_1$. M: 418.97. Available commercially as
the hydrochloride.
Production:
- desipramine + α,4-dichloroacetophenone (amine
  formation)
Uses:
antidepressant drug

long residue
atmospheric residue; crude oil, reduced
Dark, viscous oil. BP: >350°C. Pour point: 30–40°C.
d: 0.90–0.98 kg/l. The chemical composition depends
on the source of the crude oil.
Production:
• crude oil (atmospheric distillation; coproduced with
  naphtha, light/naphtha, heavy/kerosene/gas oil,
  light/gas oil, heavy/refinery gas)
Derivatives:
bitumen; gas oil, heavy; gas oil, light; gas oil, vacuum;
gasoline, catalytic-cracker; heavy cycle oil; light cycle
oil; lubricant oils, distillates; naphtha, heavy; refinery
gas; short residue; synthesis gas
Uses:
boiler/industrial/marine/locomotive fuel oil blending
component; road oils

loperamide
[53179-11-6]; [34552-83-5]

C$_{29}$H$_{33}$Cl$_1$N$_2$O$_2$. M: 477.04. Available commercially as
the hydrochloride.
Production:
• 4-(4-chlorophenyl)-4-hydroxypiperidine + ethylene
  oxide + diphenamid (epoxidation/chlorination/
  dehydrochlorination)
Uses: antidiarrheal drug

lorazepam
Ativan (American Home Products); [846-49-1]

C$_{15}$H$_{10}$Cl$_2$N$_2$O$_2$. M: 321.16.
Production:
• 2-amino-2′,5-dichlorobenzophenone + hydroxylamine sulphate + chloroacetyl chloride + acetic
  anhydride (imine formation/amide formation/
  cyclisation/acid-catalysed rearrangement/Polonovsky
  rearrangement/saponification)
Uses:
anxiolytic/muscle relaxant drug

LPG *See:* liquified petroleum gas

LTAC *See:* dodecyltrimethylammonium chloride

LTDP *See:* dilauryl thiodipropionate

lubricant oils, base
base oils; petroleum oils
Lubricant base oils vary from light, fluid spindle oils
to heavy, viscous cylinder oils. In between are the base
oils used for motor and industrial lubricants. Oils originating from naphthenic crude oils have a low wax
content but also a low viscosity index. High viscosity
index oils are prepared by solvent extraction and dewaxing of base oils from paraffinic crude oils.
Production:
• lubricant oils, refined (urea dewaxing process/
  hydrogen finishing processes)
• lubricant oils, refined (ketone dewaxing processes/
  hydrogen finishing processes)
• lubricant oils, refined (catalytic dewaxing process)
Uses: acaricide/insecticide/herbicide; lubricating oil
blending component

lubricant oils, distillates
Lubricant base oils prior to refining and dewaxing. BP:
300–550°C. Light oils of this type are called 'spindle
oils'. The chemical composition and properties of the
oil vary with the source and nature of the crude oil.
Production:
• long residue (vacuum distillation; coproduced with
  gas oil, vacuum/short residue/bitumen)
Derivatives: brightstock; lubricant oils, hydrocracked;
lubricant oils, refined; naphthenic acid; sodium petroleum sulphonate; white oil

lubricant oils, hydrocracked
High viscosity index oils used in high-performance
motor lubricants. A typical viscosity index is 120.
Production:
• lubricant oils, distillates (hydrocracking; coproduced
  with brightstock)
Derivatives: lubricant oils, refined

lubricant oils, refined
Lubricating oils are refined by various processes primarily to remove or convert aromatic components. This
improves the chemical stability and viscosity index of
the oil.
Production:
• lubricant oils, distillates/lubricant oils, hydro-
  cracked/deasphalted oil (solvent refining)
• lubricant oils, distillates + sulphuric acid (dry
  refining process)
• lubricant oils, distillates/lubricant oils, hydrocracked
  (hydrorefining)
Derivatives: lubricant oils, base

lucanthone
1-(2-diethylaminoethylamino)-4-methylthiaxanthone;
[479-50-5] (free base); [548-57-2] (hydrochloride)

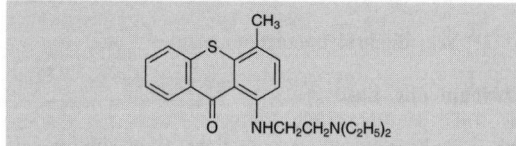

$C_{20}H_{24}N_2O_1S_1$. M: 340.48.
Production:
• 2-amino-4-nitrotoluene + thiosalicylic acid +
2-diethylaminoethyl chloride hydrochloride
(diazotisation/sulphide formation/cyclisation/nitro
reduction/amine formation)
Derivatives: hycanthone
Uses: anthelmintic drug

lumazine
2,4-dihydroxypteridine; [487-21-8]

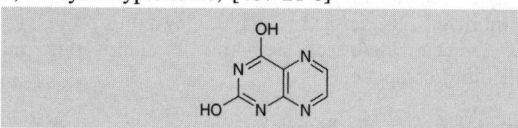

$C_6H_4N_4O_2$. M: 164.13. Yellow, crystalline solid. MP:
348°C. Soluble in oxygenated solvents.
Production:
• 2,4,5,6-tetraaminopyrimidine sulphate + glyoxal
(condensation/amide hydrolysis)
Derivatives: amiloride

2,6-lupetidine *See:* 2,6-dimethylpiperidine

2,6-lutidine
2,6-dimethylpyridine; [108-48-5]

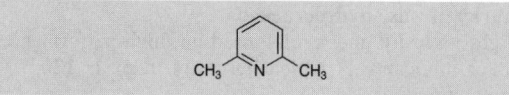

$C_7H_9N_1$. M: 107.16. Colourless to pale yellow liquid.
BP: 143–145°C. d: 0.92 kg/l (25°C). Miscible with
cold water. Less soluble in hot water.
Production:
• pyridine bases, crude (fractionation; coproduced
with pyridine/α-picoline/γ-picoline/3,4-lutidine/
pyridine bases)
Derivatives:
clopidol; 2,6-dimethylpiperidine; dipicolinic acid
Uses:
reagent (pharmaceutical manufacture); solvent

3,4-lutidine
2095115; 3,4-dimethylpyridine; [583-58-4]
$C_7H_9N_1$. M: 107.16. Pale yellow liquid. BP: 163–
164°C. d: 0.95 kg/l (25°C). Slightly soluble in water.
Soluble in oxygenated solvents.

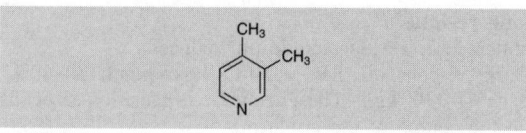

Production:
• pyridine bases, crude (fractionation; coproduced
with pyridine/α-picoline/γ-picoline/2,6-lutidine/
pyridine bases)
Derivatives: pentazocine; phenazocine

L-lysine
L-α,ε-diaminocaproic acid; Lys; [56-87-1]; [657-27-2]
(hydrochloride)

$$H_2NCH_2CH_2CH_2CH_2 - \overset{\overset{NH_2}{|}}{\underset{\underset{H}{|}}{C}} - COOH$$

$C_6H_{14}N_2O_2$. M: 146.19. Available commercially as the
naturally-occurring L(+)-enantiomer as the free base or
hydrochloride salt. White, crystalline solid. Decomposes
on heating above 220°C. Soluble in water. Slightly
soluble in alcohol.
Production:
• acetic acid + *Brevibacterium flavum* bacteria (Aji-
nomoto fermentation process)
• cyclohexene + nitrosyl chloride + ammonia (Toray
enzymatic hydrolysis process)
Derivatives: lisinopril; thymopentin
Uses: animal feed additive; raw material (peptide
drugs, pharmaceutical salts); diagnostic aids

mafenide
[138-39-6]; [138-37-4] (hydrochloride)

$C_7H_{10}N_2O_2S_1$. M: 186.23. Available commercially as the free base or as the hydrochloride or acetate salts.
Production:
• acetic anhydride + benzylamine + chlorosulphonic acid + ammonia (acetylation/chlorosulphonation/sulphonamide formation/amide hydrolysis)
Uses: sulfatolamide antibacterial drug component

magenta *See:* Basic Violet 14

magic acid *See:* trifluoromethanesulphonic acid

magnesia, caustic-calcined
magnesia, calcined; magnesia, chemical; magnesite, caustic-calcined; magnesium oxide; periclase; [1309-48-4]

MgO

Mg_1O_1. M: 40.31. White powder, granules or lumps.
Production:
• magnesium carbonate, natural/magnesium hydroxide (calcination)
• dolomite, calcined + carbon dioxide (Patterson and low pressure processes)
Derivatives: alkylbenzene sulphonates, alkali-earth salts; dialkylaryl sulphonates, alkali-earth salts; magnesium acetate; magnesium fluorosilicate; magnesium lauryl sulphate; magnesium stearate
Uses:
Sorel cement component (industrial flooring, wall plaster); dry-cleaning solvent decolouring agent; electrical heating rods; fertiliser ingredient; filler (toothpaste, cosmetics); uranium processing absorbent; animal feed ingredient; gelatine extraction agent; sulphur dioxide recovery material (sulphite pulp process); vulcanisation activator; water treatment chemical

magnesia, dead-burned
magnesia; magnesia, fused; magnesia, sintered; magnesium oxide; [1309-48-4]

MgO

Mg_1O_1. M: 40.31. Available as sintered or fused magnesia. Shaped products of fused magnesia are manufactured by melting the formed shape in an electric furnace at 2,800–3,000°C.

Production:
• magnesium carbonate, natural/magnesium hydroxide (calcination)
Uses: fused magnesia (high-temperature crucibles, electrical heating elements); magnesite-chrome refractory bricks; magnesite refractory bricks (steel furnaces); lightweight building board

magnesite *See:* magnesium carbonate, natural

magnesium
[7439-95-4]

Mg

Mg_1. M: 24.31. Silvery-white metal available as bars, wire and ribbon. MP: 651°C. BP: 1100°C. d: 1.74 kg/l.
Production:
• magnesium chloride (melt electrolysis; coproduced with chlorine)
• dolomite, calcined + ferrosilicon (silicothermal reduction)
Derivatives: beryllium; boron carbide; n-butylmagnesium chloride; 4-(4-chlorophenyl)-4-hydroxypiperidine; ethylmagnesium bromide; methylmagnesium bromide; methylmagnesium chloride; phenylmagnesium bromide; phenylmagnesium chloride; tetra-n-octyltin; titanium; titanium diboride; triphenylphosphine; uranium metal, U^{235} enriched; zirconium
Uses: deoxiding agent (nickel production); desulphurising/deoxiding agent (steel production); aluminium-magnesium alloys (can tops); fireworks ingredient; magnesium-zinc alloys; Grignard reagent; reagent (aluminothermic processes); sacrificial anodes (tanks, pipelines corrosion protection)

magnesium acetate
[142-72-3]

$(CH_3COO)_2Mg$

$C_4H_6Mg_1O_4$. M: 142.40. Available as the tetrahydrate. White solid. MP: 80°C. d: 1.45 kg/l. Soluble in water.
Production:
• magnesia, caustic-calcined/magnesium carbonate, basic + acetic acid (salt formation)
Uses: cathartic drug; textile dyeing/printing auxiliary

magnesium carbonate, basic
hydromagnesite; magnesia alba; [39409-82-0]

$4MgCO_3.Mg(OH)_2$

$C_4H_2Mg_5O_{14}$. M: 395.61. Available as the tetrahydrate.

White, bulky powder. Decomposes on heating above 700°C releasing carbon dioxide. Slightly soluble in water.
Production:
- brine, residual + ammonium bicarbonate (salt formation)
- magnesium hydroxide + carbon dioxide (salt formation)
- dolomite, calcined + carbon dioxide (salt formation/calcination)

Derivatives: magnesium acetate
Uses:
filler (paper, plastics, rubber); antacid drug; anticaking agent (salt); nitric acid concentration reagent; thermal insulation

magnesium carbonate, natural
magnesite

$$MgCO_3$$

$C_1Mg_1O_3$. M: 84.32. Naturally occurring mineral mined in many parts of the world.
Derivatives:
magnesia, caustic-calcined; magnesia, dead-burned; magnesium chloride; magnesium sulphate
Uses:
filler (paper, plastics, rubber); fire extinguishant powder; fireproofing agent; flattening agent (paints, printing inks); polishing compounds; magnesia insulation

magnesium chloride
[7791-18-6]

$$MgCl_2$$

Cl_2Mg_1. M: 95.22. Available commercially as the hexahydrate. White, deliquescent flakes. MP: 118°C with decomposition. d: 1.56 kg/l (25°C). Solubility in water: 6.09 kg/l water (25°C). Anhydrous and sesquihydrate grades are used as intermediates, particularly as feedstocks for magnesium production.
Production:
- magnesium carbonate, natural + chlorine + seawater (Norsk-Hydro process)
- magnesium carbonate, natural + chlorine + carbon monoxide (MPLC process)
- magnesium carbonate, natural + hydrochloric acid (salt formation)
- magnesium hydroxide + hydrochloric acid (salt formation)

Derivatives: chlorine; magnesium
Uses:
Sorel cement component (industrial flooring, wall plaster); curing agent (textile finishes); dust binder/road consolidation agent (construction, mining); fireproofing agent (wood); fertiliser granulation aid; sugar processing reagent; lightweight building board; refrigerant brines; thawing agent

magnesium fluorosilicate
magnesium hexafluorosilicate; magnesium silicofluoride; [16949-65-8]

$$MgSiF_6$$

$F_6Mg_1Si_1$. M: 166.39. Available commercially as the hexahydrate. White crystals. Decomposes on heating above 120°C. d: 1.79 kg/l. Solubility in water: 1.07 kg/l water (20°C) forming acidic solutions.
Production:
- magnesia, caustic-calcined + hexafluorosilicic acid (salt formation)

Uses:
insect resist agent (wool treatment); wood preservative

magnesium gluconate

$$\left[HOCH_2(CHOH)_4COO^-\right]_2 Mg^{2+}$$

$C_{12}H_{22}Mg_1O_{14}$. M: 414.61. White, crystalline powder. Soluble in water.
Production:
- sodium gluconate + magnesium sulphate (salt formation)

Uses: animal feed additive; mineral supplement

magnesium hexafluorosilicate
See: magnesium fluorosilicate

magnesium hydroxide
brucite; magnesium hydrate; [1309-42-8]

$$Mg(OH)_2$$

$H_2Mg_1O_2$. M: 58.33. White granules. Decomposes on heating above 120°C. Solubility in water: 2.81 kg/l (0°C).
Production:
- seawater + calcium oxide/dolomite, calcined (salt formation)
- natural brines + calcium oxide (precipitation; coproduced with calcium chloride)
- brine, residual + calcium oxide/dolomite, calcined (precipitation)

Derivatives:
magnesia, caustic-calcined; magnesia, dead-burned; magnesium carbonate, basic; magnesium chloride
Uses: drying agent; fire-retardant filler (plastics); flue gas desulphurisation agent; fuel oil additive; antacid drug; sugar processing reagent; ferrite ceramics raw material; raw material (sulphite pulp process); water treatment chemical

magnesium lauryl sulphate
[3097-08-3]

$$\left[CH_3(CH_2)_{11}OSO_3^-\right]_2 Mg^{2+}$$

$C_{24}H_{50}Mg_1O_8S_2$. M: 555.09. Available commercially as the pure solid or as a 25–30% solution in water.

Production:
- *n*-alkanol(C_{12}-C_{13})/*n*-alkanol(C_{12}-C_{14}) + magnesia, caustic-calcined (sulphation/salt formation)

Uses: surfactant (toothpaste, shampoos)

magnesium oxide
See: magnesia, caustic-calcined; magnesia, dead-burned

magnesium stearate
[557-04-0]

$$[CH_3(CH_2)_{16}COO]_2Mg$$

$C_{36}H_{70}Mg_1O_4$. M: 591.27. White powder. MP: 145°C. Insoluble in water and alcohol. The commercial material contains 5–10% magnesium oxide.
Production:
- magnesia, caustic-calcined + stearic acid (salt formation)

Uses: amino resins processing lubricant; cosmetics/pharmaceuticals ingredient

magnesium sulphate
Epsom salts; [7487-88-9]

$$MgSO_4$$

$Mg_1O_4S_1$. M: 120.37. The anhydrous salt is a colourless, crystalline solid. Solubility in water: 360 g/l (20°C). Kieserite is a natural mineral ($MgSO_4.1H_2O$) which is mined and used for lower grade applications. Epsomite (Epsom salts) is the heptahydrate. It loses its water of crystallisation when heated above 150°C.
Production:
- seawater/magnesium carbonate, natural + sulphuric acid (salt formation)
- brine, residual (separation)
- natural potash salt deposits (mining/separation; byproduct of potassium chloride production)

Derivatives:
magnesium gluconate; petroleum sulphonates, alkali-earth salts; potassium magnesium sulphate; potassium sulphate
Uses: cathartic drug; dyeing/printing auxiliary; fertiliser ingredient; animal feed additive; lightweight building board; raw material (magnesia refractory bricks); fireproofing agent (textiles); speciality paper additive

magnetite *See:* iron oxide black

mahogany oil *See:* sodium petroleum sulphonate

maize gluten
corn gluten
Protein component of maize seed, separated during starch production.
Production:
- maize (milling/separation; coproduced with starch/maize bran)

Derivatives: protein hydrolysates; zein
Uses: animal feed ingredient

maize oil
corn oil; [8001-30-7]
Pale yellow liquid. Titre: 14–20°C. Saponification value: 188–193 mg KOH/g. d: 0.92 kg/l (25°C). Insoluble in water. Soluble in chlorinated and aromatic solvents. The chain-length distribution is: 8–19% $C_{16:0}$, 19–50% $C_{18:1}$ and 34–62% $C_{18:2}$.
Production:
- maize bran (expression/alkali refining)

Uses: cooking/salad oil; margarine ingredient; semi-drying oil (paints)

Malachite Green *See:* Basic Green 4

malathion
S-1,2-bis(ethoxycarbonyl)ethyl-*O,O*-dimethylphosphorodithioate; [121-75-5]

$$\begin{array}{cc} O & S \\ \| & \| \\ C_2H_5OCCHSP(OCH_3)_2 \\ | \\ CH_2COOC_2H_5 \end{array}$$

$C_{10}H_{19}O_6P_1S_2$. M: 330.35.
Production:
- diethyl maleate + *O,O*-dimethyl dithiophosphoric acid (addition)

Uses: insecticide/acaricide

maleic acid
ethylenedicarboxylic acid; [110-16-7]

$$\begin{array}{c} CHCOOH \\ \| \\ CHCOOH \end{array}$$

$C_4H_4O_4$. M: 116.07. White solid. MP: 138–139°C from water, 130°C from alcohol. Rearranges partially to fumaric acid when heated above melting point. Solubility in water: 441 g/l solution (25°C).
Production:
- maleic anhydride (hydration)

Derivatives:
N-cyclohexylmaleimide; dibutyltin maleate; dioctyltin maleate; thiomalic acid
Uses: coloured aluminium anodising reagent

maleic anhydride
MA; MAN; [108-31-6]

$C_4H_2O_3$. M: 98.06. White briquettes or molten liquid. MP: 53°C. BP: 202°C. d: 1.47 kg/l (20°C). d: 1.2 kg/l (70°C). Soluble in water forming maleic acid. Soluble in oxygenated solvents.

Production:
- raffinate II/*n*-butane (oxidation)
- benzene (gas-phase oxidation)
- *o*-xylene (gas-phase oxidation; byproduct of phthalic anhydride production)
- naphthalene fraction (gas-phase oxidation; byproduct of phthalic anhydride production)

Derivatives: bismaleimide prepolymers; bismethylenedianiline maleimide; 1,4-butanediol; *t*-butyl monoperoxymaleate; diallyl maleate; di-*n*-butyl maleate; dibutyltin bis(isooctylmaleate); di-(2-ethylhexyl) maleate; diethyl maleate; dimethyl maleate; disodium coconut monoethanolamide sulphosuccinate; disodium *N*-cocoylsulphosuccinamate; disodium isodecylsulphosuccinate; disodium lauryl ether sulphosuccinate; disodium laurylsulphosuccinate; disodium oleic monoisopropanolamide sulphosuccinate; disodium *N*-oleylsulphosuccinamate; disodium *N*-stearylsulphosuccinamate; dodecenylsuccinic anhydride; endothal-sodium; ethylene-maleic anhydride copolymers; fumaric acid; HET anhydride; hydrocarbon-maleic resins; maleic acid; maleic hydrazide; maleic resins; maleinised oils; DL-malic acid; methylenebis(maleimide); methyl tetrahydrophthalic anhydride; nadic anhydride; octenylsuccinic anhydride; *m*-phenylenebismaleimide; *N*-phenylmaleimide; piperylene-maleic anhydride adducts; polyisobutenylsuccinic anhydride; poly(maleic acid); poly(methyl vinyl ether-maleic anhydride); pyridate; sodium bistridecylsulphosuccinate; sodium diamylsulphosuccinate; sodium dihexylsulphosuccinate; sodium diisobutylsulphosuccinate; sodium diisooctylsulphosuccinate; sodium starch sulphosuccinate; starch, amphoteric; styrene-maleic anhydride copolymers; succinic acid; succinic anhydride; tetrahydrofuran; tetrahydrophthalic anhydride; tetrasodium *N*-(1,2-dicarboxyethyl)-*N*-octadecylsulphosuccinamate; 2,4,6-tribromophenylmaleimide; unsaturated polyester resins, coating grades; unsaturated polyester resins, general grades; unsaturated polyester resins, isophthalate grades

Uses:
alkyd resin/poly(methyl methacrylate)/crosslinked polymer polyol comonomer

maleic hydrazide

1,2-dihydropyridazine-3,6-dione; MH; [10071-13-3]; [51542-52-0] (potassium salt); [28330-26-9] (sodium salt)

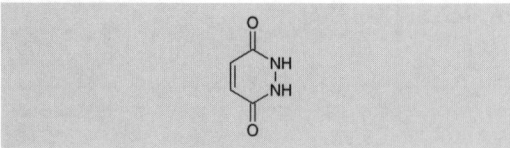

$C_4H_4N_2O_2$. M: 112.08. Available commercially as the potassium or sodium salts.

Production:
- maleic anhydride + hydrazine (amide formation)

Derivatives: 3,6-dichloropyridazine
Uses: plant growth regulator

maleic resins

fumaric resins

Available commercially in several different grades depending on the type and ratio of raw material used in the manufacture. Glycol-soluble maleic resins have a high acid value (280–320 mg KOH/g), spirit-soluble maleics, a medium acid value (90–130 mg KOH/g) and hydrocarbon-soluble maleics a low acid value (<25 mg KOH/g). Softening point: 120–160°C. Fumaric acid increases the acid value and softening point. Polyhydric alcohols reduce the acid value and alter the solubility characteristics.

Production:
- abietic acid/rosin, tall oil/rosin, wood/rosin, gum + maleic anhydride/fumaric acid + pentaerythritol/glycerol (condensation)

Uses: gloss/adhesion promoter (alkyd resins, nitrocellulose lacquers); dry-strength additive (paper); binder (varnishes, stoving lacquers, printing inks)

maleinised oils

linseed oil, maleinised
Production:
- linseed oil/tall oil fatty acid/tung oil/castor oil, dehydrated/soyabean oil + glycerol/pentaerythritol + maleic anhydride (esterification)

Derivatives: alkyd resins, water-soluble
Uses: drying oil (paints, printing inks)

DL-malic acid

hydroxysuccinic acid; [617-48-1]

$$\underset{HOOCCH_2\overset{\overset{\displaystyle OH}{|}}{C}HCOOH}{}$$

$C_4H_6O_5$. M: 134.08. White crystals. MP: 131–133°C. d: 1.60 kg/l (20°C). Soluble in water and oxygenated solvents.

Production:
- maleic anhydride (hydration/isomerisation; coproduced with fumaric acid)

Uses:
acidulant (soft drinks, fruit juice, canned vegetables, preserves); preservative (cosmetics, toiletry, pharmaceuticals); aluminium anodising reagent; sequesterant (metal cleaners); chrome plating reagent; electrodeless nickel coating reagent; textile finishing agent

L-malic acid

(*S*)-malic acid; [97-67-6]

$$\begin{array}{c} COOH \\ | \\ HO\blacktriangleright C\blacktriangleleft H \\ | \\ CH_2COOH \end{array}$$

$C_4H_6O_5$. M: 134.08. White, crystalline solid. MP:

100–103°C. Decomposes on heating above 180°C. Solubility in water: 580 g/l water (25°C). Soluble in oxygenated solvents.
Production:
• fumaric acid + *Brevibacterium ammoniagenes* bacteria (microbial conversion)
Uses: flavour enhancer/acidity regulator (soft drinks, foods, cosmetics, toothpaste)

malonamide nitrile *See:* cyanoacetamide

malonic acid
[141-82-2]

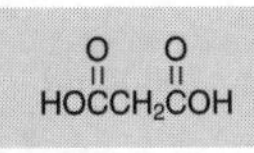

$$\underset{\text{HOCCH}_2\text{COH}}{\overset{\text{O} \quad \text{O}}{||\quad\quad||}}$$

$C_3H_4O_4$. M: 104.06. White, crystalline solid. MP: 135°C with decomposition. Solubility in water: 735 g/l water (20°C). Soluble in alcohol.
Production:
• malononitrile (nitrile hydrolysis)
• cyanoacetic acid (nitrile hydrolysis)
Derivatives:
diethyl malonate; dimethyl malonate; Meldrum's acid
Uses:
silver plating brightening agent; blowing agent (foamed plastics); tanning auxiliary

malononitrile
dicyanomethane; malonic dinitrile; malonitrile; MDN; [109-77-3]

$$\text{CH}_2(\text{CN})_2$$

$C_3H_2N_2$. M: 66.06. White solid. MP: 32–34°C. BP: 218°C. d: 1.19 kg/l (20°C). Soluble in water and oxygenated solvents.
Production:
• acetonitrile + cyanogen chloride (dehydrochlorination)
Derivatives:
o-chlorobenzalmalononitrile; 3-cyano-4-methyl-6-hydroxy-2-pyridone; Disperse Yellow 99; malonic acid; 5-nitroso-2,4,6-triaminopyrimidine

malonylurea *See:* barbituric acid

maltitol
4-*O*-α-D-glucopyranosyl-D-glucitol; [585-88-6]

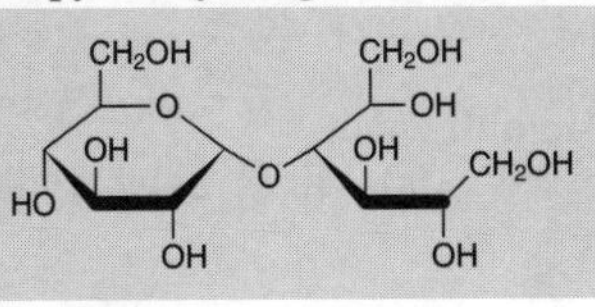

$C_{12}H_{24}O_{11}$. M: 344.31.
Production:
• high-maltose syrup (hydrogenation)
Uses: artificial sweetener

maltodextrin
Glucose syrup containing a relatively low proportion of D-glucose. Different grades are characterised by their reduced sugar content expressed in terms of dextrose equivalents (DE). Maltodextrins have DE<20.
Production:
• starch + hydrochloric acid (acid conversion)
• starch + α-amylase, bacterial (enzyme conversion)
Uses:
flavour carrier (prepared foods); food bulking agent (cake/drink mixes); baby food; salad dressing; frozen desserts

maltol
3-hydroxy-2-methyl-4-pyrone; [118-71-8]

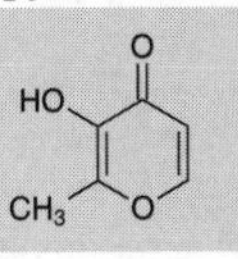

$C_6H_6O_3$. M: 126.12. White crystals with a caramel-like odour. MP: 162–164°C.
Production:
• wood tar, hardwood (extraction; coproduced with 3-methyl-2-cyclopenten-2-ol-1-one)
• 2-acetylfuran (rearrangement/oxidation)
Uses: flavour enhancer; flavouring ingredient

maltose

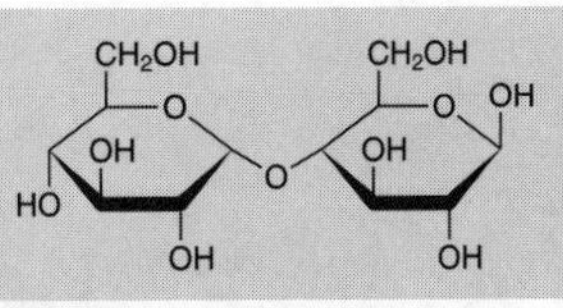

$C_{12}H_{22}O_{11}$. M: 342.30. White crystals. MP: 102–103°C. d: 1.54 kg/l. Soluble in water. Available commercially as the monohydrate.
Production:
• glucose syrup (enzymatic hydrolysis)
Uses: food ingredient; microbial fermentation nutrient; parenteral nutrient ingredient

MAN *See:* methacrylonitrile; maleic anhydride

mancozeb
[8018-01-7]

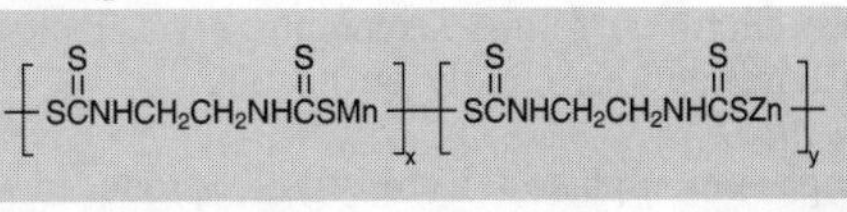

Complex, polymeric salt of ethylenebis(dithiocarbanic acid) with manganese (20%) and zinc (2.55%).
Production:
• nabam + manganous chloride + zinc chloride (salt formation)
Uses: fungicide

D-mandelic acid

D-α-hydroxyphenylacetic acid; D-2-hydroxy-2-phenyl-acetic acid; D-phenylglycollic acid; [17199-29-0]

$C_8H_8O_3$. M: 152.15. Crystalline solid comprising the (R)-$(-)$-enantiomer. MP: 131–134°C. d: 1.34 kg/l. Soluble in water and oxygenated solvents.
Production:
• DL-mandelic acid (racemate separation)
Derivatives: azidocillin; cefamandole
Uses: racemate separation agent

DL-mandelic acid

phenylglycollic acid; phenylglyconic acid; α-phenyl-hydroxyacetic acid; [90-64-2]

$C_8H_8O_3$. M: 152.15. White, crystalline solid. MP: 120–121°C. d: 1.30 kg/l (20°C). Soluble in water and oxygenated solvents.
Production:
• benzaldehyde + sodium cyanide (cyanohydrin formation/nitrile hydrolysis)
Derivatives: cyclandelate; D-mandelic acid
Uses: urinary antibacterial drug

maneb

[12427-38-2]

Complex, polymeric salt of ethylenebis(dithiocarbanic acid) with manganese.
Production:
• nabam + manganese sulphate (salt formation)
Uses: fungicide

manganese

[7439-96-5]

Mn

Mn_1. M: 54.94. Silver-grey, hard, brittle metal. Exists in four allotropic forms. Decomposes water slowly at room temperatures, rapidly on heating.
Production:
• manganese sulphate (electrolysis; coproduced with manganese dioxide)
Derivatives: manganous chloride
Uses:
aluminium/copper/nickel/silver/titanium alloying ingredient (chemical/electrical resistance applications); manganese bronze ingredient

manganese carbonate

manganous carbonate; rhodochrosite; [598-62-9]

$MnCO_3$

$C_1Mn_1O_3$. M: 114.95. Pink powder. Insoluble in water.
Production:
• manganese sulphate + ammonium bicarbonate (salt formation)
Derivatives: manganese dioxide; manganous chloride
Uses: animal feed additive; welding rod ingredient

manganese chloride *See:* manganous chloride

manganese dioxide

manganese(IV) oxide; manganic oxide; MD; CMD; EMD; [1313-13-9]

MnO_2

Mn_1O_2. M: 86.94. Dark brown granules or crystalline powder. d: 5.03 kg/l. Several grades of manganese dioxide are available commercially. The main types of product are: battery grade, chemical manganese dioxide (CMD) and electrolytic manganese dioxide (EMD).
Production:
• manganese ores + sulphuric acid (acid extraction; coproduced with manganese sulphate)
• manganese ores (nitrogen oxides process)
• manganese carbonate + sodium chlorate (thermal oxidation)
• manganese sulphate (electrolysis; coproduced with manganese)
Derivatives:
p-anisaldehyde; ferrite; manganese tetroxide; manganic oxide; manganous chloride
Uses: dry-cell/alkali/zinc chloride/zinc-carbon batteries; polysulphide rubber curing agent; colourant (bricks, ceramics, tiles, frits); ferrite ceramics ingredient; oxidising agent

manganese dodecenylsuccinate

$C_9H_{19}CH=CHCH_2CHCOO^-$ Mn^{2+}
CH_2COO^-

$C_{16}H_{26}Mn_1O_4$. M: 337.33.
Production:
• dodecenylsuccinic anhydride + manganese sulphate (salt formation)
Uses: jet fuel antistatic additive

manganese naphthenate

Brown resin. MP: 130–140°C. Soluble in hydrocarbon solvents.
Production:
• manganese sulphate + naphthenic acid (salt formation)
Uses: unsaturated polyester resin catalyst accelerator; paint drier

manganese sulphate
manganous sulphate; [7785-87-7]

MnSO₄

$Mn_1O_4S_1$. M: 151.00. Pale red crystals. Commercial grades contain 29.5–32.0% Mn corresponding to the mono- or dihydrate. Loses water of crystallisation when heated above 400°C. Soluble in water. Manganese sulphate is also produced as a byproduct of oxidation reactions in which manganese dioxide is used as the oxidising agent.
Production:
• manganous oxide + sulphuric acid (salt formation)
• manganese ores + sulphuric acid (acid extraction; coproduced with manganese dioxide)
Derivatives: maneb; manganese; manganese carbonate; manganese dioxide; manganese dodecenylsuccinate; manganese naphthenate; manganese tallate
Uses:
fertiliser/animal feed additive; glass/porcelain ingredient

manganese tallate
Brown liquid or paste comprising 3–10% manganese in a hydrocarbon solvent.
Production:
• manganese sulphate + tall oil fatty acid (salt formation)
Uses: paint drier

manganese tetroxide
hausmannite; manganese oxide; [1317-35-7]

Mn₃O₄

Mn_3O_4. M: 228.81. Brownish-black powder. d: 4.7 kg/l. Insoluble in water.
Production:
• manganese dioxide (thermal reduction)
Uses: magnetic tape/semiconductor manufacture

manganic oxide
manganese(III) oxide; manganese sesquioxide

Mn₂O₃

Mn_2O_3. M: 157.88. Brownish-black powder. d: 4.81 kg/l. Insoluble in water. Releases oxygen when heated to 1,080°C.
Production:
• manganese dioxide (thermal reduction)
Uses: magnetic tape/semiconductor manufacture

manganous chloride
manganese chloride; [7773-01-5]

MnCl₂

Cl_2Mn_1. M: 125.85. Anhydrous grades are pink crystals. MP: 650°C. d: 2.98 kg/l (25°C). Solubility in water: 723 g/l (25°C). Tetrahydrate grades are rose-

coloured crystals which lose water when heated above 106°C. Solubility in water: 1.51 kg/l (8°C).
Production:
• manganese dioxide + hydrogen chloride, anhydrous (Weldon process)
• manganous oxide/manganese carbonate + hydrochloric acid (salt formation)
• ferromanganese/manganese + chlorine (reaction)
Derivatives: mancozeb
Uses: brick colorant; dry batteries; corrosion-resistant magnesium alloys

manganous oxide
manganese monoxide; manganese(II) oxide; manganosite

MnO

Mn_1O_1. M: 70.94. Green powder. MP: 1,650°C. d: 5.18 kg/l. Insoluble in water.
Production:
• manganese ores + metallurgical coke (reduction)
Derivatives:
manganese sulphate; manganous chloride
Uses: fertiliser additive; animal feed additive; oxide ceramics ingredient

manila resin
[9000-14-0]
Exuded, soft oleoresin from *Agathis alba* trees which grow in the Philippines. Softening point: 120–130°C (Ring and Ball Method). d: ~1.07 kg/l. Acid value: 120–150 mg KOH/g. Soluble in alcohol. Insoluble in esters and hydrocarbons.
Uses: binder (road marking paints, insulation varnishes, flexographic inks)

mannitol
manna sugar; E421 (EC); [69-65-8]

CH₂OH
HOCH
HOCH
HCOH
HCOH
CH₂OH

$C_6H_{14}O_6$. M: 182.17. White granules or powder with a sweetish taste. d: 1.52 kg/l (20°C). Soluble in water. Slightly soluble in oxygenated solvents. Insoluble in vegetable and mineral oils.
Production:
• invert sugar (hydrogenation; coproduced with sorbitol)
Uses: sweetener (bakery goods, chewing gum, confectionary, pharmaceuticals); polyvinyl chloride heat co-stabilisers

MAP *See:* monoammonium phosphate; *m*-aminophenol

maprotiline
[10262-69-8]; [10347-81-6] (hydrochloride)

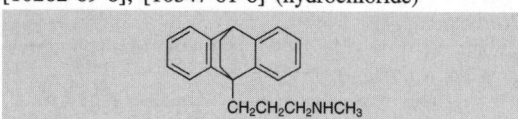

CH₂CH₂CH₂NHCH₃

$C_{20}H_{23}N_1$. M: 277.41. Available commercially as the free base or hydrochloride.
Production:
• anthracene + 3-dimethylaminopropyl chloride hydrochloride + ethylene + ethyl chloroformate (Friedel-Crafts alkylation/cycloaddition/demethylation)
Uses: antidepressant drug

MAPTAC *See:* 3-(methacrylamidopropyl)trimethyl-ammonium chloride

marjoram oil
Yellow-green liquid with a spicy odour. d: ~0.90 kg/l (25°C). Insoluble in water. Soluble in oxygenated and chlorinated solvents. Produced by steam distillation of the flowering tops of *Origanum marjorana* which is grown in France, Germany, Spain, Hungary, Tunisia and the USA.
Uses: flavouring ingredient

mastic
Exuded oleoresin from *Pistachia lentiscus* shrubs which grow in Greece. Pale yellow 'tears'. Soluble in oxygenated and aromatic solvents.
Uses:
incense; binder (paper/picture varnishes)

mazindol

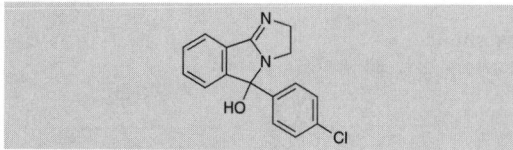

HO

Cl

$C_{16}H_{13}Cl_1N_2O_1$. M: 284.74.
Production:
• 2-(4-chlorobenzoyl)benzoic acid + ethylenediamine (multistep synthesis)
Uses: appetite reduction drug

MBA
See: 1-phenylethanol; *N,N'*-methylenebisacrylamide

MBAA *See:* bromoacetic acid

MBC *See:* carbendazim

MBI *See:* 2-mercaptobenzimidazole

MBMC *See:* 6-*t*-butyl-*m*-cresol

MBPM *See:* benzyl phenylmalonate

MBS *See:* methyl methacrylate-butadiene-styrene co-polymers; 2-morpholinobenzothiazylsulphenamide

MBSS *See:* 2-morpholinodithiobenzothiazole

MBT *See:* 2-mercaptobenzothiazole; methylene bisthio-cyanate

MBTS *See:* 2,2'-dibenzothiazyl disulphide

MC *See:* methyl cellulose

MCA *See:* chloroacetic acid

MCOPP *See:* chloro-*o*-phenylphenol

MCPA *See:* 2-methyl-4-chlorophenoxyacetic acid

MCPA-(2-hydroxybutyl)
2-hydroxybutyl (4-chloro-2-methylphenoxy)acetate

$C_{13}H_{17}Cl_1O_4$. M: 272.73. Commonly solid in mixtures with 2,4-D-2-hydroxybutyl.
Production:
• 2-methyl-4-chlorophenoxyacetic acid + 1,2-butylene oxide (epoxidation)
Uses: herbicide

MCPA-isooctyl
isooctyl 4-chloro-2-methylphenoxyacetate

$C_{17}H_{25}Cl_1O_3$. M: 312.84.
Production:
• isooctanol + 2-methyl-4-chlorophenoxyacetic acid (esterification)
Uses: herbicide

MCPA-thioethyl
sodium 4-(4-chloro-2-methylphenoxy)butyrate;
[25319-90-8]

$C_{11}H_{13}Cl_1O_2S_1$. M: 244.73.
Production:
• ethyl mercaptan + 2-methyl-4-chlorophenoxyacetic acid (thioesterification)
Uses: herbicide

MCPB-sodium
[94-81-5]

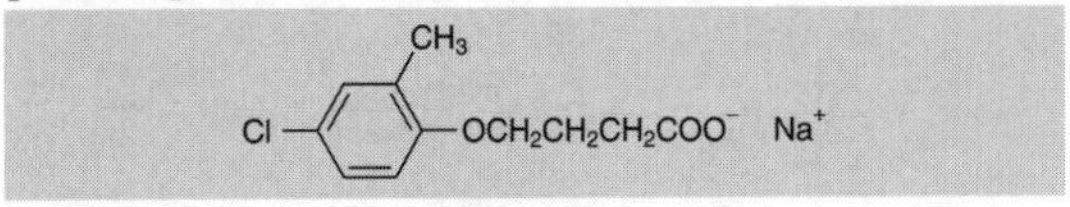

$C_{11}H_{12}Cl_1Na_1O_3$. M: 250.66.
Production:
• *p*-chloro-*o*-cresol + γ-butyrolactone + sodium
  hydroxide (esterification/salt formation)
Uses: herbicide

MD *See:* manganese dioxide

MDA *See:* 4,4′-diaminodiphenylmethane; 4,4′-diamino-diphenylmethane, pure

MDAC *See:* 7-diethylamino-4-methylcoumarin

MDC *See:* methylene chloride

MDCHA *See:* *N*-methyldicyclohexylamine

MDEA *See:* methyldiethanolamine

MDI *See:* 4,4′-diphenylmethane diisocyanate, polymeric; 4,4′-diphenylmethane diisocyanate, pure grade

MDMH *See:* monomethylol dimethylhydantoin

MDN *See:* malononitrile

MDT *See:* 2-methylmercapto-4,6-dichlorotriazine

2-ME *See:* ethylene glycol monomethyl ether

MEA
See: ethylamine; monoethanolamine; *N*-ethylaniline

mebendazole
[31431-39-7]

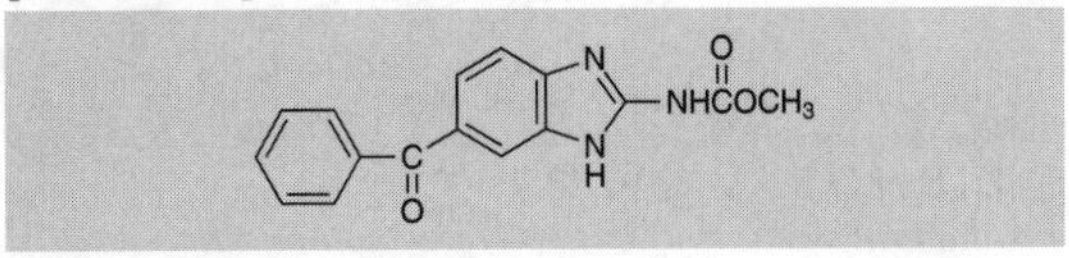

$C_{16}H_{13}N_3O_3$. M: 295.30.
Production:
• *p*-chlorobenzophenone + ammonia + *O*-methyl-isourea sulphate + methyl chloroformate (nitration/ammoniation/condensation/dehydrochlorination)
Uses: anthelmintic drug

mebeverine
[3625-06-7]; [2753-45-9] (hydrochloride)
$C_{25}H_{35}N_1O_5$. M: 429.55. Available commercially as the
hydrochloride.

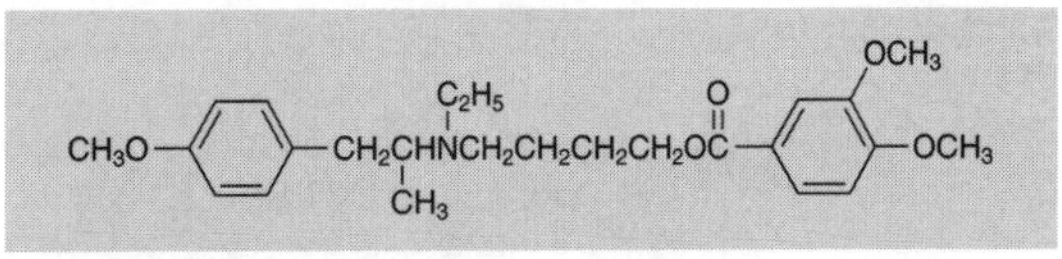

Production:
• *p*-methoxyphenylacetone + ethylamine + ethyl
  succinyl chloride + veratric acid (reductive
  amination/amide formation/ester reduction/
  esterification)
Uses: antispasmodic drug

mecarbam
S-(*N*-ethoxycarbonyl-*N*-methylcarbamoylmethyl) *O,O*-diethyl phosphorodithioate; [2595-54-2]

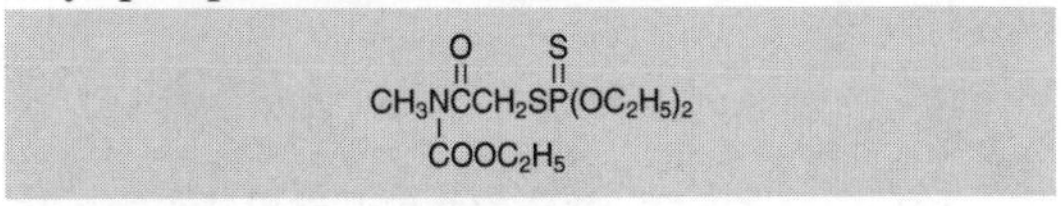

$C_{10}H_{20}N_1O_5P_1S_2$. M: 329.37.
Production:
• chloroacetyl chloride + methylamine + *O,O*-diethyl
  dithiophosphoric acid + ethyl chloroformate (amide
  formation/dehydrochlorination/dehydrochlorination)
Uses:
insecticide/acaricide

mecillinam
amdinocillin; [32887-01-7]

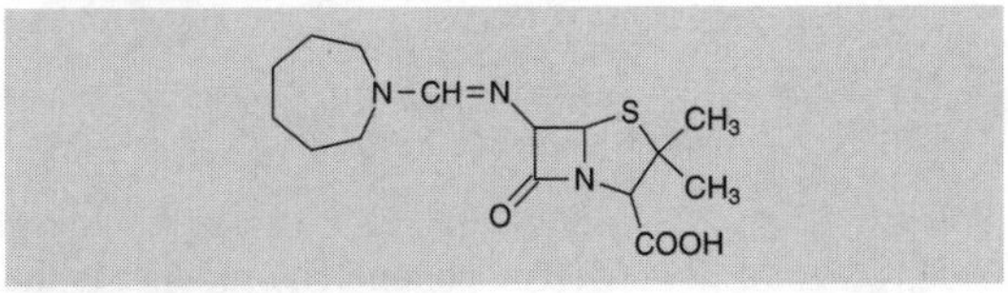

$C_{15}H_{23}N_3O_3S_1$. M: 325.42.
Production:
• hexamethyleneimine + formic acid + 6-aminopen-
  icillanic acid (amide formation/imine formation)
Derivatives:
pivmecillinam
Uses: antibacterial drug

meclofenamic acid
[644-62-2]

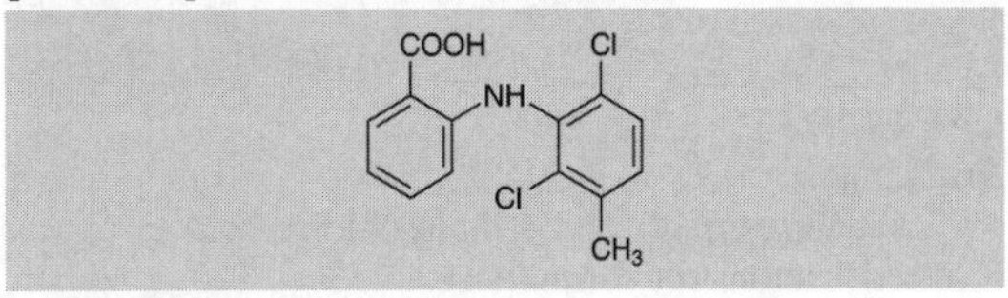

$C_{14}H_{11}Cl_2N_1O_2$. M: 296.16.
Production:
• *m*-toluidine + *o*-chlorobenzoic acid (sulphonation/
  ring chlorination/desulphonation/amine formation)
Uses:
antiinflammatory drug

meclofenoxate

[51-68-3]

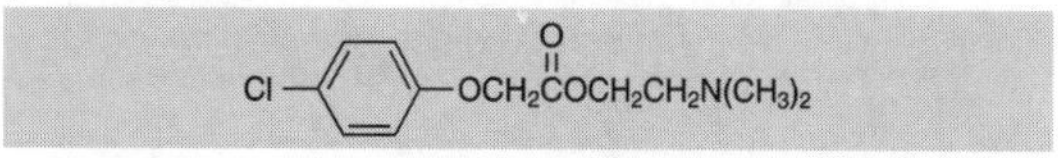

Cl—⟨benzene⟩—$OCH_2COCH_2CH_2N(CH_3)_2$

$C_{12}H_{16}Cl_1N_1O_3$. M: 257.72. Available commercially as the free base or hydrochloride.
Production:
- *p*-chlorophenol + chloroacetic acid + 2-dimethyl-aminoethyl chloride hydrochloride (ether formation/esterification)

Uses: cerebral stimulant drug

mecoprop

2-(4-chloro-2-methylphenoxy)propionic acid; [7085-19-0]

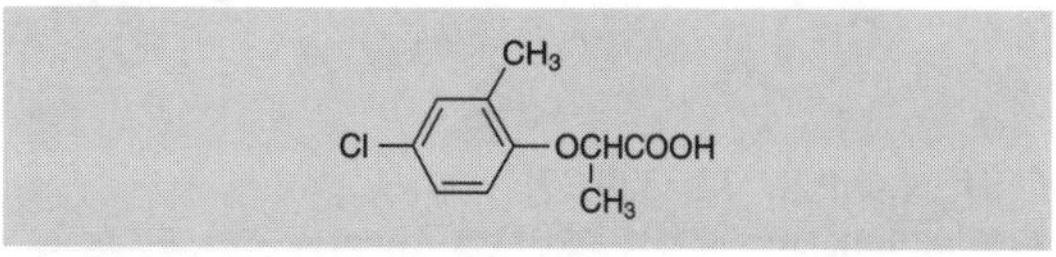

Cl—⟨benzene with CH_3⟩—$OCHCOOH$ / CH_3

$C_{10}H_{11}Cl_1O_3$. M: 214.65.
Production:
- *p*-chloro-*o*-cresol + α-chloropropionic acid (ether formation)

Uses: herbicide

mecoprop-P

(*R*)-2-(4-chloro-2-methylphenoxy)propionic acid

Cl—⟨benzene with CH_3⟩—O-C-$COOH$ with CH_3 and H

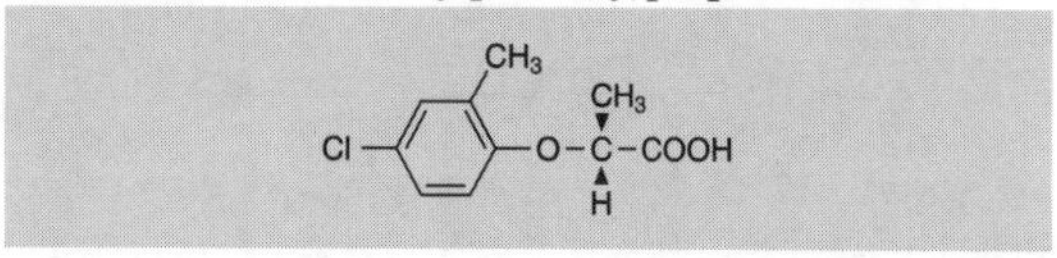

$C_{10}H_{11}Cl_1O_3$. M: 214.65. The commercial product is the (*R*)-(+)-enantiomer.
Production:
- *p*-chloro-*o*-cresol + (*S*)-α-chloropropionic acid (ether formation)

Uses: herbicide

mecysteine hydrochloride

methyl-L-cysteine hydrochloride

NH_3^+ Cl^-
$HSCH_2CHCOCH_3$
$\quad\quad\quad O$

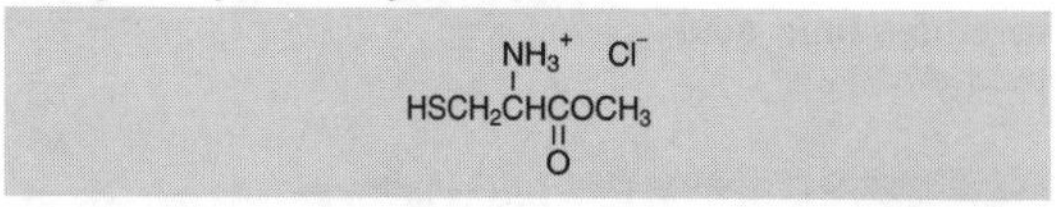

$C_4H_{10}Cl_1N_1O_2S_1$. M: 171.64.
Production:
- L-cysteine + methanol + hydrochloric acid (esterification/salt formation)

Uses:
respiratory tract drug

medazepam

[2898-12-6]
$C_{16}H_{15}Cl_1N_2$. M: 270.76.

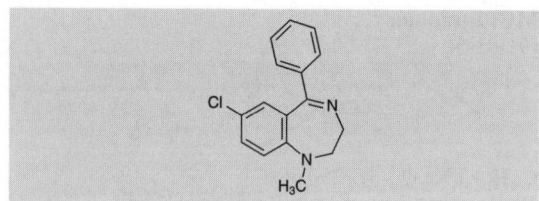

Production:
- diazepam (carbonyl reduction)

Uses: anxiolytic drug

mefenacet

2-(1,3-benzothiazol-2-yloxy)-*N*-methylacetanilide; [73250-68-7]

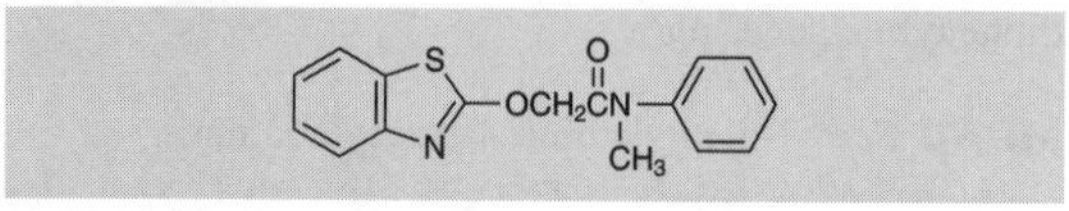

$C_{16}H_{14}N_2O_2S_1$. M: 298.36.
Production:
- 2-mercaptobenzothiazole + *N*-methylaniline + glycollic acid (amide formation/ether formation)

Uses: herbicide

mefenamic acid

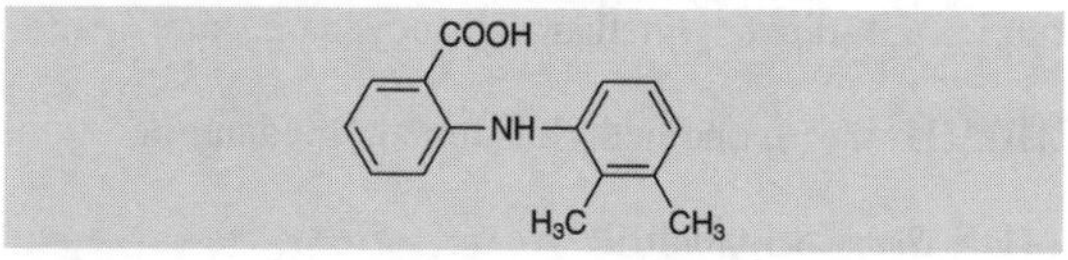

⟨benzene with COOH⟩—NH—⟨benzene with H_3C and CH_3⟩

$C_{15}H_{15}N_1O_2$. M: 241.29.
Production:
- *o*-chlorobenzoic acid + 2,3-xylidine (nitro reduction/amine formation)

Uses: analgesic drug

mefluidide

5′-(1,1,1-trifluoromethanesulphonamido)acet-2′,4′-xylidide; [53780-34-0]

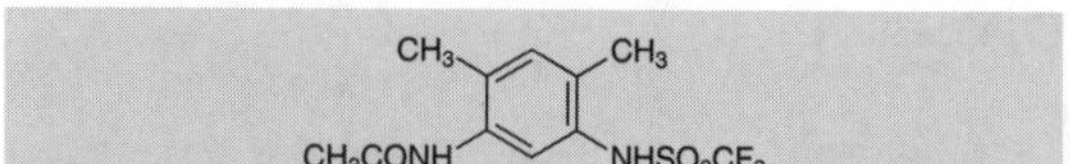

CH_3 CH_3
CH_3CONH—⟨benzene⟩—$NHSO_2CF_3$

$C_{11}H_{13}F_3N_2O_3S_1$. M: 310.28.
Production:
- 2,4-xylidine + acetic anhydride + trifluoromethane-sulphonic acid (acetylation/nitration/nitro reduction/sulphonamide formation)

Uses: plant growth regulator/herbicide

mefruside

[7195-27-9]
$C_{13}H_{19}Cl_1N_2O_5S_2$. M: 382.88.
Production:
- ethyl levulinate + sodium cyanide + 2-chloro-5-chlorosulphonylbenzenesulphonamide (cyano-

hydrin formation/transesterification/hydrogenation/
amine methylation/sulphonamide formation)

Uses: diuretic drug

MEG *See:* ethylene glycol

MEHQ *See:* hydroquinone monomethyl ether

MEK *See:* methyl ethyl ketone

MEKO *See:* methyl ethyl ketoxime

MEKP *See:* methyl ethyl ketone peroxide

melamine
2,4,6-triamino-1,3,5-triazine; 2,4,6-triamino-*sym*-triazine;
[108-78-1]

$C_3H_6N_6$. M: 126.12. Crystalline solid. MP: 347°C
(sealed tube) with decomposition. Sublimes below
250°C. Slightly soluble in water.
Production:
• dicyandiamide (cyclisation)
• urea (low-pressure catalytic process)
• urea (high-pressure catalytic process)
Derivatives: dimelamine phosphate; hexamethoxymethylmelamine; melamine cyanurate; melamine-formaldehyde resins; melamine-formaldehyde resins, butylated;
melamine phosphate
Uses: fire-retardant intumescent paint ingredient

melamine cyanurate

$C_6H_9N_9O_3$. M: 255.20.
Production:
• melamine + cyanuric acid (salt formation)
Uses:
fire-retardant additive (plastics, resins)

melamine-epoxy resins
Beetle BE647 (BIP Chemicals)
Production:
• hexamethoxymethylmelamine/melamine-form-
aldehyde resins, butylated + bisphenol A glycidyl

ether prepolymers/bisphenol A diglycidyl ether
(condensation)
Uses: curing agent (phenolic can coatings); stoved
primer/finishing paints (white goods)

melamine-formaldehyde resins
melamine resins; [9003-08-1]
Precondensated resins with varying melamine:formalde-
hyde ratios and degree of polymerisation. For fabric,
paper or leather treatment, products with a melamine:
formaldehyde ratio of 1:3 are typical, together with a
relatively low degree of polymerisation. They are
supplied either as a solution in water or in a spray-
dried form. For moulding and laminating applications,
melamine:formaldehyde ratios of 1:2 are more common, with a higher degree of crosslinking. Cured
resins are characterised by their hardness and their
good heat and chemical resistance.
Production:
• melamine + formaldehyde (carbonyl condensation)
Uses: concrete admixtures; high-pressure decorative
laminates (worktop surfaces); high-temperature/electrical
insulation laminates; hot-setting adhesive (plywood);
moulding powders (electrical fittings, tableware, household appliances); flame-retardant textile treatment
agent; textile/leather finishing agent; wet-strength additive (paper)

melamine-formaldehyde resins, butylated

x, y, z = 0, 1. Oil-soluble resins. Commercial products
are mixtures containing 3–6 butylated methylol groups
on each molecule. They are usually supplied as solutions in *n*-butanol or *n*-butanol/xylene.
Production:
• melamine + formaldehyde + *n*-butanol (carbonyl
  condensation/ether formation)
Derivatives:
melamine-epoxy resins
Uses: hydroxyl-terminated thermosetting acrylic resin
crosslinking agent; alkyd-amino resins (printing inks);
alkyd-amino stoving resins (domestic equipment, vehicle finishes)

melamine phosphate

$C_3H_9N_6O_4P_1$. M: 224.11. White powder. d: 1.69 kg/l.
Solubility in water: 7 g/l water. Decomposition starts
at 300°C.

Production:
• melamine + phosphoric acid, pure (salt formation)
Uses: fire-retardant (paper, plastics); intumescent paint/
mastic ingredient

melamine resins *See:* melamine-formaldehyde resins

Meldrum's acid
[2033-24-1]
$C_6H_8O_4$. M: 144.13. Crystalline solid. Decomposes on
heating above 95°C. Soluble in water and oxygenated
solvents.

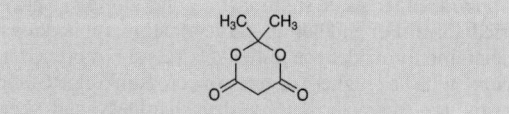

Production:
• malonic acid + acetone + acetic anhydride (ketal
formation)
Uses: malonic ester synthesis reagent

melinite *See:* picric acid

melitracen
[5118-29-6]

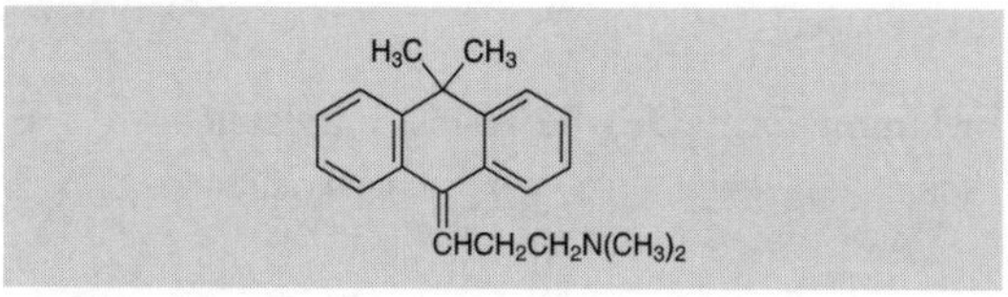

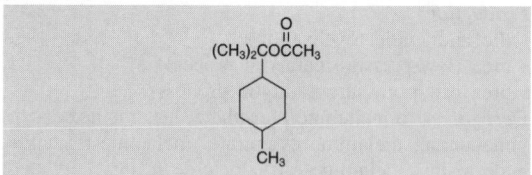

$C_{21}H_{25}N_1$. M: 291.44. Available commercially as the
hydrochloride.
Production:
• anthrone + 3-dimethylaminopropyl chloride
hydrochloride + methyl iodide (methylation/
Grignard reagent formation/Grignard reaction/
dehydration)
Uses: antidepressant drug

menadione
2-methyl-1,4-naphthoquinone; vitamin K_3; [58-27-5]

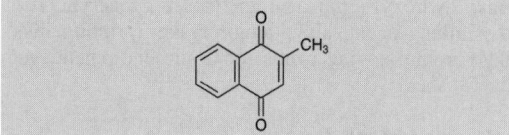

$C_{11}H_8O_2$. M: 172.18. Yellow, crystalline solid. MP:
105–107°C. Insoluble in water. Soluble in aromatic
solvents.
Production:
• β-methylnaphthalene + nitric acid, concentrated
(oxidation)
Derivatives: menadoxime; vitamin K_1
Uses: animal feed additive; antihaemorrhagic drug

menadoxime
[573-01-3]

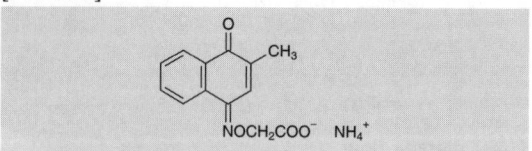

$C_{13}H_{14}N_2O_4$. M: 262.26.
Production:
• menadione + hydroxylamine hydrochloride +
sodium chloroacetate + ammonia (oxime
formation/dehydrochlorination/salt formation)
Uses: antihaemorrhagic drug

1,4-*p*-menthadiene *See:* γ-terpinene

1,5-*p*-menthadiene *See:* (+)-α-phellandrene

(+)-1,8-*p*-menthadiene *See:* (+)-limonene

(−)-1,8-*p*-menthadien-6-one *See:* (−)-carvone

***p*-menthan-3-ol** *See:* menthol

***p*-menthan-3-one** *See:* menthone

menthanyl acetate
8-*p*-menthanyl acetate; *p*-menthan-8-yl acetate;
[80-25-1]

$C_{12}H_{22}O_2$. M: 198.31. Colourless liquid with a citrus
odour.
Production:
• terpinyl acetate (hydrogenation)
Uses: fragrance ingredient (household products)

***p*-menthan-3-yl acetate** *See:* menthyl acetate

***p*-menthan-8-yl acetate** *See:* menthanyl acetate

1-*p*-menthen-8-ol *See:* α-terpineol

8-*p*-menthen-3-ol *See:* isopulegol

(−)-menthol
(−)-*p*-menthan-3-ol; [2216-51-5]
$C_{10}H_{20}O_1$. M: 156.27. White, crystalline solid with a
characteristic odour and taste. MP: 43°C. BP: 216°C.
d: 0.89 kg/l (20°C). Slight soluble in water. Soluble
in oxygenated and hydrocarbon solvents.

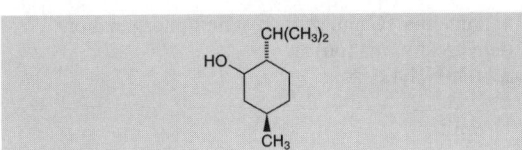

Production:
- peppermint oil, Japanese (extraction)
- *Eucalyptus dives* oil (hydrogenation/isomer separation)
- (±)-menthol (racemate separation)
- peppermint oil, dementholised (fractionation)

Derivatives: menthone; menthyl acetate

Uses: flavouring ingredient (cigarettes, chewing gum, toothpaste, cosmetics)

(±)-menthol

(±)-*p*-menthan-3-ol; DL-menthol; [89-78-1]

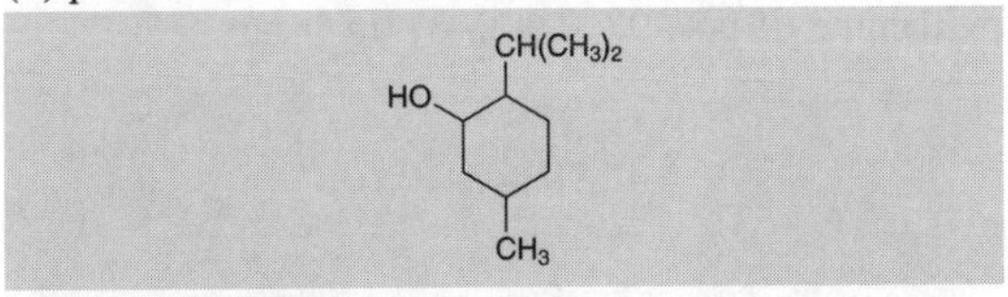

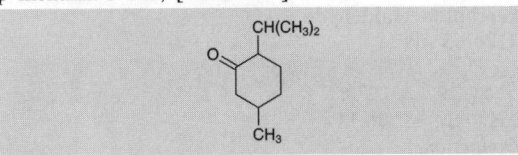

$C_{10}H_{20}O_1$. M: 156.27. Crystalline solid with a peppermint odour. MP: 38°C. Slightly soluble in water. Soluble in oxygenated and chlorinated solvents.

Production:
- thymol (hydrogenation)
- menthone (hydrogenation)

Derivatives:
(–)-menthol; menthyl acetate; menthyl salicylate

Uses: flavouring/fragrance/medicine/liniment ingredient

menthone

p-menthan-3-one; [1074-95-9]

$C_{10}H_{18}O_1$. M: 154.25. Colourless liquid with a minty odour. Usually a mixture of enantiomers. BP: 210°C. d: 0.89 kg/l (20°C). Slightly soluble in water.

Production:
- peppermint oil, dementholised (fractionation)
- thymol (hydrogenation)
- (–)-menthol (alcohol oxidation)

Derivatives: (±)-menthol

Uses: flavouring ingredient

menthyl acetate

p-menthan-3-yl acetate; [2623-23-6] ((–) enantiomer);
[89-48-5] (racemic mixture)

$C_{12}H_{22}O_2$. M: 198.31. Colourless liquid with a minty odour. BP: 227°C. d: 0.93 kg/l (20°C). Miscible with oxygenated solvents. Available commercially as the racemic mixture or pure (–)-enantiomer.

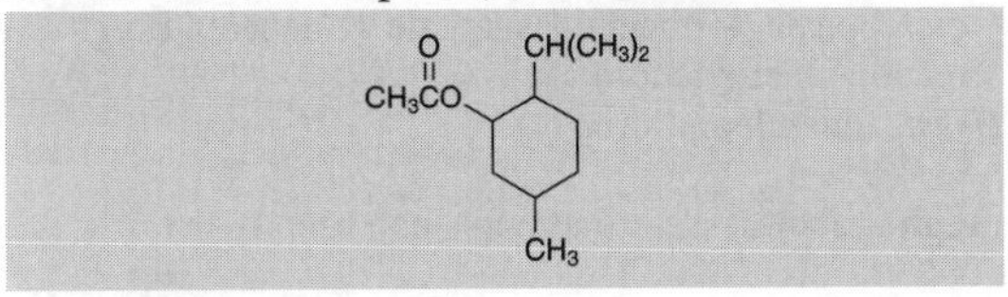

Production:
- (±)-menthol/(–)-menthol + acetic anhydride (esterification)

Uses: flavouring ingredient

menthyl salicylate

[89-46-3]

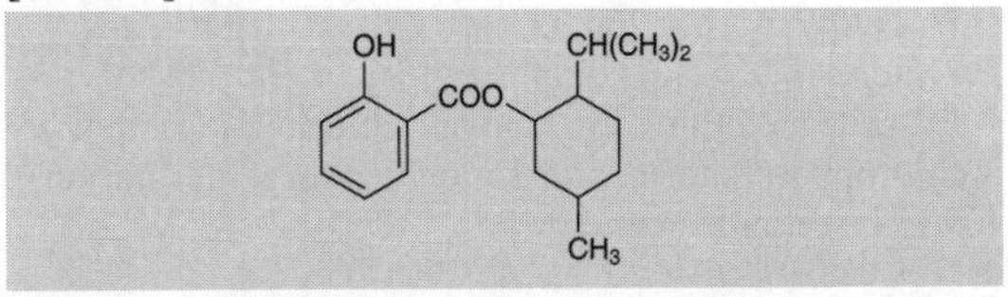

$C_{17}H_{24}O_3$. M: 276.38. Yellow, viscous liquid. d: 1.04 kg/l (25°C). Insoluble in water. Soluble in oxygenated and aromatic solvents.

Production:
- (±)-menthol + salicylic acid (esterification)

Uses: sunscreening agent

MEP *See:* 2-methyl-5-ethylpyridine

mepacrine

quinacrine; [83-89-6]; [69-05-6] (hydrochloride)

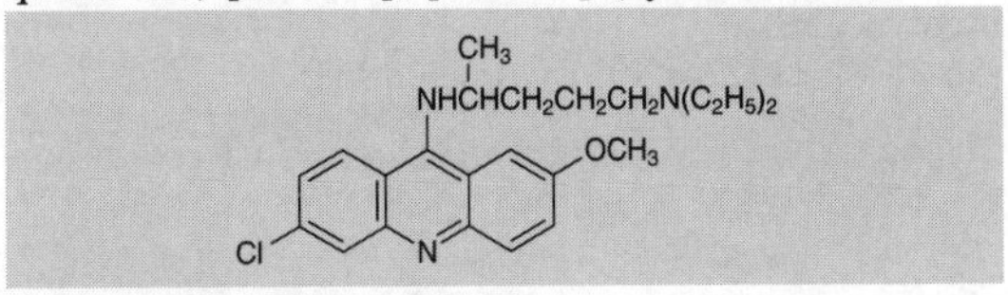

$C_{23}H_{30}Cl_1N_3O_1$. M: 399.96.

Production:
- 2,4-dichlorobenzoyl chloride + *p*-anisidine + 4-amino-1-diethylaminopentane (Friedel-Crafts acylation/amine formation/reductive amination)

Uses: antimalarial drug

meperidine *See:* pethidine

mephenytoin

5-ethyl-3-methyl-5-phenylhydantoin; [50-12-4]

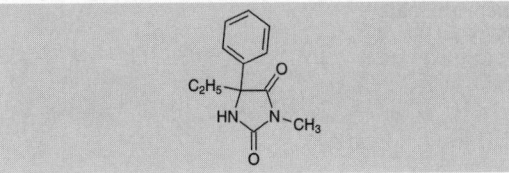

$C_{12}H_{14}N_2O_2$. M: 218.25.

Production:
- propiophenone + hydrogen cyanide + ammonium bicarbonate + dimethyl sulphate (Bucherer-Bergs reaction/methylation)

Uses: antiepileptic drug

mephobarbital *See:* methylphenobarbital

mephosfolan
diethyl 4-methyl-1,3-dithiolan-2-ylidenephosphoramidate; [950-10-7]

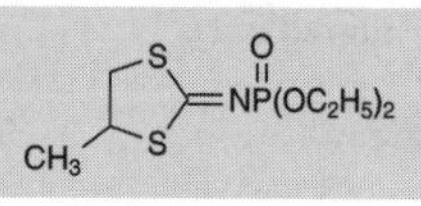

$C_8H_{16}N_1O_3P_1S_2$. M: 269.33.
Production:
- 1,2-propanedithiol + cyanogen chloride + diethyl chlorophosphate (condensation/dehydrochlorination)

Uses: insecticide/acaricide

mepiquat chloride
1,1-dimethylpiperidinium chloride; [24307-26-4]

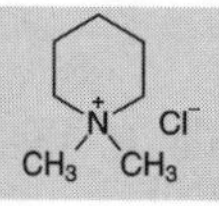

$C_7H_{16}Cl_1N_1$. M: 149.67.
Production:
- piperidine + methyl chloride (methylation)

Uses: plant growth regulator

mepivacaine
[96-88-8]; [1722-62-9] (hydrochloride)

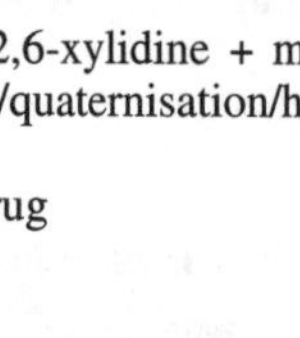

$C_{15}H_{22}N_2O_1$. M: 246.35. Available commercially as the hydrochloride.
Production:
- picolinic acid + 2,6-xylidine + methyl bromide (amide formation/quaternisation/hydrogenation)

Uses:
local anaesthetic drug

meprobamate
[57-53-4]

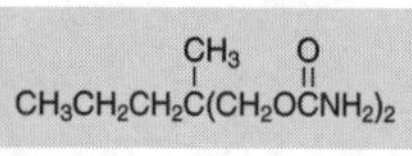

$C_9H_{18}N_2O_4$. M: 218.25.
Production:
- 2-methylvaleraldehyde + formaldehyde + phosgene

+ ammonia (Cannizzaro reaction/phosgenation/dehydrochlorination)

Uses: anxiolytic drug

mepronil
3'-isopropoxy-*o*-toluanilide; [55814-41-0]

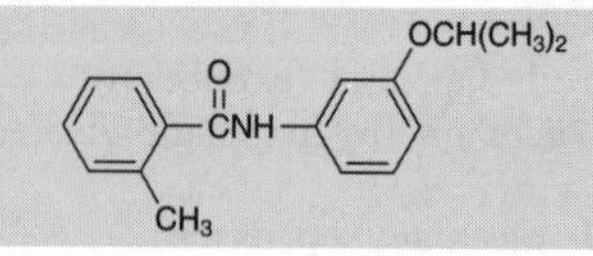

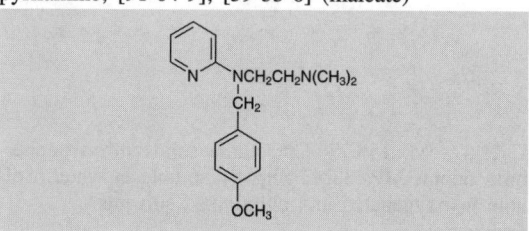

$C_{17}H_{19}N_1O_2$. M: 269.34.
Production:
- *o*-toluic acid + *m*-aminophenol + isopropanol (amide formation/ether formation)

Uses: fungicide

mepyramine
pyrilamine; [91-84-9]; [59-33-6] (maleate)

$C_{17}H_{23}N_3O_1$. M: 285.39. Available commercially as the free base, maleate or 8-bromotheophyllinate.
Production:
- 2-aminopyridine + anisyl alcohol + 2-dimethylaminoethyl chloride hydrochloride (amine formation/amine formation)

Uses: antihistamine drug

mercaptoacetaldehyde
[4124-63-4]

$HSCH_2CHO$

$C_2H_4O_1S_1$. M: 76.11.
Production:
- methyl mercaptan + chloroacetaldehyde (sulphide formation)

Derivatives: DL-cysteine hydrochloride; polythiazide

mercaptoacetic acid *See:* thioglycollic acid

2-mercaptoaniline *See:* 2-aminothiophenol

2-mercaptobenzimidazole
benzimidazole-2-thiol; MBI; [583-39-1]

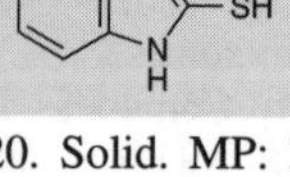

$C_7H_6N_2S_1$. M: 150.20. Solid. MP: 303°C. Slightly sol-

uble in water. Soluble in alcohol.
Production:
- *o*-phenylenediamine + carbon disulphide (condensation)

Derivatives: zinc 2-mercaptobenzimidazole
Uses:
nickel plating brightening agent; antioxidant (rubber)

o-mercaptobenzoic acid *See:* thiosalicylic acid

2-mercaptobenzothiazole
MBT; [149-30-4]

C$_7$H$_5$N$_1$S$_2$. M: 167.26. Pale yellow crystals with an unpleasant odour. MP: 175–179°C. d: 1.42 kg/l (20°C). Insoluble in water. Slightly soluble in oxygenated solvents.
Production:
- aniline + carbon disulphide + sulphur (addition)

Derivatives: benzthiazuron; *N-t*-butyl-2-benzothiazolesulphenamide; *N*-cyclohexyl-2-benzothiazolesulphenamide; 2,2′-dibenzothiazyl disulphide; *N,N*-dicyclohexyl-2-benzothiazolesulphenamide; mefenacet; methabenzthiazuron; 2-morpholinobenzothiazylsulphenamide; 2-morpholinodithiobenzothiazole; sodium 2-mercaptobenzothiazole; 2-(thiocyanomethylthio)benzothiazole; zinc mercaptobenzothiazole
Uses: flotation collector (sulphide ores); vulcanisation accelerator

2-mercaptoethanol
[60-24-2]

HSCH$_2$CH$_2$OH

C$_2$H$_6$O$_1$S$_1$. M: 78.13. Liquid with an unpleasant odour. BR: 150–158°C. d: 1.12 kg/l (15°C). Miscible with water, oxygenated and aromatic solvents.
Production:
- hydrogen sulphide + ethylene oxide (epoxidation; coproduced with thiodiglycol)

Derivatives:
carboxin; dibutyltin bis(2-mercaptoethyl oleate); dimethyltin bis(2-mercaptoethyl oleate); 1,2-ethanedithiol; monobutyltin tris(2-mercaptoethyl oleate); monomethyltin tris(2-mercaptoethyl oleate); vamidothion
Uses: flotation depressant (copper ores)

2-mercaptoethylamine hydrochloride
2-aminoethanethiol hydrochloride; cysteamine hydrochloride; 2-thiolethanolamine hydrochloride;
[156-57-0]

HSCH$_2$CH$_2$NH$_3$$^+$ Cl$^-$

C$_2$H$_8$N$_1$S$_1$. M: 78.15. Crystalline solid with an unpleasant odour. MP: 67–69°C. Soluble in water and alcohol.

Production:
- monoethanolamine + sodium hydrosulphide + hydrochloric acid (thiolation/salt formation)

Derivatives: cimetidine; ranitidine

2-mercaptoimidazoline *See:* ethylenethiourea

2-mercaptomethylbenzimidazole
mercaptomethylbenzimidazole; MMBI

C$_8$H$_8$N$_2$S$_1$. M: 164.22.
Production:
- 3,4-diaminotoluene + carbon disulphide (condensation)

Derivatives: zinc 2-mercaptomethylbenzimidazole
Uses: antioxidant (rubber)

3-mercaptopropionic acid
β-mercaptopropionic acid; mercaptopropionic acid; [107-96-0]

HSCH$_2$CH$_2$COOH

C$_3$H$_6$O$_2$S$_1$. M: 106.14. Colourless liquid. MP: 17°C. d: 1.22 kg/l (21°C). Soluble in water and oxygenated solvents.
Production:
- hydrogen sulphide + acrylonitrile (cyanoethylation/ nitrile hydrolysis)

Derivatives:
dioctyltin β-mercaptopropionate
Uses: polyvinyl chloride heat costabilisers

γ-mercaptopropyltrimethoxysilane
[4420-74-0]

HSCH$_2$CH$_2$CH$_2$Si(OCH$_3$)$_3$

C$_6$H$_{16}$O$_3$S$_1$Si$_1$. M: 196.35.
Production:
- trichlorosilane + allyl mercaptan + methanol (hydrosilation/dehydrochlorination)

Uses: plastics coupling agent

6-mercaptopurine
6MP; [50-44-2]

C$_5$H$_4$N$_4$S$_1$. M: 152.17.
Production:
- 6-chloropurine + sodium thiocyanate (dehydrochlorination/thiocyanate hydrolysis)

Uses: antineoplastic drug

2-mercaptosuccinic acid *See:* thiomalic acid

mercuric acetate
mercury acetate; [1600-27-7]

$$O$$
$$\parallel$$
$$(CH_3CO)_2Hg$$

$C_4H_6Hg_1O_4$. M: 318.68. White, crystalline powder. MP: 178–180°C with decomposition. d: 3.28 kg/l. Soluble in water.
Production:
• mercuric oxide, yellow + acetic acid (salt formation)
Derivatives: phenylmercury acetate

mercuric chloride
mercury chloride; [7487-94-7]

$$HgCl_2$$

Cl_2Hg_1. M: 271.50. White, crystalline powder. MP: 277–280°C. BP: 302°C. Solubility in water: 70 g/l water (20°C).
Production:
• mercury + chlorine (reaction)
Derivatives: di-(phenylmercury) dodecenylsuccinate; mercuric chloride, ammoniated; mercuric oxide, yellow
Uses: vinyl chloride production catalyst; photographic image intensifying agent; dry battery cases; turf fungicide; topical antiseptic

mercuric chloride, ammoniated
ammoniated mercury; white precipitate

$$H_2NHgCl$$

$H_2Cl_1Hg_1N_1$. M: 252.07. White powder. d: 5.38 kg/l. Insoluble in water and alcohol.
Production:
• mercuric chloride + ammonia (salt formation)
Uses: medical antiseptic

mercuric nitrate
[10045-94-0]

$$Hg(NO_3)_2$$

$Hg_1N_2O_6$. M: 324.59. Available as the hemihydrate. White, deliquescent, crystalline powder. MP: 79°C. d: 4.79 kg/l. Soluble in cold water. Decomposed by hot water.
Production:
• mercury + nitric acid (salt formation)
Derivatives: mercuric oxide, yellow
Uses: analytical reagent

mercuric oxide, red
mercuric oxide; mercury oxide; [21908-53-2]

$$HgO$$

Hg_1O_1. M: 216.59.

Production:
• mercury + nitric acid (salt formation/thermal conversion)
Uses: wound protectant (fruit/ornamental trees)

mercuric oxide, yellow
[21908-53-2]

$$HgO$$

Hg_1O_1. M: 216.59. Yellow powder. Decomposes on heating above 500°C. d: 11.1 kg/l (4°C). Insoluble in water.
Production:
• mercuric chloride/mercuric nitrate + sodium hydroxide (salt formation)
Derivatives:
mercuric acetate; phenylmercuric propionate

mercurous chloride
calomel; [10294-44-7]

$$Hg_2Cl_2$$

Cl_2Hg_2. M: 472.09. White powder. Sublimes when heated above 400°C. Insoluble in water. Soluble in most organic solvents.
Production:
• mercury + chlorine (reaction)
Uses: insecticide/soil fungicide

mercury
[7439-97-6]

$$Hg$$

Hg_1. M: 200.59. Silver-white, liquid metal. BP: 357°C. MP: -39°C. d: 13.5 kg/l (25°C). Mercury is not corroded by at at normal temperatures nor is it attacked by dilute acids or alkalis. It is attacked by oxidising acids.
Production:
• mercury ore (ore roasting/sublimation)
Derivatives: mercuric chloride; mercuric nitrate; mercuric oxide, red; mercurous chloride; mercury fulminate
Uses: mercury-cell cathode (chloride production); electrical conductors, contact breakers, rocker switches; instrument indicator fluid; mercury vapour arc lamps; vacuum pumps

mercury fulminate
mercury cyanate

$$Hg(CNO)_2$$

$C_2Hg_1N_2O_2$. M: 284.62. Grey, crystalline powder. Explodes when dry and when heated. d: 4.42 kg/l. Slightly soluble in water.
Production:
• mercury + ethanol + nitric acid (salt formation)
Uses: explosive primers (detonators, cartridge caps)

mesidine
2,4,6-trimethylaniline; [88-05-1]

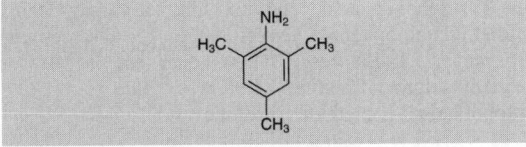

$C_9H_{13}N_1$. M: 135.21. Liquid. BP: 232–234°C. MP: -5°C. d: 0.96 kg/l. Insoluble in water.
Production:
• mesitylene (nitration/nitro reduction)
Derivatives:
Acid Blue 80; Acid Blue 129

mesitylene
1,3,5-trimethylbenzene; [108-67-8]

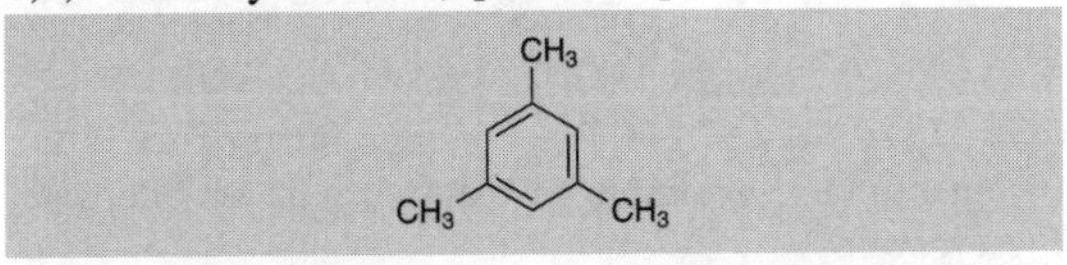

C_9H_{12}. M: 120.20. Colourless liquid. BP: 163–165°C. MP: -45°C. d: 0.87 kg/l (20°C). Insoluble in water. Miscible with oxygenated and aromatic solvents.
Production:
• trimethylbenzene fraction (fractionation; coproduced with pseudocumene/durene)
Derivatives: mesidine; trimesic acid; 2,4,6-tris(3,5-di-*t*-butyl-4-hydroxybenzyl)mesitylene

mesityl oxide
methyl isobutenyl ketone; 4-methyl-3-penten-2-one; [141-79-7]

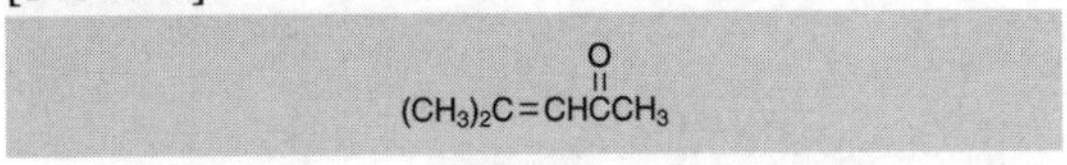

$(CH_3)_2C = CHCCH_3$

$C_6H_{10}O_1$. M: 98.14. Colourless liquid with a sweet odour. BP: 130°C. FP: -46°C. d: 0.85 kg/l (20°C). Slightly soluble in water. Miscible with oxygenated solvents.
Production:
• diacetone alcohol (dehydration)
Derivatives:
methyl isobutyl ketone; methyl 3-methyl-2-butenoate

mestranol
[72-33-3]

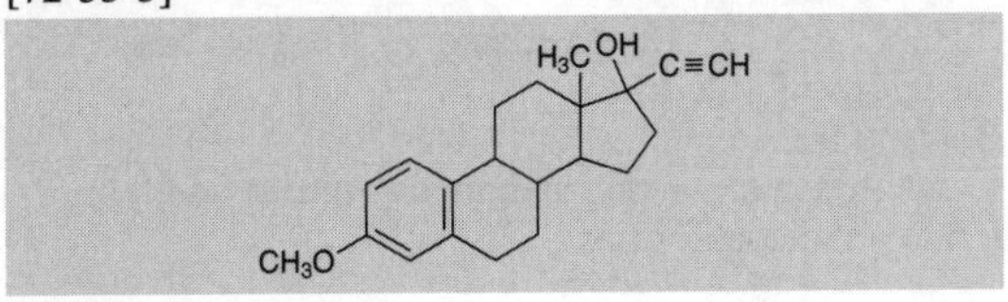

$C_{21}H_{26}O_2$. M: 310.44.
Production:
• estrone + acetylene (methylation/ethynylation)

• 3-methoxyestra-2,5-diene-17-ol + acetylene (Oppenauer oxidation/ethynylation)
Uses:
contraceptive/female hormone therapy drug

mesuximide
methsuximide; [77-41-8]

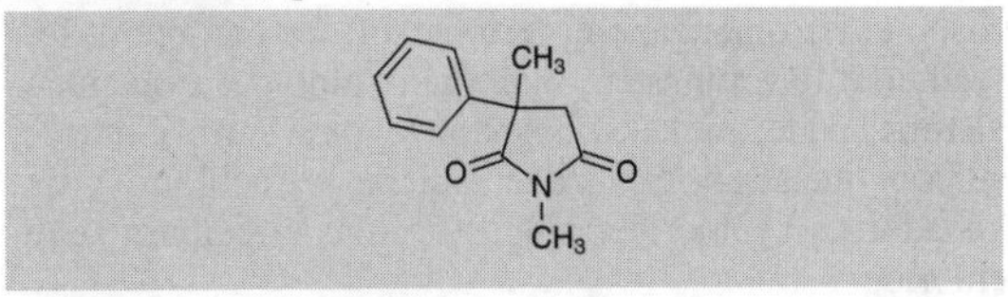

$C_{12}H_{13}N_1O_2$. M: 203.24.
Production:
• acetophenone + ethyl cyanoacetate + hydrogen cyanide + methylamine (Cope reaction/addition/nitrile hydrolysis/decarboxylation/amide formation)
Uses: antiepileptic drug

mesyl chloride *See:* methanesulphonyl chloride

Met *See:* L-methionine

metalaxyl
methyl *N*-(2-methoxyacetyl)-*N*-(2,6-xylyl)-DL-alaninate; [57837-19-1]

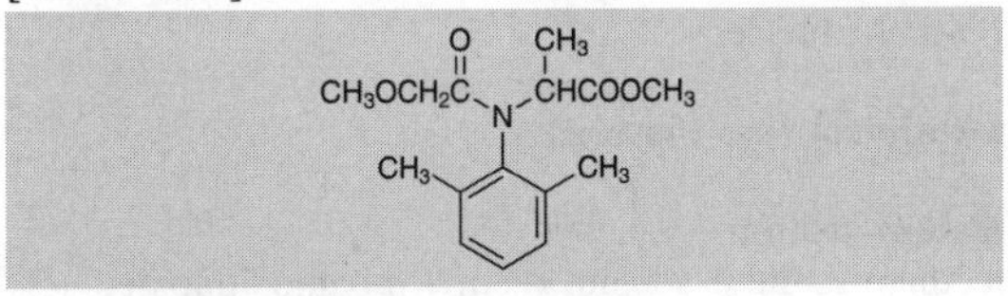

$C_{15}H_{21}N_1O_4$. M: 279.34.
Production:
• 2-methoxyacetic acid + 2,6-xylidine + methyl α-chloropropionate (amide formation/amine formation)
Uses: fungicide

metaldehyde
[108-62-3]

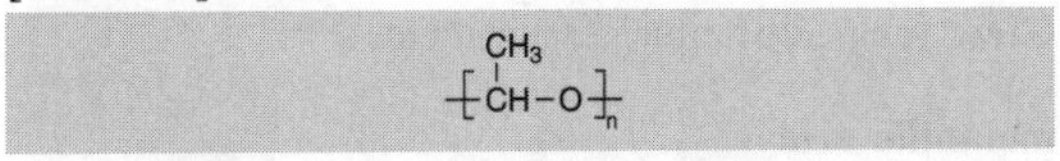

n = 4–6. White, crystalline solid. MP: 246°C (sealed tube). Sublimes when heated to 110°C. Insoluble in water. Soluble in aromatic and chlorinated solvents.
Production:
• acetaldehyde (condensation)
Uses:
portable stove fuel; molluscicide

metallurgical coke
coke; furnace coke
Grey-black, porous lumps. d: 0.8–1.0 kg/l. Ash: 8–10%. Volatile matter: ~1%. Sulphur content: ~1%.

Production:
- coal (high-temperature carbonisation)
- sponge coke, green (high-temperature carbonisation)

Derivatives: alumina, fused; aluminium chloride, anhydrous; arsenic; barium oxide; boron carbide; cadmium; calcium carbide; carbon, moulded; carbon disulphide; chromium; chromium oxide; ferroboron; ferrochrome; ferromanganese; ferronickel; ferroniobium; ferrosilicon; ferrotungsten; hydrogen sulphide; iron; manganous oxide; nickel; phosphorus; rare earth chloride; silicon, metallurgical grade; silicon tetrachloride; tin; vanadium oxychloride; zinc; zirconia; zirconium tetrachloride

Uses: filter medium; fuel

metamitron

4-amino-3-methyl-6-phenyl-1,2,4-triazin-5-one; [41394-05-2]

$C_{10}H_{10}N_4O_1$. M: 202.22.
Production:
- acetic anhydride + hydrazine + methyl phenylglyoxylate (amide formation/condensation)

Uses: herbicide

metamizol *See:* dipyrone

metam-sodium

metham-sodium; sodium methylcarbamodithioate; sodium methyldithiocarbamate; [137-42-8]

$C_2H_4N_1Na_1S_2$. M: 129.18.
Production:
- methylamine + carbon disulphide + sodium hydroxide (thiocarbonylation/salt formation)

Derivatives: dazomet; methyl isothiocyanate
Uses: fungicide/herbicide/nematicide

metanilic acid

3-aminobenzenesulphonic acid; aniline-3-sulphonic acid; *m*-sulphanilic acid; [121-47-1]

$C_6H_7N_1O_3S_1$. M: 173.20. White needles. Decomposed by heating. Slightly soluble in water and oxygenated solvents.
Production:
- *m*-nitrobenzenesulphonic acid (nitro reduction)

Derivatives: Acid Blue 113; Acid Red 119; Acid Yellow 29; Acid Yellow 36; 4-amino-3-methoxyazobenzene-3'-sulphonic acid, sodium salt; *m*-aminophenol; *m*-diethylaminophenol; Direct Blue 75; Fluorescent Brightener 24; Fluorescent Brightener 86; *m*-(β-hydroxyethylsulphonyl)aniline; Reactive Blue 5; 1-(3'-sulphophenyl)-3-methylpyrazolone

metaphyllin *See:* theophylline

metaproterenol *See:* orciprenaline

metaraminol

[54-49-9]; [33402-03-8] (hydrogen tartrate)

$C_9H_{13}N_1O_2$. M: 167.21. The commercial product is the (−)-enantiomer, available as the free base or bitartrate.
Production:
- propiophenone + *n*-butyl nitrite (nitration/nitro reduction/diazotisation/hydrolysis/alpha carbonylation/ammoniation/hydrogenation/racemate separation)

Uses: adrenergic drug

metazachlor

2-chloro-*N*-(pyrazol-1-ylmethyl)acet-2',6'-xylidide; [67129-08-2]

$C_{14}H_{16}Cl_1N_3O_1$. M: 277.75.
Production:
- 1,1,3,3-tetramethoxypropane + hydrazine + formaldehyde + 2,6-xylidine + chloroacetyl chloride (condensation/aminomethylation/amide formation)

Uses: herbicide

metformin

1,1-dimethylbiguanide; [657-24-9]

$C_4H_{11}N_5$. M: 129.16. Available as the free base or as the hydrochloride salt.
Production:
- dimethylamine + dicyandiamide (nitrile addition)

Uses: antidiabetic drug

methabenzthiazuron

1-benzothiazol-2-yl-1,3-dimethylurea; [18691-97-9]
$C_{10}H_{11}N_3O_1S_1$. M: 221.28.

$$CH_2 = \underset{\underset{CH_3}{|}}{C} \underset{\underset{CH_3}{|}}{\overset{\overset{O}{\|}}{C}} NNHCH_3$$

Production:
• 2-mercaptobenzothiazole + methylamine + methyl-isocyanate (amine formation/isocyanate addition)
Uses: herbicide

methacillin *See:* meticillin

methacrifos
O-2-methoxycarbonylprop-1-enyl *O,O*-dimethyl phos-phorothioate; [30864-28-9]

$$(CH_3O)_2 \underset{\underset{O}{\|}}{\overset{\overset{S}{\|}}{P}} OCH = \underset{\underset{CH_3}{|}}{C} \underset{\underset{O}{\|}}{\overset{}{C}} COCH_3$$

$C_7H_{13}O_5P_1S_1$. M: 240.20.
Production:
• methanol + propionic acid + formaldehyde + *O,O*-dimethyl phosphorochlorothioate (esterification/condensation/dehydrochlorination)
Uses: insecticide/acaricide

methacrolein
methacrylaldehyde; [78-85-3]

$$\underset{\underset{CH_2 = C}{|}}{\overset{CH_3}{}} CHO$$

$C_4H_6O_1$. M: 70.09. Liquid. BP: 68°C. d: 0.83 kg/l (30°C). Miscible with water and oxygenated solvents. Not a generally traded product.
Production:
• propionaldehyde + formaldehyde (BASF methacrolein process)
• isobutylene/*t*-butanol (catalytic oxidation processes)
Derivatives: methacrylic acid; 1-methyl-4-(4-methyl-3-penten-1-yl)-3-cyclohexenecarboxaldehyde

methacrylamide
[79-39-0]

$$CH_2 = \underset{\underset{CH_3}{|}}{C} \underset{\underset{}{}}{\overset{\overset{O}{\|}}{C}} CNH_2$$

$C_4H_7N_1O_1$. M: 85.11. Solid. MP: 109–110°C. Soluble in alcohol.
Production:
• methacrylamide sulphate (neutralisation)
Derivatives: *N*-methylol methacrylamide
Uses: reactive comonomer (acrylic resins)

methacrylamide sulphate
$C_8H_{16}N_2O_6S_1$. M: 268.28. Intermediate in methyl methacrylate and methacrylic acid production. Not a commercially traded product.

$$CH_2 = \underset{\underset{CH_3}{|}}{C} CONH_3^+ \quad \tfrac{1}{2}SO_4^{2+}$$

Production:
• acetone cyanohydrin + sulphuric acid (acid-catalysed hydrolysis)
• methacrylonitrile + sulphuric acid (nitrile hydrolysis)
Derivatives:
methacrylamide; methacrylic acid; methyl methacrylate

3-(methacrylamidopropyl)trimethylammonium chloride
N-(trimethylammoniumpropyl)methacrylamide chloride; MAPTAC; [51410-72-1]

$$CH_2 = \underset{\underset{CH_3}{|}}{C} \overset{\overset{O}{\|}}{C} NHCH_2CH_2CH_2N(CH_3)_3^+ \quad Cl^-$$

$C_{10}H_{21}Cl_1N_2O_1$. M: 220.74.
Production:
• dimethylaminopropyl methacrylamide + methyl chloride (quaternisation)
Derivatives:
acrylamide copolymers, cationic

methacrylatochromic chloride
methacrylato chromic chloride hydroxide; Volan (Du Pont); [15096-41-0]

$$CH_2 = \underset{\underset{CH_3}{|}}{C} \overset{\overset{O}{\|}}{C} CO.Cr_2Cl_5OH$$

$C_4H_6Cl_5Cr_2O_3$. M: 383.34.
Production:
• chromic chloride + methacrylic acid (reaction)
Uses: plastics coupling agent

methacrylic acid
MAA; [79-41-4]

$$CH_2 = \underset{\underset{CH_3}{|}}{C} COOH$$

$C_4H_6O_2$. M: 86.09. Colourless liquid with a penetrating odour. BP: 159–163°C. FP: 14°C. d: 1.02 kg/l (20°C). Miscible with water. Flash point: 77°C (COC). Commercial products contain hydroquinone or hydroquinone methyl ether to inhibit polymerisation.
Production:
• methacrylamide sulphate (hydrolysis)
• methacrolein (air oxidation)
Derivatives:
acrylic resins, carboxylated; ammonium polymethacryl-ate; aztreonam; captopril; ceftazidime; ethylene-meth-acrylic acid copolymers; glycidyl methacrylate; 2-hydr-oxyethyl methacrylate; 2-hydroxypropyl methacrylate; iocetamic acid; isocyanatoethyl methacrylate; meth-acrylatochromic chloride; methacrylyl chloride; methyl

methacrylate; polyacrylate resins, crosslinked; poly-(methacrylic acid); poly(methacrylimide); styrene-butadiene copolymers, carboxylated; tributyltin methacrylate; vinyl ester resins
Uses:
thermosetting acrylic resin comonomer; carboxylated comonomer (styrene-butadiene/nitrile latex); engineering adhesives

methacrylonitrile
MAN; 2-methyl-2-propenenitrile; [126-98-7]

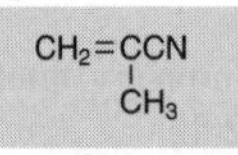

$$CH_2=CCN$$
$$CH_3$$

$C_4H_5N_1$. M: 67.09. Colourless liquid. BP: 90°C. MP: -36°C. d: 0.80 kg/l (20°C). Solubility in water: 26 g/l water (20°C).
Production:
• isobutylene + ammonia (Sohio ammoxidation process)
Derivatives:
methacrylamide sulphate; poly(methacrylimide)
Uses: nitrile rubber comonomer

γ-methacryloxypropyltrimethoxysilane
[2530-85-0]

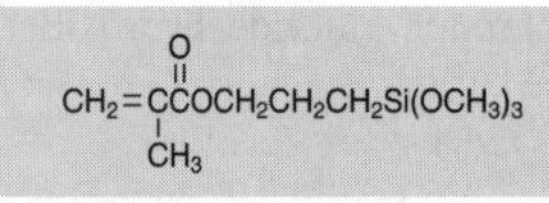

$$O$$
$$||$$
$$CH_2=CCOCH_2CH_2CH_2Si(OCH_3)_3$$
$$CH_3$$

$C_{10}H_{20}O_5Si_1$. M: 248.35.
Production:
• trichlorosilane + allyl methacrylate + methanol (hydrosilation/dehydrochlorination)
Uses: plastics coupling agent

methacrylyl chloride
[920-46-7]

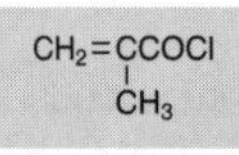

$$CH_2=CCOCl$$
$$CH_3$$

$C_4H_5Cl_1O_1$. M: 104.53. Liquid. BP: 95°C. Hydrolysed by water.
Production:
• methacrylic acid (acid chloride formation)
Derivatives:
bisphenol AF dimethacrylate; dimethylaminopropyl methacrylamide; perfluoroalkyl methacrylates

(±)-1,8-*p*-menthadiene *See:* dipentene

methadone
[76-99-3]; [1095-90-5] (hydrochloride)
$C_{21}H_{27}N_1O_1$. M: 309.45. Available commercially as the racemic hydrochloride. The L(−)-enantiomer also has pharmacological properties. It is called levomethadone (*qv*).

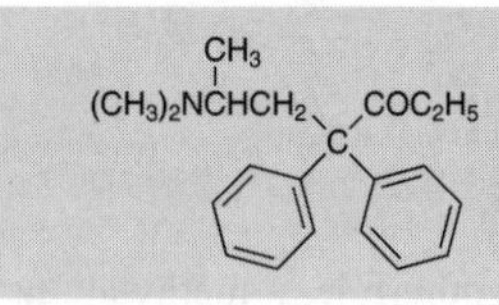

$$CH_3$$
$$(CH_3)_2NCHCH_2\quad COC_2H_5$$

Production:
• dimethylisopropanolamine + diphenylacetonitrile + ethylmagnesium bromide (alcohol chlorination/dehydrochlorination/Grignard reaction/hydrolysis)
Derivatives:
levomethadone
Uses: analgesic drug

methallyl chloride
3-chloro-2-methylpropene; β-methylallyl chloride; MAC

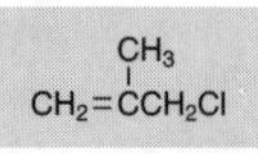

$$CH_3$$
$$CH_2=CCH_2Cl$$

$C_4H_7Cl_1$. M: 90.55. Colourless liquid with a pungent odour. BP: 71–73°C. d: 0.93 kg/l (20°C). Insoluble in water.
Production:
• isobutylene + chlorine (chlorination)
Derivatives:
carbofuran; 3-dimethylamino-2-methylpropyl chloride hydrochloride; ethalfluralin; fenbutatin oxide

methamidophos
O,S-dimethyl phosphoroamidothioate; [10265-92-6]

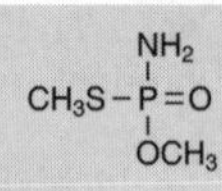

$$NH_2$$
$$|$$
$$CH_3S-P=O$$
$$|$$
$$OCH_3$$

$C_2H_8N_1O_2P_1S_1$. M: 141.12.
Production:
• *O,O*-dimethyl phosphorochlorothioate + ammonia (dehydrochlorination/dealkylation/methylation)
Derivatives:
acephate
Uses: acaricide/insecticide

methamphetamine
desoxyephedrine hydrochloride

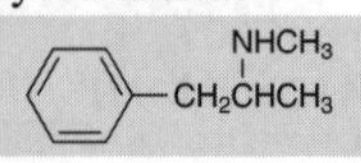

$$NHCH_3$$
$$-CH_2CHCH_3$$

$C_{10}H_{15}N_1$. M: 149.24. Available commercially as the free amine or hydrochloride.
Production:
• phenylacetone + methylamine (reductive amination)
Uses: anorexic drug

metham-sodium *See:* metam-sodium

methane *See:* natural gas

methanesulphonic acid

methylsulphonic acid; MSA; [75-75-2]

$$CH_3SO_3H$$

$C_1H_4O_3S_1$. M: 96.10. Liquid or solid. MP: 20°C. d: 1.48 kg/l (18°C). Soluble in water and oxygenated solvents.

Production:
• methyl mercaptan + sodium hypochlorite (oxidation)
Derivatives: methanesulphonyl chloride; trifluoromethanesulphonic acid
Uses: esterification/alkylation catalyst; polymeric coatings/thermosetting resin curing agent

methanesulphonyl chloride

mesyl chloride; methylsulphonyl chloride; MSC; [124-63-0]

$$CH_3SO_2Cl$$

$C_1H_3Cl_1O_2S_1$. M: 114.54. Liquid. d: 1.48 kg/l (20°C). Insoluble in water. Soluble in oxygenated solvents.

Production:
• methanesulphonic acid (acid chloride formation)
Derivatives:
2-amino-5-[N-ethyl-N-(2-methylsulphonaminoethyl)-amino]toluene; 2-amino-4-methylsulphonylphenol; ethofumesate; fomesafen; mezlocillin; sotalol; thiamphenicol; tiapride
Uses: amino/alcohol group formation/protection reagent

methanethiol *See:* methyl mercaptan

methanol

methyl alcohol; methyl hydrate; [67-56-1]

$$CH_3OH$$

$C_1H_4O_1$. M: 32.04. Colourless liquid with a mild odour. BP: 65°C. FP: -98°C. d: 0.79 kg/l (20°C). Miscible with water and most organic solvents. Flash point: 6°C (CC).

Production:
• synthesis gas (high/medium/low-pressure processes)
• *n*-butane (Celanese LPO process; coproduced with ethanol/acetone/methyl ethyl ketone/formic acid/acetic acid/propionic acid/*n*-butyric acid/methyl formate)
• oxygenates, Fischer-Tropsch, mixed (fractionation; coproduced with ethanol/isopropanol/*n*-butanol/isobutanol/amyl alcohol, primary/acetaldehyde/acetone/methyl ethyl ketone)
Derivatives: acetic acid; acetic anhydride; amiloride; 2-amino-5-nitroanisole; *t*-amyl methyl ether; *p*-anisidine; aspartame; bifenox; N,N′-bis(methoxymethyl)urone; carbomethoxybenzenesulphonyl isocyanate; chlorflurenol-methyl; chloromethyl methyl ether; chloroneb; 4-chloro-2-nitroanisole; γ-chloropropyltrimethoxysilane; citral dimethyl acetal; cloethocarb; *o*-cresol; 2,6-

di-*t*-butyl-4-methoxymethylphenol; diclofop-methyl; diethylene glycol monomethyl ether; 2,5-dimethoxyaniline; dimethyl acetonedicarboxylate; dimethyl adipate; dimethyl alkylene(C$_4$-C$_6$)dicarboxylates; dimethylamine; N,N-dimethylaniline; dimethyl carbonate; N,N-dimethylcyclohexylamine; O,O-dimethyl dithiophosphoric acid; dimethyl isophthalate; dimethyl maleate; dimethyl malonate; dimethyl naphthalene-2,6-dicarboxylate; dimethyl 5-nitroisophthalate; dimethyl phosphite; dimethyl phthalate; dimethyl succinate; dimethyl sulphate; dimethyl sulphide; dimethyl terephthalate; N,N-dimethyl-*p*-toluidine; 2,4-dinitroanisole; dioxabenzofos; dipropylene glycol monomethyl ether; enflurane; β-(3,4-epoxycyclohexyl)ethyltrimethoxysilane; ethylene glycol monomethyl ether; formaldehyde; formamide; formic acid; gas oil, light; gasoline, mixed ether; γ-glycidoxypropyltrimethoxysilane; 2,2,3,4,4,4-hexafluorobutanol; hexamethoxymethylmelamine; hydratropaldehyde dimethyl acetal; hydroxycitronellal dimethyl acetal; ibuprofen; imazamethabenz-methyl; imipenem; mecysteine hydrochloride; γ-mercaptopropyltrimethoxysilane; methacrifos; γ-methacryloxypropyltrimethoxysilane; 2-methoxyacetic acid; 3-methoxybutanol; methoxyflurane; 3-methoxypropionitrile; methyl abietate; methyl acetoacetate; methyl acrylate; methylamine; N-methylaminoacetaldehyde dimethyl acetal; methyl 3-amino-4-methylthiophene-2-carboxylate; N-methylaniline; methyl anthranilate; methyl bromide; methyl *t*-butyl ether; methyl chloride; methyl chloroacetate; methyl γ-chloroacetoacetate; methyl chloroformate; methyl α-chloropropionate; methyl cinnamate; methyl cocoate; methyl cyanoacetate; N-methylcyclohexylamine; N-methyldicyclohexylamine; methyl 3-fluorocarbonylperfluoropropionate; methyl formate; α-methylglucoside; methylglyoxal dimethyl acetal; methyl glyoxylate methyl hemiacetal; methyl 4-hydroxybenzoate; methyl isonicotinate; O-methylisourea sulphate; methyl laurate; methyl mercaptan; methyl methacrylate; methyl 3-methyl-2-butenoate; methyl myristate; methyl 2-nonynoate; methyl 2-octynoate; methyl oleate; methyl palmitate; methyl phenylglyoxylate; methyl pivalate; methyl ricinoleate; methyl salicylate; methyl stearate; methyl *p*-toluenesulphonate; N-methyl-*m*-toluidine; methyl valerate; methyl vinyl ether; metolachlor; metoxuron; naphtha, heavy; naphtha, light; naproxen; *o*-nitroanisole; palm kernel methyl ester; phenylacetaldehyde dimethyl acetal; Pigment Yellow 120; polyethylene glycol monomethyl ether; prometon; propetamphos; propylene glycol monomethyl ether; raffinate II; refinery gas; L-serine; sodium methoxide; 2,2,3,3-tetrafluoropropanol; 1,1,3,3-tetramethoxypropane; tetramethylammonium hydroxide; tetrapropylene glycol monomethyl ether; thiafensulfuron-methyl; tolycaine; triethylene glycol monomethyl ether; 1,1,ω-trihydroperfluoroalkanol; trimethoxyphenylsilane; 3-(trimethoxysilyl)propyldimethyloctadecylammonium chloride; trimethylamine; trimethyl borate; trimethyl orthoacetate;

trimethyl orthoformate; trimethyl phosphite; tripropylene glycol monomethyl ether; 2,6-xylenol; 2,6-xylidine
Uses:
ethanol denaturant; extraction agent (phosphoric acid purification); extraction solvent (Rectisol process); petrol/diesel fuel antiicing additive; antifreeze/hydraulic fluid blending component; petrol octane booster; process solvent (chemical/pharmaceutical production); isobutylene production reagent (Exxon process)

methazole
2-(3,4-dichlorophenyl)-4-methyl-1,2,4-oxadiazolidine-3,5-dione; [20354-26-1]

$C_9H_6Cl_2N_2O_3$. M: 261.07.
Production:
• 3,4-dichloronitrobenzene + methyl isocyanate + phosgene (nitro reduction/isocyanate addition/ phosgenation)
Uses: herbicide

methicone *See:* silicone oils

methidathion
[950-37-8]

$C_6H_{11}N_2O_4P_1S_3$. M: 302.33.
Production:
• hydrazine + carbonyl sulphide + formaldehyde + O,O-dimethyl dithiophosphoric acid (condensation/ chloromethylation/dehydrochlorination)
Uses: insecticide/acaricide

methimazole *See:* thiamazole

methiocarb
3,5-dimethyl-4-(methylthio)phenyl methylcarbamate; [2032-65-7]

$C_{11}H_{15}N_1O_2S_1$. M: 225.31.
Production:
• 3,5-xylenol + methylsulphenyl chloride + methyl isocyanate (dehydrochlorination/isocyanate addition)
Uses:
acaricide/molluscicide/insecticide

DL-methionine
2-amino-4-methylthiobutyric acid; racemethionine; [59-51-8]

$C_5H_{11}N_1O_2S_1$. M: 149.21. Feed grade is a yellowish powder with a slight, mouldy odour. MP: 281°C with decomposition. d: 1.34 kg/l. Solubility in water: 33 g/l (20°C). Insoluble in all organic solvents.
Production:
• methyl mercaptan + acrolein + hydrogen cyanide + ammonium bicarbonate (Michael addition/Bucherer-Bergs reaction)
Derivatives: L-methionine
Uses: animal feed additive

L-methionine
L-2-amino-4-methylthiobutyric acid; Met; [63-68-3]

$C_5H_{11}N_1O_2S_1$. M: 149.21. Available commercially as the naturally-occurring L(−)-enantiomer. White, crystalline solid. MP: 280°C (sealed tube). Soluble in water.
Production:
• DL-methionine + acetic anhydride + *Aspergillus oryzae* mould (acetylation/enzymatic hydrolysis)
Derivatives: pentagastrin
Uses: infusion solutions; peptide drug intermediate

methionine hydroxy analogue
Alimet (Monsanto)

$C_5H_{10}O_3S_1$. M: 150.19. Available commercially as the free acid or calcium salt.
Production:
• methyl mercaptan + acrolein + hydrogen cyanide (Michael addition/cyanohydrin formation/nitrile hydrolysis)
Uses: animal feed additive

methocarbamol
[532-03-6]

$C_{11}H_{15}N_1O_5$. M: 241.25.
Production:
• guaifenesin + phosgene + ammonia (phosgenation/ dehydrochlorination)
Uses: muscle relaxant drug

methohexital

[151-83-7]; [309-36-4] (sodium salt)

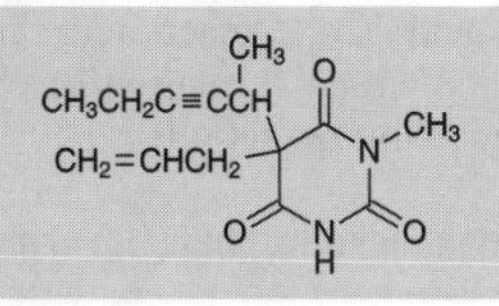

$C_{14}H_{18}N_2O_3$. M: 262.30.
Production:
- 2-chloro-3-hexyne + diethyl malonate + allyl bromide + N-methylurea (dehydrochlorination/dehydrobromination/cyclisation)

Uses: anaesthetic drug

methomyl

S-methyl N-(methylcarbamoyloxy)thioacetimidate; Lannate (Du Pont); [16752-77-5]

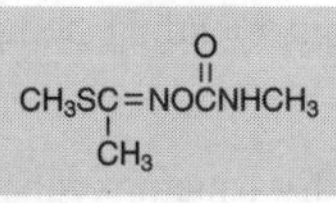

$C_5H_{10}N_2O_2S_1$. M: 162.20.
Production:
- acetaldehyde + hydroxylamine sulphate + methyl mercaptan + methyl isocyanate (oxime formation/chlorination/sulphide formation/isocyanate addition)

Uses: insecticide

methoprene

isopropyl 11-methoxy-3,7,11-trimethyldodeca-2,4-dienoate; [40596-69-8]

$C_{19}H_{34}O_3$. M: 310.48. The commercial product is the *trans,trans*-isomer.
Production:
- isopropanol + bromoacetic acid + chloroacetone + methoxycitronellal (esterification/Reformatsky reaction/dehydration/Wittig reaction)

Uses: insect growth regulator

methoprotryne

2-isopropylamino-4-(3-methoxypropylamino)-6-methyl-thio-1,3,5-triazine; [841-06-5]

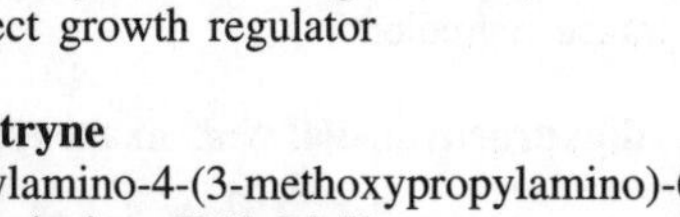

$C_{11}H_{21}N_5O_1S_1$. M: 271.38.
Production:
- 2-methylmercapto-4,6-dichlorotriazine + 3-methoxypropylamine + isopropylamine (amine formation/amine formation)

Uses: herbicide

methotrexate

MTX; [59-05-2]

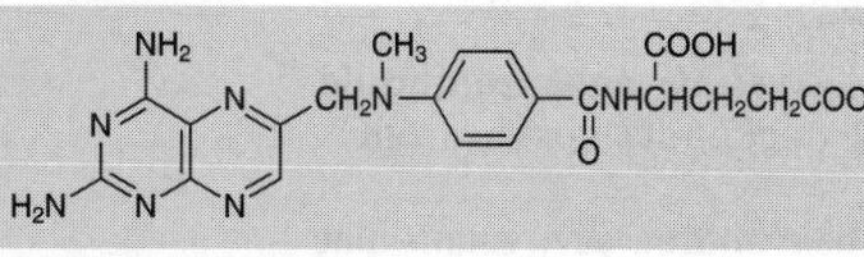

$C_{20}H_{22}N_8O_5$. M: 454.45. Available commercially as the acid or disodium salt.
Production:
- p-nitrobenzoyl chloride + L-glutamic acid + formaldehyde + 2,4,5,6-tetraaminopyrimidine sulphate + 1,1,3-trichloroacetone (amide formation/nitro reduction/methylation/condensation/amine formation)

Uses: antineoplastic/antirheumatic drug

methotrimeprazine *See:* levomepromazine

methoxsalen

ammoidin; 8-methoxypsoralen; xanthotoxin; 8-MOP; [298-81-7]

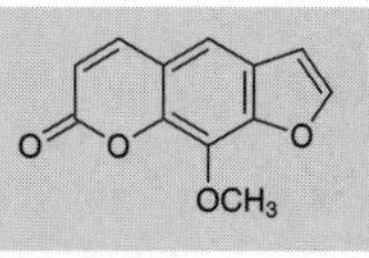

$C_{12}H_8O_4$. M: 216.19.
Production:
- lemon oil/lime oil (extraction/saponification/methylation)

Uses: skin pigmentation drug

2-methoxyacetic acid

methylglycollic acid; [625-45-6]

CH_3OCH_2COOH

$C_3H_6O_3$. M: 90.08. Hygroscopic liquid. BP: 202–204°C. d: 1.42 kg/l (20°C). Soluble in water and oxygenated solvents.
Production:
- methanol + chloroacetic acid (ether formation)

Derivatives: metalaxyl; oxadixyl

4-methoxyacetophenone

4-acetylanisole; [100-06-1]

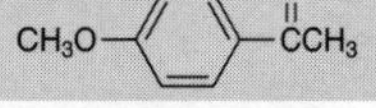

$C_9H_{10}O_2$. M: 150.18. White crystals with sweet odour. MP: 36–38°C. BP: 265°C. d: 1.08 kg/l (41°C). Slightly soluble in water. Soluble in oxygenated solvents.
Production:
- p-hydroxyacetophenone + dimethyl sulphate (methylation)

Derivatives: butyl 2-cyano-3-methyl-*p*-methoxycinnamate; 4-methoxyphenylacetic acid
Uses:
fragrance ingredient (soap)

6-methoxy-2-aminobenzothiazole
See: 2-amino-6-methoxybenzothiazole

2-methoxyaniline *See: o*-anisidine

4-methoxyaniline *See: p*-anisidine

2-methoxyaniline-4-(β-hydroxyethyl)sulphone
See: 5-(β-hydroxyethylsulphonyl)-2-methoxyaniline

2-methoxyaniline-5-sulphonic acid
See: 2-aminoanisole-4-sulphonic acid

4-methoxybenzaldehyde *See: p*-anisaldehyde

methoxybenzene *See:* anisole

4-methoxybenzoic acid
p-anisic acid; [100-09-4]

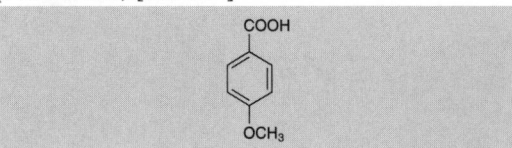

$C_8H_8O_3$. M: 152.15. Solid. MP: 182–185°C. BP: 275–280°C. d: 1.38 kg/l (4°C). Soluble in oxygenated solvents and hot water.
Production:
• *p*-methoxytoluene (side-chain oxidation)
Derivatives:
3-amino-4-methoxybenzoic acid; anisoyl chloride

***p*-methoxybenzoyl chloride** *See:* anisoyl chloride

4-methoxybenzyl alcohol *See:* anisyl alcohol

***p*-methoxybenzylidenemalonic acid, dimethyl ester**
See: methyl 2-carbomethoxy-4′-methoxycinnamate

1-(4-methoxybenzyl)-1,2,3,4,5,6,7,8-octahydroisoquinoline

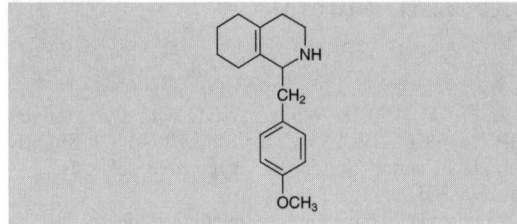

$C_{17}H_{23}N_1O_1$. M: 257.38.

Production:
• cyclohexanone + cyanoacetic acid + 4-methoxyphenylacetic acid (Cope reaction/decarboxylation/nitrile reduction/amide formation/Bischler-Napieralski reaction/reduction)
Derivatives:
dextromethorphan; levallorphan; levorphanol

3-methoxybutanol
[2517-43-3]

$$OCH_3$$
$$CH_3CHCH_2CH_2OH$$

$C_5H_{12}O_2$. M: 104.15. Colourless liquid. BP: 159–163°C. d:0.921 kg/l (20°C). Miscible with water. Flash point: 60°C (CC).
Production:
• crotonaldehyde + methanol (addition/hydrogenation)
Uses: hydraulic fluid blending component

methoxychlor
1,1,1-trichloro-2,2-di-(4-methoxyphenyl)ethane; [72-43-5]

$$CH_3O—⟨⟩—CH—⟨⟩—OCH_3$$
$$CCl_3$$

$C_{16}H_{15}Cl_3O_2$. M: 345.66.
Production:
• anisole + chloral (carbonyl addition)
Uses: insecticide

methoxycitronellal
3,7-dimethyl-7-methoxyoctan-1-al; 7-methoxydihydrocitronellal; [3613-30-7]

$$OCH_3 \quad CH_3$$
$$(CH_3)_2CCH_2CH_2CH_2CHCH_2CHO$$

$C_{11}H_{22}O_2$. M: 186.30. Colourless liquid with a floral odour.
Production:
• hydroxycitronellal + dimethyl sulphate (methylation)
Derivatives: methoprene
Uses: fragrance ingredient

7-methoxydihydrocitronellal *See:* methoxycitronellal

2-methoxydihydropyran
2-methoxy-2,3-dihydropyran; [4454-05-1]

$C_6H_{10}O_2$. M: 114.15. Liquid. BP: 126°C. MP: <60°C.
Production:
• acrolein + methyl vinyl ether (cycloaddition)
Derivatives:
5-bromovaleric acid; glutaraldehyde

3-methoxyestra-2,5-diene-17-ol

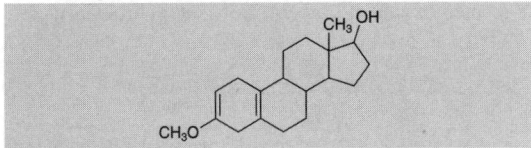

$C_{19}H_{28}O_2$. M: 288.43.
Production:
• estrone (methylation/Birch reduction)
• 6-methoxy-1-tetralone + acetylene + 2-methyl-
  cyclopentane-1,3-dione (multistep synthesis)
Derivatives: estradiol; mestranol; norethisterone; 19-
nortestosterone; trenbolone acetate

2-methoxyethanol
See: ethylene glycol monomethyl ether

2-methoxyethyl acrylate
β-methoxyethyl acrylate; [3121-61-7]

$$CH_2{=}CHCOCH_2CH_2OCH_3$$

$C_6H_{10}O_3$. M: 130.15.
Production:
• ethylene glycol monomethyl ether + acrylic acid
  (esterification)
Derivatives: acrylic rubber

2-methoxyethyl chloroformate
[628-12-6]

$$CH_3OCH_2CH_2OCCl$$

$C_4H_7Cl_1O_3$. M: 138.55. Liquid. Decomposes on heating
above 100°C. MP: <-70°C.
Production:
• ethylene glycol monomethyl ether + phosgene
  (phosgenation)
Derivatives: methylol carbamate resins

β-methoxyethyl cyanoacrylate

$$CH_2{=}CCOCH_2CH_2OCH_3$$
$$CN$$

$C_7H_9N_1O_3$. M: 155.16.
Production:
• ethylene glycol monomethyl ether + cyanoacetic
  acid + formaldehyde (esterification/aldol
  condensation/thermal depolymerisation)
• ethylene glycol monomethyl ether acetate +
  cyanogen chloride + formaldehyde (dehydro-
  chlorination/aldol condensation/thermal
  depolymerisation)
Uses:
low-odour cyanoacrylate adhesives

methoxyflurane
2,2-dichloro-1,1-difluoroethyl methyl ether; [76-38-0]
$C_3H_4Cl_2F_2O_1$. M: 164.97.

$$CH_3OCF_2CHCl_2$$

Production:
• 1,1-dichloro-2,2-difluoroethylene + methanol
  (addition)
Uses: inhalation anaesthetic drug

2-methoxy-3'-hydroxy-2'-naphthanilide
See: 3-hydroxy-2-naphth-*o*-anisidide

4-methoxy-3'-hydroxy-2'-naphthanilide
See: 3-hydroxy-2-naphth-*p*-anisidide

methoxymethylamine
See: *N,O*-dimethylhydroxylamine

2-methoxy-5-methylaniline *See:* *p*-cresidine

2-methoxynaphthalene *See:* β-naphthyl methyl ether

2-methoxy-4-nitroaniline *See:* 2-amino-5-nitroanisole

2-methoxy-5-nitroaniline *See:* 2-amino-4-nitroanisole

4-methoxy-2-nitroaniline *See:* 4-amino-3-nitroanisole

methoxyphenamine
[93-30-1]; [5588-10-3] (hydrochloride)

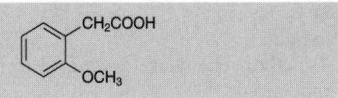

$C_{11}H_{17}N_1O_1$. M: 179.27.
Production:
• methylamine + *o*-methoxyphenylacetone (amine
  formation)
Uses: bronchodilator drug

p-methoxyphenethyl alcohol
See: 2-(*p*-methoxyphenyl)ethanol

o-methoxyphenol *See:* guaiacol

p-methoxyphenol
See: hydroquinone monomethyl ether

2-methoxyphenylacetic acid
[93-25-4]

$C_9H_{10}O_3$. M: 166.18. Solid. MP: 121–125°C.

Production:
- *o*-hydroxyacetophenone + dimethyl sulphate
  (methylation/Willgerodt reaction)

Derivatives:
o-methoxyphenylacetone

4-methoxyphenylacetic acid

$$CH_3O\text{—}\underset{}{\bigcirc}\text{—}CH_2COOH$$

$C_9H_{10}O_3$. M: 166.18. Yellowish flakes. MP: 86–88°C. Insoluble in cold water. Soluble in alcohol.
Production:
- 4-methoxyacetophenone (Willgerodt reaction)

Derivatives: 1-(4-methoxybenzyl)-1,2,3,4,5,6,7,8-octa-hydroisoquinoline; *p*-methoxyphenylacetone; 2-(*p*-methoxyphenyl)ethanol

o-methoxyphenylacetone
2-methoxyphenylacetone; 1-(2-methoxyphenyl)-2-propanone; [5211-62-1]

$$\underset{OCH_3}{\overset{\overset{O}{\parallel}}{\underset{}{\bigcirc}}CH_2CCH_3}$$

$C_{10}H_{12}O_2$. M: 164.21. Liquid. BP: 135–139°C (2.0 kPa).
Production:
- 2-methoxyphenylacetic acid + methyl acetate
  (nitrile formation/condensation)

Derivatives: methoxyphenamine

p-methoxyphenylacetone
4-acetonylanisole; *p*-acetonylanisole; 4-methoxybenzyl methyl ketone; 4-methoxyphenylacetone; [122-84-9]

$$CH_3O\text{—}\underset{}{\bigcirc}\text{—}CH_2\overset{\overset{O}{\parallel}}{C}CH_3$$

$C_{10}H_{12}O_2$. M: 164.21. Liquid. BP: 110–113°C. Slightly soluble in water and oxygenated solvents.
Production:
- 4-methoxyphenylacetic acid + methyl acetate
  (esterification/condensation)

Derivatives:
fenoterol; mebeverine

2-(*p*-methoxyphenyl)ethanol
p-methoxyphenethyl alcohol

$$CH_3O\text{—}\underset{}{\bigcirc}\text{—}CH_2CH_2OH$$

$C_9H_{12}O_2$. M: 152.20. Solid. MP: 28–30°C. BP: 334–336°C.
Production:
- 4-methoxyphenylacetic acid (esterification/ester reduction)

Derivatives: astemizole

1-(2-methoxyphenyl)piperazine hydrochloride
N-(*o*-methoxyphenyl)piperazine monohydrochloride; [66373-53-3]

$$\underset{}{\bigcirc}\overset{OCH_3}{}\text{—N}\underset{}{\bigcirc}\text{NH .HCl}$$

$C_{11}H_{17}Cl_1N_2O_1$. M: 228.72. Off-white, crystalline solid. Soluble in water and oxygenated solvents.
Production:
- *o*-anisidine + diethanolamine (amine formation)

Derivatives:
urapidil

methoxypropanol
See: propylene glycol monomethyl ether

p-methoxypropenylbenzene *See:* anethole

2-methoxy-4-propenylphenol *See:* isoeugenol

3-methoxypropionitrile
[110-67-8]

$$CH_3OCH_2CH_2C\equiv N$$

$C_4H_7N_1O_1$. M: 85.11. Liquid. BP: 64–66°C (2.7 kPa). MP: <-20°C.
Production:
- methanol + acrylonitrile (cyanoethylation)

Derivatives:
3-methoxypropylamine; trimethoprim
Uses: process solvent

methoxypropoxypropanol
See: dipropylene glycol monomethyl ether

3-methoxypropylamine
3-MPA; [5332-73-0]

$$CH_3OCH_2CH_2CH_2NH_2$$

$C_4H_{11}N_1O_1$. M: 89.14. Liquid. BP: 117–119°C. MP: <-70°C. d: 0.87 kg/l (20°C). Soluble in water and most organic solvents.
Production:
- 3-methoxypropionitrile (nitrile reduction)

Derivatives:
methoprotryne
Uses: optical brightener intermediate

6-methoxy-1-tetralone
6-methoxy-α-tetralone; [1078-19-9]

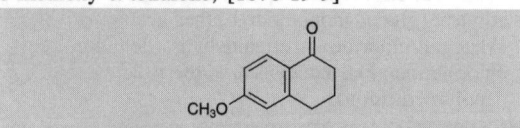

$C_{11}H_{12}O_2$. M: 176.22. Solid. MP: 77–80°C.

Production:
- β-naphthol + dimethyl sulphate (methylation/ reduction/side-chain oxidation)

Derivatives: 3-methoxyestra-2,5-diene-17-ol; norgestrel

p-methoxytoluene
p-cresyl methyl ether; 4-methylanisole; methyl *p*-cresol; [104-93-8]

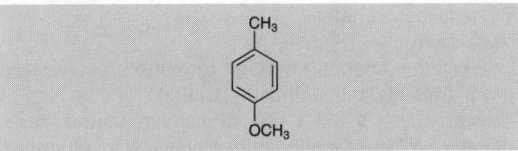

$C_8H_{10}O_1$. M: 122.17. Colourless liquid with strong, floral odour. BP: 176°C. d: 0.97 kg/l (25°C). Insoluble in water. Soluble in alcohol.
Production:
- *p*-cresol + dimethyl sulphate (methylation)

Derivatives:
p-anisaldehyde; 4-methoxybenzoic acid

methsuximide *See:* mesuximide

methyl abietate
methyl rosinate; Abalyn (Hercules); [127-25-3]

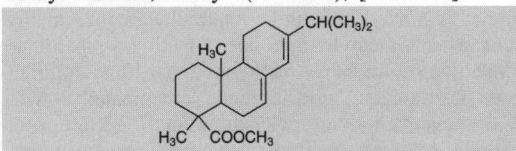

$C_{21}H_{32}O_2$. M: 316.49. Pale yellow liquid. BP: 365°C with decomposition. d: 1.04 kg/l (20°C). Insoluble in water. Soluble in most organic solvents.
Production:
- rosin, wood + methanol (alcoholysis/isomerisation)

Derivatives:
hydroabietyl alcohol; methyl abietate, hydrogenated

methyl abietate, hydrogenated
methyl rosinate, hydrogenated (CTFA); Hercolyn D (Hercules)

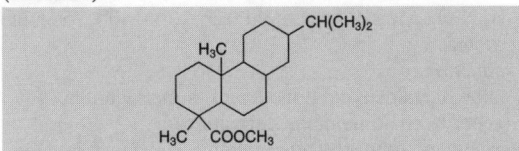

$C_{21}H_{36}O_2$. M: 320.52.
Production:
- methyl abietate (hydrogenation)

Uses: plasticiser

N-methylacetamide
[79-16-3]
$C_3H_7N_1O_1$. M: 73.10.

Production:
- acetic acid + methylamine (amide formation)

Derivatives:
N-methyl-*N*-vinylacetamide
Uses: solvent

methyl acetate
[79-20-9]

$C_3H_6O_2$. M: 74.08. Colourless liquid with pleasant odour. BP: 57°C. d: 0.93 kg/l (25°C). Soluble in water. Miscible with alcohol.
Production:
- methanol + carbon monoxide (BASF/Monsanto carbonylation processes; byproduct of acetic acid production)
- methanol + carbon monoxide (BP acetyls process; byproduct of acetic acid/acetic anhydride production)

Derivatives:
chlorophacinone; diphacinone; fenfluramine; *o*-methoxyphenylacetone; *p*-methoxyphenylacetone; methyl cinnamate; methyl cyanoacetate; methyldopa; phenylacetone

N-methylacetoacetamide
acetoacet-*N*-methylamide; [20306-75-6]

$C_5H_9N_1O_2$. M: 115.13.
Production:
- diketene + methylamine (amide formation)

Derivatives: monocrotophos

methyl acetoacetate
[105-45-3]

$C_5H_8O_3$. M: 116.11. Colourless liquid. BP: 169–170°C. MP: -80°C. d: 1.08 kg/l (20°C). Soluble in water. Miscible with oxygenated solvents.
Production:
- diketene + methanol (esterification)

Derivatives:
acetonylacetone; chloroacetone; 3-(2-chloro-6-fluorophenyl)-5-methylisoxazole-4-carboxylic acid; 3-(2-chlorophenyl)-5-methylisoxazole-4-carboxylic acid; 3-cyano-4-methyl-6-hydroxy-2-pyridone; diacetoacet-*o*-tolidide; 3-(2,6-dichlorophenyl)-5-methylisoxazole-4-carboxylic acid; dilauryl 1,4-dihydro-2,6-dimethylpyridine-3,5-dicarboxylate; epirizole; fenfuram; methyl *n*-amyl ketone; β-methylheptenone; methyl isoamyl ketone; methyl iso-

propyl ketone; methyl *n*-nonyl ketone; 5-methyl-3-phen-
ylisoxazole-4-carboxylic acid; methyl propyl ketone;
mevinphos; nicardipine; nimodipine; nitrendipine; oxamyl; pseudoionone; 3-pyridino-4-methyl-6-hydroxy-2-
pyridone chloride; sulfamerazine; sulfamethoxazole
Uses:
reagent (Dane salt formation)

p-methylacetophenone
p-acetotoluene; methyl *p*-tolyl ketone; [122-00-9]

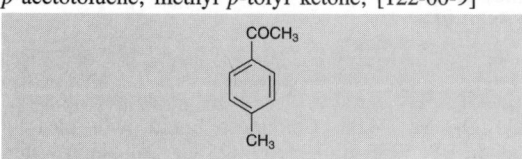

C$_9$H$_{10}$O$_1$. M: 134.18. Colourless, crystalline solid with
a floral odour. MP: 28°C. BP: 226°C. d: 1.01 kg/l
(20°C). Insoluble in water. Soluble in oxygenated
solvents.
Production:
• toluene + acetic anhydride (Friedel-Crafts acylation)
Derivatives:
N-methyl-2-*p*-tolylindole; triprolidine
Uses: fragrance ingredient

methyl acrylate
[96-33-3]

$$CH_2=CHCOCH_3$$

C$_4$H$_6$O$_2$. M: 86.09. Liquid with an acrid odour. BP:
79–81°C. FP: -77°C. d: 0.95 kg/l (25°C). Slightly
soluble in water. The commercial product is stabilised
against polymerisation with hydroquinone monomethyl
ether or a similar inhibitor.
Production:
• methanol + acrylic acid (esterification)
Derivatives:
acrylic resins, solvent-based; caproamphocarboxypropionate; caryloamphocarboxypropionate; cocoaminopropionic acid; cocoamphocarboxypropionate; cocoamphopropionate; dimyristyl thiodipropionate; ditridecyl thiodipropionate; ethylene-methyl acrylate copolymers; ethylene-methyl acrylate terpolymer, ionomeric; isobornyl acrylate; isostearoamphopropionate;
lauroamphocarboxypropionate; lauryl acrylate; methyl
3,5-di-*t*-butyl-4-hydroxyphenylpropionate; oleoamphopropionate; 15-pentadecanolide; polyacrylonitrile; triethylene glycol bis[3-(3-*t*-butyl-4-hydroxy-5-methyl-
phenyl)propionate]; vinyl chloride-acrylic ester copolymers; vinylidene chloride copolymers, latex; vinylidene
chloride-methyl acrylate copolymers
Uses: acrylic/vinyl acetate resin comonomer (textile,
paper, leather finishes)

β-methylallyl chloride *See:* methallyl chloride

methylamine
monomethylamine; MMA; [74-89-5]

$$CH_3NH_2$$

C$_1$H$_5$N$_1$. M: 31.06. Colourless liquified gas with a
strong, ammoniacal odour. BP: -6°C. FP: -94°C. d:
0.67 kg/l (4°C). Soluble in water and oxygenated
solvents. Also available commercially as a 40% or
50% aqueous solution.
Production:
• methanol + ammonia (amine formation; coproduced
with trimethylamine/dimethylamine)
Derivatives: Acid Black 60; adrenalone; amitraz; benzoctamine; *N*-benzylmethylamine; betahistine; chlordiazepoxide; 5-chloro-2-methyl-4-isothiazolinone; cimetidine; dazomet; desmetryn; dimethoate; *N,N'*-dimethyl-
urea; *N,N'*-dinitroso-*N,N'*-dimethylterephthalamide; Disperse Blue 3; Disperse Blue 14; Disperse Red 9; DL-
ephedrine; L-ephedrine; Fluorescent Brightener 162;
fluridone; furathiocarb; iocarmic acid; iotalamic acid;
mecarbam; mesuximide; metam-sodium; methabenzthiazuron; methamphetamine; methoxyphenamine; *N*-meth-
ylacetamide; *N*-methylacetoacetamide; *N*-methylamino-
acetaldehyde dimethyl acetal; 1-methylamino-1-methyl-
thio-2-nitroethylene; 3-methylaminopropylamine; methyldidecylamine; methyldiethanolamine; methylethanolamine; *N*-methylformamide; methylhydrazine; methyl
isocyanate; *N*-methylmorpholine; 1-methyl-4-piperidone;
N-methylpyrrolidone; *N*-methylurea; naftifine; nomifensine; norflurazon; nortriptyline; omethoate; *N,N,N'*,
N'',N''-pentamethyldipropylenetriamine; 1,2,2,6,6-penta-
methyl-4-hydroxypiperidine; phenolic resins, amino-
substituted; phenylephrine hydrochloride; Pigment Red
179; Pigment Red 185; Pigment Violet 32; polyacrylamide, aminomethylated; polystyrene, crosslinked,
aminated; sarcosine; sodium *N*-methyltaurate; synephrine; vamidothion; 3,5-xylyl methylcarbamate; zomepirac

N-methylaminoacetaldehyde dimethyl acetal
2,2-dimethoxyethylethylamine; [122-07-6]

$$CH_3NHCH_2CH(OCH_3)_2$$

C$_5$H$_{13}$N$_1$O$_2$. M: 119.16. Liquid. BP: 139–140°C. Soluble
in water.
Production:
• chloroacetaldehyde + methanol + methylamine
(acetal formation/amine formation)
Derivatives: epinephrine; tolmetin

1-methylamino-1-methylthio-2-nitroethylene
N-methyl-1-methylthio-2-nitroethenamine; [61832-41-5]

$$CH_3S\diagdown C=CHNO_2$$
$$CH_3NH\diagup$$

C$_4$H$_8$N$_2$O$_2$S$_1$. M: 148.17.

Production:
- carbon disulphide + nitromethane + dimethyl sulphate + methylamine (addition/methylation/ amine formation)

Derivatives: ranitidine

methyl 3-amino-4-methylthiophene-2-carboxylate
[85006-31-1]

$C_7H_9N_1O_2S_1$. M: 171.22. Solid.
Production:
- 3-methylthiophene + acetyl chloride + methanol (Friedel-Crafts acylation/nitration/esterification/nitro reduction)

Derivatives: carticaine

N-methyl-*p*-aminophenol
p-methylaminophenol; metol; [150-75-4]

$C_7H_9N_1O_1$. M: 123.16. Available commercially as the bisulphate.
Production:
- *p*-aminophenol (methylation)

Uses: photographic developing agent

3-methylaminopropylamine
3-amino-1-methylaminopropane; *N*-methyldiaminopropane; [6291-84-5]

CH₃NHCH₂CH₂CH₂NH₂

$C_4H_{12}N_2$. M: 88.15. Liquid. BP: 138–144°C. MP: <-72°C. Soluble in oxygenated solvents.
Production:
- methylamine + acrylonitrile (cyanoethylation/nitrile reduction)

Derivatives: oxantel; pyrantel

methyl *n*-amyl ketone
2-heptanone; [110-43-0]

CH₃(CH₂)₄CCH₃

$C_7H_{14}O_1$. M: 114.19. Colourless liquid with fruity odour. BP: 152°C. d: 0.82 kg/l (20°C). Slightly soluble in water. Soluble in oxygenated solvents.
Production:
- methyl acetoacetate + *n*-butyl chloride (acetoacetate ester synthesis)

Uses: fragrance ingredient

N-methylaniline
[100-61-8]

$C_7H_9N_1$. M: 107.16. Colourless or yellow liquid. BP: 196°C. FP: -57°C. d: 0.99 kg/l (20°C). Insoluble in water. Soluble in oxygenated solvents.
Production:
- aniline + methanol (amine formation; coproduced with *N,N*-dimethylaniline)

Derivatives: *N*-(2-cyanoethyl)-*N*-methylaniline; *N,N′*-dimethyldiphenylthiuram disulphide; *N*-(*p*-ethoxycarbonylphenyl)-*N′*-methyl-*N′*-phenylformamidine; Fischer's base; mefenacet; methyldymron

methyl anthranilate
methyl *o*-aminobenzoate; [134-20-3]

$C_8H_9N_1O_2$. M: 151.17. Colourless to pale yellow liquid or solid with a grape-like odour. MP: 24°C. BP: 131–133°C (1.9 kPa). Slightly soluble in water. Soluble in oxygenated solvents.
Production:
- methanol + anthranilic acid (esterification)

Derivatives: bentazone; hydroxycitronellal-anthranilate adduct; methyl *N*-methylanthranilate; α-methyl-β-3,4-methylenedioxyphenylpropionaldehyde-anthranilate adduct; Pigment Red 175

Uses: fragrance/flavouring ingredient

2-methylanthraquinone
[84-54-8]

$C_{15}H_{10}O_2$. M: 222.24. Pale yellow needles. MP: 168–170°C. Sublimes on further heating. Insoluble in water. Soluble in aromatic solvents.
Production:
- toluene + phthalic anhydride (Friedel-Crafts acylation/acid-catalysed coupling)

Derivatives: 1-chloro-2-methylanthraquinone; 1-nitroanthraquinone-2-carboxylic acid

p-methylbenzaldehyde
4-methylbenzaldehyde; *p*-tolylaldehyde; [104-87-0]
$C_8H_8O_1$. M: 120.15. Colourless liquid with a floral

odour. BP: 204°C. MP: -6°C. d: 1.02 kg/l. Slightly soluble in water.

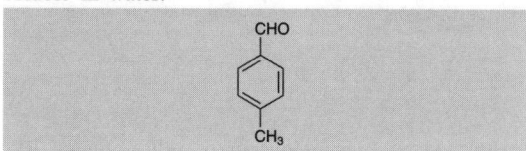

Production:
• toluene + dimethylformamide (Vilsmeier reaction)
• toluene + carbon monoxide (Gattermann-Koch reaction)
Derivatives: 4-methylphenylacetaldehyde
Uses: flavouring ingredient

methyl benzoate
[93-58-3]

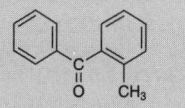

$C_8H_8O_2$. M: 136.15. Colourless liquid with a pleasant odour. BP: 199–200°C. MP: -15°C. d: 1.09 kg/l (20°C). Insoluble in water. Miscible with oxygenated solvents.
Production:
• p-xylene + methanol (side-chain oxidation/esterification; byproduct of dimethyl terephthalate production)
Uses: dyestuffs intermediate; fragrance ingredient

m-**methylbenzoic acid** *See:* m-toluic acid

o-**methylbenzoic acid** *See:* o-toluic acid

p-**methylbenzoic acid** *See:* p-toluic acid

2-methylbenzophenone
[131-58-8]

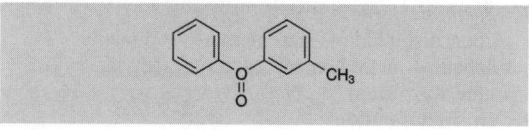

$C_{14}H_{12}O_1$. M: 196.25. Liquid. BP: 310°C. Insoluble in water. Soluble in oxygenated and aromatic solvents.
Production:
• o-toluic acid + benzene (acid chloride formation/ Friedel-Crafts acylation)
Derivatives: orphenadrine
Uses: perfume fixative

3-methylbenzophenone
m-methylbenzophenone; *m*-phenyltolyl ketone; [643-65-2]
$C_{14}H_{12}O_1$. M: 196.25. Colourless liquid. BP: 315°C. Insoluble in water. Soluble in oxygenated and chlorinated solvents.

Production:
• benzene + *m*-toluic acid (acid chloride formation/ Friedel-Crafts acylation)
Derivatives: ketoprofen

2-methylbenzothiazole
[120-75-2]

$C_8H_7N_1S_1$. M: 149.22.
Production:
• acetic acid + 2-aminothiophenol (condensation)
Uses: photographic sensitising dyestuff intermediate

o-**methylbenzoyl chloride** *See:* o-toluoyl chloride

p-**methylbenzoyl chloride** *See:* p-toluoyl chloride

α-**methylbenzyl alcohol** *See:* 1-phenylethanol

N-**methylbenzylamine** *See:* N-benzylmethylamine

methylbenzyl ketone *See:* phenylacetone

methyl blue *See:* Acid Blue 93

methyl borate *See:* trimethyl borate

methyl bromide
bromomethane; [74-83-9]

CH_3Br

$C_1H_3Br_1$. M: 94.93. Colourless, odourless, liquified gas. BP: 4°C. FP: -94°C. d: 1.73 kg/l (liquid, 20°C). Insoluble in water. Soluble in most organic solvents.
Production:
• methanol + hydrobromic acid (alcohol bromination)
Derivatives: cetyltrimethylammonium bromide; clidinium bromide; clobazam; distigmine bromide; fenpiverinium bromide; hexobarbital; mepivacaine; methylmagnesium bromide; myristyltrimethylammonium bromide; pirimicarb; propantheline bromide; pyridostigmine bromide; tetramethylammonium bromide
Uses: soil/grain fumigant

2-methyl-1,3-butadiene *See:* isoprene

2-methyl-1-butanol
amyl alcohol, active; *s*-butylcarbinol; [137-32-6]
$C_5H_{12}O_1$. M: 88.15. Colourless liquid. BP: 129°C. FP: -70°C. d: 0.82 kg/l (20°C). Flash point: 43°C (TCC).

Solubility in water: 30 g/l water (25°C).

$$CH_3CH_2\overset{\overset{\displaystyle CH_3}{|}}{CH}CH_2OH$$

Production:
- amyl alcohol, primary (fractionation; coproduced with *n*-amyl alcohol)

Uses: solvent

2-methyl-2-butanol *See:* *t*-amyl alcohol

3-methylbutanol *See:* isoamyl alcohol

3-methylbutan-2-one *See:* methyl isopropyl ketone

2-methyl-2-butene
β-amylene; 2-methylbutene-2; [513-35-9]

$$(CH_3)_2C = CHCH_3$$

C_5H_{10}. M: 70.13. Colourless liquid with an unpleasant odour. BP: 38–39°C. d: 0.66 kg/l (20°C). Insoluble in water. Soluble in alcohol. Commercial grades contain 92–95% 2-methyl-2-butene.
Production:
- isoamylene (fractionation)

Derivatives: 6-acetyl-1,1,2,3,3,5-hexamethylindane; 4,5,5,6,7,7-hexamethylindanopyran

2-methyl-3-buten-2-ol
3-methyl-1-buten-3-ol; [115-18-4]

$$CH_2 = CH\overset{\overset{\displaystyle OH}{|}}{C}(CH_3)_2$$

$C_5H_{10}O_1$. M: 86.13. Liquid. BP: 96–98°C.
Production:
- methylbutynol (hydrogenation)

Derivatives:
(*1RS*)-*cis/trans*-3-(2,2-dichlorovinyl)-2,2-dimethylcyclopropanecarboxylic acid; β-methylheptenone

3-methyl-2-buten-1-ol
3,3-dimethylallyl alcohol; prenol; prenyl alcohol; [556-82-1]

$$(CH_3)_2C = CHCH_2OH$$

$C_5H_{10}O_1$. M: 86.13. Liquid. BP: 139–140°C.
Production:
- isobutylene + formaldehyde (Prins reaction)

Derivatives:
(*1RS*)-*trans*-chrysanthemic acid; lavandulyl acetate; methyl 3,3-dimethyl-4-pentenoate; pentazocine

2-methyl-2-butenonitrile

$$CH_3CH = \overset{\overset{\displaystyle CH_3}{|}}{C}CH_2CN$$

$C_6H_7N_1$. M: 93.13.

Production:
- butadiene + hydrogen cyanide (Du Pont HMDA process; byproduct of adiponitrile production)

Derivatives: tiglic acid

3-methyl-2-butylamine
2-amino-3-methylbutane; 1,2-dimethylpropylamine; [598-74-3]

$$(CH_3)_2CH\overset{\overset{\displaystyle CH_3}{|}}{CH}NH_2$$

$C_5H_{13}N_1$. M: 85.15. Liquid. BP: 80–83°C. MP: <-50°C. d: 0.75 kg/l (20°C). Miscible with water and oxygenated solvents. The commercial product contains 10% water.
Production:
- methyl isopropyl ketone + hydroxylamine sulphate (oxime formation/hydrogenation)

Derivatives: dimethametryn

methyl *t*-butyl ether
MTBE; [1634-04-4]

$$(CH_3)_3COCH_3$$

$C_5H_{12}O_1$. M: 88.15. Colourless liquid. BP: 55°C. MP: -109°C. d: 0.74 kg/l. Solubility in water: 48 g/l water (25°C). Flash point : -28°C.
Production:
- raffinate I + methanol (ether formation; coproduced with raffinate II)
- *t*-butanol + methanol (Arco MTBE process)
- isobutylene + methanol (ether formation)

Uses: extraction solvent; petrol blending component

methylbutynol
2-methyl-3-butyn-2-ol; 3-methyl-1-butyn-3-ol; [115-19-5]

$$HC \equiv C\overset{\overset{\displaystyle OH}{|}}{C}(CH_3)_2$$

$C_5H_8O_1$. M: 84.11. Colourless liquid with a pleasant odour. BP: 102–105°C. MP: 2°C. d: 0.86 kg/l (20°C). Miscible with water. Soluble in most organic solvents.
Production:
- acetylene + acetone (ethynylation)

Derivatives:
Fischer's base; 2-methyl-3-buten-2-ol; propyzamide
Uses: electroplating brightening agent; corrosion inhibitor (oilfield acidising, steel pickling acids); stabiliser (chlorinated solvents)

2-methylbutyraldehyde
[96-17-3]

$$CH_3CH_2\overset{\overset{\displaystyle CH_3}{|}}{CH}CHO$$

$C_5H_{10}O_1$. M: 86.13.

Production:
• pentaldehydes, mixed (separation; coproduced with valeraldehyde)
Derivatives: 2-methylbutyric acid

2-methylbutyric acid
[116-53-0]

$$CH_3CH_2\overset{\overset{\displaystyle CH_3}{|}}{C}HCOOH$$

$C_5H_{10}O_2$. M: 102.13. Liquid with strong, unpleasant odour. BP: 174–177°C. MP: <70°C. d: 0.94 kg/l (20°C). Slightly soluble in water. Soluble in oxygenated solvents. The commercial product is a racemic mixture.
Production:
• 2-methylbutyraldehyde (carbonyl oxidation)
Uses: fragrance/flavouring intermediate

3-methylbutyric acid *See:* isovaleric acid

methyl caprate
methyl decanoate; [110-42-9]

$$CH_3(CH_2)_8\overset{\overset{\displaystyle O}{||}}{C}OCH_3$$

$C_{11}H_{22}O_2$. M: 186.30. Colourless liquid with a pleasant odour. BP: 223–225°C. FP: -13°C. d: 0.87 kg/l (20°C). Insoluble in water. Soluble in oxygenated solvents.
Production:
• C_8-C_{10} fatty acids, methyl ester (fractionation; coproduced with methyl caproate/methyl caprylate)
Uses: flavouring ingredient

methyl caproate
methyl hexanoate; [106-70-7]

$$CH_3(CH_2)_4\overset{\overset{\displaystyle O}{||}}{C}OCH_3$$

$C_7H_{14}O_2$. M: 130.19. Colourless liquid with a pleasant odour. BP: 150–151°C. FP: -71°C. d: 0.89 kg/l (20°C). Insoluble in water. Soluble in oxygenated solvents.
Production:
• C_8-C_{10} fatty acids, methyl ester (fractionation; coproduced with methyl caprate/methyl caprylate)
Uses: flavouring ingredient

methyl caprylate
methyl octanoate; [111-11-5]

$$CH_3(CH_2)_6\overset{\overset{\displaystyle O}{||}}{C}OCH_3$$

$C_9H_{18}O_2$. M: 158.24. Colourless liquid. BP: 195°C. MP: -63°C. d: 0.95 kg/l (15°C). Insoluble in water.
Production:
• C_8-C_{10} fatty acids, methyl ester (fractionation; coproduced with methyl caprate/methyl caproate)
Uses: flavouring ingredient

methyl 2-carbomethoxy-4′-methoxycinnamate
dimethyl anisylidenemalonate; *p*-methoxybenzylidene-malonic acid, dimethyl ester; methyl 2-carbomethoxy-3-(*p*-methoxyphenyl)acrylate; Cyanasorb UV-1088 (American Cyanamid)

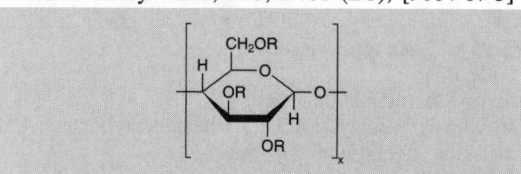

$C_{13}H_{14}O_5$. M: 250.25. White powder. MP: 58°C.
Production:
• *p*-anisaldehyde + dimethyl malonate (carbonyl condensation)
Uses: light stabiliser (plastics)

methylcatechol *See:* guaiacol

Methyl Cellosolve
See: ethylene glycol monomethyl ether

methyl cellulose
cellulose methyl ether; MC; E461 (EC); [9004-67-5]

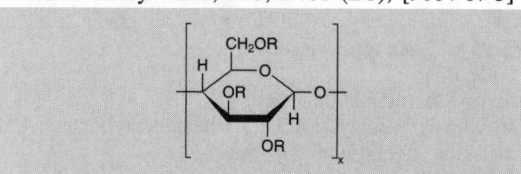

R = H, methyl-. White, granular powder. Soluble in cold water forming viscous solutions. Degree of polymerisation: 800–2,400 depending on the source of the cellulose. Degree of substitution: 1.40–1.95, equivalent to a methoxyl content of 24–32% w/w.
Production:
• alkali cellulose + methyl chloride (ether formation)
Derivatives: methyl hydroxypropyl cellulose
Uses: tobacco binder/film-forming agent; plasticiser/adhesion additive (plaster, tile cements); protective colloid (vinyl chloride suspension polymerisation); thickening agent/ protective colloid (latex paints, adhesives, decorative stuccos); wallpaper adhesive

methyl chloride
chloromethane; [74-87-3]

$$CH_3Cl$$

$C_1H_3Cl_1$. M: 50.48. Colourless gas. BP: -24°C. FP: -98°C. Slightly soluble in water. Soluble in methanol.
Production:
• methanol + hydrogen chloride, anhydrous (gas-phase chlorination)
• natural gas + hydrogen chloride, anhydrous/oxygen (Lummus oxychlorination process; coproduced with chloroform/methylene chloride/carbon tetrachloride)
Derivatives:
alkyl(C_{13}-C_{15})trimethylammonium chloride; Basic Red 29; Basic Yellow 25; behenyltrimethylammonium chl-

oride; carbon tetrachloride; cetyltrimethylammonium chloride; chloroform; chlorotrimethylsilane; diallyldimethylammonium chloride; dichlorodimethylsilane; dichloromethylsilane; didecyldimethylammonium chloride; dimethyldicocoammonium chloride; dimethyldistearylammonium chloride; dimethylditallowammonium chloride; disodium methylarsonate; dodecyltrimethylammonium chloride; glufosinate-ammonium; mepiquat chloride; 3-(methacrylamidopropyl)trimethylammonium chloride; methyl cellulose; methylene chloride; methyl hydroxyethylcellulose; methyl iodide; methyl isopropyl ketone; methylmagnesium chloride; methyl *N*-methylanthranilate; monosodium methylarsonate; naphtholactam blue; paraquat dichloride; pentamethyl-*N*-tallow-1,3-propanediammonium chloride; sodium cacodylate; soyatrimethylammonium chloride; suxamethonium chloride; tallowtrimethylammonium chloride; tetramethylammonium chloride; tetramethyllead; thioridazine; tri-*n*-butylmethylammonium chloride; trichloromethylsilane; trimethylammoniumethyl methacrylate chloride; *N,N,N*-trimethyl-2-hydroxypropylammonium 2-ethylhexanoate
Uses:
methylation reagent

methyl chloroacetate
[96-34-4]

$$CICH_2COCH_3$$

$C_3H_5Cl_1O_2$. M: 108.52. Colourless liquid. BP: 127–130°C. MP: -33°C. d: 1.24 kg/l (20°C). Insoluble in water. Miscible with oxygenated solvents.
Production:
• methanol + chloroacetic acid (esterification)
Derivatives: chloroacetonitrile; (*RS*)-α-(4-chlorophenyl)-isovaleric acid; diltiazem; dimethoate; etretinate; ibuprofen; methyl nonylacetaldehyde; 4-methylphenylacetaldehyde; naproxen; piroxicam; sodium fluoroacetate

methyl γ-chloroacetoacetate
methyl 4-chloroacetoacetate; methyl 4-chloro-3-oxobutanoate; [32807-28-6]

$$CICH_2CCH_2COOCH_3$$

$C_5H_7Cl_1O_3$. M: 150.56. Colourless liquid. BP: 50°C (0.13 kPa). d: 1.29 kg/l (20°C). Slightly soluble in water. Soluble in oxygenated and aromatic solvents.
Production:
• diketene + hydrogen chloride, anhydrous + methanol (alpha chlorination/esterification)
Derivatives:
acetone-1,3-dicarboxylic acid; 1,3-dichloroacetone; dimethyl acetonedicarboxylate; flurochloridone; 1,1,3-trichloroacetone

methyl chloroform *See:* 1,1,1-trichloroethane

methyl chloroformate
methyl chlorocarbonate; [79-22-1]

$$CH_3OCCl$$

$C_2H_3Cl_1O_2$. M: 94.49. Liquid. BP: 71–72°C. MP: -81°C. d: 1.22 kg/l (20°C). Slightly soluble in water with gradual hydrolysis. Miscible with most organic solvents.
Production:
• methanol + phosgene (phosgenation)
Derivatives:
asulam; carbendazim; flubendazole; hexazinone; mebendazole; methyl 2-nonynoate; methyl 2-octynoate; methylol carbamate resins; phenmedipham; thiophanate-methyl

2-methyl-4-chlorophenoxyacetic acid
MCPA; [94-74-6]

$C_9H_9Cl_1O_3$. M: 200.62. Available commercially as the acid, potassium, sodium or dimethylammonium salts.
Production:
• *p*-chloro-*o*-cresol + chloroacetic acid (ether formation)
Derivatives:
MCPA-(2-hydroxybutyl); MCPA-isooctyl; MCPA-thioethyl
Uses: herbicide

methyl α-chloropropionate
methyl 2-chloropropionate; [17639-93-9]

$$CH_3CHCOOCH_3$$

$C_4H_7Cl_1O_2$. M: 122.55. Colourless liquid. BP: 132-133°C. d: 1.08 kg/l (4°C). Soluble in oxygenated solvents. The commercial product is a racemic mixture.
Production:
• methanol + α-chloropropionic acid (esterification)
Derivatives:
benalaxyl; flamprop-methyl; furalaxyl; metalaxyl

α-methylcinnamaldehyde
[101-39-3]

$C_{10}H_{10}O_1$. M: 146.19. Liquid. BP: 138–140°C (1.9 kPa).
Production:
• benzaldehyde + propionaldehyde (carbonyl condensation)
Derivatives: 4-*t*-butyl-α-methylhydrocinnamaldehyde; cyclamen aldehyde

methyl cinnamate
[103-26-4]

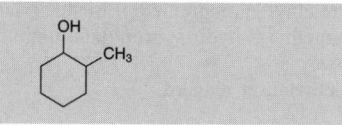

$C_{10}H_{10}O_2$. M: 162.19. Colourless crystals with fruity odour. MP: 36.5°C, BP: 262°C. d: 1.09 kg/l (20°C). Insoluble in water. Soluble in oxygenated solvents.
Production:
• cinnamic acid + methanol (esterification)
• benzaldehyde + methyl acetate (Claisen condensation)
Uses:
perfume ingredient

methyl cocoate
coconut acid methyl ester

R = coco-. A typical chain-length distribution is: 3% C_8, 5% C_{10}, 49% C_{12}, 19% C_{14}, 11% C_{16}, 3% $C_{18:0}$, 6% $C_{18:1}$, 1% $C_{18:2}$.
Production:
• coconut oil + methanol (transesterification)
Derivatives:
coconut acid diethanolamide; C_8-C_{10} fatty acids, methyl ester; methyl cocoate, topped

methyl cocoate, topped

n = 10, 12, 14, 16. Residual fraction from first distillation of coconut acid methyl ester. A typical chain-length distribution is: 50% C_{12}, 19% C_{14}, 12% C_{16}, 18% C_{18}.
Production:
• methyl cocoate (fractionation; coproduced with C_8-C_{10} fatty acids, methyl ester)
Derivatives: n-alkanol(C_{12}-C_{18}); C_{14}-C_{18} fatty acids, methyl ester; methyl laurate

2-methylcrotonic acid *See:* tiglic acid

methyl cyanide *See:* acetonitrile

methyl cyanoacetate
[105-34-0]

NCCH_2COOCH_3

$C_4H_5N_1O_2$. M: 99.09.
Production:
• methanol + cyanoacetic acid (esterification)
• methyl acetate + cyanogen chloride (dehydrochlorination)
Derivatives:
cefotetan; sulfadimethoxine

methylcyclohexanol
[25639-42-3]

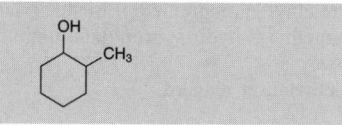

$C_7H_{14}O_1$. M: 114.19. Colourless liquid. BP: 168°C. d: 0.93 kg/l (20°C). Slightly soluble in water. Mixed isomer product.
Production:
• m/p-cresol (hydrogenation)
Derivatives:
di-(methylcyclohexyl) phthalate; methylcyclohexanone
Uses: solvent (resins, printing inks)

2-methylcyclohexanol
hexahydro-o-cresol; [583-59-5] (mixed isomers); [7443-70-1] (*cis*-isomer)

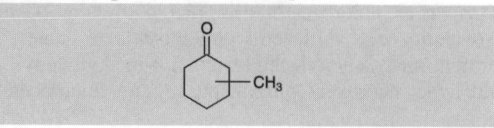

$C_7H_{14}O_1$. M: 114.19. Colourless, viscous liquid with a menthol-like odour. BP: 155–180°C. d: 0.92 kg/l.
Production:
• o-cresol (hydrogenation)
Derivatives:
2,4-dimethyl-6-(α-methylcyclohexyl)phenol; 2,2′-methylenebis[4-methyl-6-(α-methylcyclohexyl)phenol]

methylcyclohexanone
Sextone B (Laporte); [1331-22-2]

$C_7H_{12}O_1$. M: 112.18. Colourless to pale yellow liquid with a strong ketone odour. BP: 170°C. d: 0.91 kg/l. The commercial product is a mixture of isomers.
Production:
• methylcyclohexanol (alcohol oxidation)
Uses: solvent (lacquers, printing inks)

2-methylcyclohexylamine
[7003-32-9]

$C_7H_{15}N_1$. M: 113.21. Pale yellow liquid. BP: 149–150°C. FP: -78°C. d: 0.86 kg/l (4°C). Slightly soluble in water. Soluble in oxygenated solvents. The commercial product is a mixture of *cis* and *trans*-isomers.

Production:
- *o*-nitrotoluene (reduction)

Derivatives: siduron

N-methylcyclohexylamine

NMCHA; [100-60-7]

$C_7H_{15}N_1$. M: 113.21. Colourless to amber liquid. BP: 149°C. FP: -9°C. d: 0.85 kg/l (4°C). Slightly soluble in water. Soluble in oxygenated solvents.

Production:
- cyclohexylamine + methanol (amine formation; coproduced with *N,N*-dimethylcyclohexylamine)

Derivatives: bromhexine

2-methylcyclopentane-1,3-dione

$C_6H_8O_2$. M: 112.13. Solid. MP: 213–215°C.

Production:
- diethyl maleate + ethyl propionate (Claisen condensation/decarboxylation/hydrogenation)

Derivatives: 3-methoxyestra-2,5-diene-17-ol

3-methyl-2-cyclopenten-2-ol-1-one

[80-71-7]

$C_6H_8O_2$. M: 112.12. Crystalline solid. MP: 106°C.

Production:
- wood tar, hardwood (extraction; coproduced with maltol)
- 2-acetylfuran (rearrangement/oxidation)

Uses: flavouring ingredient

methyl 3,5-di-*t*-butyl-4-hydroxyphenylpropionate

$C_{18}H_{28}O_3$. M: 292.42.

Production:
- 2,6-di-*t*-butylphenol + methyl acrylate (Friedel-Crafts alkylation)

Derivatives:
N,N'-hexamethylenebis[3-(3,5-di-*t*-butyl-4-hydroxyphenyl)propionamide]; 1,6-hexanediyl bis[3-(3,5-di-*t*-butyl-4-hydroxyphenyl)propionate]; hydrazinobis[3-(3,5-di-*t*-butyl-4-hydroxyphenyl)propionate]; 2,2'-oxamidobis[eth-yl-3-(3,5-di-*t*-butyl-4-hydroxyphenyl)propionate]; penta-erythritol tetrakis[3-(3,5-di-*t*-butyl-4-hydroxyphenyl)-propionate]; stearyl 3-(3',5'-di-*t*-butyl-4'-hydroxyphen-yl)propionate; thiodiglycol bis[3-(3,5-di-*t*-butyl-4-hydr-oxyphenyl)propionate]; 1,3,5-tris[3-(3,5-di-*t*-butyl-4-hyd-roxyphenyl)propanoxyethyl] isocyanurate

N-methyldicyclohexylamine

N,N-dicyclohexylmethylamine; MDCHA; [7560-83-0]

$C_{13}H_{25}N_1$. M: 195.35. Colourless to amber liquid. BP: 265°C. FP: <-78°C. d: 0.92 kg/l (4°C). Flash point: 118°C (CC).

Production:
- dicyclohexylamine + methanol (amine formation)

Uses: polyurethane catalyst

methyldidecylamine

didecylmethylamine

$C_{21}H_{45}N_1$. M: 311.60. Liquid with a characteristic amine odour. MP: <-10°C. d: 0.80 kg/l (25°C). Flash point: 165°C (TOC).

Production:
- *n*-decanol + methylamine (amine formation)

Derivatives:
didecyldimethylammonium chloride

methyldiethanolamine

MDEA; 2,2'-(methylimino)diethanol; [105-59-9]

$C_5H_{13}N_1O_2$. M: 119.16. Colourless liquid with a mild, ammoniacal odour. BP: 115–118°C (0.7 kPa). Pour point: -55°C. Absorbs water and carbon dioxide from the air. Soluble in water and oxygenated solvents. Insoluble in aliphatic solvents. Flash point: 137°C.

Production:
- methylamine + ethylene oxide (epoxidation; coproduced with methylethanolamine)

Derivatives: pethidine

Uses: hydrogen sulphide extraction solvent (gas processing); photoactivator (printing inks, lacquers)

methyl dihydrojasmonate

3-(carbomethoxymethyl)-2-pentylcyclopentanone; Hedione (Firmenich); [24851-98-7]

$C_{13}H_{22}O_3$. M: 226.32. Liquid with a jasmine-like odour.

Production:
- cyclopentanone + valeraldehyde + diethyl malonate (aldol condensation/isomerisation/Michael addition/hydrolysis/decarboxylation)

Uses: fragrance ingredient

methyl 3,3-dimethyl-4-pentenoate
[63721-05-1]

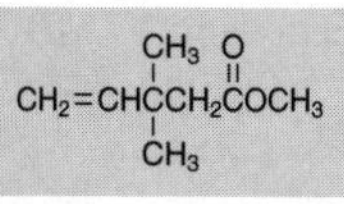

$C_8H_{14}O_2$. M: 142.20.
Production:
- 3-methyl-2-buten-1-ol + trimethyl orthoacetate (condensation)

Derivatives: 3-(2-chloro-3,3,3-trifluoropropenyl)-2,2-dimethylcyclopropanecarboxylic acid; (*1RS*)-*cis*-3-(2,2-dichlorovinyl)-2,2-dimethylcyclopropanecarboxylic acid

methyldopa
[555-30-6]

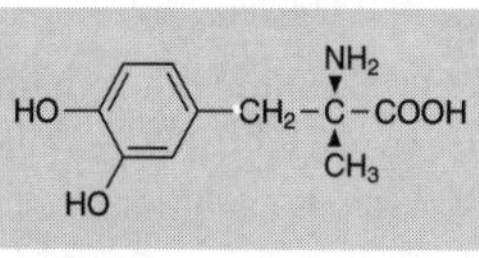

$C_{10}H_{13}N_1O_4$. M: 211.22.
Production:
- homoveratric acid + methyl acetate + hydrogen cyanide + ammonia (condensation/decarboxylation/Strecker synthesis/racemate separation/demethylation)

Uses: antihypertensive drug

methyldymron
1-methyl-3-(1-methyl-1-phenylethyl)-1-phenylurea

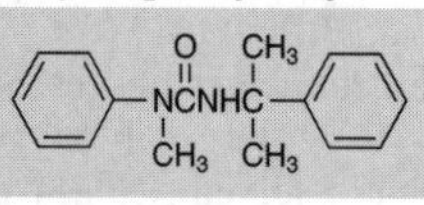

$C_{17}H_{20}N_2O_1$. M: 268.36.
Production:
- 2-phenyl-2-propylamine + phosgene + *N*-methyl-aniline (phosgenation/dehydrochlorination)

Uses: herbicide

N,N'-methylenebisacrylamide
MBA

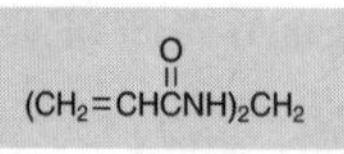

$C_7H_{10}N_2O_2$. M: 154.17. Colourless, crystalline powder. MP: 185°C.
Production:
- acrylamide + formaldehyde (carbonyl addition)

Uses: crosslinking agent (superabsorbent polymers, polyacrylamide, acrylic resin)

4,4'-methylenebis(2-chloroaniline)
3,3'-dichloro-4,4'-diaminodiphenylmethane; MOCA; [101-14-4]

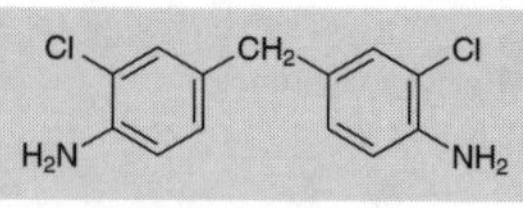

$C_{13}H_{12}Cl_2N_2$. M: 267.17. Light brown flakes. MP: 105°C. Slightly soluble in water. Soluble in oxygenated solvents.
Production:
- *o*-chloroaniline + formaldehyde (carbonyl condensation)

Derivatives:
polyurethane, cast elastomers
Uses: polyurethane crosslinking agent

4,4'-methylenebis(3-chloro-2,6-diethylaniline)

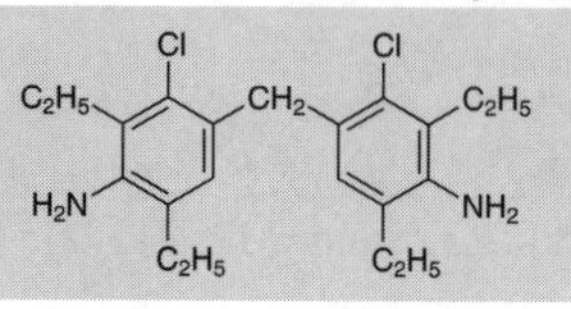

$C_{21}H_{28}Cl_2N_2$. M: 379.37.
Production:
- 2,6-diethylaniline + formaldehyde (carbonyl condensation/ring chlorination)

Uses: polyurethane elastomer curing agent

4,4'-methylenebiscyclohexanol
2,2-bis(4-hydroxycyclohexyl)propane; bisphenol H; bisphenol A, hydrogenated; HBPA; Millad (Milliken); [80-04-6]

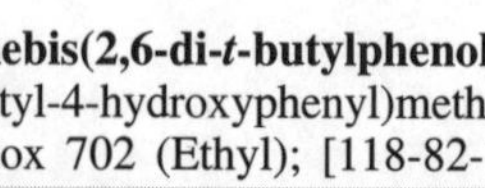

$C_{15}H_{28}O_2$. M: 240.38.
Production:
- bisphenol A (hydrogenation)

Derivatives:
bisphenol H diglycidyl ether

4,4'-methylenebis(2,6-di-*t*-butylphenol)
bis(2,6-di-*t*-butyl-4-hydroxyphenyl)methane; Ionox WTE (Shell); Ethanox 702 (Ethyl); [118-82-1]

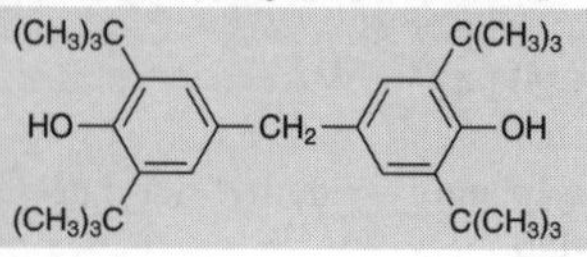

$C_{29}H_{44}O_2$. M: 424.67.
Production:
- 2,6-di-*t*-butylphenol + formaldehyde (carbonyl condensation)

Uses: antioxidant

methylenebis(dimethylcyclohexylamine)
bis(*p*-dimethylaminocyclohexyl)methane

$$(CH_3)_2N \text{—} \bigcirc \text{—} CH_2 \text{—} \bigcirc \text{—} N(CH_3)_2$$

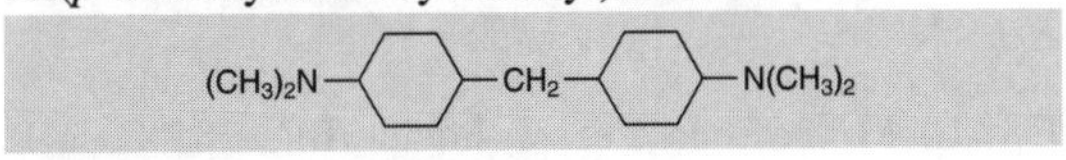

$C_{17}H_{34}N_2$. M: 266.47.
Production:
• bis(*p*-aminocyclohexyl)methane + dimethyl sulphate
  (amine formation/methylation)
Uses: polyurethane foam catalyst

2,2'-methylenebis(4-ethyl-6-*t*-butylphenol)
Cyanox 425 (American Cyanamid)

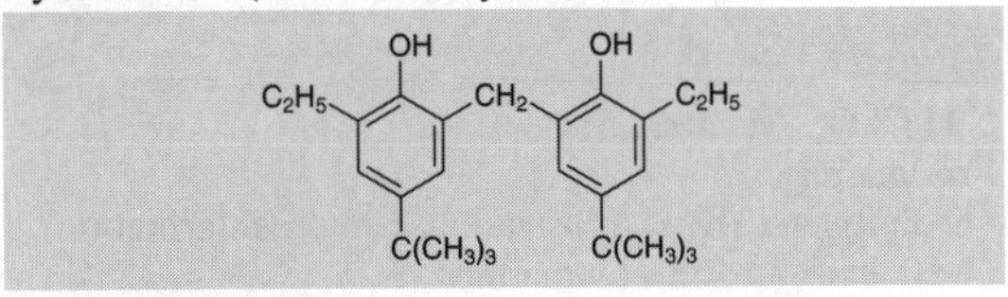

$C_{25}H_{36}O_2$. M: 368.56.
Production:
• *o-t*-butylphenol + ethylene + formaldehyde
  (Friedel-Crafts alkylation/carbonyl condensation)
Uses: antioxidant (plastics)

methylenebis(maleimide)
HVA-2 (Du Pont)

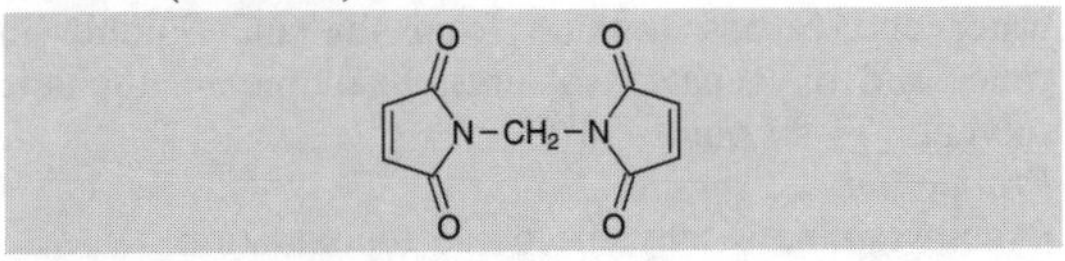

$C_9H_6N_2O_4$. M: 206.16.
Production:
• maleic anhydride + ammonia + formaldehyde
  (imide formation/carbonyl condensation)
Uses:
peroxide crosslinking coactivator

2,2'-methylenebis(4-methyl-6-*t*-butylphenol)
2,2'-methylenebis(6-*t*-butylcresol); BPH; CAO-5 (PMC);
[119-47-1]

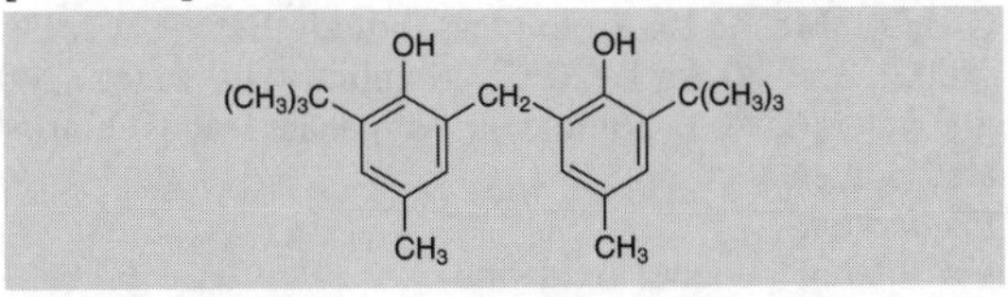

$C_{23}H_{32}O_2$. M: 340.51. Off-white powder. MP: 118–
128°C. d: 1.07–1.10 kg/l. Soluble in oxygenated and
aromatic solvents.
Production:
• 2-*t*-butyl-*p*-cresol + formaldehyde (carbonyl
  condensation)
Uses:
antioxidant (ABS, polypropylene, polyacetal, rubber,
latex, adhesives)

2,2'-methylenebis(4-methyl-6-cyclohexylphenol)
CPH

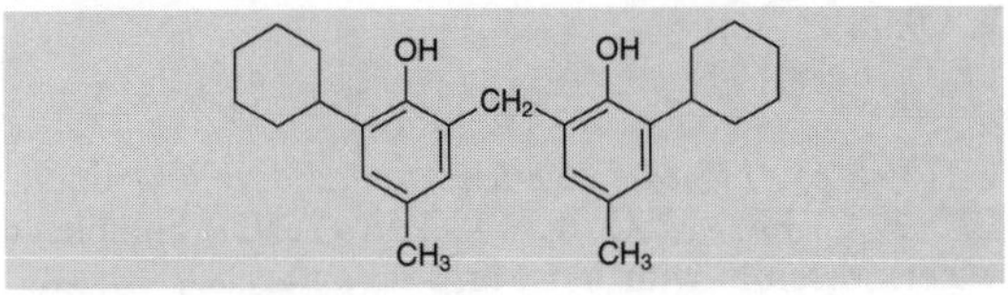

$C_{27}H_{36}O_2$. M: 392.59.
Production:
• *p*-cresol + cyclohexanol + formaldehyde (Friedel-
  Crafts alkylation/carbonyl condensation)
Uses:
antioxidant (plastics, rubber)

**2,2'-methylenebis[4-methyl-6-(α-methylcyclohexyl)-
phenol]**
Nonox WSP (ICI)

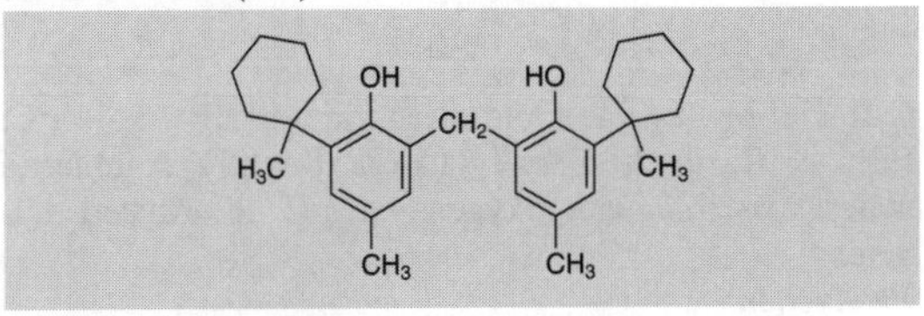

$C_{29}H_{40}O_2$. M: 420.64.
Production:
• *p*-cresol + formaldehyde + 2-methylcyclohexanol
  (Friedel-Crafts alkylation/carbonyl condensation)
Uses: antioxidant (plastics)

2,2'-methylenebis(4-methyl-6-nonylphenol)
6,6'-methylenebis(4-methyl-2-nonylphenol)

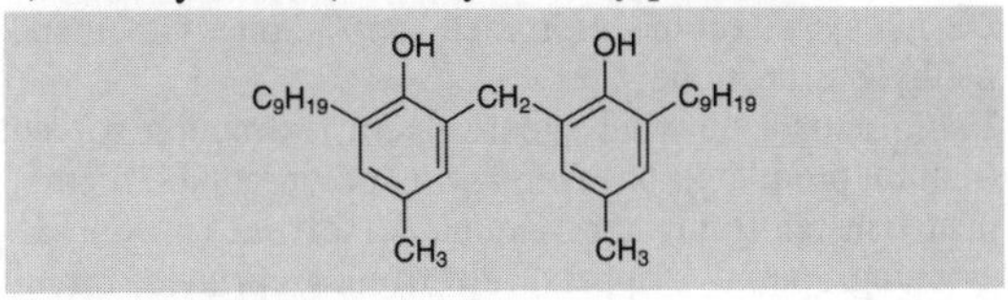

$C_{33}H_{52}O_2$. M: 480.78.
Production:
• *p*-cresol + formaldehyde + nonene, branched
  (Friedel-Crafts alkylation/carbonyl condensation)
Uses: antioxidant (plastics)

methylene bisthiocyanate
methylene dithiocyanate; MBT; [6317-18-6]

$$CH_2(NCS)_2$$

$C_3H_2N_2S_2$. M: 130.19.
Production:
• methylene bromide + sodium thiocyanate
  (thiocyanate addition)
Uses:
biocide (cooling water systems); wood preservative

Methylene Blue *See:* Basic Blue 9

methylene bromide

dibromomethane; methylene dibromide; DBM; [74-95-3]

$$CH_2Br_2$$

$C_1H_2Br_2$. M: 173.84. Colourless to pale yellow liquid. BP: 99°C. FP: -52°C. d: 2.48 kg/l (25°C). Soluble in water. Miscible with most organic solvents.
Production:
• methylene chloride + bromine (bromination; coproduced with bromochloromethane)
Derivatives: 1,2-benzodioxole; methylene bisthiocyanate
Uses: high-density solvent (mineral separation, gauge fluid); process solvent

methylene chloride

dichloromethane; methylene dichloride; MDC; [75-09-2]

$$CH_2Cl_2$$

$C_1H_2Cl_2$. M: 84.94. Colourless liquid. BP: 39–40°C. FP: -98°C. d: 1.34 kg/l (15°C). Slightly soluble in water. Miscible with oxygenated and chlorinated solvents.
Production:
• methyl chloride + chlorine (thermal chlorination; coproduced with chloroform/carbon tetrachloride)
• natural gas + hydrogen chloride, anhydrous/oxygen (Lummus oxychlorination process; coproduced with chloroform/methyl chloride/carbon tetrachloride)
• natural gas + hydrogen chloride, anhydrous (oxychlorination; coproduced with chloroform/carbon tetrachloride)
Derivatives: bromochloromethane; diphenylmethane; methylene bromide
Uses: aerosol blowing agent/solvent; extraction solvent (natural products); blowing agent (polyurethane foams); heat-transfer fluid; non-flammable solvent (vapour degreasing, paint strippers, electronics, printed circuit board cleaning); non-flammable solvent (polyurethane, polyester resin cleaners, adhesives, tablet coatings); process solvent (cellulose acetate/triaceate production, butyl rubber production, Di-Me oil dewaxing process)

4,4′-methylenedianiline

See: 4,4′-diaminodiphenylmethane, crude

3,4-methylenedioxyaniline

[14268-66-7]

$C_7H_7N_1O_2$. M: 137.15.
Production:
• 1,2-benzodioxole (nitration/nitro reduction)
Derivatives: oxolinic acid

methylene iodide

diiodomethane; [75-11-6]

$$CH_2I_2$$

$C_1H_2I_2$. M: 267.84. Yellow liquid. BP: 181°C. MP: 6°C. d: 3.33 kg/l (20°C). Insoluble in water.
Production:
• iodoform (reduction)
Uses: high-density solvent (mineral separation)

β-methylepichlorohydrin

$C_4H_7Cl_1O_1$. M: 106.55.
Production:
• isobutylene (hypochlorination/dehydrochlorination)
Uses: epoxy resin comonomer

methylethanolamine

2-methylaminoethanol; *N*-methylaminoethanol; monomethylethanolamine; [109-83-1]

$$CH_3NHCH_2CH_2OH$$

$C_3H_9N_1O_1$. M: 75.11. Colourless liquid with a mild, ammoniacal odour. BP: 158–163°C. MP: -5°C. Absorbs water and carbon dioxide from the air. Soluble in water and oxygenated solvents. Insoluble in aliphatic solvents. Flash point: 74°C.
Production:
• methylamine + ethylene oxide (epoxidation; coproduced with methyldiethanolamine)
Derivatives:
Fluorescent Brightener DMEA; nefopam; nicardipine; xanthinol nicotinate

methyl ethyl ketone

2-butanone; ethyl methyl ketone; MEK; [78-93-3]

$C_4H_8O_1$. M: 72.10. Colourless liquid. BP: 79°C. FP: -86°C. d: 0.80 kg/l (20°C). Solubility in water: 240 g/l water (20°C). Soluble in oxygenated and chlorinated solvents.
Production:
• *s*-butanol (alcohol oxidation)
• naphtha, heavy (liquid-phase oxidation; coproduced with formic acid/acetic acid/propionic acid/acetone)
• *n*-butane (Celanese LPO process; coproduced with methanol/ethanol/acetone/formic acid/acetic acid/propionic acid/*n*-butyric acid/methyl formate)
• oxygenates, Fischer-Tropsch, mixed (fractionation; coproduced with methanol/ethanol/isopropanol/*n*-butanol/isobutanol/amyl alcohol, primary/acetaldehyde/acetone)

Derivatives: butocarboxim; 2,2-di-(*t*-butylperoxy)butane; dimethyl octynediol; ethionamide; ethosuximide; ethyl amyl ketone; α-isomethylionone; methyl ethyl ketone peroxide; methyl ethyl ketoxime; methylionone; methyl isopropenyl ketone; methylpentynol; quinolinic acid
Uses:
process solvent (Dilchill lubricating oil dewaxing process); solvent (paints, lacquers, printing inks, adhesives)

methyl ethyl ketone peroxide
MEKP; [1338-23-4]

$$\underset{\underset{OOH}{|}}{\overset{\overset{CH_3}{|}}{C_2H_5C}}-O-O-\underset{\underset{OOH}{|}}{\overset{\overset{CH_3}{|}}{CC_2H_5}}$$

$C_8H_{18}O_6$. M: 210.24. Liquid comprising 5–11% active oxygen content in dimethyl phthalate. The product has a 10-hour half-life at 105°C. Mixed product consisting of dimers (50%), trimers (25%) and monomeric peroxy compounds.
Production:
• methyl ethyl ketone + hydrogen peroxide (peroxidation)
Uses: unsaturated polyester resin crosslinking agent

methyl ethyl ketoxime
MEKO

$$\underset{CH_3CH_2CCH_3}{\overset{\overset{NOH}{||}}{}}$$

$C_4H_9N_1O_1$. M: 87.12. Liquid. BP: 153°C. MP: -30°C. d: 0.92 kg/l (20°C). Soluble in water and oxygenated solvents.
Production:
• methyl ethyl ketone + hydroxylamine sulphate (oxime formation)
Uses: antioxidant; antiskinning agent (oil-based paints, lacquers); isocyanate blocking agent; oxygen scavenger (boiler water treatment)

2-methyl-5-ethylpyridine
5-ethyl-2-methylpyridine; 5-ethyl-2-picoline; MEP; [104-90-5]

$C_8H_{11}N_1$. M: 121.19. Colourless liquid with a strong, aromatic odour. BP: 178°C. FP: -70°C. d: 0.92 kg/l (20°C). Insoluble in water. Soluble in oxygenated and aromatic solvents.
Production:
• paraldehyde + ammonia (liquid-phase condensation; coproduced with α-picoline/γ-picoline)
Derivatives:
5-ethylquinolinic acid; isocinchomeronic acid

methyl eugenol
4-allyl-1,2-dimethoxybenzene; 4-allylveratrole; 3-(3,4-dimethoxyphenyl)propene; eugenol methyl ether; [93-15-2]

$C_{11}H_{14}O_2$. M: 178.23. Colourless liquid with mild odour. BP: 128–130°C (1.3 kPa). d: 1.03 kg/l (25°C). Insoluble in water. Soluble in alcohol.
Production:
• eugenol + dimethyl sulphate (methylation)
Uses: flavouring/fragrance ingredient

methyl 3-fluorocarbonylperfluoropropionate

$$\overset{\overset{O}{||}}{FCCF_2}CF_2\overset{\overset{O}{||}}{C}OCH_3$$

$C_5H_3F_5O_3$. M: 206.05.
Production:
• tetrafluoroethylene + iodine + methanol (addition/telomerisation/cyclisation/esterification)
Derivatives: tetrafluoroethylene-perfluoro(vinyl ether carboxylate) copolymers

N-methylformamide
[123-39-7]

$$\overset{\overset{O}{||}}{HCNHCH_3}$$

$C_2H_5N_1O_1$. M: 59.07. Liquid. BP: 199–201°C. MP: -3°C. d: 1.01 kg/l (20°C). Soluble in water and alcohol.
Production:
• methyl formate + methylamine (amide formation)
Derivatives: Fischer's aldehyde; formothion
Uses: process solvent; selective solvent (aromatics, butadiene, acetylene extraction)

methyl formate
[107-31-3]

$$\overset{\overset{O}{||}}{HCOCH_3}$$

$C_2H_4O_2$. M: 60.05. Colourless, volatile liquid with a pleasant odour. MP: -99°C. BP: 31°C. d: 0.97 kg/l. Soluble in water.
Production:
• carbon monoxide + methanol (two-stage formate process; coproduced with formic acid)
• *n*-butane (Celanese LPO process; coproduced with methanol/ethanol/acetone/methyl ethyl ketone/formic acid/acetic acid/propionic acid/*n*-butyric acid)
Derivatives: dimethylformamide; Direct Red 149; fosamine-ammonium; *N*-methylformamide
Uses: cold-box foundry mould process curing agent

α-methylglucoside
[97-30-3]

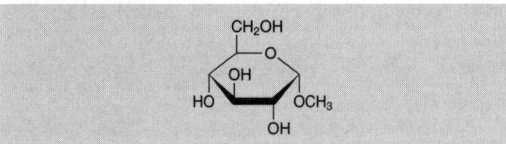

$C_7H_{14}O_6$. M: 194.18. White crystals. MP: 168°C. d: 1.46 kg/l (30°C). Soluble in water.
Production:
• starch hydrolysate + methanol (ether formation)
Derivatives:
methyl glucoside ethoxylates; polyether polyols, rigid
Uses: alkyd resin polyol comonomer

methyl glucoside ethoxylates

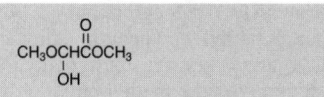

k+l+m+n = 10–20.
Production:
• α-methylglucoside + ethylene oxide (epoxidation)
Uses: emollient (cosmetics, toiletries)

2-methylglutaronitrile
[4553-62-2]

$$\underset{\underset{NCCHCH_2CH_2CN}{|}}{CH_3}$$

$C_6H_8N_2$. M: 108.14.
Production:
• butadiene + hydrogen cyanide (Du Pont HMDA process; byproduct of adiponitrile production)
Derivatives:
2-methylpentamethylenediamine

methylglycollic acid *See:* 2-methoxyacetic acid

methylglyoxal dimethyl acetal
1,1-dimethoxypropan-2-one; pyruvaldehyde dimethyl acetal; [6342-56-9]

$$\underset{CH_3CCH(OCH_3)_2}{\overset{O}{\parallel}}$$

$C_5H_{10}O_3$. M: 118.13. Liquid. BP: 136–139°C. MP: -57°C.
Production:
• propylene glycol + nitric acid, concentrated + methanol (oxidation/acetal formation)
Derivatives:
allethrolone; 5-methylpyrazine-2-carboxylic acid

methyl glyoxylate methyl hemiacetal
$C_4H_8O_4$. M: 120.10.

$$\underset{\underset{OH}{|}}{\overset{O}{\underset{CH_3OCHCOCH_3}{\parallel}}}$$

Production:
• dimethyl maleate + ozone + methanol (ozonolysis)
• glyoxylic acid + methanol (esterification/acetal formation)
Derivatives: glyoxylic acid

methylheptenol
6-methyl-5-hepten-2-ol; [1569-60-4]

$$(CH_3)_2C=CHCH_2CH_2\underset{\underset{CHOH}{|}}{\overset{CH_3}{}}$$

$C_8H_{16}O_1$. M: 128.22.
Production:
• β-methylheptenone (carbonyl reduction)
Uses: insect pheromone

α-methylheptenone
2-methyl-1-hepten-6-one; 6-methyl-6-hepten-2-one

$$\underset{CH_2=CCH_2CH_2CH_2CCH_3}{\overset{CH_3 \qquad O}{|\qquad\quad\parallel}}$$

$C_8H_{14}O_1$. M: 126.20.
Production:
• isobutylene + formaldehyde + acetone (carbonyl condensation)
Derivatives: hydroxycitronellal; octodrine

β-methylheptenone
2-methyl-2-hepten-6-one; 6-methyl-5-hepten-2-one; [110-93-0]

$$(CH_3)_2C=CHCH_2CH_2\overset{O}{\overset{\parallel}{C}}CH_3$$

$C_8H_{14}O_1$. M: 126.20. Colourless liquid. BP: 173°C. MP: -67°C. d: 0.86 kg/l (20°C). Insoluble in water. Miscible with oxygenated solvents.
Production:
• 2-methyl-3-buten-2-ol + methyl acetoacetate (esterification/Carroll reaction)
• isoprene + acetone (hydrochlorination/dehydrchlorination)
Derivatives: dehydrolinalool; 2,6-dimethyl-2-heptanol; geranonitrile; methylheptenol

methyl hexahydrophthalic anhydride
MHHPA

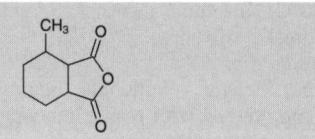

$C_9H_{12}O_3$. M: 168.20.

Production:
• methyl tetrahydrophthalic anhydride (hydrogenation)
Uses: epoxy resin curing agent

methyl hexyl ketone
2-octanone; [111-13-7]

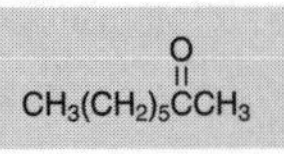

$$CH_3(CH_2)_5\overset{\overset{O}{\|}}{C}CH_3$$

$C_8H_{16}O_1$. M: 128.22. Liquid with an apple-like odour. BP: 172–173°C. MP: -21°C. d: 0.82 kg/l (20°C). Slightly soluble in water. Soluble in oxygenated solvents.
Production:
• 2-octanol (alcohol oxidation)
Uses: fragrance/flavouring ingredient

methyl hydrate *See:* methanol

methyl hydrazine
monomethylhydrazine; MMH; [60-34-4]

$$CH_3NHNH_2$$

$C_1H_6N_2$. M: 46.07. Colourless liquid with an amine odour. BP: 87°C. FP: -52°C. d: 0.87 kg/l (20°C). Miscible with water and alcohol.
Production:
• ammonia + methylamine (chlorination/ dehydrochlorination)
Derivatives: difenzoquat methosulphate; procarbazine
Uses: rocket fuel

methyl 4-hydroxybenzoate
E218 (EC); methyl *p*-hydroxybenzoate; methylparaben; [99-76-3]

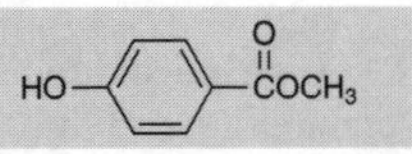

$$HO-\!\!\!\!\bigcirc\!\!\!\!-\overset{\overset{O}{\|}}{C}OCH_3$$

$C_8H_8O_3$. M: 152.15. White, crystalline solid. MP: 126–128°C. BP: ~275°C with decomposition. Very slightly soluble in water. Soluble in oxygenated solvents. Also available as the sodium salt. The latter is not approved for food use in the USA.
Production:
• methanol + *p*-hydroxybenzoic acid (esterification)
Uses: biocide (latices, emulsions, cosmetics); preservative (fruit, preserves, soft drinks)

methyl hydroxyethylcellulose
MHEC; [9032-42-2]

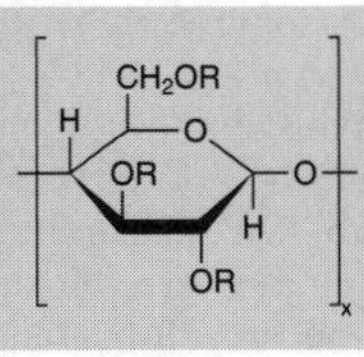

R = methyl, poly(oxyethyl)-. White powder. Soluble in

cold water forming colloidal solutions which gel as the temperature is increased.
Production:
• hydroxyethyl cellulose + methyl chloride (ether formation)
Uses: adhesion promotion agent (tile cements); water retention aid/thickening agent (sprayable plasters, mortar, stucco, fillers)

2-methyl-3′-hydroxy-2′-naphthanilide
See: 3-hydroxy-2-naphth-*o*-toluidide

4-methyl-3′-hydroxy-2′-naphthanilide
See: 3-hydroxy-2-naphth-*p*-toluidide

methylhydroxypropylcellulose
MHPC; E464 (EC); [9004-65-3]

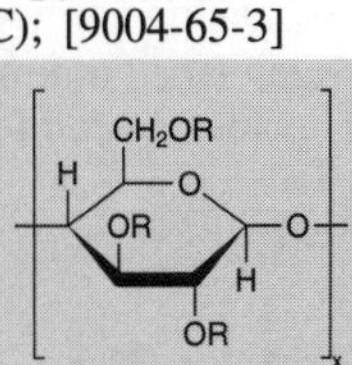

R = methyl, poly(oxypropyl)-. White, granular powder. Degree of polymerisation: 800–2,400, depending on the source of the cellulose and the PO content. The methoxyl content is, typically, 25–30% w/w and the PO content, 3–12% w/w. Soluble in cold water.
Production:
• methyl cellulose + propylene oxide (epoxidation)
Uses: protective colloid (emulsion paints); thickening agent (prepared foods)

2-methylimidazole
2-MI; 2MZ; [693-98-1]

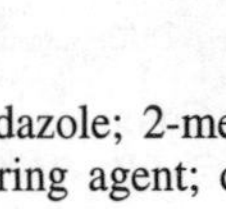

$C_4H_6N_2$. M: 82.10. Crystalline powder or flake. MP: 142–146°C, 136–138°C (90% flake grade). BP: 264°C. Soluble in water and oxygenated solvents.
Production:
• acetaldehyde + glyoxal + ammonia (Radziszewski reaction)
Derivatives:
1-benzyl-2-methylimidazole; 2-methyl-4-nitroimidazole
Uses: epoxy resin curing agent; dyeing auxiliary

2-methylindole
[95-20-5]

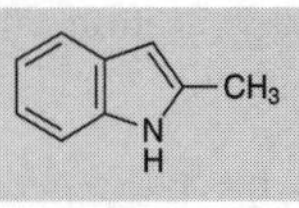

$C_9H_9N_1$. M: 131.18. Moist, crystalline solid. MP: 53–

55°C (dry). BP: 124–126°C (0.4 kPa). Slightly soluble in hot water and oxygenated solvents.
Production:
• acetone + phenylhydrazine (Fischer indole synthesis)
Derivatives:
Acid Yellow 87; Basic Orange 21

methyl iodide
iodomethane; [74-88-4]

$$CH_3I$$

$C_1H_3I_1$. M: 141.93. Colourless liquid. Discoloured by light. BP: 41–43°C. d: 2.28 kg/l (20°C). Slightly soluble in water. Miscible with oxygenated solvents.
Production:
• methyl chloride + sodium iodide (Finkelstein reaction)
Derivatives: benoxaprofen; 6-dimethylamino-1,2-dimethylquinolinium iodide; ketoprofen; melitracen; *N*-methylquinolinium iodide
Uses: methylation reagent

methylionone
1-(2,6,6-trimethyl-1-cyclohex-1-yl)-1-penten-3-one (β-isomer); 1-(2,6,6-trimethyl-2-cyclohex-1-yl)-1-penten-3-one (α-isomer); [127-42-4] (α-isomer); [127-43-5] (β-isomer)

$C_{14}H_{22}O_1$. M: 206.33. Yellow liquid with a floral odour. BP: 144°C (2.0 kPa). d: 0.94 kg/l (20°C). Insoluble in water. Soluble in alcohol. Mixed product containing the α- and β-isomers as well as the isomethylionone analogues.
Production:
• citral + methyl ethyl ketone (carbonyl condensation/acid-catalysed rearrangement)
Uses: fragrance ingredient

methyl isoamyl ketone
5-methyl-2-hexanone; MIAK; [110-12-3]

$$(CH_3)_2CHCH_2CH_2\overset{O}{\overset{\|}{C}}CH_3$$

$C_7H_{14}O_1$. M: 114.19. Colourless liquid with a pleasant odour. BP: 142–145°C. FP: -74°C. d: 0.81 kg/l (20°C). Slightly soluble in water. Miscible with oxygenated, chlorinated and hydrocarbon solvents.
Production:
• isobutylene + methyl acetoacetate (acetoacetate ester synthesis)
Derivatives:
N,N'-bis(1,4-dimethylpentyl)-*p*-phenylenediamine
Uses: high-boiling lacquer solvent

methyl isobutyl carbinol
methyl amyl alcohol; 4-methyl-2-pentanol; 4-methyl-pentan-2-ol; MIBC; [108-11-2]

$$\overset{OH}{\overset{|}{(CH_3)_2CHCH_2CHCH_3}}$$

$C_6H_{14}O_1$. M: 102.18. Colourless liquid. d: 0.81 kg/l (20°C). BP: 132°C. FP: -90°C. Solubility in water: 16.4 g/l (25°C).
Production:
• methyl isobutyl ketone (hydrogenation)
Derivatives: sodium dihexylsulphosuccinate; sodium *O,O*-di-(methylamyl) dithiophosphate; zinc dihexyl dithiophosphate
Uses:
flotation frothing agent; high-boiling lacquer solvent

methyl isobutyl ketone
4-methyl-2-pentanone; MIBK; [108-10-1]

$$(CH_3)_2CHCH_2\overset{O}{\overset{\|}{C}}CH_3$$

$C_6H_{12}O_1$. M: 100.17. Colourless liquid. BP: 114–117°C. d: 0.80 kg/l (20°C). Insoluble in water. Miscible with most organic solvents and oils. Flash point: 16°C (TCC).
Production:
• mesityl oxide (hydrogenation)
Derivatives: dimethyl hexynol; *N*-hexyl-*N'*-phenyl-*p*-phenylenediamine; methyl isobutyl carbinol; methyl isobutyl ketone peroxide; tetramethyl decynediol
Uses: extraction solvent (mineral processing); process solvent (Dilchill lubricating oil dewaxing process); solvent (resins, stoving enamels, lacquers, printing inks)

methyl isobutyl ketone peroxide
Mixed product containing α-hydroxy- and α-peroxyhydroperoxides. Commercial grades have 9% active oxygen and are usually dissolved in DMP.
Production:
• methyl isobutyl ketone + hydrogen peroxide (peroxidation)
Uses: unsaturated polyester resin crosslinking agent

methyl isocyanate
MIC; [624-83-9]

$$CH_3NCO$$

$C_2H_3N_1O_1$. M: 57.05. Liquid. BP: 43–45°C. d: 0.96 kg/l (20°C). Highly toxic. Soluble in water.
Production:
• methylamine + phosgene (phosgenation)
Derivatives:
aldicarb; bendiocarb; benzthiazuron; butocarboxim; carbaryl; carbofuran; cloethocarb; dioxacarb; ethidimuron; ethiofencarb; fenobucarb; formetanate hydrochloride; isoprocarb; methabenzthiazuron; methazole; methiocarb;

methomyl; metolcarb; oxamyl; promecarb; propoxur; pyricarbate; tebuthiuron; thiazafluron; thiodicarb; thiofanox; xylylcarb

methyl isoeugenol
1-(3,4-dimethoxyphenyl)propene; propenylguaiacol; isoeugenol methyl ether

CH₃O—⟨benzene ring⟩—CH=CHCH₃ with CH₃O substituent

$C_{11}H_{14}O_2$. M: 178.23. Colourless or yellowish liquid with a clove-like odour. Commercial grades are a mixture of the *cis* and *trans*-isomers with BP: 264°C. d: 1.05 kg/l (20°C). Soluble in 70% alcohol.
Production:
• isoeugenol + dimethyl sulphate (methylation)
Uses: fragrance ingredient

methyl isonicotinate
methyl 4-pyridinecarboxylate; [2459-09-8]

COOCH₃ on pyridine ring

$C_7H_7N_1O_2$. M: 137.15. Liquid with a mild, pleasant odour. MP: 8°C. BP: 207–209°C with some decomposition. Slightly soluble in water. Soluble in oxygenated and aromatic solvents.
Production:
• methanol + isonicotinic acid (esterification)
Derivatives: isoniazid

methyl isopropenyl ketone
MIPK; [814-78-8]

O
||
CH₃CC=CH₂
|
CH₃

$C_5H_8O_1$. M: 84.11. Colourless liquid with a pleasant odour. BP: 98°C. d: 0.85 kg/l (20°C). Slightly soluble in water. Soluble in oxygenated solvents.
Production:
• methyl ethyl ketone + formaldehyde (carbonyl condensation)
Uses:
photodegradable polymer comonomer

methyl isopropyl ketone
3-methylbutan-2-one; [563-80-4]

(CH₃)₂CHCCH₃
||
O

$C_5H_{10}O_1$. M: 86.13. Liquid. BP: 91–94°C. MP: -92°C. d: 0.80 kg/l (15°C). Slightly soluble in water. Soluble in oxygenated solvents.

Production:
• methyl acetoacetate + methyl chloride (acetoacetate ester synthesis)
Derivatives:
2-amino-2-methylisopentamide; 3-methyl-2-butylamine
Uses: dyestuffs intermediate

methyl-*p*-isopropylphenylpropionaldehyde
See: cyclamen aldehyde

methyl isothiocyanate
methyl mustard oil; MIT; MITC; [556-61-6]

CH₃NCS

$C_2H_3N_1S_1$. M: 73.11.
Production:
• metam-sodium (dethiolation)
Derivatives: 4-methyl thiosemicarbazide; thiamazole; 5-thio-1-methyltetrazole
Uses: soil fungicide

O-methylisourea sulphate
O-methylpseudourea sulphate; [52328-05-9]

NH₂
|
CH₃OC=NH₂⁺ ½SO₄²⁻

$C_2H_6N_2O_1$. M: 74.08.
Production:
• cyanamide + methanol (nitrile addition)
Derivatives: 2-amino-4-methoxy-6-methyltriazine; flubendazole; guanethidine; guanoclor; hexazinone; mebendazole; pipemidic acid; piromidic acid

methyl laurate
[111-82-0]

O
||
CH₃(CH₂)₁₀COCH₃

$C_{13}H_{26}O_2$. M: 214.35. Liquid. BP: 148°C (1.8 kPa). d: 0.87 kg/l (20°C). Insoluble in water. Chain-length distribution depends on the source and processing of the raw materials.
Production:
• lauric acid, broad cut + methanol (esterification)
• palm kernel methyl ester, topped/methyl cocoate, topped (fractionation; coproduced with C_{14}-C_{18} fatty acids, methyl ester)
Derivatives:
n-alkanol(C_{12}-C_{14}); lauric acid diethanolamide
Uses: lubricant (textile spin finishes)

methylmagnesium bromide
[75-16-1]

CH₃MgBr

$C_1H_3Br_1Mg_1$. M: 119.24. Available as a solution in tetrahydrofuran or tetrahydrofuran/toluene mixtures.

Production:
• methyl bromide + magnesium (Grignard reagent formation)

Derivatives: spironolactone

Uses: Grignard reagent

methylmagnesium chloride
[676-58-4]

CH₃MgCl

$C_1H_3Cl_1Mg_1$. M: 74.79. Available commercially as a 20–24% solution in tetrahydrofuran.

Production:
• methyl chloride + magnesium (Grignard reagent formation)

Derivatives: chlorphenoxamine; clemastine; 2,6-dimethyl-2-heptanol; dimethyl phenethyl carbinol; hydroxycitronellal; propenylguethol; tetramethyltin

Uses: Grignard reagent

methyl mercaptan
methanethiol; [74-93-1]

CH₃SH

$C_1H_4S_1$. M: 48.10. Liquified gas with a strong, unpleasant odour. BP: 6°C. MP: -122°C. d: 0.90 kg/l (0°C). Soluble in water and oxygenated solvents.

Production:
• methanol + hydrogen sulphide (thiolation)

Derivatives:
aldicarb; butocarboxim; mercaptoacetaldehyde; methanesulphonic acid; DL-methionine; methionine hydroxy analogue; methomyl; 2-methylmercapto-4,6-dichlorotriazine; methyl sulphenyl chloride; nifuratel; oxamyl; prometryn; sulindac; terbutryn; thiodicarb; thiofanox; thioridazine

2-methylmercapto-4,6-dichlorotriazine
MDT; 2-methylthio-4,6-dichloro-*sym*-triazine

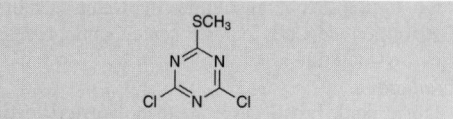

$C_4H_3Cl_2N_3S_1$. M: 196.05.

Production:
• cyanuric chloride + methyl mercaptan (dehydrochlorination)

Derivatives: ametryn; aziprotryne; desmetryn; dimethametryn; methoprotryne

p-methylmercaptophenol
4-(methylthio)phenol; *p*-thiocresol; [1073-72-9]
$C_7H_8O_1S_1$. M: 140.20.

Production:
• phenol + methyl sulphenyl chloride (dehydrochlorination)

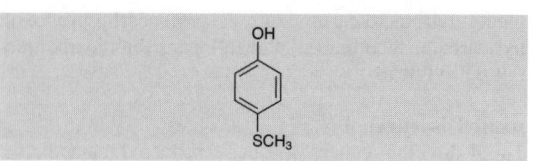

Derivatives: fensulfothion; propaphos; sulprofos

2-methyl-5-mercapto-1,3,4-thiadiazole
2-methyl-1,3,4-thiadiazole-5-thiol

$C_3H_4N_2S_2$. M: 132.20.

Production:
• acetic anhydride + hydrazine + carbon disulphide (amide formation/thiocarbonylation)

Derivatives: cefazedone; cefazolin

methyl methacrylate
MMA; [80-62-6]

$C_5H_8O_2$. M: 100.11. Colourless liquid with ester-like odour. BP: 100–101°C. MP: -48°C. d: 0.94 kg/l (25°C). Solubility in water: 15 g/l solution (20°C). Flash point: 13°C (TOC). Commercial products contain hydroquinone methyl ether or similar polymerisation inhibitors.

Production:
• methanol + methacrylamide sulphate (alcoholysis)
• methanol + methacrylic acid (esterification)

Derivatives:
acrylic resins, hydroxylated; acrylic resins, latex; acrylic resins, solvent-based; allyl methacrylate; benzyl methacrylate; bisphenol A dimethacrylate; 1,3-butanediol dimethacrylate; 1,4-butanediol dimethacrylate; *t*-butylaminoethyl methacrylate; *n*-butyl methacrylate; 2-cyanoethyl methacrylate; cyclohexyl methacrylate; dicyclopentenyl methacrylate; 2-diethylaminoethyl methacrylate; diethylene glycol dimethacrylate; 2-dimethylaminoethyl methacrylate; 1,12-dodecanediyl dimethacrylate; ethylene glycol dimethacrylate; 2-ethylhexyl methacrylate; ethyl methacrylate; 1,6-hexanediol dimethacrylate; isobornyl methacrylate; isobutyl methacrylate; isodecyl methacrylate; isotridecyl methacrylate; lauryl methacrylate; methyl methacrylate-butadiene-styrene copolymers; methyl methacrylate copolymers, high molecular weight; neopentyl glycol dimethacrylate; *n*-nonyl methacrylate; poly(acrylate-methacrylate) graft copolymers; polyacrylonitrile; polyethylene glycol dimethacrylate; polymethacrylates, oil-soluble; polymethacrylates, oil-soluble dispersants; poly-(methyl methacrylate); procymidone; stearyl methacrylate; styrene-acrylic copolymers; tetraethylene glycol

dimethacrylate; tetrahydrofurfuryl methacrylate; triethylene glycol dimethacrylate; trimethylolpropane trimethacrylate; vinyl ester resins; vinylidene chloride copolymers, latex
Uses: poly(methyl methacrylate) block bonding agent; marble-like surfaces/basins/panels (kitchens, bathrooms); nitrile rubber comonomer; engineering adhesives; industrial flooring compositions; precast concrete composites; reactive diluent (unsaturated polyester resins); resin mortars (self-levelling floors, jointless floor/wall coatings)

methyl methacrylate-butadiene-styrene copolymers
MBS
Thermoplastic blend produced by polymerisation of styrene and methyl methacrylate in the presence of polybutadiene latex. The polymers are transparent with higher clarity and light resistance than ABS.
Production:
• methyl methacrylate + styrene + polybutadiene latex (emulsion polymerisation)
Derivatives: polyvinyl chloride, high-impact
Uses: food/drug packaging; polyvinyl chloride processing aid/impact modifier

methyl methacrylate copolymers, high molecular weight
Thermoplastics. M: ~10^6. These polymers should not be confused with the methacrylate copolymers used in emulsion paints.
Production:
• methyl methacrylate + ethyl acrylate/*n*-butyl acrylate/*n*-butyl methacrylate/styrene (emulsion polymerisation)
Uses: processing aid (polyvinyl chloride)

methyl *N*-methylanthranilate
dimethyl anthranilate; methyl 2-methylaminobenzoate; [85-91-6]

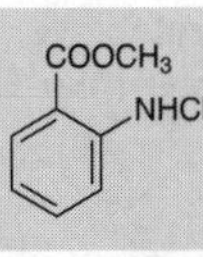

$C_9H_{11}N_1O_2$. M: 165.20. Solid or liquid. MP: 19°C. BP: 255°C. d: 1.13 kg/l (20°C). Insoluble in water. Soluble in oxygenated solvents.
Production:
• methyl anthranilate + methyl chloride (methylation)
Derivatives: dibenzepin
Uses: fragrance ingredient

methyl 3-methyl-2-butenoate

$C_6H_{10}O_2$. M: 114.15.

Production:
• mesityl oxide + methanol (haloform reaction/esterification)
Derivatives: (*1RS*)-*trans*-chrysanthemic acid

α-methyl-β-3,4-methylenedioxyphenylpropionaldehyde-anthranilate adduct

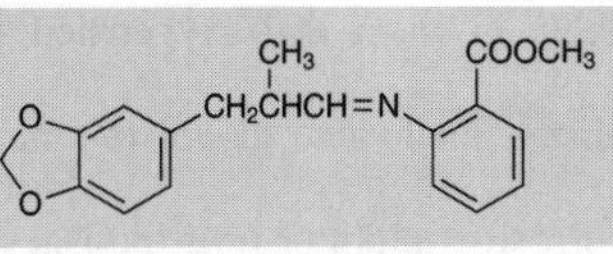

$C_{19}H_{19}N_1O_4$. M: 325.36.
Production:
• piperonal + propionaldehyde + methyl anthranilate (carbonyl condensation/imine formation)
Uses: fragrance ingredient

3-methyl-4-(methylmercapto)phenol

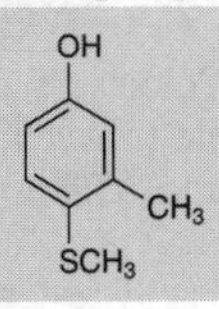

$C_8H_{10}O_1S_1$. M: 154.23.
Production:
• *m*-cresol + methyl sulphenyl chloride (dehydrochlorination)
Derivatives: fenamiphos; fenthion

methyl 3-methylorsellinate
methyl 2,4-dihydroxy-3,6-dimethylbenzoate; methyl 3,6-dimethyl-2,4-dihydroxybenzoate; [4707-47-5]

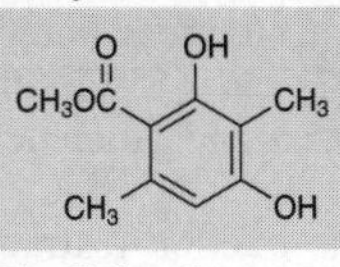

$C_{10}H_{12}O_4$. M: 196.21. Colourless crystals with an earthy odour. MP: 145°C.
Production:
• propionyl chloride + propylene + dimethyl malonate (acylation/carbonyl condensation/oxidation)
Uses: fragrance ingredient (soap, cosmetics)

1-methyl-4-(4-methyl-3-penten-1-yl)-3-cyclohexenecarboxaldehyde
vernaldehyde

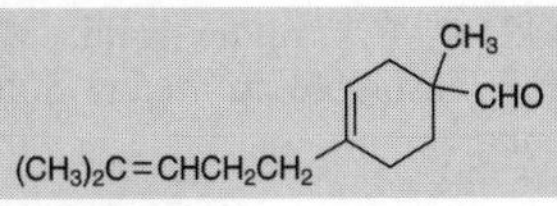

$C_{14}H_{22}O_1$. M: 206.33.
Production:
• myrcene + methacrolein (Diels-Alder cycloaddition)
Uses: fragrance ingredient

N-methylmorpholine
[109-02-4]

CH_3N O (morpholine ring structure)

$C_5H_{11}N_1O_1$. M: 101.15. Colourless liquid with a penetrating, ammoniacal odour. FP: -66°C. d: 0.92 kg/l (20°C). Soluble in water and oxygenated solvents.
Production:
• methylamine + diethylene glycol (amine formation)
Uses:
emulsifier/corrosion inhibitor (oils, polishes); extraction solvent; polyurethane catalyst; stabiliser (chlorinated solvents)

methyl myristate
methyl tetradecanoate; [124-10-7]

$CH_3(CH_2)_{12}COCH_3$ (with C=O)

$C_{15}H_{30}O_2$. M: 242.40. Colourless liquid. MP: 18°C. BP: 187°C (3 kPa). Insoluble in water. Chain-length distribution is generally around 95% C_{14}.
Production:
• methanol + myristic acid (esterification)
Derivatives: myristyl myristate

α-methylnaphthalene
1-methylnaphthalene; [90-12-0]

(naphthalene with CH₃ structure)

$C_{11}H_{10}$. M: 142.20. Colourless liquid. BP: 240–243°C. FP: -19°C. d: 1.02 kg/l (15°C). Insoluble in water. Soluble in oxygenated and aromatic solvents.
Production:
• methylnaphthalene fraction (extraction; coproduced with β-methylnaphthalene)
Derivatives:
1-chloromethylnaphthalene; 1-naphthaldehyde

β-methylnaphthalene
2-methylnaphthalene; [91-57-6]

(naphthalene with CH₃ structure)

$C_{11}H_{10}$. M: 142.20. Crystalline solid. MP: 34–36°C. BP: 241–243°C. Insoluble in water. Soluble in oxygenated solvents.
Production:
• methylnaphthalene fraction (extraction; coproduced with α-methylnaphthalene)
Derivatives:
menadione; sodium alkylnaphthalene sulphonate

methylnaphthalene fraction
methylnaphthalene oil

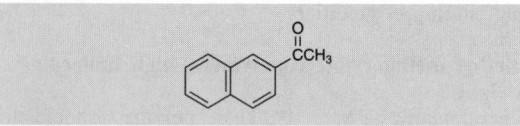

$C_{11}H_{10}$. M: 142.20. Mixed aromatic stream. BP: 235–260°C.
Production:
• C_{10+} aromatics (fractionation; coproduced with naphthalene fraction/dimethylnaphthalene fraction)
Derivatives:
isoquinoline; α-methylnaphthalene; β-methylnaphthalene; perfluoromethyldecalin; quinoline; sodium alkylnaphthalene sulphonate
Uses: heat-transfer oil; solvent

methyl β-naphthyl ether
See: β-naphthyl methyl ether

methyl β-naphthyl ketone
β-acetylnaphthalene; 2-acetylnaphthalene; methyl naphthyl ketone; β-naphthyl methyl ketone; Oranger crist; [93-08-3]

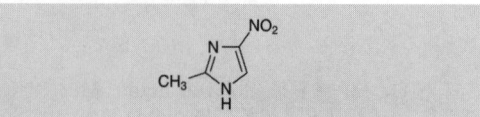

$C_{12}H_{10}O_1$. M: 170.21. White, crystalline solid with a floral odour. MP: 56°C.
Production:
• naphthalene + acetyl chloride (Friedel-Crafts acylation)
Uses: fragrance/flavouring ingredient

2-methyl-4-nitroaniline *See:* 2-amino-5-nitrotoluene

4-methyl-2-nitroaniline *See:* 4-amino-3-nitrotoluene

2-methyl-4-nitroimidazole
2-methyl-5-nitroimidazole; [696-23-1]

(imidazole ring with NO_2 and CH_3 substituents, N–H)

$C_4H_5N_3O_2$. M: 127.10. Solid. MP: 244°C.
Production:
• 2-methylimidazole (nitration)
Derivatives:
metronidazole; ornidazole; tinidazole

3-methyl-4-nitrophenol *See:* 4-nitro-*m*-cresol

3-methyl-6-nitrophenol *See:* 6-nitro-*m*-cresol

4-methyl-2-nitrophenol *See:* *m*-nitro-*p*-cresol

2-methyl-2-nitropropanol
2-nitro-2-methyl-1-propanol; NMP

$$NO_2$$
$$(CH_3)_2CCH_2OH$$

$C_4H_9N_1O_3$. M: 119.12. Solid. MP: 90°C. Solubility in water: 350 g/l water (20°C).
Production:
• 2-nitropropane + formaldehyde (hydroxymethylation)
Derivatives:
2-amino-2-methyl-1-propanol
Uses: crosslinking agent

methylnonylacetaldehyde
aldehyde C-12 MNA; 2-methylundecanal; methylundecanal; MNA; [110-41-8]

$$CH_3$$
$$CH_3(CH_2)_8CHCHO$$

$C_{12}H_{24}O_1$. M: 184.32. Colourless liquid with a strong, herbal odour. BP: 114°C (1.3 kPa). d: 0.83 kg/l (15°C). Soluble in alcohol and aliphatic solvents.
Production:
• methyl *n*-nonyl ketone + methyl chloroacetate (Darzens reaction/hydrolysis/decarboxylation)
• *n*-undecanal + formaldehyde (carbonyl condensation/hydrogenation)
Uses: fragrance ingredient

methyl *n*-nonyl ketone
methyl nonyl ketone; rue ketone; 2-undecanone; [112-12-9]

$$O$$
$$CH_3(CH_2)_8CCH_3$$

$C_{11}H_{22}O_1$. M: 170.30. Colourless liquid with a strong, herbal odour. BP: 225°C. MP: 12–13°C d: 0.82 kg/l. Insoluble in water. Soluble in oxygenated and aromatic solvents.
Production:
• *n*-octyl bromide + methyl acetoacetate (acetoacetate ester synthesis)
Derivatives:
methylnonylacetaldehyde
Uses: fragrance/flavouring ingredient

methyl 2-nonynoate
methyl octyne carbonate; [111-80-8]

$$O$$
$$CH_3(CH_2)_5C \equiv CCOCH_3$$

$C_{10}H_{16}O_2$. M: 168.24.
Production:
• acetylene + *n*-hexyl bromide + methyl chloroformate + methanol (ethynylation/ dehydrobromination/esterification)
Uses: fragrance ingredient (soap, detergents)

methyl 2-octynoate
methyl heptyne carbonate; methyl octynoate; [111-12-6]

$$O$$
$$CH_3(CH_2)_4C \equiv CCOCH_3$$

$C_9H_{14}O_2$. M: 154.21.
Production:
• acetylene + *n*-amyl bromide + methyl chloroformate + methanol (ethynylation/ dehydrochlorination/esterification)
Uses: fragrance ingredient (soap, detergents)

N-methylolacrylamide
N-(hydroxymethyl)acrylamide; NMA; [924-42-5]

$$O$$
$$CH_2 = CHCNHCH_2OH$$

$C_4H_7N_1O_2$. M: 101.11.
Production:
• acrylamide + formaldehyde (hydroxymethylation)
Uses: reactive comonomer (vinyl acetate, styrene-butadiene resins); starch modifier

5-methylol 1-aza-3,7-dioxabicyclo[3,3,0]octane
Neosept 95 (Tenneco)

$$(CH_2O)_nH$$

n = 1–4. Mixed product. The major component is the monomethylol derivative.
Production:
• tris(hydroxymethyl)aminomethane + formaldehyde (condensation)
Uses: preservative (water-based paints)

methylol carbamate resins

$$O$$
$$ROCN(CH_2OH)_2$$

R = methyl, isopropyl, isobutyl, 2-methoxyethyl-.
Production:
• methyl chloroformate/isopropyl chloroformate/ isobutyl chloroformate/2-methoxyethyl chloroformate + ammonia + formaldehyde (dehydrochlorination/condensation)
Uses: permanent-press textile finishing agent

1-methyl-1-(oleamidoethyl) oleylimidazoline methosulphate

$$CH_3(CH_2)_7CH = CH(CH_2)_7$$
$$H_3C \quad CH_3SO_4^-$$
$$CH_2CH_2NHC(CH_2)_7CH = CH(CH_2)_7CH_3$$
$$O$$

$C_{42}H_{81}N_3O_5S_1$. M: 740.18. Available as a 75% solution in water.

Production:
- aminoethyl oleyl imidazoline + oleic acid + dimethyl sulphate (amide formation/quaternisation)

Uses: fabric softener

methyl oleate
[112-62-9]

$$CH_3(CH_2)_7CH=CH(CH_2)_7\overset{\overset{\displaystyle O}{\|}}{C}OCH_3$$

$C_{19}H_{36}O_2$. M: 296.50. Pale yellow liquid. BP: 202–210°C (2 kPa). Pour point: -15°C. Flash point: 180°C (COC). Insoluble in water. Miscible with oxygenated solvents.

Production:
- methanol + oleic acid (esterification)

Derivatives:
2-ethylhexyl oleate; fatty oils, sulphurised; oleic acid diethanolamide

Uses: lubricant (textile spin finishes); lubricity additive (metalworking fluids)

N-methylol methacrylamide
N-(hydroxymethyl)methacrylamide; [923-02-4]

$$CH_2=\overset{\overset{\displaystyle O}{\|}}{\underset{\underset{\displaystyle CH_3}{|}}{C}}CNHCH_2OH$$

$C_5H_9N_1O_2$. M: 115.13.
Production:
- methacrylamide + formaldehyde (carbonyl condensation)

Uses: reactive comonomer (acrylic resins)

methyl palmitate
methyl hexadecanoate; [112-39-0]

$$CH_3(CH_2)_{14}\overset{\overset{\displaystyle O}{\|}}{C}OCH_3$$

$C_{17}H_{34}O_2$. M: 270.46. Solid. MP: 30°C. BP: 418°C. Insoluble in water. Soluble in oxygenated, chlorinated and aromatic solvents. Properties vary with the source and purity of palmitic acid fraction.
Production:
- methanol + palmitic acid (esterification)

Derivatives: cetyl alcohol

methylparaben *See:* methyl 4-hydroxybenzoate

methyl parathion *See:* parathion-methyl

2-methylpentadiene
[926-54-5]

$$CH_2=\overset{\overset{\displaystyle CH_3}{|}}{C}CH=CHCH_3$$

C_6H_{10}. M: 82.15. Colourless liquid. BP: 75–76°C. d:

0.72 kg/l (20°C). Insoluble in water. Mixed product containing some 4-methyl isomer.
Production:
- hexylene glycol (dehydration)

Derivatives: dimethyl-3-cyclohexenecarboxaldehyde; trimethyl 3-cyclohexenecarboxaldehyde

2-methylpentamethylenediamine
Dytek A (Du Pont)

$$H_2NCH_2\overset{\overset{\displaystyle CH_3}{|}}{C}HCH_2CH_2CH_2NH_2$$

$C_6H_{16}N_2$. M: 116.21.
Production:
- 2-methylglutaronitrile (nitrile reduction)

Derivatives: polyamide resins, non-reactive; polyamide resins, reactive

2-methylpentane-2,4-diol *See:* hexylene glycol

2-methylpentanoic acid *See:* 2-methylvaleric acid

2-methylpentanol
2-methylpentan-1-ol; [105-30-6]

$$CH_3CH_2CH_2\overset{\overset{\displaystyle CH_3}{|}}{C}HCH_2OH$$

$C_6H_{14}O_1$. M: 102.18. Liquid. BP: 148°C. d: 0.82 kg/l (20°C). Almost insoluble in water. Flash point: 51°C (TCC).
Production:
- 2-methylvaleraldehyde (hydrogenation)

Uses: solvent

4-methyl-2-pentanol *See:* methyl isobutyl carbinol

4-methyl-2-pentanone *See:* methyl isobutyl ketone

methylpentene, mixed
Mixed isohexene component of steam-cracker C_5 streams.
Production:
- C_5-stream, steam-cracked (NMP solvent separation process; byproduct of dicyclopentadiene/isoprene production)

Derivatives: 2,2-dimethylpentanoic acid; 2-ethyl-2-methylbutanoic acid

4-methyl-1-pentene
1-isohexene; 4-methylpentene-1; 4-MP1; 4MP-1; [691-37-2]

$$(CH_3)_2CHCH_2CH=CH_2$$

C_6H_{12}. M: 84.17. Colourless liquid. MP: -154°C. BP: 53°C. d: 0.67 kg/l (20°C).
Production:
- propylene (alkali metal dimerisation process)

Derivatives: polyethylene, linear low-density; polyethylene, very low-density; polymethylpentene

4-methyl-3-penten-2-one *See:* mesityl oxide

3/4-(4-methyl-3-penten-1-yl)-3-cyclohexenecarboxaldehyde
Myrac aldehyde (IFF); Myraldene (Givaudan-Roure); [37677-14-8]

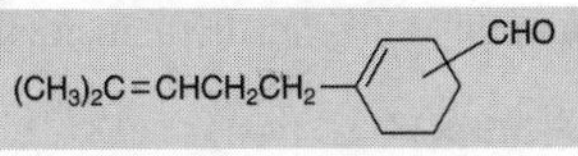

$(CH_3)_2C=CHCH_2CH_2$ —CHO

$C_{13}H_{20}O_1$. M: 192.30. Mixed product containing the 3- and 4-(hydroxymethylpentenyl) isomers.
Production:
• myrcene + acrolein (Diels-Alder cycloaddition)
Uses: fragrance ingredient (technical products)

methyl pentenynol
cis-3-methyl-2-penten-4-yn-1-ol

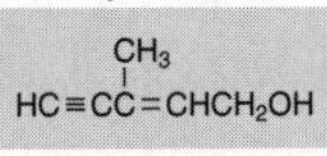

$$HC\equiv C\overset{\overset{\displaystyle CH_3}{|}}{C}=CHCH_2OH$$

$C_6H_8O_1$. M: 96.13. Intermediate in the Roche process for vitamin A production.
Production:
• methyl vinyl ketone + acetylene (ethynylation/ acid-catalysed rearrangement)
Derivatives: vitamin A

methylpentynol
3-methylpentyn-3-ol; [565-68-4]

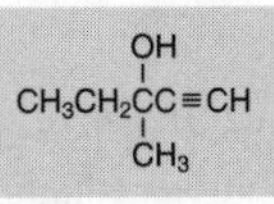

$$CH_3CH_2\overset{\overset{\displaystyle OH}{|}}{\underset{\underset{\displaystyle CH_3}{|}}{C}}C\equiv CH$$

$C_6H_{10}O_1$. M: 98.15. Colourless liquid. BP: 120–121°C. FP: -30°C. d: 0.87 kg/l (20°C). Soluble in water. Miscible with oxygenated, chlorinated and aromatic solvents.
Production:
• methyl ethyl ketone + acetylene (ethynylation)
Uses: electroplating brightening agent; fish tranquilliser; acid corrosion inhibitor; stabiliser (chlorinated solvents)

methylphenobarbital
mephobarbital; methylphenobarbitone; [115-38-8]

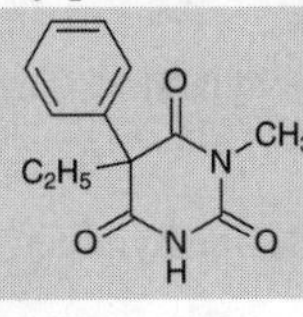

$C_{13}H_{14}N_2O_3$. M: 246.26.
Production:
• phenobarbital + dimethyl sulphate (methylation)
Uses: anticonvulsant drug

2-methylphenol *See:* *o*-cresol

3-methylphenol *See:* *m*-cresol

4-methylphenol *See:* *p*-cresol

4-methylphenylacetaldehyde
p-methylphenylacetaldehyde; [104-09-6]

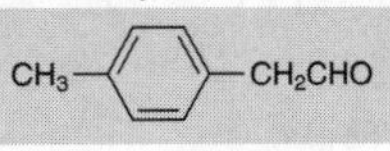

CH_3 —CH_2CHO

$C_9H_{10}O_1$. M: 134.18. Colourless liquid with a strong odour.
Production:
• *p*-methylbenzaldehyde + methyl chloroacetate (Darzens reaction/hydrolysis/decarboxylation)
Uses: fragrance ingredient

2-methyl-3-phenylbenzyl alcohol
HMBP; 3-hydroxymethyl-2-methylbiphenyl

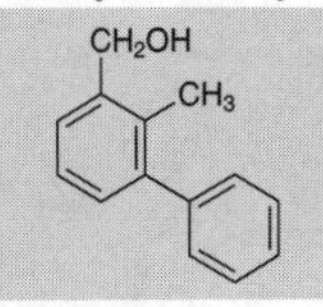

$C_{14}H_{14}O_1$. M: 198.26.
Production:
• fluorenone + formaldehyde (hydroxymethylation/ reductive decarboxylation)
Derivatives: bifenthrin

methyl phenylglyoxylate
methyl α-ketophenylacetate

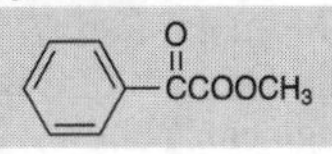

$C_9H_8O_3$. M: 164.16.
Production:
• benzoyl cyanide + methanol (nitrile hydrolysis/ esterification)
Derivatives: metamitron

5-methyl-3-phenylisoxazole-4-carboxylic acid
PMIC acid (Shell); [1136-45-4]

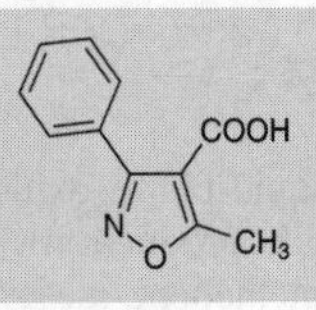

$C_{11}H_9N_1O_3$. M: 203.20. Solid.
Production:
• benzaldehyde + methyl acetoacetate + hydroxylamine hydrochloride (Knoevenagel condensation/ chlorination/cyclisation)
Derivatives: oxacillin

1-(4′-methylphenyl)-3-methylpyrazolone
1-(p-tolyl)-3-methyl-5-pyrazolone; [86-92-0]

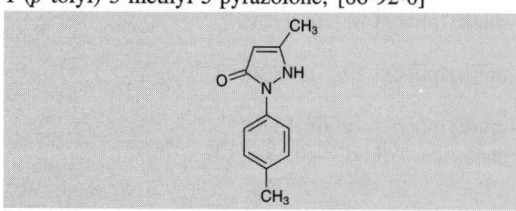

$C_{11}H_{12}N_2O_1$. M: 188.23.
Production:
• p-toluidine + diketene (diazotisation/azo reduction/ condensation)
Derivatives:
Pigment Orange 34; Pigment Red 37

3-methyl-1-phenyl-5-pyrazolone
3-methyl-1-phenyl-2-pyrazol-5-one; 1-phenyl-3-methyl-5-pyrazolone; PMP; [89-25-8]

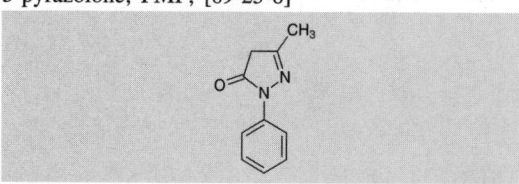

$C_{10}H_{10}N_2O_1$. M: 174.20. White, crystalline powder. MP: 129–130°C. Soluble in water. Slightly soluble in alcohol.
Production:
• diketene + phenylhydrazine (condensation)
Derivatives: Acid Orange 60; Acid Orange 74; Acid Orange 92; Acid Orange 148; Acid Yellow 42; Disperse Yellow 16; Mordant Red 7; Mordant Red 19; phenazone; Pigment Orange 6; Pigment Orange 13; Pigment Red 41; Pigment Yellow 10; Pigment Yellow 60; propyphenazone; Solvent Yellow 21

4-methylphthalic anhydride
toluene-3,4-dicarboxylic anhydride; [19438-61-0]

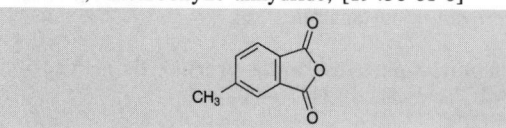

$C_9H_6O_3$. M: 162.15.
Production:
• pseudocumene (liquid-phase oxidation; byproduct of trimellitic anhydride production)
Derivatives: imazamethabenz-methyl

N-methylpiperazine
[109-01-3]
$C_5H_{12}N_2$. M: 100.16. Colourless, hygroscopic liquid with an unpleasant odour. BP: 137–139°C. FP: -6°C. Soluble in water and oxygenated solvents.

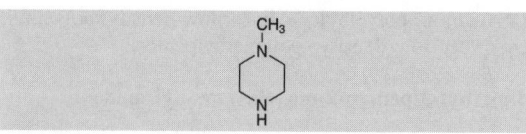

Production:
• piperazine + formaldehyde (methylation; coproduced with N,N′-dimethylpiperazine)
Derivatives: diethylcarbamazine; pirenzepine; prochlorperazine; rifampin; tiotixene; trifluoperazine

2-methylpiperidine
α-pipecoline; [109-05-7]

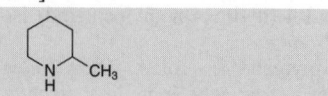

$C_6H_{13}N_1$. M: 99.18. Liquid with an unpleasant odour. BP: 118–119°C. MP: -5°C. d: 0.84 kg/l (25°C). Soluble in water and oxygenated solvents.
Production:
• α-picoline (electrolytic reduction)
Derivatives:
cyclomethycaine; piperocaine; piperophos

3-methylpiperidine
3MP; [626-56-2]

$C_6H_{13}N_1$. M: 99.18. Liquid. BP: 125°C. d: 0.85 kg/l (20°C). Soluble in water.
Production:
• 2-methylglutaronitrile (nitrile reduction; byproduct of 2-methylpentamethylenediamine production)
Uses: epoxy resin curing agent

1-methyl-4-piperidone
N-methyl-4-piperidone; [1445-73-4]

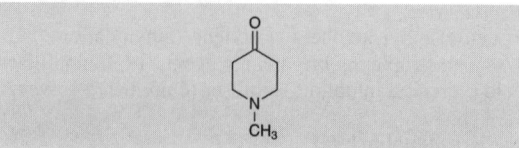

$C_6H_{11}N_1O_1$. M: 113.17. Liquid. BP: 55–58°C (1.3 kPa).
Production:
• ethyl acrylate + methylamine (amine formation/ condensation/decarboxylation)
Derivatives:
bamipine; 4-hydroxy-1-methylpiperidine; thenalidine

methyl pivalate
methyl 2,2′-dimethylpropionate; methyl trimethylacetate; [598-98-1]
$C_6H_{12}O_2$. M: 116.17. Liquid.

$(CH_3)_3CCOCH_3$

Production:
• methanol + pivalic acid (esterification)
Derivatives:
ethyl pivaloacetate

2-methyl-1-propanol *See:* isobutanol

2-methyl-2-propanol *See:* *t*-butanol

2-methylpropionic acid *See:* isobutyric acid

methyl propyl ketone
2-pentanone; MPK; [107-87-9]

$CH_3CH_2CH_2CCH_3$ (with O double bond)

$C_5H_{10}O_1$. M: 86.13. Colourless liquid. BP: 102–103°C. MP: -77°C. d: 0.81 kg/l (20°C). Slightly soluble in water. Soluble in oxygenated solvents.
Production:
• ethylene + methyl acetoacetate (acetoacetate ester synthesis)
Derivatives:
pentobarbital; prothionamide; thiopental sodium

methylpropynol *See:* 3-butyn-2-ol

***O*-methylpseudourea sulphate**
See: O-methylisourea sulphate

5-methylpyrazine-2-carboxylic acid
2-methylpyrazine-5-carboxylic acid; [5521-55-1]

$C_6H_6N_2O_2$. M: 138.13.
Production:
• 5-nitroso-2,4,6-triaminopyrimidine + methylglyoxal dimethyl acetal (imine formation/nitro reduction/ amine formation/amide hydrolysis/diazotisation/ reduction)
Derivatives: glipizide

2-methylpyridine *See:* α-picoline

3-methylpyridine *See:* β-picoline

4-methylpyridine *See:* γ-picoline

***N*-methylpyrrole**
[96-54-8]
$C_5H_7N_1$. M: 81.12. Liquid. BP: 112–113°C. Insoluble in water. Miscible with oxygenated solvents.

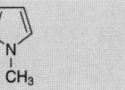

Production:
• pyrrole + dimethyl sulphate (methylation)
Derivatives:
tolmetin

***N*-methylpyrrolidone**
1-methyl-2-pyrrolidone; *N*-methyl-2-pyrrolidone; NMP; [872-50-4]

$C_5H_9N_1O_1$. M: 99.13. Liquid. BP: 202–205°C. MP: -25°C. d: 1.02 kg/l (25°C). Soluble in water and most organic solvents.
Production:
• γ-butyrolactone + methylamine (amide formation)
Derivatives:
2-aminomethyl-1-ethylpyrrolidine
Uses: aprotic process solvent (chemical synthesis); solvent (polyimide coatings); selective solvent (aromatics/ acetylene/butadiene extraction, Purisol carbon monoxide process, lubricating oil dearomatisation)

2-methylquinoline *See:* quinaldine

***N*-methylquinolinium iodide**
[3947-76-0]

$C_{10}H_{10}I_1N_1$. M: 271.10.
Production:
• quinoline + methyl iodide (quaternisation)
Uses: nickel plating brightening agent

methyl ricinoleate
methyl 12-hydroxyoleate; [141-24-2]

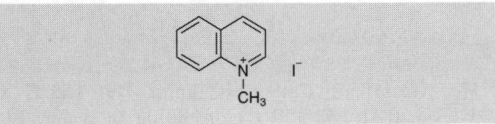

$C_{19}H_{36}O_3$. M: 312.50. Colourless liquid. d: 0.92 kg/l (20°C). Insoluble in water. Soluble in oxygenated solvents.
Production:
• castor oil + methanol (transesterification)
Derivatives:
n-heptaldehyde; methyl undecylenate
Uses: lubricity additive (cutting fluids)

methyl rosinate *See:* methyl abietate

methyl salicylate
oil of wintergreen; [119-36-8]

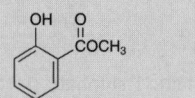

$C_8H_8O_3$. M: 152.15. Colourless liquid with a pleasant odour. BP: 221–224°C. MP: -9°C. d: 1.18 kg/l (25°C). Very slightly soluble in water. Soluble in oxygenated and chlorinated solvents.
Production:
• methanol + salicylic acid (esterification)
Derivatives:
doxepin; salbutamol; salicyl alcohol; salicylamide
Uses: fragrance/flavouring ingredient; antiseptic

methyl stearate
methyl *n*-octadecanoate; [112-61-8]

$$CH_3(CH_2)_{16}COCH_3$$

$C_{19}H_{38}O_2$. M: 298.51. White crystals. MP: 38°C. Insoluble in water.
Production:
• methanol + stearic acid (esterification)
Derivatives: stearyl alcohol

α-methylstyrene
isopropenylbenzene; AMS; [98-83-9]

$$CH_3C=CH_2$$

C_9H_{10}. M: 118.18. Colourless liquid. BP: 165°C. FP: -23°C. d: 0.91 kg/l (20°C). Insoluble in water. Flash point: 58°C (COC).
Production:
• cumene hydroperoxide (acid-catalysed hydrolysis; byproduct of phenol/acetone production)
• cumene (dehydrogenation)
Derivatives:
t-butylcumyl peroxide; diaminophenylindane; *p*-dicumyldiphenylamine; dicumyl peroxide; 4,5,5,6,7,7-hexamethylindanopyran; 2-[2′-hydroxy-3′,5′-bis(1-methyl-1-phenylethyl)]benzotriazole; α-methylstyrene-vinyltoluene copolymers; 2-phenyl-2-propylamine; styrene-α-methylstyrene copolymers; styrene-α-methylstyrene copolymers, low molecular weight
Uses:
polyvinyl chloride/high-temperature ABS comonomer; reactive diluent (unsaturated polyester resins)

p-methylstyrene
PMS; *p*-vinyltoluene; [622-97-9]
C_9H_{10}. M: 118.18.

Production:
• toluene + acetaldehyde (Mobil process)
Uses: polystyrene comonomer

α-methylstyrene-vinyltoluene copolymers
Piccotex (Hercules)

Low molecular weight hydrocarbon resin. Softening point: 75–120°C (Ring and Ball Method).
Production:
• α-methylstyrene + vinyltoluene (polymerisation)
Uses: tackifier/modifier resin (adhesives)

methyl sulphenyl chloride
[5813-48-9]

$$CH_3SCl$$

$C_1H_3Cl_1S_1$. M: 82.54.
Production:
• methyl mercaptan + chlorine (chlorination)
Derivatives:
3,5-di-(methylthio)toluenediamine; methiocarb; *p*-methylmercaptophenol; 3-methyl-4-(methylmercapto)phenol

methylsulphonic acid *See:* methanesulphonic acid

methylsulphonyl chloride
See: methanesulphonyl chloride

1-methyl-1-(tallowamidoethyl)tallowimidazoline methosulphate
quaternium-27 (CTFA)

R = tallow-.
Production:
• aminoethyl tallow imidazoline + tallow acid + dimethyl sulphate (amide formation/quaternisation)
Uses: fabric softener

methyltaurine, sodium salt
See: sodium *N*-methyltaurate

2-methyltetrahydrofuran
[25265-68-3]
$C_5H_{10}O_1$. M: 86.13. Colourless liquid with ether-like odour. BP: 80°C. d: 0.85 kg/l (20°C). Solubility in

water: 150 g/l water (25°C). Solubility increases at higher temperatures.

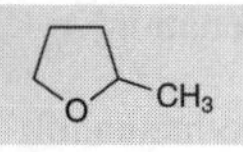

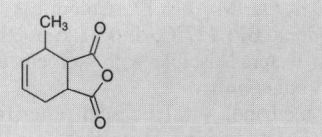

Production:
• furfural (hydrogenation)
Derivatives: primaquine

methyl tetrahydrophthalic anhydride
MTHPA

$C_9H_{10}O_3$. M: 166.18.
Production:
• piperylene + maleic anhydride (Diels-Alder cycloaddition)
Derivatives:
methyl hexahydrophthalic anhydride
Uses: polyester resin comonomer

1-methyltetrazole-5-thiol *See:* 5-thio-1-methyltetrazole

2-methyl-1,3,4-thiadiazole-5-thiol
See: 2-methyl-5-mercapto-1,3,4-thiadiazole

4-methylthiazole
[693-95-8]

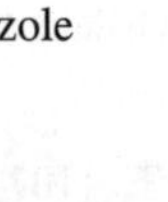

$C_4H_5N_1S_1$. M: 99.15. Liquid. BP: 130°C. d: 1.11 kg/l (20°C). Soluble in water and oxygenated solvents.
Production:
• chloroacetone + ammonium thiocyanate (condensation)
Derivatives: thiabendazole

3-methylthiophene
[616-44-4]

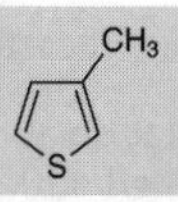

$C_5H_6S_1$. M: 98.16. Pale yellow liquid. BP: 115–117°C. MP: -69°C. d: 1.02 kg/l (25°C). Insoluble in water. Miscible with oxygenated solvents.
Production:
• isoamylene + sulphur (reaction)
Derivatives:
methyl 3-amino-4-methylthiophene-2-carboxylate; 3-thienylmalonic acid

4-methyl thiosemicarbazide
methylthiocarbamyl hydrazine; [6610-29-3]

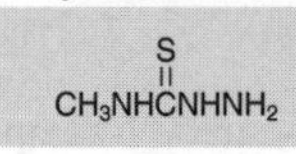

$$CH_3NHCNHNH_2$$

$C_2H_7N_3S_1$. M: 105.17. Solid. MP: 135–138°C.
Production:
• hydrazine + methyl isothiocyanate (thiocyanate addition)
Derivatives:
ethidimuron; tebuthiuron; thiazafluron

methyl *p*-toluenesulphonate
methyl 4-toluenesulphonate; methyl tosylate; [80-48-8]

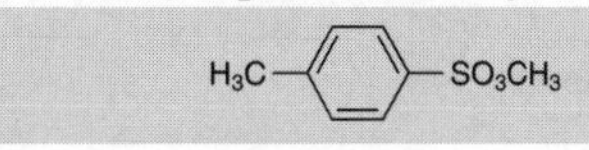

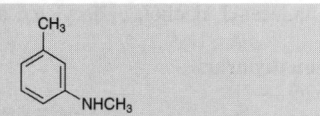

$C_8H_{10}O_3S_1$. M: 186.23. White, crystalline solid. MP: 28°C. BP: 292°C. Slightly soluble in water. Soluble in oxygenated, chlorinated and aromatic solvents.
Production:
• *p*-toluenesulphonyl chloride + methanol (dehydrochlorination)
Uses: methylation reagent

N-methyl-*m*-toluidine
3-(methylamino)toluene; [696-44-6]

$C_8H_{11}N_1$. M: 121.19. Liquid. BP: 206–207°C. Insoluble in water. Miscible with oxygenated solvents.
Production:
• *m*-toluidine + methanol (amine formation)
Derivatives: tolnaftate

N-methyl-2-*p*-tolylindole

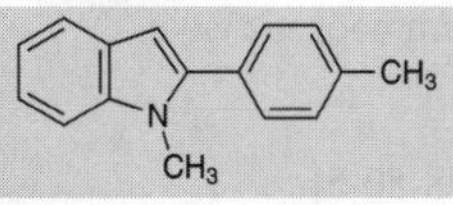

$C_{16}H_{15}N_1$. M: 221.31.
Production:
• phenylhydrazine + *p*-methylacetophenone + dimethyl sulphate (Fischer indole synthesis/ methylation)
Derivatives:
Basic Red 29; Basic Yellow 25

methyl triacetoxysilane
[4253-34-3]

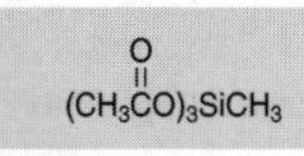

$C_7H_{12}O_6Si_1$. M: 220.25.

Production:
- trichloromethylsilane + acetic acid (dehydrochlorination)

Derivatives:
silicone rubber, cold-cured, 1-component

methyltrichlorosilane *See:* trichloromethylsilane

methyl triglycol
See: triethylene glycol monomethyl ether

methyl trimethylacetate *See:* methyl pivalate

2-methylundecanal *See:* methylnonylacetaldehyde

methyl undecylenate
[111-81-9]

$$CH_2=CH(CH_2)_8COCH_3$$

$C_{12}H_{22}O_2$. M: 198.31. Colourless liquid. BP: 248°C. MP: -28°C. d: 0.89 kg/l (15°C). Soluble in oxygenated solvents.
Production:
- methyl ricinoleate (catalytic dehydrogenation; coproduced with *n*-heptaldehyde)

Derivatives: 12-oxa-16-hexadecanolide; *n*-undecanol; *n*-undecenyl alcohol; undecylenic acid

6-methyluracil
[626-48-2]

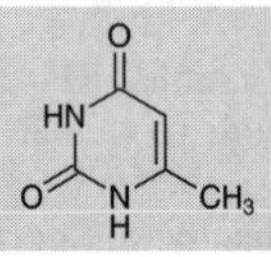

$C_5H_6N_2O_2$. M: 126.11.
Production:
- ethyl acetoacetate + urea (condensation)

Derivatives: 5-aminoorotic acid

N-methylurea
methylurea; [598-50-5]

$$CH_3NHCNH_2$$

$C_2H_6N_2O_1$. M: 74.08.
Production:
- methylamine + sodium cyanate (isocyanate addition)

Derivatives: 6-amino-1-methyluracil; methohexital

2-methylvaleraldehyde
2-methylpentanal; α-methylvaleraldehyde; [123-15-9]

$$CH_3CH_2CH_2CHCHO$$

$C_6H_{12}O_1$. M: 100.17. Liquid. BP: 118°C. MP: <100°C.

Production:
- propionaldehyde (carbonyl condensation/ dehydration/hydrogenation)

Derivatives:
meprobamate; 2-methylpentanol; 2-methylvaleric acid

methyl valerate
[624-24-8]

$$CH_3CH_2CH_2CH_2COCH_3$$

$C_6H_{12}O_2$. M: 116.17. Colourless liquid with a fruity odour. BP: 127°C. d: 0.91 kg/l (21°C). Slightly soluble in water. Miscible with oxygenated solvents.
Production:
- methanol + valeric acid (esterification)

Uses: flavouring ingredient

2-methylvaleric acid
2-methylpentanoic acid; [97-61-0]

$$CH_3CH_2CH_2CHCOOH$$

$C_6H_{12}O_2$. M: 116.17. Liquid. BP: 193°C. d: 0.93 kg/l (20°C). Soluble in water and oxygenated solvents.
Production:
- 2-methylvaleraldehyde (carbonyl oxidation)

Derivatives: pentanochlor

N-methyl-N-vinylacetamide
[3195-78-6]

$$CH_3CNCH=CH_2$$

$C_5H_9N_1O_1$. M: 99.13.
Production:
- *N*-methylacetamide + acetylene (ethynylation)

Uses: acrylic/acrylamide resin comonomer

methylvinyldichlorosilane
See: dichloromethylvinylsilane

methyl vinyl ether
vinyl methyl ether; MVE; [107-25-5]

$$CH_2=CHOCH_3$$

$C_3H_6O_1$. M: 58.08. Colourless, liquified gas. BP: 6°C. MP: -122°C. d: 0.75 kg/l (20°C). Slightly soluble in water. Soluble in oxygenated solvents.
Production:
- methanol + acetylene (ethynylation)

Derivatives: 2-methoxydihydropyran; poly(methyl vinyl ether-maleic anhydride); poly(vinyl methyl ether)

methyl vinyl ether-maleic anhydride copolymers
See: poly(methyl vinyl ether-maleic anhydride)

methyl vinyl ketone
3-butene-2-one; vinyl methyl ketone; [78-94-4]

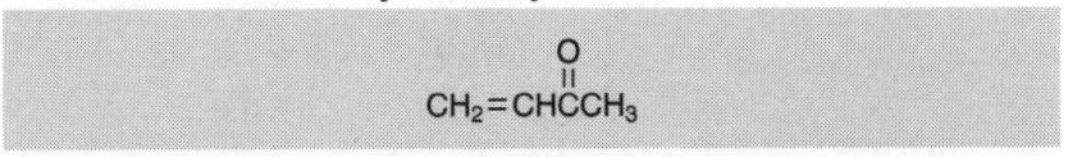

$$CH_2=CHCCH_3$$
(O)

$C_4H_6O_1$. M: 70.09. Liquid with an unpleasant, pungent odour. BP: 81°C. d: 0.86 kg/l (20°C). Soluble in water and oxygenated solvents. Commercial products are stabilised with 1% hydroquinone.
Production:
• formaldehyde + acetone (carbonyl condensation/dehydration)
Derivatives:
dihydrojasmone; 6-dimethylamino-1,2-dimethylquinolinium iodide; methyl pentenynol; vinclozolin
Uses:
photodegradable polymer comonomer

methyl violet *See:* Basic Violet 1

methyprylon
[125-64-4]

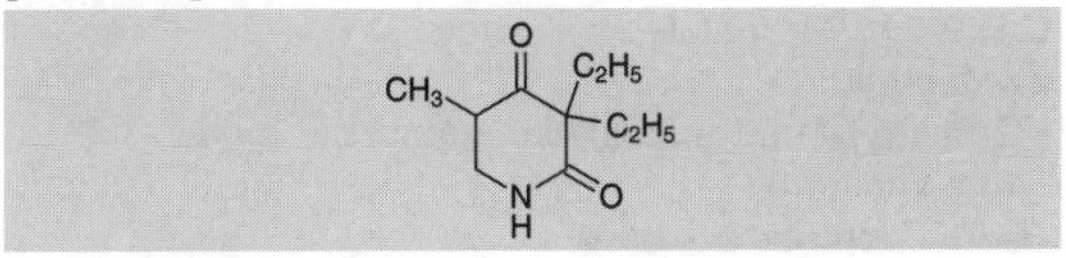

$C_{10}H_{17}N_1O_2$. M: 183.26.
Production:
• ethyl acetoacetate + ethyl bromide + ethyl formate + ammonia (dehydrobromination/carbonyl condensation/amine formation/cyclisation/hydrogenation/carbonyl condensation/hydrogenation)
Uses:
hypnotic/sedative drug

meticillin
methacillin; [61-32-5]; [132-92-3] (sodium salt)

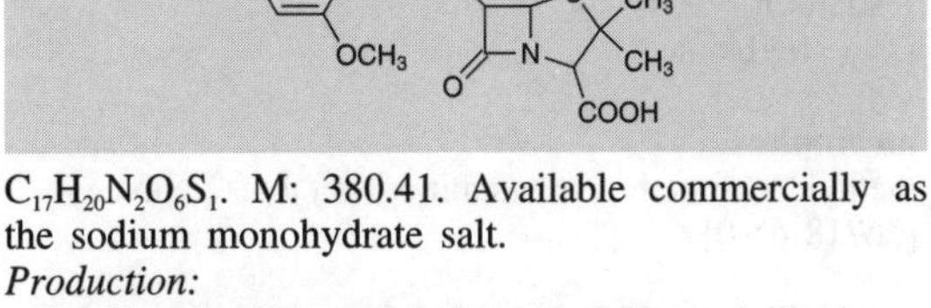

$C_{17}H_{20}N_2O_6S_1$. M: 380.41. Available commercially as the sodium monohydrate salt.
Production:
• 2,6-dimethoxybenzoic acid + 6-aminopenicillanic acid (amide formation)
Uses: antibacterial drug

metiram
Polyram (BASF); [9006-42-2]
Mixed product based on the zinc and ammonium salts of ethylenebis(dithiocarbamate), together with poly-(ethylenethiuram disulphide).

Production:
• ethylenediamine + carbon disulphide + zinc sulphate + ammonia (reaction)
Uses: fungicide

metobromuron
3-(4-bromophenyl)-1-methoxy-1-methylurea; [3060-89-7]

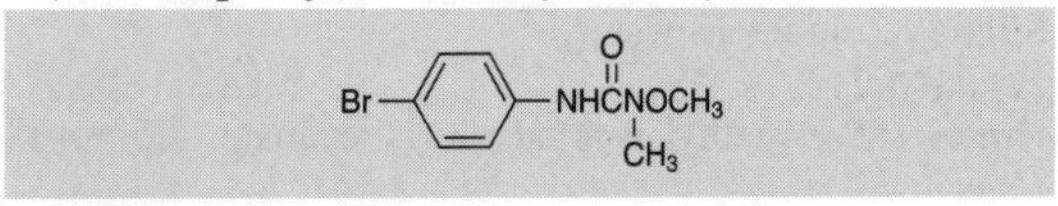

$C_9H_{11}Br_1N_2O_2$. M: 259.10.
Production:
• *p*-bromoaniline + phosgene + *N,O*-dimethyl-hydroxylamine (phosgenation/isocyanate addition)
Uses: herbicide

metoclopramide
[364-62-5]

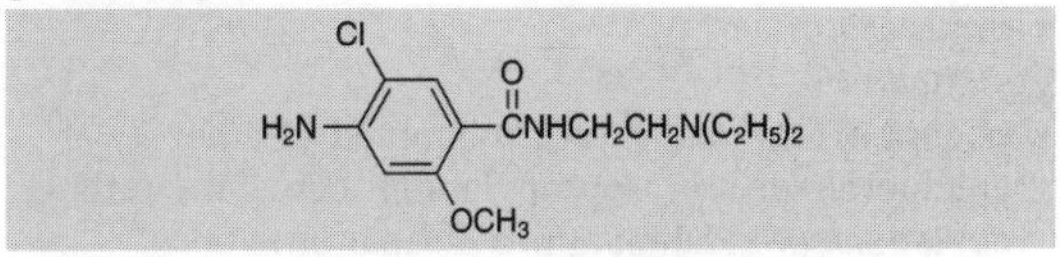

$C_{14}H_{22}Cl_1N_3O_2$. M: 299.80. Available commercially as the monohydrochloride or dihydrochloride monohydrate salts.
Production:
• *p*-aminosalicylic acid + *N,N*-diethylethylenediamine (acetylation/methylation/ring chlorination/amide formation/amide hydrolysis)
Uses:
antiemetic/stomach therapy drug

metol *See:* *N*-methyl-*p*-aminophenol

metolachlor
2-chloro-6′-ethyl-*N*-(2-methoxy-1-methylethyl)acet-*o*-toluidide; [51218-45-2]

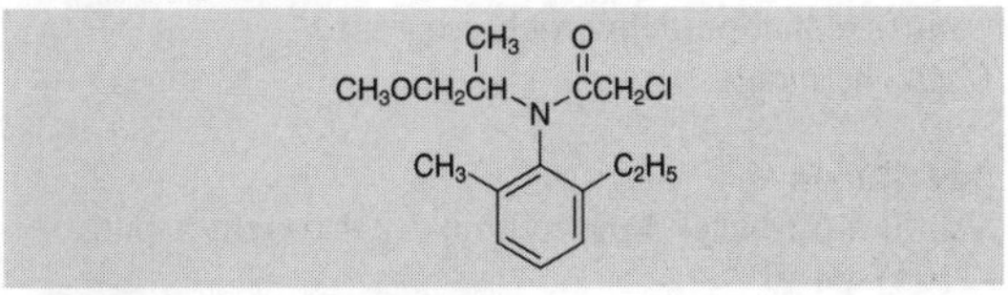

$C_{15}H_{22}Cl_1N_1O_2$. M: 283.80.
Production:
• methanol + allyl chloride + hydrogen bromide, anhydrous + 2-ethyl-6-methylaniline + chloroacetyl chloride (ether formation/addition/amine formation/amide formation)
Uses: herbicide

metolcarb
Metacrate (Nihon Nohyaku); 3-methylphenyl methyl-carbamate; MTMC; Tsumacide (Sumitomo); [1129-41-5]

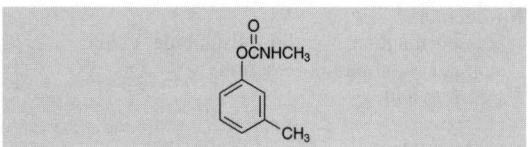

$C_9H_{11}N_1O_2$. M: 165.20. Colourless solid. MP: 74–75°C. Slightly soluble in water.
Production:
• *m*-cresol + methyl isocyanate (isocyanate addition)
Uses:
insecticide

metoprolol
[37350-58-6]

$(CH_3)_2CHNHCH_2CHCH_2O$—⬡—$CH_2CH_2OCH_3$

$C_{15}H_{25}N_1O_3$. M: 267.37. Available commercially as the tartrate salt.
Production:
• phenol + ethylene glycol monomethyl ether + epichlorohydrin + isopropylamine (Friedel-Crafts acylation/epoxidation/amine formation)
Uses:
antianginal drug

metoxuron
3-(3-chloro-4-methoxyphenyl)-1,1-dimethylurea; [19937-59-8]

CH_3O—⬡—$NHCN(CH_3)_2$

$C_{10}H_{13}Cl_1N_2O_2$. M: 228.67.
Production:
• 3,4-dichloronitrobenzene + methanol + dimethylcarbamoyl chloride (ether formation/ nitro reduction/dehydrochlorination)
Uses: herbicide

metribuzin
4-amino-6-*t*-butyl-3-methylthio-1,2,4-triazin-5-one; [21087-64-9]

$C_8H_{14}N_4O_1S_1$. M: 214.29.
Production:
• hydrazine + carbon disulphide + pivaloyl chloride + sodium cyanide (thiocarbonylation/methylation/ cyanidation/nitrile hydrolysis/condensation)
Uses:
herbicide

metrizoic acid
[1949-45-7]

$C_{12}H_{11}I_3N_2O_4$. M: 627.94. Available commercially as the sodium salt.
Production:
• amidotrizoic acid + dimethyl sulphate (methylation)
Uses:
x-ray diagnostic aid

metronidazole
1-(2-hydroxyethyl)-2-methyl-5-nitroimidazole; [443-48-1]

O_2N—⬡—CH_3 / CH_2CH_2OH

$C_6H_9N_3O_3$. M: 171.16.
Production:
• 2-methyl-4-nitroimidazole + ethylene oxide (epoxidation)
Uses: antiprotazoal drug

metsulfuron-methyl
2-[-3-(4-methoxy-6-methyl-1,3,5-triazin-2-yl)ureido-sulphonyl]benzoic acid; [74223-64-6]

$C_{14}H_{15}N_5O_6S_1$. M: 381.35.
Production:
• carbomethoxybenzenesulphonyl isocyanate + 2-amino-4-methoxy-6-methyltriazine (isocyanate addition)
Uses: herbicide

mevinphos
methyl 3-(dimethoxyphosphinoyloxy)but-2-enoate; [26718-65-0]

$CH_3OCCH=COP(OCH_3)_2$ / CH_3

$C_7H_{13}O_6P_1$. M: 224.14.
Production:
• methyl acetoacetate + trimethyl phosphite (alpha chlorination/Perkow reaction)
Uses:
insecticide/acaricide

mexiletine
[31828-71-4]

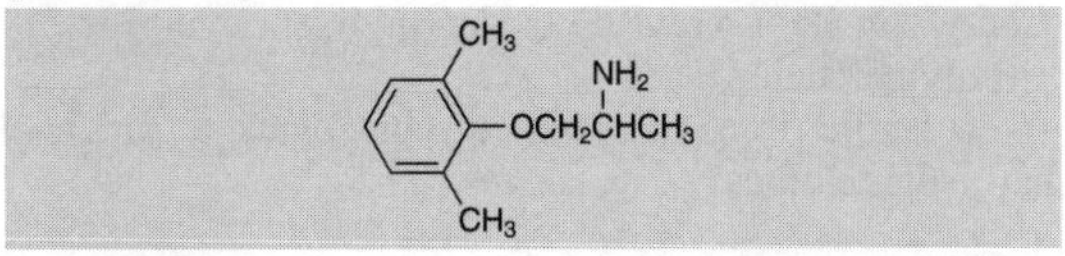

$C_{11}H_{17}N_1O_1$. M: 179.27. Available commercially as the hydrochloride.
Production:
• 2,6-xylenol + chloroacetone + ammonia (ether formation/ammoniation)
Uses: antiarrhythmic/anticonvulsant drug

mezlocillin
[51481-65-3]

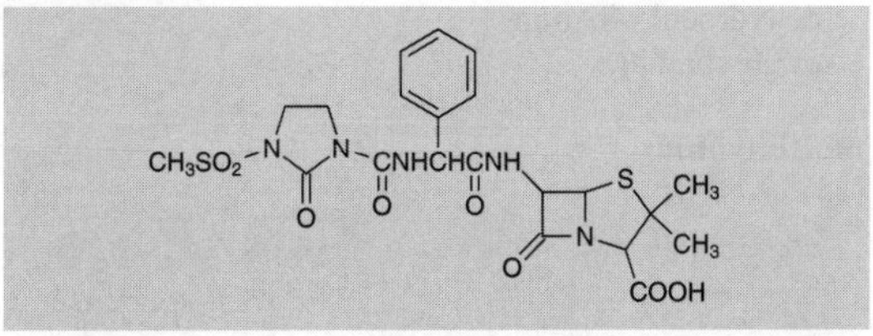

$C_{21}H_{25}N_5O_8S_2$. M: 539.58. Available commercially as the sodium monohydrate salt.
Production:
• ethylene urea + methanesulphonyl chloride + ethyl chloroformate + ampicillin (sulphonamide formation/dehydrochlorination/amide formation)
Uses: antibacterial drug

MH *See:* maleic hydrazide

MHEC *See:* methyl hydroxyethylcellulose

MHHPA *See:* methyl hexahydrophthalic anhydride

MHPC *See:* methylhydroxypropylcellulose

2-MI *See:* 2-methylimidazole

MIAK *See:* methyl isoamyl ketone

MIBC *See:* methyl isobutyl carbinol

MIBK *See:* methyl isobutyl ketone

MIC *See:* methyl isocyanate

mica
77019 (CI); [12001-26-2]
Mica is one of several aluminosilicate minerals (muscovite, phlogipite, biotite, vermiculite) that have been laid down with a planar grain that allows them to be cleaved into thin sheets or films. The product is available as block, sheet, punch, splittings and wet or dry ground grades. Treated, organophilic grades are also available. Sheet mica is the most expensive. It is mined and cut in India, Brazil and Madagascar.
Uses:
electrical/thermal insulation sheets; lubricants/ greases; oil-well drilling lost circulation material; reinforcing filler (paints, plastics, sealants)

Michler's base
See: bis(*p*-dimethylaminophenyl)methane

Michler's hydrol
See: 4,4'-bis(dimethylamino)benzhydrol

Michler's ketone
See: 4,4'-bis(dimethylamino)benzophenone

miconazole
[22916-47-8]

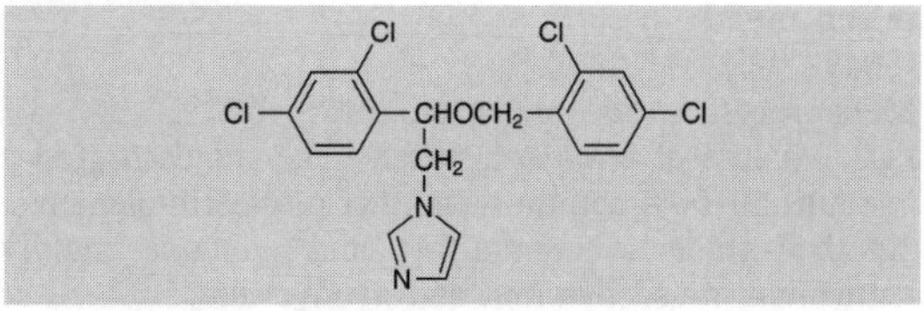

$C_{18}H_{14}Cl_4N_2O_1$. M: 416.13. Available commercially as the nitrate.
Production:
• α,2,4-trichloroacetophenone + imidazole + 2,4-dichlorobenzyl chloride (amine formation/ carbonyl reduction/ether formation)
Uses: antifungal drug

microcrystalline wax
[63231-60-7]
White, yellow or brown solid. Mixture of mainly isoparaffins and cycloparaffins averaging 30–75 carbon atoms per molecule. Softening point: 70–90°C.
Production:
• petroleum jelly (Sweating process)
Derivatives:
wax, oxidised
Uses: candle wax; coating wax (packaging, textiles); electrical insulation impregnation wax; heat-seal/hot melt flow additive; shoe/car polish ingredient; slip improvement additive (printing, carbon-copying inks)

middle oil *See:* naphthalene fraction

milk protein *See:* casein

milk sugar *See:* lactose

Milori Blue *See:* Prussian Blue

minium *See:* red lead

minocycline
[10118-90-8]

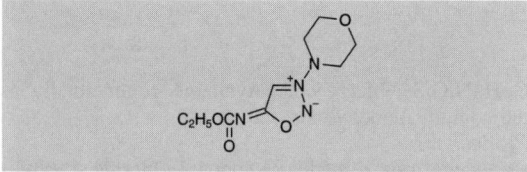

$C_{23}H_{27}N_3O_7$. M: 457.48. Available commercially as the free base or hydrochloride.
Production:
• sancycline (nitration/nitro reduction/amine methylation)
Uses: antibacterial drug

MIPA *See:* isopropylamine; monoisopropanolamine

MIPK *See:* methyl isopropenyl ketone

misch metal
[8049-20-5]
Metal sheets stored under oil. MP: ~650°C. d: ~6.7 kg/l. Mixture of rare-earth metals. The standard grades contains 50–60% cerium with other rare-earth elements. Another grade is cerium-free and contains mainly lanthanum, praseodymium and neodymium.
Production:
• rare earth chloride (electrolysis)
Uses: ductile iron/steel desulphurisation reagent; non-ferrous metal additive; lighter flints

MITC *See:* methyl isothiocyanate

MMA *See:* methyl methacrylate; methylamine

MMBI *See:* 2-mercaptomethylbenzimidazole

MMH *See:* methyl hydrazine

MNA *See:* methylnonylacetaldehyde

MNBA *See:* n-butylamine

MNPC *See:* m-nitro-p-cresol

MNPT *See:* 4-amino-3-nitrotoluene

MOCA *See:* 4,4′-methylenebis(2-chloroaniline)

modacrylic fibre

$$\left[CH_2 - \underset{\underset{CN}{|}}{CH} \right]_x \left[CH_2 - CH_{2-n}Cl_n \right]_y$$

n = 1, 2. Chloroacrylonitrile copolymers containing 35–85% acrylonitrile characterised by their high resilience, good abrasion resistance, low moisture uptake, chemical inertness and inherent fire resistance. MP: ~200°C.

d: 1.30–1.37 kg/l. Tenacity: 2.0–3.5 g/d (wet and dry).
Production:
• acrylonitrile + vinyl chloride/vinylidene chloride (polymerisation)
Uses: textile fibres (carpets, curtains, blankets, artificial hair, nightclothes)

molinate
S-ethyl *N,N*-hexamethylenethiocarbamate; [2212-67-1]

$C_9H_{17}N_1O_1S_1$. M: 187.31.
Production:
• hexamethyleneimine + ethyl chlorothioformate (dehydrochlorination)
Uses: herbicide

molsidomine
[25717-80-0]

$C_9H_{14}N_4O_4$. M: 242.24.
Production:
• morpholine + sodium cyanate + formaldehyde + hydrogen cyanide + sodium nitrite + ethyl chloroformate (cyanate addition/Hofmann degradation/cyanomethylation/nitrosation/condensation/dehydrochlorination)
Uses: antianginal drug

Molybdate Orange *See:* Pigment Red 104

Molybdate Red *See:* Pigment Red 104

molybdenum
[7439-98-7]

Mo

Mo_1. M: 95.94. Silvery-grey metal. MP: 2,625°C. BP: 5,560°C. d: 10.2 kg/l. Good corrosion and chemical resistance except under oxidising conditions. Available as bar, rod, wire, sheet, foil, powder and single crystals. See also ferromolybdenum.
Production:
• molybdenum trioxide/ammonium molybdate + hydrogen (hydrogenation)
Derivatives:
molybdenum hexacarbonyl
Uses: electrical/electronic filaments and contacts; non-ferrous alloy ingredient

molybdenum carbonyl *See:* molybdenum hexacarbonyl

molybdenum di-(2-ethylhexyl) dithiophosphate

$$\left[CH_3(CH_2)_3\overset{\overset{\displaystyle C_2H_5}{|}}{C}HCH_2O\right]_2\overset{\overset{\displaystyle S}{\|}}{P}SH$$

The chemical is the molybdenum complex of the displayed structure.
Production:
• phosphorus pentasulphide + 2-ethylhexanol + molybdenum trioxide (condensation)
Uses: antiwear additive (lubricants)

molybdenum disulphide
molybdenum sulphide; molybdic sulphide; [1317-33-5]

$$MoS_2$$

Mo_1S_2. M: 160.07. Shiny, grey powder. d: 4.8 kg/l. Sublimes on heating to 450°C. Insoluble in water. Molybdenite is a natural mineral form of molybdenum disulphide.
Production:
• molybdenite concentrate (separation)
Uses: friction modifier (lubricating oils); lubricating filler (engineering plastics)

molybdenum hexacarbonyl
molybdenum carbonyl; [13939-06-5]

$$Mo(CO)_6$$

$C_6Mo_1O_6$. M: 264.00.
Production:
• molybdenum + carbon monoxide (complex formation)
Uses: latex polymerisation initiator

molybdenum trioxide
molybdic oxide; [1313-27-5]

$$MoO_3$$

Mo_1O_3. M: 143.94. White, crystalline powder. MP: 795°C. d: 4.69 kg/l. Slightly soluble in hot water.
Production:
• molybdenite concentrate (thermal oxidation)
Derivatives: ammonium molybdate; calcium zinc molybdate; ferromolybdenum; molybdenum; molybdenum di-(2-ethylhexyl) dithiophosphate; sodium molybdate; zinc molybdate, basic
Uses: fire-retardant additive

molybdophosphoric acid *See:* phosphomolybdic acid

monalide
N-(4-chlorophenyl)-2,2-dimethylvaleramide; [7287-36-7]
$C_{13}H_{18}Cl_1N_1O_1$. M: 239.74.
Production:
• 2,2-dimethylpentanoic acid + p-chloroaniline (amide formation)

Uses: herbicide

monazite
Rare earth phosphate concentrate containing 5–10% thorium dioxide. Produced mainly in Australia, India, Brazil, Malaysia and Russia. Brazil and India process monazite before release into the market in order to remove the thorium for strategic nuclear purposes.
Production:
• mineral sands (separation; coproduced with rutile/zircon/ilmenite)
Derivatives: rare earth oxide, hydrate; thorium dioxide

monoammonium phosphate
ammonium acid phosphate; ammonium dihydrogen phosphate; ammonium phosphate, monobasic; MAP; [7722-76-1]

$$NH_4H_2PO_4$$

$H_6N_1O_4P_1$. M: 115.03. Available commercially as fertiliser, technical and food grades according to the source and purity of the phosphoric acid. Pure product: White crystals. d: 1.80 kg/l. Solubility in water: 299 g/l water (20°C). A typical fertiliser grade has a 13% N and 52% P_2O_5 content.
Production:
• ammonia + phosphoric acid, pure (salt formation)
• ammonia + phosphoric acid, crude (salt formation)
Uses: dyeing auxiliary; fertiliser ingredient; fire extinguishant powder; fire-retardant (paper, textiles, wood, cellulosics); leavening agent/dough conditioner; yeast/microbial fermentation nutrient

monobutyltin sulphide
butylthiostannoic acid

$$(CH_3CH_2CH_2CH_2)_4Sn_4S_6$$

$C_{16}H_{36}S_6Sn_4$. M: 895.61.
Production:
• n-butyltin trichloride + sodium sulphide (dehydrochlorination)
Uses: polyvinyl chloride heat stabiliser

monobutyltin tris(isooctylthioglycollate)
n-butyltin tris(isooctylmercaptoacetate)

$$CH_3CH_2CH_2CH_2Sn\left[SCH_2\overset{\overset{\displaystyle O}{\|}}{C}OCH_2C_7H_{15}\right]_3$$

$C_{34}H_{66}O_6S_3Sn_1$. M: 785.77.
Production:
• n-butyltin trichloride + isooctyl thioglycollate (dehydrochlorination)
Uses: polyvinyl chloride heat stabiliser

monobutyltin tris(2-mercaptoethyl oleate)

$$CH_3CH_2CH_2CH_2Sn\left[SCH_2CH_2O\overset{\overset{O}{\|}}{C}(CH_2)_7CH=CH(CH_2)_7CH_3\right]_3$$

$C_{64}H_{120}O_6S_3Sn_1$. M: 1200.53.
Production:
- 2-mercaptoethanol + oleic acid + *n*-butyltin trichloride (carbonyl condensation)

Uses: polyvinyl chloride heat stabiliser

monocalcium phosphate

calcium phosphate; calcium phosphate, monobasic; [7758-23-8]

$$Ca(H_2PO_4)_2$$

$H_4Ca_1O_8P_2$. M: 234.05. Colourless crystals. Releases water of crystallisation when heated above 100°C. Decomposes at 200°C. d: 2.22 kg/l (16°C). Solubility in water: 18 g/l water (30°C).
Production:
- calcium hydroxide + phosphoric acid, pure (salt formation)

Uses:
animal feed supplement; baking powder ingredient

n-monochloroparaffins (C$_{10}$-C$_{13}$)

chloro-oil

$$\underset{CH_3(CH_2)_mCH(CH_2)_nCH_3}{\overset{\overset{Cl}{|}}{}}$$

m+n = 7–10.
Production:
- *n*-paraffins (C$_{10}$-C$_{13}$) + chlorine (chlorination)

Derivatives:
dodecylbenzene, linear; *n*-olefins(C$_{10}$-C$_{13}$)

n-monochloroparaffins (C$_{11}$-C$_{14}$)

chloro-oil

$$\underset{CH_3(CH_2)_mCH(CH_2)_nCH_3}{\overset{\overset{Cl}{|}}{}}$$

m+n = 8–11.
Production:
- *n*-paraffins (C$_{11}$-C$_{14}$) + chlorine (chlorination)

Derivatives:
n-olefins(C$_{11}$-C$_{14}$)

monochloropivaloyl chloride

3-chloro-2,2-dimethylpropanoyl chloride; [4300-97-4]

$$\underset{(CH_3)_2CCOCl}{\overset{\overset{CH_2Cl}{|}}{}}$$

$C_5H_8Cl_2O_1$. M: 155.02. Liquid.
Production:
- pivalic acid (chlorination)

Derivatives:
clomazone; 4,4-dimethyl-1-phenyl-3-pyrazolidinone

monocrotophos

dimethyl 1-methyl-2-(methylcarbamoyl)vinyl phosphate; [6923-22-4]

$$\underset{CH_3}{\underset{|}{CH_3NHC\overset{\overset{O}{\|}}{C}H=C\overset{\overset{O}{\|}}{O}P(OCH_3)_2}}$$

$C_7H_{14}N_1O_5P_1$. M: 223.16.
Production:
- *N*-methylacetoacetamide + trimethyl phosphite (alpha chlorination/Perkow reaction)

Uses: insecticide/acaricide

monoethanolamine

2-aminoethanol; ethanolamine; 2-hydroxyethylamine; MEA; MELA; [141-43-5]

$$H_2NCH_2CH_2OH$$

$C_2H_7N_1O_1$. M: 61.09. Colourless liquid. BP: 166–174°C. FP: 10°C. d: 1.01 kg/l (25°C). Miscible with water, most oxygenated and some chlorinated solvents. Flash point: 91°C (CC).
Production:
- ammonia + ethylene oxide (epoxidation; coproduced with diethanolamine/triethanolamine)

Derivatives:
N-acetylethanolamine; aminoethylethanolamine; 2-amino-5-[*N*-ethyl-*N*-(2-methylsulphonaminoethyl)amino]-toluene; aminoethylpiperazine; bensulide; coconut acid monoethanolamide; diethylenetriamine; Disperse Blue 3; Disperse Blue 7; ethanolamine thioglycollate; ethylenediamine; ethyleneimine; fenetylline; fenoxycarb; Fluorescent Brightener 142; *N*-hydroxyethylpiperazine; 2-[(hydroxymethyl)amino]ethanol; 4-hydroxy-2,2,6,6-tetramethyl-1-piperidine ethanol; ifosfamide; isocyanatoethyl methacrylate; lauric acid monoethanolamide; 2-mercaptoethylamine hydrochloride; monoethanolamine lauryl sulphate; niridazole; 2,2′-oxamidobis[ethyl 3-(3,5-di-*t*-butyl-4-hydroxyphenyl)propionate]; oxetacaine; piperazine; polyethylenepolyamine; sodium *N*-hydroxyethylglycine; stearic acid monoethanolamide; taurine; tetraethylenepentamine; triethylenetetramine; *N,N′,N″*-tris(2-hydroxyethyl)hexahydrotriazine; urea-formaldehyde resins, cationic; viloxazine

Uses:
neutralising agent (detergents, cleaners, personal-care products); selective solvent (carbon dioxide, hydrogen sulphide); soap-based emulsifier solubilising agent (metalworking fluids, textile auxiliaries); solubiliser (water-based printing inks, agrochemicals)

monoethanolamine lauryl sulphate

MEA-lauryl sulphate; [4722-98-9]

$$CH_3(CH_2)_{11}OSO_3^-\quad HOCH_2CH_2NH_3^+$$

$C_{14}H_{33}N_1O_5S_1$. M: 327.47. Pale yellow liquid consisting of 30% active matter in water.

Production:
- *n*-alkanol(C$_{12}$-C$_{13}$)/*n*-alkanol(C$_{12}$-C$_{14}$)/*n*-alkanol(C$_{12}$-C$_{18}$) + monoethanolamine (sulphation/salt formation)

Uses: shampoos/bubble baths

monoethyl 5-nitroisophthalate
ethyl 5-nitroisophthalate

C$_{10}$H$_9$N$_1$O$_6$. M: 239.18.
Production:
- 5-nitroisophthalic acid + ethanol (dehydration/alcoholysis)

Derivatives: iocarmic acid; iotalamic acid

monoisopropanolamine
1-aminopropan-2-ol; isopropanolamine; MIPA; [78-96-6]

C$_3$H$_9$N$_1$O$_1$. M: 75.11. Colourless liquid with mild, ammoniacal odour. BP: 159°C. FP: 3°C. d: 0.96 kg/l (25°C). Completely miscible with water and oxygenated solvents.
Production:
- ammonia + propylene oxide (epoxidation; coproduced with diisopropanolamine/triisopropanolamine)

Derivatives:
lauric acid monoisopropanolamide; monoisopropanolamine alkylbenzenesulphonate; oleic acid monoisopropanolamide; 1,2-propanediamine
Uses: emulsifier (polishes, cleaners, textile auxiliaries, pesticides); corrosion inhibitor (metalworking fluids)

monoisopropanolamine alkylbenzenesulphonate
MIPA-dodecylbenzenesulphonate (CTFA)

C$_{21}$H$_{39}$N$_1$O$_4$S$_1$. M: 401.61. Yellow, viscous liquid usually sold as a 90% solution in water. Soluble in oils and organic solvents.
Production:
- dodecylbenzenesulphonic acid, linear + monoisopropanolamine (salt formation)

Uses:
emulsifier (oils, solvents, waxes); surfactant/gelling agent (hand cleaners)

monolinuron
3-(4-chlorophenyl)-1-methoxy-1-methylurea; [1746-81-2]
C$_9$H$_{11}$Cl$_1$N$_2$O$_2$. M: 214.65.

Production:
- *N,O*-dimethylhydroxylamine + *p*-chlorophenyl isocyanate (isocyanate addition)

Uses: herbicide

monomethylol dimethylhydantoin
MDMH

C$_6$H$_{10}$N$_2$O$_3$. M: 158.16.
Production:
- 5,5-dimethylhydantoin + formaldehyde (condensation)

Uses: hair lacquer resin

monomethyltin trichloride

CH$_3$SnCl$_3$

C$_1$H$_3$Cl$_3$Sn$_1$. M: 240.08. Colourless crystals. MP: 43°C. BP: 171°C. Soluble in water.
Production:
- stannic chloride + tetramethyltin (Kocheshkov redistribution)

Derivatives: monomethyltin tris(isooctylthioglycollate); monomethyltin tris(2-mercaptoethyl oleate)

monomethyltin tris(isooctylthioglycollate)
monomethyltin tris(isooctylmercaptoacetate)

CH$_3$Sn[SCH$_2$COCH$_2$C$_7$H$_{15}$]$_3$

C$_{31}$H$_{60}$O$_6$S$_3$Sn$_1$. M: 743.69.
Production:
- monomethyltin trichloride + isooctyl thioglycollate (dehydrochlorination)

Uses: polyvinyl chloride heat stabiliser

monomethyltin tris(2-mercaptoethyl oleate)

CH$_3$Sn[SCH$_2$CH$_2$OC(CH$_2$)$_7$CH=CH(CH$_2$)$_7$CH$_3$]$_3$

C$_{61}$H$_{114}$O$_6$S$_3$Sn$_1$. M: 1158.45.
Production:
- 2-mercaptoethanol + oleic acid + monomethyltin trichloride (esterification/dehydrochlorination)

Uses: polyvinyl chloride heat stabiliser

monopotassium glutamate
monopotassium L-glutamate; MPG
C$_5$H$_8$K$_1$N$_1$O$_4$. M: 185.22. White solid. Soluble in water.
Available commercially as the natural L(+)-enantiomer.

$$HOOCCH_2CH_2-\overset{\overset{\displaystyle NH_2}{\displaystyle |}}{\underset{\underset{\displaystyle H}{\displaystyle |}}{C}}-COO^- \;\; K^+$$

Production:
• potassium hydroxide + L-glutamic acid (salt formation)
Uses: salt substitute/flavour enhancer

monosodium glutamate
monosodium L-glutamate; sodium glutamate; MSG; [142-47-2]

$$HOOCCH_2CH_2-\overset{\overset{\displaystyle NH_2}{\displaystyle |}}{\underset{\underset{\displaystyle H}{\displaystyle |}}{C}}-COO^- \;\; Na^+$$

$C_5H_8N_1Na_1O_4$. M: 169.11. White, odourless solid. Soluble in water. Available commercially as the natural L(+)-enantiomer.
Production:
• L-glutamic acid + sodium hydroxide (salt formation)
Uses:
flavour enhancer; animal feed additive

monosodium methylarsonate
monosodium methanearsonate; sodium methanearsonate; MSMA; [2163-80-6]

$$CH_3\overset{\overset{\displaystyle O^- \;\; Na^+}{\displaystyle \|}}{\underset{\underset{\displaystyle OH}{\displaystyle |}}{As}}=O$$

$C_1H_4As_1Na_1O_3$. M: 161.95.
Production:
• methyl chloride + arsenic trioxide + sulphuric acid + sodium hydroxide (reaction/neutralisation)
Uses: herbicide

monosodium phosphate
sodium dihydrogen phosphate; sodium phosphate; sodium phosphate, monobasic; MSP; E339 (EC); [7558-80-7]

$$NaH_2PO_4$$

$H_2Na_1O_4P_1$. M: 119.98. White, hygroscopic, granules or crystalline powder. Soluble in water. Insoluble in alcohol.
Production:
• sodium carbonate/sodium hydroxide + phosphoric acid, pure (salt formation)
Derivatives: sodium metaphosphate, insoluble; sodium tetraphosphate; starch, sodium phosphate
Uses: buffering agent (electroplating baths); acidulant (processed meats, egg products, powdered drinks); builder (industrial cleaning formulations); metal phosphatising reagent; mineral supplement; softening/conditioning agent (boiler water treatment); textile dyeing/printing auxiliary

montan ester waxes
Production:
• montanic acid + ethylene glycol/1,4-butanediol (esterification)
Uses: thickening/rubproofing/water repellency agent (printing inks)

montanic acid
montan acid wax
Production:
• montan wax + sulphuric acid + sodium dichromate (chromate oxidation)
Derivatives: calcium montanate; glycerol trimontanate; montan ester waxes
Uses: plastics processing lubricant

montan wax
lignite wax; [8002-53-7]
Solid. MP: 82–87°C. Saponification value: 92–112 mg KOH/g. Acid value: 32–48 mg KOH/g. The wax consists of 50% C_{24}–C_{30} esters, 20% C_{24}–C_{30} free fatty acids, 12% resins and 10% asphalt.
Production:
• lignite (solvent extraction)
Derivatives: montanic acid
Uses: polish/carbonpaper ink ingredient; internal polyvinyl chloride/rubber processing lubricant

8-MOP *See:* methoxsalen

Mordant Black 7
16505 (CI)

$C_{16}H_{10}Cl_1N_2Na_1O_6S_1$. M: 416.76.
Production:
• 2-amino-4-chlorophenol-6-sulphonic acid + 1,5-naphthalenediol (diazotisation/azo coupling)
Uses: dye (wool)

Mordant Black 9
16500 (CI)

$C_{16}H_{11}N_2Na_1O_6S_1$. M: 382.32.
Production:
• 2-aminophenol-4-sulphonic acid + 1,5-naphthalenediol (diazotisation/azo coupling)
Uses: dye (wool)

Mordant Black 11
14645 (CI); [1787-61-7]

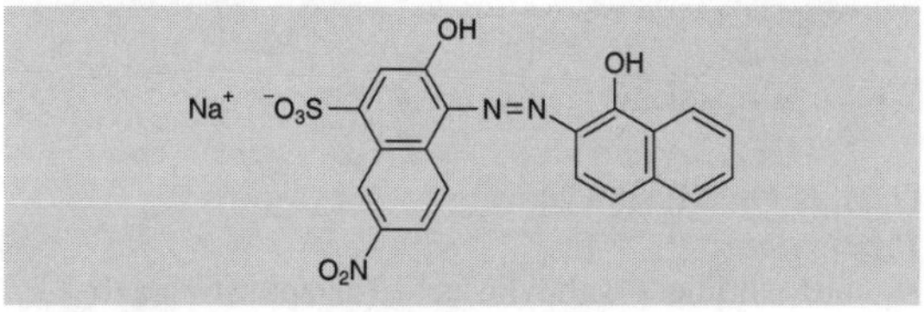

$C_{20}H_{12}N_3Na_1O_7S_1$. M: 461.38.
Production:
- 1-amino-6-nitro-2-naphthol-4-sulphonic acid + α-naphthol (diazotisation/azo coupling)

Uses:
dye (wool, silk, polyamide)

Mordant Black 13
63615 (CI)

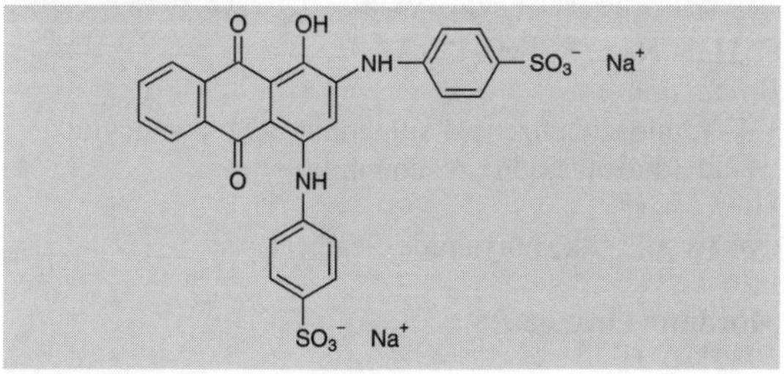

$C_{26}H_{16}N_2Na_2O_9S_2$. M: 610.53.
Production:
- 1-hydroxyanthraquinone + sulphanilic acid (ring bromination/amine formation)

Uses:
dye (wool)

Mordant Black 38
18160 (CI)

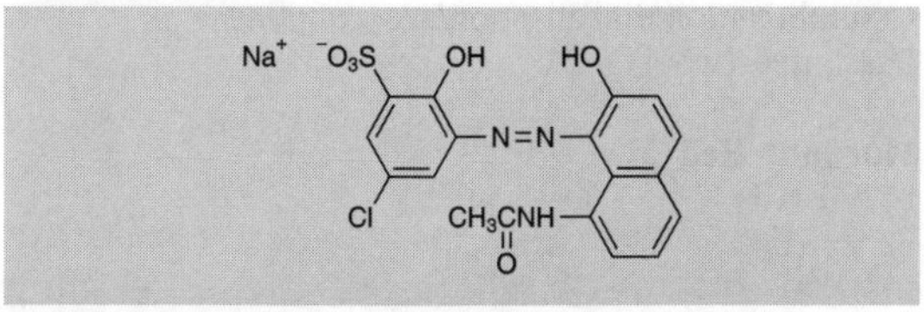

$C_{18}H_{13}Cl_1N_3Na_1O_6S_1$. M: 457.82.
Production:
- 2-amino-4-chlorophenol-6-sulphonic acid + 8-amino-2-naphthol (diazotisation/azo coupling)

Uses:
dye (wool, silk, polyamide)

Mordant Blue 1
43830 (CI)
$C_{23}H_{15}Cl_2Na_2O_6$. M: 504.25.
Production:
- o-cresotic acid + 2,6-dichlorobenzaldehyde (carbonyl condensation/oxidation)

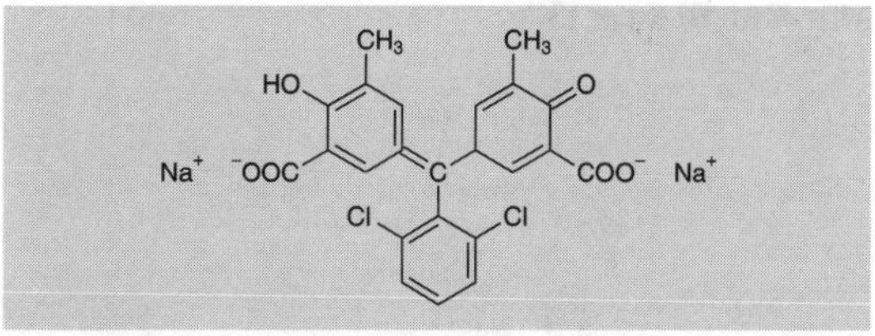

Uses: dye (wool, silk, polyamide, leather); pigments intermediate

Mordant Blue 3
43820 (CI)

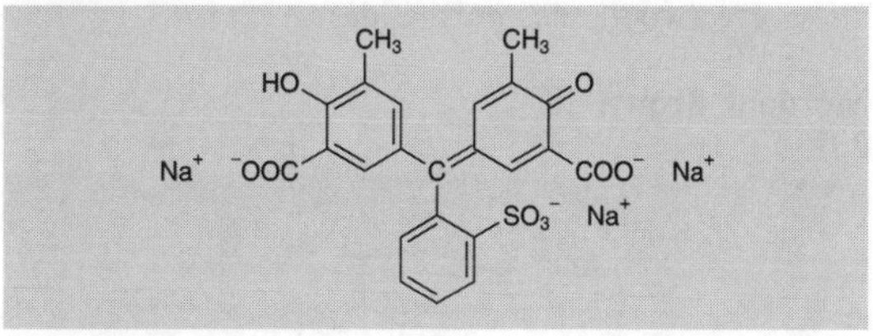

$C_{23}H_{16}Na_3O_9S_1$. M: 537.40.
Production:
- o-cresotic acid + benzaldehyde-2-sulphonic acid (condensation)

Uses: dye (wool)

Mordant Blue 13
16680 (CI)

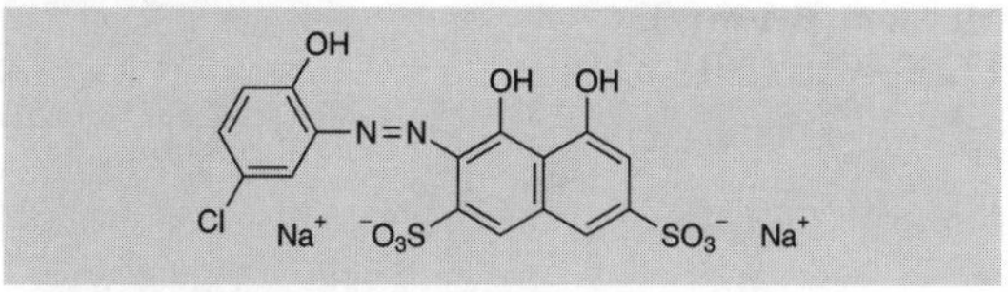

$C_{16}H_9Cl_1N_2Na_2O_9S_2$. M: 518.81.
Production:
- 2-amino-4-chlorophenol + chromotropic acid (diazotisation/azo coupling)

Uses: dye (wool)

Mordant Blue 79 *See:* Acid Red 14

Mordant Brown 1
20110 (CI); [3564-15-6]

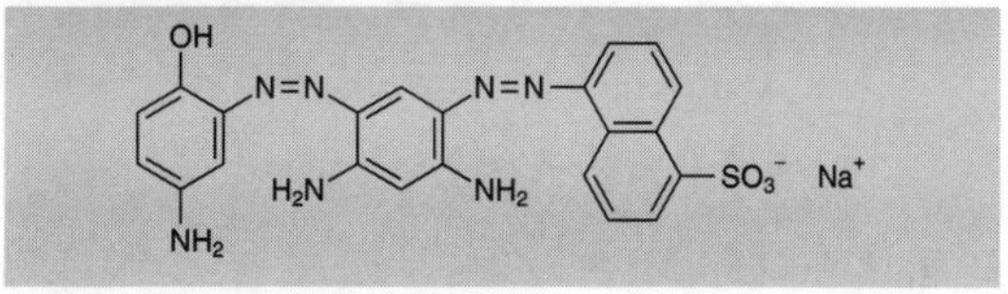

$C_{22}H_{18}N_7Na_1O_4S_1$. M: 499.48.
Production:
- 2-amino-4-nitrophenol + 1-naphthylamine-5-sulphonic acid + m-phenylenediamine (diazotisation/azo coupling/diazotisation/azo coupling)

Uses: dye (wool, silk, polyamide, leather)

Mordant Brown 13
13225 (CI)

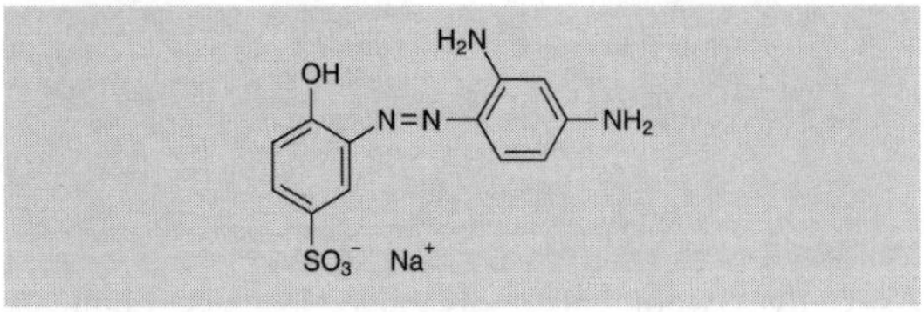

$C_{12}H_{11}N_4Na_1O_4S_1$. M: 330.30.
Production:
• 2-aminophenol-4-sulphonic acid + *m*-phenylene-diamine (diazotisation/azo coupling)
Uses: dye (wool, silk, polyamide)

Mordant Brown 18
20150 (CI)

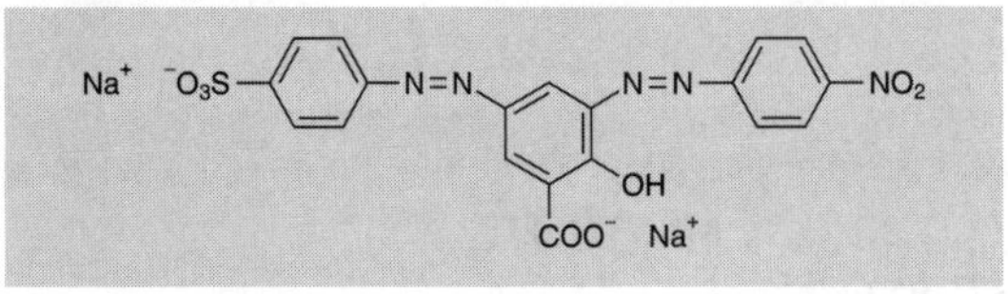

$C_{19}H_{11}N_5Na_2O_8S_1$. M: 515.37.
Production:
• *p*-nitroaniline + sulphanilic acid + salicylic acid (diazotisation/azo coupling/diazotisation/azo coupling)
Uses: dye (wool, polyamide)

Mordant Brown 33
13250 (CI); [3618-62-0]

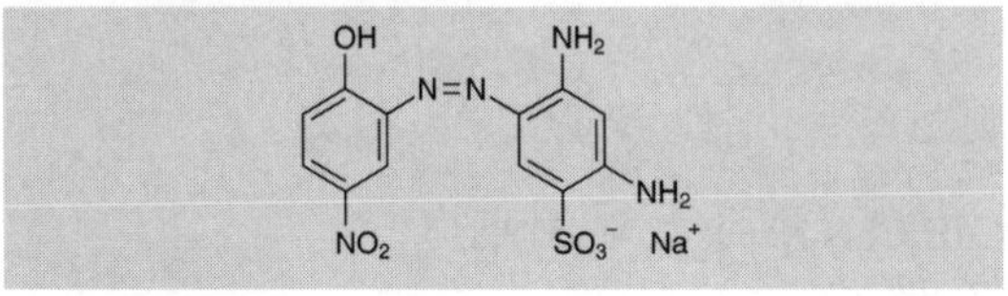

$C_{12}H_{10}N_5Na_1O_6S_1$. M: 375.29.
Production:
• 2-amino-4-nitrophenol + 2,4-diaminobenzene-sulphonic acid (diazotisation/azo coupling)
Uses: dye (wool)

Mordant Brown 40
17590 (CI)

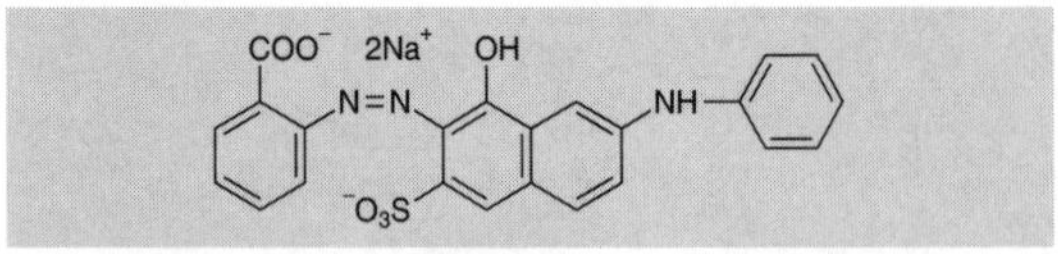

$C_{23}H_{15}N_3Na_2O_6S_1$. M: 507.42.
Production:
• anthranilic acid + *N*-phenylgamma acid (diazotisation/azo coupling)
Uses: dye (wool, polyamide)

Mordant Green 11 *See:* Acid Green 19

Mordant Orange 1
14030 (CI); [2243-76-7]

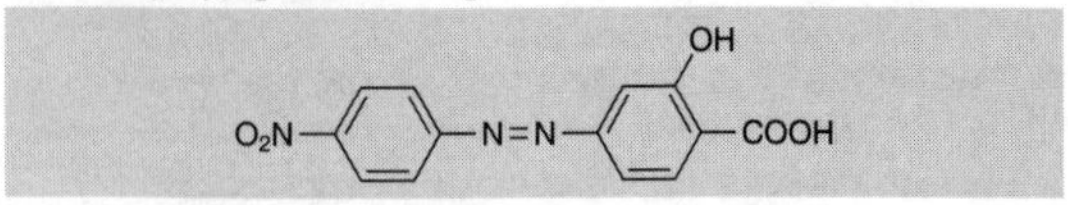

$C_{13}H_{11}N_3O_5$. M: 289.24.
Production:
• *p*-nitroaniline + salicylic acid (diazotisation/azo coupling)
Uses:
dye (wool, silk, polyamide, leather, paper)

Mordant Orange 6
26520 (CI); [3564-27-0]

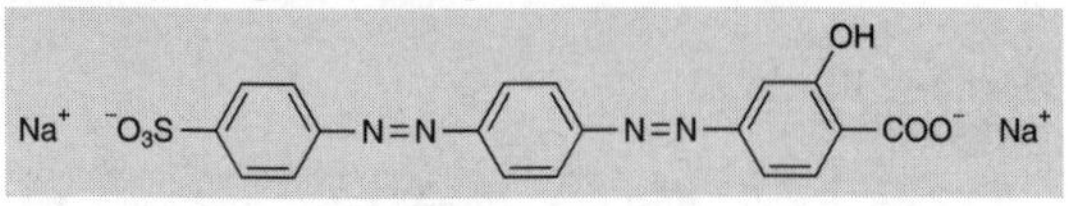

$C_{19}H_{12}N_4Na_2O_6S_1$. M: 470.37.
Production:
• 4′-aminoazobenzene-4-sulphonic acid + salicylic acid (diazotisation/azo coupling)
Uses:
dye (wool, silk, polyamide, leather)

Mordant Orange 26
19325 (CI)

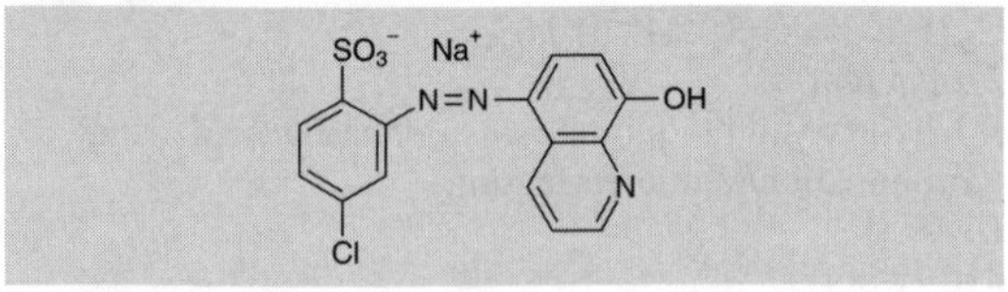

$C_{15}H_9Cl_1N_3Na_1O_4S_1$. M: 385.76.
Production:
• *m*-chloroaniline + 8-hydroxyquinoline (sulphonation/diazotisation/azo coupling)
Uses: dye (wool)

Mordant Red 5
14290 (CI)

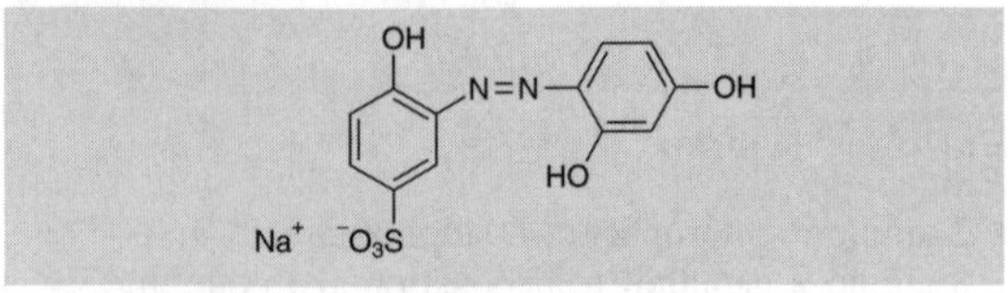

$C_{12}H_9N_2Na_1O_6S_1$. M: 332.25.
Production:
• 2-aminophenol-4-sulphonic acid + resorcinol (diazotisation/azo coupling)
Uses: dye (wool)

Mordant Red 7
18760 (CI)
$C_{20}H_{15}N_4Na_1O_5S_1$. M: 446.41.

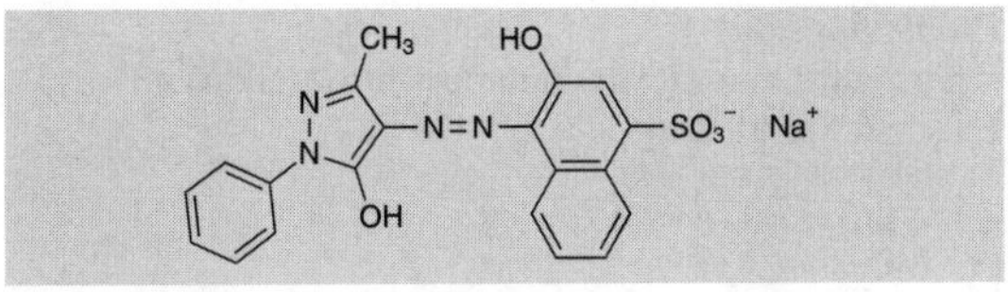

Production:
• 1-amino-2-naphthol-4-sulphonic acid + 3-methyl-1-phenyl-5-pyrazolone (diazotisation/azo coupling)
Uses:
dye (wool, silk, polyamide, leather)

Mordant Red 9
Pigment Red 60 (CI, barium salt); 16105 (CI); 16105:1 (barium salt)

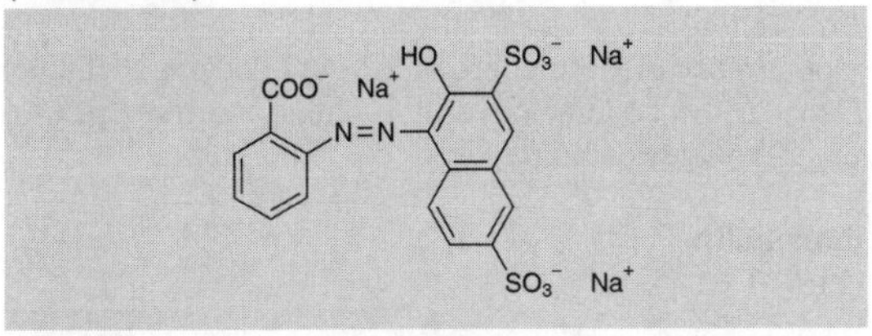

$C_{17}H_9N_2Na_3O_9S_2$. M: 518.36.
Production:
• anthranilic acid + R acid (diazotisation/azo coupling)
Uses:
dye (wool)

Mordant Red 11 *See:* alizarin

Mordant Red 15
45305 (CI)

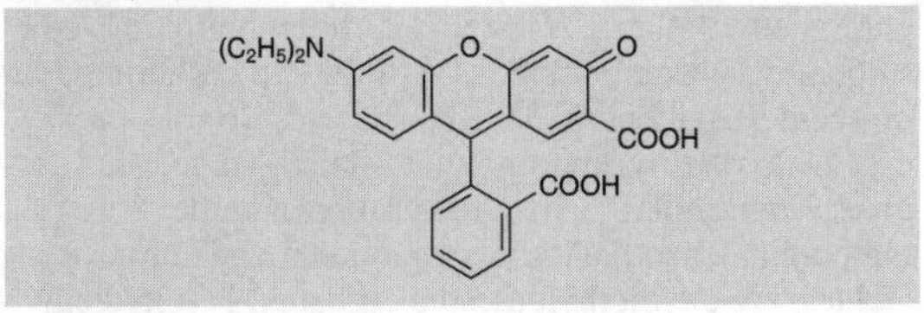

$C_{25}H_{21}N_1O_6$. M: 431.44.
Production:
• *m*-diethylaminophenol + phthalic anhydride + 2,4-dihydroxybenzoic acid (condensation/condensation)
Uses: dye (wool)

Mordant Red 19
18735 (CI); [1934-24-3]

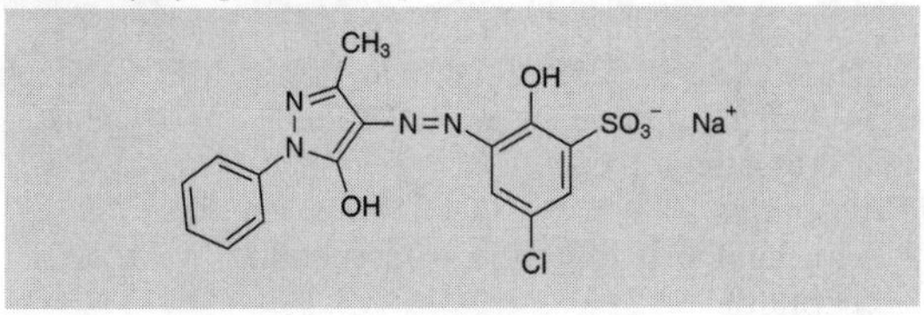

$C_{16}H_{12}Cl_1N_4Na_1O_5S_1$. M: 430.81.

Production:
• 2-amino-4-chlorophenol-6-sulphonic acid + 3-methyl-1-phenyl-5-pyrazolone (diazotisation/azo coupling)
Uses: dye (wool, silk, polyamide, leather)

Mordant Violet 5
15670 (CI)

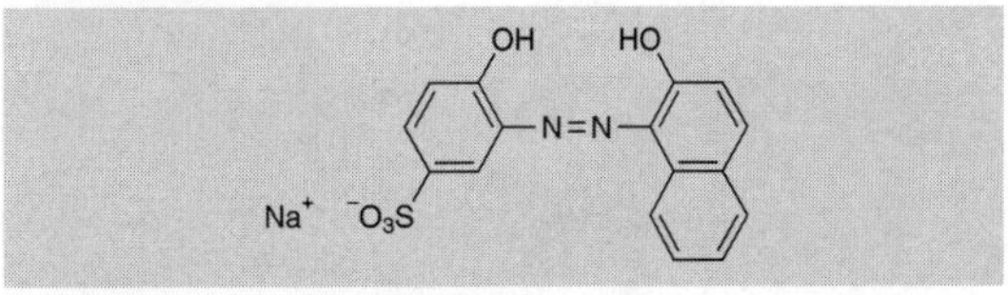

$C_{16}H_{11}N_2Na_1O_5S_1$. M: 366.32.
Production:
• 2-aminophenol-4-sulphonic acid + β-naphthol (diazotisation/azo coupling)
Uses: dye (wool, silk, polyamide, leather)

Mordant Violet 15
43560 (CI)

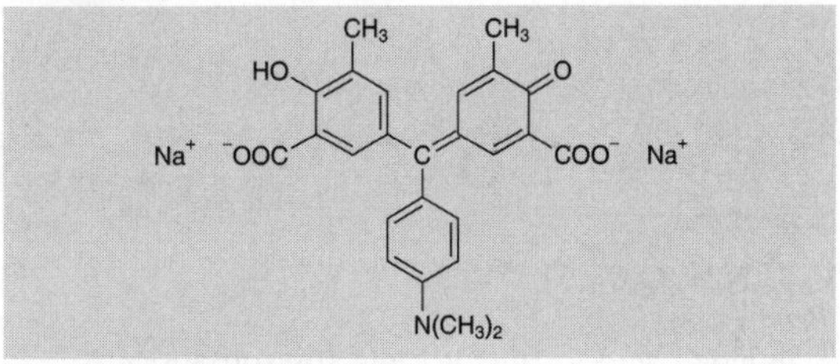

$C_{25}H_{22}N_1Na_2O_6$. M: 478.43.
Production:
• *o*-cresotic acid + *p*-dimethylaminobenzaldehyde (carbonyl condensation/oxidation)
Uses: dye (wool, silk, polyamide, cotton)

Mordant Yellow 1
14025 (CI); [584-42-9]

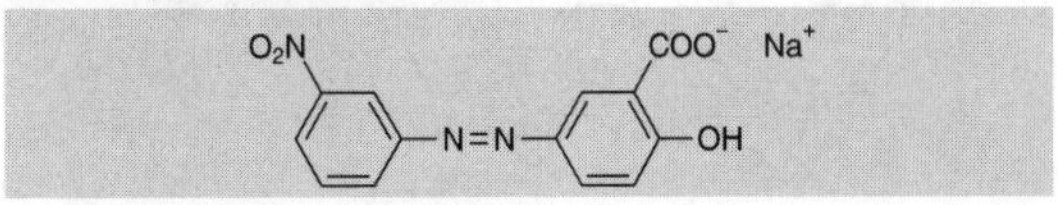

$C_{13}H_8N_3Na_1O_5$. M: 309.20.
Production:
• *m*-nitroaniline + salicylic acid (diazotisation/azo coupling)
Uses: dye (wool, silk, polyamide, cotton, leather)

Mordant Yellow 3
14095 (CI)

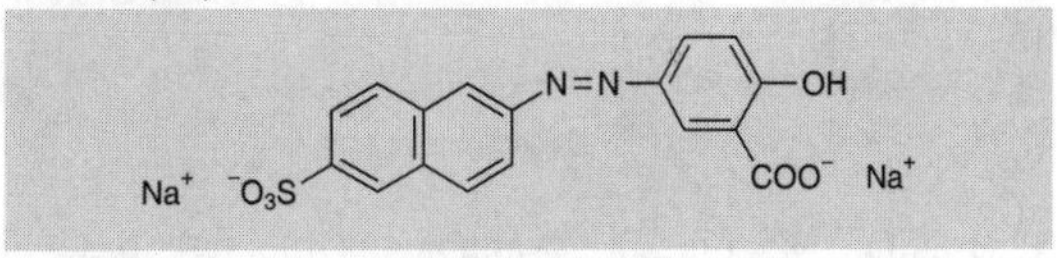

$C_{17}H_{10}N_2Na_2O_6S_1$. M: 416.31.

Production:
- Broenner's acid + salicylic acid (diazotisation/azo coupling)

Uses: dye (wool)

Mordant Yellow 8
18821 (CI)

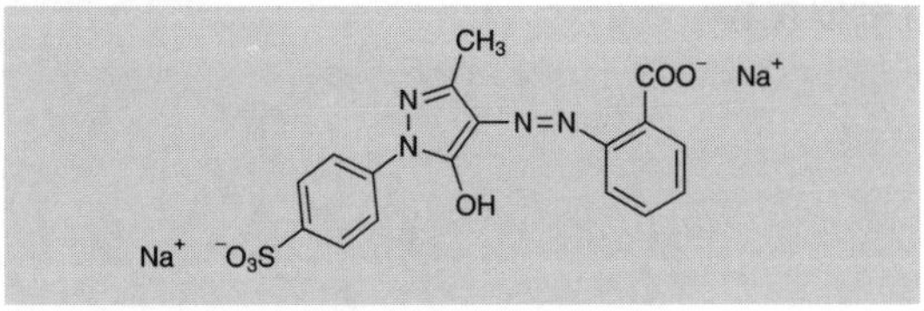

$C_{17}H_{12}N_4Na_2O_6S_1$. M: 446.35.
Production:
- anthranilic acid + 1-(4′-sulphophenyl)-3-methyl-pyrazolone (diazotisation/azo coupling)

Uses: dye (wool, silk, leather)

Mordant Yellow 20
14110 (CI)

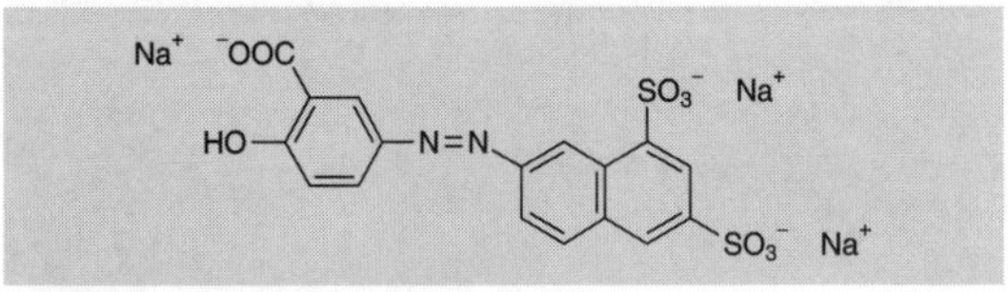

$C_{17}H_9N_2Na_3O_9S_2$. M: 518.36.
Production:
- amino-G acid + salicylic acid (diazotisation/azo coupling)

Uses:
dye (wool, leather)

Mordant Yellow 26
22880 (CI)

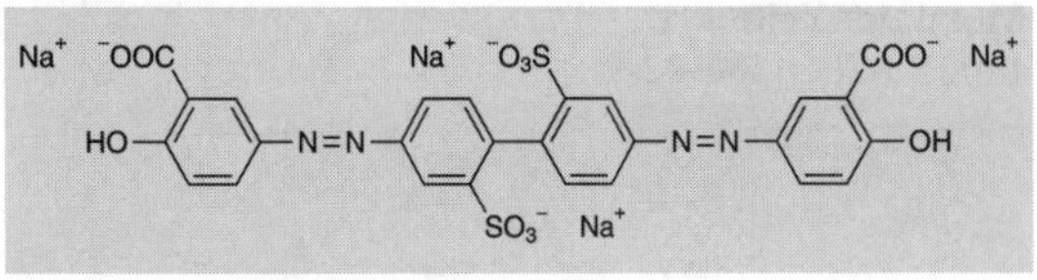

$C_{26}H_{14}N_4Na_4O_{12}S_2$. M: 730.51.
Production:
- benzidine-2,2′-disulphonic acid + salicylic acid (diazotisation/azo coupling)

Uses:
dye (wool, silk, polyamide, cotton, leather)

moroxydine
[3731-59-7]

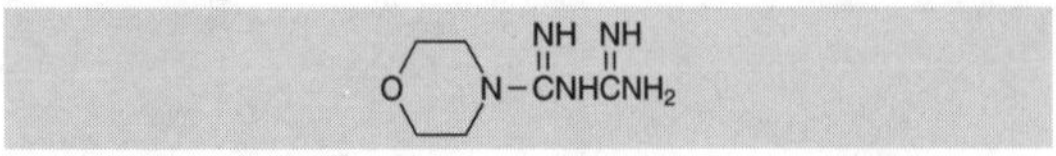

$C_6H_{13}N_5O_1$. M: 171.20. Available as the free base or hydrochloride.

Production:
- morpholine + dicyandiamide (nitrile addition)

Uses: antiviral drug

morphine
[57-27-2]

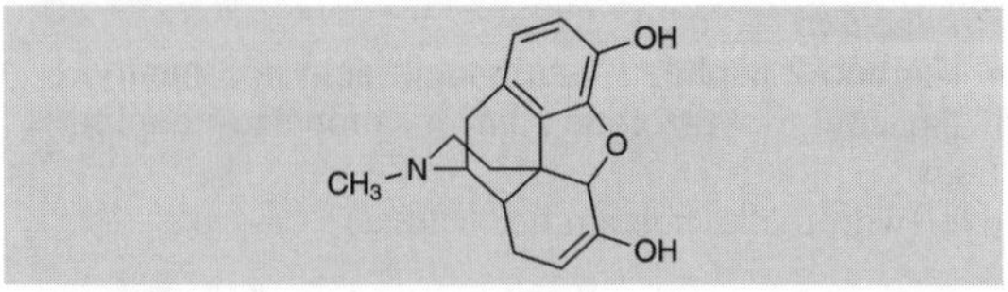

$C_{17}H_{19}N_1O_3$. M: 285.35. Available commercially as the free base monohydrate, acetate trihydrate, tartrate tetrahydrate, various phosphate and other derivatives.
Production:
- opium (extraction; coproduced with codeine/thebaine)

Derivatives: codeine; hydromorphone; normorphine
Uses: analgesic drug

morpholine
[110-91-8]

$C_4H_9N_1O_1$. M: 87.12. Colourless liquid with an amine-like odour. BP: 127–130°C. FP: -5°C. d: 1.00 kg/l (20°C). Soluble in water.
Production:
- diethylene glycol + ammonia (amine formation)
- diethanolamine (dehydration)

Derivatives: N-(3-aminopropyl)morpholine; bis(2-morpholinoethyl)ether; N-cetyl ethylmorpholinium ethosulphate; dextromoramide; 4,4′-dithiodimorpholine; Fluorescent Brightener 103; Fluorescent Brightener DM; 4-(2-hydroxyethyl)morpholine; molsidomine; moroxydine; 2-morpholinobenzothiazylsulphenamide; 2-morpholinodithiobenzothiazole; morpholinomethylnitropropane adduct; N-oxydiethylenedithiocarbamyl-N′-oxydiethylenesulphenamide; timolol
Uses: corrosion inhibitor (boilers, steam distribution systems); solubiliser (water-based printing inks); solvent

2-morpholinobenzothiazylsulphenamide
benzothiazyl-2-(oxydiethylene)sulphenamide; MBS; 2-(morpholinothio)benzothiazole

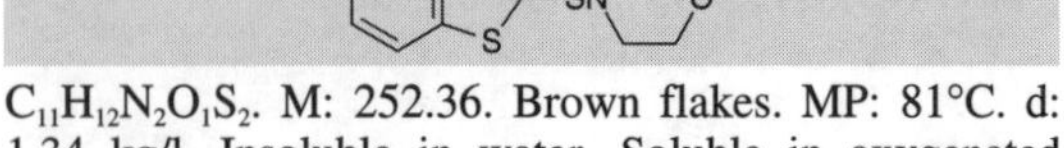

$C_{11}H_{12}N_2O_1S_2$. M: 252.36. Brown flakes. MP: 81°C. d: 1.34 kg/l. Insoluble in water. Soluble in oxygenated and aromatic solvents.
Production:
- 2-mercaptobenzothiazole + morpholine (oxidative coupling)

Uses: vulcanisation accelerator

2-morpholinodithiobenzothiazole
MBSS

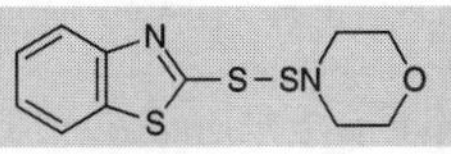

$C_{11}H_{12}N_2O_1S_3$. M: 284.42.
Production:
* 2-mercaptobenzothiazole + morpholine + sulphur monochloride (dehydrochlorination/oxidation/ chlorosulphurisation)
Uses: vulcanisation agent

morpholinomethyl-nitropropane adduct
Bioban P-1487 (Angus Chemical)

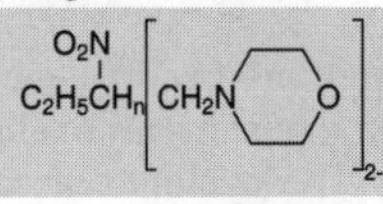

n = 1, 2. Liquid. d: 1.1 kg/l (25°C). Solubility in water: 11 g/l (20°C). Soluble in hydrocarbons.
Production:
* 1-nitropropane + formaldehyde + morpholine (Mannich reaction)
Uses: biocide (metalworking fluids)

2-(morpholinothio)benzothiazole
See: 2-morpholinobenzothiazylsulphenamide

moskene *See:* 4,6-dinitro-1,1,3,3,5-pentamethylindane

MP *See:* propylene glycol monomethyl ether

3MP *See:* 3-methylpiperidine

4MP-1 *See:* 4-methyl-1-pentene

6MP *See:* 6-mercaptopurine

MPA *See:* propylene glycol monomethyl ether acetate

3-MPA *See:* 3-methoxypropylamine

MPD *See:* *m*-phenylenediamine

MPG *See:* propylene glycol; monopotassium glutamate

MPK *See:* methyl propyl ketone

MPTD *See:* *N,N'*-dimethyldiphenylthiuram disulphide

MSA *See:* methanesulphonic acid

MSC *See:* methanesulphonyl chloride

MSG *See:* monosodium glutamate

MSMA *See:* monosodium methylarsonate

MSP *See:* monosodium phosphate

MTAB *See:* myristyltrimethylammonium bromide

MTBE *See:* methyl *t*-butyl ether

MTD *See:* 2,4/2,6-diaminotoluene

MTHPA *See:* methyl tetrahydrophthalic anhydride

MTMC *See:* metolcarb

MTN *See:* *m*-tolunitrile

MTX *See:* methotrexate

mucic acid
galactaric acid; tetrahydroxyadipic acid; [526-99-8]

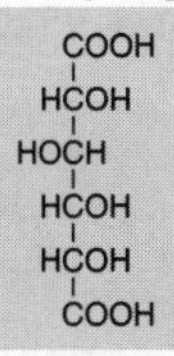

$C_6H_{10}O_8$. M: 210.14. Crystalline powder. Slightly soluble in water.
Production:
* lactose + nitric acid (oxidation)
Uses:
baking/effervescent powder ingredient

mucochloric acid
2,3-dichloro-4-oxo-2-butenoic acid; [87-56-9]

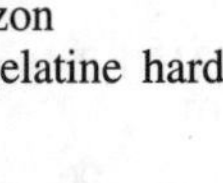

$C_4H_2Cl_2O_3$. M: 168.97. Solid. MP: 125–127°C. Soluble in hot water, oxygenated and chlorinated solvents.
Production:
* 1,4-butynediol + chlorine (addition/alcohol oxidation)
Derivatives:
chloridazon; norflurazon
Uses: photographic gelatine hardening agent

mullite
aluminium silicate, fused
Synthetic aluminosilicate mineral containing 48–70% Al_2O_3.
Production:
* sodium metasilicate + kaolin (calcination)
Uses: refractories raw material (steel/glass/cement furnace linings)

muriatic acid
See: hydrochloric acid

musk ketone
3,5-dinitro-2,6-dimethyl-4-*t*-butylacetophenone;
[81-14-1]

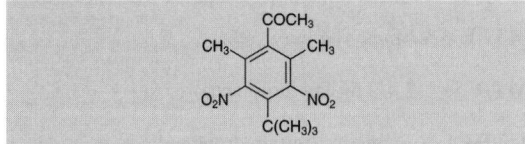

$C_{14}H_{18}N_2O_5$. M: 294.29. Yellow crystals with musk odour. MP: 135°C. Insoluble in water, slightly soluble in alcohol.
Production:
• 5-*t*-butyl-*m*-xylene + acetic anhydride (Friedel-Crafts acylation/nitration)
Uses: perfume fixative

musk xylol
musk xylene; 2,4,6-trinitro-3,5-dimethyl-*t*-butylbenzene;
[81-15-2]

$C_{12}H_{15}N_3O_6$. M: 297.26. Yellow, crystalline solid with musk odour. MP: 113°C. Insoluble in water. Soluble in hot alcohol and ether.
Production:
• 5-*t*-butyl-*m*-xylene (nitration)
Uses: fragrance ingredient (musk substitute)

mustard oil *See:* allyl isothiocyanate

MVE *See:* methyl vinyl ether

MX *See:* *m*-xylene

MXD6 *See:* poly(*m*-xylyleneadipamide)

MXDA *See:* *m*-xylylenediamine

myclobutanil
2-(4-chlorophenyl)-2-(1H-1,2,4-triazol-1-ylmethyl)hex-anenitrile; [88671-89-0]

$C_{15}H_{17}Cl_1N_4$. M: 288.78.
Production:
• α,4-dichloroacetophenone + *n*-butyl chloride + 1,2,4-triazole + hydrogen cyanide (amine formation/Grignard reagent formation/Grignard

reaction/alcohol bromination/cyanidation)
Uses: fungicide

myrcene
2-methyl-6-methylene-2,7-octadiene; 7-methyl-3-methyl-ene-1,6-octadiene; [123-35-3]

$C_{10}H_{16}$. M: 136.24. Liquid with terpene odour. d: 0.79 kg/l (20°C). Insoluble in water. Soluble in oxygenated and chlorinated solvents.
Production:
• β-pinene (thermal rearrangement)
Derivatives:
geraniol-nerol, mixed; myrcenol; 1-methyl-4-(4-methyl-3-penten-1-yl)-3-cyclohexenecarboxaldehyde; 3/4-(4-methyl-3-penten-1-yl)-3-cyclohexenecarboxaldehyde

myrcenol
2-methyl-6-methylene-7-octen-2-ol; [543-39-5]

$C_{10}H_{18}O_1$. M: 154.25. Colourless liquid with a floral odour. BP: 78°C (6.7 kPa). d: 0.87 kg/l (20°C). Insoluble in water. Soluble in alcohol.
Production:
• myrcene (hydrochlorination/hydration)
Derivatives: 3/4-(4-hydroxy-4-methylpentyl)-3-cyclohex-enecarboxaldehyde
Uses: perfume ingredient

myrcia oil *See:* bay oil

myristalkonium chloride
See: myristyldimethylbenzylammonium chloride

myristamine oxide *See:* myristyldimethylamine oxide

myristic acid
tetradecanoic acid; [544-63-8]

$$CH_3(CH_2)_{12}COOH$$

$C_{14}H_{28}O_2$. M: 228.37. White, crystalline solid. The odour should be faint with no rancidity. MP: 54°C. BP: 326°C. d: 0.84 kg/l (80°C). Insoluble in water. Soluble in aromatic and chlorinated solvents. Commercial products contain 91–93% C_{14} or 96–99% C_{14}.
Production:
• lauric acid, broad cut (fractionation; coproduced with lauric acid, narrow cut)
Derivatives:
isopropyl myristate; methyl myristate; myristyl alcohol; myristylamidopropyldimethylamine; *n*-tetradecylamine
Uses: soap/cosmetics ingredient; non-drying oil (amino stoving resins)

myristica oil *See:* nutmeg oil

myristyl alcohol
1-tetradecanol; *n*-tetradecyl alcohol; [112-72-1]

$$CH_3(CH_2)_{13}OH$$

$C_{14}H_{30}O_1$. M: 214.39. White waxy solid. MP: 38°C. d: 0.82 kg/l (4°C). Insoluble in water. Available commercially in broad or narrow cuts. Narrow cuts contain, typically, 98% C_{14}, broad cuts, 62% C_{14}, 36% C_{16}.
Production:
• ethylene (Alfol/Epal processes; coproduced with *n*-hexanol/*n*-octanol/*n*-decanol/*n*-alkanol(C_8-C_{10})/ lauryl alcohol, narrow-cut/*n*-alkanol(C_{12}-C_{14})/cetyl alcohol/stearyl alcohol/*n*-alkanol(C_{12}-C_{18})/cetyl stearyl alcohol/*n*-alkanol(C_{20+}))
• *n*-alkanol(C_{12}-C_{14}) (fractionation; coproduced with lauryl alcohol, narrow-cut)
• myristic acid (hydrogenation)
Derivatives: dimethylmyristylamine; dimyristyl thiodipropionate; myristyl bromide; myristyl chloride; myristyl lactate; myristyl myristate

myristylamidopropyldimethylamine

$$CH_3(CH_2)_{14}\overset{O}{\overset{\|}{C}}NHCH_2CH_2CH_2N(CH_3)_2$$

$C_{21}H_{44}N_2O_1$. M: 340.59.
Production:
• myristic acid + 3-dimethylaminopropylamine (amide formation)
Uses: cationic emulsifier (cosmetics, toiletries); softening agent (textile finishes)

myristylamine *See:* *n*-tetradecylamine

myristyl bromide
1-bromotetradecane; *n*-tetradecyl bromide; [112-71-0]

$$CH_3(CH_2)_{13}Br$$

$C_{14}H_{29}Br_1$. M: 277.28. Liquid. BP: 181°C (2.1 kPa). MP: 6°C. d: 1.01 kg/l (25°C). Insoluble in water. Soluble in oxygenated and aromatic solvents.
Production:
• myristyl alcohol + hydrogen bromide, anhydrous (alcohol bromination)
Derivatives:
myristyltrimethylammonium bromide

myristyl chloride
1-chlorotetradecane; *n*-tetradecyl chloride; [2425-54-9]

$$CH_3(CH_2)_{13}Cl$$

$C_{14}H_{29}Cl_1$. M: 232.83. Colourless liquid. MP: 0°C. d: 0.86 kg/l (20°C). Insoluble in water. A typical chain-length distribution is: >95% C_{14} (narrow cut) or 40% C_{12}, 50% C_{14}, 10% C_{16} (wide cut).

Production:
• myristyl alcohol (alcohol chlorination)
Derivatives: myristyldimethylbenzylammonium chloride

myristyldimethylamine *See:* dimethylmyristylamine

myristyldimethylamine oxide
myristamine oxide (CTFA)

$$CH_3(CH_2)_n\overset{CH_3}{\underset{CH_3}{N}}\!\rightarrow\!O$$

n = 11, 13, 15. $C_{16}H_{35}N_1O_1$. M: 257.47. Liquid. Available commercially as a 25–30% solution in water. d: 0.96 kg/l (25°C).
Production:
• dimethylmyristylamine + hydrogen peroxide (oxidation)
Uses: foam stabiliser (dishwashing liquids)

myristyldimethylammonium-3-sulphopropylbetaine
Ralufon DM (Raschig)

$$CH_3(CH_2)_{13}\overset{CH_3}{\underset{CH_3}{N}}CH_2CH_2CH_2SO_3^{-}$$

$C_{19}H_{41}N_1O_3S_1$. M: 363.61.
Production:
• dimethylmyristylamine + propane sultone (quaternisation)
Uses: amphoteric surfactant (shampoos/detergents)

myristyldimethylbenzylammonium chloride
dimethylmyristylbenzylammonium chloride; myristalkonium chloride; tetradecyldimethylbenzylammonium chloride; [139-08-2]

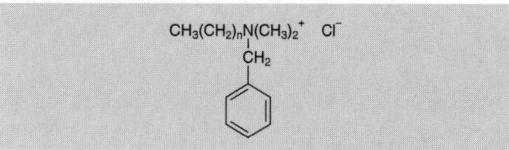

n = 11, 13, 15. $C_{23}H_{42}Cl_1N_1$. M: 368.05. White, crystalline powder or a solution containing 50–80% active matter in water.
Production:
• dimethylmyristylamine + benzyl chloride (quaternisation)
• myristyl chloride + benzyldimethylamine (quaternisation)
Uses: biocide (cooling water systems, swimming pools, disinfectant cleaners, sanitisers, deodorant blocks)

myristyl lactate
$C_{17}H_{34}O_3$. M: 286.46. Pale yellow liquid.
Production:
• myristyl alcohol + DL-lactic acid (esterification)

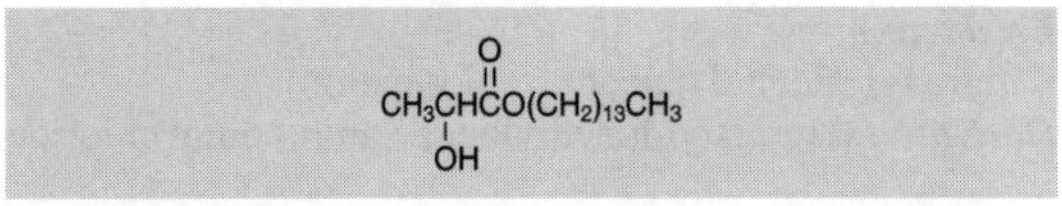

$$CH_3CHCO(CH_2)_{13}CH_3$$
$$|$$
$$OH$$

Uses: wetting agent (cosmetics, skin products)

myristyl myristate
[3234-85-3]

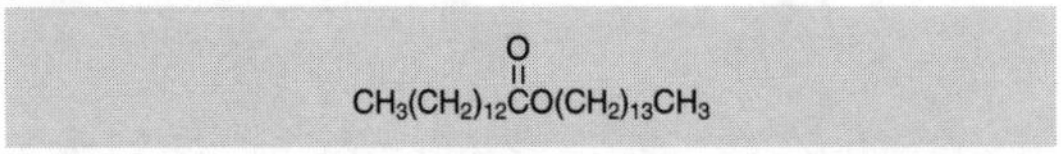

$$CH_3(CH_2)_{12}CO(CH_2)_{13}CH_3$$

$C_{28}H_{56}O_2$. M: 424.76. White, waxy solid. MP: 37–40°C.
Production:
• myristyl alcohol + methyl myristate (esterification)
Uses: emollient/lubricant (cosmetics, toiletries)

myristyltrimethylammonium bromide
myrtrimonium bromide (CTFA); tetradecyltrimethylam-
monium bromide; trimethylmyristylammonium bromide;
MTAB; TTAB

$$CH_3(CH_2)_{13}N(CH_3)_3^+ \quad Br^-$$

$C_{17}H_{38}Br_1N_1$. M: 336.40.
Production:
• dimethylmyristylamine + methyl bromide
  (quaternisation)
• trimethylamine + myristyl bromide (quaternisation)
Uses: biocide (cosmetics, toiletries); medical antiseptic

nabam

disodium 1,2-ethanebis(carbamodithioate); disodium ethylenebis(dithiocarbamate); [142-59-6]

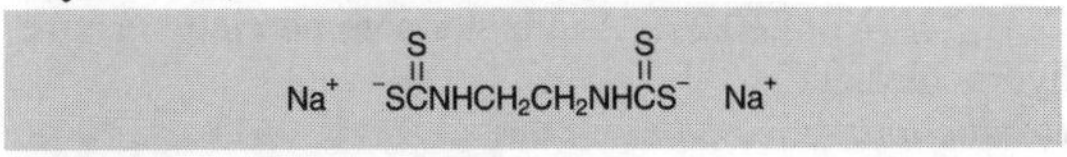

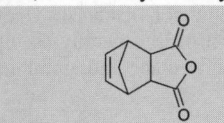

$C_4H_6N_2Na_2S_4$. M: 256.34.
Production:
• ethylenediamine + carbon disulphide + sodium hydroxide (thiocarbonylation/salt formation)
Derivatives: mancozeb; maneb; zineb
Uses: algicide/fungicide; biocide (paper production)

NaDCC *See:* sodium dichloroisocyanurate

NADEC *See:* sodium diethyldithiocarbamate

nadic anhydride

5-norbornene-2,3-dicarboxylic anhydride; [129-64-6]

$C_9H_8O_3$. M: 164.16. Crystalline solid. Soluble in oxygenated, chlorinated and aromatic solvents. Hydrolysed by water to the dicarboxylic acid.
Production:
• dicyclopentadiene + maleic anhydride (Diels-Alder cycloaddition)
Derivatives: bismaleimide prepolymers; ethylene bis-(5,6-dibromonorbornane-2,3-dicarboximide)
Uses:
heat-resistant unsaturated polyester resin comonomer

nadolol

[42200-33-9]

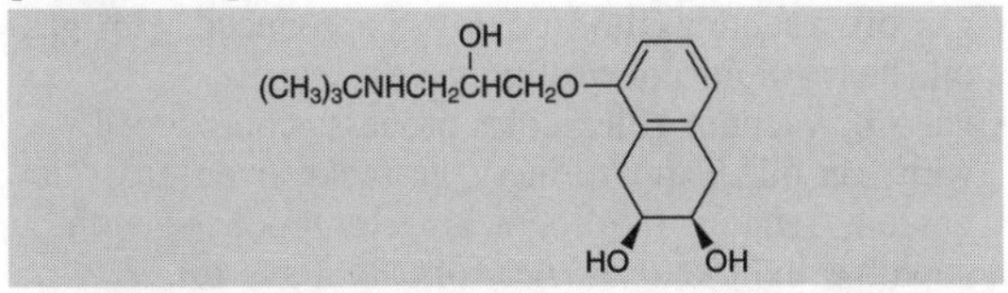

$C_{17}H_{27}N_1O_4$. M: 309.42.
Production:
• α-naphthol + epichlorohydrin + *t*-butylamine (Birch reduction/oxidation/epoxidation/amine formation)
Uses: antianginal/antihypertensive drug

Nafion *See:* tetrafluoroethylene-perfluoro(vinyl ether sulphonate) copolymers

nafronyl *See:* naftidrofuryl

naftidrofuryl

nafronyl; [31329-57-4]

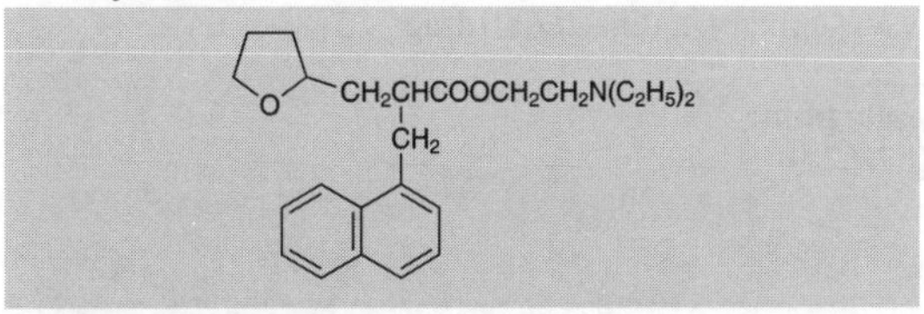

$C_{24}H_{33}N_1O_3$. M: 383.53.
Production:
• diethyl malonate + 1-chloromethylnaphthalene + furfuryl alcohol + 2-diethylaminoethyl chloride hydrochloride (alcohol chlorination/dehydro-chlorination/hydrogenation/dehydrochlorination/decarboxylation/esterification)
Uses: vasodilator drug

naftifine

[65472-88-0]

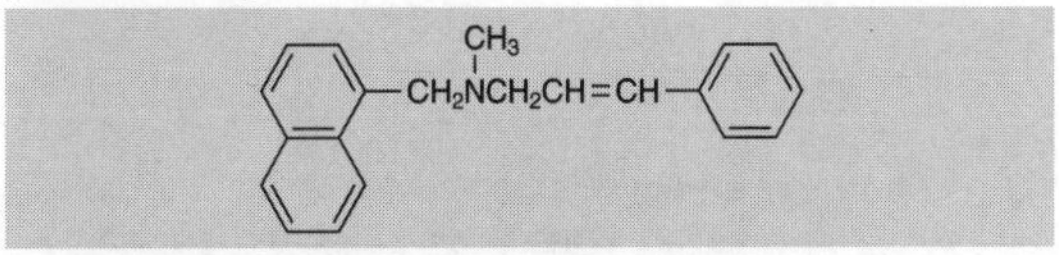

$C_{21}H_{21}N_1$. M: 287.41. The commercial product is the *trans*-isomer. Available commercially as the free base or hydrochloride.
Production:
• 1-chloromethylnaphthalene + methylamine + cinnamyl alcohol (amine formation/amine formation)
Uses: antifungal drug

naled

1,2-dibromo-2,2-dichloroethyl dimethyl phosphate; [300-76-5]

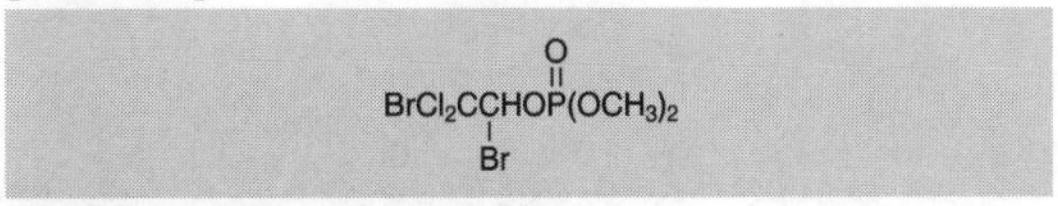

$C_4H_7Br_2Cl_2O_4P_1$. M: 380.79.
Production:
• dichlorvos + bromine (addition)
Uses: insecticide/acaricide

nalidixic acid

1-ethyl-7-methyl-1,8-naphthyridin-4-one-3-carboxylic acid; [389-08-2]
$C_{12}H_{12}N_2O_3$. M: 232.24.
Production:
• 2-amino-6-methylpyridine + diethyl ethoxy-methylenemalonate + ethyl iodide (condensation/saponification/ethylation)

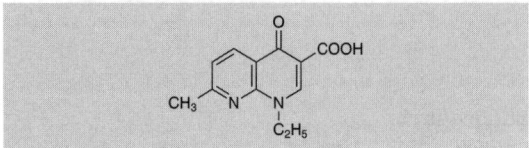

Uses: urinary antibacterial drug

nalorphine
[62-67-9]

$C_{19}H_{21}N_1O_3$. M: 311.39. Available commercially as the hydrobromide or hydrochloride.
Production:
• normorphine + allyl bromide (amine formation)
Uses: morphine antagonist drug

naloxone
[465-65-6]

$C_{19}H_{21}N_1O_4$. M: 327.39. Available commercially as the free base or as the hydrochloride salt.
Production:
• normorphine + allyl chloride (oxidation/hydrogenation/amine formation)
Uses:
morphine antagonist drug

naltrexone
[16590-41-3]

$C_{20}H_{23}N_1O_4$. M: 341.41. Available commercially as the free base or as the hydrochloride salt.
Production:
• normorphine + cyclopropylmethyl bromide (oxidation/hydrogenation/amide formation)
Uses:
morphine antagonist drug

NaMBT *See:* sodium 2-mercaptobenzothiazole

nandrolone *See:* 19-nortestosterone

naphazoline
[835-31-4]

$C_{14}H_{14}N_2$. M: 210.27. Available commercially as the hydrochloride.
Production:
• naphthylacetonitrile + ethylenediamine (condensation)
Uses: vasoconstrictor drug

naphtha, coal-derived *See:* carbolic oil

naphtha, heavy
benzin; benzine; [8030-30-6]
Liquid. BP: 85–150°C. d: 0.77 kg/l (15°C). The chemical composition is essentially mixed C_7–C_9 hydrocarbons, the isomer content of which varies with the source of the crude oil. Naphtha from synthetic sources is relatively paraffinic and usually unsaturated. Straight-run gasoline from the Synthol Fischer-Tropsch process has a 65% olefin content, for instance. Heavy naphtha intended for use in petrol is generally desulphurised by hydrotreatment and its octane rating improved by reforming.
Production:
• crude oil (atmospheric distillation; coproduced with naphtha, light/kerosene/gas oil, light/gas oil, heavy/long residue/refinery gas)
• long residue (thermal cracking; coproduced with gas oil, light/gas oil, heavy/refinery gas)
• long residue (visbreaking; coproduced with refinery gas/gas oil, heavy)
• heavy cycle oil/pyrolysis tar/coal tar pitch (delayed coking process; coproduced with gas oil, light/gas oil, heavy/needle coke/refinery gas)
• short residue (delayed coking process; coproduced with gas oil, light/gas oil, heavy/sponge coke, green/shot coke/refinery gas)
• gas oil, vacuum (fluid coking; coproduced with gas oil, heavy/fluid coke/refinery gas)
• gas oil, vacuum (Flexicoke process; coproduced with gas oil, heavy/refinery gas/coke oven gas)
• gas oil, vacuum (hydrocracking; coproduced with naphtha, light/kerosene/gas oil, light/gas oil, heavy/refinery gas)
• lubricant oils, distillates (hydrocracking; byproduct of lubricant oils, hydrocracked/brightstock production)
• synthesis gas (Synthol Fischer-Tropsch process; coproduced with naphtha, light, Synthol/gas oil, light/wax, Fischer-Tropsch/oxygenates, Fischer-Tropsch, mixed/refinery gas)
• synthesis gas (Arge Fischer-Tropsch process; coproduced with gas oil, light, Arge/wax, Fischer-

Tropsch/oxygenates, Fischer-Tropsch, mixed/ refinery gas)
- methanol (Mobil MTG process; coproduced with naphtha, light/gas oil, light/refinery gas)
- synthesis gas (Shell MDS process; coproduced with kerosene/gas oil, light/wax, Fischer-Tropsch/refinery gas)

Derivatives: acetic acid; acetone; acetylene; C_4-stream, steam-cracked; ethylene; formic acid; gasoline, pyrolysis; methyl ethyl ketone; propionic acid; propylene; pyrolysis tar; refinery gas; reformate; special boiling-point solvents; synthesis gas; white spirit
Uses: petrol/aviation gasoline blending component

naphtha, light
gasoline, straight-run
Liquid. BP: 30–90°C. d: 0.68 kg/l (15°C). The chemical composition is essentially mixed C_5 and C_6 hydrocarbons, the isomer content of which varies with the source of the crude oil. The product is usually desulphurised by caustic washing before use.
Production:
- crude oil (atmospheric distillation; coproduced with naphtha, heavy/kerosene/gas oil, light/gas oil, heavy/long residue/refinery gas)
- gas oil, vacuum (hydrocracking; coproduced with naphtha, heavy/kerosene/gas oil, light/gas oil, heavy/refinery gas)
- lubricant oils, refined (catalytic dewaxing process; byproduct of lubricant oils, base production)
- methanol (Mobil MTG process; coproduced with naphtha, heavy/gas oil, light/refinery gas)

Derivatives: petroleum ether
Uses: petrol blending component

naphtha, light, Synthol
Highly linear, olefinic, C_5–C_6 hydrocarbon stream.
Production:
- synthesis gas (Synthol Fischer-Tropsch process; coproduced with naphtha, heavy/gas oil, light/wax, Fischer-Tropsch/oxygenates, Fischer-Tropsch, mixed/refinery gas)

Derivatives: 1-hexene; 1-pentene

naphtha, VM+P *See:* white spirit

1-naphthaldehyde
[66-77-3]

$C_{11}H_8O_1$. M: 156.18.
Production:
- α-methylnaphthalene (side-chain oxidation)
Uses: dyestuffs intermediate

naphthalene
[91-20-3]

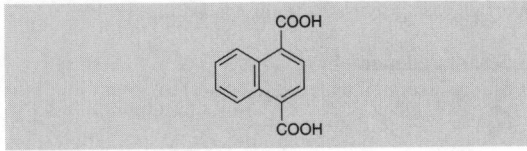

$C_{10}H_8$. M: 128.17. White flakes or balls. MP: 79–80°C. Sublimes. BP: 218°C. d: 1.16 kg/l (20°C). Commercial products range from technical grade (MP: 76°C) to refined grade (MP: 80°C). Insoluble in water. Soluble in oxygenated and aromatic solvents.
Production:
- naphthalene fraction (crystallisation/separation)
Derivatives:
decahydronaphthalene; dibenzopyrenequinone; diisopropylnaphthalene; 1,5/1,8-dinitronaphthalene; dinonylnaphthalene; methyl β-naphthyl ketone; naphthalene-2,7-disulphonic acid; naphthalene-1-sulphonic acid; naphthalene-2-sulphonic acid; α-naphthol; naphthoquinone; 1-naphthylamine; perfluorodecalin; phthalic anhydride; sodium dinaphthalenemethane sulphonate; sodium polynaphthalenemethane sulphonate; tetralin
Uses: moth repellant

α-naphthaleneacetic acid *See:* 1-naphthylacetic acid

α-naphthaleneacetonitrile *See:* naphthylacetonitrile

naphthalene-1-carboxylic acid *See:* α-naphthoic acid

naphthalene-1,4-dicarboxylic acid
[605-70-9]

$C_{12}H_8O_4$. M: 216.19.
Production:
- pyrene (ring bromination/oxidation/side-chain oxidation; byproduct of naphthalene-1,4,5,8-tetracarboxylic acid production)
Derivatives:
1,4-bis(benzoxazol-2-yl)naphthalene

naphthalene-2,6-dicarboxylic acid
2,6-NDA

$C_{12}H_8O_4$. M: 216.19. Needles. MP: >300°C.
Production:
- dimethylnaphthalene fraction (side-chain oxidation)
Derivatives:
dimethyl naphthalene-2,6-dicarboxylate; polyarylate, liquid-crystalline

1,5-naphthalene diisocyanate
NDI

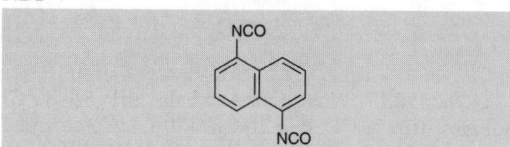

$C_{12}H_6N_2O_2$. M: 210.19. White to yellow flakes. MP: 129–131°C. BP: 263°C. Hydrolysed by water. Flash point: 155°C (COC).
Production:
• 1,5-diaminonaphthalene + phosgene (phosgenation)
Derivatives: naphthalene diisocyanate prepolymer

naphthalene diisocyanate prepolymer
NDI prepolymer

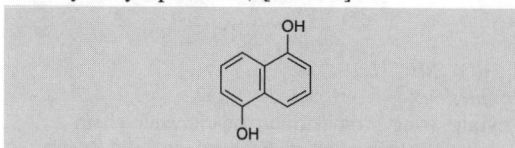

R = polyester polyol group. The product has a limited storage life and is therefore made on site immediately prior to use.
Production:
• 1,5-naphthalene diisocyanate + polyester polyols, linear/poly(ethylene-adipate)/polycaprolactone diols (isocyanate addition)
Derivatives: polyurethane, cast elastomers

1,5-naphthalenediol
1,5-dihydroxynaphthalene; [83-56-7]

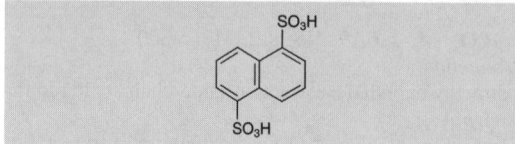

$C_{10}H_8O_2$. M: 160.17. Solid. MP: 259–261°C with decomposition. Slightly soluble in water. Soluble in oxygenated solvents.
Production:
• naphthalene-1,5-disulphonic acid (alkali fusion)
Derivatives: Mordant Black 7; Mordant Black 9

naphthalene-1,5-disulphonic acid
Armstrong's acid; [81-04-9]

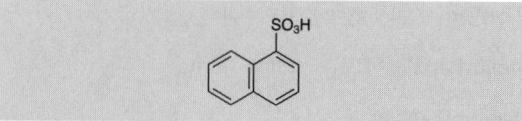

$C_{10}H_8O_6S_2$. M: 288.29.

Production:
• naphthalene-1-sulphonic acid (sulphonation)
Derivatives: 1,5-naphthalenediol; 2-naphthylamine-4,8-disulphonic acid

naphthalene-2,7-disulphonic acid
[92-41-1]

$C_{10}H_8O_6S_2$. M: 288.29. White, crystalline solid. MP: 119°C. Soluble in water and alcohol.
Production:
• naphthalene (sulphonation)
Derivatives:
Acid Green 16; naphthalene-1,3,6-trisulphonic acid

naphthalene-formaldehyde sulphonate dimer
See: sodium dinaphthalenemethane sulphonate

naphthalene fraction
middle oil; naphthalene oil
Mixed aromatic hydrocarbon stream containing naphthalene. BR: 210–230°C. Naphthalene oil from coal tar has a 85–90% naphthalene content. The naphthalene content directly affects the crystallisation point of the oil which varies from 77–79°C for technical oil to 80°C for refined naphthalene.
Production:
• coal tar, crude (alkali extraction/fractionation; coproduced with tar acid liquor/light oil/carbolic oil/creosote oil/fluorene oil/anthracene oil/coal tar pitch)
• C_{10+} aromatics/light cycle oil (hydrodealkylation)
• C_{10+} aromatics (fractionation; coproduced with methylnaphthalene fraction/dimethylnaphthalene fraction)
Derivatives: naphthalene; phthalic anhydride

naphthalene-1-sulphonic acid
α-naphthalenesulphonic acid; [85-47-2]

$C_{10}H_8O_3S_1$. M: 208.23. Available as the dihydrate. Crystalline solid. MP: 90°C. Soluble in water and alcohol.
Production:
• naphthalene (sulphonation)
Derivatives:
naphthalene-1,5-disulphonic acid; α-naphthol; 1-naphthylamine-5-sulphonic acid; peri acid

naphthalene-2-sulphonic acid
β-naphthalenesulphonic acid; [120-18-3]

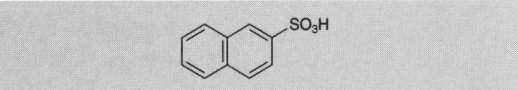

$C_{10}H_8O_3S_1$. M: 208.23. White, hygroscopic flakes. MP: 124°C. Soluble in water and oxygenated solvents.
Production:
• naphthalene (sulphonation)
Derivatives:
1,6-Cleve's acid; Cleve's acid, mixed; β-naphthol
Uses: acid-resistant phenolic resin curing agent

naphthalene-1,4,5,8-tetracarboxylic acid
[128-97-2]

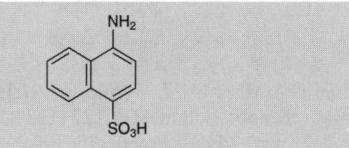

$C_{14}H_8O_8$. M: 304.20. Solid. MP: 150°C with decomposition. Soluble in hot water and acetone.
Production:
• pyrene (ring bromination/oxidation/side-chain oxidation)
Derivatives: Vat Orange 7; Vat Red 15

naphthalene-1,3,6-trisulphonic acid

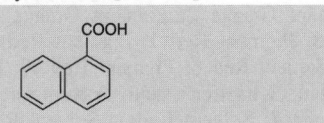

$C_{10}H_8O_9S_3$. M: 368.35.
Production:
• naphthalene-2,7-disulphonic acid (sulphonation)
Derivatives: Koch acid
Uses: nickelplating brightening agent

naphthalic anhydride
1,8-naphthalic anhydride; [81-84-5]

$C_{12}H_6O_3$. M: 198.18. Light brown needles. MP: 267–269°C. Insoluble in water. Slightly soluble in oxygenated solvents.
Production:
• acenaphthene (oxidation)
Derivatives: Fluorescent Brightener 162; perylenetetracarboxylic anhydride

naphthenic acid
[1338-24-5]
The extracted acidic component of refinery products

with BP: >150°C. Mixed product consisting of linear and cyclic aliphatic hydrocarbons containing carboxylic acid groups.
Production:
• kerosene/gas oil, heavy/lubricant oils, distillates/gas oil, light (alkali extraction/acidification)
Derivatives:
barium-zinc heat stabilisers; cadmium-barium heat stabilisers; cadmium-zinc heat stabilisers; calcium naphthenate; cobalt naphthenate; copper naphthenate; lead naphthenate; manganese naphthenate; zinc naphthenate
Uses: emulsifier (metalworking fluids)

naphthenic solvents
Series of mainly cyclic hydrocarbon fractions in the boiling range: 120–210°C. d: 0.78–0.86 kg/l. Aromatic content: 0.01–1.2%.
Production:
• trimethylbenzene fraction (hydrogenation/fractionation)
Uses:
cosolvent (mineral extraction); solvent (printing inks)

naphthionic acid
1-aminonaphthalene-4-sulphonic acid; 4-aminonaphthalene-1-sulphonic acid; 4-naphthylamine-1-sulphonic acid; [84-86-6]

$C_{10}H_9N_1O_3S_1$. M: 223.25. White needles. Decompose on heating. d: 1.67 kg/l (25°C). Soluble in water. Very slightly soluble in oxygenated solvents.
Production:
• 1-naphthylamine (sulphonation)
Derivatives:
Acid Brown 14; Acid Red 13; Acid Red 14; Acid Red 18; Acid Red 27; Acid Red 88; dichlone; Direct Red 2; Direct Red 26; Direct Yellow 106; Food Brown 3; Nevile-Winther acid

α-naphthoic acid
naphthalene-1-carboxylic acid; [86-55-5]

$C_{11}H_8O_2$. M: 172.18. White crystals. MP: 160–162°C. d: 1.40 kg/l. Insoluble in water. Soluble in oxygenated and chlorinated solvents.
Production:
• 1-chloromethylnaphthalene (oxidation)
Derivatives: 4-chloronaphtholactam; tetryzoline
Uses: dyestuffs intermediate

α-naphthol

1-hydroxynaphthalene; 1-naphthol; [90-15-3]

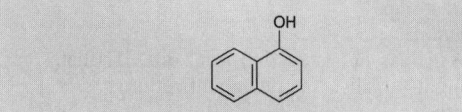

$C_{10}H_8O_1$. M: 144.17. Yellow crystals with a phenolic odour. MP: 95–96°C. BP: 288°C. Slightly soluble in hot water. Soluble in oxygenated and aromatic solvents.

Production:
• naphthalene (hydrogenation/oxidation/ dehydrogenation)
• 1-naphthylamine (hydrolysis)
• naphthalene-1-sulphonic acid (alkali fusion)

Derivatives: Acid Orange 20; carbaryl; *N*-ethyl-1-naphthylamine; α-hydroxynaphthoic acid; Mordant Black 11; nadolol; α-naphthyl glycidyl ether; napropamide; Nevile-Winther acid; *N*-phenyl-α-naphthylamine

β-naphthol

2-hydroxynaphthalene; 2-naphthol; Azoic Coupling Component 1 (CI); Developer 5 (CI); 37500 (CI); [135-19-3]

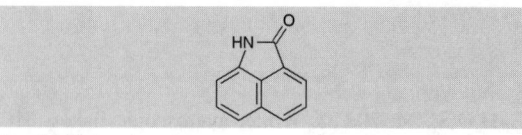

$C_{10}H_8O_1$. M: 144.17. White, crystalline solid with a mild, phenolic odour. MP: 122–123°C. BP: 285–286°C. d: 1.22 kg/l (4°C). Practically insoluble in water. Soluble in oxygenated solvents.

Production:
• naphthalene-2-sulphonic acid (alkali fusion)

Derivatives: Acid Black 52; Acid Black 63; Acid Orange 7; Acid Orange 8; Acid Red 88; Acid Red 97; Acid Red 151; Acid Red 296; Acid Red 308; Acid Violet 78; Basic Blue 6; crocein acid; decahydro-β-naphthyl acetate; *N,N'*-di-β-naphthyl-*p*-phenylenediamine; G acid; 2-hydroxy-1-naphthaldehyde; 6-methoxy-1-tetralone; Mordant Violet 5; β-naphthyl ethyl ether; β-naphthyl isobutyl ether; β-naphthyl methyl ether; (2-naphthyloxy)acetic acid; 1-nitroso-2-naphthol; β-oxynaphthoic acid; *N*-phenyl-β-naphthylamine; Pigment Orange 2; Pigment Orange 5; Pigment Orange 46; Pigment Red 1; Pigment Red 3; Pigment Red 4; Pigment Red 6; Pigment Red 49; Pigment Red 53; R acid; Schaeffer's acid; Solvent Orange 2; Solvent Orange 7; Solvent Red 1; Solvent Red 19; Solvent Red 22; Solvent Red 23; Solvent Red 24; Solvent Red 26; Solvent Red 27; Solvent Red 80; Solvent Yellow 14; Sulphur Black 11; Tobias acid; tolnaftate

naphtholactam

1-amino-8-naphtholactam; 8-amino-1-naphtholactam
$C_{11}H_7N_1O_1$. M: 169.19.

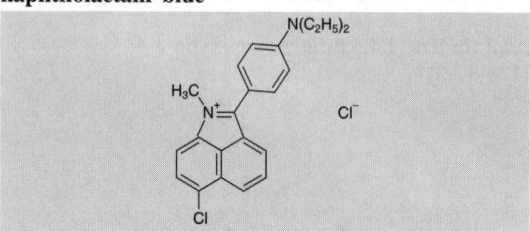

Production:
• peri acid (diazotisation/Sandmeyer reaction/nitrile hydrolysis/base-catalysed cyclisation)

Derivatives: Vat Orange 3

naphtholactam blue

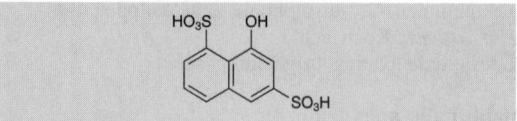

$C_{22}H_{22}Cl_2N_2$. M: 385.34.

Production:
• 4-chloronaphtholactam + *N,N*-diethylaniline + methyl chloride (condensation/quaternisation)

Uses: dye (polyacrylonitrile)

1-naphthol-2-carboxylic acid

See: α-hydroxynaphthoic acid

2-naphthol-3-carboxylic acid

See: β-oxynaphthoic acid

1-naphthol-3,8-disulphonic acid

1-hydroxynaphthalene-3,8-disulphonic acid; 8-hydroxynaphthalene-1,6-disulphonic acid

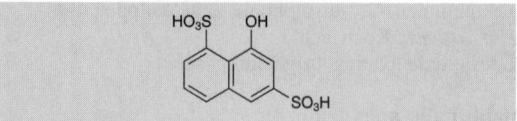

$C_{10}H_8O_7S_2$. M: 304.29.

Production:
• Koch acid (Bucherer reaction/desulphonation)

Derivatives: Direct Blue 98

2-naphthol-3,6-disulphonic acid *See:* R acid

2-naphthol-6,8-disulphonic acid *See:* G acid

3-naphthol-2,7-disulphonic acid *See:* R acid

7-naphthol-1,3-disulphonic acid *See:* G acid

1-naphthol-4-sulphonic acid *See:* Nevile-Winther acid

1-naphthol-8-sulphonic acid

See: 8-hydroxynaphthalene-1-sulphonic acid

2-naphthol-6-sulphonic acid *See:* Schaeffer's acid

naphthoquinone
α-naphthoquinone; 1,4-naphthoquinone; [130-15-4]

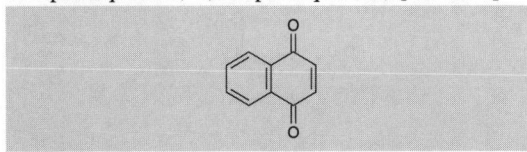

$C_{10}H_6O_2$. M: 158.16. Light yellow powder with a benzoquinone-like odour. MP: 128–129°C. Sublimes at 100°C. d: 1.42 kg/l. Insoluble in water. Soluble in oxygenated, chlorinated and aromatic solvents.
Production:
• naphthalene (gas-phase oxidation; coproduced with phthalic anhydride)
Derivatives: anthraquinone

1-naphthylacetamide
[86-86-2]

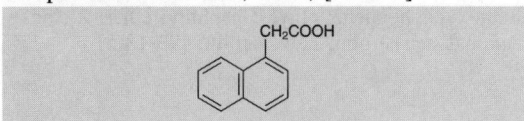

$C_{12}H_{11}N_1O_1$. M: 185.23.
Production:
• naphthylacetonitrile (nitrile hydration)
Uses: plant growth regulator

1-naphthylacetic acid
α-naphthaleneacetic acid; NAA; [86-87-3]

$C_{12}H_{10}O_2$. M: 186.21.
Production:
• naphthylacetonitrile (nitrile hydrolysis)
Derivatives: ethyl 1-naphthylacetate
Uses: plant growth regulator

naphthylacetonitrile
α-naphthaleneacetonitrile; [132-75-2]

$C_{12}H_9N_1$. M: 167.21. Waxy solid. MP: 32–33°C. Soluble in alcohol.
Production:
• 1-chloromethylnaphthalene + sodium cyanide (cyanidation)

Derivatives:
naphazoline; 1-naphthylacetamide; 1-naphthylacetic acid

1-naphthylamine
α-aminonaphthalene; 1-aminonaphthalene; α-naphthylamine; [134-32-7]

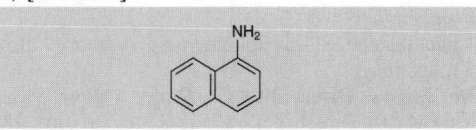

$C_{10}H_9N_1$. M: 143.19. Reddish, crystalline solid with an unpleasant odour. MP: 50°C. Sublimes. Insoluble in water. Soluble in oxygenated solvents.
Production:
• naphthalene (nitration/nitro reduction)
Derivatives:
Acid Blue 113; Acid Green 19; Acid Red 119; Direct Black 3; Direct Blue 71; Direct Blue 78; Disperse Black 1; Fluorescent Brightener 46; naphthionic acid; α-naphthol; 8-naphthylamine-1,3,5-trisulphonic acid; *N*-(1-naphthyl)-3-hydroxy-2-naphthamide; naptalam-sodium; tramazoline

1-naphthylamine-4,8-disulphonic acid
1-aminonaphthalene-4,8-disulphonic acid; 4-aminonaphthalene-1,5-disulphonic acid; 8-aminonaphthalene-1,5-disulphonic acid

$C_{10}H_9N_1O_6S_2$. M: 303.31.
Production:
• peri acid (sulphonation)
Derivatives: Chicago acid; S acid

2-naphthylamine-1,5-disulphonic acid
2-aminonaphthalene-1,5-disulphonic acid; [117-62-4]

$C_{10}H_9N_1O_6S_2$. M: 303.31.
Production:
• Tobias acid (sulphonation)
Derivatives: Reactive Orange 13; Reactive Orange 4; Reactive Yellow 4

2-naphthylamine-4,8-disulphonic acid
2,4,8-acid; 2-aminonaphthalene-4,8-disulphonic acid; 3-aminonaphthalene-1,5-disulphonic acid; [131-27-1]
$C_{10}H_9N_1O_6S_2$. M: 303.31.

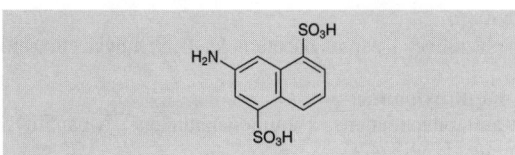

Production:
• naphthalene-1,5-disulphonic acid (nitration/nitro reduction)
Derivatives: Direct Blue 71; Direct Yellow 34; Direct Yellow 50; Direct Yellow 51; Reactive Blue 13; Reactive Yellow 3

2-naphthylamine-6,8-disulphonic acid
See: amino-G acid

1-naphthylamine-5-sulphonic acid
1-aminonaphthalene-5-sulphonic acid; 5-aminonaphthalene-1-sulphonic acid; Laurent's acid; [84-89-9]

$C_{10}H_9N_1O_3S_1$. M: 223.25. White crystals. Slightly soluble in water.
Production:
• naphthalene-1-sulphonic acid (nitration/nitro reduction/isomer separation; coproduced with peri acid)
Derivatives: 5-hydroxynaphthalene-1-sulphonic acid; Mordant Brown 1
Uses: dyestuffs intermediate

1-naphthylamine-6-sulphonic acid
See: 1,6-Cleve's acid

1-naphthylamine-7-sulphonic acid
See: 1,7-Cleve's acid

1-naphthylamine-8-sulphonic acid *See:* peri acid

2-naphthylamine-1-sulphonic acid
See: Tobias acid

2-naphthylamine-6-sulphonic acid
See: Broenner's acid

4-naphthylamine-1-sulphonic acid
See: naphthionic acid

1-naphthylamine-3,6,8-trisulphonic acid
See: Koch acid

1-naphthylamine-4,6,8-trisulphonic acid
See: 8-naphthylamine-1,3,5-trisulphonic acid

2-naphthylamine-1,5,7-trisulphonic acid
3-aminonaphthalene-4,6,8-trisulphonic acid; 6-aminonaphthalene-1,3,5-trisulphonic acid; 6-naphthylamine-1,3,5-trisulphonic acid

$C_{10}H_9N_1O_9S_3$. M: 383.37.
Production:
• Tobias acid (sulphonation)
Derivatives: J acid; sulpho-J acid

6-naphthylamine-1,3,5-trisulphonic acid
See: 2-naphthylamine-1,5,7-trisulphonic acid

8-naphthylamine-1,3,5-trisulphonic acid
1-aminonaphthalene-4,6,8-trisulphonic acid; 8-aminonaphthalene-1,3,5-trisulphonic acid; 1-naphthylamine-4,6,8-trisulphonic acid

$C_{10}H_9N_1O_9S_3$. M: 383.37.
Production:
• 1-naphthylamine (sulphonation)
Derivatives: K acid; suramin sodium

β-naphthyl ethyl ether
β-ethoxynaphthalene; ethyl β-naphthyl ether; 2-ethoxynaphthalene; nerolin; new nerolin; [93-18-5]

$C_{12}H_{12}O_1$. M: 172.23. White crystals with orange-blossom odour. MP: 37–38°C. BP: 282°C. d: 1.06 kg/l (20°C). Insoluble in water. Soluble in oxygenated and hydrocarbon solvents.
Production:
• β-naphthol + diethyl sulphate (ethylation)
Uses: fragrance ingredient

α-naphthyl glycidyl ether
[2461-42-9]

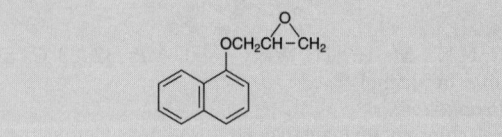

$C_{13}H_{12}O_2$. M: 200.24. Liquid.

Production:
- α-naphthol + epichlorohydrin (dehydrochlorination)

Derivatives: propranolol

N-(1-naphthyl)-3-hydroxy-2-naphthamide

N-(1-naphthyl)-2-hydroxy-3-naphthamide; Naphthol AS-BO; Azoic Coupling Component 4 (CI); 37560 (CI); [132-68-3]

$C_{21}H_{15}N_1O_2$. M: 313.36.
Production:
- β-oxynaphthoic acid + 1-naphthylamine (amide formation)

Uses: azoic dye coupling component

N-(2-naphthyl)-3-hydroxy-2-naphthamide

N-(β-naphthyl)-3-hydroxy-2-naphthamide; Naphthol AS-SW; Azoic Coupling Component 7 (CI); Developer 23 (CI); 37565 (CI)

$C_{21}H_{15}N_1O_2$. M: 313.36.
Production:
- β-oxynaphthoic acid + Tobias acid (amide formation/hydrolysis)

Uses: azoic dye diazo component

β-naphthyl isobutyl ether

2-isobutoxynaphthalene; isobutyl β-naphthyl ether; [2173-57-1]

$C_{14}H_{16}O_1$. M: 200.28. White crystals with orange-blossom odour. MP 33°C. Insoluble in water. Soluble in alcohol.
Production:
- β-naphthol + isobutyl bromide (ether formation)

Uses:
fragrance ingredient

β-naphthyl methyl ether

2-methoxynaphthalene; methyl β-naphthyl ether; Yara yara; [93-04-9]

$C_{11}H_{10}O_1$. M: 158.20. White, crystalline solid with a

floral odour. MP: 73–74°C. Slightly soluble in water. Soluble in oxygenated solvents.
Production:
- β-naphthol + dimethyl sulphate (methylation)

Derivatives: naproxen
Uses: fragrance ingredient

(2-naphthyloxy)acetic acid

[120-23-0]

$C_{12}H_{10}O_3$. M: 202.21.
Production:
- β-naphthol + chloroacetic acid (ether formation)

Uses: plant growth regulator

napropamide

N,N-diethyl-2-(1-naphthyloxy)propionamide; [15299-99-7]

$C_{17}H_{21}N_1O_2$. M: 271.37.
Production:
- α-naphthol + α-chloropropionic acid + diethylamine (ether formation/amide formation)

Uses: herbicide

naproxen

[22204-53-1]

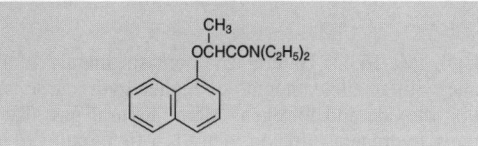

$C_{14}H_{14}O_3$. M: 230.26.
Production:
- β-naphthyl methyl ether + α-bromopropionic acid (ring bromination/Grignard reagent formation/Grignard coupling/racemate separation)
- β-naphthyl methyl ether + acetyl chloride + methyl chloroacetate (Friedel-Crafts acylation/Darzens reaction/hydrolysis/decarboxylation/carbonyl oxidation/racemate separation)
- β-naphthyl methyl ether + propionyl chloride + methanol (Friedel-Crafts acylation/ketal formation/alpha bromination/1,2-aryl shift/racemate separation)
- β-naphthyl methyl ether + propionyl chloride + tartaric acid (Friedel-Crafts acylation/ketal formation/alpha bromination/1,2-aryl shift)

Uses:
antiinflammatory/antipyretic drug

naptalam-sodium
sodium *N*-1-naphthylphthalamate; [132-67-2]

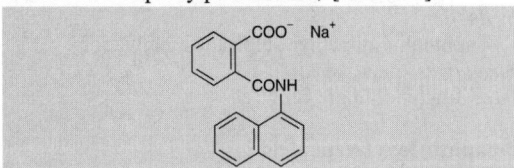

$C_{18}H_{12}N_1Na_1O_3$. M: 313.30.
Production:
- phthalic anhydride + 1-naphthylamine (amide formation)

Uses: herbicide

natamycin *See:* pimaricin

natron *See:* sodium carbonate

natural gas
LNG; methane; [74-82-8] (methane)

$$CH_4$$

C_1H_4. M: 16.04. Natural gas consists mainly of methane with smaller amounts of higher hydrocarbons, carbon dioxide and nitrogen. 'Sour' natural gas also contains hydrogen sulphide. This is often removed at an early stage in processing the gas because of its corrosive nature. Condensible hydrocarbons are separated as natural gas liquids (NGL). A typical chain-length distribution of dried, sweetened natural gas is: 80% C_1, 2% C_2, 1% C_3, 0.3% C_4, 8% CO_2, 7% N_2. Sour natural gas contains, typically, 5% H_2S. Natural gas is usually transported by pipeline but is also cooled and liquified for carriage in specially-designed ships as 'liquified natural gas' (LNG).
Production:
- natural gas, wet (fractionation; coproduced with ethane/liquified petroleum gas/gasoline, natural)

Derivatives:
acetylene; carbon black; carbon dioxide; carbon disulphide; carbon tetrachloride; chloroform; dichlorodifluoromethane; ethylene; helium; hydrogen cyanide; hydrogen sulphide; methyl chloride; methylene chloride; synthesis gas; trichlorofluoromethane
Uses:
domestic/industrial heating fuel; fuel gas (electricity/steam generation)

natural gas, wet
Natural gas containing higher, condensible hydrocarbons.
Derivatives:
ethane; gasoline, natural; liquified petroleum gas; natural gas

natural gas liquids *See:* gasoline, natural

natural rubber
cis-1,4-polyisoprene; NR; [9006-04-6]

$$\overset{CH_3}{\underset{}{{-}\!\!\left[CH_2CH{=}CHCH_2\right]\!\!-}_x}$$

Pale yellow to dark brown elastomeric solid sold in the form of compressed bales. The product is the co-agulated and dried exudate of the rubber tree (*Hevea brasiliensis*). Available as ribbed smoked sheet, air-dried sheet, crepe or in various special grades. The different types are classified according to the Standardised Malaysian Rubber (SMR) system by impurity, ash and nitrogen content, as well as by the Plasticity Retention Index (PRI) which indicates the degree of degradation in physical properties on heating. Natural rubber contains, typically, 89–92% elastomeric hydrocarbon, all of which is linear *cis*-1,4-polyisoprene. M: 200,000–400,000. The main producing countries are Indonesia, Malaysia, Thailand, India, China and Sri Lanka. The product is usually vulcanised with sulphur or sulphur chloride.
Production:
- field latex (coagulation)

Derivatives: ebonite; levulinic acid; rubber, chlorinated; rubber, cyclised; rubber hydrochloride
Uses: vehicle engine/suspension mounts; adhesives (pressure-sensitive tape); solvent-based adhesives; balls/moulded extrusions; print rollers; road repairing compounds; rubber bands; tank/container linings; truck/earthmoving vehicle tyres; vulcanising cement

natural rubber latex
White, viscous liquid containing over 60% rubber. The product is classified according to the method of concentration and the preservative used. The most common types are low-ammonia, centrifuged grades preserved with zinc diethyldithiocarbamate or tetramethylthiuram disulphide. Sodium pentachlorophenate is also used as a preservative in some countries. Other types of latex are high-ammonia, centrifuged latex, with or without other preservatives, creamed latex and evaporated latex. The latter two types have higher solids contents than centrifuged grades. Creamed latex is produced by gravity separation with the aid of a creaming agent such as ammonium alginate. Evaporated latex contains up to 8% non-rubber solids and is generally stabilised with potassium hydroxide and ammonia or soap. Most latex is sold unvulcanised, although pre-vulcanised grades are available.
Production:
- field latex (concentration/blending)

Uses: cement admixture; elastomeric textile thread; adhesives (cold-sealable packaging products, self-sealing envelopes, leather/tile adhesives); resealable/pressure-sensitive adhesives; binder (tufted carpet anchor coatings, flock attachment, non-woven fabrics); pressure-injection/surface sealing damp-proofing formulations;

latex dipping compounds (gloves, contraceptives, balloons); leatherboard; moulded latex foam; natural rubber castings; rubberised hair products; tufted carpet foam backings

NBN *See:* 1-nitroso-2-naphthol; *n*-butyronitrile

NBR *See:* acrylonitrile-butadiene copolymers

NBS *See:* *N*-bromosuccinimide

NCS *See:* *N*-chlorosuccinimide

2,6-NDA *See:* naphthalene-2,6-dicarboxylic acid

NDBC *See:* nickel di-*n*-butyldithiocarbamate

NDI *See:* 1,5-naphthalene diisocyanate

neatsfoot oil
[8002-64-0]
Pale yellow liquid with a characteristic odour. Produced by rendering cattle feet. Solidification point: -10–0°C. d: 0.92 kg/l. Saponification value: 188–198 mg KOH/g. Insoluble in water.
Derivatives: neatsfoot oil, sulphonated
Uses:
leather fat-liquoring agent; lubricant

neatsfoot oil, sulphonated
Production:
• neatsfoot oil (sulphonation)
Uses: lubricity/detergent additive (lubricants)

neburon
1-butyl-3-(3,4-dichlorophenyl)-1-methylurea; [555-37-3]

$C_{12}H_{16}Cl_2N_2O_1$. M: 275.18.
Production:
• *n*-butylamine + dimethyl sulphate + 3,4-dichlorophenyl isocyanate (methylation/isocyanate addition)
Uses: herbicide

needle coke
green coke; petroleum coke
Premium petroleum coke characterised by its needle-like appearance, low volatiles and high carbon content.
Production:
• heavy cycle oil/pyrolysis tar/coal tar pitch (delayed coking process; coproduced with naphtha, heavy/gas oil, light/gas oil, heavy/refinery gas)
Derivatives: carbon, moulded
Uses: electrodes

nefopam
[13669-70-0]

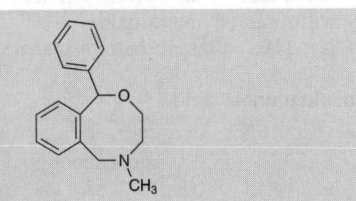

$C_{17}H_{19}N_1O_1$. M: 253.35. Available commercially as the hydrochloride.
Production:
• *o*-benzoylbenzoic acid + methylethanolamine (amide formation/carbonyl reduction/ether formation)
Uses: analgesic/antidepressant drug

NEM *See:* *N*-ethylmorpholine

neodecanoic acid
Versatic 10 acid (Shell); [26896-20-8]

$$C_6H_{13}\overset{\underset{\displaystyle CH_3}{|}}{\underset{\underset{\displaystyle CH_3}{|}}{C}}COOH$$

$C_{10}H_{20}O_2$. M: 172.27. Clear, yellow liquid. BP: 243–253°C. Solubility in water: 0.34 g/l water (25°C).
Production:
• nonene, branched + carbon monoxide (Koch carbonylation)
Derivatives: barium-zinc heat stabilisers; cadmium-barium heat stabilisers; cadmium-zinc heat stabilisers; glycidyl neodecanoate; neodecanoyl chloride; vinyl neodecanoate; zinc neodecanoate; zirconium neodecanoate
Uses:
coupling solvent (metalworking fluids); metal extraction agent

neodecanoyl chloride

$$C_6H_{13}\overset{\underset{\displaystyle CH_3}{|}}{\underset{\underset{\displaystyle CH_3}{|}}{C}}COCl$$

$C_{10}H_{19}Cl_1O_1$. M: 190.71. Liquid. BP: 63°C (0.5 kPa). d: 0.95 kg/l (20°C). Hydrolysed by water and alcohol.
Production:
• neodecanoic acid (acid chloride formation)
Derivatives:
t-amyl peroxyneodecanoate; *t*-butyl peroxyneodecanoate; cumyl peroxyneodecanoate; didecanoyl peroxide

neodymium oxide
[1313-97-9]

Nd_2O_3

Nd_2O_3. M: 336.48. Blue powder. MP: 1,900°C. d: 7.24 kg/l. Insoluble in water.

Production:
- didymium oxide (solvent extraction; coproduced with praseodymium oxide)

Uses: glass colorant; barium titanate capacitors

neoheptanoic acid

$$CH_3$$
$$C_3H_7\overset{|}{\underset{|}{C}}COOH$$
$$CH_3$$

$C_7H_{14}O_2$. M: 130.19. Mixed product of C_7 trialkylacetic acid isomers. Yellow liquid. BP: 205–213°C. Pour point: <-65°C. d: 0.92 kg/l (20°C). Acid value: 425 mg KOH/g. Slightly soluble in water. Soluble in oxygenated solvents. Flash point: 94°C (COC).
Production:
- hexene, branched + carbon monoxide (Koch carbonylation)

Derivatives: neoheptanoyl chloride
Uses: metalworking fluids

neoheptanoyl chloride

$$CH_3$$
$$C_3H_7\overset{|}{\underset{|}{C}}COCl$$
$$CH_3$$

$C_7H_{13}Cl_1O_1$. M: 148.63.
Production:
- neoheptanoic acid (acid chloride formation)

Derivatives: t-amyl peroxyneoheptanoate; t-butyl peroxyneoheptanoate; cumyl peroxyneoheptanoate; 1,1-dimethyl-3-hydroxybutyl peroxyneoheptanoate

neohexene
3,3-dimethyl-1-butene

$$(CH_3)_3CCH=CH_2$$

C_6H_{12}. M: 84.17. Clear liquid. BP: 41°C. d: 0.65 kg/l (20°C). Flash point: 7°C.
Production:
- 2,4,4-trimethylpentene + ethylene (Phillips ethenylation process)

Derivatives: 6-acetyl-1,1,2,4,4,7-hexamethyltetralin

neon
[7440-01-9]

$$Ne$$

Ne_1. M: 20.18. Colourless odourless, inert gas. BP: -246°C. d: 0.900 g/l (gas, 0°C). Slightly soluble in water.
Production:
- air (cryogenic separation; byproduct of oxygen-/nitrogen production)

Uses: inert filler gas (display lighting, instruments)

neopentanoic acid *See:* pivalic acid

neopentyl glycol
1,3-dihydroxy-2,2-dimethylpropane; 2,2-dimethyl-1,3-propanediol; NPG; [126-30-7]

$$(CH_3)_2C(CH_2OH)_2$$

$C_5H_{12}O_2$. M: 104.15. White, crystalline solid. MP: 125–130°C. d: 1.06 kg/l (25°C). Soluble in water and oxygenated solvents.
Production:
- isobutyraldehyde + formaldehyde (aldol condensation/Cannizzaro reaction)

Derivatives:
alkyd resins, water-soluble; hydramethylnon; neopentyl glycol diacrylate; neopentyl glycol dicocoate; neopentyl glycol dimethacrylate; neopentyl glycol dioleate; neopentyl glycol dipelargonate; unsaturated polyester resins, isophthalate grades
Uses: unsaturated polyester resin comonomer; polyurethane chain-extender

neopentyl glycol diacrylate
NPGDA

$$(CH_3)_2C(CH_2O\overset{O}{\overset{||}{C}}CH=CH_2)_2$$

$C_{11}H_{16}O_4$. M: 212.25.
Production:
- neopentyl glycol + acrylic acid (esterification)

Uses: reactive diluent (radiation-cured coatings)

neopentyl glycol dicocoate

$$(CH_3)_2C(CH_2O\overset{O}{\overset{||}{C}}R)_2$$

R = coco-. Amber, viscous liquid. Pour point: ~5°C.
Production:
- neopentyl glycol + coconut acid (esterification)

Uses: rolling oils

neopentyl glycol dimethacrylate

$$(CH_3)_2C\left[CH_2O\overset{O}{\overset{||}{C}}\underset{CH_3}{\overset{|}{C}}=CH_2\right]_2$$

$C_{13}H_{20}O_4$. M: 240.30.
Production:
- neopentyl glycol + methyl methacrylate (transesterification)

Uses: crosslinked acrylic/vinyl resin comonomer

neopentyl glycol dioleate

$$(CH_3)_2C\left[CH_2O\overset{O}{\overset{||}{C}}(CH_2)_7CH=CH(CH_2)_7CH_3\right]_2$$

$C_{41}H_{76}O_4$. M: 633.06.
Production:
- neopentyl glycol + oleic acid (esterification)

Uses: lubricity additive (metalworking fluids); synthetic lubricant base oils

neopentyl glycol dipelargonate

$$(CH_3)_2C \left[CH_2O \overset{\overset{O}{\|}}{C}(CH_2)_7CH_3 \right]_2$$

$C_{23}H_{44}O_4$. M: 384.60.
Production:
• neopentyl glycol + pelargonic acid (esterification)
Uses: lubricant (textile spin finishes); synthetic lubricant base oils

neopentyl glycol monohydroxypivalate
HPN; [1115-20-4]

$$\underset{\underset{CH_3}{|}}{\overset{\overset{CH_3}{|}}{HOCH_2C}}COOCH_2\underset{\underset{CH_3}{|}}{\overset{\overset{CH_3}{|}}{C}}CH_2OH$$

$C_{10}H_{20}O_4$. M: 204.27. Solid. MP: 46–50°C.
Production:
• isobutyraldehyde + formaldehyde (condensation/ Cannizzaro reaction/esterification)
Uses: alkyd/polyester paint resin comonomer; photographic coupling agent intermediate

neoprene *See:* polychloroprene

NEPD *See:* 2-ethyl-2-nitro-1,3-propanediol

nerol
3,7-dimethyl-*cis*-2,6-octadien-1-ol; [106-25-2]

$$(CH_3)_2C=CHCH_2CH_2 \quad \overset{H_3C}{\underset{}{}}C=C\overset{H}{\underset{CH_2OH}{}}$$

$C_{10}H_{18}O_1$. M: 154.25. Colourless liquid with a rose-like odour. BP: 225°C. d: 0.88 kg/l (20°C). Insoluble in water. Soluble in oxygenated solvents. The corresponding *trans*-isomer is geraniol.
Production:
• geraniol-nerol, mixed (isomer separation; coproduced with geraniol)
Derivatives: neryl acetate
Uses:
fragrance ingredient

nerolidol
3,7,11-trimethyl-1,6,10-didecatrien-3-ol; [7212-44-4]

$$(CH_3)_2C=CHCH_2CH_2\underset{\underset{OH}{|}}{\overset{\overset{CH_3}{|}}{C}}=CHCH_2CH_2\underset{\underset{OH}{|}}{\overset{\overset{CH_3}{|}}{C}}CH=CH_2$$

$C_{15}H_{26}O_1$. M: 222.37. Colourless liquid with a floral odour. BP: 145°C (1.6 kPa). d: 0.88 kg/l (20°C). Insoluble in water. Soluble in alcohol. Mixed isomer product.

Production:
• geranylacetone + acetylene (ethynylation/ hydrogenation)
Derivatives: farnesol; phytol
Uses: fragrance ingredient

nerolin *See:* β-naphthyl ethyl ether

neryl acetate
[141-12-8]

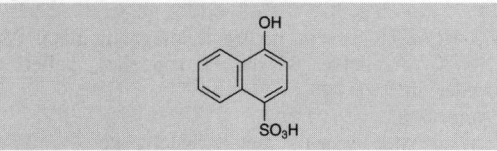

$C_{12}H_{20}O_2$. M: 196.29. Colourless liquid with a floral odour.
Production:
• nerol + sodium acetate (esterification)
Uses: fragrance ingredient

Nevile-Winther acid
4-hydroxynaphthalene-1-sulphonic acid; 1-naphthol-4-sulphonic acid; NW acid; [84-87-7]

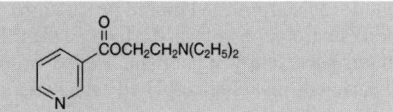

$C_{10}H_8O_4S_1$. M: 224.23. Crystals. Decompose on heating above 170°C. Soluble in water.
Production:
• α-naphthol (sulphonation)
• naphthionic acid (Bucherer reaction)
Derivatives: Acid Orange 19; Acid Red 4; Acid Red 14; 2-diazo-1-naphthol-4-sulphonic acid chloride; Direct Blue 8; Direct Blue 120

NG *See:* nitroglycerine

NGL *See:* gasoline, natural

niacin *See:* nicotinic acid

niacinamide *See:* nicotinamide

nicamete
[3099-52-3]

$$\overset{\overset{O}{\|}}{COCH_2CH_2N(C_2H_5)_2}$$

$C_{12}H_{18}N_2O_2$. M: 222.28.
Production:
• diethylaminoethanol + nicotinic acid (esterification)
Uses:
vasodilator drug

nicardipine
[55985-32-5]

$C_{26}H_{29}N_3O_6$. M: 479.53. Available commercially as the hydrochloride.
Production:
• methylethanolamine + benzyl chloride + methyl acetoacetate + *m*-nitrobenzaldehyde + ammonia (amine formation/esterification/carbonyl condensation/condensation)
Uses: antianginal/antihypertensive drug

nickel
[7440-02-0]

Ni

Ni_1. M: 58.71. Silvery, malleable, magnetic metal. MP: 1,454°C. Available as squares, rondelles, pellets or powder. d: 8.91 kg/l.
Production:
• nickel oxide, green + metallurgical coke (pyrometallurgical reduction)
• nickel oxide, green + metallurgical coke (electric furnace reduction/electrolysis)
• nickel oxide, green + hydrogen (reduction/carbonyl gas refining process)
• nickel-copper matte/nickel matte + hydrogen (pressure leaching/reduction; coproduced with cobalt)
• lateritic ore (pressure leaching/solvent extraction/electrolysis; coproduced with cobalt)
Derivatives: 2,2'-bipyridine; nickel carbonate, basic; nickel chloride; nickel formate; nickel sulphate; nickel tetracarbonyl
Uses: corrosion-resistant copper-nickel alloys (chemical plant, marine applications); corrosion-resistant nickel-chromium-iron alloys (electric cookers, furnace, boiler components); cupronickel (desalination plants, ship and marine applications); electroplating anodes (chrome-nickel plated handles, fixings, trim); electroplating anodes (electroformed mould production); heat-resistant nickel-chromium alloys (turbine blades, heating elements); super alloy ingredient; leaded bronze ingredient (bearings); nickel-silverplated tableware/keys/springs

nickel acetate
nickel diacetate; [373-02-4]

$(CH_3COO)_2Ni$

$C_4H_6Ni_1O_4$. M: 176.80. Available as the tetrahydrate.

Green powder. Decomposes on heating. d: 1.74 kg/l. Soluble in water and alcohol.
Production:
• nickel oxide, black + acetic acid (salt formation)
Uses: electrodeless nickel-hydrazine coating reagent

nickel acetylacetonate
[3264-82-2]

$C_{10}H_{14}Ni_1O_4$. M: 256.93. Green crystals. MP: 230°C. d: 1.45 kg/l.
Production:
• nickel oxide, black + acetylacetone (complex formation)
Uses: organonickel catalyst intermediate

nickel bis[2,2'-thiobis(4-*t*-octylphenol)]
2,2'-thiobis(4-*t*-octylphenolato)nickel

$C_{56}H_{82}Ni_1O_4S_2$. M: 942.12. Powder.
Production:
• 2,2'-thiobis(4-*t*-octylphenol) + nickel sulphate (complex formation)
Uses: light stabiliser (plastics)

nickel carbonate, basic
nickel carbonate hydroxide; [3333-67-3]

$NiCO_3.2Ni(OH)_2$

$C_1H_2Ni_3O_7$. M: 302.15. Available commercially as the tetrahydrate. Light green powder. Insoluble in water.
Production:
• nickel + carbon dioxide + ammonia (salt formation)
Derivatives: cobalt green; nickel nitrate; nickel oxide, black; titanium nickel yellow
Uses: glaze/ceramics ingredient; nickel catalysts

nickel carbonyl *See:* nickel tetracarbonyl

nickel chloride
[7718-54-9]

$NiCl_2$

Cl_2Ni_1. M: 129.62. Available commercially as the hexa-

hydrate. Green crystals. Solubility in water: 2.54 kg/l water (20°C). Soluble in alcohol.
Production:
• nickel/nickel oxide, black + hydrochloric acid (salt formation)
Uses: SHOP process catalyst; electroplating bath ingredient; electrodeless coating reagent (window glass)

nickel-copper matte
Crude copper-nickel sulphide smelter product containing, typically, 47% nickel, 30% copper, 22% sulphur and 0.5% iron.
Production:
• copper-nickel sulphide ores (froth flotation/ore roasting/smelting)
Derivatives: cobalt; nickel; nickel matte

nickel di-*n*-butyldithiocarbamate
NDBC; Naugard NBC (Uniroyal Chemical); UV-Chek AM 104 (Ferro)

$$\left[(CH_3CH_2CH_2CH_2)_2N\overset{S}{\overset{\|}{C}}S\right]_2 Ni$$

$C_{18}H_{36}N_2Ni_1S_4$. M: 467.47. Olive green powder. MP: 85°C.
Production:
• di-*n*-butylamine + carbon disulphide + nickel oxide, black (condensation)
Uses: neoprene/chlorosulphonated polyethylene heat-ageing inhibitor

nickel fluoroborate
nickel fluoborate; [14708-14-6]

$$Ni(BF_4)_2$$

$B_2F_8Ni_1$. M: 232.31.
Production:
• nickel oxide, black + fluoboric acid (salt formation)
Uses: electroplating bath ingredient

nickel formate
[3349-06-2]

$$(HCOO)_2Ni$$

$C_2H_2Ni_1O_4$. M: 148.75. Available as the dihydrate. Green crystals. Loses water of crystallisation when heated over 130°C. Decomposes when heated above 180°C. d: 2.15 kg/l (20°C). Soluble in water.
Production:
• nickel + formic acid (salt formation)
Uses: fatty acid hydrogenation catalyst

nickelic oxide *See:* nickel oxide, black

nickel matte
Crude nickel sulphide containing 70–80% nickel. The main producing countries are Canada and Russia (using

copper-nickel ores), Cuba, Indonesia and New Caledonia (using lateritic ores).
Production:
• lateritic ore (smelting)
• nickel-copper matte (Inco matte separation process)
Derivatives: cobalt; nickel; nickel oxide, green

nickel nitrate
nickelous nitrate; [13138-45-9]

$$Ni(NO_3)_2$$

$N_2Ni_1O_6$. M: 182.71. Available commercially as the hexahydrate. Green, deliquescent crystals. MP: 57°C. BP: 137°C. d: 2.05 kg/l. Highly soluble in water producing acidic solutions.
Production:
• nickel carbonate, basic + nitric acid (salt formation)
Uses: nickelplating reagent; nickel catalysts; raw material (pressed battery plates)

nickelous oxide *See:* nickel oxide, green

nickel oxide, black
nickelic oxide; nickel sesquioxide; [1314-06-3]

$$Ni_2O_3$$

Ni_2O_3. M: 165.42. Black powder. Converts to green nickel oxide (NiO) if heated to 1000°C. Insoluble in water.
Production:
• nickel carbonate, basic (calcination)
Derivatives: bis[*O*-ethyl-(3,5-di-*t*-butyl-4-hydroxybenzyl)phosphonic acid], nickel salt; ferrite; nickel acetate; nickel acetylacetonate; nickel chloride; nickel di-*n*-butyldithiocarbamate; nickel fluoroborate; nickel sulphamate; titanium nickel yellow

nickel oxide, green
nickelous oxide; [1313-99-1]

$$NiO$$

Ni_1O_1. M: 74.71. Green, crystalline solid. MP: 2,090°C. d: 7.45 kg/l. Insoluble in water.
Production:
• nickel matte (calcination)
Derivatives: nickel
Uses: ceramics/frits ingredient; alloy steel/stainless steel ingredient

nickel sulphamate
[13770-89-3]

$$Ni(SO_3NH_2)_2$$

$H_4N_2Ni_1O_6S_2$. M: 250.87.
Production:
• nickel oxide, black + sulphamic acid (salt formation)
Uses: electroplating bath ingredient

nickel sulphate
[7786-81-4]

NiSO₄

$Ni_1O_4S_1$. M: 154.77. Available commercially as the hexahydrate. Green, crystalline solid. Starts to lose water of crystallisation when heated above 100°C, eventually forming the anhydrous salt at 280°C. d: 2.03 kg/l. Solubility in water: 700 g/l water (20°C).
Production:
• nickel + sulphuric acid (salt formation)
Derivatives:
n-butylaminonickel-2,2'-thiobis(4-*t*-octylphenol); nickel bis[2,2'-thiobis(4-*t*-octylphenol)]; Pigment Green 10
Uses:
nickelplating/electrodeless coating reagent; mordant

nickel tetracarbonyl
nickel carbonyl; [13463-39-3]

Ni(CO)₄

$C_4Ni_1O_4$. M: 170.75. Colourless liquid. BP: 43°C. MP: -25°C. Explodes when heated above 60°C. d: 1.32 kg/l (15°C). Oxidised by air. Insoluble in water. Soluble in chlorinated and aromatic solvents. Intermediate in nickel production by the Mond process.
Production:
• nickel + carbon monoxide (complex formation)
Uses: Reppe hydrocarbonylation catalyst; vapour deposition nickelplating reagent

nickel titanate *See:* titanium nickel yellow

niclosamide
5-chloro-*N*-(2-chloro-4-nitrophenyl)salicylamide; [50-65-7]

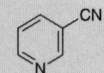

$C_{13}H_8Cl_2N_2O_4$. M: 327.12. Available commercially as the free acid or as the monoethanolamine salt.
Production:
• 5-chlorosalicylic acid + 2-chloro-4-nitroaniline (amide formation)
Uses: anthelmintic drug; molluscicide

nicotinamide
niacinamide; vitamin B₃; NSA; [98-92-0]

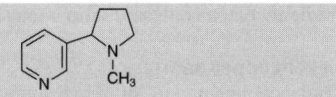

$C_6H_6N_2O_1$. M: 122.13. White needles. MP: 130–133°C. Soluble in water and oxygenated solvents.

Production:
• nicotinonitrile (nitrile hydrolysis)
Uses: antipellagra factor drug; animal feed additive

nicotine
[54-11-5]

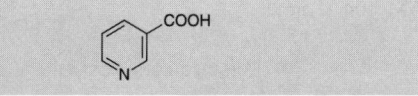

$C_{10}H_{14}N_2$. M: 162.23. Available commercially as the (−)-enantiomer sulphate salt.
Production:
• tobacco wastes (alkali extraction/steam distillation)
Uses: insecticide/fumigant

nicotinic acid
niacin; 3-pyridinecarboxylic acid; pyridine-3-carboxylic acid; vitamin B₃; [59-67-6]

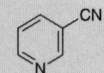

$C_6H_5N_1O_2$. M: 123.12. White needles. MP: 236–239°C. Sublimes. Soluble in hot water and aqueous alkali. Also available commercially as the potassium, sodium or zinc salts.
Production:
• isocinchomeronic acid (decarboxylation)
• nicotinonitrile (base-catalysed hydrolysis)
Derivatives: azatadine; benzyl nicotinate; 2-chloronicotinic acid; etofibrate; inositol nicotinate; nicametate; nicotinyl alcohol; nifenazone; nikethamide; xanthinol nicotinate
Uses: electroplating bath ingredient; vasodilator/lipid reduction drug; cereal/animal feed additive

nicotinonitrile
3-cyanopyridine; [100-54-9]

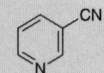

$C_6H_4N_2$. M: 104.11. White needles. MP: 49–51°C. BP: 202–205°C. Soluble in water, oxygenated and aromatic solvents.
Production:
• β-picoline + ammonia (ammoxidation)
Derivatives:
3-aminopyridine; nicotinamide; nicotinic acid

nicotinyl alcohol
pyridylcarbinol; [100-55-0]
$C_6H_7N_1O_1$. M: 109.14. Available commercially as the free alcohol or as the (+)-tartrate ester.
Production:
• nicotinic acid (esterification/ester reduction)

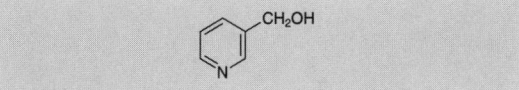

Uses: vasodilator drug

nifedipine
[21829-25-4]

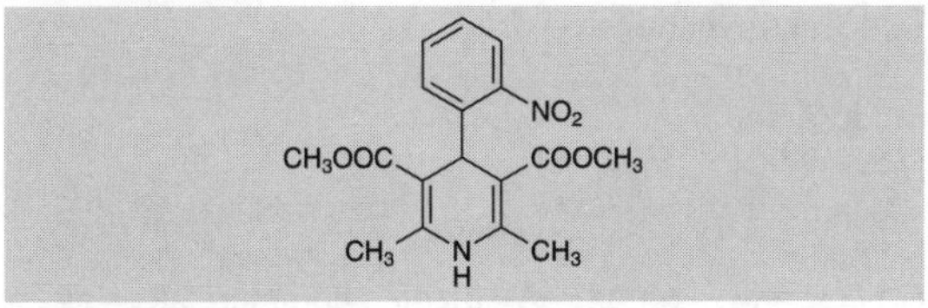

$C_{17}H_{18}N_2O_6$. M: 346.33.
Production:
- *o*-nitrobenzaldehyde + ethyl acetoacetate + ammonia (Hantzsch synthesis)

Uses:
antianginal/antihypertensive drug

nifenazone
[2139-47-1]

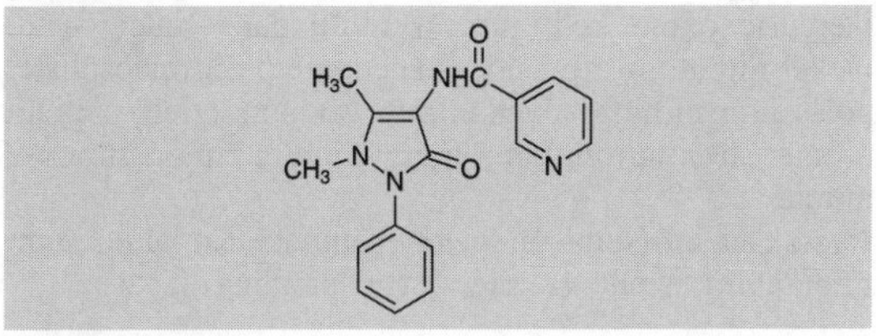

$C_{17}H_{16}N_4O_2$. M: 308.35.
Production:
- 4-aminoantipyrine + nicotinic acid (amide formation)

Uses: antirheumatic drug

niflumic acid
[4394-00-7]

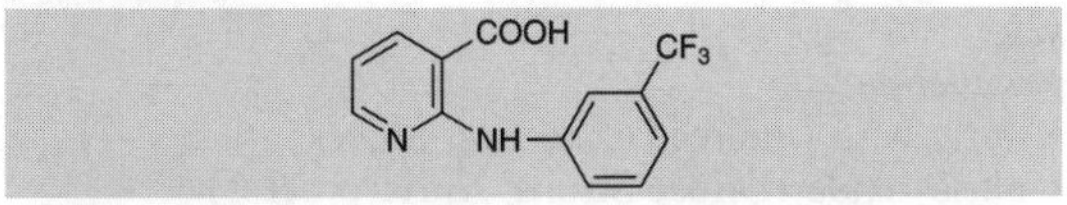

$C_{13}H_9F_3N_2O_2$. M: 282.21.
Production:
- 2-chloronicotinic acid + *m*-aminobenzotrifluoride (amine formation)

Uses: antirheumatic drug

nifuratel
[4936-47-4]

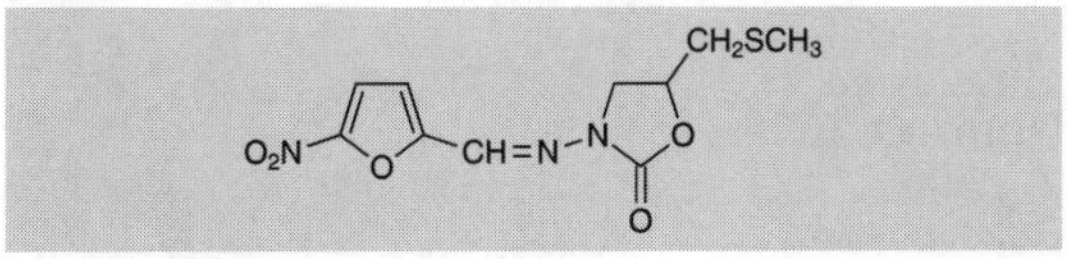

$C_{10}H_{11}N_3O_5S_1$. M: 285.28.

Production:
- methyl mercaptan + epichlorohydrin + hydrazine + diethyl carbonate + 5-nitrofurfural diacetate (epoxidation/amine formation/condensation/imine formation)

Uses: antiprotazoal drug

nifurtoinol
[1088-92-2]

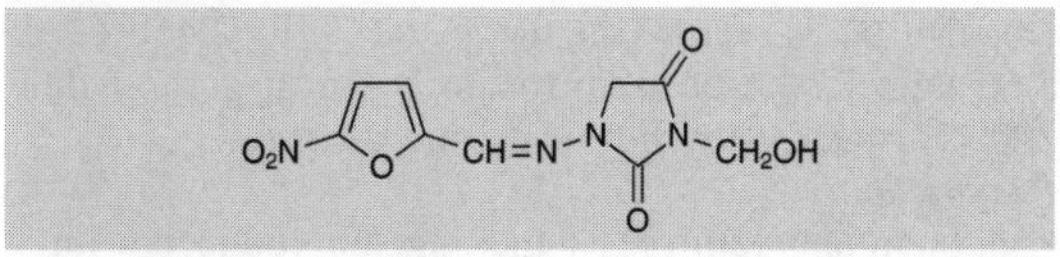

$C_9H_8N_4O_6$. M: 268.18.
Production:
- nitrofurantoin + formaldehyde (hydroxymethylation)

Uses: chemotherapeutic drug

nikethamide
[59-26-7]

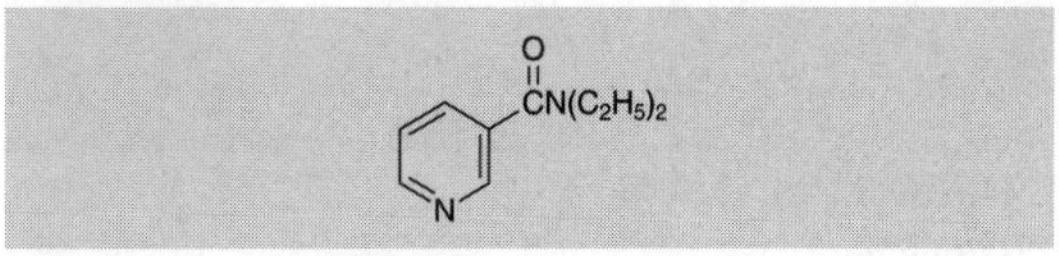

$C_{10}H_{14}N_2O_1$. M: 178.23.
Production:
- diethylamine + nicotinic acid (amide formation)

Uses: respiratory tract drug

nimodipine
[66085-59-4]

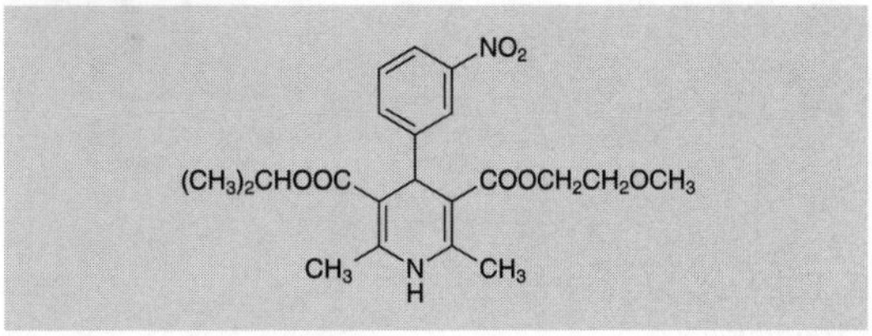

$C_{21}H_{26}N_2O_7$. M: 418.44.
Production:
- ethylene glycol monomethyl ether + methyl acetoacetate + *m*-nitrobenzaldehyde + isopropyl acetoacetate + ammonia (transesterification/carbonyl condensation/condensation)

Uses: vasodilator drug

nimorazole
1-(2-*N*-morpholinylethyl)-5-nitroimidazole; [6506-37-2]

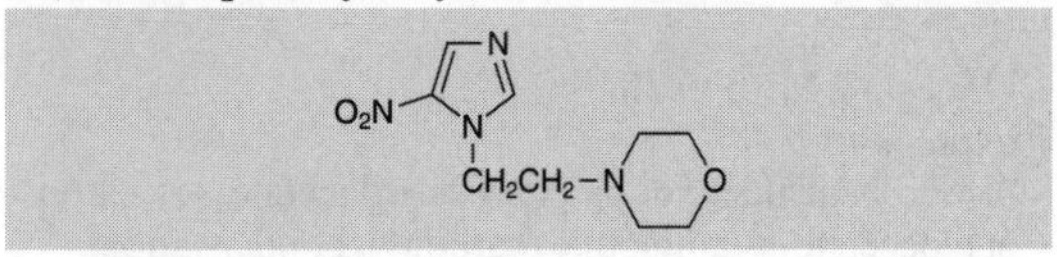

$C_9H_{14}N_4O_3$. M: 226.24.

Production:
- 4-nitroimidazole + 4-(2-hydroxyethyl)morpholine (amine formation)

Uses: antiprotazoal drug

niobium
[7440-03-1]

Nb

Nb_1. M: 92.91. Grey, ductile metal. MP: 2,468°C. d: 8.66 kg/l. Resistant to corrosion by most gases below 200°C. Attacked by hot acids and alkalis.
Production:
- niobium-tantalum ores (smelting; coproduced with tantalum)

Uses: high-temperature niobium-tungsten alloys (rocket motors, jet engines); superconducting alloys (magnets)

niridazole
[61-57-4]

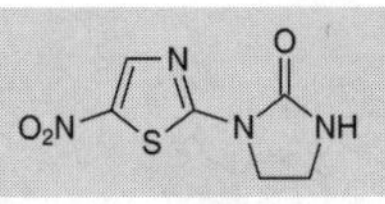

$C_6H_6N_4O_3S_1$. M: 214.21.
Production:
- monoethanolamine + phosgene + 2-amino-5-nitro-thiazole (phosgenation/isocyanate addition)

Uses: anthelmintic drug

nitrazepam
[146-22-5]

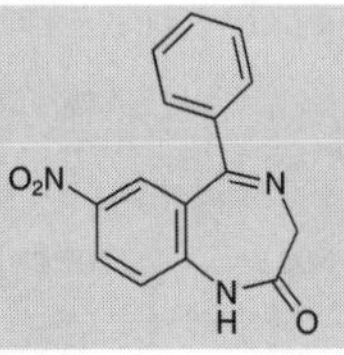

$C_{15}H_{11}N_3O_3$. M: 281.27.
Production:
- 2-amino-5-chlorobenzophenone + chloroacetyl chloride + ammonia (dechlorination/amide formation/condensation/nitration)

Uses: hypnotic/anticonvulsant drug

nitre *See:* potassium nitrate

nitre cake *See:* sodium bisulphate

nitrendipine
[39562-70-4]
$C_{18}H_{20}N_2O_6$. M: 360.36.
Production:
- *m*-nitrobenzaldehyde + ethyl acetoacetate + methyl acetoacetate + ammonia (carbonyl condensation/condensation)

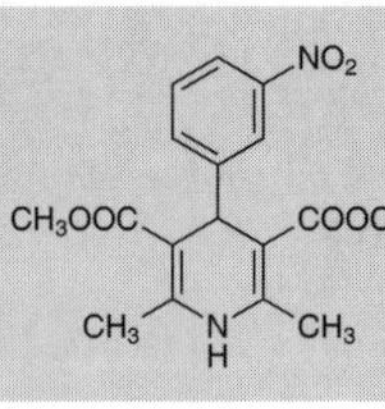

Uses: antihypertensive drug

nitric acid
[7697-37-2]

HNO₃

$H_1N_1O_3$. M: 63.02. Available commercially as a 50–70% HNO_3 solution in water. Colourless to pale yellow, fuming liquid. d: 1.33–1.40 kg/l. Soluble in water. See also nitric acid, concentrated.
Production:
- nitric oxide (oxidation process)

Derivatives: aluminium nitrate; ammonium nitrate; arsenic acid; barium nitrate; bismuth nitrate; cadmium nitrate; chloroauric acid; chloroplatinic acid; copper nitrate; glyoxylic acid; lead nitrate; mercuric nitrate; mercuric oxide, red; mercury fulminate; mucic acid; nickel nitrate; nitric acid, concentrated; nitrophosphate; potassium nitrate; silver nitrate; sodium azide; sodium nitrate; strontium nitrate; uranyl nitrate; zirconium oxy-nitrate

Uses: etchant (semiconductor manufacture); aluminium brightening agent; stainless steel pickling agent

nitric acid, concentrated
nitric acid, fuming; CNA; [7697-37-2]

HNO₃

$H_1N_1O_3$. M: 63.02. Anhydrous nitric acid containing 95–98% active matter. Colourless to yellow liquid. d: 1.50 kg/l (20°C). BP: 86°C. MP: -42°C. Soluble in water.
Production:
- nitric acid (indirect extraction process)
- nitric oxide (Direct Strong Nitric process)

Derivatives: adipic acid; anthraquinone; clopyralid; cyclonite; dinitroglycoluril; glyoxal; lead trinitroresorcinate; menadione; methylglyoxal dimethyl acetal; nitroethane; nitromethane; 1-nitropropane; 2-nitropropane; octogen; oxalic acid; pentaerythritol tetranitrate; tetranitroglycoluril; 1,3,5-triamino-2,4,6-trinitrobenzene; trimethyladipic acid; 1,3,5-trinitrobenzene

Uses: nitration/oxidation reagent

nitric oxide
[10102-43-9]

NO

N_1O_1. M: 30.01. Colourless gas. MP: -163°C. BP:

-152°C. Soluble in water. Reacts spontaneously with air to form nitrogen dioxide.

Production:
• ammonia (oxidation)

Derivatives: hydroxylamine phosphate; hydroxylamine sulphate; nitric acid; nitric acid, concentrated; nitrosyl hydrogen sulphate; sodium nitrite

nitrile rubber *See:* acrylonitrile-butadiene copolymers

nitrile rubber, hydrogenated
HNBR; Tornac (Nova)

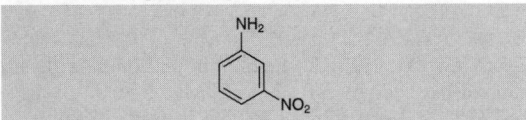

Rubber. Vulcanised by peroxides. The vulcanisate is characterised by its good thermal, oxidation, oil and chemical resistance.

Production:
• acrylonitrile-butadiene copolymers (hydrogenation)

Uses: automotive rubber components

nitrilotriacetic acid
NTA; [139-13-9]

$$N(CH_2COOH)_3$$

$C_6H_9N_1O_6$. M: 191.14. White, crystalline solid. MP: 230–235°C with decomposition. Solubility in water: 1.4 g/l (25°C) forming acidic solutions.

Production:
• hydrogen cyanide + formaldehyde + ammonia (cyanomethylation/nitrile hydrolysis; coproduced with iminodiacetic acid/glycine)

Derivatives: trisodium nitrilotriacetate

Uses: chelant/builder (industrial cleaners, detergents)

p-nitroacetanilide
4-acetamidonitrobenzene; [104-04-1]

$C_8H_8N_2O_3$. M: 180.16. Yellow, crystalline solid. MP: 216°C. Slightly soluble in water. Soluble in oxygenated solvents.

Production:
• acetic anhydride + *p*-nitroaniline (amide formation)
• acetanilide (nitration)

Derivatives: Acid Blue 41; *p*-aminoacetanilide

m-nitroaniline
3-nitroaniline; [99-09-2]

$C_6H_6N_2O_2$. M: 138.13. Yellow, crystalline solid. MP:

112–114°C. d: 0.91 kg/l (20°C). Insoluble in water. Slightly soluble in oxygenated solvents.

Production:
• *m*-dinitrobenzene (partial nitro reduction)

Derivatives: Acid Blue 29; *m*-aminoacetanilide; Direct Red 149; Disperse Blue 183; iocetamic acid; Mordant Yellow 1; 3-nitro-3'-hydroxy-2'-naphthanilide

o-nitroaniline
2-nitroaniline; [88-74-4]

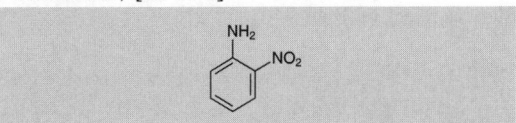

$C_6H_6N_2O_2$. M: 138.13. Yellow, crystalline solid. MP: 71–73°C. BP: 284°C. d: 0.90 kg/l (20°C). Soluble in hot water, oxygenated and chlorinated solvents.

Production:
• *o*-chloronitrobenzene + ammonia (ammoniation)

Derivatives: astemizole; 2-[2'-hydroxy-3',5'-bis(1-methyl-1-phenylethyl)]benzotriazole; 2-(2-hydroxy-3,5-di-*t*-butylphenyl)benzotriazole; 2-(2-hydroxy-5-methylphenyl)benzotriazole; 2-(2-hydroxy-5-*t*-octylphenyl)benzotriazole; *o*-phenylenediamine; Pigment Orange 2; Pigment Yellow 5

p-nitroaniline
4-nitroaniline; [100-01-6]

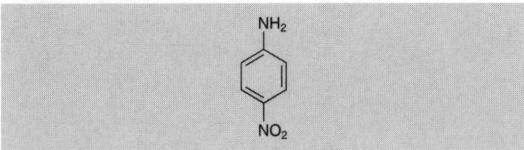

$C_6H_6N_2O_2$. M: 138.13. Yellow needles. MP: 147-149°C. Insoluble in water. Soluble in alcohol and ether.

Production:
• *p*-chloronitrobenzene + ammonia (ammoniation)

Derivatives: Acid Black 1; Acid Violet 3; 4'-amino-4-nitrodiphenylamine-2-sulphonic acid; 4,4'-diaminodiphenylamine-2-sulphonic acid; 2,6-dibromo-4-nitroaniline; 2,6-dichloro-4-nitroaniline; Direct Black 9; Direct Black 19; Direct Black 78; Direct Blue 120; Direct Green 26; Direct Yellow 44; Disperse Black 1; Disperse Black 2; Disperse Orange 3; Disperse Orange 25; Disperse Orange 29; Disperse Orange 138; Disperse Red 1; Disperse Red 17; Mordant Brown 18; Mordant Orange 1; *p*-nitroacetanilide; 4-nitroaniline-2-sulphonic acid; 4-(*p*-nitrophenyl)azo-2,5-dimethoxyaniline; *p*-phenylenediamine; Pigment Red 1; Pigment Yellow 4

4-nitroaniline-2-sulphonic acid
2-amino-5-nitrobenzenesulphonic acid; 5-nitro-2-aminobenzenesulphonic acid

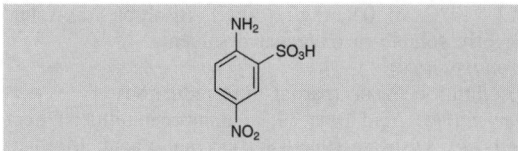

$C_6H_6N_2O_5S_1$. M: 218.18.
Production:
• *p*-nitroaniline (sulphonation)
Derivatives: Acid Violet 1; Direct Green 28; Reactive Blue 2; Reactive Blue 94

o-nitroanisole
[91-23-6]

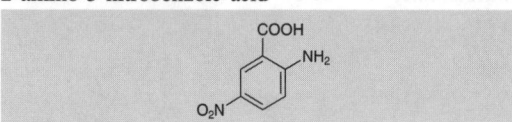

$C_7H_7N_1O_3$. M: 153.15. Yellow liquid. BP: 277°C. MP: 9°C. d: 1.25 kg/l (20°C). Insoluble in water. Soluble in oxygenated solvents.
Production:
• *o*-chloronitrobenzene + methanol (ether formation)
Derivatives:
o-anisidine; *o*-dianisidine

5-nitroanthranilic acid
2-amino-5-nitrobenzoic acid

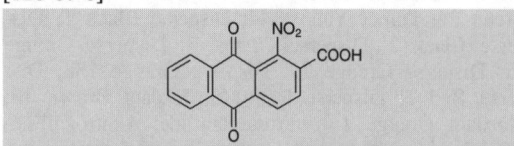

$C_7H_6N_2O_4$. M: 182.14. Yellow crystals. MP: 270-272°C. Soluble in hot water.
Production:
• phthalic anhydride + ammonia + sodium hypochlorite (nitration/amide formation/Hofmann degradation/decarboxylation)
Derivatives:
2-amino-5-nitrobenzonitrile; Direct Black 91

1-nitroanthraquinone-2-carboxylic acid
[128-67-6]

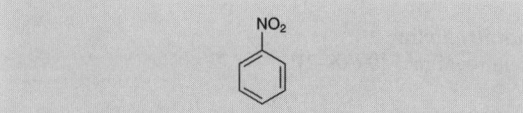

$C_{15}H_7N_1O_6$. M: 297.22. Solid. MP: 283–286°C. Soluble in alcohol and hot acetic acid.
Production:
• 2-methylanthraquinone (nitration/side-chain oxidation)
Derivatives:
Vat Blue 30; Vat Red 10; Vat Yellow 20

m-nitrobenzaldehyde
3-nitrobenzaldehyde; [99-61-6]

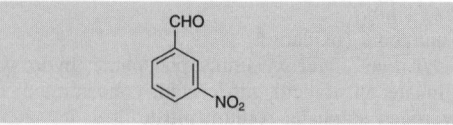

$C_7H_5N_1O_3$. M: 151.13. Yellow, crystalline powder. MP: 57–59°C. Insoluble in water. Soluble in oxygenated and chlorinated solvents.
Production:
• *m*-nitrotoluene (side-chain oxidation)
Derivatives: Acid Blue 3; *m*-hydroxybenzaldehyde; iopanoic acid; nicardipine; nimodipine; nitrendipine

o-nitrobenzaldehyde
2-nitrobenzaldehyde; [552-89-6]

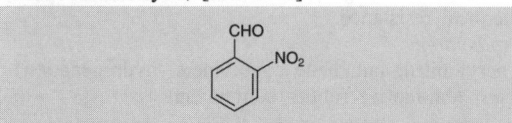

$C_7H_5N_1O_3$. M: 151.13. Pale yellow, crystalline solid. MP: 43–46°C. Slightly soluble in water. Soluble in oxygenated and chlorinated solvents.
Production:
• *o*-nitrotoluene (side-chain oxidation)
Derivatives: ambroxol; bromhexine; Fluorescent Brightener 199; nifedipine; nomifensine
Uses: analytical reagent

p-nitrobenzaldehyde
4-nitrobenzaldehyde; [555-16-8]

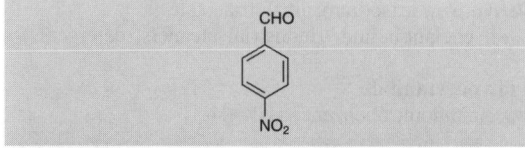

$C_7H_5N_1O_3$. M: 151.13. White crystals. MP: 104–106°C. Sublimes. d: 1.50 kg/l. Slightly soluble in water. Soluble in alcohol and aromatic solvents.
Production:
• *p*-nitrotoluene (side-chain oxidation)
Derivatives: acenocoumarol; chloramphenicol

nitrobenzene
[98-95-3]

$C_6H_5N_1O_2$. M: 123.12. Pale yellow liquid with an almond-like odour. BP: 211°C. MP: 5–6°C. d: 1.20 kg/l (15°C). Very slightly soluble in water. Soluble in most organic solvents.

Production:
• benzene (nitration)
Derivatives: p-aminophenol; aniline; Basic Violet 14; m-chloronitrobenzene; 3,3′-diaminodiphenyl sulphone; m-dinitrobenzene; hydrazobenzene; m-nitrobenzenesulphonic acid; quintozene; Solvent Black 5
Uses: extraction solvent (lubricating oil refining); process solvent (Friedel-Crafts reactions)

5-nitrobenzene-1,3-dicarboxylic acid
See: 5-nitroisophthalic acid

m-nitrobenzenesulphonic acid
3-nitrobenzenesulphonic acid; [5337-19-9]

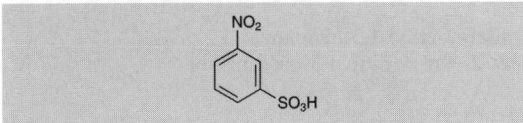

$C_6H_5N_1O_5S_1$. M: 203.17. Crystalline solid. MP: 70°C. Soluble in hot water and oxygenated solvents.
Production:
• nitrobenzene (sulphonation)
Derivatives: aniline-2,5-disulphonic acid; benzidine-2,2′-disulphonic acid; metanilic acid
Uses: dyestuffs intermediate

m-nitrobenzoic acid
3-nitrobenzoic acid; [121-92-6]

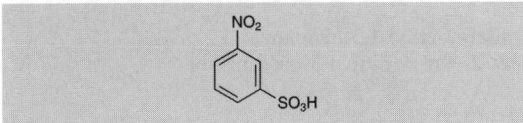

$C_7H_5N_1O_4$. M: 167.13. Yellow, crystalline solid. MP: 140–142°C. d: 1.49 kg/l (20°C). Slightly soluble in water. Soluble in oxygenated and chlorinated solvents.
Production:
• m-nitrotoluene (side-chain oxidation)
Derivatives: m-aminobenzoic acid; m-nitrobenzoyl chloride; Sulphur Red 7

o-nitrobenzoic acid
2-nitrobenzoic acid; [552-16-9]

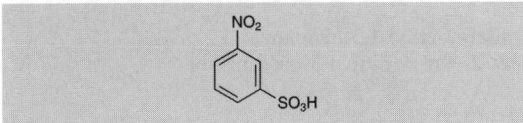

$C_7H_5N_1O_4$. M: 167.13. Yellowish-white crystals. MP: 147–148°C. d: 1.58 kg/l. Slightly soluble in water. Soluble in oxygenated solvents.
Production:
• o-nitrotoluene (side-chain oxidation)
Derivatives:
Acid Yellow 54; benzidine-3,3′-dicarboxylic acid; o-nitrobenzoyl chloride

p-nitrobenzoic acid
4-nitrobenzoic acid; [62-23-7]

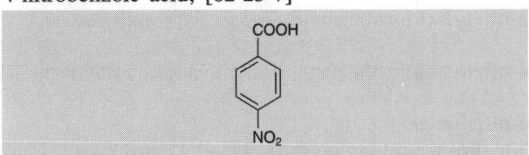

$C_7H_5N_1O_4$. M: 167.13. Colourless crystals. MP: 242°C. d: 1.55 kg/l (32°C). Sublimes. Insoluble in cold water. Soluble in hot water and acetone.
Production:
• p-nitrotoluene (side-chain oxidation)
Derivatives: p-aminobenzamide; p-aminobenzoic acid; n-butyl p-aminobenzoate; ethyl p-nitrobenzoate; p-nitrobenzoyl chloride

m-nitrobenzoyl chloride
3-nitrobenzoyl chloride; [121-90-4]

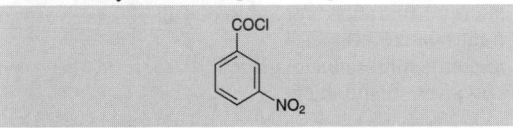

$C_7H_4Cl_1N_1O_3$. M: 185.57.
Production:
• m-nitrobenzoic acid (acid chloride formation)
Derivatives: N-m-aminobenzoyl-J acid; Diazo Brilliant Scarlet ROD; Direct Orange 75

o-nitrobenzoyl chloride
2-nitrobenzoyl chloride; [610-14-0]

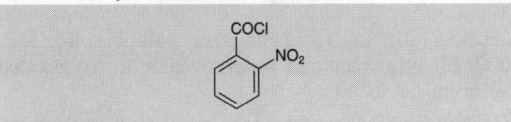

$C_7H_4Cl_1N_1O_3$. M: 185.57.
Production:
• o-nitrobenzoic acid (acid chloride formation)
Derivatives: glafenine; pirenzepine

p-nitrobenzoyl chloride
4-nitrobenzoyl chloride; [122-04-3]

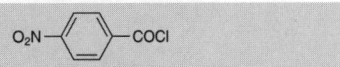

$C_7H_4Cl_1N_1O_3$. M: 185.57. Yellow, hygroscopic, crystalline solid with an unpleasant odour. MP: 72–74°C. Decomposed by water and alcohol.
Production:
• p-nitrobenzoic acid (acid chloride formation)
Derivatives:
folic acid; leucinocaine; methotrexate; procainamide
Uses: esterification reagent

nitrocellulose *See:* cellulose nitrate

4-nitro-2-chloroaniline *See:* 2-chloro-4-nitroaniline

3-nitro-1-chlorobenzene *See:* *m*-chloronitrobenzene

4-nitro-1-chlorobenzene *See:* *p*-chloronitrobenzene

4-nitro-*m*-cresol
5-hydroxy-2-nitrotoluene; 3-methyl-4-nitrophenol;
2-nitro-5-hydroxytoluene; [2581-34-2]

$C_7H_7N_1O_3$. M: 153.15. Crystalline solid. MP: 127-129°C. Slightly soluble in hot water. Soluble in oxygenated, chlorinated and aromatic solvents.
Production:
• *m*-cresol (nitration; coproduced with 6-nitro-*m*-cresol)
• *m*-cresol (nitrosation/oxidation)
Derivatives: fenitrothion

6-nitro-*m*-cresol
3-hydroxy-4-nitrotoluene; 3-methyl-6-nitrophenol;
2-nitro-5-methylphenol; [700-38-9]

$C_7H_7N_1O_3$. M: 153.15. Yellow, crystalline solid. MP: 56°C. Slightly soluble in water. Soluble in oxygenated and aromatic solvents.
Production:
• *m*-cresol (nitration; coproduced with 4-nitro-*m*-cresol)
Derivatives: butamifos; oxybuprocaine

m-nitro-*p*-cresol
4-hydroxy-3-nitrotoluene; 4-methyl-2-nitrophenol;
2-nitro-*p*-cresol; MNPC; [119-33-5]

$C_7H_7N_1O_3$. M: 153.15. Yellow solid. MP: 32–35°C. d: 1.24 kg/l (40°C). Slightly soluble in hot water. Soluble in oxygenated solvents.
Production:
• *p*-cresol (nitration)
Derivatives:
4-amino-3-nitrotoluene; *p*-cresidine
Uses: dyestuffs intermediate

nitroethane
[625-58-1]

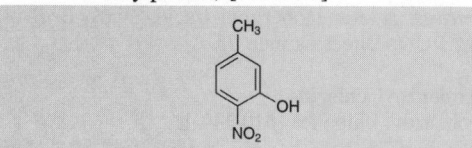

$C_2H_5N_1O_2$. M: 75.07. Liquid with a pleasant odour. BP: 112–115°C. MP: -50°C. d: 1.05 kg/l (20°C). Soluble in water. Miscible with oxygenated solvents.
Production:
• propane + nitric acid, concentrated (vapour-phase nitration; coproduced with nitromethane/2-nitropropane/1-nitropropane)
Derivatives: 2-amino-2-methyl-1,3-propanediol; hexetidine; norephedrine
Uses: solvent (adhesives)

2-nitro-2-ethyl-1,3-propanediol
See: 2-ethyl-2-nitro-1,3-propanediol

nitrofural
nitrofurazone; [59-87-0]

$C_6H_6N_4O_4$. M: 198.15.
Production:
• 5-nitrofurfural diacetate + semicarbazide hydrochloride (imine formation)
Uses: topical antiseptic

nitrofurantoin
[67-20-9]

$C_8H_6N_4O_5$. M: 238.16.
Production:
• hydrazine + chloroacetic acid + potassium cyanate + 5-nitrofurfural diacetate (amine formation/cyanate addition/condensation/imine formation)
Derivatives: nifurtoinol
Uses: antibacterial drug

nitrofurazone *See:* nitrofural

5-nitrofurfural diacetate
5-nitrofurfurylidene diacetate; [92-55-7]

$C_9H_9N_1O_7$. M: 243.17. Solid. MP: 90–92°C.
Production:
• furfural + acetic anhydride (diacetal formation/ esterification/nitration)
Derivatives:
nifuratel; nitrofural; nitrofurantoin

nitrogen
[7727-37-9]

$$N_2$$

N_2. M: 28.01. Colourless gas. BP: -196°C. d: 0.81 kg/l (-196°C). Sparingly soluble in water. The product is usually stored and transported in the liquified form. Nitrogen present in natural gas is often used as a source of this chemical in ammonia production.
Production:
• air (cryogenic separation; coproduced with oxygen)
Derivatives:
aluminium nitride; calcium cyanamide; silicon nitride
Uses:
cryogenic agent (food freezing and processing); blanketing gas (chemical, food, metallurgical production); hydraulic fluid (pneumatic controls, liquid transfer)

nitroglycerine
glycerol trinitrate; nitroglycerol; trinitrine; NG; [55-63-0]

$$\begin{array}{c} CH_2ONO_2 \\ | \\ CHONO_2 \\ | \\ CH_2ONO_2 \end{array}$$

$C_3H_5N_3O_9$. M: 227.08. Pale yellow liquid. MP: 13°C. d: 1.60 kg/l (15°C). Decomposes explosively if heated rapidly. Slightly soluble in water. Soluble in oxygenated, chlorinated and aromatic solvents.
Production:
• glycerol (nitration)
Uses: explosives; antianginal drug

nitroguanidine
NQ; [556-88-7]

$$\begin{array}{c} NH \\ || \\ H_2NCNHNO_2 \end{array}$$

$C_1H_4N_4O_2$. M: 104.07.
Production:
• guanidine nitrate (dehydration)
Uses: cartridge propellant

3-nitro-3'-hydroxy-2'-naphthanilide
3-hydroxy-2-naphth-3'-nitroanilide; Naphthol AS-BT; Azoic Coupling Component 17 (CI); 37515 (CI); [135-65-9]

$C_{17}H_{12}N_2O_4$. M: 308.30.
Production:
• β-oxynaphthoic acid + *m*-nitroaniline (amide formation)
Derivatives: Pigment Red 23
Uses: azoic dye coupling component

3-nitro-4-hydroxyphenylarsonic acid
4-hydroxy-3-nitrophenylarsonic acid; 3-nitro; Roxarsone; [121-19-7]

$C_6H_6As_1N_1O_6$. M: 337.96.
Production:
• phenol + arsenic trioxide (reaction/nitration)
Uses: growth stimulant (pigs, poultry)

4-nitroimidazole
5-nitroimidazole; [3034-38-6]

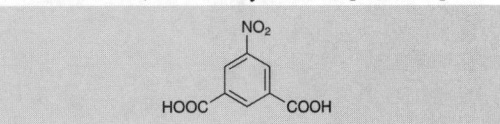

$C_3H_3N_3O_2$. M: 113.07. Solid. MP: 305°C.
Production:
• imidazole (nitration)
Derivatives: nimorazole

5-nitroimidazole *See:* 4-nitroimidazole

5-nitroisophthalic acid
5-nitrobenzene-1,3-dicarboxylic acid; [618-88-2]

$C_8H_5N_1O_6$. M: 211.13. Green crystals. MP: 250°C. Soluble in hot water. Insoluble in cold water.
Production:
• isophthalic acid (nitration)
Derivatives: 5-aminoisophthalic acid; dimethyl 5-nitroisophthalate; monoethyl 5-nitroisophthalate; nitrothalisopropyl; zinc 5-nitroisophthalate

nitro-lime *See:* calcium cyanamide

nitromethane
[75-52-5]

$$CH_3NO_2$$

$C_1H_3N_1O_2$. M: 61.04. Liquid with an unpleasant odour. BP: 101°C. MP: -29°C. d: 1.13 kg/l (25°C). Slightly soluble in water. Miscible with oxygenated and aromatic solvents.
Production:
• propane + nitric acid, concentrated (vapour-phase nitration; coproduced with nitroethane/1-nitropropane/2-nitropropane)
Derivatives: alitame; 2-aminomethyl-1-ethylpyrrolidine; 2-aminopropane-1,3-diol; azathioprine; 2-bromo-2-nitro-

propane-1,3-diol; chloropicrin; epinephrine; 1-methyl-amino-1-methylthio-2-nitroethylene; tris(hydroxymethyl)nitromethane
Uses: high-performance motor fuel; process solvent; solvent (coatings, printing inks, adhesives)

2-nitro-4-methoxyaniline *See:* 4-amino-3-nitroanisole

5-nitro-2-methoxyaniline *See:* 2-amino-4-nitroanisole

o-nitrophenol
2-nitrophenol; [88-75-5]

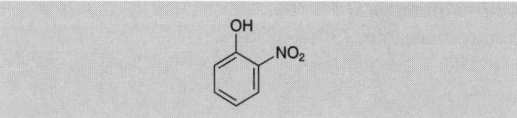

$C_6H_5N_1O_3$. M: 139.12. Pale yellow, crystalline solid. MP: 43–45°C. BP: 215°C. d: 1.29 kg/l (45°C). Soluble in hot water, aqueous alkali and aromatic solvents.
Production:
• *o*-chloronitrobenzene (hydration)
Derivatives: Acid Red 308; 2-amino-4-methylsulphonyl-phenol; *o*-aminophenol; carbofuran; Direct Red 180

p-nitrophenol
4-nitrophenol; [100-02-7]

$C_6H_5N_1O_3$. M: 139.12. Pale yellow, crystalline solid. MP: 112–114°C. Sublimes. Soluble in water, aqueous alkali, oxygenated and chlorinated solvents.
Production:
• *p*-chloronitrobenzene (hydrolysis)
Derivatives: *p*-aminophenol; *O*-ethyl *O*-(4-nitrophenyl) phenylphosphonothioate; 4,4'-oxydianiline; parathion; parathion-methyl; poly[(3,4'-diphenyl ether)-(*p*-phenyl-eneterephthalamide)]; Sulphur Green 1; Sulphur Green 11; tris(*p*-isocyanatophenyl) thiophosphate

4-(*p*-nitrophenyl)azo-2,5-dimethoxyaniline
Azoic Diazo Component 38 (CI); 37190 (CI)

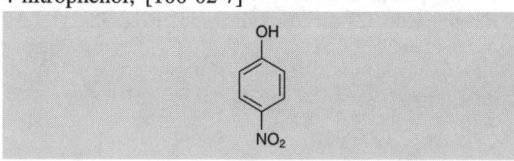

$C_{14}H_{14}N_4O_4$. M: 302.29.
Production:
• *p*-nitroaniline + 2,5-dimethoxyaniline (diazotisation/azo coupling)
Uses: azoic dye diazo component

nitrophosphate
Production:
• apatite + nitric acid + ammonia + carbon dioxide (Carbonitric process)
• apatite + nitric acid + sulphuric acid/ammonium sulphate/potassium sulphate (Sulphonitric process)
• apatite + nitric acid + ammonia + carbon dioxide (calcium separation process)
Uses: fertiliser

1-nitropropane
[108-03-2]

$CH_3CH_2CH_2NO_2$

$C_3H_7N_1O_2$. M: 89.10. Colourless liquid. BP: 129–131°C. MP: -108°C. d: 1.00 kg/l (20°C). Slightly soluble in water. Miscible with most organic solvents.
Production:
• propane + nitric acid, concentrated (vapour-phase nitration; coproduced with nitromethane/2-nitro-propane/nitroethane)
Derivatives: 2-aminobutanol; 2-ethyl-2-nitro-1,3-prop-anediol; morpholinomethyl-nitropropane adduct
Uses:
solvent (resins, lacquers, oils)

2-nitropropane
[79-46-9]

$(CH_3)_2CHNO_2$

$C_3H_7N_1O_2$. M: 89.10. Colourless liquid. BP: 118–120°C. MP: -93°C. d: 0.99 kg/l (20°C). Slightly soluble in water. Miscible with oxygenated and chlorinated solvents.
Production:
• propane + nitric acid, concentrated (vapour-phase nitration; coproduced with nitromethane/nitroethane/1-nitropropane)
Derivatives: 2-methyl-2-nitropropanol; oxetacaine
Uses: solvent (resins, coatings, printing inks, organic synthesis)

1-nitroso-2-naphthol
α-nitroso-β-naphthol; NBN; [131-91-9]

$C_{10}H_7N_1O_2$. M: 173.18. Yellow needles. MP: 104-106°C. Insoluble in water. Soluble in oxygenated and aromatic solvents.
Production:
• β-naphthol (nitrosation)
Derivatives:
1-amino-2-naphthol-4-sulphonic acid; Pigment Green 8
Uses: flotation collector

p-nitrosophenol
1,4-benzoquinone monooxime; [104-91-6]

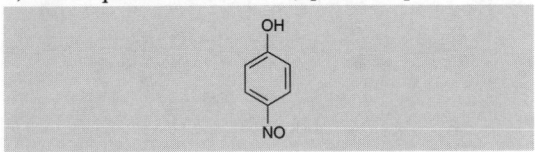

$C_6H_5N_1O_2$. M: 123.12. Pale yellow needles. MP: 126°C with decomposition. Slightly soluble in water. Soluble in oxygenated solvents.
Production:
• phenol + sodium nitrite (nitrosation)
Derivatives: *p*-quinonedioxime; Sulphur Blue 7; Sulphur Green 1; Sulphur Green 3; Sulphur Green 11; Vat Blue 42; Vat Blue 43

5-nitroso-2,4,6-triaminopyrimidine
5-nitroso-2,4,6-pyrimidinetriamine; [1006-23-1]

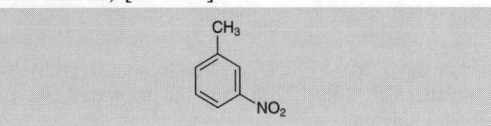

$C_4H_6N_6O_1$. M: 154.13. Red powder. MP: 345°C. Bulk density: 0.3 kg/l.
Production:
• malononitrile + guanidine hydrochloride (nitrile addition/nitrosation)
Derivatives: 5-chloro-2,4,6-trifluoropyrimidine; 5-methylpyrazine-2-carboxylic acid; 2,4,5,6-tetraaminopyrimidine sulphate; triamterene

nitrosyl chloride
[2696-92-6]

NOCl

$Cl_1N_1O_1$. M: 65.46. Orange-yellow gas. BP: -6°C. FP: -65°C. Hydrolysed by water. Manufactured *in situ*. Not a traded product.
Production:
• nitrosyl hydrogen sulphate + hydrogen chloride, anhydrous (reaction)
Derivatives: (−)-carvone; cyclohexanone oxime; lauryllactam; L-lysine

nitrosyl hydrogen sulphate
nitrosylsulphuric acid; [7782-78-7]

NO_2SO_3H

$H_1N_1O_5S_1$. M: 127.07. Crystalline solid. Decomposes in moist air or at temperatures above 50°C. Soluble in concentrated sulphuric acid.
Production:
• nitric oxide + sulphuric acid (addition)
Derivatives: caprolactam; nitrosyl chloride
Uses: diazotisation reagent

nitrothal-isopropyl
diisopropyl 5-nitroisophthalate; [10552-74-6]

$C_{14}H_{17}N_1O_6$. M: 295.29.
Production:
• isopropanol + 5-nitroisophthalic acid (esterification)
Uses:
fungicide

m-nitrotoluene
3-nitrotoluene; [99-08-1]

$C_7H_7N_1O_2$. M: 137.15. Yellow liquid. BP: 232°C. FP: 16°C. d: 1.16 kg/l (15°C). Insoluble in water. Soluble in oxygenated and aromatic solvents.
Production:
• toluene (nitration; byproduct of *p*-nitrotoluene/ *o*-nitrotoluene production)
• 4-amino-3-nitrotoluene (diazotisation/reduction)
Derivatives:
m-nitrobenzaldehyde; *m*-nitrobenzoic acid; *m*-toluidine

o-nitrotoluene
2-methylnitrobenzene; 2-nitrotoluene; [88-72-2]

$C_7H_7N_1O_2$. M: 137.15. Yellow liquid. BP: 222°C. MP: -4°C. d: 1.16 kg/l (20°C). Insoluble in water. Miscible with oxygenated and aromatic solvents.
Production:
• toluene (nitration; coproduced with *p*-nitrotoluene)
Derivatives:
o-aminobenzotrifluoride; dinitrotoluene; iminodibenzyl; 2-methylcyclohexylamine; *o*-nitrobenzaldehyde; *o*-nitrobenzoic acid; *o*-tolidine; *o*-toluidine

p-nitrotoluene
4-methyl-1-nitrobenzene; 4-nitrotoluene;
[99-99-0]

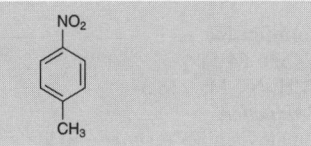

$C_7H_7N_1O_2$. M: 137.15. Colourless crystals. MP: 52–

54°C. BP: 238°C. d: 1.29 kg/l. Insoluble in water. Soluble in oxygenated and aromatic solvents.
Production:
• toluene (nitration; coproduced with *o*-nitrotoluene)
Derivatives:
2-chloro-4-nitrotoluene; dinitrotoluene; *p*-nitrobenzaldehyde; *p*-nitrobenzoic acid; 4-nitrotoluene-2-sulphonic acid; *p*-toluidine

4-nitrotoluene-2-sulphonic acid
p-nitrotoluene-2-sulphonic acid; [121-03-9]

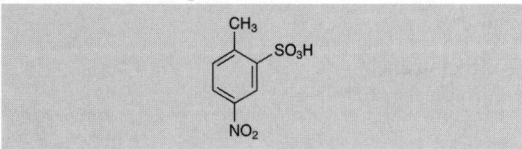

$C_7H_7N_1O_5S_1$. M: 217.20. Available as the dihydrate. Platelets. MP: 130–133°C. Soluble in water and oxygenated solvents.
Production:
• *p*-nitrotoluene (sulphonation)
Derivatives:
Acid Orange 19; Acid Yellow 25; 4-aminostilbene-2-sulphonic acid; 4,4′-dinitrostilbene-2,2′-disulphonic acid; Direct Orange 34; Direct Yellow 6

m-nitro-p-toluidine *See:* 4-amino-3-nitrotoluene

p-nitro-o-toluidine *See:* 2-amino-5-nitrotoluene

nitrous oxide
[10024-97-2]

N_2O

N_2O_1. M: 44.01. Colourless, liquified gas. BP: -88°C. MP: -91°C. Soluble in water and oxygenated solvents.
Production:
• ammonium nitrate (pyrolysis)
Uses:
inhalation anaesthetic drug; aerosol propellant gas

NMA *See:* *N*-methylolacrylamide

NMCHA *See:* *N*-methylcyclohexylamine

NMP
See: 2-methyl-2-nitropropanol; *N*-methylpyrrolidone

Nomex *See:* poly(*m*-phenyleneisophthalamide)

nomifensine
[24526-64-5]
$C_{16}H_{18}N_2$. M: 238.33.
Production:
• methylamine + styrene oxide + *o*-nitrobenzaldehyde (epoxidation/reductive amination/cyclisation)

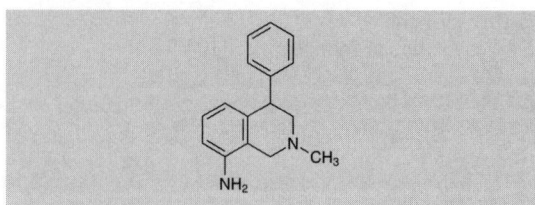

Uses: antidepressant drug

γ-nonalactone
4-hydroxynonanoic acid lactone; [104-61-0]

$CH_3(CH_2)_4$

$C_9H_{16}O_2$. M: 156.23. Yellowish liquid with a coconut-like odour. BP: 136°C (1.7 kPa). d: 0.97 kg/l (20°C).
Production:
• *n*-hexanol + acrylic acid (free-radical addition)
Uses: fragrance/flavouring ingredient

n-nonaldehyde
aldehyde C-9; *n*-nonanal; *n*-nonyl aldehyde; pelargonaldehyde; pelargonic aldehyde; [124-19-6]

$CH_3(CH_2)_7CHO$

$C_9H_{18}O_1$. M: 142.24. Colourless liquid with a floral odour. BP: 190–192°C. d: 0.83 kg/l (20°C). Insoluble in water. Soluble in alcohol.
Production:
• *n*-nonanol (alcohol oxidation)
Uses: fragrance ingredient

1,7-nonanedioic acid *See:* azelaic acid

n-nonanoic acid *See:* pelargonic acid

nonanol
3,5,5-trimethylhexan-1-ol; [2081-44-9]

$(CH_3)_3CCH_2CHCH_2CH_2OH$

$C_9H_{20}O_1$. M: 144.26. Colourless liquid. BP: 192–200°C. d: 0.83 kg/l (20°C). Insoluble in water. Flash point: 79°C (PMCC). See also isononanol.
Production:
• 2,4,4-trimethylpentene + synthesis gas (hydroformylation)
Derivatives: dinonyl phthalate; isononyl acetate; trinonyl trimellitate
Uses:
froth flotation foam modifier; antifoam (pesticide formulations); process solvent

n-nonanol
alcohol C-9; 1-nonanol; *n*-nonyl alcohol; pelargonic alcohol; [143-08-8]

$$CH_3(CH_2)_8OH$$

$C_9H_{20}O_1$. M: 144.26. Colourless liquid with a citrus odour. BP: 215°C. d: 0.83 kg/l (20°C). Insoluble in water. Miscible with oxygenated solvents.
Production:
• 1-octene + synthesis gas (hydroformylation)
Derivatives: n-nonaldehyde; pelargonic acid
Uses: fragrance ingredient

nonene, branched
isononene; propylene trimer

$$C_9H_{18}$$

C_9H_{18}. M: 126.24. Colourless liquid. BP: 134–139°C. d: 0.74 kg/l (15°C). Insoluble in water. The product is a mixture of isomers.
Production:
• propylene (phosphoric acid-catalysed oligomerisation; coproduced with dodecene, branched)
• gasoline, polymer (fractionation; coproduced with hexene, branched/heptene, branched/octene, branched/dodecene, branched)
Derivatives: dinonylnaphthalene; dinonylphenol; isodecanol; isoparaffin solvents; 2,2′-methylenebis(4-methyl-6-nonylphenol); neodecanoic acid; nonylphenol

nonoxynol *See:* nonylphenol ethoxylates

n-nonyl alcohol *See:* n-nonanol

n-nonyl methacrylate

$$CH_2=\underset{\underset{CH_3}{|}}{C}CO(CH_2)_8CH_3$$

$C_{13}H_{24}O_2$. M: 212.33.
Production:
• n-alkanol(C_8-C_{10}) + methyl methacrylate (transesterification)
Derivatives: polymethacrylates, oil-soluble; polymethacrylates, oil-soluble dispersants

nonylphenol
p-nonylphenol; [25154-52-3]

$$\text{(OH on benzene ring with } C_9H_{19} \text{)}$$

$C_{15}H_{24}O_1$. M: 220.35. Yellow liquid. BP: 288–302°C. d: 0.94 kg/l (30°C). Insoluble in water. Soluble in most organic solvents.
Production:
• nonene, branched + phenol (Friedel-Crafts alkylation; coproduced with dinonylphenol)

Derivatives: alkylphenol-polyamine adducts; calcium alkyl salicylates; 2-hydroxy-5-nonylacetophenoxime; 2-hydroxy-5-nonylbenzophenoxime; nonylphenol ethoxylates; nonylsalicylaldoxime; phenates, alkali-earth salts; phenates, sulphurised, alkali-earth salts; phenolic resins, oil-soluble, oil-reactive; Solvent Yellow 107; tris(nonylphenyl) phosphite
Uses: non-reactive epoxy resin diluent

nonylphenol ether phosphoric acid

$$\left[C_9H_{19}\text{—}\langle \rangle\text{—}O(CH_2CH_2O)_n \right]_x P(OH)_{3-x}$$

n = 4–12, x = 1, 2. Commercial products contain 4–12 moles EO. Viscous, amber liquids.
Production:
• nonylphenol ethoxylates + phosphorus pentoxide (esterification)
Uses: emulsifier (emulsion polymerisation); surfactant (acid/alkaline cleaners)

nonylphenol ethoxylates
nonoxynol (CTFA)

$$C_9H_{19}\text{—}\langle \rangle\text{—}O(CH_2CH_2O)_nH$$

n = 4–50. Liquid (4–7 moles EO), paste (13–15 moles EO) or solid (20–50 moles EO). Ranges in colour from pale yellow to white at higher EO contents. HLB: 8.9–18.2. Products with 4–7 moles EO are oil soluble, the remainder are water soluble.
Production:
• nonylphenol + ethylene oxide (epoxidation)
Derivatives:
ammonium nonylphenol ether sulphates; nonylphenol ether phosphoric acid; nonylphenol polyether amines; sodium nonylphenol ether sulphate
Uses: crude oil demulsifier ingredient; defoaming agent; emulsifier (oils, solvents, waxes); emulsifier (pesticides); emulsifier/protective colloid (emulsion polymerisation); spermicide preparations; surfactant (dishwashing detergents); surfactant/wetting agent (household/industrial cleaners); textile scouring agent; wetting/dispersing agent (household/industrial cleaners)

nonylphenol polyether amines
Surfonamine MNPA (Texaco Chemical)

$$C_9H_{19}\text{—}\langle \rangle\text{—}(OCH_2CH_2)_n(O\underset{\underset{CH_3}{|}}{C}HCH_2)_2NH_2$$

n = 1–10.
Production:
• nonylphenol ethoxylates + propylene oxide + ammonia (epoxidation/ammoniation)
Uses: corrosion inhibitor (fuel additives, lubricant additives, oilfield chemicals)

nonylsalicylaldoxime
P50 (ICI)

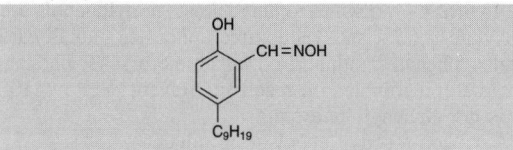

$C_{16}H_{25}N_1O_2$. M: 263.39.
Production:
• nonylphenol + chloroform + hydroxylamine
  sulphate (Reimer-Tiemann reaction/oxime formation)
Uses: copper extraction reagent

nootkatone
[4674-50-4]

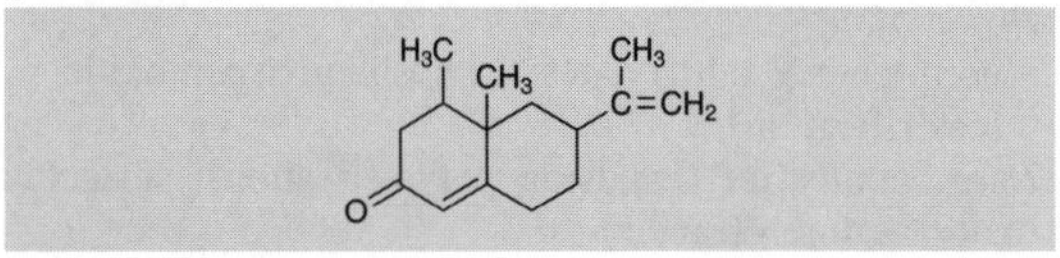

$C_{15}H_{22}O_1$. M: 218.34.
Production:
• orange oil (separation/oxidation)
Uses: flavouring ingredient

nopinene *See:* β-pinene

nopyl acetate
2-(2-acetoxyethyl)-6,6-dimethylnorpin-2-ene; [128-51-8]

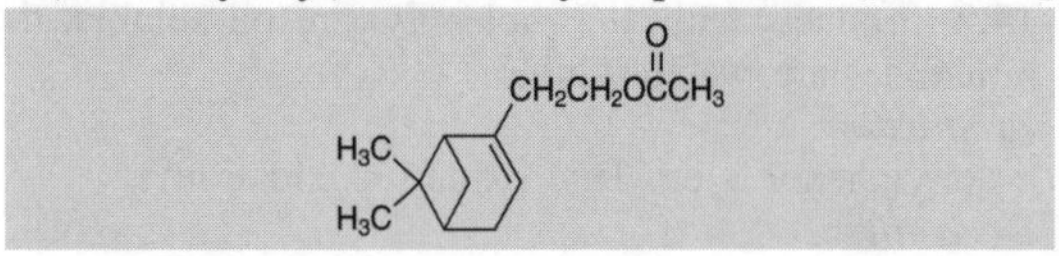

$C_{13}H_{20}O_2$. M: 208.30. The commercial product is the
(−)-enantiomer.
Production:
• β-pinene + paraformaldehyde + acetic anhydride
  (Prins reaction/esterification)
Uses:
fragrance ingredient (soap, household products)

norbornene
bicyclo[2.2.1]hept-2-ene; norbornylene; [498-66-8]

C_7H_{10}. M: 94.16.
Production:
• dicyclopentadiene + ethylene (Diels-Alder cycloaddition)
Derivatives: polynorbornene

nordazepam
desmethyldiazepam; DMDZ; [1088-11-5]
$C_{15}H_{11}Cl_1N_2O_1$. M: 270.71.

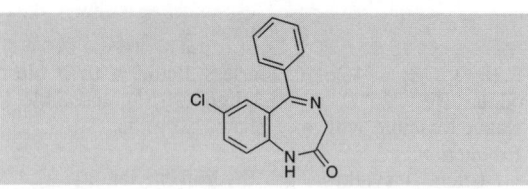

Production:
• 2-amino-5-chlorobenzophenone + ethyl glycinate
  hydrochloride (condensation)
• 2-amino-5-chlorobenzophenone + chloroacetyl
  chloride + hydroxylamine sulphate (imine
  formation/amide formation/cyclisation/acid-catalysed
  rearrangement/reduction)
Derivatives:
alprazolam; diazepam; prazepam
Uses: anxiolytic drug

norephedrine
phenylpropanolamine; PPA; [700-65-2]; [154-41-6]
(hydrochloride)

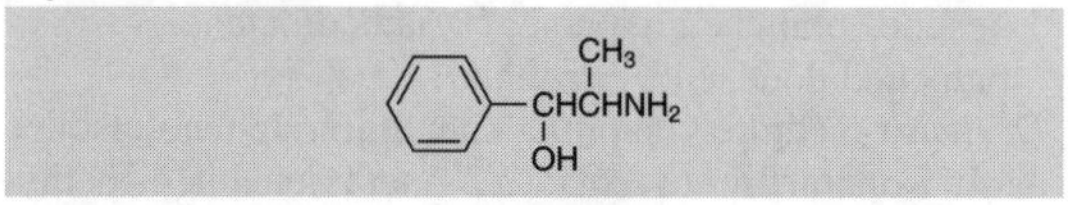

$C_9H_{13}N_1O_1$. M: 151.21. Available commercially as the
racemic salt. The D-*threo*-isomer, called norpseudo-
ephedrine, also has pharmacological properties.
Production:
• benzaldehyde + nitroethane (condensation/nitro
  reduction)
• propiophenone + isoamyl nitrite + ammonia (alpha
  carbonylation/reductive ammoniation)
Derivatives: DL-ephedrine
Uses:
anorexic/bronchodilator drug

norethisterone
norethindrone; [68-22-4]; [51-98-9] (acetate)

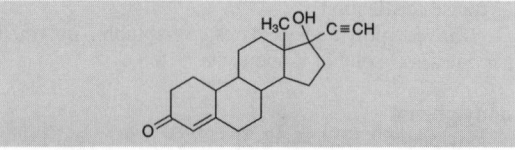

$C_{20}H_{26}O_2$. M: 298.43. Available as the alcohol or as
the acetate ester.
Production:
• 3-methoxyestra-2,5-diene-17-ol + acetylene
  (Oppenauer oxidation/ethynylation/hydrolysis)
Uses:
contraceptive drug

norfenefrine
[536-21-0]
$C_8H_{11}N_1O_2$. M: 153.19. Available commercially as the
racemic hydrochloride.

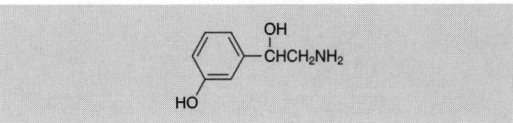

Production:
- *m*-hydroxyacetophenone + hexamethylenetetramine (alpha bromination/Delepine reaction/carbonyl reduction)

Uses: adrenergic drug

norfloxacin
[70458-96-7]

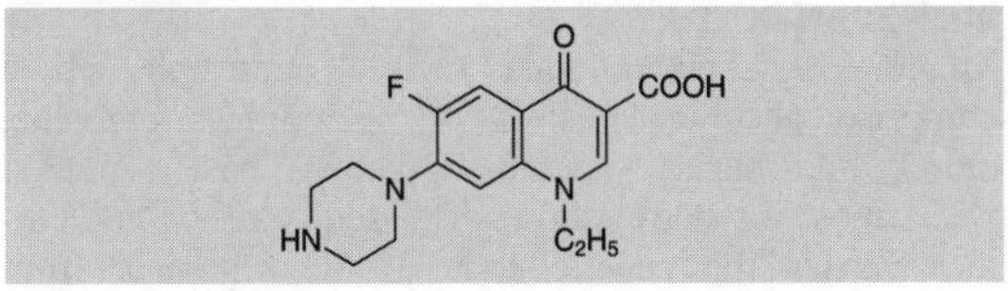

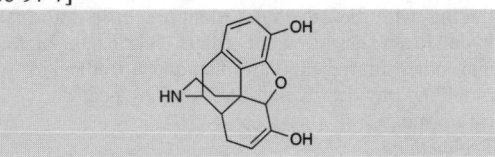

$C_{16}H_{18}F_1N_3O_3$. M: 319.34.
Production:
- 3-chloro-4-fluoroaniline + diethyl ethoxy-methylenemalonate + ethyl bromide + piperazine (amine formation/dehydration/amine formation/saponification/amine formation)

Uses:
antibacterial drug

norflurazon
4-chloro-5-methylamino-2-(3-trifluoromethylphenyl)pyr-idazin-3-one; [27314-13-2]

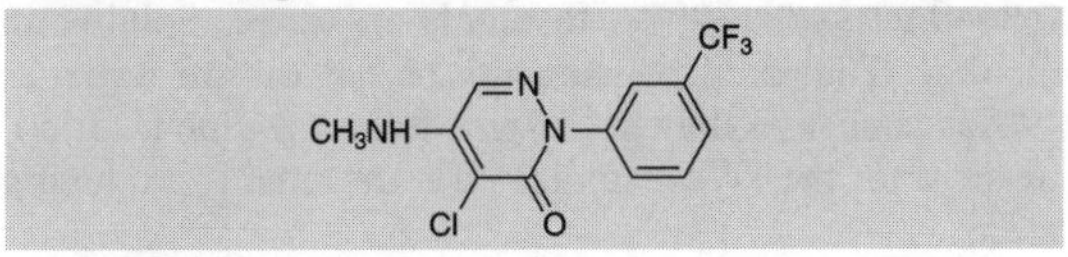

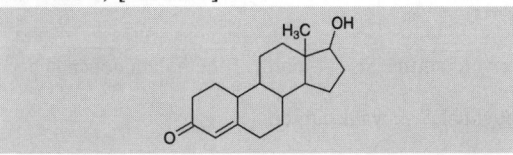

$C_{12}H_9Cl_1F_3N_3O_1$. M: 303.66.
Production:
- *m*-aminobenzotrifluoride + mucochloric acid + methylamine (diazotisation/reduction/condensation/amine formation)

Uses: herbicide

norgestrel
[6533-00-2]

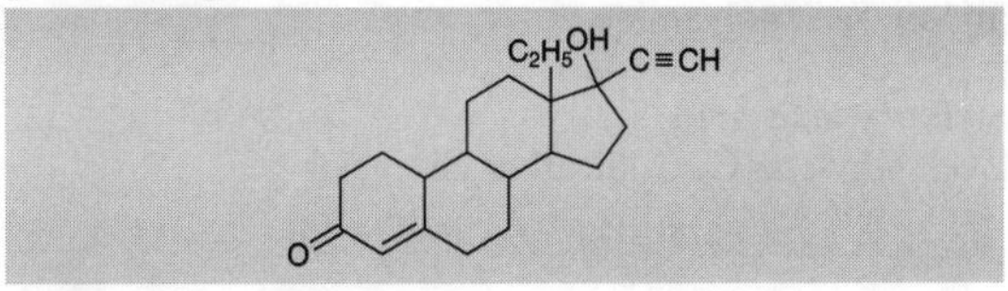

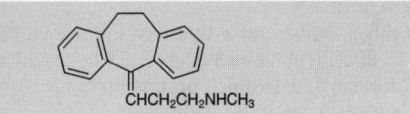

$C_{21}H_{28}O_2$. M: 312.45.
Production:
- 6-methoxy-1-tetralone + acetylene + 2-ethyl-cyclopentane-1,3-dione (multistep synthesis)

Uses:
contraceptive drug

normorphine
[466-97-7]

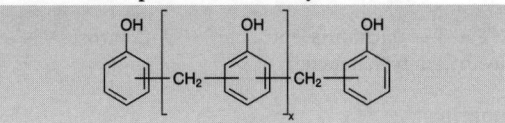

$C_{16}H_{17}N_1O_3$. M: 271.33.
Production:
- morphine + acetic anhydride (acetylation/demethylation/ester hydrolysis)

Derivatives:
nalorphine; naloxone; naltrexone
Uses: analgesic drug

19-nortestosterone
nandrolone; [434-22-0]

$C_{18}H_{26}O_2$. M: 274.41. Available as the dodecanoate, the cyclohexanecarboxylate, the cyclohexanepropionate or the furylpropionate salts.
Production:
- 3-methoxyestra-2,5-diene-17-ol (hydrolysis/rearrangement)

Uses: animal growth stimulant

nortriptyline

$C_{19}H_{21}N_1$. M: 263.39. The product is available as the free base or hydrochloride.
Production:
- dibenzosuberone + cyclopropyl bromide + methylamine (Grignard reaction/rearrangement/amine formation)

Uses: antidepressant drug

Noryl *See:* poly(phenylene oxide)

novolac resins
novolak resins; phenol-formaldehyde resin; PF

Thermosetting resin prepolymers formed by using a small (typically, 25%) molar excess of phenol over

formaldehyde. Bridging between the 2,4'- and 4,4'-positions is prevalent. The resin is usually cured by cross-linking with hexamethylenediamine or paraformaldehyde. Resin, curing agent, fillers, lubricants, pigments and other ingredients are blended together to form moulding powders which are cured by heat during thermoforming.
Production:
• phenol/xylenol, mixed/*m/p*-cresol/*o*-cresol + formaldehyde (acid-catalysed condensation)
Derivatives: epoxy-novolac resins
Uses:
fibre (flame-resistant clothing); rubber strength/hardness additive; binder (photoresists); binders (foundry moulds, grinding wheels, brake linings); moulding compounds (electrical housings/components, saucepan/cooker/iron handles, bottle caps, closures); moulding compounds (engine covers, pump vanes, generator parts)

novoldiamine *See:* 4-amino-1-diethylaminopentane

novonal *See:* valdetamide

noxiptiline hydrochloride
[3362-45-6] (free base)

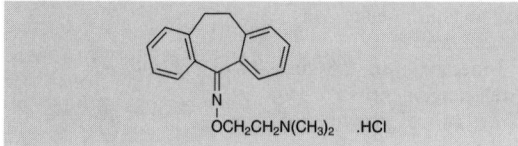

$C_{19}H_{23}Cl_1N_2O_1$. M: 330.86.
Production:
• dibenzosuberone + hydroxylamine hydrochloride + 2-dimethylaminoethyl chloride hydrochloride (imine formation/dehydrochlorination)
Uses: psychostimulant drug

NPG *See:* neopentyl glycol

NPGDA *See:* neopentyl glycol diacrylate

NQ *See:* nitroguanidine

NR *See:* natural rubber

NSA *See:* nicotinamide

NSP *See:* calcium superphosphate

NTA *See:* nitrilotriacetic acid; *N,N'*-dinitroso-*N,N'*-dimethylterephthalamide

nuarimol
2-chloro-4'-fluoro-α-(pyrimidin-5-yl)benzhydryl alcohol; [63284-71-9]

$C_{17}H_{12}Cl_1F_1N_2O_1$. M: 314.75.
Production:
• *o*-chlorobenzoyl chloride + fluorobenzene + 5-bromopyrimidine (Friedel-Crafts acylation/Grignard reagent formation/Grignard reaction)
Uses: fungicide

nucleic acids
Mixed, long-chain polymers of nucleotide units which comprise phosphate esters of pyrimidine (cytosine, uracil) and purine (adenine, guanine) bases coupled with ribose or deoxyribose. The sequence of nucleotides carries the genetic code of the organism from which they are extracted. Soluble in water.
Production:
• yeast (extraction)
Derivatives:
D-2-deoxyribose; D-ribose; sodium 5'-guanylate; sodium 5'-inosate

nutmeg oil
myristica oil; [8008-45-5]
Colourless to pale yellow liquid with a spicy odour. Produced from the nutmegs (fruit kernels) and arils (mace) of the nutmeg tree (*Myristica fragrans*). d: 0.86–0.92 kg/l (20°C). Insoluble in water. Soluble in alcohol. The main constituents of the oil are terpenes (90%) such as sabinene, α-pinene and β-pinene. Indonesia and the West Indies are the main producing areas.
Uses:
flavouring ingredient

NVP *See:* *N*-vinyl-2-pyrrolidone

NW acid *See:* Nevile-Winther acid

nylidrin *See:* buphenine

nylon *See:* polyamide

nylon waste acid
See: alkylene(C_4-C_6)dicarboxylic acids

OBCP *See:* *o*-benzyl-*p*-chlorophenol

OBSH *See:* 4,4'-oxybis(benzenesulphohydrazide)

ochre *See:* iron oxide yellow

OCNB *See:* *o*-chloronitrobenzene

Ocotea cymbarum oil
sassafras oil, Brazilian; [68153-14-0]
Yellow liquid with safrole odour. Produced from wild trees growing in Brazil, Paraguay and Colombia. MP: 8°C. d: ~1.09 kg/l (20°C). Miscible with alcohol.
Production:
• *Ocotea pretiosa* wood (steam distillation)
Derivatives: safrole
Uses:
flavouring ingredient

OCP
See: ethylene-propylene copolymers; *o*-chlorophenol

octabromodiphenyl oxide
octabrom; octabromodiphenyl ether; Saytex 111 (Ethyl)

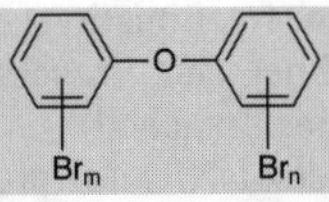

m+n = 8. $C_{12}H_2Br_8O_1$. M: 801.38. Solid. MP: 70-150°C. d: 2.8 kg/l. Insoluble in water. Soluble in chlorinated and aromatic solvents.
Production:
• diphenyl oxide + bromine (ring bromination)
Uses: fire-retardant additive (ABS resins, polyamides, polyethylene)

octadecyl alcohol *See:* stearyl alcohol

octadecyl vinyl ether
[930-02-9]

$$CH_2=CHO(CH_2)_{17}CH_3$$

$C_{20}H_{40}O_1$. M: 296.54. Solid or liquid. MP: 27°C. BP: 179–192°C (0.7 kPa).
Production:
• acetylene + stearyl alcohol (vinylation)
Derivatives:
poly(vinyl octadecyl ether)

octafluorocyclobutane
[115-25-3]
C_4F_8. M: 200.02.

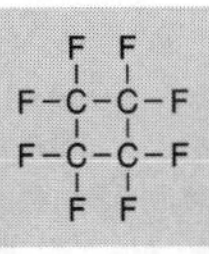

Production:
• chlorodifluoromethane (pyrolysis; byproduct of tetrafluoroethylene production)
Uses: aerosol propellant; refrigerant gas

γ-octalactone
4-hydroxyoctanoic acid lactone; [104-50-7]

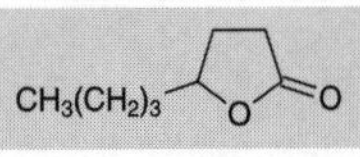

$C_8H_{14}O_2$. M: 142.20. Yellowish liquid with a fruity odour. BP: 116–117°C (1.3 kPa). d: 0.98 kg/l (20°C).
Production:
• *n*-amyl alcohol + acrylic acid (free-radical addition)
Uses: fragrance/flavouring ingredient

n-octaldehyde
aldehyde C-8; capryl aldehyde; caprylic aldehyde; *n*-octanal; *n*-octyl aldehyde; [124-13-0]

$$CH_3(CH_2)_6CHO$$

$C_8H_{16}O_1$. M: 128.22. Colourless liquid with a strong, citrus odour. BP: 168°C. MP: -21°C. d: 0.82 kg/l (20°C). Slightly soluble in water. Soluble in oxygenated and aliphatic solvents.
Production:
• *n*-octanol (alcohol oxidation)
Derivatives: α-hexylcinnamaldehyde
Uses: fragrance ingredient

octamethylcyclotetrasiloxane
[556-67-2]

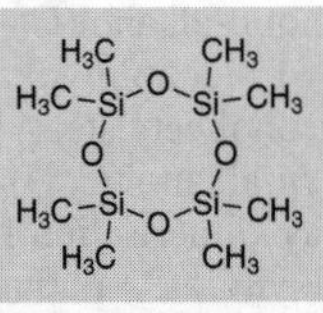

$C_8H_{24}O_4Si_4$. M: 296.62. Silicone oligomer available in a very pure form and therefore suitable for the production of high molecular weight polymers.
Production:
• dimethylsiloxane oligomers (fractionation/equilibration)
Derivatives:
poly(dimethylsiloxane), vinylated

octane-1,8-dicarboxylic acid *See:* sebacic acid

octane-1,8-dioic acid *See:* suberic acid

***n*-octanoic acid** *See:* caprylic acid

2-octanol
[123-96-6]

$$\underset{CH_3(CH_2)_5CHCH_3}{\overset{OH}{\mid}}$$

$C_8H_{18}O_1$. M: 130.23. Viscous liquid. BP: 180°C. MP: -39°C. d: 0.82 kg/l (20°C). Insoluble in water. Soluble in oxygenated solvents.
Production:
• ricinoleic acid (alkali fusion; coproduced with sebacic acid)
Derivatives: fluroxypyr-1-methylheptyl; methyl hexyl ketone; 1-octene
Uses: antifoam

3-octanol
[589-98-0]

$$\underset{CH_3CH_2CH_2CH_2CH_2CHCH_2CH_3}{\overset{OH}{\mid}}$$

$C_8H_{18}O_1$. M: 130.23. Colourless liquid with a mushroom-like odour.
Production:
• ethyl *n*-amyl ketone (carbonyl reduction)
Uses: fragrance ingredient

n-octanol
alcohol C-8; caprylic alcohol; 1-octanol; octan-1-ol; *n*-octyl alcohol; [111-87-5]

$$CH_3(CH_2)_7OH$$

$C_8H_{18}O_1$. M: 130.23. Colourless liquid with pungent odour. MP: -16°C. BP: 194–195°C. d: 0.83 kg/l (20°C). Insoluble in water. Soluble in oxygenated solvents. Competes with *n*-alkanol(C_7–C_9).
Production:
• ethylene (Alfol/Epal processes; coproduced with *n*-hexanol/*n*-decanol/*n*-alkanol(C_8-C_{10})/lauryl alcohol, narrow-cut/myristyl alcohol/*n*-alkanol(C_{12}-C_{14})/cetyl alcohol/stearyl alcohol/cetylstearyl alcohol/ *n*-alkanol(C_{12}-C_{18})/*n*-alkanol(C_{20+}))
• butadiene (Kuraray dimerisation-hydration process)
Derivatives: di-*n*-alkyl(C_7-C_9) phthalate; dimethyloctylamine; *n*-octaldehyde; *n*-octyl bromide; *n*-octyl chloride; *n*-octyl gallate; tri-*n*-alkyl(C_7-C_9) trimellitate; tri-*n*-octylamine; γ-undecalactone

2-octanone *See:* methyl hexyl ketone

3-octanone *See:* ethyl *n*-amyl ketone

1-octene
octene-1; 1-octylene; [111-66-0]

$$CH_3(CH_2)_5CH=CH_2$$

C_8H_{16}. M: 112.22. Colourless liquid. FP: -101°C. BP: 121°C. d: 0.72 kg/l (20°C). Insoluble in water. Soluble in alcohol, hydrocarbon and chlorinated solvents.
Production:
• ethylene (Ziegler oligomerisation; coproduced with 1-butene/1-hexene/1-decene/1-dodecene/α-olefins (C_{12}-C_{14})/α-olefins(C_{14}-C_{16})/α-olefins(C_{16}-C_{18})/ α-olefins(C_{18+}))
• 2-octanol (dehydration)
Derivatives:
n-alkanol(C_7-C_9); *n*-alkanol(C_9-C_{11}); dinocap; *n*-nonanol; octenylsuccinic anhydride; *n*-octyl mercaptan; polyethylene, very low-density; tri-*n*-octylaluminium; tri-*n*-octylphosphine oxide

octene, branched
di-*n*-butene; DNB

$$C_8H_{16}$$

C_8H_{16}. M: 112.22. Colourless liquid with pungent odour. BP: 100–105°C. d: 0.72 kg/l (15°C). The isomer distribution varies somewhat with the production route. Octene produced from raffinate II has greater linearity than that from polymer gasoline but still has an average of 1.1–1.3 side-chains per molecule. See also 2,4,4-trimethylpentene.
Production:
• gasoline, polymer (fractionation; coproduced with hexene, branched/heptene, branched/nonene, branched/dodecene, branched)
• raffinate II (Dimersol X/Octol processes; coproduced with dodecene, branched)
Derivatives:
isononanol; isoparaffin solvents

1-octen-3-ol
[3391-86-4]

$$\underset{CH_3(CH_2)_4CHCH=CH_2}{\overset{OH}{\mid}}$$

$C_8H_{16}O_1$. M: 128.22.
Production:
• *n*-hexaldehyde + acetylene (ethynylation/ hydrogenation)
Derivatives: ethyl *n*-amyl ketone
Uses: fragrance ingredient

octenylsuccinic anhydride
n-octenylsuccinic anhydride; OSA

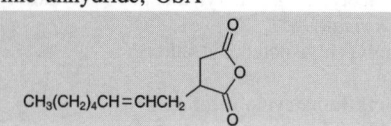

$C_{12}H_{18}O_3$. M: 210.27.

Production:
• 1-octene + maleic anhydride (ene reaction)
Uses: corrosion inhibitor

octhilinone *See:* 2-*n*-octyl-4-isothiazolinone

octodrine
1,5-dimethylhexylamine; [543-82-8]

$$(CH_3)_2CHCH_2CH_2CH_2\overset{\overset{\displaystyle CH_3}{|}}{C}HNH_2$$

$C_8H_{19}N_1$. M: 129.25. Liquid. BP: 155°C.
Production:
• α-methylheptenone + ammonia (amine formation)
Uses: decongestant drug

octogen
cyclotetramethylenetetranitramine; 1,3,5,7-tetranitro-1,3,5,7-tetraazacyclooctane; HMX; [2691-41-0]

$$\begin{array}{c} NO_2 \\ | \\ N \\ O_2N-N \qquad N-NO_2 \\ N \\ | \\ NO_2 \end{array}$$

$C_4H_8N_8O_8$. M: 296.15.
Production:
• hexamethylenetetramine + ammonium nitrate + paraformaldehyde + nitric acid, concentrated (Bachmann process)
Uses: explosives

N-t-octylacrylamide

$$CH_2=CH\overset{\overset{\displaystyle O}{\|}}{C}NHC_8H_{17}$$

$C_{11}H_{21}N_1O_1$. M: 183.30.
Production:
• acrylonitrile + 2,4,4-trimethylpentene (Ritter reaction/hydration)
Uses:
acrylic resin hydrophobic comonomer

n-octyl alcohol *See:* *n*-octanol

n-octylamine
1-aminooctane; [111-86-4]

$$CH_3(CH_2)_7NH_2$$

$C_8H_{19}N_1$. M: 129.25. Liquid. MP: -7°C. d: 0.78 kg/l (25°C). Insoluble in water. Flash point: 70°C (OC).
Production:
• caprylic acid + ammonia (nitrile formation/nitrile reduction)
Derivatives:
2-*n*-octyl-4-isothiazolinone

t-octylamine
octylamine

$$C_5H_{11}\overset{\overset{\displaystyle CH_3}{|}}{\underset{\underset{\displaystyle CH_3}{|}}{C}}-NH_2$$

$C_8H_{19}N_1$. M: 129.25.
Production:
• 2,4,4-trimethylpentene + hydrogen cyanide (Ritter reaction)
Derivatives: hindered-amine cyanurates, polymeric

n-octyl bromide
1-bromooctane; [111-83-1]

$$CH_3(CH_2)_7Br$$

$C_8H_{17}Br_1$. M: 193.13. Liquid. BP: 202°C. MP: -55°C. d: 1.12 kg/l (20°C). Insoluble in water. Soluble in oxygenated solvents.
Production:
• *n*-octanol + hydrogen bromide, anhydrous (alcohol bromination)
Derivatives: 2-hydroxy-4-octoxybenzophenone; methyl *n*-nonyl ketone

n-octyl chloride
caprylic chloride; octyl chloride; [111-85-3]

$$CH_3(CH_2)_7Cl$$

$C_8H_{17}Cl_1$. M: 148.68. Liquid. d: 0.87 kg/l (20°C). Flash point: 62°C (PMCC). Commercial products have 95% C_8 content.
Production:
• *n*-octanol + hydrogen chloride, anhydrous (alcohol chlorination)
Derivatives:
dimethyldioctylammonium chloride; tetra-*n*-octyltin

n-octyldimethylamine *See:* dimethyloctylamine

octyl epoxystearate *See:* 2-ethylhexyl epoxystearate

octyl epoxytallate *See:* isooctyl epoxytallate

n-octyl gallate
octyl gallate; E311 (EC); [1034-01-1]

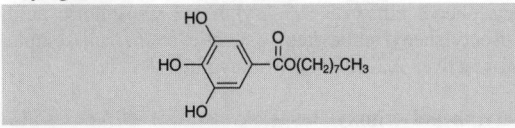

$C_{15}H_{22}O_5$. M: 282.33. White crystals. MP: 98–100°C. Insoluble in water. Soluble in oxygenated solvents. Not approved for food use in the USA.
Production:
• *n*-octanol + gallic acid (esterification)
Uses: antioxidant (oils, fats, cereals)

2-n-octyl-4-isothiazolinone
octhilinone; Kathon LM (Rohm and Haas); Skane M-8 (Rohm and Haas); [26530-20-1]

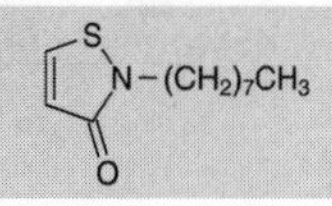

$C_{11}H_{19}N_1O_1S_1$. M: 213.34.
Production:
• acryloyl chloride + *n*-octylamine + sulphur dichloride (amide formation/sulphurisation/ dehydrochlorination)
Uses:
fungicide/wound protectant (fruit trees); biocide (water treatment, paints, latices); preservative (fabrics, leather)

n-octyl mercaptan
1-octanethiol; [111-88-6]

$C_8H_{18}S_1$. M: 146.29. Colourless liquid with a mild odour. BR: 194–202°C. FP: -49°C. d: 0.84 kg/l (15°C). Insoluble in water. Soluble in alcohol.
Production:
• 1-octene + hydrogen sulphide (anti-Markownikoff addition)
Derivatives: 2,4-bis(*n*-octylthio)-6-(4-hydroxy-3,5-di-*t*-butylanilino)-1,3,5-triazine; octylthiochloroformate; perfluorooctanesulphonic acid

octyl methacrylate *See:* 2-ethylhexyl methacrylate

octyl nitrate *See:* 2-ethylhexyl nitrate

octyl palmitate *See:* 2-ethylhexyl palmitate

p-t-octylphenol

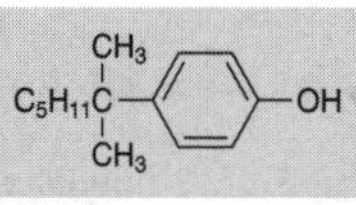

$C_{14}H_{22}O_1$. M: 206.33.
Production:
• 2,4,4-trimethylpentene + phenol (Friedel-Crafts alkylation)
Derivatives: 2-(2-hydroxy-5-*t*-octylphenyl)benzotriazole; octylphenol ethoxylates; octylphenyl phosphoric acid; *p-t*-octylphenyl salicylate; phenolic resins, oil-soluble, oil-reactive; 2,2'-thiobis(4-*t*-octylphenol)

octylphenol ethoxylates
octoxynol (CTFA)

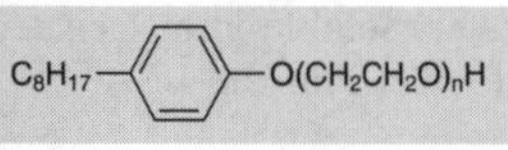

n = 6–40. Liquid (6–11 moles EO). Product is usually sold as a solution in water when the EO content is greater than 11 moles. HLB: 11.0–17.3. Soluble in water when EO content greater than 8 moles.
Production:
• *p-t*-octylphenol + ethylene oxide (epoxidation)
Uses: emulsifier (aromatic oils, solvents); surfactant/ wetting agent (household/industrial cleaners)

octylphenyl phosphoric acid
octylphenyl acid phosphate

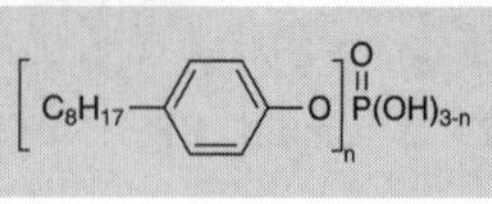

n = 1, 2.
Production:
• *p-t*-octylphenol + phosphorus pentoxide (esterification)
Uses: extraction agent (uranium ore)

p-t-octylphenyl salicylate
OPS

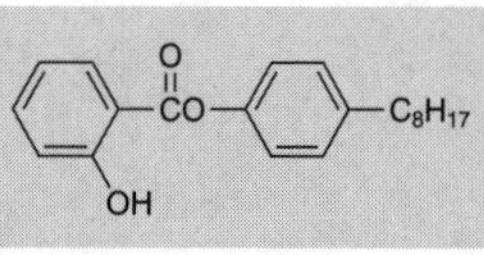

$C_{21}H_{26}O_3$. M: 326.44.
Production:
• *p-t*-octylphenol + salicylic acid (esterification)
Uses: light stabiliser (plastics)

octyl salicylate *See:* 2-ethylhexyl salicylate

octyl stearate *See:* 2-ethylhexyl stearate

octylthiochloroformate
[13889-96-8]

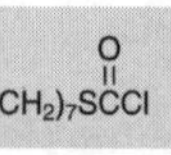

$C_9H_{17}Cl_1O_1S_1$. M: 208.75. Liquid. BP: 132°C (1.4 kPa). MP: <-15°C.
Production:
• *n*-octyl mercaptan + phosgene (phosgenation)
Derivatives: pyridate

ODA *See:* 4,4'-oxydianiline

ODCB *See:* *o*-dichlorobenzene

ODPA *See:* diphenylamine, octylated; 4,4'-oxydiphthalic anhydride

ofurace
α-2-chloro-*N*-2,6-xylylacetamido-γ-butyrolactone; [58810-48-3]
$C_{14}H_{16}Cl_1N_1O_3$. M: 281.74.

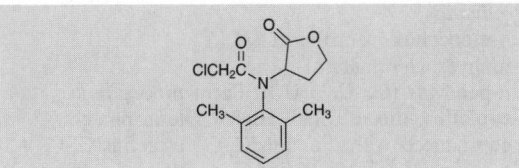

Production:
- γ-butyrolactone + 2,6-xylidine + chloroacetyl chloride (alpha chlorination/amine formation/amide formation)

Uses: fungicide

oil, vulcanised *See:* factice

OIP *See:* o-isopropylphenol

oiticica oil
Drying oil containing about 75% (+)-licanic acid ($C_{18:3}$, conjugated with a γ-ketone group). d: 0.97 kg/l. Varnishes made from oiticica oil are similar to those made from tung oil. The oil is extracted from *Licania rigida* nuts which are collected from wild trees in NE Brazil.
Uses: alkyd resin comonomer; drying oil (paints, printing inks)

olealkonium chloride
See: oleylbenzyldimethylammonium chloride

oleamide
octadecenamide; oleic acid amide; [301-02-0]

$$CH_3(CH_2)_7CH=CH(CH_2)_7CONH_2$$

$C_{18}H_{35}N_1O_1$. M: 281.49. White, waxy beads. MP: 66–76°C. Iodine value: 80–95 g I_2/100 g. Insoluble in water.
Production:
- oleic acid + ammonia (amide formation)
Derivatives: oleamide ethoxylates
Uses: plastics processing lubricant; slip improvement additive (printing ink); polyethylene slip agents; solubiliser (oil-soluble dyestuffs)

oleamide ethoxylates

$$CH_3(CH_2)_7CH=CH(CH_2)_7CNH(CH_2CH_2O)_nH$$

n = 2–10.
Production:
- oleamide + ethylene oxide (epoxidation)
Uses:
emulsifier/dispersant (emulsion polymerisation, cleaners)

oleamidopropyl betaine
[25054-76-6]
$C_{25}H_{48}N_2O_3$. M: 424.66. Available as a 30% solution in water.

$$CH_3(CH_2)_7CH=CH(CH_2)_7CNHCH_2CH_2CH_2\overset{+}{N}CH_2COO^-$$

Production:
- oleamidopropyldimethylamine + sodium chloroacetate (quaternisation)
Uses:
mild, high-foaming surfactant (shampoos, toiletries)

oleamidopropyldimethylamine
[109-28-4]

$$CH_3(CH_2)_7CH=CH(CH_2)_7CNHCH_2CH_2CH_2N(CH_3)_2$$

$C_{23}H_{46}N_2O_1$. M: 366.63. Soft solid.
Production:
- oleic acid + 3-dimethylaminopropylamine (amide formation)
Derivatives: oleamidopropyl betaine

oleamine *See:* oleylamine

olefin copolymers *See:* ethylene-propylene copolymers

α-olefins, mixed

$$CH_3(CH_2)_nCH=CH_2$$

n = 6–18. Intermediate stream forming the feed to the metathesis section of the Shell Higher Olefin process. Not a commercial product.
Production:
- ethylene (Ziegler oligomerisation)
Derivatives:
n-olefins(C_6-C_8); n-olefins(C_8-C_{10}); n-olefins(C_{10}-C_{13}); n-olefins(C_{11}-C_{12}); n-olefins(C_{11}-C_{14}); n-olefins(C_{13}-C_{14})

α-olefins(C_{12}-C_{14})

$$CH_3(CH_2)_nCH=CH_2$$

n = 9, 11. Colourless liquid. BP: 213–250°C. d: 0.76 kg/l (25°C). Commercial products contain 62–72% C_{12}, 28–38% C_{14}.
Production:
- ethylene (Ziegler oligomerisation; coproduced with 1-butene/1-hexene/1-octene/1-decene/1-dodecene/α-olefins(C_{14}-C_{16})α-olefins(C_{16}-C_{18})/α-olefins(C_{18+})/)
Derivatives: n-alkanol(C_{13}-C_{15}); dialkylbenzene; dodecylbenzene, linear

α-olefins(C_{14}-C_{16})

$$CH_3(CH_2)_nCH=CH_2$$

n = 11, 13.
Production:
- ethylene (Ziegler oligomerisation; coproduced with 1-butene/1-hexene/1-octene/1-decene/1-dodecene/

α-olefins(C$_{12}$-C$_{14}$)α-olefins(C$_{16}$-C$_{18}$)/α-olefins(C$_{18+}$))
Derivatives: sodium α-olefin(C$_{14}$-C$_{16}$) sulphonate

α-olefins(C$_{16}$-C$_{18}$)

$$CH_3(CH_2)_nCH=CH_2$$

n = 13–15. C$_{17}$H$_{34}$. M: 238.46. Colourless liquid. BP: 285–316°C. d: 0.78 kg/l (25°C). The commercial product is available with various proportions of C$_{16}$ to C$_{18}$.
Production:
• ethylene (Ziegler oligomerisation; coproduced with 1-butene/1-hexene/1-octene/1-decene/1-dodecene/ α-olefins(C$_{12}$-C$_{14}$)/α-olefins(C$_{14}$-C$_{16}$)/α-olefins(C$_{18+}$))
Derivatives:
sodium α-olefin(C$_{15}$-C$_{18}$) sulphonate

α-olefins(C$_{18+}$)

$$CH_3(CH_2)_nCH=CH_2$$

n ≥ 15.
Production:
• ethylene (Ziegler oligomerisation; coproduced with 1-butene/1-hexene/1-octene/1-decene/1-dodecene/ α-olefins(C$_{12}$-C$_{14}$)/α-olefins(C$_{14}$-C$_{16}$)α-olefins(C$_{16}$-C$_{18}$))
Derivatives: alkylbenzene, long-chain

n-olefins(C$_6$-C$_8$)

$$CH_3(CH_2)_mCH=CH(CH_2)_nCH_3$$

m+n = 2–4. C$_7$H$_{14}$. M: 98.19. Colourless liquid. BP: 63–123°C. d: 0.61–0.71 kg/l (25°C).
Production:
• α-olefins, mixed (Shell Higher Olefin process; coproduced with *n*-olefins(C$_8$-C$_{10}$)/*n*-olefins(C$_{10}$-C$_{13}$)/ *n*-olefins(C$_{11}$-C$_{12}$)/*n*-olefins(C$_{11}$-C$_{14}$)/*n*-olefins(C$_{13}$-C$_{14}$))
Derivatives: *n*-alkanol(C$_7$-C$_9$)

n-olefins(C$_8$-C$_{10}$)

$$CH_3(CH_2)_mCH=CH(CH_2)_nCH_3$$

m+n = 4–6. C$_9$H$_{18}$. M: 126.24. Colourless liquid. BP: 121–171°C. d: 0.71–0.73 kg/l (25°C).
Production:
• α-olefins, mixed (Shell Higher Olefin process; coproduced with *n*-olefins(C$_6$-C$_8$)/*n*-olefins(C$_{10}$-C$_{13}$)/ *n*-olefins(C$_{11}$-C$_{12}$)/*n*-olefins(C$_{11}$-C$_{14}$)/*n*-olefins(C$_{13}$-C$_{14}$))
Derivatives: *n*-alkanol(C$_9$-C$_{11}$)

n-olefins(C$_{10}$-C$_{13}$)

$$CH_3(CH_2)_mCH=CH(CH_2)_nCH_3$$

m+n = 6–9. Mixed stream comprising alkanes and linear olefins used as the feedstock for linear dodecylbenzene manufacture. The double bond is located at any point along the olefin chain. A typical chain-length distribution is: 15% C$_{10}$, 35% C$_{11}$, 30% C$_{12}$, 20% C$_{13}$.

Production:
• *n*-monochloroparaffins (C$_{10}$-C$_{13}$) (dehydrochlorination)
• *n*-paraffins (C$_{10}$-C$_{13}$) (UOP Pacol process)
• α-olefins, mixed (Shell Higher Olefin process; coproduced with *n*-olefins(C$_6$-C$_8$)/*n*-olefins(C$_8$-C$_{10}$)/ *n*-olefins(C$_{11}$-C$_{12}$)/*n*-olefins(C$_{11}$-C$_{14}$)/*n*-olefins(C$_{13}$-C$_{14}$))
Derivatives:
dialkylbenzene; dodecylbenzene, linear

n-olefins(C$_{11}$-C$_{12}$)

$$CH_3(CH_2)_mCH=CH(CH_2)_nCH_3$$

m+n = 7, 8.
Production:
• α-olefins, mixed (Shell Higher Olefin process; coproduced with *n*-olefins(C$_6$-C$_8$)/*n*-olefins(C$_8$-C$_{10}$)/ *n*-olefins(C$_{10}$-C$_{13}$)/*n*-olefins(C$_{11}$-C$_{14}$)/*n*-olefins(C$_{13}$-C$_{14}$))
Derivatives:
n-alkanol(C$_{12}$-C$_{13}$)

n-olefins(C$_{11}$-C$_{14}$)

$$CH_3(CH_2)_mCH=CH(CH_2)_nCH_3$$

m+n = 7–10.
Production:
• α-olefins, mixed (Shell Higher Olefin process; coproduced with *n*-olefins(C$_6$-C$_8$)/*n*-olefins(C$_8$-C$_{10}$)/ *n*-olefins(C$_{10}$-C$_{13}$)/*n*-olefins(C$_{11}$-C$_{12}$)/*n*-olefins(C$_{13}$-C$_{14}$))
• *n*-monochloroparaffins (C$_{11}$-C$_{14}$) (dehydrochlorination)
Derivatives:
n-alkanol(C$_{12}$-C$_{15}$)

n-olefins(C$_{13}$-C$_{14}$)

$$CH_3(CH_2)_mCH=CH(CH_2)_nCH_3$$

m+n = 9–10. Colourless liquid. BP: 230–250°C. d: 0.76 kg/l (25°C).
Production:
• α-olefins, mixed (Shell Higher Olefin process; coproduced with *n*-olefins(C$_6$-C$_8$)/*n*-olefins(C$_8$-C$_{10}$)/ *n*-olefins(C$_{10}$-C$_{13}$)/*n*-olefins(C$_{11}$-C$_{12}$)/*n*-olefins(C$_{11}$-C$_{14}$))
Derivatives: *n*-alkanol(C$_{14}$-C$_{15}$)

oleic acid
9-octadecenoic acid; olein; [112-80-1]

$$CH_3(CH_2)_7CH=CH(CH_2)_7COOH$$

C$_{18}$H$_{34}$O$_2$. M: 282.47. Clear yellow to brown liquid. Titre: 5–17°C. d: 0.90 kg/l (25°C). Commercial products contain 67–80% oleic acid, 6–12% linoleic and linolenic acids, and 7–12% saturated acids. Insoluble in water. Soluble in oxygenated, chlorinated and aromatic solvents.
Production:
• tallow acid (selective crystallisation/solvent separation; coproduced with stearic acid)

- coconut acid/palm kernel fatty acids (fractionation; coproduced with C_8-C_{10} fatty acids/lauric acid, broad cut)
- rapeseed fatty acids (fractionation; coproduced with erucic acid)
- palm acid (selective crystallisation; coproduced with palmitic acid)

Derivatives: aminoethyl oleyl imidazoline; ammonium oleate; azelaic acid; *n*-butyl oleate; copper oleate; cyclohexyl epoxystearate; *n*-decyl oleate; dibutyltin bis-(2-mercaptoethyl oleate); diethylene glycol monooleate; di-(hydroxymethyl) oleyloxazoline; dimethylhydantoin ether monooleate; dimethyltin bis(2-mercaptoethyl oleate); ethyl hydroxymethyl oleyloxazoline; glycerol dioleate; glycerol monooleate; isobutyl oleate; isooctyl oleate; isopropyl oleate; 1-methyl-1-(oleamidoethyl) oleylimidazoline methosulphate; methyl oleate; monobutyltin tris(2-mercaptoethyl oleate); monomethyltin tris(2-mercaptoethyl oleate); neopentyl glycol dioleate; oleamide; oleamidopropyldimethylamine; oleic acid diethanolamide; oleic acid monoisopropanolamide; oleoyl sarcosine; oleyl alcohol; oleylamine; oleyl imidazoline; oleyl oleate; pelargonic acid; pentaerythritol tetraoleate; polyethylene glycol dioleate; polyethylene glycol monooleate; polyglycerol fatty esters; potassium oleate; sodium oleate; sodium *N*-oleyl-*N*-methyltaurate; sorbitan monooleate; sorbitan trioleate; stannous oleate; *N*-tallow-1,3-propanediamine dioleate; triethanolamine monooleate ester; triethanolamine oleate diester; trimethylolpropane trioleate; triolein

Uses:
emollient/superfatting agent (cosmetics); emulsifier (metalworking fluids); emulsifier (resins, surface coatings); emulsifier/solubiliser/stabiliser (pharmaceuticals, food); flotation frothing agent; hair dyeing/tinting ingredient; rubber processing lubricant; soap ingredient (household products, textile auxiliaries); polyvinyl chloride heat costabilisers; thickening/lubricity additive (lubricants); waterproofing agent

oleic acid diethanolamide

$$CH_3(CH_2)_7CH=CH(CH_2)_7\overset{O}{\overset{\|}{C}}N(CH_2CH_2OH)_2$$

$C_{22}H_{43}N_1O_3$. M: 369.59. Available as 1:1 or 2:1 types. The former is made by reacting the methyl ester with an equimolar quantity of diethanolamine. It is a brownish liquid containing 85–100% active matter. The 2:1 type is made from the acid using an excess of diethanolamine. It is an amber liquid comprising 60% fatty diethanolamide and 25% diethanolamine.
Production:
- oleic acid + diethanolamine (Kritchevsky reaction)
- methyl oleate + diethanolamine (amide formation)
Uses: emulsifier/corrosion inhibitor (soluble cutting oils); emulsifier/thickening agent (cleaners, household products)

oleic acid monoisopropanolamide
oleamide MIPA; [111-05-7]

$$CH_3(CH_2)_7CH=CH(CH_2)_7\overset{O}{\overset{\|}{C}}NHCH\overset{CH_3}{\underset{|}{C}}H_2OH$$

$C_{21}H_{41}N_1O_2$. M: 339.57. Soft paste.
Production:
- oleic acid + monoisopropanolamine (amide formation)
Derivatives:
disodium oleic monoisopropanolamide sulphosuccinate
Uses: foam/superfatting agent (cosmetics, toiletries)

olein *See:* oleic acid

oleoamphopropionate

$$CH_3(CH_2)_7CH=CH(CH_2)_7 \quad \underset{HOCH_2CH_2}{\overset{N}{\diagdown}} \underset{CH_2CH_2COO^-}{}$$

$C_{25}H_{46}N_2O_3$. M: 422.65. Available as a 37% solution in water.
Production:
- oleyl imidazoline + methyl acrylate (addition)
Uses: surfactant (conditioning shampoos)

oleoyl sarcosine
N-oleyl sarcosine; [110-25-8]

$$CH_3(CH_2)_7CH=CH(CH_2)_7\overset{O}{\overset{\|}{C}}N\underset{CH_3}{CH_2COOH}$$

$C_{21}H_{39}N_1O_3$. M: 353.55. Yellow liquid usually available as the sodium salt.
Production:
- oleic acid + sarcosine (amide formation)
Uses: corrosion inhibition/foaming/wetting agent (industrial detergents); emulsifier (metalworking fluids, emulsion polymerisation); surfactant (carpet shampoos, fabric detergents, dishwashing liquids, cosmetics, toiletries, toothpaste)

oleum
sulphuric acid, fuming; [8014-95-7]

$$H_2SO_4.nSO_3$$

Colourless or yellow, hygroscopic, fuming, viscous liquid comprising a solution of sulphur trioxide in sulphuric acid. Available commercially with free SO_3 contents of 20–75% w/w. Hydrolysed violently by water. Oleum with 20–35% SO_3 is produced by the Contact process. Oleum with a higher sulphur trioxide content is manufactured by distillation of 20–35% oleum.
Production:
- sulphur dioxide, raw (Contact process)
Derivatives: boron trifluoride; caprolactam; diethyl sulphate; dimethyl sulphate; sodium petroleum sulphonate;

sulphamic acid; sulphuric acid; sulphur trioxide; titanium dioxide, hydrate; white oil
Uses: sulphonation/sulphation/nitration reagent

oleyl alcohol
1-octadecenol; octadec-9-en-1-ol; [143-28-2]

$$CH_3(CH_2)_7CH=CH(CH_2)_8OH$$

$C_{18}H_{36}O_1$. M: 268.49. Pale yellow, oily liquid. MP: 13–19°C. BP: 305–370°C. d: 0.85 kg/l (20°C). Insoluble in water.
Production:
• oleic acid (selective hydrogenation)
Derivatives: oleyl alcohol ethoxylates; oleyl oleate
Uses: lubricity additive (cutting fluids); softening agent/lubricant (textile processing)

oleyl alcohol ethoxylates
oleth (CTFA); polyoxyl oleyl ether

$$CH_3(CH_2)_7CH=CH(CH_2)_8(OCH_2CH_2)_nOH$$

n = 2–20. Pale yellow liquid to white, waxy solid, depending on ethoxylate content. HLB: 4.9–15.3 (2–20 moles EO).
Production:
• oleyl alcohol + ethylene oxide (epoxidation)
Derivatives: oleyl ether phosphoric acid
Uses: emulsifier (metalworking fluids, degreasers, liquid cleaners, wax emulsions, cosmetics)

oleylamine
oleamine; [112-90-3]

$$CH_3(CH_2)_7CH=CH(CH_2)_8NH_2$$

$C_{18}H_{37}N_1$. M: 267.51. Solid or liquid. MP: 18–26°C. A typical chain-length distribution is: 4% C_{14}, 30% C_{16}, 65% C_{18}, 1% C_{20}.
Production:
• oleic acid + ammonia (nitrile formation/nitrile reduction)
Derivatives: bis(2-hydroxyethyl)oleylamine; disodium *N*-oleylsulphosuccinamate; oleylamine ethoxylates; oleyldimethylamine; *N*-oleyl-1,3-propanediamine; palmitic acid oleylamide
Uses: pigment grinding/dispersing agent

oleylamine ethoxylates
PEG oleamine

$$CH_3(CH_2)_7CH=CH(CH_2)_8N\begin{matrix}(CH_2CH_2O)_mH\\(CH_2CH_2O)_nH\end{matrix}$$

m+n = 5–15. Liquids. HLB: 14.6–19.2 (5–15 moles EO).
Production:
• oleylamine + ethylene oxide (epoxidation)
Uses: cationic emulsifier (wax, oil, solvent emulsions)

oleylbenzyldimethylammonium chloride
olealkonium chloride (CTFA)

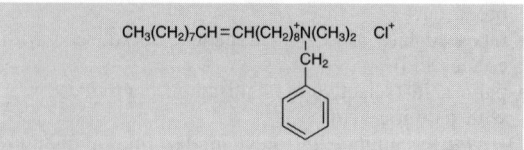

$C_{27}H_{48}Cl_1N_1$. M: 422.14.
Production:
• oleyldimethylamine + benzyl chloride (quaternisation)
Uses: conditioning agent (hair products)

oleyldimethylamine
N,N-dimethyloleylamine

$$CH_3(CH_2)_7CH=CH(CH_2)_8N(CH_3)_2$$

$C_{20}H_{41}N_1$. M: 295.56.
Production:
• oleylamine (methylation)
Derivatives:
oleylbenzyldimethylammonium chloride; oleyldimethylamine oxide

oleyldimethylamine oxide
oleamine oxide (CTFA); [14351-50-9]; [61792-38-9]

$$CH_3(CH_2)_7CH=CH(CH_2)_8\overset{\overset{\displaystyle CH_3}{|}}{\underset{\underset{\displaystyle CH_3}{|}}{N}}\rightarrow O$$

$C_{20}H_{41}N_1O_1$. M: 311.56. Available as a 50% solution in water.
Production:
• oleyldimethylamine + hydrogen peroxide (peroxidation)
Uses: foam stabiliser/viscosifier (toiletries, household products)

oleyl ether phosphoric acid

$$\left[CH_3(CH_2)_7CH=CH(CH_2)_8(OCH_2CH_2)_mO\right]_n\overset{\overset{\displaystyle O}{||}}{P}(OH)_{3-n}$$

m = 2–20, n = 1–2. Yellow, viscous liquid or paste. Mixture of the mono- and di-esters.
Production:
• oleyl alcohol ethoxylates + phosphorus pentoxide (reaction)
Uses: extreme-pressure/emulsifier/corrosion inhibitor additives (metalworking fluids); antistatic agent/lubricant/softening agent (textile processing); surfactant (household/industrial cleaners)

oleyl imidazoline
2-oleyl-1-(hydroxyethyl)imidazoline (CTFA)
$C_{22}H_{42}N_2O_1$. M: 350.59.
Production:
• oleic acid + aminoethylethanolamine (condensation)

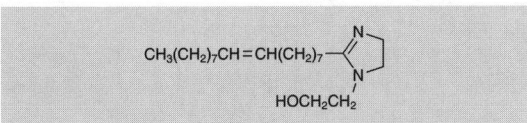

Derivatives: oleoamphopropionate

oleyl oleate
[3687-45-4]

$$CH_3(CH_2)_7CH=CH(CH_2)_7CO(CH_2)_8CH=CH(CH_2)_7CH_3$$

$C_{36}H_{68}O_2$. M: 532.94. Yellow liquid. MP: 14–16°C. Insoluble in water.
Production:
• oleyl alcohol + oleic acid (esterification)
Uses: lubricant (textile spin finishes); solubiliser (pharmaceuticals)

N-oleyl-1,3-propanediamine
N-oleylpropane-1,3-diamine; *N*-oleyl-1,3-propylene-diamine

$$CH_3(CH_2)_7CH=CH(CH_2)_8NHCH_2CH_2CH_2NH_2$$

$C_{21}H_{44}N_2$. M: 324.59. Liquid or paste. MP: 15°C.
Production:
• oleylamine + acrylonitrile (addition/nitrile reduction)
Uses: corrosion inhibitor (metalworking fluids); bitumen emulsifier (car underseal)

olive oil
[8001-25-0]
Greenish-yellow oil. Produced by expression of the fruit from the olive tree (*Olea europaea*). Titre: 17–26°C. Solidification point: about -7°C. d: 0.91 kg/l (20°C). Insoluble in water. Slightly soluble in alcohol. The chain-length distribution is: 7–16% $C_{16:0}$, 65–85% $C_{18:1}$ and 4–15% $C_{18:2}$.
Derivatives: olive oil, sulphated
Uses: cooking/salad oil; emollient/cosolvent (cosmetics, pharmaceuticals); soap raw material

olive oil, sulphated
Production:
• olive oil (sulphation)
Uses: emulsifier (cosmetics)

omethoate
O,O-dimethyl *S*-methylcarbamoylmethyl phosphorothioate; [1113-02-6]

$$CH_3NHCCH_2SP(OCH_3)_2$$

$C_5H_{12}N_1O_4P_1S_1$. M: 213.19.
Production:
• chloroacetyl chloride + methylamine + *O,O*-di-methyl phosphorochlorothioate (amide formation/hydrolysis/dehydrochlorination)
Uses: insecticide/acaricide

OPD *See:* *o*-phenylenediamine

opipramol
[315-72-0]

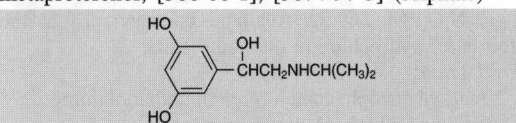

$C_{23}H_{29}N_3O_1$. M: 363.50. Available commercially as the dihydrochloride salt.
Production:
• iminostilbene + 1-bromo-3-chloropropane + *N*-hydroxyethylpiperazine (amine formation/amine formation)
Uses: antidepressant drug

opium
Latex extracted from the pods, stems and leaves of the opium poppy (*Paperver sumniferum*). Produced mainly in Burma, Thailand, Laos, China, India, Pakistan and the CIS countries.
Derivatives: codeine; morphine; thebaine

OPP *See:* *o*-phenylphenol

OPS *See:* *p-t*-octylphenyl salicylate

orange oil
citrus oil; orange peel oil; [8008-57-9]
Yellow or reddish-yellow liquid with a citrus odour. d: ~0.84 kg/l (20°C). The main constituent of the oil is (+)-limonene (>90%). The oil is extracted from sweet oranges (*Citrus aurantium*) at the same time as the juice. It is produced in many countries, particularly Brazil, the USA, Italy, Spain, Israel and South Africa.
Derivatives:
(+)-limonene; nootkatone
Uses: food/drink flavouring ingredient

orciprenaline
metaproterenol; [586-06-1]; [5874-97-5] (sulphate)

$C_{11}H_{17}N_1O_3$. M: 211.27. Available commercially as the free base or sulphate.
Production:
• 3,5-diacetoxyacetophenone + isopropylamine (alpha bromination/amine formation/hydrolysis/carbonyl reduction)
Uses: bronchodilator/asthmatic drug

origanum oil

Pale yellow liquid. Produced by the steam distillation of the flowering tops of origanum (*Origanum vulgare* and *Thymus capitatus*) which is grown in Spain, Greece, Turkey and Mexico. d: ~0.89 kg/l (15°C). Soluble in alcohol.
Uses: fragrance/flavouring ingredient

ornidazole

1-(3-chloro-2-hydroxypropyl)-2-methyl-5-nitroimidazole; [16773-42-5]

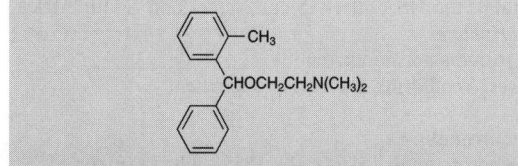

$C_7H_{10}Cl_1N_3O_3$. M: 219.63.
Production:
• 2-methyl-4-nitroimidazole + epichlorohydrin (epoxidation)
Uses: antiprotazoal drug

orotic acid

uracil-6-carboxylic acid; [65-86-1]

$C_5H_4N_2O_4$. M: 156.09.
Production:
• glycine + glyoxylic acid + sodium cyanate (cyanate addition/carbonyl condensation)
Uses: liver therapy/electrolyte carrier drug

orphenadrine

[83-98-7]; [341-69-5] (hydrochloride); [4682-36-4] (hydrogen citrate)

$C_{18}H_{23}N_1O_1$. M: 269.39. Available commercially as the free base, hydrochloride or citrate salts.
Production:
• 2-methylbenzophenone + dimethylethanolamine (carbonyl reduction/ether formation)
Uses: antiparkinsonian/muscle relaxant drug

orthanilic acid

2-aminobenzenesulphonic acid; aniline-2-sulphonic acid; [88-21-1]
$C_6H_7N_1O_3S_1$. M: 173.20. Crystalline solid. MP: 188°C. Slightly soluble in water. Insoluble in alcohol.

Production:
• 2-aminothiophenol (thiol oxidation)
Derivatives:
Acid Red 57; Reactive Blue 2; Reactive Orange 1; Reactive Red 1; Reactive Red 3; Reactive Red 12; Reactive Red 17; Reactive Red 96

orthophosphoric acid *See:* phosphoric acid, pure

oryzalin

3,5-dinitro-*N,N*-dipropylsulphanilamide; [19044-88-3]

$C_{12}H_{18}N_4O_6S_1$. M: 346.35.
Production:
• *p*-chlorobenzenesulphonyl chloride + ammonia + di-*n*-propylamine (nitration/sulphonamide formation/amine formation)
Uses:
herbicide

OSA *See:* octenylsuccinic anhydride

OSBP *See:* o-s-butylphenol

ossein

Demineralised bone consisting of collagen together with fats, mucopolysaccharides and albumens.
Production:
• bone, degreased (acid extraction; coproduced with dicalcium phosphate)
Derivatives: gelatine

OTBG *See:* o-tolylbiguanide

OTBP *See:* o-t-butylphenol

OTD *See:* 3,4-diaminotoluene

OTOS *See:* *N*-oxydiethylenedithiocarbamyl-*N'*-oxydiethylenesulphenamide

ouricury wax

[68917-70-4]
Brown solid. Produced by scrapping the fronds of the *Cocus caronapa* palm which is grown in Brazil.
Uses:
car/floor/shoe polish ingredient

oxabetrinil

α-[1,3-dioxolan-2-ylmethoxyimino]benzeneacetonitrile;
[74782-23-3]

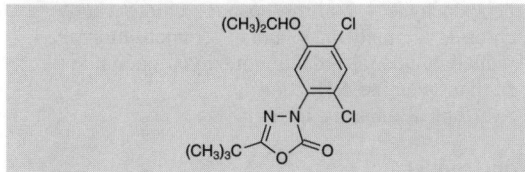

$C_{12}H_{12}N_2O_3$. M: 232.24.
Production:
• benzyl cyanide + sodium nitrite + chloroacetaldehyde + ethylene glycol (oxime formation/
  diacetal formation/dehydrochlorination)
Uses: herbicide adjunct

oxacillin

[66-79-5]

$C_{19}H_{19}N_3O_5S_1$. M: 401.43. Available commercially as
the sodium monohydrate salt.
Production:
• 5-methyl-3-phenylisoxazole-4-carboxylic acid +
  6-aminopenicillanic acid (amide formation)
Uses: antibacterial drug

oxadiazon

5-t-butyl-3-(2,4-dichloro-5-isopropoxyphenyl)-1,3,4-oxa-
diazol-3-one; [19666-30-9]

$C_{15}H_{18}Cl_2N_2O_3$. M: 345.22.
Production:
• 1,2,4,5-tetrachlorobenzene + isopropanol +
  hydrazine + pivaloyl chloride + phosgene (ether
  formation/amine formation/amide formation/
  phosgenation)
Uses: herbicide

oxadixyl

2-methoxy-N-(2-oxo-1,3-oxazolidin-3-yl)acet-2′,6′-xyl-
idide; [77732-09-3]
$C_{14}H_{18}N_2O_4$. M: 278.30.
Production:
• 2,6-xylidine + sodium nitrite + ethylene oxide +
  phosgene + 2-methoxyacetic acid (diazotisation/
  reduction/epoxidation/phosgenation/amide formation)

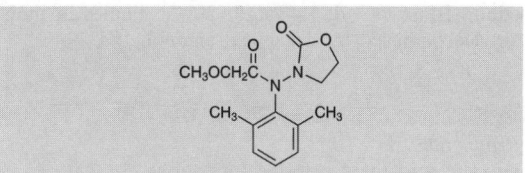

Uses: fungicide

12-oxa-16-hexadecanolide

16-hydroxy-12-oxahexadecanoic acid lactone;
[6707-60-4]

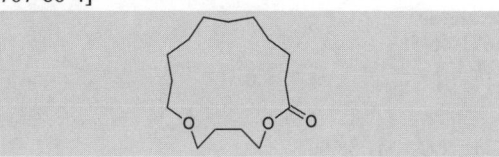

$C_{15}H_{28}O_3$. M: 256.38. Colourless crystals with musk-like
odour.
Production:
• methyl undecylenate + 1,4-butanediol (multistep
  synthesis)
Uses: fragrance ingredient (synthetic musk)

oxalic acid

ethanedioic acid; [144-62-7]

$$\begin{array}{c} COOH \\ | \\ COOH \end{array}$$

$C_2H_2O_4$. M: 90.04. Available commercially as the dihydrate. White, crystalline solid. MP: 101°C with the
release of the water of crystallisation. d: 1.65 kg/l
(20°C). Soluble in water and oxygenated solvents. Insoluble in chlorinated and hydrocarbon solvents.
Production:
• acetaldehyde + nitric acid, concentrated (oxidation;
  byproduct of glyoxal production)
• glyoxal + nitric acid (carbonyl oxidation; byproduct
  of glyoxylic acid production)
• starch/molasses + nitric acid, concentrated
  (oxidative cleavage)
• propylene + nitric acid, concentrated (oxidation)
• n-butanol + carbon monoxide (Ube process)
• ethylene glycol + nitric acid, concentrated (oxidation)
Derivatives:
ceftriaxone; N,N′-dibenzaloxalyldihydrazide; diethyl
oxalate; oxalyl chloride; 2,2′-oxamidobis[ethyl 3-(3,5-
di-t-butyl-4-hydroxyphenyl)propionate]; potassium oxalate; sodium oxalate; thiocyclam hydrogen oxalate
Uses: novolac resin production catalyst; aluminium
anodising reagent; rust/ink stain removers; textile dye-
ing/bleaching adjunct

oxalyl chloride

[79-37-8]
$C_2Cl_2O_2$. M: 126.93. Colourless liquid with a pungent

odour. BP: 63°C. d: 1.48 kg/l (20°C). Fumes in moist air. Decomposed by water and alcohol.

Production:
• oxalic acid (acid chloride formation)
Derivatives: chinomethionat; 2,3-dichloroquinoxaline-6-carboxyl chloride; diclofenac
Uses:
chlorination reagent; stabiliser (sulphur trioxide)

oxamide
[471-46-5]

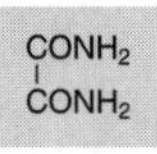

$C_2H_4N_2O_2$. M: 88.06.
Production:
• hydrogen cyanide (oxidation/nitrile hydration)
Derivatives: sulfametrole; timolol
Uses:
controlled-release fertiliser

2,2′-oxamidobis[ethyl 3-(3,5-di-*t*-butyl-4-hydroxy-phenyl)propionate]
Naugard XL-1 (Uniroyal Chemical); [70331-94-1]

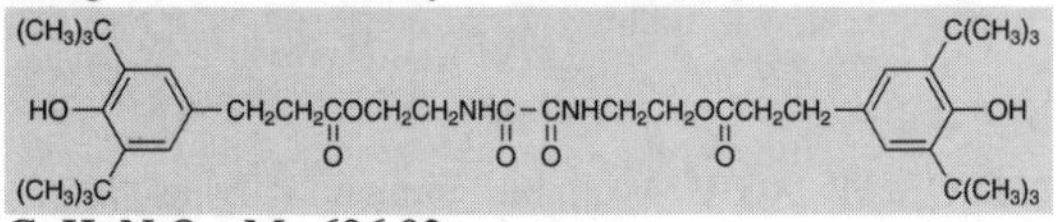

$C_{40}H_{60}N_2O_8$. M: 696.92.
Production:
• monoethanolamine + oxalic acid + methyl 3,5-di-*t*-butyl-4-hydroxyphenylpropionate (amide formation/transesterification)
Uses: antioxidant/metal deactivator (plastics)

oxamyl
N-dimethyl-2-methylcarbamoyloxyimino-2-(methylthio)-acetamide; Vydate (Du Pont); [23135-22-0]

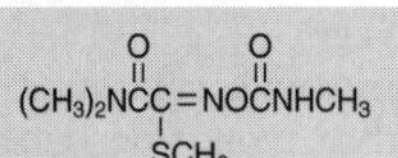

$C_7H_{13}N_3O_3S_1$. M: 219.26.
Production:
• methyl acetoacetate + sodium nitrite + methyl mercaptan + dimethylamine + methyl isocyanate (oxime formation/deacetylation/sulphide formation/amide formation/isocyanate addition)
Uses: insecticide/acaricide/nematicide

oxantel
[36531-26-7] (free base); [68813-55-8] (pamoate salt)
$C_{13}H_{16}N_2O_1$. M: 216.28. Available as the free base or as the pamoate salt.

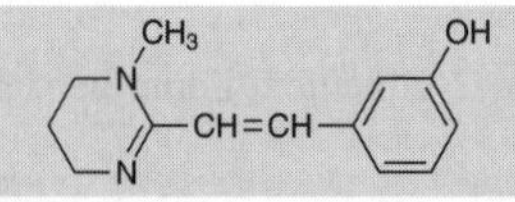

Production:
• *m*-hydroxybenzaldehyde + cyanoacetic acid + 3-methylaminopropylamine (Cope reaction/decarboxylation/condensation)
Uses: anthelmintic drug

oxazepam
[604-75-1]

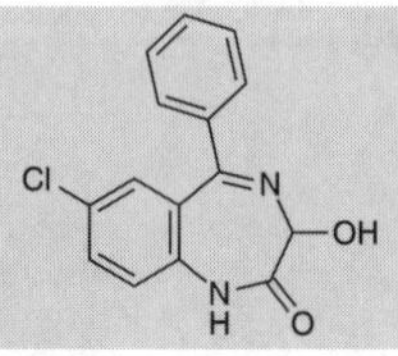

$C_{15}H_{11}Cl_1N_2O_2$. M: 286.71.
Production:
• chlordiazepoxide + acetic anhydride (deamination/Polonovsky rearrangement/saponification)
Uses: anxiolytic drug

oxetacaine
oxethazaine; [126-27-2]; [13930-31-9] (hydrochloride)

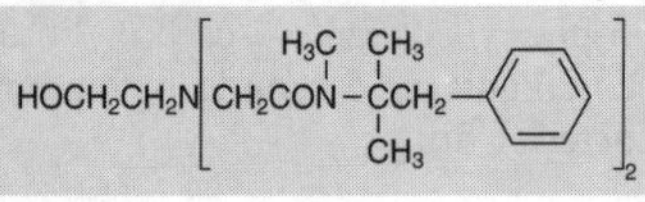

$C_{28}H_{41}N_3O_3$. M: 467.66. Available commercially as the free base or hydrochloride.
Production:
• benzaldehyde + 2-nitropropane + chloroacetyl chloride + monoethanolamine (condensation/nitro reduction/alcohol reduction/methylation/amide formation/amine formation)
Uses: topical anaesthetic drug

oxine-copper
bis(quinolin-8-olato)copper; copper 8-hydroxyquinoline; copper oxinate; copper 8-quinolinolate; [10380-28-6]

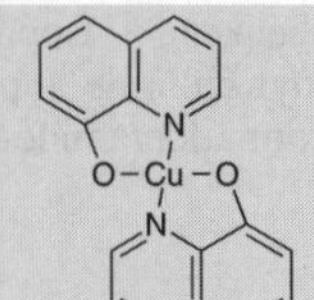

$C_{18}H_{12}Cu_1N_2O_2$. M: 351.86.
Production:
• copper sulphate + 8-hydroxyquinoline (complex formation)
Uses: seed treatment fungicide; biostabiliser (thermoplastics, wood, adhesives, paper products); wound protectant (fruit trees)

oxolinic acid

1-ethyl-6,7-methylenedioxy-4-quinolinol-3-carboxylic acid; [14698-29-4]

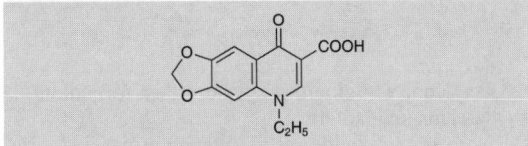

$C_{13}H_{11}N_1O_5$. M: 261.23.
Production:
- 3,4-methylenedioxyaniline + diethyl ethoxymethylenemalonate + ethyl iodide (condensation/ethylation)

Uses: urinary antibacterial drug

4-oxopentanoic acid *See:* levulinic acid

oxprenolol
[6452-71-7]

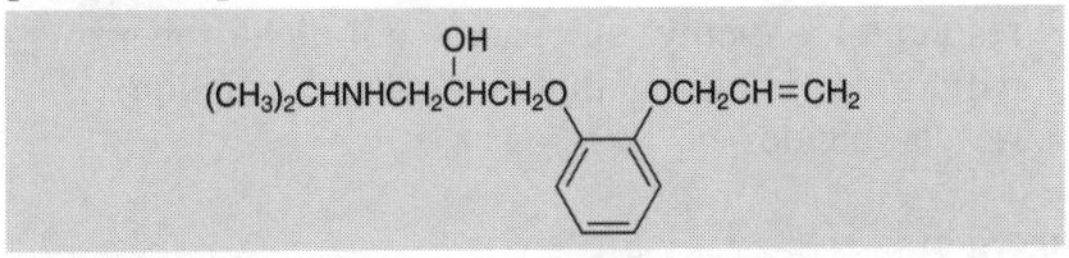

$C_{15}H_{23}N_1O_3$. M: 265.35. Available commercially as the hydrochloride.
Production:
- catechol + allyl chloride + epichlorohydrin + isopropylamine (ether formation/epoxidation/amine formation)

Uses:
antianginal drug

oxybenzone *See:* 2-hydroxy-4-methoxybenzophenone

4,4′-oxybis(benzenesulphohydrazide)

4,4′-oxybis(benzenesulphonyl hydrazine); OBSH;
[80-51-3]

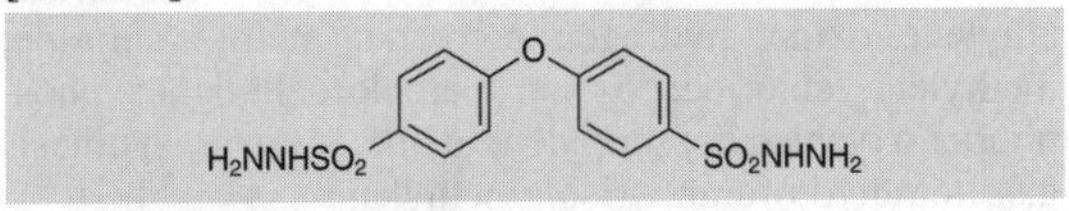

$C_{12}H_{14}N_4O_5S_2$. M: 358.39.
Production:
- diphenyl ether 4,4′-bis(sulphonyl chloride) + hydrazine (sulphonamide formation)

Uses:
blowing agent (foamed plastics)

4,4′-oxybis(benzenesulphonyl chloride)
See: diphenyl ether 4,4′-bis(sulphonyl chloride)

10,10′-oxybisphenoxyarsine

Durotex; Vinyzene BP (Morton International); Vinyzene SB-1 (Morton International); [58-36-6]
$C_{24}H_{16}As_2O_3$. M: 502.23.

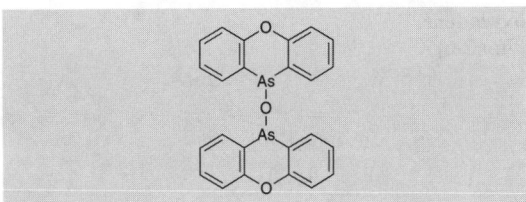

Production:
- diphenyl oxide + arsenic trioxide + sodium hydroxide (condensation)
Uses:
plastics biostabiliser

2,2′-oxybis(4,4,6-trimethyl)-1,3,2-dioxaborinane
Biobor JF (Borax Consolidated); [14697-50-8]

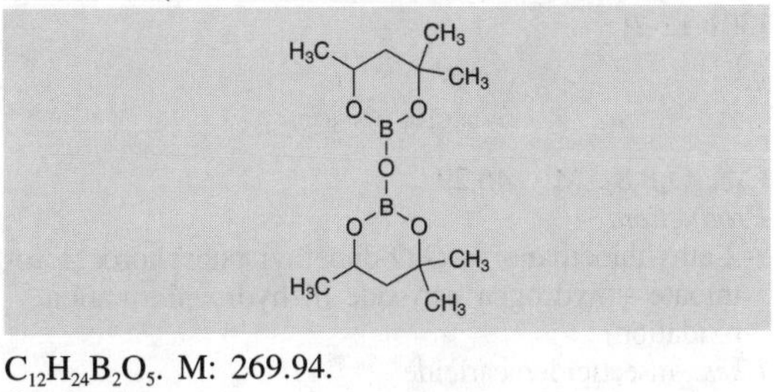

$C_{12}H_{24}B_2O_5$. M: 269.94.
Production:
- boric acid + hexylene glycol (dehydration)
Uses: biocide (jet fuels)

oxybuprocaine
benoxinate; [99-43-4]

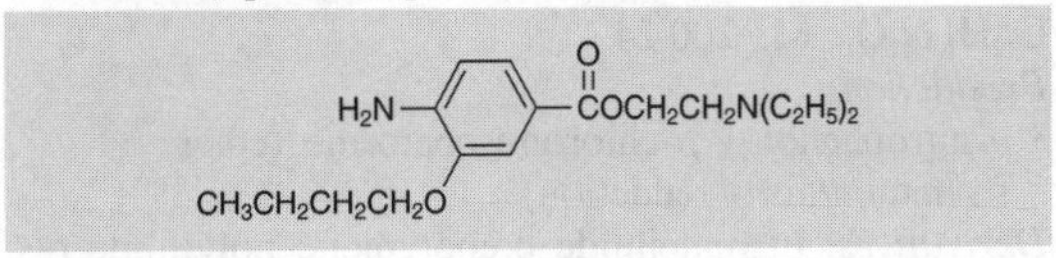

$C_{17}H_{28}N_2O_3$. M: 308.42. Available commercially as the hydrochloride.
Production:
- 6-nitro-*m*-cresol + *n*-butyl bromide + diethylaminoethanol (side-chain oxidation/ether formation/esterification/nitro reduction)
Uses: local anaesthetic drug

oxycarboxin
5,6-dihydro-2-methyl-1,4-oxathiine-3-carboxanilide 4,4-dioxide; [5259-88-1]

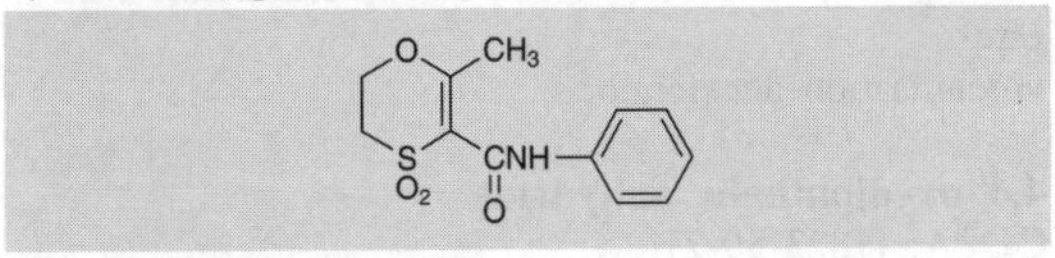

$C_{12}H_{13}N_1O_4S_1$. M: 267.30.
Production:
- carboxin + hydrogen peroxide (oxidation)
Uses: fungicide

oxycodone
[76-42-6]

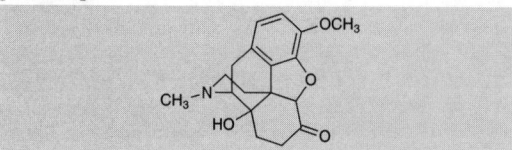

$C_{18}H_{21}N_1O_4$. M: 315.38. Available commercially as the hydrochloride.
Production:
• codeine/thebaine (oxidation/hydrogenation)
Uses: analgesic drug

oxydemeton-methyl
S-2-ethylsulphinylethyl *O,O*-dimethyl phosphorothioate; [301-12-2]

$$C_2H_5SCH_2CH_2SP(OCH_3)_2$$

$C_6H_{15}O_4P_1S_2$. M: 246.29.
Production:
• 2-ethylthioethanol + *O,O*-dimethyl phosphorochloro-thioate + hydrogen peroxide (dehydrochlorination/oxidation)
Uses: insecticide/acaricide

4,4′-oxydianiline
4,4′-diaminodiphenyl ether; ODA

$$H_2N-\langle\rangle-O-\langle\rangle-NH_2$$

$C_{12}H_{12}N_2O_1$. M: 200.24.
Production:
• *p*-nitrophenol + *p*-chloronitrobenzene (ether formation/nitro reduction)
Derivatives: bismaleimide prepolymers; polyimide resins; polyimide resins, prepolymers

N-oxydiethylenedithiocarbamyl-*N*′-oxydiethylene sulphenamide
OTOS; Cure Rite 18 (B.F. Goodrich)

$$O\langle\rangle N-CS-N\langle\rangle O$$

$C_9H_{16}N_2O_2S_2$. M: 248.37.
Production:
• morpholine + carbon disulphide (condensation)
Uses:
vulcanisation accelerator

4,4′-oxydiphthalic anhydride
ODPA; [1823-59-2]
$C_{16}H_6O_7$. M: 310.22. White, crystalline powder. MP: 226–227°C. d: 1.59 kg/l. Hydrolysed by water. Soluble in *N,N*-dimethylformamide, *N*-methyl-2-pyrrolidone and dimethyl sulphoxide.

Production:
• 3,4-xylenol + 4-chloro-*o*-xylene (ether formation/side-chain oxidation)
Derivatives: polyimide resins, prepolymers

oxyfluorfen
2-chloro-4-(trifluoromethylphenyl) 3-ethoxy-4-nitro-phenyl ether; [42874-03-3]

$C_{15}H_{11}Cl_1F_3N_1O_4$. M: 361.70.
Production:
• resorcinol + diethyl sulphate + 3,4-dichlorobenzo-trifluoride (nitration/ethylation/ether formation)
Uses: herbicide

oxygen
[7782-44-7]

$$O_2$$

O_2. M: 32.00. Colourless gas. BP: -183°C. d: 1.33 g/l (gas, 20°C). Solubility in water: 31 g/l water (20°C). Available in both liquified and gaseous form.
Production:
• water (electrolysis; coproduced with hydrogen)
• air (cryogenic separation; coproduced with nitrogen)
Derivatives:
acetaldehyde; acetic acid; acetic anhydride; acetylene; acrolein; acrylic acid; allyl alcohol; 1,4-butanediol; *t*-butyl hydroperoxide; carbon tetrachloride; chlorine; chloroform; cumene hydroperoxide; ethylene dichloride; ethylene oxide; hydrogen peroxide; methyl chloride; methylene chloride; ozone; perchloroethylene; phosphorus oxychloride; propylene oxide; styrene; synthesis gas; tetrahydrofuran; trichloroethylene
Uses:
medical/diving/aerospace gas component; steel smelting/oxygen lancing reagent; effluent/sewage treatment; oxidising agent; rocket propellant; welding/cutting gas

oxygenates, Fischer-Tropsch, mixed
Intermediate aqueous stream from Fischer-Tropsch production containing water-soluble products. Not a commercially-traded product.
Production:
• synthesis gas (Synthol Fischer-Tropsch process; coproduced with naphtha, light, Synthol/naphtha, heavy/gas oil, light/wax, Fischer-Tropsch/refinery gas)

- synthesis gas (Arge Fischer-Tropsch process; coproduced with naphtha, heavy/gas oil, light, Arge/wax, Fischer-Tropsch/refinery gas)

Derivatives: acetaldehyde; acetone; amyl alcohol, primary; *n*-butanol; ethanol; isobutanol; isopropanol; methanol; methyl ethyl ketone

oxymetazoline
[1491-59-4]

$C_{16}H_{24}N_2O_1$. M: 260.38. Available commercially as the free base or hydrochloride.
Production:
- 6-*t*-butyl-2,4-dimethylphenol + formaldehyde + sodium cyanide + ethylenediamine (chloromethylation/cyanidation/condensation)

Uses: vasoconstrictor drug

β-oxynaphthoic acid
β-hydroxynaphthoic acid; 3-hydroxy-2-naphthoic acid; 2-naphthol-3-carboxylic acid; BONA; BON acid; [92-70-6]

$C_{11}H_8O_3$. M: 188.18. Pale yellow, crystalline solid. MP: 218–221°C. Insoluble in water. Soluble in most organic solvents.
Production:
- β-naphthol + carbon dioxide (Kolbe-Schmitt reaction)

Derivatives: bephenium hydroxynaphthoate; *N,N'*-bis-(3-hydroxy-2-naphthoyl)dianisidine; 4-chloro-2,5-dimethoxy-3'-hydroxy-2'-naphthanilide; 5-chloro-2,4-dimethoxy-3'-hydroxy-2'-naphthanilide; 4-chloro-3'-hydroxy-2'-naphth-*m*-toluidide; 5-chloro-3'-hydroxy-2'-naphth-*o*-toluidide; 3-hydroxy-2-naphthanilide; 3-hydroxy-2-naphth-*o*-anisidide; 3-hydroxy-2-naphth-*p*-anisidide; 5-(2'-hydroxy-3'-naphthoyl)aminobenzimidazolone; 3-hydroxy-2-naphth-*p*-phenethidide; 3-hydroxy-2-naphth-*o*-phenetidide; 3-hydroxy-2-naphth-*o*-toluidide; 3-hydroxy-2-naphth-*p*-toluidide; 3-hydroxy-2-naphth-2',4'-xylidide; *N*-(1-naphthyl)-3-hydroxy-2-naphthamide; *N*-(2-naphthyl)-3-hydroxy-2-naphthamide; 3-nitro-3'-hydroxy-2'-naphthanilide; pamoic acid; Pigment Orange 38; Pigment Red 8; Pigment Red 48; Pigment Red 52; Pigment Red 57; Pigment Red 63; Pigment Red 184; Pigment Red 200; Pigment Red 214; Pigment Red 221; Pigment Red 222; Pigment Red 242

oxyphenbutazone
[129-20-4]
$C_{19}H_{20}N_2O_3$. M: 324.38. Available commercially as the

free base monohydrate or piperazine monohydrate salt.

Production:
- diethyl *n*-butylmalonate + phenol + benzyl chloride + aniline (diazotisation/ether formation/azo coupling/reduction/amide formation/hydrogenation)

Uses: antiinflammatory drug

oxyquinaldine carboxylic acid
3-hydroxyquinaldine-4-carboxylic acid; [117-57-7]

$C_{11}H_9N_1O_3$. M: 203.20. Solid. MP: 215–225°C with decomposition.
Production:
- isatin + hydroxyacetone (condensation)

Derivatives:
Disperse Yellow 64; quinophthalone

oxytetracycline
terramycin; [79-57-2]

$C_{22}H_{24}N_2O_9$. M: 460.43. Available commercially as the free base or hydrochloride.
Production:
- microbial fermentation medium + *Streptomyces rimosus* bacteria (fermentation)

Derivatives: doxycycline
Uses: antibacterial drug

oxythioquinox *See:* chinomethionat

oxytocin
[50-56-6]; [74499-03-9] (dihydrogen citrate)

H-Cys-Tyr-Ile-Gln-Asn-Cys-Pro-Leu-Gly-NH₂

$C_{43}H_{66}N_{12}O_{12}S_2$. M: 1007.20. Available as the free base or as the dihydrogen citrate salt.
Production:
- L-cysteine + L-tyrosine + L-isoleucine + L-glutamic acid + L-aspartic acid + L-proline +

L-leucine + glycine + ammonia (peptide synthesis)
Uses: labour induction drug

ozocerite

ozokerite wax; [8021-55-4]
Not longer manufactured. The term is still used, however, for blended microcrystalline and paraffin waxes.

ozone

[10028-15-6]

O_3

O_3. M: 48.00. Colourless gas with a characteristic odour. BP: -112°C. Explosive, particularly when liquified. Not transportable.
Production:
• air/oxygen (electrical discharge)
Derivatives: 2,5-dimethyl-4-hydroxy-3-furanone; levulinic acid; methyl glyoxylate methyl hemiacetal; vanillin
Uses:
industrial/municipal wastewater treatment; ozonolysis reagent; swimming pool disinfectant

P

paclobutrazol
1-(4-chlorophenyl)-4,4-dimethyl-2-(1H-1,2,4-triazol-1-yl)pentan-3-ol; [76738-62-0]

$$(CH_3)_3CCHCHCH_2 \text{—} \text{—} Cl$$
OH

$C_{15}H_{20}Cl_1N_3O_1$. M: 293.79.
Production:
• α-chloropinacolone + 1,2,4-triazole + *p*-chloro-benzyl chloride (amine formation/dehydrochlorination)
Uses: plant growth regulator

PACM *See:* bis(*p*-aminocyclohexyl)methane

PAG *See:* polyalkylene glycol; pentaacetylglucose

PAI *See:* poly(amide-imide)

palladium
[7440-05-3]

Pd

Pd_1. M: 106.40. Silvery-white metal. MP: 1,554°C. d: 12.0 kg/l. Available commercially as powder, foil, wire, single crystals and as coatings on activated alumina or charcoal.
Production:
• copper anodic slimes/nickel refinery anode slimes/Mond process residues (sulphating roast process/hydrometallurgical refining; coproduced with platinum/gold/silver/selenium/tellurium)
Uses: hydrogenation/oxidation catalyst; electrical contacts; brazing alloy ingredient

palm acid
Solid. Titre: 40–43°C. Saponification value: 202–220 mg KOH/g.
Production:
• palm oil (hydrolysis)
Derivatives: oleic acid; palmitic acid
Uses: soap raw material

palmarosa oil
geranium oil, Turkish; [8014-19-5]
Pale yellow liquid with a rose-like odour. d: ~0.89 kg/l (20°C). Soluble in alcohol. The main constituent of the oil is geraniol (70–85%). Extracted from palmarosa grass (*Cymbopogon martinii*) by steam distillation.
Derivatives: geraniol
Uses:
fragrance ingredient (soap, cosmetics)

palm butter *See:* palm oil

palmitic acid
hexadecanoic acid; [57-10-3]

$CH_3(CH_2)_{14}COOH$

$C_{16}H_{32}O_2$. M: 256.44. White solid. MP: 63°C. BP: 351°C. d: 0.85 kg/l (80°C). Insoluble in water, soluble in aromatic, chlorinated and oxygenated solvents. Several grades are available commercially: 'Eutectic' grades are a mixture of 60% palmitic acid and 30% stearic acid. Other grades containing 80%, 92% and 97% palmitic acid are also available.
Production:
• palm acid (selective crystallisation; coproduced with oleic acid)
Derivatives: ascorbyl palmitate; cetyl alcohol; cetyl palmitate; 2-ethylhexyl palmitate; *n*-hexadecylamine; isopropyl palmitate; methyl palmitate; palmitic acid oleylamide; sorbitan monopalmitate
Uses: soap/cosmetics ingredient; non-drying oil (surface coatings)

palmitic acid oleylamide

$$CH_3(CH_2)_{14}CNH(CH_2)_8CH=CH(CH_2)_7CH_3$$
O

$C_{34}H_{67}N_1O_1$. M: 505.92. Solid. MP: 151–158°C.
Production:
• palmitic acid + oleylamine (amide formation)
Uses: internal plastics processing lubricant

palmityl alcohol *See:* cetyl alcohol

palmitylamine *See:* *n*-hexadecylamine

palmityldimethylammonium-3-sulphopropylbetaine
Ralufon DP (Raschig)

$$CH_3(CH_2)_{15}NCH_2CH_2CH_2SO_3^-$$
CH_3 / CH_3

$C_{21}H_{45}N_1O_3S_1$. M: 391.66.
Production:
• dimethylcetylamine + propane sultone (quaternisation)
Uses:
amphoteric surfactant (shampoos/industrial detergents)

palm kernel fatty acids

RCOOH

R = palm kernel-. Pale yellow solid. MP: 25–30°C. Acid value: 245–255 mg KOH/g. Insoluble in water.

A typical chain-length distribution is: 50% C_{12}, 20% C_{14}, 10% C_{16}, 15% $C_{18:1}$.
Production:
• palm kernel oil (hydrolysis)
Derivatives:
C_8-C_{10} fatty acids; lauric acid, broad cut; oleic acid
Uses: soap/cosmetics ingredient; soap raw material

palm kernel methyl ester

$$\underset{\text{RCOCH}_3}{\overset{\overset{\displaystyle O}{\|}}{}}$$

R = palm kernel-.
Production:
• palm kernel oil + methanol (alcoholysis)
Derivatives: C_8-C_{10} fatty acids, methyl ester; palm kernel methyl ester, topped

palm kernel methyl ester, topped

$$\underset{\text{CH}_3(\text{CH}_2)_n\text{COCH}_3}{\overset{\overset{\displaystyle O}{\|}}{}}$$

n = 10–16. Residual fraction from first distillation of palm kernel acid methyl ester. A typical chain-length distribution is: 47% C_{12}, 16% C_{14}, 12% C_{16}, 22% C_{18}.
Production:
• palm kernel methyl ester (fractionation; coproduced with C_8-C_{10} fatty acids, methyl ester)
Derivatives: C_{14}-C_{18} fatty acids, methyl ester; *n*-alkanol (C_{12}-C_{18}); methyl laurate

palm kernel oil

Elaeis guineensis seed oil; [8023-79-8]
Yellowish fat. MP: 26–30°C. d: 0.95 kg/l. Produced by extraction from the kernels of the oil palm (*Elaeis guineensis*). A typical chain-length distribution is: 5% $C_{8:0}$, 4% $C_{10:0}$, 46% $C_{12:0}$, 16% $C_{14:0}$, 8% $C_{16:0}$, 2% $C_{18:0}$, 13% $C_{18:1}$, 2% $C_{18:2}$.
Derivatives:
palm kernel fatty acids; palm kernel methyl ester
Uses: margarine ingredient; soap ingredient

palm oil

Elaeis guineensis oil; palm butter; [8002-75-3]
Reddish-yellow fat. MP: 27–42°C. d: 0.92–0.93 kg/l. Produced by expression/solvent extraction of the fruit of the oil palm (*Elaeis guineensis*). A typical chain-length distribution is: 1% C_{14}, 43% $C_{16:0}$, 5% $C_{18:0}$, 41% $C_{18:1}$, 10% $C_{18:2}$.
Derivatives:
fatty oils, sulphurised; palm acid
Uses: cooking oil; margarine ingredient; plasticiser (rubber); soap ingredient; steel cold-rolling oil

pamaquine

[635-05-2]
$C_{19}H_{29}N_3O_1$. M: 315.46.

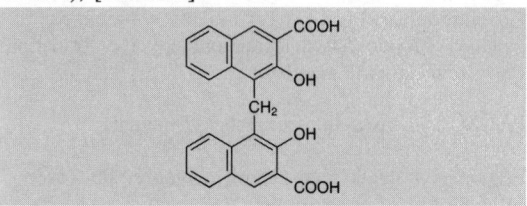

Production:
• 4-amino-3-nitroanisole + glycerol + 5-diethylamino-2-pentanone (Skraup synthesis/amine formation)
Uses: antimalarial drug

pamoic acid

embonic acid; 1,1-methylenebis(2-naphthol-3-carboxylic acid); [130-85-8]

$C_{23}H_{16}O_6$. M: 388.37. Crystalline solid. Decomposes on heating above 280°C. Insoluble in water and oxygenated solvents.
Production:
• β-oxynaphthoic acid + formaldehyde (carbonyl condensation)
Derivatives: pyrvinium pamoate

PAMXD6 *See:* poly(*m*-xylyleneadipamide)

PAN *See:* *N*-phenyl-α-naphthylamine; polyacrylonitrile

pancreatin

[8049-47-6]
Production:
• pig pancreas (drying)
Uses: animal feed digestion aid; leather tanning auxiliary; spotting solvent (dry cleaning)

pantolactone

2,4-dihydroxy-3,3-dimethylbutyric acid γ-lactone; [599-04-2]

$C_6H_{10}O_3$. M: 130.15. Crystals. MP: 80°C (racemic mixture), 91°C (resolved isomers). d: 1.18 kg/l (20°C). Soluble in water, oxygenated and chlorinated solvents. Available commercially both as a racemic mixture and as the D(−) or L(+)-enantiomers.
Production:
• isobutyraldehyde + formaldehyde + hydrogen cyanide (condensation/nitrile hydrolysis)
Derivatives: calcium pantothenate; pantothenol

pantothenol
panthenol; pantothenyl alcohol; [81-13-0]

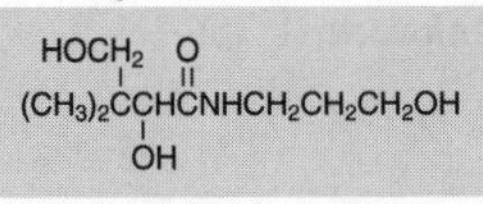

$$HOCH_2\ O$$
$$(CH_3)_2CCHCNHCH_2CH_2CH_2OH$$
$$OH$$

$C_9H_{19}N_1O_4$. M: 205.26. Viscous liquid. Soluble in water and oxygenated solvents. Both the racemic and (+)-form of this chemical are produced.
Production:
• pantolactone + 3-aminopropanol (amide formation)
Uses: cholinergic drug; animal feed additive

PAO *See:* polyalphaolefins

PAPA *See:* polyazelaic polyanhydride

papain
E.C.3.4.22.2 (Enzyme Commission); [9001-73-4]
The commercial product is the dried latex of papaya fruit (pawpaw, *Carica papaya*). It is available as the crude product, in a purified form or as a solution in glycerol.
Uses: beer chillproofing agent; gluten softening agent (prepared food); leather batting reagent; meat tenderiser

papaverine
6,7-dimethoxy-1-veratrylisoquinoline;
[58-74-2]; [6183-83-1] (hydrochloride)

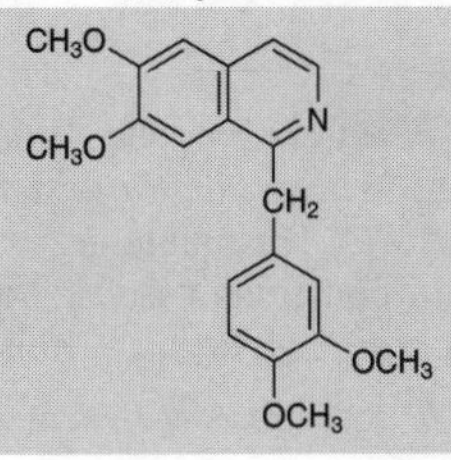

$C_{20}H_{21}N_1O_4$. M: 339.40. Available commercially as the hydrochloride.
Production:
• homoveratric acid + homoveratrylamine (amide formation/carbonyl condensation/dehydrogenation)
Uses:
spasmolytic/vasodilator drug

PAPI
See: 4,4′-diphenylmethane diisocyanate, polymeric

paracetamol
p-acetamidophenol (INN); acetaminophen; *N*-acetyl-4-aminophenol; 4-hydroxyacetanilide; APAP; Tylenol (Johnson & Johnson); [103-90-2]

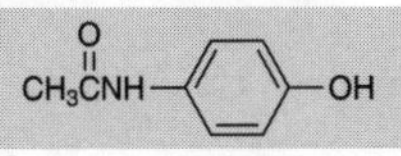

$C_8H_9N_1O_2$. M: 151.17. White, crystalline solid. MP:

170°C. d: 1.29 kg/l (20°C). Soluble in hot water, oxygenated and chlorinated solvents.
Production:
• acetic anhydride + *p*-aminophenol (amide formation)
• *p*-hydroxyacetophenone + hydroxylamine sulphate (Hoechst Celanese process)
Derivatives: ambroxol
Uses: dyestuffs intermediate; analgesic/antipyretic drug

paraffin *See:* kerosene

paraffin, chlorinated *See:* chloroparaffin

_n_-paraffins (C_{10}-C_{13})

$$CH_3(CH_2)_nCH_3$$

n = 8–11.
Production:
• kerosene (molecular sieve separation; coproduced with *n*-paraffins (C_{11}-C_{14})/*n*-paraffins (C_{14}-C_{18}))
Derivatives:
n-monochloroparaffins (C_{10}-C_{13}); *n*-olefins(C_{10}-C_{13})
Uses: domestic lamp oil; aluminium cold-rolling oils; pharmaceutical solvent, lubricant

_n_-paraffins (C_{11}-C_{14})

$$CH_3(CH_2)_nCH_3$$

n = 9–12.
Production:
• kerosene (molecular sieve separation; coproduced with *n*-paraffins (C_{10}-C_{13})/*n*-paraffins (C_{14}-C_{18}))
Derivatives: *n*-monochloroparaffins (C_{11}-C_{14}); sodium alkane(C_{11}-C_{14}) sulphonate

_n_-paraffins (C_{14}-C_{18})

$$CH_3(CH_2)_nCH_3$$

n = 12–16. Solid or liquid. BP: 240–300°C. d: 0.78 kg/l. Insoluble in water. Soluble in ether.
Production:
• kerosene (molecular sieve separation; coproduced with *n*-paraffins (C_{10}-C_{13})/*n*-paraffins (C_{11}-C_{14}))
• gas oil, light (molecular sieve separation)
Derivatives:
chloroparaffin; sodium alkane(C_{14}-C_{18}) sulphonate

_n_-paraffins (C_{24}-C_{60}) *See:* wax, Fischer-Tropsch

paraffin wax
Solid. MP: 45–70°C. Mixed hydrocarbon wax containing a high proportion of C_{15}–C_{40} alkanes. The macrocrystalline paraffin wax produced by solvent dewaxing processes is a mixture of normal, iso and cycloparaffins. The urea dewaxing processes produces wax comprising ≥70% *n*-paraffins.

Production:
- slack wax (sweating process)

Derivatives: chloroparaffin

Uses:

candles; casting wax; electrical insulation; barrier/antiblocking/heat sealing agent (hot melt adhesives); base oil (toiletries, creams); match impregnating material; paper impregnation/coating material; floor/shoe/car polish ingredient; poultry defeathering aid; plastics processing lubricant; rubber compounding ingredient; tack reduction additive (printing/carbon-copying inks); textile waterproofing agent

paraformaldehyde
[30525-89-4]

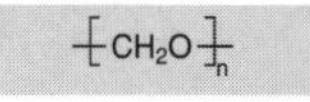

$$\left[CH_2O \right]_n$$

White, crystalline powder. Hydrolysed by hot water and alkali forming formaldehyde.

Production:
- formaldehyde (polymerisation)

Derivatives:

chloromethyl chlorosulphate; cyclonite; hexachlorophene; nopyl acetate; octogen; triprolidine

Uses:

resorcinol-formaldehyde resin curing agent; disinfectant; amino/phenolic resin formaldehyde substitute; chloromethylation reagent

paraldehyde
2,4,6-trimethyl-1,3,5-trioxane; [123-63-7]

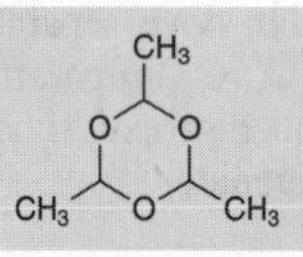

$C_6H_{12}O_3$. M: 132.17. Liquid with a characteristic odour. BP: 124–127°C. FP: 12°C. d: 0.99 kg/l (20°C). Soluble in hot water. Miscible with oxygenated and chlorinated solvents.

Production:
- acetaldehyde (carbonyl addition)

Derivatives:

2-methyl-5-ethylpyridine; α-picoline; γ-picoline

paramorphine *See:* thebaine

paraquat dichloride
1,1′-dimethyl-4,4′-bipyridinium chloride; [1910-42-5]

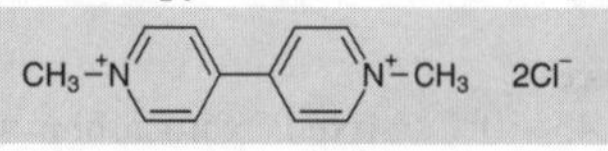

$C_{12}H_{14}Cl_2N_2$. M: 257.16.

Production:
- pyridine + sodium + methyl chloride (oxidative coupling/quaternisation)

Uses: herbicide

parathion
O,O-diethyl *O*-4-nitrophenyl phosphorothioate; ethyl parathion; parathion-ethyl; [56-38-2]

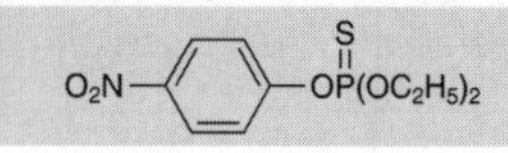

$C_{10}H_{14}N_1O_5P_1S_1$. M: 291.25.

Production:
- *p*-nitrophenol + *O,O*-diethyl phosphorochlorothioate (dehydrochlorination)

Uses: insecticide/acaricide

parathion-methyl
O,O-dimethyl-*O*-4-nitrophenyl phosphorothioate; methyl parathion; [298-00-0]

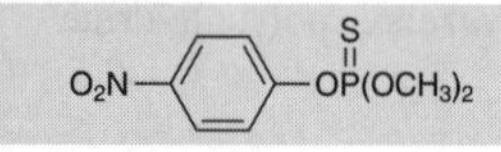

$C_8H_{10}N_1O_5P_1S_1$. M: 263.20.

Production:
- *p*-nitrophenol + *O,O*-dimethyl phosphorochlorothioate (dehydrochlorination)

Uses: insecticide/acaricide

paroxypropione *See:* *p*-hydroxypropiophenone

PAS *See:* *p*-aminosalicylic acid

PASA *See:* *p*-aminosalicylic acid

patchouli oil
Brown oil with an intense odour. Produced by steam distillation of the leaves of *Pogostemon cablin*. d: 0.97–0.98 kg/l (15°C). Insoluble in water. Soluble in alcohol. The main constituent is patchoulol. The oil is produced in Indonesia, Malaysia, China, Brazil, Africa and the CIS countries.

Uses:

fragrance ingredient

patent blue *See:* Acid Blue 3

PB *See:* polybutene-1

1,2-PBD *See:* 1,2-polybutadiene

PBI *See:* polybenzimidazole

PBN *See:* *N*-phenyl-β-naphthylamine

PBT *See:* poly(butylene terephthalate)

PC *See:* polycarbonate

PCMC *See:* *p*-chloro-*m*-cresol

PCMX *See:* 4-chloro-3,5-xylenol

PCNB *See: p*-chloronitrobenzene; quintozene

PCOC *See: p*-chloro-*o*-cresol

PCP *See: p*-chlorophenol; pentachlorophenol

PCT
See: poly(1,4-cyclohexylenedimethylene terephthalate)

PCTFE *See:* polychlorotrifluoroethylene

PCTP *See:* pentachlorothiophenol

77PD
See: N,N'-bis(1,4-dimethylpentyl)-*p*-phenylenediamine

PDA *See:* 1,2-propanediamine

PDCB *See: p*-dichlorobenzene

PDMS *See:* silicone oils

peach kernel oil
peach nut oil; [8023-98-1]
Pale yellow oil. Produced by expression of the kernels from the fruit of the peach (*Prunus persica*). d: ~0.92 kg/l (15°C). Slightly soluble in alcohol. Soluble in water.
Uses: emollient (cosmetics)

peanut oil
arachis oil; groundnut oil; [8002-03-7]
Colourless to pale yellow liquid. Titre: 26–32°C. Solidification point: -3–0°C. d: 0.92 kg/l (15°C). The chain-length distribution is : 5–16% $C_{16:0}$, 51–71% $C_{18:1}$, 13–26% $C_{18:2}$.
Uses:
drying oil (paints); ingredient (mayonnaise, salad oil, shortening, margarine, baked goods); soap ingredient

Pebax *See:* poly(ether-amide) elastomers

pebulate
S-propyl butyl(ethyl)thiocarbamate; [1114-71-2]

$$CH_3CH_2CH_2CH_2\overset{\overset{O}{\|}}{N}\underset{\underset{C_2H_5}{|}}{}CSCH_2CH_2CH_3$$

$C_{10}H_{21}N_1O_1S_1$. M: 203.35.
Production:
• *n*-propyl mercaptan + phosgene + *n*-butylethyl-
  amine (phosgenation/dehydrochlorination)
Uses:
herbicide

pectin
E440 (EC); [9000-69-5]

Yellow-white powder. Soluble in water. Insoluble in oxygenated solvents. Polysaccharide gum in which 70–75% of the acid groups in the initial extract are methylated. These are hydrolysed to varying degrees by acid, alkali or ammonia producing different grades of pectin.
Production:
• orange peel/apple pomace/lemon peel (extraction)
Uses:
stabiliser/thickening agent (foods, preserves)

PEEA *See:* 2-phenoxyethyl acrylate

PEEK *See:* polyether ether ketone

PEG *See:* polyethylene glycol

PEI *See:* polyethyleneimine; poly(ether-imide)

PEK *See:* polyether ketone

PEKEKK *See:* polyether ketone ether ketone ketone

PEKK *See:* polyether ketone ketone

pelargonaldehyde *See: n*-nonaldehyde

pelargonic acid
nonanoic acid; *n*-nonanoic acid; [112-05-0]

$$CH_3(CH_2)_7COOH$$

$C_9H_{18}O_2$. M: 158.24. Colourless liquid. BP: 249–271°C. d: 0.90 kg/l (20°C). Acid value: 351 mg KOH/g. Insoluble in water. Soluble in oxygenated solvents.
Production:
• oleic acid (ozonolysis; coproduced with azelaic
  acid)
• *n*-nonanol (alcohol oxidation)
Derivatives: alkyd resins, non-drying; complex ester oils; dipentaerythritol hexapelargonate; neopentyl glycol dipelargonate; *N*-pelagonoyl-*p*-aminophenol; pentaerythritol tetrapelargonate; propylene glycol dipelargonate; sodium nonanoyloxybenzene sulphonate; triethylene glycol dipelargonate; trimethylolpropane tripelargonate
Uses: butter marker; alkyd resin comonomer; cosmetics ingredient

N-pelagonoyl-p-aminophenol
4-hydroxypelagonanilide; Suconox-9 (Hexcel); [101-95-1]

$$CH_3(CH_2)_7\overset{\overset{O}{\|}}{C}NH\text{—}\langle\ \rangle\text{—}OH$$

$C_{15}H_{23}N_1O_2$. M: 249.35.
Production:
• pelargonic acid + *p*-aminophenol (amide formation)
Uses: antioxidant (plastics)

PEN *See:* poly(ethylene naphthalate)

penconazole
1-(2,4-dichloro-β-propylphenethyl)-1H-1,2,4-triazole; [66246-88-6]

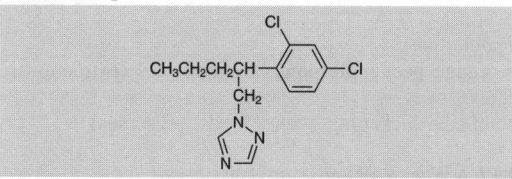

$C_{13}H_{15}Cl_2N_3$. M: 284.19.
Production:
• α,2,4-trichloroacetophenone + 1,2,4-triazole + *n*-propyl bromide (amine formation/Grignard reagent formation/Grignard reaction/alcohol reduction)
Uses: fungicide

pencycuron
1-(4-chlorobenzyl)-1-cyclopentyl-3-phenylurea; [66063-05-6]

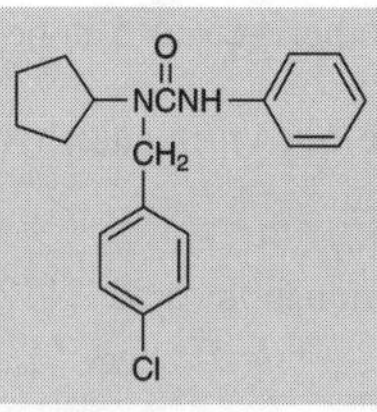

$C_{19}H_{21}Cl_1N_2O_1$. M: 328.84.
Production:
• cyclopentylamine + *p*-chlorobenzaldehyde + phenyl isocyanate (reductive amination/isocyanate addition)
Uses: fungicide

pendimethalin
N-(1-ethylpropyl)-2,6-dinitro-3,4-xylidine; [40487-42-1]

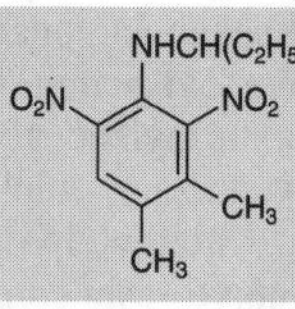

$C_{13}H_{19}N_3O_4$. M: 281.31.
Production:
• *o*-xylene + diethyl ketone + ammonia (ring chlorination/nitration/ammoniation/amine formation)
Uses: herbicide

penfluridol
[26864-56-2]
$C_{28}H_{27}Cl_1F_5N_1O_1$. M: 523.98.
Production:
• *o*-chlorobenzotrifluoride + 1-benzyl-4-piperidone + 4,4-bis(*p*-fluorophenyl)butyl chloride (ring bromination/Grignard reagent formation/Grignard reaction/amide dealkylation/dehydrochlorination)

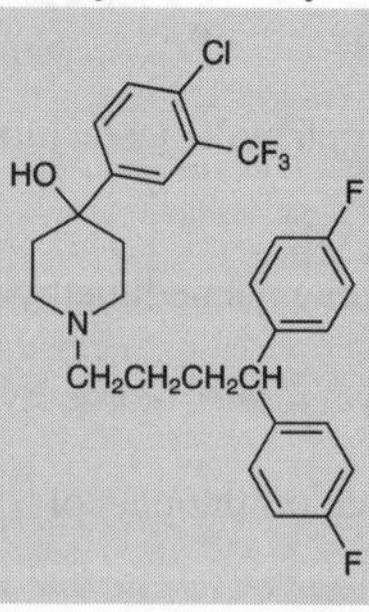

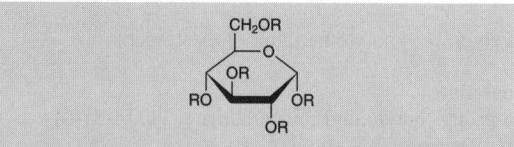

Uses: neuroleptic drug

penicillamine
3-mercapto-D-valine; [52-67-5]

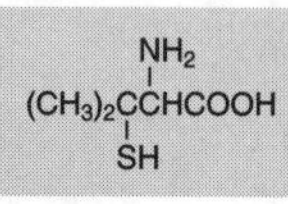

$C_5H_{11}N_1O_2S_1$. M: 149.21.
Production:
• benzylpenicillin (hydrolysis)
Uses: antirheumatic drug

penicillin G *See:* benzylpenicillin

penicillin V *See:* phenoxymethylpenicillin

pennyroyal oil
Oil produced by steam distillation of *Mentha pulegium* flowers, which are grown in Spain and North Africa, or *Hedeoma pulegioides* flowers, grown in USA.
Uses: fragrance ingredient (soaps, toiletries)

pentaacetylglucose
PAG

R = acetyl-. $C_{16}H_{22}O_{11}$. M: 390.35.
Production:
• starch hydrolysate + acetic anhydride (acetylation)
Uses: bleach activator (laundry detergents)

pentabromodiphenyl oxide
pentabrom; pentabromobiphenyl ether

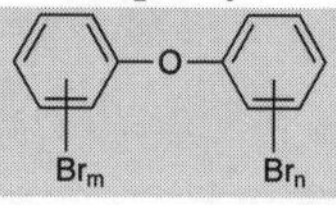

m+n = 5. $C_{12}H_5Br_5O_1$. M: 564.69. Liquid. d: 2.3 kg/l.

Insoluble in water. Soluble in oxygenated, chlorinated and aromatic solvents. Also available in a blended form with phosphate ester fire retardants.
Production:
• diphenyl oxide + bromine (ring bromination)
Uses: fire-retardant additive (polyurethane flexible foam, unsaturated polyester resin, textile coatings)

α,α,2,4,5-pentachloroacetophenone
2,2,2′,4′,5′-pentachloroacetophenone

$C_8H_3Cl_5O_1$. M: 292.37.
Production:
• 2,4,5-trichloroacetophenone (alpha chlorination)
Derivatives: tetrachlorvinphos

pentachloronitrobenzene *See:* quintozene

pentachlorophenol
PCP; [608-93-5]

$C_6H_1Cl_5O_1$. M: 266.34.
Production:
• hexachlorobenzene (base-catalysed hydrolysis)
• phenol + chlorine (ring chlorination)
Derivatives:
sodium pentachlorophenate
Uses: wood preservative/fungicide

pentachlorothiophenol
pentachlorobenzenethiol; PCTP; [133-49-3]

$C_6H_1Cl_5S_1$. M: 282.40.
Production:
• hexachlorobenzene + hydrogen sulphide (thiolation)
Uses: rubber peptising agent

15-pentadecanolide
15-hydroxypentadecanoic acid lactone; pentadeca-lactone; [106-02-5]
$C_{15}H_{28}O_2$. M: 240.38. Colourless crystals with a musk-like odour. MP: 37–38°C. BP: 169°C (1.3 kPa). d: 0.94 kg/l (40°C).

Production:
• cyclododecanone + allyl alcohol (carbonyl condensation/ether formation/oxidative cleavage)
• 1,12-dodecanediol + methyl acrylate (multistep synthesis)
Uses: fragrance ingredient (musk substitute, fixative)

1,3-pentadiene *See:* piperylene

pentaerythritol
tetramethylolmethane; [115-77-5]

$C(CH_2OH)_4$

$C_5H_{12}O_4$. M: 136.15. White, crystalline solid. MP: 260°C. Soluble in water and alcohol. Insoluble in aromatic and chlorinated solvents. Different grades are available commercially containing different levels of dipentaerythritol.
Production:
• acetaldehyde + formaldehyde (aldol condensation/Cannizzaro reaction)
Derivatives: alkyd resins, long-oil; alkyd resins, medium-oil; bis(2,4-di-*t*-butylphenyl)pentaerythrityl diphosphite; dibromoneopentyl glycol; distearylpentaerythrityl diphosphite; maleic resins; maleinised oils; pentaerythritol tetraacrylate; pentaerythritol tetrabehenate; pentaerythritol tetrakis[3-(3,5-di-*t*-butyl-4-hydroxyphenyl)-propionate]; pentaerythritol tetranitrate; pentaerythritol tetraoleate; pentaerythritol tetrapelargonate; pentaerythritol tetrastearate; pentaerythritol triacrylate; pentaerythritol triallyl ether; phenolic resins, rosin-modified; polyether polyols, rigid; rosin ester gum; tribromoneopentyl alcohol
Uses: polyvinyl chloride heat costabilisers

pentaerythritol tetraacrylate

$C[CH_2OCCH=CH_2]_4$

$C_{17}H_{20}O_8$. M: 352.34.
Production:
• pentaerythritol + acrylic acid (esterification)
Derivatives:
pentaerythritol tetrakis(3-mercaptopropionate)
Uses: reactive diluent (radiation-cured inks, lacquers)

pentaerythritol tetrabehenate
[61682-73-3]
$C_{93}H_{180}O_8$. M: 1426.46. Solid. MP: 73°C.
Production:
• pentaerythritol + behenic acid (esterification)

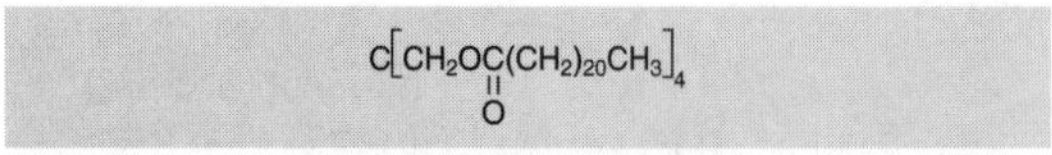

$$C[CH_2OC(CH_2)_{20}CH_3]_4$$

Uses: plastics processing lubricant

pentaerythritol tetrakis[3-(3,5-di-*t*-butyl-4-hydroxyphenyl)propionate]

tetrakis[methylene (3,5-di-*t*-butyl-4-hydroxy)hydrocinnamate]methane; Irganox 1010 (Ciba-Geigy); [6683-19-8]

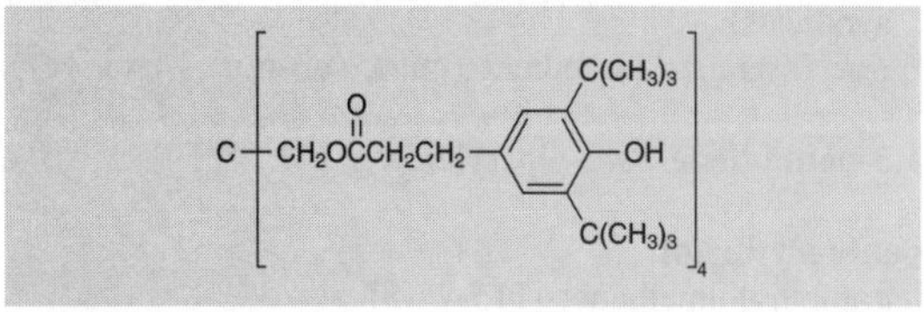

$C_{73}H_{108}O_{12}$. M: 1177.65.
Production:
• pentaerythritol + methyl 3,5-di-*t*-butyl-4-hydroxyphenylpropionate (transesterification)
Uses:
antioxidant (plastics)

pentaerythritol tetrakis(3-mercaptopropionate)

Mercaptate Q-43 (Carstab); [7575-23-7]

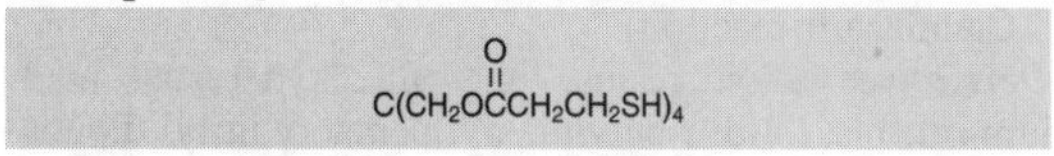

$$C(CH_2OCCH_2CH_2SH)_4$$

$C_{17}H_{28}O_8S_4$. M: 488.66. Liquid. d: 1.28 kg/l (25°C). Insoluble in water.
Production:
• pentaerythritol tetraacrylate + hydrogen sulphide (addition)
Uses:
polymerisation modifier

pentaerythritol tetranitrate

PETN; [78-11-5]

$$C(CH_2ONO_2)_4$$

$C_5H_8N_4O_{12}$. M: 316.13.
Production:
• pentaerythritol + nitric acid, concentrated (nitration)
Uses:
detonator cords; *angina pectoris* drug

pentaerythritol tetraoleate

[19321-40-5]

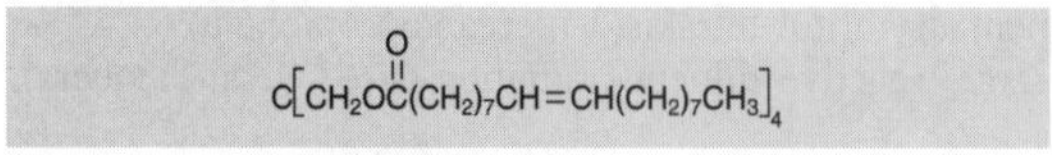

$$C[CH_2OC(CH_2)_7CH=CH(CH_2)_7CH_3]_4$$

$C_{77}H_{140}O_8$. M: 1193.96.
Production:
• pentaerythritol + oleic acid (esterification)
Uses: lubricity additive (hot rolling, forming, drawing lubricants)

pentaerythritol tetrapelargonate

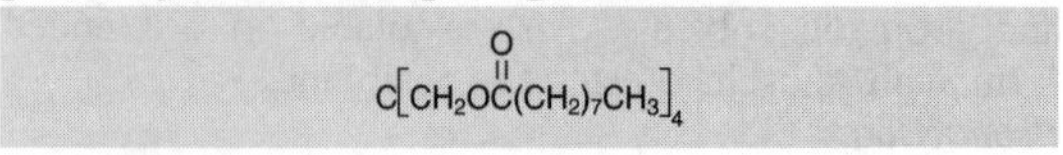

$$C[CH_2OC(CH_2)_7CH_3]_4$$

$C_{41}H_{76}O_8$. M: 697.06.
Production:
• pentaerythritol + pelargonic acid (esterification)
Uses: synthetic lubricant base oils

pentaerythritol tetrastearate

[115-83-3]

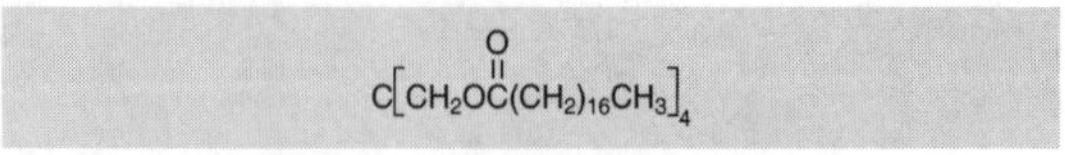

$$C[CH_2OC(CH_2)_{16}CH_3]_4$$

$C_{77}H_{148}O_8$. M: 1202.02. Solid. MP: 62°C.
Production:
• stearic acid + pentaerythritol (transesterification)
Uses: rubber/plastics processing lubricant

pentaerythritol triacrylate

PETA

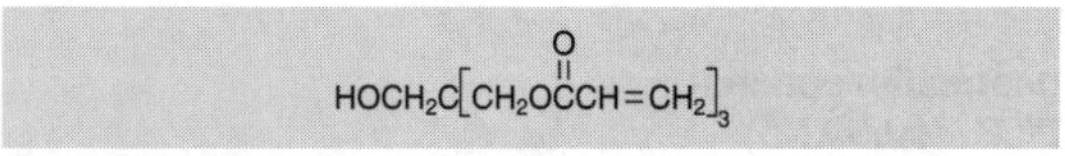

$$HOCH_2C[CH_2OCCH=CH_2]_3$$

$C_{14}H_{18}O_7$. M: 298.28.
Production:
• pentaerythritol + acrylic acid (esterification)
Uses:
reactive diluent (radiation-cured inks, lacquers)

pentaerythritol triallyl ether

[1471-17-6]

$$HOCH_2C(CH_2OCH_2CH=CH_2)_3$$

$C_{14}H_{24}O_4$. M: 256.34. Liquid.
Production:
• pentaerythritol + allyl chloride (ether formation)
Derivatives:
unsaturated polyester resins, coating grades
Uses: unsaturated polyester resin comonomer

pentafluoroethane

R125

$$CHF_2CF_3$$

$C_2H_1F_5$. M: 120.02.
Production:
• 1,1-dichloro-2,2,2-trifluoroethane + hydrogen fluoride (halogen exchange; coproduced with 1-chloro-1,2,2,2-tetrafluoroethane)
Uses: refrigerant gas

pentagastrin

[5534-95-2]

$$BOC\text{-}\beta\text{-}Ala\text{-}Trp\text{-}Met\text{-}Asp\text{-}Phe\text{-}NH_2$$

BOC = *t*-butoxycarbonyl-. $C_{37}H_{49}N_7O_9S_1$. M: 767.90.

Production:
- *t*-butanol + phosgene + β-alanine + L-tryptophan + L-methionine + L-phenylalanine + L-aspartic acid + ammonia (peptide synthesis)

Uses: medical diagnostic aid

pentaldehyde *See:* valeraldehyde

pentaldehydes, mixed

$$C_4H_9CHO$$

$C_5H_{10}O_1$. M: 86.13. Intermediate stream containing mainly 2-methylbutyraldehyde and valeraldehyde. Not a commercially traded product.

Production:
- raffinate II + synthesis gas (hydroformylation)

Derivatives: amyl alcohol, primary; 2-methylbutyraldehyde; valeraldehyde

pentamethyldiethylenetriamine

N,N,N′,N″,N″-pentamethyldiethylenetriamine; [3030-47-5]

$$\underset{\underset{CH_3}{|}}{(CH_3)_2NCH_2CH_2NCH_2CH_2N(CH_3)_2}$$

$C_9H_{23}N_3$. M: 173.30. Liquid with strong, ammoniacal odour. BP: 70–85°C (1.1 kPa). MP: <20°C.

Production:
- diethylenetriamine (methylation)

Uses: polyurethane foam catalyst

pentamethyldipropylenetriamine

N,N,N′,N″,N″-pentamethyldipropylenetriamine; 2,6,10-trimethyl-2,6,10-triazaundecane; Polycat 77 (Air Products and Chemical);

$$\underset{\underset{CH_3}{|}}{(CH_3)_2NCH_2CH_2CH_2NCH_2CH_2CH_2N(CH_3)_2}$$

$C_{11}H_{27}N_3$. M: 201.36.

Production:
- methylamine + 3-dimethylaminopropyl chloride hydrochloride (amine formation)

Uses:
polyurethane foam catalyst

pentamethyleneamine *See:* piperidine

pentamethylene glycol *See:* 1,5-pentanediol

1,2,2,6,6-pentamethyl-4-hydroxypiperidine

$C_{10}H_{21}N_1O_1$. M: 171.29.

Production:
- phorone + methylamine (carbonyl condensation)

Derivatives: di-(pentamethylhydroxypiperidyl) butyl-(di-3,5-*t*-butyl-4-hydroxybenzyl)malonate; di-(1,2,2,6,6-pentamethyl-4-piperidyl) sebacate

pentamethyl-*N*-tallow-1,3-propanediammonium chloride

$$R\overset{\underset{CH_3}{|}}{\underset{\underset{CH_3}{|}}{-\overset{+}{N}CH_2CH_2CH_2\overset{+}{N}(CH_3)_3}}\ \ 2Cl^-$$

R = tallow-. $C_{26}H_{58}Cl_2N_2$. M: 469.67. Available commercially as a 50% solution in water.

Production:
- *N*-tallow-1,3-propanediamine + methyl chloride (quaternisation)

Uses: cationic emulsifier (solvent cleaners, pesticides)

n-pentane
[109-66-0]

$$CH_3CH_2CH_2CH_2CH_3$$

C_5H_{12}. M: 72.15. Colourless liquid. BP: 36°C. FP: -130°C. d: 0.63 kg/l (20°C). Insoluble in water. Soluble in oxygenated, chlorinated and hydrocarbon solvents.

Production:
- gasoline, polymer (molecular sieve separation; coproduced with isopentane/*n*-hexane/isohexane)

Derivatives: perfluoro-*n*-pentane

Uses: blowing agent (expandable polystyrene); process solvent (lubricant deasphalting); thermometer fluid

pentane-1,5-dioic acid *See:* glutaric acid

1,5-pentanediol
pentamethylene glycol; [111-29-5]

$$HOCH_2CH_2CH_2CH_2CH_2OH$$

$C_5H_{12}O_2$. M: 104.15. Liquid. BP: 242°C. FP: -15°C. d: 0.99 kg/l (20°C). Flash point: 147°C (PMCC). Miscible with water.

Production:
- glutaraldehyde (hydrogenation)

Derivatives: dicycloverine

2,4-pentanedione *See:* acetylacetone

pentanochlor
3′-chloro-2-methylvaler-*p*-toluidide; [2307-68-8]

$C_{13}H_{18}Cl_1N_1O_1$. M: 239.74.

Production:
- 2-methylvaleric acid + 4-amino-2-chlorotoluene (amide formation)

Uses: herbicide

n-pentanoic acid *See:* valeric acid

1-pentanol *See:* *n*-amyl alcohol

2-pentanone *See:* methyl propyl ketone

3-pentanone *See:* diethyl ketone

pentapotassium triphosphate
See: potassium tripolyphosphate

pentasodium diethylenetriaminepentaacetate *See:* diethylenetriaminepentaacetic acid, pentasodium salt

pentazocine
[359-83-1]

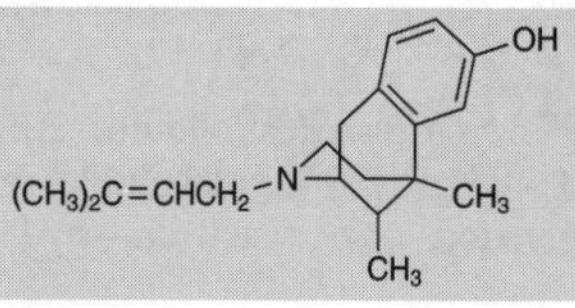

$C_{19}H_{27}N_1O_1$. M: 285.44.
Production:
- 3,4-lutidine + anisyl alcohol + 3-methyl-2-buten-1-ol (quaternisation/Grignard reaction/hydrogenation/cyclisation/demethylation/amine formation)

Uses: analgesic drug

pentenamide
See: valdetamide

1-pentene
[109-67-1]

$CH_3CH_2CH_2CH=CH_2$

C_5H_{10}. M: 70.13. Colourless liquid. BP: 29°C. MP: -138°C. d: 0.64 kg/l (20°C). Insoluble in water. Miscible with oxygenated solvents.
Production:
- naphtha, light, Synthol (extraction; coproduced with 1-hexene)

Derivatives:
propiconazole
Uses: linear, low-density polyethylene comonomer

pentifylline
[1028-33-7]
$C_{13}H_{20}N_4O_2$. M: 264.33.
Production:
- *n*-hexyl chloride + theobromine (dehydrochlorination)

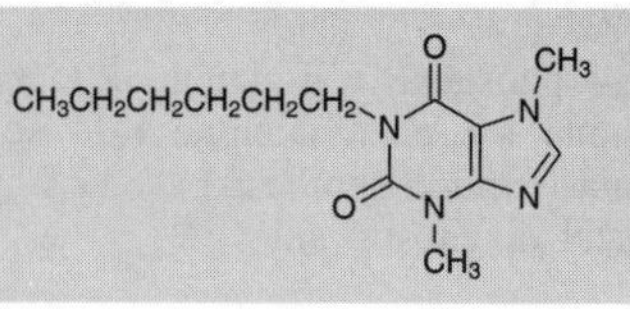

Uses: vasodilator drug

pentobarbital
5-ethyl-5-(2′-pentyl)barbituric acid; [76-74-4]; [57-33-0] (sodium salt)

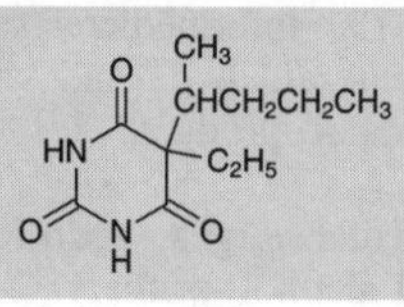

$C_{11}H_{18}N_2O_3$. M: 226.27. Available commercially as the sodium or calcium salts.
Production:
- ethyl cyanoacetate + methyl propyl ketone + ethyl bromide + dicyandiamide (Cope reaction/hydrogenation/dehydrobromination/cyclisation/nitrile hydrolysis/decarboxylation)

Uses: sedative/hypnotic drug

pentothal *See:* thiopental sodium

pentoxifylline
[6493-05-6]

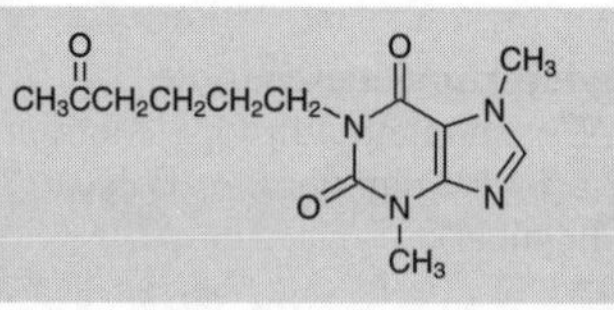

$C_{13}H_{18}N_4O_3$. M: 278.31.
Production:
- ethyl acetoacetate + 1-bromo-3-chloropropane + theobromine (dehydrobromination/decarboxylation/amine formation)

Uses: vasodilator drug

pentoxyverine
carbetapentane; [77-23-6]; [23142-01-0] (citrate)

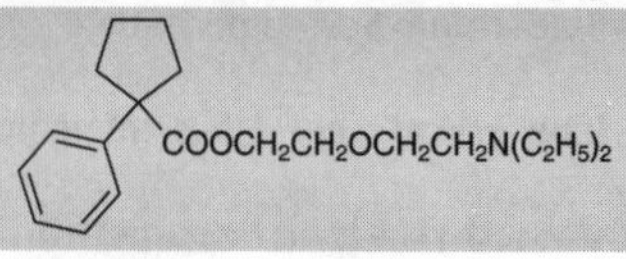

$C_{20}H_{31}N_1O_3$. M: 333.48. Available commercially as the free base or as the citrate salt.
Production:
- benzyl cyanide + 1,4-dibromobutane + diethylaminoethanol + ethylene oxide (dehydrobromination/nitrile hydrolysis/epoxidation/esterification)

Uses: antitussive drug

2-pentyl-3-phenyl-2-propenal
See: α-amylcinnamaldehyde

PEO *See:* polyethylene glycol

PEOX *See:* poly(ethylene oxide) resins

PEP *See:* polyethylenepolyamine

PEPA *See:* poly(ether-amide) elastomers

peppermint oil
[8006-90-4]
Pale yellow liquid with a characteristic odour. d: 0.90–0.92 kg/l (20°C). Soluble in alcohol. The main components of the oil are (−)-menthol (50%), (−)-menthone (20%), and menthyl acetate (10%). The oil is extracted from the peppermint plant (*Mentha piperata*) which is grown mainly in the USA, but also in some parts of Europe.
Uses: flavouring ingredient (toothpaste, chewing gum, confectionery)

peppermint oil, dementholised
Japanese peppermint oil from which a proportion of the (−)-menthol has been separated out by crystallisation.
Production:
• peppermint oil, Japanese (extraction)
Derivatives: (−)-menthol; menthone

peppermint oil, Japanese
cornmint oil; *Mentha arvensis* oil
Colourless to yellow liquid with a penetrating, minty odour. Produced by steam distillation of flowering *Mentha arvensis* plants. d: ~0.89 kg/l (25°C). Soluble in alcohol. The major constituent of the oil is (−)-menthol. Brazil, Paraguay and China are the main producing countries.
Derivatives:
(−)-menthol; peppermint oil, dementholised
Uses: flavouring ingredient (confectionery)

peracetic acid
peroxyacetic acid; PAA; [79-21-0]

$$\underset{CH_3CO-OH}{\overset{\overset{\text{O}}{\|}}{}}$$

$C_2H_4O_3$. M: 76.05. Liquid with an acrid odour. Explodes on heating above 110°C. Soluble in water and oxygenated solvents. Available commercially as a 40–45% solution in acetic acid.
Production:
• acetaldehyde (air oxidation; coproduced with acetic acid)
• acetic acid + hydrogen peroxide (sulphuric acid process)

Derivatives:
aldoxycarb; 7-amino-3-desacetoxycephalosporanic acid; butoxycarboxim; *n*-butyl epoxystearate; campholenic aldehyde; caprolactone; cedrene epoxide; cyclohexyl epoxystearate; dicyclopentadiene alcohol epoxide; dicyclopentadiene dioxide; diisodecyl 4,5-epoxytetrahydrophthalate; β-(3,4-epoxycyclohexyl)ethyltrimethoxysilane; 3,4-epoxycyclohexylmethyl 3,4-epoxycyclohexylcarboxylate; 3,4-epoxy-6-methylcyclohexylmethyl 3,4-epoxy-6-methylcyclohexane carboxylate; 2-ethylhexyl epoxystearate; hydroxycitronellal; isooctyl epoxystearate; linalool oxide; linseed oil, epoxidised; polybutadiene, epoxidised; soyabean oil, epoxidised; tinidazole; vinylcyclohexene dioxide
Uses:
disinfectant (food and beverage equipment); biocide (paper production)

perchloro-1,1′-bicyclopenta-2,4-diene *See:* dienochlor

perchlorocyclopentadiene
See: hexachlorocyclopentadiene

perchloroethane *See:* hexachloroethane

perchloroethylene
tetrachloroethylene; Perklone (ICI); [127-18-4]

$$CCl_2=CCl_2$$

C_2Cl_4. M: 165.83. Colourless, non-flammable liquid with a pleasant odour. BP: 121°C. FP: -22°C. d: 1.63 kg/l (20°C). Insoluble in water. Miscible with most organic solvents.
Production:
• ethylene dichloride + chlorine (chlorination; coproduced with trichloroethylene)
• ethane/propane + chlorine (chlorinolysis; coproduced with carbon tetrachloride)
• ethylene dichloride + chlorine + oxygen (oxychlorination/dehydrochlorination; coproduced with trichloroethylene)
• carbon tetrachloride (thermal dechlorination)
Derivatives:
chloropentafluoroethane; 1,2-dichloro-1,1,2,2-tetrafluoroethane; 1,1-dichloro-2,2,2-trifluoroethane; tetrachlorodifluoroethane; 1,1,2-trichloro-1,2,2-trifluoroethane
Uses: oil/fat extraction solvent; flotation solvent (coal separation); anthelmintic drug; solvent (dry cleaning, vapour degreasing); textile finishing agent

perchloromethyl mercaptan
See: trichloromethanesulphenyl chloride

perfluidone
1,1,1-trifluoro-2′-methyl-4′-(phenylsulphonyl)methanesulphonanilide; [37924-13-3]
$C_{14}H_{12}F_3N_1O_4S_2$. M: 379.38.

Production:
- *o*-toluidine + benzenesulphonyl chloride + trifluoro-methanesulphonic acid (sulphonation/amide formation)

Uses: herbicide

perfluoroacetic acid *See:* trifluoroacetic acid

perfluoroalkyl acrylates

R = fluorinated alkyl-.
Production:
- 1,1-hydroperfluorooctanol/2,2,3,4,4,4-hexafluoro-butanol/2,2,3,3-tetrafluoropropanol/hexafluoro-isopropanol + acryloyl chloride (esterification)

Uses: comonomers (water/oil repellent textile coatings, optical wave guides, photoresists, medical plastics)

2-[perfluoroalkyl(C_6-C_{12})]ethanol

$CF_3(CF_2)_nCH_2CH_2OH$

n = 5–11.
Production:
- perfluoroalkyl(C_6-C_{12}) iodide + ethylene (addition/hydration)

Derivatives:
diethanolamine 2-[perfluoroalkyl(C_6-C_{12})]ethyl phosphate

perfluoroalkyl(C_6-C_{12}) iodide

$CF_3(CF_2)_nI$

n = 5–11.
Production:
- tetrafluoroethylene + iodine pentafluoride (addition/telomerisation; coproduced with perfluorohexyl iodide/perfluorooctyl iodide)

Derivatives: 2-[perfluoroalkyl(C_6-C_{12})]ethanol

perfluoroalkyl methacrylates

R = fluorinated alkyl-.
Production:
- 2-(perfluorooctyl)ethanol/2,2,3,4,4,4-hexafluoro-butanol/1,1-hydroperfluorooctanol/hexafluoro-isopropanol/2,2,3,3-tetrafluoropropanol + methacrylyl chloride (transesterification)

Uses:
comonomers (water/oil repellent textile coatings, optical wave guides, photoresists, medical plastics)

perfluorobutanesulphonic acid
perfluoro-*n*-butyl sulphonic acid; [59933-66-3]

$CF_3CF_2CF_2CF_2SO_3H$

$C_4H_1F_9O_3S_1$. M: 300.09.
Production:
- *n*-butyl mercaptan + hydrogen fluoride (Simon electrochemical fluorination)

Uses: antistatic agents

perfluorocaprylic acid *See:* perfluorooctanoic acid

perfluorodecalin
[306-94-5]

$C_{10}F_{18}$. M: 462.07.
Production:
- naphthalene + fluorine (vapour-phase fluorination)

Uses: dielectric fluids (transformers, switchgear); heat-transfer fluid (vapour-phase soldering, electronics cooling systems); leak testing fluid

perfluorodimethylcyclohexane
PP3 (Rhône-Poulenc)

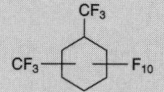

C_8F_{16}. M: 400.06. Colourless fluid. BP: 92–104°C. Pour point: -70°C. d: 1.83 kg/l (20°C). Insoluble in water.
Production:
- xylene, mixed + fluorine (vapour-phase fluorination)

Uses: heat-transfer fluid (electronic cooling systems, vacuum systems); leak testing fluid

perfluoroethercarboxylic acid oligomers

$F(CFCF_2O)_nCFCOOH$ with CF_3 substituents

n = 2–35.
Production:
- hexafluoropropylene oxide (fluoride-initiated polymerisation)

Derivatives: poly(perfluoropropyl ether)
Uses: fluorocarbon surfactant intermediate

perfluoroethylene *See:* tetrafluoroethylene

perfluoroheptanoic acid
[375-85-9]

$CF_3(CF_2)_5COOH$

$C_7H_1F_{13}O_2$. M: 364.06. Liquid. BP: 175°C. d: 1.79 kg/l (20°C).

Production:
- perfluorohexylethylene (oxidative cleavage)

Uses: fluorocarbon surfactant intermediate

perfluoro-*n*-hexane
PP1 (Rhône-Poulenc)

$$CF_3CF_2CF_2CF_2CF_2CF_3$$

C_6F_{14}. M: 338.04. Colourless liquid. BP: 54–60°C. Pour point: -90°C. d: 1.68 kg/l (20°C). Insoluble in water.
Production:
- *n*-hexane + fluorine (vapour-phase fluorination)

Uses: heat-transfer fluid

perfluorohexanesulphonic acid
perfluoro-*n*-hexyl sulphonic acid; [355-46-4]

$$CF_3(CF_2)_5SO_3H$$

$C_6H_1F_{13}O_3S_1$. M: 400.11.
Production:
- *n*-hexyl mercaptan + hydrogen fluoride (Simon electrochemical fluorination)

Uses: fire extinguishant additives

perfluorohexylethylene

$$CF_3(CF_2)_5CH=CH_2$$

$C_8H_3F_{13}$. M: 346.08.
Production:
- perfluorohexyl iodide + ethylene (addition/dehydroiodination)

Derivatives: dichloromethyl-2-(perfluoroalkyl)ethylsilane; perfluoroheptanoic acid

perfluorohexyl iodide
[355-43-1]

$$CF_3(CF_2)_5I$$

$C_6F_{13}I_1$. M: 445.94. Liquid. BP: 117°C.
Production:
- tetrafluoroethylene + iodine pentafluoride (addition/telomerisation; coproduced with perfluorooctyl iodide/perfluoroalkyl(C_6-C_{12}) iodide)

Derivatives:
perfluorohexylethylene

perfluoro-1-iodooctane *See:* perfluorooctyl iodide

perfluoromethylcyclohexane
PP2 (Rhône-Poulenc); [355-02-2]

C_7F_{14}. M: 350.05. Colourless fluid. BP: 73–78°C. Pour point: -30°C. d: 1.79 kg/l (20°C). Insoluble in water.

Production:
- toluene + fluorine (vapour-phase fluorination)

Derivatives: tetrafluoro-*p*-methylbenzyl alcohol
Uses: heat-transfer fluid (electronic cooling systems, vacuum systems); leak testing fluid

perfluoromethyldecalin

$C_{11}F_{20}$. M: 512.08.
Production:
- methylnaphthalene fraction + fluorine (vapour-phase fluorination)

Uses: dielectric fluids (transformers, switchgear); heat-transfer fluid (vapour-phase soldering, electronics cooling systems); leak testing fluid

perfluoro(methyl vinyl ether)
FMVE; [1187-93-5]

$$CF_2=CFOCF_3$$

$C_3F_6O_1$. M: 166.02.
Production:
- carbon monoxide + fluorine + hexafluoropropylene oxide (fluorination/addition/hydrolysis/decarboxylative fluorination)

Derivatives: tetrafluoroethylene-perfluoro(methyl vinyl ether) copolymers

perfluorononanoic acid
[375-95-1]

$$CF_3(CF_2)_7COOH$$

$C_9H_1F_{17}O_2$. M: 464.08. Liquid. BP: 110°C (2.1 kPa).
Production:
- perfluorooctylethylene (oxidative cleavage)

Uses: fluorocarbon surfactant intermediate

perfluorooctanesulphonic acid
[1763-23-1]

$$CF_3(CF_2)_7SO_3H$$

$C_8H_1F_{17}O_3S_1$. M: 500.13. Liquid. BP: 133°C (0.8 kPa).
Production:
- *n*-octyl mercaptan + hydrogen fluoride (Simon electrochemical fluorination/oxidation)

Derivatives: 2-(*N*-ethylperfluorooctylsulphonamido)ethanol; tetraethylammonium perfluorooctyl sulphonate
Uses: spray-control additive (electroplating)

perfluorooctanoic acid
perfluorocaprylic acid; [335-67-1]
$C_8H_1F_{15}O_2$. M: 414.07. Colourless liquid. BP; 189°C. d: 1.8 kg/l. Strongly acidic.

CF$_3$(CF$_2$)$_6$COOH

Production:
• caprylic acid + hydrogen fluoride (Simon electrochemical fluorination/hydrolysis)
• perfluorooctyl iodide (oxidation)
Derivatives: ammonium perfluorooctoate; 1,1-hydroperfluorooctanol; potassium perfluorooctoate

2-(perfluorooctyl)ethanol
1H,1H,2H,2H-perfluorodecanol

CF$_3$(CF$_2$)$_7$CH$_2$CH$_2$OH

C$_{10}$H$_5$F$_{17}$O$_1$. M: 464.12.
Production:
• perfluorooctyl iodide + ethylene (addition/hydration)
Derivatives: perfluoroalkyl methacrylates; 2-(perfluorooctyl)ethyl ethoxylates

perfluorooctylethylene

CF$_3$(CF$_2$)$_7$CH=CH$_2$

C$_{10}$H$_3$F$_{17}$. M: 446.10.
Production:
• perfluorooctyl iodide + ethylene (addition/dehydroiodination)
Derivatives: dichloromethyl-2-(perfluoroalkyl)ethylsilane; perfluorononanoic acid

2-(perfluorooctyl)ethyl ethoxylates
Fluorad FC-170-C (3M)

CF$_3$(CF$_2$)$_7$(CH$_2$CH$_2$O)$_n$H

Production:
• 2-(perfluorooctyl)ethanol + ethylene oxide (epoxidation)
Uses: surfactant (electronic etchant, refractories, inks, polishes)

perfluorooctyl iodide
perfluoro-1-iodooctane

CF$_3$(CF$_2$)$_7$I

C$_8$F$_{17}$I$_1$. M: 545.96.
Production:
• tetrafluoroethylene + iodine pentafluoride (addition/telomerisation; coproduced with perfluoroalkyl(C$_6$-C$_{12}$) iodide/perfluorohexyl iodide)
Derivatives: perfluorooctanoic acid; 2-(perfluorooctyl)-ethanol; perfluorooctylethylene

perfluoro-*n*-pentane
PP50 (Rhône-Poulenc)

CF$_3$CF$_2$CF$_2$CF$_2$CF$_3$

C$_5$F$_{12}$. M: 288.03. Colourless liquid. BP: 28–32°C. Pour point: -120°C. d: 1.60 kg/l (20°C).

Production:
• *n*-pentane + fluorine (vapour-phase fluorination)
Uses: heat-transfer fluid

perfluoro(propyl vinyl ether)
PPVE; [1623-05-8]

CF$_2$=CFOCF$_2$CF$_2$CF$_3$

C$_5$F$_{10}$O$_1$. M: 266.03.
Production:
• hexafluoropropylene oxide (dimerisation/decarboxylation/hydrolysis)
Derivatives: tetrafluoroethylene-perfluoro(propyl vinyl ether) copolymers

perfluorotriamylamine
Fluorinert FC-70 (3M)

N(CF$_2$CF$_2$CF$_2$CF$_2$CF$_3$)$_3$

C$_{15}$F$_{33}$N$_1$. M: 821.10. Liquid. BP: 203–216°C. Pour point: -25°C. d: 1.94 kg/l (20°C).
Production:
• triamylamine + hydrogen fluoride (Simon electrochemical fluorination)
Uses: heat-transfer fluid (vapour-phase soldering)

perfluorotributylamine
Fluorinert FC-43 (3M)

N(CF$_2$CF$_2$CF$_2$CF$_3$)$_3$

C$_{12}$F$_{27}$N$_1$. M: 671.09. Liquid. BP: 165–185°C. Pour point: -50°C. d: 1.86 kg/l (20°C).
Production:
• tri-*n*-butylamine + hydrogen fluoride (Simon electrochemical fluorination)
Uses: heat-transfer fluid (vapour-phase soldering)

perfluorotrihexylamine
Fluorinert FC-71 (3M); [432-08-6]

N[(CF$_2$)$_5$CF$_3$]$_2$

C$_{18}$F$_{39}$N$_1$. M: 971.13. Liquid. BP: 250–260°C. FP: 33°C. d: 1.90 kg/l (25°C).
Production:
• tri-*n*-hexylamine + hydrogen fluoride (Simon electrochemical fluorination)
Uses: heat-transfer fluid (vapour-phase soldering)

performic acid
peroxyformic acid; [107-32-4]

O
||
HCO−OH

C$_1$H$_2$O$_3$. M: 62.03. Colourless liquid produced *in situ*. Not a commercially traded product.
Production:
• formic acid + hydrogen peroxide (peroxidation)

Derivatives:
n-butyl epoxystearate; diisodecyl 4,5-epoxytetrahydro-phthalate; isooctyl epoxystearate; linseed oil, epoxidised; soyabean oil, epoxidised
Uses: peroxidation reagent

perhexiline
[6621-47-2]

$C_{19}H_{35}N_1$. M: 277.50.
Production:
• α-picoline + *n*-butyllithium + benzophenone (Grignard reagent formation/Grignard reaction/dehydration/hydrogenation)
Uses: vasodilator drug

peri acid
8-aminonaphthalene-1-sulphonic acid; 1-naphthylamine-8-sulphonic acid; [82-75-7]

$C_{10}H_9N_1O_3S_1$. M: 223.25. White crystals. Slightly soluble in water.
Production:
• naphthalene-1-sulphonic acid (nitration/nitro reduction/isomer separation; coproduced with 1-naphthylamine-5-sulphonic acid)
Derivatives:
Acid Blue 118; 8-hydroxynaphthalene-1-sulphonic acid; naphtholactam; 1-naphthylamine-4,8-disulphonic acid; *N*-phenyl-peri acid

perlite
Natural volcanic, porous glass containing interstitial water. The ore is pulverised and calcined at 1,000°C causing the glass to expand into light, porous granules.
Uses:
hydroponic agriculture substrate; lightweight concrete aggregate; packaging material; wall, floor insulation

permethrin
[52645-53-1]

$C_{21}H_{20}Cl_2O_3$. M: 391.30.

Production:
• 3-phenoxybenzyl alcohol + (*1RS*)-*cis/trans*-3-(2,2-dichlorovinyl)-2,2-dimethylcyclopropanecarboxylic acid (esterification)
Uses: insecticide

peroxysulphuric acid
Caro's acid; peroxymonosulphuric acid; persulphuric acid; [7722-86-3]

$$HO-O-SO_3H$$

$H_2O_5S_1$. M: 114.07. Available commercially as a 15–40% solution in water.
Production:
• sulphuric acid + hydrogen peroxide (peroxidation)
Uses: disinfectant (detergent sanitisers); oxidising agent (effluent treatment)

perphenazine
PZC; [58-39-9]

$C_{21}H_{26}Cl_1N_3O_1S_1$. M: 403.97.
Production:
• 2-chlorophenothiazine + 1-bromo-3-chloropropane + *N*-hydroxyethylpiperazine (amine formation/amine formation)
Uses: neuroleptic/antiemetic drug

Perspex *See:* poly(methyl methacrylate)

Peru balsam oil
Production:
• balsam, Peru (solvent extraction)
Uses:
flavouring ingredient; perfume fixative

perylenetetracarboxylic anhydride
perylene-3,4,9,10-tetracarboxylic anhydride; Perylene Red Y; Pigment Red 224 (CI); 71127 (CI)

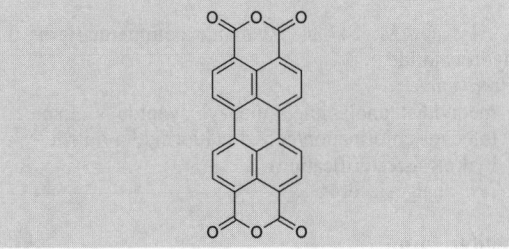

$C_{24}H_8O_6$. M: 392.31.
Production:
• naphthalic anhydride (oxidative coupling)

Derivatives: perylimide; Pigment Red 123; Pigment Red 149; Pigment Red 178; Pigment Red 179; Pigment Red 190; Vat Red 32
Uses: pigment (printing inks, paints)

perylimide
perylenetetracarboxylic diimide; Pigment Violet 29 (CI); 34910 (CI); [81-33-4]

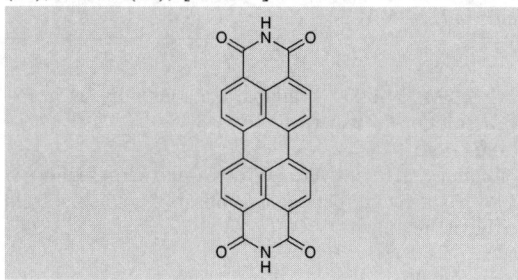

$C_{24}H_{10}N_2O_4$. M: 390.35. Solid. MP: >360°C.
Production:
• perylenetetracarboxylic anhydride + ammonia (imide formation)
Uses: pigment (plastics)

PES *See:* poly(4,4'-phenoxybiphenyl sulphone); polyether sulphone

PET *See:* poly(ethylene terephthalate)

PETA *See:* pentaerythritol triacrylate

PETG *See:* poly(1,4-cyclohexylenedimethylene terephthalate-isophthalate); poly(ethylene-1,4-cyclohexanedimethylene-terephthalate)

pethidine
meperidine; [57-42-1]; [50-13-5] (hydrochloride)

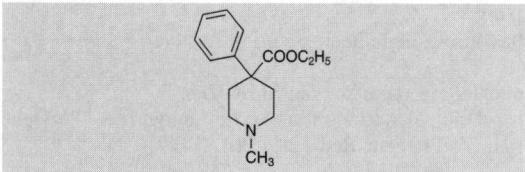

$C_{15}H_{21}N_1O_2$. M: 247.34. Available commercially as the hydrochloride.
Production:
• methyldiethanolamine + benzyl cyanide + ethanol (alcohol chlorination/dehydrochlorination/nitrile hydrolysis/esterification)
Uses: analgesic drug

petitgrain oil
Pale yellow liquid with a pleasant, characteristic odour. Produced by steam distillation of the leaves/twigs of various species of Seville orange (*Citrus aurantium*). d:

0.89 kg/l (15°C). Insoluble in water. Soluble in alcohol. The main constituent of the oil is linalyl acetate. There is some variation in the composition of the oil from different sources and subspecies. Major producing countries are Paraguay, France and Italy.
Uses:
fragrance ingredient (soap, cosmetics)

PETN *See:* pentaerythritol tetranitrate

petrolatum *See:* petroleum jelly

petroleum coke *See:* sponge coke, green; needle coke; fluid coke; flexicoke; shot coke

petroleum ether
ligroin
Aliphatic solvents boiling between 25°C and 80°C comprising mainly pentanes and hexanes. Various cuts with 10–20°C boiling ranges are produced. d: 0.63–0.68 kg/l (15°C). The aromatic content is usually below 0.2%.
Production:
• naphtha, light (fractionation)
Uses: solvent (paints, printing inks); extraction solvent (vegetable oil processing)

petroleum jelly
petrolatum; vaseline; [8027-32-5]; [8009-03-8]
White, yellow or brown soft gel with a characteristic odour. Softening point: 65–70°C. Insoluble in water and alcohol. Available in various technical or medicinal grades.
Production:
• deasphalted oil (solvent extraction; byproduct of brightstock production)
Derivatives:
microcrystalline wax
Uses: cable lubricants; cheese coatings; chewing gum ingredient; electrical insulation impregnation wax; adhesive diluent; insecticide spray ingredient; leather grease/polish; ointment base (pharmaceuticals, cosmetics); rust prevention coatings; tack reduction additive (printing inks)

petroleum resins, C₅ aliphatic types
See: hydrocarbon resins, C_5 aliphatic types

petroleum resins, C₉ aromatic types
See: hydrocarbon resins, C_9 aromatic types

petroleum resins, dicyclopentadiene types
See: hydrocarbon resins, dicyclopentadiene types

petroleum sulphonates, alkali-earth salts
naphtha sulphonates, alkali-earth salts
The equivalent weights of these products are 450–500

g, expressed as the sodium salt. Neutral and over-based grades are both available.
Production:
• sodium petroleum sulphonate + calcium chloride/ barium chloride/magnesium sulphate (salt formation)
Uses:
corrosion inhibitor/detergent additive (lubricating oils)

petroleum sulphonates, sodium salts *See:* sodium petroleum sulphonate

PF *See:* novolac resins; resol resins

PFA *See:* tetrafluoroethylene-perfluoro(propyl vinyl ether) copolymers

PG *See:* n-propyl gallate

PGA *See:* folic acid

PGE *See:* phenyl glycidyl ether

PGML *See:* propylene glycol monolaurate

PGMS *See:* propylene glycol monostearate

PHB *See:* p-hydroxybenzoic acid; poly(hydroxybutyrate-hydroxyvalerate)

PHBA *See:* p-hydroxybenzoic acid

Phe *See:* L-phenylalanine

(+)-α-phellandrene
1,5-p-menthadiene; [4221-98-1]

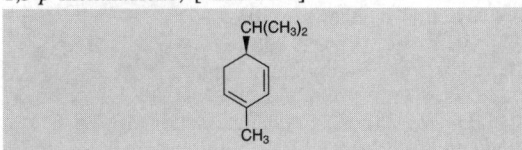

$C_{10}H_{16}$. M: 136.24. Colourless liquid with a citrus-like odour. BP: 172°C. d: 0.84 kg/l (20°C). Insoluble in water.
Production:
• *Eucalyptus dives* oil (fractionation)
Uses: fragrance ingredient

phenacetin
acetophenetidine; 4-ethoxyacetanilide; N-(4-ethoxyphenyl)acetamide; [62-44-2]

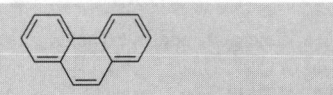

$C_{10}H_{13}N_1O_2$. M: 179.22.
Production:
• p-phenetidine + acetic anhydride (acetylation)

Derivatives: Disperse Blue 79
Uses: analgesic/antipyretic drug

phenanthrene
[85-01-8]

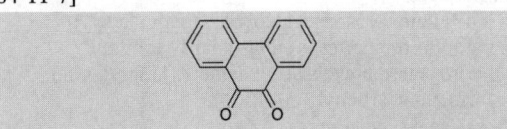

$C_{14}H_{10}$. M: 178.23. Crystalline solid. MP: 99–101°C. BP: 340°C. d: 1.18 kg/l (25°C). Insoluble in water. Soluble in aromatic solvents.
Production:
• anthracene oil (fractionation; byproduct of anthracene production)
Derivatives: diphenic acid; 9,10-phenanthrenequinone

9,10-phenanthrenequinone
[84-11-7]

$C_{14}H_8O_2$. M: 208.21. Orange crystals. MP: 206–207°C. Sublimes on heating above 360°C. d: 1.40 kg/l. Insoluble in water. Soluble in oxygenated and aromatic solvents.
Production:
• phenanthrene (oxidation)
Derivatives: chlorflurenol-methyl; flurenol-butyl

phenates, alkali-earth salts

n = 7–28, M = Ca, Ba, Mg. Phenates used as detergents in lubricants have a side-chain produced by oligomerisation of propylene containing 9–30 carbon atoms. They are usually supplied in mixed additive packages with sulphonates and antioxidants all dissolved in mineral oil and are often in an 'over-based' form containing stabilised micelles of alkali-earth hydroxide/oxide.
Production:
• nonylphenol/dodecylphenol/alkyl(C_9-C_{30})phenol/ phenolic resins, oil-soluble, oil-reactive + calcium hydroxide/barium oxide/barium hydroxide (salt formation)
Uses: detergent additive (lubricants)

phenates, sulphurised, alkali-earth salts
calcium phenate, sulphurized
m = 7–28, n = 1–3.
Production:
• nonylphenol/dodecylphenol/alkyl(C_9-C_{30})phenol + sulphur + calcium hydroxide/barium oxide/barium hydroxide (sulphurisation/salt formation)

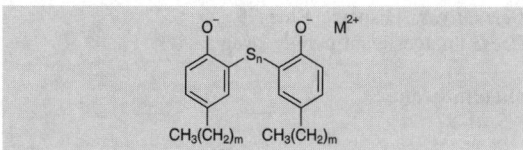

Uses: detergent additive (lubricants)

phenazocine
[127-35-5]

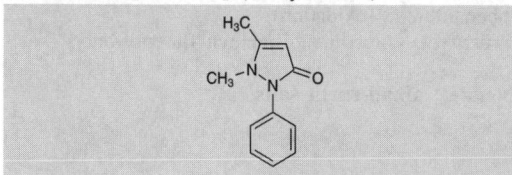

$C_{22}H_{27}N_1O_1$. M: 321.47. Available commercially as the racemic hydrobromide salt.
Production:
- 3,4-lutidine + anisyl alcohol + phenylacetyl chloride (quaternisation/Grignard reaction/hydrogenation/cyclisation/demethylation/amine formation/carbonyl reduction)
Uses: analgesic drug

phenazone
antipyrine; 2,3-dimethyl-1-phenyl-3-pyrazolin-5-one; [60-80-0]; [569-84-6] (O-acetylsalicylate); [603-64-5] (mandelate); [520-07-0] (salicylacetate)

$C_{11}H_{12}N_2O_1$. M: 188.23. Available commercially as the acetylsalicylate, mandelate, methylethyl glycollate or salicylacetate salts.
Production:
- 3-methyl-1-phenyl-5-pyrazolone + dimethyl sulphate (methylation)
Derivatives: 4-aminoantipyrine
Uses: analgesic drug

phenazopyridine
[94-78-0]; [136-40-3] (hydrochloride)

$C_{11}H_{11}N_5$. M: 213.24. Available commercially as the free base or as the hydrochloride salt.
Production:
- 2,6-diaminopyridine + benzenediazonium chloride (azo coupling)
Uses: urinary antibacterial drug

phenethyl acetate
2-phenylethyl acetate; [103-45-7]

$C_{10}H_{12}O_2$. M: 164.21. Colourless liquid with a floral odour. BP: 232°C.
Production:
- phenethyl alcohol + acetic acid (esterification)
Uses: fragrance ingredient

phenethyl alcohol
2-phenylethyl alcohol; [60-12-8]

$C_8H_{10}O_1$. M: 122.17. Colourless liquid with a rose-like odour. BP: 219°C. FP: -27°C. d: 1.01 kg/l (25°C). Slightly soluble in water. Soluble in oxygenated solvents.
Production:
- ethylbenzene + propylene + oxygen (Arco SM-PO process; byproduct of propylene oxide/styrene production)
- benzene + ethylene oxide (epoxidation)
Derivatives:
fentanyl; phenethyl acetate; phenethyl cinnamate; phenethyl formate; phenethyl isobutyrate; phenethyl isovalerate; phenethyl phenylacetate; phenethyl propionate; phenethyl salicylate; phenylacetaldehyde; 2-phenylethylamine
Uses: fragrance ingredient/fixative

phenethylamine *See:* 2-phenylethylamine

phenethyl cinnamate
2-phenylethyl cinnamate; [103-53-7]

$C_{17}H_{16}O_2$. M: 252.32. Crystalline solid. MP: 68°C.
Production:
- phenethyl alcohol + cinnamic acid (esterification)
Uses: fragrance ingredient

phenethyl formate
2-phenylethyl formate; [104-62-1]

$C_9H_{10}O_2$. M: 150.18.
Production:
- phenethyl alcohol + formic acid (esterification)
Uses: fragrance ingredient

phenethyl isobutyrate
2-phenylethyl isobutyrate; [103-48-0]
$C_{12}H_{16}O_2$. M: 192.26. Liquid with a floral odour.

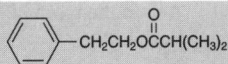

Production:
• phenethyl alcohol + isobutyric acid (esterification)
Uses:
flavouring/fragrance ingredient

phenethyl isovalerate
2-phenylethyl isovalerate; [140-26-1]

$C_{13}H_{18}O_2$. M: 206.28. Colourless liquid with a fruity odour.
Production:
• phenethyl alcohol + isovaleric acid (esterification)
Uses:
flavouring/fragrance ingredient

phenethyl phenylacetate
2-phenylethyl phenylacetate; [102-20-5]

$C_{16}H_{16}O_2$. M: 240.31. Colourless liquid or crystalline solid with floral odour. MP: 26.5°C. Insoluble in water, soluble in alcohol.
Production:
• phenylacetic acid + phenethyl alcohol (esterification)
Uses: perfume fixative

phenethyl propionate
2-phenylethyl propionate; [122-70-3]

$C_{11}H_{14}O_2$. M: 178.23. Colourless liquid with a floral-fruity odour. d: 1.01 kg/l (25°C). Soluble in alcohol.
Production:
• phenethyl alcohol + propionic acid (esterification)
Uses:
flavouring/fragrance ingredient

phenethyl salicylate
2-phenylethyl salicylate; [87-22-9]

$C_{15}H_{14}O_3$. M: 242.27. White crystals with a floral odour. MP: 44°C.
Production:
• phenethyl alcohol + salicylic acid (esterification)
Uses:
fragrance ingredient

pheneticillin
[147-55-7]; [132-93-4] (potassium salt)

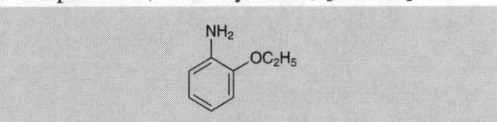

$C_{17}H_{20}N_2O_5S_1$. M: 364.41. Available commercially as the potassium salt.
Production:
• 2-phenoxypropionic acid + 6-aminopenicillanic acid (amide formation)
Uses: antibacterial drug

o-phenetidine
o-aminophenetole; 2-ethoxyaniline; [94-70-2]

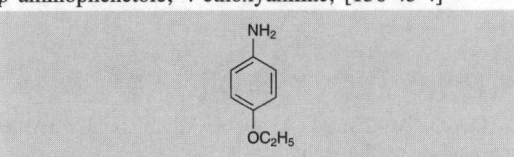

$C_8H_{11}N_1O_1$. M: 137.19. Brown liquid. BP: 232°C. Slightly soluble in water. Soluble in oxygenated solvents.
Production:
• *o*-chloronitrobenzene + ethanol (ether formation/ nitro reduction)
Derivatives:
3-hydroxy-2-naphth-*o*-phenetidide

p-phenetidine
p-aminophenetole; 4-ethoxyaniline; [156-43-4]

$C_8H_{11}N_1O_1$. M: 137.19. Colourless liquid. Discoloured by light and air. BP: 253–255°C. MP: 2–4°C. d: 1.07 kg/l (15°C). Insoluble in water. Soluble in oxygenated solvents.
Production:
• *p*-chloronitrobenzene + ethanol (ether formation/ nitro reduction)
Derivatives:
acetoacet-*p*-phenetidide; Acid Blue 213; 6-ethoxy-2,2, 4-trimethyl-1,2-dihydroquinoline; 3-hydroxy-2-naphth-*p*-phenethidide; lactophenetide; phenacetin; Pigment Red 123; Pigment Yellow 152; Vat Orange 5

phenidone *See:* 1-phenyl-3-pyrazolidone

pheniramine
[86-21-5]; [132-20-7] (hydrogen maleate)
$C_{16}H_{20}N_2$. M: 240.35. Available commercially as the free base and as the maleate.

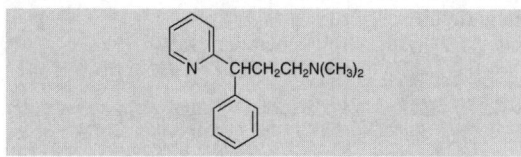

Production:
- benzyl cyanide + 2-chloropyridine + 2-dimethyl-aminoethyl chloride hydrochloride (condensation/condensation/nitrile hydrolysis/decarboxylation)

Uses:
antihistamine drug

phenmedipham

3-methoxycarbonylaminophenyl-3′-methylcarbanilate; [13684-63-4]

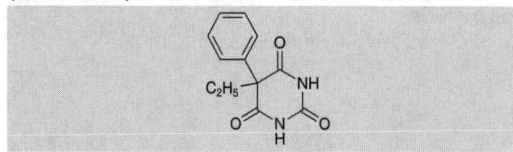

$C_{16}H_{16}N_2O_4$. M: 300.32.
Production:
- *m*-aminophenol + methyl chloroformate + phosgene + *m*-toluidine (dehydrochlorination/phosgenation/dehydrochlorination)

Uses: herbicide

phenobarbital

5-ethyl-5-phenylbarbituric acid; [50-06-6]; [57-30-7] (sodium salt)

$C_{12}H_{12}N_2O_3$. M: 232.24. Available commercially as the free acid or as the sodium salt.
Production:
- phenylmalonic acid + ethyl bromide + urea (esterification/dehydrobromination/cyclisation)

Derivatives:
methylphenobarbital
Uses: sedative/hypnotic drug

phenol

carbolic acid; [108-95-2]

$C_6H_6O_1$. M: 94.12. White, crystalline solid with a characteristic odour. Discoloured by light and air. MP: 41–43°C. BP: 182°C. d: 1.04 kg/l (60°C). Slightly soluble in water forming acidic solutions. Miscible with oxygenated and chlorinated solvents. Usually stored and transported in bulk as a molten liquid. Also available as a 10% aqueous solution.

Production:
- cumene hydroperoxide (acid-catalysed hydrolysis; coproduced with acetone)
- benzoic acid (oxydecarboxylation)
- chlorobenzene (hydration)
- cresylic acid (fractionation; coproduced with *o*-cresol/*m/p*-cresol/xylenol, mixed)

Derivatives:
Acid Red 114; Acid Red 249; Acid Violet 41; aclonifen; alkyl(C_9-C_{30})phenol; *o*-allylphenol; *p-t*-amylphenol; aniline; anisole; bephenium hydroxynaphthoate; bisacodyl; bisphenol A; bisphenol AF; bisphenol F diglycidyl ether; bumetanide; *n*-butyl diphenyl phosphate; *o-s*-butylphenol; *o-t*-butylphenol; *p-t*-butylphenol; *t*-butylphenyl diphenyl phosphate; cashew nutshell-phenol condensate diglycidyl ether; catechol; *o*-chlorophenol; *p*-chlorophenol; *o*-cresol; cyclohexanol; 2,4-di-*t*-butylphenol; 2,6-di-*t*-butylphenol; 2,4-dichlorophenol; didecyl phenyl phosphite; 4,4′-dihydroxydiphenyl sulphone; dimethylaminomethylphenol; dinocap; dinonylphenol; diphenyl carbonate; diphenyl decyl phosphite; diphenyl 2-ethylhexyl phosphate; diphenyl isophthalate; diphenyl oxide; *N,N*′-diphenyl-*p*-phenylenediamine; diphenyl phthalate; Direct Yellow 4; Disperse Orange 29; Disperse Red 60; Disperse Yellow 23; dodecylphenol; ethylene glycol monophenyl ether; fenothiocarb; fenoxycarb; flocoumafen; 4-fluoro-3-phenoxybenzaldehyde cyanohydrin; flurprimidol; hydroquinone; *p*-hydroxybenzaldehyde; *p*-hydroxybenzoic acid; 2-[2′-hydroxy-3′,5′-bis(1-methyl-1-phenylethyl)]benzotriazole; D-α-(4-hydroxyphenyl)glycine; *p*-hydroxypropiophenone; isopropylphenol; *o*-isopropylphenol; isopropylphenyl diphenyl phosphate; isoxsuprine; *p*-methylmercaptophenol; metoprolol; 3-nitro-4-hydroxyphenylarsonic acid; *p*-nitrosophenol; nonylphenol; novolac resins; *p-t*-octylphenol; oxyphenbutazone; pentachlorophenol; phenol, styrenated; phenol-formaldehyde sulphonates; phenolphthalein; *p*-phenolsulphonic acid; phenoxyacetic acid; 3-phenoxybenzaldehyde; 2-phenoxybutyric acid; 1-phenoxy-2-propanol; 2-phenoxypropionic acid; phenyl acetate; phenyl chloroformate; phenylene-phenolic resins; phenyl glycidyl ether; phenyl *p*-hydroxybenzoate; phenyl salicylate; polyether ketone ether ketone ketone; propantheline bromide; resol resins; resorcinol-formaldehyde resins; salicylaldehyde; salicylic acid; sodium nonanoyloxybenzene sulphonate; Sulphur Red 10; 1,1,2,2-tetra[*p*-(2,3-epoxypropoxy)phenyl]ethane; 4,4′-thiodiphenol; 2,4,6-tribromophenol; 2,4,6-trichlorophenol; *p,p′,p″*-tri-(2,3-epoxypropoxy)triphenylmethane; triphenyl phosphate; triphenyl phosphite; triphenyl phosphorothionate; 2,4,6-tris(dimethylaminomethyl)phenol; tris(hydroxyphenyl)methane triglycidyl ether; 2,6-xylenol

Uses: disinfectant; isocyanate blocking agent; selective solvent (lubricating oil dearomatisation)

phenol, styrenated
SPH

$C_{14}H_{14}O_1$. M: 198.26. Pale yellow, viscous liquid or powder, depending on the degree of alkylation. Insoluble in water. Soluble in oxygenated or aromatic solvents.
Production:
• phenol + styrene (Friedel-Crafts alkylation)
Uses: antioxidant (ABS, rubber, latex, adhesives)

phenol-formaldehyde alkoxylates
Production:
• phenolic resins, oil-soluble, oil-reactive + propylene oxide/ethylene oxide (epoxidation)
Uses: crude oil demulsifier component

phenol-formaldehyde resin
See: novolac resins; resol resins

phenol-formaldehyde sulphonates
resole sulphonates
Water-soluble oligomers. See also phenolic resins, sulphonated.
Production:
• phenol + formaldehyde + sodium sulphite (carbonyl addition/sulphonation)
Uses: crude oil/lubricant demulsifier component; milling/dispersing agent (pigments, dyes)

phenolic-epoxy resins
Production:
• resol resins + bisphenol A glycidyl ether prepolymers (condensation)
Uses: stoving lacquers (drum linings)

phenolic resins, amino-substituted
Yellow-brown granules. Bulk density: 0.60–0.70 kg/l.
Production:
• resol resins + chloromethyl methyl ether + dimethylamine/methylamine/ammonia (chloromethylation/amine formation)
Uses:
weakly basic ion-exchange resins (chemical, pharmaceutical, food purification); weakly basic ion-exchange resins (water softening, demineralisation)

phenolic resins, oil-soluble, non oil-reactive
resol resins, oil-soluble
Softening point: ~100°C. Soluble in aromatic solvents.
Production:
• p-phenylphenol + formaldehyde (acid-catalysed condensation)

Uses: carbonless paper coatings; spar varnish/machinery paints

phenolic resins, oil-soluble, oil-reactive
resol resins, oil-soluble

n ≥ 4. Softening point: 75–80°C. Soluble in hydrocarbons.
Production:
• p-t-butylphenol/p-t-amylphenol/p-t-octylphenol/nonylphenol/dinonylphenol/p-phenylphenol + formaldehyde (base-catalysed condensation)
Derivatives: phenates, alkali-earth salts; phenol-formaldehyde alkoxylates; phenolic resins, rosin-modified
Uses: chemically-resistant surface finishes; tung oil-phenolic resin (aluminium decorative, structural, maintenance paints, spar varnishes); binder (printing inks)

phenolic resins, rosin-modified
Brittle solid. Softening point: 100–175°C (Ring and Ball Method). Soluble in esters and aromatic solvents. Limited solubility in aliphatic solvents.
Production:
• phenolic resins, oil-soluble, oil-reactive + rosin, tall oil/rosin, wood/rosin, gum + glycerol/pentaerythritol (condensation)
Uses: binder (decorative undercoats, marine varnishes, primer paints, printing inks)

phenolic resins, sulphonated
Yellow-brown granules. Bulk density: 0.65–1.00 kg/l. Used for sodium and hydrogen exchange in water treatment. See also phenol-formaldehyde sulphonates.
Production:
• resol resins (sulphonation)
Uses: strongly acidic ion-exchange resins (water softening, demineralisation); strongly acidic ion-exchange resins (food, chemical, pharmaceutical purification)

phenolphthalein
[77-09-8]
$C_{20}H_{14}O_4$. M: 318.33. Crystalline solid. MP: 261°C. d: 1.28 kg/l (30°C). Slightly soluble in water. Soluble in

alcohol. Available in white or yellow forms. The monosodium salt is the most common form sold commercially.

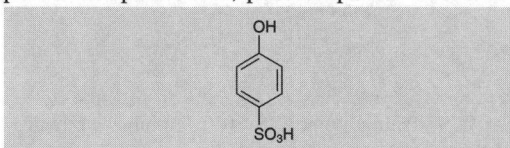

Production:
• phenol + phthalic anhydride (condensation)
Uses: analytical reagent; laxative drug

p-phenolsulphonic acid
phenol-4-sulphonic acid; phenolsulphonic acid

$C_6H_6O_4S_1$. M: 174.18. Commercially available as a 33–75% solution in water. Soluble in water and alcohol.
Production:
• phenol (sulphonation)
Derivatives: 2-aminophenol-4-sulphonic acid; famphur; zinc *p*-phenolsulphonate
Uses: reagent (coloured aluminium anodising, Ferrostan tin plating process)

phenothiazine
dibenzo-1,4-thiazine; thiodiphenylamine; PTZ; [92-84-2]

$C_{12}H_9N_1S_1$. M: 199.27. Greenish-yellow powder. MP: 182–185°C. BP: 371°C. Insoluble in water. Slightly soluble in alcohol and mineral oils. Soluble in aromatic solvents.
Production:
• diphenylamine + sulphur (Bernthsen synthesis)
Derivatives:
promazine; promethazine
Uses: chain transfer agent (rubber production); anthelmintic drug; antioxidant (lubricants, rubber, wax); polymerisation inhibitor (acrylic ester monomers)

phenothrin
[26002-80-2]

$C_{23}H_{26}O_3$. M: 350.46.

Production:
• 3-phenoxybenzyl alcohol +
  (*1RS*)-*cis/trans*-chrysanthemic acid (esterification)
Uses: insecticide

phenoxyacetic acid
[122-59-8]

$C_8H_8O_3$. M: 152.15. Off-white, crystalline solid. MP: 98–100°C. BP: 285°C with decomposition. Slightly soluble in water. Soluble in oxygenated and aromatic solvents.
Production:
• phenol + chloroacetic acid (ether formation)
Derivatives:
allyl phenoxyacetate; phenoxymethylpenicillin

3-phenoxybenzaldehyde
[39515-51-0]

$C_{13}H_{10}O_2$. M: 198.22.
Production:
• benzaldehyde + phenol (ring bromination/ether formation)
Derivatives: 3-phenoxybenzyl alcohol; 3-phenoxybenzaldehyde cyanohydrin

3-phenoxybenzaldehyde cyanohydrin
[39515-47-4]

$C_{14}H_{11}N_1O_2$. M: 225.25.
Production:
• 3-phenoxybenzaldehyde + sodium cyanide (cyanohydrin formation)
Derivatives: acrinathrin; cyhalothrin; cypermethrin; deltamethrin; esfenvalerate; fenpropathrin; fenvalerate; flucythrinate; D-fluvalinate

3-phenoxybenzyl alcohol
[13826-35-2]

$C_{13}H_{12}O_2$. M: 200.24.
Production:
• 3-phenoxybenzaldehyde (carbonyl reduction)
Derivatives: permethrin; phenothrin

2-phenoxybutyric acid
[13794-14-4]

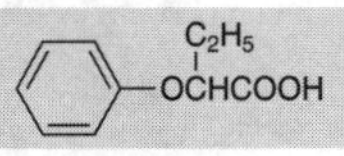

$C_{10}H_{12}O_3$. M: 180.21. Crystalline solid. MP: 79–83°C. BP: 258°C. Soluble in hot water.
Production:
• phenol + α-bromobutyric acid (ether formation)
Derivatives: propicillin

2-phenoxyethanol
See: ethylene glycol monophenyl ether

2-phenoxyethyl acrylate
phenoxyethyl acrylate; PEEA

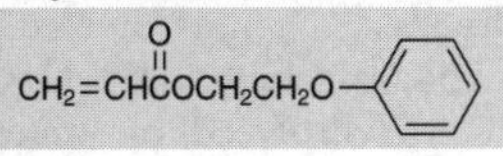

$C_{11}H_{12}O_3$. M: 192.22.
Production:
• ethylene glycol monophenyl ether + acrylic acid (esterification)
Uses: reactive diluent (radiation-cured inks, lacquers)

2-phenoxyethyl isobutyrate
[103-60-6]

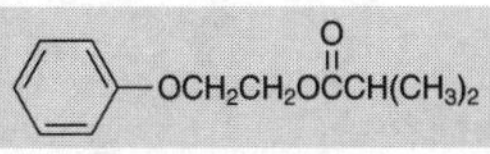

$C_{12}H_{16}O_3$. M: 208.26. Colourless liquid with floral odour. BP: 125–127°C (0.53 kPa). d: 1.05 kg/l.
Production:
• ethylene glycol monophenyl ether + isobutyric acid (esterification)
Uses: perfume fixative

β-phenoxyisopropanol *See:* 1-phenoxy-2-propanol

phenoxymethylpenicillin
penicillin V; [87-08-1]; [132-98-9] (potassium salt)

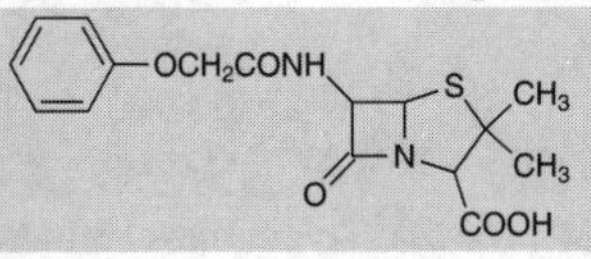

$C_{16}H_{18}N_2O_5S_1$. M: 350.38. Available commercially as the acid, potassium or calcium salts.
Production:
• corn steep liquor + phenoxyacetic acid + *Penicillium chrysogenum* mould (fermentation)
Uses: antibacterial drug

1-phenoxy-2-propanol
β-phenoxyisopropanol; phenoxyisopropanol; α-propylene glycol 1-phenyl ether; [770-35-4]
$C_9H_{12}O_2$. M: 152.20.

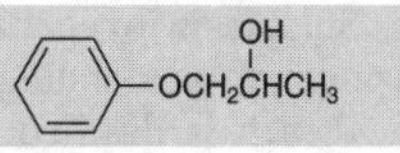

Production:
• phenol + propylene oxide (epoxidation)
Uses:
pharmaceutical intermediate

2-phenoxypropionic acid
[940-31-8]

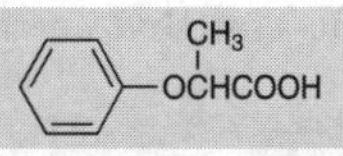

$C_9H_{10}O_3$. M: 166.18. Crystalline solid. MP: 116–119°C. BP: 265°C. Slightly soluble in water. Soluble in oxygenated solvents.
Production:
• phenol + α-chloropropionic acid (ether formation)
Derivatives:
pheneticillin

phenprocoumone
[435-97-2]

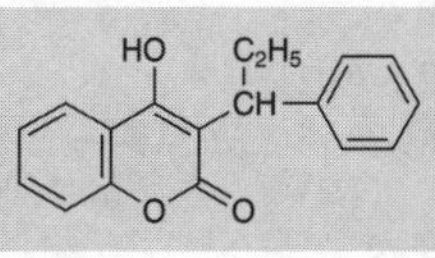

$C_{18}H_{16}O_3$. M: 280.33.
Production:
• propiophenone + diethyl malonate + acetylsalicylic acid (carbonyl condensation/hydrogenation/condensation/decarboxylation)
Uses: anticoagulant drug

phenthoate
S-α-ethoxycarbonylbenzyl O,O-dimethyl phosphorodithioate; [2597-03-7]

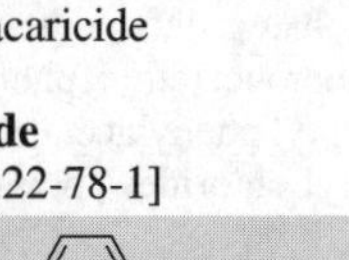

$C_{12}H_{17}O_4P_1S_2$. M: 320.37.
Production:
• ethyl phenylacetate + O,O-dimethyl dithiophosphoric acid (alpha bromination/dehydrobromination)
Uses: insecticide/acaricide

phenylacetaldehyde
α-tolualdehyde; [122-78-1]

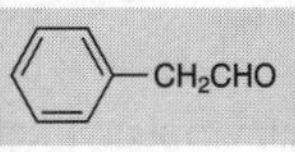

$C_8H_8O_1$. M: 120.15. Colourless liquid with a pleasant odour. BP: 194–196°C. d: 1.02 kg/l (20°C). Slightly

soluble in water. Soluble in oxygenated solvents. The product forms a polymer on standing which reconverts to the monomer when it is distilled.
Production:
• styrene oxide (isomerisation)
• phenethyl alcohol (alcohol oxidation)
Derivatives:
phenylacetaldehyde dimethyl acetal; DL-phenylalanine
Uses: fragrance ingredient

phenylacetaldehyde dimethyl acetal
[101-48-4]

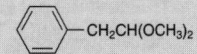

$C_{10}H_{14}O_2$. M: 166.22. Colourless liquid with a rose-like odour.
Production:
• phenylacetaldehyde + methanol (acetal formation)
Uses: fragrance ingredient

N-phenylacetamide *See:* acetanilide

phenyl acetate
acetylphenol; [122-79-2]

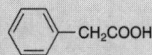

$C_8H_8O_2$. M: 136.15. Colourless liquid. BP: 195°C. d: 1.07 kg/l (20°C). Insoluble in water. Miscible with oxygenated and chlorinated solvents.
Production:
• phenol + acetic acid (esterification)
Derivatives: *o*-hydroxyacetophenone; *p*-hydroxyacetophenone; synephrine
Uses: high-boiling aprotic solvent

phenylacetic acid
α-toluic acid; [103-82-2]

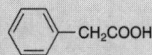

$C_8H_8O_2$. M: 136.15. White flakes. MP: 75–77°C. BP: 263–265°C. Soluble in hot water, oxygenated and chlorinated solvents.
Production:
• benzyl cyanide (base-catalysed hydrolysis)
Derivatives:
benzyl phenylmalonate; cefsulodin; *p*-cresyl phenylacetate; dibenzosuberone; ethyl phenylacetate; geranyl phenylacetate; isobutyl phenylacetate; phenethyl phenylacetate; phenylacetyl chloride; potassium phenylacetate

phenylacetone
acetonylbenzene; benzyl methyl ketone; methyl benzyl ketone; [103-79-7]
$C_9H_{10}O_1$. M: 134.18. Liquid. BP: 214–216°C. d: 1.02

kg/l (20°C). Insoluble in water. Soluble in oxygenated and aromatic solvents.

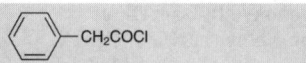

Production:
• benzyl cyanide + methyl acetate (condensation)
Derivatives: amphetamine; fenetylline; methamphetamine; prenylamine

phenylacetonitrile *See:* benzyl cyanide

phenylacetyl chloride
α-toluoyl chloride; [103-80-0]

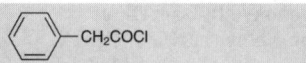

$C_8H_7Cl_1O_1$. M: 154.60. Liquid. BP: 11°C (3.0 kPa). d: 1.17 kg/l (20°C). Hydrolysed by water and alcohol. Soluble in ether.
Production:
• phenylacetic acid (acid chloride formation)
Derivatives: bamifylline; benalaxyl; difenacoum; flocoumafen; phenazocine

DL-phenylalanine
α-amino-β-phenylpropionic acid; [150-30-1]

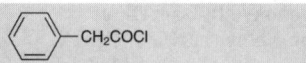

$C_9H_{11}N_1O_2$. M: 165.20.
Production:
• phenylacetaldehyde + hydrogen cyanide + ammonia (Strecker synthesis)
• benzaldehyde + hydantoin (carbonyl condensation/hydrogenation/hydrolysis)
Derivatives:
aspartame; L-phenylalanine

L-phenylalanine
L-α-amino-β-phenylpropionic acid; Phe; [63-91-2]

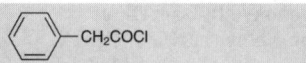

$C_9H_{11}N_1O_2$. M: 165.20. Available commercially as the naturally-occurring L(+)-enantiomer. White crystalline solid. Decomposes on heating above 280°C. Soluble in water.
Production:
• 2-acetamidocinnamic acid + hydrogen (chiral catalytic hydrogenation/amide hydrolysis)
• microbial fermentation medium + *Corynebacterium glutamicum* bacteria (fermentation/separation; byproduct of L-glutamic acid production)
• DL-phenylalanine + acetic anhydride + *Aspergillus oryzae* mould (acetylation/enzymatic hydrolysis)

• 2-acetamidocinnamic acid + *Corynebacterium glutamicum* bacteria + L-aspartic acid + *Paracoccus dinitrificans* bacteria (microbial deamination/microbial transamination)
• cinnamic acid + ammonia (enzymatic amination)
Derivatives: aspartame; pentagastrin
Uses: raw material (peptide drugs); infusion solutions/ diagnostic aids

p-phenylazoaniline
4-aminoazobenzene; Aniline Yellow; Solvent Yellow 1 (CI); 11000 (CI); [60-09-3]

$C_{12}H_{11}N_3$. M: 197.24. Yellowish-brown crystals. MP: 127°C. Slightly soluble in water. Soluble in oxygenated solvents.
Production:
• aniline + sodium nitrite (condensation)
Derivatives:
Acid Red 73; 4-aminoazobenzene-3,4'-disulphonic acid; Disperse Yellow 23; Pigment Red 178; Solvent Red 19; Solvent Red 23
Uses: nickel plating brightening agent; solvent dye (lacquer, varnish, wax)

4-phenylazoaniline-2,4'-disulphonic acid
See: 4-aminoazobenzene-3,4'-disulphonic acid

p-phenylbenzoic acid
See: biphenyl-4-carboxylic acid

p-phenylbenzophenone
Trigonal 12 (Akzo); [2128-93-0]

$C_{19}H_{14}O_1$. M: 258.32.
Production:
• biphenyl + benzoyl chloride (Friedel-Crafts acylation)
Uses:
photoinitiator (radiation-cured lacquers, printing inks)

4-phenylbutan-2-one *See:* benzylacetone

phenylbutazone
[50-33-9]

$C_{19}H_{20}N_2O_2$. M: 308.38. Available commercially as the free base or piperazinium salt.

Production:
• diethyl *n*-butylmalonate + hydrazobenzene (amide formation)
Uses: antiinflammatory drug

4-phenyl-3-buten-2-one *See:* benzylideneacetone

1-phenyl-3-carbethoxy-5-pyrazolone
See: ethyl 1-phenylpyrazolone-3-carboxylate

phenyl chloroformate
[1885-14-9]

$C_7H_5Cl_1O_2$. M: 156.57. Liquid. BP: 85°C (2.5 kPa). MP: <-35°C.
Production:
• phenol + phosgene (phosgenation)
Uses: phosgenation/protection reagent

phenyl cyanide *See:* benzonitrile

phenyl didecyl phosphite
See: didecyl phenyl phosphite

m-phenylenebismaleimide
bis-*m*-phenylenediamine maleimide; *N,N'*-(*m*-phenylene)dimaleimide; BMP; BPI

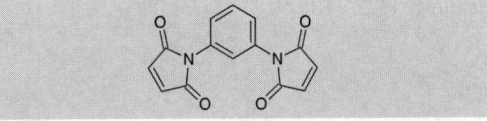

$C_{14}H_8N_2O_4$. M: 268.22.
Production:
• *m*-phenylenediamine + maleic anhydride (imide formation)
Uses: peroxide crosslinking coactivator; high-performance resin comonomer

m-phenylenediamine
1,3-diaminobenzene; *m*-diaminobenzene; 1,3-phenylenediamine; MPD; [108-45-2]

$C_6H_8N_2$. M: 108.14. White solid. Discoloured by light and air. MP: 64–66°C. BP: 287°C. Soluble in water and oxygenated solvents.
Production:
• *m*-dinitrobenzene (nitro reduction)
Derivatives: Basic Brown 1; bismaleimide prepolymers; chrysoidine; 2,4-diaminobenzenesulphonic acid; Direct Black 9; Direct Black 19; Direct Black 22; Mordant

Brown 1; Mordant Brown 13; *m*-phenylenebismaleimide; poly(ether-imide); polyhydantoin resins; polyimide resins, prepolymers; poly(*m*-phenyleneisophthalamide)
Uses: polyurea foam crosslinking agent; epoxy resin curing agent

o-phenylenediamine
1,2-diaminobenzene; *o*-diaminobenzene; 1,2-phenylenediamine; OPD; [95-54-5]

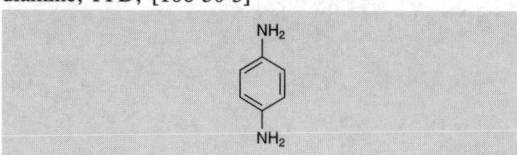

$C_6H_8N_2$. M: 108.14. White solid. Discoloured by light and air. MP: 100–102°C. BP: 256–258°C. Soluble in hot water. Soluble in oxygenated solvents.
Production:
• *o*-nitroaniline (nitro reduction)
Derivatives: 5-aminobenzimidazolone; benzotriazole; carbendazim; droperidol; Fluorescent Brightener 133; fuberidazole; 2-mercaptobenzimidazole; 1-(4-piperidyl)-2-benzodiazolinone; quinalphos; quinoxaline; sulphaquinoxaline; thiabendazole; thiophanate-methyl; Vat Orange 7; Vat Red 15
Uses: dyestuffs intermediate

p-phenylenediamine
1,4-diaminobenzene; *p*-diaminobenzene; 1,4-phenylenediamine; PPD; [106-50-3]

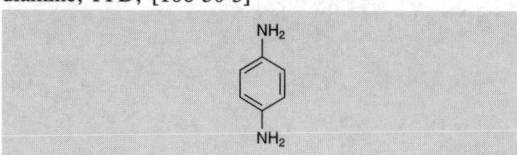

$C_6H_8N_2$. M: 108.14. White, crystalline solid. MP: 139–141°C. BP: 268°C. Soluble in hot water, hot alcohol and chlorinated solvents.
Production:
• *p*-nitroaniline (nitro reduction)
Derivatives:
p-aminoacetanilide; *N,N'*-bis(1,4-dimethylpentyl)-*p*-phenylenediamine; bismaleimide prepolymers; bitoscanate; *N,N'*-di-β-naphthyl-*p*-phenylenediamine; *N,N'*-diphenyl-*p*-phenylenediamine; Disperse Yellow 9; Pigment Yellow 110; poly[(3,4'-diphenyl ether)-(*p*-phenyleneterephthalamide)]; polyimide resins, prepolymers; poly(*p*-phenyleneterephthalamide)
Uses: hair colorant

p-phenylene diisocyanate
PPDI; [104-49-4]

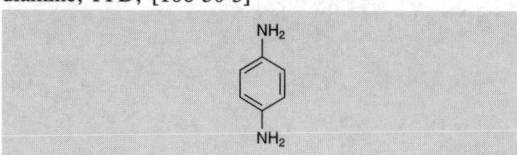

$C_8H_4N_2O_2$. M: 160.23. Solid. MP: 95°C.

Production:
• dimethyl terephthalate + ammonia (amide formation/Hofmann rearrangement)
Uses:
polyurethane elastomers

phenylene-phenolic resins
Xylok (Albright and Wilson)

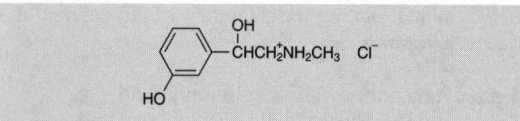

Thermosetting prepolymers cured by hexamethylenetetramine. The product is characterised by its excellent high temperature/fire performance combined with good chemical resistance and electrical properties.
Production:
• phenol + 1,4-bis(methoxymethyl)benzene (condensation)
Uses: laminating resins (electrical components)

phenylephrine hydrochloride
[61-76-7]

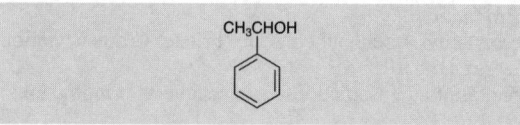

$C_9H_{14}Cl_1N_1O_2$. M: 203.67.
Production:
• *m*-hydroxyacetophenone + methylamine (alcohol group protection/alpha bromination/amine formation/carbonyl reduction/quaternisation)
Uses: decongestant/mydriatic drug

1-phenylethanol
α-methylbenzyl alcohol; 1-phenylethyl alcohol; styrallyl alcohol; MBA; [589-18-4]

$C_8H_{10}O_1$. M: 122.17. Colourless liquid with a mild, rose-like odour. BP: 203°C. MP: 21°C. d: 1.01 kg/l (25°C). Slightly soluble in water. Soluble in oxygenated and hydrocarbon solvents.
Production:
• ethylbenzene + propylene + oxygen (Arco SM-PO process; byproduct of propylene oxide/styrene production)
Derivatives:
1-phenylethyl acetate
Uses: fragrance ingredient; solvent

phenyl ether *See:* diphenyl oxide

1-phenylethyl acetate

α-methylbenzyl acetate; methyl phenyl carbinol acetate; s-phenylethyl acetate; styrallyl acetate; [50373-55-2]

$C_{10}H_{12}O_2$. M: 164.21. Liquid with a floral odour.
Production:
• 1-phenylethanol + acetic acid (esterification)
Uses: fragrance ingredient

1-phenylethyl alcohol *See:* 1-phenylethanol

2-phenylethyl alcohol *See:* phenethyl alcohol

2-phenylethylamine

1-amino-2-phenylethane; phenethylamine; β-phenylethylamine; [64-04-0]

$C_8H_{11}N_1$. M: 121.19. Liquid with an amine odour. BP: 194–195°C. d: 0.96 kg/l (24°C). Soluble in water and oxygenated solvents. Absorbs carbon dioxide from the air.
Production:
• benzyl cyanide (nitrile reduction)
• phenethyl alcohol + ammonia (amine formation)
Derivatives:
glibenclamide; glipizide; glisoxepide

D-α-phenylethylamine

[3886-69-9]

$C_8H_{11}N_1$. M: 121.19. Liquid comprising the (*R*)-(+)-enantiomer. BP: 181–183°C. d: 0.95 kg/l (20°C). Soluble in water. Miscible with oxygenated solvents.
Production:
• acetophenone + ammonia (reductive ammoniation/racemate separation)
Derivatives:
etomidate
Uses: racemate separation agent

2-phenylethyl formate *See:* phenethyl formate

N-phenylgamma acid

6-anilino-4-naphthol-2-sulphonic acid; 2-(phenylamino)-8-naphthol-6-sulphonic acid; 7-(phenylamino)-1-naphthol-3-sulphonic acid; *N*-phenyl-γ acid; [119-19-7]
$C_{16}H_{13}N_1O_4S_1$. M: 315.35.

Production:
• gamma acid + aniline (amine formation)
Derivatives: Mordant Brown 40

phenyl glycidyl ether

1,2-epoxy-3-phenoxypropane; PGE; [122-60-1]

$C_9H_{10}O_2$. M: 150.18. Colourless liquid. BP: 245°C. d: 1.11 kg/l (25°C). Viscosity: 0.04–0.07 poise (25°C).
Production:
• phenol + epichlorohydrin (dehydrochlorination)
Uses: reactive diluent (epoxy resins); stabiliser (vinylidene chloride-vinyl chloride copolymers)

D-α-phenylglycine

D-α-aminophenylacetic acid; [875-74-1]

$C_8H_9N_1O_2$. M: 151.17. Needles. MP: 305°C with decomposition. Soluble in alkali. The commercial product is the natural D(−)-enantiomer.
Production:
• benzaldehyde + hydrogen cyanide + ammonia (Strecker synthesis/racemate separation)
Derivatives:
ampicillin; cefaclor; cefalexin; cefradine; epicillin

N-phenylglycine

anilinoacetic acid; [103-01-5]

$C_8H_9N_1O_2$. M: 151.17. Crystalline solid. MP: 127°C. Soluble in water and alcohol.
Production:
• aniline + formaldehyde + hydrogen cyanide (cyanomethylation/nitrile hydrolysis)
Derivatives: indigo

phenylglycollic acid *See:* DL-mandelic acid

phenylhydrazine

[100-63-0]; [59-88-1] (hydrochloride)

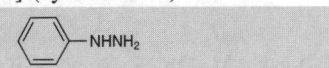

$C_6H_8N_2$. M: 108.14. Colourless liquid. Discoloured by air. BP: 238–241°C. Slightly soluble in water. Soluble

in oxygenated, chlorinated and aromatic solvents. Also available as the hydrochloride salt.
Production:
• benzenediazonium chloride (reduction)
Derivatives: 3-amino-1-phenyl-5-pyrazolone; chloridazon; 4,4-dimethyl-1-phenyl-3-pyrazolidinone; ethyl 1-phenylpyrazolone-3-carboxylate; 2-methylindole; 3-methyl-1-phenyl-5-pyrazolone; *N*-methyl-2-*p*-tolylindole; 2-phenylindole; 1-phenyl-3-pyrazolidone; sulfaphenazole; triazophos; L-tryptophan
Uses: reducing agent

phenylhydrazine-4-sulphonic acid
4-sulphophenylhydrazine; [98-71-5]

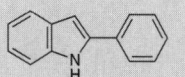

$C_6H_8N_2O_3S_1$. M: 188.20. Crystalline solid. MP: 286°C. Slightly soluble in water.
Production:
• sulphanilic acid (diazotisation/reduction)
Derivatives: 1-(4'-sulphophenyl)-3-methylpyrazolone

phenyl *p*-hydroxybenzoate
phenyl 4-hydroxybenzoate; [17696-62-7]

$C_{13}H_{10}O_3$. M: 214.22.
Production:
• phenol + *p*-hydroxybenzoic acid (esterification)
Derivatives: poly(*p*-hydroxybenzoate)

2-phenylindole
β-phenylindole; [948-65-2]

$C_{14}H_{11}N_1$. M: 193.25.
Production:
• phenylhydrazine + acetophenone (Fischer indole synthesis)
Derivatives:
Acid Blue 213
Uses: polyvinyl chloride heat stabiliser

phenyl isocyanate
carbanil; [103-71-9]

$C_7H_5N_1O_1$. M: 119.13. Liquid with an acrid odour. BP: 158–168°C. MP: -30°C. d: 1.10 kg/l (20°C). Hydrolysed by water and alcohol.

Production:
• aniline + phosgene (phosgenation)
Derivatives: carbetamide; desmedipham; fenuron; pencycuron; siduron; thidiazuron

phenyl isothiocyanate
phenyl mustard oil; thiocarbanil; [103-72-0]

$C_7H_5N_1S_1$. M: 135.19. Liquid. BP: 221°C. MP: -21°C. d: 1.14 kg/l (20°C). Insoluble in water. Soluble in oxygenated solvents.
Production:
• aniline + carbon disulphide (addition/oxidation)
Derivatives:
1-phenyl-5-mercaptotetrazole
Uses: analytical reagent

N-phenyl-J acid
2-anilino-5-naphthol-7-sulphonic acid; phenyl-J acid; [119-40-4]

$C_{16}H_{13}N_1O_4S_1$. M: 315.35.
Production:
• J acid + chlorobenzene (amine formation)
Derivatives:
Direct Blue 67; Direct Blue 75; Direct Blue 78; Direct Blue 98; Direct Violet 9

phenylmagnesium bromide
[100-58-3]

$C_6H_5Br_1Mg_1$. M: 181.32. Available commercially as a 45% solution in diethyl ether.
Production:
• bromobenzene + magnesium (Grignard reagent formation)
Derivatives:
azacyclonol; 4,4'-dimethoxytriphenylmethyl chloride; doxylamine; fendiline; prenylamine
Uses: Grignard reagent

phenylmagnesium chloride
[100-59-4]

$C_6H_5Cl_1Mg_1$. M: 136.87. Available commercially as a 25% solution in tetrahydrofuran.

Production:
- chlorobenzene + magnesium (Grignard reagent formation)

Derivatives: clotrimazole; dichloromethylphenylsilane; tetraphenyltin

N-phenylmaleimide
[941-69-5]

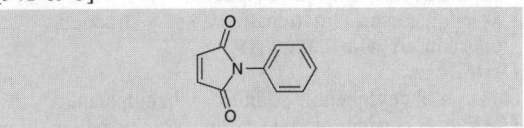

$C_{10}H_7N_1O_2$. M: 173.18. Yellow needles. MP: 88–89°C. Slightly soluble in water. Soluble in oxygenated, chlorinated and aromatic solvents.
Production:
- maleic anhydride + aniline (imide formation)

Uses: analytical reagent; binder (heat resistant coatings)

phenylmalonic acid
2-phenylmalonic acid; [2613-89-0]

$$\text{—CH(COOH)}_2$$

$C_9H_8O_4$. M: 180.16. Solid. MP: 153–155°C.
Production:
- ethyl phenylacetate + diethyl carbonate (condensation/ester hydrolysis)

Derivatives: phenobarbital

phenylmalonic acid, benzyl ester
See: benzyl phenylmalonate

phenyl mercaptan
See: thiophenol

1-phenyl-5-mercaptotetrazole
1-phenyltetrazole-5-thiol; PMT; [86-93-1]

$$\text{N—N}$$

$C_7H_6N_4S_1$. M: 178.22.
Production:
- phenyl isothiocyanate + sodium azide (condensation)

Uses: photographic antifogging agent

phenylmercuric nitrate, basic
[8003-05-2]

$$\left[\text{—Hg—} \right]_2 \text{OH.NO}_3$$

$C_{12}H_{11}Hg_2N_1O_4$. M: 634.41. Greyish-white, crystalline

powder. MP: 185°C with decomposition. Almost insoluble in water and alcohol.
Production:
- phenylmercury acetate + sodium nitrate (salt formation)

Uses: medical antiseptic/disinfectant

phenylmercuric oleate

$$\text{—HgOC(CH}_2)_7\text{CH} = \text{CH(CH}_2)_7\text{CH}_3$$

$C_{24}H_{38}Hg_1O_2$. M: 559.15. White, crystalline powder. MP: 45°C. Insoluble in water.
Production:
- phenylmercury acetate + sodium oleate (salt formation)

Uses: biocide (paints)

phenylmercuric propionate
phenyl(propanoato-O)mercury; [103-27-5]

$$\text{—HgOCCH}_2\text{CH}_3$$

$C_9H_{10}Hg_1O_2$. M: 350.77. White powder. MP: 70°C.
Production:
- benzene + mercuric oxide, yellow + propionic acid (condensation)

Uses: polyurethane catalyst

phenylmercury acetate
PMA; [62-38-4]

$$\text{—HgOCCH}_3$$

$C_8H_8Hg_1O_2$. M: 336.74.
Production:
- benzene + mercuric acetate (reaction)

Derivatives:
phenylmercuric nitrate, basic; phenylmercuric oleate
Uses: fungicide; preservative (paint)

5-phenyl-3-methyl-2-pentenonitrile
[53243-59-7] (*cis*-isomer); [53243-60-0] (*trans*-isomer)

$$\text{—CH}_2\text{CH}_2\text{C} = \text{CHCN} \quad (\text{CH}_3)$$

$C_{12}H_{13}N_1$. M: 171.24. Colourless crystals with fruity odour. The commercial product consists of 40% *cis*-isomer and 60% *trans*-isomer. BP: 82–88°C (0.02 kPa). d: 0.98 kg/l (25°C).
Production:
- benzylacetone + cyanoacetic acid (Cope reaction/decarboxylation)

Uses: fragrance ingredient

1-phenyl-2-methyl-2-propanol
See: dimethyl benzyl carbinol

1-phenyl-3-methyl-5-pyrazolone
See: 3-methyl-1-phenyl-5-pyrazolone

N-phenyl-α-naphthylamine
PAN; [90-30-2]

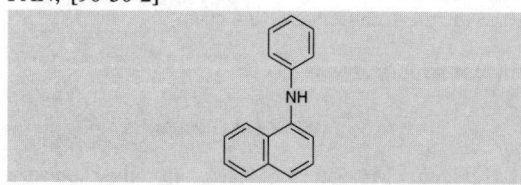

$C_{16}H_{13}N_1$. M: 219.29. White, crystalline solid. MP: 62°C. d: 1.17 kg/l. Very slightly soluble in water. Soluble in oxygenated and aromatic solvents.
Production:
• α-naphthol + aniline (amine formation)
Derivatives: Solvent Blue 4
Uses: antioxidant (rubber, lubricants)

N-phenyl-β-naphthylamine
PBN; [135-88-6]

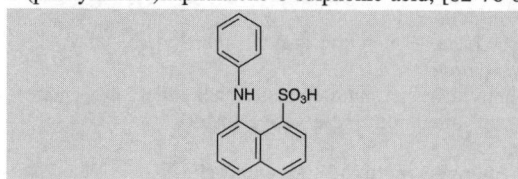

$C_{16}H_{13}N_1$. M: 219.29. Crystalline solid. MP: 107–108°C. BP: 398–400°C. d: 1.18 kg/l. Very slightly soluble in water. Soluble in hot alcohol.
Production:
• β-naphthol + aniline (amine formation)
Uses: antioxidant (rubber, lubricants)

N-phenyl-peri acid
1-(phenylamino)naphthalene-8-sulphonic acid; [82-76-8]

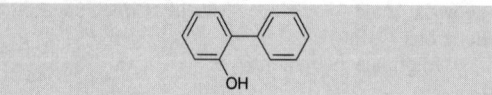

$C_{16}H_{13}N_1O_3S_1$. M: 299.35.
Production:
• peri acid + chlorobenzene (amine formation)
Derivatives:
Acid Blue 92; Acid Blue 113; Sulphur Green 3

o-phenylphenol
2-hydroxybiphenyl; o-hydroxydiphenyl; 2-phenylphenol; OPP; E231 (EC); [90-43-7]

$C_{12}H_{10}O_1$. M: 170.21. Off-white flakes with a sweetish odour. MP: 56–57°C. BP: 288°C. Bulk density: 0.62

kg/l. Sparingly soluble in water. Soluble in aqueous alkali and oxygenated solvents. Flash point: 138°C (PMCC).
Production:
• biphenyl (sulphonation/alkali fusion; coproduced with *p*-phenylphenol)
• chlorobenzene (arylation/base-catalysed hydrolysis; coproduced with *p*-phenylphenol)
• xylenol, mixed (fractionation/alkali extraction; coproduced with biphenyl)
Derivatives:
chloro-*o*-phenylphenol; sodium *o*-phenylphenate
Uses: dye carrier; biocide (adhesives, paper, building products, leather); antiseptic ingredient

p-phenylphenol
4-hydroxybiphenyl; 4-phenylphenol; [92-69-3]
$C_{12}H_{10}O_1$. M: 170.21. White flakes. MP: 165°C. BP: 321°C. d: 1.27 kg/l (25°C). Insoluble in water. Soluble in oxygenated solvents.

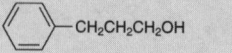

Production:
• biphenyl (sulphonation/alkali fusion; coproduced with *o*-phenylphenol)
• chlorobenzene (arylation/base-catalysed hydrolysis; coproduced with *o*-phenylphenol)
Derivatives: bitertanol; phenolic resins, oil-soluble, non oil-reactive; phenolic resins, oil-soluble, oil-reactive

N-phenyl-p-phenylenediamine
See: p-aminodiphenylamine

phenylphosphonic dichloride
See: phosphenyl chloride

3-phenylpropanol
dihydrocinnamic alcohol; hydrocinnamic alcohol; 3-phenyl-1-propanol; phenylpropyl alcohol; [122-97-4]

$C_9H_{12}O_1$. M: 136.20. Colourless liquid with a floral odour. BP: 237°C. d: 1.01 kg/l (20°C). Slightly soluble in water. Miscible with oxygenated solvents.
Production:
• cinnamaldehyde (hydrogenation)
Uses: fragrance ingredient

phenylpropanolamine *See:* norephedrine

3-phenyl-2-propenoic acid *See:* cinnamic acid

3-phenyl-2-propen-1-ol *See:* cinnamyl alcohol

2-phenylpropionaldehyde *See:* hydratropaldehyde

3-phenylpropionaldehyde
dihydrocinnamaldehyde; hydrocinnamic aldehyde; phenylpropyl aldehyde; [104-53-0]

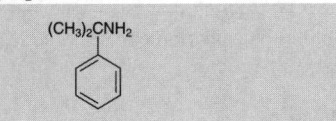

$C_9H_{10}O_1$. M: 134.18. Colourless liquid with a floral odour.
Production:
• cinnamaldehyde (hydrogenation)
• styrene + synthesis gas (hydroformylation; coproduced with hydratropaldehyde)
Derivatives: enalapril; lisinopril
Uses: fragrance ingredient

3-phenylpropionic acid *See:* hydrocinnamic acid

2-phenyl-2-propylamine
2-amino-2-phenylpropane

$C_9H_{13}N_1$. M: 135.21.
Production:
• α-methylstyrene + hydrogen cyanide (Ritter reaction)
Derivatives: bromobutide; daimuron; methyldymron

1-phenyl-3-pyrazolidone
phenidone

$C_9H_{10}N_2O_1$. M: 162.19. Solid. MP: 121°C. Solubility in water: 100 g/l (100°C).
Production:
• phenylhydrazine + 3-chloropropionyl chloride (condensation)
Uses: photographic developing agent

phenyl salicylate
salol; [118-55-8]

$C_{13}H_{10}O_3$. M: 214.22. White, crystalline powder with a pleasant odour. MP: 42–44°C. d: 1.26 kg/l (30°C). Insoluble in water. Soluble in organic solvents.
Production:
• phenol + salicylic acid (esterification)
Uses: drug coatings; sunscreening agent (cosmetics); analgesic/antiinflammatory drug

phenylsulphonic acid *See:* benzenesulphonic acid

5-phenyltetrazole

$C_7H_6N_4$. M: 146.16.
Production:
• benzonitrile + sodium azide (condensation)
Uses: blowing agent (foamed plastics); photographic antifogging agent

phenyltoloxamine
[92-12-6]; [1176-08-5] (dihydrogen citrate)

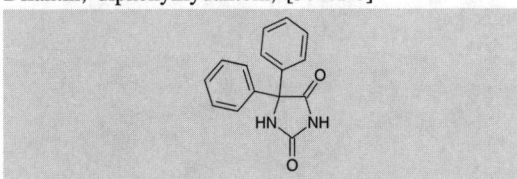

$C_{17}H_{21}N_1O_1$. M: 255.37. Available commercially as the free base and the dihydrogen citrate salt.
Production:
• benzene + salicylic acid + 2-dimethylaminoethyl chloride hydrochloride (acid chloride formation/ Friedel-Crafts acylation/carbonyl reduction/ether formation)
Uses: antihistamine drug

phenyltrichlorosilane *See:* trichlorophenylsilane

phenyltrimethoxysilane *See:* trimethoxyphenylsilane

phenyltrimethylammonium hydroxide
See: trimethylphenylammonium hydroxide

phenyramidol *See:* fenyramidol

phenytoin
Dilantin; diphenylhydantoin; [57-41-0]

$C_{15}H_{12}N_2O_2$. M: 252.27. Available commercially as the acid or sodium salt.
Production:
• benzophenone + hydrogen cyanide + ammonium bicarbonate (Bucherer-Bergs reaction)
• benzil + urea (amide formation/rearrangement)
Uses: antiepileptic drug

phloroglucinol
1,3,5-trihydroxybenzene; [108-73-6]
$C_6H_6O_3$. M: 126.12. White crystals. MP: 218°C. Sub-

limes on further heating. Slightly soluble in water. Soluble in oxygenated solvents.

Production:
- 1,3,5-trinitrobenzene (nitro reduction/diazotisation/hydrolysis)

Derivatives: 1,3,5-triamino-2,4,6-trinitrobenzene
Uses: analytical reagent; printing, dyeing auxiliary

phorate

O,O-diethyl *S*-ethylthiomethyl phosphorodithioate; [298-02-2]

$C_7H_{17}O_2P_1S_3$. M: 260.38.
Production:
- ethyl mercaptan + formaldehyde + *O,O*-diethyl dithiophosphoric acid (carbonyl condensation)

Uses:
insecticide/acaricide/nematicide

phorone

diisopropylidene acetone; [504-20-1]

$C_9H_{14}O_1$. M: 138.21.
Production:
- acetone (carbonyl condensation)

Derivatives:
diisobutyl ketone; 4-hydroxy-2,2,6,6-tetramethylpiperidine; 4-hydroxy-2,2,6,6-tetramethyl-1-piperidine ethanol; 1,2,2,6,6-pentamethyl-4-hydroxypiperidine

phosalone

[2310-17-0]

$C_{12}H_{15}Cl_1N_1O_4P_1S_2$. M: 367.81.
Production:
- benzoxazolone + formaldehyde + *O,O*-diethyl dithiophosphoric acid (ring chlorination/chloromethylation/dehydrochlorination)

Uses: insecticide/acaricide

phosdiphen

bis(2,4-dichlorophenyl) ethyl phosphate; [36519-00-3]
$C_{14}H_{11}Cl_4O_4P_1$. M: 416.02.

Production:
- phosphorus oxychloride + 2,4-dichlorophenol + ethanol (dehydrochlorination/dehydrochlorination)

Uses: fungicide

phosfolan

diethyl 1,3-dithiolan-2-ylidenephosphoramidate; [947-02-4]

$C_7H_{14}N_1O_3P_1S_2$. M: 255.30.
Production:
- 1,2-ethanedithiol + cyanogen chloride + diethyl chlorophosphate (condensation/dehydrochlorination)

Uses: insecticide

phosgene

carbonyl chloride; [75-44-5]

$C_1Cl_2O_1$. M: 98.92. Colourless gas/liquid. BP: 7°C. MP: -128°C. d: 1.39 kg/l (20°C). Highly toxic. Slightly soluble in water, with which it reacts. Soluble in hydrocarbon, ester and organic acid solvents.
Production:
- carbon monoxide + chlorine (addition)

Derivatives:
5-aminobenzimidazolone; azamethiphos; Basic Violet 3; Basic Violet 4; benzoxazolone; benzyl chloroformate; biotin; bis(4-*t*-butylcyclohexyl) peroxydicarbonate; 4,4'-bis(diethylamino)benzophenone; 4,4'-bis(dimethylamino)benzophenone; *N,N'*-bis(2-methoxy-5-methylphenyl) urea; buprofezin; *n*-butyl chloroformate; *n*-butyl isocyanate; carbamazepine; carbomethoxybenzenesulphonyl isocyanate; cartap; cetyl chloroformate; chinomethionat; chlorbromuron; chlorbufam; 2-chlorobenzenesulphonyl isocyanate; *p*-chlorophenyl isocyanate; chlozolinate; cyclohexyl isocyanate; daimuron; 3,4-dichlorophenyl isocyanate; diethylcarbamoyl chloride; diethylene glycol bis(chloroformate); 4,4'-diisocyanatodicyclohexylmethane; dimefuron; dimethylcarbamoyl chloride; diphenyl carbonate; 4,4'-diphenylmethane diisocyanate, polymeric; 4,4'-diphenylmethane diisocyanate, pure grade; Direct Yellow 44; Direct Yellow 49; Direct Yellow 50; Direct Yellow 51; Direct Yellow 118; ethyl chloroformate; ethyl chlorothioformate; 2-ethylhexyl chloroformate; ethyl isocyanate; flucofenuron; hexamethylene diisocyanate; iprodione; isobutyl chloroformate; isocyanatoethyl methacrylate; isophorone diisocyanate; isopropyl chloroformate; isoprothiolane; J acid urea;

karbutilate; meprobamate; methazole; methocarbamol; 2-methoxyethyl chloroformate; methyl chloroformate; methyldymron; methyl isocyanate; metobromuron; 1,5-naphthalene diisocyanate; niridazole; octylthiochloroformate; oxadiazon; oxadixyl; pebulate; pentagastrin; phenmedipham; phenyl chloroformate; phenyl isocyanate; pipazetate; polycarbonate; polyester carbonate; prochloraz; n-propyl chloroformate; propylene carbonate; suramin sodium; teflubenzuron; tetrabromobisphenol A carbonate oligomer; thiafensulfuron-methyl; toluene diisocyanate; p-toluenesulphonyl isocyanate; trimethylhexamethylene diisocyanate; triphenylmethane triisocyanate; tris(p-isocyanatophenyl) thiophosphate; Vat Yellow 20; vernolate; vinclozolin; xylene diisocyanate, hydrogenated; 3,5-xylyl methylcarbamate

Uses:
acid chlorination/phosgenation reagent

phosmet
O,O-dimethyl *S*-phthalimidomethyl phosphorodithioate; [732-11-6]

$C_{11}H_{12}N_1O_4P_1S_2$. M: 317.33.
Production:
• phthalimide + formaldehyde + *O,O*-dimethyl dithiophosphoric acid (chloromethylation/ dehydrochlorination)
Uses: insecticide/acaricide

phosphamidon
2-chloro-2-diethylcarbamoyl-1-methylvinyl dimethyl phosphate; [13171-21-6]

$(C_2H_5)_2NCC=COP(OCH_3)_2$
with Cl and CH₃ substituents

$C_{10}H_{19}Cl_1N_1O_5P_1$. M: 299.68.
Production:
• *N,N*-diethylacetoacetamide + trimethyl phosphite (alpha chlorination/Perkow reaction)
Uses: insecticide/acaricide

phosphenyl chloride
benzenephosphorus dichloride; phenylphosphonic dichloride; phenyl phosphonodichloridite; [824-72-6]

PCl₂ attached to benzene ring

$C_6H_5Cl_2P_1$. M: 178.99. Colourless, fuming liquid. BP: 225°C. MP: -51°C. d: 1.32 kg/l (20°C). Hydrolysed by water. Soluble in chlorinated and aromatic solvents.

Production:
• benzene + phosphorus trichloride (addition)
Derivatives:
O-ethyl *O*-(4-nitrophenyl) phenylphosphonothioate

phosphine
[7803-51-2]

PH₃

H_3P_1. M: 34.00. Colourless gas. BP: -88°C. MP: -133°C. Spontaneously ignites on contact with air. Slightly soluble in water.
Production:
• phosphorus + calcium hydroxide (salt formation)
• phosphorus + sodium hydroxide (salt formation)
• phosphorus + water (hydration)
Derivatives: tetrakis(hydroxymethyl)phosphonium chloride; tetrakis(hydroxymethyl)phosphonium sulphate; tri-*n*-butylphosphine; tri-*n*-octylphosphine oxide
Uses: semiconductor dopant

phosphomolybdic acid
molybdophosphoric acid; triple salt acid; PMA; [11104-88-4]

$H_3PO_4.12MoO_3$

$H_3Mo_{12}O_{40}P_1$. M: 1825.23. Yellow crystals. MP: 78°C. Soluble in water with dissociation. The common molar ratio of P:Mo is 1:12 although values down to 1:9 are also used occasionally.
Production:
• sodium molybdate/ammonium molybdate + phosphoric acid, pure (salt formation)
Uses: laking agent (basic dyes)

phosphomolybdotungstic acid
phosphotungstomolybdic acid; triple salt acid; PMTA

$H_3PO_4.mMoO_3.nWO_3$

m = 8–9, n = 9–10. Mixed phosphate-molybdate-tungstate salt with a variable water content. The most commonly-used molar ratios of P:Mo:W are 1:8:10 or 1:9:9.
Production:
• phosphoric acid, pure + sodium tungstate + sodium molybdate (salt formation)
Uses: laking agent (basic dyes); reagent (PMTA salt formation)

phosphonic acid *See:* phosphorous acid

phosphoric acid, crude
orthophosphoric acid, crude

H_3PO_4

$H_3O_4P_1$. M: 97.99. Yellow to black liquid available as solutions in water containing 40–54% P_2O_5.

Production:
- apatite + sulphuric acid (wet phosphoric acid dihydrate process; coproduced with gypsum)
- apatite + sulphuric acid (wet phosphoric acid hemihydrate process; coproduced with calcium sulphate hemihydrate)

Derivatives: ammonium polyphosphate, solution; calcium triple superphosphate; diammonium phosphate; monoammonium phosphate; phosphoric acid, pure; vanadium pentoxide; yellow cake

phosphoric acid, pure
orthophosphoric acid; E338 (EC); [7664-38-2]

$H_3O_4P_1$. M: 97.99. Colourless liquid or solid. MP: 42°C. d: 1.87 kg/l (25°C). Starts to decompose forming polyphosphoric acids when heated above 200°C. Soluble in water and alcohol. Also available as aqueous solutions containing 75–85% w/w H_3PO_4.

H_3PO_4

Production:
- phosphorus (furnace process)
- phosphoric acid, crude (heavy metal precipitation/ solvent extraction)
- phosphorus + water (hydration; byproduct of phosphine production)
- cyclohexanone + hydroxylamine phosphate (DSM HPO process; byproduct of cyclohexanone oxime production)

Derivatives: aluminium phosphate, monobasic; ammonium polyphosphate, solid; diammonium phosphate; dicalcium phosphate; dimelamine phosphate; disodium acid pyrophosphate; disodium phosphate; guanidine phosphate, dibasic; guanidine phosphate, monobasic; hydroxylamine phosphate; melamine phosphate; monoammonium phosphate; monocalcium phosphate; monosodium phosphate; phosphomolybdic acid; phosphotungstic acid; phosphomolybdotungstic acid; potassium pyrophosphate; potassium tripolyphosphate; sodium aluminium phosphate; sodium hexametaphosphate; sodium tripolyphosphate; tetrasodium pyrophosphate; tricalcium phosphate; triethanolamine phosphate; trisodium phosphate; zirconium phosphate

Uses:
polymer gasoline catalyst; etchant (semiconductor manufacture); acidulant (soft drinks, prepared foods); aluminium brightening/anodising agent; aluminium/steel/ magnesium/zinc anticorrosion treatment reagent; microbial fermentation nutrient; refractories raw material

phosphorous acid
orthophosphorous acid; phosphonic acid; [13598-36-2]

H_3PO_3

$H_3O_3P_1$. M: 81.99. White, deliquescent, crystalline solid or flakes. MP: 74°C. Soluble in water forming acidic solutions. The product is also available as a 70% aq-

ueous solution. Phosphorous acid is formed as a by-product in acid chlorination reactions using phosphorus trichloride. This is a further source of the chemical.

Production:
- phosphorus trichloride (hydrolysis)

Derivatives: aminotris(methylene phosphonic acid); bis-[O-ethyl-(3,5-di-t-butyl-4-hydroxybenzyl)phosphonic acid], calcium salt; diethylenetriaminepenta-(methylene phosphonic acid); ethylenediaminetetra-(methylene phosphonic acid); 2-ethylhexyliminobis(methylenephosphonic acid); hexamethylenediaminetetra-(methylenephosphonic acid); hydroxyethylidene(diphosphonic acid); lead phosphite, dibasic

Uses: reducing/resin decolorisation agent

phosphorus
phosphorus, white; phosphorus, yellow; [7723-14-0]

P

P_1. M: 30.97. White, waxy solid. Discoloured by light. MP: 44°C. BP: 280°C. Emits green light and ignites spontaneously in air. Insoluble in water.

Production:
- apatite + metallurgical coke + quartz (electric furnace reduction)

Derivatives: aluminium phosphide; calcium hypophosphite; phosphine; phosphoric acid, pure; phosphorus, red; phosphorus pentasulphide; phosphorus pentoxide; phosphorus sesquisulphide; phosphorus trichloride; sodium hypophosphite; thiophenol; zinc phosphide

Uses: alphabromination catalyst

phosphorus, red
[7723-14-0]

P

P_1. M: 30.97. Reddish-brown powder. Sublimes on heating above 416°C. Insoluble in water.

Production:
- phosphorus (thermal conversion)

Uses: fire-retardant additive (polyamides); ingredient (matchheads, fireworks)

phosphorus oxychloride
phosphoryl chloride; [10025-87-3]

$POCl_3$

$Cl_3O_1P_1$. M: 153.33. Colourless, fuming liquid with a pungent odour. BP: 106°C. MP: -1°C. d: 1.65 kg/l (25°C). Hydrolysed by water and alcohol.

Production:
- phosphorus trichloride + oxygen (oxidation)

Derivatives:
bis(2-ethylhexyl) hydrogen phosphate; n-butyl diphenyl phosphate; t-butylphenyl diphenyl phosphate; cyclophosphamide; diethyl chlorophosphate; diphenyl cresyl phosphate; diphenyl 2-ethylhexyl phosphate; edifen-

phos; fenamiphos; hexamethylphosphoramide; ifosfamide; isopropylphenyl diphenyl phosphate; phosdiphen; profenofos; starch, amphoteric; starch, crosslinked; tetrakis(2-chloroethyl)ethylene diphosphate; triallyl phosphate; tri-n-butyl phosphate; S,S,S-tributyl phosphorotrithioate; tricresyl phosphate; triethylenephosphoramide; tri-(2-ethylhexyl) phosphate; triethyl phosphate; triphenyl phosphate; tris(2-chloroethyl) phosphate; tris(1-chloro-2-propyl) phosphate; tris(1,3-dichloro-2-propyl) phosphate; tris(isopropylphenyl) phosphate; trixylyl phosphate; trofosfamide

Uses: starch crosslinking agent; semiconductor dopant; reagent (Vilsmeier reaction, chlorination)

phosphorus pentachloride
phosphoric chloride; [10026-13-8]

PCl_5

Cl_5P_1. M: 208.23. Pale greenish-yellow solid with a pungent odour. MP: 167°C (sealed tube). Sublimes at 159°C. d: 1.6 kg/l. Fumes in air. Hydrolysed by water forming hydrochloric acid.
Production:
• phosphorus trichloride + chlorine (reaction)
Derivatives: poly(fluoroalkoxyphosphazene) elastomers
Uses: ring chlorination/acid chloride formation reagent

phosphorus pentasulphide
[1314-80-3]

P_2S_5

P_2S_5. M: 222.27. Light yellow, hygroscopic, crystalline solid. MP: 286–290°C. BP: 513–515°C. Decomposed by water releasing hydrogen sulphide. Soluble in alkali.
Production:
• phosphorus + sulphur (thermal combination)
Derivatives:
ammonium O,O-dicresyl dithiophosphate; O,O-diethyl dithiophosphoric acid; O,O-diisopropyl phosphorodithioic acid; O,O-dimethyl dithiophosphoric acid; O,O-di-n-propyl phosphorochlorothioate; molybdenum di-(2-ethylhexyl) dithiophosphate; polybutene thiophosphonate propoxylates, alkali-earth salts; sodium O,O-di-s-butyl dithiophosphate; sodium O,O-diisoamyl dithiophosphate; sodium O,O-diisobutyl dithiophosphate; sodium O,O-diisopropyl dithiophosphate; sodium O,O-di-(methylamyl) dithiophosphate; zinc di-n-butyl dithiophosphate; zinc didecyl dithiophosphate; zinc didodecyl dithiophosphate; zinc dihexyl dithiophosphate; zinc dioctyl dithiophosphate
Uses: flotation depressant (copper ores)

phosphorus pentoxide
phosphoric anhydride; [1314-56-3]

P_4O_{10}

$O_{10}P_4$. M: 283.88. White, deliquescent, crystalline powder. MP: 580°C. Sublimes 300°C. d: 2.39 kg/l. Violently hydrolysed by water forming phosphoric acid.
Production:
• phosphorus (air oxidation)
Derivatives:
n-alkanol(C_{12}-C_{15}) ether phosphoric acid; ammonium polyphosphate, solid; amyl phosphoric acid; n-butyl phosphoric acid; cetyloleyl ether phosphoric acid; cetylstearyl ether phosphoric acid; diethanolamine 2-[perfluoroalkyl(C_6-C_{12})]ethyl phosphate; 2-(N-ethylperfluorooctylsulphonamido)ethyl phosphate, ammonium salt; isodecyl ether phosphoric acid; isooctyl phosphoric acid; isotridecanol ether phosphoric acid; nonylphenol ether phosphoric acid; octylphenyl phosphoric acid; oleyl ether phosphoric acid; stearyl phosphoric acid
Uses:
drying agent; dehydration/condensation reagent; asphalt additives; Nokes froth flotation reagent component;

phosphorus sesquisulphide
tetraphosphorus trisulphide; [1314-85-8]

P_4S_3

P_4S_3. M: 220.09. Yellow-green solid. MP: 172°C. BP: 408°C. Insoluble in water. Soluble in carbon disulphide.
Production:
• phosphorus + sulphur (reaction)
Uses: match head ingredient

phosphorus trichloride
[7719-12-2]

PCl_3

Cl_3P_1. M: 137.33. Colourless, fuming liquid with a pungent, irritating odour. BP: 75°C. MP: -112°C. d: 1.57 kg/l (20°C). Hydrolysed by water and alcohol. Soluble in chlorinated and aromatic solvents.
Production:
• phosphorus + chlorine (chlorination)
Derivatives:
bis(2,4-di-t-butylphenyl)pentaerythrityl diphosphite; cadusafos; di-n-butyl butylphosphonate; didecyl phenylphosphite; diethyl phosphite; dimethyl phosphite; dioctyl octylphosphonate; diphenyl decyl phosphite; distearylpentaerythrityl diphosphite; ethoprophos; fosetyl-aluminium; glufosinate-ammonium; glyphosate; haloxon; phosphenyl chloride; phosphorous acid; phosphorus oxychloride; phosphorus pentachloride; propaphos; tetrakis(2,4-di-t-butylphenyl)-4,4′-biphenyl diphosphonite; thiophosphoryl chloride; tributoxyethyl phosphate; triethyl phosphite; triisooctyl phosphite; trimethyl phosphite; triphenylphosphine; triphenyl phosphite; tris(2-chloroethyl) phosphite; tris(2,4-di-t-butylphenyl) phosphite; tris(nonylphenyl) phosphite
Uses:
acid chloride formation reagent

phosphoryl chloride
See: phosphorus oxychloride

phosphotungstic acid
triple salt acid; tungstophosphoric acid; PTA

$$H_3PO_4.12WO_3$$

$H_3O_{40}P_1W_{12}$. M: 2880.15. White or yellow-green crystals with a variable water content. Soluble in water. The commonly used molar ratio of P:W is 1:12 although values down to 1:6 are also produced for special applications.
Production:
• sodium tungstate + phosphoric acid, pure (salt formation)
Uses: laking agent (basic dyes)

phoxim
O,O-diethyl α-cyanobenzylideneaminooxyphosphonothioate; [14816-18-3]

$C_{12}H_{15}N_2O_3P_1S_1$. M: 298.29.
Production:
• benzyl cyanide + sodium nitrite + *O,O*-diethyl phosphorochlorothioate (oxime formation/dehydrochlorination)
Uses: insecticide

PHPA
See: acrylamide-sodium acrylate copolymers

phthalic anhydride
PA; [85-44-9]

$C_8H_4O_3$. M: 148.12. White flakes or molten liquid. MP: 131°C. Sublimes. BP: 295°C (sealed tube). d: 1.53 kg/l. Slightly soluble in hot water with hydrolysis to phthalic acid. Soluble in alcohol.
Production:
• *o*-xylene (gas-phase oxidation)
• naphthalene fraction (gas-phase oxidation)
• naphthalene (gas-phase oxidation; coproduced with naphthoquinone)
Derivatives:
Acid Red 308; alkyd resins, long-oil; alkyd resins, medium-oil; alkyd resins, non-drying; alkyd resins, short-oil; alkyd resins, water-soluble; amylanthraquinone; azatadine; Basic Red 1; Basic Violet 10; benzothienocycloheptanone; *o*-benzoylbenzoic acid; 2-*t*-butylanthraquinone; *n*-butyl benzyl phthalate; *n*-butyl isodecyl phthalate; *n*-butyl octyl phthalate; 2-(4-chloro-

benzoyl)benzoic acid; 1-chloro-4-hydroxyanthraquinone; copper phthalocyanine; di-*n*-alkyl(C_7-C_9) phthalate; di-*n*-alkyl(C_8-C_{10}) phthalate; di-*n*-alkyl(C_9-C_{11}) phthalate; diallyl phthalate; dibenzosuberone; dibutoxyethyl phthalate; di-*n*-butyl phthalate; dicyclohexyl phthalate; di-(2-ethylhexyl) phthalate; diethyl phthalate; dihydralazine; diisobutyl phthalate; diisodecyl phthalate; diisononyl phthalate; diisooctyl phthalate; diisotridecyl phthalate; di-(2-methoxyethyl) phthalate; di-(methylcyclohexyl) phthalate; dimethyl phthalate; dinonyl phthalate; diphenyl phthalate; Disperse Yellow 64; 2-ethylanthraquinone; fluorescein; hydroabietyl phthalate; lead phthalate, dibasic; 2-methylanthraquinone; Mordant Red 15; naptalam-sodium; 5-nitroanthranilic acid; phenolphthalein; phthalimide; phthaloyl chloride; polyester resins, carboxylated; polyester resins, hydroxylated; polymeric plasticisers; quinophthalone; Solvent Green 4; Sulphur Yellow 9; talampicillin; tetrabromophthalic anhydride; 2,2,4-trimethyl-1,3-pentanediol benzyl phthalate; unsaturated polyester resins, coating grades; unsaturated polyester resins, general grades
Uses: heat-cured epoxy resin curing agent; vulcanisation retarder

phthalide
fthalide; 4,5,6,7-tetrachlorophthalide; TCP; [27355-22-2]

$C_8H_2Cl_4O_2$. M: 271.92.
Production:
• *o*-xylene (chlorination/acid-catalysed cyclisation)
Uses: fungicide

phthalimide
[85-41-6]

$C_8H_5N_1O_2$. M: 147.14. White powder or flakes. MP: 235–236°C. Slightly soluble in water. Soluble in aqueous alkali.
Production:
• phthalic anhydride + ammonia (amide formation)
Derivatives: N-(cyclohexylthio)phthalimide; N-(dichlorofluoromethylthio)phthalimide; folpet; isatoic anhydride; phosmet; primaquine

phthalocyanine blue *See:* copper phthalocyanine

phthalocyanine green
See: Pigment Green 7; Pigment Green 36

phthalodinitrile

1,2-dicyanobenzene; *o*-dicyanobenzene; phthalonitrile; [91-15-6]

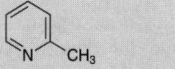

$C_8H_4N_2$. M: 128.13. Pale brown solid. MP: 141°C. Insoluble in water.
Production:
• *o*-xylene + ammonia (ammoxidation)
Derivatives:
copper phthalocyanine; 1,3-diiminoisoindoline; 3,3,4,5,6,7-hexachloroisoindolinone; Pigment Blue 16
Uses:
Ingrain Blue dyestuffs intermediate

phthaloyl chloride

phthaloyl dichloride; [88-95-9]

$C_8H_4Cl_2O_2$. M: 203.03. Colourless liquid or solid. MP: 15–16°C. BP: 280–282°C. Hydrolysed by water and alcohol.
Production:
• phthalic anhydride (acid chloride formation)
Uses: chemical intermediate

phyloquinone *See:* vitamin K$_1$

phytic acid

inositolhexaphosphoric acid; [83-86-3]; [7776-28-5] (calcium salt)

R = dihydrogen phosphate. $C_6H_{18}O_{24}P_6$. M: 660.03. Yellowish, viscous liquid. Decomposes on heating. Soluble in water. The product is available as the acid, sodium, calcium, calcium-magnesium or calcium-iron salts.
Production:
• corn steep liquor (extraction)
Derivatives: inositol
Uses: vegetable oil clarification/purification agent; dispersant (cleaning formulations)

phytol

3,7,11,15-tetramethyl-2-hexadecen-1-ol; [150-86-7]

$(CH_3)_2CHCH_2CH_2CH_2CHCH_2CH_2CH_2CHCH_2CH_2CH_2C=CHCH_2OH$

$C_{20}H_{40}O_1$. M: 296.54. Involatile liquid. Insoluble in water. Soluble in oxygenated, chlorinated and aromatic solvents.
Production:
• nerolidol + ethyl acetoacetate + acetylene (carbonyl condensation/ethynylation/hydrogenation/isomerisation)
Derivatives: α-tocopherol; vitamin K$_1$

phytomenadione *See:* vitamin K$_1$

phytosterols, mixed

soyabean sterols
Mixed product containing β-sitosterol, stigmasterol and related products.
Production:
• soyabean soap stock (acidification/fractionation; byproduct of soyabean acid production)
Derivatives:
androstadienedione; stigmasterol

PIB *See:* polyisobutylene, low molecular weight

PIBSA *See:* polyisobutenylsuccinic anhydride

picloram

[1918-02-1]

$C_6H_3Cl_3N_2O_2$. M: 241.46.
Production:
• α-picoline + chlorine + ammonia (chlorination/ammoniation/acid-catalysed hydrolysis)
Uses:
herbicide; flow stimulant (natural rubber, pine gum)

α-picoline

2-methylpyridine; 2-picoline; [109-06-8]

$C_6H_7N_1$. M: 93.14. Colourless liquid with an unpleasant odour. BP: 128–129°C. FP: -64°C. d: 0.95 kg/l (20°C). Miscible with water and oxygenated solvents.
Production:
• paraldehyde + ammonia (liquid-phase condensation; coproduced with γ-picoline/2-methyl-5-ethyl-pyridine)
• pyridine bases, crude (fractionation; coproduced with pyridine/γ-picoline/2,6-lutidine/3,4-lutidine/pyridine bases)
• acetaldehyde + formaldehyde + ammonia (Reilly synthesis; coproduced with pyridine/β-picoline/γ-picoline)
• acetone + acrylonitrile (cyanoethylation/cyclisation)

Derivatives: 2-amino-6-methylpyridine; betahistine; bisacodyl; clopyralid; 2-methylpiperidine; perhexiline; picloram; picolinic acid; thioridazine; 2-vinylpyridine

β-picoline
3-methylpyridine; 3-picoline; [108-99-6]

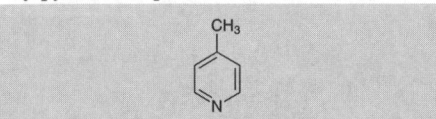

$C_6H_7N_1$. M: 93.14. Colourless liquid. BP: 143–144°C. d: 0.96 kg/l (20°C). Miscible with water and alcohol.
Production:
- acetaldehyde + formaldehyde + ammonia (Reilly synthesis; coproduced with pyridine/α-picoline/γ-picoline)
- acrolein + ammonia (Daicel process; coproduced with pyridine)

Derivatives:
3-chloro-2-hydroxy-5-trifluoromethylpyridine; 2-hydroxy-5-(trifluoromethyl)pyridine; nicotinonitrile
Uses: process solvent

γ-picoline
4-methylpyridine; 4-picoline; [108-89-4]

$C_6H_7N_1$. M: 93.14. Liquid with an unpleasant odour. BP: 144–145°C. d: 0.96 kg/l (15°C). Soluble in water and oxygenated solvents.
Production:
- paraldehyde + ammonia (liquid-phase condensation; coproduced with α-picoline/2-methyl-5-ethylpyridine)
- pyridine bases, crude (fractionation; coproduced with pyridine/α-picoline/2,6-lutidine/3,4-lutidine/pyridine bases)
- acetaldehyde + formaldehyde + ammonia (Reilly synthesis; coproduced with pyridine/α-picoline/β-picoline)

Derivatives: isonicotinic acid; 4-vinylpyridine

picolinic acid
2-pyridinecarboxylic acid; pyridine-2-carboxylic acid; [98-98-6]

$C_6H_5N_1O_2$. M: 123.12. Red, crystalline solid. MP: 136–138°C. Sublimes. Soluble in hot water and alcohol.
Production:
- α-picoline (side-chain oxidation)

Derivatives: 2-acetylpyridine; bromazepam; bupivacaine; mepivacaine

picric acid
melinite; 2,4,6-trinitrophenol; trinitrophenol; TNP; 10305 (CI); [88-89-1]

$C_6H_3N_3O_7$. M: 229.10. Pale yellow crystals. MP: 122–123°C. Explodes on heating above 300°C. d: 1.76 kg/l (20°C). Slightly soluble in hot water. Commercially available as a paste containing 10–20% water.
Production:
- 2,4-dinitrophenol (nitration)

Derivatives: ammonium picrate; sodium picramate; Sulphur Black 2
Uses: wool/silk dyeing; explosives; analytical reagent

Pigment Black 7 *See:* carbon black

Pigment Black 11 *See:* iron oxide black

Pigment Blue 1 *See:* Basic Blue 7

Pigment Blue 2 *See:* Solvent Blue 4

Pigment Blue 9 *See:* Basic Blue 1

Pigment Blue 14 *See:* Basic Violet 4

Pigment Blue 15 *See:* copper phthalocyanine

Pigment Blue 16
phthalocyanine blue, copper-free; 74100 (CI)

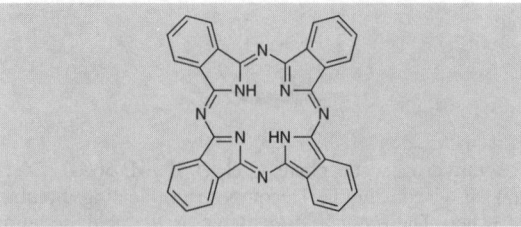

$C_{32}H_{18}N_8$. M: 514.55.
Production:
- phthalodinitrile (condensation)

Uses: pigment (printing inks, emulsion paints, paper coatings, plastics)

Pigment Blue 17 *See:* Direct Blue 86

Pigment Blue 18
Alkali Blue G; Reflex Blue 2G; 42770:1 (CI)
$C_{37}H_{29}N_3O_6S_2$. M: 675.78.
Production:
- aniline + benzoic acid (condensation/sulphonation)

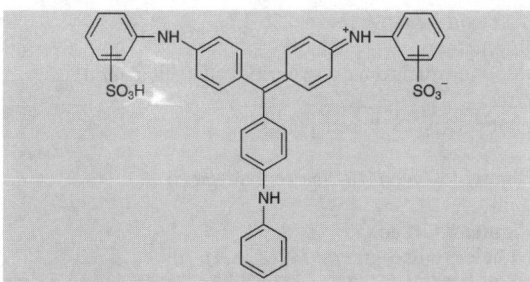

Uses: pigment (lacquers, printing inks)

Pigment Blue 24 *See:* Acid Blue 9

Pigment Blue 27 *See:* Prussian Blue

Pigment Blue 28 *See:* cobalt blue

Pigment Blue 29
Ultramarine Blue; 77007 (CI); [57455-37-5];
[1317-97-1]

$$Na_{6-8}Al_6Si_6S_{2-4}O_{24}$$

A series of blue pigments, sometimes with a reddish
or violet hue. d: 2.35 kg/l.
Production:
• sodium carbonate + kaolin + sulphur (thermal
  reduction)
Derivatives: Pigment Violet 15
Uses: Pigment Green 16 component; pigment (paints,
printing inks, plastics)

Pigment Blue 56
Reflex Blue 2G; 42800 (CI)

$C_{40}H_{35}N_3O_3S_1$. M: 637.80.
Production:
• *m*-toluidine + benzoic acid (condensation/
  sulphonation)
Uses: pigment (printing inks)

Pigment Blue 60 *See:* indanthrone

Pigment Blue 61
Alkali Blue G; 42765:1 (CI)
$C_{37}H_{29}N_3O_3S_1$. M: 595.72.

Production:
• aniline + benzoic acid (condensation/sulphonation)
Uses: pigment (lacquers, printing inks)

Pigment Blue 62 *See:* Basic Blue 7

Pigment Blue 63 *See:* Acid Blue 74

Pigment Blue 64 *See:* Vat Blue 6

Pigment Brown 3 *See:* Solvent Brown 12

Pigment Brown 7 *See:* iron oxide brown

Pigment Brown 24
See: chrome antimony titanium buff

Pigment Brown 25
Fast Brown HFR; 12510 (CI)

$C_{24}H_{15}Cl_2N_5O_3$. M: 492.32.
Production:
• 2,5-dichloroaniline + 5-(2′-hydroxy-3′-naphthoyl)-
  aminobenzimidazolone (diazotisation/azo coupling)
Uses:
pigment (printing inks, polyvinyl chloride)

Pigment Brown 29 *See:* chrome iron brown

Pigment Green 1 *See:* Basic Green 1

Pigment Green 3 *See:* Basic Yellow 2

Pigment Green 4 *See:* Basic Green 4

Pigment Green 7
phthalocyanine green; 74260 (CI); [1328-53-6]
$C_{32}Cl_{16}Cu_1N_8$. M: 1127.21.
Production:
• copper phthalocyanine (ring chlorination)

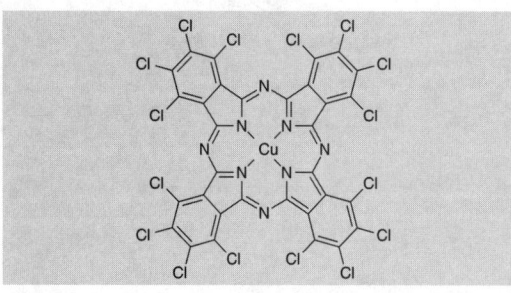

Uses:
pigment (paints, printing inks, lacquers, plastics)

Pigment Green 8
Pigment Green B; Paliotol Green K9781 (BASF); 10006 (CI); [16143-80-9]

$C_{30}H_{18}Fe_1N_3Na_1O_6$. M: 595.32.
Production:
• 1-nitroso-2-naphthol + ferrous sulphate (complex formation)
Uses:
pigment (plastics, water-based paints)

Pigment Green 10
Nickel Azo Yellow; 12775 (CI)

The pigment is the 2:1 nickel complex of the displayed structure.
Production:
• p-chloroaniline + 2,4-dihydroxyquinoline + nickel sulphate (diazotisation/azo coupling/complex formation)
Uses: pigment (alkyd resin enamels, lacquers)

Pigment Green 12 *See:* Acid Green 1

Pigment Green 15 *See:* chrome green

Pigment Green 17 *See:* chromium oxide

Pigment Green 18
chromium hydroxide, green; chromium oxide hydrate; Guignet's Green; viridian; 77289 (CI)

Cr_2O_3

Cr_2O_3. M: 151.99. Green powder. d: 3.2 kg/l. Decom-

poses on heating above 250°C.
Production:
• sodium dichromate + boric acid (calcination)
Uses:
pigment (water-based paints)

Pigment Green 19 *See:* cobalt green

Pigment Green 36
phthalocyanine green; 74265 (CI)

$C_{32}Br_6Cl_{10}Cu_1N_8$. M: 1393.91.
Production:
• copper phthalocyanine (ring chlorination/ring bromination)
Uses:
pigment (paints, printing inks, plastics)

Pigment Metal 1
See: aluminium

Pigment Orange 2
12060 (CI)

$C_{16}H_{11}N_3O_3$. M: 293.29.
Production:
• o-nitroaniline + β-naphthol (diazotisation/azo coupling)
Uses:
pigment (paints, printing inks, paper, leather finishes)

Pigment Orange 5
Dinitroaniline Red; DNA Orange; Orange 2G; Permanent Red 2G; 12075 (CI); D&C Orange No. 17 (FDC); [3468-63-1]

$C_{16}H_{10}N_4O_5$. M: 338.28.

Production:
- 2,4-dinitroaniline + β-naphthol
  (diazotisation/azo coupling)

Uses: pigment (paints, printing inks)

Pigment Orange 6
12730 (CI)

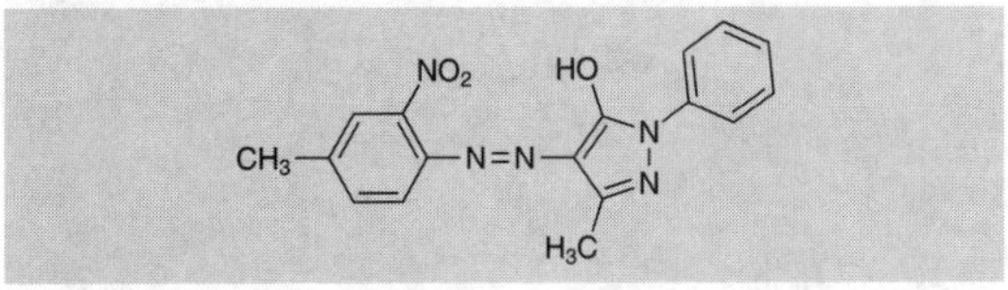

$C_{17}H_{15}N_5O_3$. M: 337.34.
Production:
- 4-amino-3-nitrotoluene + 3-methyl-1-phenyl-
  5-pyrazolone (diazotisation/azo coupling)

Uses:
pigment (plastics, resins)

Pigment Orange 13
Permanent Orange G; 21110 (CI)

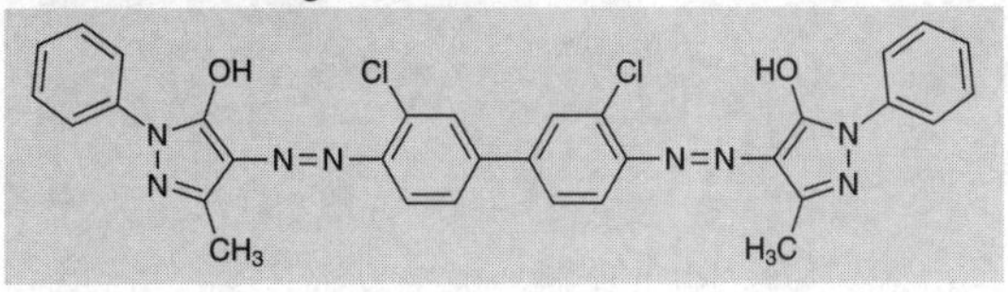

$C_{32}H_{24}Cl_2N_8O_2$. M: 623.51.
Production:
- 3,3′-dichlorobenzidine dihydrochloride + 3-methyl-
  1-phenyl-5-pyrazolone (diazotisation/azo coupling)

Uses:
pigment (paints, printing inks, plastics, rubber)

Pigment Orange 14
21165 (CI)

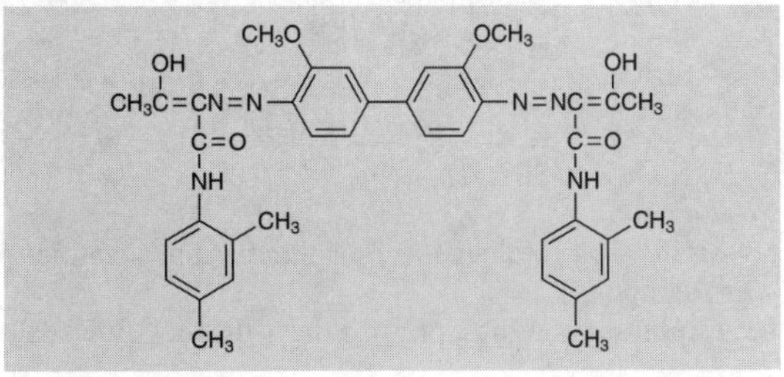

$C_{38}H_{40}N_6O_6$. M: 676.77.
Production:
- o-dianisidine + acetoacet-2,4-xylidide
  (diazotisation/azo coupling)

Uses:
pigment (rubber)

Pigment Orange 15
21130 (CI)
$C_{34}H_{32}N_6O_4$. M: 588.67.

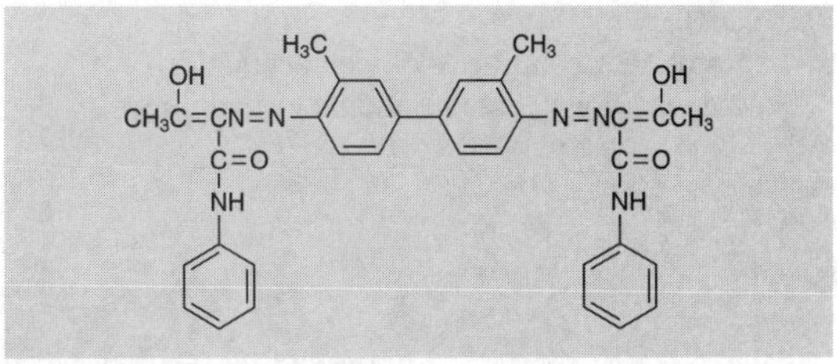

Production:
- o-tolidine + acetoacetanilide (diazotisation/azo
  coupling)

Uses: pigment (printing inks)

Pigment Orange 16
Dianisidine Orange; 21160 (CI)

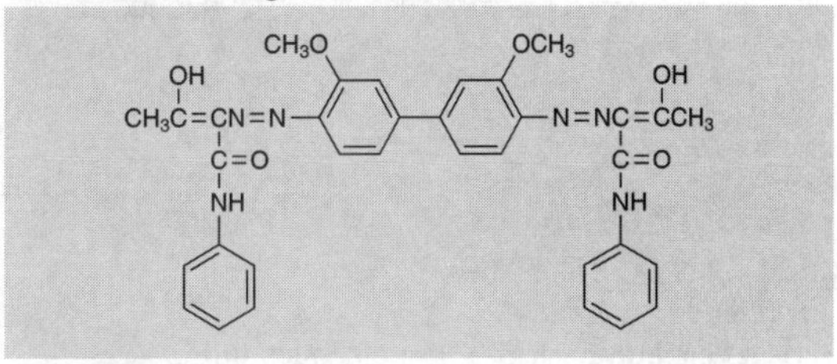

$C_{34}H_{32}N_6O_6$. M: 620.66.
Production:
- o-dianisidine + acetoacetanilide (diazotisation/azo
  coupling)

Uses:
pigment (printing inks, lacquer, plastics, rubber)

Pigment Orange 20 *See:* cadmium red

Pigment Orange 34
Fast Orange F2G; 21115 (CI)

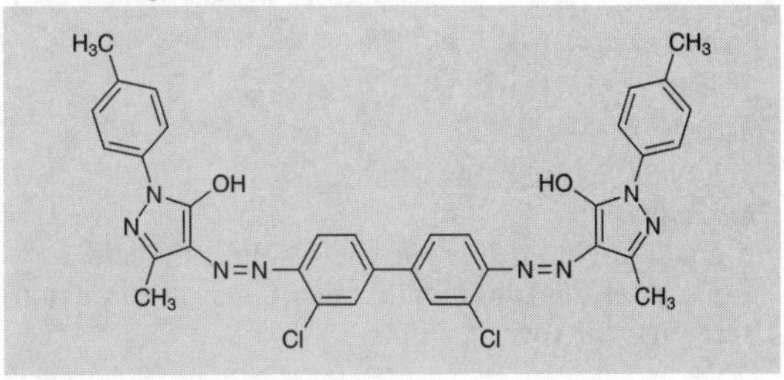

$C_{34}H_{28}Cl_2N_8O_2$. M: 651.56.
Production:
- 3,3′-dichlorobenzidine dihydrochloride +
  1-(4′-methylphenyl)-3-methylpyrazolone
  (diazotisation/azo coupling)

Uses:
pigment (plastics, resins, inks)

Pigment Orange 36
Benzimidazolone Orange HL; 11780 (CI)
$C_{17}H_{13}Cl_1N_6O_5$. M: 416.77.

Production:
• 4-chloro-2-nitroaniline + 5-acetoacetamido-
benzimidazolone (diazotisation/azo coupling)

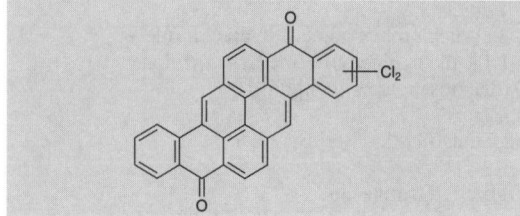

Uses: pigment (paints, printing inks)

Pigment Orange 38
12367 (CI)

$C_{26}H_{20}Cl_1N_5O_4$. M: 501.94.
Production:
• β-oxynaphthoic acid + *p*-aminoacetanilide +
3-amino-4-chlorobenzamide (amide formation/
diazotisation/azo coupling)
Uses: pigment (paints, printing inks, plastics)

Pigment Orange 40 *See:* pyranthrone

Pigment Orange 46
15602 (CI)

$C_{18}H_{14}Cl_1N_2Na_1O_4S_1$. M: 412.82.
Production:
• 5-amino-2-chloroethylbenzene-4-sulphonic acid +
β-naphthol (diazotisation/azo coupling/salt formation)
Uses: pigment (printing inks)

Pigment Orange 51

$C_{30}H_{12}Cl_2O_2$. M: 475.34.

Production:
• pyranthrone (ring chlorination)
Uses: pigment (paints, plastics, printing inks)

Pigment Red 1
Paranitroaniline Red; 12070 (CI)

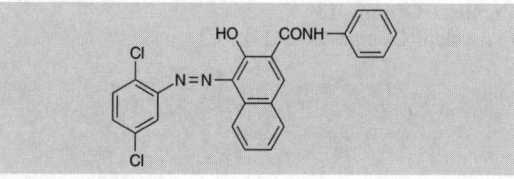

$C_{16}H_{11}N_3O_3$. M: 293.29.
Production:
• *p*-nitroaniline + β-naphthol (diazotisation/azo
coupling)
Uses: pigment (paints, printing inks)

Pigment Red 2
Naphthol Red; Permanent Red FRR (CI); 12310 (CI)

$C_{23}H_{15}Cl_2N_3O_2$. M: 436.30.
Production:
• 2,5-dichloroaniline + 3-hydroxy-2-naphthanilide
(diazotisation/azo coupling)
Uses: pigment (printing inks, lacquers, paints, plastics)

Pigment Red 3
Toluidine Red; 12120 (CI);

$C_{17}H_{13}N_3O_3$. M: 307.31.
Production:
• 4-amino-3-nitrotoluene + β-naphthol (diazotisation/
azo coupling)
Uses: pigment (paints, printing inks, leather finishes)

Pigment Red 4
Paranitroaniline Red, chlorinated; Permanent Red R;
12085 (CI); D&C Red No. 36 (FDC); [2814-77-9]

$C_{16}H_{10}Cl_1N_3O_3$. M: 327.73.

Production:
- 2-chloro-4-nitroaniline + β-naphthol (diazotisation/ azo coupling)

Uses: pigment (printing inks, resins, paper, cosmetics)

Pigment Red 5
Carmine FB; 12490 (CI)

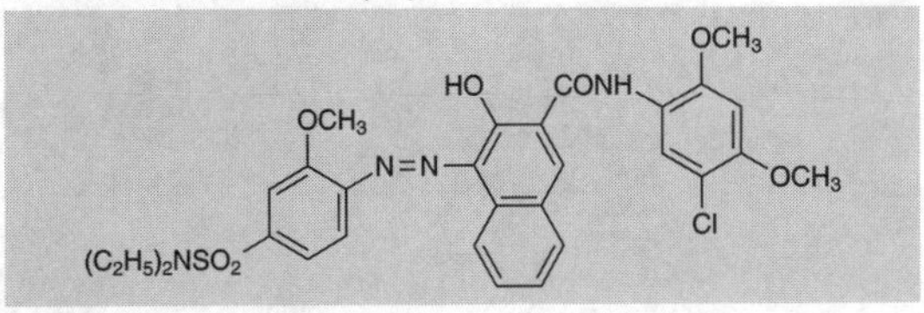

$C_{30}H_{31}Cl_1N_4O_7S_1$. M: 627.11.
Production:
- *N,N*-diethyl-3-amino-4-methoxybenzenesulphon- amide + 5-chloro-2,4-dimethoxy-3′-hydroxy- 2′-naphthanilide (diazotisation/azo coupling)

Uses: pigment (printing inks)

Pigment Red 6
12090 (CI)

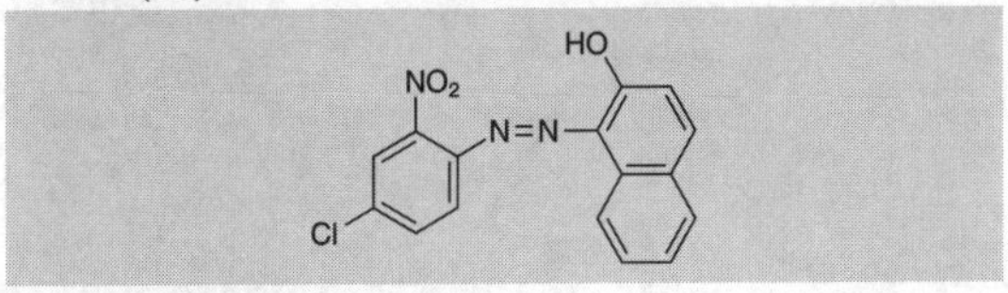

$C_{16}H_{10}Cl_1N_3O_3$. M: 327.73.
Production:
- 4-chloro-2-nitroaniline + β-naphthol (diazotisation/ azo coupling)

Uses: pigment (paint, lacquers)

Pigment Red 7
Permanent Red F4RH; 12420 (CI)

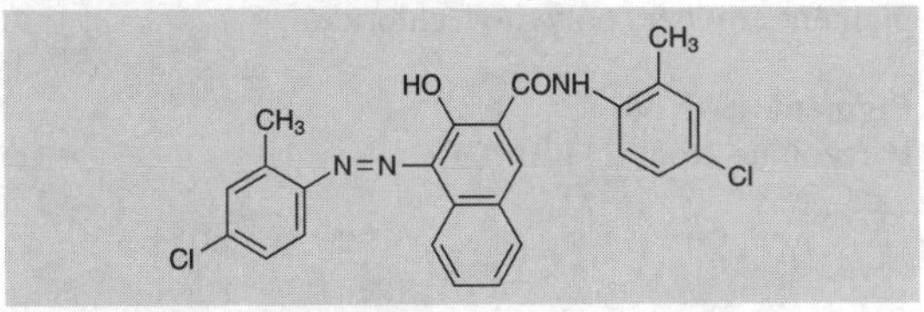

$C_{25}H_{19}Cl_2N_3O_2$. M: 464.35.
Production:
- 2-amino-5-chlorotoluene + 4-chloro-3′-hydroxy- 2′-naphth-*m*-toluidide (diazotisation/azo coupling)

Uses: pigment (paints, printing inks)

Pigment Red 8
Naphthol Red F4R; 12335 (CI)
$C_{24}H_{17}Cl_1N_4O_4$. M: 460.88.
Production:
- β-oxynaphthoic acid + *p*-chloroaniline + 2-amino- 4-nitrotoluene (amide formation/diazotisation/azo coupling)

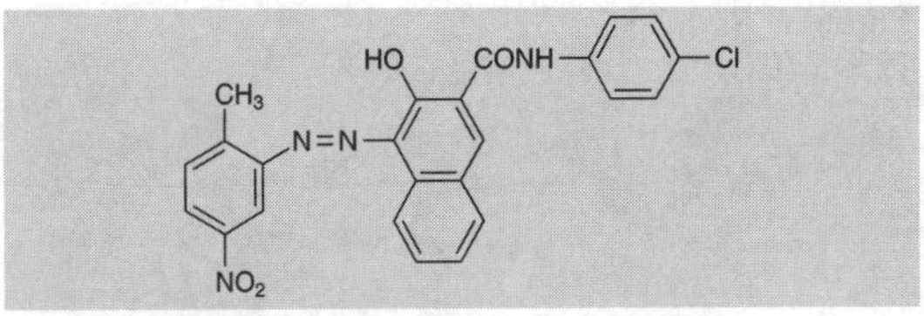

Uses: pigment (printing inks)

Pigment Red 9
Naphthol Red LF; Red FRLL; 12460 (CI)

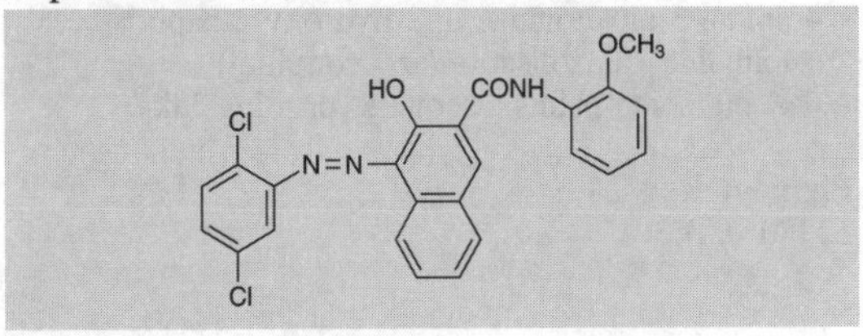

$C_{24}H_{17}Cl_2N_3O_3$. M: 466.33.
Production:
- 2,5-dichloroaniline + 3-hydroxy-2-naphth- *o*-anisidide (diazotisation/azo coupling)

Uses:
pigment (paints, printing inks)

Pigment Red 10
Permanent Red FRL; 12440 (CI)

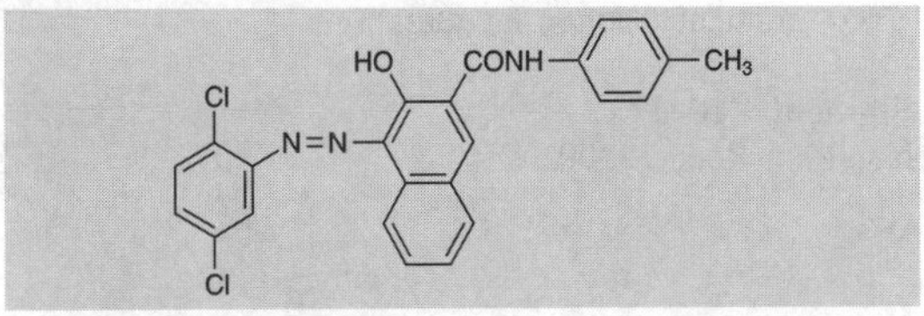

$C_{24}H_{17}Cl_2N_3O_2$. M: 450.33.
Production:
- 2,5-dichloroaniline + 3-hydroxy-2-naphth-*p*-toluidide (diazotisation/azo coupling)

Uses:
pigment (paints, printing inks)

Pigment Red 12
Bordeaux F2R; 12385 (CI)

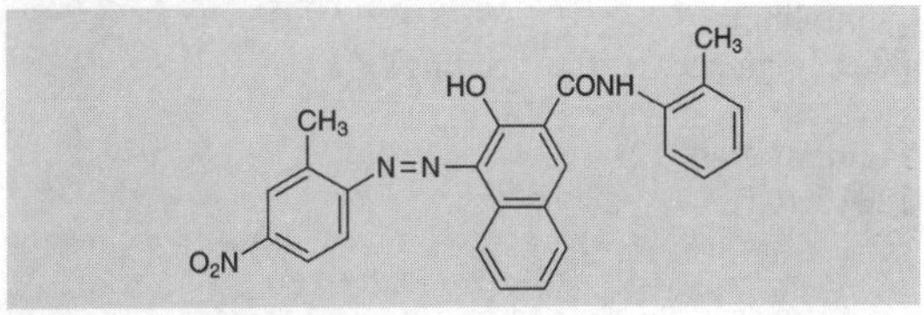

$C_{25}H_{20}N_4O_4$. M: 440.46.
Production:
- 2-amino-5-nitrotoluene + 3-hydroxy-2-naphth- *o*-toluidide (diazotisation/azo coupling)

Uses:
pigment (paints, printing inks)

Pigment Red 13
12395 (CI)

$C_{25}H_{20}N_4O_4$. M: 440.46.
Production:
• 4-amino-3-nitrotoluene + 3-hydroxy-2-naphth-
o-toluidide (diazotisation/azo coupling)
Uses: pigment (paints, lacquers, printing inks)

Pigment Red 14
12380 (CI)

$C_{24}H_{18}Cl_1N_4O_4$. M: 461.88.
Production:
• 4-chloro-2-nitroaniline + 3-hydroxy-2-naphth-
o-toluidide (diazotisation/azo coupling)
Uses: pigment (paints, lacquers)

Pigment Red 17
Naphthol Red; 12390 (CI)

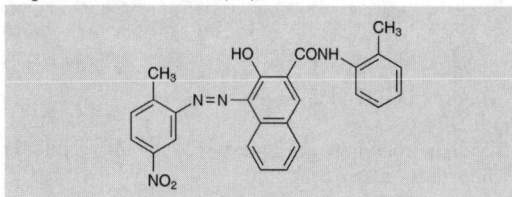

$C_{25}H_{20}N_4O_4$. M: 440.46.
Production:
• 2-amino-4-nitrotoluene + 3-hydroxy-2-naphth-
o-toluidide (amide formation/diazotisation/azo
coupling)
Uses: pigment (textile printing)

Pigment Red 22
12315 (CI)

$C_{24}H_{18}N_4O_4$. M: 426.43.

Production:
• 2-amino-4-nitrotoluene + 3-hydroxy-2-naphthanilide
(diazotisation/azo coupling)
Uses: pigment (printing inks, paints)

Pigment Red 23
12355 (CI)

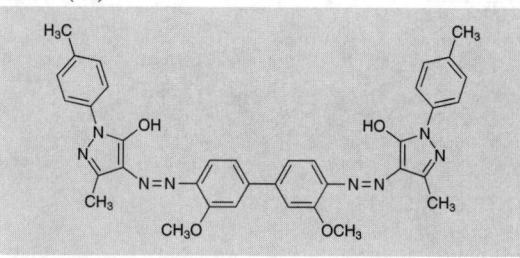

$C_{24}H_{17}N_5O_7$. M: 487.43.
Production:
• 2-amino-4-nitroanisole + 3-nitro-3′-hydroxy-
2′-naphthanilide (diazotisation/azo coupling)
Uses: pigment (printing inks, paints)

Pigment Red 37
21205 (CI)

$C_{36}H_{34}N_8O_4$. M: 642.73.
Production:
• o-dianisidine + 1-(4′-methylphenyl)-3-methyl-
pyrazolone (diazotisation/azo coupling)
Uses:
pigment (rubber, polyvinyl chloride)

Pigment Red 38
Pyrazolone Red; 21120 (CI)

$C_{36}H_{28}Cl_2N_8O_6$. M: 739.58.
Production:
• 3,3′-dichlorobenzidine dihydrochloride + ethyl
1-phenylpyrazolone-3-carboxylate (diazotisation/azo
coupling)
Uses: pigment (rubber, plastics)

Pigment Red 41
21200 (CI)
$C_{34}H_{30}N_8O_4$. M: 614.67.

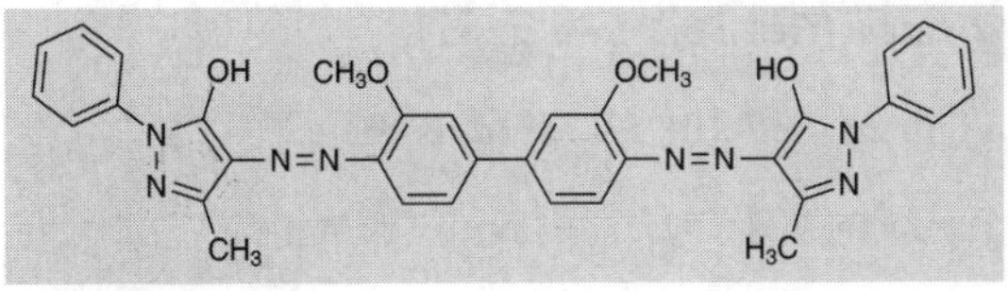

Production:
* *o*-dianisidine + 3-methyl-1-phenyl-5-pyrazolone
  (diazotisation/azo coupling)

Uses:
pigment (rubber, polyvinyl chloride)

Pigment Red 42
21210 (CI)

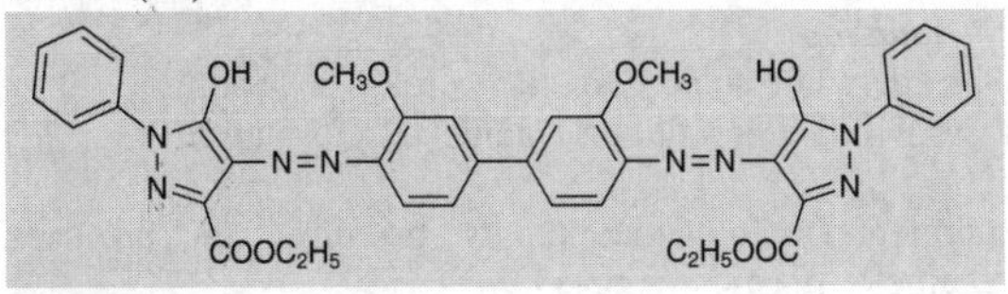

$C_{38}H_{34}N_8O_8$. M: 730.74.
Production:
* *o*-dianisidine + ethyl 1-phenylpyrazolone-
  3-carboxylate (diazotisation/azo coupling)

Uses:
pigment (paints, plastics, rubber)

Pigment Red 48
BON Red; Permanent Red 2B; Rubine 2B; Pigment Red 48:1 (CI, barium salt); Pigment Red 48:2 (CI, calcium salt); Pigment Red 48:3 (CI, strontium salt); Pigment Red 48:4 (CI, manganese salt); 15865 (CI, sodium salt); 15865:1 (CI, barium salt); 15865:2 (CI, calcium salt); 15865:3 (CI, strontium salt); 15865:4 (CI, manganese salt)

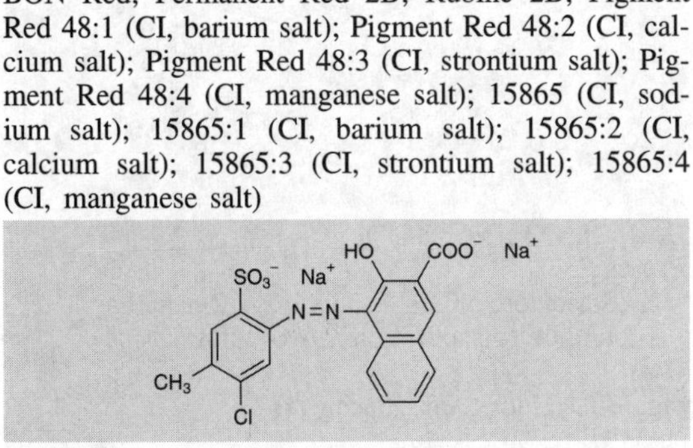

$C_{18}H_{11}Cl_1N_2Na_2O_6S_1$. M: 464.78.
Production:
* 2B acid + β-oxynaphthoic acid (diazotisation/azo
  coupling)

Uses:
pigment (printing inks, paints, resins, lacquers, rubber, vinyls, aminoplasts)

Pigment Red 49
barium toner (barium salt); calcium toner (calcium salt); Lithol Red (sodium salt); Lithol Toner BS (calcium salt); Lithol Toner YS (barium salt); Pigment Red 49:1 (CI, barium salt); Pigment Red 49:2 (CI, calcium salt); 15630 (CI, sodium salt); 15630:1 (Ci, barium salt); 15630:2 (CI, calcium salt)

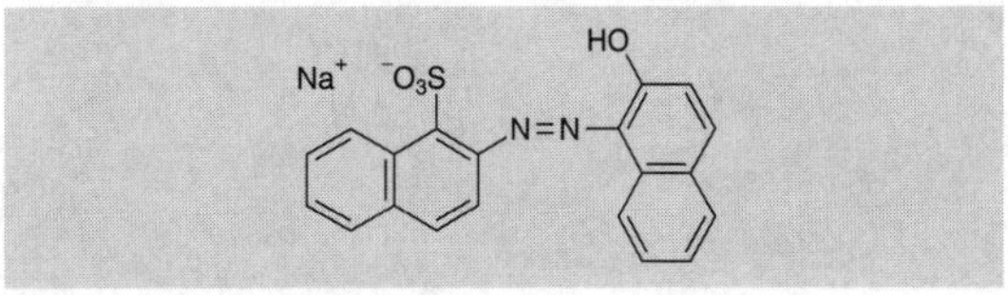

$C_{20}H_{13}N_2Na_1O_4S_1$. M: 400.38.
Production:
* Tobias acid + β-naphthol (diazotisation/azo coupling)

Uses: plastics colorant; toner (paints, printing inks)

Pigment Red 52
BON Red; Pigment Red 52:1 (CI, calcium salt); Pigment Red 52:2 (CI, manganese salt); 15860 (CI, sodium salt); 15860:1 (CI, calcium salt); 15860:2 (CI, manganese salt);

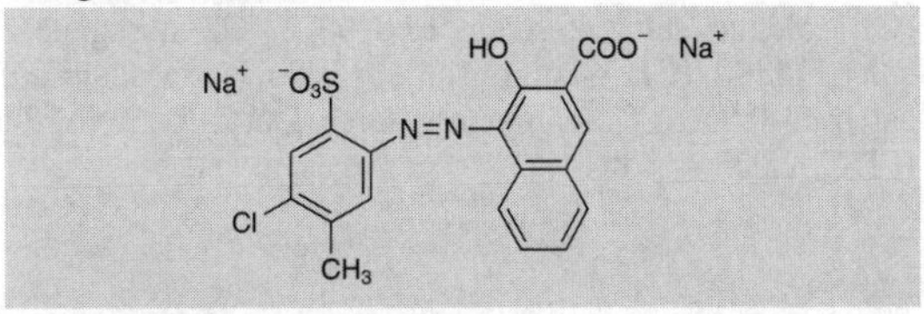

$C_{18}H_{11}Cl_1N_2Na_2O_6S_1$. M: 464.78.
Production:
* 5-amino-2-chlorotoluene-4-sulphonic acid + β-oxynaphthoic acid (diazotisation/azo coupling/sodium
  salt formation)

Uses:
pigment (printing inks, paints, lacquers, plastics)

Pigment Red 53
Pigment Red 53:1 (CI, barium salt); Pigment Red 53:2 (CI, calcium salt); 15585 (CI, sodium salt); 15585:1 (CI, barium salt); 15585:2 (CI, calcium salt); D&C Red No. 9 (FDC); [5160-02-1]

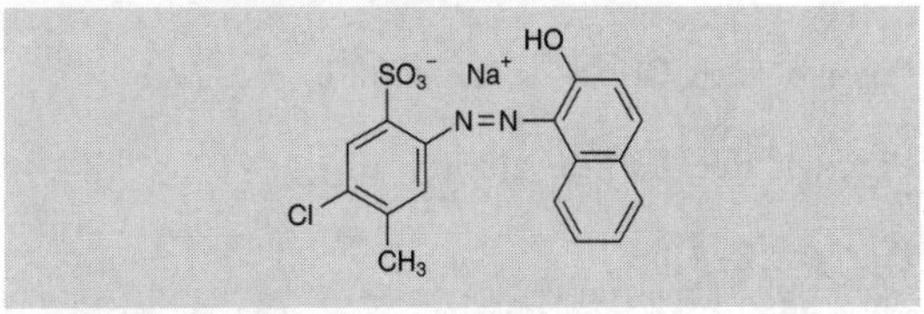

$C_{17}H_{12}Cl_1N_2Na_1O_4S_1$. M: 398.80.
Production:
* 5-amino-2-chlorotoluene-4-sulphonic acid +
  β-naphthol (diazotisation/azo coupling/sodium salt
  formation)

Uses:
pigment (printing inks, plastics)

Pigment Red 57
crimson toner; Lithol Rubine BK; Permanent Red 4B; Pigment Red 57:1 (CI, calcium salt); Pigment Red 57:2 (CI, barium salt); 15850 (CI, sodium salt); 15850:1 (CI, calcium salt); 15850:2 (CI, barium salt); D&C Red No. 7 (FDC); E180 (EC); [5281-04-9]

$C_{18}H_{12}N_2Na_2O_6S_1$. M: 430.34.
Production:
• 4B acid + β-oxynaphthoic acid (diazotisation/azo coupling/sodium salt formation)
Uses: cheese rind dye; pigment (plastics, printing inks)

Pigment Red 60 *See:* Mordant Red 9

Pigment Red 63
BON Maroon; Lake Bordeaux B; Pigment Red 63:1 (CI, calcium salt); Pigment Red 63:2 (CI, manganese salt); 15880 (CI, sodium salt); 15880:1 (CI, calcium salt); 15880:2 (CI, manganese salt); D&C Red No. 34 (FDC, calcium salt)

$C_{21}H_{12}N_2Na_2O_6S_1$. M: 466.37.
Production:
• Tobias acid + β-oxynaphthoic acid (diazotisation/ azo coupling)
Uses: pigment (paint, enamels, lacquers, resins, printing inks, vinyl plastics)

Pigment Red 66 *See:* Acid Red 108

Pigment Red 67 *See:* Acid Red 107

Pigment Red 81 *See:* Basic Red 1

Pigment Red 83 *See:* alizarin

Pigment Red 88
Thioindigo Red; 73312 (CI)

$C_{16}H_4Cl_4O_2S_2$. M: 434.15.
Production:
• 2,5-dichloroaniline + sodium hydrosulphide + chloroacetic acid (diazotisation/thiolation/ reduction/amine formation/dehydrative coupling/ decarboxylation)
Uses:
pigment (industrial paints, printing inks, plastics)

Pigment Red 90:1 *See:* eosine

Pigment Red 101 *See:* iron oxide red

Pigment Red 102 *See:* iron oxide red

Pigment Red 104
Chrome Scarlet; Molybdate Orange; Molybdate Red; Orange Chrome; 77605 (CI)

$PbCrO_4.mPbMoO_4.nPbSO_4$

Series of pigments which range in colour from orange to red, depending on the chromate:molybdate:sulphate ratio.
Production:
• lead nitrate + sodium dichromate + sodium molybdate + sulphuric acid (salt formation)
Uses:
pigment (maintenance paints, printing inks, lacquers, enamels, plastics, rubber)

Pigment Red 105 *See:* red lead

Pigment Red 108 *See:* cadmium red

Pigment Red 112
Permanent Red FGR; 12370 (CI); [6535-46-2]

$C_{24}H_{16}Cl_3N_3O_2$. M: 484.77.
Production:
• 2,4,5-trichloroaniline + 3-hydroxy-2-naphth-*o*-toluidide (diazotisation/azo coupling)
Uses:
pigment (printing inks, lacquers)

Pigment Red 122
See: 2,9-dimethylquinacridone

Pigment Red 123
Paliogen Red K3871 (BASF)

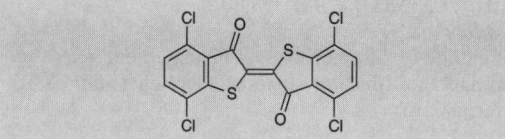

$C_{40}H_{26}N_2O_6$. M: 630.65.
Production:
• perylenetetracarboxylic anhydride + *p*-phenetidine (amide formation)
Uses: plastics colorant

Pigment Red 146
Permanent Carmine FBB; 12485 (CI)

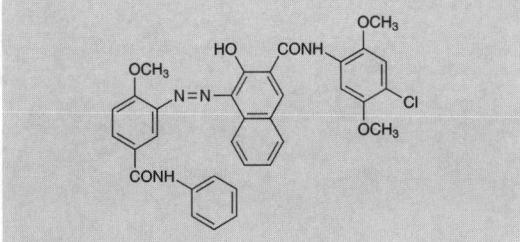

$C_{33}H_{27}Cl_1N_4O_6$. M: 611.05.
Production:
• 3-amino-4-methoxybenzoic acid + aniline +
  4-chloro-2,5-dimethoxy-3'-hydroxy-2'-naphthanilide
  (amide formation/diazotisation/azo coupling)
Uses:
pigment (paints, printing inks, lacquers)

Pigment Red 147
12433 (CI)

$C_{32}H_{25}Cl_1N_4O_4$. M: 565.02.
Production:
• 3-amino-4-methoxybenzoic acid + aniline +
  5-chloro-3'-hydroxy-2'-naphth-*o*-toluidide (amide
  formation/diazotisation/azo coupling)
Uses:
pigment (printing inks)

Pigment Red 149
Perylene Red; 71137 (CI); PV Fast Red B (Hoechst);
Permanent Red BL (Hoechst)

$C_{40}H_{26}N_2O_4$. M: 598.66.
Production:
• perylenetetracarboxylic anhydride + 3,5-xylidine
  (amide formation)
Uses: plastics colorant

Pigment Red 168 *See:* Vat Orange 3

Pigment Red 169 *See:* Basic Red 1

Pigment Red 170
Naphthol Red F5RK; 12475 (CI)

$C_{26}H_{22}N_4O_4$. M: 454.50.
Production:
• *p*-aminobenzamide + 3-hydroxy-2-naphth-
  o-phenetidide (diazotisation/azo coupling)
Uses:
pigment (printing inks, lacquers)

Pigment Red 171
Benzimidazolone Maroon HFM; 12521 (CI); PV Fast
Maroon HFM (Hoechst)

$C_{25}H_{18}N_6O_6$. M: 498.44.
Production:
• 5-(2'-hydroxy-3'-naphthoyl)aminobenzimidazolone +
  2-amino-5-nitroanisole (diazotisation/azo coupling)
Uses: plastics colorant

Pigment Red 172 *See:* Acid Red 51

Pigment Red 173 *See:* Basic Violet 10

Pigment Red 175
Benzimidazolone Red HFT; 12513 (CI)

$C_{26}H_{19}N_5O_5$. M: 481.47.
Production:
• 5-(2'-hydroxy-3'-naphthoyl)aminobenzimidazolone +
  methyl anthranilate (diazotisation/azo coupling)
Uses:
plastics colorant

Pigment Red 176
Benzimidazolone Carmine HF3C; 12515 (CI)
$C_{32}H_{24}N_6O_5$. M: 572.57.
Production:
• 3-amino-4-methoxybenzoic acid + aniline +
  5-(2'-hydroxy-3'-naphthoyl)aminobenzimidazolone
  (amide formation/diazotisation/azo coupling)

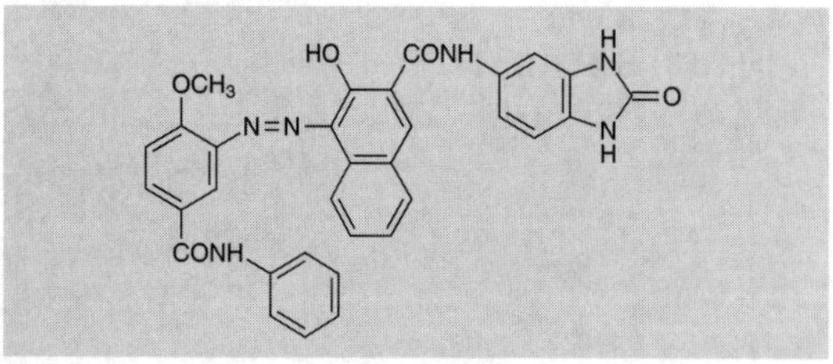

Uses:
pigment (plastics, printing inks)

Pigment Red 177
Anthraquinone Red; 65300 (CI); Chromophtal Red
A3B (Ciba-Geigy); [4051-63-2]

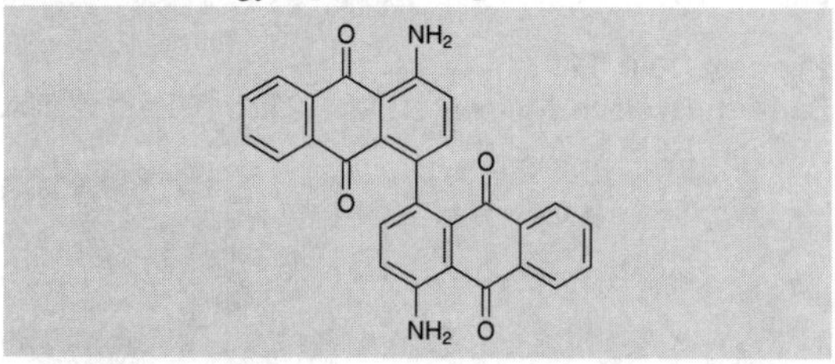

$C_{28}H_{16}N_2O_4$. M: 444.45.
Production:
• bromamine acid (condensation/desulphonation)
Uses:
plastics colorant

Pigment Red 178
Paliogen Red K3911HD (BASF)

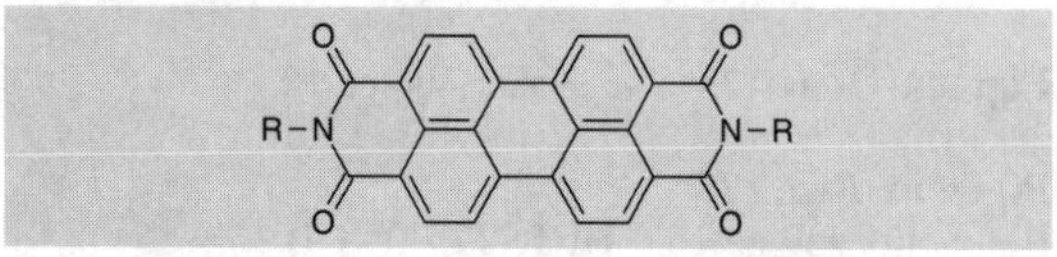

R = *p*-azobenzene-. $C_{48}H_{26}N_6O_4$. M: 750.78.
Production:
• perylenetetracarboxylic anhydride + *p*-phenyl-
azoaniline (amide formation)
Uses: plastics colorant

Pigment Red 179
Perylene Maroon; Vat Red 23 (CI); 71130 (CI)

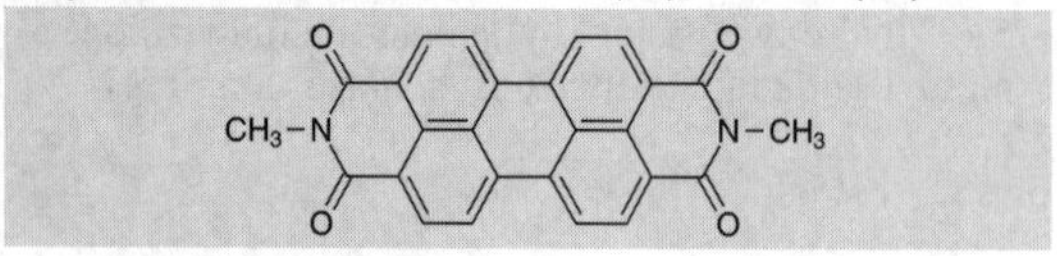

$C_{26}H_{14}N_2O_4$. M: 418.41.
Production:
• perylenetetracarboxylic anhydride + methylamine
(methylation)
Uses:
dye (cotton); pigment (industrial/vehicle/architectural
paints, plastics, printing inks)

Pigment Red 184
Naphthol Rubine F6B

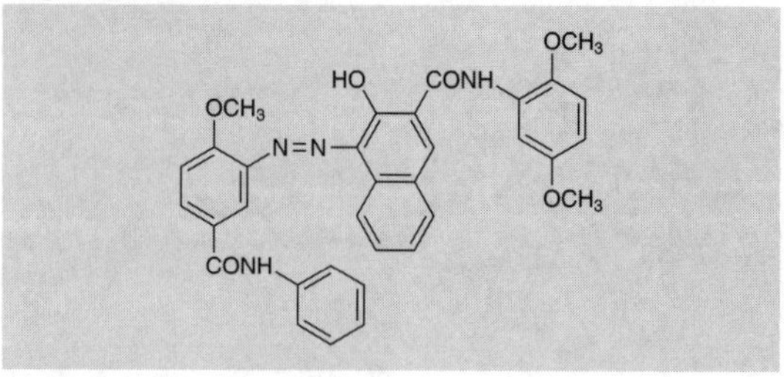

$C_{33}H_{28}N_4O_6$. M: 576.60.
Production:
• 3-amino-4-methoxybenzoic acid + aniline +
β-oxynaphthoic acid + 2,5-dimethoxyaniline
(amide formation/amide formation/diazotisation/
azo coupling)
Uses: pigment (printing inks, lacquers, plastics)

Pigment Red 185
Benzimidazolone Carmine HF4C; 12516 (CI)

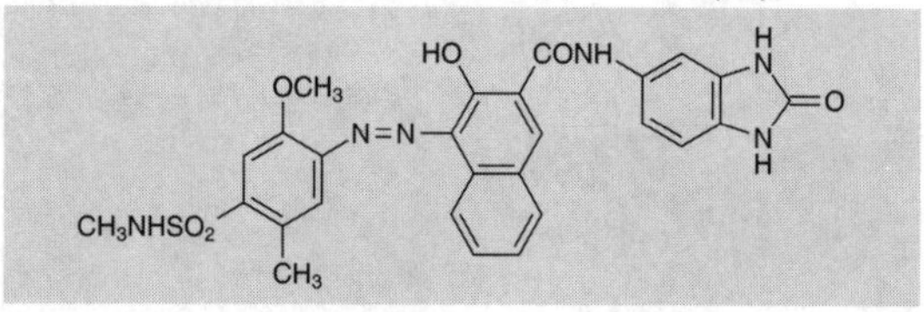

$C_{27}H_{24}N_6O_6S_1$. M: 560.58.
Production:
• 5-amino-4-methoxytoluene-2-sulphonic acid +
methylamine + 5-(2'-hydroxy-3'-naphthoyl)amino-
benzimidazolone (sulphonamide formation/
diazotisation/azo coupling)
Uses:
pigment (printing inks, lacquers, resins, plastics)

Pigment Red 187
12486 (CI)

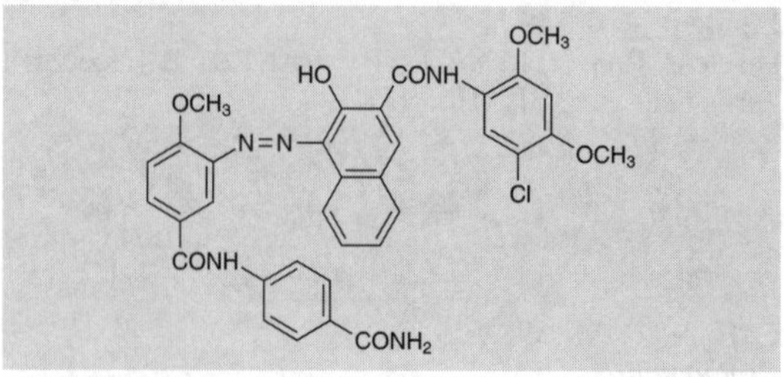

$C_{34}H_{28}Cl_1N_5O_7$. M: 654.06.
Production:
• 3-amino-4-methoxybenzoic acid + *p*-amino-
benzamide + 5-chloro-2,4-dimethoxy-3'-hydroxy-
2'-naphthanilide (diazotisation/azo coupling/amide
formation)
Uses: pigment (paints, lacquers)

Pigment Red 188
12467 (CI)

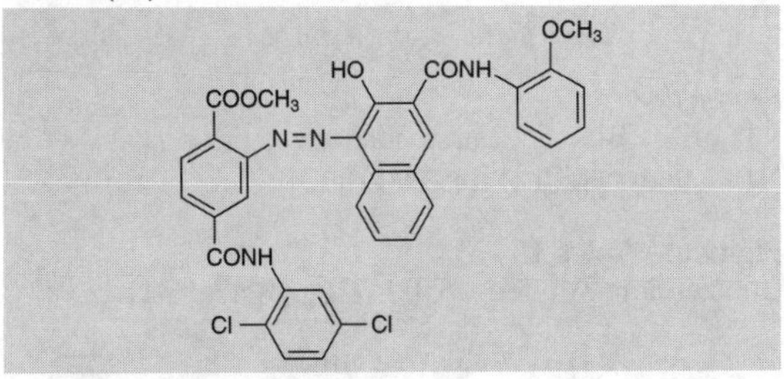

$C_{33}H_{24}Cl_2N_4O_6$. M: 643.48.
Production:
- dimethyl terephthalate + 2,5-dichloroaniline + 3-hydroxy-2-naphth-*o*-anisidide (nitration/nitro reduction/amide formation/diazotisation/ azo coupling)

Uses: pigment (plastics, lacquers, printing inks)

Pigment Red 189 *See:* Vat Red 32

Pigment Red 190
Vat Red 29 (CI); 71140 (CI)

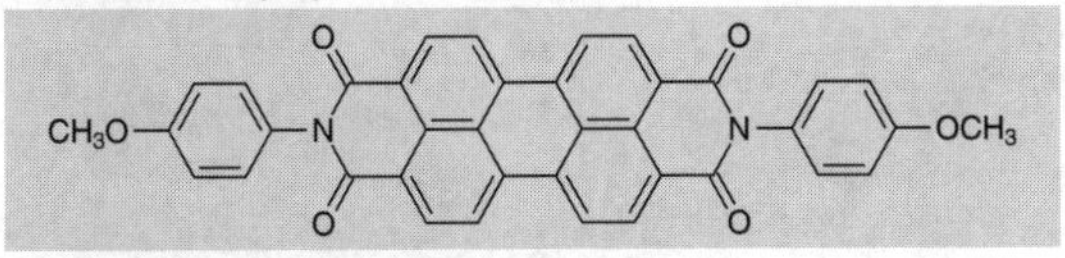

$C_{38}H_{22}N_2O_6$. M: 602.60.
Production:
- perylenetetracarboxylic anhydride + *p*-anisidine (amide formation)

Uses: pigment (plastics, industrial/vehicle/architectural paints, printing inks); vat dye (cotton)

Pigment Red 193 *See:* Acid Red 27

Pigment Red 194 *See:* Vat Red 15

Pigment Red 195 *See:* Vat Red 13

Pigment Red 200
Rubine Red 6B; 15867 (CI)

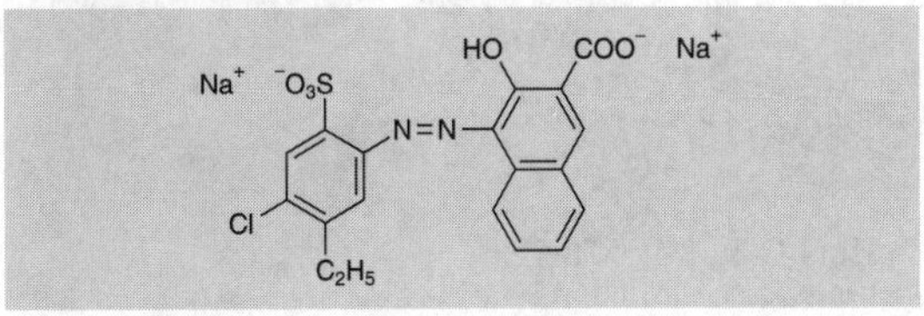

$C_{19}H_{13}Cl_1Na_2O_6S_1$. M: 450.79.
Production:
- 5-amino-2-chloroethylbenzene-4-sulphonic acid + β-oxynaphthoic acid (diazotisation/azo coupling/ sodium salt formation)

Uses: pigment (printing inks)

Pigment Red 202 *See:* 2,9-dichloroquinacridone

Pigment Red 208
Benzimidazolone Red HF2B; 12514 (CI)

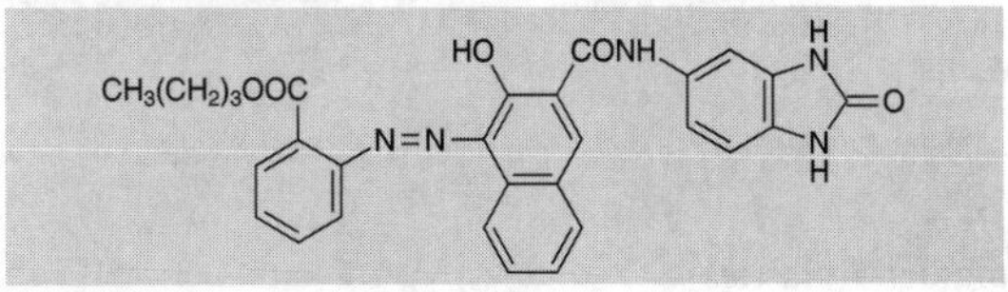

$C_{29}H_{25}N_5O_5$. M: 523.55.
Production:
- anthranilic acid + *n*-butanol + 5-(2′-hydroxy-3′-naphthoyl)aminobenzimidazolone (esterification/ diazotisation/azo coupling)

Uses: pigment (plastics, printing inks)

Pigment Red 209 *See:* 3,10-dichloroquinacridone

Pigment Red 214

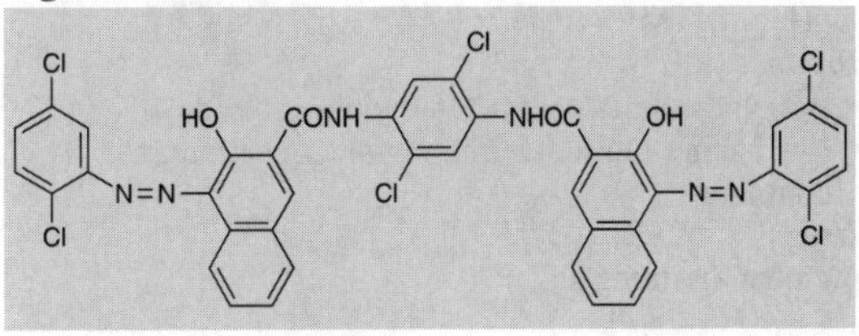

$C_{40}H_{22}Cl_6N_6O_4$. M: 863.38.
Production:
- 2,5-dichloro-*p*-phenylenediamine + β-oxynaphthoic acid + 2,5-dichloroaniline (amide formation/ diazotisation/azo coupling)

Uses: pigment (paints, plastics)

Pigment Red 216
Vat Orange 4 (CI); 59710 (CI)

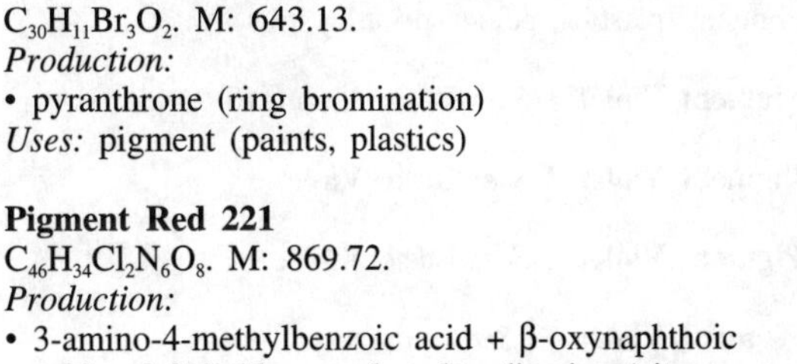

$C_{30}H_{11}Br_3O_2$. M: 643.13.
Production:
- pyranthrone (ring bromination)

Uses: pigment (paints, plastics)

Pigment Red 221
$C_{46}H_{34}Cl_2N_6O_8$. M: 869.72.
Production:
- 3-amino-4-methylbenzoic acid + β-oxynaphthoic acid + 2,5-dichloro-*p*-phenylenediamine (nitro reduction/diazotisation/azo coupling/amide formation)

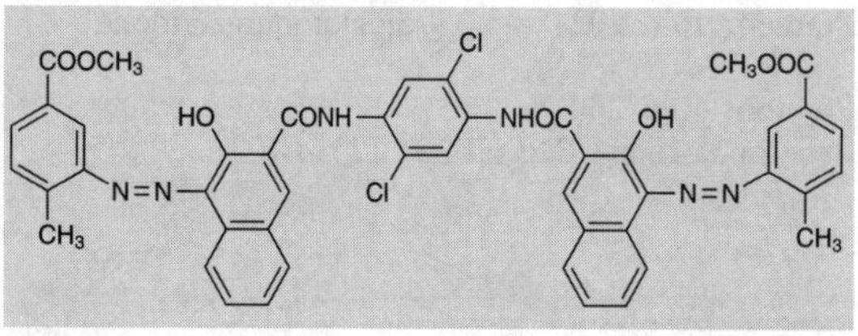

Uses:
pigment (plastics)

Pigment Red 222
Azo Magenta G (CI)

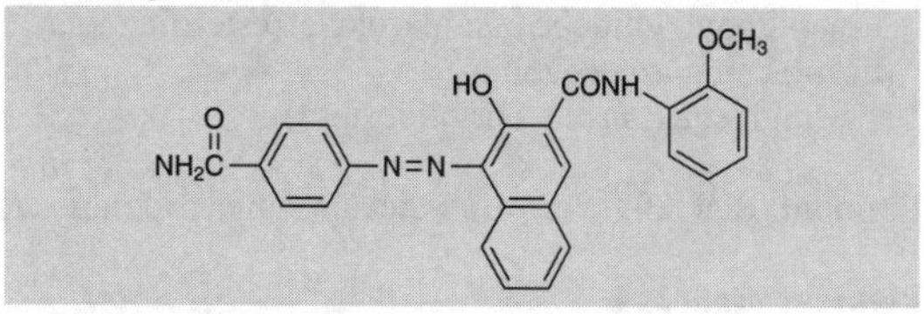

$C_{25}H_{20}N_4O_4$. M: 440.46.
Production:
• β-oxynaphthoic acid + p-aminobenzamide + o-anisidine (amide formation/diazotisation/azo coupling)
Uses:
pigment (printing inks)

Pigment Red 224
See: perylenetetracarboxylic anhydride

Pigment Red 242

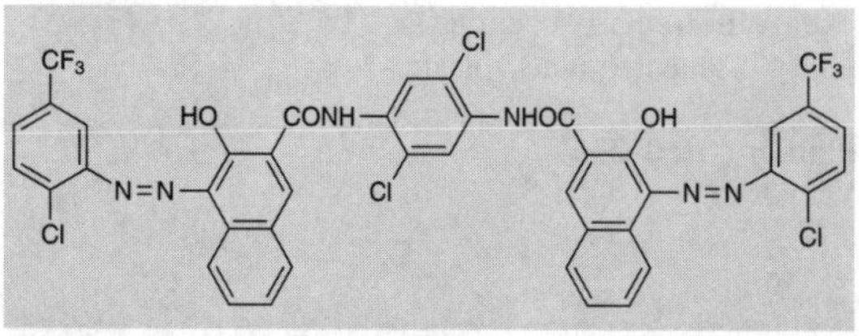

$C_{42}H_{22}Cl_4F_6N_6O_4$. M: 930.48.
Production:
• 3-amino-4-chlorobenzotrifluoride + β-oxynaphthoic acid + 2,5-dichloro-p-phenylenediamine (diazotisation/azo coupling/amide formation)
Uses:
pigment (plastics, paints, printing inks)

Pigment Violet 1 See: Basic Violet 10

Pigment Violet 3 See: Basic Violet 1

Pigment Violet 4 See: Basic Violet 14

Pigment Violet 12 See: quinizarin

Pigment Violet 14 See: cobalt phosphate

Pigment Violet 15
Ultramarine Violet; 77007 (CI); [12769-96-9]

$$Na_{4-6}H_2Al_6Si_6S_2O_{24}$$

Production:
• Pigment Blue 29 (air oxidation)
Uses: pigment (printing inks)

Pigment Violet 19
Quinacridone Violet; 46500 (CI); [1047-16-1]

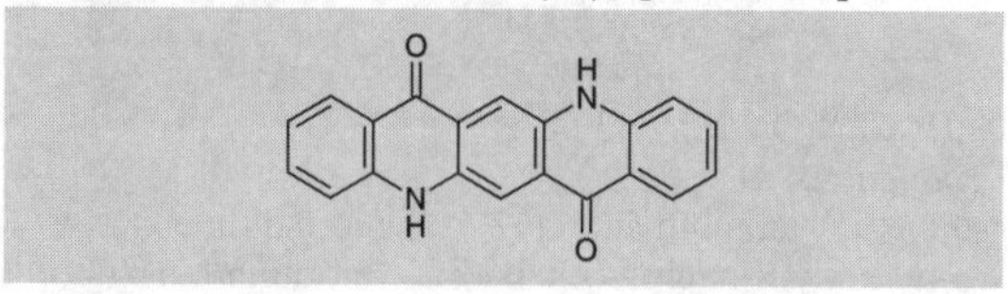

$C_{20}H_{12}N_2O_2$. M: 312.33.
Production:
• dimethyl succinylosuccinate + aniline (amine formation/condensation)
Uses: pigment (paints, printing inks, enamels, lacquers)

Pigment Violet 23
Carbazole Violet; Dioxazine Violet RL; 51319 (CI)

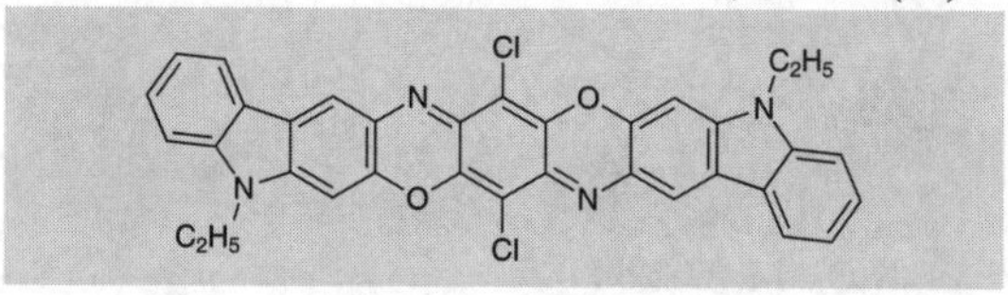

$C_{34}H_{22}Cl_2N_4O_2$. M: 589.49.
Production:
• 3-amino-N-ethylcarbazole + chloranil (amine formation/carbonyl condensation)
Uses: pigment (paints, printing inks, lacquers, plastics)

Pigment Violet 27 See: Basic Violet 1

Pigment Violet 29 See: perylimide

Pigment Violet 32
Benzimidazolone Bordeaux HF3R; 12517 (CI)

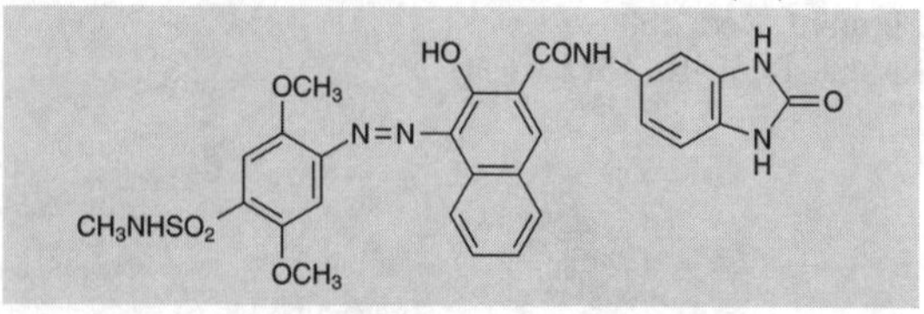

$C_{27}H_{24}N_6O_7S_1$. M: 576.58.
Production:
• 4-amino-2,5-dimethoxybenzenesulphonic acid + methylamine + 5-(2'-hydroxy-3'-naphthoyl)amino-benzimidazolone (sulphonamide formation/diazotisation/azo coupling)
Uses:
pigment (printing inks, paints, plastics)

Pigment Violet 37
Dioxazine Violet B; 51319 (CI)

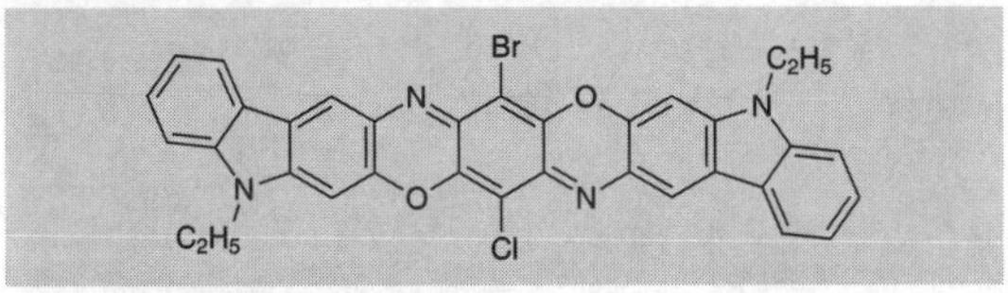

$C_{34}H_{22}Br_1Cl_1N_4O_2$. M: 633.93.
Production:
• chloranil + 3-amino-*N*-ethylcarbazole + sodium bromide (amine formation/carbonyl condensation/halogen exchange)
Uses: pigment (printing inks, paints, plastics)

Pigment Violet 39 *See:* Basic Violet 3

Pigment White 1 *See:* lead carbonate, basic

Pigment White 2 *See:* lead sulphate, monobasic

Pigment White 4 *See:* zinc oxide

Pigment White 5 *See:* lithopone

Pigment White 6 *See:* titanium dioxide

Pigment White 7 *See:* zinc sulphide

Pigment White 11 *See:* antimony trioxide

Pigment White 18 *See:* calcite; calcium carbonate

Pigment White 19 *See:* kaolin

Pigment White 21 *See:* blanc fixe

Pigment White 24 *See:* alumina trihydrate

Pigment White 26 *See:* talc

Pigment White 27 *See:* silica, fumed

Pigment White 32 *See:* zinc phosphate

Pigment Yellow 1
Arylamide Yellow G; 11680 (CI); [2512-29-0]

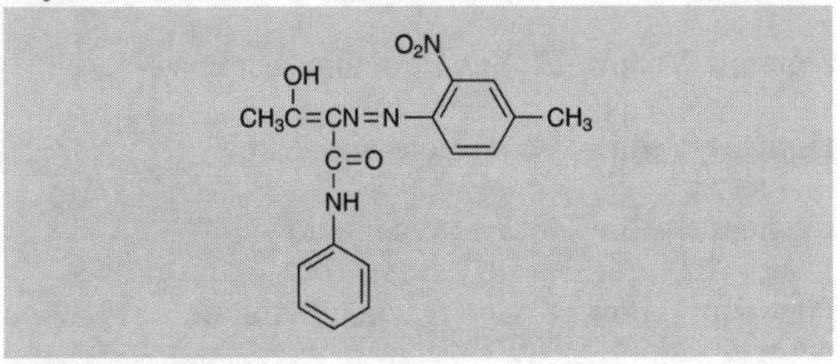

$C_{17}H_{16}N_4O_4$. M: 340.35.

Production:
• 4-amino-3-nitrotoluene + acetoacetanilide (diazotisation/azo coupling)
Uses:
pigment (paints, resins, printing inks)

Pigment Yellow 3
Arylamide Yellow 10G; 11710 (CI); [6486-23-3]

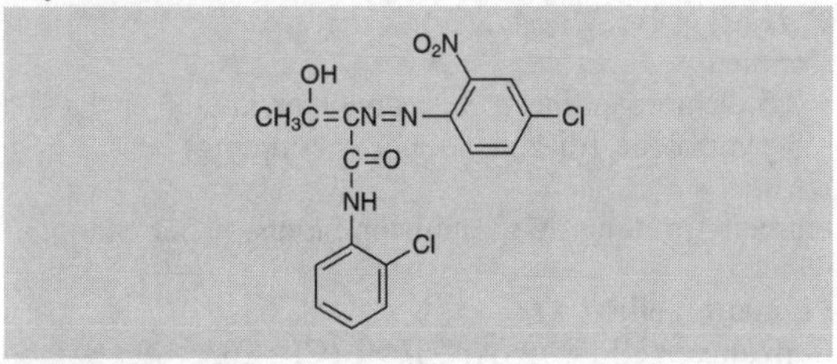

$C_{16}H_{12}Cl_2N_4O_4$. M: 395.22.
Production:
• 4-chloro-2-nitroaniline + acetoacet-*o*-chloroanilide (diazotisation/azo coupling)
Uses:
pigment (paints, printing inks)

Pigment Yellow 4
Arylamide Yellow 13G; 11665 (CI)

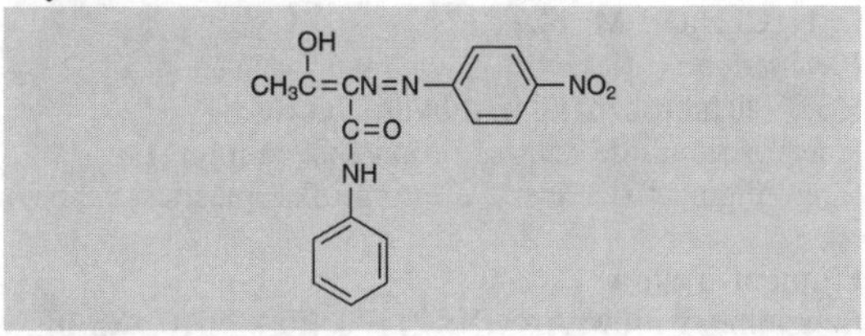

$C_{16}H_{14}N_4O_4$. M: 326.32.
Production:
• *p*-nitroaniline + acetoacetanilide (diazotisation/azo coupling)
Uses:
pigment (printing inks)

Pigment Yellow 5
Arylide Yellow 5G; 11660 (CI)

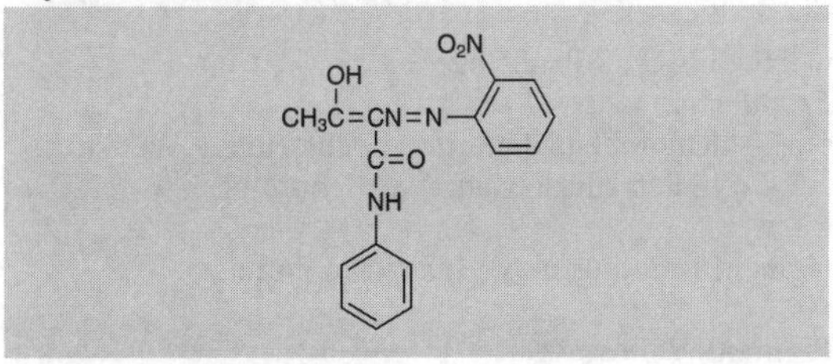

$C_{16}H_{14}N_4O_4$. M: 326.32.
Production:
• *o*-nitroaniline + acetoacetanilide (diazotisation/azo coupling)
Uses: pigment (printing inks)

Pigment Yellow 10
12710 (CI)

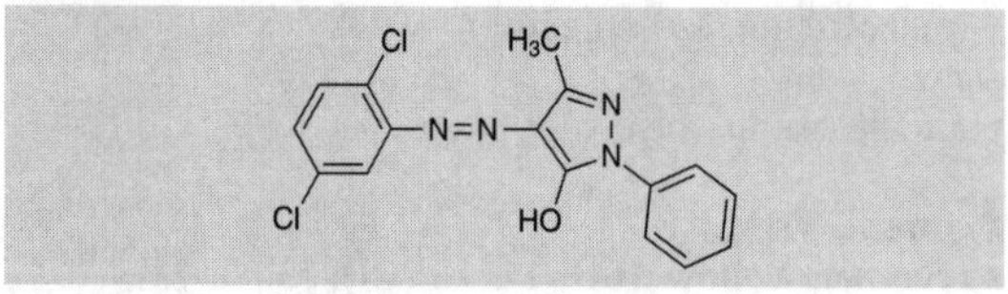

$C_{16}H_{12}Cl_2N_4O_1$. M: 347.22.
Production:
- 2,5-dichloroaniline + 3-methyl-1-phenyl-
  5-pyrazolone (diazotisation/azo coupling)

Uses:
pigment (printing inks, emulsion paints, paper coatings)

Pigment Yellow 12
Benzidine Yellow AAA; 21090 (CI); [6358-85-6]

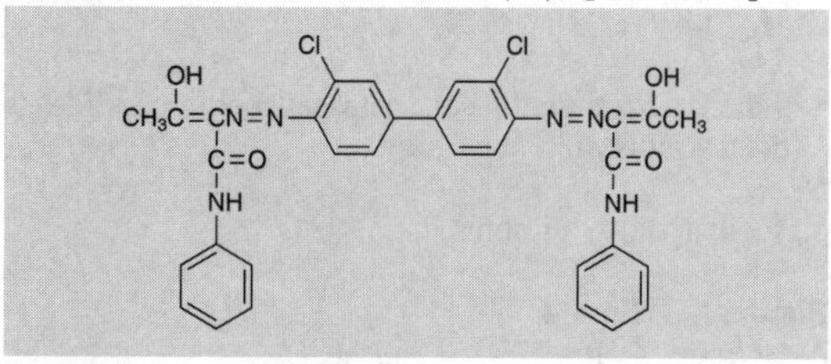

$C_{32}H_{26}Cl_2N_6O_4$. M: 629.51.
Production:
- 3,3'-dichlorobenzidine dihydrochloride +
  acetoacetanilide (diazotisation/azo coupling)

Uses: pigment (lacquers, printing inks, plastics, rubber)

Pigment Yellow 13
Benzidine Yellow AAMX; 21100 (CI); [5102-83-0]

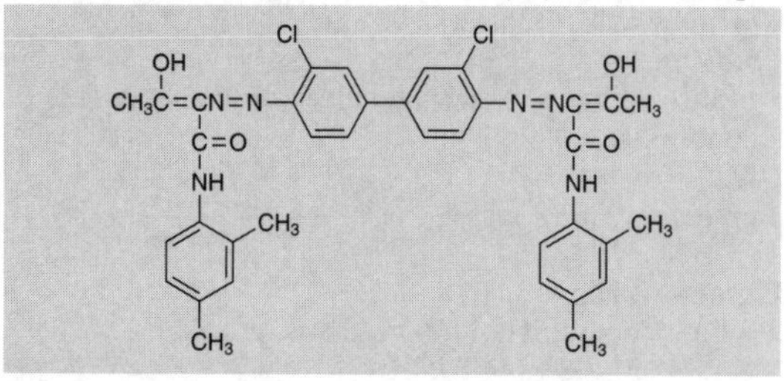

$C_{36}H_{34}Cl_2N_6O_4$. M: 685.62.
Production:
- 3,3'-dichlorobenzidine dihydrochloride + acetoacet-
  2,4-xylidide (diazotisation/azo coupling)

Uses:
pigment (printing inks); plastics colorant

Pigment Yellow 14
Benzidine Yellow AAOT; 21095 (CI)
$C_{34}H_{30}Cl_2N_6O_4$. M: 657.56.
Production:
- 3,3'-dichlorobenzidine dihydrochloride +
  acetoacet-*o*-toluidide (diazotisation/azo coupling)

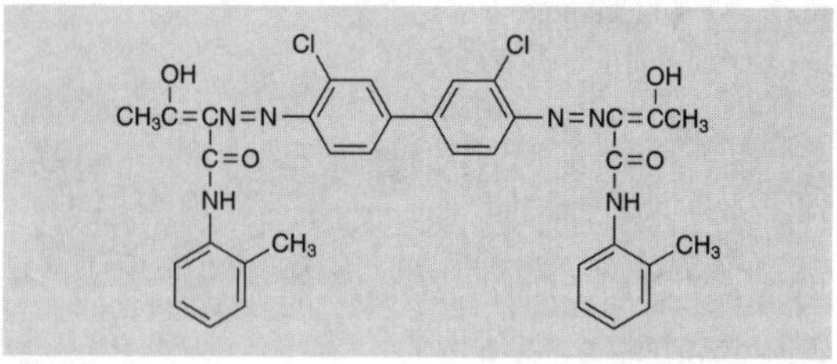

Uses:
pigment (printing inks, resins, plastics, rubber)

Pigment Yellow 17
Benzidine Yellow AAOA; 21105 (CI)

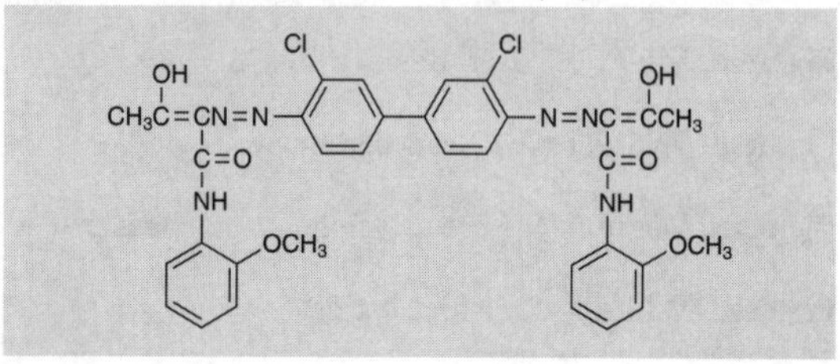

$C_{34}H_{30}Cl_2N_6O_6$. M: 689.55.
Production:
- 3,3'-dichlorobenzidine dihydrochloride +
  acetoacet-*o*-anisidide (diazotisation/azo coupling)

Uses: pigment (printing inks)

Pigment Yellow 18
49005:1 (CI)

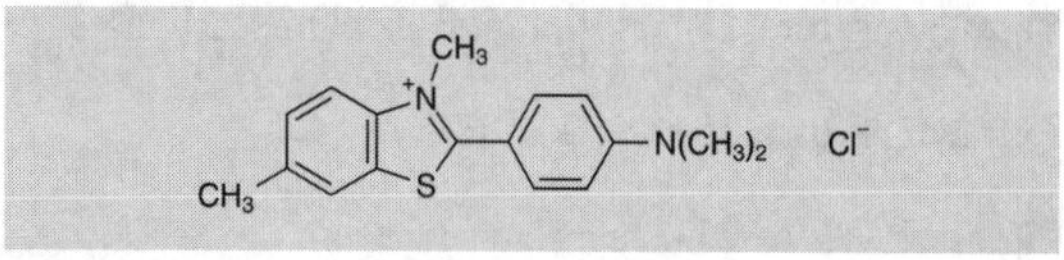

The pigment is the PMTA salt of the displayed
structure.
Production:
- *p*-toluidine + sulphur + dimethyl sulphate + (bake
  process/methylation)

Uses:
Pigment Green 2 component; pigment (printing inks)

Pigment Yellow 24 *See:* flavanthrone

Pigment Yellow 31 *See:* barium chromate

Pigment Yellow 32 *See:* strontium chromate

Pigment Yellow 34 *See:* chrome yellow

Pigment Yellow 36 *See:* zinc yellow

Pigment Yellow 37 *See:* cadmium yellow

Pigment Yellow 42 *See:* iron oxide yellow

Pigment Yellow 53 *See:* titanium nickel yellow

Pigment Yellow 55
Benzidine Yellow AAPT; 21096 (CI)

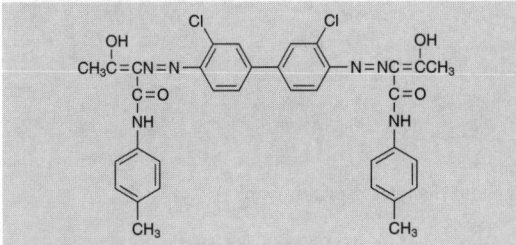

$C_{34}H_{30}Cl_2N_6O_4$. M: 657.56.
Production:
• 3,3′-dichlorobenzidine dihydrochloride +
  acetoacet-*p*-toluidide (diazotisation/azo coupling)
Uses:
pigment (printing inks)

Pigment Yellow 60
Arylamide Yellow 4R; 12705 (CI)

$C_{16}H_{13}Cl_1N_4O_1$. M: 312.76.
Production:
• *o*-chloroaniline + 3-methyl-1-phenyl-5-pyrazolone
  (diazotisation/azo coupling)
Uses:
pigment (printing inks, lacquers, stains, plastics)

Pigment Yellow 63
21091 (CI)

$C_{32}H_{24}Cl_4N_6O_4$. M: 698.39.
Production:
• 3,3′-dichlorobenzidine dihydrochloride +
  acetoacet-*o*-chloroanilide (diazotisation/azo coupling)
Uses:
pigment (printing inks, lacquers, resins, rubber, paper)

Pigment Yellow 65
Arylamide Yellow RN; 11740 (CI)
$C_{18}H_{18}N_4O_6$. M: 386.36.

Production:
• 4-amino-3-nitroanisole + acetoacet-*o*-anisidide
  (diazotisation/azo coupling)
Uses:
pigment (emulsion paints)

Pigment Yellow 73
Arylamide Yellow GX; 11738 (CI); [13515-40-7]

$C_{17}H_{15}Cl_1N_4O_5$. M: 390.78.
Production:
• 4-chloro-2-nitroaniline + acetoacet-*o*-anisidide
  (diazotisation/azo coupling)
Uses:
pigment (paints, rubber, printing inks)

Pigment Yellow 74
Arylamide Yellow 5GX; 11741 (CI)

$C_{18}H_{18}N_4O_6$. M: 386.36.
Production:
• 2-amino-5-nitroanisole + acetoacet-*o*-anisidide
  (diazotisation/azo coupling)
Uses:
pigment (printing inks)

Pigment Yellow 75
11770 (CI)
$C_{18}H_{17}Cl_1N_4O_5$. M: 404.81.
Production:
• 4-chloro-2-nitroaniline + acetoacet-*p*-phenetidide
  (diazotisation/azo coupling)

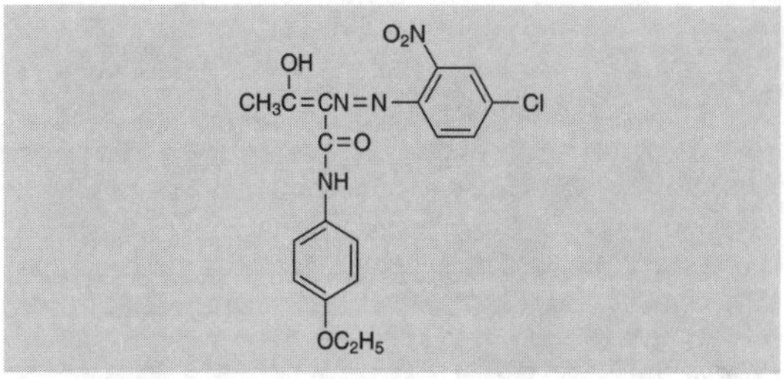

Uses: pigment (paints, printing inks)

Pigment Yellow 81
Diarylide Yellow H10G; PV Yellow H10G (Hoechst)

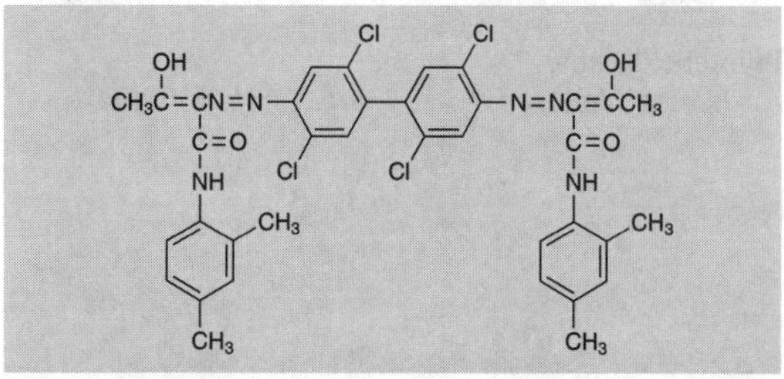

$C_{36}H_{32}Cl_4N_6O_4$. M: 754.51.
Production:
- 2,2',5,5'-tetrachlorobenzidine + acetoacet-2,4-xylidide (diazotisation/azo coupling)

Uses: plastics colorant

Pigment Yellow 83
Benzidine Yellow AADMC; 21108 (CI)

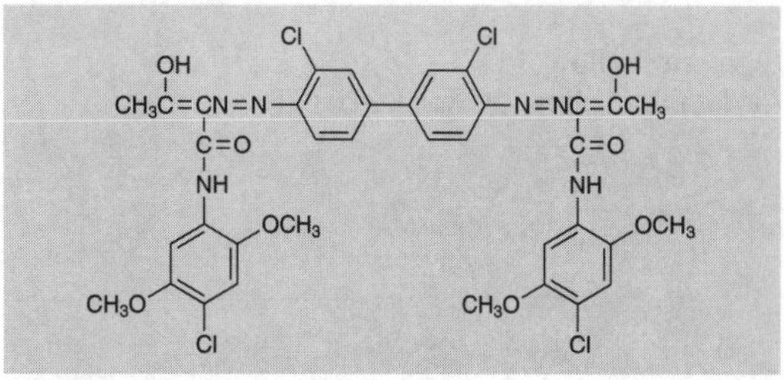

$C_{36}H_{32}Cl_4N_6O_8$. M: 818.50.
Production:
- 3,3'-dichlorobenzidine dihydrochloride + acetoacet-4-chloro-2,5-dimethoxyanilide (diazotisation/azo coupling)

Uses:
pigment (printing inks, plastics)

Pigment Yellow 97
Arylide Yellow FGL; 11767 (CI)
$C_{26}H_{27}Cl_1N_4O_8S_1$. M: 591.04.
Production:
- acetoacet-4-chloro-2,5-dimethoxyanilide + 4-amino-2,5-dimethoxybenzenesulphonic acid + aniline (sulphonamide formation/diazotisation/azo coupling)

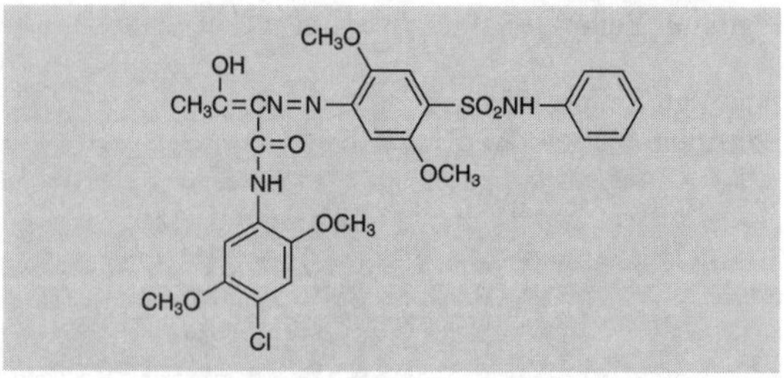

Uses:
pigment (lacquers, printing inks)

Pigment Yellow 100 *See:* tartrazine

Pigment Yellow 101
Fluorescent Yellow; Brilliant Yellow 8GF; 48052 (CI)

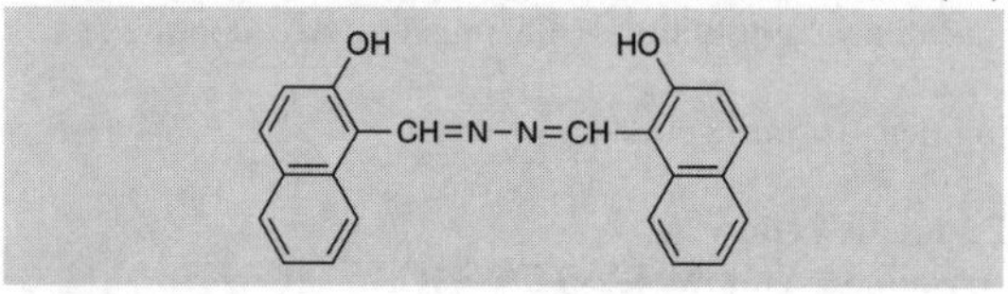

$C_{22}H_{16}N_2O_2$. M: 340.38.
Production:
- 2-hydroxy-1-naphthaldehyde + hydrazine (imine formation)
Uses:
fluorescent pigment (printing inks, paints, lacquers)

Pigment Yellow 104 *See:* Food Yellow 3

Pigment Yellow 108 *See:* Vat Yellow 20

Pigment Yellow 110
Tetrachloroisoindolinone Yellow 2RLTS; Chromophtal Yellow 2RLTS (Ciba-Geigy); Irgazin Yellow 3RLTN (Ciba-Geigy)

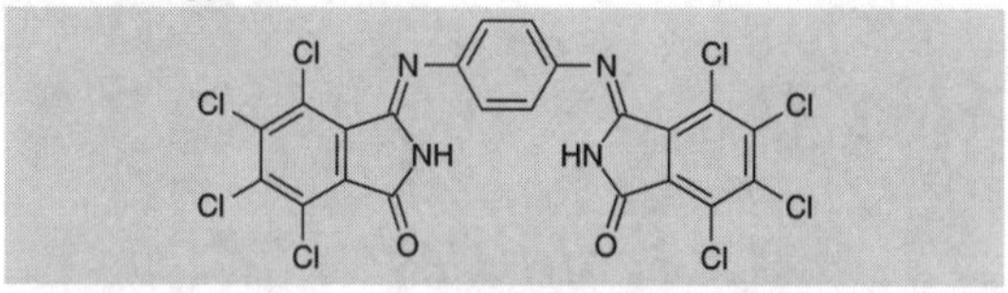

$C_{22}H_6Cl_8N_4O_2$. M: 641.94.
Production:
- *p*-phenylenediamine + 3,3,4,5,6,7-hexachloro-isoindolinone (imine formation)
Uses:
plastics colorant

Pigment Yellow 113
21126 (CI)
$C_{34}H_{26}Cl_6N_6O_4$. M: 795.34.
Production:
- 2,2',5,5'-tetrachlorobenzidine + acetoacet-4-chloro-2-methylanilide (diazotisation/azo coupling)

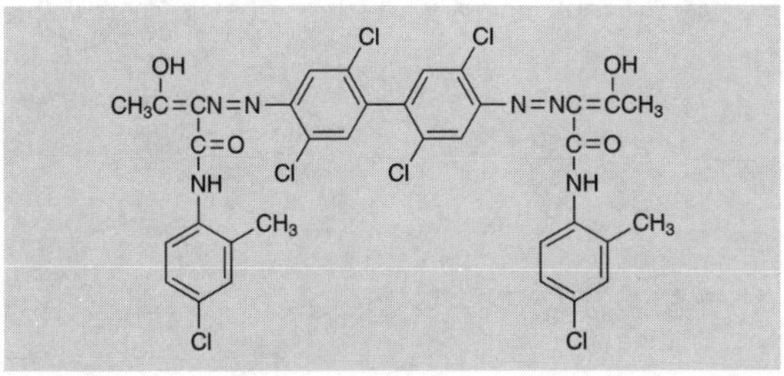

Uses: pigment (printing inks)

Pigment Yellow 115 *See:* Acid Yellow 3

Pigment Yellow 118
See: chrome antimony titanium buff

Pigment Yellow 119
See: zinc ferrite

Pigment Yellow 120
Benzimidazolone Yellow H2G; 11783 (CI); PV Fast Yellow H2G (Hoechst)

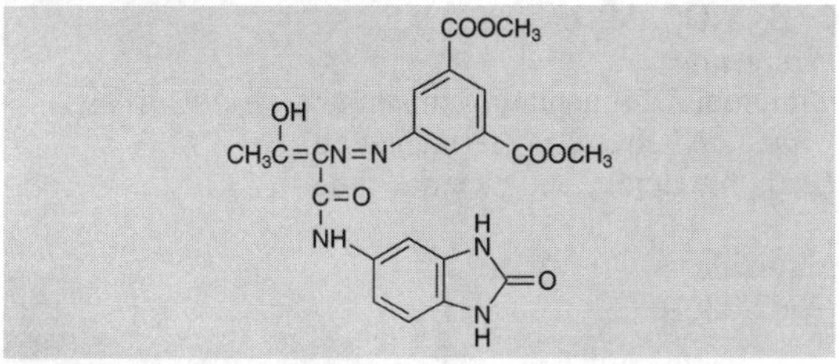

$C_{21}H_{19}N_5O_7$. M: 453.41. Orange solid.
Production:
• 5-aminoisophthalic acid + methanol + 5-acetoacetamidobenzimidazolone (esterification/diazotisation/azo coupling)
Uses: pigment (paints, plastics)

Pigment Yellow 124
21107 (CI)

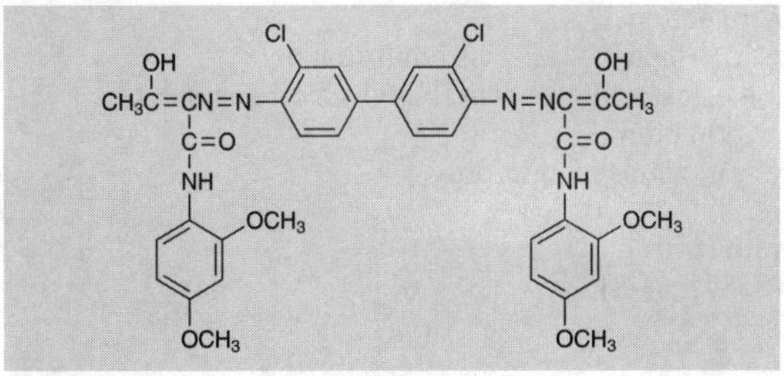

$C_{36}H_{34}Cl_2N_6O_8$. M: 749.61.
Production:
• diketene + 2,4-dimethoxyaniline + 3,3'-dichlorobenzidine dihydrochloride (amide formation/diazotisation/azo coupling)
Uses: pigment (printing inks)

Pigment Yellow 127

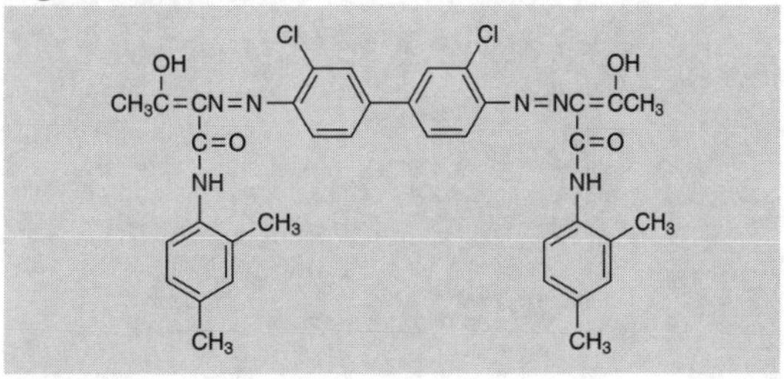

$C_{36}H_{34}Cl_2N_6O_4$. M: 685.62.
Production:
• 3,3'-dichlorobenzidine dihydrochloride + acetoacet-2,4-xylidide (diazotisation/azo coupling)
Uses: pigment (plastics)

Pigment Yellow 138 *See:* quinophthalone

Pigment Yellow 139
Paliotol Yellow K1841D (BASF)

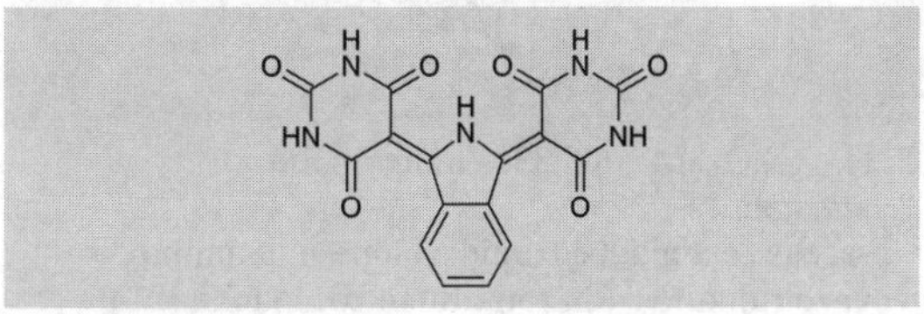

$C_{16}H_9N_5O_6$. M: 367.28.
Production:
• 1,3-diiminoisoindoline + barbituric acid (carbonyl condensation)
Uses: pigment (paints, plastics)

Pigment Yellow 151
Benzimidazolone Yellow H4G; Hostaperm Yellow H4G (Hoechst)

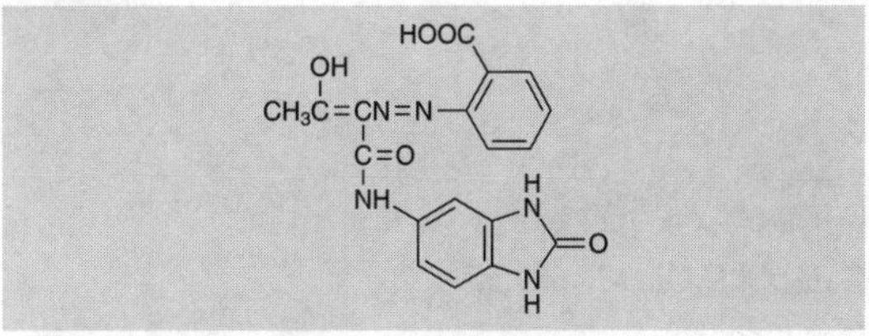

$C_{18}H_{15}N_5O_5$. M: 381.35. Orange solid.
Production:
• 5-acetoacetamidobenzimidazolone + anthranilic acid (diazotisation/azo coupling)
Uses: pigment (paints, plastics)

Pigment Yellow 152
$C_{36}H_{34}Cl_2N_6O_6$. M: 717.61.
Production:
• diketene + *p*-phenetidine + 3,3'-dichlorobenzidine dihydrochloride (amide formation/diazotisation/azo coupling)

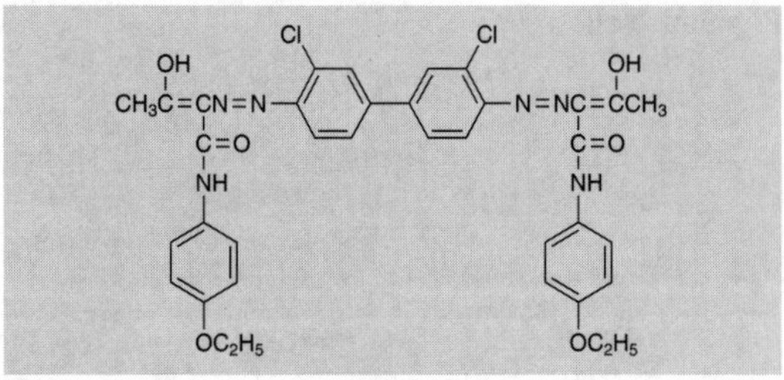

Uses:
pigment (paints, printing inks)

Pigment Yellow 154
Benzimidazolone Yellow H3G; Hostaperm Yellow H3G (Hoechst)

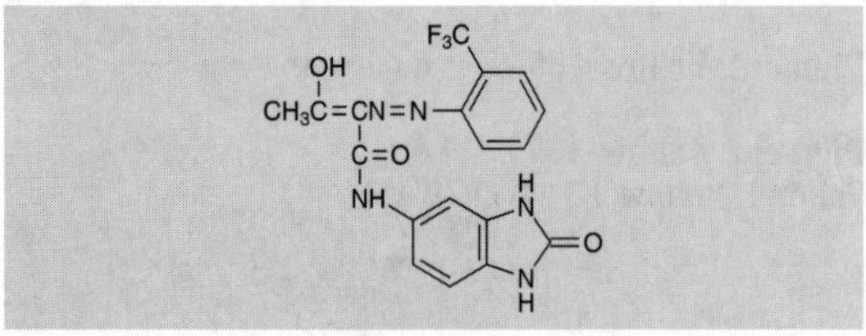

$C_{18}H_{14}F_3N_5O_3$. M: 405.33. Orange solid.
Production:
• 5-acetoacetamidobenzimidazolone + *o*-amino-benzotrifluoride (diazotisation/azo coupling)
Uses:
pigment (paints, plastics)

Pigment Yellow 170
21104 (CI)

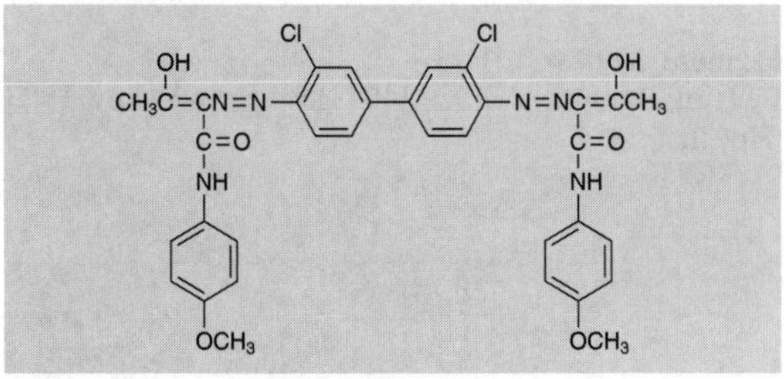

$C_{34}H_{30}Cl_2N_6O_6$. M: 689.55.
Production:
• diketene + *p*-anisidine + 3,3′-dichlorobenzidine dihydrochloride (amide formation/diazotisation/azo coupling)
Uses:
pigment (printing inks)

Pigment Yellow 171
21106 (CI)
$C_{34}H_{28}Cl_4N_6O_4$. M: 726.45.
Production:
• 3,3′-dichlorobenzidine dihydrochloride + acetoacet-4-chloro-2-methylanilide (diazotisation/azo coupling)

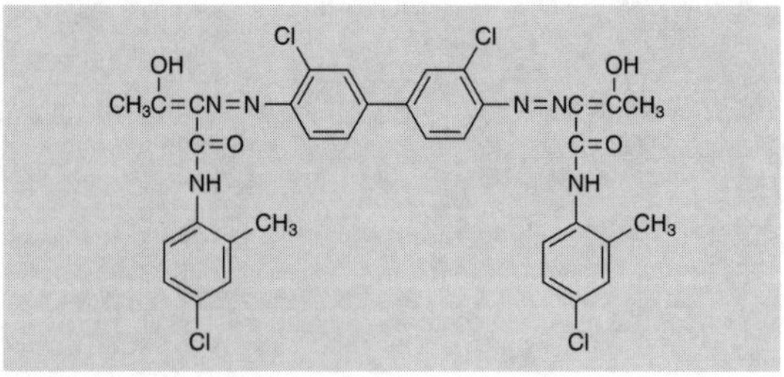

Uses: pigment (plastics)

pimaricin
natamycin; [7681-93-8]

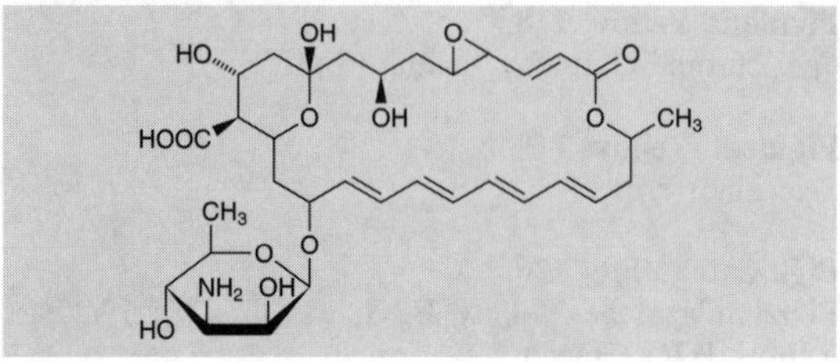

$C_{33}H_{47}N_1O_{13}$. M: 665.74.
Production:
• microbial fermentation medium + *Streptomyces natalensis* bacteria (fermentation)
Uses: fungicide; antibacterial drug

pimozide
[2062-78-4]

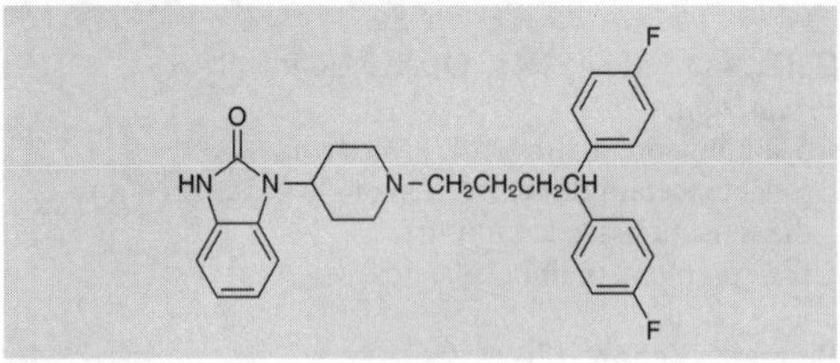

$C_{28}H_{29}F_2N_3O_1$. M: 461.56.
Production:
• 1-(4-piperidyl)-2-benzodiazolinone + 4,4-bis(*p*-fluorophenyl)butyl chloride (amine formation)
Uses: antipsychotic drug

pinacidil
[85371-64-8]

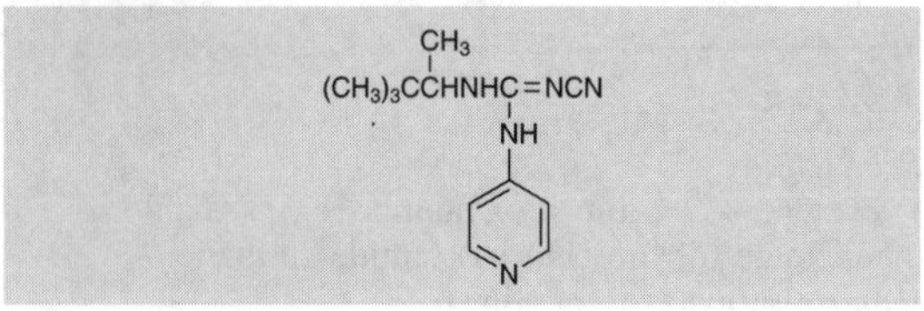

$C_{13}H_{19}N_5$. M: 245.32.

Production:
- pinacolone + ammonia + *N*-cyanoimido-*S,S*-dimethyldithiocarbamate + 4-aminopyridine (amine formation/amine formation/amine formation)

Uses: antihypertensive drug

pinacolone
3,3-dimethylbutan-2-one; methyl *t*-butyl ketone; 1,1,1-trimethylacetone; [75-97-8]

$$O$$
$$(CH_3)_3C\overset{\parallel}{C}CH_3$$

$C_6H_{12}O_1$. M: 100.17. Liquid with a mint-like odour. BP: 105–106°C. MP: -53°C. d: 0.80 kg/l (25°C). Slightly soluble in water. Soluble in oxygenated solvents.
Production:
- pivalic acid + acetic anhydride (decarboxylation)

Derivatives:
buprenorphine; α-chloropinacolone; pinacidil; pindone

pinane
2,6,6-trimethylbicyclo[3.1.1]heptane

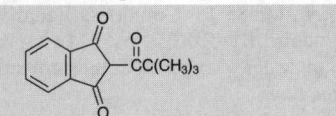

$C_{10}H_{18}$. M: 138.25. The standard product is the *cis*-isomer. Not commercially traded.
Production:
- α-pinene (hydrogenation)

Derivatives: dihydromyrcenol; linalool

pindone
2-pivaloyl-1,3-indanedione; [83-26-1]

$C_{14}H_{14}O_3$. M: 230.26.
Production:
- pinacolone + diethyl phthalate (carbonyl condensation)

Uses: rodenticide

pine gum
pine balsam; turpentine gum
Pine gum is the exuded oleoresin from living trees of the *Pinus* species. China, Brazil, France and Portugal are important producing countries.
Derivatives:
dipentene; pine oil; rosin, gum; turpentine oil, gum

α-pinene
2,6,6-trimethylbicyclo[3.1.1]hept-2-ene; [80-56-8]
$C_{10}H_{16}$. M: 136.24. Colourless liquid. BP: 156°C. MP: -50°C. d: 0.86 kg/l (20°C). Insoluble in water. Soluble

in oxygenated and chlorinated solvents. The ratio of the two enantiomers in the product varies with the source of the turpentine oil.

Production:
- turpentine oil, wood (fractionation/isomerisation; coproduced with β-pinene)
- turpentine oil, sulphate (fractionation; coproduced with β-pinene)

Derivatives: camphene; campholenic aldehyde; fenchone; pinane; terpene resins

β-pinene
nopinene; 6,6-dimethyl-2-methylene[3.1.1]heptane; [127-91-3]

$C_{10}H_{16}$. M: 136.24. Colourless liquid with a terpene-like odour. Most commonly available as the (–)-isomer. BP: 163°C. d: 0.87 kg/l (15°C). Insoluble in water. Soluble in most organic solvents.
Production:
- turpentine oil, wood (fractionation/isomerisation; coproduced with α-pinene)
- turpentine oil, sulphate (fractionation; coproduced with α-pinene)

Derivatives:
bornyl acetate; myrcene; nopyl acetate; terpene resins
Uses: fragrance ingredient (technical products)

pine oil
[8002-09-3]
Yellowish liquid with turpentine-like odour. d: 0.93 kg/l. BP: 200–225°C. Insoluble in water.
Production:
- sulphate pulp black liquor evaporator condensate (separation/fractionation; coproduced with turpentine oil, sulphate)
- pinewood stumps (steam distillation; coproduced with turpentine oil, wood/dipentene/rosin, wood)
- pine gum (fractionation; coproduced with dipentene/rosin, gum/turpentine oil, gum)
- pyrolysis oil, pinewood (fractionation; coproduced with turpentine oil, wood/wood pitch/tar oil, wood)

Derivatives:
anethole; 3-carene; dipentene; α-terpineol
Uses:
flotation frothing agent; sanitiser/fragrance ingredient (cleaning/disinfectant formulations, paints); non-reactive epoxy resin diluent

PIP *See:* piperazine

pipazetate
pipazethate; [2167-85-3]; [6056-11-7] (hydrochloride)

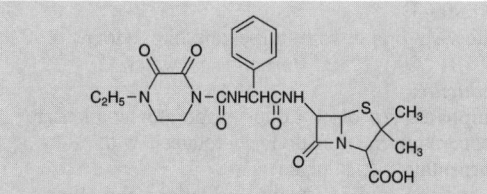

$C_{21}H_{25}N_3O_3S_1$. M: 399.51. Available commercially as the hydrochloride.
Production:
- piperidine + ethylene oxide + 1-azaphenothiazine + phosgene (epoxidation/phosgenation/dehydrochlorination)

Uses: antitussive drug

α-pipecoline *See:* 2-methylpiperidine

pipemidic acid
[51940-44-4]

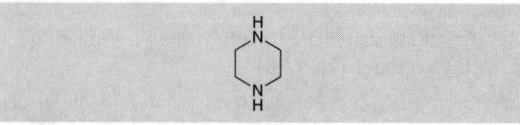

$C_{14}H_{17}N_5O_3$. M: 303.32.
Production:
- acrylonitrile + *O*-methylisourea sulphate + diethyl ethoxymethylenemalonate + piperazine (condensation/condensation/saponification/ethylation/amine formation)

Uses: antibacterial drug

piperacillin
[61477-96-1]; [59703-84-3] (sodium salt)

$C_{23}H_{27}N_5O_7S_1$. M: 517.55. Available commercially as the acid or sodium salts.
Production:
- *N*-ethylethylenediamine + diethyl oxalate + ethyl chloroformate + ampicillin (condensation/dehydrochlorination/amide formation)

Uses: antibacterial drug

piperazine
diethylenediamine; PIP; [110-85-0]; [16832-43-2] (hydrate)
$C_4H_{10}N_2$. M: 86.13. White, hygroscopic flakes with a mild, ammoniacal odour. MP: 109°C. Sublimes on heating. BP: 148°C. d: 1.11 kg/l (20°C). Miscible with water. Soluble in oxygenated and aromatic solvents. Also available as the hydrate containing 65–68% piperazine. MP: 35–45°C. d: 1.02 kg/l (50°C), and as the hydrochloride, sulphate, phosphate and citrate salts for veterinary use.

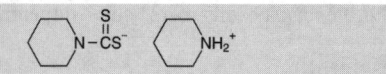

Production:
- ethylene dichloride + ammonia (amine formation; coproduced with ethylenediamine/diethylenetriamine/triethylenetetramine/tetraethylenepentamine/polyethylenepolyamine/aminoethylpiperazine)
- monoethanolamine + ammonia (ammoniation; coproduced with ethylenediamine/diethylenetriamine/*N*-hydroxyethylpiperazine/aminoethylpiperazine/aminoethylethanolamine)

Derivatives:
aminoethylpiperazine; cinnarizine; *N,N'*-dimethylpiperazine; eprazinone; flunarizine; lidoflazine; *N*-methylpiperazine; norfloxacin; pipemidic acid; polyamide resins, non-reactive; polyamide resins, reactive; prazosin; triforine
Uses: rubber curing agent; anthelmintic drug

piperidine
pentamethyleneamine; [110-89-4]

$C_5H_{11}N_1$. M: 85.15. Colourless liquid with a characteristic odour. BP: 106°C. MP: -11°C. d: 0.86 kg/l. Soluble in water, oxygenated and aromatic solvents.
Production:
- pyridine (reduction)
Derivatives:
dipentamethylenethiuram tetrasulphide; dipyridamole; etozolin; fenpiverinium bromide; fenpropidin; mepiquat chloride; pipazetate; piperidinium pentamethylenedithiocarbamate; piproctanyl bromide; piprozolin; zinc pentamethylenedithiocarbamate
Uses: condensation catalyst; epoxy resin curing agent

piperidine-4-carboxylic acid *See:* isonipecotic acid

piperidinium pentamethylenedithiocarbamate
PPC; PPD; [98-77-1]

$C_{11}H_{22}N_2S_2$. M: 246.44. Creamy-white powder with characteristic smell. MP: 168°C. d: 1.2 kg/l. Soluble in hot water and aromatic solvents.

Production:
- piperidine + carbon disulphide (condensation/ quaternisation)

Uses: vulcanisation accelerator

1-(4-piperidyl)-2-benzodiazolinone

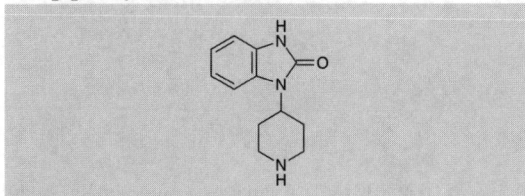

$C_{12}H_{15}N_3O_1$. M: 217.27.
Production:
- 1-benzyl-3-carbethoxy-4-piperidone hydrochloride + *o*-phenylenediamine (imine formation/ rearrangement/debenzylation)
- 4-amino-*N*-benzylpiperidine + *o*-chloronitrobenzene + sodium cyanate (amine formation/nitro reduction/ cyanate addition/debenzylation)

Derivatives:
benperidol; pimozide

piperocaine
[136-82-3]; [24561-10-2] (hydrochloride)

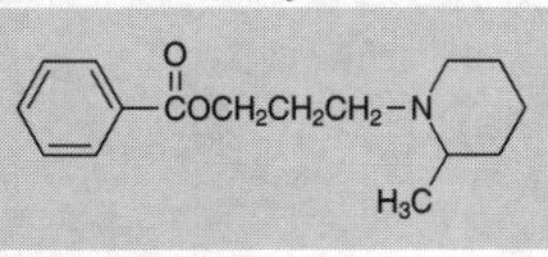

$C_{16}H_{23}N_1O_2$. M: 261.37.
Production:
- 1-bromo-3-chloropropane + 2-methylpiperidine + benzoic acid (amine formation/esterification)

Uses: local anaesthetic drug

piperonal
heliotropin; 3,4-methylenedioxybenzaldehyde; [120-57-0]

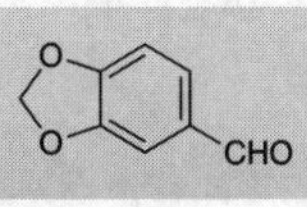

$C_8H_6O_3$. M: 150.14. White crystals with a floral odour. MP: 35–36°C. Practically insoluble in water. Soluble in oxygenated solvents.
Production:
- 1,2-benzodioxole + glyoxylic acid (carbonyl addition/oxidation/decarboxylation)
- isosafrole (oxidative cleavage)

Derivatives: epinephrine; α-methyl-β-3,4-methylenedioxyphenylpropionaldehyde-anthranilate adduct; piperonyl isobutyrate
Uses:
flavouring/fragrance ingredient

piperonyl butoxide
2-(2-butoxyethoxy)ethyl 6-propylpiperonyl ether; [51-03-6]

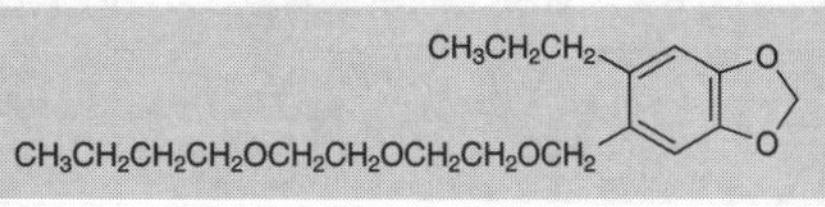

$C_{19}H_{30}O_5$. M: 338.44.
Production:
- safrole + formaldehyde + diethylene glycol monobutyl ether (hydrogenation/alkoxymethylation)

Uses:
pyrethroid synergist

piperonyl isobutyrate

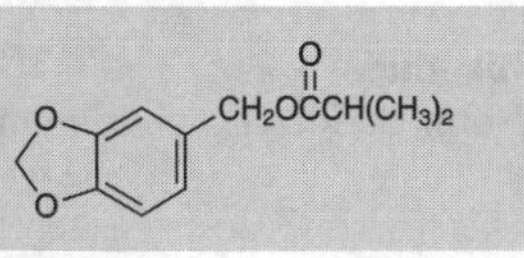

$C_{12}H_{14}O_4$. M: 222.24.
Production:
- piperonal + isobutyric acid (carbonyl reduction/ esterification)

Uses: flavouring ingredient

piperophos
S-2-methylpiperidinocarbonylmethyl *O,O*-dipropyl phosphorodithioate; [24151-93-7]

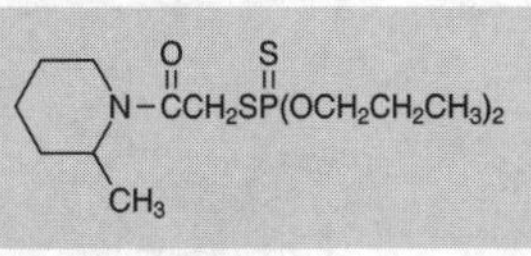

$C_{14}H_{28}N_1O_3P_1S_2$. M: 353.48.
Production:
- 2-methylpiperidine + chloroacetyl chloride + *O,O*-di-*n*-propyl dithiophosphoric acid (amide formation/dehydrochlorination)

Uses: herbicide

piperylene
1,3-pentadiene

$$CH_3CH=CH-CH=CH_2$$

C_5H_8. M: 68.11. Aliphatic hydrocarbon liquid containing, typically, 30% *cis*- and *trans*-piperylene.
Production:
- C_4-stream, steam-cracked/C_4-stream, refinery (solvent extraction; byproduct of butadiene/ raffinate I production)
- C_5-stream, steam-cracked (NMP solvent separation process; byproduct of dicyclopentadiene/isoprene production)

Derivatives:
methyl tetrahydrophthalic anhydride; piperylene-maleic anhydride adducts

piperylene-maleic anhydride adducts
Epiclon B-4400 (Dainippon Ink and Chemicals)

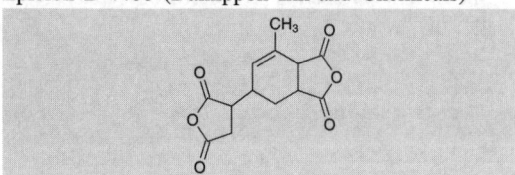

$C_{13}H_{12}O_6$. M: 264.23.
Production:
• piperylene + maleic anhydride (Diels-Alder cycloaddition/ene reaction)
Uses:
epoxy resin curing agent

piproctanyl bromide
1-allyl-1-(3,7-dimethyloctyl)piperidinium bromide; [56717-11-4]

$CH_2=CHCH_2$ $CH_2CH_2CHCHCH_2CH_2CH_2CH(CH_3)_2$ Br^-

$C_{18}H_{36}Br_1N_1$. M: 346.40.
Production:
• piperidine + tetrahydrogeraniol + allyl bromide (amine formation/quaternisation)
Uses:
plant growth regulator

piprozolin
[17243-64-0]

$C_{14}H_{22}N_2O_3S_1$. M: 298.40.
Production:
• ethyl cyanoacetate + thioglycollic acid + diethyl sulphate + piperidine (condensation/ethylation/alpha bromination/amine formation)
Uses: choleretic drug

piracetam
[7491-74-9]

$C_6H_{10}N_2O_2$. M: 142.16.
Production:
• 2-pyrrolidone + ethyl chloroacetate + ammonia (amine formation/amide formation)
Uses:
cerebral stimulant drug

pirenzepine
[28797-61-7]

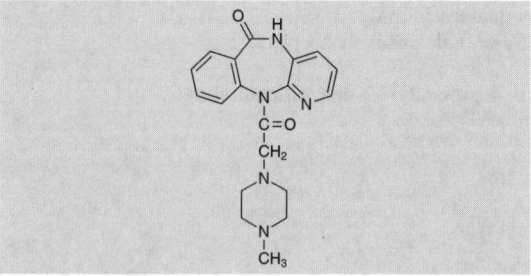

$C_{19}H_{21}N_5O_2$. M: 351.42. Available commercially as the dihydrochloride salt.
Production:
• 3-aminopyridine + chloroacetyl chloride + *o*-nitrobenzoyl chloride + *N*-methylpiperazine (ring chlorination/amide formation/nitro reduction/amine formation/amide formation/amine formation)
Uses: ulcer therapy drug

pirimicarb
2-dimethylamino-5,6-dimethylpyrimidin-4-yl dimethylcarbamate; [23103-98-2]

$C_{11}H_{18}N_4O_2$. M: 238.29.
Production:
• methyl bromide + ethyl acetoacetate + *N,N*-dimethylguanidine + dimethylcarbamoyl chloride (dehydrobromination/condensation/dehydrochlorination)
Uses: insecticide

pirimiphos-ethyl
O-2-diethylamino-6-methylpyrimidin-4-yl *O,O*-diethyl phosphorothioate; [23505-41-1]

$C_{13}H_{24}N_3O_3P_1S_1$. M: 333.38.
Production:
• diethylamine + cyanamide + ethyl acetoacetate + *O,O*-diethyl phosphorochlorothioate (nitrile addition/condensation/dehydrochlorination)
Uses: insecticide

pirimiphos-methyl
O-2-dimethylamino-6-methylpyrimidin-4-yl *O,O*-dimethyl phosphorothioate; [29232-93-7]

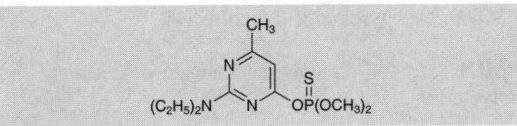

$C_{11}H_{20}N_3O_3P_1S_1$. M: 305.33.
Production:
• diethylamine + cyanamide + ethyl acetoacetate +
  O,O-dimethyl phosphorochlorothioate (nitrile
  addition/condensation/dehydrochlorination)
Uses: insecticide/acaricide

piromidic acid
[19562-30-2]

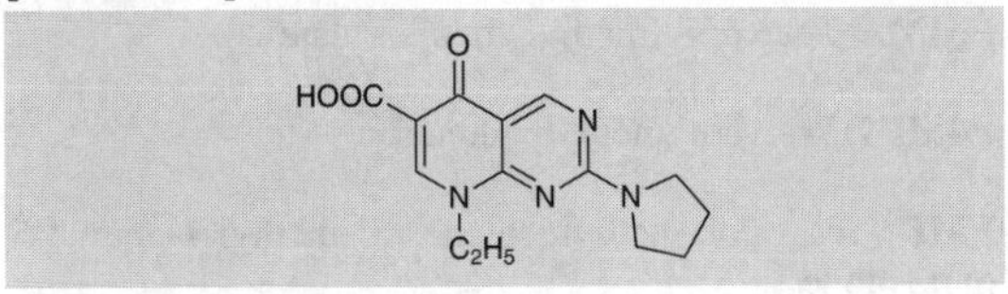

$C_{14}H_{16}N_4O_3$. M: 288.31.
Production:
• acrylonitrile + *O*-methylisourea sulphate + diethyl
  ethoxymethylenemalonate + pyrrolidine
  (condensation/condensation/saponification/
  ethylation/amine formation)
Uses: antibacterial drug

piroxicam
[36322-90-4]

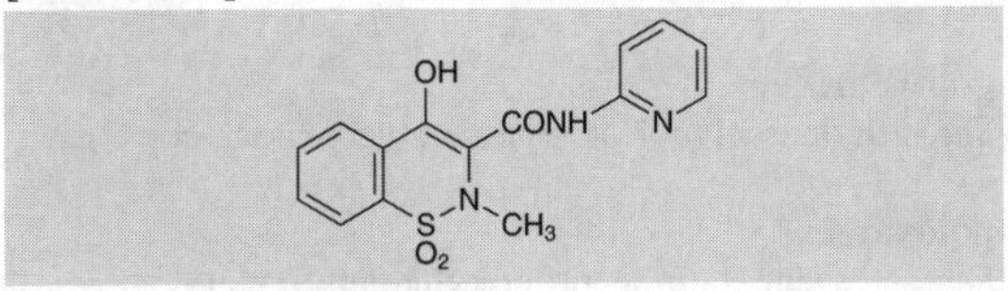

$C_{15}H_{13}N_3O_4S_1$. M: 331.35.
Available commercially as the free base and as the
cinnamic acid ester.
Production:
• sodium saccharin + methyl chloroacetate +
  2-aminopyridine (amine formation/rearrangement/
  methylation/amide formation)
Uses: antiinflammatory drug

PISO *See:* poly(imide-sulphone)

pitch *See:* coal tar pitch; tall oil pitch

pivalic acid
2,2-dimethylpropanoic acid; neopentanoic acid; trimethylacetic acid; [75-98-9]

(CH₃)₃CCOOH

$C_5H_{10}O_2$. M: 102.13. White, crystalline solid. MP:
36°C. BP: 160–162°C. d: 0.90 kg/l (40°C). Slightly
soluble in water. Soluble in oxygenated solvents.

Production:
• isobutylene + carbon monoxide (Koch carbonylation)
Derivatives:
dimefuron; isostearyl pivalate; methyl pivalate; monochloropivaloyl chloride; pinacolone; pivaloyl chloride
Uses:
fuel oil additive; metalworking fluids

pivaloacetonitrile *See:* cyanopinacolone

pivaloyl chloride
2,2-dimethylpropanoyl chloride; neopentanoyl chloride;
pivalyl chloride; trimethylacetyl chloride; [3282-30-2]

(CH₃)₃CCOCl

$C_5H_9Cl_1O_1$. M: 120.57. Hygroscopic liquid. BP: 105–
106°C. Hydrolysed by water and alcohol. Soluble in
ether.
Production:
• pivalic acid (acid chloride formation)
Derivatives:
t-amyl peroxypivalate; *t*-butyl peroxypivalate; chloromethyl pivalate; metribuzin; oxadiazon; tebutam; tebuthiuron
Uses:
alcohol group protection reagent (steroid synthesis)

pivampicillin
[33817-20-8]

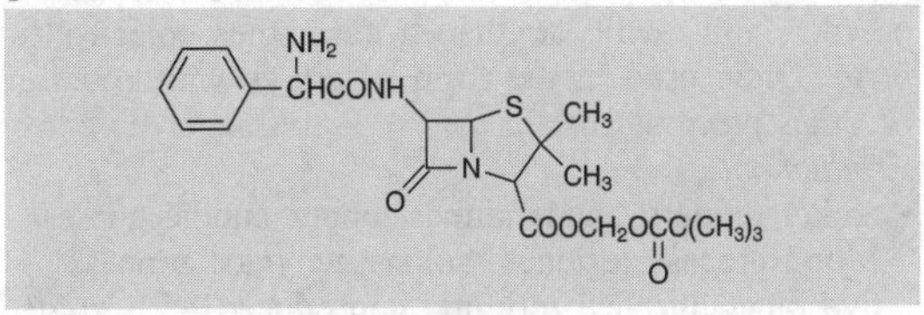

$C_{22}H_{29}N_3O_6S_1$. M: 463.54. Available commercially as
the free base or hydrochloride.
Production:
• ampicillin + chloromethyl pivalate (Dane salt
  formation/esterification/hydrolysis)
Uses: antibacterial drug

pivmecillinam
amdinocillin pivoxil; [32886-97-8]

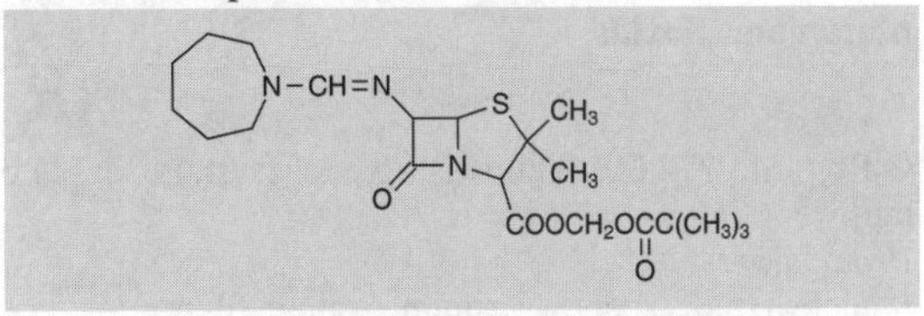

$C_{21}H_{33}N_3O_5S_1$. M: 439.56. Available commercially as
the free base or hydrochloride.
Production:
• mecillinam + chloromethyl pivalate (esterification)
Uses: antibacterial drug

pizotifen
pizotyline; [15574-96-6]

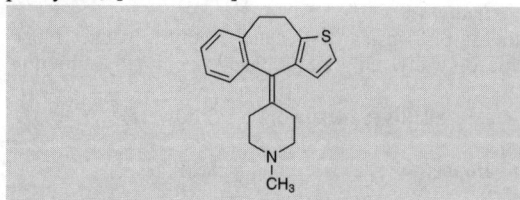

$C_{19}H_{21}N_1S_1$. M: 295.45. Available commercially as the free base and as the malate salt.
Production:
• benzothienocycloheptanone + isonipecotic acid
  (condensation/decarboxylation)
Uses: migraine therapy drug

plaster of Paris *See:* calcium sulphate hemihydrate

plasticisers, polymeric *See:* polymeric plasticisers

platformate *See:* reformate

platinum
[7440-06-4]

Pt

Pt_1. M: 195.09. Silvery-grey, ductile metal. MP: 1,769 °C. d: 21.5 kg/l. Relatively unreactive. Available in powder, foil, wire or shaped (crucibles, electrodes) form. Often used in the form of alloys with rhodium or other precious metals.
Production:
• nickel refinery anode slimes/copper anodic slimes/
  Mond process residues (sulphating roast process/
  hydrometallurgical refining; coproduced with gold/
  silver/palladium/selenium/tellurium)
Derivatives: chloroplatinic acid
Uses:
car catalytic converters; catalyst (petroleum reforming, acetic/nitric/sulphuric acid production); jewellery; scientific equipment/crucibles

Plexiglas *See:* poly(methyl methacrylate)

plutonium dioxide

PuO₂

O_2Pu_1. M: 274.00. Yellowish-green crystals. d: 11.5 kg/l.
Production:
• nuclear fuel, spent + sodium oxalate (Purex
  process/salt formation/calcination)
Uses: fast-breeder reactor fuels

PMA *See:* propylene glycol monomethyl ether acetate; phenylmercury acetate; phosphomolybdic acid

PMDA *See:* pyromellitic dianhydride

PMDI *See:* 4,4′-diphenylmethane diisocyanate, polymeric

PMDS *See:* di-(phenylmercury) dodecenylsuccinate

PMI *See:* poly(methacrylimide)

PMIC acid *See:* 5-methyl-3-phenylisoxazole-4-carboxylic acid

PMM *See:* poly(methyl methacrylate)

PMMA *See:* poly(methyl methacrylate)

P4MP1 *See:* polymethylpentene

PMP *See:* polymethylpentene; 3-methyl-1-phenyl-5-pyrazolone

PMS *See:* p-methylstyrene

PMT *See:* 1-phenyl-5-mercaptotetrazole

PMTA *See:* phosphotungstomolybdic acid

PNF *See:* poly(fluoroalkoxyphosphazene) elastomers

PNR *See:* polynorbornene

poloxamer
See: ethylene glycol-propylene glycol block copolymers

poloxamine
See: ethylenediamine propoxylate/ethoxylates

polyacetal, copolymers
acetal resins; poly(oxymethylene); POM; Celcon (Hoechst Celanese)

$-[CH_2O]_x-[CH_2CH_2O]_y-$

Highly crystalline thermoplastic characterised by its good tensile strength, rigidity and toughness as well as its excellent creep resistance. The polymer is resistant to alkali, solvents and hot water and can be used at temperatures up to 80°C. MP: 160–170°C. The polymers are processed by standard thermoplastic techniques and are available as basic, glass fibre or mineral-filled grades.
Production:
• trioxane + dioxolane/ethylene oxide (carbonyl
  addition)
Uses: domestic plumbing fittings/taps/valves; moulded bearings/gears/rollers/cams (household equipment, toys); pens/pencils; small precision moulded components (electronic equipment, aerosol valves/snap closures

polyacetal, homopolymers

acetal resins; poly(oxymethylene); POM; Delrin (Du Pont); Hostaform (Hoechst); Kemetal (Hoechst Celanese); Ultraform (BASF)

$$\text{---}\!\left[\!\text{CH}_2\text{O}\right]_{\!x}\!\text{---}$$

Highly crystalline thermoplastic. d: 1.425 kg/l. Tensile strength: 70 MPa. Elongation at break: 15–75%. Vicat softening point: 185°C. The polymer is characterised by its high tensile strength, rigidity and good fatigue endurance. They are usable at 100°C, have reasonably water and solvent resistance, a low coefficient of friction and good surface appearance. Processing is by conventional thermoplastic techniques.
Production:
• formaldehyde + acetic anhydride (carbonyl addition/acetylation)
Uses: domestic pipe fittings/taps/shower heads; moulded buttons/bearings/rollers/cams (household equipment); moulded pump/valve housings; small precision moulded components (electronics, measuring equipment)

polyacrylamide

[9003-05-8]

$$\text{---}\!\left[\!\text{CH}_2\text{--CH}\right]_{\!x}\!\text{---}\quad\overset{\text{CONH}_2}{|}$$

Water-soluble polymer. M: 40,000–1,500,000.
Production:
• acrylamide (solution polymerisation)
Derivatives: acrylamide-sodium acrylate copolymers; polyacrylamide, aminomethylated; polyacrylamide, glyoxylic acid-modified; polyacrylamide, methylolated; polyacrylamide, sulphomethylated; poly(vinylamine)
Uses: thickening/filtration/clarifying aid (oil-well drilling mud, mineral processing, mine effluent treatment)

polyacrylamide, aminomethylated

[25765-48-4]

$$\text{---}\!\left[\!\text{CH}_2\text{--CH}\right]_{\!x}\!\left[\!\text{CH}_2\text{--CH}\right]_{\!y}\!\text{---}$$
$$\overset{\text{CONHCH}_2\text{NHCH}_3}{|}\qquad\overset{\text{CONH}_2}{|}$$

Production:
• polyacrylamide + formaldehyde + methylamine/dimethylamine (Mannich reaction)
Uses: cationic flocculants (water treatment)

polyacrylamide, glyoxylic acid-modified

acrylamidoglycollate-acrylamide copolymers

$$\text{---}\!\left[\!\text{CH}_2\text{--CH}\right]_{\!x}\!\left[\!\text{CH}_2\text{--CH}\right]_{\!y}\!\text{---}$$
$$\overset{\text{OH}}{\underset{}{\overset{|}{\text{CONHCHCOOH}}}}\qquad\overset{\text{CONH}_2}{|}$$

Production:
• polyacrylamide + glyoxylic acid (carbonyl addition)

Uses: amphoteric polyelectrolytes (flotation depressant)

polyacrylamide, methylolated

$$\text{---}\!\left[\!\text{CH}_2\text{--CH}\right]_{\!x}\!\text{---}\quad\overset{\text{CONHCH}_2\text{OH}}{|}$$

Production:
• polyacrylamide + formaldehyde (hydroxymethylation)
Uses: fabric back-coatings; adhesives; textile sizing/crease-proofing agent

polyacrylamide, partially-hydrolysed

See: acrylamide-sodium acrylate copolymers

polyacrylamide, sulphomethylated

$$\text{---}\!\left[\!\text{CH}_2\text{--CH}\right]_{\!x}\!\left[\!\text{CH}_2\text{--CH}\right]_{\!y}\!\text{---}$$
$$\overset{\text{NHCH}_2\text{SO}_3^-\ \text{Na}^+}{\underset{}{\overset{|}{\text{CO}}}}\qquad\overset{\text{COOH}}{|}$$

High molecular weight polymers containing >50% sulphomethyl groups. The carbonyl groups are formed by amide hydrolysis under normal sulphomethylation reaction conditions.
Production:
• polyacrylamide + formaldehyde + sodium bisulphite (sulphomethylation)
Uses: strongly anionic flocculants (water, wastewater treatment)

poly(acrylamide-sodium acrylate)

See: acrylamide-sodium acrylate copolymers

poly(acrylate-methacrylate) graft copolymers

ACE
Production:
• acrylic resins, latex + methyl methacrylate (graft polymerisation)
Derivatives: polyvinyl chloride, high-impact
Uses: polyvinyl chloride impact modifier

polyacrylate resins, aminated

Beads.
Production:
• 2-dimethylaminoethyl acrylate (polymerisation)
Uses: weakly basic ion-exchange resins (water softening, demineralisation, food/chemical/pharmaceutical purification)

polyacrylate resins, crosslinked

Beads. Bulk density: 0.70–0.95 kg/l. Several grades available commercially with crosslinking varying from 0% to 10%.
Production:
• acrylic acid/methacrylic acid (polymerisation)
Uses: weakly acidic ion-exchange resins (effluent treatment, food/chemical/pharmaceutical purification)

poly(acrylic acid)

$$\begin{array}{c} COOH \\ | \\ \{CH_2-CH\}_x \end{array}$$

Available commercially as aqueous solutions containing 25–30% solids. pH: 2.0. d: 1.02 kg/l. M: 50,000–250,000.

Production:
• acrylic acid (solution polymerisation)

Uses: dispersant (heavy-duty liquid laundry cleaners); nickel plating reagent; glass coatings; hydrazine rocket fuel binder; polyamide/polyester textile sizing; stabiliser (polystyrene, methyl methacrylate organosols)

polyacrylonitrile

acrylic fibre; PAN; Courtelle (Courtaulds); Dralon (Bayer); Orlon (Du Pont); [25014-41-9]

$$\{CH_2-CH\}_x \begin{array}{c} | \\ CN \end{array}$$

White powder. Decomposes when heated above 180°C. M_v: 100,000–150,000. Several different grades are available. Variation in properties is brought about by the inclusion of comonomers and by the polymerisation conditions.

Production:
• acrylonitrile + methyl methacrylate/methyl acrylate/vinyl acetate (solution polymerisation)
• acrylonitrile + methyl methacrylate/methyl acrylate/vinyl acetate (aqueous heterogeneous polymerisation)

Derivatives: carbon fibre

Uses: fibre (textiles, household furnishings, industrial applications)

poly(acrylonitrile-butadiene-styrene)

See: acrylonitrile-butadiene-styrene copolymers

polyalkylene glycol
PAG

$$\{CH_2-CHO\}_x \begin{array}{c} R \\ | \\ \end{array}$$

R = H, methyl, ethyl-. Oils comprising ethylene oxide-propylene oxide random copolymers with the EO:PO ratio varying between 0:1 and 3:1. Polyalkylene glycols made with a high proportion of EO are soluble in water. As the PO content increases, the water solubility decreases. d: 1.00–1.15 kg/l. The oils have good lubricity, a low pour point and high viscosity index.

Production:
• propylene oxide + ethylene oxide (epoxidation)

Uses: compressor/textile lubricants; metal cutting fluid/brake fluid blending component; industrial gear oils and greases; rubber processing lubricant; water-based fire-resistant hydraulic fluids

polyalphaolefins
PAO

$$\{CH_2-CH\}_n \begin{array}{c} (CH_2)_7CH_3 \\ | \\ \end{array}$$

n = 3–5. High viscosity-index lubricating oils. Pour point: -100 – -5°C. Viscosity range: 100–6,500 mm^2/s (38°C). Good high-temperature stability.

Production:
• 1-decene (cationic polymerisation/hydrogenation)

Uses:
synthetic lubricant base oils

polyaluminium chloride
aluminium chloride, basic; PAC

$$Al_2(OH)_nCl$$

n = 1.0–5.0. Basic aluminium chloride with an OH:Al ratio of 0.5–2.5. Usually sold as a solution in water.

Production:
• alumina trihydrate + hydrochloric acid (salt formation)
• aluminium sulphate + calcium hydroxide (salt formation)

Uses: flocculant (water treatment); alum replacement (alkaline papermaking processes); fire-resistant ceramic paste binder; alumina fibre raw material; catalyst raw material; textile finishing agent

polyamide 6
nylon 6; PA 6; Durathan B (Bayer); Sniamid (Snia Tecnopolimeri); Ultramid B (BASF)

$$\{NHCH_2CH_2CH_2CH_2CH_2C\}_x \begin{array}{c} O \\ || \\ \end{array}$$

Thermoplastic available as unfilled or glass fibre-reinforced pellets. d: 1.13 kg/l. Tensile strength: 76 MPa. Tensile modulus: 2,800 MPa. Elongation at break: 100–200%. The polymer has excellent abrasion resistance and reasonable electrical insulation properties when dry. It absorbs up to 9.5% water, however, which adversely affects its insulation value. MP: 215°C. The polymer has a high degree of crystallinity. In some applications, polyamide 6 is cast directly *in situ* from caprolactam.

Production:
• caprolactam (amide formation)

Uses: cast resins (propellers, larger gears, liners); filaments (fishing nets/lines, musical instruments); gears/cams/bearings/bushes/valve seats (machinery, vehicle components); textile fibres

polyamide 6 terpolymers
polyamide 6/66/12; polyamide 6/66/610; polyamide 6/66/612; polyamide 6/69/612

Thermoplastic resins. Melting range: 80–150°C. d: 1.05–1.10 kg/l. Various grades available with differing

viscosities, melting ranges, adhesion characteristics and moisture absorption. Available commercially as powders, pellets, filament, spun-bonded web and film.
Production:
- caprolactam + adipic acid/azelaic acid/ 1,12-dodecanedioic acid + hexamethylenediamine + lauryllactam (amide formation)
Uses: hot melt adhesives (fabric bonding)

polyamide 6-(3)T
poly(trimethylhexamethyleneterephthalamide); PA 6-(3)T; Trogamid T (Hüls)

Thermoplastic pellets. d: 1.12 kg/l. Tensile strength: 83 MPa. Elongation at break: 9.5%. Vicat softening point: 145°C. The polymer has high clarity, rigidity, low water absorption and good thermal properties. It has an amorphous plastic structure.
Production:
- dimethyl terephthalate + trimethylhexamethylene-diamine (amide formation)
Uses: transparent instrument/electrical components

polyamide 6I
nylon 6I; PA 6I

Amorphous, transparent polyamide.
Production:
- dimethyl isophthalate + hexamethylenediamine (amide formation)
Uses: barrier resins (food packaging film); transparent instrument components

polyamide 11
nylon 11; PA 11

Thermoplastic available as unfilled or glass fibre-reinforced pellets. d: 1.04 kg/l. Tensile strength: 38 MPa. Tensile modulus: 1,400 MPa. Elongation at break: 30–300%. The polymer has a high degree of crystallinity, excellent abrasion resistance and good electrical insulation properties. It absorbs up to 1.9% water. MP: 185°C.
Production:
- ω-aminoundecanoic acid (amide formation)
Uses:
chemically-resistant powder coatings; extruded automotive fuel/hydraulic hoses; filaments (sports equip-

ment, brushes, braiding); gears/cams/bearings/bushes/ valve seats; transparent films (food, pharmaceutical packaging)

polyamide 12
nylon 12; PA 12; [25038-74-8]

Thermoplastic available as unfilled or glass fibre-reinforced pellets. d: 1.02 kg/l. Tensile strength: 45 MPa. Tensile modulus: 1,400 MPa. Elongation at break: 200%. The polymer has a high degree of crystallinity, excellent abrasion resistance and good electrical insulation properties. It absorbs up to 1.4% water. MP: 175°C.
Production:
- lauryllactam (amide formation)
Uses: chemically-resistant powder coatings; extruded automotive fuel/hydraulic hoses; gears/cams/bearings/ bushes/valve seats

polyamide 46
nylon 46; PA 46; Standyl (DSM)

Semicrystalline thermoplastic. MP: 295°C. Heat distortion temperature: 149°C or up to 285°C with glass fibre-reinforcing filler.
Production:
- adipic acid + 1,4-diaminobutane (amide formation)
Uses:
automotive/electronic/domestic appliance components

polyamide 66
nylon 66; PA 66; Enkalon (Akzo); Maranyl A (ICI); Technyl A (Rhône-Poulenc); Ultramid A (BASF); Durethan A (Bayer); Vydyne (Monsanto); Zytel 66 (Du Pont)

Thermoplastic available as unfilled or glass fibre-reinforced pellets. d: 1.14 kg/l. Tensile strength: 80 MPa. Tensile modulus: 3,000 MPa. Elongation at break: 80–100%. The polymer is highly crystalline, has excellent abrasion resistance and reasonable electrical insulation properties when dry. It absorbs up to 9% water, however, which adversely affects its insulation value. MP: 264°C.
Production:
- adipic acid + hexamethylenediamine (amide formation)
Uses: gears/cams/bearings/bushes/valve seats; abrasion-resistant pneumatic transport piping; ribbon (artificial turf); textile fibres

polyamide 66/610
nylon 66/610

$$\left[\!\!\left[C(CH_2)_nCNH(CH_2)_6NH\right]\!\!\right]_x$$

n = 4–8. Thermoplastic consisting of 65% sebacic acid and 35% adipic acid. d: 1.08 kg/l. Tensile strength: 38 MPa. Tensile modulus: 1,400 MPa.
Production:
• adipic acid + sebacic acid + hexamethylenediamine (amide formation)
Uses: filaments (fishing nets/lines)

polyamide 69
nylon 69; PA 69

$$\left[\!\!\left[C(CH_2)_7CNH(CH_2)_6NH\right]\!\!\right]_n$$

Solid. MP: 205°C. d: 1.09 kg/l.
Production:
• azelaic acid + hexamethylenediamine (amide formation)
Uses: brush bristles/industrial monofilament; cable/wire jacketing; electrical/automotive parts

polyamide 610
nylon 610; PA 610; Technyl (Rhône-Poulenc); Ultramid S (BASF)

$$\left[\!\!\left[C(CH_2)_8CNH(CH_2)_6NH\right]\!\!\right]_x$$

Thermoplastic available as unfilled or glass fibre-reinforced pellets. d: 1.09 kg/l. Tensile strength: 55 MPa. Tensile modulus: 2,100 MPa. Elongation at break: 100–150%. The polymer has a high degree of crystallinity, excellent abrasion resistance and good electrical insulation properties. It absorbs up to 3.5% water. MP: 215°C.
Production:
• sebacic acid + hexamethylenediamine (amide formation)
Uses: fibres; filaments (sports equipment, brushes, braiding); gears/cams/bearings/bushes/valve seats

polyamide 612
nylon 612; PA 612

$$\left[\!\!\left[C(CH_2)_{10}CNH(CH_2)_6NH\right]\!\!\right]_x$$

Solid. MP: 210°C. d: 1.07 kg/l. Tensile stress at the yield point: 60 MPa. Better dimensional stability, electrical resistance and water absorption properties than polyamide 66. Available in standard and glass fibre-filled grades for injection moulding and extrusion.
Production:
• 1,12-dodecanedioic acid + hexamethylenediamine (amide formation)

Uses: brush bristles/industrial monofilament; cable/wire jacketing; electrical/automotive parts

polyamide 1212
nylon 1212; PA 1212

$$\left[\!\!\left[C(CH_2)_{10}CNH(CH_2)_{12}NH\right]\!\!\right]_x$$

Production:
• 1,12-dodecanedioic acid + 1,12-diaminododecane (amide formation)
Uses: chemically-resistant tubing/components

poly(amide-imide)
PAI; Torlon (Amoco)

Thermoplastic. d: 1.40 kg/l. Tensile strength: 186 MPa. Elongation at break: 12%.
Production:
• trimellitic anhydride + 4,4′-diphenylmethane diisocyanate, polymeric (isocyanate addition)
Uses:
low-temperature/high-performance plastics; binder (high temperature surface coatings)

polyamide-polyamine-epichlorohydrin resins
See: adipic acid-dimethylaminohydroxypropyldiethylenetriamine copolymers

polyamide resins, non-reactive
polyamide resins, neutral; polyamide resins, thermoplastic

$$\left[\!\!\left[C-R-CNH-R'-NH\right]\!\!\right]_x$$

Thermoplastic solids. d: 0.98 kg/l (25°C). Hot melt grades have softening points between 90 and 190°C.
Production:
• dimer acid/trimer acid + ethylenediamine/triethylenetetramine/diethylenetriamine/2-methylpentamethylenediamine/hexamethylenediamine/piperazine (amide formation)
Uses:
heat-seal coatings; hot melt adhesives; binder (printing inks)

polyamide resins, reactive
Versamid (Henkel)
Liquids or low-melting solids, sometimes dissolved in solvent. d: 0.95–1.02 kg/l. Amine value: 130–600 mg KOH/g. Wide range of viscosities and epoxy curing rates available. Mixed products.

Production:
- dimer acid/trimer acid + ethylenediamine/bis-
  (hexamethylene)triamine/polyethylenepolyamine/
  diethylenetriamine/triethylenetetramine/piperazine/
  2-methylpentamethylenediamine/tetraethylene-
  pentamine/polyether polyols, flexible, amine-
  terminated (amide formation)

Uses:
flexible epoxy resin curing agent; phenolic/acrylic resin
modifiers (paints, lacquers); thixotropic alkyd resin comonomers (non-drip decorative paints)

polyamide TR55
Amidel (Union Carbide); Grilamid TR55
(EMS-Chemie)

Thermoplastic amorphous polymer.
Production:
- dimethyl isophthalate + bis(4-amino-3-methylcyclo-
  hexyl)methane + lauryllactam (amide formation)

Uses:
transparent instrument/electrical components

polyarylate, amorphous
Ardel (Amoco); Arylef (Solvay); Arylon (Du Pont);
Durel (Occidental Chemical); U-Polymer (Unitika)

x = y. Thermoplastic. d: 1.21 kg/l. Tensile strength: 62
MPa. Elongation at break: 40%. The polymer is transparent and tough with good flame-resistant properties.
Production:
- bisphenol A + terephthaloyl chloride + isophthaloyl
  chloride (esterification)

Uses:
moulded electrical/medical components; microwaveable
kitchenware; transparent glazing (solar panels)

polyarylate, liquid-crystalline
Ekkcel (Solvay); Xydar (Amoco)
Group of thermoplastics characterised by their excellent
fire-resistance, toughness, chemical inertness and good
electrical properties. The polymers are described as
'liquid crystalline' because, during processing, they exhibit anisotropy (a property of crystals) while behaving
as a liquid. Molecular alignments formed during processing provide secondary intermolecular bonds which
enhance the strength of the polymer, particularly at
high temperatures.
Production:
- dimethyl terephthalate/terephthalic acid +
  p-hydroxybenzoic acid + dimethyl naphthalene-

2,6-dicarboxylate/naphthalene-2,6-dicarboxylic acid
+ 4,4'-dihydroxybiphenyl (esterification)
Uses: heat-resistant film (microwaveable food packaging); injection-moulded electronic/medical equipment
components

polyazelaic polyanhydride
PAPA

Production:
- azelaic acid (acid chloride
  formation/dehydrochlorination)

Uses:
epoxy resin flexibiliser; speciality polyurethane polyol

polyaziridine *See:* polyethyleneimine

poly(p-benzhydrazoterephthalamide)
PABH-T X-500 (Monsanto)

Production:
- terephthaloyl chloride + hydrazine + p-aminobenzoic acid (amide formation/amide formation)

Uses:
high-strength, heat-resistant fibre

polybenzimidazole
PBI

Production:
- diphenyl isophthalate + 3,3'-diaminobenzidine
  (condensation)

Uses: high-temperature textile/insulation fibre

1,2-polybutadiene
1,2-PBD

Thermoplastic consisting of 50–65% syndiotactic polybutadiene with >90% of the monomer units linked at
their 1,2-positions. The polymer is partially crystalline,
but transparent. MP: 90°C. T_g: -23°C. The film has a
high gas permeability and a high tear/puncture resistance. T_g: -23°C.
Production:
- butadiene (Ziegler polymerisation)

Uses: bottles; food packaging film

polybutadiene, epoxidised
poly(butadiene) oxide; polyoil, epoxidised

$$\left[CH_2CH-CHCH_2\right]_m \left[CH_2CH=CHCH_2\right]_n$$

Light yellow to amber liquids. d:0.98–1.02 kg/l. M: 9,000–15,000. Epoxide equivalent: 150–250 g. The resin is generally cured with an acid anhydride hardening agent.
Production:
• polybutadiene latex + peracetic acid (epoxidation)
Uses: epoxy resin comonomer (sealants, electronic encapsulation)

polybutadiene, hydrogenated

$$\left[CH_2CH_2CH_2CH_2\right]_x \left[CH_2CH\overset{CH_2CH_3}{|}\right]_y$$

y > 30%.
Production:
• butadiene (polymerisation/hydrogenation)
Uses: viscosity modifier (lubricating oils)

polybutadiene, hydroxyl-terminated
poly BD glycol; polybutadiene glycol; HTBD; Butarez (Phillips Petroleum); R-15M (Arco Chemical); R-45M (Arco Chemical)
The polymers have an average molecular weight of 2,000–3,000 with a hydroxyl functionality of ~2.0. The product from Arco contains 60% *trans*-isomers whereas that from Japan Synthetic Rubber contains 55% vinylbutadiene and 35% *trans*-isomers.
Production:
• butadiene (polymerisation)
Uses:
cable joint potting compounds/pipe sealants; alkyd resin modifier; polyurethane adhesives/rocket fuel binders

polybutadiene latex
polybutadiene; BR

$$\left[CH_2CH=CHCH_2\right]_x$$

Latex emulsion. The polymer comprises, typically, 70% *trans*-1,4-butadiene, 15% *cis*-1,4-butadiene and 15% 1,2-butadiene units.
Production:
• butadiene (emulsion polymerisation)
Derivatives: acrylonitrile-butadiene-styrene copolymers; methyl methacrylate-butadiene-styrene copolymers; polybutadiene, epoxidised; polystyrene, high-impact
Uses: binder (paper sizing)

polybutadiene oil

$$\left[CH_2CH=CHCH_2\right]_x$$

Stereospecific, low molecular weight, liquid polybutadiene. M: 500–30,000. Dries in air to produce films.

Production:
• butadiene (Ziegler polymerisation)
Uses:
corrosion protection coatings; soil consolidation agent

polybutadiene rubber
butadiene rubber; polybutadiene; BR

$$\left[CH_2CH=CHCH_2\right]_x$$

Elastomers vulcanised using sulphur systems. Often used in blends with styrene-butadiene and nitrile rubber because of its relatively poor tear and tensile strength. Blends also have higher resilience, better abrasion and low temperature performance. Grades produced using Ziegler-Natta catalysts are >90% *cis*-1,4-butadiene. With lithium catalysts a lower *cis*-1,4-butadiene (40%) content is obtained, but a higher 1,2-isomer content (10%).
Production:
• butadiene (solution polymerisation)
Uses: conveyor belts/drive belts; shoe-soling/bumpers/ shock absorber pads; tyre treads

polybutene
Hyvis (BP Chemicals); [9003-28-5]
Low molecular weight, mixed C_4 polymers. Colourless, viscous liquids. Pour point: -60–+50°C. Viscosity: 3–42,000 cSt (100°C). Insoluble in water. Miscible with mineral oil. M: 300–6,000. See also polyisobutylene.
Production:
• raffinate I (Amoco/Cosden Oil polybutene processes; coproduced with raffinate II)
Derivatives: polybutene thiophosphonate propoxylates, alkali-earth salts; polyisobutenylsuccinic anhydride
Uses:
cable filling compounds; linear low density polyethylene comonomer (cling film); adhesives/sealants; viscosity modifier (lubricating oils); metalworking/2-stroke/ compressor/gear/wire-rope oils and greases

polybutene-1
polybutylene; PB

$$\left[CH_2-CH\overset{C_2H_5}{|}\right]_x$$

Thermoplastic beads. d: 0.915–0.925 kg/l. MP: 124–126°C. Tensile strength: 29–33 MPa. Elongation at break: 280–350%. The polymers have excellent creep and stress cracking resistance, together with chemical properties is similar to polypropylene. Polybutene-1 has a predominantly isotactic structure, a high molecular weight and around 50% crystallinity.
Production:
• 1-butene (Ziegler polymerisation)
Uses:
heat-sealable packaging film; hot water system piping; processing aid (polyolefins)

polybutene-1, atactic
APB

$$\left[CH_2-\underset{\underset{C_2H_5}{|}}{CH}\right]_x$$

Tacky, rubbery solid consisting of amorphous polybutene-1. M: 50,000–150,000. Softening point: 100°C (Ring and Ball Method). Soluble in aliphatic hydrocarbons.
Production:
• 1-butene (Ziegler polymerisation; byproduct of polybutene-1 production)
Uses: ingredient (bitumen sealants/roofing sheets)

polybutene thiophosphonate propoxylates, alkaliearth salts

$$RPS(CHCH_2O)_xH \quad nM(OH)_2$$
(with S double bond and CH₃ substituents shown)

R = polybutenyl-, M = Ca, Ba.
Production:
• polybutene/polyisobutylene, low molecular weight + phosphorus pentasulphide + propylene oxide + calcium hydroxide/barium oxide/barium hydroxide (condensation/epoxidation/salt formation)
Uses: detergent/oxidation inhibition/extreme pressure additives (lubricants)

poly(butylene terephthalate)
poly(tetramethylene terephthalate); PBT; PBTP; PTMT; Pocan B (Bayer); Rynite (Du Pont); [26062-94-2]

$$\left[CH_2CH_2CH_2CH_2O\overset{O}{\underset{||}{C}}-\bigcirc-\overset{O}{\underset{||}{C}}O\right]_x$$

Crystalline thermoplastic. d: 1.31 kg/l. Tensile strength: 56 MPa. Vicat softening point: 175°C. The polymer has a 30°C lower melting point and heat distortion temperature than polyethylene terephthalate. It is characterised by its good heat stability, mechanical properties, electrical insulation, surface finish, water absorption and grease/oil/petrol resistance. Often sold reinforced with glass fibre which increases its heat distortion temperature to >200°C.
Production:
• 1,4-butanediol + dimethyl terephthalate (esterification)
Uses: domestic power tool, cooker components; electrical plugs, sockets, switches, circuit breaker housings; vehicle grilles, fuel caps, door handles, wing mirrors, headlights; polybutylene terephthalate/polycarbonate blends; pump housings, impellers, gears, hinges

polycaprolactone diols

$$H\left[OCH_2CH_2CH_2CH_2CH_2\overset{O}{\underset{||}{C}}\right]_x OH$$

Liquid. M_w: 15,000–40,000.

Production:
• caprolactone (esterification)
Derivatives: naphthalene diisocyanate prepolymer; polyester polyurethane prepolymers, hydroxyl-terminated; polyester polyurethane prepolymers, isocyanate-terminated; polyurethane, cast elastomers; polyurethane, thermoplastic elastomers
Uses: antiblocking/dyeing aid (polyolefins)

polycarbonate
PC; Lexan (General Electric); Makrolon (Bayer)

$$\left[O-\bigcirc-\underset{\underset{CH_3}{|}}{\overset{\overset{CH_3}{|}}{C}}-\bigcirc-O\overset{O}{\underset{||}{C}}\right]_x$$

Thermoplastics available in pellets, including glass-filled and flame-retarded grades. d: 1.2 kg/l. Tensile strength: 65 MPa. Tensile modulus: 2,400 MPa. Elongation at break: 80–120%. The polymer is transparent with a high initial impact strength, good heat resistance, electrical insulation and self-extinguishing properties. The solvent resistance is relatively poor, however.
Production:
• bisphenol A + phosgene (phosgenation)
• bisphenol A + diphenyl carbonate (transesterification)
Uses:
compact disks; covers/housings/components (electrical/electronic/measuring equipment); domestic utensils, babies bottles and large containers; ABS/polycarbonate blends (electrical components and housings); industrial fibres; polyarylene ether/polycarbonate blends (vehicle fuel/oil/antifreeze resistant components); polybutylene terephthalate/polycarbonate blends; polyethylene terephthalate/polycarbonate blends; safety helmets/goggles/shields; unbreakable/vandal-proof glazing (lamp housings, transparent sheeting)

polycarbonate diols

$$HO\left[(CH_2)_6O\overset{O}{\underset{||}{C}}O\right]_x(CH_2)_6OH$$

Waxy solid. MP: 55–60°C.
Production:
• 1,6-hexanediol + diphenyl carbonate (transesterification)
Uses:
polyol component (polyurethane coatings/adhesives)

polychloroprene
chloroprene; poly(2-chlorobutadiene); CR; neoprene (Du Pont);

$$\left[CH_2\underset{\underset{Cl}{|}}{C}=CHCH_2\right]_n$$

Elastomer available as baled rubber or latex. The vulcanisate is characterised by its good flame and oil res-

istance compared with standard rubber materials. Heat and weather resistance are also good.
Production:
• chloroprene (emulsion polymerisation)
Uses:
cable jacketing/hoses/wire coverings; contact adhesives (shoe soling, laminates, construction, automotive applications); extruded profiles, seals, drive belts; flexible mechanical components; roofing membranes; foil-paper laminating adhesives; latex dipping compounds (gloves, contraceptives, balloons); oil-resistant moulded latex foam; leatherboard impregnating agent

polychlorotrifluoroethylene
PCTFE; Aclar (Allied-Signal); [9002-83-9]

$$\left[CF_2-CF \right]_x \quad Cl$$

Thermoplastic available as a moulding compound or as transparent sheet/film. d: 2.1 kg/l. Tensile strength: 30–40 MPa. Tensile modulus: 1,300 MPa. Elongation at break: 150–200%. The polymer is stronger and has a lower softening point than polytetrafluoroethylene. It has low gas permeability and water absorption properties.
Production:
• chlorotrifluoroethylene (polymerisation)
Uses: chemically-resistant seals/O-rings; transparent vapour barrier layer (electroluminescent devices, pharmaceutical packaging); transparent chemically resistant mouldings

poly(1,4-cyclohexylenedimethylene terephthalate)
PCT; Ektar (Eastman Chemical)

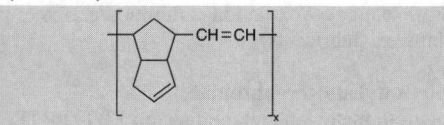

Thermoplastic with a 20°C higher melting and heat distortion temperature than polyethylene terephthalate.
Production:
• 1,4-cyclohexanedimethanol + dimethyl terephthalate (esterification)
Uses: biaxially-oriented film; injection-moulded vehicle engine components; textile fibres

poly(1,4-cyclohexylenedimethylene terephthalate-isophthalate)
PETG

Thermoplastic. d: 1.2 kg/l. Tensile strength: 50 MPa. The polymer is amorphous, producing tough film/mouldings of high clarity with good barrier and solvent resistance properties.

Production:
• 1,4-cyclohexanedimethanol + dimethyl terephthalate + dimethyl isophthalate (transesterification)
Uses: film (packaging, building panel linings); transparent moulded items

poly(diallyldimethylammonium chloride)
poly(dimethyldiallylammonium chloride)

$$\left[CH_2-CH \right]_m \\ CH_2 \\ {}^+N(CH_3)_2 \quad Cl^- \\ CH_2 \\ \left[CH_2-CH \right]_n$$

Viscous liquid comprising a 40% polymer solution in water. M: 100,000–1,000,000.
Production:
• diallyldimethylammonium chloride (aqueous polymerisation)
Uses: cationic flocculants (water treatment, mineral processing); conditioning agent (shampoos, hair conditioners, cosmetics, toiletries)

poly(dicyclopentadiene)
Metton (Hercules)

Production:
• dicyclopentadiene (polymerisation)
Uses:
RRIM injection-moulded automotive components

poly(diethylene adipate)
See: polyester polyols, slightly-branched

poly(dimethyl-2-hydroxypropylammonium chloride)
See: poly(2-hydroxypropyl dimethylammonium chloride)

poly(2,6-dimethyl-*p*-phenylene oxide)
See: poly(phenylene oxide)

poly(dimethylsiloxane)
See: silicone oils

poly(dimethylsiloxane), crosslinking
Silicone oil containing hydrogen atoms which can react with vinyl groups on other suitable polymers.
Production:
• dimethylsiloxane oligomers + dichloromethylsilane (base-catalysed polymerisation)
Derivatives:
silicone rubber, cold-cured, 2-component, polyaddition-types

poly(dimethylsiloxane), hydroxyl-terminated

H—[O—Si(CH₃)(CH₃)]ₙ—OH

Reactive oils consisting of linear silicone chains with terminal hydroxyl groups. M: 1,000–100,000.
Production:
• dimethylsiloxane oligomers (hydrolysis)
Derivatives:
silicone rubber, cold-cured, 1-component; silicone rubber, cold-cured, 2-component, polycondensation-types
Uses:
liquid silicone rubber component (moulded baby bottle teats, electronics)

poly(dimethylsiloxane), vinylated

Reactive gums consisting of linear silicone chains containing a small proportion of vinyl groups. M: 300,000–700,000.
Production:
• octamethylcyclotetrasiloxane + dichloromethylphenylsilane + dichloromethylvinylsilane
  (polymerisation)
Derivatives: silicone rubber, cold-cured, 2-component, polyaddition-types; silicone rubber, heat-cured

poly[(3,4′-diphenyl ether)-(p-phenyleneterephthalamide)]

Technora (Teijin)

Production:
• p-nitrophenol + m-chloronitrobenzene + p-phenylenediamine + terephthaloyl chloride (ether
  formation/nitro reduction/amide formation)
Uses: honeycomb panel core (aircraft, public transport); high-temperature textile/insulation fibre

polydodecylbenzene *See:* heavy alkylate, branched

polyepichlorohydrin

Hydrin (B.F. Goodrich)

—[CH₂—CHO(CH₂Cl)]ₓ—

Elastomers. Homopolymer, copolymer with ethylene oxide, and terpolymer with ethylene oxide and allyl glycidyl ether are produced. Homo and copolymers are vulcanised with diamine and lead compounds. The terpolymer is vulcanised with sulphur or peroxides. Vulcanisates are characterised by good heat, weather, flame and oil resistance, excellent low temperature properties and an upper working temperature of about 150°C.

Production:
• epichlorohydrin + ethylene oxide (epoxidation)
Uses:
automotive seals, diaphragms, membranes, hoses, vibration damping components; paper/printing/copier roller coverings

polyester, linear, high molecular weight
See: poly(ethylene terephthalate)

polyester-acrylate resins

CH₂=CCO—R′—OCC=CH₂ (R) (R)

R = H, methyl-, R′ = polyester. Complex, acrylate-terminated polyester prepolymers. Inks and coatings made with polyester-acrylate resins exhibit good pigment wetting and good adhesion characteristics.
Production:
• polyester resins, hydroxylated + acrylic acid
  (esterification)
• polyester resins, carboxylated + 2-hydroxyethyl
  methacrylate/2-hydroxypropyl methacrylate/
  2-hydroxypropyl acrylate/2-hydroxyethyl acrylate
  (esterification)
Uses:
binder (radiation-cured printing inks, wood/textile finishes, paper-foil lacquers)

polyester carbonate

Apec (Bayer); Lexan PPC (General Electric)

Tough, transparent, high-temperature form of polycarbonate resin. T$_g$: >195°C.
Production:
• bisphenol A + phosgene + dimethyl terephthalate
  (phosgenation/esterification)
Uses:
impact-resistant lights/electrical equipment

polyester polyols, aromatic

HOCH₂CH₂OCH₂CHO—[C(O)—C₆H₄—C(O)OCH₂CH₂OCH₂CH₂O]ₓ—H

Production:
• poly(ethylene terephthalate), scrap/dimethyl
  terephthalate production residues + diethylene
  glycol (transesterification)
Derivatives:
polyisocyanurate, rigid foam; polyurethane, rigid foam

polyester polyols, crosslinked
See: polyester resins, hydroxylated

polyester polyols, linear
polyols, flexible
Viscous liquids/waxy solids made from diacids and diols. Hydroxyl value: 45–60 mg KOH/g. See also poly-(ethylene-adipate), polyester polyols, slightly-branched, polycaprolactone diols, polycarbonate diols.
Production:
- adipic acid/sebacic acid/alkylene(C_4-C_6)dicarboxylic acids/azelaic acid + ethylene glycol/1,4-butanediol/ alkylene(C_4-C_6) diol/1,6-hexanediol (esterification)

Derivatives:
naphthalene diisocyanate prepolymer; polyester polyurethane prepolymers, hydroxyl-terminated; polyurethane, cast elastomers; polyurethane, flexible foam, slabstock; polyurethane, microcellular foam; polyurethane, thermoplastic elastomers
Uses: elastomeric fabric coatings; polyurethane impact-resistant floor coverings

polyester polyols, slightly-branched
poly(diethylene adipate)
Polyester polyols for flexible polyurethane foam are slightly branched with M: 1,500–2,000. For semi-rigid foam applications a more highly-branched polyol is used.
Production:
- diethylene glycol + adipic acid/dimethyl adipate (esterification)

Derivatives: polyurethane, flexible foam, slabstock; polyurethane, low-resilience elastomers; polyurethane, semi-rigid foam

polyester polyurethane prepolymers, hydroxyl-terminated
Production:
- 4,4′-diphenylmethane diisocyanate, pure + polycaprolactone diols/polyester polyols, linear (isocyanate addition)

Uses: 2-pack elastomeric polyurethane coatings (fabric coatings, impact-resistant floor coatings)

polyester polyurethane prepolymers, isocyanate-terminated

R = polyester diol.
Production:
- poly(ethylene-adipate)/polycaprolactone diols + 4,4′-diphenylmethane diisocyanate, pure (isocyanate addition)

Derivatives: polyurethane, cast elastomers; polyurethane, microcellular foam

polyester resins, carboxylated
Saturated polyester prepolymers with a high free carboxylic acid content. have good pigment wetting and adhesion properties, but relatively poor chemical resistance.
Production:
- glycerol/trimethylolpropane/1,3-butanediol + phthalic anhydride/dimethyl adipate/adipic acid (esterification)

Derivatives: polyester-acrylate resins

polyester resins, hydroxylated
polyester polyols, crosslinked
Saturated polyester prepolymers with a high free hydroxyl content.
Production:
- glycerol/trimethylolpropane/1,3-butanediol + phthalic anhydride/adipic acid/dimethyl adipate (esterification)

Derivatives: polyester-acrylate resins
Uses: epoxy-terminated thermosetting acrylic resin curing agent; polyester/amino stoving resins (high-solids industrial finishes); polyester/isocyanate electrostatic powder coatings; 2-pack polyurethane coatings (aluminium, plastic, wood, marine, aircraft, self-levelling floor paints)

polyester resins, linear, medium molecular weight
White or yellow pellets. Melting range: 94–182°C. d: 1.25–1.28 kg/l. M: 10,000–30,000. Available commercially as powder, granules, pellets, web or film.
Production:
- ethylene glycol/1,4-butanediol/1,6-hexanediol/ 1,4-cyclohexanedimethanol + dimethyl adipate/ dimethyl isophthalate/dimethyl terephthalate/ dimethyl cyclohexane-1,4-dicarboxylate (esterification)

Uses:
hot melt adhesives (shoe production, fabric bonding)

poly(ether-amide) elastomers
PEPAP; Pebax (Elf-Atochem)

R = polyamide, R′ = polyether. Thermoplastic elastomer consisting of hard, crystallised polyamide segments linked by flexible polyether polyol. Several different grades are available which vary in the polyamide and polyether constituents as well as in the degree of polymerisation. Tensile strength: 30–50 MPa. Elongation at break: 400–700%. Young's modulus: 10–250 MPa.
Production:
- lauryllactam/caprolactam/ω-aminoundecanoic acid + hexamethylenediamine + adipic acid/azelaic acid/ 1,12-dodecanedioic acid + polypropylene glycol/ poly(tetramethylene ether) glycol (amide formation/esterification)

Uses: sports shoes/ski boots; wiper blades, pump membranes, flexible drives

polyether ether ketone
polyarylene ether ether ketone; PEEK;
Vitrex PEEK (ICI)

Partially crystalline thermoplastic characterised by its excellent chemical, heat, flame and tear resistance. Its electrical insulation properties are similar to those of fluoropolymers. d: 1.3 kg/l (unreinforced). Tensile strength: 91 MPa at yield. Flexural modulus: 3800 MPa. Processed by extrusion or injection moulding on conventional equipment.
Production:
• hydroquinone + 4,4'-difluorobenzophenone (ether formation)
Uses: cable/wire insulation (aircraft and aerospace applications); fibre (high-temperature industrial fabrics); piping/moulded components (chemical, petroleum processing equipment)

poly(ether-imide)
PEI; Ultem (General Electric)

Transparent thermoplastic characterised by its high flexural strength, good high-temperature performance (continuous usage up to 170°C) and excellent flame resistance. It is moderately resistant to chemicals/solvents and has good hydrolytic stability. Processed by injection moulding, extrusion and thermoforming.
Production:
• bisphenol A + 4-fluorophthalic anhydride + *m*-phenylenediamine (ether formation/imide formation)
Uses: aircraft interior equipment; high-temperature vehicle/electronic components

polyether ketone
polyarylene ether ketone; PEK

Thermoplastics characterised by their excellent flame and chemical resistance, toughness and abrasion resistance. Working temperature range: -250°C to +250°C.
Production:
• 4,4'-difluorobenzophenone + 4,4'-dihydroxybenzophenone (ether formation)
Uses: fibre-reinforced laminates (aircraft, aerospace components); injection-moulded components (aircraft, aerospace, petroleum applications); pipe/wire insulation

polyether ketone ether ketone ketone
PEKEKK; Ultrapek (BASF)

Semi-crystalline thermoplastic characterised by its excellent thermal properties. T_g: 173°C. T_m: 380°C. The material is processed at 400–420°C.
Production:
• 4,4'-difluorobenzophenone + phenol + terephthaloyl chloride (ether formation/Friedel-Crafts acylation)
Uses:
plastic composite reinforcing fibre (aircraft)

polyether ketone ketone
PEKK

Semi-crystalline thermoplastic characterised by its excellent thermal properties. T_g: 156°C. T_m: 310–338°C.
Production:
• diphenyl oxide + terephthaloyl chloride + isophthaloyl chloride (Friedel-Crafts acylation)
Uses: plastic composite reinforcing fibre (aircraft)

polyether polyols, flexible
polyols, flexible; polyoxypropylene triols

$$R\left[O(CHCH_2O)_nCH_2CH_2OH\right]_3$$
$$\overset{CH_3}{|}$$

R = triol. Triol consisting of PO-extended arms tipped with ethylene oxide to improve reactivity. M: 1,000–6,500. Hydroxyl value: 28–160 mg KOH/g.
Production:
• trimethylolpropane/glycerol + propylene oxide/ethylene oxide (epoxidation)
Derivatives: polyols, epoxy dispersion; polyols, polyisocyanate polyaddition; polyols, polymer; polyols, polyurea dispersion; polyurethane, flexible foam, cold-moulded; polyurethane, flexible foam, hot-moulded; polyurethane, flexible foam, slabstock; polyurethane, integral-skin foam; polyurethane, microcellular foam; polyurethane, semi-rigid foam; polyurethane-polyurea, reaction injection-moulded elastomers
Uses: moisture-cured polyurethane varnish (interior woodwork, flooring)

polyether polyols, flexible, amine-terminated
polyols, flexible, amine-terminated; polyoxypropyleneamines; Jeffamine (Texaco Chemical)

$$R\left[(OCH_2CH)_nNH_2\right]_3$$
$$\overset{CH_3}{|}$$

R = diol, triol. Colourless to pale yellow liquids con-

sisting of polypropylene glycols, poly(ethylene-propylene) glycols and triols with terminal amine groups. M: 230–5,000.
Production:
• trimethylolpropane/glycerol + propylene oxide/ ethylene oxide + ammonia (epoxidation/ammoniation)
Derivatives:
polyamide resins, reactive; polyurethane-polyurea, reaction injection-moulded elastomers
Uses: epoxy resin curing agent

polyether polyols, rigid
polyols, rigid

$$R\left[O(CHCH_2O)_mH\right]_n$$
$$\overset{\displaystyle CH_3}{}$$

n = 3–8, R = base polyol. Colourless, viscous liquid polyol consisting of propylene oxide-extended arms with an average functionality of 4–5. M: 150– 1,600. Hydroxyl value: 250–1000 mg KOH/g.
Production:
• glycerol/trimethylolpropane/pentaerythritol/sorbitol/ sucrose/α-methylglucoside/triethanolamine/ethylenediamine/diethylenetriamine/4,4′-diaminodiphenylmethane, crude/2,4/2,6-diaminotoluene + propylene oxide (epoxidation)
Derivatives:
polyisocyanurate, rigid foam; polyurethane, rigid foam

polyether sulphone
PES; Ultrason E (BASF); Vitrex PES (ICI)

$$\left[\begin{array}{c}\end{array}\right]_x$$

Transparent, amber engineering thermoplastic characterised by its good creep resistance, thermal and electrical properties. Self-extinguishing. Resistant to attack by aqueous acid, alkali and most solvents. T_g: 220°C. d: 1.37 kg/l. Tensile strength: 84 N/mm². Tensile modulus: 2.4 N/mm². Elongation at break : 40%. Available as unreinforced and glass fibre-filled grades as well as in blends with styrene-butadiene thermoplastic elastomers.
Production:
• diphenyl oxide + diphenyl ether 4,4′-bis(sulphonyl chloride) (chlorosulphonation)
Uses: high-temperature/electrical insulation mouldings (hair drier/oven/fan heater components)

polyethylbenzene *See:* diethylbenzene, mixed

polyethylene, chlorinated
Bayer CM (Bayer); CM; Elaslen (Showa Denko); Kelrinal (DSM); Solpolac (Caffaro)
Elastomer vulcanised by peroxide crosslinking. The vulcanisates are characterised by their good chemical,

weather and flame resistance. The mechanical properties of the polymer are also reasonably good. Chlorine content: 25–40% w/w.

$$\left[CH_2-CH_2\right]_x\left[CH_2-\overset{\displaystyle Cl}{CH}\right]_y$$

Production:
• polyethylene, high-density + chlorine (chlorination)
Derivatives: polyvinyl chloride, high-impact
Uses: cable/wire jacketing; fire-retardant textile finishes; industrial hosing/sheeting; pool liner/roof covering membranes; polyvinyl chloride impact modifier/ processing aid

polyethylene, chlorosulphonated
CSM; CSPE; Hypalon (Du Pont)

$$\left[CH_2-\overset{\displaystyle Cl}{CH}\right]_x\left[CH_2-\overset{\displaystyle SO_2Cl}{CH}\right]_y$$

Elastomers used in vulcanised and unvulcanised form. Vulcanisation is achieved by crosslinking with magnesium oxide, dibasic lead phthalate or other chemicals. The vulcanisates are characterised by their excellent oil, chemical, ozone and weather resistance. Most grades contain 25–43% chlorine and 1–1.5% sulphur.
Production:
• polyethylene, low-density + sulphur dioxide, pure + chlorine (photochlorosulphonation)
Uses: cable/wire insulation; fabric coatings (construction sheet, membrane liners, roof coverings); engineering adhesives; hoses/moulded goods

polyethylene, crosslinked
XLPE; XPE

$$\left[CH_2-CH_2\right]_x$$

Thermoplastic beads crosslinked during processing or by post-treatment. The product has better impact, stress cracking and flexural properties than uncrosslinked grades. A typical grade contains one crosslink per two hundred carbon atoms.
Production:
• polyethylene, low-density (radiation process)
• polyethylene, low-density (peroxide crosslinking process)
• polyethylene, low-density (Dow Sioplas process)
Uses: dielectric insulator (high-voltage cables); foam (sports equipment, life jackets, protective clothing, pipe insulation, vehicle sound insulation/floor coverings); domestic floor heating piping

polyethylene, high-density
HDPE

$$\left[CH_2-CH_2\right]_x$$

Thermoplastic beads. d: 0.94–0.96 kg/l. MP: 120–

130°C. Tensile strength: 24–28 MPa. Tensile modulus: 1050–1500 MPa. Elongation at break: 350–400%. Insoluble in water and cold organic solvents. Swollen by hydrocarbon and chlorinated solvents. High-density polyethylene has a linear structure with a few, short side-chains per molecule. M: ~50,000 for grades produced by the Phillips process.

Production:
- ethylene (Ziegler slurry process)
- ethylene + propylene/1-butene/1-hexene (Phillips solution polymerisation process)
- ethylene (gas-phase polymerisation)

Derivatives: polyethylene, chlorinated; polyethylene wax, high-density

Uses: cable/wire jacketing; fibres; fibrillated yarn; packaging film (carrier bags, food wrappers); blow-moulded food/household containers; blow-moulded fuel tank/canisters; injection-moulded products (crates, buckets, tubs, containers, toys, caps); pipe/profile extrusions; rotationally-moulded items

polyethylene, high-density, high molecular weight
HMWPE

$$+CH_2-CH_2+_x$$

Available as high-tenacity film of 10–30 μ thickness. d: 0.95 kg/l. Melt index: 0.3 dg/min. M: 200,000–400,000.

Production:
- ethylene (Ziegler polymerisation)

Uses: paper-like packaging film (carrier bags)

polyethylene, high-density, ultra-high molecular weight
UHMWPE

$$+CH_2-CH_2+_x$$

Thermoplastic characterised by its high impact and stress cracking resistance over a temperature range -200–+90°C. MP: 135–138°C. d: 0.94 kg/l. Very low melt flow index (<0.01 dg/min). M: 4–6 x 10^6. Special processing is required.

Production:
- ethylene (Ziegler polymerisation)

Uses:
high-strength fibre (body armour); wear-resistant chute linings, slides, gears, rollers and seals

polyethylene, linear low-density
LLDPE

$$+CH_2-CH_2+_x$$

Thermoplastic beads. d: 0.91–0.94 kg/l. MP: 122–124°C. Tensile strength: 18–25 MPa. Tensile modulus: 350–500 MPa. Elongation at break: 300–400%. Insoluble in water and cold organic solvents. Swollen by hydrocarbon and chlorinated solvents. Linear low-

density polyethylene has a linear structure with short side-chains produced by the comonomer. Mean molecular weights vary widely.

Production:
- ethylene + 1-butene/1-hexene (solution processes)
- ethylene + 4-methyl-1-pentene (BP gas-phase process)
- ethylene + 1-butene/1-hexene (Phillips slurry process)
- ethylene + 1-butene/1-hexene (gas-phase polymerisation)

Uses: cable/wire jacketing; pipe/profile extrusions; film (sacks, food wrapping, carrier bags, general packaging); injection-moulded products (toys, electrical fittings, bushes, seals, components); rotationally-moulded tanks/boats;

polyethylene, low-density
LDPE; [9002-88-4]

$$+CH_2-CH_2+_x$$

Thermoplastic beads. d: ≤0.92 kg/l. MP: 107–115°C. Tensile strength: 12–15 MPa. Tensile modulus: 140 MPa. Elongation at break: 550–650%. Insoluble in water and cold organic solvents. Swollen by hydrocarbon and chlorinated solvents. Low-density polyethylene has a branched structure with many, long side-chains per molecule. M: ≤70,000.

Production:
- ethylene (high-pressure bulk polymerisation)

Derivatives:
polyethylene, chlorosulphonated; polyethylene, cross-linked; polyethylene wax, low-density

Uses:
cable/wire insulation; construction/agricultural film; extrusion coatings (paper laminates); fibres; film (sacks, food wrapping, carrier bags, general packaging); blow-moulded flexible bottles/drum linings; injection-moulded products (toys, electrical fittings, bushes, seals, components); piping; powder coatings; shrink film (food wrapping); stretch film (pallet wrapping)

polyethylene, very low-density
polyethylene, linear low-density, high α-olefin content; ULDPE; VLDPE

$$+CH_2-CH_2+_x$$

Rubbery thermoplastic consisting of long chain ethylene copolymers containing up to 10% comonomers. The polymer is characterised by its high impact and tensile strength with elongation at break close to 900%.

Production:
- ethylene + propylene/4-methyl-1-pentene/1-octene (Ziegler polymerisation)

Uses:
polyolefin compound elasticity improver; heavy-duty stretch packaging film

poly(ethylene-adipate)

$$-[C(CH_2)_4COCH_2CH_2O]_x-$$

Waxy solid.
Production:
• ethylene glycol + adipic acid (esterification)
Derivatives:
naphthalene diisocyanate prepolymer; polyester polyurethane prepolymers, isocyanate-terminated; polyurethane, thermoplastic elastomers
Uses:
polyol component (polyurethane elastomers, adhesives)

poly(ethylene-chlorotrifluoroethylene)
ECTFE; Halar (Allied-Signal)

$$-[CH_2-CH_2]_x-[CF_2-CF]_y-$$
$$\quad\quad\quad\quad\quad\quad\quad\quad Cl$$

Thermoplastic. d: 1.68 kg/l. Tensile strength: 42–48 MPa. Tensile modulus: 1,400 MPa. Elongation at break: 200%. The polymer has good impact resistance, chemical resistance and electrical insulation properties.
Production:
• ethylene + chlorotrifluoroethylene (polymerisation)
Uses:
industrial fibres; injection-moulded products

poly(ethylene-1,4-cyclohexanedimethylene-terephthalate)
PETG; Kodar (Eastman Chemical)

$$-[OCH_2CH_2O\overset{O}{\overset{\|}{C}}-\langle\rangle-\overset{O}{\overset{\|}{C}}]_x-[OCH_2-\langle\rangle-CH_2O\overset{O}{\overset{\|}{C}}-\langle\rangle-\overset{O}{\overset{\|}{C}}]_y-$$

Thermoplastic polymer characterised by its high clarity, toughness and good melt strength.
Production:
• ethylene glycol + 1,4-cyclohexanedimethanol + dimethyl terephthalate (esterification)
Uses: extrusion blow-moulded bottles (soft drinks, mineral water, sauces, preserves); injection-moulded automotive/electrical components; packaging film

polyethylene glycol
poly(ethylene oxide); PEG; PEO; Carbowax (Union Carbide); [25322-68-3]

$$HO-[CH_2CH_2O]_n-H$$

Colourless liquids or white, soft or hard waxes, depending on the molecular weight. M: 150–20,000. d: 1.13 kg/l (20°C). The products have good lubricity, heat stability and chemical resistance. Their solubility in water ranges from complete miscibility at low molecular weight to about 500 g/l solution at high molecular weight.
Production:
• ethylene oxide (epoxidation)

Derivatives: complex ester oils; polyethylene glycol dilaurate; polyethylene glycol dimethacrylate; polyethylene glycol dioleate; polyethylene glycol distearate; polyurethane, latex
Uses:
nickel plating brightening agent; crude oil demulsifier component; gas desulphurisation agent; antistatic agent/lubricant (textile spin finishes, rubber); brake/hydraulic/transmission fluid blending component; lubricant (paper calenders, metal drawing/extrusion oils); glass/ceramics binder; rubber mould release agent; plasticiser (casein, gelatine, glue, regenerated cellulose); softening agent (paper); solvent (pigments, printing inks); solvent/thickening agent/ointment base (pharmaceuticals, cosmetics, soap, toiletries)

polyethylene glycol dilaurate
PEG dilaurate (CTFA)

$$CH_3(CH_2)_{10}\overset{O}{\overset{\|}{C}}(OCH_2CH_2)_n O\overset{O}{\overset{\|}{C}}(CH_2)_{10}CH_3$$

n = 4–150. Yellow liquid to white solid. HLB: 5.9–18.5 (4–150 moles EO).
Production:
• lauric acid, narrow cut + polyethylene glycol (esterification)
Uses: emulsifier (cosmetics, pharmaceuticals)

polyethylene glycol dimethacrylate

$$CH_2=\overset{O}{\overset{\|}{C}}CO(CH_2CH_2O)_n C\overset{O}{\overset{\|}{C}}CH=CH_2$$
$$\quad\quad CH_3\quad\quad\quad\quad\quad\quad\quad\quad CH_3$$

Production:
• polyethylene glycol + methyl methacrylate (transesterification)
Uses: crosslinking comonomer

polyethylene glycol dioleate
PEG dioleate (CTFA)

$$CH_3(CH_2)_7CH=CH(CH_2)_7\overset{O}{\overset{\|}{C}}O(CH_2CH_2O)_n \overset{O}{\overset{\|}{C}}(CH_2)_7CH=CH(CH_2)_7CH_3$$

n = 4–23. Yellow liquid or solid. HLB: 4.6–12.6 (4.5–23 moles EO).
Production:
• polyethylene glycol + oleic acid (esterification)
Uses: emulsifier (oil-based cleaners, oil-spill dispersants); emulsifier/lubricity additive (metalworking fluids, textile auxiliaries); antifoam; antistatic agent

polyethylene glycol distearate
PEG distearate

$$CH_3(CH_2)_{16}\overset{O}{\overset{\|}{C}}(OCH_2CH_2)_n O\overset{O}{\overset{\|}{C}}(CH_2)_{16}CH_3$$

n = 9–14. Solid. HLB: 7.7–10.1 (9–14 moles EO).

Production:
• polyethylene glycol + stearic acid (esterification)
Uses: emulsifier/opacifier (cosmetics, toiletries)

polyethylene glycol monocetyl ether
See: cetyl alcohol ethoxylates

polyethylene glycol monocetyloleyl ether
See: cetyloleyl alcohol ethoxylates

polyethylene glycol monolaurate
polyoxyethylene monolaurate; PEG laurate (CTFA)

$$CH_3(CH_2)_{10}C(OCH_2CH_2)_nOR$$

R = H, methyl-, n = 4–100. Pale yellow liquids to white, waxy solids. HLB: 9–19. Dispersible in water at low EO content, soluble at higher EO content. The solubility decreases with increasing temperature.
Production:
• lauric acid, broad cut + ethylene oxide (epoxidation)
• polyethylene glycol monomethyl ether + lauric acid, broad cut/lauric acid, narrow cut (esterification)
Uses: emulsifier (polyvinyl chloride production); lubricant (textile/glassfibre processing); printing/dyeing auxiliary; wetting agent/solubiliser/emulsifier (flavourings, perfumes, cosmetics)

polyethylene glycol monomethyl ether

$$CH_3O(CH_2CH_2O)_nH$$

n = 7–16. Colourless, viscous liquids or soft waxes. MP: -5–+25°C. M: 350–750. Miscible with water.
Production:
• methanol + ethylene oxide (epoxidation)
Derivatives:
polyethylene glycol monolaurate; polyethylene glycol monooleate; polyethylene glycol monostearate

polyethylene glycol monooleate
polyoxyethylene monooleate; PEG monooleate

$$CH_3(CH_2)_7CH=CH(CH_3)_7C(OCH_2CH_2)_nOR$$

R = H, methyl-, n = 4–130. Pale yellow to white, waxy solid. HLB: 7–19 (4–130 moles EO). Dispersible in water at low EO content, soluble at higher EO content. Solubility decreases with increasing temperature.
Production:
• oleic acid + ethylene oxide (epoxidation)
• polyethylene glycol monomethyl ether + oleic acid (esterification)
Uses:
lubricant/antistatic agent (textile spin finishes); emulsifier (metalworking fluids, polyvinyl chloride production); antifoam; surfactant (oil spill dispersants)

polyethylene glycol monostearate
polyoxyethylene monostearate; PEG stearate

$$CH_3(CH_2)_{16}C(OCH_2CH_2)_nOR$$

R = H, methyl-. White or yellow paste or solid. Properties vary with the length of the ethoxylate chain. MP: 31–33°C. HLB: 7.5–18.0 (4–100 moles EO). Insoluble in water below 8 moles EO.
Production:
• stearic acid + ethylene oxide (epoxidation)
• polyethylene glycol monomethyl ether + stearic acid (esterification)
Uses: emulsifier (pesticides, metalworking fluids); foam boosters/antiredeposition agents (shampoos); emulsifier/thickening agent (cosmetics); antistatic agent (textile spin finishes, paper tissue); nonionic surfactant (textile scouring, hard-surface/metal/concrete cleaners)

polyethylene glycol monotallate
PEG tallate

$$RC(OCH_2CH_2)_nOH$$

R = tall-, n = 3–10. Liquid or waxy solid.
Production:
• tall oil fatty acid + ethylene oxide (epoxidation)
Uses:
emulsifier/wetting agent (pesticides); low-foaming surfactant (hard surface cleaners, paper desliming aid)

polyethyleneimine
polyaziridine; PEI; Polymin (BASF); [9002-98-6]

$$[CH_2CH_2NH]_x$$

Water-soluble cationic polyelectrolyte available with a branched or linear structure.
Production:
• ethyleneimine (polymerisation)
Uses: cationic polyelectrolytes (paper retention aid, wet strength additive, pigment dispersion); flocculant (water treatment); adhesion promotion agent; ion-exchange media; textile dyeing/printing auxiliary

poly(ethylene naphthalate)
PEN

Production:
• dimethyl naphthalene-2,6-dicarboxylate + ethylene glycol (esterification)
Uses: magnetic recording tape/packaging film

poly(ethylene oxide) resins
PEOX; Polyox (Union Carbide)

$$HO\text{—}[CH_2CH_2O]_x\text{—}H$$

High molecular weight, thermoplastic ethylene oxide available as powder, slurry or film. MP: 65°C. Soluble in water. Tensile strength: 15–20 MPa. Elongation at break: 700–1,200%. M: 100,000–5,000,000.
Production:
• ethylene oxide (epoxidation)
Uses: coagulant (water treatment); extruded water-soluble/heat-sealable packaging films; water-soluble antimist/antisplash additives; thickening agent (water/acid/solvents); wet tack/levelling agent (adhesives)

polyethylenepolyamine
PEP; polyamines; [84238-53-9]; [68910-05-4]
Dark brown, viscous liquid with an ammoniacal odour. MP: -20°C to 20°C. BP: > 270°C. d: 1.00–1.10 kg/l (20°C). Flash point: >130°C. Miscible with water, oxygenated and aromatic solvents. The product is a mixture of high-boiling ethyleneamines and ethanolamines.
Production:
• ethylene dichloride + ammonia (amine formation; coproduced with ethylenediamine/diethylenetriamine/triethylenetetramine/tetraethylenepentamine/piperazine/aminoethylpiperazine)
• ethylenediamine + monoethanolamine (reductive amination; coproduced with diethylenetriamine/triethylenetetramine/tetraethylenepentamine)
Derivatives: alkylphenol-polyamine adducts; fatty acid imidazoline polyamines; polyamide resins, reactive
Uses: cement grinding aid; epoxy resin curing agent; vulcanisation accelerator

poly(ethylene terephthalate)
polyester, linear, high molecular weight; PET; Arnite (Akzo); Kodar (Eastman Chemical); Melinex (ICI); [25038-59-9]

$$[CH_2CH_2OC\text{—}\bigcirc\text{—}CO]_x$$

Amorphous or crystalline thermoplastic. Slow crystallisation rates at processing temperatures allow the polymer to be quenched into its amorphous state. Crystallisation can be induced by orientating the polymer as film or fibre, or by the inclusion of nucleation additives. d: 1.37–1.39 kg/l. Tensile strength: 140 MPa (biaxially-oriented film), 50 MPa (moulding grades). Vicat softening point: 261°C. The polymer is characterised by its high clarity in amorphous or biaxially-oriented forms. Highly crystalline, opaque moulding resin is also produced. Glass fibre is commonly used in moulding compounds giving a heat distortion temperature of 245°C. Recycled material is available in some countries.

Production:
• ethylene glycol + terephthalic acid (esterification)
• ethylene glycol + dimethyl terephthalate (transesterification)
Uses:
crystalline moulding compounds (cooking containers); amorphous moulding compounds (boil-in-bag pouches, microwaveable containers); biaxially-oriented coated/metallised/embossed film; biaxially-oriented film (packaging, recording tape, floppy disks, capacitors, electronic insulation); biaxially-oriented film (photographic, reprographic, drawing media); blow-moulded soft drink/condiment containers; moulding compounds (vehicle engine components, electrical/electronic connectors and components); partially-oriented fibre (textiles, nonwoven fabrics); polyethylene terephthalate/polycarbonate blends; strapping tapes/ropes

poly(ethylene-tetrafluoroethylene)
See: ethylene-tetrafluoroethylene copolymers

polyethylene wax, high-density

$$[CH_2\text{–}CH_2]_n$$

n = 70–350.
Production:
• ethylene (Ziegler polymerisation)
• polyethylene, high-density (thermomechanical cleavage)
Derivatives: alkanol (C_{30}-C_{50}) ethoxylates; wax, oxidised
Uses: antistatic agent/lubricant (textile spin finishes); hot melt adhesives; plastics processing lubricant; rubproofing additive (printing inks)

polyethylene wax, low-density

$$[CH_2\text{–}CH_2]_n$$

n = 50–500.
Production:
• ethylene (high-pressure bulk polymerisation)
• polyethylene, low-density (thermomechanical cleavage)
Derivatives: wax, oxidised
Uses: antistatic agent/lubricant (textile spin finishes); hot melt adhesives

poly(fluoroalkoxyphosphazene) elastomers
PNF; Eypel-F (Ethyl); PNF Rubber (Bridgestone/Firestone)

$$[P=N]_x \begin{array}{l} OCH_2(CF_2CF_2)_nH \\ OCH_2CF_3 \end{array}$$

n = 1–3. Elastomer characterised by its excellent low-temperature flexibility, its good mechanical properties over the temperature range -75–+150°C and its good resistance to weather, solvents and acid.

Production:
- ammonium chloride + phosphorus pentachloride + 1,1,ω-trihydroperfluoroalkanol/2,2,2-trifluoroethanol (reaction/salt formation/dehydrochlorination)

Uses:
O-rings/seals (aerospace, military, industrial applications); low-temperature fuel hoses; vibration shock mountings

polyglycerol

$$\left[CH_2CHCH_2O\right]_n \quad \overset{OH}{|}$$

Viscous liquids. Various grades contain 2–10 glycerol units joined by ether linkages. Soluble in water and alcohol.
Production:
- glycerol (ether formation)

Derivatives: polyglycerol fatty esters
Uses: humectant

polyglycerol fatty esters

polyglyceryl-10 decaoleate (CTFA); polyglyceryl-6 dioleate (CTFA); polyglyceryl-3 oleate (CTFA); polyglyceryl-4 oleate (CTFA); polyglyceryl-2 sesquioleate (CTFA); polyglyceryl-10 tetraoleate (CTFA); A(1) 6.28 (FAO/WHO); E475 (EC)
Mixed products based on polyglycerol containing 3–10 glycerol units condensed with 2–10 moles of fatty acid.
Production:
- polyglycerol + oleic acid/stearic acid/ricinoleic acid (esterification)

Uses: food emulsifier

poly(glycidyltrimethylammonium chloride)
[51838-31-4]

$$\left[CH_2-CHO\right]_x \quad CH_2N(CH_3)_3^+ \quad Cl^-$$

Production:
- 2,3-epoxypropyltrimethylammonium chloride (polymerisation)

Uses:
cationic polyelectrolytes (water/sewage clarification); retention aids/drainage aids (paper production)

poly(hexafluoropropylene oxide)
Krytox (Du Pont)

$$CF_3CF_2CF_2O(CFCF_2O)_nCF_2CF_3 \quad \overset{CF_3}{|}$$

n = 0–18. Thermally stable and chemically inert liquids.
Production:
- hexafluoropropylene oxide (polymerisation/ decarboxylative fluorination)

Uses: heat-transfer fluid; synthetic lubricant base oils

poly(hexamethylenebiguanide) hydrochloride

$$\left[NHCNHCNH(CH_2)_6\right]_n \quad nHCl \quad \overset{NH}{\overset{||}{}} \overset{NH}{\overset{||}{}}$$

Production:
- dicyandiamide + hexamethylenediamine (amidine formation)

Uses: disinfectant

polyhydantoin resins

Films characterised by their excellent electrical insulation characteristics. Continuously usable up to 160°C. T_g: 273°C. d: 1.27 kg/l.
Production:
- ethyl chloroacetate + *m*-phenylenediamine + 4,4′-diphenylmethane diisocyanate, polymeric (amine formation/isocyanate addition)

Uses:
electrical insulation films (electric motors, capacitors)

poly(p-hydroxybenzoate)
Ekonol (BP Chemicals)

$$\left[O-\underset{}{}-\overset{O}{\overset{||}{C}}\right]_x$$

High melting point polymer shaped by impact moulding, pressure sintering or flame spraying.
Production:
- phenyl *p*-hydroxybenzoate (transesterification)

Uses: heat-resistant bearings

poly(hydroxybutyrate-hydroxyvalerate)
PHB; Biopol (ICI)

$$\left[CHCH_2CO\right]_x\left[CHCH_2CO\right]_y \quad \overset{O}{\overset{||}{}} \quad \overset{O}{\overset{||}{}} \quad \underset{CH_3}{} \quad \underset{C_2H_5}{}$$

Thermoplastic. Softening point: 150–180°C. The hydroxyvalerate content varies from 0% to 25%. At 0%, the polymer is rigid whereas at 25% it is soft and tough like polyethylene.
Production:
- microbial fermentation medium + *Alcaligenes eutrophus* bacteria (fermentation)

Uses: biodegradable medical/agricultural/packaging uses

poly(2-hydroxyethyl methacrylate)
Production:
- 2-hydroxyethyl methacrylate (polymerisation)

Uses: contact lenses; hydrophilic coatings (technical/medical applications)

poly(*N*-β-hydroxyethyl-2,2,6,6-tetramethyl-4-hydroxy-piperidyl succinate)

Production:
- 4-hydroxy-2,2,6,6-tetramethyl-1-piperidine ethanol + dimethyl succinate (transesterification)

Uses: light stabiliser (plastics)

poly(2-hydroxypropyl dimethylammonium chloride)
poly(dimethyl-2-hydroxypropylammonium chloride); [39660-17-8]

Highly cationic polyelectrolyte. M: <500,000.
Production:
- epichlorohydrin + dimethylamine (amine formation/polymerisation)

Uses:
cationic flocculants (coal clarification)

polyimide resins
Kapton (Du Pont); Vespel (Du Pont)

Thermoset polymers in the form of blocks or film. These polymers have excellent heat resistance and electrical properties as well as good chemical, solvent and abrasion resistance. d: 1.42 kg/l. Tensile strength: 90 Mpa. Elongation at break: 8%.
Production:
- pyromellitic dianhydride + 4,4′-oxydianiline (imide formation)

Uses:
high-temperature/high-strength machinable blocks/film

polyimide resins, prepolymers
Prepolymers cured by stoving at temperatures above 150°C. The cured resin is characterised by its excellent high temperature and insulation properties. Many grades can be used continuously at 300°C.

Production:
- pyromellitic dianhydride/4,4′-oxydiphthalic anhydride/biphenyl-3,3′,4,4′-tetracarboxylic dianhydride/benzophenonetetracarboxylate dianhydride + *p*-phenylenediamine/4,4′-oxydianiline/*m*-phenylenediamine (imide formation)

Uses: binder (stoving enamels)

poly(imide-sulphone)
PISO; Vectra (Hoechst)

Production:
- benzophenonetetracarboxylate dianhydride + 4,4′-diaminodiphenyl sulphone (amide formation)

Uses: high-temperature/electrical insulation mouldings (hair dryer/oven/fan heater components)

polyisobutenylsuccinic anhydride
PIBSA

n = 10–15 (mixed isomer).
Production:
- polybutene/polyisobutylene, low molecular weight + maleic anhydride (ene reaction)

Derivatives: *N,N′*-(tetraethylenepentamino)-bispolyisobutenylsuccinimide; *N*-(tetraethylenepentamino)mono-polyisobutenylsuccinimide

polyisobutylene, high molecular weight
Oppanol B (BASF); Vistanex MM (Exxon Chemical)

Light-coloured, rubbery polymer characterised by its excellent chemical and ozone resistance. M: 70,000–250,000.

Production:
- isobutylene (polymerisation)

Uses: chewing gum base; caulks/sealants; rubber/polyethylene impact modifier; tank liner/roof covering membranes; pressure-sensitive adhesives

polyisobutylene, low molecular weight

PIB; Oppanol B (BASF); Paratone N (Exxon Chemical); Vistanex LM (Exxon Chemical)

$$\left[CH_2-\underset{\underset{CH_3}{|}}{\overset{\overset{CH_3}{|}}{C}} \right]_x$$

Colourless to pale yellow, viscous liquids. M: 500–5,000. Competes with polybutene (*qv*).

Production:
- isobutylene (polymerisation)

Derivatives: polybutene thiophosphonate propoxylates, alkali-earth salts; polyisobutenylsuccinic anhydride

Uses: metalworking/compressor/2-stroke/electrical insulation oils; tackifier (sealants, mastics, hot melt/pressure-sensitive adhesives); viscosity modifier (lubricating oils)

poly(isobutyl vinyl ether-vinyl chloride)

poly(vinyl chloride-isobutyl vinyl ether); Vinoflex (BASF)

$$\left[CH_2-\underset{\underset{OCH_2CH(CH_3)_2}{|}}{CH} \right]_y \left[CH_2-\underset{\underset{Cl}{|}}{CH} \right]_x$$

Latex.

Production:
- isobutyl vinyl ether + vinyl chloride (polymerisation)

Uses: binder (paints, sealants)

polyisocyanurate, rigid foam

Rigid foam in which a high proportion of the isocyanate has self-condensed into isocyanurate rings. Such foam has better flame resistance than rigid polyurethane foam, although inferior impact properties.

Production:
- /4,4'-diphenylmethane diisocyanate, polymeric + polyether polyols, rigid/polyester polyols, aromatic (isocyanate addition)

Uses:
slabstock/laminated foam-cored panels/composite building boards; sprayed insulation foam (tanks, roofs, pipe insulation)

polyisoprene

isoprene rubber; *cis*-1,4-polyisoprene; IR

$$\left[CH_2\underset{\overset{|}{CH_3}}{C}=CHCH_2 \right]_x$$

Solid bales available in a range of standard, oil-extended and carbon black-filled grades. d: 0.90–0.94 kg/l.

Properties vary with the type of catalyst used in their manufacture. Lithium-catalysed grades have a higher, but narrower, chain-length distribution but a lower *cis*-isomer content than titanium-catalysed grades. Titanium-catalysed grades are therefore closer to natural rubber in their physical properties. A liquid grade of polyisoprene is also available.

Production:
- isoprene (Ziegler polymerisation)

Derivatives:
rubber, chlorinated

Uses: footwear/moulded goods; latex (foam, dipped goods, adhesives); tyres

cis-**1,4-polyisoprene** *See:* natural rubber; polyisoprene

polyisoprene, hydrogenated

$$\left[CH_2CHCH_2CH_2 \right]_x \quad \overset{CH_3}{|}$$

Production:
- isoprene (polymerisation/hydrogenation)

Uses: viscosity modifier (lubricating oils)

poly(maleic acid)

poly(maleic anhydride)

$$\left[\underset{\underset{COOH}{|}}{\overset{\overset{COOH}{|}}{CH}}-CH \right]_x$$

Production:
- maleic anhydride (polymerisation)

Uses: scale inhibitor (water treatment)

polymeric plasticisers

plasticisers, polymeric

$$A\left[B-C \right]_x B-A$$

A = monohydric alcohol, B = dibasic acid, C = diol. Pale yellow liquids. Several grades available which vary in viscosity from 3,000 mPa.s (25°C) to >10^6 mPa.s (25°C). d: 1.0–1.2 kg/l (25°C). M: 1,300 (low-viscosity grades). Soluble in aromatic, ketone, ether and chlorinated solvents. Insoluble in water and aliphatic solvents.

Production:
- 2-ethylhexanol/isooctanol/isodecanol + ethylene glycol/propylene glycol/1,3-butanediol/ 1,4-butanediol/dipropylene glycol + adipic acid/ azelaic acid/sebacic acid/isosebacic acid/phthalic anhydride (esterification)

Uses: plasticiser (polyvinyl chloride, rubber)

polymethacrylates, oil-soluble

A molecular weight range of ~20,000 is optimum for viscosity modification applications. Pour-point depression requires higher molecular weight polymers.

$$\left[CH_2-\underset{\underset{COOR}{|}}{\overset{\overset{CH_3}{|}}{C}} \right]_x$$

R = mixed C_1-C_{20} alkyl-.
Production:
- methyl methacrylate/*n*-butyl methacrylate/2-ethyl-hexyl methacrylate/*n*-nonyl methacrylate/isodecyl methacrylate/lauryl methacrylate/isotridecyl methacrylate/stearyl methacrylate (polymerisation)
Uses:
viscosity modifier/pour point depressants (lubricating oils)

polymethacrylates, oil-soluble dispersants

$$\left[CH_2-\underset{\underset{COOR}{|}}{\overset{\overset{CH_3}{|}}{C}} \right]_x \left[CH_2-\underset{\underset{COOR'}{|}}{\overset{\overset{CH_3}{|}}{C}} \right]_y$$

R = mixed C_1-C_{20} alkyl-, R' = polar groups.
Production:
- methyl methacrylate/*n*-butyl methacrylate/2-ethyl-hexyl methacrylate/*n*-nonyl methacrylate/isodecyl methacrylate/lauryl methacrylate/stearyl methacrylate + 2-hydroxyethyl methacrylate/2-dimethyl-aminoethyl methacrylate/2-diethylaminoethyl methacrylate/dimethylaminopropyl methacrylamide (polymerisation)
Uses: ashless dispersants (lubricants)

poly(methacrylic acid)

$$\left[CH_2-\underset{\underset{COOH}{|}}{\overset{\overset{CH_3}{|}}{C}} \right]_x$$

Available commercially as aqueous solutions containing about 20% solids. pH: 2.0. d: 1.07 kg/l.
Production:
- methacrylic acid (solution polymerisation)
Uses:
cement grinding aid; textile soil-release finishes; rayon textile sizing agent; stabiliser (polyvinyl chloride suspension production)

poly(methacrylimide)
PMI; Kamax (Rohm and Haas); Rohacell (Roehm)

$$\left[CH_2-\underset{O=\overset{}{\underset{}{}}}{\overset{H_3C \quad CH_3}{}}\underset{N \atop H}{} =O \right]_x$$

Foam characterised by its good heat distortion properties, solvent resistance and stiffness.
Production:
- methacrylic acid + methacrylonitrile (polymerisation)
Uses: cellular foam (engine housings, aircraft body components, sports equipment)

poly(methylene-thiodiethyl ether)

$$\left[CH_2CH_2SCH_2CH_2OCH_2O \right]_x$$

Production:
- thiodiglycol + formaldehyde (carbonyl condensation)
Uses:
rubber heat stabiliser/plasticiser

poly(methyl methacrylate)
PMM; PMMA; Lucite (Du Pont); Perspex (ICI); Plexiglas (Rohm and Haas);

$$\left[CH_2-\underset{\underset{COOCH_3}{|}}{\overset{\overset{CH_3}{|}}{C}} \right]_x$$

Granules, beads, cast sheet and block. d: 1.18 kg/l. Tensile strength: 72 MPa. Tensile modulus: 2,400 MPa. The polymer is a hard, transparent, amorphous material soluble in ethyl acetate and chlorinated solvents. M_n: 60,000 (moulding grades), 1,000,000 (cast sheet).
Production:
- methyl methacrylate (bulk polymerisation)
- methyl methacrylate (suspension polymerisation)
Uses:
extruded decorative strips/furniture hardware; extruded optical fibres; machinable blocks (spectacle lenses, instrument components); moulded decorative plaques (cars, household equipment); moulded domestic furniture/electronics covers; moulded transparent vehicle, ship, traffic lights; sheet (display signs, baths, wash basins, cover panes, display screens, instrument components); sheet (motorcycle windscreens, tractor cabs, roof lights, transparent wall, ceiling, roof, dome building material); tubing (food processing, chemical, medical equipment components)

polymethylpentene
poly(4-methyl-1-pentene); P4MP1; PMP; TPX (Mitsui); Crystalor (Phillips Petroleum)

$$\left[CH_2-\underset{}{\overset{\overset{CH_2CH(CH_3)_2}{|}}{CH}} \right]_x$$

Thermoplastic beads available unfilled or glass fibre-reinforced. d: 0.83–0.84 kg/l. MP: 230–240°C. Tensile strength: 26–27 MPa. Tensile modulus: ~1500 MPa. Elongation at break: 25–40%. The polymer is characterised by its high transparency and good heat performance with chemical resistance similar to polypropylene. It is relatively brittle and has poor age resistance, however.
Production:
- 4-methyl-1-pentene (Ziegler polymerisation)
Uses:
injection-moulded electrical/electronic components; transparent sterilisable laboratory/medical equipment

poly(methyl vinyl ether-maleic anhydride)
methyl vinyl ether-maleic anhydride copolymers; poly-(maleic anhydride-methyl vinyl ether); PVM/MA; Gantrez AN (ISP)

White powder. Linear polymer with a 1:1 ratio of methyl vinyl ether to maleic anhydride. M: 20,000–67,000. Soluble in oxygenated solvents. Polymers of this type are also produced in the form of a lightly crosslinked gels.
Production:
• methyl vinyl ether + maleic anhydride (cationic polymerisation)
Uses:
drilling mud fluid loss control agent; gelling agent (textile printing pastes); viscosity modifier (emulsion paints, cosmetics, hair spray, textile size)

polymyxin
[1406-11-7]
Mixed group of cyclic polypeptides made of L-α,γ-diaminobutyric acid, L-threonine, L-leucine and other amino acid units. M: ~1,000.
Production:
• microbial fermentation medium + *Bacillus polymyxa* bacteria (fermentation)
Uses: antibacterial drug

polynorbornamide
Hostamid LP700 (Hoechst)

Thermoplastic pellets. d: 1.17 kg/l. Tensile strength: 91–95 MPa. The polymer has high clarity, rigidity, low water absorption and good thermal properties. It has an amorphous plastic structure.
Production:
• dimethyl terephthalate + caprolactam + bis(amino-methyl)norbornane (amide formation)
Uses:
transparent instrument/electrical components

polynorbornene
PNR; Norsorex (Total Chimie)

Elastomer vulcanised by sulphur or peroxide methods. The vulcanisate is characterised by its ability to produce very soft, but strong, rubber goods. The double bond can be either in the *cis* or *trans* configuration depending on the catalyst used in the polymerisation.

Production:
• norbornene (cycloaddition/polymerisation)
Uses:
bellows/vibration damping componants; profiles/ seals; roller coverings

polyoctenylene, rubber
polyoctenamer; Vestenamer (Hüls)

Two grades are available: one has a high *trans*-isomer content and high crystallinity, the other a medium *trans*-isomer content and low crystallinity.
Production:
• cyclooctene (metathesis)
Uses: processing aid (diene rubbers)

polyoil, epoxidised
See: polybutadiene, epoxidised

polyols, epoxy dispersion
Flexible polyurethane triols containing a stable dispersion of amine-cured epoxy resin particles formed by the *in situ* reaction of ethylenediamine with bisphenol A diglycidyl ether in polyol. A dispersion content of up to 20% is possible.
Production:
• bisphenol A diglycidyl ether + ethylenediamine + polyether polyols, flexible (epoxidation)
Derivatives:
polyurethane, flexible foam, high-resilience

polyols, flexible *See:* polyether polyols, flexible; polyester polyols, linear

polyols, flexible, amine-terminated
See: polyether polyols, flexible, amine-terminated

polyols, PHD
See: polyols, polyurea dispersion

polyols, polyisocyanate polyaddition
PIPA polyols
Flexible polyurethane triols containing a dispersion of polyurethane particles formed by reaction of isocyanate with alkanolamine. Products with a dispersion content of over 80% are possible.
Production:
• toluene diisocyanate/4,4'-diphenylmethane diisocyanate, polymeric + diethanolamine + polyether polyols, flexible (isocyanate addition)
Derivatives: polyurethane, flexible foam, cold-moulded; polyurethane, flexible foam, high-resilience

polyols, polymer
Ethylene oxide-tipped triols containing stable dispersions of styrene-acrylonitrile formed *in situ*. Where

high dispersion concentrations and high styrene contents are required in order to meet smouldering ignition tests, stabilisers produced by grafting styrene onto polyether polyols are used. These are formed using polyols containing maleic anhydride or isocyanatoethyl methacrylate as reactive sites or by addition polymerisation techniques.
Production:
• polyether polyols, flexible + styrene + acrylonitrile
  (polymerisation)
Derivatives:
polyurethane, flexible foam, cold-moulded; polyurethane, flexible foam, high-resilience

polyols, polyurea dispersion
polyols, PHD
Flexible polyurethane triols containing a dispersion of polyurea particles formed by reaction of a diamine, such as hydrazine, with toluene diisocyanate. Products with a dispersion content of up to 28% are possible.
Production:
• toluene diisocyanate + hydrazine + polyether
  polyols, flexible (isocyanate addition)
Derivatives:
polyurethane, flexible foam, cold-moulded; polyurethane, flexible foam, high-resilience

polyols, rigid *See:* polyether polyols, rigid

polyoxin
[19396-06-6]

R = hydroxymethyl- (polyoxin B), -carboxylic acid (polyoxin D). Mixed product consisting of polyoxin B and polyoxin D.
Production:
• microbial fermentation medium + *Streptomyces
  cacaoi* bacteria (fermentation/extraction)
Uses:
fungicide

poly(oxymethylene)
See: polyacetal, copolymers; polyacetal, homopolymers

polyoxypropyleneamines
See: polyether polyols, flexible, amine-terminated

polyoxypropylene triols
See: polyether polyols, flexible

poly(perfluoropropyl ether)
Fomblin (Ausimont); Galden (Ausimont); Krytox (Du Pont)

Colourless liquids. All low molecular weight polymers. BP: 95–125°C (HS grade), 215–240°C (LS grade). d: 1.84 kg/l (HS grade, 20°C), 1.82 kg/l (LS grade, 20°C).
Production:
• hexafluoropropylene (photooxidation/thermal
  rearrangement)
• perfluoroethercarboxylic acid oligomers (decarb-
  oxylation/fluorination)
Uses: heat-transfer fluid (vapour phase soldering, electronic cooling systems); leak testing fluid; non-flammable aircraft/aerospace lubricant

poly(4,4'-phenoxybiphenyl sulphone)
PES; Radel (Amoco)

Transparent, amorphous, amber thermoplastic characterised by its good creep resistance, thermal and electrical properties. Self-extinguishing. Resistant to attack by aqueous acid, alkali and most solvents. T_g: 220°C. d: 1.29 kg/l. Tensile strength: 72 N/mm^2. Tensile modulus: 2.1 N/mm^2. Elongation at break: 60%. Available as unreinforced and glass fibre-filled grades as well as in blends with ABS.
Production:
• 4,4'-dihydroxybiphenyl + 4,4'-dichlorodiphenyl
  sulphone (ether formation)
Uses: hair driers/oven/fan heater components; high-temperature/electrical insulation mouldings

polyphenyl *See:* terphenyl

poly(*m*-phenyleneisophthalamide)
m-aramid; Nomex (Du Pont)

Fibre and machineable blocks characterised by their excellent heat resistance. Suitable for continuous service at 200°C. The fibre is spun from lyotropic, liquid-crystalline, oriented solutions. It does not melt but decomposes at temperatures above 400°C. d: 1.35–1.45 kg/l.
Production:
• isophthaloyl chloride + *m*-phenylenediamine (amide
  formation)

Uses: heat-insulating paper fibre (electrical equipment); honeycomb panel core (aircraft, public transport); textile fibres (heat protective clothing, industrial fabrics)

poly(phenylene oxide)

polyarylene ether; poly(phenylene ether); poly(2,6-dimethyl-*p*-phenylene oxide); PPE; PPO; Noryl (General Electric)

Amorphous thermoplastic. The commercial product is usually sold as an alloy with polystyrene. d: 1.06 kg/l. Tensile strength: 72 MPa. Elongation at break: 50%. The polymer is characterised by its high heat distortion temperature (up to 120°C), its excellent impact strength, flame resistance and rigidity. Available in various glass or mineral-filled grades.
Production:
• 2,6-xylenol (oxidative coupling)
Uses: high-temperature precision engineering, electrical components; polystyrene/polyamide/polycarbonate blends (vehicle panels, ducts, components, electrical housings, mountings); water distribution, pumping, handling equipment

poly(phenylene sulphide)

PPS; Ryton (Phillips Petroleum); Tedur (Bayer)

Polymer characterised by its good heat, flame and chemical resistance as well as reasonable electrical insulation properties. Tensile strength: 70–150 MPa. Flexural modulus: 1,000–20,000 MPa (40% glass fibre). Available either as a viscous thermoplastic processed by injection moulding at 340–370°C or as compression moulding compounds crosslinked by air oxidation at elevated temperatures.
Production:
• *p*-dichlorobenzene + sodium sulphide (sulphide formation)
Uses: compression moulding powders (kitchen, plant, laboratory equipment); injection-moulded electrical formers, holders, switches, relays; vehicle fuel system components, air control fittings; industrial fibres

poly(*p*-phenyleneterephthalamide)

p-aramid; PPDT; PPTA; Kevlar (Du Pont)

Fibre characterised by its high strength and excellent heat resistance. It also possesses good dielectric properties and chemical resistance. The polymer does not melt but decomposes at temperatures in excess of 400°C. d: 1.45 kg/l.
Production:
• terephthaloyl chloride + *p*-phenylenediamine (amide formation)
Uses: asbestos substitute (brake lining reinforcement); high-strength/heat-resistant fibre (cables, fabrics); plastic composite reinforcing fibre (aircraft); reinforcing fibre (tyres, conveyor belts, drive belts); textile fibres (heat protective clothing, industrial fabrics)

polypropylene

PP; [9003-07-0]

Thermoplastic beads available as the homopolymer or as the copolymer with a few percent ethylene. d: 0.90 kg/l. Tensile strength: 28–35 MPa. Flexural modulus: 1,000–1,700 MPa. Copolymers have a higher impact strength but less rigidity than homopolymers. Polypropylene has a predominantly isotactic structure with a high degree of crystallinity.
Production:
• propylene (slurry process)
• propylene (Himont Spheripol process)
• propylene (gas-phase polymerisation)
• propylene (Himont-Mitsui process)
• propylene (Novolen process)
Derivatives:
polypropylene, elastomer-modified; polypropylene wax
Uses:
fibrillated oriented polypropylene tape/fibre; biaxially-oriented film (food, tobacco, confectionery display packaging); blow-moulded drums/water tanks; injection-moulded automobile components, housings, battery cases; injection-moulded kitchen/household equipment; injection-moulded tool, storage boxes; melt-spun fibres; industrial drain/vent/waste piping; domestic floor heating piping; powder coatings; thin-walled food packaging; transparent films (general display packaging)

polypropylene, atactic

polypropylene, amorphous; APP

Tacky, rubbery solid consisting of amorphous polypropylene with a small degree of crystallinity. M: 20,000–80,000. d: 0.86 kg/l. Softening point: 155°C (Ring and Ball Method).
Production:
• propylene (slurry process; byproduct of polypropylene production)
• propylene (polymerisation)

Uses: corrosion protection wrappings; back-coating compositions (carpet tiles); hot melt adhesives (paper lamination); road marking compounds; ingredient (bitumen sealants/roofing sheets); vehicle vibration damping material

polypropylene, elastomer-modified
polyolefin elastomers, thermoplastic; EMP; EMPP; EPDM/PP; TPE; TPOR; Santoprene (Monsanto)
Production:
- polypropylene + ethylene-propylene-diene terpolymer, rubber/ethylene-propylene copolymers, rubber (compounding)

Uses:
cable/wire insulation; automotive spoilers, bumpers, dashboards, shelves, wheel-well linings, door handles; industrial tubing/hosing; shoe heels; sports goods

polypropylene glycol
poly(propylene oxide); PPG; Dowfroth 400 (Dow Chemical); [25322-69-4]

$$HO\text{-}\left[CHCH_2O\right]_n\text{-}H \quad (CH_3)$$

n = 4–70. Viscous liquids. M: 400–4000. Low molecular weight grades have d: 1.01 kg/l, viscosity: 70 mPa.s (25°C) and are completely miscible with water and alcohol. High molecular weight grades have d: 1.00 kg/l (25°C), viscosity: 1,100 mPa.s (25°C) and are immiscible in water although miscible with alcohol.
Production:
- propylene oxide (epoxidation)

Derivatives:
dodecyl succinate propoxylates; ethylene glycol-propylene glycol block copolymers; poly(ether-amide) elastomers; polypropylene glycol diglycidyl ether
Uses: flotation frothing agent; high-temperature lubricants (ovens, dryers, furnaces); polyurethane chain-extender; rubber processing lubricant; water-based fire-resistant hydraulic fluids

polypropylene glycol diglycidyl ether

$$CH_2\text{-}CH\text{CH}_2O\left[CH_2\text{CHO}\right]_n CH_2CH\text{-}CH_2 \quad (CH_3)$$

Production:
- polypropylene glycol + epichlorohydrin (dehydrochlorination)

Uses:
epoxy resin flexibiliser

polypropylene glycol monocetyl ether
See: cetyl alcohol propoxylates

polypropylene glycol monolanolin ether
See: lanolin propoxylates

polypropylene wax

$$\left[CH_2\text{-}CH\right]_n \quad (CH_3)$$

n = 30–100. Waxy solid. Drop point: ~160°C. Viscosity: 100–35,000 mPa.s (170°C).
Production:
- propylene (Ziegler polymerisation)
- polypropylene (thermomechanical cleavage)

Uses: plastics processing lubricant

polystyrene, crosslinked
See: styrene-divinylbenzene copolymers

polystyrene, crosslinked, aminated
Yellow-brown beads. Bulk density: 0.59–0.70 kg/l.
Production:
- styrene-divinylbenzene copolymers + chloromethyl methyl ether + ammonia/methylamine/dimethylamine (chloromethylation/amine formation)

Uses: weakly basic ion-exchange resins (water softening, demineralisation, food/chemical/pharmaceutical purification)

polystyrene, crosslinked, hydroxyethyldimethylbenzylammoniated
Yellow-brown beads. Bulk density: 0.72 kg/l. 'Type 2' resin, used for chloride and hydroxide exchange in water treatment. Several grades available commercially with crosslinking varying from 1% to 8%.
Production:
- styrene-divinylbenzene copolymers + chloromethyl methyl ether + dimethylethanolamine (dehydrochlorination/quaternisation)

Uses: strongly basic ion-exchange resins (water softening, demineralisation, food/chemical/pharmaceutical purification)

polystyrene, crosslinked, phosphonated
Production:
- styrene-divinylbenzene copolymers + chloromethyl methyl ether + ammonia + ethephon (chloromethylation/amine formation/amine formation)

Uses: weakly acidic ion-exchange resins (effluent treatment, ion extraction)

polystyrene, crosslinked, sulphonated
Yellow-brown beads. Bulk density: 0.70–0.95 kg/l. Used for sodium and hydrogen exchange in water treatment. Several grades available commercially with crosslinking varying from 1% to 20%.
Production:
- styrene-divinylbenzene copolymers (sulphonation/neutralisation)

Uses: strongly acidic ion-exchange resins (water softening, demineralisation, food/chemical/pharmaceutical purification)

polystyrene, crosslinked, trimethylbenzylammoniated

Yellow-brown beads. Bulk density: 0.67 kg/l. 'Type 1' resin, used for chloride and hydroxide exchange in water treatment. Several grades available commercially with crosslinking varying from 1% to 8%.
Production:
• styrene-divinylbenzene copolymers + chloromethyl methyl ether + trimethylamine (dehydrochlorination/quaternisation)
Uses: strongly basic ion-exchange resins (water softening, demineralisation, food/chemical/pharmaceutical purification)

polystyrene, expandable

EPS; XPS

Amorphous polystyrene beads containing pentane as a blowing agent and coated with a lubricant. Bead diameter: 0.4–1.5 mm. The polymer is converted to foamed articles with a closed cell structure by the application of steam.
Production:
• styrene (suspension polymerisation)
Uses: expanded polystyrene (protective packaging, insulation, disposable cups)

polystyrene, general-purpose

PS; [9003-53-6]

Thermoplastic pellets. d: 1.05 kg/l. Tensile strength: 52 MPa. Tensile modulus: 3,900 MPa. Softening point: 80–102°C. The polymer is amorphous, hard, rigid and highly transparent. It has low moisture absorption, good chemical resistance and is easily processed to dimensionally stable mouldings. High molecular weight grades have better impact strength while retaining their transparency.
Production:
• styrene (suspension polymerisation)
• styrene (bulk polymerisation)
Derivatives:
sodium polystyrene sulphonate
Uses:
biaxially-oriented film (food packaging); electric/electronic equipment housings/knobs/fittings; injection-moulded bottle caps, jars, containers; household equipment; plastic pigments (emulsion paints); polyarylene ether blends (vehicle panels, ducts, components, electrical housings, mountings); vacuum-formed box liners

polystyrene, high-impact

HIPS; polystyrene, toughened

Thermoplastic pellets formed by the polymerisation of styrene in the presence of rubber latex. d: 1.04 kg/l. Tensile strength: 30 MPa. Tensile modulus: 2,750MPa. Vicat softening point: 94°C. It differs from general purpose polystyrene by its higher impact strength, its lack of transparency and its lower surface gloss.
Production:
• styrene + polybutadiene latex/ethylene-propylene-diene terpolymer, rubber (polymerisation)
Uses:
household/office equipment; refrigerator fittings/linings

polystyrene, sulphonated

See: sodium polystyrene sulphonate

polysulphide, liquid

Thermosetting resin cured by a variety of methods. M: 300–7,500. The vulcanisates have excellent solvent and weather resistance.
Production:
• polysulphide, rubber (reductive cleavage)
Uses: caulks/sealants (aircraft, insulated glass panels, general construction applications); flexible epoxy resin curing agent; solid rocket fuel binder

polysulphide, rubber

TM; Thiokol A (Morton International); Thiokol B (Morton International); Thiokol ST (Morton International) Elastomers characterised by the presence of sulphide or disulphide linkages in the polymer chain. M: >500,000. Cured using hot vulcanisation in which the mercaptan groups are oxidised to form disulphide linkages. The vulcanisate has excellent solvent and weather resistance.
Production:
• ethylene dichloride/di-(2-chloroethyl)ether + sodium sulphide + sulphur (dehydrochlorination)
Derivatives: polysulphide, liquid
Uses:
highly oil/water resistant seals, hoses and couplings

polysulphone

PSU; Udel (Union Carbide)

Transparent, pale yellow engineering thermoplastic characterised by its good creep resistance, thermal and electrical properties. Self-extinguishing. Resistant to

attack by aqueous acid, alkali and most solvents. T_g: 185°C. d: 1.24 kg/l. Tensile strength: 70 N/mm². Tensile modulus: 2.5 N/mm². Elongation at break: 75%. Available as unreinforced and glass fibre-filled grades as well as in blends with ABS.
Production:
• bisphenol A + 4,4′-dichlorodiphenyl sulphone (ether formation)
Uses:
high-temperature/electrical insulation mouldings (hair drier/oven/fan heater components)

polytetrafluoroethylene
PTFE; Fluon (ICI); Teflon (Du Pont); [9002-84-0]

$$-\left[CF_2-CF_2\right]_x-$$

Thermoplastic. d: 2.1–2.3 kg/l. Tensile strength: 17–21 MPa. Elongation at break: 200–300%. The polymer is characterised by its excellent thermal and chemical resistance, its low coefficient of friction and its high electrical insulation. It has a high degree of crystallinity with a linear molecular structure, essentially free from branching. M: 400,000–9,000,000.
Production:
• tetrafluoroethylene (emulsion polymerisation)
Uses:
chemically-resistant Raschig rings/heat exchanger linings/filter media/seals; construction fabrics (architectural tents, pneumatic structures); electrical insulation; aircraft seals/tubes/gearing components; antiadhesion coatings (pans, trays, irons); industrial fibres; low-friction coatings; rubproofing additive (printing inks); thread guides/belts/slides

polytetrafluoroethylene wax

$$-\left[CF_2-CF_2\right]_n-$$

Production:
• tetrafluoroethylene (emulsion polymerisation)
Uses: processing aid (polyolefins)

poly(tetramethylene ether) glycol
poly(tetrahydrofuran); Poly-THF; PTHF; PTMEG; [25190-06-1]

$$H-\left[OCH_2CH_2CH_2CH_2\right]_n-OH$$

n = 10–30. Solid. Softening point: 25–35°C.
Production:
• tetrahydrofuran (polycondensation)
Derivatives:
copolyester, thermoplastic elastomers; elastane; poly-(ether-amide) elastomers; polyurethane, thermoplastic elastomers; toluene diisocyanate polyether prepolymers
Uses: polyvinyl chloride processing lubricant

poly(tetramethylene terephthalate)
See: poly(butylene terephthalate)

polythiazide
[346-18-9]

$C_{11}H_{13}Cl_1F_3N_3O_4S_3$. M: 439.87.
Production:
• 5-chloroaniline-2,4-disulphonamide + 2,2,2-trifluoroethanol + mercaptoacetaldehyde (sulphide formation/carbonyl condensation/methylation)
Uses: diuretic/antihypertensive drug

poly(trifluoropropylmethylsiloxane)

Production:
• dichloromethyl-3,3,3-trifluoropropylsilane (base-catalysed polymerisation)
Uses: chemically-resistant lubricating oils/greases

poly(trimethylhexamethyleneterephthalamide)
See: polyamide 6-(3)T

polyurethane, cast elastomers
CPU
Elastomers made by reaction of an isocyanate prepolymer with a short chain-extending agent either at ambient or high temperature. Both one and two-pack systems are available, the former relying on blocked isocyanate prepolymers. Tensile strength: 20–40 MPa. Elongation at break: 350–700%.
Production:
• naphthalene diisocyanate prepolymer + 1,4-butanediol/1,3-butanediol/trimethylolpropane (isocyanate addition)
• toluene diisocyanate polyether prepolymers + 1,4-butanediol/trimethylolpropane/4,4′-methylenebis(2-chloroaniline) (isocyanate addition)
• polyester polyurethane prepolymers, isocyanate-terminated + 1,4-butanediol (isocyanate addition)
• 4,4′-diphenylmethane diisocyanate polyether prepolymers + polyester polyols, linear/polycaprolactone diols (isocyanate addition)
Uses: castors/rollers; fork-lift/industrial machinery tyres; oil seals; diaphragms

polyurethane, flexible foam, cold-moulded
Soft, lightweight, open-celled foam usually made *in situ* by mixing isocyanate, polyol and blowing agent, and letting the foam cure within a closed mould at 25–60°C. d: 35–55 kg/m³. The product is characterised by its good flexibility, resilience and high tensile strength.

Production:
* 4,4′-diphenylmethane diisocyanate, polymeric/
  4,4′-diphenylmethane diisocyanate trimer/toluene
  diisocyanate/toluene diisocyanate trimers +
  polyether polyols, flexible/polyols, polymer/
  polyols, polyisocyanate polyaddition/polyols,
  polyurea dispersion (isocyanate addition)

Uses: vehicle seating/interior padding; furniture/seating
cushioning

polyurethane, flexible foam, high-resilience

Soft, lightweight, open-celled foam usually made *in
situ* by mixing isocyanate, polyol and blowing agent.
d: 10–80 kg/m². The resilience of the foam increases
sharply as it is compressed giving better support in
furniture cushioning.

Production:
* toluene diisocyanate + polyols, polymer/polyols,
  epoxy dispersion/polyols, polyisocyanate
  polyaddition/polyols, polyurea dispersion
  (isocyanate addition)

Uses:
vehicle seating/arm-rests; furniture/seating cushioning;
mattresses

polyurethane, flexible foam, hot-moulded

Soft, lightweight, open-celled foam usually made *in
situ* by mixing isocyanate, polyol and blowing agent,
and letting the foam cure within a closed mould at
temperatures of ~120*C. d: 30–40 kg/m². The product
is characterised by its good flexibility, resilience and
high tensile strength.

Production:
* toluene diisocyanate + polyether polyols, flexible
  (isocyanate addition)

Uses:
vehicle seating/interior padding; furniture cushioning

polyurethane, flexible foam, slabstock

Soft, lightweight, open-celled foam usually made *in
situ* by mixing isocyanate, polyol and blowing agent.
d: 10–80 kg/m². The foam is characterised by its good
flexibility, resilience and high tensile strength.

Production:
* toluene diisocyanate + polyether polyols, flexible/
  polyester polyols, linear/polyester polyols,
  slightly-branched (isocyanate addition)

Uses:
furniture/seating cushioning; mattresses; packaging;
sound insulation; air filters; laminated foam-backed
fabric; sponges; underwear padding

polyurethane, integral-skin foam

Elastomeric moulding with a foamed core but an intact
surface. d: 200–500 kg/m² in the centre of the moulding, 600–900 kg/m² at the surface. Both open and closed-cell foams are produced.

Production:
* 4,4′-diphenylmethane diisocyanate, polymeric/
  4,4′-diphenylmethane diisocyanate polyether
  prepolymers + polyether polyols, flexible
  (isocyanate addition)

Uses: vehicle steering wheels/head rests/arm rests/cons-
oles/knobs; furniture arm rests/padding; cycle/toy tyres;
shoe-soling/balls

polyurethane, latex

Nonionic, anionic or cationic emulsions with particle
sizes in the range 50–500 nm and containing 50–60%
solids.

Production:
* 4,4′-diphenylmethane diisocyanate, polymeric +
  polyethylene glycol (solution polymerisation/
  mechanical dispersion)

Uses: water-based fabric coatings/finishing agent

polyurethane, low-resilience elastomers

PUR

Cast elastomers made by mixing the two components.
Tensile strength: 7–24 MPa. Elongation at break: 650–
850%.

Production:
* toluene diisocyanate + castor oil/polyester polyols,
  slightly-branched (isocyanate addition)

Uses: electrical/electronic encapsulation; print rollers

polyurethane, microcellular foam

High-density, closed-cell elastomeric foam. d: ~500
kg/m² at the centre of the moulding and ~700 kg/m²
at the skin.

Production:
* 4,4′-diphenylmethane diisocyanate polyether
  prepolymers + polyester polyurethane prepolymers,
  isocyanate-terminated/polyether polyols, flexible/
  polyester polyols, linear (isocyanate addition)

Uses: microcellular shoe-soling; vehicle bumper mount-
ings/suspension bump absorbers

polyurethane, rigid foam

Closed cell foam usually made *in situ* by mixing isocyanate, polyol and blowing agent. Several density
foams are available, depending on the intended purpose. d: 25–50 kg/m² (insulation, buoyancy), 50–200
kg/m² (chairs, furniture), 250–800 kg/m² (computer terminal housings).

Production:
* 4,4′-diphenylmethane diisocyanate, polymeric +
  polyether polyols, rigid/polyester polyols, aromatic
  (isocyanate addition)

Uses: cavity-filling buoyancy foam (boats); refrigerator
insulation; slabstock/laminated foam-cored panels/com-
posite building boards; sprayed insulation foam (tanks,
roofs, piping); structural foam mouldings (chairs, furniture, electronic/computer terminal housings)

polyurethane, semi-rigid foam

High-density, flexible foam with a predominantly open-celled structure. Produced *in situ* by mixing isocyanate and polyol and allowing the polyurethane to cure in a closed mould. The foam is generally blown by including a little water in the polyol component. d: 40–100 kg/m^2.

Production:
- 4,4'-diphenylmethane diisocyanate, polymeric + polyether polyols, flexible/polyester polyol, slightly-branched (isocyanate addition)

Uses: vehicle crash-padded dashboards/interior trim/bumper cores

polyurethane, thermoplastic elastomers

TPU

Solid. The polymer consists of hard segments embedded in a soft, elastomeric polyol phase. The hard segments are formed by linking MDI units together with 1,4-butanediol. Processing is by the standard techniques for thermoplastics. The rubber is characterised by its excellent abrasion and impact resistance, coupled with high strength and a wide working temperature range.

Production:
- 4,4'-diphenylmethane diisocyanate, pure + poly(ethylene-adipate)/polyester polyols, linear/polycaprolactone diols/poly(tetramethylene ether) glycol + 1,4-butanediol (isocyanate addition)

Uses: flexible gaskets/bellows/tubing/coverings; abrasion-resistant rollers and guides; hydraulic hoses; cable sheathing; injection-moulded gears, bearings, ball cups, seals, wear plates; sports shoes/ski boots

polyurethane-polyurea, reaction injection-moulded elastomers

Elastomers produced *in situ* by simultaneous injection moulding of the isocyanate and polyol components. The polyol component often includes fillers and glass-fibre or flake reinforcement, as well pigments and the usual catalysts and chain extenders.

Production:
- 4,4'-diphenylmethane diisocyanate polyether pre-polymers + polyether polyols, flexible/polyether polyols, flexible, amine-terminated (isocyanate addition)

Uses: vehicle body parts/spoilers/bumpers/front grilles/mud guards

polyvinyl acetate

PVA; PVAC; [9003-20-7]

Latex emulsion containing 45–60% solids and a particle size in the range 0.5–30 μ. Stabilised with polyvinyl alcohol, methyl cellulose, hydroxyethyl cellulose or surfactants. pH: 4–5. Viscosity: 1,000–35,000 mPa.s. See also vinyl acetate-butyl acrylate copolymers, vinyl acetate-ethylene-vinyl chloride copolymers and vinyl acetate-vinyl neodecanoate cpolymers.

Production:
- vinyl acetate (emulsion polymerisation)

Derivatives:
polyvinyl alcohol; polyvinyl formal

Uses: cement admixture; paper sizing ingredient; non-woven fabric sizing; textile/packaging/construction adhesives; transparent foil/heat sealing lacquers; binder (water-based paints)

poly(vinyl acetate-crotonic acid)

See: vinyl acetate-crotonic acid copolymers

polyvinyl alcohol

PVA; PVAL; PVOH; [9002-89-5]

Amorphous, atactic, water-soluble thermoplastic. The solubility in water varies with the degree of hydrolysis, the optimum being ~88%. The polymer is available as cast film, fibre or as a solution in water. The film is characterised by its oil resistance, toughness and high tensile strength.

Production:
- polyvinyl acetate + ethanol (transesterification)

Derivatives:
polyvinyl butyral; polyvinyl cinnamate

Uses: dispersant (polyvinyl chloride suspension polymerisation); binder (speciality paper coatings); thermosetting resin mould release agents; protective colloid (emulsion polymerisation); colour photography polymeric coupler raw material; textile fibres; textile sizing; thickening agent (polyvinyl acetate adhesives); water-resistance additive (starch adhesives)

poly(vinylamine)

polyamines

Mixed product of high molecular weight.

Production:
- polyacrylamide (Hofmann degradation)

Uses:
cationic flocculants (wastewater treatment); retention aids (paper production)

polyvinyl butyral

PVB; [63148-65-2]

White powder, aqueous dispersion or film. The powder is dissolved in solvent for use in coatings and adhesives. Aqueous dispersions are plasticised for use in textile coatings.

Production:
- polyvinyl alcohol + *n*-butyraldehyde (acetal formation)

Uses:
safety glass interleaving film; hot melt/structural adhesives; modifying resin (surface coatings, printing inks); water/abrasion-resistant textile finishes

polyvinylcarbazole

Photoconductive thermoplastic. d: 1.19 kg/l. Tensile strength: 10 MPa. Elongation at break: 0.5%. The polymer is brittle with a high softening point.

Production:
- *N*-vinylcarbazole (polymerisation)

Uses:
photoconductor (photocopiers); electronics photoresistive coatings

polyvinyl chloride
vinyon; PVC; [9002-86-2]

Thermoplastic available as powder or in various compounded forms. The base material has a particle size of 30 μ to 300 μ. The particles also vary in shape, mean molecular weight and molecular weight distribution, depending on the method of manufacture. M: 100,000–200,000. Rigid PVC compounds are available as powder or pellets. d: 1.35 kg/l. Softening point: 68–80°C. Tensile strength: 35–50 MPa. Elongation at break: 35–40%. Standard and high-impact grades are available. The compounds contain stabilisers, UV absorbers, fillers, antistatic agents, processing aids and other ingredients. Plasticised PVC compounds are available as pellets. d: 1.15–1.50 kg/l. Tensile strength: 10–25 MPa. The ratio of resin to plasticiser varies from 80:20 to 50:50. PVC pastes consist of PVC granules in plasticiser. The size of the granules is selected so as to ensure a low viscosity with 55–75% resin content. The plasticiser swells the resin particles as the temperature increases, causing gelling. Eventually the particles fuse when the temperature reaches, typically, 170–200°C. Organosols are PVC pastes thinned with solvent.

Production:
- vinyl chloride (suspension polymerisation)

- vinyl chloride (bulk polymerisation)
- vinyl chloride (solution polymerisation)

Derivatives: polyvinyl chloride, chlorinated; polyvinyl chloride, high-impact

Uses:
industrial fibres; plastic gloves; car underseal pastes; calendered packaging film/sheeting pastes; calendered leathercloth sheeting pastes; dip coating, coil coating, stoved industrial finish pastes; powder coating pastes; rotationally-casted flexible hollow product pastes; surface coverings (wallpaper, wallcoverings, furniture, doors); tiles/cushioned floor covering pastes; tarpaulins/work clothes/waterproof membranes/equipment covers; plasticised compounds (extruded flexible piping, mine belting, electrical wire insulation/covering, blow moulded tubes, bottles, balls, toys, extruded window seals, edging, stair protectors, injection moulded shoesoling, gaskets, mats, pads, thermoformed machine covers, displays, signs); plasticised foam (cushioning, sound, vibration damping); reinforcing additive (rubber); rigid compounds (clear plastic bottles, extruded window, door frames, roller shutter blades, guttering, profiles, conduit, foamed door frames, window boards, drain, vent, waste, sewage, soil drainage piping, chemical/gas piping and equipment, translucent glazing panels)

polyvinyl chloride, chlorinated
CPVC; PVCC
Commercial material has a chlorine content of ~65% and $T_g = 110°C$.

Production:
- polyvinyl chloride (chlorination)

Uses:
chemical handling equipment; hot water plumbing components/pipe joints

polyvinyl chloride, high-impact
HI-PVC
Production:
- acrylic resins, latex/ethylene-vinyl acetate copolymers, 40-50% vinyl acetate + vinyl chloride (graft polymerisation)
- polyvinyl chloride + polyethylene, chlorinated/methyl methacrylate-butadiene-styrene copolymers/acrylonitrile-butadiene-styrene copolymers/poly(acrylate-methacrylate) graft copolymers (compounding)

Uses:
extruded profiles (windows, fence posts, door frames, furniture, cladding boards); guttering/cable conduit/corrugated sheet; blister packaging; oil/water/soft drinks bottles

polyvinyl cinnamate
Production:
- polyvinyl alcohol + cinnamoyl chloride (esterification)

Uses: electronics photoresistive coatings

polyvinyl fluoride
PVF; Tedlar (Du Pont); [24981-14-4]

Thermoplastic available as transparent or pigmented extruded film.
Production:
• vinyl fluoride (polymerisation)
Uses: thermosetting resin mould release agents; weather-resistant films (building laminates)

polyvinyl formal
PVF; PVFM

x = 350–500. White, amorphous powder. Contains 5–9% vinyl alcohol and 9–50% vinyl acetate monomers. Soluble in phenols, alcohols, aromatic and some chlorinated solvents.
Production:
• polyvinyl acetate + formaldehyde (acetal formation)
Uses: phenolic/polyvinyl formal resins (wire enamels, adhesives, can coatings)

polyvinylidene fluoride
PVDF; Foraflon (Elf-Atochem); Kynar (Elf-Atochem); [24937-79-9]

Thermoplastic. MP: 154–184°C. d: 1.75–1.80 kg/l. Tensile strength: 35–55 MPa. The polymer is characterised by its strength, toughness and flexibility. It has relatively good chemical resistance. The dielectric properties of the polymer are frequency dependent which renders the material unsuitable for some electrical insulation purposes.
Production:
• vinylidene fluoride (polymerisation)
Uses:
bonded liners (steel machinery/equipment); chemically-resistant piping/equipment; pyroelectric device housings

poly(vinyl methyl ether)
PVM; Gantraz M (ISP); Lutonal (BASF); [9003-09-2]
Available commercially as dry powder or as an aqueous solution. Soluble in water.

Production:
• methyl vinyl ether (cationic polymerisation)
Uses: flexibiliser/viscosity control agent (photoresist coatings); semipermeable membranes (reverse osmosis plants); tackifier/adhesion promoter (acrylic pressure-sensitive adhesives)

poly(vinyl octadecyl ether)

Production:
• octadecyl vinyl ether (polymerisation)
Uses:
high-gloss polish ingredient

poly(vinyl propionate)
Propiofan (BASF)

Production:
• vinyl propionate (emulsion polymerisation)
Uses: binder (alkali-resistant surface coatings)

poly(4-vinylpyridine)
PVP; Reillex (Reilly Industries)
Production:
• 4-vinylpyridine + divinylbenzene (polymerisation)
Uses: catalyst support; immobilised basic catalyst; immobilised chelant (metal recovery)

polyvinylpyrrolidone
povidone; PVP; Polyclar AT (ISP)

White powder. Soluble in water and organic solvents. pH: 3.0–7.0 (5% solution in water).
Production:
• N-vinyl-2-pyrrolidone (aqueous polymerisation)
Derivatives: povidone-iodine
Uses: beer/wine/fruit juice clarifying agent; film-forming agent (hairsprays, cosmetics); parenteral/ophthalmic solutions; pharmaceutical compounding auxiliary; polymeric dyeing substrate (polyacrylonitrile fibres); thickening agent (cosmetics)

polyvinylpyrrolidone, crosslinked
PVPP; [9003-39-8]
White powder. Insoluble in water but swells instantly on contact. Insoluble in organic solvents.

Production:
• *N*-vinyl-2-pyrrolidone (polymerisation)
Uses: pharmaceutical tablet disintegrant

poly-*p*-xylylene
Parylene (Union Carbide)

The product is supplied in the form of the dimer which is vacuum deposited onto the substrate. The polymer is formed as a coating which can be peeled off if required.
Production:
• *p*-xylene (thermal combination/vacuum deposition)
Uses:
dielectric coatings (electronic components)

poly(*m*-xyleneadipamide)
PAMXD6; Ixef (Solvay); MXD6 (Mitsubishi)

Thermoplastic, usually glass fibre-reinforced. d: 1.43 kg/l (30% glass fibre). Tensile strength: 165 MPa (30% glass fibre).
Production:
• adipic acid + *m*-xylylenediamine (amide formation)
Uses: automotive components

POM
See: polyacetal, copolymers; polyacetal, homopolymers

potash *See:* potassium carbonate

potash alum *See:* aluminium potassium sulphate

potash blue *See:* Prussian Blue

potassium
[7440-09-7]

K_1. M: 39.10. Soft, silver-white metal. MP: 98°C. BP: 760°C. d: 0.98 kg/l (20°C). Reacts with water and alcohol releasing hydrogen. Soluble in liquid ammonia.
Production:
• potassium chloride + sodium (reduction/fractionation)
Uses: low-melting, sodium-potassium heat-transfer alloys; reducing agent

potassium acetate
E261 (EC); [127-08-2]

$C_2H_3K_1O_2$. M: 98.14. Colourless, deliquescent crystals. MP: 292°C. d: 1.57 kg/l (25°C). Soluble in water forming alkaline solutions. Soluble in oxygenated solvents.
Production:
• potassium carbonate + acetic acid (salt formation)
Uses: polyurethane foam catalyst; colour fixative/buffering agent (soups, vegetables); dehydration agent; diuretic drug; glass raw material; penicillin purification reagent; softening agent (paper, textiles)

potassium *n*-alkanol (C_{13}-C_{15}) ether propylsulphonate

m = 13–15, n = 3–12.
Production:
• *n*-alkanol(C_{13}-C_{15}) ethoxylates + propane sultone (addition/potassium salt formation)
Uses: emulsifier (industrial detergents, cleaners)

potassium aluminium sulphate
See: aluminium potassium sulphate

potassium amyl xanthate
KAX

$C_6H_{11}K_1O_1S_2$. M: 202.39.
Production:
• carbon disulphide + amyl alcohol, primary + potassium hydroxide (thiocarbonylation)
Uses:
flotation collector (sulphide ores)

potassium antimony tartrate
See: antimony potassium tartrate

potassium benzoate
E212 (EC); [582-25-2]

$C_6H_5K_1O_2$. M: 148.21. Available as the trihydrate. White powder. Loses water of crystallisation when heated above 110°C. Soluble in water and alcohol. Not approved for food use in the USA.
Production:
• benzoic acid + potassium hydroxide (salt formation)
Uses: corrosion inhibitor (antifreeze); preservative (soft drinks, fruit juices, sauces, adhesives, cosmetics)

potassium bicarbonate

potassium acid carbonate; [298-14-6]

KHCO₃

$C_1H_1K_1O_3$. M: 100.12. Colourless crystals. Decomposes on heating to 100–200°C. Solubility in water: 224 g/l (0°C) forming alkaline solutions.

Production:
• potassium carbonate + carbon dioxide (neutralisation)

Derivatives: p-aminosalicylic acid; 2,4-dihydroxybenzoic acid; 2,6-dihydroxybenzoic acid

Uses:
fire extinguishant powder; raising agent (bakery goods)

potassium bifluoride

potassium hydrogen fluoride; [7789-29-9]

KHF₂

$H_1F_2K_1$. M: 78.11. White, crystalline solid. MP: 238°C. d: 2.37 kg/l. Solubility in water: 390 g/l (20°C).

Production:
• potassium carbonate + hydrofluoric acid (salt formation)

Uses: alkylation catalyst; fluorine production electrolyte; glass frosting agent

potassium bitartrate

cream of tartar; monopotassium tartrate; potassium acid tartrate; E336 (EC); [868-14-4]

```
        COO⁻  K⁺
         |
        HCOH
         |
        HOCH
         |
        COOH
```

$C_4H_5K_1O_6$. M: 188.17. White, crystalline powder. Slightly soluble in water. Insoluble in alcohol.

Production:
• Rochelle salt + tartaric acid (salt formation)

Derivatives: antimony potassium tartrate

Uses: dyeing auxiliary; baking powder/cake mixes

potassium bromate

[7758-01-2]

KBrO₃

$Br_1K_1O_3$. M: 167.00. White, crystalline powder. Decomposes when heated above 370°C, releasing oxygen. d: 3.27 kg/l. Soluble in water.

Production:
• potassium carbonate + bromine (salt formation)

Uses: dough conditioner; flour bleach/oxidising agent; analytical reagent; industrial cleaning agent

potassium bromide

[7758-02-3]

Br_1K_1. M: 119.00. White, crystalline powder. MP: 730°C. d: 2.75 kg/l. Soluble in water.

KBr

Production:
• potassium carbonate + bromine (salt formation; byproduct of potassium bromate production)
• potassium carbonate + hydrobromic acid (salt formation)

Derivatives: p-bromobenzyl cyanide

Uses: photographic chemical; process engraving, lithographic reagent

potassium carbonate

potash; [584-08-7]

K₂CO₃

$C_1K_2O_3$. M: 138.21. Available commercially as the anhydrous, granular solid, as potash hydrate with 1.5 moles of water and as a 47% solution in water.

Production:
• potassium hydroxide + carbon dioxide (salt formation)

Derivatives: acesulfame-K; potassium acetate; potassium bicarbonate; potassium bifluoride; potassium bromate; potassium bromide; potassium fluoride; potassium oxalate; potassium silicate; potassium xylene sulphonate

Uses:
chocolate ingredient; crystal/television tube glass ingredient; soap ingredient; enamels; process solvent (Benfield/Catacarb processes)

potassium chlorate

[3811-04-9]

KClO₃

$Cl_1K_1O_3$. M: 122.55. White crystals. MP: 368°C. Decomposes when heated above 400°C forming potassium perchlorate. d: 2.32 kg/l. Soluble in water.

Production:
• potassium chloride + sodium chlorate (salt formation)

Derivatives: potassium iodate; Prussian Blue

Uses: match head/explosives ingredient; analytical/dyestuffs oxidation reagent

potassium chloride

muriate of potash; [7447-40-7]

KCl

Cl_1K_1. M: 74.55. The agricultural grade of potassium chloride is obtained by upgrading natural potassium-containing minerals such as carnallite ($KCl.MgCl_2$. $6H_2O$) and sylvite (KCl). The pure grade of potassium chloride is a white, crystalline powder. MP: 790°C. d: 1.99 kg/l. Solubility in water: 276 g/l (0°C).

Production:
• natural potash salt deposits (mining/separation)
• brine, natural borate (extraction; coproduced with sodium borate/sodium carbonate/sodium sulphate)

• brine, natural potash (extraction)
Derivatives:
chlorine; potassium; potassium chlorate; potassium dichromate; potassium hexafluorosilicate; potassium hydroxide; potassium magnesium sulphate; potassium nitrate; potassium perchlorate; potassium sulphate; potassium tetraborate
Uses: lithium production electrolyte; fertiliser ingredient; photographic chemical

potassium chromate
[7789-00-6]

$$K_2CrO_4$$

$Cr_1K_2O_4$. M: 194.20. Yellow crystals. MP: 970°C. d: 2.73 kg/l (18°C). Solubility in water: 630 g/l water (20°C) forming alkaline solutions.
Production:
• potassium hydroxide + chromite (salt formation)
Uses: enamel ingredient; leather tanning auxiliary; metal chromating agent

potassium citrate
tripotassium citrate; tripotassium 2-hydroxypropane-1,2,3-tricarboxylate; E332 (EC); [866-83-1]

$$\begin{array}{l} CH_2COO^- \ \ K^+ \\ | \\ HO-C-COO^- \ \ K^+ \\ | \\ CH_2COO^- \ \ K^+ \end{array}$$

$C_6H_5K_3O_7$. M: 306.41. Available as the monohydrate. White crystals. Loses water of crystallisation at 180°C, decomposing at 230°C. Soluble in water. Insoluble in alcohol.
Production:
• citric acid + potassium hydroxide (salt formation)
Uses: emulsifier/acidity regulator (foodstuffs)

potassium cyanate
[590-28-3]

$$KOCN$$

$C_1K_1N_1O_1$. M: 81.12. White, crystalline powder. MP: 315°C. d: 2.06 kg/l. Soluble in water.
Production:
• potassium hydroxide + urea (reaction)
Derivatives:
domperidone; nitrofurantoin; sulfacarbamide
Uses: case hardening salts; herbicide

potassium cyanide
[151-50-8]

$$KCN$$

$C_1K_1N_1$. M: 65.12. White granules or briquettes. MP: 634°C. d: 1.52 kg/l. Soluble in water forming alkaline solutions. Very toxic. Liberates hydrogen cyanide gas on contact with moist air.

Production:
• potassium hydroxide + hydrogen cyanide (salt formation)
Derivatives: 5-ethylquinolinic acid; ibuprofen; potassium ferrocyanide; potassium gold cyanide; praziquantel; quinoline-2,3-dicarboxylic acid
Uses:
benzoin condensation catalyst; gold/silver/copper plating reagent; metal surface hardening salts component

potassium dichloroisocyanurate
potassium dichlorotriazine-2,4,6-trione; troclosene potassium; KDCC; [2244-21-5]

$C_3Cl_2K_1N_3O_3$. M: 236.06. White granules containing 60% available chlorine. Solubility in water: 90 g/l solution (25°C).
Production:
• trichloroisocyanuric acid + potassium hydroxide (salt formation)
Uses: bleaching agent (household cleaners); swimming pool disinfectant

potassium dichromate
potassium bichromate; [7778-50-9]

$$K_2Cr_2O_7$$

$Cr_2K_2O_7$. M: 294.18. Orange-red crystals. MP: 398°C. d: 2.69 kg/l (25°C). Solubility in water: 45 g/l (25°C) producing acidic solutions. Not hygroscopic.
Production:
• potassium chloride + sodium dichromate (salt formation)
Derivatives: chrome alum; zinc yellow
Uses: brake linings; chrome plating reagent; safety match ingredient; oil/wax bleaching agent; oxidation reagent; tin/chromium pink pigments

potassium ethyl xanthate
ethyl potassium carbonate; potassium ethyldithiocarbonate; KEX; [140-89-6]

$C_3H_5K_1O_1S_2$. M: 160.30. Pale yellow, crystalline powder. d: 1.56 kg/l (20°C). Soluble in water forming alkaline solutions.
Production:
• ethanol + carbon disulphide + potassium hydroxide (thiocarbonylation)
Derivatives: pyritinol
Uses: flotation collector (sulphide ores); analytical reagent; dehydration reagent (antibacterial drug synthesis)

potassium ferricyanide

red prussiate of potash; [13746-66-2]

K₃Fe(CN)₆

$C_6Fe_1K_3N_6$. M: 329.27. Ruby-red crystals. d: 1.85 kg/l (25°C). Solubility in water: 460 g/l water (20°C).
Production:
• potassium ferrocyanide + chlorine (oxidation)
Uses: blueprint paper production; etchant; flotation depressant; photographic bleaching/reducing agent; rust conversion agent

potassium ferrocyanide

yellow prussiate of potash; [13943-58-3]

K₄Fe(CN)₆

$C_6Fe_1K_4N_6$. M: 368.37. Available as the trihydrate. Amber to lemon-yellow crystals. Lose water on heating above 60°C. d: 1.85 kg/l (15°C). Solubility in water: 280 g/l water (20°C). Insoluble in alcohol.
Production:
• potassium cyanide + ferrous sulphate (complex formation)
Derivatives: potassium ferricyanide; Prussian Blue
Uses: electroplating bath ingredient; flotation depressant; analytical reagent (ferric salts); anticaking agent (table salt); heavy metal scavenger (fruit juice, wine); dyeing/printing reagent

potassium fluoborate

potassium borofluoride; potassium tetrafluoroborate; [14075-53-7]

KBF₄

$B_1F_4K_1$. M: 125.90. Colourless crystals. Decompose on heating to 350°C. d: 2.50 kg/l (20°C). Soluble in water, slowly forming acidic solutions.
Production:
• potassium hydroxide + fluoboric acid (salt formation)
Uses:
reactive filler (resin-based grinding wheels); soldering/brazing flux; surface hardening filler (magnesium/aluminium casting moulds)

potassium fluoride

[7789-23-3]

KF

F_1K_1. M: 58.10. White, deliquescent crystals. MP: 860°C. Solubility in water: 1.02 kg/l (25°C).
Production:
• potassium carbonate + hydrofluoric acid (salt formation)
Derivatives:
potassium fluorozirconate; sodium fluoroacetate
Uses:
brazing/soldering flux; fluorination reagent

potassium fluorotitanate

potassium titanium fluoride; titanium potassium fluoride

K₂TiF₆

$F_6K_2Ti_1$. M: 240.09. Available commercially as the monohydrate. Colourless, lustrous crystals. Releases water of crystallisation when heated over 32°C. Slightly soluble in water.
Production:
• potassium hexafluorosilicate + titanium dioxide, hydrate (salt formation)
Uses: flux (non-ferrous metals production); aluminium grain refining agent

potassium fluorozirconate

potassium zironifluoride; potassium zirconium fluoride; zirconium potassium fluoride; [16923-95-8]

K₂ZrF₆

$F_6K_2Zr_1$. M: 283.41. Colourless crystals. d: 3.48 kg/l. Slightly soluble in cold water.
Production:
• potassium hexafluorosilicate + zircon (reaction)
• potassium fluoride + hydrofluoric acid + zirconium carbonate, basic (salt formation)
Uses:
aluminium/magnesium grain refining agent; aluminium conversion coatings; wool flame resistance treatment agent

potassium fluosilicate

See: potassium hexafluorosilicate

potassium gluconate

[299-27-4]

HOCH₂(CHOH)₄COO⁻ K⁺

$C_6H_{11}K_1O_7$. M: 234.25. Pale yellow crystals. Decompose when heated above 180°C. Soluble in water giving mildly alkaline solutions.
Production:
• sodium gluconate + potassium hydroxide (salt formation)
Uses: mineral supplement

potassium gold cyanide

gold potassium cyanide; potassium dicyanoaurate; [13967-50-5]

KAu(CN)₂

$C_2Au_1K_1N_2$. M: 288.10. White, crystalline powder. Soluble in water.
Production:
• potassium cyanide + chloroauric acid + ammonia (salt formation)
Uses:
electroplating bath ingredient

potassium hexafluorosilicate

potassium fluosilicate; potassium silicofluoride;
[16871-90-2]

K_2SiF_6

$F_6K_2Si_1$. M: 220.28. White, crystalline solid. Decomposes on heating. Solubility in water: 70 g/l water (20°C) forming acidic solutions.
Production:
• potassium chloride + hexafluorosilicic acid (salt formation)
Derivatives:
potassium fluorotitanate; potassium fluorozirconate
Uses: chrome plating reagent; speciality glass/enamel ingredient

potassium hydroxide

caustic potash; [1310-58-3]

KOH

$H_1K_1O_1$. M: 56.11. White, 88–92% flakes or pellets. MP: ~360°C. BP: 1,320–1,324°C. d: 2.04 kg/l. Solubility in water: 1,100 g/l water (15°C). Also available commercially as a 45–50% solution in water.
Production:
• potassium chloride (mercury cell electrolysis; coproduced with chlorine)
• potassium chloride (membrane cell electrolysis; coproduced with chlorine)
Derivatives: N-cyanoimido-S,S-dimethyldithiocarbamate; monopotassium glutamate; potassium amyl xanthate; potassium benzoate; potassium carbonate; potassium chromate; potassium citrate; potassium cyanate; potassium cyanide; potassium dichloroisocyanurate; potassium ethyl xanthate; potassium fluoborate; potassium gluconate; potassium iodide; potassium isopropyl xanthate; potassium metabisulphite; potassium oleate; potassium pentaborate; potassium perfluorooctoate; potassium permanganate; potassium persulphate; potassium phenylacetate; potassium pyrophosphate; potassium silicate; potassium sorbate; potassium stannate; potassium stearate; potassium tetraborate; potassium thiocyanate; potassium tripolyphosphate; silver peroxide; zeolite X
Uses:
liquid fertiliser ingredient; electroplating/photographic reagent; battery electrolyte; soap raw material; reagent (carbon dioxide absorption processes)

potassium iodate

[7758-05-6]

KIO_3

$I_1K_1O_3$. M: 214.00. White crystals. d: 3.9 kg/l. Slow decomposition on heating. Soluble in water.
Production:
• potassium chlorate + iodine (reaction)
Uses: analytical reagent; animal feed additive

potassium iodide

[7681-11-0]

KI

I_1K_1. M: 166.00. Colourless crystals. MP: 686°C. d: 3.13 kg/l. Solubility in water: 1.27 kg/l water (0°C). Soluble in oxygenated solvents.
Production:
• potassium hydroxide + iodine (salt formation)
Derivatives: iodoform; thymol iodide
Uses: animal feed/table salt additive; raw material (photographic film production); ring iodination reagent

potassium isopropyl xanthate

KIPX

$(CH_3)_2CHOC\overset{\overset{\displaystyle S}{\|}}{S^-}$ K^+

$C_4H_7K_1O_1S_2$. M: 174.33.
Production:
• carbon disulphide + isopropanol + potassium hydroxide (condensation)
Uses: flotation collector (sulphide ores)

potassium magnesium sulphate

langbeinite

$K_2SO_4.2MgSO_4$

$K_2Mg_2O_{12}S_3$. M: 415.00. Langbeinite is a natural mineral form of potassium dimagnesium sulphate.
Production:
• potassium chloride + magnesium sulphate (salt formation)
Derivatives: potassium sulphate
Uses: fertiliser ingredient

potassium metabisulphite

KMS; E224 (EC); [16731-55-8]

$K_2S_2O_5$

$K_2O_5S_2$. M: 222.32. White, granular powder with a pungent odour. Solubility in water: 310 g/kg solution (20°C) forming acidic solutions.
Production:
• potassium hydroxide + sulphur dioxide, pure (salt formation)
Uses: beer/wine fermentation control agent; preservative (dried fruit, dried vegetables, meat, soups, sauces)

potassium nitrate

nitre; saltpetre; E252 (EC); [7757-79-1]

KNO_3

$K_1N_1O_3$. M: 101.11.
Production:
• caliche ore (Guggenheim process; coproduced with sodium nitrate/sodium iodate liquor)

- potassium chloride + nitric acid (salt formation)
- potassium chloride + sodium nitrate (salt formation)

Uses:
glass/enamel/porcelain production clarifying agent; fertiliser; heat treatment salts; fireworks/gunpowder ingredient; preservative/colour fixative (cured meat, fish); tobacco burning aid

potassium oleate
[143-18-0]

$$CH_3(CH_2)_7CH=CH(CH_2)_7COO^- \quad K^+$$

$C_{18}H_{33}K_1O_2$. M: 320.56. Brown solid. Soluble in water forming alkaline solutions.
Production:
- oleic acid + potassium hydroxide (salt formation)

Uses: emulsifier (latex); surfactant (textile detergents)

potassium oxalate
[583-52-8]

$$\begin{array}{c} COO^- \\ | \\ COO^- \end{array} \quad 2K^+$$

$C_2K_2O_4$. M: 166.22. The commercial product is the monohydrate. Colourless crystals. Loses water of crystallisation when heated above 160°C. d: 2.13 kg/l. Solubility in water: 330 g/l water (16°C).
Production:
- potassium carbonate + oxalic acid (esterification)

Uses: textile finishing agent

potassium pentaborate
[11128-29-3]; [12229-13-9] (octahydrate)

$$K_2O.5B_2O_3$$

$B_{10}K_2O_{16}$. M: 442.29. Available commercially as the octahydrate. White, crystalline solid. MP: 780°C. d: 1.74 kg/l. Soluble in water. Less soluble than sodium pentaborate.
Production:
- potassium hydroxide + boric acid (salt formation)

Uses: speciality welding/brazing fluxes

potassium perchlorate
[7778-74-7]

$$KClO_4$$

$Cl_1K_1O_4$. M: 138.55. Colourless crystals. Decomposes on heating to 400°C. Solubility in water: 15 g/l (25°C).
Production:
- sodium perchlorate + potassium chloride (salt formation)

Uses: explosives/pyrotechnics

potassium perfluorooctoate
Fluorad FC-129 (3M)
$C_8F_{15}K_1O_2$. M: 452.16.

$$CF_3(CF_2)_6COO^- \quad K^+$$

Production:
- perfluorooctanoic acid + potassium hydroxide (salt formation)

Uses: emulsifier (cleaners, polishes, water-based coatings); photographic chemical

potassium permanganate
[7722-64-7]

$$KMnO_4$$

$K_1Mn_1O_4$. M: 158.04. Purple crystals. Decompose when heated to 240°C releasing oxygen. d: 2.70 kg/l. Soluble in water.
Production:
- manganese ores + potassium hydroxide (thermal oxidation/electrolytic oxidation)

Derivatives: demeton-S-methylsulphon
Uses:
effluent/flue-gas purification; oxidation reagent; sanitising agent (water treatment)

potassium persulphate
potassium peroxydisulphate; [7727-21-1]

$$K_2S_2O_8$$

$K_2O_8S_2$. M: 270.32. White, crystalline salt which decomposes on heating. Solubility in water: 48 g/l water (20°C) with gradual decomposition.
Production:
- potassium hydroxide + ammonium persulphate (salt formation)
- potassium sulphate + sulphuric acid (membrane cell electrolysis)

Uses: polymerisation initiator

potassium phenylacetate
[13005-36-2]

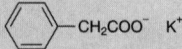

$C_8H_7K_1O_2$. M: 174.25.
Production:
- potassium hydroxide + phenylacetic acid (salt formation)

Derivatives: benzylpenicillin

potassium pyrophosphate
tetrapotassium pyrophosphate; TKPP; [7320-34-5]

$$K_4P_2O_7$$

$K_2O_7P_2$. M: 252.14. White powder. Solubility in water: 1.91 kg/l (25°C) forming alkaline solutions.
Production:
- potassium hydroxide + phosphoric acid, pure (salt formation/thermal rearrangement)

Uses: buffering agent (electroplating baths); liquid soap clarifying agent; detergent builder (liquid cleaners); scale inhibitor (boiler water treatment); stabiliser/dispersant (emulsion paints, synthetic latex production)

potassium silicate

$$K_2O.nSiO_2$$

n = 2.25–3.90. The commercial products are glass chips or colourless solutions in water containing 27.5–52.5% total solids and silica:alkali ratios in the range 1.45–2.48 w/w. All solutions are alkaline.
Production:
• potassium carbonate + quartz (reaction/furnace process)
• potassium hydroxide + quartz (hydrothermal process)
Uses:
detergent builder (household and industrial cleaners); adhesives (paper tubes, drums); binder (plaster, heat-resistant paints, welding electrode coatings, refractories, insulation, fire-resistant barriers)

potassium silicofluoride
See: potassium hexafluorosilicate

potassium sodium tartrate *See:* Rochelle salt

potassium sorbate
potassium 2,4-hexadienoate; E202 (EC); [590-00-1]

$$CH_3CH=CHCH=CHCOO^-\ K^+$$

$C_6H_7K_1O_2$. M: 150.23. Crystalline powder/granules. MP: 270°C with decomposition. d: 1.36 kg/l (20°C). Soluble in water and alcohol. The commercial product is the *trans,trans*-isomer.
Production:
• potassium hydroxide + sorbic acid (salt formation)
Uses: preservative (food, animal feed)

potassium stannate
dipotassium tin trioxide; [12142-33-5]

$$K_2SnO_3$$

$K_2O_3Sn_1$. M: 244.89. The commercial product is the trihydrate. Colourless crystals. d: 3.20 kg/l. Solubility in water: 1.10 kg/l water (20°C) forming alkaline solutions.
Production:
• potassium hydroxide + stannic oxide (fusion)
Uses: tin plating reagent

potassium stearate
[593-29-3]

$$CH_3(CH_2)_{16}COO^-\ K^+$$

$C_{18}H_{35}K_1O_2$. M: 322.58. White powder. Soluble in hot water producing alkaline solutions. Soluble in alcohol.

Production:
• stearic acid + potassium hydroxide (salt formation)
Uses: cosmetics/toiletries/soaps

potassium sulphate
sulphate of potash; [7778-80-5]

$$K_2SO_4$$

$K_2O_4S_1$. M: 174.26. White crystals. Solubility in water: 120 g/l (20°C).
Production:
• potassium chloride + sulphuric acid (salt formation)
• potassium chloride + sulphur dioxide, pure (Hargreaves process)
• potassium chloride + potassium magnesium sulphate/magnesium sulphate (salt formation)
Derivatives: aluminium potassium sulphate; nitrophosphate; potassium persulphate
Uses: chrome plating reagent; fertiliser ingredient; glass raw material

potassium tetraborate
dipotassium tetraborate; potassium borate; [1332-77-0]; [12045-78-2] (tetrahydrate)

$$K_2B_4O_7$$

$B_4K_2O_7$. M: 233.43. Available commercially as the tetrahydrate. White, crystalline powder. Loses 2 moles of water of crystallisation when heated above 112°C and a further 2 moles above 180°C. d: 1.92 kg/l. Soluble in water.
Production:
• potassium hydroxide + boric acid (salt formation)
• potassium chloride + sodium borate (salt formation)
Uses:
diazo developer solutions; casein crosslinking agent; welding flux; cutting fluid ingredient

potassium tetrafluoroborate *See:* potassium fluoborate

potassium thiocyanate
[333-20-0]

$$KSCN$$

$C_1K_1N_1S_1$. M: 97.18. White, hygroscopic, crystalline solid. MP: 173°C. d: 1.89 kg/l. Soluble in water and alcohol.
Production:
• potassium hydroxide + ammonium thiocyanate (salt formation)
Derivatives:
allyl isothiocyanate; 2-amino-6-methoxybenzothiazole; benazolin; etomidate; sulfathiourea; 5-thio-1-(β-dimethylaminoethyl)tetrazole; thiophanate-methyl
Uses: chelating agent (metal purification); electroplating bath ingredient; analytical reagent; photographic chemical; textile dyeing/printing auxiliary

potassium titanium fluoride
See: potassium fluorotitanate

potassium tripolyphosphate
pentapotassium triphosphate; KTPP; [13845-36-8]

$$K_5P_3O_{10}$$

$K_5O_{10}P_3$. M: 448.42. White, crystalline solid. MP: 620–640°C. d: 2.54 kg/l. Soluble in water.
Production:
• potassium hydroxide + phosphoric acid, pure (salt formation/thermal dehydration)
Uses:
dispersant/sequesterant (boiler water treatment, liquid cleaners)

potassium xylene sulphonate
PXS

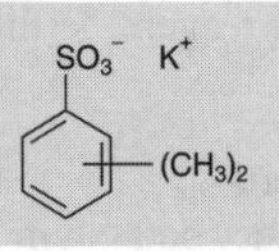

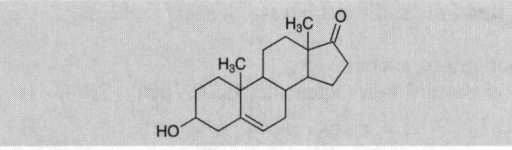

$C_8H_9K_1O_3S_1$. M: 224.32. Available commercially as a 40% solution in water or as 90% powder.
Production:
• xylenesulphonic acid + potassium carbonate (salt formation)
Uses: hydrotrope (light-duty liquid detergents)

potassium zirconium fluoride
See: potassium fluorozirconate

povidone *See:* polyvinylpyrrolidone

povidone-iodine
Yellow powder with a characteristic odour. Soluble in water forming acidic solutions.
Production:
• polyvinylpyrrolidone + iodine (complex formation)
Uses:
medical disinfectant

PP *See:* polypropylene

PPA *See:* norephedrine

PPD *See:* p-phenylenediamine; piperidinium pentamethylenedithiocarbamate

6PPD *See:* N-hexyl-N'-phenyl-p-phenylenediamine

PPDI *See:* p-phenylene diisocyanate

PPDT *See:* poly(p-phenyleneterephthalamide)

PPE *See:* poly(phenylene oxide)

PPG *See:* polypropylene glycol

PPO *See:* poly(phenylene oxide)

PPS *See:* poly(phenylene sulphide)

PPTA *See:* poly(p-phenyleneterephthalamide)

PPVE *See:* perfluoro(propyl vinyl ether)

PQD *See:* p-quinonedioxime

praseodymium oxide
[12037-29-5]

$$Pr_2O_3$$

O_3Pr_2. M: 329.81.
Production:
• didymium oxide (solvent extraction; coproduced with neodymium oxide)
Uses: ceramic tiles/sanitaryware colorant

prasterone
androstenolone; 5-androsten-17-one; dehydroepiandrosterone; DHA; [53-43-0]

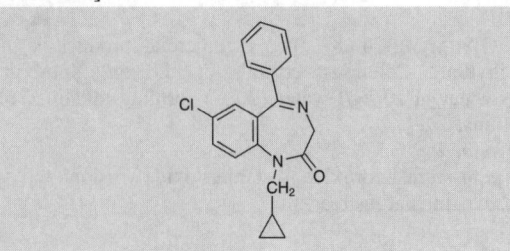

$C_{19}H_{28}O_2$. M: 288.43. Commonly used as the 3-acetoxy derivative for synthesis purposes.
Production:
• dehydropregnenolone acetate + hydroxylamine hydrochloride (oxime formation/Beckmann rearrangement)
Derivatives:
androstadienedione; spironolactone; testosterone

prazepam
[2955-38-6]

$C_{19}H_{17}Cl_1N_2O_1$. M: 324.81.
Production:
• nordazepam + cyclopropylmethyl bromide (amine formation)
Uses: anxiolytic/muscle relaxant drug

praziquantel
[55268-74-1]

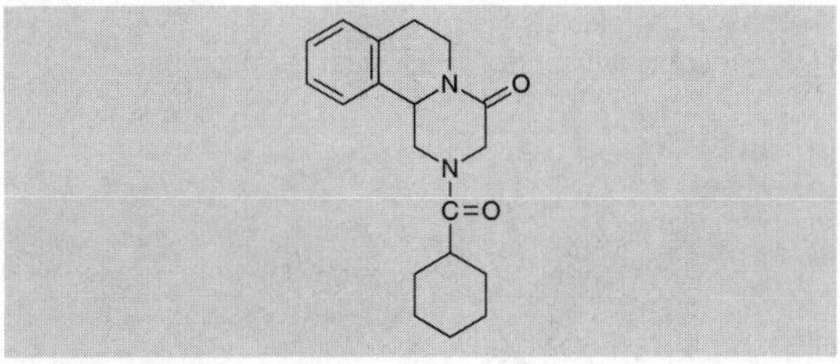

$C_{19}H_{24}N_2O_2$. M: 312.41.
Production:
• isoquinoline + cyclohexanecarboxylic acid +
  potassium cyanide + chloroacetyl chloride (amide
  formation/cyanidation/Reissert reaction/amide
  formation/amine formation)
Uses:
anthelmintic drug

prazosin
[19216-56-9]

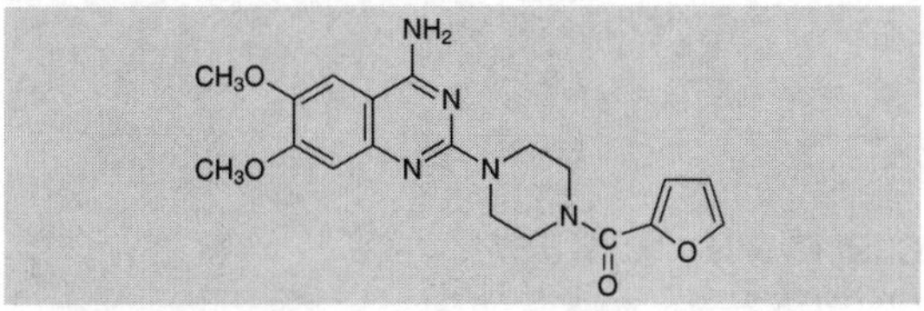

$C_{19}H_{21}N_5O_4$. M: 383.42. Available commercially as the
hydrochloride.
Production:
• piperazine + 2-furoic acid + 4-amino-2-chloro-
  6,7-dimethoxyquinazoline (amide formation/amine
  formation)
Uses: antihypertensive drug

prednisolone
[50-24-8]

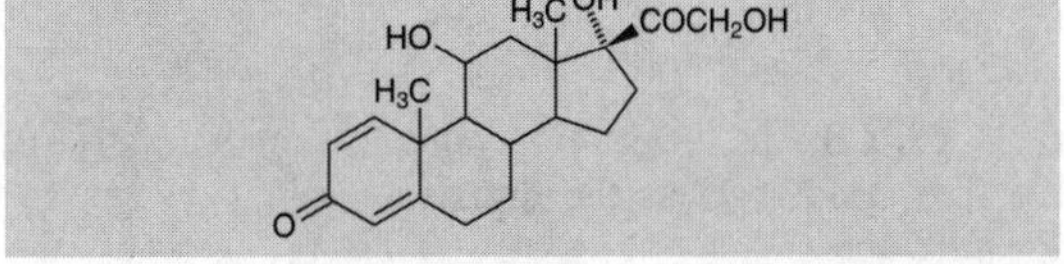

$C_{21}H_{28}O_5$. M: 360.44. Available commercially as the
alcohol, the 21-acetate, the 21-phosphate, disodium salt
and as a variety of other derivatives.
Production:
• hydrocortisone (microbial conversion)
Derivatives: prednisone
Uses: antiinflammatory drug

prednisone
[53-03-2]
$C_{21}H_{26}O_5$. M: 358.44. Available commercially as the
free alcohol and as the 21-acetate ester.

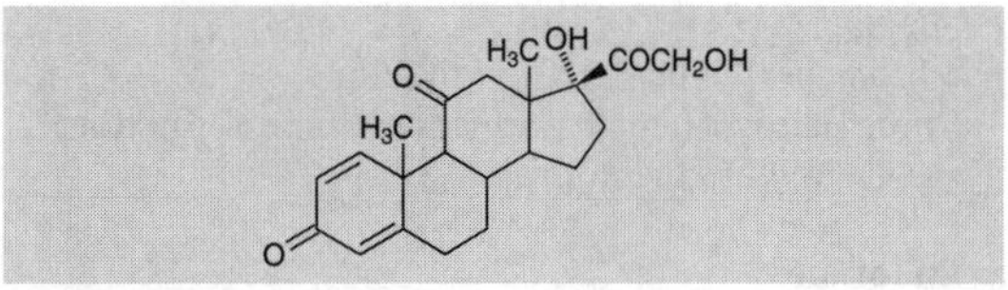

Production:
• prednisolone (alcohol oxidation)
Uses: antiinflammatory drug

Δ⁴-pregnene-3,20-dione *See:* progesterone

prenyl alcohol *See:* 3-methyl-2-buten-1-ol

prenylamine
[390-64-7]; [69-43-2] (lactate)

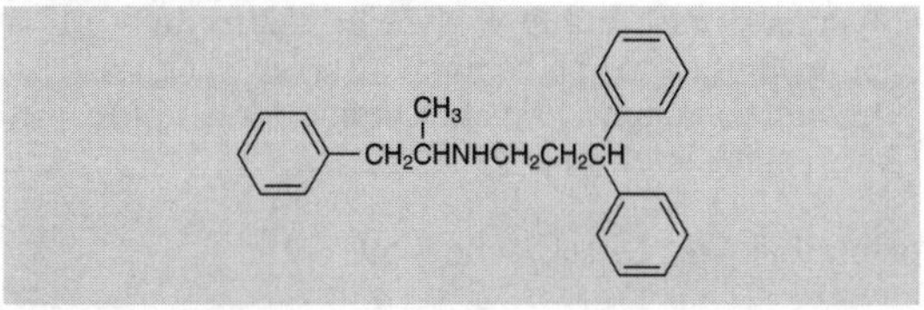

$C_{24}H_{27}N_1$. M: 329.49. Available commercially as the
free base or lactate.
Production:
• benzaldehyde + ethyl cyanoacetate + phenylmagnesium bromide + phenylacetone (Cope reaction/
  Grignard reaction/decarboxylation/nitrile reduction/
  reductive amination)
Uses: vasodilator drug

pretilachlor
2-chloro-2',6'-diethyl-*N*-(2-propoxyethyl)acetanilide;
[51218-49-6]

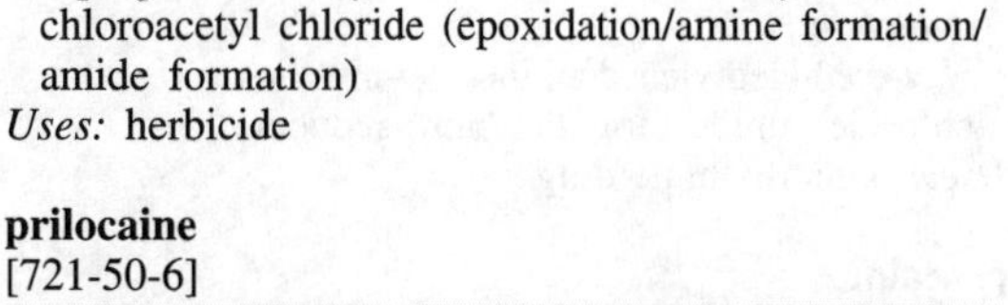

$C_{17}H_{26}Cl_1N_1O_2$. M: 311.86.
Production:
• *n*-propanol + ethylene oxide + 2,6-diethylaniline +
  chloroacetyl chloride (epoxidation/amine formation/
  amide formation)
Uses: herbicide

prilocaine
[721-50-6]

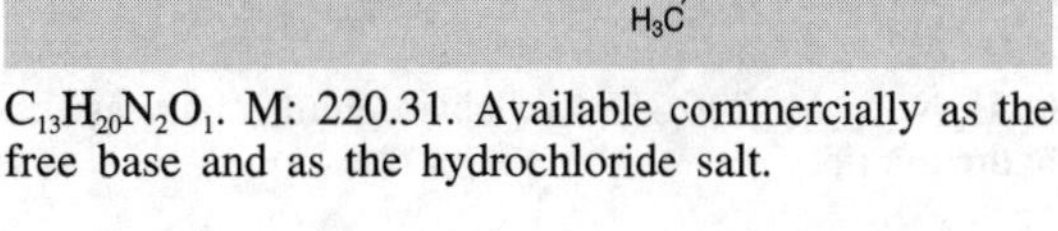

$C_{13}H_{20}N_2O_1$. M: 220.31. Available commercially as the
free base and as the hydrochloride salt.

Production:
- α-bromopropionic acid + *o*-toluidine + *n*-propylamine (amide formation/amine formation)

Uses: local anaesthetic drug

primaquine
[90-34-6]

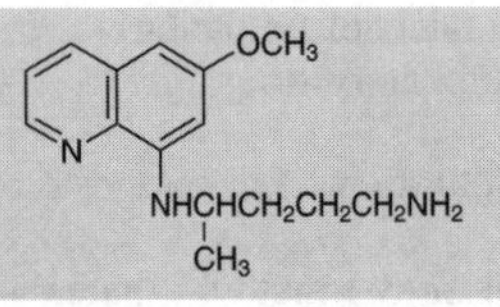

$C_{15}H_{21}N_3O_1$. M: 259.35. Available as the free amine and as the phosphate salt.
Production:
- 4-amino-3-nitroanisole + glycerol + 2-methyl-tetrahydrofuran + phthalimide (Skraup synthesis/bromination/amine formation/amine formation)

Uses: antimalarial drug

primuline *See:* Direct Yellow 59

Pro *See:* L-proline

probenecid
[57-66-9]

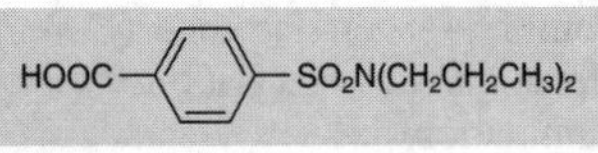

$C_{13}H_{19}N_1O_4S_1$. M: 285.36.
Production:
- sulphanilic acid + copper cyanide + di-*n*-propyl-amine (diazotisation/Sandmeyer reaction/sulphonamide formation/nitrile hydrolysis)

Uses: gout treatment drug

procainamide
[51-06-9]; [614-39-1] (hydrochloride)

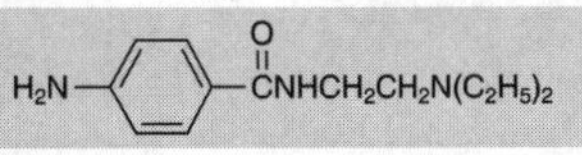

$C_{13}H_{21}N_3O_1$. M: 235.33. Available commercially as the hydrochloride.
Production:
- N,N-diethylethylenediamine + *p*-nitrobenzoyl chloride (amide formation/nitro reduction)

Uses: antiarrhythmic drug

procaine
2-(diethylamino)ethyl 4-aminobenzoate; [59-46-1]; [51-05-8] (hydrochloride)

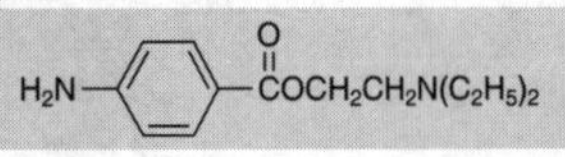

$C_{13}H_{20}N_2O_2$. M: 236.31. Available commercially as the hydrochloride.

Production:
- diethylaminoethanol + ethyl *p*-aminobenzoate (transesterification)

Uses: local anaesthetic drug; penicillin adjunct

procarbazine
[671-16-9]

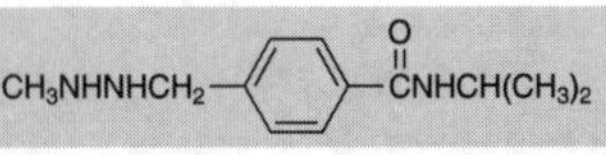

$C_{12}H_{19}N_3O_1$. M: 221.30.
Production:
- *p*-toluic acid + methyl hydrazine + isopropylamine (side-chain bromination/amine formation/amide formation)

Uses: cytostatic drug

prochloraz
1-N-propyl-N-[2-(2,4,6-trichlorophenoxy)ethyl]carbam-oylimidazole; [67747-09-5]

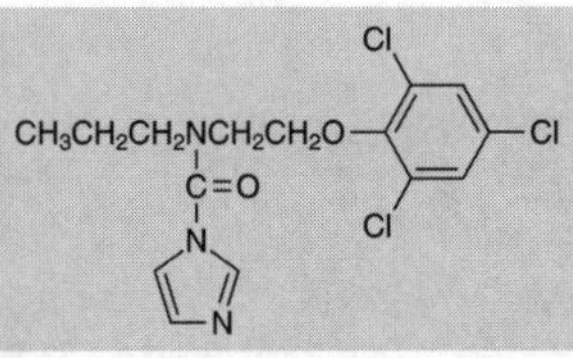

$C_{15}H_{16}Cl_3N_3O_2$. M: 376.67.
Production:
- *n*-propylethanolamine + 2,4,6-trichlorophenol + phosgene + imidazole (ether formation/phosgenation/dehydrochlorination)

Uses: fungicide

prochlorperazine
[58-38-8]; [84-02-6] (maleate)

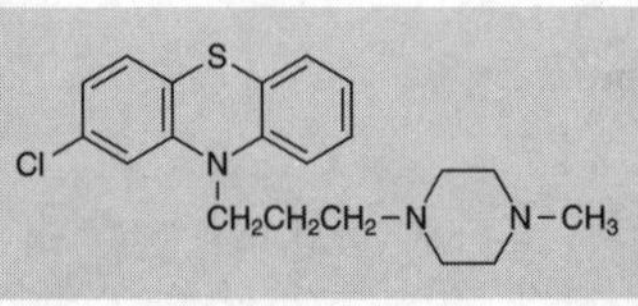

$C_{20}H_{24}Cl_1N_3S_1$. M: 373.94. Available commercially as the free amide and as the dimaleate salt.
Production:
- 2-chlorophenothiazine + 1-bromo-3-chloropropane + N-methylpiperazine (dehydrobromination/dehydrochlorination)

Uses: neuroleptic drug

procymidone
N-(3,5-dichlorophenyl)-1,2-dimethylcyclopropane-1,2-dicarboximide; [32809-16-8]
$C_{13}H_{11}Cl_2N_1O_2$. M: 284.15.
Production:
- DL-alanine + methyl methacrylate + 3,5-dichloro-aniline (diazotisation/addition/amide formation)

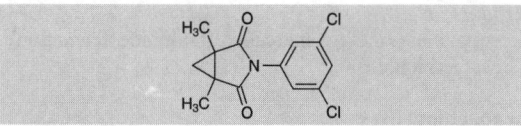

Uses: fungicide

prodiamine
2-amino-4-dipropylamino-3,5-dinitrobenzotrifluoride;
[29091-21-2]

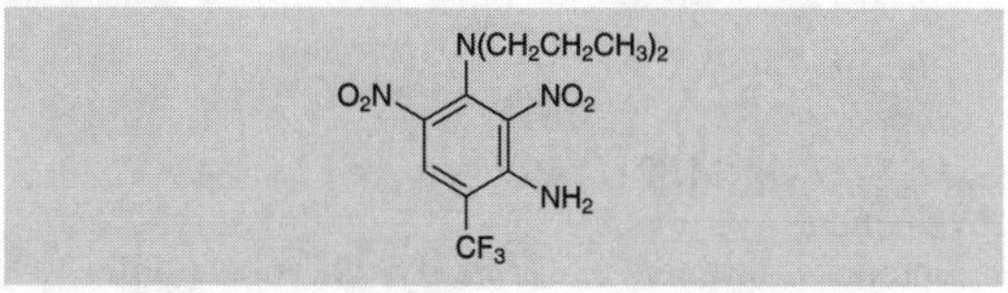

$C_{13}H_{17}F_3N_4O_4$. M: 350.30.
Production:
• 2,4-dichlorobenzotrifluoride + di-*n*-propylamine +
ammonia (nitration/amine formation/amine formation)
Uses: herbicide

profenofos
[41198-08-7]

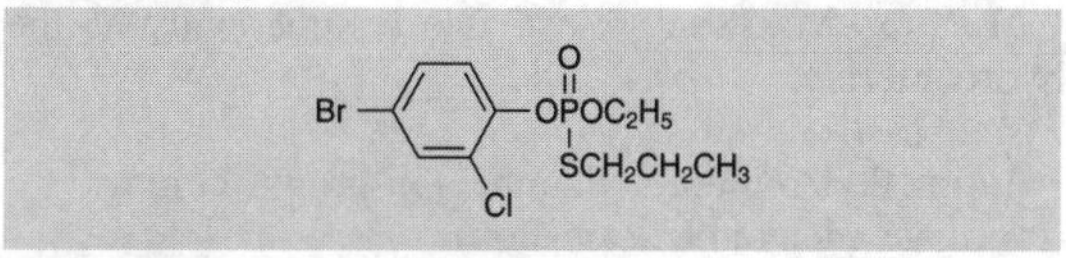

$C_{11}H_{15}Br_1Cl_1O_3P_1S_1$. M: 373.62.
Production:
• *o*-chlorophenol + phosphorus oxychloride +
n-propyl mercaptan + ethanol (ring bromination/
dehydrochlorination/dehydrochlorination/
dehydrochlorination)
Uses: insecticide/acaricide

profluralin
4-[*N*-(cyclopropylmethyl)-*N*-propylamino]-3,5-dinitro-
benzotrifluoride; [26399-36-0]

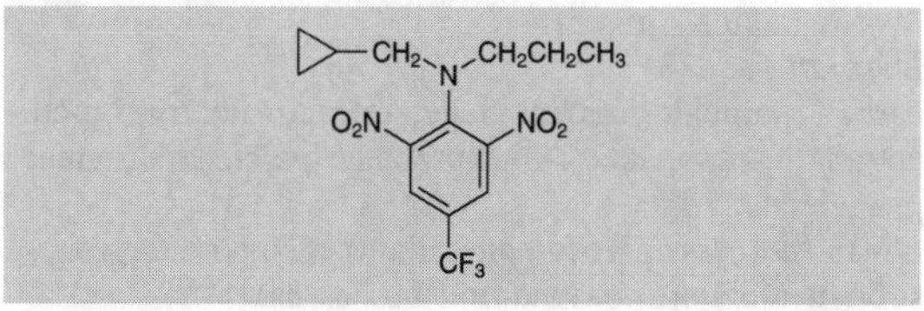

$C_{14}H_{16}F_3N_3O_4$. M: 347.29.
Production:
• 4-chloro-3,5-dinitrobenzotrifluoride + *n*-propylamine
+ cyclopropylmethyl bromide (amine formation/
amine formation)
Uses: herbicide

progesterone
Δ^4-pregnene-3,20-dione; [57-83-0]
$C_{21}H_{30}O_2$. M: 314.47.

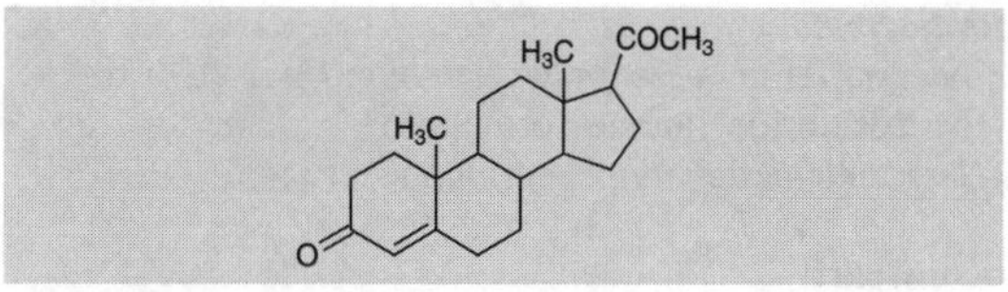

Production:
• dehydropregnenolone acetate (hydrogenation/
Oppenauer oxidation)
• stigmasterol (multistep synthesis)
Derivatives:
11-α-hydroxyprogesterone
Uses: progestogenic drug

proglinazine-ethyl
N-(4-chloro-6-isopropylamino)-1,3,5-triazin-2-yl)glycine;
[68228-18-2]

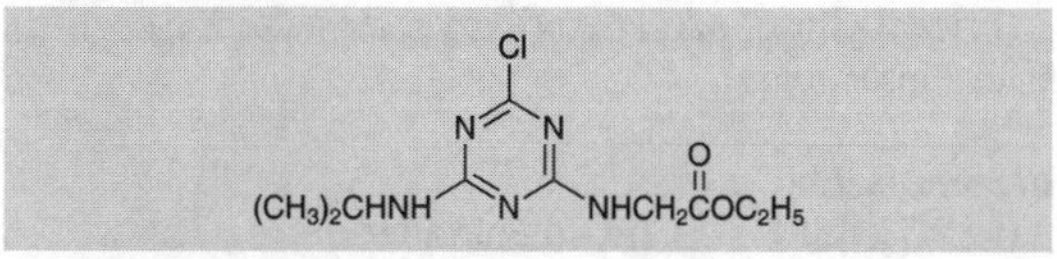

$C_{10}H_{16}Cl_1N_5O_2$. M: 273.72.
Production:
• cyanuric chloride + isopropylamine + ethyl
glycinate hydrochloride (amine formation/amine
formation)
Uses: herbicide

L-proline
Pro; pyrrolidine-2-carboxylic acid; [147-85-3]

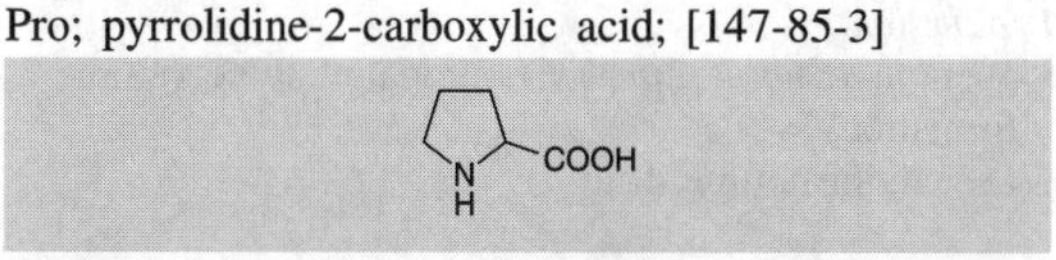

$C_5H_9N_1O_2$. M: 115.13. Available commercially as the
natural L(−)-enantiomer. White, crystalline solid. Decomposes when heated above 220°C. Soluble in water
and alcohol.
Production:
• microbial fermentation medium + *Corynebacterium
glutamicum* bacteria (fermentation/separation;
byproduct of L-glutamic acid production)
Derivatives:
captopril; enalapril; lisinopril; oxytocin
Uses: infusion solutions/diagnostic aids; raw material
(peptide drugs)

promazine
[58-40-2]; [53-60-1] (hydrochloride)

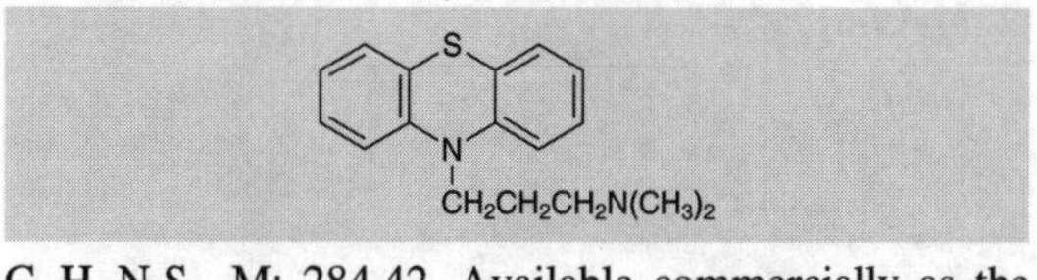

$C_{17}H_{20}N_2S_1$. M: 284.42. Available commercially as the
free base and as the hydrochloride salt.

Production:
- phenothiazine + 3-dimethylaminopropyl chloride hydrochloride (amine formation)

Uses: antiemetic drug; neuroleptic drug

promecarb

3-isopropyl-5-methylphenyl methylcarbamate; [2631-37-0]

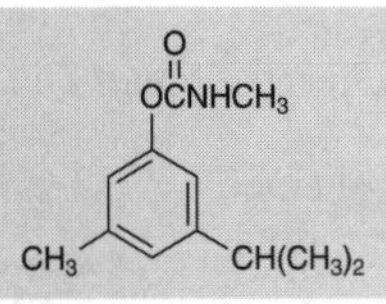

$C_{12}H_{17}N_1O_2$. M: 207.28.
Production:
- *m*-cresol + propylene + methyl isocyanate (Friedel-Crafts alkylation/isocyanate addition)

Uses: insecticide

promethazine

[60-87-7]; [58-33-3] (hydrochloride)

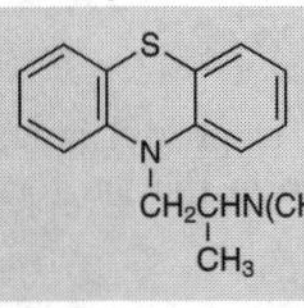

$C_{17}H_{20}N_2S_1$. M: 284.42. Available commercially as the hydrochloride.
Production:
- phenothiazine + dimethylisopropanolamine (amine formation)

Uses: antihistamine drug

prometon

2,4-bis(isopropylamino)-6-methoxy-1,3,5-triazine; [1610-18-0]

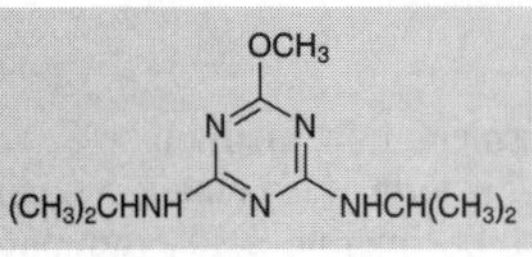

$C_{10}H_{19}N_5O_1$. M: 225.29.
Production:
- propazine + methanol (ether formation)

Uses: herbicide

prometryn

2,4-bis(isopropylamino)-6-methylthio-1,3,5-triazine; [7287-19-6]

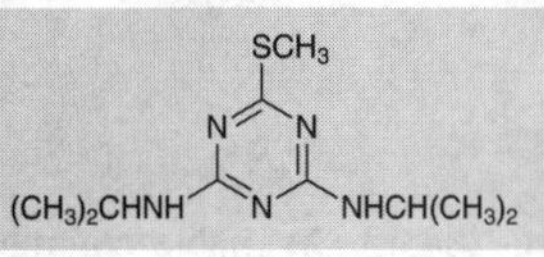

$C_{10}H_{19}N_5S_1$. M: 241.35.

Production:
- propazine + methyl mercaptan (sulphide formation)

Uses: herbicide

propachlor

2-chloro-*N*-isopropylacetanilide; Ramrod (Monsanto); [1918-16-7]

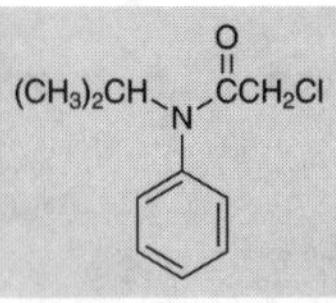

$C_{11}H_{14}Cl_1N_1O_1$. M: 211.69.
Production:
- acetone + aniline + chloroacetyl chloride (amine formation/amide formation)

Uses: herbicide

propamocarb

propyl 3-(dimethylamino)propylcarbamate; [24579-73-5]

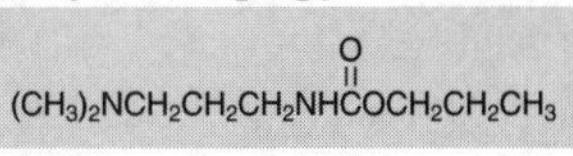

$C_9H_{20}N_2O_2$. M: 188.27. Available commercially as the hydrochloride.
Production:
- 3-dimethylaminopropylamine + *n*-propyl chloroformate (dehydrochlorination)

Uses: fungicide

propane

[74-98-6]

C_3H_8. M: 44.10. Colourless, liquified gas. BP: -42°C. FP: -187°C. d: 0.585 kg/l (-45°C). Slightly soluble in water. Soluble in organic solvents.
Production:
- liquified petroleum gas (fractionation; coproduced with butane, mixed)

Derivatives:
carbon tetrachloride; ethylene; nitroethane; nitromethane; 1-nitropropane; 2-nitropropane; perchloroethylene; propylene

Uses: fuel gas; aerosol propellant; refrigerant; process solvent (solvent deasphalting processes)

propane/butane, mixed *See:* liquified petroleum gas

1,2-propanediamine

1,2-diaminopropane; propane-1,2-diamine; 1,2-propylenediamine; PDA; [78-90-0]

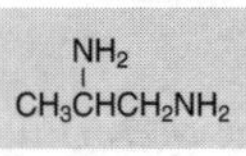

$C_3H_{10}N_2$. M: 74.12. Liquid with an ammoniacal odour.

BP: 120–123°C. MP: -37°C. Soluble in water and chlorinated solvents.
Production:
• propylene dichloride + ammonia (amine formation)
• monoisopropanolamine + ammonia (ammoniation)
Derivatives:
N,N'-disalicylidene-1,2-propanediamine; propineb

1,3-propanediamine
1,3-diaminopropane; propane-1,3-diamine; 1,3-propylenediamine; [109-76-2]

$$H_2NCH_2CH_2CH_2NH_2$$

$C_3H_{10}N_2$. M: 74.12. Colourless liquid. BP: 137–140°C. FP: -12°C. d: 0.89 kg/l (20°C). Soluble in water and oxygenated solvents.
Production:
• ammonia + acrylonitrile (cyanoethylation/nitrile reduction; coproduced with dipropylenetriamine)
Derivatives:
propylene urea
Uses: pharmaceutical raw material

1,2-propanedithiol

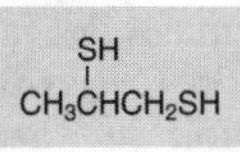

$$\overset{SH}{CH_3CHCH_2SH}$$

$C_3H_8S_2$. M: 108.22.
Production:
• propylene dichloride + hydrogen sulphide (dehydrochlorination)
Derivatives:
mephosfolan

propane sultone
[1120-71-4]

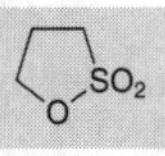

$C_3H_6O_3S_1$. M: 122.14.
Production:
• allyl alcohol + sodium bisulphite (addition)
Derivatives: cocoamidopropyldimethylammonium-3-sulphopropyl betaine; cocodimethylammonium-3-sulphopropylbetaine; lauryldimethylammonium-3-sulphopropylbetaine; myristyldimethylammonium-3-sulphopropylbetaine; palmityldimethylammonium-3-sulphopropylbetaine; potassium n-alkanol (C_{13}-C_{15}) ether propylsulphonate; stearyldimethylammonium-3-sulphopropylbetaine; tallowamidopropyldimethylammonium-3-sulphopropyl betaine

propanidid
[1421-14-3]
$C_{18}H_{27}N_1O_5$. M: 337.42.
Production:
• homovanillic acid + n-propanol + chloroacetyl

chloride + diethylamine (esterification/amide formation/ether formation)

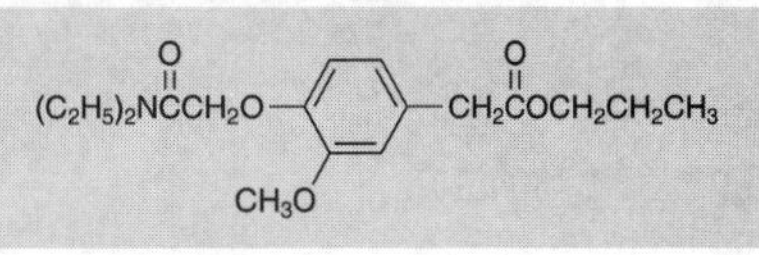

Uses: anaesthetic drug

propanil
3',4'-dichloropropionanilide; [709-98-8]

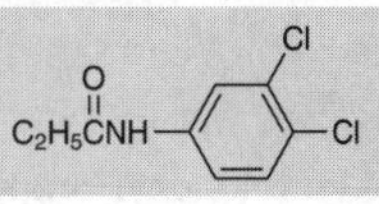

$C_9H_9Cl_2N_1O_1$. M: 218.09.
Production:
• propionic acid + 3,4-dichloroaniline (amide formation)
Uses: herbicide

2-propanol *See:* isopropanol

n-propanol
1-propanol; n-propyl alcohol; [71-23-8]

$$CH_3CH_2CH_2OH$$

$C_3H_8O_1$. M: 60.09. Colourless liquid. BP: 97°C. FP: -126°C. d: 0.81 kg/l (20°C). Miscible with water and oxygenated solvents. Flash point: 23°C (TCC).
Production:
• propionaldehyde (hydrogenation)
Derivatives:
O,O-di-n-propyl phosphorochlorothioate; pretilachlor; propanidid; propaphos; n-propyl acetate; n-propyl bromide; n-propyl butyrate; n-propyl chloroformate; n-propyl gallate; propyl 4-hydroxybenzoate; propyliodone; triflumizole
Uses: solvent (paints, printing inks)

2-propanone *See:* acetone

propantheline bromide
[50-34-0]

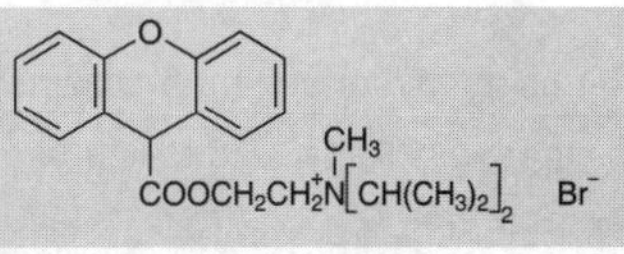

$C_{23}H_{30}Br_1N_1O_3$. M: 448.40.
Production:
• formaldehyde + phenol + carbon dioxide + 2-diisopropylaminoethanol + methyl bromide (carbonyl addition/cyclisation/Grignard reagent formation/Grignard reaction/esterification/quaternisation)
Uses: anticholinergic drug

propaphos
4-(methylthio)phenyl dipropyl phosphate; [7292-16-2]

CH$_3$S—⟨ ⟩—OP(OCH$_2$CH$_2$CH$_3$)$_2$ (with O double bond on P)

C$_{13}$H$_{21}$O$_4$P$_1$S$_1$. M: 304.34.
Production:
• *n*-propanol + phosphorus trichloride + *p*-methyl-mercaptophenol (dehydrochlorination/Michaelis-Arbuzov reaction)
Uses:
insecticide

propargite
2-(4-*t*-butylphenoxy)cyclohexyl prop-2-ynyl sulphite; [2312-35-8]

CH≡CCH$_2$OSO—O—⟨cyclohexyl⟩—O—⟨ ⟩—C(CH$_3$)$_3$

C$_{19}$H$_{26}$O$_4$S$_1$. M: 350.48.
Production:
• *p*-*t*-butylphenol + cyclohexene oxide + thionyl chloride + propargyl alcohol (epoxidation/chlorosulphonation/sulphonation)
Uses: acaricide

propargyl alcohol
2-propyn-1-ol; [107-19-7]

HC≡CCH$_2$OH

C$_3$H$_4$O$_1$. M: 56.06. Liquid with a floral odour. BP: 114–115°C. MP: -52°C. d: 0.95 kg/l. Miscible with water, oxygenated, chlorinated and aromatic solvents. Also available as a 45% solution in water.
Production:
• acetylene + formaldehyde (ethynylation; byproduct of 1,4-butynediol production)
Derivatives:
2-aminopyrimidine; heptopargil; propargite; tri-allate
Uses: corrosion inhibitor (oil-well acidising, electro-plating baths)

propazine
2-chloro-4,6-diisopropylamino-1,3,5-triazine; [139-40-2]

(CH$_3$)$_2$CHNH—⟨triazine⟩—NHCH(CH$_3$)$_2$ with Cl

C$_9$H$_{16}$Cl$_1$N$_5$. M: 229.71.
Production:
• cyanuric chloride + isopropylamine (amine formation)
Derivatives:
dipropetryn; prometon; prometryn
Uses: herbicide

propentofylline
[55242-55-2]

CH$_3$COCH$_2$CH$_2$CH$_2$CH$_2$— (purine ring with CH$_2$CH$_2$CH$_3$, two O, CH$_3$, N)

C$_{15}$H$_{22}$N$_4$O$_3$. M: 306.37.
Production:
• 6-amino-1-methyluracil + *n*-propyl bromide + ethyl acetoacetate + 1-bromo-3-chloropropane (nitrosation/nitro reduction/condensation/amine formation/dehydrobromination/decarboxylation/ amine formation)
Uses: vasodilator drug

propenylguethol
1-(4-ethoxy-3-hydroxyphenyl)propene; 2-ethoxy-5-propenylphenol; 4-propenylguethol; [94-86-0]

C$_2$H$_5$O—⟨ ⟩—CH=CHCH$_3$ with HO

C$_{11}$H$_{14}$O$_2$. M: 178.23. White powder with vanilla-like odour. Commercial grades are a mixture of *cis*- and *trans*-isomers. MP: 35°C (*cis*-isomer), 86°C (*trans*-isomer). Slightly soluble in water. Soluble in alcohol and hydrocarbon solvents.
Production:
• isosafrole + methylmagnesium chloride (Grignard reaction)
• isoeugenol + diethyl sulphate (ethylation/demethylation)
Uses:
flavouring/fragrance ingredient (soap, detergents)

propetamphos
isopropyl 3-[ethylamino(methoxy)phosphinothioyloxy]-isocrotonate; [31218-83-4]

(CH$_3$)$_2$CHOCCH=C—O—PNHC$_2$H$_5$ with CH$_3$, OCH$_3$, O and S

C$_{10}$H$_{20}$N$_1$O$_4$P$_1$S$_1$. M: 281.31.
Production:
• thiophosphoryl chloride + ethylamine + methanol + isopropyl acetoacetate (dehydrochlorination/dehydrochlorination/alpha chlorination/Perkow reaction)
Uses: insecticide

propham
isopropyl phenylcarbamate; IPC; [122-42-9]

⟨ ⟩—NHCOCH(CH$_3$)$_2$ with O

C$_{10}$H$_{13}$N$_1$O$_2$. M: 179.22.

Production:
- aniline + isopropyl chloroformate
  (dehydrochlorination)

Uses:
herbicide/plant growth regulator

propicillin
[551-27-9]; [1245-44-9] (potassium salt)

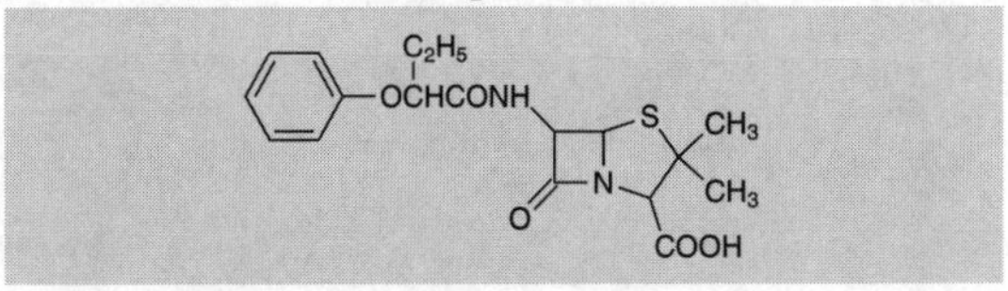

$C_{18}H_{22}N_2O_5S_1$. M: 378.44. Available commercially as the acid or potassium salts.
Production:
- 2-phenoxybutyric acid + 6-aminopenicillanic acid
  (amide formation)

Uses: antibacterial drug

propiconazole
1-[2-(2,4-dichlorophenyl)-4-propyl-1,3-dioxolan-2-yl-methyl]-1H-1,2,4-triazole; [60207-90-1]

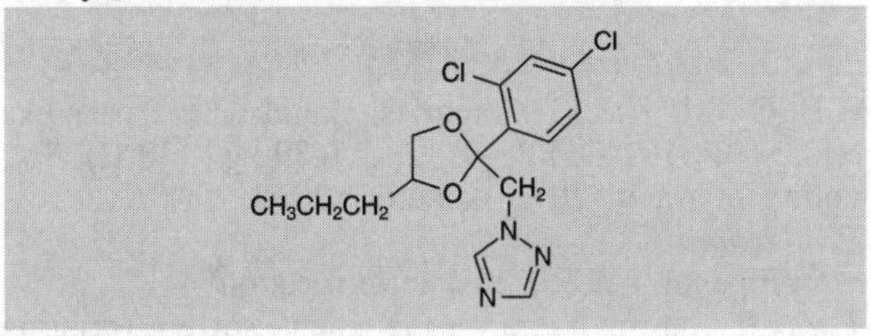

$C_{15}H_{17}Cl_2N_3O_2$. M: 342.23.
Production:
- α,2,4-trichloroacetophenone + 1,2,4-triazole +
  1-pentene + sodium hypochlorite (amine
  formation/hypochlorination/diacetal formation)

Uses: fungicide

propineb
[9016-72-2]

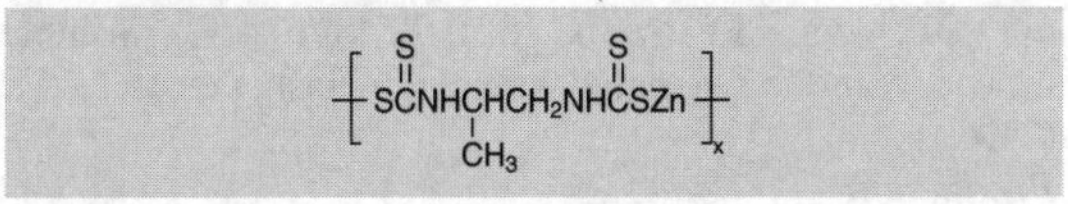

Complex, polymeric salt of propylenebis(dithiocarbanic acid) with zinc.
Production:
- 1,2-propanediamine + carbon disulphide + zinc
  sulphate (amine formation/salt formation)

Uses: fungicide

propionaldehyde
propanal; propyl aldehyde; [123-38-6]

$C_3H_6O_1$. M: 58.08. Liquid with a pungent odour. BP:

47–49°C. MP: -81°C. d: 0.81 kg/l (20°C). Soluble in water. Miscible with oxygenated solvents.
Production:
- ethylene + synthesis gas (hydroformylation)

Derivatives: 4-*t*-butyl-α-methylhydrocinnamaldehyde; β-carotene; cyclamen aldehyde; di-*n*-propylamine; emp-enthrin; etretinate; isoeugenol; methacrolein; α-methyl-cinnamaldehyde; α-methyl-β-3,4-methylenedioxyphen-ylpropionaldehyde-anthranilate adduct; 2-methylvaler-aldehyde; *n*-propanol; propionic acid; propionitrile; *n*-propylamine; trimethylolethane

propionic acid
propanoic acid; E280 (EC); [79-09-4]

$C_3H_6O_2$. M: 74.08. Colourless liquid with a pungent, rancid odour. BP: 141°C. FP: -21°C. d: 0.99 kg/l (20°C). Miscible with water. Soluble in oxygenated and chlorinated solvents. Flash point: 52°C (TCC).
Production:
- ethylene + carbon monoxide (Reppe hydrocarbonylation)
- propionaldehyde (carbonyl oxidation)
- naphtha, heavy (liquid-phase oxidation; coproduced
  with acetone/methyl ethyl ketone/formic acid/acetic
  acid)
- *n*-butane (Celanese LPO process; coproduced with
  methanol/ethanol/acetone/methyl ethyl ketone/formic
  acid/acetic acid/*n*-butyric acid/methyl formate)

Derivatives:
benzoyl chloride; benzyl propionate; α-bromopropionic acid; *n*-butyl propionate; calcium propionate; cellulose propionate; α-chloropropionic acid; citronellyl propion-ate; cocoamidopropyldimethylamine propionate; α,α-di-chloropropionic acid; diethyl ketone; ethyl propionate; geranyl propionate; *p*-hydroxypropiophenone; isoamyl propionate; linalyl propionate; methacrifos; phenethyl propionate; phenylmercuric propionate; propanil; prop-ionyl chloride; sodium propionate; vinyl propionate
Uses:
preservative (bread, grain)

propionitrile
ethyl cyanide; [107-12-0]

$C_3H_5N_1$. M: 55.08. Colourless liquid with an ethereal odour. BP: 97°C. MP: -92°C. d: 0.78 kg/l (20°C). Soluble with water. Miscible with oxygenated solvents.
Production:
- propionaldehyde + hydroxylamine sulphate (oxime
  formation/dehydration)
- acrylonitrile (Monsanto electrohydrodimerisation
  process; byproduct of adiponitrile production)

Derivatives: diethyl methylmalonate; 2-ethyl-4-methyl-imidazole; etrimfos; sulfafurazole

propionyl chloride
[79-03-8]

CH₃CH₂COCl

$C_3H_5Cl_1O_1$. M: 92.52. Liquid with a pungent odour. BP: 77–79°C. MP: -94°C. Hydrolysed by water and alcohol.
Production:
- propionic acid (chlorination)
- propionic acid + benzotrichloride (acid chloride formation; coproduced with benzoyl chloride)

Derivatives:
alfentanil; anethole; dextropropoxyphene; Disperse Blue 125; Disperse Blue 183; fentanyl; ibuprofen; methyl 3-methylorsellinate; naproxen; 2-propionylfuran; propiophenone; sulfaethidole

2-propionylfuran
ethyl 2-furyl ketone

$C_7H_8O_2$. M: 124.14. Crystalline solid. MP: 28°C. d: 1.06 kg/l (28°C). Insoluble in water. Soluble in oxygenated solvents.
Production:
- furan + propionyl chloride (Friedel-Crafts acylation)

Derivatives:
3-ethyl-2-cyclopenten-2-ol-1-one; ethyl maltol

propiophenone
ethyl phenyl ketone; phenyl ethyl ketone; 1-phenyl-propan-1-one; [93-55-0]

$C_9H_{10}O_1$. M: 134.18. Solid or liquid with a pleasant, floral odour. MP: 18°C. BP: 217–218°C. d: 1.01 kg/l (20°C). Insoluble in water. Miscible with alcohol and aromatic solvents.
Production:
- benzene + propionyl chloride (Friedel-Crafts acylation)

Derivatives: amfepramone; dextropropoxyphene; DL-ephedrine; eprazinone; mephenytoin; metaraminol; norephedrine; phenprocoumone; tamoxifen
Uses: fragrance ingredient

propoxur
2-isopropoxyphenyl methylcarbamate; [114-26-1]

$C_{11}H_{15}N_1O_3$. M: 209.25.

Production:
- catechol + propylene + methyl isocyanate (ether formation/isocyanate addition)
Uses: insecticide

propoxyphene *See:* dextropropoxyphene

propranolol
[525-66-6]

$C_{16}H_{21}N_1O_2$. M: 259.36. Available commercially as the hydrochloride.
Production:
- isopropylamine + α-naphthyl glycidyl ether (epoxidation)
Uses: antianginal/antihypertensive drug

n-propyl acetate
[109-60-4]

$C_5H_{10}O_2$. M: 102.13. Colourless liquid with a pear-like odour. BP: 102°C. FP: -95°C. d: 0.89 kg/l (20°C). Solubility in water: 20 g/l solution (20°C).
Production:
- n-propanol + acetic acid (esterification)
Uses: flavouring/fragrance ingredient; solvent (printing inks, cellulose derivatives)

n-propyl alcohol *See:* n-propanol

n-propylamine
1-aminopropane; monopropylamine; [107-10-8]

CH₃CH₂CH₂NH₂

$C_3H_9N_1$. M: 59.11. Colourless liquid with an amine odour. BP: 48°C. FP: -83°C. d: 0.72 kg/l (4°C). Soluble in water and oxygenated solvents. Flash point: -37°C (TOC).
Production:
- propionaldehyde + ammonia (reductive ammoniation; coproduced with di-n-propylamine)
Derivatives: carticaine; chlorpropamide; prilocaine; n-propylethanolamine; profluralin

2-(propylamino)ethanol *See:* n-propylethanolamine

n-propyl bromide
1-bromopropane; [106-94-5]

CH₃CH₂CH₂Br

$C_3H_7Br_1$. M: 122.99. Colourless liquid. BP: 71°C. MP:

-110°C. d: 1.35 kg/l (20°C). Insoluble in water. Miscible with oxygenated and chlorinated solvents.
Production:
• *n*-propanol + hydrobromic acid (alcohol bromination)
Derivatives:
penconazole; propentofylline; valproic acid

n-propyl butyrate
[105-66-8]

$$CH_3CH_2CH_2COCH_2CH_2CH_3$$

$C_7H_{14}O_2$. M: 130.19. Colourless liquid. BP: 143°C. MP: -97°C. Slightly soluble in water. Soluble in oxygenated solvents.
Production:
• *n*-propanol + *n*-butyric acid (esterification)
Uses: flavouring ingredient

n-propyl chloroformate
n-propyl chlorocarbonate; [109-61-5]

$$CH_3CH_2CH_2OCCl$$

$C_4H_7ClO_2$. M: 122.55. Colourless liquid. BP: 106°C. MP: <-70°C. Hydrolysed by water and alcohol. Soluble in chlorinated and aromatic solvents.
Production:
• *n*-propanol + phosgene (phosgenation)
Derivatives:
di-(*n*-propyl) peroxydicarbonate; propamocarb

n-propyl cyanide *See: n*-butyronitrile

propylene
propene; [115-07-1]

$$CH_3CH=CH_2$$

C_3H_6. M: 42.08. Propylene is available in the form of either a relatively pure stream, from steam cracking and dehydrogenation plants, or as a mixed propane-propylene stream from refinery sources. The C_3 component of the gases from a refinery catalytic cracking unit contains, typically, 70% propylene. For most applications mixed streams of this type are acceptable. A notable exception to this is polypropylene production, for which relatively pure, 'polymer grade' propylene is needed. Pure propylene is a colourless gas which is liquified for storage and transportation. BP: -48°C. FP: -185°C. d: 0.61 kg/l (-50°C). Slightly soluble in water. Soluble in oxygenated solvents.
Production:
• propane (dehydrogenation)
• propane (steam cracking; coproduced with ethylene)
• liquified petroleum gas (steam cracking; coproduced with ethylene/C_4-stream, steam-cracked/gasoline, pyrolysis/pyrolysis tar)

• naphtha, heavy/gasoline, natural/gasoline, dearomatised (steam cracking; coproduced with ethylene/C_4-stream, steam-cracked/gasoline, pyrolysis/pyrolysis tar)
• gas oil, light (steam cracking; coproduced with ethylene/C_4-stream, steam-cracked/gasoline, pyrolysis/pyrolysis tar)
• refinery gas (fractionation; coproduced with liquified petroleum gas/C_4-stream, refinery)
• ethylene (Phillips metathesis process)
Derivatives:
acetone; acrolein; acrylic acid; acrylonitrile; alkyl(C_9-C_{30})phenol; allyl alcohol; allyl chloride; benzoin isopropyl ether; *n*-butanol; *t*-butanol; *n*-butylbenzene; *n*-butyraldehyde; carvacrol; *m/p*-cresol; cumene; cyclamen aldehyde; *m*-diisopropylbenzene; *p*-diisopropylbenzene; diisopropylnaphthalene; 2,3-dimethyl-2-butene; dodecene, branched; ethylene-propylene copolymers; ethylene-propylene copolymers, rubber; ethylene-propylene-diene terpolymer, rubber; 2-ethylhexanol; gasoline, alkylate; hexene, branched; isobutanol; isobutylbenzene; isobutyraldehyde; isopropanol; isopropyl mercaptan; isopropylphenol; *o*-isopropylphenol; methyl 3-methylorsellinate; 4-methyl-1-pentene; nonene, branched; oxalic acid; polyethylene, high-density; polyethylene, very low-density; polypropylene; polypropylene, atactic; polypropylene wax; promecarb; propoxur; propylene oxide; *n*-propyl mercaptan; styrene; tetrafluoroethylene-propylene terpolymers; thymol; vinyl chloride-propylene copolymers

propylene carbonate
[108-32-7]

$C_4H_6O_3$. M: 102.09. Colourless liquid with mild odour. FP: -49°C. BP: 242°C. d: 1.20 kg/l (20°C).
Production:
• propylene oxide + carbon dioxide (epoxidation)
• propylene glycol + phosgene (dehydrochlorination)
Uses: bentonite/montmorillonite gelling agent (greases, cosmetics); polar process solvent (chemical synthesis); hydraulic fluid additive; hydroxypropylation reagent; setting agent (sodium silicate foundry mould binders); solvent (Fluor-solvent carbon monoxide separation process)

1,2-propylenediamine *See:* 1,2-propanediamine

1,3-propylenediamine *See:* 1,3-propanediamine

propylene dichloride
1,2-dichloropropane; [78-87-5]
$C_3H_6Cl_2$. M: 112.99. Colourless liquid. BP: 96°C. FP: -100°C. d: 1.15 kg/l (25°C). Flash point: 60°C (TCC).

Slightly soluble in water. Soluble in oxygenated solvents.

$$\underset{\underset{\displaystyle Cl}{|}}{CH_3CHCH_2Cl}$$

Production:
- propylene + chlorine + calcium hydroxide (hypochlorination/dehydrochlorination; byproduct of propylene oxide production)

Derivatives: 1,2-propanediamine; 1,2-propanedithiol

1,2-propylene glycol *See:* propylene glycol

1,3-propylene glycol *See:* trimethylene glycol

propylene glycol
monopropylene glycol; propane-1,2-diol; 1,2-propylene glycol; MPG; [57-55-6]

$$\underset{\underset{\displaystyle CH_3}{|}}{HOCHCH_2OH}$$

$C_3H_8O_2$. M: 76.09. Colourless liquid available as industrial or pharmaceutical grade material. BP: 187–189°C. d: 1.04 kg/l (20°C). Miscible with water and oxygenated solvents.
Production:
- propylene oxide (hydration; coproduced with dipropylene glycol/tripropylene glycol)

Derivatives: hydroxyacetone; methylglyoxal dimethyl acetal; polymeric plasticisers; propylene carbonate; propylene glycol dicaprylate/caprate; propylene glycol dipelargonate; unsaturated polyester resins, coating grades; unsaturated polyester resins, general grades; unsaturated polyester resins, isophthalate grades
Uses: brake/hydraulic fluid component; coalescing solvent (water-based paints); low-toxicity antifreeze; moisturising agent/preservative (foodstuffs, pet foods); polyurethane chain-extender; solvent (printing inks, pharmaceuticals, cosmetics); tobacco humectant

propylene glycol alginate
hydroxypropyl alginate; E405 (EC); [9005-37-2]
Modified polysaccharide gum. Soluble in water forming viscous solutions.
Production:
- alginic acid + propylene oxide (epoxidation)
Uses: thickening agent/emulsifier (prepared foods)

1,3-propylene glycol di-(*p*-aminobenzoate)

$$H_2N-\!\!\!\!\bigcirc\!\!\!\!-\underset{O}{\overset{O}{C}}OCH_2CH_2CH_2O\underset{O}{\overset{O}{C}}-\!\!\!\!\bigcirc\!\!\!\!-NH_2$$

$C_{17}H_{18}N_2O_4$. M: 314.34.
Production:
- trimethylene glycol + *p*-aminobenzoic acid (esterification)
Uses: cast polyurethane elastomer crosslinking agent

propylene glycol dicaprylate/caprate

$$CH_3(CH_2)_n\overset{O}{\overset{||}{C}}OCH_2\underset{\underset{\displaystyle CH_3}{|}}{CH}O\overset{O}{\overset{||}{C}}(CH_2)_nCH_3$$

n = 8–10. Liquid. Pour point: -40°C. d: 0.92 kg/l (25°C). Insoluble in water. Flash point: 184°C (COC).
Production:
- propylene glycol + C_8-C_{10} fatty acids (esterification)
Uses: emollient/cosolvent (toiletries)

propylene glycol dipelargonate
[41395-83-9]

$$CH_3(CH_2)_7\overset{O}{\overset{||}{C}}OCH_2\underset{\underset{\displaystyle CH_3}{|}}{CH}O\overset{O}{\overset{||}{C}}(CH_2)_7CH_3$$

$C_{21}H_{40}O_4$. M: 356.55. Liquid. MP: -21°C.
Production:
- propylene glycol + pelargonic acid (esterification)
Uses: emollient/cosolvent (toiletries)

propylene glycol mono-*t*-butyl ether
Arcosolv PTB (Arco Chemical)

$$\underset{\underset{\displaystyle CH_3}{|}}{(CH_3)_3COCHCH_2OH}$$

$C_7H_{16}O_2$. M: 132.21.
Production:
- *t*-butanol + propylene oxide (epoxidation)
Uses: coupling solvent

propylene glycol monoethyl ether
ethoxypropanol; EP

$$\underset{\underset{\displaystyle CH_3}{|}}{C_2H_5OCHCH_2OH}$$

$C_5H_{12}O_2$. M: 104.15. Colourless liquid. BP: 132°C. d: 0.90 kg/l.
Production:
- ethanol + propylene oxide (epoxidation)
Derivatives: propylene glycol monoethyl ether acetate
Uses: coalescing solvent (water-based paints); solvent (paints, printing inks)

propylene glycol monoethyl ether acetate
ethoxypropyl acetate; EPA

$$\underset{\underset{\displaystyle CH_3}{|}}{C_2H_5OCHCH_2O}\overset{O}{\overset{||}{C}}CH_3$$

$C_7H_{14}O_3$. M: 146.19. Colourless liquid. BP: 158°C. d: 0.95 kg/l (20°C). Soluble in water. Miscible with most organic solvents. Flash point: 54°C (PMCC).
Production:
- propylene glycol monoethyl ether + acetic acid (esterification)
Uses: solvent (paints, printing inks)

propylene glycol monoisobutyl ether
isobutoxypropanol; [23436-19-3]

$$CH_3$$
$$(CH_3)_2CHCH_2OCHCH_2OH$$

$C_7H_{16}O_2$. M: 132.21. Liquid. BP: 161°C. d: 0.87 kg/l. Soluble in water and most organic solvents. Flash point: 60°C (PMCC).

Production:
• isobutanol + propylene oxide (epoxidation)

Uses:
coalescing solvent (water-based paints); solvent (paints)

propylene glycol monolaurate
propylene glycol laurate (CTFA); PGML

$$O \quad CH_3$$
$$CH_3(CH_2)_{10}COCHCH_2OH$$

$C_{15}H_{30}O_3$. M: 258.40. Pale amber liquid.

Production:
• lauric acid, narrow cut + propylene oxide (epoxidation)

Uses: emollient (cosmetics)

propylene glycol monomethyl ether
methoxypropanol; MP; [107-98-2]

$$CH_3$$
$$CH_3OCHCH_2OH$$

$C_4H_{10}O_2$. M: 90.12. Colourless liquid. BP: 120°C. FP: -95°C. d: 0.92 kg/l (20°C). Completely miscible with water and oxygenated solvents.

Production:
• methanol + propylene oxide (epoxidation)

Derivatives:
propylene glycol monomethyl ether acetate

Uses: coalescing solvent (water-based paints/inks)

propylene glycol monomethyl ether acetate
methoxypropyl acetate; propylene glycol methyl ether acetate; MPA; PMA

$$CH_3 \quad O$$
$$CH_3OCHCH_2OCCH_3$$

$C_6H_{12}O_3$. M: 132.17. Colourless liquid. BP: 146°C. d: 0.97 kg/l (20°C). Soluble in water. Miscible with most organic solvents. Flash point: 50°C (PMCC).

Production:
• propylene glycol monomethyl ether + acetic acid (esterification)

Uses:
solvent (paints, printing inks)

propylene glycol monostearate
PGMS

$C_{21}H_{42}O_3$. M: 342.57. Yellow paste. MP: 35–40°C. HLB: 3.5 (self-emulsifying grades), 2.5 (non self-emulsifying grades). Self-emulsifying grades contain some free fatty acid.

$$O \quad CH_3$$
$$CH_3(CH_2)_{16}COCHCH_2OH$$

Production:
• stearic acid + propylene oxide (epoxidation)

Uses: auxiliary emulsifier/viscosifier (food, cosmetics)

propylene oxide
1,2-epoxypropane; [75-56-9]

$$O$$
$$CH_3CH-CH_2$$

$C_3H_6O_1$. M: 58.08. Colourless liquid. BP: 34–35°C. FP: -112°C. d: 0.82 kg/l (25°C). Solubility in water: 590 g/l solution (25°C). Miscible with oxygenated solvents. Flash point: <-25°C (TCC).

Production:
• ethylbenzene + propylene + oxygen (Arco SM-PO process; coproduced with styrene)
• *t*-butyl hydroperoxide + propylene (Arco TBA-PO process; coproduced with *t*-butanol)
• propylene + chlorine + calcium hydroxide (hypochlorination/dehydrochlorination)

Derivatives:
allyl alcohol; *N,N'*-bis(2-hydroxypropyl)-2-methylpiperazine; bisphenol A propoxylates; cetyl alcohol propoxylates; dextromoramide; di-(2-hydroxypropyl)bisphenol A; diisopropanolamine; dimethylisopropanolamine; dipropylene glycol; dipropylene glycol monohexyl ether; dipropylene glycol monoisobutyl ether; dipropylene glycol monomethyl ether; ethylenediamine propoxylate/ethoxylates; glycerol propoxylate triacrylate; 4,5,5,6,7,7-hexamethylindanopyran; 2-hydroxypropyl acrylate; hydroxypropyl cellulose; hydroxypropyl guar; 1-(2-hydroxypropyl)imidazole; 2-hydroxypropyl methacrylate; hydroxypropyl starch; isoxsuprine; lanolin propoxylates; lauryl alcohol ethoxylate/propoxylates; methylhydroxypropylcellulose; monoisopropanolamine; nonylphenol polyether amines; phenol-formaldehyde alkoxylates; 1-phenoxy-2-propanol; polyalkylene glycol; polybutene thiophosphonate propoxylates, alkali-earth salts; polyether polyols, flexible; polyether polyols, flexible, amine-terminated; polyether polyols, rigid; polypropylene glycol; propylene carbonate; propylene glycol; propylene glycol alginate; propylene glycol mono-*t*-butyl ether; propylene glycol monoethyl ether; propylene glycol monoisobutyl ether; propylene glycol monolaurate; propylene glycol monomethyl ether; propylene glycol monostearate; propylene oxide copolymers, rubber; protheobromine; proxyphylline; silicone-polyol block copolymers; tetrabromophthalate diol; tetrahydroxypropyl ethylenediamine; tetrapropylene glycol monomethyl ether; triisopropanolamine; tripropylene glycol; tripropylene glycol monomethyl ether; tris(1-chloro-2-propyl) phosphate

propylene oxide copolymers, rubber

poly(propylene oxide); Parel (B.F. Goodrich)

Rubber. Vulcanisates are characterised by their excellent resilience and hysteresis. Moderate resistance to oil and solvents. Service range: -60–+150°C.
Production:
• propylene oxide + allyl glycidyl ether (epoxidation)
Uses: automotive/aerospace components

propylene tetramer *See:* dodecene, branched

propylene trimer *See:* nonene, branched

propylene urea

tetrahydro-2-pyrimidinone; *N,N'*-trimethyleneurea; [1852-17-1]

$C_4H_8N_2O_1$. M: 100.11. Solid. MP: 261–265°C.
Production:
• 1,3-propanediamine + urea (condensation)
Derivatives: dimethylolpropylene urea

n-propylethanolamine

N-(2-hydroxyethyl)propylamine; 2-(propylamino)ethanol; [16369-21-4]

$CH_3CH_2CH_2NHCH_2CH_2OH$

$C_5H_{13}N_1O_1$. M: 103.16. Liquid. BP: 179–182°C. Soluble in water.
Production:
• *n*-propylamine + ethylene oxide (epoxidation)
Derivatives: fluchloralin; prochloraz

n-propyl gallate

propyl gallate; PG; E310 (EC); [121-79-9]

$C_{10}H_{12}O_5$. M: 212.20. White crystals. MP: 148–150°C. Very slightly soluble in water. Soluble in oxygenated solvents.
Production:
• *n*-propanol + gallic acid (esterification)
Uses: antioxidant (oils, fats, waxes, prepared foods)

propyl 4-hydroxybenzoate

E216 (EC); propylparaben; *n*-propyl *p*-hydroxybenzoate; [94-13-3]

$C_{10}H_{12}O_3$. M: 180.21. White, crystalline solid. MP: 95–98°C. Insoluble in water. Soluble in oxygenated solvents. Also available as the sodium salt. The latter is not approved for food use in the USA.
Production:
• *n*-propanol + *p*-hydroxybenzoic acid (esterification)
Uses: preservative (fruit, preserves, soft drinks)

propyliodone

[587-61-1]

$C_{10}H_{11}I_2N_1O_3$. M: 447.03.
Production:
• *n*-propanol + diodone (esterification)
Uses: x-ray diagnostic aid

n-propyl mercaptan

propane-1-thiol; [107-03-9]

$CH_3CH_2CH_2SH$

$C_3H_8S_1$. M: 76.15. Liquid with an unpleasant odour. BR: 67–71°C. d: 0.84 kg/l (15°C). Slightly soluble in water. Soluble in oxygenated solvents.
Production:
• propylene + hydrogen sulphide (anti-Markownikoff addition)
Derivatives: ethoprophos; pebulate; profenofos; prothiofos; sulprofos; vernolate
Uses: gas odorant

propylparaben *See:* propyl 4-hydroxybenzoate

2-propyn-1-ol *See:* propargyl alcohol

propyphenazone

[479-92-5]

$C_{14}H_{18}N_2O_1$. M: 230.30.
Production:
• 3-methyl-1-phenyl-5-pyrazolone + acetone + dimethyl sulphate (carbonyl condensation/hydrogenation/methylation)
Uses: analgesic drug adjunct

propyzamide
3,5-dichloro-N-(1,1-dimethylpropynyl)benzamide;
[23950-58-5]

$C_{12}H_{11}Cl_2N_1O_1$. M: 256.14.
Production:
• methylbutynol + ammonia + 3,5-dichlorobenzoyl
  chloride (ammoniation/amide formation)
Uses: herbicide

proquazone
[22760-18-5]

$C_{18}H_{18}N_2O_1$. M: 278.35.
Production:
• m-cresotic acid + benzene + isopropylamine + urea
  (Friedel-Crafts acylation/amine formation/cyclisation)
Uses: antirheumatic drug

protease, bacterial, alkaline
detergent enzyme; subtilisin; E.C.3.4.21.14 (Enzyme
Commission); [9014-01-1]
Granules. Serine-active proteolytic enzyme. Reactive
in the pH range 7.0–11.0.
Production:
• microbial fermentation medium + *Bacillus
  licheniformis* bacteria (fermentation)
Uses:
laundry detergent ingredient

protease, bacterial, neutral
E.C.3.4.24.4 (Enzyme Commission); [9068-59-1]
Metalloprotease enzymes active over the pH range 6–9.
Production:
• microbial fermentation medium + *Bacillus
  amyloliquefaciens* bacteria/*Bacillus thermo-
  proteolyticus* bacteria (fermentation)
Derivatives:
protein hydrolysates
Uses: beer production; tanning agent

protease, fungal
rennin, fungal
Mixed extract containing acidic protease used as a substitute for calf rennet. Other types are used in baking
and soya sauce production.

Production:
• mould fermentation medium + *Mucor pusillus*
  mould (fermentation)
Uses: cheese/casein/soya sauce production reagent

protein hydrolysates
casamino acid
Mixture of amino acids and peptides, the composition
of which varies with the raw materials.
Production:
• animal glue/maize gluten/casein/soyabean meal +
  protease, bacterial, neutral (enzymatic hydrolysis)
Uses: flavour enhancer; moisturising agent (shampoos,
cosmetics); parenteral nutrient ingredient

protheobromine
[50-39-5]

$C_{10}H_{14}N_4O_3$. M: 238.25.
Production:
• theobromine + propylene oxide (epoxidation)
Uses: diuretic drug

prothiofos
O-2,4-dichlorophenyl O-ethyl S-propyl phosphorodithioate; [34643-46-4]

$C_{11}H_{15}Cl_2O_2P_1S_2$. M: 345.25.
Production:
• thiophosphoryl chloride + ethanol + 2,4-dichloro-
  phenol + n-propyl mercaptan (dehydrochlorination/
  dehydrochlorination/dehydrochlorination)
Uses: insecticide

prothionamide
[14222-60-7]

$C_9H_{12}N_2S_1$. M: 180.27.
Production:
• methyl propyl ketone + diethyl oxalate + cyanoacetamide + ammonia + hydrogen sulphide (carbonyl condensation/cyclisation/nitrile hydrolysis/
  decarboxylation/nitrile formation/nitrile addition)
Uses: tuberculostatic drug

prothipendyl

[303-69-5]; [74525-36-3] (hydrochloride)

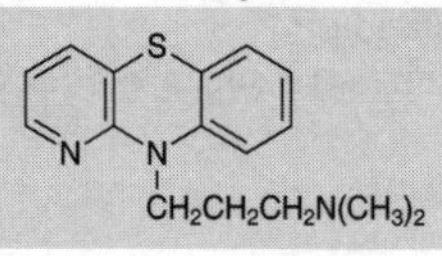

$C_{16}H_{19}N_3S_1$. M: 285.41. Available commercially as the free base or as the hydrochloride salt.

Production:

• 1-azaphenothiazine + 3-dimethylaminopropyl chloride hydrochloride (amine formation)

Uses:

psychosedative/antihistamine drug

prothoate

O,O-diethyl *S*-isopropylcarbamoylmethyl phosphorodithioate; [2275-18-5]

$C_9H_{20}N_1O_3P_1S_2$. M: 285.37.

Production:

• chloroacetic acid + isopropylamine + *O,O*-diethyl dithiophosphoric acid (amide formation/ dehydrochlorination)

Uses: insecticide/acaricide

protriptyline

[438-60-8]; [1225-55-4] (hydrochloride)

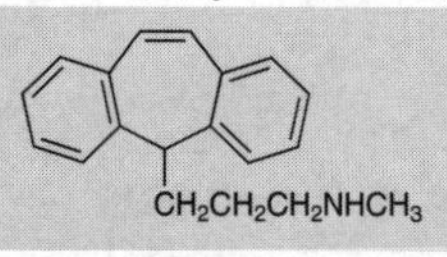

$C_{19}H_{21}N_1$. M: 263.39. Available commercially as the free base or as the hydrochloride salt.

Production:

• dibenzosuberenone-5 + 3-dimethylaminopropyl chloride hydrochloride + ethyl chloroformate (reduction/dehydrochlorination/demethylation)

Uses: antidepressant drug

proxyphylline

[603-00-9]

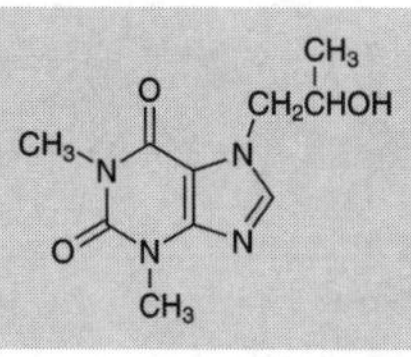

$C_{10}H_{14}N_4O_3$. M: 238.25.

Production:

• theophylline + propylene oxide (epoxidation)

Uses:

bronchodilator/vasodilator drug

Prussian Blue

Bronze Blue; Chinese Blue; iron blue; Milori Blue; non-bronze blue; potash blue; ferric ferrocyanide (CTFA); Pigment Blue 27 (CI); 77510 (CI); 77520 (CI)

$$MFe\left[Fe(CN)\right]_6$$

M = potassium, sodium or ammonium. A series of blue pigments, sometimes with a reddish or greenish hue, or with a bronze lustre (bronze blue, Chinese blue). d: 1.97 kg/l. Decomposed by alkali.

Production:

• ferrous sulphate + potassium ferrocyanide + potassium chlorate (indirect potash blue process)

• potassium ferrocyanide + sodium ferrocyanide + ammonium sulphate + sodium chlorate (indirect ammonia-soda process)

• ferric chloride + potassium ferrocyanide (direct potash blue process)

Derivatives: chrome green

Uses: zinc green pigment component; pigment (printing inks, paints, paper coatings)

PS *See:* polystyrene, general-purpose

PSBR *See:* vinylpyridine copolymers, latex

pseudocumene

1,2,4-trimethylbenzene; [95-63-6]

C_9H_{12}. M: 120.20. Liquid. BP: 168–170°C. MP: -44°C. d: 0.88 kg/l (15°C). Insoluble in water. Flash point: 44°C.

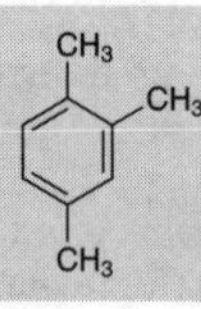

Production:

• trimethylbenzene fraction (fractionation; coproduced with mesitylene/durene)

Derivatives: trimellitic anhydride

pseudoionone

6,10-dimethyl-3,5,9-undecatrien-2-one; [141-10-6]

$C_{13}H_{20}O_1$. M: 192.30. Pale yellow liquid. BP: 143–145°C (1.6 kPa). d: 0.90 kg/l (20°C). Soluble in oxygenated solvents.

Production:

• citral + acetone (carbonyl condensation)

• dehydrolinalool + methyl acetoacetate (ether formation/Carroll reaction)

Derivatives:

β-ionone; ionone; 2,6,10-trimethylundecenal

PSS *See:* sodium polystyrene sulphonate

PSU *See:* polysulphone

PSVS *See:* sodium poly(vinyl sulphonate)

psyllium seed gum
Polysaccharide gum extracted by boiling water from the seed coats of the psyllium (*Plantago ovata*) plants. India is the main producing country.
Uses:
hair-setting lotion ingredient; laxative drug

PTA *See:* phosphotungstic acid; terephthalic acid

PTFE *See:* polytetrafluoroethylene

PTHF *See:* poly(tetramethylene ether) glycol

PTMEG *See:* poly(tetramethylene ether) glycol

PTMT *See:* poly(butylene terephthalate)

PTSA *See:* *p*-toluenesulphonic acid

PTSI *See:* *p*-toluenesulphonyl isocyanate

PTZ *See:* phenothiazine

pumice
[1332-09-8]
Grey, highly porous, natural volcanic glass. Italy, USA, Canada, New Zealand and Japan are major producing countries.
Uses:
burnishing stone (metal and wood surface preparation); catalyst carrier; metal polishing compounds; scouring soap ingredient; lightweight concrete aggregate; heat/sound insulation

PUR *See:* polyurethane, low-resilience elastomers

putrescine *See:* 1,4-diaminobutane

PVA *See:* polyvinyl acetate; polyvinyl alcohol

PVAC *See:* polyvinyl acetate

PVAL *See:* polyvinyl alcohol

PVB *See:* polyvinyl butyral

PVC *See:* polyvinyl chloride

PVCA *See:* vinyl chloride-vinyl acetate copolymers

PVCC *See:* polyvinyl chloride, chlorinated

PVDF *See:* polyvinylidene fluoride

PVF *See:* polyvinyl fluoride; polyvinyl formal

PVM *See:* poly(vinyl methyl ether)

PVM/MA
See: poly(methyl vinyl ether-maleic anhydride)

PVOH *See:* polyvinyl alcohol

PVP *See:* polyvinylpyrrolidone; poly(4-vinylpyridine)

PVPP *See:* polyvinylpyrrolidone, crosslinked

PVP/VA
See: vinylpyrrolidone-vinyl acetate copolymers

PXS
See: potassium xylene sulphonate

pyrantel
[15686-83-6] (free base); [33401-94-4] (hydrogen tartrate); [22204-24-6] (pamoate)

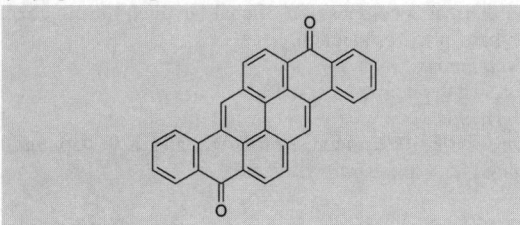

$C_{11}H_{14}N_2S_1$. M: 206.30. Available commercially as the tartrate and pamoate salts.
Production:
• thiophene + dimethylformamide + cyanoacetic acid + 3-methylaminopropylamine (Vilsmeier reaction/Cope reaction/decarboxylation/condensation)
Uses:
anthelmintic drug

pyranthrone
Pigment Orange 40 (CI); Vat Orange 9 (CI); 59700 (CI); [128-70-1]

$C_{30}H_{14}O_2$. M: 406.44.
Production:
• 1-chloro-2-methylanthraquinone (base-catalysed coupling)
Derivatives:
Pigment Orange 51; Pigment Red 216; Vat Orange 2
Uses: dye (cotton)

pyrazinamide
pyrazine-2-carboxamide; [98-96-4]

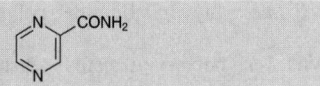

$C_5H_5N_3O_1$. M: 123.11.
Production:
- quinoxaline + ammonia (side-chain oxidation/
  decarboxylation/amide formation)

Uses: antituberculosis drug

1,9-pyrazolanthrone *See:* anthrapyrazolone

pyrazon *See:* chloridazon

pyrazophos
[13457-18-6]

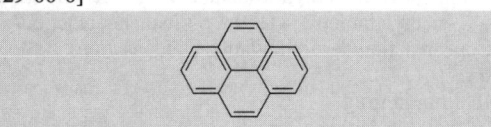

$C_{14}H_{20}N_3O_5P_1S_1$. M: 373.35.
Production:
- cyanoacetic acid + hydrazine + ethyl acetoacetate +
  triethyl orthoformate + *O,O*-diethyl
  phosphorochlorothioate (condensation/condensation/
  dehydrochlorination)

Uses: fungicide

pyrene
[129-00-0]

$C_{16}H_{10}$. M: 202.26. Pale yellow crystals. MP: 149–
150°C. d: 1.27 kg/l (20°C). Insoluble in water. Soluble
in oxygenated and aromatic solvents. Pyrene is formed
by thermal decomposition of coal tar pitch during coke
or hard pitch production.
Production:
- coal tar pitch (pyrolysis)

Derivatives:
Direct Blue 109; Fluorescent Brightener 179; naphthal-
ene-1,4,5,8-tetracarboxylic acid

pyrethrum
[8003-34-7]
Extract of pyrethrum (*Chrysanthemum cinerariaefolium*)
flowers which are grown in Kenya, Japan, New Guinea
and Ecuador. The extract contains 20–25% mixed esters formed from pyrethrolone, cinerolone and jasmol-
one alcohols with chrysanthemic and pyrethric acids.
Uses: insecticide

pyricarbate
2,6-pyridinedimethanol bis(methylcarbamate); pyridinol
carbamate; [1882-26-4]

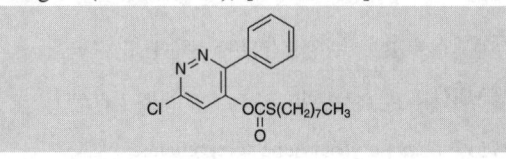

$C_{11}H_{15}N_3O_4$. M: 253.26.
Production:
- dipicolinic acid + methyl isocyanate (esterification/
  ester reduction/isocyanate addition)

Uses: antiarteriosclerotic drug

pyridate
Lentagran (Chemie Linz); [55512-33-9]

$C_{19}H_{23}Cl_1N_2O_2S_1$. M: 378.91.
Production:
- benzoic acid + maleic anhydride + hydrazine +
  octylthiochloroformate (acylation/amide formation/
  rearrangement/dehydrochlorination)

Uses: herbicide

pyridine
[110-86-1]

$C_5H_5N_1$. M: 79.10. Pale yellow liquid with a characteristic odour. BP: 115°C. FP: -42°C. d: 0.98 kg/l
(20°C). Miscible with water, oxygenated and aromatic
solvents.
Production:
- pyridine bases, crude (fractionation; coproduced
  with α-picoline/γ-picoline/2,6-lutidine/3,4-lutidine/
  pyridine bases)
- acetaldehyde + formaldehyde + ammonia (Reilly
  synthesis; coproduced with α-picoline/β-picoline/
  γ-picoline)
- acrolein + ammonia (Daicel process; coproduced
  with β-picoline)

Derivatives:
2-aminopyridine; 4-aminopyridine; Basic Blue 119;
Basic Orange 30:1; Basic Red 18:1; 2,2′-bipyridine;
2-bromopyridine; cefaloridine; cefapirin; cefazedone;
ceftazidime; cetylpyridinium bromide; cetylpyridinium
chloride; 2-chloropyridine; diodone; doxylamine; laurylpyridinium chloride; paraquat dichloride; piperidine;
pyridine-*N*-oxide; 3-pyridino-4-methyl-6-hydroxy-2-pyr-
idone chloride; pyrifenox; stearamidomethylpyridinium
chloride

pyridine bases
[68391-11-7]

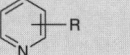

R = mixed alkyl-. Liquid available in several grades within the distillation range 60–210°C.
Production:
• pyridine bases, crude (fractionation; coproduced with pyridine/α-picoline/γ-picoline/2,6-lutidine/3,4-lutidine)
Uses: alcohol denaturant

pyridine bases, crude
Production:
• light oil (acid extraction/alkali extraction; byproduct of benzole production)
Derivatives: 2,6-lutidine; 3,4-lutidine; α-picoline; γ-picoline; pyridine; pyridine bases

pyridine-2-carboxylic acid *See:* picolinic acid

pyridine-3-carboxylic acid *See:* nicotinic acid

pyridine-4-carboxylic acid *See:* isonicotinic acid

pyridine-2,3-dicarboxylic acid *See:* quinolinic acid

pyridine-2,5-dicarboxylic acid *See:* isocinchomeronic acid

pyridine-2,6-dicarboxylic acid *See:* dipicolinic acid

pyridine-N-oxide
pyridine-1-oxide; [694-59-7]

$C_5H_5N_1O_1$. M: 95.10. Crystalline solid. MP: 66°C.
Production:
• pyridine + hydrogen peroxide (oxidation)
Uses: chemical intermediate

3-pyridino-4-methyl-6-hydroxy-2-pyridone chloride

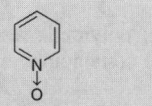

$C_{11}H_{11}Cl_1N_2O_2$. M: 238.67.
Production:
• ethyl chloroacetate + pyridine + methyl acetoacetate + ammonia (amide formation/quaternisation/condensation)

Uses: azoic dye coupling component (acrylic fibre, Cartesol-K paper dyes)

pyridostigmine bromide
[101-26-8]

$C_9H_{13}Br_1N_2O_2$. M: 261.11.
Production:
• 3-hydroxypyridine + dimethylcarbamoyl chloride + methyl bromide (dehydrochlorination/quaternisation)
Uses: cholinergic drug

pyridoxine
4,5-dimethylol-3-hydroxy-2-methylpyridine; vitamin B_6; [65-23-6]; [58-56-0] (hydrochloride); [4372-46-7] (tri-palmitate)

$C_8H_{11}N_1O_3$. M: 169.19. Available commercially as the hydrochloride, phosphate or tripalmitate derivatives.
Production:
• β-aminocrotononitrile + formic acid + 1,4-butenediol (condensation/alcohol protection/cycloaddition/rearrangement/alcohol deprotection)
Derivatives:
pyritinol
Uses: dietary supplement ingredient

α-pyridylamine *See:* 2-aminopyridine

β-pyridylamine *See:* 3-aminopyridine

γ-pyridylamine *See:* 4-aminopyridine

pyrifenox
2′,4′-dichloro-2-(3-pyridyl)acetophenone O-methyl-oxime; [88283-41-4]

$C_{14}H_{12}Cl_2N_2O_1$. M: 295.17.
Production:
• pyridine + α,2,4-trichloroacetophenone + hydroxyl-amine sulphate + dimethyl sulphate (Friedel-Crafts alkylation/oxime formation/methylation)
Uses: fungicide

pyritinol
[1098-97-1] (free base); [10049-83-9] (hydrochloride)

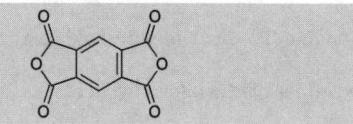

$C_{16}H_{20}N_2O_4S_2$. M: 368.48. Available commercially as the free base or hydrochloride.
Production:
• pyridoxine + potassium ethyl xanthate (alcohol bromination/dehydrobromination/sulphide formation)
Uses: nootropic drug

pyrocatechol *See:* catechol

pyrogallic acid *See:* pyrogallol

pyrogallol
pyrogallic acid; 1,2,3-trihydroxybenzene; 76515 (CI); [87-66-1]

$C_6H_6O_3$. M: 126.12. White, crystalline solid. Discoloured by light and air. MP: 131–133°C. BP: 309°C. d: 1.45 kg/l. Soluble in water and oxygenated solvents.
Production:
• gallic acid (decarboxylation)
• cyclohexanone (alpha chlorination/hydration/dehydrochlorination)
Derivatives: bendiocarb; 2,3,4-trihydroxybenzophenone mono-2,1,5-diazoester
Uses:
dyestuffs intermediate; mordant (wool/leather dyeing); analytical reagent (antimony, bismuth, gas analysis)

pyroligneous acid *See:* wood vinegar

pyrolysis oil, hardwood
Condensible vapours from charcoal production consisting of water, tars and low molecular weight organic acids and alcohols. The tar contains both water-soluble and water-insoluble fractions.
Production:
• hardwood (carbonisation; byproduct of charcoal production)
Derivatives:
wood spirit; wood tar, hardwood; wood vinegar
Uses: fuel

pyrolysis oil, pinewood
Production:
• pinewood logs (carbonisation; byproduct of charcoal production)

Derivatives: turpentine oil, wood; tar oil, wood; pine oil; wood pitch
Uses: fuel

pyrolysis tar
Involatile tar produced by steam cracking of heavy hydrocarbon feedstocks. Mixed product with 75–80% aromatics content.
Production:
• liquified petroleum gas (steam cracking; coproduced with ethylene/propylene/C_4-stream, steam-cracked/gasoline, pyrolysis)
• naphtha, heavy/gasoline, natural/gasoline, dearomatised (steam cracking; coproduced with ethylene/propylene/C_4-stream, steam-cracked/gasoline, pyrolysis)
• gas oil, light (steam cracking; coproduced with ethylene/propylene/C_4-stream, steam-cracked/gasoline, pyrolysis)
Derivatives: carbon black; gas oil, heavy; gas oil, light; naphtha, heavy; needle coke; refinery gas
Uses: fuel oil; road tars; wood preservative

pyromellitic dianhydride
PMDA; [89-32-7]

$C_{10}H_2O_6$. M: 218.12. White powder. MP: 283–285°C. Hydrolysed to acid by water. Soluble in oxygenated and aromatic solvents.
Production:
• durene (side-chain oxidation)
Derivatives:
polyimide resins; polyimide resins, prepolymers
Uses: alkyd resin comonomer; epoxy resin curing agent

pyroquilon
1,2,5,6-tetrahydropyrrolo[3,2,1-ij]quinolin-4-one; [57369-32-1]

$C_{11}H_{11}N_1O_1$. M: 173.22.
Production:
• aniline + 3-chloropropionyl chloride + chloroacetyl chloride (amide formation/condensation/amide formation/condensation/carbonyl condensation)
Uses: fungicide

pyrrole
[109-97-7]
$C_4H_5N_1$. M: 67.09. Yellow liquid. d: 0.97 kg/l (20°C). BP: 130°C.

Production:
• furan + ammonia (amine formation)
Derivatives: clemastine; *N*-methylpyrrole

pyrrolidine
[123-75-1]

$C_4H_9N_1$. M: 71.12. Colourless to pale yellow liquid with an ammoniacal odour. BP: 86–88°C. MP: <−60°C. Miscible with water forming alkaline solutions. Soluble in oxygenated and chlorinated solvents.
Production:
• 1,4-butanediol + ammonia (amine formation)
• succinonitrile (nitrile reduction; byproduct of 1,4-diaminobutane production)
Derivatives:
clemizole; dextromoramide; piromidic acid; triprolidine

pyrrolidine-2-carboxylic acid *See:* L-proline

2-pyrrolidone
γ-butyrolactam; [616-45-5]

$C_4H_7N_1O_1$. M: 85.11. Colourless liquid or solid. MP: 25°C. BP: 245°C. d: 1.11 kg/l (20°C). Miscible with water, oxygenated, chlorinated and aromatic solvents. Insoluble in aliphatic solvents.
Production:
• γ-butyrolactone + ammonia (ammoniation)
Derivatives: piracetam; *N*-vinyl-2-pyrrolidone
Uses: plasticiser/emulsifier (styrene-acrylic floor-wax); selective solvent (acetylene, acrylonitrile production); process solvent (pharmaceutical manufacture)

pyruvic acid
2-ketopropionic acid; [127-17-3]

$C_3H_4O_3$. M: 88.06. Colourless liquid with an odour of acetic acid. MP: 11–12°C. BP: 164–166°C. Miscible with water and oxygenated solvents.
Production:
• natural rubber + ozone (ozonolysis; byproduct of levulinic acid production)
• DL-lactic acid (oxidation)
Derivatives: levodopa

pyrvinium pamoate
pyrvinium embonate; [3546-41-6]

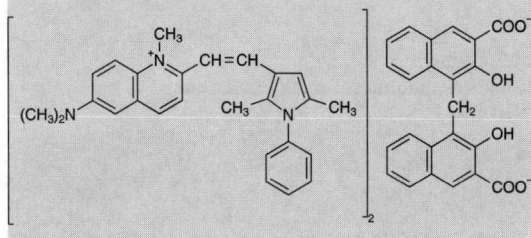

$C_{75}H_{70}N_6O_6$. M: 1151.44.
Production:
• acetonylacetone + aniline + 6-dimethylamino-1,2-dimethylquinolinium iodide + pamoic acid (reductive amination/Vilsmeier reaction/carbonyl condensation/salt formation)
Uses: anthelmintic drug

Q

quinaldine
α-methylquinoline; 2-methylquinoline;
[91-63-4]

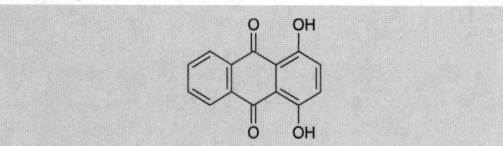

$C_{10}H_9N_1$. M: 143.19. Brown liquid. BP: 246°C. MP:
-2°C. d: 1.06 kg/l. Insoluble in water. Soluble in oxygenated and chlorinated solvents.
Production:
• aniline + acetaldehyde (Doebner-von Miller
  synthesis)
Derivatives:
quinoline-2,3-dicarboxylic acid
Uses: photographic sensitising dyestuff intermediate

quinalphos
O,O-diethyl *O*-quinoxalin-2-yl phosphorothioate;
[13593-03-8]

$C_{12}H_{15}N_2O_3P_1S_1$. M: 298.29.
Production:
• *o*-phenylenediamine + glyoxylic acid + *O,O*-diethyl
  phosphorochlorothioate (condensation/dehydro-
  chlorination)
Uses: insecticide/acaricide

quinizarin
1,4-dihydroxyanthraquinone; Pigment Violet 12 (CI,
aluminium salt); 58050 (CI); 58050:1 (aluminium salt);
[81-64-1]

$C_{14}H_8O_4$. M: 240.21. Red solid. MP: 192–195°C. Soluble in hot water and ether.
Production:
• 1-chloro-4-hydroxyanthraquinone (hydrolysis)
• 1-hydroxyanthraquinone (sulphonation/alkali fusion)
Derivatives:
Acid Blue 80; Acid Green 27; Acid Green 75; Disperse Blue 3; Disperse Blue 7; Disperse Blue 14; Solvent Blue 35; Solvent Blue 36; Solvent Blue 59; Solvent Green 3
Uses: pigment (paints, resins)

quinoline
[91-22-5]

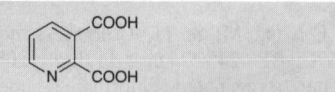

$C_9H_7N_1$. M: 129.17. Colourless, hygroscopic liquid with
an unpleasant odour. BP: 236–238°C. d: 1.09 kg/l
(25°C). Soluble in hot water. Miscible with oxygenated solvents.
Production:
• methylnaphthalene fraction (acid extraction;
  coproduced with isoquinoline)
Derivatives: 8-hydroxyquinoline; *N*-methylquinolinium
iodide; quinolinic acid

quinoline-2,3-dicarboxylic acid

$C_{11}H_7N_1O_4$. M: 217.19.
Production:
• quinaldine + potassium cyanide (sulphonation/
  cyanidation/side-chain oxidation)
Derivatives: imazaquin-ammonium

quinolinic acid
pyridine-2,3-dicarboxylic acid; [89-00-9]

$C_7H_5N_1O_4$. M: 167.13. Yellow powder. MP: 190°C with
decomposition. Bulk density: 0.6 kg/l. Very slightly
soluble in water. Soluble in aqueous alkali.
Production:
• quinoline (oxidative cleavage)
• methyl ethyl ketone + acrylonitrile (cyano-
  ethylation/side-chain oxidation)
Derivatives: imazapyr-isopropylammonium
Uses: flotation depressant (copper ores)

quinomethionate *See:* chinomethionat

quinone *See:* *p*-benzoquinone

_p_-quinonedioxime
1,4-benzoquinone dioxime; PQD; [105-11-3]
$C_6H_6N_2O_2$. M: 138.13. Yellow needles. Decomposes on
heating above 240°C. Soluble in hot water.
Production:
• *p*-nitrosophenol + hydroxylamine sulphate
  (oxidation/imine formation)

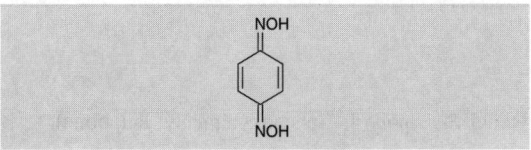

Derivatives: dibenzoyl-*p*-quinonedioxime
Uses: crosslinking agent (rubber)

quinophthalone
Disperse Yellow 54 (CI); Pigment Yellow 138 (CI); Solvent Yellow 33 (CI); 47000 (CI); D&C Yellow No. 11 (FDC); Paliotol Yellow K0961HD (BASF); [8003-22-3]; [12223-85-7]

$C_{18}H_{11}N_1O_3$. M: 289.30.
Production:
• oxyquinaldine carboxylic acid + phthalic anhydride (condensation/decarboxylation)
Derivatives: Acid Yellow 3
Uses:
solvent dye (oils, varnishes, solvents); dye (polyamide, polyester tri-chromatic dyeing); plastics colorant

quinoxaline
1,4-benzodiazine; *p*-benzodiazine; [91-19-0]

$C_8H_6N_2$. M: 130.15. Crystalline solid. MP: 29–32°C. BP: 230°C. Soluble in water, oxygenated and aromatic solvents.
Production:
• *o*-phenylenediamine + glyoxal (imine formation)
Derivatives: pyrazinamide

quintozene
pentachloronitrobenzene; PCNB; [82-68-8]

$C_6Cl_5N_1O_2$. M: 295.34.
Production:
• nitrobenzene (ring chlorination)
Uses: fungicide

quinuclidin-3-ol
3-hydroxy-1-azabicyclo[2,2,2]octane; 3-hydroxyquinuclidine; [1619-34-7]

$C_7H_{13}N_1O_1$. M: 127.20. Cream, crystalline powder. MP: 220–225°C. Soluble in water and alcohol.
Production:
• isonipecotic acid + ethyl bromoacetate (quaternisation/Claisen condensation/ester hydrolysis/decarboxylation/carbonyl reduction)
Derivatives: aceclidine; clidinium bromide

3-quinuclidinyl acetate *See:* aceclidine

quizalofop-ethyl
ethyl 2-[4-(6-chloroquinoxalin-2-yloxy)phenoxy]propionate; [76578-14-8]

$C_{19}H_{17}Cl_1N_2O_4$. M: 372.81.
Production:
• 4-chloro-*o*-phenylenediamine + glyoxylic acid + 2-(4-chlorophenoxy)propionic acid + ethanol (condensation/ether formation/esterification)
Uses: herbicide

R

R11 *See:* trichlorofluoromethane

R12 *See:* dichlorodifluoromethane

R12B1 *See:* bromochlorodifluoromethane

R13 *See:* chlorotrifluoromethane

R13B1 *See:* bromotrifluoromethane

R21 *See:* dichlorofluoromethane

R22 *See:* chlorodifluoromethane

R23 *See:* trifluoromethane

R112 *See:* tetrachlorodifluoroethane

R113 *See:* 1,1,2-trichloro-1,2,2-trifluoroethane

R114 *See:* 1,2-dichloro-1,1,2,2-tetrafluoroethane

R115 *See:* chloropentafluoroethane

R123 *See:* 1,1-dichloro-2,2,2-trifluoroethane

R124 *See:* 1-chloro-1,2,2,2-tetrafluoroethane

R125 *See:* pentafluoroethane

R134a *See:* 1,1,1,2-tetrafluoroethane

R141b *See:* 1,1-dichloro-1-fluoroethane

R142b *See:* 1-chloro-1,1-difluoroethane

R152a *See:* difluoroethane

racemethionine *See:* DL-methionine

R acid
2-hydroxynaphthalene-3,6-disulphonic acid; 3-naphthol-2,7-disulphonic acid; R salt (sodium salt)

$C_{10}H_8O_7S_2$. M: 304.29. Available commercially as the acid and sodium salts.
Production:
• β-naphthol (sulphonation; coproduced with G acid)
Derivatives: Acid Green 50; Acid Red 26; Acid Red 27; Direct Blue 80; Mordant Red 9

Radel *See:* poly(4,4′-phenoxybiphenyl sulphone)

raffinate I
C_4 refinery or cracker stream after removal of the butadiene component. A typical composition is: 40–50% isobutene, 25–35% 1-butene, 10–20% 2-butene and 10–15% mixed butanes.
Production:
• C_4-stream, refinery/C_4-stream, steam-cracked (solvent extraction; coproduced with butadiene)
• C_4-stream, steam-cracked + chlorine (BP/Du Pont chloroprene processes; coproduced with chloroprene)
• C_4-stream, steam-cracked (cycloaddition; coproduced with 1,5,9-cyclododecatriene/1,5-cyclooctadiene)
Derivatives:
dodecene, branched; isobutylene; methyl *t*-butyl ether; polybutene; raffinate II; 2,4,4-trimethylpentene

raffinate II
n-butenes, mixed
C_4H_8. M: 56.10. C_4 refinery or steam-cracker stream after removal of the butadiene and isobutylene components. A typical composition is: 45–60% 1-butene, 20–40% 2-butene, 10–20% *n*-butane, 5% isobutane.
Production:
• raffinate I (molecular sieve separation; coproduced with isobutylene)
• raffinate I (Amoco/Cosden Oil polybutene processes; coproduced with polybutene)
• raffinate I (acid-catalysed alkylation; coproduced with dodecene, branched/2,4,4-trimethylpentene)
• raffinate I + methanol (ether formation; coproduced with methyl *t*-butyl ether)
• raffinate I (sulphuric acid separation processes; coproduced with isobutylene)
Derivatives:
butadiene; *s*-butanol; 1-butene; *s*-butyl mercaptan; dodecene, branched; gasoline, alkylate; hydrogen cyanide; maleic anhydride; octene, branched; pentaldehydes, mixed

ranitidine
Zantac (Glaxo); [66357-35-5]

$C_{13}H_{22}N_4O_3S_1$. M: 314.41. Available commercially as the hydrochloride.
Production:
• furfuryl alcohol + formaldehyde + dimethylamine + 2-mercaptoethylamine hydrochloride + 1-methyl-

amino-1-methylthio-2-nitroethylene (Mannich reaction/sulphide formation/amine formation)
Uses: ulcer therapy drug

rapeseed fatty acids

RCOOH

R = rapeseed-. A typical chain-length distribution is: 8% $C_{16:0}$, 25% $C_{18:1}$, 20% $C_{18:2}$, 10% $C_{20:0}$, 30% $C_{22:1}$.
Production:
• rapeseed oil (hydrolysis)
Derivatives: erucic acid; oleic acid

rapeseed oil

canola oil (low erucic acid grades); [8002-13-9]
Pale yellow liquid. Titre: 15–23°C. Saponification value: 170–185 mg KOH/g. Iodine value: 90–110 g I_2/100 g. Low erucic acid rapeseed oil is also produced for animal and human food use.
Production:
• rapeseed, high erucic acid (solvent extraction)
Derivatives:
factice; fatty oils, sulphurised; rapeseed fatty acids
Uses: leather fat-liquoring agent; lubricity additive (rolling, cutting oils); quenching oil; textile finishing agent

rare earth chloride

RCl₃

R = rare earth-.
Production:
• rare earth oxide + metallurgical coke + chlorine (thermal reduction/chlorination)
• rare earth chloride, hydrate (calcination)
Derivatives: mischmetal

rare earth chloride, hydrate

RCl₃.6H₂O

R = rare earth-.
Production:
• rare earth oxide/rare earth oxide, hydrate/ lanthanum-praseodymium-neodymium oxide concentrate + hydrochloric acid (reaction)
Derivatives:
rare earth chloride
Uses: raw material (pure rare earth chemicals); zeolite gasoline cracking catalysts

rare earth fluoride

RF₃

R = rare earth-.
Production:
• rare earth oxide, hydrate + hydrofluoric acid (salt formation)
Uses: carbon arc cores

rare earth oxide

R₂O₃

R = rare earth-. Concentrate containing, typically, 70% rare earth oxides.
Production:
• bastnasite ore (froth flotation/acid leaching)
Derivatives: cerium oxide; lanthanum-praseodymium-neodymium oxide concentrate; rare earth chloride; rare earth chloride, hydrate; samarium oxide

rare earth oxide, hydrate

Rare earth concentrate containing about 45% cerium, 20% lanthanum, 19% neodymium, 5% praseodymium, 4% samarium and smaller quantities of other rare earth elements.
Production:
• monazite + sodium hydroxide (salt formation/ separation; coproduced with thorium dioxide)
Derivatives: cerium oxide; didymium oxide; lanthanum oxide; rare earth chloride, hydrate; rare earth fluoride; samarium oxide

raspberry ketone *See:* p-hydroxybenzylacetone

rayon *See:* cellulose, regenerated

RDX *See:* cyclonite

Reactive Black 5
20505 (CI)

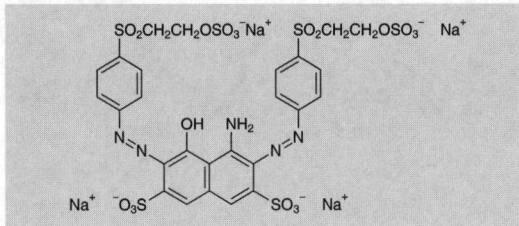

$C_{26}H_{21}N_5Na_4O_{19}S_6$. M: 991.81.
Production:
• p-(β-hydroxyethylsulphonyl)aniline + H acid (diazotisation/azo coupling/sulphation)
Uses: dye (cotton)

Reactive Blue 2
Procion Blue H-B (ICI); 61211 (CI); [12236-82-7]

$C_{29}H_{17}Cl_1Na_3N_7O_{11}S_3$. M: 840.11.

Production:
- bromamine acid + 4-nitroaniline-2-sulphonic acid + orthanilic acid + cyanuric chloride (amine formation/amine formation/nitro reduction/amine formation)

Uses: dye (cotton, polyamide, silk)

Reactive Blue 4
61205 (CI); Procion Blue MX-R (ICI)

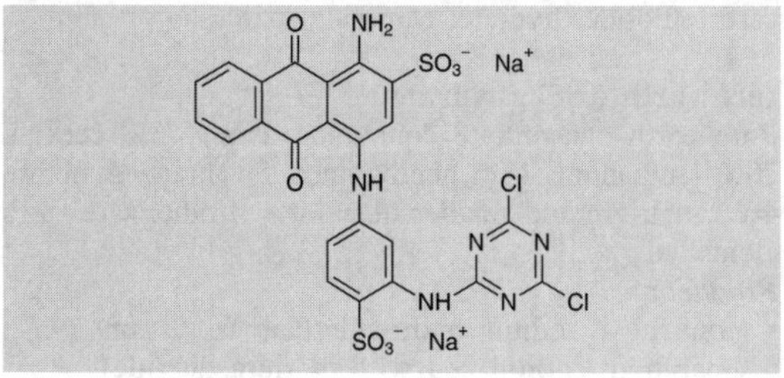

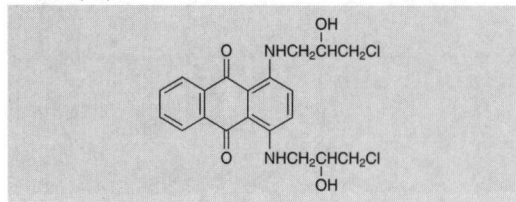

$C_{23}H_{12}Cl_2N_6Na_2O_8S_2$. M: 681.40.
Production:
- bromamine acid + 2,4-diaminobenzenesulphonic acid + cyanuric chloride (amine formation/amine formation)

Derivatives:
Reactive Blue 5
Uses: dye (cotton)

Reactive Blue 5
61205:1 (CI)

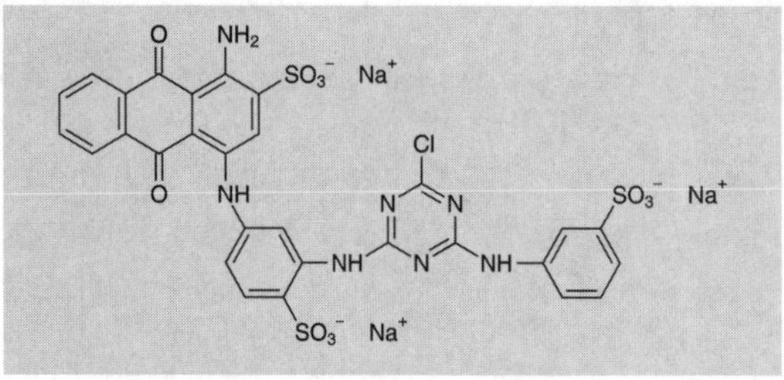

$C_{29}H_{17}Cl_1N_7Na_3O_{11}S_3$. M: 840.11.
Production:
- Reactive Blue 4 + metanilic acid (amine formation)

Uses:
dye (cotton)

Reactive Blue 6
61549 (CI)

$C_{20}H_{20}Cl_2N_2O_4$. M: 423.30.

Production:
- 1,4-diaminoanthraquinone + epichlorohydrin (epoxidation)

Uses: dye (cotton, polyamide, acetate fibres)

Reactive Blue 7
74460 (CI)

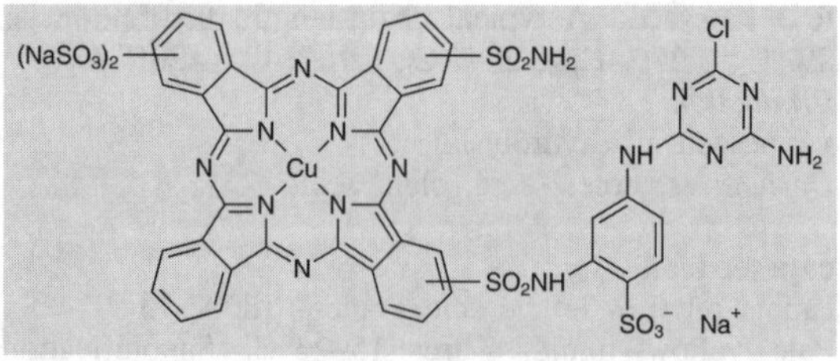

Mixed product consisting of copper phthalocyanine sulphonate and sulphonamide derivatives.
Production:
- copper phthalocyanine + 2,4-diaminobenzene-sulphonic acid + cyanuric chloride + ammonia (sulphonation/sulphonamide formation/dehydrochlorination)

Uses: dye (cotton)

Reactive Blue 13
Procion Blue H-5R (ICI)

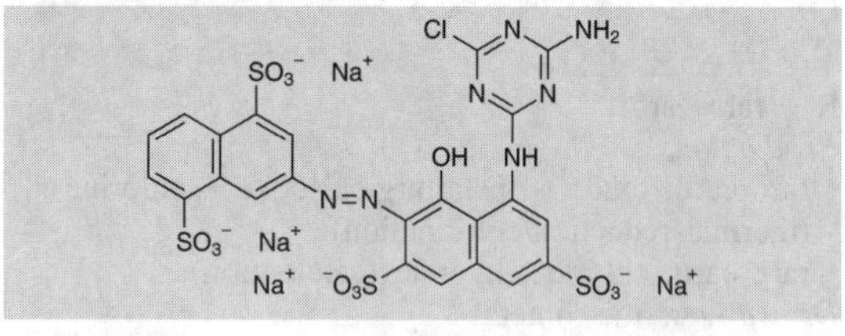

The dye is the copper complex of the displayed structure.
Production:
- N-acetyl-H acid + 2-naphthylamine-4,8-disulphonic acid + cyanuric chloride + ammonia + copper sulphate (diazotisation/azo coupling/amine formation/amine formation)

Uses: dye (cotton)

Reactive Blue 19
61200 (CI); [2580-78-1]

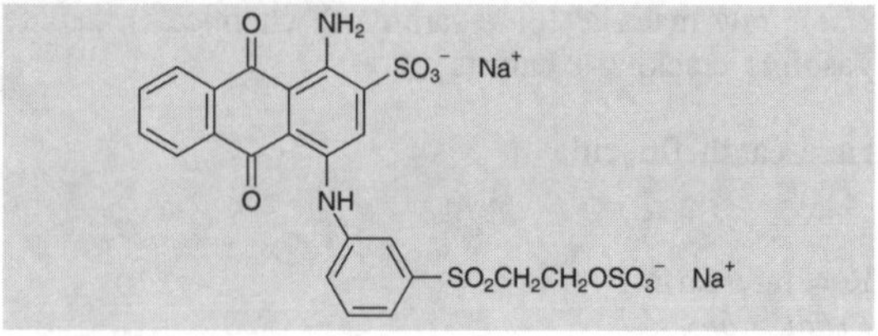

$C_{22}H_{16}N_2Na_2O_{11}S_3$. M: 626.54.
Production:
- m-(β-hydroxyethylsulphonyl)aniline + bromamine

acid (amine formation/sulphonation)
Uses: dye (cotton)

Reactive Blue 94

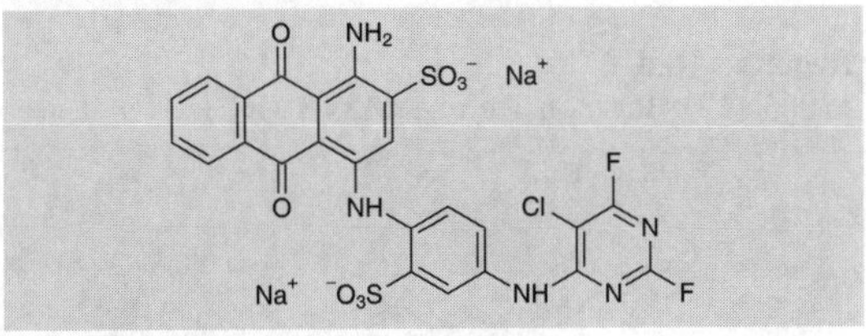

$C_{24}H_{12}Cl_1F_2N_5Na_2O_8S_2$. M: 681.94.
Production:
• bromamine acid + 4-nitroaniline-2-sulphonic acid + 5-chloro-2,4,6-trifluoropyrimidine (dehydro-bromination/nitro reduction/dehydrofluorination)
Uses: dye (wool, polyamide)

Reactive Brown 1
26440 (CI); Procion Orange Brown H-G (ICI)

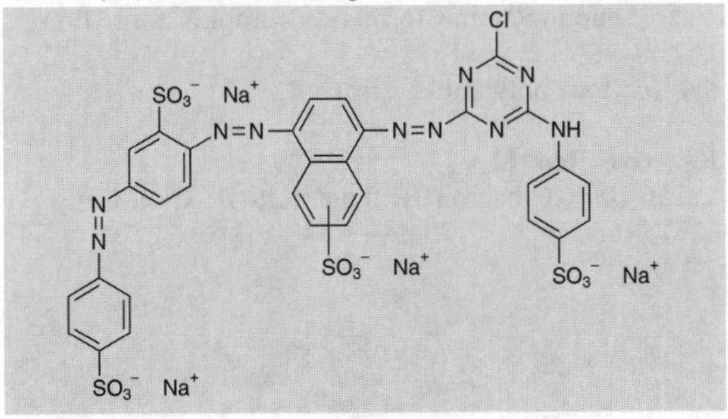

$C_{31}H_{17}Cl_1N_{10}Na_4O_{12}S_4$. M: 977.20.
Production:
• 4-aminoazobenzene-3,4′-disulphonic acid + Cleve's acid, mixed + cyanuric chloride + sulphanilic acid (diazotisation/azo coupling/amine formation/amine formation)
Uses: dye (cotton)

Reactive Orange 1
Procion Brilliant Orange MX-GS (ICI)

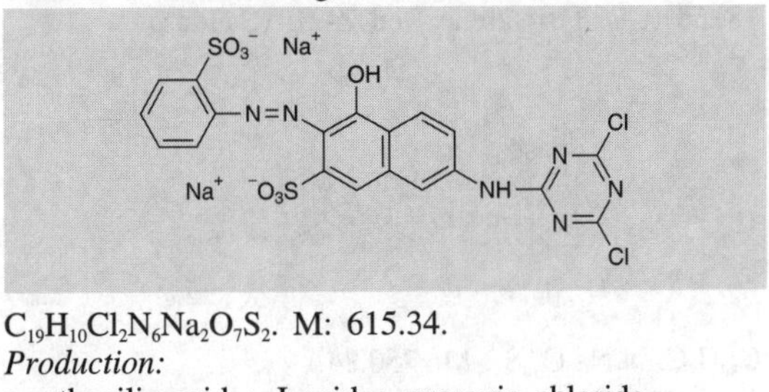

$C_{19}H_{10}Cl_2N_6Na_2O_7S_2$. M: 615.34.
Production:
• orthanilic acid + J acid + cyanuric chloride (diazotisation/azo coupling/amine formation)
Uses:
dye (cotton, polyamide, silk)

Reactive Orange 4
18260 (CI)

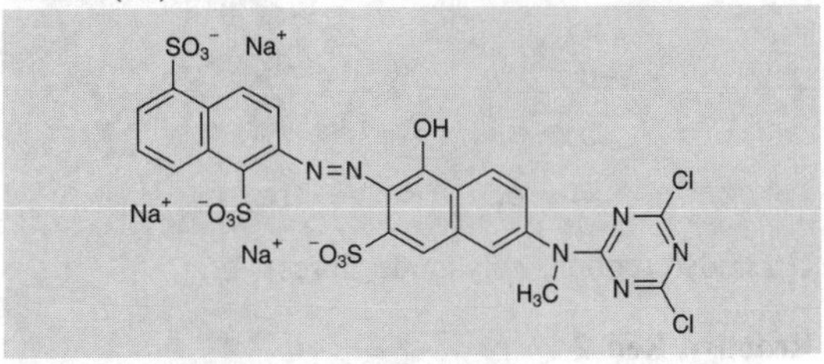

$C_{24}H_{13}Cl_2N_6Na_3O_{10}S_3$. M: 781.46.
Production:
• 2-naphthylamine-1,5-disulphonic acid + J acid + cyanuric chloride (methylation/diazotisation/azo coupling/amine formation)
Uses:
dye (cellulose, wool, polyamide fibres)

Reactive Orange 13
18270 (CI)

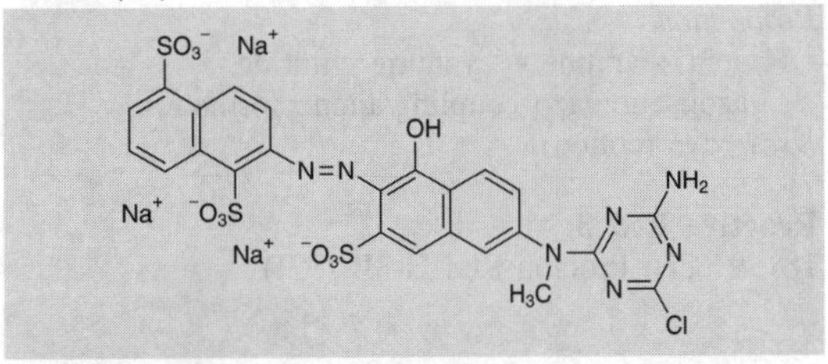

$C_{24}H_{15}Cl_1N_7Na_3O_{10}S_3$. M: 762.03.
Production:
• 2-naphthylamine-1,5-disulphonic acid + J acid + cyanuric chloride + ammonia (diazotisation/azo coupling/amine formation/amine formation)
Uses: dye (cotton)

Reactive Orange 16
17757 (CI)

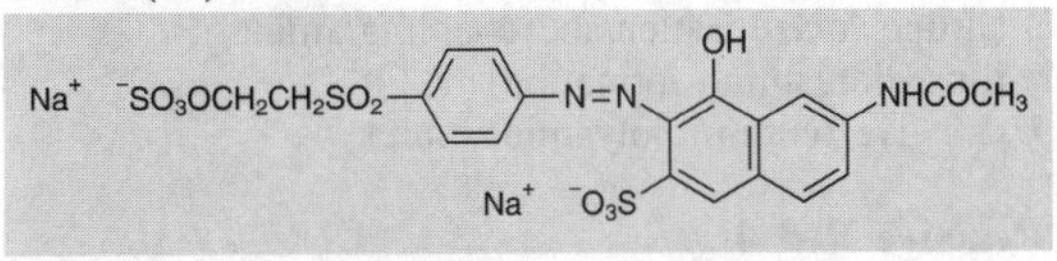

$C_{20}H_{17}N_3Na_2O_{11}S_3$. M: 617.54.
Production:
• *p*-(β-hydroxyethylsulphonyl)aniline + acetic anhydride + gamma acid (acetylation/diazotisation/azo coupling/sulphation)
Uses: dye (cotton)

Reactive Red 1
Procion Red MX-2B (ICI); 18158 (CI)
$C_{19}H_9Cl_2N_6Na_3O_{10}S_3$. M: 717.39.
Production:
• H acid + orthanilic acid + cyanuric chloride (diazotisation/azo coupling/amine formation)

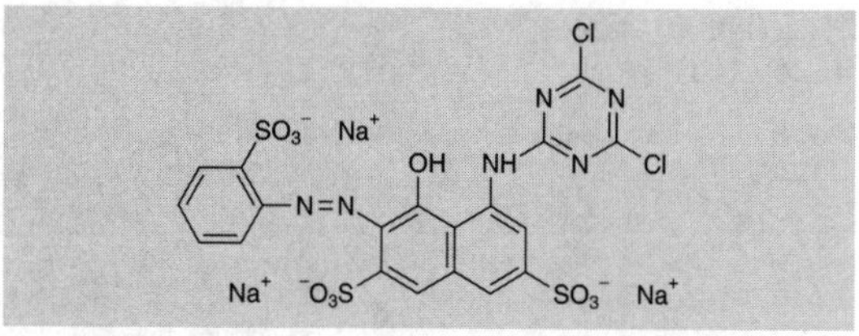

Uses: dye (cotton, polyamide fibres)

Reactive Red 2
18200 (CI); Procion Red MX-5B (ICI)

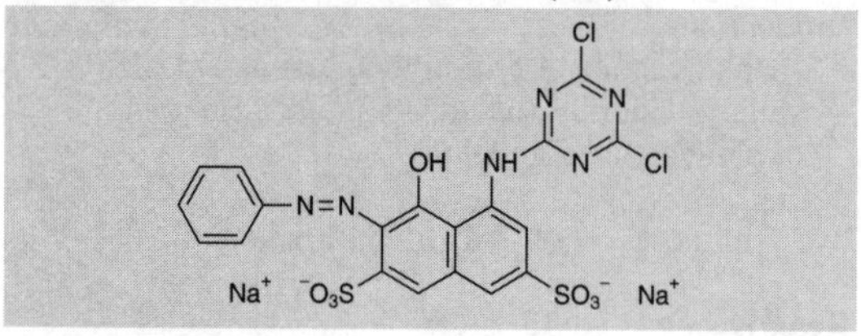

$C_{19}H_{10}Cl_2N_6Na_2O_7S_2$. M: 615.34.
Production:
• H acid + aniline + cyanuric chloride
  (diazotisation/azo coupling/amine formation)
Uses: dye (cotton)

Reactive Red 3
18159 (CI); Procion Red H-3B (ICI)

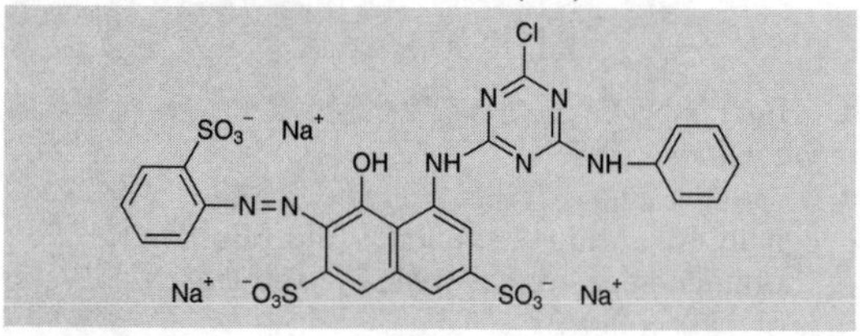

$C_{25}H_{15}Cl_1N_7Na_3O_{10}S_3$. M: 774.04.
Production:
• H acid + orthanilic acid + cyanuric chloride +
  aniline (diazotisation/azo coupling/amine
  formation/amine formation)
Uses: dye (cotton, polyamide fibres)

Reactive Red 4
18105 (CI)

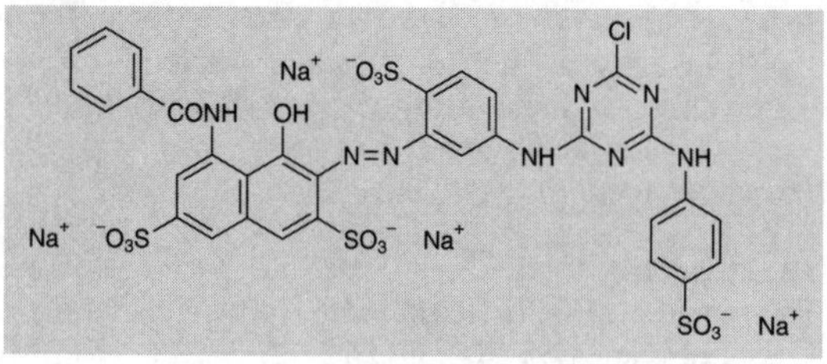

$C_{32}H_{19}Cl_1N_8Na_4O_{14}S_4$. M: 995.22.
Production:
• sulphanilic acid + cyanuric chloride + 2,4-diamino-

benzenesulphonic acid + H acid + benzoyl chloride
(amide formation/diazotisation/azo coupling/amine
formation/amine formation)
Uses: dye (polyamide, silk)

Reactive Red 6
17965 (CI); Procion Rubine MX-B (ICI)

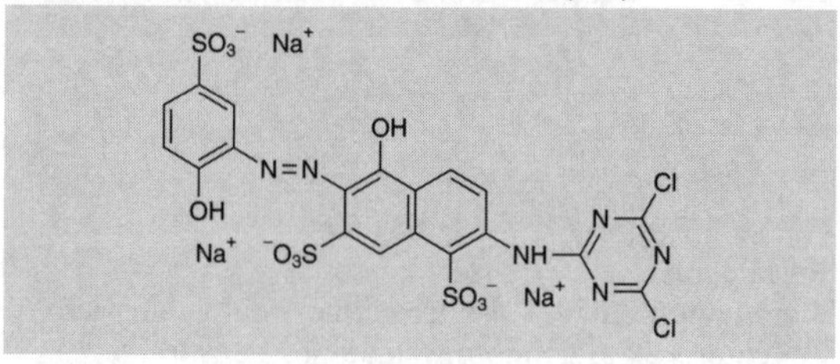

The dye is the copper complex of the displayed
structure.
Production:
• 2-aminophenol-4-sulphonic acid + sulpho-J acid +
  cyanuric chloride + copper sulphate (diazotisation/
  azo coupling/amine formation/complex formation)
Uses:
dye (cotton, polyamide, silk)

Reactive Red 12
18156 (CI); Cibacron Brilliant Red B (Ciba-Geigy)

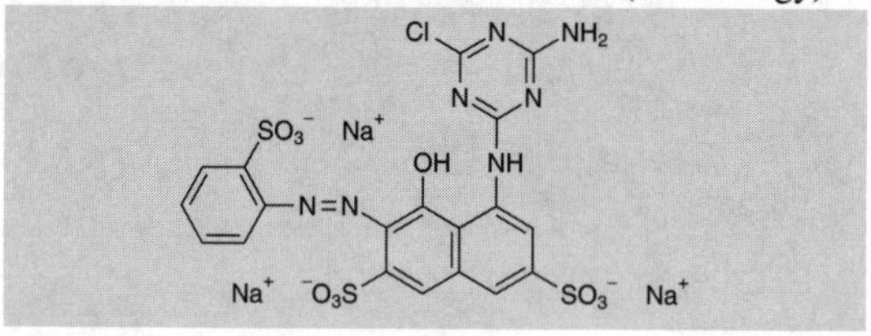

$C_{19}H_{11}Cl_1N_7Na_3O_{10}S_3$. M: 697.95.
Production:
• H acid + orthanilic acid + cyanuric chloride +
  ammonia (diazotisation/azo coupling/amine
  formation/amine formation)
Uses: dye (cotton)

Reactive Red 17
18155 (CI); Drimarene Red Z-2B (Sandoz)

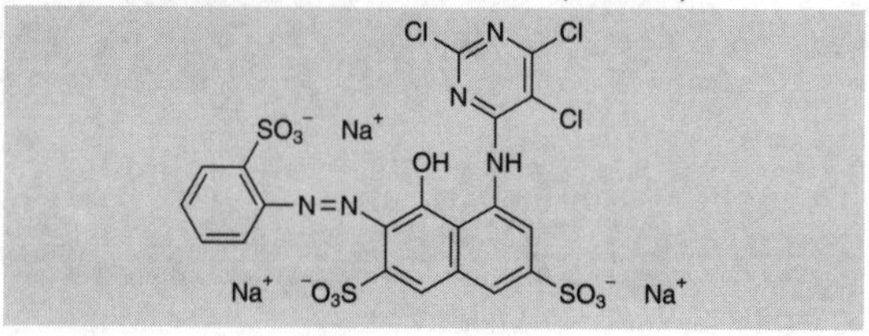

$C_{20}H_9Cl_3N_5Na_3O_{10}S_3$. M: 750.84.
Production:
• H acid + orthanilic acid + 2,4,5,6-tetrachloropyrim-
  idine (diazotisation/azo coupling/amine formation)
Uses: dye (cotton)

Reactive Red 96

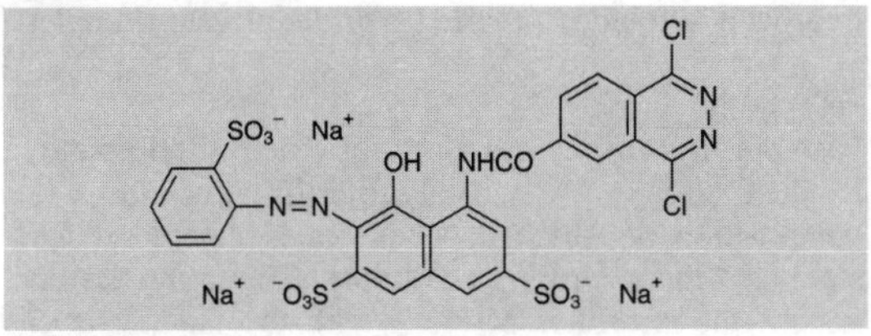

$C_{25}H_{12}Cl_2N_5Na_3O_{11}S_3$. M: 794.47.
Production:
• orthanilic acid + H acid + 1,4-dichlorophthalazine-6-carboxyl chloride (amide formation/diazotisation/azo coupling)
Uses: dye (cotton)

Reactive Violet 5
18097 (CI)

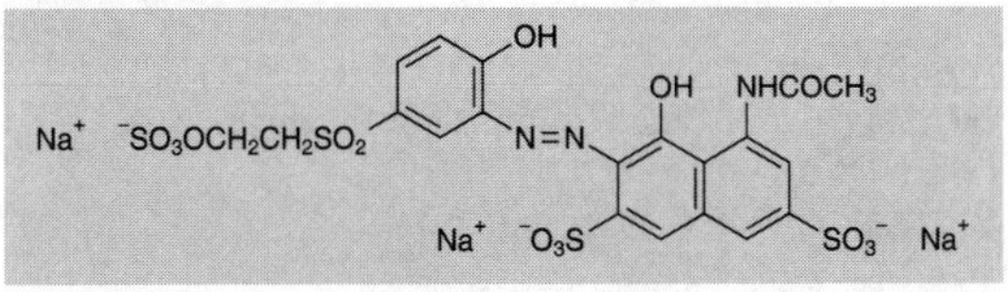

The dye is the 2:1 copper complex of the displayed structure.
Production:
• 5-(β-hydroxyethylsulphonyl)-2-methoxyaniline + N-acetyl-H acid + copper sulphate (diazotisation/azo coupling/sulphation/complex formation)
Uses: dye (cotton)

Reactive Yellow 1
18971 (CI); Procion Brilliant Yellow MX-6G (ICI)

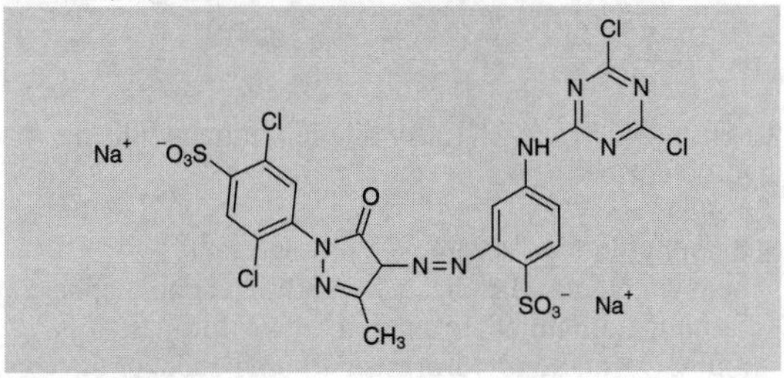

$C_{19}H_9Cl_4N_8Na_2O_7S_2$. M: 713.25.
Production:
• 2,4-diaminobenzenesulphonic acid + cyanuric chloride + 1-(2′,5′-dichloro-4′-sulphophenyl)-3-methylpyrazolone (amine formation/diazotisation/azo coupling)
Uses: dye (cotton)

Reactive Yellow 3
13245 (CI); Procion Yellow H-A (ICI)
$C_{21}H_{13}Cl_2N_7Na_2O_7S_2$. M: 656.39.
Production:
• 2-naphthylamine-4,8-disulphonic acid + m-amino-acetanilide + cyanuric chloride (diazotisation/azo coupling/amine formation)

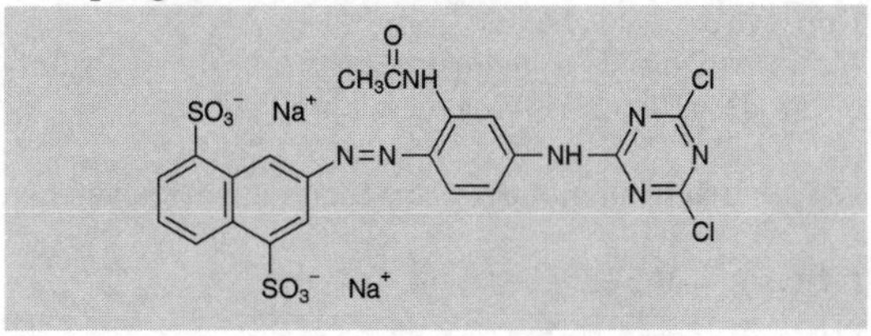

Uses: dye (cotton, polyamide, wool, silk)

Reactive Yellow 4
13190 (CI); Procion Yellow MX-R (ICI)

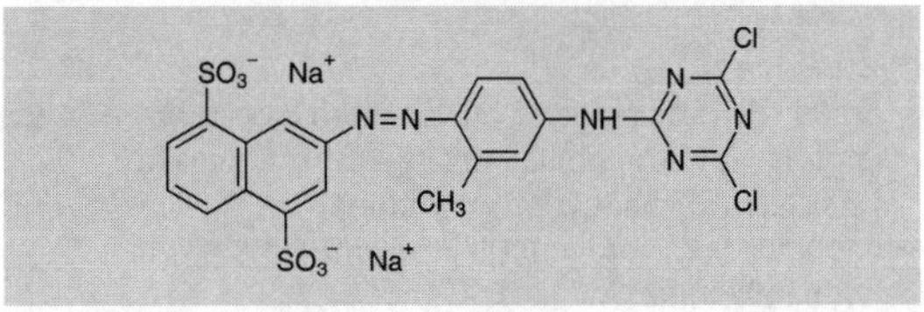

$C_{20}H_{12}Cl_2N_6Na_2O_6S_2$. M: 613.36.
Production:
• 2-naphthylamine-1,5-disulphonic acid + m-toluidine + cyanuric chloride (diazotisation/azo coupling/dehydrochlorination)
Uses: dye (cotton, polyamide, silk)

Reactive Yellow 17
Remazol Golden Yellow G (Hoechst)

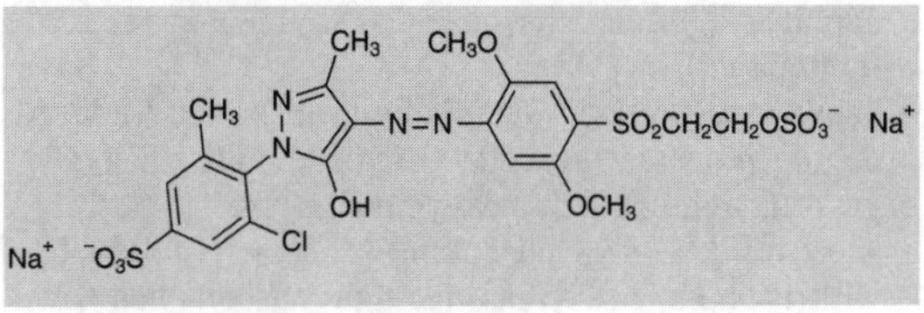

$C_{21}H_{21}Cl_1N_4Na_2O_{12}S_3$. M: 699.04.
Production:
• 2,5-dimethoxy-5-(β-hydroxyethylsulphonyl)aniline + 1-(6′-chloro-2′-methyl-4′-sulphophenyl)-4-methyl-pyrazolone (diazotisation/azo coupling/sulphonation)
Uses: dye (cotton)

red iron oxide *See:* iron oxide red

red lead
lead oxide, red; lead tetroxide; minium; Pigment Red 105 (CI); 77578 (CI); [1314-41-6]

2PbO.PbO$_2$

O_4Pb_3. M: 685.57. Orange-red pigment. d: 8.8 kg/l. Insoluble in water and alcohol. Available in different grades which vary in their PbO content. Grades containing >95% Pb_3O_4 are required for paint applications. The product is highly toxic and its use is controlled in many countries.

Production:
- litharge (air oxidation)

Derivatives: lead dioxide

Uses: anticorrosion pigment (primer paints); battery electrode paste; glass/ceramics ingredient

red prussiate of potash *See:* potassium ferricyanide

refinery B-B *See:* C_4-stream, refinery

refinery gas
Refinery gas is a variable mixture of light hydrocarbons produced in petroleum refinery operations. It is used as a source of C_3 and C_4 hydrocarbons as well as sulphur.
Production:
- crude oil (atmospheric distillation; coproduced with naphtha, light/naphtha, heavy/kerosene/gas oil, light/gas oil, heavy/long residue)
- naphtha, heavy (catalytic reforming; coproduced with reformate)
- long residue (thermal cracking; coproduced with naphtha, heavy/gas oil, light/gas oil, heavy)
- long residue (visbreaking; coproduced with naphtha, heavy/gas oil, heavy)
- gas oil, vacuum/long residue/deasphalted oil (fluidised-bed catalytic cracking; coproduced with gasoline, catalytic-cracker/light cycle oil/heavy cycle oil)
- gas oil, vacuum (hydrocracking; coproduced with naphtha, light/naphtha, heavy/kerosene/gas oil, light/gas oil, heavy)
- heavy cycle oil/coal tar pitch/pyrolysis tar (delayed coking process; coproduced with naphtha, heavy/ gas oil, light/gas oil, heavy/needle coke)
- short residue (delayed coking process; coproduced with naphtha, heavy/gas oil, light/gas oil, heavy/ sponge coke, green/shot coke)
- gas oil, vacuum (fluid coking; coproduced with naphtha, heavy/gas oil, heavy/fluid coke)
- gas oil, vacuum (Flexicoke process; coproduced with naphtha, heavy/gas oil, heavy/coke oven gas)
- lubricant oils, refined (catalytic dewaxing process; byproduct of lubricant oils, base production)
- synthesis gas (Synthol Fischer-Tropsch process; coproduced with naphtha, light, Synthol/naphtha, heavy/gas oil, light/wax, Fischer-Tropsch/ oxygenates, Fischer-Tropsch, mixed)
- synthesis gas (Arge Fischer-Tropsch process; coproduced with naphtha, heavy/gas oil, light, Arge/wax, Fischer-Tropsch/oxygenates, Fischer-Tropsch, mixed)
- methanol (Mobil MTG process; coproduced with naphtha, light/naphtha, heavy/gas oil, light)
- synthesis gas (Shell MDS process; coproduced with naphtha, heavy/gas oil, light/kerosene/wax, Fischer-Tropsch)

Derivatives: C_4-stream, refinery; gasoline, polymer; hydrogen sulphide; liquified petroleum gas; propylene

reformate
gasoline, reformate; gasoline, reformed; platformate
Product stream from catalytic reforming, the exact composition of which depends on the crude oil feedstock and the reforming conditions. The aromatics content of the stream is 50–65% with the naphthene and paraffin content correspondingly lower than in the reformer feedstock. Research octane Number (RON): 90–105.
Production:
- naphtha, heavy (catalytic reforming; coproduced with refinery gas)

Derivatives: aromatics, mixed; gasoline, dearomatised
Uses:
petrol/aviation gasoline/jet fuel blending component

rennin, calf
E.C.3.4.4.3 (Enzyme Commission); rennet, calf; [9001-98-3]
Enzyme extracted from calf offal.
Uses:
cheese/casein/leather production reagent

rennin, fungal *See:* protease, fungal

reproterol
[54063-54-6]

$C_{18}H_{23}N_5O_5$. M: 389.41. Available commercially as the hydrochloride.
Production:
- theophylline + 1-bromo-3-chloropropane + benzylamine + 3,5-diacetoxyacetophenone (alpha bromination/amine formation/amine formation/ amine formation/hydrolysis/carbonyl reduction)

Uses:
bronchodilator drug

resacetophenone *See:* 2,4-dihydroxyacetophenone

resmethrin
[10453-86-8]

$C_{22}H_{26}O_3$. M: 338.45.

Production:
- 5-benzyl-3-furylmethyl alcohol +
  (*1RS*)-*cis/trans*-chrysanthemic acid (esterification)

Uses: insecticide

resol resins

phenol-formaldehyde resin; resole; resole resins; PF;

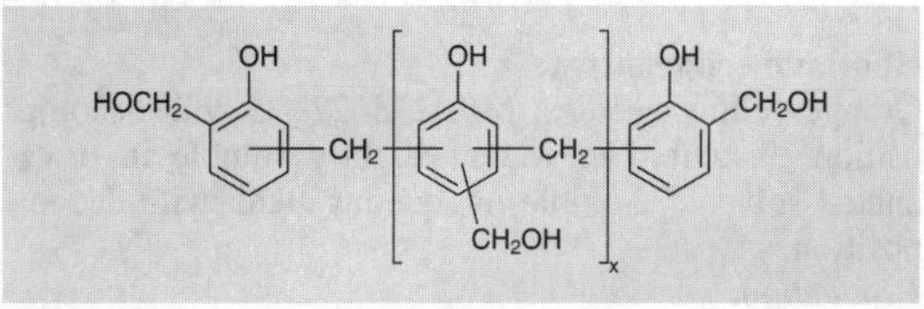

Thermosetting prepolymer formed using a molar excess (typically, 50%) of formaldehyde over phenol. Available as water-soluble resins containing about 70% solids in water. Oil-soluble grades are also produced. The resins are cured by heat.

Production:
- phenol/*o*-cresol/*m/p*-cresol + formaldehyde
  (base-catalysed condensation)

Derivatives:

phenolic-epoxy resins; phenolic resins, amino-substituted; phenolic resins, sulphonated

Uses: butyl rubber crosslinking agent; adhesives (plywood, chipboard, moulded fibreboard, grinding discs, sandpaper); binders (mineral fibre insulation); fabric-reinforced laminates (bushes, slides, gear wheels, disks, rollers, ball bearing cages); paper laminates (decorative laminate baselayer, electrical insulation components); nitrile-phenolic structural/laminating adhesives; speciality phenolic moulding compounds; phenolic resin foam; tackifier (nitrile rubbers); paper sizing deposition aid

resol resins, oil-soluble

See: phenolic resins, oil-soluble, oil-reactive; phenolic resins, oil-soluble, non oil-reactive

resorantel

[20788-07-2]

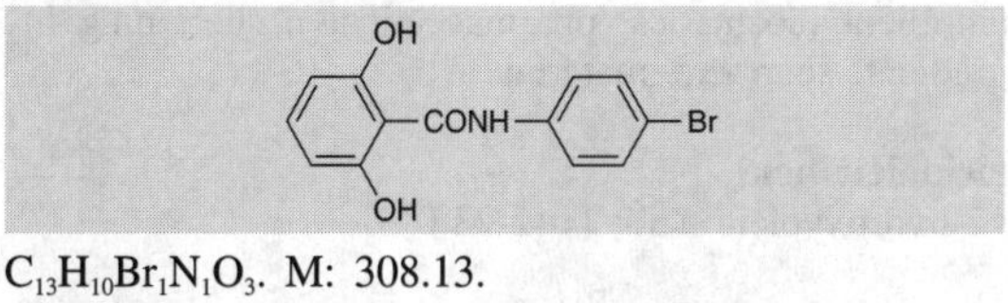

$C_{13}H_{10}Br_1N_1O_3$. M: 308.13.

Production:
- 2,6-dihydroxybenzoic acid + *p*-bromoaniline (amide formation)

Uses: anthelmintic drug

resorcinic acid

See: 3,5-dihydroxybenzoic acid

resorcinol

1,3-dihydroxybenzene; *m*-dihydroxybenzene; 3-hydroxyphenol; [108-46-3]

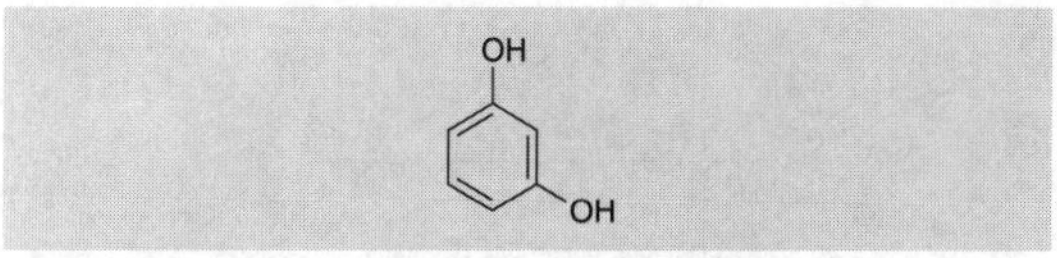

$C_6H_6O_2$. M: 110.12. White, crystalline solid. Discoloured by light and air. MP: 109–110°C. BP: 277°C. d: 1.27 kg/l (15°C). Soluble in water and oxygenated solvents.

Production:
- benzene (sulphonation/alkali fusion)
- *m*-diisopropylbenzene (oxidation/acid-catalysed hydrolysis; coproduced with acetone)

Derivatives:

Acid Brown 14; Acid Orange 24; *m*-aminophenol; carbocromen; 2,4-dihydroxyacetophenone; 2,6-dihydroxyacetophenone; 2,4-dihydroxybenzaldehyde; 2,4-dihydroxybenzoic acid; 2,6-dihydroxybenzoic acid; 2,4-dihydroxybenzophenone; 2,2′-dihydroxy-4-methoxybenzophenone; Direct Orange 18; fluorescein; haloxon; hexylresorcinol; lead trinitroresorcinate; Mordant Red 5; oxyfluorfen; resorcinol di-(2-hydroxyethyl) ether; resorcinol dimethyl ether; resorcinol-formaldehyde resins

Uses:

urea-formaldehyde resin comonomer; tanning agent

resorcinol di-(2-hydroxyethyl) ether

1,3-di-(2-hydroxyethoxy)benzene;

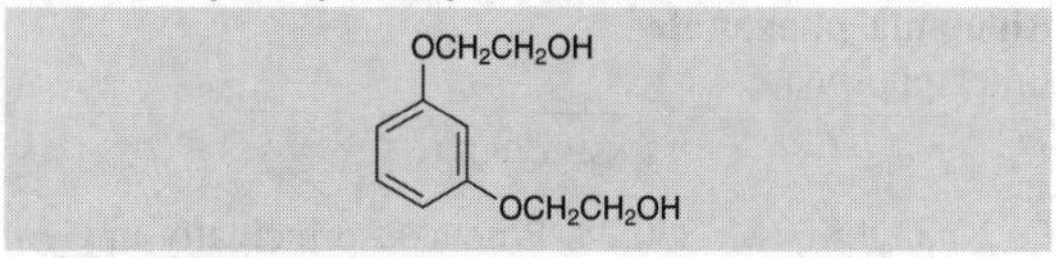

$C_{10}H_{14}O_4$. M: 198.22.

Production:
- resorcinol + ethylene oxide (epoxidation)

Uses:

polyurethane elastomer crosslinking agent

resorcinol dimethyl ether

1,3-dimethoxybenzene; [151-10-0]

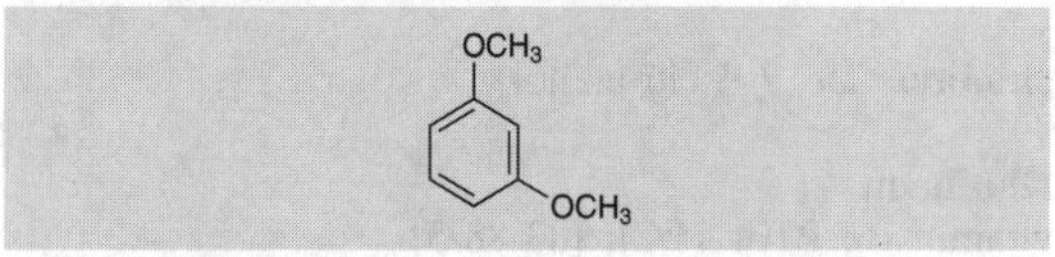

$C_8H_{10}O_2$. M: 138.17.

Production:
- resorcinol/dimethyl sulphate (methylation)

Derivatives:

5-chloro-2,4-dimethoxyaniline; 2,4-dimethoxyaniline

Uses: flavouring ingredient

resorcinol-formaldehyde resins

resorcinol resins

Thermosetting prepolymer cured by reaction with paraformaldehyde.

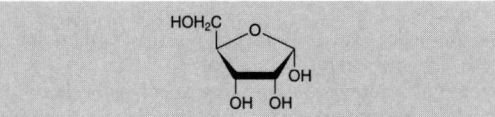

Production:
• resorcinol/phenol + formaldehyde (carbonyl condensation)

Uses: water-resistant additive (starch adhesives); wood adhesives; tackifier (nitrile rubbers); tyre-cord adhesive

resorcinol fraction
Amber, viscous liquid. BR: 275–315°C. d: 1.18 kg/l (20°C). Soluble in water. Miscible with oxygenated and aromatic solvents. Comprises 80% dihydric phenols of which 30–37% is resorcinol.

Production:
• tar acid liquor (fractionation; coproduced with tar acids, crude/catechol)

Uses:
phenolic resin comonomer (adhesives, resins, paints)

α-resorcylic acid
See: 3,5-dihydroxybenzoic acid

retinol *See:* vitamin A

Rhenania phosphate
sinter phosphate

$$CaNaPO_4.Ca_2SiO_4$$

$Ca_3Na_1O_8P_1Si_1$. M: 330.28. Produced principally in Germany and Poland, but available elsewhere. Standard grades have 25–30% P_2O_5.

Production:
• apatite + quartz + sodium carbonate/sodium hydroxide (sintering)

Uses: fertiliser

rho acid *See:* anthraquinone-1,5-disulphonic acid

rhodinol *See:* (−)-citronellol

riboflavin
vitamin B_2; E101 (EC); [83-88-5]

$C_{17}H_{20}N_4O_6$. M: 376.37. Orange-yellow needles. De-composes at 280°C. Slightly soluble in oxygenated solvents and water.

Production:
• D-ribose + 3,4-xylidine + benzenediazonium chloride + barbituric acid (reductive amination/azo coupling/condensation/deamination/cyclisation)

Uses: food colorant

riboflavin concentrate
Orange-yellow needles. MP: 278–279°C with decomposition. Insoluble in water. Slightly soluble in oxygenated solvents. Soluble in aqueous alkali with decomposition.

Production:
• microbial fermentation medium + *Eremothecium ashbyii* bacteria/*Ashbya gossypii* bacteria (fermentation)

Uses:
dietary supplement; animal feed additive

D-ribose
[50-69-1]

$C_5H_{10}O_5$. M: 150.12. White platelets. MP: 87°C. Soluble in water.

Production:
• nucleic acids (hydrolysis; coproduced with D-2-deoxyribose)

Derivatives: riboflavin

rice bran oil
[68553-81-1]
Yellow liquid. Produced by solvent extraction of rice bran. Titre: 24–28°C. d: 0.92 kg/l (25°C). Insoluble in water. The chain-length distribution is: 12–18% $C_{16:0}$, 40–50% $C_{18:1}$ and 29–42% $C_{18:2}$.

Uses:
emollient (cosmetics, pharmaceuticals); shortening ingredient; soap raw material

ricinoleic acid
12-hydroxyoleic acid; [141-22-0]

$$\overset{OH}{\underset{|}{CH_3(CH_2)_5CHCH_2CH=CH(CH_2)_7COOH}}$$

$C_{18}H_{34}O_3$. M: 298.47. Pale yellow, viscous liquid. MP: 4–5°C. d: 0.96 kg/l (15°C). BP: 227°C (1.3 kPa). Insoluble in water. Soluble in oxygenated solvents.

Production:
• castor oil (hydrolysis)

Derivatives: barium ricinoleate; *n*-butyl ricinoleate; 12-hydroxystearic acid; 2-octanol; polyglycerol fatty esters; sebacic acid

rifampin
[13292-46-1]

Cyclic structure joined at the positions marked *.
$C_{43}H_{58}N_4O_{12}$. M: 822.95.
Production:
• rifamycin SV + dimethylformamide + *N*-methyl-piperazine (Vilsmeier reaction/diazotisation/reduction/imine formation)
Uses:
antituberculosis drug

rifamycin SV

cyclic structure, joined at *. $C_{37}H_{47}N_1O_{12}$. M: 697.79.
Production:
• microbial fermentation medium + *Streptomyces mediterranei* bacteria (fermentation)
Derivatives: rifampin

rimantidine
[13392-28-4]

$C_{12}H_{21}N_1$. M: 179.31.
Production:
• 1-bromoadamantane + ethyl acetate + ammonia (cyanidation/nitrile hydrolysis/esterification/Claisen condensation/decarboxylation/reductive ammoniation)
Uses: antiviral drug

RMDI
See: 4,4′-diisocyanatodicyclohexylmethane

robenidine
[25875-51-8]

$C_{15}H_{13}Cl_2N_5$. M: 334.20.

Production:
• hydrazine + cyanogen chloride + *p*-chloro-benzaldehyde (imine formation/condensation)
Uses: coccidiostat

Rochelle salt
potassium sodium tartrate; E337 (EC); [304-59-6]

$C_4H_4K_1Na_1O_6$. M: 210.15. Available as the tetrahydrate. White, crystalline powder. MP: 70–80°C. d: 1.79 kg/l. Soluble in water forming slightly alkaline solutions. Insoluble in alcohol.
Production:
• wine argols + sodium carbonate (salt formation)
Derivatives: potassium bitartrate
Uses: food additive; analytical reagent; copper plating reagent; reagent (mirror production)

rosemary oil
[8000-25-7]
Pale yellow liquid with a characteristic odour. Produced by steam distillation of rosemary (*Rosmarinus officinalis*) twigs and flowering tops. d: ~0.90 kg/l (25°C). Insoluble in water. Soluble in alcohol. The major constituents of the oil are 1,8-cineole (50%), α-pinene (30%) and camphor (20%). Produced in Mediterranean countries, particularly Spain and Tunisia.
Uses: perfume ingredient

rose oxide
4-methyl-2-(2-methyl-1-propenyl)tetrahydropyran; [876-17-5] (*cis*-isomer); [876-18-6] (*trans*-isomer)

$C_{10}H_{18}O_1$. M: 154.25. Colourless liquid with strong floral odour. BP: 70°C (1.6 kPa). d: 0.88 kg/l (20°C). Commercial grades are variable mixtures of the *cis* and *trans*-isomers.
Production:
• (±)-citronellol (photooxidation/reduction/allylic rearrangement/ether formation)
Uses: fragrance ingredient (soap)

rosewood oil *See:* bois de rose oil

rosin, gum
colophony
Pale yellow to amber solid. Softening point: 78°C (Ring and Ball Method). Melting point: 110°C. d: 1.04–1.08 kg/l.

Production:
- pine gum (fractionation; coproduced with dipentene/pine oil/turpentine oil, gum)

Derivatives: calcium rosinate; maleic resins; phenolic resins, rosin-modified; rosin, polymerised; rosin ester gum; sodium rosinate; zinc rosinate

Uses:
paper sizing ingredient; tackifier (rubber, adhesives); tung oil/rosin varnish ingredient (machinery paints)

rosin, hydrogenated

Foral AX (Hercules); Staybelite (Hercules)
Solid. Softening point: 68°C (Ring and Ball Method). Acid value: ~160 mg KOH/g. Available as 50% or 65% hydrogenated grades.
Production:
- rosin, wood (hydrogenation)

Derivatives: rosin ester gum
Uses: tackifier/modifier resin (adhesives)

rosin, lime-hardened *See:* calcium rosinate

rosin, polymerised

Available in various grades depending on the degree of polymerisation. 'Dimerised' grades have a softening range of 150–170°C and contain about 80% dimer acids. The remainder is monomer acid and neutrals. 'Polymerised' grades have lower softening points, typically, 95°C (Ring and Ball Method).
Production:
- rosin, tall oil/rosin, wood/rosin, gum (thermal polymerisation)

Derivatives:
calcium rosinate; rosin ester gum; zinc rosinate
Uses: tackifier (polyamide hot melt adhesives); binder (printing inks, lacquers)

rosin, tall oil

TOR
Yellow or brown solid. Softening point: 80°C (Ring and Ball method). Typical acid value: 163 mg KOH/g. The product is a mixture of resins acids and varies somewhat with source.
Production:
- tall oil, crude (fractionation; coproduced with tall oil fatty acid/tall oil, distilled)

Derivatives: abietic acid; calcium rosinate; maleic resins; phenolic resins, rosin-modified; rosin, polymerised; rosin ester gum; sodium rosinate; zinc rosinate
Uses: binder (rust preventative storage coatings); oil-well drilling mud lubricant; plasticiser (rubber)

rosin, wood

Brittle solid when cold varying in colour from colourless to yellow or brown. Softening point: 80°C (Drop method), 73°C (Ring and Ball method). Typical acid value: 160. d: 1.04–1.08 kg/l. Insoluble in water.

Soluble in most organic solvents when fresh. Exposure to air produces insoluble oxidation products.
Production:
- pinewood stumps (steam distillation; coproduced with turpentine oil, wood/dipentene/pine oil)

Derivatives: calcium rosinate; maleic resins; methyl abietate; phenolic resins, rosin-modified; rosin, hydrogenated; rosin, polymerised; rosin ester gum; sodium rosinate; zinc rosinate
Uses: tackifier (rubber)

rosin ester gum

Amber solid. Softening point: 85–90°C (glycerol esters, Ring and Ball Method) and 110–115°C (pentaerythritol esters, Ring and Ball Method). Soluble in hydrocarbons, ester and ketone solvents. Insoluble in alcohol.
Production:
- rosin, wood/rosin, hydrogenated/abietic acid/rosin, tall oil/rosin, gum/rosin, polymerised + glycerol/pentaerythritol/triethylene glycol (esterification)

Uses: binder (paints/printing inks); tackifier/plasticiser (elastomer-based adhesives, hot melt adhesives)

rotenone

derris; [83-79-4]

$C_{23}H_{22}O_6$. M: 394.42. Produced in Malaysia from *Derris elipitica* roots and in South America from *Lonchocarpus* roots. White, crystalline solid separated from the root by solvent extraction followed by crystallisation.
Production:
- derris root/*Lonchocarpus* root (solvent extraction)

Uses: acaricide/insecticide

rubber, chlorinated

Alloprene (ICI)
White powder characterised by its good film-forming and electrical/thermal insulation properties. Good resistance to acids and alkalis, non-flammable and non-toxic. Soluble in aromatic and chlorinated solvents. Compatible with drying oils, alkyd and acrylic resins. Chlorine content: 65%.
Production:
- natural rubber/polyisoprene + chlorine (chlorination)

Uses:
fire-resistant textile coatings; heat-seal coatings; synthetic rubber adhesives; binder (anticorrosion/chemical-resistant/fire-resistant paints); binder (swimming pool/marine/road-marking/concrete paints, printing inks, paper coatings)

rubber, cyclised
Horn-like thermoplastic formed by self-condensation of the polyisoprene such that the unsaturation is reduced to around half that of natural rubber. The product is inelastic and denser than natural rubber.
Production:
• natural rubber (acid-catalysed condensation)
Uses: rubber-metal bonding agent; binder (lacquers)

rubber hydrochloride
Pliofilm (Goodyear Tire & Rubber)

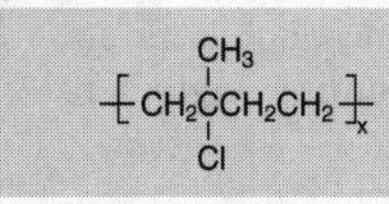

$$\begin{array}{c} CH_3 \\ | \\ \left[CH_2CCH_2CH_2 \right]_x \\ | \\ Cl \end{array}$$

Compounded plastic characterised by its good resistance to fats, oils, acids and alkalis. Swollen by most organic solvents.
Production:
• natural rubber + hydrogen chloride, anhydrous (addition)
Uses: cast resins (packaging films); lacquer resin; rubber-metal bonding agent

rue ketone *See:* methyl *n*-nonyl ketone

rutile
Titanium dioxide mineral used as the feedstock for the chloride process to titanium dioxide. Both occurs naturally and is produced by synthesis. Concentrates of natural material contain >90% TiO_2. Synthetic rutile normally contains 85–90% TiO_2.
Production:
• mineral sands (separation; coproduced with zircon/ilmenite/monazite)
• ilmenite + hydrochloric acid (reduction)
Derivatives: titanium dioxide; titanium tetrachloride
Uses: acid refractory bricks raw material

S

S acid

1-amino-8-hydroxynaphthalene-4-sulphonic acid;
4-amino-5-naphthol-1-sulphonic acid; [83-64-7]

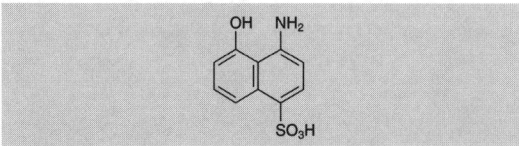

$C_{10}H_9N_1O_4S_1$. M: 239.25. Off-white needles. Slightly soluble in water.
Production:
• 1-naphthylamine-4,8-disulphonic acid (alkali fusion)
Derivatives: Direct Black 78
Uses: dyestuffs intermediate

SADH *See:* daminozide

safflower acid

Production:
• safflower seeds (extraction/alkali refining;
  byproduct of safflower oil production)
Derivatives: alkyd resins, long-oil; alkyd resins, medium-oil; alkyd resins, short-oil

safflower oil

[8001-23-8]
Pale yellow liquid. Produced by extraction from safflower (*Carthamus tintorius*) seeds. Titre: 15–18°C. d: 0.92 kg/l (25°C). Insoluble in water. The chain-length distribution is: 6% $C_{16:0}$, 26–38% $C_{18:1}$ and 51–67% $C_{18:2}$.
Production:
• safflower seeds (extraction/alkali refining)
Uses: cooking/salad oil; margarine/shortening; drying oil (paints, alkyd resins)

safrole

4-allyl-1,2-methylenedioxybenzene; 3,4-methylenedioxy-1-allylbenzene; [94-59-7]

$C_{10}H_{10}O_2$. M: 162.19. Viscous, colourless liquid with characteristic odour. MP: 11°C. BP: 232–234°C. d: 1.09 kg/l (25°C). Insoluble in water. Soluble in alcohol and chlorinated solvents.
Production:
• *Ocotea cymbarum* oil (extraction)
Derivatives:
isosafrole; piperonyl butoxide
Uses: fragrance/flavouring ingredient

sage oil, Clary

Salvia sclarea oil; [8022-56-8]
Yellow liquid with a herbal odour. d: ~0.90 kg/l (25°C). Produced by steam distillation of *Salvia sclarea* flowers and leaves which are grown in the Mediterranean and Balkan countries as well as in the USA.
Derivatives:
tetramethyldodecahydronaphthofuran
Uses: fragrance/flavouring ingredient

sage oil, Dalmatian

Pale yellow liquid with a camphor-like odour. d: ~0.92 kg/l (25°C). Obtained by steam distillation of *Salvia officinalis*. Insoluble in water. Soluble in alcohol. The major components of the oil are camphor and α-thujone.
Uses: flavouring ingredient

sage oil, Spanish

Pale yellow liquid with a camphor-like odour. d: ~0.92 kg/l (20°C). Obtained by steam distillation of *Salvia lavandulaefolia*. Insoluble in water. Soluble in alcohol. Produced in Spain.
Uses:
perfume ingredient (soap)

SAIB *See:* sucrose acetate isobutyrate

salacetamide

[487-48-9]

$C_9H_9N_1O_3$. M: 179.18.
Production:
• salicylamide + acetic anhydride (acetylation)
Uses:
analgesic/antipyretic drug

salazosulfapyridine

sulfasalazine; [599-79-1]

$C_{18}H_{14}N_4O_5S_1$. M: 398.39.
Production:
• 2-aminopyridine + 4-acetamidobenzenesulphonyl chloride + sodium nitrite + salicylic acid (sulphonamide formation/amide hydrolysis/diazotisation/azo coupling)
Uses: anticolitis drug

salbutamol

albuterol; [18559-94-9]; [51022-70-9] (sulphate)

$C_{13}H_{21}N_1O_3$. M: 239.32. Available commercially as free base or sulphate.

Production:
• methyl salicylate + chloroacetyl chloride + benzyl-*t*-butylamine (Friedel-Crafts acylation/amine formation/ester reduction/carbonyl reduction)

Uses: bronchodilator drug

salicyl alcohol

2-hydroxybenzyl alcohol; [90-01-7]

$C_7H_8O_2$. M: 124.14. White, crystalline solid. MP: 84–86°C. Slightly soluble in water. Soluble in most organic solvents.

Production:
• methyl salicylate (ester reduction)

Derivatives: dioxabenzofos; ethiofencarb

Uses: local anaesthetic drug

salicylaldehyde

2-hydroxybenzaldehyde; *o*-hydroxybenzaldehyde; salicylal; salicylic aldehyde; [90-02-8]

$C_7H_6O_2$. M: 122.13. Straw-coloured liquid. BP: 195–196°C. FP: 1°C. d: 1.16 kg/l (25°C). Slightly soluble in water. Soluble in oxygenated and aromatic solvents. Flash point: 77°C.

Production:
• phenol + chloroform (Reimer-Tiemann reaction; coproduced with *p*-hydroxybenzaldehyde)

Derivatives:
Acid Orange 148; coumarin; dioxacarb; *N,N'*-disalicylideneethylenediamine; *N,N'*-disalicylidene-1,2-propanediamine; *N*-salicylideneethylamine; *N*-salicylidene-*N'*-salicoylhydrazine

Uses: mineral extraction agent

salicylamide

2-hydroxybenzamide; *o*-hydroxybenzamide; [65-45-2]
$C_7H_7N_1O_2$. M: 137.15. White, crystalline powder. MP: 139–141°C. Slightly soluble in water. Soluble in oxygenated and chlorinated solvents.

Production:
• methyl salicylate + ammonia (amide formation)

Derivatives: ethenzamide; labetalol; salacetamide

Uses: analgesic drug

3-salicylamido-1,2,4-triazole

$C_9H_8N_4O_2$. M: 204.19.

Production:
• 3-amino-1,2,4-triazole + salicylic acid (amide formation)

Uses: metal deactivator (plastics)

salicylanilide

[87-17-2]

$C_{13}H_{11}N_1O_2$. M: 213.24. White crystals. MP: 136°C. Slightly soluble in water. Soluble in oxygenated and aromatic solvents.

Production:
• salicylic acid + aniline (amide formation)

Uses: topical antifungal drug

salicylic acid

2-hydroxybenzoic acid; *o*-hydroxybenzoic acid; [69-72-7]

$C_7H_6O_3$. M: 138.13. White crystals. Discoloured by light. MP: 158–160°C. Sublime. d: 1.44 kg/l (20°C). Slightly soluble in hot water. Soluble in oxygenated and chlorinated solvents. Flash point: 157°C (TCC).

Production:
• phenol + carbon dioxide (Kolbe-Schmitt reaction)

Derivatives:
acetylsalicylic acid; 5-aminosalicylic acid; benzyl salicylate; *p-t*-butylphenyl salicylate; 5-chlorosalicylic acid; 2,2'-dihydroxy-4-methoxybenzophenone; dipropylene glycol monosalicylate; Direct Black 91; Direct Green 26; Direct Orange 6; Direct Yellow 44; *N,N'*-disalicylhydrazide; 2-ethylhexyl salicylate; fluorosalan; *n*-hexyl sal-

icylate; homomenthyl salicylate; isoamyl salicylate; isobutyl salicylate; isofenphos; menthyl salicylate; methyl salicylate; Mordant Brown 18; Mordant Orange 1; Mordant Orange 6; Mordant Yellow 1; Mordant Yellow 3; Mordant Yellow 20; Mordant Yellow 26; *p-t*-octylphenyl salicylate; phenethyl salicylate; phenyl salicylate; phenyltoloxamine; salazosulfapyridine; 3-salicylamido-1,2,4-triazole; salicylanilide; *N*-salicylidene-*N'*-salicoylhydrazine; sodium salicylate; sulphosalicylic acid; sulpiride; tiapride

Uses:
foundry resin curing accelerator; vulcanisation retarder

N-salicylideneethylamine
N-ethylsalicylimide

$C_9H_{11}N_1O_1$. M: 149.20.
Production:
• salicylaldehyde + ethylamine (imine formation)
Uses:
metal deactivator (lubricants)

N-salicylidene-*N'*-salicoylhydrazine

$C_{14}H_{12}N_2O_3$. M: 256.26.
Production:
• salicylaldehyde + hydrazine + salicylic acid (imine formation/amide formation)
Uses:
metal deactivator (plastics)

salol *See:* phenyl salicylate

SALP *See:* sodium aluminium phosphate

sal soda *See:* sodium carbonate

salt cake *See:* sodium sulphate

saltpetre *See:* potassium nitrate

***Salvia sclarea* oil** *See:* sage oil, Clary

samarium oxide
[12060-58-1]

O_3Sm_2. M: 348.70. Off-white powder. d: 8.35 kg/l. Insoluble in water. A grade containing 96% samarium is used for magnet production.

Production:
• rare earth oxide (solvent extraction; coproduced with cerium oxide/lanthanum-praseodymium-neodymium oxide concentrate)
• rare earth oxide, hydrate (solvent extraction; coproduced with didymium oxide/cerium oxide/lanthanum oxide)
• mischmetal electrolysis slag (solvent extraction)
Uses:
nuclear reactor control rods; samarium-cobalt magnets

SAN *See:* styrene-acrylonitrile copolymers

sancycline
[808-26-4]

$C_{21}H_{22}N_2O_7$. M: 414.41. Available commercially as the free base or hydrochloride.
Production:
• demeclocycline (hydrogenation)
Derivatives: minocycline
Uses: antibacterial drug

sandalwood oil
[8006-87-9]
Pale yellow liquid with a characteristic odour. Produced by solvent extraction of wood from *Eucarya spicata* trees which grow in Western Australia. It is also produced by steam distillation of wood from *Santalum album* trees which grow in India. d: ~0.97 kg/l (20°C). Soluble in ethanol.
Uses:
perfume ingredient

sandarac
[9000-57-1]
Exuded oleoresin from *Callitris quadrivalvis* trees which grow in North Africa, as well as from similar trees growing in Australia. White to yellow 'tears'. Soluble in alcohol and acetone. Insoluble in hydrocarbons and esters.
Uses:
binder (paper/picture varnishes)

SAPP *See:* disodium acid pyrophosphate

sarcosine
methylaminoacetic acid; *N*-methylglycine; [107-97-1]

$C_3H_7N_1O_2$. M: 89.10. White, crystalline solid. Decomposes on heating above 100°C. Soluble in water.

Production:
• methylamine + formaldehyde + hydrogen cyanide (carbonyl condensation/nitrile hydrolysis)
Derivatives: cocoyl sarcosine; lauroyl sarcosine; oleoyl sarcosine; sodium sarcosinate

SAS *See:* sodium alkane(C_{14}-C_{18}) sulphonate; sodium alkane(C_{11}-C_{14}) sulphonate

sassafras oil, Brazilian *See: Ocotea cymbarum* oil

SBA *See:* s-butanol

SBP *See:* special boiling-point solvents

SBR *See:* styrene-butadiene copolymers

SBS *See:* styrene-butadiene triblock copolymers

Schaeffer's acid
2-hydroxynaphthalene-6-sulphonic acid; 2-naphthol-6-sulphonic acid; Schaeffer's beta acid; [93-01-6]

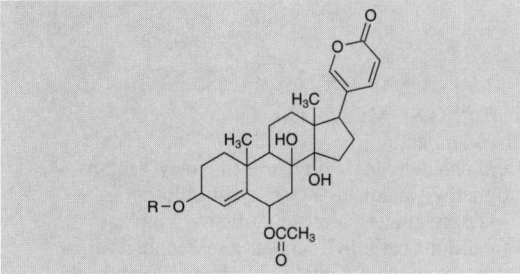

$C_{10}H_8O_4S_1$. M: 224.23. White platelets. MP: 122–125°C. Soluble in water and alcohol. Also available as the sodium salt.
Production:
• β-naphthol (sulphonation)
Derivatives:
Acid Green 1; Acid Red 13; Broenner's acid; 2-ethoxy-1-naphthylamine-6-sulphonic acid; Food Red 17; Food Yellow 3

scilliroside
[507-60-8]

R = β-D-glucopyranosyl-. $C_{32}H_{44}O_{12}$. M: 620.69. Extract of the bulbs of the red squill (*Urginea maritima*).
Uses: rodenticide

SCMC *See:* sodium carboxymethyl cellulose

scopolamine
hyoscine; (−)-scopolamine; [51-34-3]

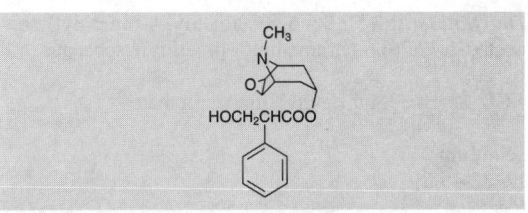

$C_{17}H_{21}N_1O_4$. M: 303.37. Extracted with atropine from thorn apple (*Datura stramonium*) fruit.
Derivatives:
butylscopolamine bromide; cimetropium bromide
Uses: anticholinergic drug

SCP *See:* single cell protein

SCS *See:* sodium cumene sulphonate

SDA *See:* stilbene-4,4'-dicarboxylic acid

SDDC *See:* sodium dimethyldithiocarbamate

SDEC *See:* sodium diethyldithiocarbamate

SDPA *See:* diphenylamine, styrenated

SDS *See:* sodium lauryl sulphate

sebacic acid
decandioic acid; octane-1,8-dicarboxylic acid; [111-20-6]

$$HOOCCH_2CH_2CH_2CH_2CH_2CH_2CH_2CH_2COOH$$

$C_{10}H_{18}O_4$. M: 202.25. White powder. MP: 131–134°C. d: 1.21 kg/l (20°C). Soluble in oxygenated solvents and hot water.
Production:
• butadiene (dimerisation/hydrogenation/hydroformylation)
• ricinoleic acid (alkali fusion; coproduced with 2-octanol)
Derivatives:
complex ester oils; di-*n*-butyl sebacate; diester oils; di-(2-ethylhexyl) sebacate; polyamide 66/ 610; polyamide 610; polyester polyols, linear; polymeric plasticisers; sebacoyl chloride
Uses: alkyd resin comonomer

sebacoyl chloride
sebacoyl dichloride; [111-19-3]

$$ClC(CH_2)_8CCl$$

$C_{10}H_{16}Cl_2O_2$. M: 239.15. Liquid. BP: 220°C (10 kPa). d: 1.12 kg/l (20°C). Hydrolysed by water.
Production:
• sebacic acid (acid chloride formation)

Derivatives: di-(1,2,2,6,6-pentamethyl-4-piperidyl) sebacate; di-(2,2,6,6-tetramethyl-4-piperidyl) sebacate

SED *See:* sodium diethyldithiocarbamate

selenium
[7782-49-2]

Se

Se_1. M: 78.96. Dark red to black solid. MP: 217°C. BP: 685°C. d: 4.82 kg/l (25°C). Available as pellets or powder.
Production:
• copper anodic slimes/copper anodic slimes (sulphating roast process/hydrometallurgical refining; coproduced with platinum/gold/silver/palladium/tellurium)
Derivatives: selenium dioxide
Uses: glass colorant; animal feed additive; iron/copper/nickel/lead alloy ingredient; photoconductor (photocopiers, photocells, temperature gauges)

selenium dioxide
[7446-08-4]

SeO_2

O_2Se_1. M: 110.96. White, lustrous powder. Sublimes when heated to 315°C. Solubility in water: 400 g/l water (20°C). Soluble in alcohol.
Production:
• selenium (air oxidation)
Derivatives:
sodium selenite
Uses: analytical reagent; oxidising agent

semicarbazide hydrochloride
aminourea hydrochloride; [57-56-7] (free base); [563-41-7] (hydrochloride)

$C_1H_6Cl_1N_3O_1$. M: 111.53. White, crystalline solid. MP: 175–177°C with decomposition. Soluble in water. Insoluble in oxygenated solvents.
Production:
• sodium cyanate + hydrazine + hydrochloric acid (addition/salt formation)
Derivatives:
2-amino-5-methyl-1,3,4-thiadiazole; isazofos; nitrofural; trazodone
Uses: analytical reagent (carbonyl compounds)

semicoke
Coalite (Anglo United); Disco
Production:
• coal (low-temperature carbonisation)
Uses: domestic/industrial heating fuel

Senegal phosphate
aluminium phosphate, natural; [7784-30-7]
Granules. Standard grades contain about 30% P_2O_5.
Uses: fertiliser

L-serine
L-β-hydroxyalanine; Ser; [56-45-1]

$C_3H_7N_1O_3$. M: 105.10. Available commercially as the naturally-occurring L(−)-enantiomer. Crystalline solid. Decomposes on heating to 230°C. Soluble in water.
Production:
• glycine + methanol (microbial conversion)
Derivatives: L-tryptophan
Uses: infusion solutions/diagnostic aids; raw material (peptide drugs)

Serisol Blue RD

$C_{14}H_{17}N_5O_3S_1$. M: 335.38.
Production:
• 2-amino-5-nitrothiazole + *N*-ethyl-*N*-(2-hydroxyethyl)-*m*-toluidine (diazotisation/azo coupling)
Uses: dye (acetate)

sethoxydim
[74051-80-2]

$C_{17}H_{29}N_1O_3S_1$. M: 327.49.
Production:
• crotonaldehyde + ethyl mercaptan + acetone + dimethyl malonate + *n*-butyryl chloride + hydroxylamine sulphate + diethyl sulphate (addition/ carbonyl condensation/condensation/decarboxylation/dehydrochlorination/oxime formation/ethylation)
Uses: herbicide

SFS *See:* sodium formaldehyde sulphoxylate

shark liver oil
[68990-63-6]
Yellow liquid. Produced by expression of shark's liver.

d: 0.92 kg/l. Soluble in oxygenated and chlorinated solvents.
Derivatives: squalane

shellac
lac; [9000-59-3]
Exudate of the lac insect (*Laccifer lacca*) which feeds on the sap of host trees, excreting the lac as it does so. The lac is collected from the trees and purified. Pale yellow to brown flakes. MP: 115–120°C. d: ~1.15 kg/l. Produced in India.
Production:
• lac insects (extraction)
Uses:
floor polishes; sealing wax/optical cements; binder (knot-sealing paints)

short residue
vacuum residue
Black solid. BP: >535°C. Pour point: 25–50°C. d: 0.95–1.01 kg/l. The chemical composition varies considerably with the source of the crude oil.
Production:
• long residue (vacuum distillation; coproduced with bitumen/gas oil, vacuum/lubricant oils, distillates)
Derivatives:
bitumen; brightstock; deasphalted oil; gas oil, heavy; gas oil, light; naphtha, heavy; refinery gas; shot coke; sponge coke, green
Uses: boiler/industrial/marine fuel oil component

shot coke
petroleum coke
Spherically-shaped black particles.
Production:
• short residue (delayed coking process; coproduced with naphtha, heavy/sponge coke, green/gas oil, light/refinery gas/gas oil, heavy)
Uses:
fuel (electricity generation, cement/lime production)

SIBX *See:* sodium isobutyl xanthate

siduron
1-(2-methylcyclohexyl)-3-phenylurea; [1982-49-6]

$C_{14}H_{20}N_2O_1$. M: 232.32.
Production:
• 2-methylcyclohexylamine + phenyl isocyanate (isocyanate addition)
Uses: herbicide

sienna *See:* iron oxide yellow

silane
[7803-62-5]

H_4Si_1. M: 32.12. Gas with an unpleasant odour. BP: -112°C. Slowly decomposed by water. Soluble in most organic solvents.
Production:
• trichlorosilane (disproportionation)
• silicon tetrachloride + lithium aluminium hydride (reduction)
Uses: semiconductor fabrication material

silica *See:* quartz

silica, fumed
silica, pyrogenic; Pigment White 27 (CI); 77711 (CI)

O_2Si_1. M: 60.09. Colourless to white, lightweight powder. BET surface area: 200–300 m²/g.
Production:
• silicon tetrachloride/silicon tetrafluoride + hydrogen (flame hydrolysis process)
Derivatives: silicone rubber, heat-cured
Uses: filler (plastics, rubber, caulks, sealants); flattening agent/pigment (paints, printing inks); viscosifier (paints, adhesives, cosmetics)

silica, precipitated
silica, colloidal

O_2Si_1. M: 60.09. White, crystalline powder with a primary particle size of 5–50 nm, a specific surface area of 30–500 m²/g and a relatively low porosity. d: 2.05 kg/l. The manufacturing process differs from that of silica gel in that the silica is flocculated and precipitated rather than being allowed to form a gel. When intended as a filler, further treatment with chlorosilanes or other reagents is common in order to render the surface organophilic.
Production:
• sodium silicate + sulphuric acid (acidification)
Uses: beer clarifying agent; extender (paints); flow conditioner/anticaking agent (fire extinguisher powders, foodstuffs); pesticide carrier; abrasive/thickening agent (toothpaste); reinforcing filler (rubber, plastics, sealants, cleaners, grease)

silica gel
silica, amorphous

O_2Si_1. M: 60.09. A form of amorphous silica in which the colloidal particles have fused together into a rigid, hydrogel matrix. This is dried to the xerogel which is

the silica gel of commerce. Gels produced under different conditions have different pore sizes and surface areas. Grades with pore sizes of ~2 nm are used as desiccants. Those with pore sizes of ~20 nm are preferred as matt pigments and antiblocking agents.
Production:
• sodium silicate + sulphuric acid (salt formation)
Uses: gas/liquid drying agent; machinery/electronics storage sachets; flattening agent (matt paints); flow conditioner/anticaking agent (plastics, food, chemicals); chromatographic adsorption agent

silicon, electronic grade
[7440-21-3]

Si

Si_1. M: 28.09. Grey, lustrous semiconductive solid. MP: 1,410°C. d: 2.33 kg/l (25°C). Sold in the form of rod, usually of 15 mm or 50 mm diameter.
Production:
• trichlorosilane + hydrogen (dehydrochlorination)
Uses: semiconductor devices/chips/solar cells substrate

silicon, metallurgical grade

Si

Si_1. M: 28.09. Grey lumps or powder. MP: 1,410°C. d: 2.33 kg/l (25°C). Insoluble in water.
Production:
• quartz + metallurgical coke (arc reduction)
Derivatives: chlorotrimethylsilane; dichlorodimethylsilane; dichlorodiphenylsilane; dichloromethylsilane; silicon nitride; silicon tetrachloride; trichloromethylsilane; trichlorophenylsilane; trichlorosilane
Uses: aluminium alloys, silicon bronze, iron/steel

silicon carbide
[409-21-2]

SiC

C_1Si_1. M: 40.10. Hard, black or green granules. d: 3.2 kg/l. Decomposes when heated above 2800°C.
Production:
• sponge coke, green/anthracite + quartz (Acheson electrothermal process)
Uses: ceramic components (combustion engines, turbines, heat exchangers); grinding wheel abrasive; refractory ceramics (furnace linings)

silicon nitride

Si_3N_4

N_4Si_3. M: 140.29. Hard, powder or shaped, reaction-sintered parts. Stable to 1,900°C. d: 3.2 kg/l.
Production:
• silicon, metallurgical grade + nitrogen (thermal conversion)

Uses: cutting tools; refractory ceramics (coatings, crucibles, furnace components)

silicon tetrachloride
tetrachlorosilane; [10026-04-7]

$SiCl_4$

Cl_4Si_1. M: 169.90. Colourless liquid. BP: 58°C. Decomposed by water forming hydrogen chloride. Fumes in air.
Production:
• silicon, metallurgical grade + chlorine (chlorination)
• silicon, metallurgical grade + hydrogen chloride, anhydrous (reaction; coproduced with trichlorosilane)
• rutile/anatase + chlorine + sponge coke, calcined/titanium slag (chloride process; byproduct of titanium tetrachloride production)
• zircon + metallurgical coke + chlorine (thermal reduction/chlorination; byproduct of silicon tetrachloride/zirconium tetrachloride production)
• trichlorosilane (disproportionation; byproduct of silane production)
Derivatives: etacelasil; ethyl silicate; silicone resin; silane; silica, fumed
Uses: semiconductor fabrication raw material

silicon tetrafluoride
tetrafluorosilane; [7783-61-1]

SiF_4

F_4Si_1. M: 104.08. Colourless gas with pungent odour. Decomposed by water. Fumes in moist air forming hydrofluoric acid.
Production:
• fluorspar + sulphuric acid (acidification; byproduct of hydrogen fluoride production)
• apatite + quartz (calcination; byproduct of apatite, defluorinated production)
Derivatives: hexafluorosilicic acid; silica, fumed

silicone alkyd resins
Production:
• silicone resin + alkyd resins, long-oil (compounding)
Uses: coil coating (metallic building materials); durable industrial paints; heat-resistant stoving enamel (heating appliances, cookers, utensils); scratch resistant coatings (plastics)

silicone oils
methicone (CTFA); poly(dimethylsiloxane); PDMS

$$\left[O-\underset{\underset{CH_3}{|}}{\overset{\overset{CH_3}{|}}{Si}} \right]_n$$

Colourless, odourless, tasteless fluids characterised by

their chemical and physiological inertness, water repellency, low surface tension and excellent dielectric properties. Viscosities vary over the range 1–10⁶ mm²/s, depending on the molecular weight. The oils are usable over a wide temperature range, typically, -70–+250°C. They are available as pure material or formulated into pastes, greases or emulsions in water.
Production:
• dimethylsiloxane oligomers + hexamethyldisiloxane (acid-catalysed polymerisation)
Uses: defoaming agent (oil processing); flow/gloss improver (alkyd paints, varnishes); lubricant (polishes, maintenance products); antiadhesion coatings; hydraulic/dielectric/heat-transfer/diffusion pump oils; barrier creams/lipstick/pharmaceutical ingredient; lubricant (motors, instruments, precision bearings); silicone emulsions (antifoam, antiadherence coatings, mould-release agents, textile waterproofing); silicone greases (gear/bearing lubricants); silicone pastes (valve lubricants, mould-release agents, electrical/electronic protection); textile/paper sizing additive

silicone-polyol block copolymers
Production:
• dichlorodimethylsilane + triethylene glycol monobutyl ether (dehydrochlorination)
• dichloromethylsilane + ethylene oxide/propylene oxide (epoxidation)
Uses: polyurethane foam stabiliser; antifoam; textile auxiliaries

silicone resin
Production:
• dimethylsiloxane oligomers + trichloromethylsilane/trichlorophenylsilane + silicon tetrachloride (polymerisation)
Derivatives: silicone alkyd resins
Uses: electrical insulation lacquer/coatings/tapes; glass fibre/mica laminating resin (electrical, electronic components); pressure-injected damp-proofing formulations; polish ingredient; plastics mould release agents; moulding powders (electrical, electronic components); silicone emulsions (masonry, glass surface treatment, textile waterproofing); surface sealing compounds (brickwork, masonry); binder (heat-resistant/coil coating paints)

silicone rubber, cold-cured, 1-component
Elastomers characterised by their excellent heat, chemical and weather resistance with low-temperature flexibility down to -40°C. Moisture-cured with the release of acetic acid.
Production:
• poly(dimethylsiloxane), hydroxyl-terminated + methyl triacetoxysilane (condensation)
Uses: caulks/sealants (expansion joints, windows); sealants/gaskets/shock-absorbing fixings (vehicles, domestic appliances); heat-resistant adhesives

silicone rubber, cold-cured, 2-component, polyaddition-types
Presented as liquids or pastes which are cured, sometimes at slightly elevated temperatures, using catalysts such as hexachloroplatinic acid.
Production:
• poly(dimethylsiloxane), vinylated + poly(dimethylsiloxane), crosslinking (addition-cured process)
Uses: dielectric gels; electrical/electronic encapsulation; fire-resistant cable coatings; foamed sealants; resin casting moulds

silicone rubber, cold-cured, 2-component, polycondensation-types
Elastomers characterised by their excellent heat, chemical and weather resistance with low-temperature flexibility down to -40°C. Cured by mixing resin with crosslinking component.
Production:
• poly(dimethylsiloxane), hydroxyl-terminated + ethyl silicate (condensation-cured process)
Uses: moulding compounds (furniture, construction); paper antiadhesion coatings; electrical component sealant; roofing membranes; window/curtain walling sealant

silicone rubber, heat-cured
Elastomers characterised by their excellent heat, chemical and weather resistance with low-temperature flexibility down to -40°C. Cured by incorporation of peroxides and heating.
Production:
• poly(dimethylsiloxane), vinylated + silica, fumed (compounding)
Uses: chemically-resistant/medical tubing and mouldings; flexible/rigid foams; press-formed automobile seals; wire/cable jacketing

silver
[7440-22-4]

Ag

Ag_1. M: 107.87. Greyish-white, malleable, ductile metal. MP: 961°C. BP: 2,212°C. d: 10.5 kg/l. High electrical and thermal conductivity. Available as powder, grains, pieces, wire, foil, sheet, tubing, ingots and as shaped objects. Often sold alloyed with copper and sometimes cadmium. 'Sterling' silver contains 92.5% silver. The CIS, Mexico, Canada, Peru, USA and Australia are the main producing countries.
Production:
• silver ores (cyanidation/reduction)
• copper anodic slimes (sulphating roast process/hydrometallurgical refining; coproduced with platinum/gold/palladium/selenium/tellurium)
• lead bullion (pyrometallurgical refining/Parkes process/Betterton-Kroll process; byproduct of lead production)

- lead bullion (electrochemical refining; byproduct of lead production)

Derivatives:
silver nitrate
Uses: formaldehyde/ethylene oxide production catalyst; conductive filler (electronic plastics, coatings); dental alloys; electrical conductors, radar waveguides; non-corrosive chemical/food/brewing equipment; ornaments/jewellery/tableware/coinage

silver bromide
[7785-23-1]

AgBr

Ag_1Br_1. M: 187.77. Pale yellow, crystalline powder. MP: 434°C. d: 6.47 kg/l (25°C). Insoluble in water. Darkened by light.
Production:
- silver nitrate + sodium bromide (salt formation)
Uses: photographic chemical

silver chloride
[7783-90-6]

AgCl

Ag_1Cl_1. M: 143.32. White powder which turns blue on exposure to light. MP: 455°C. d: 5.56 kg/l. Insoluble in water.
Production:
- silver nitrate + sodium chloride, refined (salt formation)
Uses: phototropic glass additive

silver cyanide
[506-64-9]

AgCN

$C_1Ag_1N_1$. M: 133.89. White powder. Decomposes at 320°C with the release of cyanogen. d: 3.95 kg/l. Insoluble in water. Darkened by light.
Production:
- silver nitrate + sodium cyanide (salt formation)
Uses: electroplating bath ingredient

silver nitrate
[7761-88-8]

AgNO₃

$Ag_1N_1O_3$. M: 169.88. Colourless crystals. MP: 212°C. d: 4.35 kg/l. Solubility in water: 1.22 kg/l water (0°C).
Production:
- silver + nitric acid (reaction)
Derivatives: silver bromide; silver chloride; silver cyanide; silver peroxide
Uses:
raw material (photographic film production, silver salt production); reagent (mirror production)

silver peroxide
argentic oxide; silver oxide

AgO

Ag_1O_1. M: 123.87.
Production:
- silver nitrate + potassium hydroxide + sodium persulphate (reaction/oxidation)
Uses: silver oxide-zinc alkali batteries

simazine
2-chloro-4,6-di-(ethylamino)-1,3,5-triazine; 2-di-(ethylamino)-6-chloro-*sym*-triazine; [122-34-9]

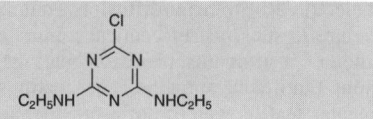

$C_7H_{12}Cl_1N_5$. M: 201.66.
Production:
- cyanuric chloride + ethylamine (amine formation)
Uses: herbicide

single cell protein
SCP
Production:
- sulphite pulp waste liquor + *Paecilomyces varioti* bacteria (Pekito process)
- sulphite pulp waste liquor + torula yeast (fermentation)
- whey + *Kusyeromyces fragilis* bacteria (fermentation)
- ethanol + torula yeast (Amoco process)
Uses: animal feed ingredient

sinter phosphate *See:* Rhenania phosphate

SIPX *See:* sodium isopropyl xanthate

SIS *See:* styrene-isoprene triblock copolymers

slack wax
Wax containing 2–7% lubricant base oil. d: 0.76–0.79 kg/l (20°C). Congealing point: 20–55°C.
Production:
- lubricant oils, refined (urea dewaxing process/hydrogen finishing processes; byproduct of lubricant oils, base production)
- lubricant oils, refined (ketone dewaxing processes/hydrogen finishing processes; byproduct of lubricant oils, base production)
Derivatives:
paraffin wax
Uses: cable filling compounds; binder (pressed woodchip logs, particleboard)

SMCA *See:* sodium chloroacetate

SMS *See:* sodium metabisulphite; styrene-α-methyl-styrene copolymers, low molecular weight; styrene-α-methylstyrene copolymers

SNOBS *See:* sodium nonanoyloxybenzene sulphonate

soda ash *See:* sodium carbonate

soda cellulose *See:* alkali cellulose

sodamide
sodium amide; [7782-92-5]

NaNH₂

$H_2N_1Na_1$. M: 39.02. White, crystalline solid. MP: 210°C. Violently hydrolysed by water and alkali producing ammonia.
Production:
• sodium + ammonia (reaction)
Derivatives: 2-amino-6-methylpyridine; 2-aminopyridine; 2,6-diaminopyridine; indigo; sodium azide
Uses: dehydration agent; reagent (Madelung synthesis, base-catalysed condensation/amidation)

soda nitre *See:* sodium nitrate

soda pulp *See:* alkali cellulose

sodium
[7440-23-5]

Na

Na_1. M: 22.99. Soft, silver-white metal. MP: 98°C. BP: 881°C. d: 0.97 kg/l (20°C). Reacts with water and alcohol, releasing hydrogen. Soluble in liquid ammonia.
Production:
• sodium chloride, refined (Downs process; coproduced with chlorine)
Derivatives:
arsine; paraquat dichloride; potassium; sodamide; sodium borohydride; sodium ethoxide; sodium hydride; sodium methoxide; sodium peroxide; tetra-n-butyltin; tetraethyl lead; tetramethyl lead; titanium
Uses: heat-transfer fluid (nuclear reactors); reagent (Birch/Bouveault-Blanc reductions, waste oil/hydrocarbon refining); sodium vapour lamps; sodium-sulphur batteries

sodium acetate
[127-09-3]

CH₃COO⁻ Na⁺

$C_2H_3Na_1O_2$. M: 82.03. Available commercially as anhydrous or 60% (trihydrate) grades. The anhydrous product is a white, hygroscopic powder. MP: 324°C. The 60% grade is a white crystalline or granular solid which loses its water of crystallisation when heated above 120°C. Soluble in water forming slightly alkaline solutions. Soluble in alcohol.
Production:
• sodium hydroxide + acetic acid (salt formation)
Derivatives: acetyl chloride; chromium acetate; cinnamic acid; 2-ethylhexyl p-methoxycinnamate; fentin acetate; neryl acetate
Uses: buffering agent (dried soups, bakery products); esterification/Perkin's reaction catalyst; electrodeless nickel coating reagent; acetylation reagent

sodium alginate
algin
Cream powder containing, typically, 13% water. Decomposes on heating above 150°C. d: 1.59 kg/l. Soluble in water forming a gel.
Production:
• alginic acid + sodium hydroxide (salt formation)
Uses: plasticiser/binding agent (welding rod coatings); stabiliser/gelling agent (prepared food products); thickening agent (textile printing pastes)

sodium alkane(C_{11}-C_{14}) sulphonate
paraffin(C_{11}-C_{14}) sulphonate, sodium salt; secondary alkane sulphonate; SAS

SO_3^- Na^+ $CH_3(CH_2)_mCH(CH_2)_nCH_3$

m+n = 8–11. Yellowish-white flakes. Sold as pure product or as a 30–76% solution in water. Soluble in water producing alkaline solutions.
Production:
• n-paraffins (C_{11}-C_{14}) + sulphur dioxide, pure (photochlorosulphonation)
Uses: textile/leather cleaning agent

sodium alkane(C_{14}-C_{18}) sulphonate
paraffin(C_{14}-C_{18}) sulphonate, sodium salt; secondary alkane sulphonate; SAS

SO_3^- Na^+ $CH_3(CH_2)_mCH(CH_2)_nCH_3$

m+n = 11–15. Yellowish-white flakes. Sold as pure product or as 30–76% solution in water. Dissolves in water producing alkaline solutions.
Production:
• n-paraffins (C_{14}-C_{18}) + sulphur dioxide, pure (photochlorosulphonation)
• n-paraffins (C_{14}-C_{18}) + sulphur dioxide, pure (photosulphoxidation)
Uses: surfactant (light-duty liquid cleaners, dishwashing detergents)

sodium n-alkanol (C_{13}-C_{15}) ether sulphates

$C_mH_{2m+1}CH_2(OCH_2CH_2)_nOSO_3^-$ Na^+

m = 12–14, n = 2–3. Pale yellow liquids available as

either 27% or 70% solutions in water.
Production:
- *n*-alkanol(C_{13}-C_{15}) ethoxylates (sulphation/sodium salt formation)

Uses:
high-foaming surfactant (dishwashing liquid, shampoos, bath products); wetting agent (drilling muds, plasterboard production)

sodium alkylbenzenesulphonate, branched
See: sodium dodecylbenzenesulphonate

sodium alkylbenzenesulphonate, linear
LABS; LAS

n = 10–13. Cream-coloured flakes or powder (80–85% active matter content), pale yellow pastes (65% active matter content) or liquids (30% active matter content). Soluble in water forming alkaline solutions. The chain-length distribution is, typically: 13% C_{10}, 34% C_{11}, 31% C_{12}, 22% C_{13} for broad-cut products.
Production:
- dodecylbenzenesulphonic acid, linear + sodium hydroxide/sodium carbonate (salt formation)

Uses:
concrete air-entrainment agents; crude oil demulsifier component; emulsifier (emulsion polymerisation); mineral flotation agent; mortar plasticiser; scouring/degreasing agent (leather, fur production); scouring/wetting agents (textile production); surfactant (powder laundry detergents, light-duty detergents); wetting agent (polyvinyl acetate adhesives)

sodium alkylnaphthalene sulphonate
[26264-58-4] (methyl substituent)

$C_{11}H_9Na_1O_3S_1$. M: 244.24.
Production:
- methylnaphthalene fraction/β-methylnaphthalene (sulphonation/sodium salt formation)

Uses: emulsifier/dispersant (emulsion polymerisation, paints, inks, pesticides); wetting agent (textile/leather/pesticide auxiliaries)

sodium allyl sulphonate

$C_3H_5Na_1O_3S_1$. M: 144.12. The commercial product is sold as a solution in water.
Production:
- allyl chloride + sodium bisulphite (sulphonation)

Uses:
nickel plating brightening agent; anionic comonomer

sodium alum
sodium aluminium sulphate; [10102-71-3]

$Al_1Na_1O_8S_2$. M: 242.09. Available commercially as the dodecahydrate. Colourless crystals. MP: 61°C. d: 1.67 kg/l. Highly soluble in water.
Production:
- sodium sulphate + alumina trihydrate + sulphuric acid (salt formation)

Uses: leavening agent

sodium aluminate
[1302-42-7]

$Al_1Na_1O_2$. M: 81.97. White powder. MP: 1,650°C. Soluble in water forming alkaline solutions.
Production:
- sodium hydroxide + alumina trihydrate (salt formation)

Derivatives: cryolite; zeolite A; zeolite X; zeolite Y; zeolite ZSM 5
Uses: curing agent (brinks, tiles); aluminosilicate catalyst raw material; reagent (titanium dioxide post-treatment); sizing/retention aid (paper production); textile auxiliary; flocculant (water treatment)

sodium aluminium phosphate
SALP

$H_{14}Al_3Na_1O_{32}P_8$. M: 877.81. Available as the tetrahydrate. White powder. Insoluble in water.
Production:
- sodium hydroxide + alumina trihydrate + phosphoric acid, pure (salt formation)

Uses: leavening agent

sodium amalgam
[11110-52-4]

Silver, crystalline solid. A sodium/mercury alloy containing 2-20% sodium. The physical properties vary with the composition. Decomposed by water evolving hydrogen.
Production:
- sodium chloride, natural (mercury cell electrolysis; byproduct of chlorine/sodium hydroxide production)

Derivatives: sodium hydrosulphite; sodium sulphide
Uses: reducing agent

sodium anisaldehyde bisulphite
sodium 4-methoxybenzaldehyde bisulphite;
[68083-31-8]
$C_8H_9Na_1O_5S_1$. M: 240.20.

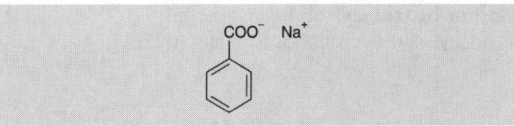

Production:
• *p*-anisaldehyde + sodium bisulphite (bisulphite addition)
Uses: electroplating brightening agent

sodium ascorbate
E301 (EC); [134-03-2]

$C_6H_7Na_1O_6$. M: 198.11. White, crystalline powder. Decomposes on heating to 218°C. Soluble in water with gradual air oxidation. The commercial product is the natural L(+)-enantiomer.
Production:
• ascorbic acid + sodium hydroxide (salt formation)
Uses:
dietary supplement ingredient; antioxidant/colour fixative (prepared meat, dairy, baby products)

sodium azide
[26628-22-8]

NaN_3

N_3Na_1. M: 65.01. White crystals. Decomposes on heating forming sodium and nitrogen. d: 1.85 kg/l. Highly toxic. Soluble in water and liquid ammonia. Slightly soluble in alcohol.
Production:
• sodamide + nitric acid (reaction)
Derivatives:
alfentanil; azidocillin; aziprotryne; cefazolin; lead azide; 1-phenyl-5-mercaptotetrazole; 5-phenyltetrazole; thidiazuron; 5-thio-1-(β-dimethylaminoethyl)tetrazole; 5-thio-1-methyltetrazole
Uses: inflatable vehicle safety bag propellant

sodium β-carboxyethyl acrylate

$CH_2=CHCOCH_2CH_2COO^-$ Na^+

$C_6H_7Na_1O_4$. M: 166.12.
Production:
• acrylic acid (Michael addition/sodium salt formation)
Uses: acrylic resin comonomer (metal adhesives)

sodium benzoate
E211 (EC); [532-32-1]
$C_7H_5Na_1O_2$. M: 144.11. White, hygroscopic granules or powder. MP: >300°C. Soluble in water. Slightly soluble in alcohol.

COO^- Na^+

Production:
• benzoic acid + sodium hydroxide (salt formation)
Uses: preservative (soft drinks, fruit juices, sauces, adhesives, cosmetics); corrosion inhibitor (antifreeze)

sodium bicarbonate
[144-55-8]

$NaHCO_3$

$C_1H_1Na_1O_3$. M: 84.01. White granules or crystalline powder. Decomposes with loss of carbon dioxide on heating. Solubility in water: 92 g/l solution (25°C).
Production:
• sodium carbonate + carbon dioxide (salt formation)
Derivatives:
sodium sesquicarbonate
Uses: animal feed ingredient; baking powder/self-raising flour ingredient; blowing agent (foamed plastics/rubber); fire extinguishant powder; stomach powder ingredient; leaching agent (uranium ores); neutralising agent (leather, rayon production)

sodium bis(2-hydroxyethyl)-5-sulphoisophthalate
ethylene glycol sodium sulphoisophthalic acid ester; EGSSIPA

$C_{12}H_{13}Na_1O_9S_1$. M: 356.27.
Production:
• sodium sulphoisophthalic acid + ethylene oxide (epoxidation)
Uses: dyeable polyester/polyamide comonomer

sodium 4,4'-bis(4-phenyl-1,2,3-triazol-2-yl)stilbene-2,2'-disulphonate
[23743-28-4] (disodium salt)

$C_{30}H_{20}N_6Na_2O_6S_2$. M: 670.63.
Production:
• acetophenone + isoamyl nitrite + 4,4'-diaminostilbene-2,2'-disulphonic acid (nitrosation/diazotisation/reduction/condensation)
Uses: fluorescent brightening agent (detergents)

sodium bistridecylsulphosuccinate
ditridecyl sodium sulphosuccinate (CTFA)

$$Na^+ \quad {}^-O_3SCHCOCH_2C_{12}H_{25}$$
$$CH_2COCH_2C_{12}H_{25}$$

$C_{30}H_{57}Na_1O_7S_1$. M: 584.83.
Production:
• maleic anhydride + tridecanol + sodium bisulphite
  (esterification/sulphonation)
Uses: emulsifier (emulsion polymerisation)

sodium bisulphate
nitre cake; sodium acid sulphate; sodium hydrogen sulphate; [7681-38-1]

NaHSO$_4$

$H_1Na_1O_4S_1$. M: 120.06. Colourless crystals. Solubility in water: 500 g/l water (0°C). Forms acidic solutions.
Production:
• sodium chloride, natural + sulphuric acid (salt
  formation)
• sodium sulphate + sulphuric acid (salt formation)
• sodium dichromate + sulphuric acid (reaction;
  byproduct of chromic acid production)
Uses: cleaning agent; flux; leather bleaching, swelling agent; pH control (water treatment); metal pickling agent; wool carbonising agent

sodium bisulphite
sodium hydrogen sulphite; E222 (EC); [7631-90-5]

NaHSO$_3$

$H_1Na_1O_3S_1$. M: 104.06. Available commercially as a 38–43% aqueous solution.
Production:
• sodium hydroxide + sulphur dioxide, pure (salt
  formation)
Derivatives: dipyrone; disodium coconut monoethanolamide sulphosuccinate; disodium *N*-cocoylsulphosuccinamate; disodium isodecylsulphosuccinate; disodium lauryl ether sulphosuccinate; disodium laurylsulphosuccinate; disodium oleic monoisopropanolamide sulphosuccinate; disodium *N*-oleylsulphosuccinamate; disodium *N*-stearylsulphosuccinamate; polyacrylamide, sulphomethylated; propane sultone; sodium allyl sulphonate; sodium anisaldehyde bisulphite; sodium bistridecylsulphosuccinate; sodium 3-chloro-2-hydroxypropylsulphonate; sodium diamylsulphosuccinate; sodium di-(2-ethylhexyl)sulphosuccinate; sodium dihexylsulphosuccinate; sodium diisobutylsulphosuccinate; sodium diisooctylsulphosuccinate; sodium isethionate; sodium starch sulphosuccinate; sodium vinyl sulphonate; starch, amphoteric; tetrasodium *N*-(1,2-dicarboxyethyl)-*N*-octadecylsulphosuccinamate; urea-formaldehyde resins, anionic

Uses: skin/hide depilatory agent; sulphomethylation/aldehyde purification reagent

sodium borate
borax; disodium tetraborate; [1303-96-4]; [1330-43-4] (anhydrous)

Na$_2$O.2B$_2$O$_3$

$B_4Na_2O_7$. M: 201.21. Natural ores. The commercially exploited minerals are tincal (decahydrate), sborgite (pentahydrate) and kernite (tetrahydrate). The product is also made from other natural borate sources. Available commercially as the decahydrate, the pentahydrate, the anhydrous salt and as a mixed salt with boric acid ('Polybor', Borax Consolidated).
Production:
• sodium borate, natural (extraction/purification)
• calcium borate, natural + sodium carbonate
  (extraction/salt formation)
• brine, natural borate (extraction; coproduced with
  sodium carbonate/sodium sulphate/potassium
  chloride)
Derivatives:
barium metaborate; boric acid; boron trifluoride; potassium tetraborate; sodium borohydride; sodium metaborate; sodium perborate
Uses: corrosion inhibitor (sealed water cooling systems); fire-retardant additive (cellulose, plastics); flux (glass, enamel, ceramics production); ant/cockroach bait; herbicide; soap/cleaner ingredient; neutron absorber (nuclear reactors); retarder (wall plasters); tackifier (polyvinyl alcohol); fertiliser trace element additive; welding/ soldering/metallurgical flux

sodium borohydride
sodium tetrahydroborate; Borol (Morton, caustic solution); [16940-66-2]

NaBH$_4$

$H_4B_1Na_1$. M: 37.83. White solid. Solubility in water: 550 g/l (25°C). Decomposes in heating. Stability improved by alkali. Commercially sodium borohydride is sold as a solid or in solution with sodium hydroxide.
Production:
• trimethyl borate + sodium hydride (Ventron
  process)
• sodium borate + quartz + sodium + hydrogen
  (Bayer sodium borohydride process)
Derivatives: diethylamine borane; dimethylamine borane; sodium hydrosulphite
Uses:
formaldehyde scavenger (textile finishing); carbonyl reduction reagent; SHOP process catalyst; electrodeless nickel-boron/cobalt-boron coating reagent; reagent (magnetic tape production, kaolin/process stream decolorisation, vat dye reduction); trace metal scavenger (effluent treatment)

sodium bromate
[7789-38-0]

NaBrO$_3$

Br$_1$Na$_1$O$_3$. M: 150.89. White crystals. MP: 381°C. d: 3.3 kg/l. Solubility in water: 275 g/l water (0°C).
Production:
• sodium bromide (electrolytic oxidation)
Uses: industrial cleaning agent; hair waving agent

sodium bromide
[7647-15-6]

NaBr

Br$_1$Na$_1$. M: 102.89. White powder. MP: 755°C. d: 3.20 kg/l. Solubility in water: 920 g/l water. For oilfield applications, sodium bromide is usually sold as a 45% solution in water with a density of 1.47 g/l.
Production:
• sodium hydroxide + hydrobromic acid (salt formation)
Derivatives:
Pigment Violet 37; silver bromide; sodium bromate
Uses: oil-well drilling/completion fluids

sodium cacodylate
sodium dimethylarsinate; [124-65-2]

$$(CH_3)_2\overset{\overset{O}{\|}}{As}O^- \quad Na^+$$

C$_2$H$_6$As$_1$Na$_1$O$_2$. M: 159.98.
Production:
• sodium hydroxide + arsenic trioxide + methyl chloride (reaction)
Uses: herbicide/defoliant (cotton)

sodium carbonate
natron; sal soda; soda ash; washing soda; [497-19-8]

Na$_2$CO$_3$

C$_1$Na$_2$O$_3$. M: 105.99. Soda ash is anhydrous sodium carbonate. It is a white powder or granular solid. MP: 851°C. Solubility in water: 70 g/l water (0°C). Available as a light powder (bulk density: 0.55kg/l) or as a granular, dense product (bulk density: 1.01 kg/l). Washing soda is the decahydrate salt. It consists of clear, colourless crystals which are readily soluble in water giving alkaline solutions. Heating washing soda to 30°C causes it to partially dissolve in its own water of crystallisation. Natron is the natural mineral, sodium carbonate decahydrate.
Production:
• limestone + sodium chloride, natural + ammonia (ammonia-soda process)
• trona (extraction/calcination)
• brine, natural alkali (extraction/calcination; coproduced with sodium sulphate)
• brine, natural borate (extraction; coproduced with sodium borate/sodium sulphate/potassium chloride)
Derivatives: benzyl alcohol; cadmium carbonate; calcium carbonate, precipitated; calcium hypochlorite; cobalt carbonate, basic; copper carbonate, basic; disodium acid pyrophosphate; disodium phosphate; guanidine carbonate; lithium carbonate; monosodium phosphate; Pigment Blue 29; Rhenania phosphate; Rochelle salt; sodium alkylbenzenesulphonate, linear; sodium bicarbonate; sodium borate; sodium chromate; sodium cyanate; sodium dodecylbenzenesulphonate; sodium ferrocyanide; sodium fluoborate; sodium hexametaphosphate; sodium iodide; sodium metaborate; sodium metasilicate; sodium nitrate; sodium perborate; sodium percarbonate; sodium sesquicarbonate; sodium silicate; sodium sulphide; sodium sulphite; sodium tartrate; sodium thiosulphate; sodium tripolyphosphate; sodium zirconylsilicate; strontium carbonate; tetrasodium pyrophosphate; trisodium phosphate; tungsten trioxide; zirconium carbonate, basic
Uses:
iron/steel production; leaching agent (uranium ores); neutralising agent (soap, detergent production); washing soda (household/industrial cleaner); pH control (water treatment, ore processing, pulp/paper production); glass raw material; sodium salt formation agent; textile auxiliary

sodium carboxymethyl cellulose
carboxymethylcellulose; cellulose, polyanionic; cellulose gum; CMC; E466 (EC); PAC; SCMC; [9004-32-4]

R = H, sodium carboxymethyl-. White, granular powder. Degree of substitution: 0.65– 1.45. Soluble in hot and cold water forming viscous solutions.
Production:
• alkali cellulose + sodium chloroacetate (ether formation)
Uses: dry-strength additive (paper production); flotation depressant (silicate, carbonate minerals); adhesives (wallpaper); antiredeposition agent (detergents); binder (paper coatings); protective colloid (emulsion paints, inks); thickening agent (food, cosmetics, pharmaceuticals, printing dyes); viscosifier/fluid loss agent (drilling muds); warp sizing; weakly acidic ion-exchange resins

sodium caseinate
[9005-46-3]
White, odourless powder. Insoluble in water.
Production:
• casein + sodium hydroxide (salt formation)

Uses: adhesives (beer bottle labelling pastes); foil-paper laminating adhesives; binder (paper coatings); coffee whiteners, soups, stews, cereals, prepared foods; protective colloid (emulsion polymerisation)

sodium cellulose xanthate
cellulose xanthate; viscose

R = H, sodium xanthyl-. Yellow solution. Intermediate in regenerated cellulose production. Not commercially traded. The product has 15–20% xanthate substitution.
Production:
• alkali cellulose + carbon disulphide (addition)
Derivatives:
cellulose, regenerated

sodium cetyloleyl sulphate

$$ROSO_3^- \quad Na^+$$

R = cetyl/oleyl-. Available commercially as a paste containing 27–30% active matter in water.
Production:
• cetyloleyl alcohol (sulphation/sodium salt formation)
Uses: surfactant (heavy-duty powder detergents)

sodium chlorate
[7775-09-9]

$$NaClO_3$$

$Cl_1Na_1O_3$. M: 106.44. Colourless powder. MP: 248°C. Decomposes when heated above 300°C releasing oxygen. d: 2.49 kg/l. Solubility in water: 790 g/l water (0°C).
Production:
• sodium chloride, natural (electrolytic oxidation)
Derivatives:
barium chlorate; chlorine dioxide; 1-chloroanthraquinone; manganese dioxide; potassium chlorate; Prussian Blue; sodium iodate; sodium perchlorate
Uses: match head/explosives ingredient; oxidising agent (dyestuffs); herbicide; uranium extraction agent; leather tanning auxiliary

sodium chloride, natural
brine; rock salt; [7647-14-5]

$$NaCl$$

Cl_1Na_1. M: 58.44. Available as mined ore or as brine. Often upgraded before use by precipitation of alkali-earth and sulphate impurities. Found worldwide.
Derivatives:

ammonium chloride; chlorine; copper oxychloride; sodium bisulphate; sodium carbonate; sodium chlorate; sodium chloride, refined; sodium hexafluorosilicate; sodium hydroxide; sodium sulphate
Uses: oil-well drilling/completion fluids; fertiliser ingredient; ion-exchange resin regeneration; mineral processing agent; road deicing agent; sized granules (oil-well temporary plugging material)

sodium chloride, refined

$$NaCl$$

Cl_1Na_1. M: 58.44. White crystals. MP: 801°C. d: 2.17 kg/l (20°C). Solubility in water: 357 g/l water (20°C). Available in several grades including pure dried vacuum (PDV), granular, microfine, dendritic (low-density branched crystals) and chip (6–12 mm blocks).
Production:
• sodium chloride, natural (purification/concentration)
Derivatives:
bismuth oxychloride; chlorine; silver chloride; sodium
Uses: calcium carbide eutectic additive; filler (sanitary cleansers); flavour enhancer (table salt); food preservative (butter, cheese, ham, bacon, cured fish); animal feed supplement; pottery glaze ingredient; ion-exchange resin regeneration; reagent (soap/dye salting-out processes); tanning auxiliary

sodium chlorite
[7758-19-2]

$$NaClO_2$$

$Cl_1Na_1O_2$. M: 90.44. White, crystalline powder. Decomposes on heating to 180–200°C. Solubility in water: 350 g/l (20°C). Sold commercially as a solid or aqueous solution.
Production:
• chlorine dioxide + sodium hydroxide + hydrogen peroxide (reduction)
Derivatives: chlorine dioxide
Uses: etchant (printed circuit boards); bleaching agent (paper, cellulose, textiles processing); wastewater treatment chemical

sodium chloroacetate
sodium monochloroacetate; SMCA; [3926-62-3]

$$ClCH_2COO^- \quad Na^+$$

$C_2H_2Cl_1Na_1O_2$. M: 116.48. White, crystalline solid. Soluble in water.
Production:
• chloroacetic acid + sodium hydroxide (salt formation)
Derivatives: behenamidopropyl betaine; caproamphocarboxyglycinate; capryloamphocarboxyglycinate; carboxymethyl starch; cocoamidopropyl betaine; cocoamphocarboxyglycinate; coco betaine; cocoimidazoline betaine; isostearamidopropyl betaine; lauroamphocarboxy-

glycinate; lauryl betaine; menadoxime; oleamidopropyl betaine; sodium carboxymethyl cellulose; stearylimidazoline betaine; triclopyr
Uses: herbicide

sodium 2-chloroethanesulphonate
[15484-44-3]

$$ClCH_2CH_2SO_3^- \quad Na^+$$

$C_2H_4Cl_1Na_1O_3S_1$. M: 166.55.
Production:
• ethylene + chlorosulphonic acid + sodium hydroxide (addition/salt formation)
Derivatives: sodium cocoyl isethionate; sodium vinyl sulphonate; sodium *N*-methyltaurate; taurine

sodium 3-chloro-2-hydroxypropylsulphonate
[126-83-0]

$$\underset{ClCH_2CHCH_2SO_3^-}{\overset{OH}{|}} \quad Na^+$$

$C_3H_6Cl_1Na_1O_4S_1$. M: 196.58. Available as a 25% solution in water.
Production:
• epichlorohydrin + sodium bisulphite (addition)
Derivatives: cocoamidopropyl sulphobetaine; cocoimidazoline sulphobetaine; laurylimidazoline sulphobetaine; starch, amphoteric

sodium chromate
[7775-11-3]

$$Na_2CrO_4$$

$Cr_1Na_2O_4$. M: 161.98. Anhydrous grades are yellow crystals. MP: 392°C. d: 2.72 kg/l. Solubility in water: 320 g/l (0°C) forming alkaline solutions. Tetrahydrate grades are yellow crystals. Soluble in water.
Production:
• sodium carbonate + chromite (salt formation)
Derivatives: sodium dichromate
Uses: corrosion inhibitor (sealed water cooling systems, oil-well drilling muds); water/oil-resistant coatings (textiles, plastics, fibreglass); aluminium etchant ingredient; dyeing auxiliary

sodium citrate
trisodium citrate; trisodium 2-hydroxypropane-1,2,3-tricarboxylate; E331 (EC); [68-04-2]

$$\begin{array}{l} CH_2COO^- \quad Na^+ \\ | \\ HO-C-COO^- \quad Na^+ \\ | \\ CH_2COO^- \quad Na^+ \end{array}$$

$C_6H_5Na_3O_7$. M: 258.07. White crystals. Loses water of crystallisation at 150°C. Soluble in water forming slightly alkaline solutions. Insoluble in alcohol. Also available as the anhydrous salt.
Production:

• citric acid + sodium hydroxide (salt formation)
Uses: builder (household cleaners, laundry powders); emulsifier/stabiliser/acidity regulator (pharmaceuticals, cosmetics, toiletries); acidulant (preserves, soft drinks, confectionery); electrodeless nickel coating reagent

sodium cocoyl isethionate
[61789-32-0]

$$\underset{RCOCH_2CH_2SO_3^-}{\overset{O}{\overset{||}{}}} \quad Na^+$$

R = coco-. White powder.
Production:
• coconut acid + sodium isethionate/sodium 2-chloroethanesulphonate (esterification)
Uses: surfactant (hand soaps, cosmetics, toiletries)

sodium *N*-cocoyl-*N*-methyltaurate
sodium methyl cocoyl taurate (CTFA)

$$\underset{\underset{CH_3}{|}}{\overset{O}{\overset{||}{RCNCH_2CH_2SO_3^-}}} \quad Na^+$$

R = coco-. White powder or paste containing 25–100% active matter.
Production:
• coconut acid + sodium *N*-methyltaurate (amide formation)
Uses: high-foaming surfactant (cosmetics, toiletries)

sodium cumene sulphonate
sodium isopropylbenzenesulphonate; SCS; [32073-22-6]

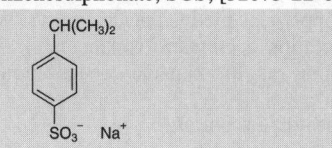

$C_9H_{11}Na_1O_3S_1$. M: 222.24.
Production:
• cumenesulphonic acid (sodium salt formation)
Uses:
hydrotrope (liquid detergents)

sodium cyanate
[917-61-3]

$$NaOCN$$

$C_1N_1Na_1O_1$. M: 65.01. White, crystalline powder. MP: 550°C. Decomposes on further heating. d: 1.89 kg/l (20°C). Soluble in water forming alkaline solutions. Practically insoluble in alcohol.
Production:
• sodium carbonate + urea (reaction)
Derivatives: 4-amino-2-chloro-6,7-dimethoxyquinazoline; bromacil; dipyridamole; *N*-methylurea; molsidomine; orotic acid; 1-(4-piperidyl)-2-benzodiazolinone;

semicarbazide hydrochloride; terbacil; *p*-toluenesulph-onyl semicarbazide; triallyl cyanurate; triazophos; γ-ur-eidopropyltriethoxysilane
Uses: case hardening salts

sodium cyanide
[143-33-9]

NaCN

$C_1N_1Na_1$. M: 49.01. White granules or briquettes. MP: 563–564°C. d: 1.60 kg/l. Soluble in water forming alk-aline solutions. Very toxic. Liberates hydrogen cyanide gas on contact with moist air.
Production:
• sodium hydroxide + hydrogen cyanide (salt formation)
Derivatives: benzoyl cyanide; benzyl cyanide; *p*-bromo-benzyl cyanide; chloramben; *p*-chlorobenzyl cyanide; chlorophacinone; cilastatin; copper cyanide; cyanoacetic acid; 2-cyanoethyl acrylate; 2-cyanoethyl methacrylate; cyanogen bromide; cyanopinacolone; dimethyl acetone-dicarboxylate; diphenylacetonitrile; Disperse Blue 165; fenoprofen; flucythrinate; Fluorescent Brightener 199; 4-fluoro-3-phenoxybenzaldehyde cyanohydrin; guaneth-idine; homovanillic acid; 1-hydroxycyclohexyl phenyl ketone; ketoprofen; DL-mandelic acid; mefruside; met-ribuzin; naphthylacetonitrile; oxymetazoline; 3-phenoxy-benzaldehyde cyanohydrin; silver cyanide; sodium ferrocyanide; sodium glucoheptonate; sodium thiocyan-ate; 3,3-tetramethyleneglutaric acid; tilidine; tolmetin; Vat Orange 5; Vat Red 1; vinclozolin; xylometazoline
Uses:
copper/zinc plating reagent; gold/silver extraction agent; flotation depressant (copper ores); metal surface hard-ening reagent; benzoin condensation catalyst; fumigant

sodium cyclamate
sodium cyclohexylsulphamate; Sucaryl (Abbott Labor-atories); [139-05-9]

$C_6H_{12}N_1Na_1O_3S_1$. M: 201.23. White crystalline solid with a strong, sweet taste. Soluble in water.
Production:
• cyclohexylamine + sulphur trioxide + sodium hydroxide (sulphonation/neutralisation)
Uses: artificial sweetener

sodium cyclohexylsulphamate
See: sodium cyclamate

sodium diamylsulphosuccinate
diamyl sodium sulphosuccinate (CTFA); Aerosol AY (American Cyanamid)
$C_{14}H_{25}Na_1O_7S_1$. M: 360.39. Available commercially as a waxy solid or as a 65% solution in water.

Production:
• amyl alcohol, primary + maleic anhydride + sodium bisulphite (esterification/sulphonation)
Uses: emulsifier (emulsion polymerisation); wetting agent (metal leaching, electroplating)

sodium *O,O*-di-*s*-butyl dithiophosphate
sodium di-*s*-butyl dithiophosphate; Aerofloat 238 (Am-erican Cyanamid)

$C_8H_{18}Na_1O_2P_1S_2$. M: 264.32.
Production:
• phosphorus pentasulphide + *s*-butanol + sodium hydroxide (condensation)
Uses: flotation collector (sulphide ores)

sodium dichloroisocyanurate
sodium dichloro-*sym*-triazine-2,4,6-trione; triclosene sodium (INN); NaDCC; [2893-78-9]

$C_3Cl_2N_3Na_1O_3$. M: 219.95. White powder available as anhydrous or dihydrate grades. Solubility in water: 227 g/l water (25°C, anhydrous product).
Production:
• cyanuric acid + sodium hypochlorite (chlorination)
Uses: bleaching/sanitising agent (scouring powders, laundry detergents); swimming pool disinfectant

sodium dichromate
sodium bichromate; [10588-01-9]

Na₂Cr₂O₇

$Cr_2Na_2O_7$. M: 261.96. Sold both as the solid dihydrate and as a solution in water containing 70% w/w sodium dichromate. The dihydrate is orange-red, deliquescent crystals. Loses water when heated above 100°C. Sol-ubility in water: 2.7 kg/l water (20°C) forming acidic solutions.
Production:
• sodium chromate + sulphuric acid (sulphuric acid process)
• sodium chromate + carbon dioxide (carbon dioxide process)
Derivatives: ammonium dichromate; anthraquinone; *p*-benzoquinone; chrome iron brown; chrome orange; chr-ome yellow; chromic acid; chromium oxide; chromium

sulphate, basic; montanic acid; Pigment Green 18; Pigment Red 104; potassium dichromate; strontium chromate
Uses: aluminium/magnesium chromatising treatments; corrosion inhibitor (industrial water treatment)

sodium dicyanamide
sodium dicyandiamide; [1934-75-4]

$$Na^+ \quad {}^-N(CN)_2$$

$C_2N_3Na_1$. M: 89.03.
Production:
- cyanamide + cyanogen chloride + sodium hydroxide (dehydrochlorination/salt formation)
Derivatives: chlorhexidine

sodium diethyldithiocarbamate
NADEC; SDEC; SED; [148-18-5]

$$\underset{(C_2H_5)_2NCS^-}{\overset{S}{\|}} \quad Na^+$$

$C_5H_{10}N_1Na_1S_2$. M: 171.26. Greenish-yellow liquid with a characteristic smell comprising a 23% solution in water. d: 1.07 kg/l (20°C).
Production:
- diethylamine + carbon disulphide + sodium hydroxide (addition/salt formation)
Derivatives:
cadmium diethyldithiocarbamate; tetraethylthiuram disulphide; zinc diethyldithiocarbamate
Uses: flotation collector; preservative (natural rubber latex); copper separation agent

sodium *O,O*-diethyl dithiophosphate
sodium diethyl dithiophosphate

$$\underset{(C_2H_5O)_2PS^-}{\overset{S}{\|}} \quad Na^+$$

$C_4H_{10}Na_1O_2P_1S_2$. M: 208.21.
Production:
- *O,O*-diethyl dithiophosphoric acid + sodium hydroxide (sodium salt formation)
Uses: flotation collector (sulphide ores)

sodium di-(2-ethylhexyl)sulphosuccinate
dioctyl sodium sulphosuccinate; sodium dioctylsulphosuccinate; DSS; Aerosol OT (American Cyanamid); [577-11-7]

$$\begin{array}{c} C_2H_5 \quad \overset{O}{\|} \\ CH_3(CH_2)_3CHCH_2OCCH_2 \\ CH_3(CH_2)_3CHCH_2OCCHSO_3^- \quad Na^+ \\ \underset{C_2H_5}{\quad} \quad \underset{O}{\|} \end{array}$$

$C_{20}H_{37}Na_1O_7S_1$. M: 444.56.
Production:
- di-(2-ethylhexyl) maleate + sodium bisulphite (sulphonation)

Uses: pigments/fillers/clay dispersant; emulsifier (emulsion polymerisation, food products); flotation collector; sugar processing aid; wetting agent (polyvinyl acetate adhesives, solvent-based products)

sodium dihexylsulphosuccinate
dihexyl sodium sulphosuccinate (CTFA); sodium di-(2-methylpentyl)sulphosuccinate

$$\begin{array}{c} \overset{O}{\|} \\ C_6H_{13}OCCH_2 \\ C_6H_{13}OCCHSO_3^- \quad Na^+ \\ \underset{O}{\|} \end{array}$$

$C_{16}H_{29}Na_1O_7S_1$. M: 388.45. Available commercially as a 60–80% solution in water.
Production:
- methyl isobutyl carbinol + maleic anhydride + sodium bisulphite (esterification/sulphonation)
Uses:
emulsifier/dispersant (emulsion polymerisation, wax, polish, hand cleaners); leaching/electroplating additive; photographic chemical; pigment dispersant; wetting/penetrating agent (glass cleaners, paint strippers, batteries)

sodium dihydroxyethylglycine
bicine; *N,N*-bis(2-hydroxyethyl)glycine, sodium salt; DHEG; [139-41-3]

$$(HOCH_2CH_2)_2NCH_2COO^- \quad Na^+$$

$C_6H_{12}N_1Na_1O_4$. M: 185.17. Available as a solution in water.
Production:
- formaldehyde + diethanolamine + hydrogen cyanide + sodium hydroxide (cyanomethylation/nitrile hydrolysis)
Uses: chelating agent/sequestrant

sodium *O,O*-diisoamyl dithiophosphate
sodium diisoamyl dithiophosphate; Aerofloat 3501 (American Cyanamid);

$$\left[(CH_3)_2CHCH_2CH_2O\right]_2\overset{S}{\underset{\|}{P}}S^- \quad Na^+$$

$C_{10}H_{22}Na_1O_2P_1S_2$. M: 292.38.
Production:
- isoamyl alcohol + phosphorus pentasulphide + sodium hydroxide (condensation)
Uses: flotation collector (sulphide ores)

sodium *O,O*-diisobutyl dithiophosphate
sodium diisobutyl dithiophosphate; Aerofloat 3477 (American Cyanamid)

$$\left[(CH_3)_2CHCH_2O\right]_2\overset{S}{\underset{\|}{P}}S^- \quad Na^+$$

$C_8H_{18}Na_1O_2P_1S_2$. M: 264.32.

Production:
- isobutanol + phosphorus pentasulphide + sodium hydroxide (addition/neutralisation)

Uses:
flotation collector (sulphide ores)

sodium diisobutylsulphosuccinate

diisobutyl sodium sulphosuccinate (CTFA); Aerosol IB (American Cyanamid); [127-39-9]

(CH₃)₂CHCH₂OCCH₂
(CH₃)₂CHCH₂OCCHSO₃⁻ Na⁺

$C_{12}H_{21}Na_1O_7S_1$. M: 332.34. Available commercially as a 45% solution in water.

Production:
- isobutanol + maleic anhydride + sodium bisulphite (esterification/sulphonation)

Uses: wetting agent (metal leaching, electroplating)

sodium diisooctylsulphosuccinate

C₇H₁₅CH₂OCCH₂
C₇H₁₅CH₂OCCHSO₃⁻ Na⁺

$C_{20}H_{37}Na_1O_7S_1$. M: 444.56. Available commercially as pure wax or as a 60–70% solution in alcohol/water or propylene glycol/water mixtures.

Production:
- isooctanol + maleic anhydride + sodium bisulphite (esterification/sulphonation)

Uses: plastics mould release agent; wetting agent (dust laying, pesticides, firefighting foams, textile processing, dry cleaning); wetting/penetrating agent (paper strippers, glass cleaners, solder fluxes); pigment dispersant (lacquers, paints, plastics);

sodium O,O-diisopropyl dithiophosphate

sodium diisopropyl dithiophosphate; Aerofloat 211 (American Cyanamid);

[(CH₃)₂CHO]₂PS⁻ Na⁺

$C_6H_{14}Na_1O_2P_1S_2$. M: 236.27.

Production:
- isopropanol + phosphorus pentasulphide + sodium hydroxide (condensation)

Uses: flotation collector (sulphide ores)

sodium diisopropylnaphthalene sulphonate

[(CH₃)₂CH]₂ — SO₃⁻ Na⁺

$C_{16}H_{19}Na_1O_3S_1$. M: 314.38. Available commercially as a powder containing 70–75% active matter.

Production:
- diisopropylnaphthalene (sulphonation/sodium salt formation)

Uses: emulsifier/dispersant (emulsion polymerisation, paints); solubiliser/wetting agent (pesticides, hard-surface cleaners, metal cleaners)

sodium O,O-di-(methylamyl) dithiophosphate

sodium di-(methylamyl) dithiophosphate; Aerofloat 249 (American Cyanamid)

[(CH₃)₂CHCH₂CHO]₂PS⁻ Na⁺

$C_{12}H_{26}Na_1O_2P_1S_2$. M: 320.43.

Production:
- phosphorus pentasulphide + methyl isobutyl carbinol + sodium hydroxide (condensation)

Uses: flotation collector (sulphide ores)

sodium dimethylarsinate *See:* sodium cacodylate

sodium dimethyldithiocarbamate

SDDC; [128-04-1]

(CH₃)₂NCS⁻ Na⁺

$C_3H_6N_1Na_1S_2$. M: 143.21. Pale greenish-yellow aqueous solution containing 40% active matter. d: 1.18 kg/l (20°C). Soluble in water.

Production:
- dimethylamine + carbon disulphide + sodium hydroxide (thiocarbonylation/salt formation)

Derivatives: bismuth dimethyldithiocarbamate; copper dimethyldithiocarbamate; ferbam; lead dimethyldithiocarbamate; tetramethylthiuram disulphide; tetramethylthiuram monosulphide; zinc dimethyldithiocarbamate

Uses: biocide (water treatment, paper sizing, adhesives, cutting fluids); termination agent (styrene-butadiene rubber production); vulcanisation accelerator

sodium dinaphthalenemethane sulphonate

naphthalene-formaldehyde sulphonate dimer; sodium methylene dinaphthalene sulphonate;

$C_{21}H_{14}Na_2O_6S_2$. M: 472.45. See also sodium polynaphthalenemethane sulphonate.

Production:
- naphthalene + formaldehyde (carbonyl condensation/sulphonation/sodium salt formation)

Uses: concrete/mortar plasticisers; dispersant/stabiliser (latices, pesticides); wetting agent (cotton, rayon)

sodium dioctylsulphosuccinate
See: sodium di-(2-ethylhexyl)sulphosuccinate

sodium dithionite *See:* sodium hydrosulphite

sodium diuranate *See:* yellow cake

sodium dodecylbenzenesulphonate
sodium alkylbenzenesulphonate, branched; [25155-30-0]

$$C_{12}H_{25}\text{—}\boxed{}\text{—}SO_3^- \quad Na^+$$

$C_{18}H_{29}Na_1O_3S_1$. M: 348.48. Available commercially as a white paste containing 62% active matter.
Production:
• dodecylbenzenesulphonic acid, branched + sodium hydroxide/sodium carbonate (salt formation)
Uses: laundry detergents (underdeveloped countries); emulsifier (emulsion polymerisation, metalworking fluids); surfactant/emulsifier (pesticides, textiles); cement admixture;

sodium *n*-dodecyl sulphate
See: sodium lauryl sulphate

sodium erythorbate
sodium isoascorbate; [6381-77-7]

$$\begin{array}{c} CH_2OH \\ | \\ HOCH \\ | \\ HCOH \\ | \\ COH \\ || \\ COH \\ | \\ COO^- \quad Na^+ \end{array}$$

$C_6H_9Na_1O_7$. M: 216.12. White, crystalline solid. Soluble in water forming alkaline solutions.
Production:
• isoascorbic acid + sodium hydroxide (salt formation)
Uses: food antioxidant

sodium ethoxide
sodium ethylate; [141-52-6]

$$C_2H_5O^- \quad Na^+$$

$C_2H_5Na_1O_1$. M: 68.05. Hygroscopic, white or pale yellow powder. Decomposes in water. Soluble in alcohol.
Production:
• ethanol + sodium (salt formation)
Derivatives: benzil diethyl acetal; 2,5-diethoxyaniline; triethyl orthoacetate; triethyl orthoformate
Uses: esterification/condensation catalyst; ethoxylation/acetoacetic ester synthesis reagent

sodium 2-ethylhexyl sulphate
sodium octyl sulphate (CTFA)
$C_8H_{17}Na_1O_4S_1$. M: 232.28. Available commercially as a 40% solution in water.

$$\begin{array}{c} C_2H_5 \\ | \\ CH_3(CH_2)_3CHCH_2OSO_3^- \quad Na^+ \end{array}$$

Production:
• 2-ethylhexanol (sulphation/sodium salt formation)
Uses: electroplating bath additive; wetting agent (alkaline textile processing aids, industrial cleaners)

sodium ferrocyanide
yellow prussiate of soda; [13601-19-9]

$$Na_4Fe(CN)_6$$

$C_6Fe_1N_6Na_4$. M: 303.92. Available as the decahydrate. Pale yellow crystals. d: 1.46 kg/l. Loses water on heating above 50°C. Solubility in water: 318 g/l (20°C).
Production:
• sodium cyanide + ferrous sulphate (complex formation)
• calcium ferrocyanide + sodium carbonate (salt formation)
Derivatives:
Prussian Blue
Uses: flotation depressant (copper ores); heavy metal scavenger; photographic oxidising/fixing agent; anticaking agent (table salt); CFA pigment formation reagent

sodium fluoborate
sodium fluoroborate

$$NaBF_4$$

$B_1F_4Na_1$. M: 109.79. White, crystalline solid. MP: 384°C with some decomposition. d: 2.47 kg/l (20°C). Soluble in water.
Production:
• sodium carbonate + fluoboric acid (salt formation)
Uses: electroplating/fluorination reagent

sodium fluoride
[7681-49-4]

$$NaF$$

F_1Na_1. M: 41.99. White powder. MP: 992–993°C. d: 2.8 kg/l. Solubility in water: 42 g/l water (10°C). Slightly soluble in alcohol.
Production:
• sodium hydroxide + hydrofluoric acid (salt formation)
• sodium hydroxide + hexafluorosilicic acid (reaction)
Derivatives:
3-chloro-4-fluoroaniline; 3-chloro-2-hydroxy-5-trifluoromethylpyridine; fentin fluoride; fluroxypyr-1-methylheptyl; sodium fluorophosphate; sulphur tetrafluoride; tributyltin fluoride
Uses: case hardening salts; electroplating bath ingredient; industrial cleaning reagent; insecticide/timber preservative; enamels/glass; steel degassing reagent; fluoridation agent (drinking water treatment)

sodium fluoroacetate
Compound 1080; [62-74-8]

$$FCH_2COO^- \quad Na^+$$

$C_2H_2F_1Na_1O_2$. M: 100.03. White, hygroscopic powder.
MP: 200–202°C with decomposition. Soluble in water.
Slightly soluble in oxygenated solvents.
Production:
• methyl chloroacetate + potassium fluoride +
  sodium hydroxide (fluorination/saponification)
Derivatives:
fluoroacetamide
Uses: rodenticide

sodium fluorophosphate
disodium fluorophosphate; sodium monofluorophosph-
ate; [10163-15-2]

$$\overset{O}{\underset{\|}{FP}}(O^- \quad Na^+)_2$$

$F_1Na_2O_3P_1$. M: 143.95. Colourless crystals. MP: 625°C.
Solubility in water: 250 g/l water.
Production:
• sodium hexametaphosphate + sodium fluoride (salt
  formation)
Uses: anticaries additive (toothpaste)

sodium fluorosilicate
See: sodium hexafluorosilicate

sodium formaldehyde hydrosulphite
See: sodium formaldehyde sulphoxylate

sodium formaldehyde sulphoxylate
sodium formaldehyde hydrosulphite; sodium hydroxy-
methanesulphinate; sodium sulphoxylate; SFS;
[149-44-0]

$$HOCH_2SO_2^- \quad Na^+$$

$C_1H_3Na_1O_3S_1$. M: 118.08. Available as the dihydrate.
White, crystalline solid. MP: 63–64°C. Decomposes
on further heating. Soluble in water. Insoluble in most
organic solvents.
Production:
• formaldehyde + sodium hydrosulphite + sodium
  hydroxide (reaction)
• formaldehyde + sulphur dioxide, pure + sodium
  hydroxide + zinc (zinc hydrosulphite process)
Uses:
redox activator (styrene-butadiene rubber production);
vat dye reducing agent

sodium formate
[141-53-7]

$$HCOO^- \quad Na^+$$

$C_1H_1Na_1O_2$. M: 68.01.

Production:
• sodium hydroxide + synthesis gas (base-catalysed
  carbonylation)
• acetaldehyde + formaldehyde (aldol condensation/
  Cannizzaro reaction; byproduct of pentaerythritol
  production)
• n-butyraldehyde + formaldehyde (aldol
  condensation/Cannizzaro reaction; byproduct of
  trimethylolpropane production)
• isobutyraldehyde + formaldehyde (aldol
  condensation/Cannizzaro reaction; byproduct of
  neopentyl glycol production)
• isobutyraldehyde + formaldehyde (condensation/
  Cannizzaro reaction; byproduct of neopentyl glycol
  monohydroxypivalate production)
Derivatives:
Basic Red 12; formic acid; sodium hydrosulphite
Uses: pH control/reducing agent (dyeing, electroplating,
pickling baths); silage fermentation additive; tanning/
textile dyeing and printing auxiliary

sodium glucoheptonate

$$HOCH_2(CHOH)_5COO^- \quad Na^+$$

$C_7H_{13}Na_1O_8$. M: 248.16.
Production:
• starch hydrolysate + sodium cyanide (cyanohydrin
  formation/nitrile hydrolysis)
Uses: chelation agent (dairy cleaners, bottle cleaners);
aluminium etchant ingredient

sodium gluconate
[527-07-1]

$$HOCH_2(CHOH)_4COO^- \quad Na^+$$

$C_6H_{11}Na_1O_7$. M: 218.14. White, crystalline powder. Solubility in water: 590 g/l (25°C).
Production:
• starch hydrolysate + *Aspergillus niger* mould
  (anaerobic fermentation)
Derivatives: calcium gluconate; gluconic acid; glucono-
lactone; magnesium gluconate; potassium gluconate
Uses: chelating agent/sequestrant (metal plating, de-
rusting, bottlewashing formulations)

sodium glutamate *See:* monosodium glutamate

sodium 5′-guanylate
disodium guanosine-5′-monophosphate; GMP;
[550-12-9]

$C_{10}H_{12}N_5Na_2O_8P_1$. M: 407.18.

Production:
- nucleic acids + *Penicillium citrium* mould (microbial cleavage; coproduced with sodium 5′-inosate)

Uses: flavour enhancer

sodium hexafluorosilicate
sodium fluorosilicate; sodium fluosilicate; sodium silicofluoride; [16893-85-9]

Na_2SiF_6

$F_6Na_2Si_1$. M: 188.06. White, crystalline powder. Decomposes on heating to red heat. d: 2.68 kg/l. Slightly soluble in water.

Production:
- sodium chloride, natural + hexafluorosilicic acid (salt formation)

Uses: water fluoridation agent; gelling agent (moulded latex foam); aluminium etchant ingredient; glass/frits/enamel raw material; soil insecticide

sodium hexametaphosphate
sodium polyphosphate; HMP; Calgon (Calgon); [68915-31-1]

$Na_2O.(NaPO_3)_n$

n = ~12. Available commercially as glassy chips or as white granules or powder. Bulk density: 1.3 kg/l (chips/powder), 0.9 kg/l (granules). Soluble in water with gradual hydrolysis at temperatures above 40°C.

Production:
- sodium hydroxide/sodium carbonate + phosphoric acid, pure (salt formation/thermal dehydration)

Derivatives:
sodium fluorophosphate

Uses: binder (refractory brinks, tiles); clay deflocculant (paper coatings, paint, ceramics); dispersant/sequesterant (boiler/drinking water treatment); bottle washing formulations; laundry rinse auxiliary; milk scale control agent (dairies, ice-cream processing equipment); reagent (pretanning/Liritan tanning process); stabiliser (jams, preserves, canned vegetables, processed meat); textile scouring/Kier boiling agent

sodium hydride
[7646-69-7]

NaH

H_1Na_1. M: 24.00. Greyish-white powder. Decomposes when heated strongly. Decomposed by water releasing hydrogen.

Production:
- sodium + hydrogen (reaction)

Derivatives:
sodium borohydride

Uses: scale prevention agent (metal processing); condensation catalyst

sodium hydrosulphide
sodium bisulphide; sodium hydrogen sulphide; sodium sulphydrate; [16721-80-5]

NaSH

$H_1Na_1S_1$. M: 56.06. Available commercially as flakes containing 71% active matter or as a pale yellow, 35% solution in water.

Production:
- sodium hydroxide + hydrogen sulphide (reaction)

Derivatives:
allyl mercaptan; benzyl mercaptan; 1,3-dimercaptoisopropyldimethylamine; 2,2′-dithiodibenzoic acid; kadethrinic acid; 2-mercaptoethylamine hydrochloride; Pigment Red 88; stearyl mercaptan; taurine; thioglycerol; thioglycollic acid; thiosalicylic acid; Vat Blue 30

Uses: skin/hide depilatory; flotation depressant (copper ores); dyestuffs processing reagent; viscose desulphurisation agent

sodium hydrosulphite
sodium dithionite; [7775-14-6]

$Na_2S_2O_4$

$Na_2O_4S_2$. M: 174.11. White, crystalline powder. MP: 55°C with decomposition. Soluble in water.

Production:
- sodium hydroxide + sulphur dioxide, pure + zinc (zinc process)
- sodium hydroxide + sulphur dioxide, pure + sodium formate (formate process)
- sodium hydroxide + sulphur dioxide, pure + sodium amalgam (amalgam process)
- sodium hydroxide + sulphur dioxide, pure + sodium borohydride (borohydride reduction process)

Derivatives: sodium formaldehyde sulphoxylate

Uses:
chromium removal reagent (effluent treatment); bleaching agent (clay, textile processing, sugar production, pulp/paper production); photographic developer ingredient; polymerisation termination agent (styrene-butadiene rubber production); vat dye reducing agent

sodium hydroxide
caustic soda; lye; [1310-73-2]

NaOH

$H_1Na_1O_1$. M: 40.00. Available commercially as a white, fused solid, flakes or beads. MP: 315°C. d: 2.12 kg/l (25°C). Solubility in water: 1,140 g/kg solution (25°C). Soluble in methanol. Also available as a colourless solution containing 50% active matter. BP: 144°C. FP: 13–16°C. d: 1.53 kg/l (20°C).

Production:
- sodium chloride, natural (mercury cell electrolysis; coproduced with chlorine)

- sodium chloride, natural (diaphram cell electrolysis; coproduced with chlorine)
- sodium chloride, natural (membrane cell electrolysis; coproduced with chlorine)
- trona + calcium oxide (salt formation)

Derivatives: acrylamide-sodium acrylate copolymers; alkali cellulose; alumina trihydrate; aluminium hydroxide gel; antimony pentasulphide; benzyltrimethylammonium hydroxide; bismuth oxide; cobalt hydroxide; copper hydroxide; diethylenetriaminepentaacetic acid, pentasodium salt; disodium acid pyrophosphate; disodium methylarsonate; disodium phosphate; endothal-sodium; ethylenediaminetetraacetic acid, calcium disodium salt; ethylenediaminetetraacetic acid, disodium salt; ethylenediaminetetraacetic acid, sodium ferric salt; ethylenediaminetetraacetic acid, tetrasodium salt; glycerol; hydroxyethylethylenediaminetriacetic acid, trisodium salt; iodoform; iron oxide, transparent; iron oxide black; iron oxide red; iron oxide yellow; MCPB-sodium; mercuric oxide, yellow; metam-sodium; monosodium glutamate; monosodium methylarsonate; monosodium phosphate; nabam; 10,10'-oxybisphenoxyarsine; phosphine; rare earth oxide, hydrate; Rhenania phosphate; sodium acetate; sodium alginate; sodium alkylbenzenesulphonate, linear; sodium aluminate; sodium aluminium phosphate; sodium ascorbate; sodium benzoate; sodium bisulphite; sodium bromide; sodium cacodylate; sodium caseinate; sodium chlorite; sodium chloroacetate; sodium 2-chloroethanesulphonate; sodium citrate; sodium cyanide; sodium cyclamate; sodium *O,O*-di-*s*-butyl dithiophosphate; sodium dicyanamide; sodium diethyldithiocarbamate; sodium *O,O*-diethyl dithiophosphate; sodium dihydroxyethylglycine; sodium *O,O*-diisoamyl dithiophosphate; sodium *O,O*-diisobutyl dithiophosphate; sodium *O,O*-diisopropyl dithiophosphate; sodium *O,O*-di-(methylamyl) dithiophosphate; sodium dimethyldithiocarbamate; sodium dodecylbenzenesulphonate; sodium erythorbate; sodium fluoride; sodium fluoroacetate; sodium formaldehyde sulphoxylate; sodium formate; sodium hexametaphosphate; sodium hydrosulphide; sodium hydrosulphite; sodium *N*-hydroxyethylglycine; sodium hypochlorite; sodium hypophosphite; sodium iodide; sodium isobutyl xanthate; sodium isopropyl xanthate; sodium lactate; sodium lignosulphonate; sodium 2-mercaptobenzothiazole; sodium metabisulphite; sodium molybdate; sodium nitrate; sodium nitrite; sodium oleate; sodium oxalate; sodium pentachlorophenate; sodium persulphate; sodium *o*-phenylphenate; sodium picramate; sodium polyacrylate, crosslinked; sodium polyaldehydocarboxylate; sodium propionate; sodium rosinate; sodium saccharin; sodium sarcosinate; sodium selenite; sodium silicate; sodium stannate; sodium stearate; sodium stearoyl-2-lactylate; sodium succinate; sodium sulphite; sodium sulphoisophthalic acid; sodium tallate; sodium thiocyanate; sodium thioglycollate; sodium trichloroacetate; sodium tungstate; sodium xylene sulphonate; stannous oxide; starch,

sodium xanthate; 2,3,6-TBA-sodium; tetrasodium pyrophosphate; thorium dioxide; tri-*n*-butyltin oxide; trisodium nitrilotriacetate; trisodium phosphate; zeolite A
Uses:
vegetable oil alkali-refining reagent; industrial cleaner ingredient; ion-exchange resin regeneration; soap raw material; aluminium/zirconium extraction agent; paint/varnish stripping; pH control (paper production, ore/chemical processing); reagent (petroleum desulphurisation); sodium salt formation agent

sodium *N*-hydroxyethylglycine

$$HOCH_2CH_2NHCH_2COO^- \quad Na^+$$

$C_4H_8N_1Na_1O_3$. M: 141.10.
Production:
- monoethanolamine + formaldehyde + hydrogen cyanide + sodium hydroxide (cyanomethylation/nitrile hydrolysis)
Uses: chelating agent

sodium hypochlorite
[7681-52-9]

$$NaOCl$$

$Cl_1Na_1O_1$. M: 74.44. Pale green, aqueous solution containing 12–14% available chlorine for commercial use or ~5% for household use.
Production:
- sodium hydroxide + chlorine (reaction)
Derivatives: calcium hypochlorite; chloral; chloramine-B; chloramine-T; chloroazodin; *o*-chlorophenol; 1,1-dimethylhydrazine; 4,4'-dinitrostilbene-2,2'-disulphonic acid; ethanesulphonyl chloride; ethylene chlorohydrin; hexanitrostilbene; hydrazine; isatoic anhydride; lithium hypochlorite; methanesulphonic acid; 5-nitroanthranilic acid; propiconazole; sodium dichloroisocyanurate; sodium saccharin; starch, oxidised; 2-thenoic acid; trisodium phosphate, chlorinated
Uses: disinfectant (cleaners, water treatment); household/textile bleach; reagent (Hofmann degradation, oxidation, reduction)

sodium hypophosphite
[7681-53-0]

$$NaH_2PO_2$$

$H_2Na_1O_2P_1$. M: 87.98. White, deliquescent granules. Decomposes with release of phosphine when heated to high temperature. Soluble in water.
Production:
- sodium hydroxide + phosphorus (salt formation)
Uses: electrodeless nickel plating reagent

sodium 5'-inosate
disodium inosine-5'-monophosphate; IMP; [4691-65-0]
$C_{10}H_{11}N_4Na_2O_8P_1$. M: 392.17.

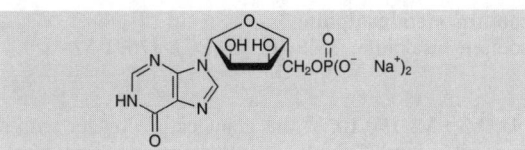

Production:
• nucleic acids + *Penicillium citrium* mould (micro-bial cleavage; coproduced with sodium 5′-guanylate)
Uses: flavour enhancer

sodium iodate
[7681-55-2]

$$NaIO_3$$

$I_1Na_1O_3$. M: 197.89. White crystals. Decomposes on heating. d: 4.2 kg/l. Solubility in water: 90 g/l water (20°C).
Production:
• sodium chlorate + iodine (metathesis)
Uses: antiseptic/disinfectant

sodium iodate liquor
Production:
• caliche ore (Guggenheim process; coproduced with sodium nitrate/potassium nitrate)
Derivatives: iodine

sodium iodide
[7681-82-5]

$$NaI$$

I_1Na_1. M: 149.89. White, hygroscopic, crystalline solid. Discoloured by air. MP: 651°C. d: 3.67 kg/l (25°C). Solubility in water: 3.0 kg/l water (0°C).
Production:
• sodium hydroxide/sodium carbonate + hydriodic acid (salt formation)
Derivatives: dipyridamole; methyl iodide
Uses: expectorant drug; animal feed supplement; iodin-ation reagent

sodium isethionate
sodium 2-hydroxyethanesulphonate; [1562-00-1]

$$HOCH_2CH_2SO_3^-\ Na^+$$

$C_2H_5Na_1O_4S_1$. M: 148.11.
Production:
• ethylene oxide + sodium bisulphite (epoxidation)
Derivatives: sodium cocoyl isethionate
Uses: dyestuffs intermediate (Remazol dyes)

sodium isoascorbate *See:* sodium erythorbate

sodium isobutyl xanthate
SIBX
$C_5H_9Na_1O_1S_2$. M: 172.24.

$$(CH_3)_2CHCH_2OCS^-\ Na^+$$

Production:
• isobutanol + carbon disulphide + sodium hydroxide (condensation)
Uses: flotation collector (sulphide ores)

sodium isopropyl xanthate
SIPX; [140-93-2]

$$(CH_3)_2CHOCS^-\ Na^+$$

$C_4H_7Na_1O_1S_2$. M: 158.22.
Production:
• isopropanol + carbon disulphide + sodium hydroxide (condensation)
Derivatives: N-ethyl O-isopropyl thionocarbamate; zinc isopropyl xanthate
Uses: flotation collector (sulphide ores); vulcanisation accelerator

sodium lactate
E325 (EC); [72-17-3]

$$CH_3CHCOO^-\ Na^+$$

$C_3H_5Na_1O_3$. M: 112.06. Colourless, hygroscopic, viscous liquid containing 20–30% water. Soluble in water.
Production:
• DL-lactic acid + sodium hydroxide (salt formation)
Uses: humectant (cheese, spreads, confectionery); cas-ein plasticiser

sodium lauroyl sarcosinate
sodium N-lauroyl sarcosinate

$$CH_3(CH_2)_{10}CNCH_2COO^-\ Na^+$$

$C_{15}H_{28}N_1Na_1O_3$. M: 293.38. Available commercially as a pure, white powder or as a 35% solution in water. The product displays corrosion inhibition, enzyme inhibition and bacteriostatic properties. See also lauroyl sarcosine.
Production:
• lauric acid, narrow cut + sodium sarcosinate (amide formation)
Uses: surfactant/foaming agent (liquid soap, shampoos, toothpastes)

sodium lauryl ether sulphate
sodium laureth sulphate (CTFA)

$$CH_3(CH_2)_{11}(OCH_2CH_2)_nOSO_3^-\ Na^+$$

n = 2–3. Yellow liquid or paste available as a 28–70% solution in water.

Production:
- *n*-alkanol(C_{12}-C_{13}) ethoxylates/*n*-alkanol(C_{12}-C_{14}) ethoxylates/*n*-alkanol(C_{12}-C_{15}) ethoxylates/*n*-alkanol(C_{13}-C_{15}) ethoxylates (sulphation/sodium salt formation)

Uses: emulsifier (emulsion polymerisation); surfactant (light-duty liquid cleaners, dishwashing detergents, shampoo, bubble bath, car shampoos); textile auxiliary; dispersant (plasterboard production); concrete air-entrainment agents

sodium lauryl sulphate
sodium *n*-dodecyl sulphate; SDS; [151-21-3]

$$CH_3(CH_2)_{11}OSO_3^-\ \ Na^+$$

n = 12–18. $C_{12}H_{25}Na_1O_4S_1$. M: 288.38. White powders containing 90% active matter, pastes containing 40–50% active matter, or aqueous solutions with <30% active matter.

Production:
- lauryl alcohol, narrow-cut/*n*-alkanol(C_{12}-C_{13})/*n*-alkanol(C_{12}-C_{14}) (sulphation/sodium salt formation)

Uses:
emulsifier (emulsion polymerisation, water-based paints, printing inks); flotation collector; foaming agent (foamed rubber/carpetbacking latex); foaming/wetting agent (toothpaste, shampoo, toiletries, carpet shampoos); low-temperature surfactant (light-duty liquids, hand cleaners, textile processing); wetting agent (pesticides, electroplating, toiletries)

sodium lignosulphonate
sodium lignin sulphonate; [8061-51-6]
Brown powder containing 70–80% lignosulphonates. Soluble in water.

Production:
- sulphite pulp waste liquor + sodium hydroxide (salt formation/separation)

Uses:
dispersant (mineral flotation, electrolytic refining, disperse dyes); emulsifier/protective colloid (emulsion polymerisation); boiler/evaporator water treatment; leather tanning auxiliary

sodium 2-mercaptobenzothiazole
sodium mercaptobenzothiazole; NaMBT

$C_7H_4N_1Na_1S_2$. M: 189.24. Available commercially as a 50% solution in water.

Production:
- 2-mercaptobenzothiazole + sodium hydroxide (neutralisation)

Uses: corrosion inhibitor (antifreeze, hydraulic fluid, coolants); flotation collector; biocide (adhesives, textiles, paper, rubber, wax)

sodium metabisulphite
sodium bisulphite; SMS; E223 (EC); [7681-57-4]

$$Na_2S_2O_5$$

$Na_2O_5S_2$. M: 190.10. White granules or powder with a pungent odour. Soluble in water forming acidic solutions. Slightly soluble in oxygenated solvents.

Production:
- sodium hydroxide + sulphur dioxide, pure (salt formation)

Uses: dechlorination reagent (drinking water, effluent); flotation depressant; food preservative (dried fruit, dried vegetables, meat, soups, sauces); preservative (photographic developers); sterilising agent (beer, wine, vinegar, glucose syrup)

sodium metaborate
[7775-19-1]

$$Na_2O.B_2O_3$$

$B_1Na_1O_2$. M: 65.80. Available commercially as the tetrahydrate or octahydrate. White granules. Dissolve in their water of crystallisation at 55°C. Soluble in water.

Production:
- sodium borate + sodium carbonate (salt formation)

Uses: herbicide; detergent/cleanser ingredient; photographic chemical; starch viscosifier

sodium metaphosphate, insoluble
Maddrell's salt; IMP

$$[NaPO_3]_n$$

White powder. Insoluble in water.

Production:
- monosodium phosphate (dehydration)

Uses: abrasive/thickening agent (toothpaste)

sodium metasilicate
[6834-92-0]

$$Na_2SiO_3$$

$Na_2O_3Si_1$. M: 122.07. Available as the anhydrous or pentahydrate salts. White granules. Soluble in water forming alkaline solutions.

Production:
- sodium carbonate + quartz (furnace process)

Derivatives: mullite

Uses: detergent builder (automatic dishwasher powders, household cleaners); stabiliser (peroxide bleaches)

sodium methallyl sulphonate
[1561-92-8]

$$CH_2{=}CCH_2SO_3^-\ \ Na^+$$
$$\qquad\quad |$$
$$\qquad\quad CH_3$$

$C_4H_7Na_1O_3S_1$. M: 158.15. Available commercially as pure powder or as a 25% solution in water.

Production:
• isobutylene (sulphonation/sodium salt formation)
Derivatives:
2-acrylamido-2-methylpropanesulphonic acid
Uses:
dyeable polyacrylonitrile/polyvinyl acetate comonomer

sodium methanearsonate
See: monosodium methylarsonate

sodium methoxide
sodium methylate; [124-41-0]

$$CH_3O^- \quad Na^+$$

$C_1H_3Na_1O_1$. M: 54.02. White powder. Decomposed by water. Soluble in alcohol. Also available as a 30% solution in methanol.
Production:
• methanol + sodium (salt formation)
Derivatives: benzil dimethyl acetal; chlomethoxyfen; Fluorescent Brightener 136; Fluorescent Brightener 162; Fluorescent Brightener 193; levomepromazine; sulfamethoxypyridazine; sulfametoxydiazine; sulfametrole; terbumeton; trimethyl orthoacetate; trimethyl orthoformate
Uses: Sol-gel glass process raw material; condensation/esterification/isomerisation/methoxylation reagent

sodium *N*-methyltaurate
methyltaurine, sodium salt; sodium 2-(methylamino)ethanesulphonate; [4316-74-9]

$$CH_3NHCH_2CH_2SO_3^- \quad Na^+$$

$C_3H_8N_1Na_1O_3S_1$. M: 161.15.
Production:
• methylamine + sodium 2-chloroethanesulphonate (amine formation)
Derivatives:
Fluorescent Brightener 86; Fluorescent Brightener 119; Fluorescent Brightener 193; sodium *N*-cocoyl-*N*-methyltaurate; sodium *N*-oleyl-*N*-methyltaurate; sodium tall oil *N*-methyltaurate
Uses: stabiliser (textile printing)

sodium molybdate
[7631-95-0]

$$Na_2MoO_4$$

$Mo_1Na_2O_4$. M: 205.92. Available commercially as anhydrous or dihydrate grades. The anhydrous product is in the form of white crystals. d: 3.28 kg/l. MP: 687°C. The dihydrate is also white crystals. These release water when heated to 100°C. Solubility in water: 562 g/l (0°C). Sodium molybdate is also sold as a 35% solution in water.
Production:
• sodium hydroxide + molybdenum trioxide (reaction)

Derivatives: phosphomolybdic acid; phosphomolybdotungstic acid; Pigment Red 104
Uses: corrosion inhibitor (cooling water systems, antifreeze, cutting fluids); metal surface treatments agent

sodium nitrate
soda nitre; E251 (EC); [7631-99-4]

$$NaNO_3$$

$N_1Na_1O_3$. M: 85.00. Colourless crystals or granular powder. MP: 308°C. d: 2.26 kg/l. Solubility in water: 730 g/l water (0°C). Slightly soluble in oxygenated solvents. Also available as an impure, fertiliser grade.
Production:
• sodium carbonate/sodium hydroxide + nitric acid (salt formation)
• caliche ore (Guggenheim process; coproduced with potassium nitrate/sodium iodate liquor)
Derivatives:
phenylmercuric nitrate, basic; potassium nitrate
Uses: glass/enamel/pottery production clarifying agent; fertiliser; aluminium etchant ingredient; preservative/colour fixative (cured meat, fish); tobacco burning aid

sodium nitrite
E250 (EC); [7632-00-0]

$$NaNO_2$$

$N_1Na_1O_2$. M: 69.00. White, hygroscopic granules or powder. MP: 271°C. Decomposes when heated further. Slowly oxidised by air. Soluble in water. Slightly soluble in oxygenated solvents.
Production:
• sodium hydroxide + nitric oxide (salt formation)
Derivatives:
4-aminoantipyrine; 2-amino-5-diethylaminotoluene; 2-amino-5-[*N*-ethyl-*N*-(2-hydroxyethyl)amino]toluene; 2-amino-5-[*N*-ethyl-*N*-(2-methoxyethyl)amino]toluene; Basic Brown 1; benzazimide; benzotriazole; *n*-butyl nitrite; ceftazidime; cymoxanil; diazodinitrophenol; dicyclohexylammonium nitrite; *N*,*N*-diethyl-*p*-phenylenediamine; 4,4'-difluorobenzophenone; 4,4'-dihydroxybenzophenone; dimefuron; *N*,*N*-dimethyl-*p*-nitrosoaniline; *N*,*N*'-dinitroso-*N*,*N*'-dimethylterephthalamide; *N*,*N*'-dinitrosopentamethylenetetramine; drazoxolon; ethyl 2-(2-aminothiazolyl)methoxyiminoacetate; ethyl diazoacetate; *N*-ethyl-*N*-(2-hydroxyethyl)-*p*-phenylenediamine; fluorobenzene; *p*-fluorotoluene; glisoxepide; hypoxanthine; isoamyl nitrite; isobutyl nitrite; molsidomine; *p*-nitrosophenol; oxabetrinil; oxadixyl; oxamyl; *p*-phenylazoaniline; phoxim; salazosulfapyridine; tetrazene; theobromine; theophylline; tolyltriazole
Uses: corrosion inhibitor (cooling water systems, metalworking fluids); phosphating accelerator; heat-treatment salts; photographic chemical; preservative/colour fixative (cured meat, fish); blowing agent; diazotisation/nitrosation/oxidation reagent; gold plating reagent

sodium nonanoyloxybenzene sulphonate
SNOBS

$C_{15}H_{21}Na_1O_5S_1$. M: 336.37.
Production:
- phenol + pelargonic acid (esterification/sulphonation/sodium salt formation)

Uses: bleach activator (laundry detergents)

sodium nonylphenol ether sulphate

n = 5–25. Available commercially as clear liquids containing 30–35% active matter in water.
Production:
- nonylphenol ethoxylates (sulphation/sodium salt formation)

Uses: emulsifier (emulsion polymerisation)

sodium oleate
[143-19-1]

$$CH_3(CH_2)_7CH = CH(CH_2)_7COO^- \quad Na^+$$

$C_{18}H_{33}Na_1O_2$. M: 304.45. White powder. MP: 232–235°C. Soluble in water and alcohol.
Production:
- oleic acid + sodium hydroxide (salt formation)

Derivatives: copper oleate; phenylmercuric oleate
Uses: emulsifier (styrene-butadiene latex production); flotation collector

sodium α-olefin(C_{14}-C_{16}) sulphonate

n = 9–11. Mixed product of alcohol/olefin sulfonates.
Production:
- α-olefins(C_{14}-C_{16}) + sulphur trioxide (sulphonation)

Uses: surfactant (household detergents, personal-care products)

sodium α-olefin(C_{15}-C_{18}) sulphonate
Hostapur OS (Hoechst)
n = 11–13. Mixed product containing alcohol and olefin sulfonates. Available as a powder or as a 40% solution in water.

Production:
- α-olefins(C_{16}-C_{18}) + sulphur trioxide (sulphonation)

Uses: high-foaming surfactant (upholstery, carpet cleaners); textile/leather conditioning agent

sodium N-oleyl-N-methyltaurate
sodium methyl oleoyl taurate (CTFA)

$C_{21}H_{40}N_1Na_1O_4S_1$. M: 425.61. Available commercially as a powder, slurry or solution in water containing 15–70% active matter.
Production:
- oleic acid + sodium N-methyltaurate (amide formation)

Uses: textile/dyeing auxiliaries

sodium oxalate
[62-76-0]

$$\begin{array}{l} COO^- \quad Na^+ \\ COO^- \quad Na^+ \end{array}$$

$C_2Na_2O_4$. M: 134.00. White crystals. d: 2.34 kg/l. MP: 250–270°C with decomposition. Solubility in water: 37 g/l (20°C).
Production:
- oxalic acid + sodium hydroxide (salt formation)

Derivatives:
ferrous oxalate; plutonium dioxide; stannous oxalate
Uses: textile/leather finishing agent

sodium pentachlorophenate
[131-52-2]

$C_6Cl_5Na_1O_1$. M: 288.32. White crystals. Solubility in water: 330 g/l.
Production:
- pentachlorophenol + sodium hydroxide (salt formation)

Uses: biocide/preservative (pulp, paper, leather, drilling mud, rubber latex, water-based paints)

sodium perborate

NaBO₃

$B_1Na_1O_3$. M: 81.80. Available as the monohydrate or tetrahydrate. The monohydrate is a white, crystalline solid with at least a 15% w/w active oxygen content. Solubility in water: 15 g/l (20°C). The tetrahydrate is a white, crystalline solid with at least a 10% w/w active oxygen content. Solubility in water: 25 g/l (20°C).
Production:
• sodium borate + sodium carbonate + hydrogen peroxide (fusion/peroxidation)
Uses:
hair bleach/cold waving ingredient; bactericide (mouthwashes); bleaching agent (laundry detergents, textile processing); dyestuffs oxidation reagent

sodium percarbonate
sodium carbonate peroxide; [4452-58-8]

Na₂CO₃.1.5H₂O₂

White, crystalline powder containing 14% w/w available oxygen. Liberates hydrogen peroxide in aqueous solution.
Production:
• sodium carbonate + hydrogen peroxide (dry/wet processes)
Uses: food bleach; bleaching agent (laundry detergents, textile processing); dyestuffs oxidation reagent

sodium perchlorate
[7601-89-0]

NaClO₄

$Cl_1Na_1O_4$. M: 122.44. White, deliquescent crystals. Decomposes on heating. Soluble in water.
Production:
• sodium chlorate (electrolysis)
• chlorine (Merck process)
Derivatives:
ammonium perchlorate; potassium perchlorate
Uses: oxidising agent (explosives)

sodium peroxide
[1313-60-6]

Na₂O₂

Na_2O_2. M: 77.98. Pale yellow granules. Soluble in water forming hydrogen peroxide and sodium hydroxide.
Production:
• sodium (air oxidation)
Derivatives: bis(4-*t*-butylcyclohexyl) peroxydicarbonate; bis(2-ethylhexyl) peroxydicarbonate
Uses: analytical reagent (mineral assay); reagent (precious metal, aluminothermic refining)

sodium persulphate
sodium peroxydisulphate; [7775-27-1]

Na₂S₂O₈

$Na_2O_8S_2$. M: 238.10. White, crystalline powder which decomposes on heating. Solubility in water: 700 g/l water (20°C) with gradual decomposition.
Production:
• sodium sulphate + sulphuric acid (membrane cell electrolysis)
• sodium hydroxide + ammonium persulphate (salt formation)
Derivatives: silver peroxide
Uses: etchant (printed circuit boards); photographic bleach bath component; bleaching agent (hair bleach formulations); polymerisation initiator

sodium petroleum sulphonate
mahogany oil; petroleum sulphonates, sodium salts; sodium naphtha sulphonate
'Natural', oil-soluble, mixed surfactants containing 61–63% sulphonates and with equivalent weights of 415–540 g.
Production:
• lubricant oils, distillates + oleum (wet refining process; coproduced with white oil)
Derivatives: petroleum sulphonates, alkali-earth salts
Uses: emulsifier/wetting agent (solvent-based cleaners, soluble cutting fluids); flotation collector

sodium *o*-phenylphenate
SOPP; E232 (EC); [132-27-4]

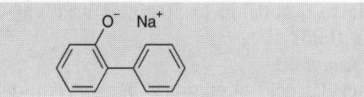

$C_{12}H_9Na_1O_1$. M: 192.19. Available commercially as the tetrahydrate. Off-white solid. d: 1.29 kg/l (20°C). Soluble in water and oxygenated solvents. Sparingly soluble in toluene and vegetable oils. Also available as aqueous solutions.
Production:
• *o*-phenylphenol + sodium hydroxide (salt formation)
Uses: disinfectant; biocide (adhesives, gums, latices, textiles, paper, hides, leather, timber)

sodium phosphate, dibasic *See:* disodium phosphate

sodium phosphate, monobasic
See: monosodium phosphate

sodium phosphate, tribasic
See: trisodium phosphate

sodium picramate
sodium 2-amino-4,6-dinitrophenolate; [96-91-3]
$C_6H_4N_3Na_1O_5$. M: 221.10.

Production:
- picric acid + sodium hydroxide (partial nitro reduction/salt formation)

Derivatives: diazodinitrophenol
Uses: dyestuffs intermediate

sodium polyacrylate

Pale yellow liquid comprising a 45% solution in water. d: 1.29 kg/l (20°C). Viscosity: 750 mPa.s (30°C). pH: 8–9 (5% solution).

Production:
- acrylic acid (solution polymerisation)

Uses:
cement grinding aid; pigments/fillers/clay dispersant (ceramics, paint, paper); film-forming agent (hairsprays); drilling-mud filtrate control agents; textile soil-release finishes; asbestos board/grinding wheel/ceramic paste binder; scale inhibitor (boiler water treatment); cotton textile sizing ingredient; thickening agent (food, toiletries, rug/fabric backing compounds)

sodium polyacrylate, crosslinked

Polymer usually held in a fibrous paper matrix. It is able to absorb up to 50 times its own weight in aqueous fluids.

Production:
- acrylic acid + ethylene bis(acrylamide) + sodium hydroxide (polymerisation)

Uses:
superabsorbent polymers (disposable nappies, sanitary towels, incontinence pads)

sodium polyaldehydocarboxylate

Production:
- acrolein + acrylic acid + sodium hydroxide (aqueous polymerisation)

Derivatives: sodium polyhydroxycarboxylate
Uses: detergent builder (household and industrial cleaners); pigment dispersant; scale inhibitor/sequestrant (water treatment, alkaline cleaners)

sodium polyhydroxycarboxylate

Production:
- sodium polyaldehydocarboxylate (Cannizzaro reaction)

Uses: scale inhibitor/sequestrant (water treatment)

sodium polynaphthalenemethane sulphonate

sodium naphthalene-formaldehyde sulphonate polymers; sodium polynaphthalene sulphonate

Available as a solution in water containing 40% active matter or as a >90% powder. See also sodium dinaphthalenemethane sulphonate.

Production:
- naphthalene + formaldehyde (carbonyl addition/ sulphonation)

Uses: concrete plasticisers; dispersant (synthetic latex production); milling/dispersing agent (pigments, dyes); synthetic tanning agents

sodium polyphosphate

See: sodium hexametaphosphate

sodium polystyrene sulphonate

poly(sodium styrenesulphonate); polystyrene, sulphonated; PSS; [9003-59-2]

Production:
- polystyrene, general-purpose (sulphonation/sodium salt formation)

Uses:
strongly anionic flocculants (water/effluent treatment)

sodium poly(vinyl sulphonate)

PSVS

Production:
- sodium vinyl sulphonate (emulsion polymerisation)

Uses: anionic flocculants (water treatment)

sodium propionate

E281 (EC); [137-40-6]

$C_3H_5Na_1O_2$. M: 96.06. Colourless, crystalline solid. Sol-

uble in water forming alkaline solutions. Slightly soluble in alcohol.
Production:
• propionic acid + sodium hydroxide (salt formation)
Uses: preservative (bread, bakery goods)

sodium 2-pyridinethiol-*N*-oxide
sodium Omadine (Olin); sodium pyrithione;
[3811-73-2]

$C_5H_4N_1Na_1O_1S_1$. M: 149.14. Available as powder or as a 40% solution in water.
Production:
• 2-chloropyridine + sodium sulphide + hydrogen peroxide (dehydrochlorination/oxidation)
Derivatives: zinc 2-pyridinethiol-*N*-oxide
Uses: biocide (metalworking fluids, latices)

sodium rhodanide *See:* sodium thiocyanate

sodium rosinate
rosin soap; sodium abietate; sodium resinate;
[14351-66-7]

$C_{20}H_{29}Na_1O_2$. M: 324.44. White powder. Slightly soluble in water. A mixed product, the main constituent of which is sodium abietate.
Production:
• rosin, tall oil/rosin, wood/rosin, gum + sodium hydroxide (salt formation)
Uses: emulsifier (emulsion polymerisation)

sodium saccharin
[128-44-9]; [6155-57-3]

$C_7H_4N_1Na_1O_3S_1$. M: 205.17. Available commercially as the dihydrate. White, crystalline powder or granules. Odourless. Intense sweet taste. Soluble in water.
Production:
• 2,2′-dithiodibenzoic acid + sodium hypochlorite + ammonia + sodium hydroxide (oxidation/amide formation/sulphonamide formation/sodium salt formation)
Derivatives: piroxicam

Uses: nickel plating brightening agent; antistatic agent (plastics, textiles); resin modifier/accelerator; sweetener (prepared foods, dentifrices, cosmetics, pharmaceuticals)

sodium salicylate
[54-21-7]

$C_7H_5Na_1O_3$. M: 160.11. White, crystalline powder. Solubility in water: 1.25 kg/l water (25°C). Soluble in oxygenated solvents.
Production:
• salicylic acid (sodium salt formation)
Uses: analgesic/antipyretic drug

sodium sarcosinate
sodium *N*-methylglycinate; [4316-73-8]

$$CH_3NHCH_2COO^- \quad Na^+$$

$C_3H_6N_1Na_1O_2$. M: 111.08. Available commercially as a 30–35% solution in water. Solutions are alkaline.
Production:
• sarcosine + sodium hydroxide (salt formation)
Derivatives: sodium lauroyl sarcosinate

sodium selenite
[10102-18-8]

$$Na_2SeO_3$$

$Na_2O_3Se_1$. M: 172.94. White crystals. Soluble in water.
Production:
• sodium hydroxide + selenium dioxide (salt formation)
Derivatives: cadmium red
Uses: glass raw material

sodium sesquicarbonate
[533-96-0]

$$Na_2CO_3.NaHCO_3$$

$C_2H_1Na_3O_6$. M: 189.99. Available commercially as the dihydrate. White needles. Decomposes on heating giving sodium carbonate. d: 2.11 kg/l. Bulk density: 0.87 kg/l. Soluble in water forming alkaline solutions. Trona is a natural form of sodium sesquicarbonate.
Production:
• trona (purification/crystallisation)
• sodium carbonate + sodium bicarbonate (salt formation)
Uses: cheese-making salts; cream neutralisation agent (butter production); detergent builder; bath salts

sodium silicate
water glass (aqueous solution); [1344-09-8]
Available as glass lumps or powder with $SiO_2{:}Na_2O$

ratios of 2:1 to 3.35:1. These products dissolve very slowly in water under normal pressures which makes then difficult to use for most applications. Also available as clear to turbid, colourless or slightly coloured, viscous solution in water. Grades with a SiO_2: Na_2O ratio of <2.85 by mass are termed 'alkaline' and ≥2.85, neutral. d: 1.35–1.70 kg/l. Viscosity: 70–90,000 cP (20°C). Absorbs carbon dioxide from the air which gradually results in a gel forming. Soluble in water. Soluble powders, produced by spray-drying sodium silicate solutions, are also available.

$$Na_2O.nSiO_2$$

n = 1.6–3.3.
Production:
• sodium carbonate + quartz (furnace process)
• sodium hydroxide + quartz (hydrothermal process)
Derivatives:
aluminium silicate, precipitated; calcium silicate; lead silicochromate, basic; silica, precipitated; silica gel; zeolite A; zeolite X; zeolite Y; zeolite ZSM 5
Uses: concrete surface hardening agents; dispersant (ceramics, cement production); detergent builder; flotation depressant; binder (pelletising fine particles, foundry moulds, heat-resistant paints); packaging adhesive (cardboard tubes, drums); peroxide bleaching adjunct (textiles, paper); soil consolidation agent; corrosion inhibitor (industrial water treatment); refractory/acid-resistant cements

sodium stannate
disodium tin trioxide; [12058-66-1]

$$Na_2SnO_3$$

$Na_2O_3Sn_1$. M: 212.67. Available commercially as the trihydrate. Colourless crystals. Releases water when heated above 140°C. Solubility in water: 600 g/l water (15°C) forming alkaline solutions.
Production:
• sodium hydroxide + stannic oxide (fusion)
Uses: tin plating reagent; textile fireproofing agent

sodium starch dodecenylsuccinate

$$\begin{array}{c} CH_2OO^- \quad Na^+ \\ | \\ C_9H_{19}CH=CHCH_2CHCOO-R \end{array}$$

R = starch-.
Production:
• starch + dodecenylsuccinic anhydride (esterification/sodium salt formation)
Uses: paper sizing ingredient

sodium starch sulphosuccinate

$$\begin{array}{c} CH_2OO^- \quad Na^+ \\ | \\ Na^+ \quad {}^-O_3SOCHCOO-R \end{array}$$

R = starch-.

Production:
• starch + maleic anhydride + sodium bisulphite (esterification/sulphonation)
Uses: anionic polyelectrolyte (water treatment)

sodium starch xanthate *See:* starch, sodium xanthate

sodium stearate
[822-16-2]

$$CH_3(CH_2)_{16}COO^- \quad Na^+$$

$C_{18}H_{35}Na_1O_2$. M: 306.47. White, fatty powder. Soluble in water producing alkaline solutions. Soluble in alcohol.
Production:
• stearic acid + sodium hydroxide (salt formation)
Derivatives:
aluminium distearate; aluminium monostearate
Uses: emulsifier (pharmaceuticals, cosmetics, toiletries); paper sizing ingredient; thickening/gelling agent (cleansing lotions, shampoo); wire-drawing lubricant

sodium stearoyl-2-lactylate
E481 (EC); [25383-99-7]

$$\begin{array}{c} O \\ || \\ CH_3(CH_2)_{16}COCHCOO^- \quad Na^+ \\ | \\ CH_3 \end{array}$$

$C_{21}H_{39}Na_1O_4$. M: 378.53. Off-white flakes or powder. MP: 52–60°C. Available in self-emulsifying or non self-emulsifying grades.
Production:
• stearic acid + DL-lactic acid + sodium hydroxide (esterification/salt formation)
Uses: dough conditioner; emulsifier (cosmetics)

sodium succinate
[150-90-3]

$$\begin{array}{c} CH_2COO^- \\ | \quad\quad\quad 2Na^+ \\ CH_2COO^- \end{array}$$

$C_4H_4Na_2O_4$. M: 162.05. Available as the hexahydrate which is a white granular solid or powder. Releases water of crystallisation when heated to 120°C. Solubility in water: 215 g/l water (0°C). Soluble in oxygenated solvents. Also available as the anhydrous salt.
Production:
• succinic acid + sodium hydroxide (salt formation)
Uses: electrodeless coating reagent

sodium sulphate
Glauber's salt; salt cake; [7757-82-6]

$$Na_2SO_4$$

$Na_2O_4S_1$. M: 142.04. The anhydrous salt is a white, crystalline powder. MP: 800°C. d: 2.7 kg/l. Soluble in water. Glauber's salt is the decahydrate. It is a white, crystalline solid which releases water on heating. d: 1.46 kg/l. Salt cake is mined sodium sulphate. This is purified and crystallised to produce Glauber's salt followed by dehydrated to anhydrous sodium sulphate.

Production:
- natural bitter salt deposits (extraction/purification)
- sodium chloride, natural + sulphur dioxide, pure (Hargreaves process)
- sodium chloride, natural + sulphuric acid (Mannheim process)
- brine, natural alkali (extraction/calcination; coproduced with sodium carbonate)
- brine, natural borate (extraction; coproduced with sodium borate/sodium carbonate/potassium chloride)
- sodium borate + sulphuric acid (neutralisation; byproduct of boric acid production)
- sodium chromate + sulphuric acid (sulphuric acid process; byproduct of sodium dichromate production)
- sodium cellulose xanthate + sulphuric acid (hydrolysis; byproduct of cellulose, regenerated production)

Derivatives: blanc fixe; sodium alum; sodium bisulphate; sodium persulphate; sodium sulphide

Uses: glass production clarifying agent; detergent builder (laundry powders); drying agent; dyeing/textile auxiliary; chrome plating reagent; animal feed ingredient; heat-storage medium; dyestuffs production reagent; reagent (wood pulp production)

sodium sulphide

[1313-82-2]; [1313-84-4] (nonahydrate)

$$Na_2S$$

Na_2S_1. M: 78.04. White to pink, crystalline solid. MP: 1,180°C. d: 1.86 kg/l. Available commercially as fused, hydrated crystals containing 30–34% sodium sulphide or as flakes containing 60–62% sodium sulphide.

Production:
- sodium carbonate + barium sulphide (reaction)
- sodium sulphate + coal (reduction)
- sodium amalgam + sulphur (reaction)
- gasoline, catalytic-cracker (alkali extraction/ acidification; coproduced with cresylic acid)

Derivatives: alitame; cadmium yellow; L-cysteine; dibenzyl disulphide; dibutyltin sulphide; dimethyl sulphide; monobutyltin sulphide; poly(phenylene sulphide); polysulphide, rubber; sodium 2-pyridinethiol-*N*-oxide; sodium thiosulphate; Sulphur Black 1; Sulphur Black 2; Sulphur Black 11; Sulphur Blue 7; Sulphur Blue 11; Sulphur Brown 1; Sulphur Brown 7; Sulphur Green 1; Sulphur Green 3; Sulphur Green 9; Sulphur Green 11; Sulphur Red 7; Sulphur Yellow 9; thiomalic acid; Vat Blue 42; Vat Blue 43

Uses: skin/hide depilatory; flotation depressant (sulphide ores); raw material (Kraft paper production); metal refining agent; reagent (sulphur dye production)

sodium sulphite

E221 (EC); [7757-83-7]

$$Na_2SO_3$$

$Na_2O_3S_1$. M: 126.04. White or pale pink, crystalline solid. Decomposes on heating. d: 2.63 kg/l. Soluble in water. Also available blended with a cobalt salt catalyst for oxygen scavenger applications.

Production:
- sodium carbonate/sodium hydroxide + sulphur dioxide, pure (salt formation)

Derivatives:
Acid Violet 41; benzaldehyde-2-sulphonic acid; phenolformaldehyde sulphonates; sodium thiosulphate

Uses:
dechlorination reagent (drinking water, effluent); flotation depressant (copper ores); bleaching agent (cellulose fibres); oxygen scavenger (boiler/industrial water treatment); preservative (fruit, fruit juice, wine, beer, frozen vegetables); preservative/fixing agent (photographic developers)

sodium sulphoisophthalic acid

5-sulpho-1,3-benzenedicarboxylic acid, monosodium salt; [6362-79-4]

$C_8H_5Na_1O_7S_1$. M: 268.17.

Production:
- isophthalic acid + sodium hydroxide (sulphonation/ sodium salt formation)

Derivatives:
sodium bis(2-hydroxyethyl)-5-sulphoisophthalate

Uses:
dyeable nylon/polyester fibre comonomer

sodium tallate

Production:
- tall oil, distilled + sodium hydroxide (neutralisation)

Uses: emulsifier (styrene-butadiene latex production); flotation collector

sodium tall oil *N*-methyltaurate

R = tall-. Liquid. Available commercially as a 20% solution in water.

Production:
- tall oil fatty acid + sodium *N*-methyltaurate (amide formation)

Uses: scale inhibitor (oilfield applications)

sodium tallow sulphate
[8052-50-4]

$$ROSO_3^-\ Na^+$$

R = tallow-. Brown paste containing about 55% active matter in water.
Production:
• tallow alcohol (sulphation/sodium salt formation)
Uses: mineral flotation agent; surfactant (heavy-duty powder detergents)

sodium tartrate
disodium tartrate; E335 (EC); [868-18-8]

$$\begin{array}{l} COO^-\ Na^+ \\ |\\ HCOH \\ |\\ HOCH \\ |\\ COO^-\ Na^+ \end{array}$$

$C_4H_4Na_2O_6$. M: 194.04. White crystals. Loses water of crystallisation when heated to 150°C. d: 1.80 kg/l. Soluble in water. Insoluble in alcohol.
Production:
• tartaric acid + sodium carbonate (salt formation)
Uses: emulsifier/buffering agent (soft drinks, preserves, confectionery)

sodium tetraphosphate
[7727-67-5]

$$Na_6P_4O_{13}$$

$Na_6O_{13}P_4$. M: 469.83.
Production:
• monosodium phosphate (thermal dehydration)
Uses: drilling mud thinning agent

sodium thiocyanate
sodium rhodanide; [540-72-7]

$$NaSCN$$

$C_1N_1Na_1S_1$. M: 81.07. White, hygroscopic, crystalline solid. MP: 287°C. Soluble in water. Also available commercially as an aqueous solution.
Production:
• sodium hydroxide + ammonium thiocyanate (salt formation)
• sodium cyanide + sulphur (reaction)
Derivatives:
ammonium thiocyanate; 6-mercaptopurine; methylene bisthiocyanate; 2-(thiocyanomethylthio)benzothiazole; thioguanine
Uses: dyeing/printing auxiliary; fibre swelling agent; acrylic fibre spinning solvent additive; metal extraction solvent; photographic chemical

sodium thioglycollate
sodium mercaptoacetate; [367-51-1]
$C_2H_3Na_1O_2S_1$. M: 114.09. White, crystalline, hygro-

scopic solid with a mild, characteristic odour. BP: >200°C. Soluble in water.

$$HSCH_2COO^-\ Na^+$$

Production:
• thioglycollic acid + sodium hydroxide (salt formation)
Uses:
froth flotation agent; microbial fermentation nutrient

sodium thiosulphate
hypo; [7772-98-7]

$$Na_2S_2O_3$$

$Na_2O_3S_2$. M: 158.11. Available as the anhydrous or pentahydrate salts. Pentahydrate: White, crystals. MP: 48°C. Loses water of crystallisation when heated to 100°C and decomposes at higher temperatures. d: 1.75 kg/l (25°C). Soluble in water.
Production:
• sodium sulphite + sulphur (salt formation)
• sodium carbonate + sodium sulphide + sulphur dioxide, raw (salt formation)
Derivatives: Basic Blue 9
Uses: dechlorination reagent (drinking water, effluent); flotation depressant (copper ores); flue gas desulphurisation agent; photographic fixative; textile/leather processing auxiliary

sodium *p*-toluenesulphinate
[873-55-2]

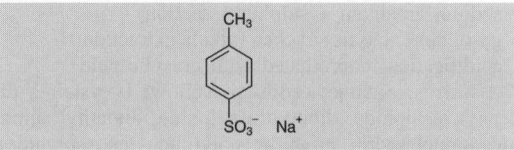

$C_7H_7Na_1O_2S_1$. M: 178.19. Available as the dihydrate.
Production:
• *p*-toluenesulphonyl chloride (sulphonate reduction)
Uses: reducing agent

sodium *p*-toluenesulphonate
sodium toluene-4-sulphonate; STS; [657-84-1]

$C_7H_7Na_1O_3S_1$. M: 194.19. Mixed product containing, typically, 80% toluene-4-sulphonate, 15% toluene-2-sulphonate and 5% toluene-3-sulphonate. Available commercially as a white, 90% active powder or as a 30–40% active liquid. Soluble in water forming acidic solutions.
Production:
• *p*-toluenesulphonic acid (sodium salt formation)
Uses:
hydrotrope (detergent liquids, powders)

sodium trichloroacetate
TCA-sodium; [650-51-1]

$$Cl_3CCOO^- \quad Na^+$$

$C_2Cl_3Na_1O_2$. M: 185.37.
Production:
• trichloroacetic acid + sodium hydroxide (salt formation)
Uses: herbicide

sodium tripolyphosphate
pentasodium triphosphate; STP; STPP; [7758-29-4]

$$Na_5P_3O_{10}$$

$Na_5O_{10}P_3$. M: 367.86. White granules or powder. The product exists in two crystal modifications, depending on the production conditions. The high-temperature modification, called STP-I, is formed by calcination at 500–550°C. The low-temperature modification (STP-II) is formed at 350–400°C. Bulk density: ~1.0 kg/l (powder), ~0.8 kg/l (granules). Both forms are soluble in water.
Production:
• sodium carbonate + phosphoric acid, pure (salt formation/calcination)
Derivatives: starch, amphoteric; starch, crosslinked; starch, sodium phosphate
Uses: clay deflocculant (oil-well drilling muds); starch crosslinking agent; curing agent (processed meats); detergent builder; softening/conditioning agent (cleaners, detergents, textile processing auxiliaries)

sodium tungstate
sodium wolframate; [13472-45-2]

$$Na_2WO_4$$

$Na_2O_4W_1$. M: 293.83. White, crystalline powder or granules. Loses water of crystallisation when heated. Soluble in water.
Production:
• sodium hydroxide + tungsten trioxide (salt formation)
Derivatives:
phosphotungstic acid; phosphomolybdotungstic acid
Uses: flame retardant textile treatment agent

sodium vinyl sulphonate
sodium ethene sulphonate; SVS; [3039-83-6]

$$CH_2=CHSO_3^- \quad Na^+$$

$C_2H_3Na_1O_3S_1$. M: 130.09.
Production:
• acetylene + sodium bisulphite (addition)
• sodium 2-chloroethanesulphonate (dehydrochlorination)
Derivatives: sodium poly(vinyl sulphonate)
Uses: ionomeric polymer comonomer; electroplating bath additive; sulphonoethylation reagent

sodium xylene sulphonate
SXS; [1300-72-7]

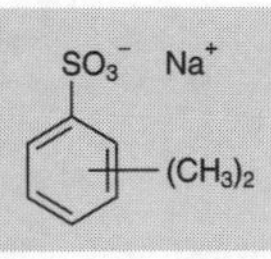

$C_8H_9Na_1O_3S_1$. M: 208.21. Available commercially as a 40% solution in water or as 90% powder.
Production:
• xylenesulphonic acid + sodium hydroxide (salt formation)
Uses: hydrotrope (heavy-duty powder/liquid detergents)

sodium zirconylsilicate

$$Na_2O.ZrO_2.SiO_2$$

$Na_2O_5Si_1Zr_1$. M: 245.28.
Production:
• sodium carbonate + zircon (alkali fusion)
Derivatives:
zirconium sulphate, basic

solasodine
[126-17-0]

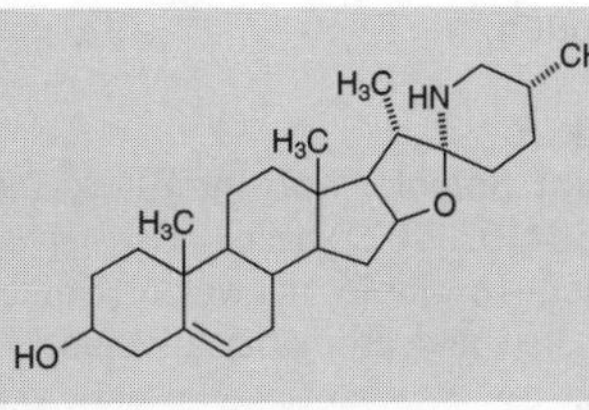

$C_{27}H_{43}N_1O_2$. M: 413.65. Obtained by extraction from bulli-bulli (*Solanum aviculare*) shrub leaves cultivated in New Zealand.
Derivatives:
dehydropregnenolone acetate

Solubilised Vat Blue 1
Indigosol O; 73002 (CI)

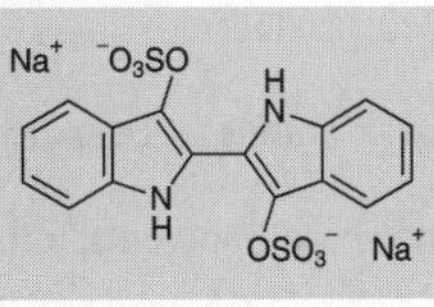

$C_{16}H_{10}N_2Na_2O_8S_2$. M: 468.37.
Production:
• indigo (sulphonation)
Uses: dye (cotton)

Solubilised Vat Yellow 1
70601 (CI)
$C_{28}H_{14}N_2Na_2O_8S_2$. M: 616.53.
Production:
• flavanthrone (sulphation)

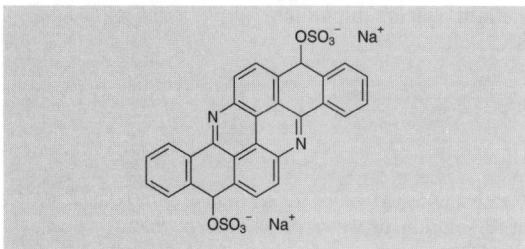

Uses: dye (cotton)

Solubilised Vat Yellow 7
60531 (CI)

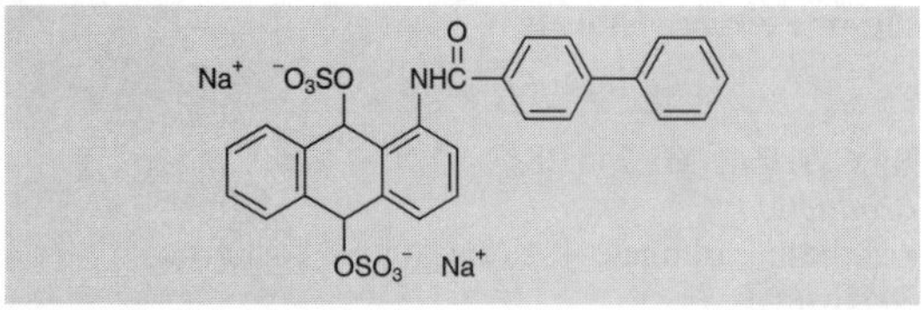

$C_{27}H_{19}N_1Na_2O_9S_2$. M: 611.57.
Production:
- 1-aminoanthraquinone + biphenyl-4-carboxylic acid (amide formation/sulphonation)

Uses: dye (cotton)

Solvent Black 5
Nigrosine Spirit Soluble; Solvent Black 7 (free base); 50415 (CI); 50415:1 (free base)
Mixed product. Insoluble in water. Soluble in fatty acids, oxygenated and aromatic solvents.
Production:
- nitrobenzene + aniline + ferrous sulphate (complex formation)

Uses: solvent dye (resin, varnish, lacquer, wood dyes, shoe polish)

Solvent Black 7 *See:* Solvent Black 5

Solvent Blue 3
42775 (CI). Mixed product.
Production:
- Basic Violet 14 + aniline + benzoic acid (condensation)

Uses: dye (alcohol-based solvents, oils, fats, waxes)

Solvent Blue 4
Victoria Blue; Basic Blue 26 (CI, chloride salt); Pigment Blue 2 (CI, PMTA salt); 44045 (CI, chloride salt); 44045:1 (CI, free base); 44045:2 (CI, PMTA salt)
$C_{33}H_{33}N_3$. M: 471.64. The chloride and PMTA salts are produced from the oxidised form of this triarylmethine *leuco* base.
Production:
- 4,4′-bis(dimethylamino)benzophenone + *N*-phenyl-α-naphthylamine (carbonyl condensation)

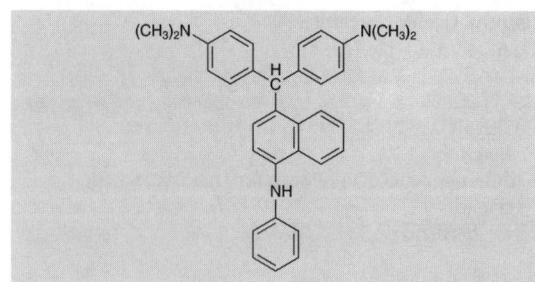

Uses: basic dye (cotton, paper); pigment (printing inks); solvent dye (ballpen inks, printer ribbons)

Solvent Blue 5 *See:* Basic Blue 7

Solvent Blue 8 *See:* Basic Blue 9

Solvent Blue 18 *See:* 1,4,5,8-tetraaminoanthraquinone

Solvent Blue 35
61554 (CI); Sudan Blue 2 (BASF); [12769-17-4]

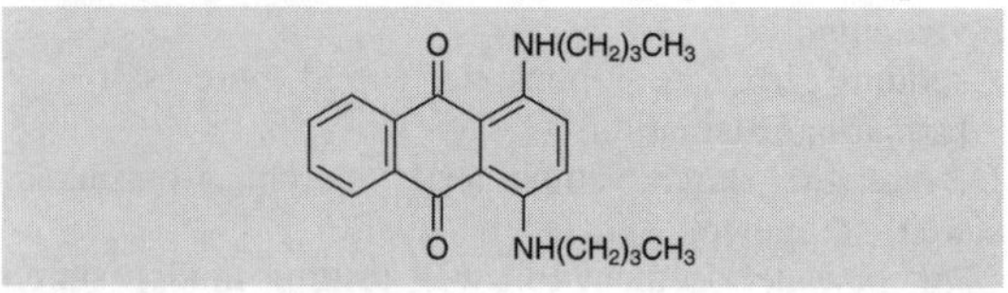

$C_{22}H_{26}N_2O_2$. M: 350.46.
Production:
- quinizarin + *n*-butylamine (amine formation)

Uses: plastics colorant

Solvent Blue 36
Disperse Blue 134 (CI); 61551 (CI)

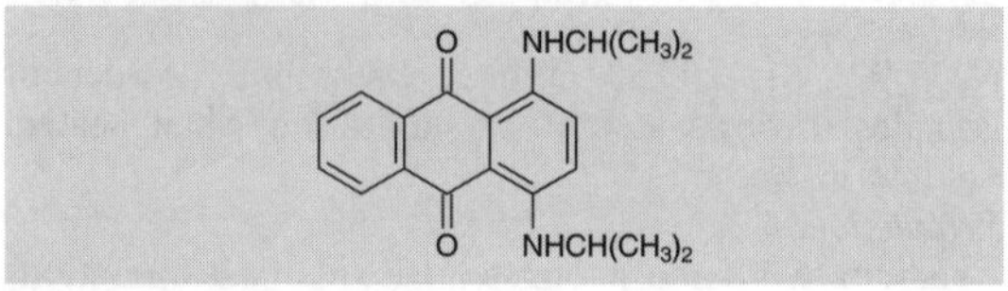

$C_{20}H_{22}N_2O_2$. M: 322.41.
Production:
- quinizarin + isopropylamine (amine formation)

Uses: dye (oils, plastics)

Solvent Blue 38 *See:* Direct Blue 86

Solvent Blue 59
61552 (CI)

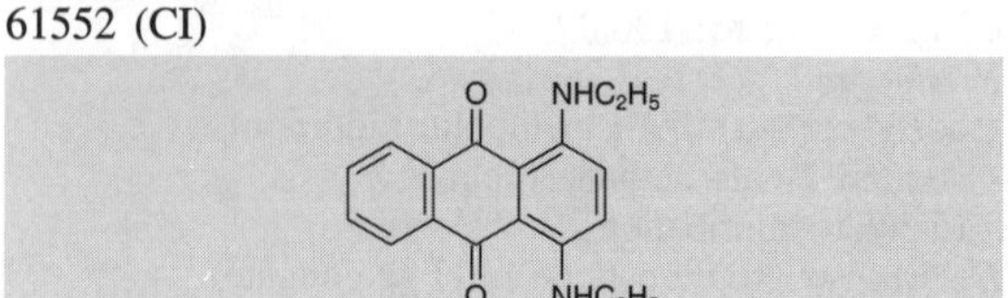

$C_{18}H_{18}N_2O_2$. M: 294.35.

Production:
• quinizarin + ethylamine (amine formation)
Uses:
dye (petroleum products, solvents, wax, polystyrene, lacquer)

Solvent Blue 69 *See:* Disperse Blue 7

Solvent Brown 12
Bismarck Brown R (hydrochloride); Pigment Brown 3 (CI, PMTA salt); 21010 (CI, hydrochloride); 21010:1 (CI, free base); 21010:2 (CI, PMTA salt); [4482-25-1] (hydrochloride)

$C_{21}H_{24}N_8$. M: 388.48. Mixed product.
Production:
• 2,4/2,6-diaminotoluene (diazotisation/azo coupling)
Uses:
basic dye (cotton, bast fibres, acrylic fibre, wool, silk, leather); solvent dye (oils, solvents, waxes, stain)

Solvent Brown 41 *See:* Basic Brown 1

Solvent Green 1 *See:* Basic Green 4

Solvent Green 3
61565 (CI); D&C Green No. 6 (FDC); [128-80-3]

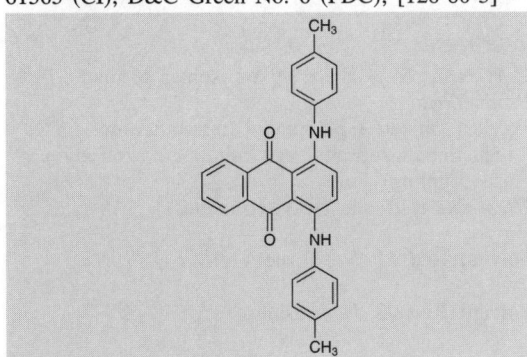

$C_{28}H_{22}N_2O_2$. M: 418.50.
Production:
• quinizarin + *p*-toluidine (amine formation)
Derivatives:
Acid Green 25
Uses: dye (oils, fats, wax, stains, petroleum products)

Solvent Green 4
Fluorescent Brightener 74 (CI); 45550 (CI)
$C_{22}H_{16}O_1$. M: 296.37. Forms dull, olive-coloured solutions in mineral oil.

Production:
• *p*-cresol + phthalic anhydride (carbonyl condensation/cyclisation/reduction)
Uses: dye (mineral oil)

Solvent Orange 2
12100 (CI)

$C_{17}H_{14}N_2O_1$. M: 262.31.
Production:
• *o*-toluidine + β-naphthol (diazotisation/azo coupling)
Uses: dye (varnish, oils, cosmetics)

Solvent Orange 5 *See:* Acid Orange 74

Solvent Orange 7
1-(2,4-dimethylphenylazo)-2-hydroxynaphthalene

$C_{18}H_{16}N_2O_1$. M: 276.34.
Production:
• 2,4-xylidine + β-naphthol (diazotisation/azo coupling)
Uses: dye (lubricating oil)

Solvent Orange 9 *See:* Disperse Orange 3

Solvent Orange 15 *See:* Basic Orange 14

Solvent Orange 42 *See:* Acid Orange 92

Solvent Orange 53 *See:* Disperse Yellow 9

Solvent Red 1
12150 (CI); Sudan Red G (BASF)

$C_{17}H_{14}N_2O_2$. M: 278.31.

Production:
- *o*-anisidine + β-naphthol (diazotisation/azo coupling)

Uses: plastics colorant

Solvent Red 19

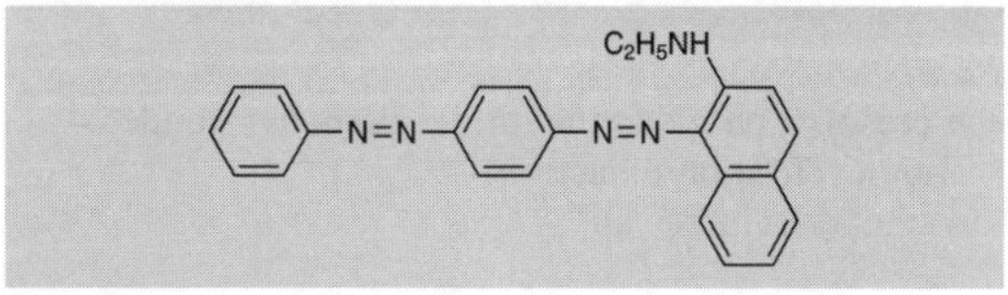

C$_{24}$H$_{21}$N$_5$. M: 379.47.

Production:
- β-naphthol + ethylamine + *p*-phenylazoaniline (amine formation/diazotisation/azo coupling)

Uses: dye (heating oil)

Solvent Red 22
21250 (CI)

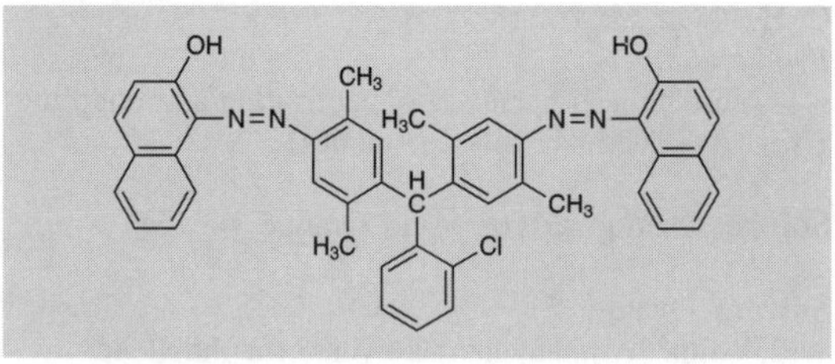

C$_{43}$H$_{35}$Cl$_1$N$_4$O$_2$. M: 675.23.

Production:
- 2,5-xylidine + *o*-chlorobenzaldehyde + β-naphthol (carbonyl condensation/diazotisation/azo coupling)

Uses:
dye (lacquers, inks, solvents, oils, fats, waxes)

Solvent Red 23
Sudan III; 26100 (CI); D&C Red No. 17 (FDC); [85-86-9]

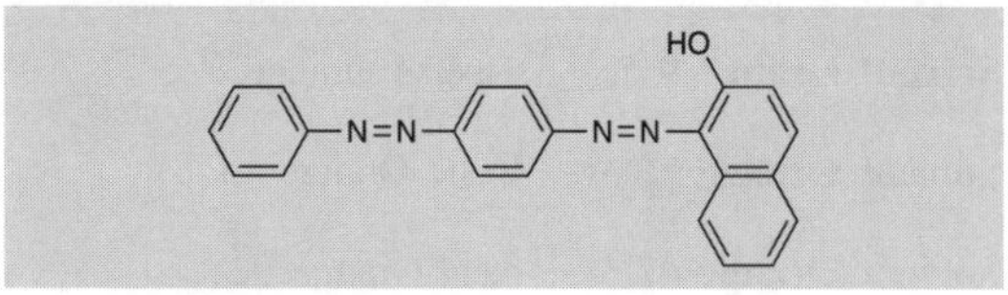

C$_{22}$H$_{16}$N$_4$O$_1$. M: 352.40.

Production:
- *p*-phenylazoaniline + β-naphthol (diazotisation/azo coupling)

Uses: dye (heating oil)

Solvent Red 24
Scarlet Red; 26105 (CI); [85-83-6]
C$_{24}$H$_{20}$N$_4$O$_1$. M: 380.45.

Production:
- *o*-toluidine + β-naphthol (diazotisation/azo coupling/diazotisation/azo coupling)

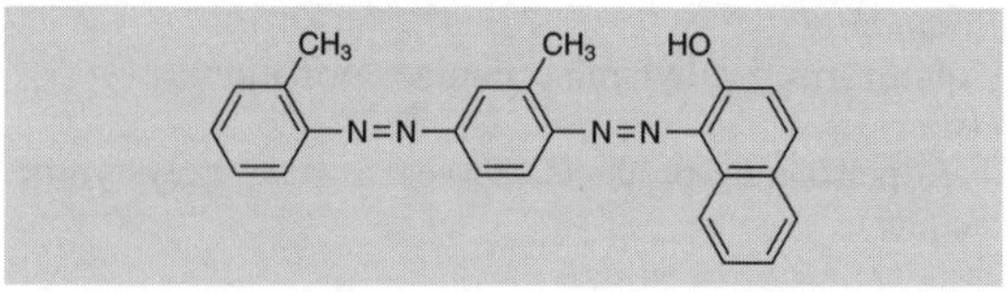

Uses:
dye (petroleum products, oils, polish, stains, lacquer, plastics, soap)

Solvent Red 26
26120 (CI)

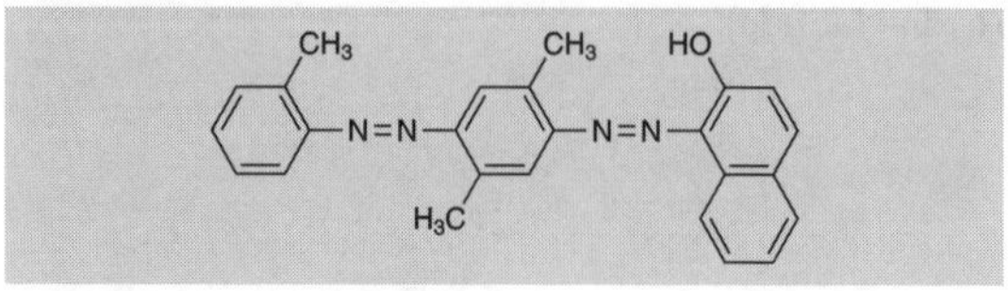

C$_{25}$H$_{22}$N$_4$O$_1$. M: 394.48.

Production:
- *o*-toluidine + 2,5-xylidine + β-naphthol (diazotisation/azo coupling/diazotisation/azo coupling)

Uses:
dye (petroleum products, oils, fats, waxes, acrylics)

Solvent Red 27
26125 (CI)

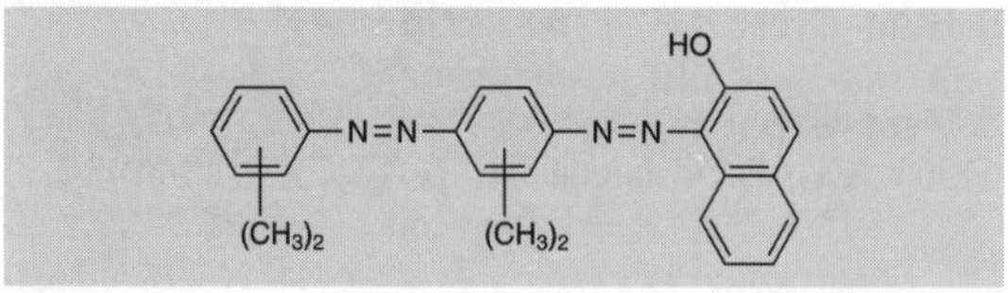

C$_{26}$H$_{24}$N$_4$O$_1$. M: 408.50. Mixed isomer product.

Production:
- xylene, mixed + β-naphthol (nitration/nitro reduction/diazotisation/azo coupling/diazotisation/azo coupling)

Uses: dye (oils, fats, wax, cosmetics)

Solvent Red 41 *See:* Basic Violet 14

Solvent Red 43 *See:* eosine

Solvent Red 49 *See:* Basic Violet 10

Solvent Red 80
Citrus Red No. 2; 12156 (CI); [6358-53-8]

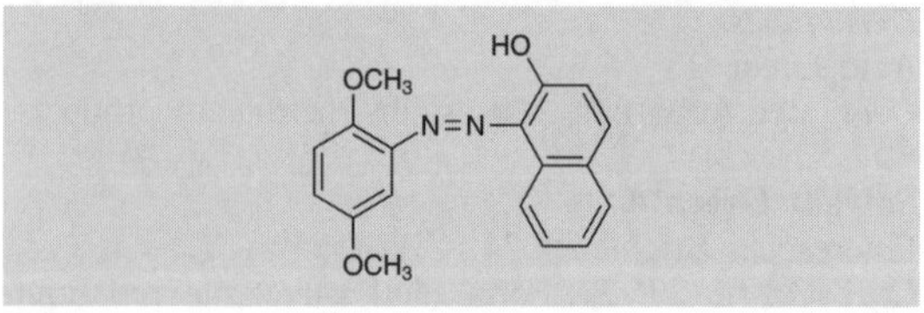

C$_{18}$H$_{16}$N$_2$O$_3$. M: 308.34.

Production:
- 2,5-dimethoxyaniline + β-naphthol (diazotisation/ azo coupling)

Uses: dye (citrus fruit)

Solvent Red 102 *See:* Acid Red 296

Solvent Red 111 *See:* Disperse Red 9

Solvent Red 117 *See:* Disperse Red 5

Solvent Red 140 *See:* Acid Red 51

Solvent Violet 8 *See:* Basic Violet 1

Solvent Violet 9 *See:* Basic Violet 3

Solvent Violet 10
Acid Violet 9 (CI, sodium salt); 45190 (CI, sodium salt); 45190:1 (CI)

$C_{34}H_{26}N_2O_6S_1$. M: 590.65.
Production:
- fluorescein + *o*-toluidine (chlorination/amine formation/sulphonation)

Uses:
acid dye (wool); solvent dye (lacquers, resins)

Solvent Violet 11
See: 1,4-diaminoanthraquinone

Solvent Violet 13
See: Disperse Blue 72

Solvent Violet 14
61705 (CI)

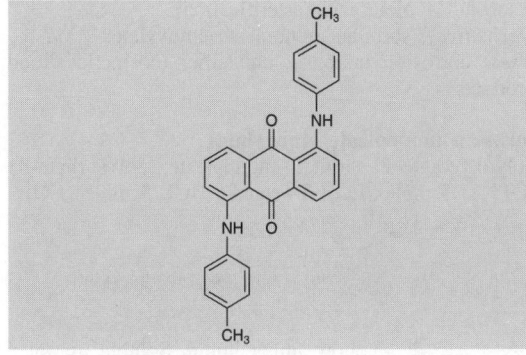

$C_{28}H_{22}N_2O_2$. M: 418.50.

Production:
- 1,5-diaminoanthraquinone + *p*-toluidine (amine formation)

Uses:
dye (oils, wax, polystyrene, stains)

Solvent Yellow 1 *See:* *p*-phenylazoaniline

Solvent Yellow 3 *See:* *o*-aminoazotoluene

Solvent Yellow 14
12055 (CI)

$C_{16}H_{12}N_2O_1$. M: 248.29.
Production:
- aniline + β-naphthol (diazotisation/azo coupling)

Uses:
dye (polish, solvents, varnish, polystyrene, soap)

Solvent Yellow 16 *See:* Disperse Yellow 16

Solvent Yellow 19
Acid Yellow 99 (CI, chromium complex); 13900 (CI, chromium complex); 13900:1 (CI, free acid)

The dye is the chromium complex of the displayed structure.
Production:
- 2-amino-4-nitrophenol-6-sulphonic acid + acetoacetanilide + chromic fluoride (diazotisation/ azo coupling/complex formation)

Uses:
solvent dye (solvents, lacquer, stains, plastics); acid dye (wool)

Solvent Yellow 21
Acid Yellow 121 (CI); 18690 (CI)

The dye is the chromium complex of the displayed structure.

Production:
- anthranilic acid + 3-methyl-1-phenyl-5-pyrazolone + chromium sulphate (diazotisation/azo coupling/ complex formation)

Uses: acid dye (polyamide fibres); solvent dye (solvents, resins, stains)

Solvent Yellow 33 *See:* quinophthalone

Solvent Yellow 34 *See:* Basic Yellow 2

Solvent Yellow 56
11021 (CI)

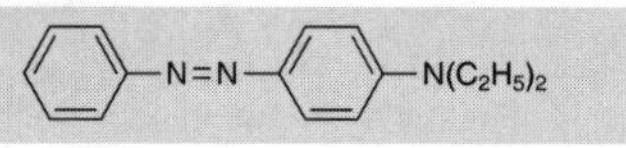

$C_{16}H_{19}N_3$. M: 253.35.
Production:
- aniline + *N,N*-diethylaniline (diazotisation/azo coupling)

Uses: dye (petroleum products, polish)

Solvent Yellow 77 *See:* Disperse Yellow 3

Solvent Yellow 94 *See:* fluorescein

Solvent Yellow 107
21140 (CI)

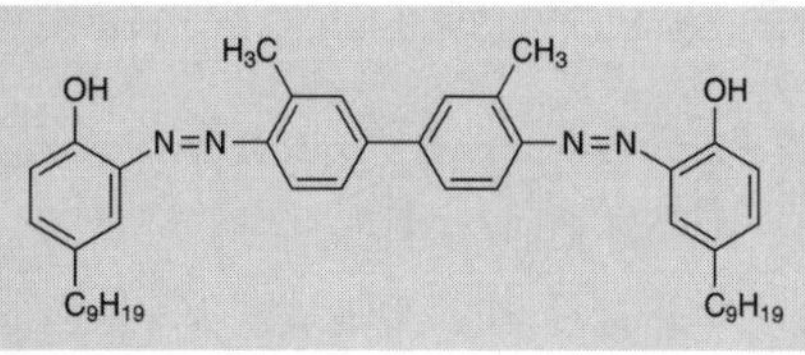

$C_{44}H_{58}N_4O_2$. M: 674.97.
Production:
- *o*-tolidine + nonylphenol (diazotisation/azo coupling)

Uses: dye (petroleum products, oils, solvents, waxes)

SOPP *See:* sodium *o*-phenylphenate

sorbic acid
2,4-hexadienoic acid; E200 (EC); [110-44-1]

$$CH_3CH=CHCH=CHCOOH$$

$C_6H_8O_2$. M: 112.13. White crystals or powder. MP: 134–135°C. BP: 228°C with decomposition. d: 1.20 kg/l (20°C). Very slightly soluble in water. Soluble in oxygenated solvents. The commercial product is the *trans,trans*-isomer.
Production:
- crotonaldehyde + ketene (condensation)

Derivatives: potassium sorbate
Uses:
preservative (food, animal feed, tobacco, cosmetics)

sorbitan monolaurate
sorbitan laurate; Span 20 (ICI)

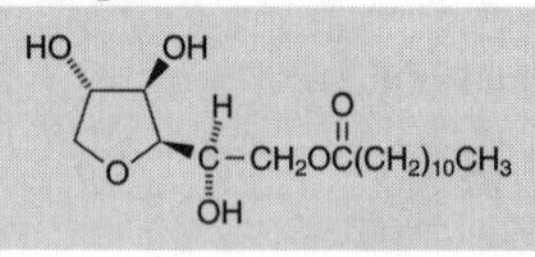

$C_{18}H_{34}O_6$. M: 346.46. Yellow-amber liquid. HLB: 8.6. Dispersible in water.
Production:
- sorbitol + lauric acid, narrow cut (esterification)

Derivatives: sorbitan monolaurate ethoxylates
Uses: emulsifier (cosmetics, food products)

sorbitan monolaurate ethoxylates
polyoxyethylene sorbitan monolaurate; polysorbate-20 (CTFA, 20 moles EO); polysorbate-21 (CTFA, 4 moles EO); Tween 20 (ICI, 20 moles EO); Tween 21 (ICI, 4 moles EO)

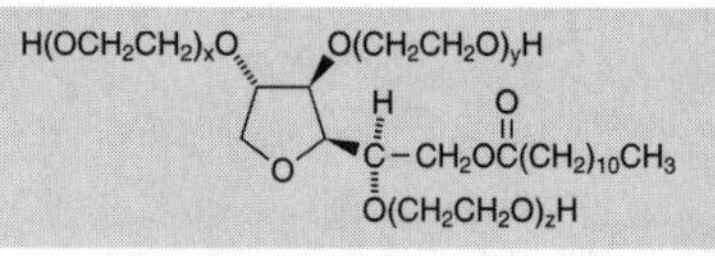

x+y+z = 4–20. Yellow liquid. Soluble in water and alcohol (20 moles EO) or dispersible in water (4 moles EO). HLB: 13.3–16.7 (4–20 moles EO).
Production:
- sorbitan monolaurate + ethylene oxide (epoxidation)

Uses: emulsifier (food, cosmetics, pharmaceuticals)

sorbitan monooleate
sorbitan oleate; Span 80 (ICI)

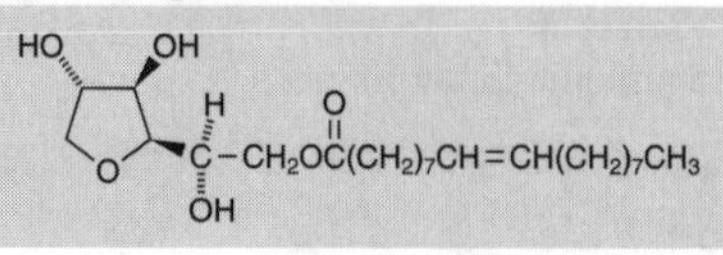

$C_{24}H_{44}O_6$. M: 428.60. Yellow-amber liquid. HLB: 4.3. Insoluble in water.
Production:
- sorbitol + oleic acid (esterification)

Derivatives: sorbitan monooleate ethoxylates
Uses: corrosion inhibitor; emulsifier (cosmetics, food products)

sorbitan monooleate ethoxylates
polyoxyethylene sorbitan monooleate; polysorbate-81 (CTFA, 5 moles EO); Tween 81 (ICI, 5 moles EO)

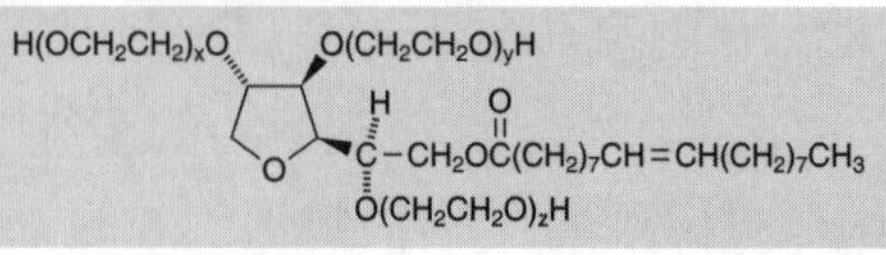

x+y+z = 5–20. Yellow-amber liquid. Soluble in water and alcohol (20 moles EO), or soluble in aliphatic sol-

vents and dispersible in water (4 moles EO). HLB: 10.0–15.0 (5–20 moles EO).
Production:
• sorbitan monooleate + ethylene oxide (epoxidation)
Uses: degreasing agent (leather processing); emulsifier (animal feed, cleaners, pesticides, waxes, silicone oils, food products, cosmetics, pharmaceuticals); lubricant/antistatic agent/detergent (textile processing); surfactant (oil spill dispersants, tank cleaners)

sorbitan monopalmitate
sorbitan palmitate; Span 40 (ICI)

$C_{22}H_{42}O_6$. M: 402.57. Cream-coloured solid. HLB: 6.7. Insoluble in water.
Production:
• sorbitol + palmitic acid (esterification)
Derivatives: sorbitan monopalmitate ethoxylates
Uses: emulsifier (cosmetics, food products)

sorbitan monopalmitate ethoxylates
polyoxyethylene sorbitan monopalmitate; Tween 40 (ICI, 20 moles EO)

x+y+z = 20. $C_{62}H_{122}O_{26}$. M: 1283.63. Yellow liquid. HLB: 15.6 (20 moles EO). Soluble in water and alcohol. Insoluble in oils and propylene glycol.
Production:
• sorbitan monopalmitate + ethylene oxide (epoxidation)
Uses: emulsifier (food products, cosmetics)

sorbitan monostearate
sorbitan stearate; Span 60 (ICI)

$C_{24}H_{46}O_6$. M: 430.61. White solid. Pour point: 51–54°C. HLB: 4.7. Insoluble in water.
Production:
• sorbitol + stearic acid (esterification)
Derivatives: sorbitan monostearate ethoxylates
Uses: emulsifier (cosmetics, food products)

sorbitan monostearate ethoxylates
polyoxyethylene sorbitan monostearate; polysorbate-60 (CTFA, 20 moles EO); polysorbate-61 (CTFA, 4 moles

EO); Tween 60 (ICI, 20 moles EO); Tween 61 (ICI, 4 moles EO)

x+y+z = 4–20. Pale yellow liquid to tan solid. Soluble in water/alcohol (20 moles EO) or dispersible in water (4 moles EO). HLB: 9.6–14.9 (4–20 moles EO).
Production:
• sorbitan monostearate + ethylene oxide (epoxidation)
Uses: dye penetration/levelling aid; emulsifier (food products, cosmetics, pharmaceuticals); emulsifier (solvent, polish, pesticides, dyes); lubricant/antistatic agent (textile spin finishes)

sorbitan trioleate
Span 85 (ICI); [26266-58-0]

$C_{60}H_{108}O_8$. M: 957.51. Yellow-amber liquid. HLB: 1.8. Insoluble in water.
Production:
• sorbitol + oleic acid (esterification)
Derivatives: sorbitan trioleate ethoxylates

sorbitan trioleate ethoxylates
polyoxyethylene sorbitan trioleate; polysorbate-85; Tween 85 (ICI, 20 moles EO)

$C_{100}H_{190}O_{28}$. M: 1840.59. Amber liquid. Soluble in organic solvents. Dispersible in water. HLB: 11.0.
Production:
• sorbitan trioleate + ethylene oxide (epoxidation)
Uses: emulsifier (food, cosmetics, pharmaceuticals)

sorbitan tristearate
Span 65 (ICI); [26658-19-5]

$C_{60}H_{114}O_8$. M: 963.56. White solid. Pour point: 48°C. HLB: 2.1. Dispersible in water.

Production:
- sorbitol + stearic acid (esterification)

Derivatives: sorbitan tristearate ethoxylates

Uses: emulsifier (food products)

sorbitan tristearate ethoxylates

polyoxyethylene sorbitan tristearate; polysorbate-65;
Tween 65 (ICI, 20 moles EO)

$C_{100}H_{194}O_{28}$. M: 1844.62. Tan-coloured solid. HLB: 10.5
(20 moles EO). Pour point: 33°C. Soluble in alcohol.
Insoluble in water and oils.

Production:
- sorbitan tristearate + ethylene oxide (epoxidation)

Uses: emulsifier (food products)

sorbitol

D-sorbitol; E420 (EC); [50-70-4]

$C_6H_{14}O_6$. M: 182.17. White, crystalline solid with a
sweet taste. MP: 93–98°C. d: 1.49 kg/l (25°C). Soluble
in water and oxygenated solvents. Insoluble in vegetable and mineral oils. Also available as a 70% w/w
aqueous solution.

Production:
- starch hydrolysate (hydrogenation)
- invert sugar (hydrogenation; coproduced with
  mannitol)

Derivatives: isosorbide; polyether polyols, rigid; sorbitan monolaurate; sorbitan monooleate; sorbitan monopalmitate; sorbitan monostearate; sorbitan trioleate;
sorbitan tristearate; L-sorbose

Uses: alkyd/rosin ester resin comonomer; humectant
(pet food, coconut, tobacco, leather, starch adhesives,
textile sizes); sugar crystallisation inhibitor (icing, pie
fillings, confectionery); sweetener (diet soft drinks,
chewing gum, pharmaceuticals); polyvinyl chloride heat
costabilisers

L-sorbose

[87-79-6]

$C_6H_{12}O_6$. M: 180.16. White, sweet-testing crystals. MP:
165°C. d: 1.61 kg/l (17°C). Soluble in water.

Production:
- sorbitol + *Acetobacter suboxydans* bacteria
  (anaerobic fermentation)

Derivatives: ascorbic acid; dikegulac-sodium

sotalol

[3930-20-9]

$C_{12}H_{20}N_2O_3S_1$. M: 272.36. Available commercially as
the hydrochloride.

Production:
- aniline + methanesulphonyl chloride + bromoacetyl
  bromide + isopropylamine (sulphonamide
  formation/Friedel-Crafts acylation/amine formation/
  carbonyl reduction)

Uses: antianginal/antiarrhythmic drug

soya amine

soyamine

R = soya-. A typical chain-length distribution is: 10%
$C_{16:0}$, 10% $C_{18:0}$, 25% $C_{18:1}$, 50% $C_{18:2}$.

Production:
- soyabean acid + ammonia (nitrile formation/
  hydrogenation)

Derivatives: soya amine ethoxylates; soyatrimethylammonium chloride

soya amine ethoxylates

PEG soyamine

n = 2–15. Amber liquid.

Production:
- soya amine + ethylene oxide (epoxidation)

Uses:
corrosion inhibitor; antistatic agent; emulsifier (emulsion polymerisation, oils, waxes)

soyabean acid

soy acid

Liquid or solid. Titre: 20–27°C. Saponification value:
195–205 mg KOH/g. Acid value: 194–204 mg KOH/g.
Iodine value: 123–140 g I_2/100 g. The chain-length
distribution is: 16–20% $\leq C_{18:0}$, 24–26% $C_{18:1}$, 47–53%
$C_{18:2}$ and 7% $C_{18:3}$.

Production:
- soyabean soap stock (acidification/fractionation)

Derivatives: alkyd resins, long-oil; alkyd resins, medium-oil; alkyd resins, short-oil; fatty acids, polyunsaturated, conjugated; linoleic acid diethanolamide; soya
amine

soyabean foots *See:* soyabean soap stock

soyabean meal
Residue from oil extraction containing 50% protein.
Production:
• soyabeans (solvent extraction/alkali refining;
  coproduced with soyabean oil)
Derivatives:
β-amylase; protein hydrolysates
Uses: casein-based wood adhesives; animal feed ingredient; binder (paper coatings); microbial fermentation nutrient

soyabean oil
soybean oil; [8001-22-7]
Yellow liquid. Titre: 22–24°C. Saponification value:
190–195 mg KOH/g. Iodine value: 120–140 g I_2/100
g. A typical chain-length distribution is: 10% C_{16}, 5%
$C_{18:0}$, 25% $C_{18:1}$, 50% $C_{18:2}$, 5% $C_{18:3}$.
Production:
• soyabeans (solvent extraction/alkali refining;
  coproduced with soyabean meal)
Derivatives: alkyd resins, long-oil; alkyd resins, medium-oil; alkyd resins, short-oil; cyclopentadienised oils;
fatty acid mono/diglycerides; fatty oils, sulphurised;
linoleic acid diethanolamide; maleinised oils; soyabean
oil, epoxidised
Uses: cooking oil; microbial fermentation nutrient;
plasticiser (rubber); prepared food ingredient

soyabean oil, epoxidised
ESBO; ESO; [8013-07-8]
Production:
• soyabean oil + peracetic acid/performic acid
  (epoxidation)
Derivatives: cadmium-zinc heat stabilisers
Uses: polyvinyl chloride costabiliser/plasticiser; plast-
iciser (printing inks)

soyabean soap stock
soyabean foots
Partially hydrolysed foots produced during alkali refining and deodorising of soyabean oil.
Production:
• soyabeans (solvent extraction/alkali refining;
  byproduct of soyabean oil/soyabean meal
  production)
Derivatives: soyabean acid

soyabean sterols *See:* phytosterols, mixed

soyatrimethylammonium chloride

$$RN(CH_3)_3^+ \quad Cl^-$$

R = soya-. Available as a 50% solution in water. The
chain-length distribution is: 15% C_{16}, 12% $C_{18:0}$, 71%
C_{18} unsaturated.

Production:
• soya amine + methyl chloride (quaternisation)
Uses: emulsifier; antistatic agent

SPAN *See:* starch-acrylamide graft copolymers

spandex *See:* elastane

spearmint oil
[8008-79-5]
Colourless to greeny-yellow liquid with a characteristic
odour. Produced by steam distillation of the flowering
tops of native or Scotch spearmint (*Mentha spicata* and
Mentha cardiaca, respectively). d: 0.93 kg/l (20°C).
Soluble in ethanol. The major constituent of this oil is
carvone (55%). The major producing country is USA.
Uses: flavouring ingredient (confectionery, chewing
gum, toothpaste, pharmaceuticals)

special boiling-point solvents
special boiling-point spirits; SBP; SBPS
Selected distillation cuts usually referred to by number
(4–11) or boiling range. BP varies with fraction selected in the range 60–160°C. d: 0.67–0.74 kg/l (15°C).
Aromatic content: 0–11% v/v.
Production:
• naphtha, heavy (fractionation; coproduced with
  white spirit)
Derivatives: special boiling-point solvents, dearomatised
Uses: catalytic stove fuel; solvent (paints, varnishes,
printing inks, polishes, rubber cements/adhesives); extraction solvent (rosin, wax); solvent (wool, bone degreasing); diluent (lacquer thinners)

special boiling-point solvents, dearomatised
Exxsol DSP (Exxon Chemical)
Selected distillation cuts usually referred to by boiling
range. BP varies with grade in the range 60–160°C. d:
0.66–0.76 kg/l (15°C). Aromatics content: ≤0.1%.
Production:
• special boiling-point solvents (hydrogenation)
Uses:
diluent (lacquer thinners); solvent (paints, varnishes,
printing inks, polishes, rubber cements/ adhesives)

SPH *See:* phenol, styrenated

spironolactone
[52-01-7]

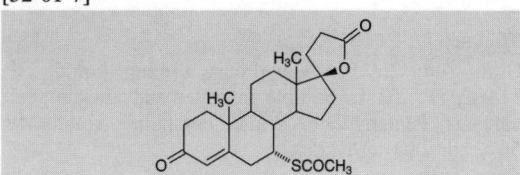

$C_{24}H_{32}O_4S_1$. M: 416.58.

Production:
- prasterone + acetylene + thioglycollic acid + methylmagnesium bromide (multistep synthesis)

Uses: diuretic drug

sponge coke, calcined

Black lumps with a sponge-like appearance. The coke is characterised by its high surface area and relatively low volatile matter content of <1%.

Production:
- sponge coke, green (calcination)

Derivatives: titanium dioxide; titanium tetrachloride

Uses: steel production; Soederberg aluminium anode raw material

sponge coke, green

green coke; petroleum coke

Black lumps with a sponge-like appearance. The coke is characterised by its high surface area and high volatile matter content of, typically 9–12%.

Production:
- short residue (delayed coking process; coproduced with naphtha, heavy/gas oil, light/gas oil, heavy/shot coke/refinery gas)

Derivatives: metallurgical coke; silicon carbide; sponge coke, calcined

Uses: electrodes (electric arc steelmaking furnaces); fuel (electricity, industrial boilers, space heating, cement/lime production); metallurgical coke modifier

squalane

[111-01-3]

$$(CH_3)_2CH(CH_2)_3\overset{\overset{\displaystyle CH_3}{|}}{C}H(CH_2)_3\overset{\overset{\displaystyle CH_3}{|}}{C}H(CH_2)_4\overset{\overset{\displaystyle CH_3}{|}}{C}H(CH_2)_3\overset{\overset{\displaystyle CH_3}{|}}{C}H(CH_3)_2$$

$C_{30}H_{62}$. M: 422.83. Oil. MP: -38°C. BP: 350°C. d: 0.81 kg/l (15°C). Soluble in hydrocarbon solvents. Slightly soluble in alcohol.

Production:
- shark liver oil (extraction/hydrogenation)
- geranylacetone + butadiene (condensation/hydrogenation)

Uses: perfume fixative/lubricant (toiletries, cosmetics)

stand oil *See:* linseed oil, heat-bodied

stannic chloride

tin chloride; tin(IV) chloride; tin tetrachloride; [7646-78-8]

SnCl$_4$

Cl_4Sn_1. M: 260.50. Anhydrous: fuming liquid. BP: 114°C. FP: -33°C. Soluble in water and most organic solvents. Pentahydrate: White, crystalline solid. MP: 56°C. d: 2.04 kg/l (25°C).

Production:
- tin + chlorine (chlorination)

Derivatives: azocyclotin; *n*-butyltin trichloride; cyhexatin; dibutyltin dichloride; dimethyltin dichloride; di-*n*-octyltin dichloride; fenbutatin oxide; fentin fluoride; fentin hydroxide; monomethyltin trichloride; tetra-*n*-butyltin; tetramethyltin; tetra-*n*-octyltin; tetraphenyltin; tributyltin chloride

Uses: Friedel-Crafts reaction/polymerisation catalyst; glass coatings/surface treatment agent; mordant (silk dyeing); perfume stabiliser (soap); sheepskin wool flame-resist treatment; ABS electroplating activator

stannic oxide

stannic acid; stannic oxide, hydrated; tin dioxide; tin oxide; tin peroxide; 77861 (CI); [18282-10-5]

SnO$_2$

O_2Sn_1. M: 150.69. White, crystalline solid. d: 6.95 kg/l. MP: 1,127°C. Insoluble in water.

Production:
- tin (air oxidation)

Derivatives: potassium stannate; sodium stannate

Uses: ceramic tiles/sanitaryware colorant; binary tin catalysts (acrolein/acetone/butadiene production); electrical resistor insulating film; opacifying ingredient (glass, pottery glazes, enamels); polishing/grinding pastes; sintered electrodes (lead glass electromelt process); silk weighing agent

stannous chloride

tin dichloride; [7772-99-8] (anhydrous); [10025-69-1] (dihydrate)

SnCl$_2$

Cl_2Sn_1. M: 189.60. Anhydrous: white solid. MP: 246°C. BP: 623°C. d: 3.95 kg/l. Solubility in water: 840 g/l water (0°C). Soluble in oxygenated solvents. Dihydrate: white solid. MP: 37°C. d: 2.63 kg/l. Soluble in water.

Production:
- tin + chlorine (chlorination)
- tin + hydrochloric acid (salt formation)

Derivatives:
stannous octoate; stannous oxalate; stannous oxide

Uses: tin plating reagent; food additive; reducing agent (mirror production, organic synthesis); photographic sensitising agent; sensitising agent (plastic/glass metallisation); soldering flux; tanning agent; wool flame retardant treatment

stannous fluoride

fluoristan; [7783-47-3]

SnF$_2$

F_2Sn_1. M: 156.69. White crystals. MP: 215°C. d: 4.57 kg/l (25°C). Solubility in water: 709 g/l water.

Production:
- stannous oxide + hydrofluoric acid (salt formation)

Uses: toothpaste ingredient

stannous fluoroborate
tin bis(tetrafluoroborate); tin fluoborate; [13814-97-6]

$$Sn(BF_4)_2$$

$B_2F_8Sn_1$. M: 292.29.
Production:
• stannous oxide + fluoboric acid (salt formation)
• tin + fluoboric acid (electrolysis)
Uses: tin plating reagent

stannous octoate
stannous 2-ethylhexoate; tin octoate; [301-10-0]

$$(C_7H_{15}COO)_2Sn$$

$C_{16}H_{30}O_4Sn_1$. M: 405.11. Yellow liquid. d: 1.25 kg/l. Insoluble in water and alcohol. Soluble in aromatic solvents.
Production:
• stannous chloride + 2-ethylhexanoic acid/ isooctanoic acid (salt formation)
Uses: polyurethane foam catalyst; RTV silicone rubber curing agent

stannous oleate
tin oleate; [1912-84-1]

$$\left[CH_3(CH_2)_7CH=CH(CH_2)_7COO\right]_2 Sn$$

$C_{36}H_{66}O_4Sn_1$. M: 681.62.
Production:
• stannous oxide + oleic acid (salt formation)
Uses:
esterification catalyst

stannous oxalate
tin oxalate; [814-94-8]

$$\begin{matrix} COO^- \\ | \\ COO^- \end{matrix} \quad Sn^{2+}$$

$C_2O_4Sn_1$. M: 206.71. White powder. Decomposes when heated above 250°C. d: 3.56 kg/l. Insoluble in water.
Production:
• sodium oxalate + stannous chloride (salt formation)
Uses:
esterification catalyst

stannous oxide
tin monoxide; [21651-19-4]

$$SnO$$

O_1Sn_1. M: 134.69. Blue-black crystals. Decomposes on heating over 385°C. d: 6.45 kg/l. Insoluble in water.
Production:
• stannous chloride + sodium hydroxide (salt formation)
Derivatives: stannous fluoride; stannous fluoroborate; stannous oleate
Uses: speciality glass raw material

stannous sulphate
tin sulphate; [7488-55-3]

$$SnSO_4$$

$O_4S_1Sn_1$. M: 214.75. White, crystalline powder. Decomposes when heated above 360°C with release of sulphur dioxide. Soluble in water.
Production:
• tin + sulphuric acid (salt formation)
Uses: tin electrodeposition raw material

starch
[9005-84-9]

Starch is a mixture of amylose and amylopectin carbohydrates, both of which are 1,4-β-linked glucose polymers. The relative proportion of each varies with the source of the starch. Physically, starch granules consist of regions ('micelles') of oriented, crystalline amylose and amylopectin molecules surrounded by polymer in a gelled state. The behaviour of the starch when cooked is governed by the ease with which water can penetrate the mass and solvate the polymers. This process causes the granule to swell and, eventually, rupture. On cooling, high-amylose starches 'retrograde' to gels whereas high-amylopectin starches remain as true polymer solutions. The different types of starch are commonly referred to by source, such as potato starch, corn starch, arrowroot starch and so on.
Production:
• maize (milling/separation; coproduced with maize gluten/maize bran)
• potatoes (hot water extraction)
• cassava tubers (hot water extraction)
• arrowroot (hot water extraction)
• taro tubers (hot water extraction)
• sorghum grains (hot water extraction)
• sago palm stems (hot water extraction)
• wheat grain (milling/separation)
• rice grain (milling/separation)
• barley grain (milling/separation)
Derivatives:
carboxymethyl starch; dextrin; glucose syrup; hydroxyethyl starch; hydroxypropyl starch; maltodextrin; oxalic acid; sodium starch dodecenylsuccinate; sodium starch sulphosuccinate; starch, acid-converted; starch, acrylamidoglycollic acid-modified; starch, cationic; starch, crosslinked; starch, oxidised; starch, pregelatinised; starch, sodium phosphate; starch, sodium xanthate; starch, thermochemically-converted; starch acetate; starch-acrylamide graft copolymers

Uses: dry-strength additive/surface sizing (paper production); flocculant (water treatment); flotation depressant (haematite ores); food ingredient; adhesives (bottle labelling, paper bag/envelope seams, corrugated cardboard, carton sealing); foil-paper laminating adhesives; binder (paper coatings); microbial fermentation nutrient; warp sizing

starch, acid-converted

Acid attacks the amorphous regions of the starch granule causing depolymerisation particularly of the amylopectin. This causes a reduction in the solution viscosity, reduced gel strength and higher gelatinisation temperatures.

Production:
• starch (acidification)

Uses: binder (plasterboard); confectionery ingredient; surface sizing (paper); warp sizing

starch, acrylamidoglycollic acid-modified

$$RO-CH_2CH_2\overset{\overset{\displaystyle O}{\|}}{C}NHCH_2COOH$$

R = starch-.
Production:
• starch + acrylonitrile + glycollic acid (cyanoethylation/nitrile addition)

Uses: anionic polyelectrolyte (flotation depressant)

starch, amphoteric

Starch containing both cationic and anionic pendant groups.

Production:
• starch, cationic + sodium tripolyphosphate/ phosphorus oxychloride (esterification)
• starch, cationic + maleic anhydride + sodium bisulphite (esterification/sulphonation)
• starch, cationic + sodium 3-chloro-2-hydroxy-propylsulphonate (ether formation)

Uses: dry-strength additive (paper production); textile finishing agent

starch, cationic

Production:
• starch + 2-dimethylaminoethyl chloride hydrochloride/2-diethylaminoethyl chloride hydrochloride/3-dimethylaminopropyl chloride hydrochloride/2,3-epoxypropyltrimethylammonium chloride (ether formation/quaternisation)

Derivatives: starch, amphoteric

Uses: dry-strength additive/internal sizing/retention aid (paper production); mineral flotation depressant; textile finishing agent

starch, crosslinked

Crosslinking is used to improve the viscosity and swelling characteristics of starch during cooking.

Production:
• starch + phosphorus oxychloride/sodium tripoly-phosphate/adipic acid/epichlorohydrin (reaction)

Uses: textile sizing; thickening agents/stabilisers (prepared foods)

starch, oxidised

Reduced viscosity form of starch with some anionic properties.

Production:
• starch + chlorine/hydrogen peroxide/sodium hypochlorite (oxidation)

Uses:
food ingredient; binder (plasterboard); surface/internal paper sizing; adhesives; textile sizing/backfilling agent

starch, pregelatinised

Production:
• starch (thermal swelling/drying)

Uses: adhesives (corrugated cardboard, multi-wall paper bags, wallpaper, posters); internal paper sizing; pie/pudding filling ingredient

starch, sodium phosphate

$$RO-PO_3^-\ Na^+$$

R = starch-.
Production:
• starch + sodium tripolyphosphate/monosodium phosphate/disodium phosphate (esterification)

Uses: dry-strength additive/retention aid (paper production); food ingredient; mineral flotation depressant; starch modifier (paper adhesives); textile sizing

starch, sodium xanthate

sodium starch xanthate

$$RO-\overset{\overset{\displaystyle S}{\|}}{C}S^-\ Na^+$$

R = starch-.
Production:
• starch + carbon disulphide + sodium hydroxide (reaction)

Uses: heavy metal scavenger (wastewater treatment)

starch, thermochemically-converted

Production:
• starch + ammonium persulphate (oxidative crosslinking)

Uses: surface sizing (paper)

starch acetate

$$RO-\overset{\overset{\displaystyle O}{\|}}{C}CH_3$$

R = starch-. Starch with usually <5% acetyl content, equivalent to a degree of substitution of <0.2. The acetyl groups prevent association of the outer branches of amylopectin and so stabilise the starch in solution.

Production:
• starch + acetic anhydride (acetylation)

Uses:
surface sizing (paper); thickening agent (prepared foods); warp sizing (polyester-cotton blends)

starch-acrylamide graft copolymers
starch-acrylonitrile graft copolymers; SPAN

$$RO-CH_2CH_2\overset{\overset{O}{\|}}{C}NH_2$$

R = starch-.

Production:
• starch + acrylonitrile (cyanoethylation/nitrile hydration)

Uses: adhesives (gummed tapes)

starch hydrolysate
dextrose hydrosylate

Glucose syrup containing principally D-glucose. Different grades are characterised by their reduced sugar content expressed in terms of dextrose equivalents (DE). Starch hydrosylates have DE>80.

Production:
• glucose syrup + glucoamylase (enzymatic hydrolysis)

Derivatives:
ethanol; D-glucose; D-glucuronolactone; high-fructose syrup; α-methylglucoside; pentaacetylglucose; sodium glucoheptonate; sodium gluconate; sorbitol

stearalkonium chloride
See: dimethylstearylbenzylammonium chloride

stearamide
[124-26-5]

$$CH_3(CH_2)_{16}\overset{\overset{O}{\|}}{C}NH_2$$

$C_{18}H_{37}N_1O_1$. M: 283.50. White solid. Drop point: 100–104°C. Insoluble in water.

Production:
• stearic acid + ammonia (amide formation)

Derivatives: stearamidomethylpyridinium chloride

Uses: lubricant (textile spinning); plastics processing lubricant; slip improvement additive (printing ink); softening agent (textile finishes); solubiliser (oil-soluble dyestuffs); shampoo thickening agent/foam booster

stearamidomethylpyridinium chloride
octadecanamidomethylpyridinium chloride

$$CH_3(CH_2)_{16}\overset{\overset{O}{\|}}{C}NHCH_2\overset{+}{N}\bigcirc \quad Cl^-$$

$C_{24}H_{43}Cl_1N_2O_1$. M: 411.06.

Production:
• stearamide + formaldehyde + pyridine + hydrochloric acid (Mannich reaction/salt formation)

Uses: textile waterproofing agent

stearamidopropyldimethylamine
[7651-02-7]

$$CH_3(CH_2)_{16}\overset{\overset{O}{\|}}{C}NHCH_2CH_2CH_2N(CH_3)_2$$

$C_{23}H_{48}N_2O_1$. M: 368.64.

Production:
• stearic acid + 3-dimethylaminopropylamine (amide formation)

Derivatives:
stearamidopropyldimethylamine lactate

Uses: conditioning agent/emulsifier (cosmetics, toiletries); softening agent (textile finishes)

stearamidopropyldimethylamine lactate
[55819-53-9]

$$CH_3(CH_2)_{16}\overset{\overset{O}{\|}}{C}NHCH_2CH_2CH_2\overset{+}{N}H(CH_3)_2 \quad CH_3\overset{\overset{OH}{|}}{C}HCOO^-$$

$C_{26}H_{54}N_2O_4$. M: 458.73.

Production:
• stearamidopropyldimethylamine + DL-lactic acid (salt formation)

Uses:
conditioning agent (cosmetics, toiletries)

stearamine *See:* stearylamine

stearic acid
palmitic/stearic acids; stearic/palmitic acids; stearine; stearin

$$CH_3(CH_2)_{16}COOH$$

$C_{18}H_{36}O_2$. M: 284.48. Colourless, waxy solid. d: 0.84 kg/l (80°C). Several grades of stearic acid are available commercially which vary in composition depending on the source and processing. A typical chain-length distribution of hydrogenated tallow is: 2% C_{14}, 38% C_{16}, 58% C_{18}, with MP: 54–59°C. Stearin, separated from the olein fraction of tallow by physical means, has a chain-length distribution like: 2.5% C_{14}, 50% C_{16}, 44% $C_{18:1}$, 3% $C_{18:2}$ for the 'triple-pressed' grade. 'Single-pressed' and 'double-pressed' grades have higher $C_{18:2}$ acid contents. Pure stearic acid, produced by fractional distillation, has a typical chain-length distribution of: 5% C_{16}, 93% C_{18}, 2% C_{20} with MP: 64–67°C.

Production:
• tallow acid (selective crystallisation or solvent separation; coproduced with oleic acid)
• tallow, hydrogenated (hydrolysis)

Derivatives: aluminium tristearate; ammonium stearate; barium stearate; barium-zinc heat stabilisers; *n*-butyl

stearate; cadmium-zinc heat stabilisers; calcium stearate; calcium stearoyl-2-lactylate; cetyl stearate; cetyl-stearyl stearate; diethylene glycol monostearate; ethylene bis(stearamide); ethylene glycol distearate; ethylene glycol monostearate; 2-ethylhexyl stearate; ethyl stearate; glycerol monostearate; guanidine stearate; hexamethylenebis(stearamide); isobutyl stearate; isooctyl stearate; isopropyl stearate; isotridecyl stearate; lead stearate, dibasic; lead stearate, normal; lithium stearate; magnesium stearate; methyl stearate; pentaerythritol tetrastearate; polyethylene glycol distearate; polyethylene glycol monostearate; polyglycerol fatty esters; potassium stearate; propylene glycol monostearate; sodium stearate; sodium stearoyl-2-lactylate; sorbitan monostearate; sorbitan tristearate; stearamide; stearamidopropyldimethylamine; stearic acid diethanolamide; stearic acid fish amide; stearic acid monoethanolamide; stearic anhydride; *N*-stearoyl-*p*-aminophenol; stearoyl chloride; stearyl alcohol; stearylamine; stearyl stearate; tristearin; zinc stearate
Uses:
candles; organophilic/antistatic coatings (calcium carbonate fillers/polystyrene beads); emollient/superfatting agent (cosmetics); lubricity additive (lubricants); paper sizing ingredient (speciality papers); plastics processing lubricant; polyvinyl chloride heat costabilisers; textile auxiliary; vulcanisation activator

stearic acid diethanolamide
stearic acid polydiethanolamide

$C_{22}H_{45}N_1O_3$. M: 371.61. Mixed Kritchevsky reaction product containing 60% fatty diethanolamide and 25% diethanolamine.
Production:
• stearic acid + diethanolamine (Kritchevsky reaction)
Uses: petrol antiicing additive; emulsifier/corrosion inhibitor (soluble cutting oils)

stearic acid fish amide

R = fish-.
Production:
• stearic acid + fish amine (amide formation)
Uses:
internal plastics processing lubricant

stearic acid monoethanolamide
stearamide MEA (CTFA); [111-57-9]

$C_{20}H_{41}N_1O_2$. M: 327.56. White or yellow flakes.

Production:
• stearic acid + monoethanolamine (amide formation)
Uses: emulsifier/pearlising/thickening agent (soaps, toiletries, cosmetics); foam stabiliser (laundry detergents)

stearic acid polydiethanolamide
See: stearic acid diethanolamide

stearic anhydride

$C_{36}H_{70}O_3$. M: 550.96. Solid. MP: 71°C. d: 0.84 kg/l. Insoluble in water and alcohol.
Production:
• stearyl ketene + stearic acid (addition)
Uses: paper sizing ingredient

stearin *See:* stearic acid

stearoamphoglycinate *See:* stearylimidazoline betaine

N-stearoyl-*p*-aminophenol
4-hydroxystearanilide; Suconox-18 (Hexcel); [103-99-1]

$C_{24}H_{41}N_1O_2$. M: 375.60.
Production:
• stearic acid + *p*-aminophenol (amide formation)
Uses: antioxidant (plastics)

stearoylbenzoylmethane

$C_{26}H_{42}O_2$. M: 386.63.
Production:
• stearyl ketene + acetophenone (condensation)
Uses: polyvinyl chloride heat costabilisers

stearoyl chloride

$C_{18}H_{35}Cl_1O_1$. M: 302.93. Liquid or solid. MP: 23°C. Soluble in hot water.
Production:
• stearic acid (acid chloride formation)
Derivatives: stearyl ketene

stearyl alcohol
1-octadecanol; octadecanol; *n*-octadecanol; octadecyl alcohol; [112-92-5]
$C_{18}H_{38}O_1$. M: 270.50.

$$CH_3(CH_2)_{17}OH$$

Production:
- ethylene (Alfol/Epal processes; coproduced with *n*-hexanol/*n*-octanol/*n*-decanol/*n*-alkanol(C_8-C_{10})/ lauryl alcohol, narrow-cut/myristyl alcohol/ *n*-alkanol(C_{12}-C_{14})/cetyl alcohol/cetylstearyl alcohol/ *n*-alkanol(C_{12}-C_{18})/*n*-alkanol(C_{20+}))
- stearic acid/methyl stearate (hydrogenation)
- cetylstearyl alcohol (fractionation; coproduced with cetyl alcohol)

Derivatives:
dimethylstearylamine; distearylpentaerythrityl diphosphite; distearyl thiodipropionate; octadecyl vinyl ether; stearyl alcohol ethoxylates; stearylamine; stearyl 3-(3′,5′-di-*t*-butyl-4′-hydroxyphenyl)propionate; stearyl mercaptan; stearyl methacrylate; stearyl phosphoric acid; stearyl stearate

Uses:
plastics processing lubricant

stearyl alcohol ethoxylates
POE stearyl ether; steareth (CTFA)

$$CH_3(CH_2)_{17}(OCH_2CH_2)_nOH$$

n = 2–100. White solids. HLB: 4.0–15.3 (2–20 moles EO). Soluble in alcohol. Higher ethoxylated grades are dispersible in water.
Production:
- stearyl alcohol + ethylene oxide (epoxidation)
Uses: emollient/lubricant, emulsifier (cosmetics, pharmaceuticals)

stearylamine
hydrogenated tallowamine; stearamine; [124-30-1]; [61788-45-2]

$$CH_3(CH_2)_{17}NH_2$$

$C_{18}H_{39}N_1$. M: 269.52. Solid. MP: 45–47°C. Typical chain-length distribution: 5% C_{14}, 30% C_{16}, 65% C_{18}.
Production:
- stearic acid + ammonia (nitrile formation/ hydrogenation)
- stearyl alcohol + ammonia (reductive ammoniation)

Derivatives:
dimethylstearylamine; distearylamine; erucic acid stearylamide; fish acid stearylamide; stearylamine acetate; stearylamine ethoxylates; stearyl-1,3-propanediamine; tetrasodium *N*-(1,2-dicarboxyethyl)-*N*-octadecylsulphosuccinamate
Uses: cationic flotation agent (potash ores); filler dispersant (paper production); motor fuel distribution improvement additive; pigment grinding/dispersing agent; bitumen adhesion promotion agents; anticaking agent (fertilisers); antistatic agent (plastics); plastics mould release agent; organophilic surface treatment agent (china clay)

stearylamine acetate
hydrogenated tallowamine acetate; stearamine acetate; stearylammonium acetate

$$CH_3(CH_2)_{17}NH_3^+ \quad CH_3COO^-$$

$C_{20}H_{43}N_1O_2$. M: 329.57. Solid. MP: 60°C. HLB: 10.7. A typical chain-length distribution is: 5% C_{14}, 30% C_{16}, 65% C_{18}.
Production:
- stearylamine + acetic acid (salt formation)
Uses: dispersant/drainage aid/pitch emulsifier (paper production); anticaking agent (fertilisers); organophilic surface treatment agent (china clay)

stearylamine ethoxylates
hydrogenated tallowamine ethoxylates; PEG stearamine

$$RN \begin{cases} (CH_2CH_2O)_mH \\ (CH_2CH_2O)_nH \end{cases}$$

R = stearyl-, m+n = 2–15. Stearylamine ethoxylates are liquids containing 5–30 moles EO. HLB: 15.0–19.0 (5–30 moles EO).
Production:
- stearylamine + ethylene oxide (epoxidation)
Uses:
corrosion inhibitor; emulsifier (wax, soluble oils, pesticides, cleaners, bitumen, silicone oils); antistatic agent (textile spin finishes, paper processing, plastics); wetting/dispersing agent (electrostatic paints, inks, dyes, pigments)

stearyl 3-(3′,5′-di-*t*-butyl-4′-hydroxyphenyl)propionate
octadecyl 3,5-di-*t*-butyl-4-hydroxyhydrocinnamate; Ethanox 376 (Ethyl); Irganox 1076 (Ciba-Geigy); Naugard 76 (Uniroyal Chemical); Oxi-Chek 116 (Ferro); Ultranox 276 (Borg-Warner Chemicals); [2082-79-3]

$C_{35}H_{62}O_3$. M: 530.88.
Production:
- stearyl alcohol + methyl 3,5-di-*t*-butyl-4-hydroxyphenylpropionate (transesterification)
Uses: antioxidant (plastics, rubber)

stearyldimethylamine *See:* dimethylstearylamine

stearyldimethylammonium-3-sulphopropylbetaine
Ralufon DS (Raschig)

$C_{23}H_{49}N_1O_3S_1$. M: 419.71.

Production:
- dimethylstearylamine + propane sultone
  (quaternisation)

Uses: amphoteric surfactant (shampoos/detergents)

stearyldimethylbenzylammonium chloride
See: dimethylstearylbenzylammonium chloride

stearyl imidazoline
2-heptadecyl-1-hydroxyethylimidazoline; 2-heptadecyl-2-imidazoline-1-ethanol; 1-hydroxyethyl-2-heptadecyl-imidazoline; tallow imidazoline

$$CH_3(CH_2)_{16} \quad \begin{array}{c} N \\ \diagdown \\ N \\ | \\ HOCH_2CH_2 \end{array}$$

$C_{22}H_{44}N_2O_1$. M: 352.60. Lipophilic surfactant. Dissolves readily in non-polar solvents. Acid salts are adsorbed on negatively charged surfaces and have excellent wetting, foam and detergent properties.
Production:
- tallow acid + aminoethylethanolamine
  (condensation)

Derivatives:
stearylimidazoline betaine

Uses: corrosion inhibitor (lubricant additives, oilfield chemicals); flotation collector (sulphide ores); petrol antiicing additive; antistatic agent (textile spin finishes); oil-soluble emulsifier (industrial detergents, cleaners, adhesives, pesticides); softening agent (textile finishes)

stearylimidazoline betaine
stearoamphoglycinate (CTFA)

$$CH_3(CH_2)_{16} \quad \begin{array}{c} N \\ \diagdown \\ N^+ \\ | \quad \diagdown \\ HOCH_2CH_2 \quad CH_2COO^- \end{array}$$

$C_{24}H_{46}N_2O_3$. M: 410.64. White paste containing 20–30% active matter in water.
Production:
- stearyl imidazoline + sodium chloroacetate
  (dehydrochlorination)

Uses:
conditioning agent (hair products); surfactant (metal polishes); antistatic agent (textile spin finishes)

stearyl ketene
alkyl ketene

$$CH_3(CH_2)_{15}CH=C=O$$

$C_{18}H_{34}O_1$. M: 266.47.
Production:
- stearoyl chloride (dehydrochlorination)

Derivatives:
alkylketene dimer; stearic anhydride; stearoylbenzoyl-methane

stearyl mercaptan
octadecan-1-thiol; octadecyl mercaptan; [2885-00-9]

$$CH_3(CH_2)_{17}SH$$

$C_{18}H_{38}S_1$. M: 286.56. Solid. MP: 25°C. BP: 205–209°C (1.4 kPa). d: 0.84 kg/l.
Production:
- stearyl alcohol + sodium hydrosulphide (thiolation)

Derivatives:
distearyl disulphide

Uses: silver antitarnishing agent

stearyl methacrylate
alkyl(C_{16}-C_{18}) methacrylate; [32360-05-7]

$$CH_2=\overset{\overset{O}{\|}}{\underset{\underset{CH_3}{|}}{C}}CO(CH_2)_{17}CH_3$$

$C_{22}H_{42}O_2$. M: 338.58. Liquid or solid. BP: 310–370°C. FP: 15°C. d: 0.86 kg/l (25°C). Insoluble in water. Commercial products are stabilised with hydroquinone or similar polymerisation inhibitors.
Production:
- stearyl alcohol + methyl methacrylate
  (transesterification)

Derivatives:
polymethacrylates, oil-soluble; polymethacrylates, oil-soluble dispersants

stearyl phosphoric acid
stearyl acid phosphate

$$\left[CH_3(CH_2)_{17}O\right]_n \overset{\overset{O}{\|}}{P}(OH)_{3-n}$$

n = 1–2.
Production:
- stearyl alcohol + phosphorus pentoxide (reaction)

Uses: emulsifier/wetting agent (industrial cleaners)

stearyl-1,3-propanediamine
hydrogenated tallow-1,3-diaminopropane; *N*-(hydrogenated tallow)-1,3-propylenediamine; stearyl-1,3-diaminopropane

$$CH_3(CH_2)_{17}NHCH_2CH_2CH_2NH_2$$

$C_{21}H_{46}N_2$. M: 326.61. Paste. MP: 40°C.
Production:
- stearylamine + acrylonitrile (cyanoethylation/nitrile
  reduction)

Uses: bitumen adhesion promotion agents

stearyl stearate
[2778-96-3]

$$CH_3(CH_2)_{16}\overset{\overset{O}{\|}}{C}O(CH_2)_{17}CH_3$$

$C_{36}H_{72}O_2$. M: 536.98.

Production:
• stearyl alcohol + stearic acid (esterification)
Uses: plastics processing lubricant

sterculia gum *See:* gum karaya

stigmasterol
[83-48-7]

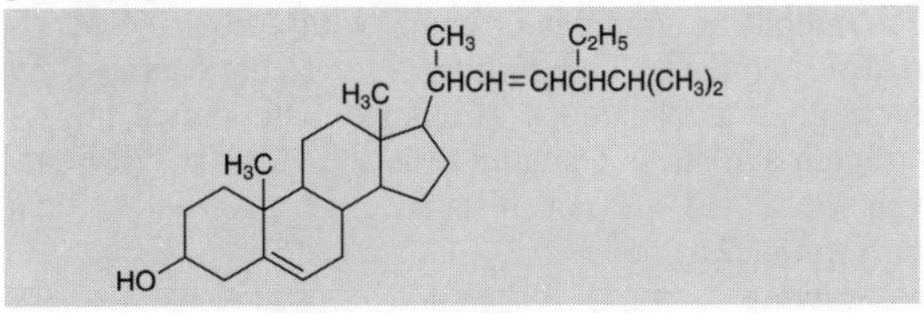

$C_{29}H_{48}O_1$. M: 412.70. Crystalline solid. MP: 170°C. Insoluble in water. Soluble in oxygenated and chlorinated solvents.
Production:
• phytosterols, mixed (separation)
Derivatives: progesterone

stilbene-4,4′-dicarboxylic acid
SDA

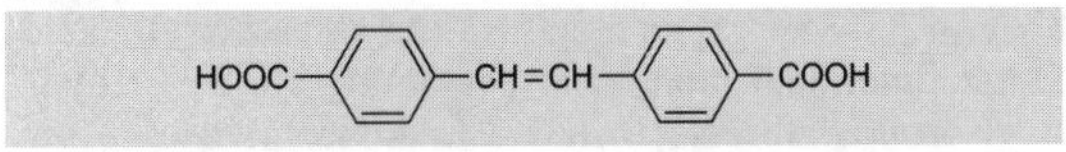

$C_{16}H_{12}O_4$. M: 268.28. The *trans*-isomer is used in liquid-crystal polymer applications.
Production:
• *p*-toluic acid (oxidative coupling)
Derivatives:
4,4′-bis(benzoxazol-2-yl)stilbene
Uses: comonomer (liquid-crystal polymers)

Stoddard solvent *See:* white spirit

STPP *See:* sodium tripolyphosphate

strawberry aldehyde *See:* ethyl methylphenylglycidate

streptomycin
[57-92-1]; [6160-32-3] (hydrochloride); [3810-74-0] (sulphate)

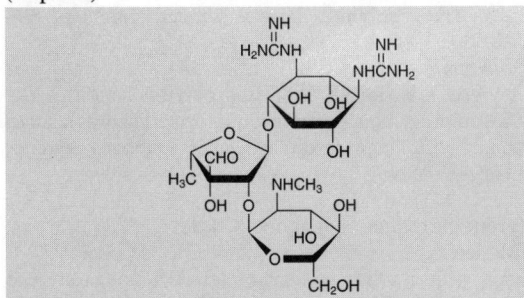

$C_{21}H_{39}N_7O_{12}$. M: 581.58.

Production:
• microbial fermentation medium + *Streptomyces griseus* bacteria (fermentation/extraction)
Uses: antituberculosis drug

strontium carbonate
[1633-05-2]

SrCO₃

$C_1O_3Sr_1$. M: 147.63. White powder. Decomposes on heating to 1,350°C. Strontianite is the natural strontium carbonate mineral.
Production:
• celestite ore + sodium carbonate (ore roasting/salt formation)
• strontium carbonate, natural (extraction)
Derivatives:
ferrite; strontium chromate; strontium nitrate
Uses: phosphor glass ingredient (television, CRT screens); ferrite ceramics raw material; reagent (electrolytic zinc production)

strontium chromate
Pigment Yellow 32 (CI); [7789-06-2]

SrCrO₄

$Cr_1O_4Sr_1$. M: 203.62. Yellow pigment. d: 3.90 kg/l. Slightly soluble in water.
Production:
• strontium carbonate + sodium dichromate (precipitation)
Uses: chrome plating reagent; anticorrosion pigment (protective paints)

strontium nitrate
[10042-76-9]

Sr(NO₃)₂

$N_2O_6Sr_1$. M: 211.62. White powder. MP: 570°C. d: 2.99 kg/l. Solubility in water: 570 g/l (25°C).
Production:
• strontium carbonate + nitric acid (neutralisation)
Uses: fireworks/flares ingredient

STS *See:* sodium *p*-toluenesulphonate

styrallyl alcohol *See:* 1-phenylethanol

styrene
styrene monomer; [100-42-5]

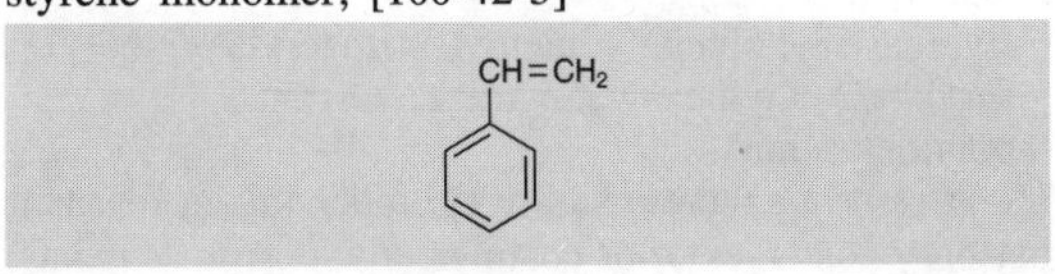

C_8H_8. M: 104.15. Colourless liquid with a strong, characteristic odour. BP: 145°C. FP: -31°C. d: 0.90 kg/l

(25°C). Polymerises on heating. Insoluble in water. Miscible with most organic solvents. Flash point: 34°C (TCC). Commercial grades are stabilised with up to 50 ppm of *t*-butylcatechol or a similar inhibitor.

Production:
- ethylbenzene (dehydrogenation)
- ethylbenzene + propylene + oxygen (Arco SM-PO process; coproduced with propylene oxide)

Derivatives: acrylic resins, amidated; acrylic resins, carboxylated; acrylic resins, hydroxylated; acrylonitrile-butadiene-styrene copolymers; acrylonitrile-(ethylene-propylene-diene)-styrene copolymers; acrylonitrile-styrene-acrylic ester copolymers; alkyd resins, styrenated/vinyltoluenated; diphenylamine, styrenated; eprazinone; hydratropaldehyde; methyl methacrylate-butadiene-styrene copolymers; methyl methacrylate copolymers, high molecular weight; phenol, styrenated; polyols, polymer; polystyrene, expandable; polystyrene, general-purpose; polystyrene, high-impact; styrene-acrylic copolymers; styrene-acrylonitrile copolymers; styrene-butadiene copolymers, carboxylated; styrene-butadiene copolymers, high-styrene; styrene-butadiene copolymers, latex; styrene-butadiene copolymers, rubber; styrene-butadiene block copolymers, branched; styrene-butadiene random copolymers, hydrogenated; styrene-butadiene triblock copolymers; styrene-divinylbenzene copolymers; styrene-fumarate copolymers; styrene-isoprene block copolymers, hydrogenated; styrene-isoprene triblock copolymers; styrene-maleic anhydride copolymers; styrene-α-methylstyrene copolymers; styrene-α-methylstyrene copolymers, low molecular weight; styrene oxide; tranylcypromine; unsaturated polyester resins, coating grades; unsaturated polyester resins, general grades; unsaturated polyester resins, isophthalate grades; vinyl ester resins; vinylpyridine copolymers, latex

Uses: cast resins (electronic components); nitrile rubber comonomer; alkyd/epoxy ester resin modifier; reactive diluent (unsaturated polyester resins)

styrene-acrylic copolymers

R = *n*-butyl, 2-ethylhexyl-. Latex containing 45–55% solids. Grades for paint applications contain, typically, 55% styrene.

Production:
- styrene/vinyltoluene + methyl methacrylate/*n*-butyl acrylate/2-ethylhexyl acrylate (emulsion polymerisation)

Uses: cement/concrete additive; binder (alkali-resistant masonry paints, exterior coatings, low-cost matt paints, metal primers); sealants/caulks/roofing compounds; tile adhesive

styrene-acrylonitrile copolymers
SAN; Kostil (ENI)

Thermoplastic granules or beads with a 20–30% acrylonitrile content. The polymers are characterised by their good transparency combined with better impact strength and stress cracking resistance than polystyrene. Chemical and solvent resistance is also better than polystyrene.

Production:
- styrene + acrylonitrile (polymerisation)

Uses: bottles/stoppers; glossy houseware/picnicware; vehicle dashboard/lighting components; telephone/office machinery/household appliance components; toilet/stationary articles

styrene-butadiene copolymers, carboxylated
XSBR

Latex with a solids content of 50–55%. These products contain 35–85% styrene and up to 5% carboxylic acid. Other functional monomers containing amino or hydroxyl groups are also included in some grades.

Production:
- styrene + butadiene + acrylic acid/methacrylic acid/itaconic acid (emulsion polymerisation)

Uses:
bonding agent (casein, protein glues); construction adhesives; textile/paper/leather/foil laminating adhesives; binder (carpet underlay, needle-punched carpet, tufted carpet secondary backing/precoating, non-woven fabric, paper coatings); cement admixture

styrene-butadiene copolymers, high-styrene
high-styrene resins; styrene resins

Latex. These polymers have a styrene content of 80–85%.

Production:
- styrene + butadiene (emulsion polymerisation)

Uses: impregnating resins (thermoformed boards); shoe-soling; stiffening/reinforcing agent (rubber, styrene-butadiene latex)

styrene-butadiene copolymers, latex
SBR latex

Latex with a solids content of 60–70% and a styrene content of 20–35% (cold polymerised grades) or 45% (hot polymerised grades).

$$\left[CH_2-CH\right]_x \left[CH_2CH=CHCH_2\right]_y$$

Production:
* styrene + butadiene (emulsion polymerisation)

Uses: adhesives (floor tiles); asbestos-sized tiles/roofing felts; paper coatings; latex foam (tufted carpet/fabric backcoating, moulded items); non-woven fabric sizing

styrene-butadiene copolymers, rubber
SBR; styrene-butadiene rubber

$$\left[CH_2-CH\right]_x \left[CH_2CH=CHCH_2\right]_y$$

Several different grades of styrene-butadiene rubber are available. Styrene contents are commonly 23–25%, but up to 40% in some grades. For emulsion grades, the monomer ratio, polymerisation temperature, emulsifier/stabiliser system and additives, particular oil or carbon black, are all important factors in determining properties. With solution grades, there is greater manufacturing flexibility allowing random, tapered and block copolymer grades to be produced. Grades with a higher 1,2-butadiene content are also produced.

Production:
* styrene + butadiene (emulsion polymerisation)
* styrene + butadiene (solution polymerisation)

Uses: cable insulation/jacketing; conveyor/drive belts; solvent-based construction, pressure-sensitive, laminating/sprayable adhesives; hoses; moulded rubber goods; shoe-soling; tyres

styrene-butadiene block copolymers, branched
K-Resin (Phillips Petroleum)

The resin is a star-shaped polymer made from styrene-butadiene blocks joined by a multifunctional coupling agent. The styrene content is about 75% giving transparent, tough polymers which are easy to process.

Production:
* styrene + butadiene (solution polymerisation)

Uses: moulded toys/household items; specialist medical/industrial mouldings

styrene-butadiene random copolymers, hydrogenated

$$\left[CH_2-CH\right]_x \left[CH_2CH_2CH_2CH_2\right]_y$$

M: 75,000–200,000.

Production:
* styrene + butadiene (polymerisation/hydrogenation)

Uses: viscosity modifier (lubricating oils)

styrene-butadiene triblock copolymers
SBS; Cariflex TR (Shell); Kraton D (Shell); Solprene (Phillips Petroleum)

Thermoplastic elastomers produced by coupling together styrene-butadiene diblock copolymers into a S-B-S triblock. Other shaped polymers are also produced using higher functionality coupling agents. The styrene content is, typically, 30%. M: 80,000–100,000.

$$\left[CH_2-CH\right]_x \left[CH_2CH=CHCH_2\right]_y \left[CH_2-CH\right]_z$$

Production:
* styrene + butadiene (solution polymerisation)

Uses: bitumen modifier; hot melt adhesives; pressure-sensitive adhesives; roller coverings; thermoplastic rubber shoe soling compounds

styrene-divinylbenzene copolymers
polystyrene, crosslinked; poly(styrene-divinylbenzene)

$$\left[CH_2-CH\right]_x \left[CH_2-CH\right]_y$$
$$\left[CH-CH_2\right]_z$$

Produced as beads of various mesh size.

Production:
* styrene + divinylbenzene (suspension polymerisation)

Derivatives: polystyrene, crosslinked, aminated; polystyrene, crosslinked, hydroxyethyldimethylbenzylammoniated; polystyrene, crosslinked, phosphonated; polystyrene, crosslinked, sulphonated; polystyrene, crosslinked, trimethylbenzylammoniated

styrene-fumarate copolymers
Oil-soluble polymers containing a small proportion of polar groups. Available as solutions containing 35–45% active matter in mineral oil. M: 350,000–700,000.

Production:
* styrene + fumaric acid + tallow alcohol + N-(3-aminopropyl)morpholine (polymerisation/esterification/amide formation)

Uses: ashless dispersants/viscosity modifiers (lubricants)

styrene-isoprene block copolymers, hydrogenated
Shellvis (Shell)

$$\left[CH_2-CH\right]_x \left[CH_2\overset{CH_3}{CH}CH_2CH_2\right]_y$$

x = 300–500, y = 6,000–12,000. M: 30,000–50,000 (styrene segment), 50,000–100,000 (isoprene segment).

Production:
- styrene + isoprene (solution polymerisation/ hydrogenation)

Uses:
viscosity modifier (lubricating oils)

styrene-isoprene triblock copolymers
SIS; Cariflex TR (Shell); Kraton D (Shell)

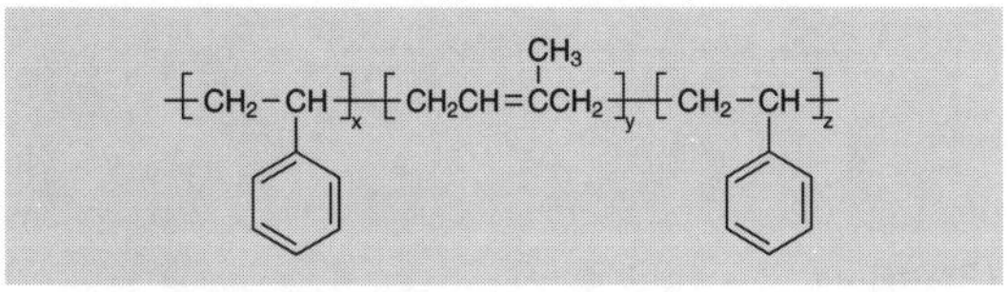

Thermoplastic elastomers produced by coupling together styrene-isoprene diblock copolymers into a S-I-S triblock. The styrene content is, typically, 14%.

Production:
- styrene + isoprene (solution polymerisation)

Uses:
bitumen modifier; hot melt/pressure-sensitive adhesives; roller coverings; thermoplastic rubber shoe soling compounds

styrene-maleic anhydride copolymers
Scripset (Monsanto); SMA Resin (Total Chimie)

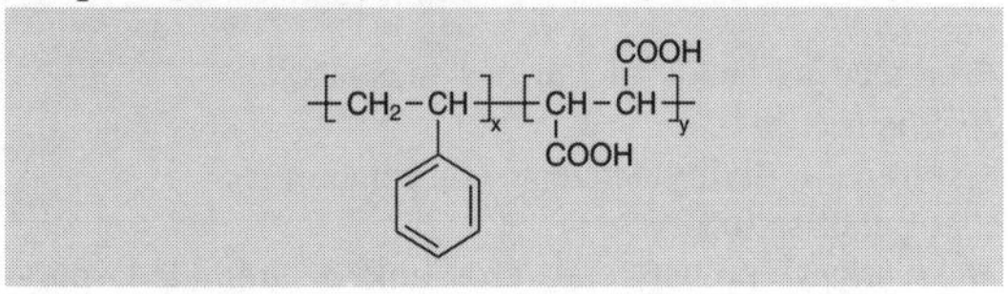

Ratios of styrene to maleic anhydride vary from 1:1 to 3:1. Some products are alkali-soluble, others solvent-soluble.

Production:
- styrene + maleic anhydride (polymerisation)

Uses:
adhesion promotion agent; floor wax ingredient; paper/ textile sizing ingredient; processing aid (polyvinyl chloride); binder/thickening agent (water-based paints, printing inks)

styrene-α-methylstyrene copolymers
SMS

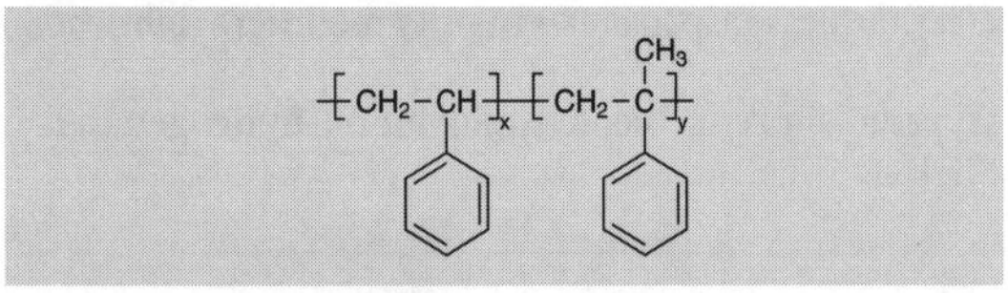

Thermoplastic similar to polystyrene but with improved heat resistance and optical properties.

Production:
- styrene + α-methylstyrene (polymerisation)

Uses:
injection-moulded household equipment

styrene-α-methylstyrene copolymers, low molecular weight
SMS; Kristalex (Hercules)

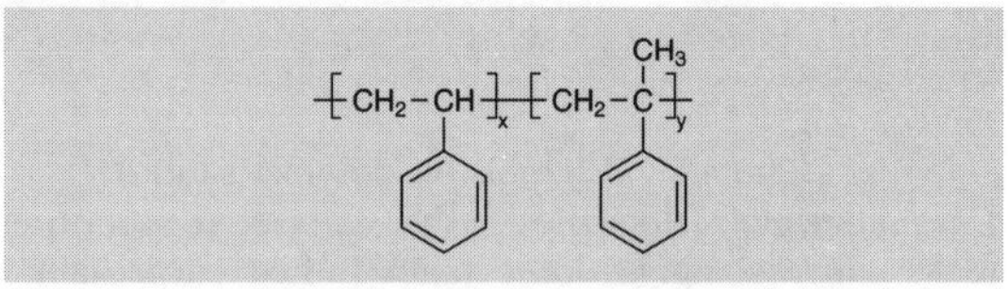

Low molecular weight hydrocarbon resin. Softening point: 25–140°C (Ring and Ball Method).

Production:
- styrene + α-methylstyrene (polymerisation)

Uses:
tackifier/modifier resin (adhesives)

styrene oxide
[96-09-3]

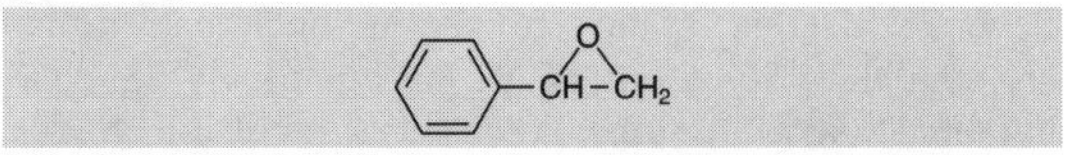

$C_8H_8O_1$. M: 120.15. Colourless liquid. BP: 194°C. FP: -37°C. d: 1.05 kg/l (25°C). Practically insoluble in water.

Production:
- styrene (hypochlorination/dehydrochlorination)

Derivatives: fenyramidol; nomifensine; phenylacetaldehyde; tetramisole

Uses: reactive diluent (epoxy resins)

suberic acid
hexane-1,6-dicarboxylic acid; octane-1,8-dioic acid; [505-48-6]

$$HOOC(CH_2)_6COOH$$

$C_8H_{14}O_4$. M: 174.20. White crystals. MP: 140–144°C. Sublimes at 300°C. Soluble in hot water. Slightly soluble in cold water.

Production:
- cyclooctene (oxidative cleavage)

Derivatives: cycloheptanone; guazatine acetate

suberone *See:* cycloheptanone

succinchlorimide *See:* N-chlorosuccinimide

succinic acid
butanedioic acid; [110-15-6]

$$CH_2COOH$$
$$CH_2COOH$$

$C_4H_6O_4$. M: 118.09. Colourless crystals. MP: 188°C with dehydration. d: 1.56 kg/l. Solubility in water: 77 g/l water (20°C).

Production:
- maleic anhydride (hydrogenation/hydration)
- dimethyl succinate (hydrolysis)

Derivatives: di-*n*-butyl succinate; diethyl succinate; dimethyl succinate; sodium succinate; succinimide; succinonitrile; suxamethonium chloride
Uses: food buffering agent; alkyd/unsaturated polyester resin comonomer

succinic acid peroxide

monoperoxysuccinic acid; succinyl peroxide; [123-23-9]

$$HOOCCH_2CH_2CO-OCCH_2CH_2COOH$$

$C_8H_{10}O_8$. M: 234.16. White powder. MP: 125°C with decomposition. Soluble in water.
Production:
• succinic anhydride + hydrogen peroxide (peroxidation)
Uses: antiseptic/disinfectant; polymerisation initiator

succinic anhydride

SAA; [108-30-5]

$C_4H_4O_3$. M: 100.07. White, hygroscopic, crystalline solid. MP: 119–120°C. BP: 261°C. d: 1.57 kg/l. Insoluble in water. Soluble in alcohol and chlorinated solvents.
Production:
• maleic anhydride (hydrogenation)
Derivatives: daminozide; ethyl succinyl chloride; succinic acid peroxide
Uses: epoxy resin curing agent

succinimide

[123-56-8]

$C_4H_5N_1O_2$. M: 99.09. White crystals. MP: 126°C. BP: 288°C. Soluble in hot water.
Production:
• succinic acid + ammonia (amide formation)
Derivatives:
N-bromosuccinimide; *N*-chlorosuccinimide

succinonitrile

1,2-dicyanoethane; ethylene dicyanide; [110-61-2]

$$NCCH_2CH_2CN$$

$C_4H_4N_2$. M: 80.08. Colourless solid. MP: 56°C. BP: 266°C. d: 0.98 kg/l (60°C). Soluble in water and oxygenated solvents.
Production:
• succinic acid + ammonia (nitrile formation)

• hydrogen cyanide + acrylonitrile (cyanoethylation)
Derivatives: 1,4-diaminobutane
Uses: nickel plating brightening agent

succinylcholine chloride *See:* suxamethonium chloride

sucralfate

[54182-58-0]

$R = Al_2(OH)_5SO_3$-. $C_{12}H_{54}Al_{16}O_{75}S_8$. M: 2086.70.
Production:
• sucrose + aluminium chlorohydrate + sulphur trioxide (complex formation)
Uses: ulcer therapy drug

sucrose

sugar; [57-50-1]

$C_{12}H_{22}O_{11}$. M: 342.30. White crystals. Decompose on heating above 170°C forming caramel. d: 1.59 kg/l (25°C). Available commercially as the naturally-occurring (+)-enantiomer. Soluble in water. Slightly soluble in alcohol.
Production:
• sugar cane juice (extraction)
• sugar beet juice (extraction)
Derivatives: dextran; polyether polyols, rigid; sucralfate; sucrose acetate isobutyrate; sucrose octaacetate
Uses: pharmaceutical compounding auxiliary; sweetener (prepared foods, soft drinks)

sucrose acetate isobutyrate

SAIB (Eastman Chemical); [126-13-6]

R = acetyl-, isobutyrl-. $C_{40}H_{62}O_{19}$. M: 846.92. White powder. Decomposes on heating to 288°C. d: 1.15 kg/l. Insoluble in water.
Production:
• sucrose + acetic anhydride + isobutyric acid (esterification)
Uses:
plasticiser (cellulose, polystyrene, polyvinyl acetate)

sucrose octaacetate
[126-14-7]

R = acetyl-. $C_{28}H_{38}O_{19}$. M: 678.59. White needles with a bitter taste. MP: 85°C. Decomposes on heating above 285°C. Slightly soluble in water. Soluble in oxygenated and aromatic solvents.
Production:
• sucrose + acetic anhydride (acetylation)
Uses:
alcohol denaturant

sulcofenuron
[3567-25-7]

$C_{19}H_{12}Cl_4N_2O_5S_1$. M: 522.18.
Production:
• 3,4-dichlorophenyl isocyanate + *p*-chlorophenol + 2,5-dichloroaniline (sulphonation/dehydrochlorination/isocyanate addition)
Uses:
insect resist agent (wool treatment)

sulfacarbamide
sulfanilylurea; [547-44-4]

$C_7H_9N_3O_3S_1$. M: 215.23.
Production:
• 4-acetylsulphanilamide + potassium cyanate (cyanate addition/amide hydrolysis)
Uses: antibacterial drug

sulfacetamide
p-aminobenzene sulphonoacetamide; [144-80-9]; [127-56-0] (sodium salt)

$C_8H_{10}N_2O_3S_1$. M: 214.24. Available commercially as the acid or sodium monohydrate salts.
Production:
• 4-acetylsulphanilamide + acetic anhydride (acetylation/amide hydrolysis)
Uses:
antibacterial drug

sulfadiazine
[68-35-9]; [547-32-0] (sodium salt)

$C_{10}H_{10}N_4O_2S_1$. M: 250.28. Available commercially as the sodium salt or in mixtures with trimethoprim.
Production:
• 4-acetamidobenzenesulphonyl chloride + 2-aminopyrimidine (sulphonamide formation/amide hydrolysis)
Uses: antibacterial drug

sulfadicramide
[115-68-4]

$C_{11}H_{14}N_2O_3S_1$. M: 254.30.
Production:
• acetone + cyanoacetic acid + 4-acetamidobenzenesulphonyl chloride (carbonyl condensation/decarboxylation/nitrile hydration/sulphonamide formation/amide hydrolysis)
Uses: antibacterial drug

sulfadimethoxine
[122-11-2]

$C_{12}H_{14}N_4O_4S_1$. M: 310.33.
Production:
• methyl cyanoacetate + urea + dimethyl sulphate + 4-acetamidobenzenesulphonyl chloride (condensation/methylation/sulphonamide formation/amide hydrolysis)
Uses:
antibacterial drug

sulfaethidole
[94-19-9]

$C_{10}H_{12}N_4O_2S_2$. M: 284.37.
Production:
• thiosemicarbazide + propionyl chloride + 4-acetamidobenzenesulphonyl chloride (condensation/sulphonamide formation/amide hydrolysis)
Uses:
antibacterial drug

sulfafurazole
sulfisoxazole; [127-69-5]

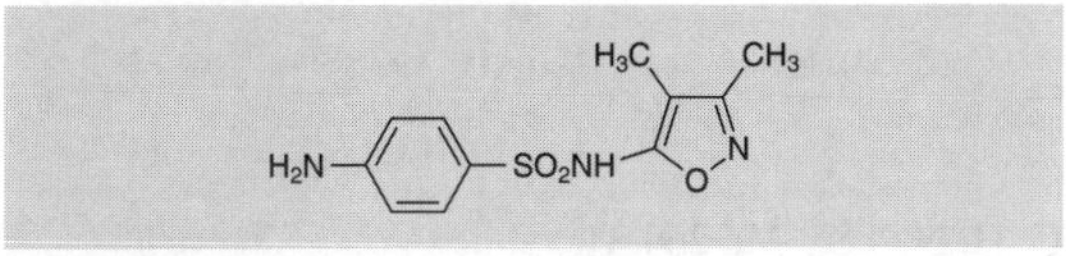

$C_{11}H_{13}N_3O_3S_1$. M: 267.30.
Production:
- propionitrile + ethyl acetate + hydroxylamine sulphate + 4-acetamidobenzenesulphonyl chloride (Claisen condensation/imine formation/cyclisation/ sulphonamide formation/amide hydrolysis)

Uses:
antibacterial drug

sulfaguanidine
[57-67-0]

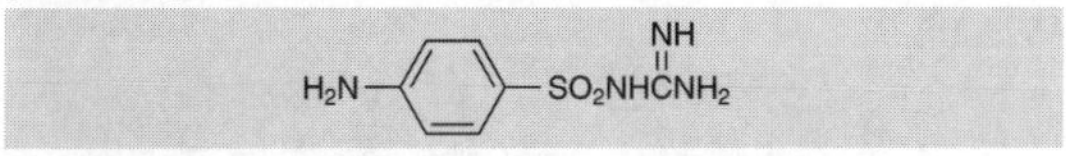

$C_7H_{10}N_4O_2S_1$. M: 214.25.
Production:
- guanidine nitrate/guanidine carbonate + 4-acetamidobenzenesulphonyl chloride (sulphonamide formation/amide hydrolysis)

Uses: antibacterial drug

sulfaguanole
[27031-08-9]

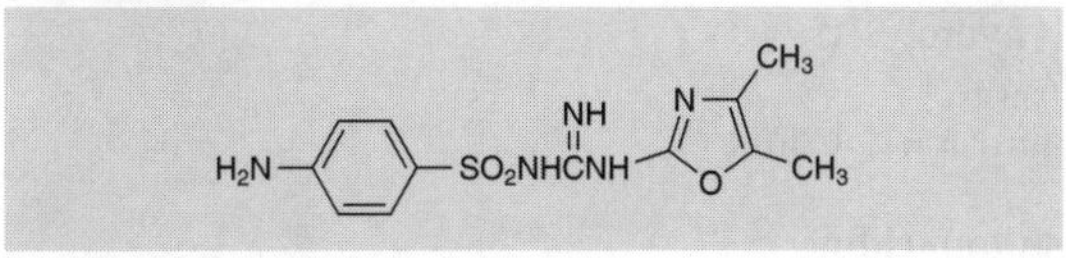

$C_{12}H_{15}N_5O_3S_1$. M: 309.34.
Production:
- 4-acetamidobenzenesulphonyl chloride + cyanamide + acetoin (sulphonamide formation/amide hydrolysis/carbonyl condensation)

Uses:
antibacterial drug

sulfalene
[152-47-6]

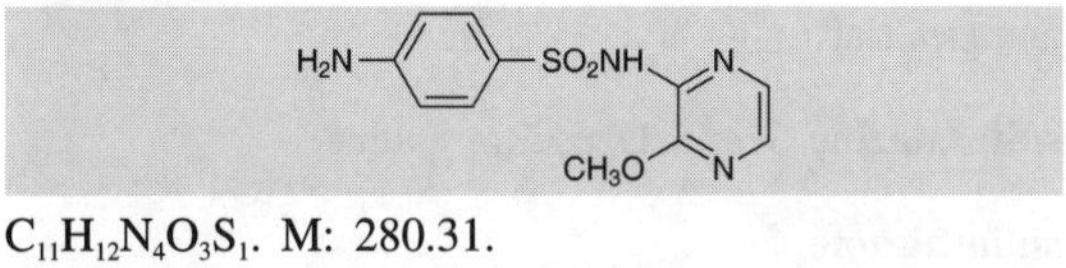

$C_{11}H_{12}N_4O_3S_1$. M: 280.31.
Production:
- glycine + ammonia + glyoxal + 4-acetamido-benzenesulphonyl chloride (amide formation/ condensation/methylation/nitration/nitro reduction/ sulphonamide formation/amide hydrolysis)

Uses:
antibacterial drug

sulfamerazine
[127-79-7]; [127-58-2] (sodium salt)

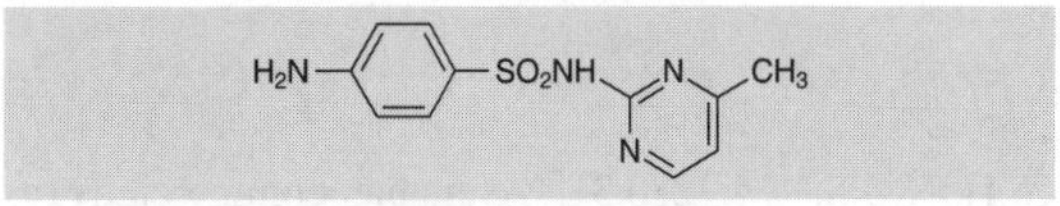

$C_{11}H_{12}N_4O_2S_1$. M: 264.31. Available commercially as the free base or as the sodium salt.
Production:
- methyl acetoacetate + guanidine hydrochloride + 4-acetamidobenzenesulphonyl chloride (condensation/reduction/sulphonamide formation/ amide hydrolysis)

Uses: antibacterial drug

sulfamethazine
[57-68-1]

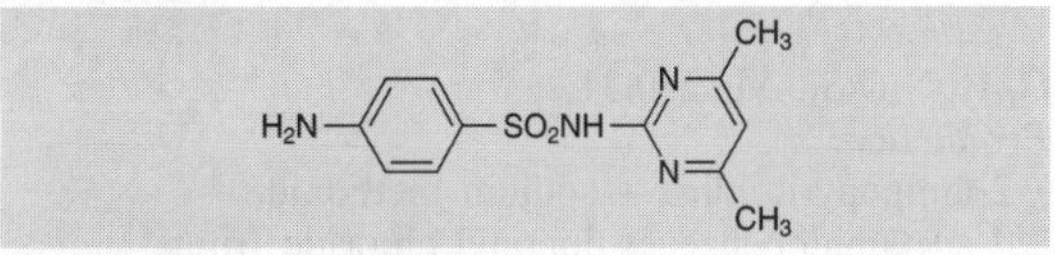

$C_{12}H_{14}N_4O_2S_1$. M: 278.33.
Production:
- 4-acetamidobenzenesulphonyl chloride + guanidine hydrochloride + acetylacetone (condensation/ sulphonamide formation/amide hydrolysis)

Uses: antibacterial drug

sulfamethizole
[144-82-1]

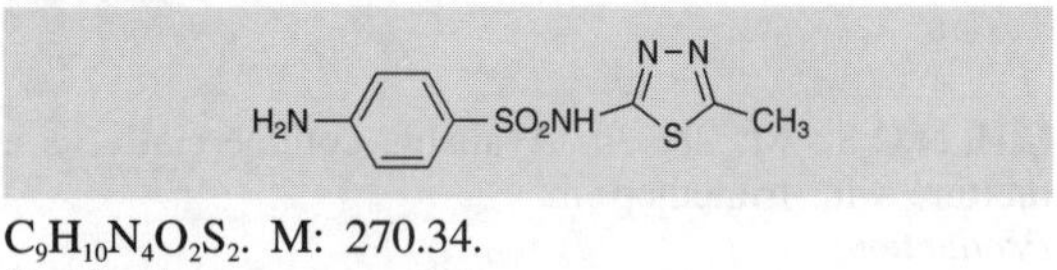

$C_9H_{10}N_4O_2S_2$. M: 270.34.
Production:
- 4-acetamidobenzenesulphonyl chloride + 2-amino-5-methyl-1,3,4-thiadiazole (sulphonamide formation/amide hydrolysis)

Uses: antibacterial drug

sulfamethoxazole
[723-46-6]

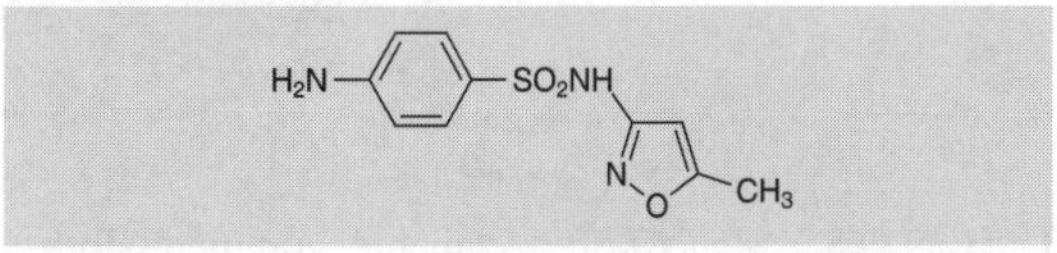

$C_{10}H_{11}N_3O_3S_1$. M: 253.28. Available commercially as the pure compound or in mixtures with trimethoprim.
Production:
- methyl acetoacetate + ammonia + hydroxylamine sulphate + 4-acetamidobenzenesulphonyl chloride (nitrile formation/amidine formation/cyclisation/ sulphonamide formation/amide hydrolysis)

Uses: antibacterial drug

sulfamethoxypyridazine
[80-35-3]

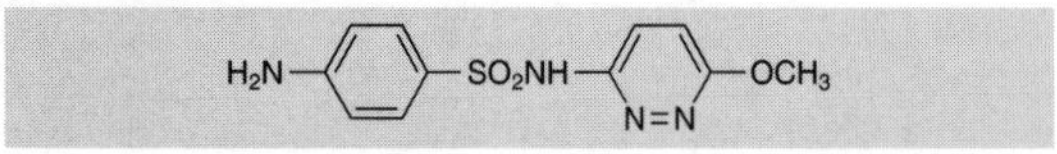

$C_{11}H_{12}N_4O_3S_1$. M: 280.31. Available commercially as the free base or acetyl derivative.
Production:
- sulphanilamide + 3,6-dichloropyridazine + sodium methoxide (amide formation/ether formation)

Uses: antibacterial drug

sulfametoxydiazine
sulfameter; [651-06-9]

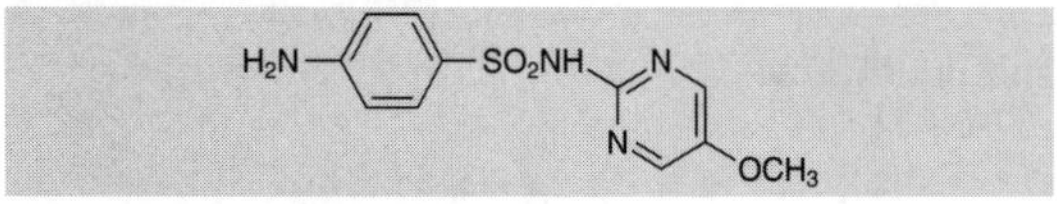

$C_{11}H_{12}N_4O_3S_1$. M: 280.31.
Production:
- 2-aminopyrimidine + sodium methoxide + 4-acetamidobenzenesulphonyl chloride (ring bromination/ether formation/sulphonamide formation/amide hydrolysis)

Uses: antibacterial drug

sulfametrole
[32909-92-5]

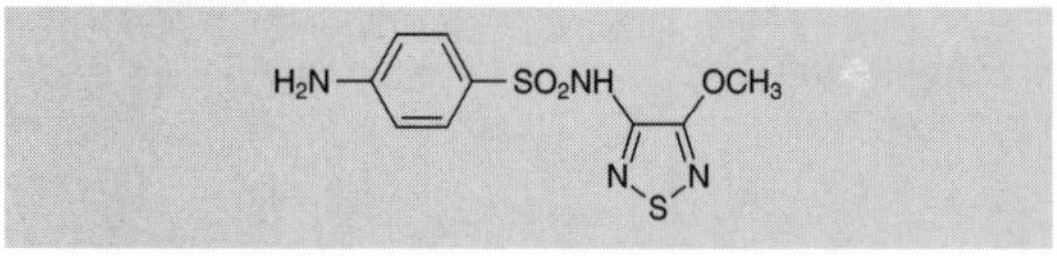

$C_9H_{10}N_4O_3S_2$. M: 286.34. Available commercially as a mixture with trimethoprim.
Production:
- oxamide + sulphur dichloride + sulphanilamide + sodium methoxide (condensation/amide formation/ether formation)

Uses: antibacterial drug

sulfamoxole
[729-99-7]

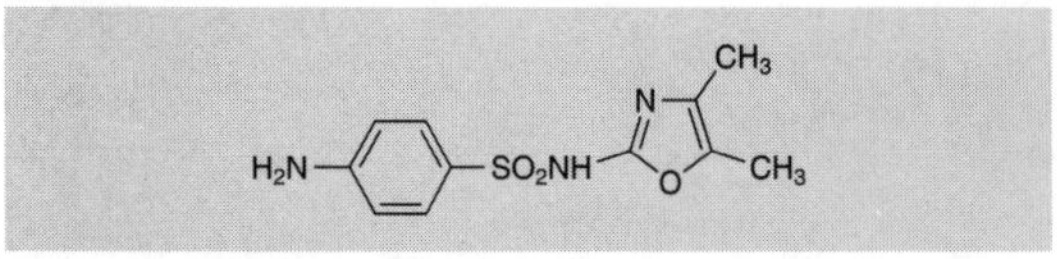

$C_{11}H_{13}N_3O_3S_1$. M: 267.30. Available commercially as the pure compound or in mixtures with trimethoprim.
Production:
- 4-acetamidobenzenesulphonyl chloride + cyanamide + acetoin (sulphonamide formation/carbonyl condensation/amide hydrolysis)

Uses: antibacterial drug

sulfanilylurea *See:* sulfacarbamide

sulfaperin
sulfaperine; [599-88-2]

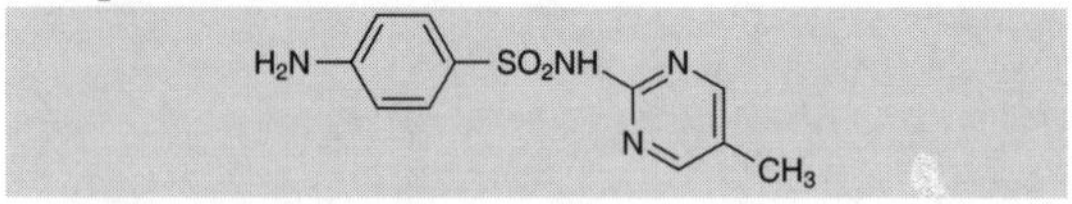

$C_{11}H_{12}N_4O_2S_1$. M: 264.31.
Production:
- diethyl methylmalonate + guanidine hydrochloride + 4-acetamidobenzenesulphonyl chloride (condensation/chlorination/reduction/sulphonamide formation/amide hydrolysis)

Uses:
antibacterial drug

sulfaperine *See:* sulfaperin

sulfaphenazole
[526-08-9]

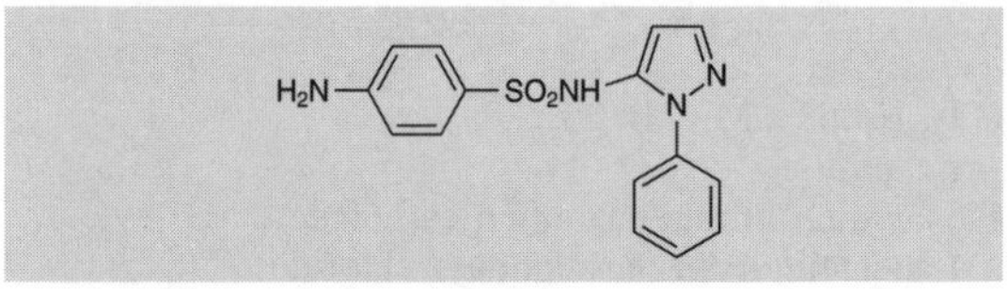

$C_{15}H_{14}N_4O_2S_1$. M: 314.36.
Production:
- phenylhydrazine + acetonitrile + formic acid + 4-acetamidobenzenesulphonyl chloride (condensation/sulphonamide formation/amide hydrolysis)

Uses:
antibacterial drug

sulfapyridine
[144-83-2]; [127-57-1] (sodium salt)

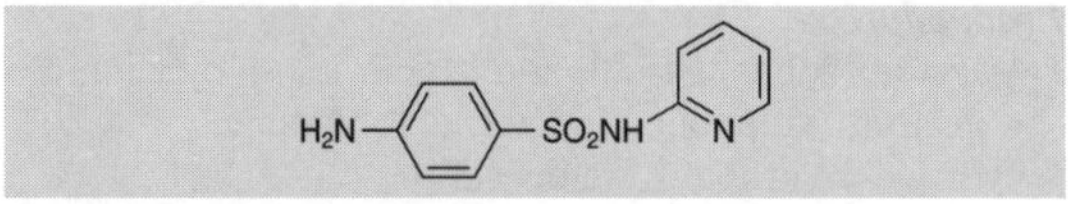

$C_{11}H_{11}N_3O_2S_1$. M: 249.29.
Production:
- 4-acetamidobenzenesulphonyl chloride + 2-amino-pyridine (sulphonamide formation/amide hydrolysis)

Uses:
antibacterial drug

sulfasalazine *See:* salazosulfapyridine

sulfathiazole
[72-14-0]; [144-74-1] (sodium salt)

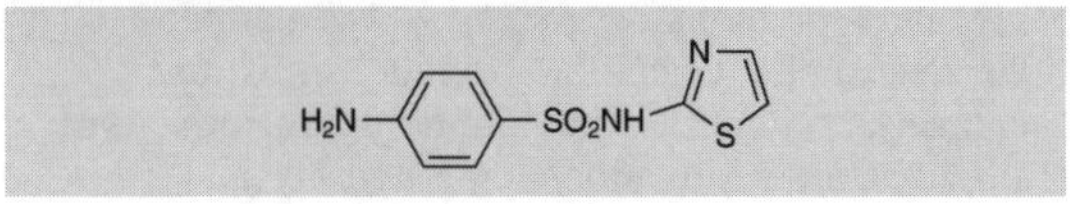

$C_9H_9N_3O_2S_2$. M: 255.32. Available commercially as the free base or as the sodium salt.

Production:
- 4-acetamidobenzenesulphonyl chloride + 2-amino-thiazole (sulphonamide formation/amide hydrolysis)

Uses:
antibacterial drug

sulfathiocarbamide *See:* sulfathiourea

sulfathiourea
sulfathiocarbamide; [515-49-1]

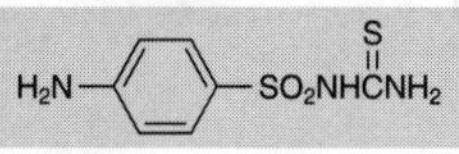

$$H_2N{-}\bigcirc{-}SO_2NH\overset{S}{\overset{\|}{C}}NH_2$$

$C_7H_9N_3O_2S_2$. M: 231.30.
Production:
- 4-acetylsulphanilamide + potassium thiocyanate (thiocyanate addition/amide hydrolysis)

Uses: sulfatolamide antibacterial drug component; antibacterial drug

sulfinpyrazone
[57-96-5]

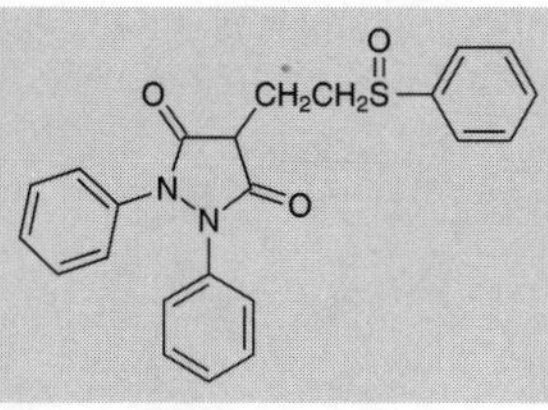

$C_{23}H_{20}N_2O_3S_1$. M: 404.48.
Production:
- thiophenol + ethylene oxide + diethyl malonate + hydrazobenzene + hydrogen peroxide (epoxidation/ alcohol chlorination/dehydrochlorination/ condensation/oxidation)

Uses:
antiphlogistic drug

sulfisomidine
[515-64-0]

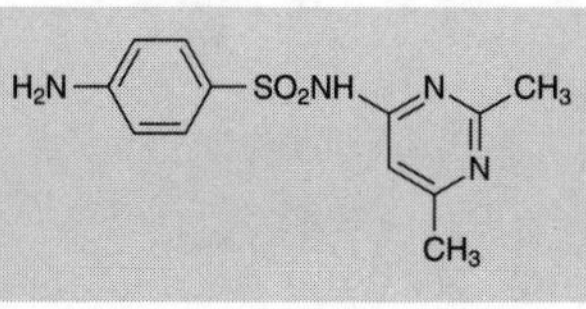

$C_{12}H_{14}N_4O_2S_1$. M: 278.33.
Production:
- β-aminocrotononitrile + acetamidine hydrochloride + 4-acetamidobenzenesulphonyl chloride (condensation/sulphonamide formation/amide hydrolysis)

Uses:
antibacterial drug

sulfisoxazole *See:* sulfafurazole

sulfolane
tetrahydrothiophene-1,1-dioxide; [126-33-0]

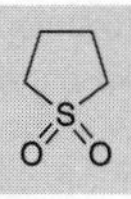

$C_4H_8O_2S_1$. M: 120.16. Liquid. MP: 27°C. BP: 287°C. d: 1.26 kg/l (30°C). Miscible with water, oxygenated and aromatic solvents. Partially miscible with aliphatic hydrocarbons.
Production:
- butadiene + sulphur dioxide, pure (addition/ hydrogenation)

Uses: Sulfinol gas-desulphurisation process cosolvent; aprotic process solvent (chemical synthesis); selective solvent (Shell-UOP aromatics extraction process)

sulfometuron-methyl
methyl 2-[3-(4,6-dimethylpyrimidin-2-yl)ureidosulphon-yl]benzoate; Oust (Du Pont); [74222-97-2]

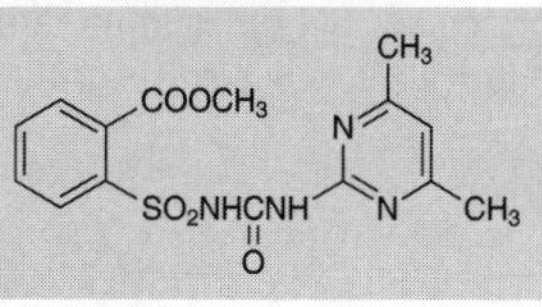

$C_{15}H_{16}N_4O_5S_1$. M: 364.37.
Production:
- 2-amino-4,6-dimethylpyrimidine + carbomethoxy-benzenesulphonyl isocyanate (isocyanate addition)

Uses: herbicide

sulfotep
O,O,O',O'-tetramethyl dithiopyrophosphate; [3689-24-5]

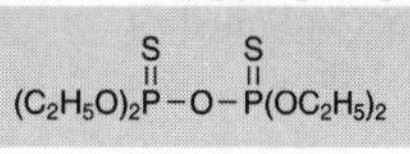

$$(C_2H_5O)_2\overset{S}{\overset{\|}{P}}{-}O{-}\overset{S}{\overset{\|}{P}}(OC_2H_5)_2$$

$C_8H_{20}O_5P_2S_2$. M: 322.33.
Production:
- O,O-diethyl phosphorochlorothioate (base hydrolysis)

Uses: insecticide

sulfur *See:* sulphur

sulindac
[38194-50-2]

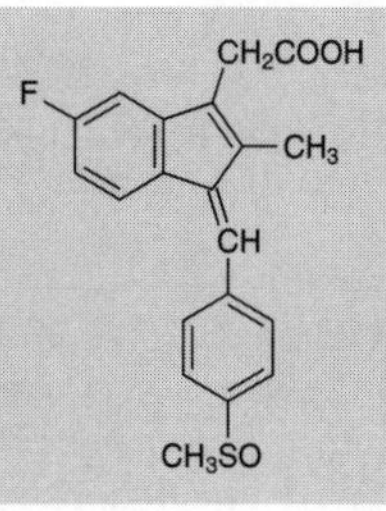

$C_{20}H_{17}F_1O_3S_1$. M: 356.42.

Production:

Production:
- 4-fluorobenzyl chloride + diethyl methylmalonate + cyanoacetic acid + *p*-chlorobenzaldehyde + methyl mercaptan (malonic ester synthesis/cyclisation/ Cope reaction/decarboxylation/nitrile hydrolysis/ sulphide formation/carbonyl condensation/oxidation)

Uses: antiinflammatory drug

sulphamic acid
[5329-14-6]

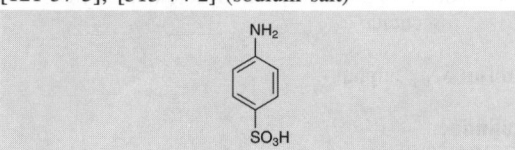

$H_3N_1O_3S_1$. M: 97.09. White crystals. MP: 205°C. Decomposes on further heating. d: 2.13 kg/l (25°C). Solubility in water: 176 g/l solution (20°C).

Production:
- urea + oleum (addition)

Derivatives: ammonium sulphamate; guanidine sulphamate; nickel sulphamate

Uses: electroplating bath ingredient; industrial cleaning/ boiler descaling agent; pulp bleaching adjunct; diazotisation/nitrite removal reagent; sulphation reagent

sulphanilamide
4-aminobenzenesulphonamide; [63-74-1]

H_2N—⟨⟩—SO_2NH_2

$C_6H_8N_2O_2S_1$. M: 172.20. Crystals. MP: 164–166°C. Slightly soluble in water. Soluble in oxygenated solvents.

Production:
- 4-acetylsulphanilamide (amide hydrolysis)

Derivatives: asulam; Fluorescent Brightener 121; sulfamethoxypyridazine; sulfametrole

Uses: antibacterial drug

sulphanilic acid
4-aminobenzenesulphonic acid; aniline-4-sulphonic acid; [121-57-3]; [515-74-2] (sodium salt)

NH_2
⟨⟩
SO_3H

$C_6H_7N_1O_3S_1$. M: 173.20. White, crystalline solid. Decomposes when heated above 280°C. Slightly soluble in water. Available commercially as the acid monohydrate and sodium dihydrate salts.

Production:
- aniline (sulphonation)

Derivatives: Acid Orange 7; Acid Orange 20; Acid Orange 24; Acid Yellow 17; 4'-aminoazobenzene-4-sulphonic acid; Direct Brown 44; Direct Orange 34; Direct Violet 9; ethyl 1-(4-sulphophenyl)-5-pyrazolone-3-carboxylate; Fluorescent Brightener DMDDEA; Food

Black 1; Food Yellow 3; *p*-(β-hydroxyethylsulphonyl)-aniline; Mordant Black 13; Mordant Brown 18; phenylhydrazine-4-sulphonic acid; probenecid; Reactive Brown 1; Reactive Red 4; tartrazine

Uses: analytical reagent (nitrite); photographic coupling agent intermediate

sulphaquinoxaline
[59-40-5]

H_2N—⟨⟩—SO_2NH—[quinoxaline]

$C_{14}H_{12}N_4O_2S_1$. M: 300.34.

Production:
- 4-acetamidobenzenesulphonyl chloride + *o*-phenylenediamine + glycollic acid (condensation/ dehydrochlorination)

Uses: coccidiostat

sulpho-J acid
2-amino-5-hydroxynaphthalene-1,7-disulphonic acid; 6-amino-1-hydroxynaphthalene-3,5-disulphonic acid; 6-amino-1-naphthol-3,5-disulphonic acid

[naphthalene structure with OH, HO₃S, NH₂, SO₃H]

$C_{10}H_9N_1O_7S_2$. M: 319.31.

Production:
- 2-naphthylamine-1,5,7-trisulphonic acid (alkali fusion)

Derivatives: Reactive Red 6

1-(4'-sulpho-2'-methylphenyl)-3-methylpyrazolone
3-methyl-1-(4'-sulpho-*o*-tolyl)-5-pyrazolone

[pyrazolone structure with CH₃, O, NH, CH₃, SO₃H]

$C_{11}H_{12}N_2O_4S_1$. M: 268.29.

Production:
- diketene + 2-aminotoluene-5-sulphonic acid (diazotisation/reduction/condensation)

Derivatives: Acid Yellow 54

sulphonyl bisphenol
See: 4,4'-dihydroxydiphenyl sulphone

sulphonyldianiline
See: 4,4'-diaminodiphenyl sulphone

1-(3'-sulphophenyl)-3-methylpyrazolone
1-(3'-sulphophenyl)-3-methyl-5-pyrazolone

$C_{10}H_{10}N_2O_4S_1$. M: 254.26.
Production:
• metanilic acid + diketene (diazotisation/reduction/condensation)
Derivatives: Acid Red 183; Acid Red 186

1-(4'-sulphophenyl)-3-methylpyrazolone
[89-36-1]

$C_{10}H_{10}N_2O_4S_1$. M: 254.26.
Production:
• phenylhydrazine-4-sulphonic acid + diketene (condensation)
Derivatives:
Acid Yellow 25; Acid Yellow 76; Mordant Yellow 8

sulphosalicylic acid
5-sulphosalicylic acid; [97-05-2]

$C_7H_6O_6S_1$. M: 218.18. Available as the dihydrate. White or pink crystalline powder. Soluble in water and oxygenated solvents.
Production:
• salicylic acid (sulphonation)
Uses: coloured aluminium anodising reagent

sulphur
[7704-34-9]

S

S_1. M: 32.06. Available commercially as a yellow solid in lump, roll, fines, flours or precipitated form. Also available as an amber-coloured molten liquid. MP: 110–113°C. BP: 444–445°C. d: 2.07 kg/l (solid, 20°C), d: 1.80 kg/l (liquid, 125°C). Insoluble in water. Soluble in carbon disulphide, chlorinated and aromatic solvents. Natural sulphur deposits are found in Canada, the USA, Poland, Russia, Italy, Japan, Chile and elsewhere.
Production:
• sulphur, natural deposits (Frasch process)
• sulphur, natural deposits (distillation)
• hydrogen sulphide (Claus process)
• hydrogen sulphide (Cope process)
• iron pyrite (Outokumpu process)
Derivatives: ammonium sulphide; ammonium thiosulphate; antimony pentasulphide; 1-azaphenothiazine; *t*-butyl polysulphide; cadmium red; cadmium yellow; calcium polysulphide; carbon disulphide; carbonyl sulphide; 2-chlorophenothiazine; chromium oxide; dehydrothio-*p*-toluidinesulphonic acid; diallyl sulphide; dimethyl sulphide; Direct Yellow 59; ebonite; *O*-ethyl *O*-(4-nitrophenyl) phenylphosphonothioate; factice; fatty oils, sulphurised; hydrogen sulphide; 2-mercaptobenzothiazole; 3-methylthiophene; phenates, sulphurised, alkali-earth salts; phenothiazine; phosphorus pentasulphide; phosphorus sesquisulphide; Pigment Blue 29; Pigment Yellow 18; polysulphide, rubber; sodium sulphide; sodium thiocyanate; sodium thiosulphate; Sulphur Black 1; Sulphur Black 2; Sulphur Black 11; Sulphur Blue 7; Sulphur Blue 11; Sulphur Brown 1; Sulphur Brown 7; Sulphur Brown 10; Sulphur Brown 52; sulphur dioxide, raw; Sulphur Green 1; Sulphur Green 3; Sulphur Green 9; Sulphur Green 11; sulphur hexafluoride; sulphur monochloride; Sulphur Orange 1; Sulphur Red 7; Sulphur Red 10; Sulphur Yellow 1; Sulphur Yellow 9; terpenes, sulphurised; thiophene; thiophosphoryl chloride; tricyclazole; 2-(trifluoromethyl)-phenothiazine; Vat Blue 19; Vat Blue 42; Vat Blue 43; Vat Green 7
Uses:
fungicide/acaricide; gunpowder ingredient; reagent (sulphur dye production); vulcanisation agent

Sulphur Black 1
Sulphur Black T; 53185 (CI); [1326-82-5]
Mixed product of undefined structure. Also sold in the pre-reduced (*leuco*) form.
Production:
• 2,4-dinitrophenol + sulphur + sodium sulphide (polysulphide melt process)
Uses: dye (cotton)

Sulphur Black 2
53195 (CI)

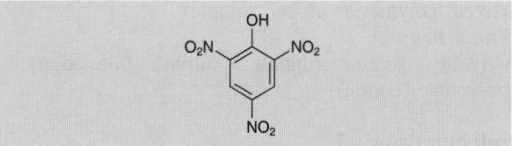

The dye is a polymeric sulphur complex of the displayed structure. Mixed product available commercially in its pre-reduced (*leuco*) form.

Production:
- picric acid + sodium sulphide + sulphur (thionation)

Uses: dye (cotton)

Sulphur Black 11
53290 (CI)

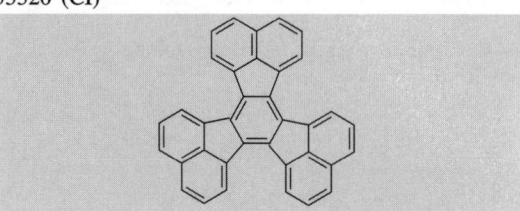

The dye is a mixed, polymeric sulphur complex of the displayed structure.

Production:
- β-naphthol + *p*-aminophenol + sodium sulphide + sulphur (amine formation/polysulphide melt process)

Uses: dye (cotton)

Sulphur Blue 7
53440 (CI)

The dye is a mixed, polymeric sulphur complex of the displayed structure.

Production:
- *o*-toluidine + *p*-nitrosophenol + sodium sulphide + sulphur (condensation/thionation)

Uses: dye (cotton)

Sulphur Blue 11
53235 (CI)

The dye is a mixed, polymeric sulphur complex of the displayed structure. Also sold in pre-reduced (*leuco*) form.

Production:
- 2,4-dinitroaniline + hydroquinone + sodium sulphide + sulphur (amine formation/thionation)

Uses: dye (cotton)

Sulphur Brown 1
53000 (CI)

Mixed, polymeric sulphur complex.

Production:
- lignite + sodium sulphide + sulphur (thionation)

Uses: dye (cotton)

Sulphur Brown 7
53275 (CI)

Dull reddish-brown solid. Mixed, polymeric sulphur complex.

Production:
- 1,5/1,8-dinitronaphthalene + sodium sulphide + sulphur (polysulphide bake process)

Uses: dye (cotton)

Sulphur Brown 10
53055 (CI)

Mixed, polymeric sulphur complex.

Production:
- 2,4/2,6-diaminotoluene + sulphur (thionation)

Uses: dye (cotton)

Sulphur Brown 52
53320 (CI)

The dye is a mixed, polymeric sulphur complex of the displayed structure.

Production:
- acenaphthene + sulphur (thionation)

Uses: dye (cotton)

sulphur chloride *See:* sulphur monochloride

sulphur dichloride
[10545-99-0]

SCl₂

Cl_2S_1. M: 102.97. Deep red, fuming liquid containing 73–79% sulphur dichloride and 21–27% sulphur monochloride. BP: 59°C with decomposition. Hydrolysed in moist air forming hydrochloric acid.

Production:
- sulphur monochloride + chlorine (reaction)

Derivatives: benfuracarb; bithionol; captafol; carbosulphan; 5-chloro-2-methyl-4-isothiazolinone; furathiocarb; 2-*n*-octyl-4-isothiazolinone; sulfametrole; 4,4′-thiobis(2-*t*-butyl-5-methylphenol); 2,2′-thiobis(4-methyl-6-*t*-butylphenol); 2,2′-thiobis(4-*t*-octylphenol); thiocyclam hydrogen oxalate; thiodicarb; 4,4′-thiodiphenol; timolol

Uses:
vulcanisation agent

sulphur dioxide, pure
E220 (EC); [7446-09-5]

SO₂

O_2S_1. M: 64.06. Colourless, liquified gas with a characteristic, pungent odour. BP: -10°C. MP: -73°C. d: 1.50 kg/l (-20°C). Soluble in water and oxygenated solvents.

Production:
• sulphur dioxide, raw (water absorption process)
• sulphur dioxide, raw (solvent extraction)
• sulphur dioxide, raw (cryogenic separation)
Derivatives: acetyl chloride; ammonium sulphite; chlorine dioxide; chlorthalidone; chrome alum; chromium sulphate, basic; cuprous chloride; hydroxylamine sulphate; iodine; polyethylene, chlorosulphonated; potassium metabisulphite; potassium sulphate; sodium alkane(C_{11}-C_{14}) sulphonate; sodium alkane(C_{14}-C_{18}) sulphonate; sodium bisulphite; sodium formaldehyde sulphoxylate; sodium hydrosulphite; sodium metabisulphite; sodium sulphate; sodium sulphite; sulfolane; sulphuryl chloride; thionyl chloride
Uses: cold-box foundry mould process curing agent; dechlorination reagent (drinking water, effluent); bleaching agent (flour, kaolin decolorisation); preservative (dried fruit, dried vegetables, meat, soups, sauces); raw material (sulphite pulp process); manganese ore dressing agent; selective solvent (Edeleanu kerosine, lubricating oil dearomatisation process); sterilising agent (beer, wine, vinegar, glucose syrup)

sulphur dioxide, raw
O_2S_1. M: 64.06.
Production:
• sulphur (oxidation)
• iron pyrite (oxidation)
• sulphuric acid, waste (pyrolysis)
• ferrous sulphate (calcination; byproduct of iron oxide red production)
• zinc sulphide ore concentrates (ore roasting; byproduct of zinc oxide concentrates production)
• lead sulphide ore concentrates (smelting; byproduct of lead bullion production)
• copper sulphide ore concentrates (smelting/air conversion; byproduct of copper, blister production)
• gypsum (Mueller-Kuehne process; coproduced with calcium oxide)
Derivatives: ammonium bisulphite; calcium bisulphite; gypsum; oleum; sodium thiosulphate; sulphur dioxide, pure; sulphuric acid

Sulphur Green 1
53166 (CI); [1326-77-8]
Mixed, polymeric sulphur complex. Also sold in the pre-reduced (*leuco*) form.
Production:
• *p*-nitrophenol/*p*-aminophenol/*p*-nitrosophenol + copper sulphate + sulphur + sodium sulphide (polysulphide bake process)
Uses: dye (cotton)

Sulphur Green 3
53570 (CI)
The dye is a polymeric sulphur complex of the displayed structure.

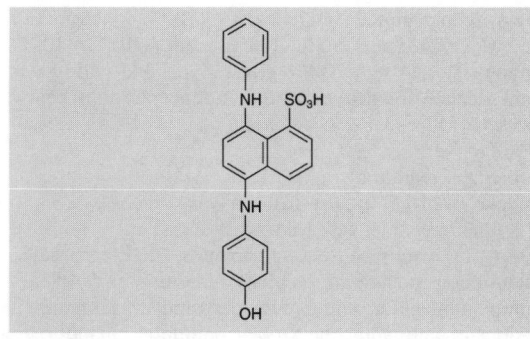

Production:
• *N*-phenyl-peri acid + *p*-nitrosophenol + sulphur + sodium sulphide (condensation/polysulphide bake process)
Uses: dye (cotton)

Sulphur Green 9
53005 (CI); [1326-39-2]
Mixed, polymeric sulphur complex. Also sold in the pre-reduced (*leuco*) form.
Production:
• *m*-dinitrobenzene/*p*-aminophenol + sulphur + sodium sulphide (polysulphide bake process)
Uses: dye (cotton)

Sulphur Green 11
53165 (CI); [12262-52-1]
Mixed, polymeric sulphur complex. Also sold in the pre-reduced (*leuco*) form.
Production:
• *p*-nitrophenol/*p*-aminophenol/*p*-nitrosophenol + sulphur + sodium sulphide (polysulphide bake process)
Uses: dye (cotton)

sulphur hexafluoride
[2551-62-4]

$$SF_6$$

F_6S_1. M: 146.05. Colourless, odourless gas. Chemically and thermally inert.
Production:
• sulphur + fluorine (fluorination)
Uses: high-dielectric gas (high voltage switching applications); magnesium casting ignition inhibitor; inert filler gas (multiply-glazed windows)

sulphuric acid
[7664-93-9]

$$H_2SO_4$$

$H_2O_4S_1$. M: 98.08. Available commercially as 78%, 93%, 96%, 98% and 100% H_2SO_4, as well as in diluted form for battery and reagent use. Colourless, hygroscopic liquid. BP: 270°C (100% grade). FP: -32°C (93% grade), 3°C (98% grade), 10°C (100% grade). d: 1.84 kg/l (100% grade). Miscible with water and alcohol. Corrosive to steel at concentrations below 95%.

Production:
• oleum (hydration)
• coke oven gas (moist gas catalysis process)
• sulphur dioxide, raw (nitrous process)

Derivatives: alkylbenzene sulphonates, alkali-earth salts; aluminium potassium sulphate; aluminium sulphate; ammonium alum; ammonium persulphate; ammonium sulphate; anthraquinone; *p*-benzoquinone; blanc fixe; boric acid; calcium sulphate hemihydrate; calcium superphosphate; cellulose, regenerated; chlorine dioxide; chrome lignosulphonate; chrome yellow; chromic acid; chromium; chromium sulphate; chromium sulphate, basic; citric acid; cobalt sulphate; copper; copper sulphate; dialkylaryl sulphonates, alkali-earth salts; dodecylbenzenesulphonic acid, branched; dodecylbenzenesulphonic acid, linear; guanylurea sulphate; gypsum; hydrogen fluoride; hydroxylamine sulphate; lead sulphate, monobasic; lead sulphate, tribasic; lithium carbonate; lubricant oils, refined; magnesium sulphate; manganese dioxide; manganese sulphate; methacrylamide sulphate; monosodium methylarsonate; montanic acid; nickel sulphate; nitrophosphate; nitrosyl hydrogen sulphate; peroxysulphuric acid; phosphoric acid, crude; Pigment Red 104; potassium persulphate; potassium sulphate; silica, precipitated; silica gel; sodium alum; sodium bisulphate; sodium dichromate; sodium persulphate; sodium sulphate; stannous sulphate; tartaric acid; tetra-*n*-butylammonium hydrogen sulphate; tetraethylammonium hydroxide; tetrakis(hydroxymethyl)phosphonium sulphate; tetramethylammonium hydroxide; zinc sulphate; zinc yellow; zirconia; zirconium sulphate; zirconium sulphate, basic

Uses: aluminium brightening agent; battery electrolyte; leaching agent (uranium/copper ores, zinc/copper production); pH control (water treatment); steel pickling agent; reagent (petroleum refining); sulphonation/nitration reagent; dehydration agent (chlorine)

sulphuric acid, fuming *See:* oleum

sulphur monochloride
disulphur dichloride; sulphur chloride; [10025-67-9]

S_2Cl_2

Cl_2S_2. M: 135.04. Yellowish-red, fuming liquid with a characteristic, pungent odour. BP: 138°C. MP: -76°C. d: 1.69 kg/l (15°C). Decomposed by water. Soluble in carbon disulphide, oxygenated and aromatic solvents.

Production:
• sulphur + chlorine (reaction)

Derivatives: caprolactam disulphide; dibutylphenol disulphide; dipentamethylenethiuram tetrasulphide; 4,4′-dithiodimorpholine; factice; lard oil, chlorosulphurised; 2-morpholinodithiobenzothiazole; sulphur dichloride; sulphur tetrafluoride; Vat Orange 5; Vat Red 1

Uses:
alphachlorination catalyst; chlorosulphurisation reagent (lubricant additive production); vulcanisation agent

Sulphur Orange 1
53050 (CI); [1326-49-4]
Mixed product of undefined structure. Also available in the pre-reduced (*leuco*) form.

Production:
• 2,4/2,6-diaminotoluene + sulphur (sulphur bake process)

Uses: dye (cotton)

sulphur oxychloride *See:* thionyl chloride

Sulphur Red 7
53810 (CI)

The dye is a mixed, polymeric sulphur complex of the displayed structure.

Production:
• 2-amino-5-nitrophenol + chloranil + *m*-nitrobenzoic acid + sulphur + sodium sulphide (condensation/amide formation/polysulphide melt process)

Uses: dye (cotton)

Sulphur Red 10
Leuco Sulphur Brown 96 (CI); 53228 (CI); [1326-96-1]

The dye is a mixed, polymeric sulphur complex of the displayed structure. Also available in the pre-reduced (*leuco*) form.

Production:
• phenol + *p*-aminophenol + sulphur (amine formation/sulphur bake process)

Uses: dye (cotton)

sulphur tetrafluoride
[7783-60-0]

SF_4

F_4S_1. M: 108.05. Colourless gas. BP: -38°C. Hydrolysed by water.

Production:
• sulphur monochloride + sodium fluoride (fluorination)

Uses: fluorination reagent

sulphur trioxide
[7446-11-9]

$$SO_3$$

O_3S_1. M: 80.06. Hygroscopic liquid. BP: 45°C. The solid exists in three phases. MP: 62°C (α-form), 32°C (β-form) and 17°C (γ-form). d: 1.92 kg/l (20°C). Fumes in air. Violently hydrolysed by water forming sulphuric acid. Usually manufactured *in situ*. The product is maintained in the γ-phase by the addition of stabilisers such as thionyl chloride or oxalyl chloride.
Production:
• oleum (distillation)
Derivatives:
calcium cyclamate; chlorosulphonic acid; chlorosulphonyl isocyanate; fluorosulphonic acid; sodium α-olefin (C_{14}-C_{16}) sulphonate; sodium α-olefin(C_{15}- C_{18}) sulphonate; sodium cyclamate; sucralfate
Uses: sulphonation/sulphation reagent

Sulphur Yellow 1
53040 (CI); [1326-47-2]
Mixed product of undefined structure. Also available in the pre-reduced (*leuco*) form.
Production:
• 2-amino-4-nitrotoluene + acetic anhydride + aniline + sulphur (amide formation/nitro reduction/sulphur bake process)
Uses: dye (cotton)

Sulphur Yellow 9
53010 (CI); [1326-40-5]
Mixed product of undefined structure. Also available in the pre-reduced (*leuco*) form.
Production:
• 2,4-dinitroaniline + phthalic anhydride/acetic anhydride + sulphur + sodium sulphide (amide formation/polysulphide bake process)
Uses:
dye (cotton)

sulphuryl chloride
[7791-25-5]

$$SO_2Cl_2$$

$Cl_2O_2S_1$. M: 134.97. Clear, yellow liquid with a pungent odour. BP: 69–70°C. FP: -54°C. d: 1.68 kg/l (15°C). Slowly decomposed by water to hydrochloric and sulphuric acids.
Production:
• sulphur dioxide, pure + chlorine (chlorination)
Derivatives:
benzene-1,3-disulphohydrazide; *p*-chlorophenol; 3,3'-diaminodiphenyl sulphone; 4,4'-diaminodiphenyl sulphone; sulpiride; thiafensulfuron-methyl
Uses: chlorosulphonation/ring chlorination/alpha chlorination reagent

sulpiride
[15676-16-1]

$C_{15}H_{23}N_3O_4S_1$. M: 341.42.
Production:
• salicylic acid + dimethyl sulphate + sulphuryl chloride + ammonia + 2-aminomethyl-1-ethyl-pyrrolidine (methylation/chlorosulphonation/sulphonamide formation/amide formation)
Uses:
antiemetic/antipsychotic drug

sulprofos
O-ethyl *O*-4-(methylthio)phenyl *S*-propyl phosphorodithioate; [35400-43-2]

$C_{12}H_{19}O_2P_1S_3$. M: 322.44.
Production:
• thiophosphoryl chloride + ethanol + *p*-methyl-mercaptophenol + *n*-propyl mercaptan (dehydrochlorination/dehydrochlorination/dehydrochlorination)
Uses: insecticide

sunflower acid
Pale yellow liquid. Titre: 18–24°C. Saponification value: 195–205 mg KOH/g. Acid value: 194–204 mg KOH/g. A typical chain-length distribution is: 12% $C_{18:0}$, 25% $C_{18:1}$, 60% $C_{18:2}$.
Production:
• sunflower soap stock (acidification/fractionation)
Derivatives:
alkyd resins, long-oil; alkyd resins, medium-oil; alkyd resins, short-oil; fatty acids, polyunsaturated, conjugated; linoleic acid diethanolamide
Uses: alkyd resin comonomer; soap raw material

sunflower oil
Helianthus annuus oil; sunflower seed oil
Pale yellow oil. MP: -18°C. d: 0.91–0.92 kg/l (25°C). A typical chain-length distribution is: 6% $C_{16:0}$, 5% $C_{18:0}$, 30% $C_{18:1}$, 58% $C_{18:2}$.
Production:
• sunflower seeds (extraction/alkali refining)
Derivatives:
alkyd resins, long-oil; alkyd resins, medium-oil; alkyd resins, short-oil; fatty acid mono/diglycerides
Uses:
cooking/salad oil; drying oil (alkyd resins); margarine ingredient; soap ingredient

sunflower soap stock

Partially hydrolysed foots produced during alkali refining and deodorising of sunflower oil.
Production:
• sunflower seeds (extraction/alkali refining; byproduct of sunflower oil production)
Derivatives: sunflower acid

Sunset Yellow FCF *See:* Food Yellow 3

superphosphate, normal *See:* calcium superphosphate

superphosphate, single *See:* calcium superphosphate

suramin sodium
[129-46-4]

$C_{51}H_{34}N_6Na_6O_{23}S_6$. M: 1429.17.
Production:
• m-aminobenzoic acid + phosgene + 3-amino-4-methylbenzoic acid + 8-naphthylamine-1,3,5-trisulphonic acid (phosgenation/amide formation/amide formation)
Uses: anthelmintic drug

suxamethonium chloride
succinylcholine chloride; [71-27-2]

$C_{14}H_{30}Cl_2N_2O_4$. M: 361.31.
Production:
• dimethylethanolamine + succinic acid + methyl chloride (esterification/quaternisation)
Uses: muscle relaxant drug

SVS *See:* sodium vinyl sulphonate

SXS *See:* sodium xylene sulphonate

synephrine
[94-07-5]

$C_9H_{13}N_1O_2$. M: 167.21. Available commercially as the tartrate salt or as the tartrate monoester.

Production:
• p-hydroxyacetophenone + methylamine (alpha bromination/amine formation/carbonyl reduction)
• phenyl acetate + chloroacetyl chloride + N-benzylmethylamine (Friedel-Crafts acylation/amine formation/hydrolysis/carbonyl reduction)
Uses: adrenergic drug

synthesis gas
syngas

$$H_2.mCO.nCO_2$$

Synthesis gas is a general term used for mixtures of hydrogen, carbon monoxide, carbon dioxide and often nitrogen used in hydroformylation and as a raw material for ammonia, methanol, acetic acid production. Synthesis gas production facilities are usually an integral part of the derived product plant. The ratio of gas components varies with the application: in ammonia production a ratio of 1:3 N_2:H_2 is required after CO conversion to CO_2 by the shift reaction; for methanol a ratio of 1:20 CO:H_2 is used for optimum equilibration; for hydroformylation the ratio is 1:1 to 1:2.
Production:
• lignite/coal + water + air/oxygen (coal gasification)
• naphtha, heavy/natural gas (desulphurisation/steam reforming)
• long residue + air + oxygen (Shell/Texaco partial oxidation processes)
• natural gas + oxygen (SBA process; coproduced with acetylene)
• naphtha, heavy/natural gas + oxygen (Montecatini autothermic process; coproduced with acetylene)
• natural gas + oxygen (BASF partial combustion process; coproduced with acetylene)
Derivatives:
n-alkanol(C_7-C_9); n-alkanol(C_9-C_{11}); n-alkanol(C_{12}-C_{13}); n-alkanol(C_{12}-C_{15}); n-alkanol(C_{13}-C_{15}); n-alkanol(C_{14}-C_{15}); ammonia; 1,4-butanediol; n-butanol; n-butyraldehyde; calcium formate; carbon dioxide; carbon monoxide; C_{10} dialdehyde; diethyl ketone; 2-ethylhexanol; 3-formylcrotonyl acetate; gas oil, light; gas oil, light, Arge; n-heptanol; hexanol, mixed; hydratropaldehyde; hydrogen; hydrogen sulphide; hydroxycitronellal; isoamyl alcohol; isobutanol; isobutyraldehyde; isodecanol; isononanol; kerosene; methanol; naphtha, heavy; naphtha, light, Synthol; nonanol; n-nonanol; oxygenates, Fischer-Tropsch, mixed; pentaldehydes, mixed; propionaldehyde; refinery gas; sodium formate; n-tridecaldehyde; tridecanol; wax, Fischer-Tropsch
Uses: hydroformylation reagent; reduction gas (pig iron manufacture)

2,4,5-T
2,4,5-trichlorophenoxyacetic acid; Agent Orange;
[93-76-5]

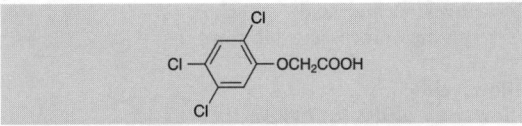

$C_8H_5Cl_3O_3$. M: 255.49. Available commercially as the acid, triethanolamine and triethylamine salts.
Production:
• 2,4,5-trichlorophenol + chloroacetic acid (ether formation)
Derivatives:
2,4,5-T-(2-butoxyethyl); 2,4,5-T-isooctyl
Uses: herbicide

2,4,6-T *See:* 2,4,6-trichlorophenol

TAA *See:* tallowamine acetate

TAB *See:* 3,3'-diaminobenzidine

TAC *See:* triallyl cyanurate

TAGN *See:* N,N',N''-triaminoguanidine nitrate

talampicillin
[47747-56-8]

$C_{24}H_{23}N_3O_6S_1$. M: 481.51. Available commercially as the free base or hydrochloride.
Production:
• phthalic anhydride + ampicillin (carbonyl reduction/esterification)
Uses: antibacterial drug

talc
French chalk; talcum; Pigment White 26 (CI); 77718 (CI); [14807-96-6]

$MgO.nSiO_2$

Finely-ground, white or light grey powder consisting of natural hydrated silicates. The product is soft, with a Mohs hardness of 1.0–2.0, is organophilic and has good lubricity. It is produced by grinding natural soap-stone, steatite or pyrophyllite ores.
Uses:
ceramics ingredient (wall tiles, dinnerware, electrical porcelain); extender/flattening agent/pigment (paints, printing inks); filler (rubber, paper, roofing asphalt); filtration aid; foundry facing/jointing cements; rice/soft metal/leather polishing compounds; antiblocking agent; insecticide carrier; toiletries/pharmaceuticals

tall oil, crude
CTO
Dark brown mixture of fatty acids, rosin and neutral wood components.
Production:
• sulphate pulp black liquor (separation/acid extraction)
Derivatives:
rosin, tall oil; tall oil, distilled; tall oil fatty acid

tall oil, distilled
Liquid. Mixed product consisting of about 60% tall oil fatty acids and 40% rosin acids.
Production:
• tall oil, crude (fractionation; coproduced with tall oil fatty acid/rosin, tall oil)
Derivatives:
cobalt tallate; copper tallate; fatty acid imidazoline polyamines; sodium tallate
Uses: emulsifier (oil-based drilling fluids)

tall oil fatty acid diethanolamide
tallamide DEA (CTFA); tall oil fatty acid polydiethanolamide

$$RCN(CH_2CH_2OH)_2$$

R = tall-. Mixed product. Clear amber liquid containing 65% amide, 23% free diethanolamine, together with free acid and secondary reaction products.
Production:
• tall oil fatty acid + diethanolamine (Kritchevsky reaction)
Uses: emulsifier (hard-surface cleaners); emulsifier/corrosion inhibitor (soluble cutting oils)

tall oil fatty acid
TOFA; [8002-26-4]
Mixed product, mainly consisting of oleic and linoleic acids, together with rosin acids. Several grades are available with varying levels of unsaponifiable matter and rosin. Commercial grades have a 6–8% or 2% rosin acid content.

Production:
- tall oil, crude (fractionation; coproduced with rosin, tall oil/tall oil, distilled)

Derivatives:
alkyd resins, long-oil; alkyd resins, medium-oil; alkyd resins, short-oil; dimer acid; fatty acid imidazoline polyamines; isooctyl epoxytallate; isostearic acid; maleinised oils; manganese tallate; polyethylene glycol monotallate; sodium tall oil *N*-methyltaurate; tall oil fatty acid diethanolamide; tall oil hydroxyethyl imidazoline; trimer acid

Uses: emulsifier (metalworking fluids); flotation collector; plasticiser (rubber)

tall oil heads

Mixed product consisting of fatty acids with a high C_{16} content. Also contains light neutral components.
Production:
- tall oil, crude (fractionation; byproduct of tall oil fatty acid/rosin, tall oil/tall oil, distilled production)

Uses: defoaming agent (phosphoric acid production); non-drying oil (surface coatings)

tall oil hydroxyethyl imidazoline

2-talloyl-1-(hydroxyethyl)imidazoline

R = tall-. Oil-soluble, nonionic surfactant.
Production:
- tall oil fatty acid + aminoethylethanolamine (condensation)

Uses: corrosion inhibitor; emulsifier (oil-based drilling fluids, industrial detergents, cleaners)

tall oil pitch

pitch, tall oil
Production:
- tall oil, crude (fractionation; byproduct of tall oil fatty acid/rosin, tall oil/tall oil, distilled production)

Uses: mastics; fuel; bitumen emulsions (roads, roofing membranes, paper coatings)

tallow

[61789-97-7]
Fat from cattle and sheep. Pale yellow solid. Titre: 40–47°C. Saponification value: 190–200 mg KOH/g. Iodine value: 35–55 g I_2/100 g. Insoluble in water. A typical chain-length distribution is: 5% C_{14}, 30% C_{16}, 20% $C_{18:0}$, 40% $C_{18:1}$.
Production:
- animal fat trimmings (rendering)
- bone, green (acid extraction; byproduct of animal glue production)

Derivatives: tallow, hydrogenated; tallow acid

Uses: lubricity additive (lubricants); steel cold-rolling lubricant; softening agent (textile warp sizing)

tallow, hydrogenated

hydrogenated tallow; tallow, hardened; [8030-12-4]
Production:
- tallow (hydrogenation)

Derivatives: stearic acid
Uses: plastics processing lubricant

tallow acid

tallow fatty acids; [61790-37-2]

RCOOH

R = tallow-. White to yellow solid. MP: 38–42°C. Acid value: 200–205 mg KOH/g. Iodine value: 50–62 g I_2/ 100 g. Insoluble in water. A typical chain-length distribution is: 2% $C_{14:0}$, 27% $C_{16:0}$, 3% $C_{16:1}$, 18% $C_{18:0}$, 43% $C_{18:1}$, 6% $C_{18:2}$.
Production:
- tallow (hydrolysis)

Derivatives: aminoethyl tallow imidazoline; *N,N*-di-tallowamidoethyl-*N*-methylammonium ethoxylate methosulphate; fatty acid imidazoline polyamines; 1-methyl-1-(tallowamidoethyl)tallowimidazoline methosulphate; oleic acid; stearic acid; stearyl imidazoline; tallow alcohol; tallowamidopropyldimethylammonium-3-sulphopropyl betaine; tallowamine
Uses: soap raw material

tallow alcohol

$CH_3(CH_2)_nOH$

n = 16, 18. Waxy solid. MP: 46°C. A typical chain-length distribution is: 5% C_{14}, 30% C_{16}, 65% C_{18}.
Production:
- tallow acid (hydrogenation)

Derivatives: sodium tallow sulphate; styrene-fumarate copolymers; tallow alcohol ethoxylates
Uses: defoaming agent; emollient (cosmetics)

tallow alcohol ethoxylates

talloweth (CTFA)

$RO(CH_2CH_2O)_nH$

R = tallow-, n = 5–50. Waxy solids. Solidification point: 30–50°C.
Production:
- tallow alcohol + ethylene oxide (epoxidation)

Uses: emulsifier (industrial detergents, cleaners, wax); low-foaming surfactant (laundry detergents)

tallowamidopropyldimethylammonium-3-sulphopropyl betaine

Production:
- tallow acid + 3-dimethylaminopropylamine + propane sultone (amide formation/quaternisation)

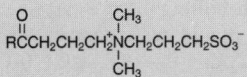

R = tallow-.
Uses:
surfactant (detergents, industrial cleaners, shampoos)

tallowamine
[61790-33-8]

$$RNH_2$$

R = tallow-. Solid. MP: 34–35°C. A typical chain-length distribution is: 5% C_{14}, 30% C_{16}, 65% C_{18}.
Production:
• tallow acid + ammonia (nitrile formation/ hydrogenation)
Derivatives: bis(2-hydroxyethyl)tallowamine; disodium N-stearylsulphosuccinamate; ditallowamine; tallowamine acetate; tallowamine ethoxylates; N-tallow-1,3-propanediamine; tallowtrimethylammonium chloride
Uses: cationic flotation agent (potash ores); pigment flushing hydrophobic agent

tallowamine acetate
TAA

$$RNH_3^+ \quad CH_3COO^-$$

R = tallow-. Solid. MP: 45–61°C. HLB: 10.8. A typical chain-length distribution is: 5% C_{14}, 30% C_{16}, 65% C_{18}.
Production:
• tallowamine + acetic acid (salt formation)
Uses:
flotation collector; pigment flushing hydrophobic agent

tallowamine ethoxylates
PEG tallow amine

$$CH_3(CH_2)_{17}N\begin{matrix}(CH_2CH_2O)_mH\\(CH_2CH_2O)_nH\end{matrix}$$

m+n = 5–15. Liquids. HLB: 14.9–19.3 (5–15 moles EO).
Production:
• tallowamine + ethylene oxide (epoxidation)
Uses: cationic emulsifier (wax, oil, solvent, dyes, acid emulsions, latex); antistatic agent (plastics); bitumen/fat liquor emulsifier

N-tallow-1,3-propanediamine
tallowaminopropylamine (CTFA); N-tallow-1,3-di-aminopropane; N-tallow-1,3-propylenediamine

$$RNHCH_2CH_2CH_2NH_2$$

R = tallow-. Paste. MP: 25°C. A typical chain-length distribution is: 5% C_{14}, 30% C_{16}, 65% C_{18}.

Production:
• tallowamine + acrylonitrile (cyanoethylation/nitrile reduction)
Derivatives:
pentamethyl-N-tallow-1,3-propanediammonium chloride; N-tallow-1,3-propanediamine dioleate; N-tallow-1,3-propanediamine ethoxylates
Uses: bitumen adhesion promotion agents; pigment wetting/adhesion agent (oil-based paints)

N-tallow-1,3-propanediamine dioleate
N-tallow-1,3-diaminopropane dioleate; tallow propylenediamine dioleate; N-tallow-1,3-propylenediamine dioleate

$$R-^+NH_2CH_2CH_2CH_2NH_3^+ \quad 2CH_3(CH_2)_7CH=CH(CH_2)_7COO^-$$

R = tallow-. Paste. MP: 30–40°C.
Production:
• N-tallow-1,3-propanediamine + oleic acid (salt formation)
Uses: pigment grinding aid/dispersant; wetting/adhesion agent (oil-based paints)

N-tallow-1,3-propanediamine ethoxylates

$$H(OCH_2CH_2)_l\begin{matrix}R\\NCH_2CH_2N\end{matrix}\begin{matrix}(CH_2CH_2O)_mH\\(CH_2CH_2O)_nH\end{matrix}$$

R = tallow-. l+m+n = 3–15. Amber liquids. d: 0.95–1.04 kg/l. HLB: 10.1–18.5 (3–15 moles EO).
Production:
• N-tallow-1,3-propanediamine + ethylene oxide (epoxidation)
Uses:
corrosion inhibitor (oilfield chemicals); bitumen emulsifier; surfactant (haircare products); textile auxiliary

tallowtrimethylammonium chloride
tallowtrimonium chloride (CTFA); trimethyltallowammonium chloride

$$RN(CH_3)_3^+ \quad Cl^-$$

R = tallow-. Available commercially as a 50% solution in water.
Production:
• tallowamine + methyl chloride (methylation)
Uses: external plastics antistatic agent

tamarind gum
Extracted from the seeds oft the tamarind (*Tamarindus indica*) tree.
Uses: cotton textile sizing ingredient

tamoxifen
[10540-29-1]; [54965-24-1] (citrate)
$C_{26}H_{29}N_1O_1$. M: 371.53. Available commercially as the citrate salt.

Production:
• anisole + benzoyl chloride + propiophenone + 2-dimethylaminoethyl chloride hydrochloride (Friedel-Crafts acylation/carbonyl reduction/alcohol chlorination/Grignard reagent formation/Grignard reaction/dehydration/ether formation)
Uses:
antioestrogen/antineoplastic drug

tannin *See:* quebracho extract; wattle bark extract; chestnut extract

tantalum
[7440-25-7]

Ta

Ta_1. M: 180.95. Ductile, hard, grey metal. MP: 2,996°C. d: 16.7 kg/l. Resistant to corrosion and attack by most acids and alkalis. Available commercially as powder, foil, wire and tubing.
Production:
• niobium-tantalum ores (smelting; coproduced with niobium)
Uses: chemical handling equipment; capacitors/rectifiers/semiconductors

TAP *See:* triallyl phosphate

tar acid liquor
Alkali-soluble portion of coal tar comprising a mixture of monohydric and dihydric phenolic compounds.
Production:
• coal tar, crude (alkali extraction/fractionation; coproduced with light oil/carbolic oil/creosote oil/naphthalene fraction/fluorene oil/anthracene oil/coal tar pitch)
Derivatives:
catechol; resorcinol fraction; tar acids, crude

tar acids, crude
Crude tar acids comprising a mixture of monohydric phenolic compounds.
Production:
• tar acid liquor (fractionation; coproduced with catechol/resorcinol fraction)
• light oil (acid extraction/alkali extraction; byproduct of benzole production)
Derivatives:
cresylic acid; cresylic pitch; tar acids, high-boiling

tar acids, high-boiling
Dark coloured liquid with distinctive carbolic odour. BR: 230–310°C. d: 1.01–1.08 kg/l (20°C). Commercial product is a mixture of alkylated phenols, indanols and naphthols.
Production:
• tar acids, crude (fractionation; coproduced with cresylic acid/cresylic pitch)
Uses:
disinfectant; epoxy-pitch/polyurethane-pitch coatings (marine paints); flotation frothing agent; non-reactive epoxy resin diluent; oxidation/gum inhibitor (fuel oils)

tar oil, coal *See:* anthracene oil

tar oil, wood
creosote
Yellow to dark brown liquids with a characteristic odour. Several grades are available varying in boiling range and viscosity.
Production:
• wood tar, hardwood (fractionation; coproduced with wood pitch)
• pyrolysis oil, pinewood (fractionation; coproduced with turpentine oil, wood/pine oil/wood pitch)
Derivatives: wood creosote
Uses: roofing felt/coatings; mineral flotation agent; wood preservative

tartar emetic *See:* antimony potassium tartrate

tartaric acid
dihydroxybutanedioic acid; dihydroxysuccinic acid; E334 (EC); [87-69-4]

$$\begin{array}{c} COOH \\ | \\ HCOH \\ | \\ HOCH \\ | \\ COOH \end{array}$$

$C_4H_6O_6$. M: 150.08. White, crystalline solid. MP: 169–170°C. d: 1.76 kg/l (20°C). Soluble in water and alcohol. The commercial product is the natural, L(+)-enantiomer.
Production:
• calcium tartrate + sulphuric acid (acidification)
Derivatives:
diacetyl fatty acid monoglyceride tartrate; naproxen; potassium bitartrate; sodium tartrate
Uses: acidulant (soft drinks, preserves, confectionery); aluminium anodising reagent; racemate separation agent

tartrazine
Acid Yellow 23 (CI); Food Yellow 4 (CI); Pigment Yellow 100 (CI, aluminium salt); 19140 (CI); 19140:1 (CI, aluminium salt); E102 (EC); FD&C Yellow No. 5 (FDC); [1934-21-0]
$C_{16}H_9N_4Na_3O_9S_2$. M: 534.37.

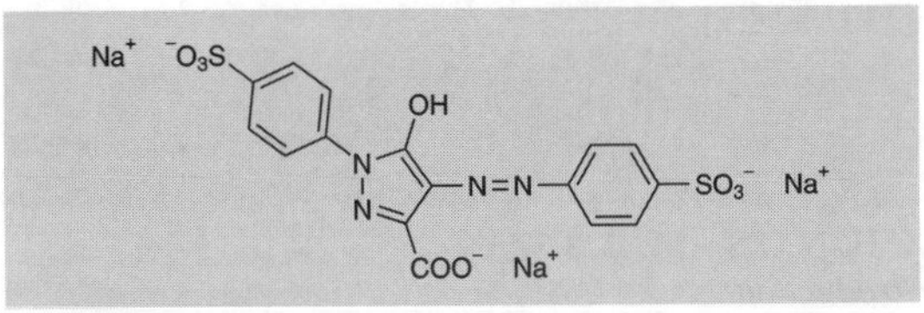

Production:
- ethyl 1-(4-sulphophenyl)-5-pyrazolone-3-carboxylate + sulphanilic acid (hydrolysis/diazotisation/azo coupling)

Uses: dye (polyamide fibres); food colorant; pigment (printing inks)

TATB *See:* 1,3,5-triamino-2,4,6-trinitrobenzene

TATM *See:* triallyl trimellitate

taurine
2-aminoethylsulphonic acid; [107-35-7]

$C_2H_7N_1O_3S_1$. M: 125.15. Solid. Decomposes when heated above 317°C. Soluble in water. Insoluble in oxygenated solvents.
Production:
- sodium 2-chloroethanesulphonate + ammonia (amine formation)
- monoethanolamine + sodium hydrosulphide (sulphation/thiolation/oxidation)

Uses:
milk enrichment additive

TBA *See:* t-butanol; 2,4,6-tribromoaniline

TBAB *See:* tetra-n-butylammonium bromide

2,3,6-TBA-sodium
sodium 2,3,6-trichlorobenzoate; [2078-42-4]

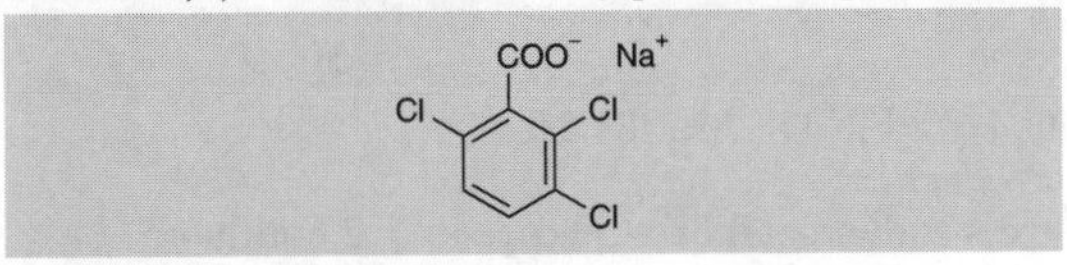

$C_7H_2Cl_3Na_1O_2$. M: 247.45.
Production:
- 2,6-dichlorotoluene + sodium hydroxide (ring chlorination/side-chain oxidation/salt formation)

Uses: herbicide

TBB *See:* p-t-butylbenzaldehyde

TBBA *See:* tetrabromobisphenol A

TBBS *See:* N-t-butyl-2-benzothiazolesulphenamide

TBC *See:* t-butylcatechol; tri-n-butyl citrate

TBDPE *See:* tetrabromodipentaerythritol

TBE *See:* tetrabromoethane

TBEP *See:* tributoxyethyl phosphate

TBHP *See:* t-butyl hydroperoxide

TBIC *See:* t-butyl peroxyisopropylcarbonate

TBMAC *See:* tri-n-butylmethylammonium chloride

TBNPA *See:* tribromoneopentyl alcohol

TBP *See:* 2,4,6-tribromophenol; tri-n-butyl phosphate

TBPA *See:* tetrabromophthalic anhydride

TBPAE *See:* 2,4,6-tribromophenyl allyl ether

TBS *See:* p-t-butylphenyl salicylate

TBT *See:* butyl titanate; tri-n-butyltin oxide; p-t-butyltoluene

TBTF *See:* tributyltin fluoride

TBTO *See:* tri-n-butyltin oxide

TBUP *See:* tri-n-butylphosphine

2,4,5-T-(2-butoxyethyl)
2-butoxyethyl (2,4,5-trichlorophenoxy)acetate; [2545-59-7]

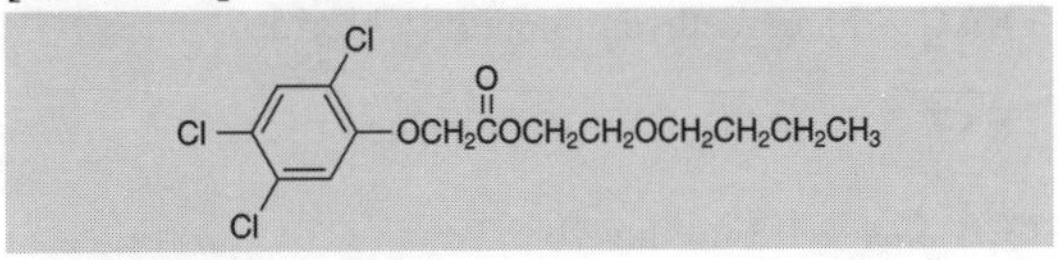

$C_{14}H_{17}Cl_3O_4$. M: 355.65.
Production:
- ethylene glycol monobutyl ether + 2,4,5-T (esterification)

Uses:
herbicide

TBZ *See:* thiabendazole

TCA *See:* trichloroacetic acid

TCBO *See:* trichlorobutylene oxide

TCC *See:* triclocarban

TCCA *See:* trichloroisocyanuric acid

TCE *See:* trichloroethylene

TCEP *See:* tris(2-chloroethyl) phosphate

TCMTB *See:* 2-(thiocyanomethylthio)benzothiazole

TCNB *See:* tecnazene

TCP *See:* phthalide; tricresyl phosphate

TCPP *See:* tris(1-chloro-2-propyl) phosphate

TCT *See:* tricrotonylidenetetramine

TDA *See:* 2,4/2,6-diaminotoluene

TDG *See:* thiodiglycol

TDI *See:* toluene diisocyanate

TDM *See:* *t*-dodecyl mercaptan

TDMAMP *See:* 2,4,6-tris(dimethylaminomethyl)phenol

TDP *See:* 4,4′-thiodiphenol

TDQP
See: 2,2,4-trimethyl-1,2-dihydroquinoline, polymeric

TDS *See:* isotridecyl stearate

TEA
See: triethylaluminium; triethylamine; triethanolamine

TEAB *See:* tetraethylammonium bromide

TEAC *See:* tetraethylammonium chloride

TEAT *See:* triethanolamine titanate

TEB *See:* 1,1,3-triethoxybutane

tebutam
N-benzyl-*N*-isopropylpivalamide; [35256-85-0]

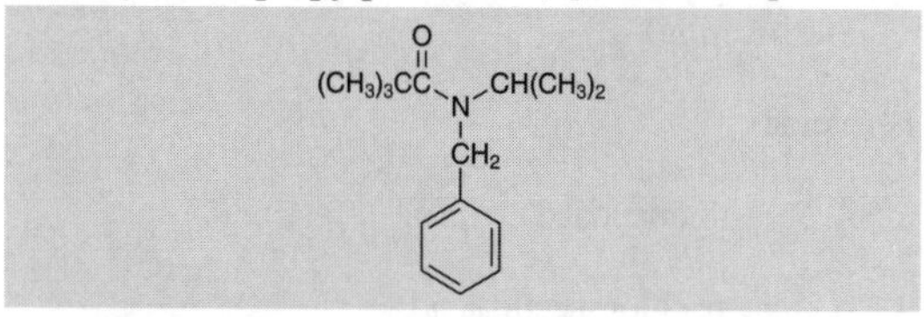

$C_{15}H_{23}N_1O_1$. M: 233.35.
Production:
• isopropylamine + benzaldehyde + pivaloyl chloride
  (reductive amination/amide formation)
Uses: herbicide

tebuthiuron
1-(5-*t*-butyl-1,3,4-thiadiazol-2-yl)-1,3-dimethylurea;

[34014-18-1]

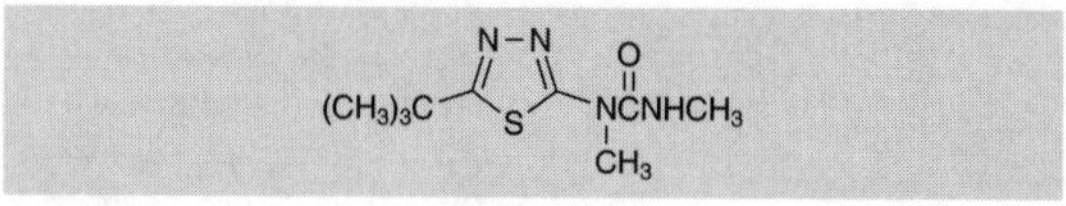

$C_9H_{16}N_4O_1S_1$. M: 228.32.
Production:
• pivaloyl chloride + 4-methyl thiosemicarbazide +
  methyl isocyanate (condensation/isocyanate addition)
Uses: herbicide

TEC *See:* triethyl citrate

tecnazene
1,2,4,5-tetrachloro-3-nitrobenzene; 2,3,5,6-tetrachloronit-
robenzene; TCNB; [117-18-0]

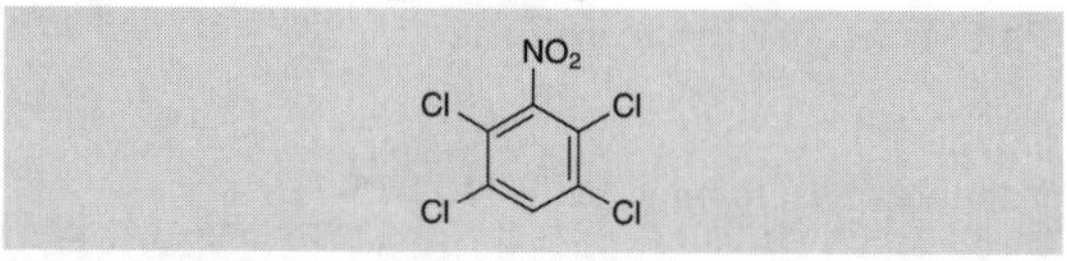

$C_6H_1Cl_4N_1O_2$. M: 260.90.
Production:
• 1,2,4,5-tetrachlorobenzene (nitration)
Uses:
fungicide; potato sprouting inhibitor

TEDA *See:* triethylenediamine

TEDMA *See:* triethylene glycol dimethacrylate

Teflon *See:* polytetrafluoroethylene

teflubenzuron
1-(3,5-dichloro-2,4-difluorophenyl)-3-(2,6-difluorobenz-
oyl)urea; [83121-18-0]

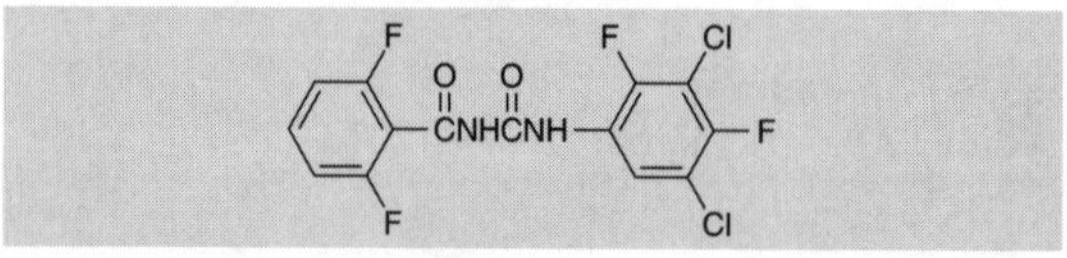

$C_{14}H_6Cl_2F_4N_2O_2$. M: 381.11.
Production:
• 2,4-difluoroaniline + phosgene + 2,6-difluoro-
  benzamide (ring chlorination/phosgenation/
  isocyanate addition)
Uses: insecticide

tefluthrin
[79538-32-2]

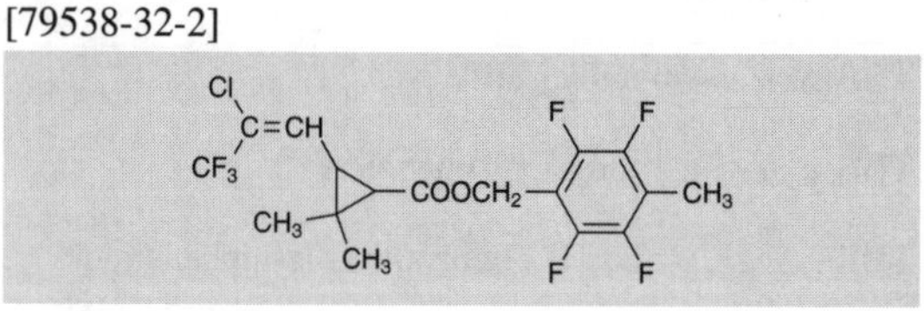

$C_{17}H_{14}Cl_1F_7O_2$. M: 418.74.

Production:
- tetrafluoro-*p*-methylbenzyl alcohol + 3-(2-chloro-3,3,3-trifluoropropenyl)-2,2-dimethylcyclo-propanecarboxylic acid (esterification)

Uses: insecticide

TEG *See:* triethylene glycol

tegafur
[17902-23-7]

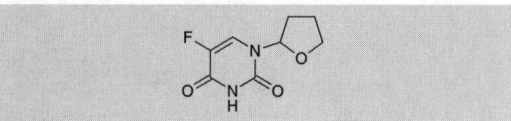

$C_8H_9F_1N_2O_3$. M: 200.17.
Production:
- furan + fluorouracil (selective hydrogenation/addition)

Uses: antineoplastic drug

TEGDA *See:* triethylene glycol diacetate

TEGMA *See:* triethylene glycol dimethacrylate

TEGN *See:* triethylene glycol dinitrate

TEL *See:* tetraethyl lead

tellurium
[13494-80-9]

Te

Te_1. M: 127.60. Grey, lustrous, crystalline solid. MP: 450°C. BP: 990°C. Attacked by acids and alkalis under oxidative conditions.
Production:
- copper anodic slimes (sulphating roast process/hydrometallurgical refining; coproduced with gold/silver/platinum/palladium/selenium)

Derivatives: tellurium dioxide
Uses: lead/copper/stainless steel alloying ingredient

tellurium dioxide
[7446-07-3]

TeO₂

O_2Te_1. M: 159.60. White crystals. MP: 733°C forming a dark-red liquid.
Production:
- tellurium (air oxidation)

Uses: glass/semiconductor ingredient; metal additive

TEM *See:* triethylenemelamine

temazepam
[846-50-4]
$C_{16}H_{13}Cl_1N_2O_2$. M: 300.74.

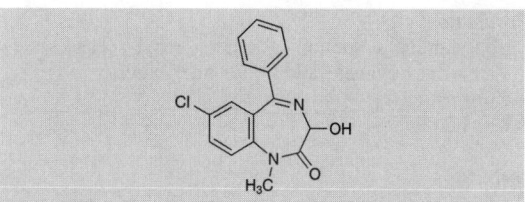

Production:
- diazepam + acetic anhydride (multistep synthesis)

Uses: hypnotic drug

temephos
O,O,O',O'-tetramethyl *O,O'*-thiodi-*p*-phenylene diphosphorothioate; [3383-96-8]

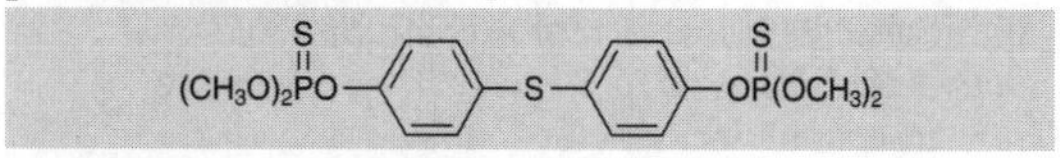

$$(CH_3O)_2PO\!-\!\!\bigcirc\!\!-\!S\!-\!\!\bigcirc\!\!-\!OP(OCH_3)_2$$

$C_{16}H_{20}O_6P_2S_3$. M: 466.47.
Production:
- 4,4'-thiodiphenol + *O,O*-dimethyl phosphorochlorothioate (dehydrochlorination)

Uses: insecticide

temocillin
[66148-78-5]

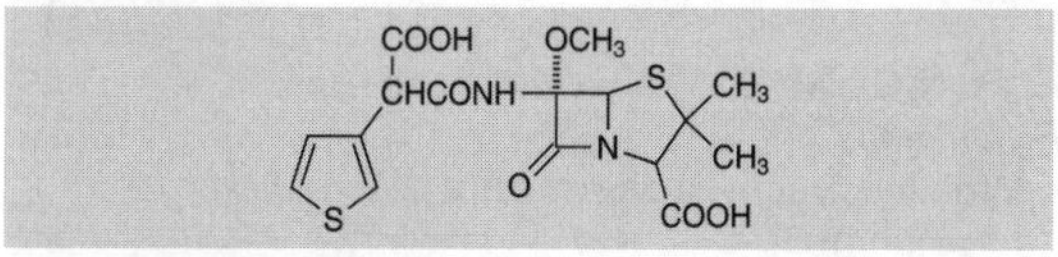

$C_{16}H_{18}N_2O_7S_2$. M: 414.45.
Production:
- 6-aminopenicillanic acid + 3-thienylmalonic acid (multistep synthesis)

Uses: antibacterial drug

TEN
See: tris(hydroxyphenyl)methane triglycidyl ether

TEOS *See:* ethyl silicate

TEP *See:* triethyl phosphate

TEPA
See: tetraethylenepentamine; triethylenephosphoramide

TEPI *See:* triethyl phosphite

terbacil
3-*t*-butyl-5-chloro-6-methyluracil; [5902-51-2]

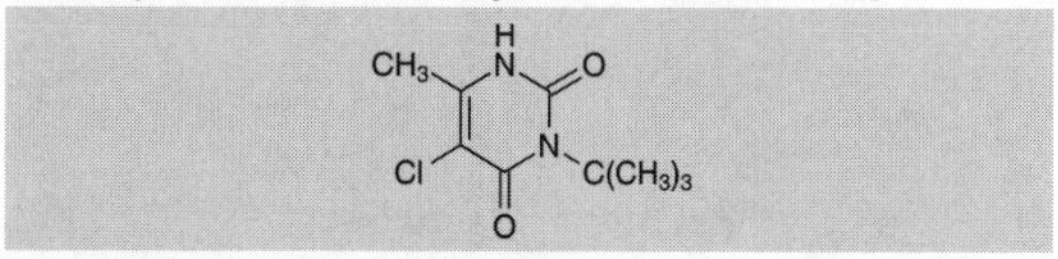

$C_9H_{13}Cl_1N_2O_2$. M: 216.66.

Production:
- *t*-butylamine + sodium cyanate + ethyl acetoacetate + chlorine (cyanate addition/condensation/chlorination)

Uses: herbicide

terbufos

S-t-butylthiomethyl *O,O*-diethyl phosphorodithioate; [13071-79-9]

$(CH_3)_3CSCH_2SP(OC_2H_5)_2$

$C_9H_{21}O_2P_1S_3$. M: 288.43.

Production:
- *t*-butyl mercaptan + formaldehyde + *O,O*-diethyl dithiophosphoric acid (chloromethylation/dehydrochlorination)

Uses: insecticide/nematicide

terbumeton

2-*t*-butylamino-4-ethylamino-6-methoxy-1,3,5-triazine; [33693-04-8]

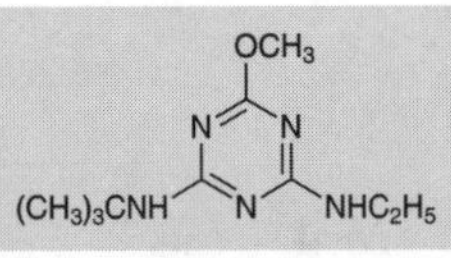

$C_{10}H_{19}N_5O_1$. M: 225.29.

Production:
- terbuthylazine + sodium methoxide (ether formation)

Uses: herbicide

terbutaline

[23031-25-6]

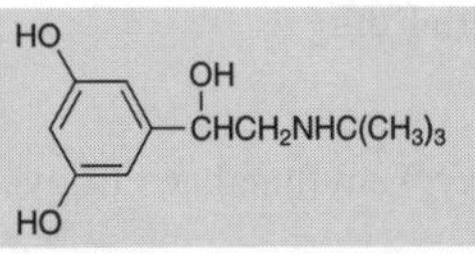

$C_{12}H_{19}N_1O_3$. M: 225.29. Available commercially as the free base or sulphate.

Production:
- 3,5-dibenzoxyacetophenone + benzyl-*t*-butylamine (alpha bromination/amine formation/hydrolysis/carbonyl reduction)

Uses: bronchodilator drug

terbuthylazine

2-*t*-butylamino-4-chloro-6-ethylamino-1,3,5-triazine; [5915-41-3]

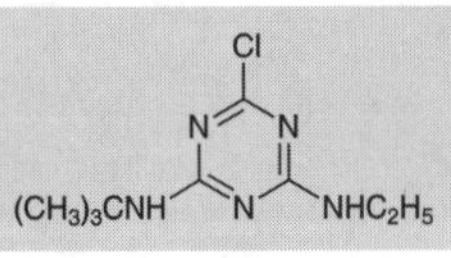

$C_9H_{16}Cl_1N_5$. M: 229.71.

Production:
- cyanuric chloride + ethylamine + *t*-butylamine (dehydrochlorination/dehydrochlorination)

Derivatives: terbumeton; terbutryn

Uses: herbicide

terbutryn

2-*t*-butylamino-4-ethylamino-6-methylthio-1,3,5-triazine; [886-50-0]

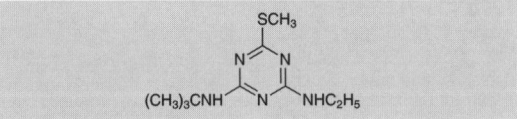

$C_{10}H_{19}N_5S_1$. M: 241.35.

Production:
- terbuthylazine + methyl mercaptan (sulphide formation)

Uses: herbicide

terephthalic acid

benzene-1,4-dicarboxylic acid; PTA (pure grade); TPA (technical grade); [100-21-0]

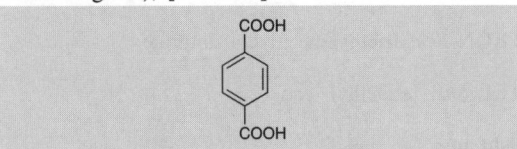

$C_8H_6O_4$. M: 166.13. White, crystalline powder. Sublimes on heating to 400°C. d: 1.51 kg/l. Insoluble in water. The product of *p*-xylene oxidation is called 'technical grade'. It is hydrogenated and separated from impurities (mainly *o*-toluic acid) by crystallisation. The resultant terephthalic acid is termed 'pure grade'. It needs a 4-formylbenzoic acid of <25 ppm to be acceptable in most applications.

Production:
- *p*-xylene (side-chain oxidation/hydrogenation)
- dimethyl terephthalate (hydrolysis)

Derivatives:
polyarylate, liquid-crystalline; poly(ethylene terephthalate); terephthaloyl chloride

Uses: alkyd/unsaturated polyester resin comonomer

terephthaloyl chloride

benzene-1,4-carbonyl chloride; 1,4-benzenedicarbonyl chloride; [100-20-9]

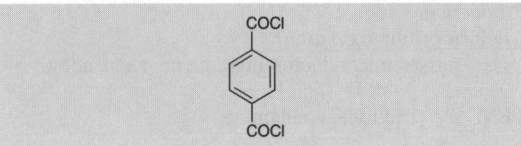

$C_8H_4Cl_2O_2$. M: 203.03. White needles. MP: 83–84°C. BP: 260°C. Hydrolysed by water and alcohol. Soluble in oxygenated solvents.

Production:
• terephthalic acid (acid chloride formation)
Derivatives:
N,N'-dinitroso-N,N'-dimethylterephthalamide; polyarylate, amorphous; poly(p-benzhydrazoterephthalamide); poly[(3,4'-diphenyl ether)-(p-phenyleneterephthalamide)]; polyether ketone ether ketone ketone; polyether ketone ketone; poly(p-phenyleneterephthalamide); Vat Yellow 13
Uses: chemical intermediate

terfenadine
[50679-08-8]

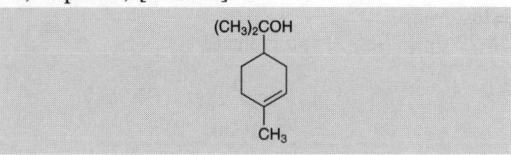

$C_{32}H_{41}N_1O_2$. M: 471.69.
Production:
• azacyclonol + 4'-t-butyl-4-chlorobutyrophenone (dehydrochlorination/carbonyl reduction)
Uses: antihistamine drug

terpene resins
Production:
• α-pinene/β-pinene/dipentene (cationic polymerisation)
Uses:
pressure-sensitive adhesives; tackifier (hot melt adhesives); binder (printing inks)

terpenes, sulphurised
Production:
• dipentene + sulphur (sulphurisation)
Uses: extreme-pressure/antioxidant additive (lubricants)

terphenyl
polyphenyl; Santosol (Monsanto)

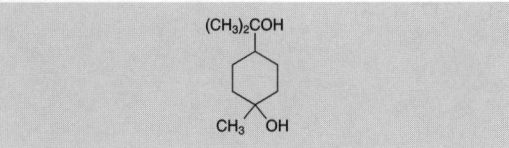

Mixed product consisting of isomeric terphenyls. A typical isomer distribution is: 8% o-, 49% m-, 23% p-terphenyl and 20% triphenylene.
Production:
• benzene (dehydrogenation; coproduced with biphenyl)
Uses: microencapsulation dye solvent (carbonless copier paper)

γ-terpinene
1,4-p-menthadiene; [99-85-4]
$C_{10}H_{16}$. M: 136.24. Colourless liquid with a citrus odour.

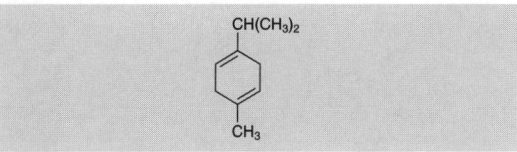

Production:
• p-cymene (Birch reduction)
Uses:
fragrance ingredient

α-terpineol
1-p-menthen-8-ol; p-menth-1-en-8-ol; pine oil, synthetic; terpineol; [98-55-5]

$C_{10}H_{18}O_1$. M: 154.25. Crystalline solid with a lilac odour. BP: 218°C. d: 0.94 kg/l (20°C). Several grades are available depending on the production process. Lower grades are mixed isomer products. Higher grades (from terpin hydrate) are used in perfumes.
Production:
• turpentine oil, sulphate/turpentine oil, wood (esterification/separation/ester hydrolysis)
• pine oil (fractionation; coproduced with anethole)
• terpin hydrate (dehydration)
Derivatives:
terpinyl acetate
Uses: flotation frothing agent; fragrance ingredient (soap, detergents); sanitiser/fragrance ingredient (cleaning/disinfectant formulations); reodorant (paints)

terpin hydrate
dipentene glycol; [2451-01-6]

$C_{10}H_{20}O_2$. M: 172.27. The commercial product is the cis-isomer.
Production:
• turpentine oil, wood (hydration)
Derivatives:
α-terpineol
Uses: expectorant drug;

terpinyl acetate
1-p-menthen-8-yl acetate; [80-26-2]
$C_{12}H_{20}O_2$. M: 196.29. Colourless liquid with a lavender-type odour. d: 0.97 kg/l (20°C). Mixed product, the main component of which is α-terpinyl acetate.

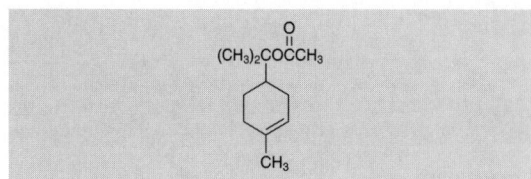

Production:
• α-terpineol + acetic anhydride (transesterification)
Derivatives: menthanyl acetate
Uses: fragrance ingredient

terramycin *See:* oxytetracycline

testosterone
[58-22-0]; [57-85-2] (propionate)

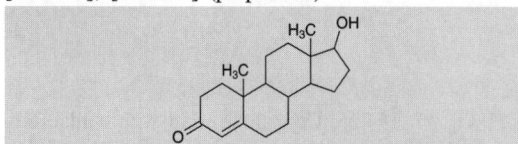

$C_{19}H_{28}O_2$. M: 288.43. Available commercially as the free alcohol, the propionate ester and as a variety of other ester derivatives.
Production:
• prasterone (carbonyl reduction/Oppenauer oxidation)
Uses: animal growth promotion agent

TET
See: tetraethylthiuram disulphide; triethylenetetramine

TETA *See:* triethylenetetramine

TETD *See:* tetraethylthiuram disulphide

1,4,5,8-tetraaminoanthraquinone
Disperse Blue 1 (CI); Solvent Blue 18 (CI); 64500 (CI); [2475-45-8]

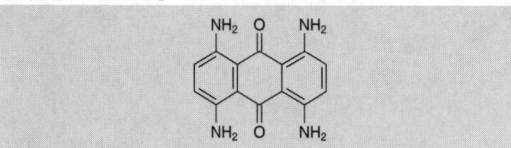

$C_{14}H_{12}N_4O_2$. M: 268.27.
Production:
• 1,5-diaminoanthraquinone (amine protection/ nitration/nitro reduction/amide hydrolysis)
Derivatives:
Disperse Blue 31; 1,4,5,8-tetrachloroanthraquinone
Uses:
disperse dye (polyester, acetate, nylon fibre); solvent dye (resins, lacquers)

3,3',4,4'-tetraaminobiphenyl
See: 3,3'-diaminobenzidine

2,4,5,6-tetraaminopyrimidine sulphate
pyrimidinetetramine sulphate; [5392-28-9]

$C_4H_{10}N_6O_4S_1$. M: 238.22. Brownish powder. Bulk density: 0.88 kg/l.MP: >300°C.
Production:
• 5-nitroso-2,4,6-triaminopyrimidine (nitro reduction)
Derivatives:
lumazine; methotrexate; 2,4,5,6-tetrachloropyrimidine

tetrabromobisphenol A
2,2',6,6'-tetrabromo-4,4'-isopropylidenediphenol; TBBA; Saytex RB-100 (Ethyl); [79-94-7]

$C_{15}H_{12}Br_4O_2$. M: 543.88. Off-white powder. MP: 179–181°C. d: 2.2 kg/l (4°C). Insoluble in water. Soluble in oxygenated solvents.
Production:
• bisphenol A + bromine (ring bromination)
Derivatives:
tetrabromobisphenol A allyl ether; tetrabromobisphenol A bis(2-hydroxyethyl ether); tetrabromobisphenol A carbonate oligomer; tetrabromobisphenol A diglycidyl ether
Uses: fire-retardant additive (ABS, phenolic, unsaturated polyester resins); fire-retardant polycarbonate comonomer

tetrabromobisphenol A allyl ether
TBBA-AE; tetrabromobisphenol A bis(allyl ether)

$C_{21}H_{20}Br_4O_2$. M: 624.01. Solid. MP: 118–120°C. d: 1.8 kg/l. Insoluble in water. Soluble in ketone, chlorinated and aromatic solvents.
Production:
• tetrabromobisphenol A + allyl chloride (ether formation)
Uses: fire-retarded expanded polystyrene/engineering thermoplastics comonomer

tetrabromobisphenol A bis(2-hydroxyethyl ether)
TBBA-EO
$C_{19}H_{20}Br_4O_4$. M: 631.99. Solid. MP: 113–119°C. d: 1.8 kg/l. Insoluble in water and aromatic solvents. Soluble in oxygenated and chlorinated solvents.

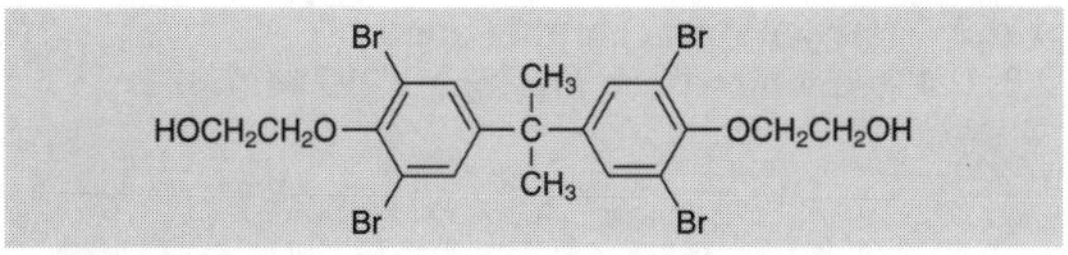

Production:
- tetrabromobisphenol A + ethylene oxide (epoxidation)

Uses: fire-retarded unsaturated polyester resin/engineering plastics comonomer

tetrabromobisphenol A carbonate oligomer

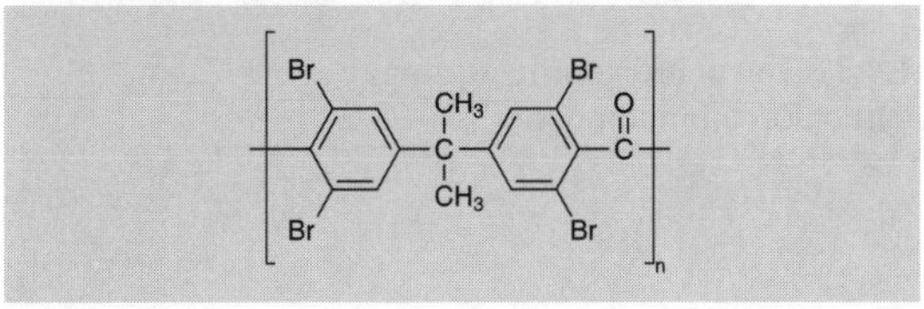

n = 4–7.
Production:
- tetrabromobisphenol A + phosgene (phosgenation)

Uses: fire-retardant polycarbonate prepolymers

tetrabromobisphenol A diglycidyl ether

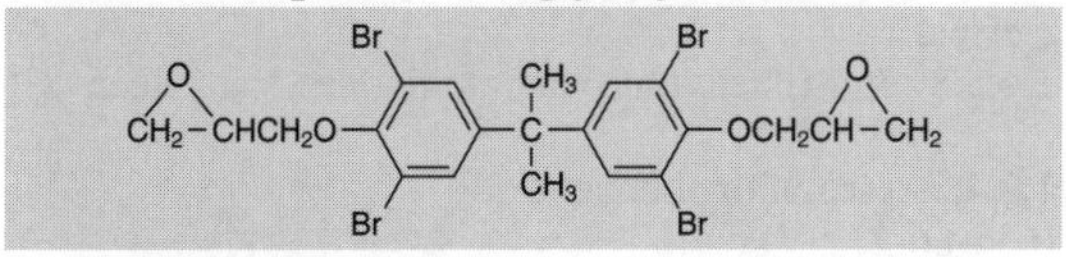

$C_{21}H_{20}Br_4O_4$. M: 656.01.
Production:
- tetrabromobisphenol A + epichlorohydrin (dehydrochlorination)

Uses: fire-retardant epoxy resin comonomer

tetrabromo-*o*-cresol
2,3,4,5-tetrabromo-*o*-cresol; [576-55-6]

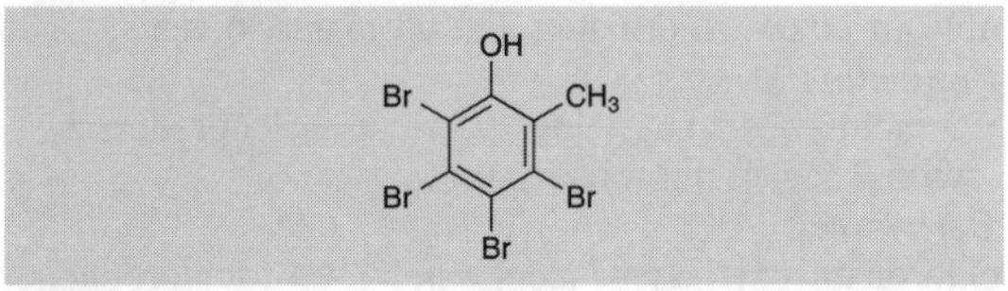

$C_7H_4Br_4O_1$. M: 423.73. White crystals. MP: 205–208°C with decomposition. Insoluble in water. Soluble in oxygenated solvents.
Production:
- *o*-cresol (ring bromination)

Uses: disinfectant

tetrabromodipentaerythritol
TBDPE
$C_{10}H_{18}Br_4O_3$. M: 505.87.
Production:
- dipentaerythritol + hydrobromic acid (alcohol bromination)

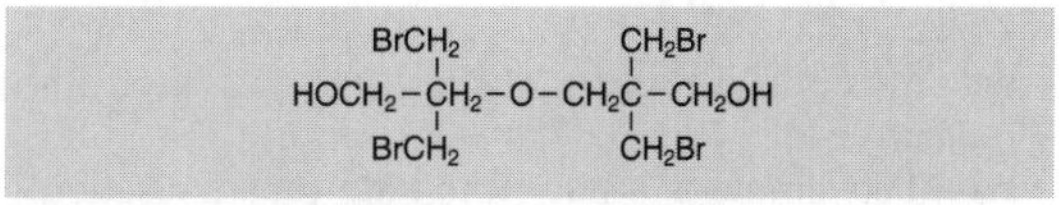

Uses: fire-retardant additive (polypropylene, styrene copolymers, unsaturated polyester resins)

tetrabromoethane
acetylene tetrabromide; TBE; 1,1,2,2-tetrabromoethane; *sym*-tetrabromoethane; [79-27-6]

$C_2H_2Br_4$. M: 345.66. Pale yellow liquid. BP: 246°C. FP: 0°C. d: 2.96 kg/l (20°C). Insoluble in water. Miscible with oxygenated and chlorinated solvents.
Production:
- acetylene + bromine (addition)

Uses: fire-retardant additive (fibres); high-density solvent (mineral separation, gauge fluid)

tetrabromophthalate diol

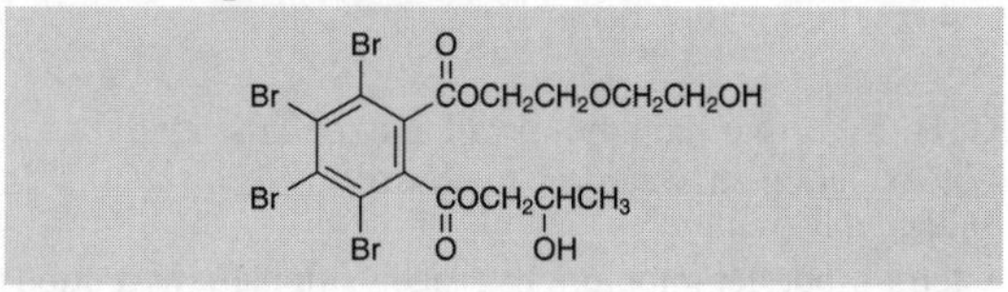

$C_{15}H_{16}Br_4O_7$. M: 627.90. Amber, viscous liquid. d: 1.80 kg/l. Insoluble in water and alcohol. Soluble in acetone and toluene.
Production:
- tetrabromophthalic anhydride + diethylene glycol + propylene oxide (esterification/epoxidation)

Uses: fire-retardant rigid polyurethane foams

tetrabromophthalic anhydride
TBPA; [632-79-1]

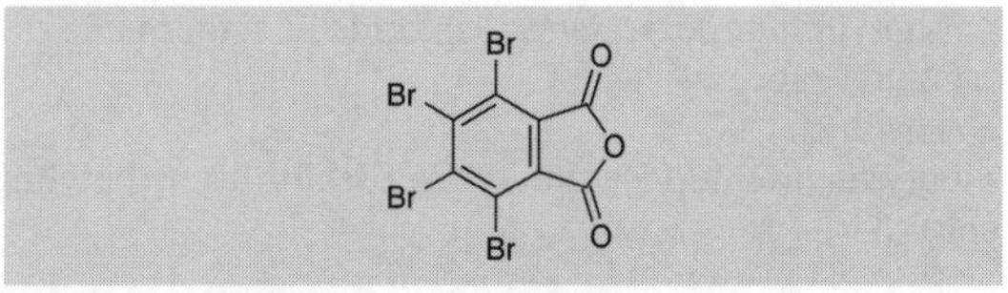

$C_8Br_4O_3$. M: 463.71. Solid. MP: 270–276°C. d: 2.9 kg/l. Insoluble in water or alcohol. Slightly soluble in ketone, chlorinated and aromatic solvents.
Production:
- phthalic anhydride + bromine (ring bromination)

Derivatives: ethylene bis(tetrabromophthalimide); tetrabromophthalate diol
Uses:
fire-retarded unsaturated polyester resin comonomer

tetra-*n*-butylammonium bromide
TBAB; [1643-19-2]
$C_{16}H_{36}Br_1N_1$. M: 322.38. Brown, hygroscopic solid. MP: 102–104°C.

$$[CH_3CH_2CH_2CH_2]_4 N^+ \quad Br^-$$

Production:
• tri-*n*-butylamine + *n*-butyl bromide (quaternisation)
Uses:
phase-transfer catalyst

tetra-*n*-butylammonium hydrogen sulphate
[32503-27-8]

$$[CH_3CH_2CH_2CH_2]_4 N^+ \quad HSO_4^-$$

$C_{16}H_{37}N_1O_4S_1$. M: 339.55.
Production:
• tri-*n*-butylamine + *n*-butanol + sulphuric acid
(quaternisation)
Derivatives:
tetra-*n*-butylammonium hydroxide
Uses: phase-transfer catalyst

tetra-*n*-butylammonium hydroxide
TBA-OH; [2052-49-5]

$$[CH_3CH_2CH_2CH_2]_4 N^+ \quad OH^-$$

$C_{16}H_{37}N_1O_1$. M: 259.49. Available commercially as a 40% solution in water or methanol.
Production:
• tetra-*n*-butylammonium hydrogen sulphate (hydration)
Uses: phase-transfer catalyst

tetra-*n*-butyltin
tetrabutyltin; tin tetrabutyl; [1461-25-2]

$$(CH_3CH_2CH_2CH_2)_4Sn$$

$C_{16}H_{36}Sn_1$. M: 347.16.
Production:
• *n*-butylmagnesium chloride + stannic chloride
(Grignard reaction)
• *n*-butyl chloride + stannic chloride + sodium
(Wurtz process)
Derivatives:
n-butyltin trichloride; dibutyltin dichloride; tributyltin chloride

tetracaine
2-dimethylaminoethyl 4-*n*-butylaminobenzoate;
[94-24-6]; [136-47-0] (hydrochloride)

$$CH_3CH_2CH_2CH_2NH - \underset{\text{benzene ring}}{} - \overset{O}{\underset{}{C}}OCH_2CH_2N(CH_3)_2$$

$C_{15}H_{24}N_2O_2$. M: 264.35. Available commercially as the hydrochloride.
Production:
• *p*-aminobenzoic acid + *n*-butyl bromide + dimethylaminoethanol (amine formation/ esterification)
Uses:
local anaesthetic drug

α,α,2,4-tetrachloroacetophenone
2,2,2',4'-tetrachloroacetophenone; [2274-66-0]

$C_8H_4Cl_4O_1$. M: 257.93.
Production:
• 2,4-dichloroacetophenone (alpha chlorination; coproduced with α,2,4-trichloroacetophenone)
Derivatives: chlorfenvinfos

1,4,5,8-tetrachloroanthraquinone
tetrachloroanthraquinone; [81-58-3]

$C_{14}H_4Cl_4O_2$. M: 345.99.
Production:
• 1,4,5,8-tetraaminoanthraquinone (diazotisation/ Sandmeyer reaction)
Derivatives:
1,4,5,8-tetra-(phenylthio)anthraquinone; Vat Green 8

1,2,4,5-tetrachlorobenzene
[634-66-2]

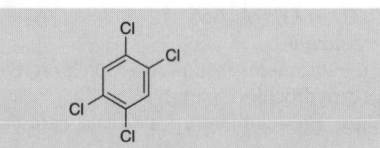

$C_6H_2Cl_4$. M: 215.90. Crystalline solid. MP: 138–140°C. BP: 243–246°C. d: 1.86 kg/l. Insoluble in water. Soluble in ether, chlorinated and aromatic solvents.
Production:
• *p*-dichlorobenzene (ring chlorination; coproduced with 1,2,4-trichlorobenzene)
Derivatives:
chloroneb; oxadiazon; tecnazene; 2,4,5-trichlorophenol

2,2',5,5'-tetrachlorobenzidine
4,4'-diamino-2,2',5,5'-tetrachlorobiphenyl

$C_{12}H_8Cl_4N_2$. M: 322.01.
Production:
• 2,5-dichloronitrobenzene (reductive coupling/ acid-catalysed rearrangement)
Derivatives: Pigment Yellow 81; Pigment Yellow 113

tetrachlorodifluoroethane

1,2-difluoro-1,1,2,2-tetrachloroethane; Freon 112 (Du Pont); R112; [76-12-0]

$$CFCl_2CFCl_2$$

$C_2Cl_4F_2$. M: 203.83. Colourless liquid or solid. MP: 26°C. BP: 93°C. Non-flammable. Insoluble in water.
Production:
• perchloroethylene + hydrogen fluoride (fluorination; coproduced with 1,1,2-trichloro-1,2,2-trifluoro-ethane/1,2-dichloro-1,1,2,2-tetrafluoroethane/chloropentafluoroethane)
Uses: degreasing solvent

2,3,5,6-tetrachloronitrobenzene *See:* tecnazene

2,4,5,6-tetrachloropyrimidine

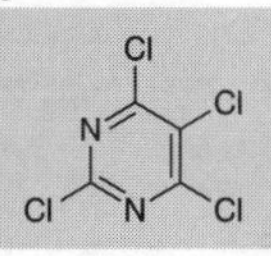

$C_4Cl_4N_2$. M: 217.86.
Production:
• 2,4,5,6-tetraaminopyrimidine sulphate + cuprous chloride (diazotisation/Sandmeyer reaction)
Derivatives: Reactive Red 17
Uses: reactive dyestuffs intermediate

tetrachlorosilane *See:* silicon tetrachloride

tetrachlorvinphos

2-chloro-1-(2,4,5-trichlorophenyl)vinyl dimethyl phosphate; [22248-79-9]

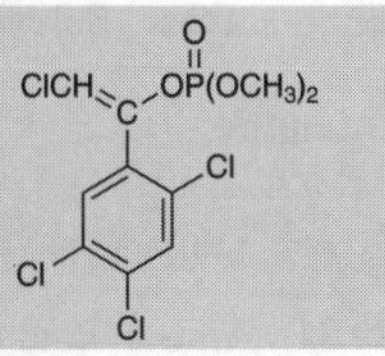

$C_{10}H_9Cl_4O_4P_1$. M: 365.96.
Production:
• α,α,2,4,5-pentachloroacetophenone + trimethyl phosphite (Perkow reaction)
Uses: acaricide/insecticide

tetracycline

[60-54-8]

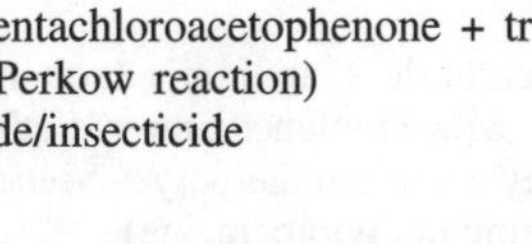

$C_{22}H_{24}N_2O_8$. M: 444.43. Available as the free amide trihydrate, or as the hydrochloride or phosphate salt.

Production:
• chlortetracycline (hydrogenation)
Uses: antibacterial drug

1-tetradecanol *See:* myristyl alcohol

n-tetradecylamine

myristylamine; tetradecylamine; [2016-42-4]

$$CH_3(CH_2)_{13}NH_2$$

$C_{14}H_{31}N_1$. M: 213.41. White solid with characteristic amine odour. MP: 31°C. A typical chain-length distribution is: 4% C_{12}, 92% C_{14}, 4% C_{16}.
Production:
• myristic acid + ammonia (nitrile formation/hydrogenation)
Derivatives:
dimethylmyristylamine
Uses: flotation collector (sulphide ores)

n-tetradecyl bromide *See:* myristyl bromide

n-tetradecyl chloride *See:* myristyl chloride

tetradifon

4-chlorophenyl 2,4,5-trichlorophenyl sulphone; [116-29-0]

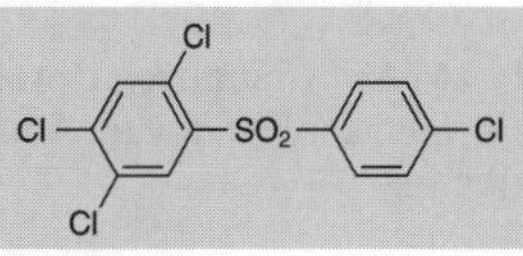

$C_{12}H_6Cl_4O_2S_1$. M: 356.05.
Production:
• 1,2,4-trichlorobenzene + chlorosulphonic acid + chlorobenzene (chlorosulphonation/chlorosulphonation)
Uses: acaricide

1,1,2,2-tetra[*p*-(2,3-epoxypropoxy)phenyl]ethane

1,1,2,2-tetra-(*p*-glycidoxyphenyl)ethane; Epon 1031 (Shell)

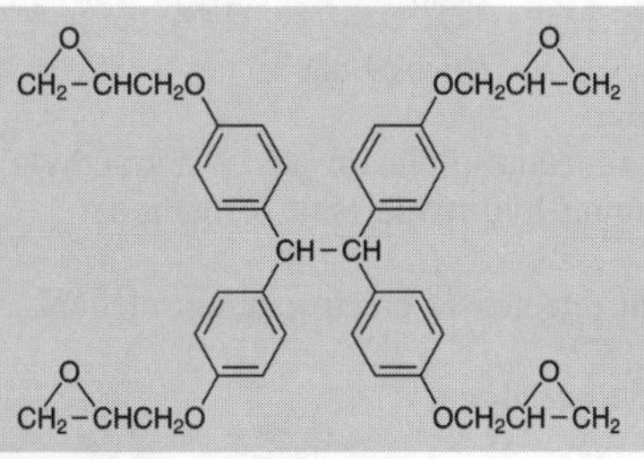

$C_{38}H_{38}O_8$. M: 622.71.
Production:
• glyoxal + phenol + epichlorohydrin (carbonyl condensation/ether formation)
Uses: high performance epoxy resin (composite aircraft bodies/components)

tetraethoxysilane *See:* ethyl silicate

tetraethylammonium bromide
tetrylammonium bromide (INN); TEAB; [71-91-0]

$(C_2H_5)_4N^+$ Br^-

$C_8H_{20}Br_1N_1$. M: 210.16. Crystalline solid. Soluble in water, oxygenated and chlorinated solvents.
Production:
• triethylamine + ethyl bromide (quaternisation)
Uses:
phase-transfer catalyst

tetraethylammonium chloride
TEAC; [56-34-8]

$(C_2H_5)_4N^+$ Cl^-

$C_8H_{20}Cl_1N_1$. M: 165.71. Crystalline solid. Soluble in water, oxygenated and chlorinated solvents.
Production:
• triethylamine + ethyl chloride (quaternisation)
Uses:
phase-transfer catalyst

tetraethylammonium hydroxide
TEA-OH; [77-98-5]

$(C_2H_5)_4N^+$ OH^-

$C_8H_{21}N_1O_1$. M: 147.27. Commercial product sold as a 25% solution in methanol or water. Aqueous solutions are strongly alkaline.
Production:
• triethylamine + ethanol + sulphuric acid (salt formation/quaternisation/hydration)
Derivatives:
tetraethylammonium perfluorooctyl sulphonate
Uses: phase-transfer catalyst

tetraethylammonium perfluorooctyl sulphonate
Fluorad FC-99 (3M)

$CF_3(CF_2)_7SO_3^-$ $(C_2H_5)_4N^+$

$C_{16}H_{20}F_{17}N_1O_3S_1$. M: 629.38.
Production:
• perfluorooctanesulphonic acid + tetraethyl-ammonium hydroxide (salt formation)
Uses:
surfactant (electronic electroplating, etchants, coatings)

tetraethylene glycol

$HO(CH_2CH_2O)_4H$

$C_8H_{18}O_5$. M: 194.22. Colourless liquid. BP: 327°C. FP: -5.5°C. d: 1.12 kg/l (25°C). Miscible with water and methanol. Flash point: 185°C (COC).
Production:
• diethylene glycol + ethylene oxide (epoxidation)

Derivatives:
tetraethylene glycol diacrylate; tetraethylene glycol dimethacrylate; tetraethylene glycol dimethyl ether
Uses: ceramic paste/printing ink binder; lubricant (metalworking fluids/textile spin finishes); softening agent (paper tissue)

tetraethylene glycol diacrylate

$CH_2=CHC(OCH_2CH_2)_4OCCH=CH_2$ (with two C=O groups)

$C_{14}H_{22}O_7$. M: 302.32.
Production:
• tetraethylene glycol + acrylic acid (esterification)
Uses: crosslinked acrylic resin comonomer

tetraethylene glycol dimethacrylate

$CH_2=CC(OCH_2CH_2)_4OCC=CH_2$ with CH_3 groups and two C=O

$C_{16}H_{26}O_7$. M: 330.38.
Production:
• tetraethylene glycol + methyl methacrylate (transesterification)
Uses: crosslinked acrylic resin comonomer

tetraethylene glycol dimethyl ether

$CH_3O(CH_2CH_2O)_4CH_3$

$C_{10}H_{22}O_5$. M: 222.28.
Production:
• tetraethylene glycol + dimethyl sulphate (methylation)
Uses:
solubiliser; selective solvent (Selexol process)

tetraethylenepentamine
TEPA; [112-57-2]

$H_2NCH_2CH_2(NHCH_2CH_2)_3NH_2$

$C_8H_{23}N_5$. M: 189.31. Amber liquid. BP: 340°C with decomposition. d: 1.00 kg/l (20°C). Soluble in water. Mixed product containing a range of oligomers.
Production:
• ethylene dichloride + ammonia (amine formation; coproduced with ethylenediamine/diethylenetri-amine/triethylenetetramine/polyethylenepolyamine/piperazine/aminoethylpiperazine)
• ethylenediamine + monoethanolamine (reductive amination; coproduced with diethylenetriamine/triethylenetetramine/polyethylenepolyamine)
Derivatives:
fatty acid imidazoline polyamines; polyamide resins, reactive; *N,N'*-(tetraethylenepentamino)bispolyisobutenylsuccinimide; *N*-(tetraethylenepentamino)monopolyisobutenylsuccinimide
Uses: nickel plating brightening agent

N,N'-(tetraethylenepentamino)-bispolyisobutenyl-succinimide

R = isobutenyl-.
Production:
- polyisobutenylsuccinic anhydride +
  tetraethylenepentamine (amide formation)
Uses:
ashless dispersants (lubricating oils, diesel fuels)

N-(tetraethylenepentamino)-monopolyisobutenyl-succinimide

m = 10–15, n = 2–5.
Production:
- polyisobutenylsuccinic anhydride +
  tetraethylenepentamine (amide formation)
Uses: motor fuel carburettor/inlet deposit control additives; ashless dispersants (lubricating oils, diesel fuels)

tetra-2-ethylhexyl orthotitanate
See: 2-ethylhexyl titanate

tetraethyl lead
TEL; [78-00-2]

$$(C_2H_5)_4Pb$$

$C_8H_{20}Pb_1$. M: 323.44. Colourless liquid. BP: 152°C (39 kPa). MP: -136°C. d: 1.66 kg/l (18°C). Insoluble in water. Soluble in oxygenated solvents.
Production:
- ethyl chloride + lead + sodium (alloy formation/ dechlorination)
Derivatives:
tetramethyl/ethyl lead, redistributed
Uses: petrol octane booster

tetraethyl silicate *See:* ethyl silicate

tetraethylthiuram disulphide
bis(diethylthiocarbamyl)disulphide; TET; TETD; [97-77-8]

$$(C_2H_5)_2NC\overset{S}{\overset{\|}{S}}SC\overset{S}{\overset{\|}{}}N(C_2H_5)_2$$

$C_{10}H_{20}N_2S_4$. M: 296.54. Pale yellow, odourless powder. MP: 65°C. d: 1.3 kg/l. Insoluble in water. Soluble in aromatic solvents.

Production:
- sodium diethyldithiocarbamate (oxidation)
Uses:
vulcanisation accelerator

1,1,1,2-tetrafluoroethane
HFC-134a; R134a

$$CH_2FCF_3$$

$C_2H_2F_4$. M: 102.03. Liquified gas. BP: -26°C. Insoluble in water. Soluble in ether.
Production:
- 1-chloro-2,2,2-trifluoroethane + hydrogen fluoride (halogen exchange)
Uses: aerosol propellant; refrigerant gas

tetrafluoroethylene
perfluoroethylene; TFE; [116-14-3]

$$CF_2=CF_2$$

C_2F_4. M: 100.01. Colourless gas. BP: -76°C. Insoluble in water.
Production:
- chlorodifluoromethane (pyrolysis)
Derivatives:
ethylene-tetrafluoroethylene copolymers; 2-hydroperfluoroethyl allyl ether; methyl 3-fluorocarbonylperfluoropropionate; perfluoroalkyl(C_6-C_{12}) iodide; perfluorohexyl iodide; perfluorooctyl iodide; polytetrafluoroethylene; polytetrafluoroethylene wax; tetrafluoroethylene-hexafluoropropylene copolymers; tetrafluoroethylene-perfluoro(methyl vinyl ether) copolymers; tetrafluoroethylene-perfluoro(propyl vinyl ether) copolymers; tetrafluoroethylene-perfluoro(vinyl ether carboxylate) copolymers; tetrafluoroethylene-perfluoro(vinyl ether sulphonate) copolymers; tetrafluoroethylene-propylene terpolymers; 2,2,3,3-tetrafluoropropanol; 1,1,ω-trihydroperfluoroalkanol; vinylidene fluoride-hexafluoropropylene-tetrafluoroethylene terpolymers

tetrafluoroethylene-hexafluoropropylene copolymers
ethylene-propylene copolymers, fluorinated; FEP; TFE/HFP; Teflon FEP (Du Pont)

Thermoplastic. d: 2.16 kg/l. Tensile strength: 19–22 MPa. Elongation at break: 250–350%. The polymer is characterised by its excellent thermal and chemical resistance, its low coefficient of friction and high electrical insulation. It has a higher impact strength than polytetrafluoroethylene.
Production:
- tetrafluoroethylene + hexafluoropropylene (emulsion polymerisation)
Uses: cable/wire insulation; chemically-resistant mouldings; fibres; shrink tubes/roller coatings

tetrafluoroethylene-perfluoro(methyl vinyl ether) copolymers
Kalrez (Du Pont)

$$-[CF_2-CF_2]_x-[CF_2-\overset{\displaystyle OCF_3}{\underset{\displaystyle |}{CF}}]_y-$$

Elastomers characterised by their excellent thermal properties as well as their chemical and solvent resistance.
Production:
• tetrafluoroethylene + perfluoro(methyl vinyl ether) (polymerisation)
Uses: high performance seals/gaskets

tetrafluoroethylene-perfluoro(propyl vinyl ether) copolymers
PFA

$$-[CF_2-CF_2]_x-[CF_2-\overset{\displaystyle OCF_2CF_2CF_3}{\underset{\displaystyle |}{CF}}]_y-$$

Thermoplastic. d: 2.16 kg/l. Tensile strength: 15–30 MPa. Tensile modulus: 600 MPa. Elongation at break: 300%. The polymer has good stress cracking resistance, chemical resistance and electrical insulation properties.
Production:
• tetrafluoroethylene + perfluoro(propyl vinyl ether) (polymerisation)
Uses: chemically-resistant mouldings; electrical insulation (wire, cables, computer components); antistick mouldings/linings

tetrafluoroethylene-perfluoro(vinyl ether carboxylate) copolymers
Flemin (Asahi Glass)

$$-[CF_2-CF_2]_x-[CF_2-\overset{\displaystyle O(CF_2\overset{CF_3}{\underset{|}{CF}}O)_nCF_2CF_2CF_2COOH}{\underset{\displaystyle |}{CF}}]_y-$$

Production:
• hexafluoropropylene oxide + methyl 3-fluorocarbonylperfluoropropionate + tetrafluoroethylene (oligomerisation/decarboxylation/polymerisation)
Uses: ion-exchange membranes

tetrafluoroethylene-perfluoro(vinyl ether sulphonate) copolymers
Nafion (Du Pont); XR resin (Du Pont)

$$-[CF_2-CF_2]_x-[CF_2-\overset{\displaystyle O(CF_2\overset{CF_3}{\underset{|}{CF}}O)_nCF_2CF_2SO_3H}{\underset{\displaystyle |}{CF}}]_y-$$

Production:
• hexafluoropropylene oxide + tetrafluoroethylene (epoxidation/decarboxylation/sulphonation/isomerisation/polymerisation)
Uses: ion-exchange membranes

tetrafluoroethylene-propylene terpolymers
Aflas (Asahi Glass)

$$-[CF_2-CF_2]_x-[\overset{\displaystyle CH_3}{\underset{\displaystyle |}{CH}}-CH_2]_y-X-$$

X = fluorinated vinyl monomer. Elastomer consisting of alternating tetrafluoroethylene and propylene monomers with a third, unspecified, monomer providing pendant vinyl groups. Crosslinked by peroxide. Vulcanisates are characterised by good heat and chemical resistance with low gas permeability.
Production:
• tetrafluoroethylene + propylene (polymerisation)
Uses:
cable/wire insulation; aerospace components; oilfield drilling and chemical equipment

tetrafluoromethane *See:* carbon tetrafluoride

tetrafluoro-*p*-methylbenzyl alcohol
[79538-03-7]

$C_8H_6F_4O_1$. M: 194.13.
Production:
• perfluoromethylcyclohexane + *n*-butyllithium + carbon dioxide (defluorination/Grignard reagent formation/Grignard reaction/esterification/ester reduction)
Derivatives: tefluthrin

2,2,3,3-tetrafluoropropanol
[76-37-9]

$$HCF_2CF_2CH_2OH$$

$C_3H_4F_4O_1$. M: 132.05.
Production:
• tetrafluoroethylene + methanol (telomerisation; coproduced with 1,1,ω-trihydroperfluoroalkanol)
Derivatives:
perfluoroalkyl acrylates; perfluoroalkyl methacrylates

tetrafluorosilane *See:* silicon tetrafluoride

tetraglycidyl methylenedianiline
N,N'-tetraglycidyl-4,4'-diaminodiphenylmethane; TGDDM; TGMDA; Araldite MY720 (Ciba-Geigy)

$C_{25}H_{30}N_2O_4$. M: 422.52.

Production:
- 4,4′-diaminodiphenylmethane, crude +
  epichlorohydrin (amine formation)

Uses:
epoxy resins (composite aircraft bodies/components)

tetrahydrofuran
THF; [109-99-9]

$C_4H_8O_1$. M: 72.10. Colourless liquid. BP: 66°C. FP: -108°C. d: 0.89 kg/l (20°C). Soluble in water and oxygenated solvents. Flash point: -14°C (CC).

Production:
- 1,4-butanediol (ether formation)
- *n*-butane (Du Pont transport-bed process/
  hydrogenation)
- maleic anhydride (hydrogenation; coproduced with
  1,4-butanediol)
- butadiene + oxygen + hydrogen (Mitsubishi
  process; coproduced with 1,4-butanediol)
- furan (hydrogenation)

Derivatives:
poly(tetramethylene ether) glycol; fenothiocarb; tetrahydrothiophene

Uses: polyacetal resin comonomer; solvent (Grignard reagents, tetraethylead production, solution styrene-butadiene rubber production, magnetic tape production, polyvinyl chloride/rubber bonding, printing plates); vinylidene copolymer solvent (cellophane coatings)

tetrahydrofurfuryl acrylate
[2399-48-6]

$$CH_2=CHCOCH_2$$

$C_8H_{12}O_3$. M: 156.19.

Production:
- tetrahydrofurfuryl alcohol + acrylic acid
  (esterification)

Uses: acrylic resin comonomer

tetrahydrofurfuryl alcohol
THFA; [97-99-4]

$$CH_2OH$$

$C_5H_{10}O_2$. M: 102.13. Colourless liquid. BP: 178°C. FP: <-80°C. d: 1.05 kg/l (20°C). Miscible with water and oxygenated solvents. Flash point: 84°C (TOC).

Production:
- furfuryl alcohol (hydrogenation)

Derivatives: tetrahydrofurfuryl acrylate; tetrahydrofurfuryl methacrylate

Uses: coupling solvent (pesticides, textile auxiliaries); solvent (paint strippers, cleaners)

tetrahydrofurfuryl methacrylate

$$CH_2=CCOCH_2$$
$$CH_3$$

$C_9H_{14}O_3$. M: 170.21.

Production:
- tetrahydrofurfuryl alcohol + methyl methacrylate
  (transesterification)

Uses: acrylic resin comonomer

tetrahydrogeraniol
3,7-dimethyloctan-1-ol; [106-21-8]

$$CH_3$$
$$(CH_3)_2CHCH_2CH_2CH_2CHCH_2CH_2OH$$

$C_{10}H_{22}O_1$. M: 158.29. Colourless liquid with a rose-like odour. BP: 212°C. d: ~0.83 kg/l (20°C). Soluble in alcohol and hydrocarbon solvents.

Production:
- geraniol/(±)-citronellol (hydrogenation)
- geraniol-nerol, mixed (hydrogenation; byproduct of
  (±)-citronellol production)

Derivatives:
piproctanyl bromide

Uses: fragrance ingredient (technical products)

tetrahydrolinalool
3,7-dimethyloctan-3-ol; [78-69-3]

$$CH_3$$
$$(CH_3)_2CHCH_2CH_2CH_2CCH_2CH_3$$
$$OH$$

$C_{10}H_{22}O_1$. M: 158.29. Colourless liquid with a floral odour. BP: 78°C (1.3 kPa). d: ~0.83 kg/l (20°C). Soluble in alcohol and hydrocarbon solvents.

Production:
- linalool (hydrogenation)

Uses:
fragrance ingredient (soap, detergents)

tetrahydronaphthalene *See:* tetralin

tetrahydrophthalic anhydride
4-cyclohexene-1,2-dicarboxylic acid; THPA; [85-43-8]

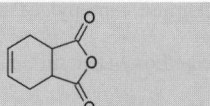

$C_8H_8O_3$. M: 152.15. White, hygroscopic, crystalline powder. MP: 101–102°C. Hydrolysed by hot water. Soluble in oxygenated and aromatic solvents. The commercial product is the *cis*-isomer.

Production:
- butadiene + maleic anhydride (Diels-Alder
  cycloaddition)

Derivatives: diisodecyl 4,5-epoxytetrahydrophthalate; hexahydrophthalic anhydride; *N*-hydroxymethyl-3,4,5,6-tetrahydrophthalimide; tetrahydrophthalimide
Uses: unsaturated polyester resin comonomer

tetrahydrophthalimide
4-cyclohexene-1,2-dicarboximide; [27813-21-4]

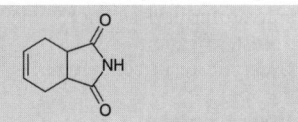

$C_8H_9N_1O_2$. M: 151.17.
Production:
• tetrahydrophthalic anhydride + ammonia (amide formation)
Derivatives: captafol; captan

tetrahydrothiophene
thiophane; THT; [110-01-0]

$C_4H_8S_1$. M: 88.16. Colourless liquid. BP: 119°C. d: 1.00 kg/l (20°C). Insoluble in water. Soluble in oxygenated solvents.
Production:
• tetrahydrofuran + hydrogen sulphide (sulphide formation)
Uses: gas odorant

tetrahydrothiophene-1,1-dioxide *See:* sulfolane

tetrahydroxypropyl ethylenediamine
N,N,N',N'-tetra-(2-hydroxypropyl)-1,2-diaminoethane; Quadrol (BASF); [102-60-3]

$C_{14}H_{32}N_2O_4$. M: 292.42. See also ethylenediamine propoxylates/ethoxylates.
Production:
• ethylenediamine + propylene oxide (epoxidation)
Uses:
propoxylated/ethoxylated surfactant intermediate

tetrahydrozoline *See:* tetryzoline

tetrakis(2-chloroethyl)ethylene diphosphate
Thermolin 101 (Olin)

$(ClCH_2CH_2O)_2POCH_2CH_2OP(OCH_2CH_2Cl)_2$

$C_{10}H_{20}Cl_4O_8P_2$. M: 472.02.

Production:
• phosphorus oxychloride + ethylene oxide (epoxidation/dehydrochlorination)
Uses:
fire-retardant additive (flexible polyurethane foam)

tetrakis(2,4-di-*t*-butylphenyl)-4,4′-biphenyl diphosphonite

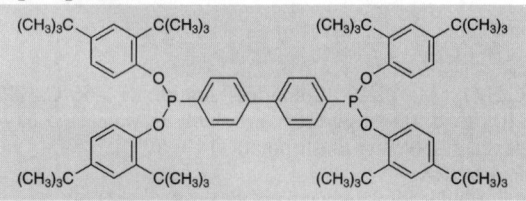

$C_{68}H_{92}O_4P_2$. M: 1035.44.
Production:
• biphenyl + phosphorus trichloride + 2,4-di-*t*-butylphenol (dehydrochlorination/ dehydrochlorination)
Uses: antioxidant (plastics)

tetrakis(hydroxymethyl)phosphonium chloride
THPC; TMPC

$(HOCH_2)_4P^+ \ Cl^-$

$C_4H_{12}Cl_1O_4P_1$. M: 190.56.
Production:
• phosphine + formaldehyde + hydrochloric acid (hydroxymethylation)
Uses: fire-retardant textile finishes

tetrakis(hydroxymethyl)phosphonium sulphate
THPS; TMPS

$(HOCH_2)_4P^+ \ \frac{1}{2}SO_4^{2-}$

$C_8H_{24}O_{12}P_2S_1$. M: 406.28.
Production:
• phosphine + formaldehyde + sulphuric acid (hydroxymethylation)
Uses: fire-retardant textile finishes

tetrakis[methylene (3,5-di-*t*-butyl-4-hydroxy)hydrocinnamate]methane *See:* pentaerythritol tetrakis-[3-(3,5-di-*t*-butyl-4-hydroxyphenyl)propionate]

tetralin
tetrahydronaphthalene; THN; [119-64-2]

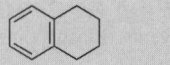

$C_{10}H_{12}$. M: 132.21. Colourless liquid with unpleasant odour. MP: -31°C. BP: 206°C. d: 0.97 kg/l (18°C). Insoluble in water.
Production:
• naphthalene (reduction)

Derivatives: coumatetralyl
Uses: heat-transfer fluid; solvent

1,1,3,3-tetramethoxypropane
[102-52-3]

$$(CH_3O)_2CHCH_2CH(OCH_3)_2$$

$C_7H_{16}O_4$. M: 164.21.
Production:
• acetaldehyde + trimethyl orthoformate + methanol (condensation/acetal formation)
Derivatives: metazachlor

tetramethrin
[7696-12-0]

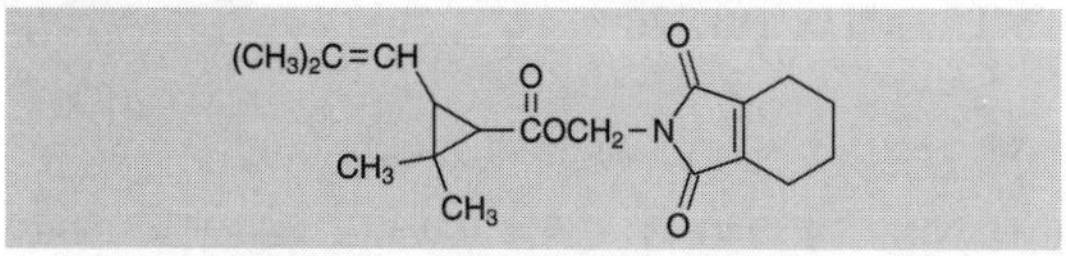

$C_{19}H_{25}N_1O_4$. M: 331.42. Available commercially as the racemic or (1R)-enriched product.
Production:
• N-hydroxymethyl-3,4,5,6-tetrahydrophthalimide + (1RS)-cis/trans-chrysanthemic acid (esterification)
Uses: insecticide

tetramethylammonium bromide
TMAB; [64-20-0]

$$(CH_3)_4N^+ \quad Br^-$$

$C_4H_{12}Br_1N_1$. M: 154.05. Solid.
Production:
• trimethylamine + methyl bromide (quaternisation)
Uses: base-catalysis reagent

tetramethylammonium chloride
TMAC; [75-57-0]

$$(CH_3)_4N^+ \quad Cl^-$$

$C_4H_{12}Cl_1N_1$. M: 109.60. Available commercially as the pure solid or as a 50% solution in water.
Production:
• trimethylamine + methyl chloride (quaternisation)
Uses: base-catalysis reagent

tetramethylammonium hydroxide
TMA-OH; [75-59-2]

$$(CH_3)_4N^+ \quad OH^-$$

$C_4H_{13}N_1O_1$. M: 91.15. Commercial product sold as a 25% solution in water or methanol.
Production:
• trimethylamine + methanol + sulphuric acid (quaternisation/hydration)
Derivatives: zeolite ZSM 5
Uses: base-catalysis reagent

1,2,4,5-tetramethylbenzene *See:* durene

tetramethyl decynediol
2,4,7,9-tetramethyl-5-decyne-4,7-diol; Surfynol 104 (Air Products and Chemical); [126-86-3]

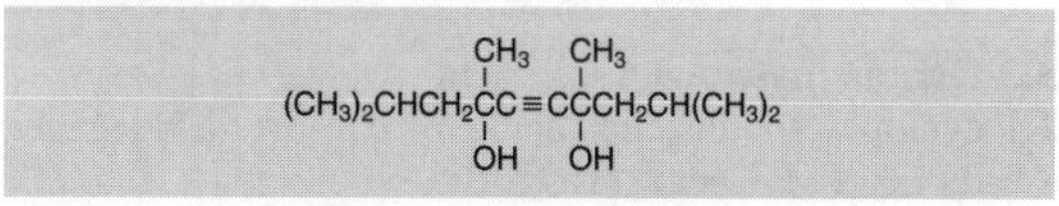

$C_{14}H_{26}O_2$. M: 226.36. White, waxy solid or pale yellow 50–85% solutions in various alcohol solvents.
Production:
• methyl isobutyl ketone + acetylene (ethynylation)
Derivatives: tetramethyl decynediol ethoxylates
Uses: defoaming agent (cement additives, dyestuffs, printing inks, pesticides); wetting agent (pesticides, industrial coatings, adhesives, rinse aids, metal cleaners)

tetramethyl decynediol ethoxylates
2,4,7,9-tetramethyl-5-decyne-4,7-diol ethoxylates; Surfynol 440 (Air Products and Chemical); Surfynol 485 (Air Products and Chemical)

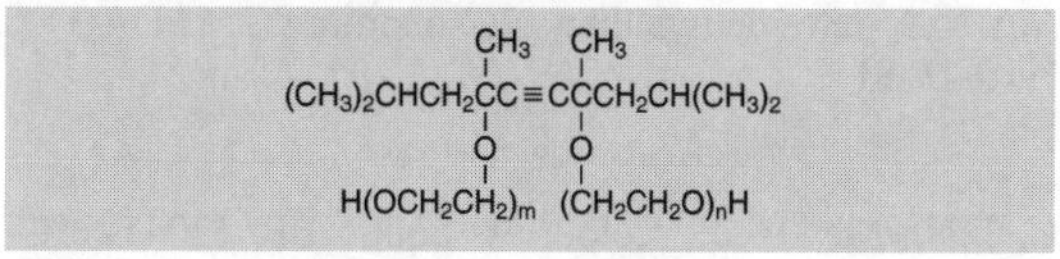

Nonionic surfactants with an ethylene oxide content of 40–85% w/w.
Production:
• tetramethyl decynediol + ethylene oxide (epoxidation)
Uses: defoaming agent; wetting agents (electroplating, metal cleaning, adhesives, paper coatings)

tetramethyldiaminobenzhydrol
See: 4,4'-bis(dimethylamino)benzhydrol

tetramethyldiaminobenzophenone
See: 4,4'-bis(dimethylamino)benzophenone

N,N,N',N'-tetramethyl-4,4'-diaminodiphenylmethane
See: bis(p-dimethylaminophenyl)methane

tetramethyldodecahydronaphthofuran
3a,6,6,9a-tetramethyldodecahydronaphtho[2,1:b]furan; [3738-00-9]

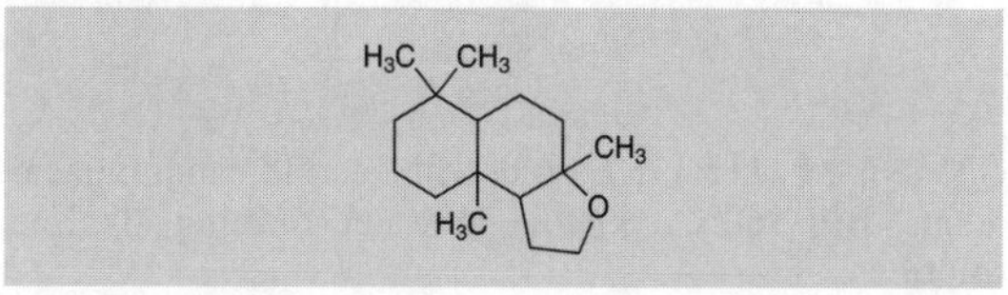

$C_{16}H_{28}O_1$. M: 236.40. Crystalline solid. MP: 75–76°C.
Production:
• sage oil, Clary (oxidative cleavage/hydrogenation/ether formation)
Uses: fragrance ingredient

tetramethylenediamine *See:* 1,4-diaminobutane

tetramethylene dibromide *See:* 1,4-dibromobutane

tetramethylene dichloride *See:* 1,4-dichlorobutane

3,3-tetramethyleneglutaric acid

1,1-cyclopentanediacetic acid; 8-oxaspiro[4,5]decane-7,9-dione; TMG acid; [16713-66-9]

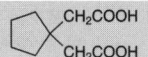

$C_9H_{14}O_4$. M: 186.21.
Production:
• 1,4-dichlorobutane + diethyl malonate + sodium cyanide (malonic ester synthesis/ester reduction/cyanidation/nitrile hydrolysis)
Derivatives:
buspirone
Uses: enzyme inactivator

tetramethylethylenediamine

N,N,N′,N′-tetramethylethane-1,2-diamine; TMEDA; [110-18-9]

$(CH_3)_2NCH_2CH_2N(CH_3)_2$

$C_6H_{16}N_2$. M: 116.21. Colourless liquid. BP: 120–122°C. d: 0.78 kg/l (20°C). Soluble in water.
Production:
• ethylenediamine (methylation)
Uses:
acrylamide polymerisation catalyst; reagent (organo-lithium compound formation)

tetramethyl/ethyl lead, redistributed

TML/TEL

$(CH_3)_m(C_2H_5)_nPb$

m+n = 4.
Production:
• tetramethyl lead + tetraethyl lead (disproportionation)
Uses: petrol octane booster

tetramethylguanidine

TMG; [80-70-6]

$(CH_3)_2NCN(CH_3)_2$
$||$
NH

$C_5H_{13}N_3$. M: 115.17. Liquid with a mild, ammoniacal odour. BP: 160°C. Soluble in water forming alkaline solutions.
Production:
• dimethylamine + cyanogen chloride (amine formation/nitrile addition)
Uses:
polyurethane foam catalyst

tetramethyl lead

TML; [75-74-1]

$(CH_3)_4Pb$

$C_4H_{12}Pb_1$. M: 267.33. Colourless liquid. MP: -30°C. BP: 110°C. d: 2.00 kg/l (20°C).
Production:
• methyl chloride + lead + sodium (alloy formation/dechlorination)
Derivatives:
tetramethyl/ethyl lead, redistributed
Uses: petrol octane booster

tetramethylthiuram disulphide

bis(dimethylthiocarbamyl)disulphide; thiram; thiuram; TMT; TMTD; [137-26-8]

$(CH_3)_2NCSSCN(CH_3)_2$, S S (=)

$C_6H_{12}N_2S_4$. M: 240.43. Creamy-white, odourless powder. MP: 145°C. d: 1.3 kg/l. Insoluble in water. Soluble in oxygenated and chlorinated solvents.
Production:
• sodium dimethyldithiocarbamate (air oxidation)
Uses: fungicide; preservative (natural rubber latex); vulcanisation accelerator

tetramethylthiuram monosulphide

TMTM; [97-74-5]

$(CH_3)_2NCSCN(CH_3)_2$, S S (=)

$C_6H_{12}N_2S_3$. M: 208.36. Yellow, odourless powder. MP: 105°C. Soluble in aromatic solvents.
Production:
• sodium dimethyldithiocarbamate (reductive coupling)
Uses:
vulcanisation accelerator

tetramethyltin

[594-27-4]

$(CH_3)_4Sn$

$C_4H_{12}Sn_1$. M: 178.83. Colourless liquid. BP: 78°C. MP: -55°C. d: 1.31 kg/l (4°C). Insoluble in water.
Production:
• methylmagnesium chloride + stannic chloride (reaction)
Derivatives:
dimethyltin dichloride; monomethyltin trichloride

tetramethylurea

TMU; [632-22-4]
$C_5H_{12}N_2O_1$. M: 116.16. Liquid. BP: 176–178°C. d: 0.97 kg/l (20°C). Miscible with water and most organic solvents.

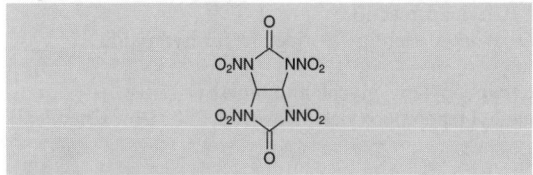

Production:
• dimethylamine + carbon dioxide (addition)
Uses:
high-boiling aprotic solvent

tetramethyl-*m*-xylene diisocyanate
m-TMXDI

$C_{14}H_{16}N_2O_2$. M: 244.29. Liquid.
Production:
• *m*-diisopropenylbenzene + isocyanic acid (hydro-chlorination/dehydrochlorination; coproduced with isopropenyldimethylbenzyl isocyanate)
Uses:
isocyanate component (polyurethane elastomers)

tetramethyl-*p*-xylene diisocyanate
p-TMDXI

$C_{14}H_{16}N_2O_2$. M: 244.29. Solid. MP: 72°C.
Production:
• *p*-diisopropenylbenzene + isocyanic acid (hydrochlorination/dehydrochlorination)
Uses:
isocyanate component (polyurethane elastomers)

tetramisole
levamisole ((–)-enantiomer); [5036-02-2]; [14769-73-4] ((–)-enantiomer)

$C_{11}H_{12}N_2S_1$. M: 204.29. Available commercially as the hydrochloride of both the racemic mixture and the L(–)-enantiomer.
Production:
• ethylene dibromide + thiourea + styrene oxide (dehydrobromination/epoxidation/alcohol chlorination/amine formation)
Uses:
anthelmintic/immunostimulant drug

tetranitroglycoluril
sorguyl

$C_4H_2N_8O_{10}$. M: 322.11.
Production:
• glycoluril + nitric acid, concentrated (nitration)
Uses: explosives

tetra-*n*-octyltin
tetraoctyltin; tin tetraoctyl; [3590-84-9]

$C_{32}H_{68}Sn_1$. M: 571.58.
Production:
• *n*-octyl chloride + magnesium + stannic chloride (Grignard reagent formation/Grignard reaction)
• tri-*n*-octylaluminium + stannic chloride (aluminium-alkyl process)
Derivatives: di-n-octyltin dichloride

1,4,5,8-tetra-(phenylthio)anthraquinone

$C_{38}H_{24}O_2S_4$. M: 640.87.
Production:
• 1,4,5,8-tetrachloroanthraquinone + thiophenol (dehydrochlorination)
Uses: dye (liquid crystal displays)

tetraphenyltin
[595-90-4]

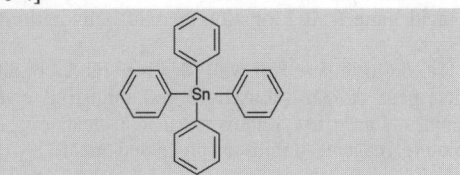

$C_{24}H_{20}Sn_1$. M: 427.11. Colourless crystals. MP: 226°C. d: 1.49 kg/l. Insoluble in water. Soluble in most organic solvents.

Production:
- phenylmagnesium chloride + stannic chloride (Grignard reaction)

Derivatives: fentin fluoride; fentin hydroxide

tetrapropylene glycol monomethyl ether

methyl tetrapropoxylate; Dowfroth 250 (Dow Chemical)

CH₃O(CHCH₂O)₄H with CH₃

$C_{13}H_{28}O_5$. M: 264.35. Colourless liquid. d: 1.04 kg/l (25°C). BP: 240°C. Miscible with water and oxygenated solvents.

Production:
- methanol + propylene oxide (epoxidation)

Uses: flotation frothing agent

tetrasodium N-(1,2-dicarboxyethyl)-N-octadecyl-sulphosuccinamate

Aerosol 22 (American Cyanamid)

$C_{26}H_{43}N_1Na_4O_{10}S_1$. M: 653.65. Available as a 35% solution in water or in water/methanol.

Production:
- maleic anhydride + stearylamine + sodium bisulphite (amine formation/amide formation/sulphonation)

Uses:
flotation collector (cassiterite ores); solubiliser/dispersing agent (industrial, household, metal cleaners)

tetrasodium ethylenediaminetetraacetate

See: ethylenediaminetetraacetic acid, tetrasodium salt

tetrasodium pyrophosphate

sodium pyrophosphate; tetrasodium diphosphate; TSPP; [7722-88-5]

Na₂O.(NaPO₃)₂

$Na_4O_7P_2$. M: 265.90. White, crystalline solid. MP: >880°C. Solubility in water: 67 g/l water (25°C).

Production:
- sodium hydroxide/sodium carbonate + phosphoric acid, pure (salt formation/thermal dehydration)

Uses:
clay deflocculant; oil-well drilling mud conditioner; detergent builder (household and industrial cleaners); sequesterant (rust removers, metal cleaners); copper plating reagent; stabiliser (processed meat)

tetrazene

[31330-63-9]
$C_2H_6N_{10}$. M: 170.13.

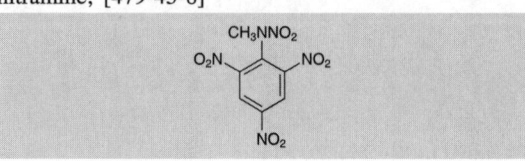

Production:
- aminoguanidine bicarbonate + sodium nitrite (diazotisation)

Uses: explosive primers

tetryl

N-methyl-2,4,6,N-tetranitroaniline; trinitrophenylmethyl-nitramine; [479-45-8]

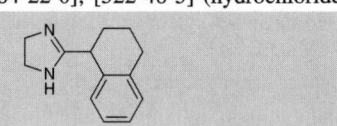

$C_7H_5N_5O_8$. M: 287.15.
Production:
- N,N-dimethylaniline (nitration)

Uses: explosives

tetryzoline

tetrahydrozoline; [84-22-0]; [522-48-5] (hydrochloride)

$C_{13}H_{16}N_2$. M: 200.28. Available commercially as the hydrochloride.
Production:
- α-naphthoic acid + ethylenediamine (condensation)

Uses:
vasoconstrictor drug

Texanol *See:* 2,2,4-trimethyl-1,3-pentanediol

TFCE *See:* chlorotrifluoroethylene

TFE *See:* tetrafluoroethylene

TFE/HFP *See:* tetrafluoroethylene-hexafluoropropylene copolymers

TFP *See:* 3,3,3-trifluoropropylene

TGDDM *See:* tetraglycidyl methylenedianiline

TGIC *See:* triglycidyl isocyanurate

TGMDA *See:* tetraglycidyl methylenedianiline

TGPAP *See:* triglycidyl-p-aminophenol

THAM *See:* tris(hydroxymethyl)aminomethane

thebaine

p-morphine; paramorphine; [115-37-7]

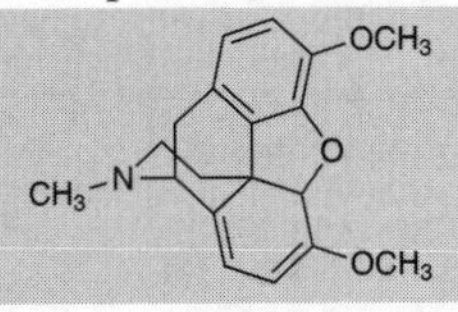

$C_{19}H_{21}N_1O_3$. M: 311.39. Crystalline solid. Sublimes at 170–180°C. Almost insoluble in water. Soluble in oxygenated, chlorinated and aromatic solvents.
Production:
• opium (extraction; coproduced with codeine/morphine)
Derivatives:
buprenorphine; oxycodone

thenalidine

thenaldine; [86-12-4]

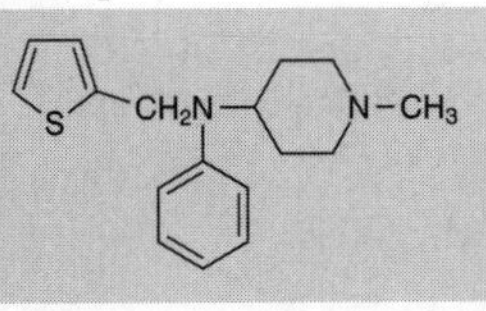

$C_{17}H_{22}N_2S_1$. M: 286.44. Available commercially as the free base or as the tartrate salt.
Production:
• 1-methyl-4-piperidone + aniline + formaldehyde + thiophene (reductive amination/Mannich reaction)
Uses:
antihistamine drug

2-thenoic acid

thiophene-2-carboxylic acid; [527-72-0]

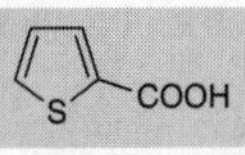

$C_5H_4O_2S_1$. M: 128.14. Needles. MP: 128–130°C. Soluble in hot water and oxygenated solvents.
Production:
• 2-acetylthiophene + sodium hypochlorite (haloform reaction)
Derivatives: thiafensulfuron-methyl
Uses: thickening agent (lubricant greases)

theobromine

3,7-dimethylxanthine; [83-67-0]

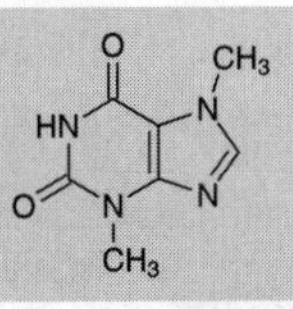

$C_7H_8N_4O_2$. M: 180.17. Crystalline solid. Sublimes at 290°C. Slightly soluble in hot water. Insoluble in most organic solvents.

Production:
• 6-amino-1-methyluracil + sodium nitrite + formamide + dimethyl sulphate (nitrosation/nitro reduction/condensation/methylation)
Derivatives: pentifylline; pentoxifylline; protheobromine
Uses: appetite stimulant drug

theodrenaline

[13460-98-5]

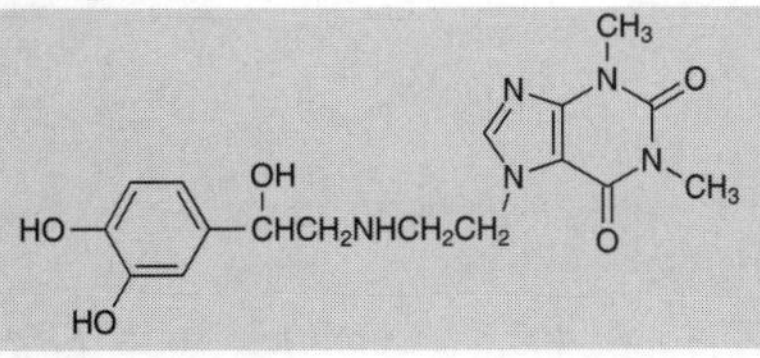

$C_{17}H_{21}N_5O_5$. M: 375.38.
Production:
• 3,4-dihydroxy-ω-chloroacetophenone + ethylene dibromide + benzylamine + theophylline (amine formation/amine formation/amine formation/debenzylation)
Uses: circulatory analeptic/antihypotensive drug

theophylline

1,3-dimethylxanthine; aminophylline (ethylenediamine salt); metaphyllin (ethylenediamine salt); [58-55-9]; [317-34-0] (ethylenediamine salt)

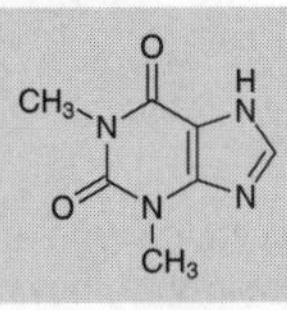

$C_7H_8N_4O_2$. M: 180.17. Available commercially as the acid, ethylenediamine, monoethanolamine, diethanolamine, isopropanolamine or sodium glycinate salts.
Production:
• 6-amino-1,3-dimethyluracil + sodium nitrite + formamide (nitrosation/nitro reduction/condensation)
Derivatives: caffeine; diprophylline; etofylline; fenetylline; proxyphylline; reproterol; theodrenaline; xanthinol nicotinate
Uses: bronchodilator drug

THF *See:* tetrahydrofuran

THFA *See:* tetrahydrofurfuryl alcohol

thiabendazole

2-(4-thiazolyl)benzimidazole; TBZ; E233 (EC); [148-79-8]

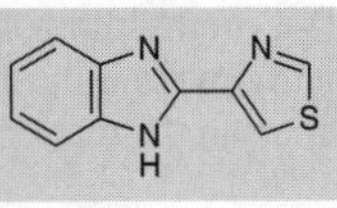

$C_{10}H_7N_3S_1$. M: 201.25. White powder. MP: 304–305°C.

Slightly soluble in water and oxygenated solvents.
Production:
• 4-methylthiazole + *o*-phenylenediamine
(ammoxidation/nitrile hydration/condensation)
Uses: fungicide; anthelmintic drug; preservative (paint, fruit, vegetables)

thiafensulfuron-methyl
[79277-27-3]

$C_{12}H_{13}N_5O_7S_2$. M: 403.38. Colourless solid. MP: 186°C. Insoluble in water. Soluble in oxygenated solvents.
Production:
• 2-thenoic acid + methanol + sulphuryl chloride + ammonia + phosgene + cyanuric acid (esterification/chlorosulphonation/sulphonamide formation/phosgenation/amine formation/isocyanate addition)
Uses: herbicide

thiamazole
methimazole; [60-56-0]

$C_4H_6N_2S_1$. M: 114.16.
Production:
• ammonia + chloroacetaldehyde + methyl isothiocyanate (amine formation/thiocyanate addition)
Uses:
electroplating bath additive; thyroid hormone drug

thiamine
vitamin B_1; [59-43-8]; [67-03-8] (hydrochloride)

$C_{12}H_{17}Cl_1N_4O_1S_1$. M: 300.81.
Production:
• 4-amino-5-aminomethyl-2-methylpyrimidine + carbon disulphide + 2-acetobutyrolactone (thiocarbonylation/alpha chlorination/decarboxylation/esterification/sulphide formation/condensation/ oxidation)
• 5-(2-hydroxyethyl)-4-methylthiazole + 4-amino-5-bromomethyl-2-methylpyrimidine hydrobromide (dehydrobromination/salt formation)
Uses:
vitamin enrichment additive (animal feed)

thiamphenicol
[15318-45-3]

$C_{12}H_{15}Cl_2N_1O_5S_1$. M: 356.22.
Production:
• toluene + methanesulphonyl chloride + glycine + chloral (sulphonation/side-chain oxidation/condensation/racemate separation/carbonyl reduction/amide formation)
Uses: antibacterial drug

3-thiapentanol *See:* 2-ethylthioethanol

thiazafluron
1,3-dimethyl-1-(5-trifluoromethyl-1,3,4-thiadiazol-2-yl)-urea; [25366-23-8]

$C_6H_7F_3N_4O_1S_1$. M: 240.21.
Production:
• trifluoroacetic anhydride + 4-methyl thiosemicarbazide + methyl isocyanate (condensation/isocyanate addition)
Uses: herbicide

1,3-thiazolinecarboxylic acid *See:* timonacic

2-thiazylamine *See:* 2-aminothiazole

thidiazuron
N-phenyl-*N'*-1,2,3-thiadiazol-5-ylurea; [51707-55-2]

$C_9H_8N_4O_1S_1$. M: 220.25.
Production:
• chloroacetonitrile + sodium azide + hydrogen sulphide + phenyl isocyanate (dehydrochlorination/condensation/isocyanate addition)
Uses:
plant growth regulator

thienamycin
[59995-64-1]

$C_{11}H_{16}N_2O_4S_1$. M: 272.32.

Production:
- corn steep liquor + *Streptomyces cattleya* bacteria (fermentation)

Derivatives: imipenem
Uses: antibacterial drug

2-thienylacetic acid
thiophene-2-acetic acid; [1918-77-0]

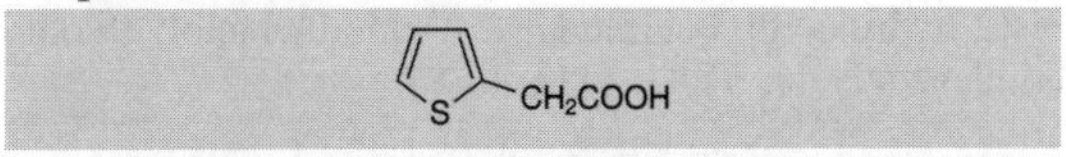

$C_6H_6O_2S_1$. M: 142.18. Crystalline solid. MP: 63–67°C. Soluble in hot water and oxygenated solvents.
Production:
- 2-acetylthiophene (Willgerodt reaction)

Derivatives:
benzothienocycloheptanone; cefalotin; cefoxitin

3-thienylmalonic acid
thiophene-3-malonic acid

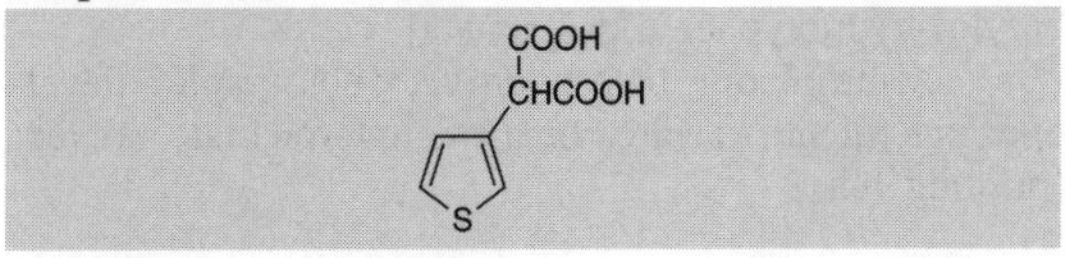

$C_7H_6O_4S_1$. M: 186.19.
Production:
- 3-methylthiophene + dimethyl carbonate (side-chain bromination/cyanidation/nitrile hydrolysis/ esterification/condensation/saponification)

Derivatives:
temocillin; ticarcillin

thioacetic acid
[507-09-5]

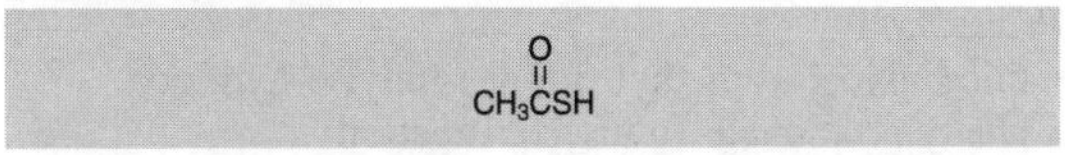

$C_2H_4O_1S_1$. M: 76.11. pale yellow liquid with a pungent odour. BP: 86–88°C with decomposition. MP: <-24°C. d: 1.07 kg/l (20°C).
Production:
- acetic anhydride + hydrogen sulphide (thiolation)

Derivatives:
biotin; captopril
Uses: reagent (steroid drug production)

thiobencarb
[28249-77-6]

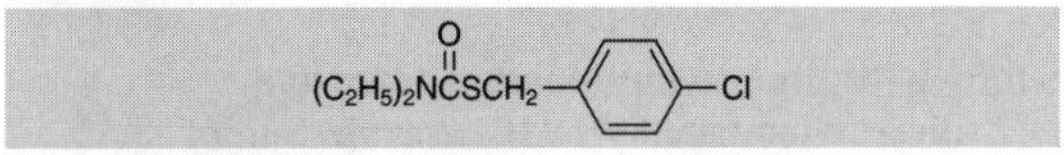

$C_{12}H_{16}Cl_1N_1O_1S_1$. M: 257.78.
Production:
- diethylamine + carbonyl sulphide + *p*-chlorobenzyl chloride (thiocarbonylation/dehydrochlorination)

Uses: herbicide

4,4'-thiobis(2-*t*-butyl-5-methylphenol)
[96-69-5]

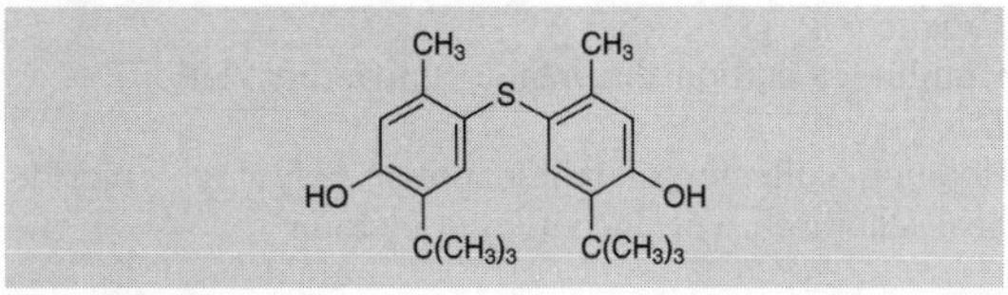

$C_{22}H_{30}O_2S_1$. M: 358.54.
Production:
- 6-*t*-butyl-*m*-cresol + sulphur dichloride (sulphurisation)

Uses: antioxidant (plastics, rubber, lubricants)

2,2'-thiobis(4,6-dichlorophenol) *See:* bithionol

2,2'-thiobis(4-methyl-6-*t*-butylphenol)
6,6'-thiobis(2-*t*-butyl-4-methylphenol)

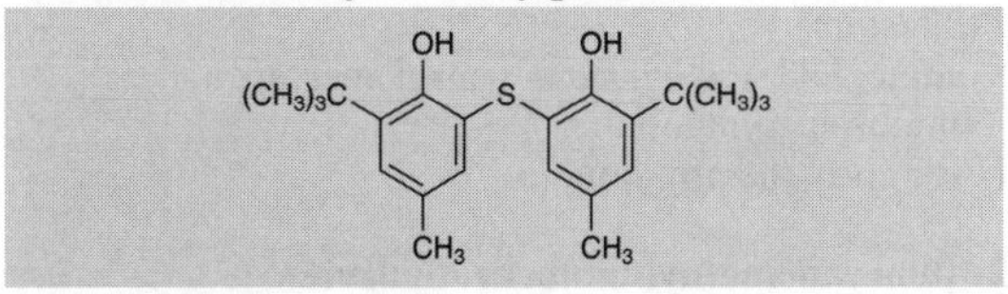

$C_{22}H_{30}O_2S_1$. M: 358.54.
Production:
- 2-*t*-butyl-*p*-cresol + sulphur dichloride (sulphurisation)

Uses: antioxidant (plastics)

2,2'-thiobis(4-*t*-octylphenol)

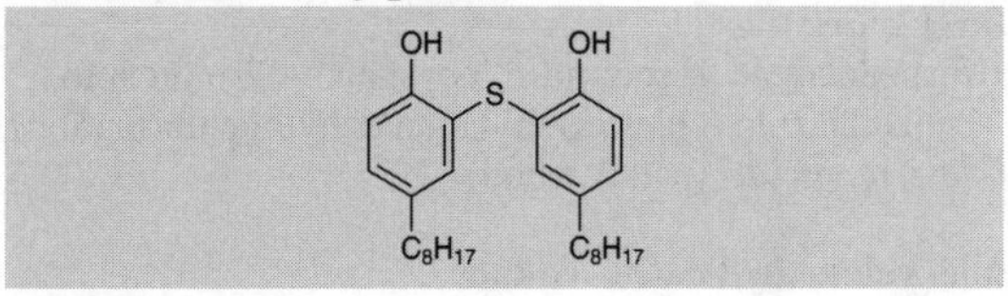

$C_{28}H_{42}O_2S_1$. M: 442.71.
Production:
- *p*-*t*-octylphenol + sulphur dichloride (sulphurisation)

Derivatives: *n*-butylaminonickel-2,2'-thiobis(4-*t*-octylphenol); nickel bis[2,2'-thiobis(4-*t*-octylphenol)]

2,2'-thiobis(4-*t*-octylphenolato)nickel
See: nickel bis[2,2'-thiobis(4-*t*-octylphenol)]

4,4'-thiobisphenol *See:* 4,4'-thiodiphenol

thiocarbamide *See:* thiourea

thiocarbanil *See:* phenyl isothiocyanate

thiocarbanilide
N,N'-diphenylthiourea; DPTU; [102-08-9]

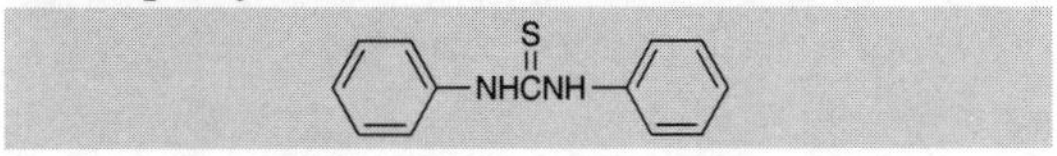

$C_{13}H_{12}N_2S_1$. M: 228.31. White, crystalline powder. MP:

150–153°C. d: 1.32 kg/l. Insoluble in water. Soluble in oxygenated and chlorinated solvents.
Production:
• aniline + carbon disulphide (thiocarbonylation)
Uses:
flotation collector (sulphide ores); polyvinyl chloride heat stabiliser; vulcanisation accelerator

thiocarbonyl chloride *See:* thiophosgene

p-thiocresol *See:* p-methylmercaptophenol

thioctic acid
lipoic acid; [62-46-4]

$C_8H_{14}O_2S_2$. M: 206.33.
Production:
• adipic acid + ethylene + benzyl mercaptan (multistep synthesis)
Uses: liver therapy drug

2-(thiocyanomethylthio)benzothiazole
(2-benzothiazolylthio)methyl isocyanate; TCMTB; Busan 72 (Buckman Laboratories)

$C_9H_6N_2S_3$. M: 238.35.
Production:
• formaldehyde + sodium thiocyanate + 2-mercapto-benzothiazole (chloromethylation/dehydrochlorination)
Uses: fungicide (paint, wood)

thiocyclam hydrogen oxalate
[31895-22-4]

$C_7H_{13}N_1O_4S_3$. M: 271.38.
Production:
• 1,3-dimercaptoisopropyldimethylamine + sulphur dichloride + oxalic acid (dehydrochlorination/salt formation)
Uses: insecticide

thiodicarb
[59669-26-0]

$C_{10}H_{18}N_4O_4S_3$. M: 354.47.

Production:
• acetaldehyde + hydroxylamine sulphate + methyl mercaptan + methyl isocyanate + sulphur dichloride (oxime formation/chlorination/sulphide formation/isocyanate addition/dehydrochlorination)
Uses: insecticide

thiodiglycol
bis(2-hydroxyethyl)sulphide; 2,2'-thiodiethanol; thiodiethylene glycol; TDG; [111-48-8]

$C_4H_{10}O_2S_1$. M: 122.18. Colourless, viscous liquid. BP: 282°C with decomposition. d: 1.18 kg/l (15°C). Soluble in water.
Production:
• hydrogen sulphide + ethylene oxide (epoxidation; coproduced with 2-mercaptoethanol)
Derivatives: poly(methylene-thiodiethyl ether); thiodiglycol di-β-aminocrotonate; thiodiglycol bis[3-(3,5-di-t-butyl-4-hydroxyphenyl)propionate]
Uses: electroplating bath additive; photographic developer ingredient; warfare chemicals intermediate; solvent (printing inks)

thiodiglycol bis[3-(3,5-di-t-butyl-4-hydroxyphenyl)-propionate]
2,2'-thiodiethyl bis(3,5-di-t-butyl-4-hydroxy)hydrocinnamate; Irganox 1035 (Ciba-Geigy)

$C_{38}H_{58}O_6S_1$. M: 642.93.
Production:
• thiodiglycol + methyl 3,5-di-t-butyl-4-hydroxy-phenylpropionate (transesterification)
Uses: antioxidant (plastics, rubber)

thiodiglycol di-β-aminocrotonate

$C_{12}H_{20}N_2O_4S_1$. M: 288.36.
Production:
• β-aminocrotononitrile + thiodiglycol (nitrile hydrolysis/esterification)
Uses: polyvinyl chloride heat stabiliser

5-thio-1-(β-dimethylaminoethyl)tetrazole
1-(2'-dimethylaminoethyl)-1H-tetrazole-5-thiol

$C_5H_{11}N_5S_1$. M: 173.23.

Production:
- 2-dimethylaminoethyl chloride hydrochloride + potassium thiocyanate + sodium azide (dehydrochlorination/cyclisation)

Derivatives:
cefotiam

4,4′-thiodiphenol

4,4′-dihydroxydiphenyl sulphide; TDP; [2664-63-3]

HO—⟨⟩—S—⟨⟩—OH

$C_{12}H_{10}O_2S_1$. M: 218.27.
Production:
- phenol + sulphur dichloride (dehydrochlorination)

Derivatives:
temephos
Uses: high-clarity polycarbonate resin comonomer

thiodipropionic acid

3,3′-thiodipropionic acid; [111-17-1]

$S(CH_2CH_2COOH)_2$

$C_6H_{10}O_4S_1$. M: 178.21. White powder. MP: 133°C. Solubility in water: 36 g/l water (25°C).
Production:
- hydrogen sulphide + acrylonitrile (cyanoethylation/ nitrile hydrolysis)

Derivatives:
dilauryl thiodipropionate; distearyl thiodipropionate
Uses: polyvinyl chloride heat costabilisers

3,3′-thiodipropionitrile

bis(2-cyanoethyl)sulphide; [111-97-7]

$S(CH_2CH_2CN)_2$

$C_6H_8N_2S_1$. M: 140.20. Pale yellow liquid. MP: 28°C. d: 1.11 kg/l (30°C). Soluble in water, oxygenated and chlorinated solvents.
Production:
- hydrogen sulphide + acrylonitrile (cyanoethylation)

Uses: nickel plating brightening agent

thiofanox

1-(2,2-dimethyl-1-methylthiomethylpropylideneamino-oxy)-*N*-methylformamide; thiofanocarb; [39196-18-4]

(CH₃)₃C   O
        \   ‖
         C=NOCNHCH₃
        /
CH₃SCH₂

$C_9H_{18}N_2O_2S_1$. M: 218.31.
Production:
- α-chloropinacolone + methyl mercaptan + hydroxylamine sulphate + methyl isocyanate (sulphide formation/oxime formation/isocyanate addition)

Uses: acaricide/insecticide

thioglycerol

monothioglycerol; thioglycerin; 1-thioglycerol; [96-27-5]

                    OH
                    |
        HSCH₂CHCH₂OH

$C_3H_8O_2S_1$. M: 108.15. Yellowish, viscous liquid. d: 1.29 kg/l (15°C). Slightly soluble in water.
Production:
- epichlorohydrin + sodium hydrosulphide (thiolation/hydration)

Uses:
polymerisation modifier; stabiliser (pharmaceuticals, cosmetics); wound healing drug

thioglycollic acid

mercaptoacetic acid; thioglycolic acid; [68-11-1]

        HSCH₂COOH

$C_2H_4O_2S_1$. M: 92.11. Available commercially as an anhydrous powder or as an aqueous solution containing 70–80% active matter. Anhydrous grade: colourless liquid with a pungent odour. BP: 94°C (0.27 kPa). MP: -10–-12°C. d: 1.32 kg/l (20°C). Miscible with water and most organic solvents.
Production:
- chloroacetic acid + sodium hydrosulphide (thiolation)

Derivatives: ammonium thioglycollate; *n*-butyl thioglycollate; cefapirin; ethanolamine thioglycollate; etozolin; isooctyl thioglycollate; piprozolin; sodium thioglycollate; spironolactone
Uses: carbonyl condensation catalyst; depilatory ingredient; hair waving agent

thioguanine

[154-42-7]

$C_5H_5N_5S_1$. M: 167.18.
Production:
- guanine + sodium thiocyanate (chlorination/ dehydrochlorination/thiocyanate hydrolysis)

Uses:
antineoplastic drug

thioindigo

Thioindigo Red B; Vat Red 41 (CI); 73300 (CI)

$C_{16}H_8O_2S_2$. M: 296.37.

Production:
• thiosalicylic acid + chloroacetic acid (sulphide formation/cyclisation/decarboxylation/oxidative coupling)
Uses: dye (cotton denim, wool, silk)

thiomalic acid
2-mercaptosuccinic acid; [70-49-5]

$$\underset{\underset{HOOCCH_2CHCOOH}{}}{SH}$$

$C_4H_6O_4S_1$. M: 150.15. White crystals. MP: 152–153°C. Soluble in water and oxygenated solvents. The commercial product is a mixture of enantiomers.
Production:
• maleic acid + hydrobromic acid + sodium sulphide (addition/thiolation)
Uses: aluminium anodising reagent; rust inhibitor; cold permanent hair waving solutions

5-thio-1-methyltetrazole
5-mercapto-1-methyltetrazole; 1-methyltetrazole-5-thiol; 1-methyl-5-thiotetrazole

$$HS-\overset{N-N}{\underset{\underset{CH_3}{N}}{}}$$

$C_2H_4N_4S_1$. M: 116.14.
Production:
• methyl isothiocyanate + sodium azide (nitrile addition)
Derivatives:
cefamandole; cefmenoxime; cefoperazone; cefotetan

thiometon
S-2-ethylthioethyl *O,O*-dimethyl phosphorodithionate; [640-15-3]

$$\underset{C_2H_5SCH_2CH_2SP(OCH_3)_2}{\overset{\overset{S}{\|}}{}}$$

$C_6H_{15}O_2P_1S_3$. M: 246.35.
Production:
• 2-ethylthioethanol + *O,O*-dimethyl dithiophosphoric acid (sulphide formation)
Uses:
acaricide/insecticide

thionyl chloride
sulphur oxychloride; [7719-09-7]

$$SOCl_2$$

$Cl_2O_1S_1$. M: 118.97. Pale yellow, fuming liquid with a pungent odour. BP: 76°C. MP: -105°C. Hydrolysed by water to sulphur dioxide and hydrochloric acid. Miscible with chlorinated and aromatic solvents.
Production:
• sulphur dioxide, pure + chlorine (addition)

Derivatives: cefapirin; cefazedone; 4-chlorobutyryl chloride; diodone; endosulphan; propargite; trimedlure
Uses: acid/alcohol chlorination/chloromethylation reagent; stabiliser (sulphur trioxide)

thiopental sodium
pentothal; [71-73-8]

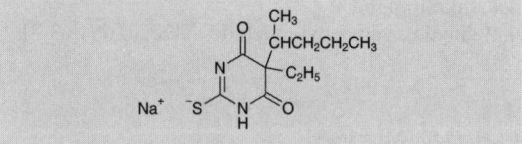

$C_{11}H_{17}N_2Na_1O_2S_1$. M: 264.32.
Production:
• diethyl malonate + methyl propyl ketone + ethyl bromide + thiourea (Knoevenagel condensation/dehydrochlorination/condensation)
Uses: anaesthetic drug

thiophanate-methyl
1,2-di-(3-methoxycarbonyl-2-thioureido)benzene; [23564-05-8]

$C_{12}H_{14}N_4O_4S_2$. M: 342.40.
Production:
• *o*-phenylenediamine + potassium thiocyanate + methyl chloroformate (addition/dehydrochlorination)
Uses: wound protectant (fruit trees)

thiophane *See:* tetrahydrothiophene

thiophene
[110-02-1]

$C_4H_4S_1$. M: 84.13. Liquid with an aromatic odour. BP: 83–85°C. Insoluble in water. Miscible with most organic solvents.
Production:
• *n*-butane + sulphur (addition)
Derivatives: 2-acetylthiophene; pyrantel; thenalidine; thiophene-2,5-dicarboxylic acid
Uses: phenol-formaldehyde resin comonomer; solvent

thiophene-2-acetic acid *See:* 2-thienylacetic acid

thiophene-2,5-dicarboxylic acid
2,5-thiophenedicarboxylic acid
$C_6H_4O_4S_1$. M: 172.16. MP: >350°C. Slightly soluble in water. Soluble in oxygenated solvents.

Production:
- thiophene + acetic anhydride (Friedel-Crafts acylation/side-chain oxidation)

Derivatives:
Fluorescent Brightener 184; Fluorescent Brightener 190

thiophenol
benzenethiol; phenyl mercaptan; [108-98-5]

$C_6H_6S_1$. M: 110.18. Liquid with an unpleasant odour. Oxidised by air to the disulphide. BP: 166–168°C. d: 1.07 kg/l (25°C). Insoluble in water. Soluble in oxygenated and aromatic solvents.

Production:
- benzenesulphonyl chloride + phosphorus (reduction)

Derivatives:
2-chlorothioxanthone; (*1RS*)-*trans*-chrysanthemic acid; 1,5-di-(*p-t*-butylphenylthio)anthraquinone; edifenphos; fonofos; sulfinpyrazone; 1,4,5,8-tetra-(phenylthio)-anthraquinone

thiophosgene
thiocarbonyl chloride; [463-71-8]

$$Cl_2C = S$$

$C_1Cl_2S_1$. M: 114.98. Reddish-yellow liquid with an unpleasant odour. BP: 73°C. d: 1.51 kg/l (15°C). Slightly soluble in water, with decomposition. Soluble in oxygenated solvents. Highly toxic.

Production:
- carbon disulphide + chlorine (reaction)

Derivatives: tolnaftate

thiophosphoryl chloride
phosphorus sulphochloride; thiophosphoric trichloride; [3982-91-0]

$$PSCl_3$$

$Cl_3P_1S_1$. M: 169.39.

Production:
- phosphorus trichloride + sulphur (reaction)

Derivatives:
butamifos; dioxabenzofos; isofenphos; propetamphos; prothiofos; sulprofos; triphenyl phosphorothionate; tris-(*p*-isocyanatophenyl) thiophosphate

thioridazine
[50-52-2]; [130-61-0] (hydrochloride)
$C_{21}H_{26}N_2S_2$. M: 370.58. Available commercially as the free base or as the hydrochloride salt.

Production:
- α-picoline + formaldehyde + methyl chloride + 2-chlorophenothiazine + methyl mercaptan (condensation/methylation/hydrogenation/sulphide formation/amine formation)

Uses: neuroleptic drug

thiosalicylic acid
o-mercaptobenzoic acid; [147-93-3]

$C_7H_6O_2S_1$. M: 154.19. Yellow flakes with an unpleasant odour. MP: 165–168°C. Sublimes. Slightly soluble in hot water. Soluble in oxygenated solvents.

Production:
- anthranilic acid + sodium hydrosulphide (diazotisation/sulphide formation)

Derivatives: flupenthixol; 2-isopropylthioxanthone; lucanthone; thioindigo; tiotixene

thiosemicarbazide
aminothiourea; TSC; [79-19-6]

$$NH_2CNHNH_2$$

$C_1H_5N_3S_1$. M: 91.13. White needles. MP: 180–181°C with decomposition. Soluble in water and alcohol.

Production:
- hydrazine + ammonium thiocyanate (thiocyanate addition)

Derivatives:
ambazone; bisthiosemi; ceftriaxone; sulfaethidole

thiosinamine *See:* allylthiourea

thiourea
thiocarbamide; [62-56-6]

$$(H_2N)_2C = S$$

$C_1H_4N_2S_1$. M: 76.11. White, crystalline solid. MP: 175–178°C. d: 1.41 kg/l. Soluble in water and alcohol.

Production:
- cyanamide + hydrogen sulphide (addition)

Derivatives:
2-aminothiazole; 2-aminothiazoline-4-carboxylic acid; aztreonam; cefotiam; ceftazidime; ethyl 2-(2-amino-thiazolyl)methoxyiminoacetate; furfuryl mercaptan; hyp-

oxanthine; tetramisole; thiopental sodium; thiourea dioxide; thiourea-urea-formaldehyde resins
Uses: dispersant (animal glue, proteins); chrome/nickel plating reagent; photographic chemical; thiolation reagent; vulcanisation accelerator

thiourea dioxide
formamidine sulphinic acid; thiourea *S,S*-dioxide; [4189-44-0]

$$\underset{HSO_2CNH_2}{\overset{\overset{NH}{\|}}{}}$$

$C_1H_4N_2O_2S_1$. M: 108.11. White, crystalline powder. Solubility in water: 30 g/l water (20°C). Insoluble in most organic solvents.
Production:
• thiourea + hydrogen peroxide (oxidation)
Uses: redox catalyst component (melamine resins); disperse dye reducing agent (textile printing, blueprint papermaking)

thiourea-urea-formaldehyde resins
Production:
• thiourea + urea + formaldehyde (condensation)
Uses: decorative laminates

thiram *See:* tetramethylthiuram disulphide

THN *See:* tetralin

Thomas slag *See:* basic slag

thorium dioxide
thorium oxide

$$ThO_2$$

O_2Th_1. M: 264.04. White, crystalline powder. d: 10.0 kg/l. MP: 3,300°C. Slightly radioactive.
Production:
• monazite + sodium hydroxide (salt formation/ separation; coproduced with rare earth oxide, hydrate)
Uses: ceramic fuel rods (nuclear reactors); gas mantles; refractory ceramics (crucibles)

THPA *See:* tetrahydrophthalic anhydride

THPC
See: tetrakis(hydroxymethyl)phosphonium chloride

THPS
See: tetrakis(hydroxymethyl)phosphonium sulphate

L-threonine
L-2-amino-3-hydroxybutyric acid; Thr; [72-19-5]
$C_4H_9N_1O_3$. M: 119.12. White crystals. Decompose on heating to 255°C. Soluble in water.

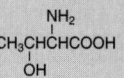

Production:
• microbial fermentation medium + *Serratia marcescens* bacteria (fermentation; coproduced with L-isoleucine)
Derivatives: aztreonam
Uses: infusion solutions

THT *See:* tetrahydrothiophene

thujopsene fraction
Cedarwood oil fraction containing *cis*-thujopsene.
Production:
• cedarwood oil, Virginia (fractionation; coproduced with cedrol)
Derivatives:
4-acetyl-1,1,6-trimethylethanooctahydronaphthalene
Uses: fragrance ingredient

thyme oil
[8007-46-3]
Colourless (purified) or reddish-brown (crude) liquid with a characteristic odour. Produced by steam distillation of thyme (*Thymus vulgaris* or *T. zygis*). d: ~0.92 kg/l (25°C). Soluble in ethanol. The main constituents of the oil are thymol and carvacrol. France, Spain, Algeria and Morocco are the main producing countries.
Uses: fragrance/flavouring ingredient

thymol
isopropyl-*m*-cresol; 2-isopropyl-5-methylphenol; [89-83-8]

$C_{10}H_{14}O_1$. M: 150.22. Colourless crystals with a herbal odour. MP: 49–51°C. BP: 231–237°C. Very slightly soluble in water. Soluble in oxygenated and chlorinated solvents.
Production:
• *m*-cresol + propylene (orthoalkylation)
Derivatives:
chlorothymol; (±)-menthol; menthone; thymol iodide
Uses: disinfectant/antiseptic/preservative; fragrance ingredient; anthelmintic drug

thymol iodide
[552-22-7]
$C_{20}H_{24}I_2O_2$. M: 550.22. Mixed product, the main component of which is dithymol diiodide.
Production:
• thymol + potassium iodide (ring iodination)

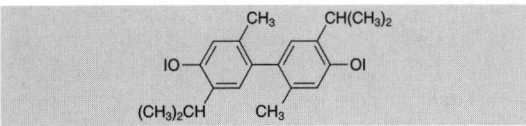

Uses: medical antiseptic

thymopentin
[69558-55-0]

H-Arg-Lys-Asp-Val-Tyr-OH

$C_{30}H_{49}N_9O_9$. M: 679.77.
Production:
• L-arginine + L-lysine + L-aspartic acid +
  L-tyrosine + L-valine (peptide synthesis)
Uses: immunostimulant drug

tiapride
[51012-32-9]

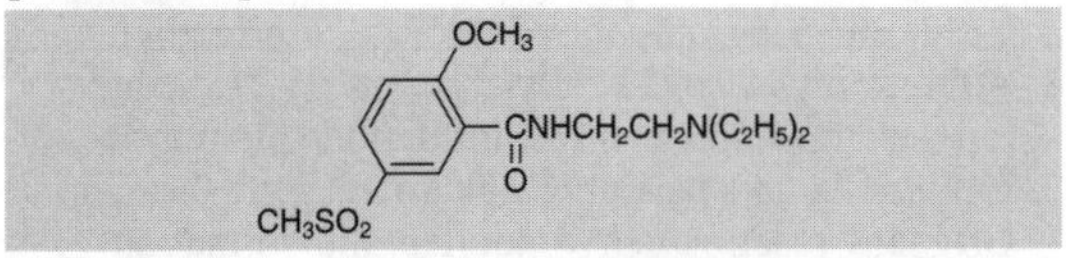

OCH₃ ... CNHCH₂CH₂N(C₂H₅)₂ / O ... CH₃SO₂

$C_{15}H_{24}N_2O_4S_1$. M: 328.42. Available commercially as
the free base or as the hydrochloride salt.
Production:
• salicylic acid + dimethyl sulphate + methanesulphonyl chloride + *N,N*-diethylethylenediamine
  (methylation/sulphonation/amide formation)
Uses:
antiemetic drug

TIB *See:* dodecene, branched

TIBA *See:* triisobutylaluminium

ticarcillin
[34787-01-4]

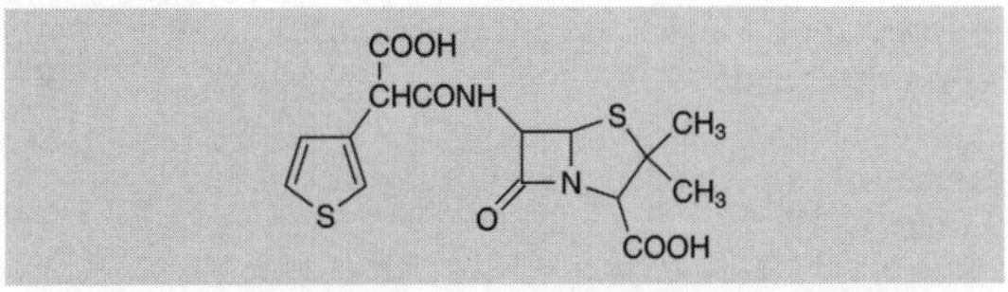

COOH / CHCONH ... S / CH₃ / O N / CH₃ / COOH

$C_{15}H_{16}N_2O_6S_2$. M: 384.42. Available commercially as
the acid or disodium salts.
Production:
• 3-thienylmalonic acid + 6-aminopenicillanic acid
  (amide formation)
Uses: antibacterial drug

tiglic acid
trans-2-methyl-2-butenoic acid; 2-methylcrotonic acid;
trans-2-methylcrotonic acid; [80-59-1]
$C_5H_8O_2$. M: 100.11. White crystals with a spicy odour.
MP: 61–64°C. BP: 199°C. d: 0.96 kg/l (15°C). Soluble

in hot water and oxygenated solvents. The *cis*-isomer
is angelic acid.

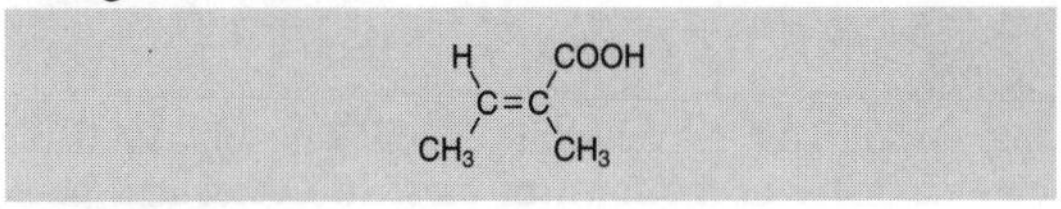

H COOH / C=C / CH₃ CH₃

Production:
• 2-methyl-2-butenonitrile (nitrile hydrolysis)
Derivatives:
citronellyl tiglate; ethyl tiglate; geranyl tiglate

tilidine
[20380-58-9]

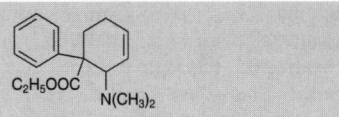

$C_{17}H_{23}N_1O_2$. M: 273.38. The commercial product is the
racemic *trans,trans*-isomer.
Production:
• crotonaldehyde + dimethylamine + acetophenone +
  sodium cyanide + ethanol (amine formation/
  cyanohydrin formation/dehydration/nitrile
  hydrolysis/esterification/cycloaddition)
Uses: analgesic drug

timolol
[26839-75-8]

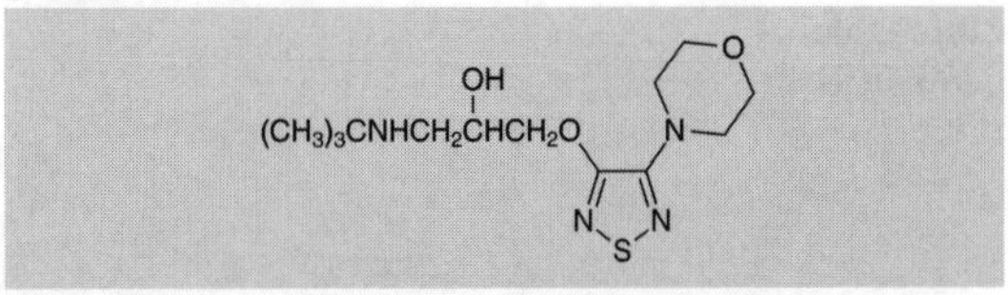

OH / (CH₃)₃CNHCH₂CHCH₂O ... N—O / N / N—S

$C_{13}H_{24}N_4O_3S_1$. M: 316.42. Available commercially as
the hydrogen maleate salt of the (*S*)-(−)-enantiomer.
Production:
• oxamide + sulphur dichloride + morpholine +
  epichlorohydrin + *t*-butylamine (condensation/amine
  formation/hydration/ether formation/epoxidation/
  racemate separation)
Uses:
antianginal/antihypertensive drug

timonacic
1,3-thiazolinecarboxylic acid; [444-27-9]

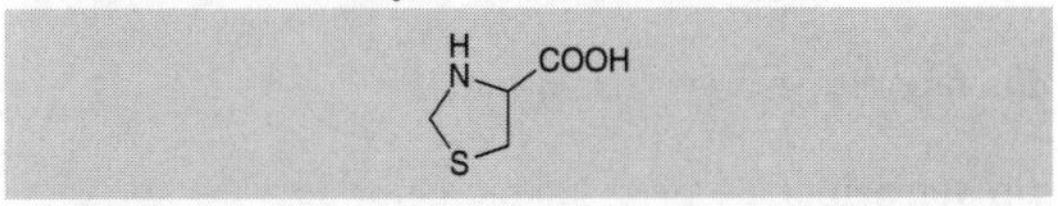

H / N COOH / S

$C_4H_7N_1O_2S_1$. M: 133.17. Available both as the racemic
mixture and as the (−)-enantiomer.
Production:
• L-cysteine/DL-cysteine hydrochloride +
  formaldehyde (condensation)
Uses: choleretic drug

tin
[7440-31-5]

Sn

Sn_1. M: 118.69. Silver-white, ductile metal. Available commercially in the form of bars, foil, shot and powder. MP: 232°C. BP: 2,507°C. d: 7.31 kg/l.
Production:
• tin ore concentrate + metallurgical coke (smelting)
Derivatives:
stannic chloride; stannic oxide; stannous chloride; stannous fluoroborate; stannous sulphate
Uses:
tinplate; conductive coatings (printed circuit boards); gunmetal; cast iron additive; aluminium-tin alloys (bearings); Pilkington float glass production bed; bronze ingredient (coins, bells, statues, pigment); leaded bronze ingredient (bearings); phosphor bronze ingredient (bearings); pewter (ornamental cups, plates); reagent (Stephen reaction, nitro reduction); tin-antimony-copper alloys (bearings); tin-lead alloys (solder, printed circuit board conductive coatings)

tin chloride *See:* stannic chloride

tin dichloride *See:* stannous chloride

tin dioxide *See:* stannic oxide

tinidazole
[19387-91-8]

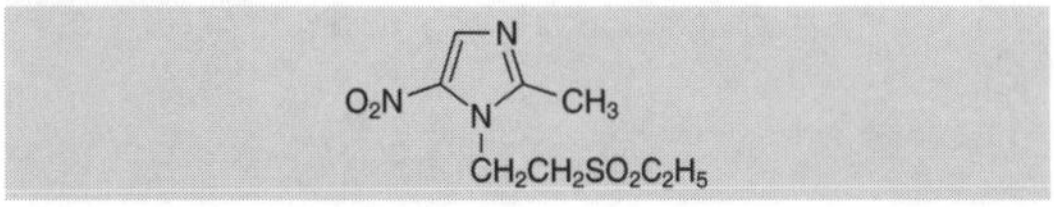

$C_8H_{13}N_3O_4S_1$. M: 247.27.
Production:
• peracetic acid + 2-ethylthioethanol + 2-methyl-4-nitroimidazole (sulphide oxidation/amine formation)
Uses:
antiprotazoal drug

tin octoate *See:* stannous octoate

tin oleate *See:* stannous oleate

tin sulphate *See:* stannous sulphate

tin tetrabutyl *See:* tetra-*n*-butyltin

tin tetrachloride *See:* stannic chloride

tin tetraoctyl *See:* tetra-*n*-octyltin

tiocarbazil
S-benzyl di-*s*-butylthiocarbamate; [36756-79-3]
$C_{16}H_{25}N_1O_1S_1$. M: 279.45.

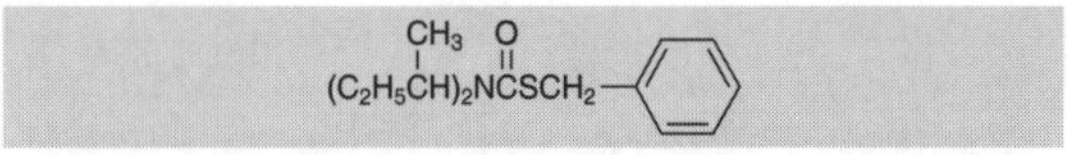

Production:
• di-*s*-butylamine + carbonyl sulphide + benzyl chloride (thiocarbonylation/dehydrochlorination)
Uses: herbicide

tiotixene
[3313-26-6]

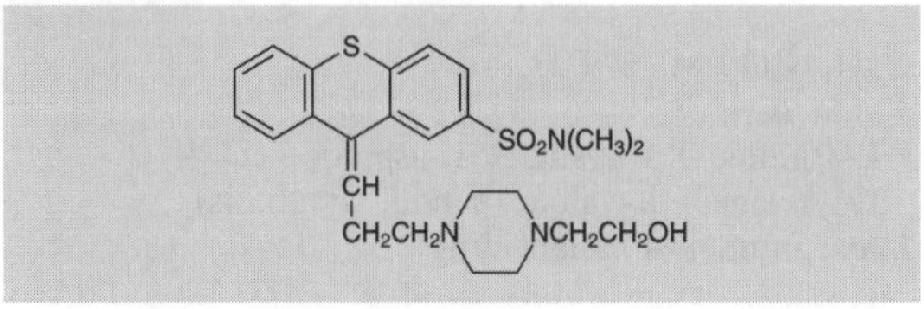

$C_{23}H_{29}N_3O_3S_2$. M: 459.63.
Production:
• *p*-chlorobenzenesulphonyl chloride + dimethylamine + thiosalicylic acid + allyl bromide + *N*-methyl-piperazine (sulphonamide formation/sulphide formation/condensation/Grignard reagent formation/Grignard reaction/dehydration/amine formation)
Uses: neuroleptic drug

TIOTM *See:* triisooctyl trimellitate

TIPA *See:* triisopropanolamine

2,4,5-T-isooctyl
isooctyl (2,4,5-trichlorophenoxy)acetate; [25168-15-4]

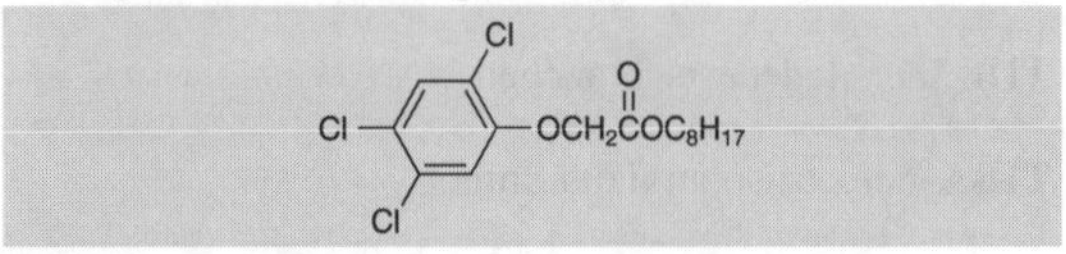

$C_{16}H_{21}Cl_3O_3$. M: 367.71.
Production:
• isooctanol + 2,4,5-T (esterification)
Uses: herbicide

titanium
[7440-32-6]

Ti

Ti_1. M: 47.90. Grey, lustrous metal. MP: 1,668°C. BP: 3,260°C. d: 4.51 kg/l. The surface of titanium is protected by an oxide film which renders the metal corrosion resistant to air, water and oxidising agents. It is attacked rapidly by acid, however. Available as sponge, foil, slugs, plate, rod and wire.
Production:
• titanium tetrachloride + sodium (Hunter process)
• titanium tetrachloride + magnesium (Kroll process)
Derivatives:
titanium hydride

Uses: chemical/petroleum refinery/electroplating plant components; aluminium grain refining agent; titanium alloy ingredient (aircraft/aerospace parts and structures); prothetic components; reagent (stainless/alloy steel refining)

titanium carbide
[12070-08-5]

TiC

C_1Ti_1. M: 59.91. Hard, grey, metallic solid. d: 4.93 kg/l. MP: 3,100°C.
Production:
• titanium dioxide, hydrate + carbon black (carburisation)
Uses: cemented carbide cutting tools

titanium diboride

TiB$_2$

B_2Ti_1. M: 69.52. Hard, chemically-resistant, electrically-conducting solid. MP: 2,850°C.
Production:
• titanium dioxide, hydrate + boron oxide + aluminium/magnesium (reaction)
Uses: electrorefining electrodes and crucibles

titanium dioxide
titanium white; Pigment White 6 (CI); E171 (EC); [13463-67-7]

TiO$_2$

O_2Ti_1. M: 79.90. White powder. Available in several grades depending on the crystal structure, surface treatment and particle size distribution. Both rutile and anatase crystal forms are available. MP: 1,855°C. d: 3.70–4.20 kg/l. Insoluble in water.
Production:
• rutile/titanium slag/anatase + chlorine + sponge coke, calcined (chloride process)
• titanium dioxide, hydrate (sulphate process)
Uses: filler/pigment (paper coatings, plastics, rubber, sealants, caulks); pigment (paints, printing inks, polishes, ceramics, vitreous enamels, food)

titanium dioxide, hydrate
titanium hydroxide; [20338-08-3]

TiO$_2$.nH$_2$O

O_2Ti_1. M: 79.90. Precipitated titanium dioxide used as a raw material for pigment production. Not a generally traded product.
Production:
• titanium slag/ilmenite/anatase + oleum (sulphate process)
Derivatives: aluminium titanate; barium titanate; chrome antimony titanium buff; cobalt green; lead zircon-ate titanate; potassium fluorotitanate; titanium carbide; titanium diboride; titanium dioxide; titanium nickel yellow

titanium hydride
[7704-98-5]

TiH$_2$

H_2Ti_1. M: 49.92. Black, metallic powder. Dissociates on heating above 290°C. d: 3.8 kg/l.
Production:
• titanium + calcium hydride + hydrogen (reaction)
Uses: getter (vacuum tubes); metal processing agent

titanium hydroxide *See:* titanium dioxide, hydrate

titanium isopropylate *See:* isopropyl titanate

titanium nickel yellow
nickel antimony titanium yellow; nickel titanate; nickel titanium yellow; Pigment Yellow 53 (CI); 77788 (CI); Light Yellow (Bayer); Sicotan Yellow K1011 (BASF)

(Ti,Ni,Sb)O$_2$

Lemon yellow, light fast powder. d: 4.5 kg/l.
Production:
• nickel carbonate, basic/nickel oxide, black + antimony trioxide + titanium dioxide, hydrate (calcination)
Uses: pigment (heat-resistant/high-durability paints); plastics colorant

titanium slag
Metallurgical slag with a high titanium content.
Production:
• ilmenite + metallurgical coke (arc furnace reduction; byproduct of iron production)
Derivatives: titanium dioxide; titanium dioxide, hydrate; titanium tetrachloride

titanium tetrabutoxide *See:* butyl titanate

titanium tetrachloride
[7550-45-0]

TiCl$_4$

Cl_4Ti_1. M: 189.71. Colourless liquid. BP: 136°C. MP: -24°C. d: 1.70 kg/l (20°C). Decomposed by water. Fumes in moist air. Soluble in most organic solvents.
Production:
• rutile/titanium slag/anatase + chlorine + sponge coke, calcined (chloride process)
Derivatives:
butyl titanate; dicyclopentadienyl titanium dichloride; isopropyl titanate; titanium; titanium trichloride
Uses:
polymerisation catalyst component

titanium tetraisopropoxide *See:* isopropyl titanate

titanium tetraoctoxide *See:* 2-ethylhexyl titanate

titanium trichloride
titanous chloride; [7705-07-9]

TiCl₃

Cl₃Ti₁. M: 154.26. Available commercially as the anhydrous or hexahydrate salts. The anhydrous grade is a dark purple, crystalline solid. Decomposed by air and water.
Production:
• titanium tetrachloride (hydrogenation)
Uses: polymerisation catalyst; dye stripping agent

TKPP *See:* potassium pyrophosphate

TMA *See:* trimethyladipic acid; trimethylamine; trimellitic anhydride

TMAB *See:* tetramethylammonium bromide

TMAC *See:* tetramethylammonium chloride

TMAEMC *See:* trimethylammoniumethyl methacrylate chloride

TMD *See:* trimethylhexamethylenediamine

TMDAU *See:* trimethylolglycoluril

TMDHQ *See:* 2,2,4-trimethyl-1,2-dihydroquinoline, polymeric

TMDI *See:* trimethylhexamethylene diisocyanate

p-TMDXI *See:* tetramethyl-p-xylene diisocyanate

TME *See:* trimethylolethane

TMEDA *See:* tetramethylethylenediamine

TMG *See:* tetramethylguanidine

TMG acid *See:* 3,3-tetramethyleneglutaric acid

TMI *See:* isopropenyldimethylbenzyl isocyanate

TML *See:* tetramethyl lead

TML/TEL *See:* tetramethyl/ethyl lead, redistributed

TMP *See:* trimethylolpropane

TMPC *See:* tetrakis(hydroxymethyl)phosphonium chloride

TMPD *See:* 2,2,4-trimethyl-1,3-pentanediol

TMPI *See:* trimethyl phosphite

TMPS *See:* tetrakis(hydroxymethyl)phosphonium sulphate

TMPTA *See:* trimethylolpropane triacrylate

TMPTMA *See:* trimethylolpropane trimethacrylate

TMQ *See:* 2,2,4-trimethyl-1,2-dihydroquinoline, polymeric

TMTD *See:* tetramethylthiuram disulphide

TMTM *See:* tetramethylthiuram monosulphide

TMU *See:* tetramethylurea

m-TMXDI *See:* tetramethyl-m-xylene diisocyanate

TNB *See:* 1,3,5-trinitrobenzene; dodecene, branched

TNBA *See:* tri-n-butylamine; tri-n-butylaluminium

TNP *See:* picric acid

TNPP *See:* tris(nonylphenyl) phosphite

TNT *See:* 2,4,6-trinitrotoluene

tobacco seed fatty acids
Production:
• tobacco seed oil (hydrolysis)
Derivatives: alkyd resins, long-oil; alkyd resins, medium-oil; alkyd resins, short-oil

tobacco seed oil
Yellowish-brown oil with characteristic odour. d: 0.92 kg/l. Saponification value: 186–197 mg KOH/g. Sold as bleached or alkaline-refined grades, or as stand oil. The chain-length distribution is: 9–10% ≤C₁₈:₀, 16–20% C₁₈:₁, 60–70% C₁₈:₂. Produced mainly in India.
Derivatives:
tobacco seed fatty acids
Uses: alkyd resin comonomer

Tobias acid
2-aminonaphthalene-1-sulphonic acid; 2-naphthylamine-1-sulphonic acid; [81-16-3]

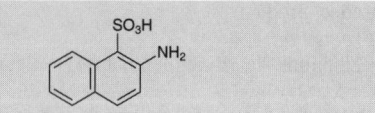

C₁₀H₉N₁O₃S₁. M: 223.25.

Production:
- β-naphthol + ammonia (sulphonation/ammoniation)

Derivatives:
Acid Yellow 19; Acid Yellow 200; 2-naphthylamine-1,5-disulphonic acid; 2-naphthylamine-1,5,7-trisulphonic acid; *N*-(2-naphthyl)-3-hydroxy-2-naphthamide; Pigment Red 49; Pigment Red 63; Vat Red 35

tobramycin
[32986-56-4]

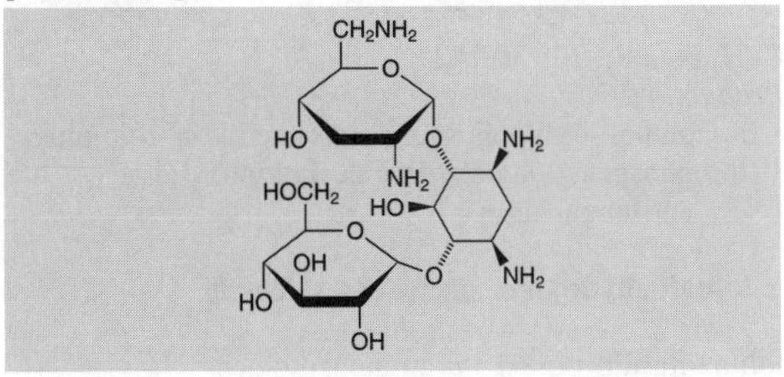

$C_{18}H_{37}N_5O_9$. M: 467.53. Commercially available as the free base or as the sulphate salt.

Production:
- microbial fermentation medium + *Streptomyces tenebrarius* bacteria (fermentation/extraction)

Uses: antibacterial drug

α-tocopherol
vitamin E; E307 (EC); [59-02-9]

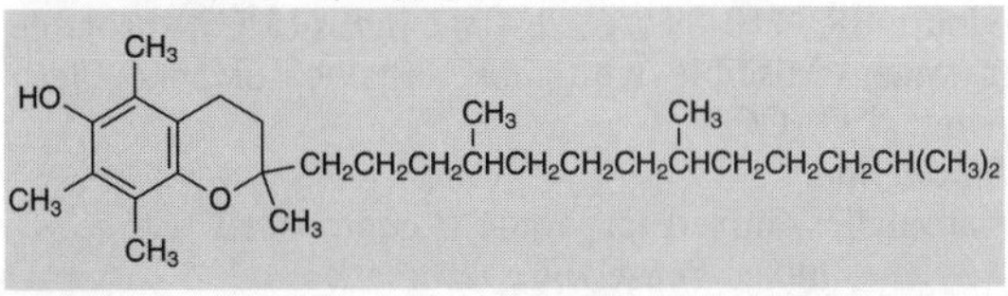

$C_{29}H_{50}O_2$. M: 430.72. Pale yellow oil. Slowly discoloured by light and air. MP: 2–4°C. d: 0.95–0.96 kg/l (25°C). Insoluble in water. Soluble in oxygenated solvents, chlorinated solvents, oils and fats. The commercial product is a racemic mixture.

Production:
- 2,3,5-trimethylphenol + phytol (oxidation/reduction/condensation)

Derivatives:
α-tocopheryl acetate

Uses: dietary supplement; animal feed additive; antioxidant (flour, bread, vegetable oils, margarine, prepared meats)

tocopherol, mixed
vitamin E; E306 (EC)
Concentrate containing >25% (R,R,R)-α-tocopherol and >25% other tocopherols.

Production:
- soyabean soap stock (acidification/fractionation; byproduct of soyabean acid production)

Uses: dietary supplement

α-tocopheryl acetate
tocopheryl acetate; vitamin E acetate; [58-95-7]

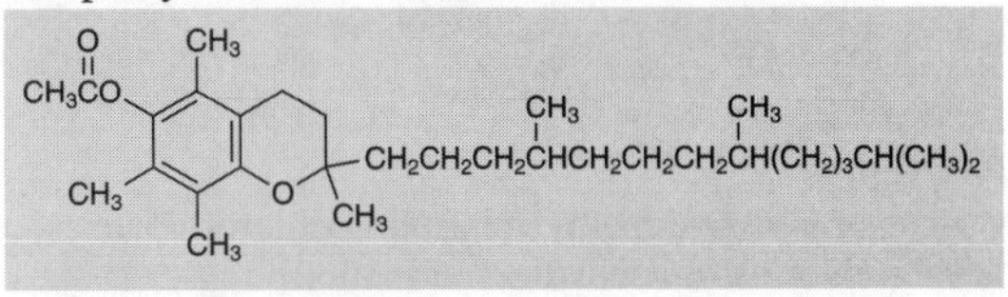

$C_{31}H_{52}O_3$. M: 472.76. Pale yellow, viscous liquid. MP: 25°C. d: 0.96 kg/l (25°C). Insoluble in water. Commercial products are usually mixtures of enantiomers although resolved forms are available. Sold as a pure product and in the form of a concentrate.

Production:
- α-tocopherol + acetic anhydride (esterification)

Uses: dietary supplement; animal/human feed additive

TOFA *See:* tall oil fatty acid

tolazamide
[1156-19-0]

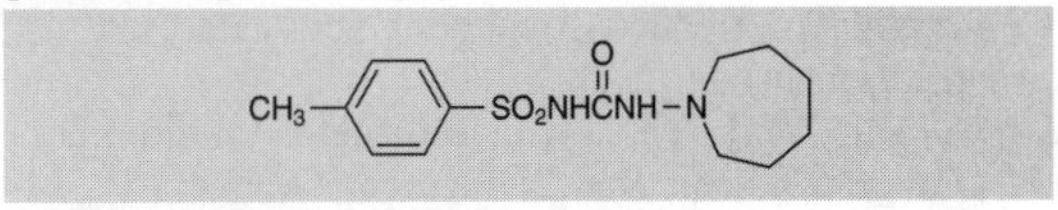

$C_{14}H_{21}N_3O_3S_1$. M: 311.40.

Production:
- hexamethyleneimine + *p*-toluenesulphonyl isocyanate (diazotisation/hydrogenation/isocyanate addition)

Uses: antidiabetic drug

tolazoline
[59-98-3]

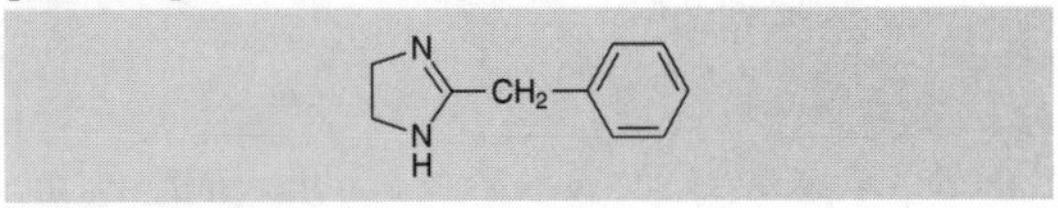

$C_{10}H_{12}N_2$. M: 160.22.

Production:
- benzyl cyanide + ethylenediamine (condensation)

Uses: vasodilator drug

tolbutamide
[64-77-7]

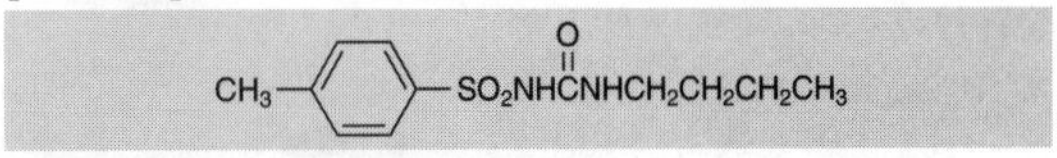

$C_{12}H_{18}N_2O_3S_1$. M: 270.34.

Production:
- *p*-toluenesulphonamide + *n*-butyl isocyanate (isocyanate addition)

Uses: antidiabetic drug

tolclofos-methyl
O-2,6-dichloro-*p*-tolyl *O,O*-dimethyl phosphorothioate; [57018-04-9]
$C_9H_{11}Cl_2O_3P_1S_1$. M: 301.13.

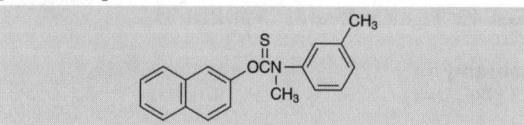

Production:
* *p*-cresol + *O,O*-dimethyl phosphorochlorothioate (ring chlorination/dehydrochlorination)
Uses: fungicide

o-tolidine

4,4′-diamino-3,3′-dimethylbiphenyl; 3,3′-dimethylbenzidine; [119-93-7]

$C_{14}H_{16}N_2$. M: 212.29. Reddish crystals. MP: 129–131°C. Slightly soluble in water. Soluble in oxygenated solvents and acids.
Production:
* *o*-nitrotoluene (reductive coupling/acid-catalysed rearrangement)
Derivatives: Acid Red 114; diacetoacet-*o*-tolidide; Direct Orange 6; Direct Red 2; Pigment Orange 15; Solvent Yellow 107
Uses: analytical reagent (free chlorine)

toliprolol

1-(isopropylamino)-3-(3-methylphenoxy)-2-propanol; [2933-94-0]

$(CH_3)_2CHNHCH_2CHCH_2O$—

OH

—CH_3

$C_{13}H_{21}N_1O_2$. M: 223.32. Available commercially as the hydrochloride.
Production:
* *m*-cresol + epichlorohydrin + isopropylamine (epoxidation/amine formation)
Uses: antianginal drug

tolmetin

[26171-23-3]

$C_{15}H_{15}N_1O_3$. M: 257.29. Available commercially as the sodium salt dihydrate.
Production:
* *N*-methylpyrrole + formaldehyde + sodium cyanide + *p*-toluoyl chloride (cyanomethylation/Friedel-Crafts acylation/nitrile hydrolysis)
* acetone-1,3-dicarboxylic acid + *N*-methylamino-acetaldehyde dimethyl acetal + *p*-toluoyl chloride

(condensation/carbonyl oxidation/decarboxylation/Friedel-Crafts acylation)
Uses: antiinflammatory drug

tolnaftate

[2398-96-1]

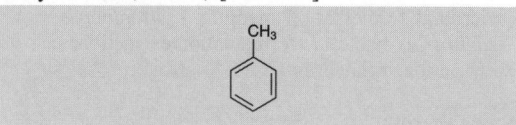

$C_{19}H_{17}N_1O_1S_1$. M: 307.42.
Production:
* β-naphthol + thiophosgene + *N*-methyl-*m*-toluidine (thiophosgenation/dehydrochlorination)
Uses: antifungal drug

α-tolualdehyde *See:* phenylacetaldehyde

toluazotoluidine *See:* o-aminoazotoluene

toluene

methylbenzene; toluol; [108-88-3]

C_7H_8. M: 92.14. Colourless liquid with an aromatic odour. BR: 110–111°C. d: 0.87 kg/l (15°C). Insoluble in water. Miscible with most organic solvents. Flash point: 5°C (CC).
Production:
* aromatics, mixed (separation; coproduced with xylene, mixed/benzene/C_{9+} aromatics)
Derivatives: acetone; benzal chloride; benzaldehyde; benzene; benzoic acid; benzonitrile; benzotrichloride; benzyl chloride; *n*-butylbenzene; *p-t*-butyltoluene; *o/p*-chlorotoluene; *m/p*-cresol; dinitrotoluene; disodium benzaldehyde-2,4-disulphonate; isobutylbenzene; *p*-methylacetophenone; 2-methylanthraquinone; *p*-methylbenzaldehyde; *p*-methylstyrene; *o*-nitrotoluene; *p*-nitrotoluene; perfluoromethylcyclohexane; thiamphenicol; *p*-toluenesulphonic acid; *p*-toluenesulphonyl chloride; 2,4,6-trinitrotoluene; vinyltoluene; xylene, mixed
Uses: alcohol denaturant; process solvent (Dilchill lubricating oil dewaxing process); solvent (paints, printing inks, adhesives, rubber product fabrication)

m-toluenediamine *See:* 2,4/2,6-diaminotoluene

o-toluenediamine *See:* 3,4-diaminotoluene

toluene diisocyanate

toluene diisocyanate (65:35); toluene diisocyanate (80:20); tolylene diisocyanate; *m*-tolylene diisocyanate; TDI; [584-84-9]

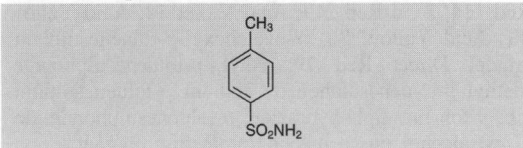

$C_9H_6N_2O_2$. M: 174.16. Yellow liquid with an unpleasant odour. BP: 251°C. FP: 9–14°C (mixed isomer), 24°C (pure). d: 1.22 kg/l (20°C). Hydrolysed by water. The most common grade is a mixed isomer product containing 80% 2,4- and 20% 2,6-isomers. A second grade containing 65% 2,4- and 35% 2,6-isomers is also available as well as the pure 2,4-isomer.
Production:
• 2,4/2,6-diaminotoluene + phosgene (phosgenation)
Derivatives:
polyols, polyisocyanate polyaddition; polyols, polyurea dispersion; polyurethane, flexible foam, cold-moulded; polyurethane, flexible foam, high-resilience; polyurethane, flexible foam, hot-moulded; polyurethane, flexible foam, slabstock; polyurethane, low-resilience elastomers; toluene diisocyanate polyether prepolymers; toluene diisocyanate trimers; toluene diisocyanate-trimethylolpropane adduct; urethane-acrylate resins; urethane-alkyd resins
Uses: moisture-cured polyurethane varnish (interior woodwork, flooring)

toluene diisocyanate polyether prepolymers

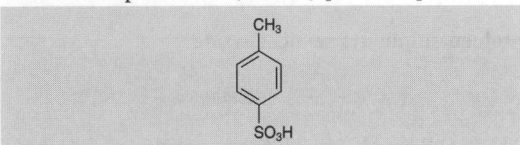

Production:
• toluene diisocyanate + poly(tetramethylene ether) glycol (isocyanate addition)
Derivatives: polyurethane, cast elastomers

toluene diisocyanate trimers

Mixed product produced by partial conversion of toluene diisocyanate to uretonimine-linked trifunctional and higher isocyanates. This has the advantage of reducing the vapour pressure of toluene diisocyanate while retaining its reactivity.
Production:
• toluene diisocyanate (isocyanate addition)
Derivatives:
polyurethane, flexible foam, cold-moulded

toluene diisocyanate-trimethylolpropane adduct

$C_{33}H_{32}N_6O_9$. M: 656.65.
Production:
• trimethylolpropane + toluene diisocyanate (isocyanate addition)
Uses: 2-pack polyurethane coatings (aluminium, plastic, wood, marine, aircraft, self-levelling floor paints); 2-pack elastomeric polyurethane coatings (fabric coatings, impact-resistant floor coatings)

p-toluenesulphohydrazide
toluene-4-sulphohydrazide; *p*-toluenesulphonyl hydrazine; [1576-35-8]

$C_7H_{10}O_2S_1N_2$. M: 172.23.
Production:
• *p*-toluenesulphonyl chloride + hydrazine (sulphonamide formation)
Derivatives: *p*-toluenesulphonyl semicarbazide
Uses: blowing agent (foamed rubber)

p-toluenesulphonamide
toluene-4-sulphonamide; [70-55-3]

$C_7H_9N_1O_2S_1$. M: 171.22. Mixed product containing, typically, 80% toluene-4-sulphonamide.
Production:
• *p*-toluenesulphonyl chloride + ammonia (sulphonamide formation)
Derivatives: chloramine-T; tolbutamide; *p*-toluenesulphonyl isocyanate
Uses: nickel plating brightening agent; plasticiser (polyamide hot melt adhesives)

p-toluenesulphonic acid
toluene-4-sulphonic acid; PTSA; [104-15-4]

$C_7H_8O_3S_1$. M: 172.20. Mixed product containing, typically, 80% toluene-4-sulphonic acid, 15% toluene-2-sulphonic acid and 5% toluene-3-sulphonic acid. Viscous brown liquid/solid. d: 1.3 kg/l (20°C). Soluble in water. Also available as amber liquids containing 63–65% active matter. Lower concentration solutions are also available for foundry use.

Production:
• toluene (sulphonation)

Derivatives: 5-amino-2-chlorotoluene-4-sulphonic acid; *p*-cresol; *N*-ethyl-*p*-toluenesulphonamide; *p*-hydroxyphenylacetonitrile; sodium *p*-toluenesulphonate

Uses: esterification/condensation/acetylation catalyst; curing agent (amino/phenolic/acrylic resins, furan foundry resins); descaling agent (industrial metal cleaners); electroplating bath additive; neutralising agent (acrylonitrile production)

p-toluenesulphonyl chloride

toluene-4-sulphonyl chloride; tosyl chloride; [98-59-9]

$C_7H_7Cl_1O_2S_1$. M: 190.65. Crystalline solid. MP: 67–68°C. Insoluble in water. Soluble in oxygenated solvents. Mixed product containing 75% *p*-isomer, 19% *o*-isomer and 6% *m*-isomer.

Production:
• toluene + chlorosulphonic acid (chlorosulphonation)

Derivatives: Acid Orange 51; Acid Orange 67; Acid Red 114; Acid Red 249; Acid Violet 14; Acid Yellow 40; Acid Yellow 76; *N*-cyclohexyl-*p*-toluenesulphonamide; Direct Red 79; ethyl *p*-toluenesulphonate; methyl *p*-toluenesulphonate; sodium *p*-toluenesulphinate; *p*-toluenesulphohydrazide; *p*-toluenesulphonamide

Uses: alcohol group reaction/protection reagent

p-toluenesulphonyl isocyanate

PTSI; [4083-64-1]

$C_8H_7N_1O_3S_1$. M: 197.22.
Production:
• *p*-toluenesulphonamide + phosgene (phosgenation)

Derivatives:
glibornuride; tolazamide

Uses: water scavenging reagent

p-toluenesulphonyl semicarbazide

$C_8H_{11}N_3O_3P_1S_1$. M: 260.23. White powder. d: 1.43 kg/l. Decomposes at 226°C when dry.

Production:
• *p*-toluenesulphohydrazide + sodium cyanate (cyanate addition)

Uses: blowing agent (foamed plastics)

m-toluic acid

3-methylbenzoic acid; *m*-methylbenzoic acid; [99-04-7]

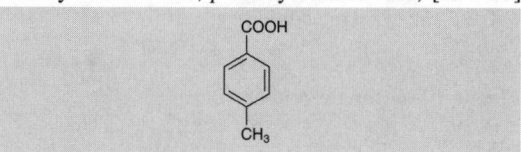

$C_8H_8O_2$. M: 136.15. White crystals. MP: 108–110°C. BP: 263°C. Slightly soluble in water. Soluble in oxygenated solvents.

Production:
• *m*-xylene (oxidation; byproduct of isophthalic acid production)

Derivatives:
N,N-diethyl-*m*-toluamide; 3-methylbenzophenone

o-toluic acid

2-methylbenzoic acid; *o*-methylbenzoic acid; [118-90-1]

$C_8H_8O_2$. M: 136.15. White, crystalline solid. MP: 103–105°C. BP: 258°C. Soluble in hot water and alcohol.

Production:
• *o*-xylene (side-chain oxidation)

Derivatives:
mepronil; 2-methylbenzophenone; *o*-toluoyl chloride

p-toluic acid

4-methylbenzoic acid; *p*-methylbenzoic acid; [99-94-5]

$C_8H_8O_2$. M: 136.15.
Production:
• *p*-xylene (side-chain oxidation/hydrogenation; byproduct of terephthalic acid production)

Derivatives: 3-amino-4-methylbenzoic acid; procarbazine; stilbene-4,4'-dicarboxylic acid; *p*-toluoyl chloride

m-toluidine

3-aminotoluene; 3-methylaniline; [108-44-1]
$C_7H_9N_1$. M: 107.16. Liquid. BP: 204–204°C. d: 0.99 kg/l (20°C). Slightly soluble in water. Soluble in oxygenated solvents and dilute acids.

Production:
• *m*-nitrotoluene (nitro reduction)

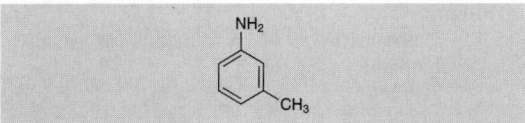

Derivatives: Acid Red 108; *m*-chlorotoluene; *N,N*-diethyl-*m*-toluidine; *N,N'*-di-(2-hydroxyethyl)-*m*-toluidine; Direct Yellow 50; Direct Yellow 118; *N*-ethyl-*m*-toluidine; meclofenamic acid; *N*-methyl-*m*-toluidine; phenmedipham; Pigment Blue 56; Reactive Yellow 4

o-toluidine

o-aminotoluene; 2-methylaniline; 2-toluidine; [95-53-4]

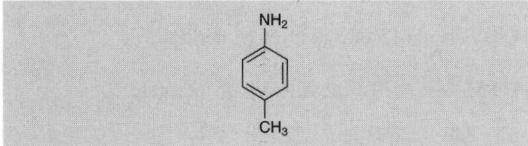

$C_7H_9N_1$. M: 107.16. Pale yellow liquid. BP: 200–201°C. MP: -23°C. d: 1.01 kg/l (20°C). Slightly soluble in water. Soluble in oxygenated solvents.
Production:
• *o*-nitrotoluene (nitro reduction)
Derivatives:
acetoacet-*o*-toluidide; *o*-aminoazotoluene; 2-amino-5-chlorotoluene; 2-amino-5-nitrotoluene; 2-aminotoluene-5-sulphonic acid; Basic Red 1; Basic Red 2; Basic Violet 14; bis(4-amino-3-methylcyclohexyl)methane; *N,N'*-diaryl-*p*-phenylenediamine; Direct Red 72; Direct Red 73; di-*o*-tolylguanidine; di-*o*-tolylthiourea; 2-ethyl-6-methylaniline; 3-hydroxy-2-naphth-*o*-toluidide; perfluidone; prilocaine; Solvent Orange 2; Solvent Red 24; Solvent Red 26; Solvent Violet 10; Sulphur Blue 7; *o*-tolylbiguanide; tricyclazole; Vat Red 1

p-toluidine

p-aminotoluene; 4-methylaniline; [106-49-0]

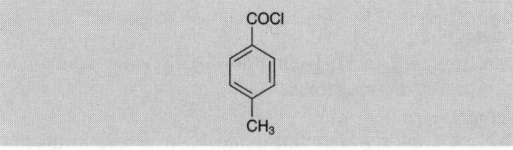

$C_7H_9N_1$. M: 107.16. White, lustrous flakes. MP: 42–44°C. BP: 199–202°C. Slightly soluble in water. Soluble in oxygenated solvents.
Production:
• *p*-nitrotoluene (nitro reduction)
Derivatives: acetoacet-*p*-toluidide; Acid Blue 27; Acid Blue 145; Acid Brown 20; Acid Violet 80; 4-amino-3-nitrotoluene; 4B acid; Basic Violet 14; *p*-bromobenzyl cyanide; daimuron; dehydrothio-*p*-toluidinesulphonic acid; 2,9-dimethylquinacridone; *N,N*-dimethyl-*p*-toluidine; Direct Yellow 59; Disperse Blue 72; *p*-fluorotoluene; 3-hydroxy-2-naphth-*p*-toluidide; 1-(4'-methylphenyl)-3-methylpyrazolone; Pigment Yellow 18; Solvent Green 3; Solvent Violet 14; tolylfluanid

m-tolunitrile

MTN; [620-22-4]

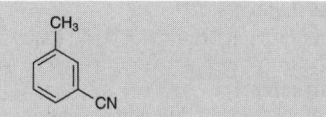

$C_8H_7N_1$. M: 117.16. Colourless liquid. BP: 205°C. MP: <-20°C.
Production:
• *m*-xylene + ammonia (ammoxidation; byproduct of isophthalodinitrile production)
Uses: chemical intermediate

o-tolunitrile

[529-19-1]

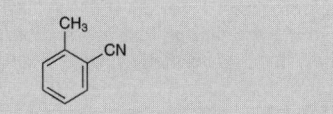

$C_8H_7N_1$. M: 117.16. Liquid. BP: 205–207°C. MP: -13°C. d: 1.00 kg/l (20°C). Insoluble in water. Miscible with oxygenated solvents.
Production:
• *o*-xylene + ammonia (ammoxidation; byproduct of phthalodinitrile production)
Uses: chemical intermediate

toluol *See:* toluene

o-toluoyl chloride

2-methylbenzoyl chloride; *o*-methylbenzoyl chloride; [933-88-0]

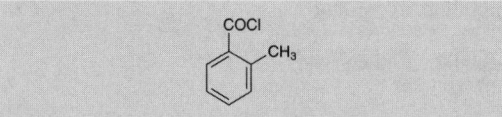

$C_8H_7Cl_1O_1$. M: 154.60. Liquid. BP: 213–214°C. Hydrolysed by water and hot alcohol.
Production:
• *o*-toluic acid (acid chloride formation)
Derivatives:
t-butyl peroxy-*o*-toluate

p-toluoyl chloride

4-methylbenzoyl chloride; *p*-methylbenzoyl chloride; [874-60-2]

$C_8H_7Cl_1O_1$. M: 154.60. Hygroscopic liquid. BP: 225–227°C. MP: -2°C. Hydrolysed by water and alcohol.

Production:
• *p*-toluic acid (acid chloride formation)
Derivatives:
Fluorescent Brightener 354; tolmetin

tolycaine
methyl 2-(2-diethylaminoacetamido)-*m*-toluate;
[3686-58-6]

$C_{15}H_{22}N_2O_3$. M: 278.35.
Production:
• *o*-cresotic acid + methanol + ammonia +
  chloroacetyl chloride + diethylamine (esterification/
  amine formation/amide formation/amine formation)
Uses: local anaesthetic drug

p-tolylaldehyde *See:* p-methylbenzaldehyde

o-tolylbiguanide
OTBG; [93-69-6]

$C_9H_{13}N_5$. M: 191.23. Cream-coloured powder. MP:
138°C.
Production:
• *o*-toluidine + dicyandiamide (reaction)
Uses: epoxy resin curing agent; antioxidant (soap); vulcanisation accelerator

4-tolyl-2,1,5-diazoester
[80370-33-8]

$C_{17}H_{12}N_2O_4S_1$. M: 340.36.
Production:
• *p*-cresol + 2-diazo-1-naphthol-5-sulphonic acid
  chloride (rearrangement)
Uses:
positive photoreprographic plate light sensitive agent

tolylene diisocyanate *See:* toluene diisocyanate

tolylfluanid
N-dichlorofluoromethylthio-*N*′,*N*′-dimethyl-*N*-(4-methyl-
phenyl)sulphamide; [731-27-1]

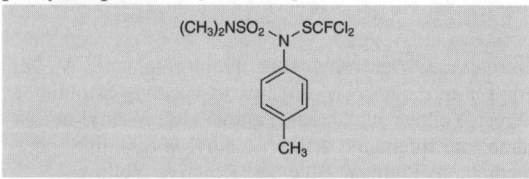

$C_{10}H_{13}Cl_2F_1N_2O_2S_2$. M: 347.26.
Production:
• dimethylsulphamyl chloride + *p*-toluidine +
  dichlorofluoromethanesulphenyl chloride (sulphide
  formation/dehydrochlorination)
Uses: fungicide

tolyltriazole

$C_7H_7N_3$. M: 133.16. Brown granules. Insoluble in water.
Production:
• 3,4-diaminotoluene + sodium nitrite (condensation)
Uses: copper corrosion inhibitor (lubricants, antifreeze)

TOP *See:* tri-(2-ethylhexyl) phosphate

TOPO *See:* tri-*n*-octylphosphine oxide

TOR *See:* rosin, tall oil

Torlon *See:* poly(amide-imide)

tosyl chloride *See:* p-toluenesulphonyl chloride

TOT *See:* tri-(2-ethylhexyl) trimellitate

TOTM *See:* tri-(2-ethylhexyl) trimellitate

TPA *See:* terephthalic acid

TPE *See:* polypropylene, elastomer-modified

TPE-E *See:* copolyester, thermoplastic elastomers

TPG *See:* tripropylene glycol

TPGDA *See:* tripropylene glycol diacrylate

TPM *See:* tripropylene glycol monomethyl ether

TPOR *See:* polypropylene, elastomer-modified

TPP *See:* triphenyl phosphite; triphenyl phosphate

TPPT *See:* triphenyl phosphorothionate

TPT *See:* fentin acetate; fentin hydroxide; isopropyl titanate

TPU *See:* polyurethane, thermoplastic elastomers

TPX polymers *See:* polymethylpentene

tragacanth gum *See:* gum tragacanth

tralomethrin
[66841-25-6]

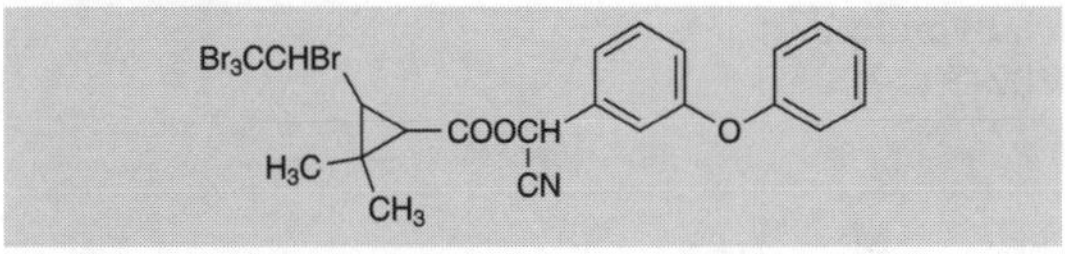

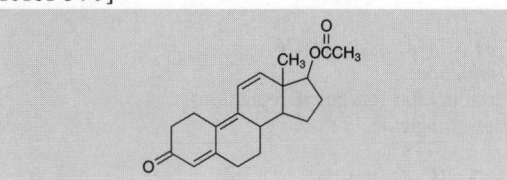

$C_{22}H_{19}Br_4N_1O_3$. M: 665.02.
Production:
• deltamethrin + bromine (addition)
Uses: insecticide

tramazoline
[1082-57-1]

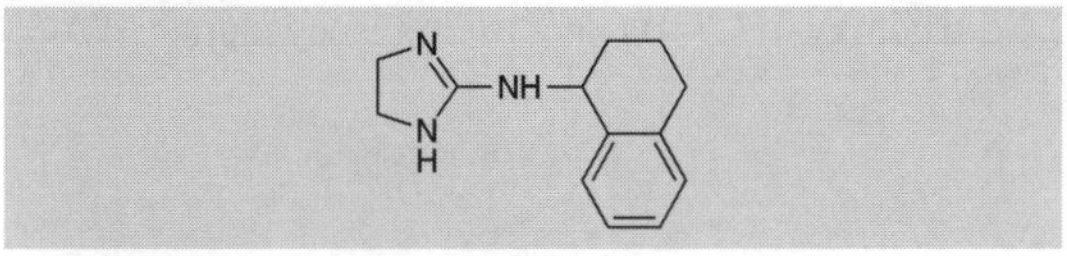

$C_{13}H_{17}N_3$. M: 215.30.
Production:
• 1-naphthylamine + ammonium thiocyanate + ethylenediamine (hydrogenation/thiocyanate addition/condensation)
Uses: vasoconstrictor drug

tranylcypromine
[155-09-9]; [13492-01-8] (sulphate)

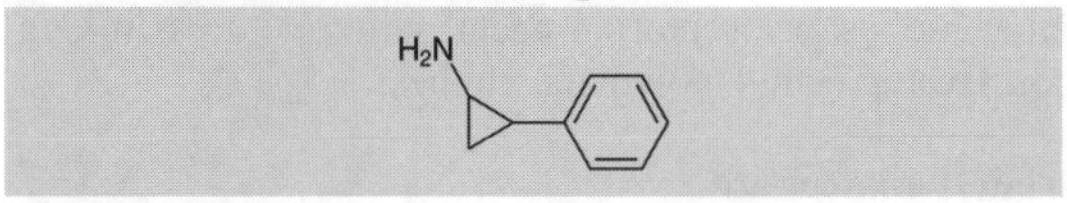

$C_9H_{11}N_1$. M: 133.20. The commercial product is the racemic *trans*-isomer.
Production:
• styrene + ethyl diazoacetate (addition/acid azide formation/Curtius degradation)
Uses: antidepressant drug

trazodone
[19794-93-5]

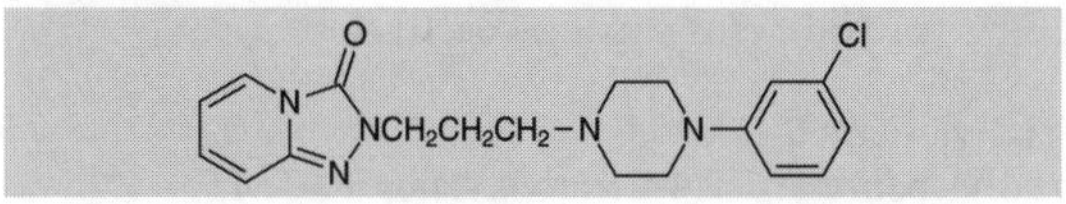

$C_{19}H_{22}Cl_1N_5O_1$. M: 371.87. Available commercially as the hydrochloride.
Production:
• 2-chloropyridine + semicarbazide hydrochloride + 1-bromo-3-chloropropane + 1-(3-chlorophenyl)-piperazine hydrochloride (condensation/amine formation/amine formation)
Uses: antidepressant/anxiolytic drug

trenbolone acetate
[10161-34-9]

$C_{20}H_{24}O_3$. M: 312.41.
Production:
• 3-methoxyestra-2,5-diene-17-ol (microbial conversion/hydrolysis/selective dehydrogenation)
Uses: animal growth stimulant

triacetin
glycerol triacetate; glyceryl triacetate; [102-76-1]

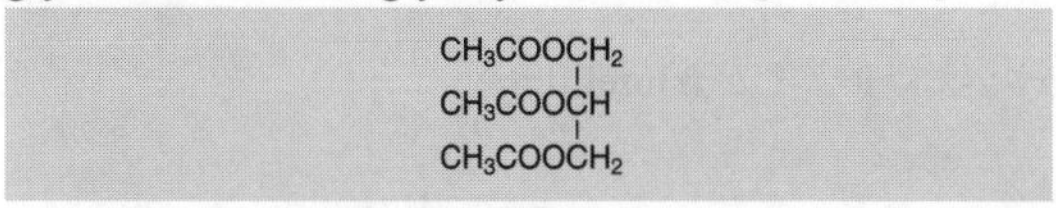

$$CH_3COOCH_2$$
$$CH_3COOCH$$
$$CH_3COOCH_2$$

$C_9H_{14}O_6$. M: 218.20. Colourless or pale yellow liquid. d: 1.16 kg/l (20°C). Saponification value: 765–775 mg KOH/g. Slightly soluble in water. Soluble in oxygenated solvents.
Production:
• glycerol + acetic anhydride (acetylation)
Uses:
perfume fixative; plasticiser (cellulosic, acrylic, vinyl acetate resins); setting agent (sodium silicate foundry mould/soil consolidation binders); solvent (dyes); topical antifungal agent

triadimefon
[43121-43-3]

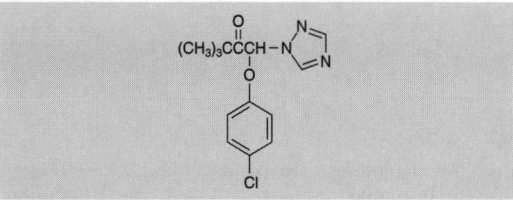

$C_{14}H_{16}Cl_1N_3O_2$. M: 293.75.
Production:
• α-chloropinacolone + *p*-chlorophenol + 1,2,4-triazole (dehydrochlorination/amine formation)
Derivatives: triadimenol
Uses: fungicide

triadimenol

1-(4-chlorophenoxy)-3,3-dimethyl-1-(1H-1,2,4-triazol-1-yl)butan-2-ol; [82200-72-4]

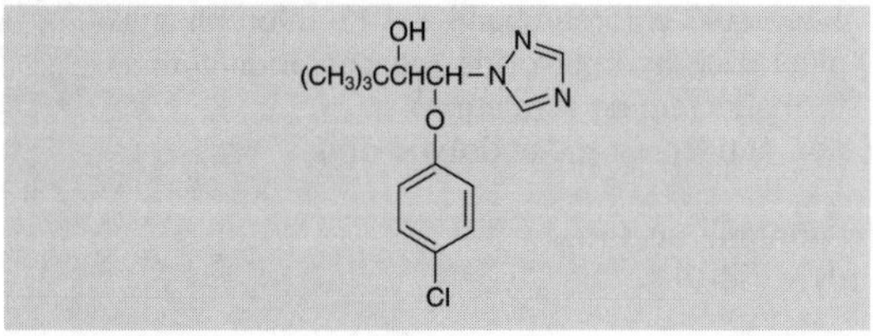

$C_{14}H_{18}Cl_1N_3O_2$. M: 295.76.
Production:
• triadimefon (carbonyl reduction)
Uses: fungicide

trialkyl(C$_8$-C$_{10}$)amine

n = 7–9.
Production:
• C$_8$-C$_{10}$ fatty acids + ammonia (nitrile formation/nitrile reduction/amine formation)
Uses:
mineral flotation agent

tri-*n*-alkyl(C$_7$-C$_9$) trimellitate

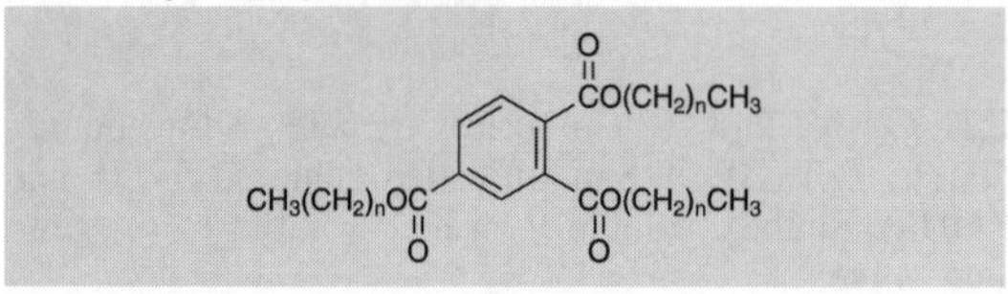

n = 6–8. Colourless, involatile liquid. d: 0.99 kg/l (20°C). Viscosity: 139 mPa.s (20°C). Insoluble in water.
Production:
• *n*-alkanol(C$_7$-C$_9$)/*n*-octanol + trimellitic anhydride (esterification)
Uses: plasticiser (polyvinyl chloride/chlorosulphonated polyethylene sealants)

tri-*n*-alkyl(C$_8$-C$_{10}$) trimellitate

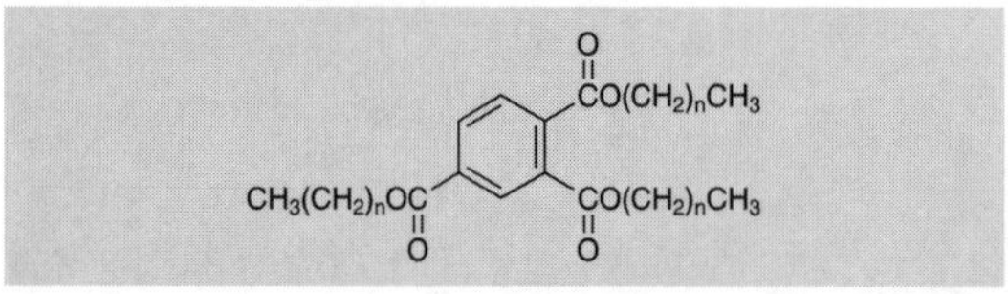

n = 7–9. Colourless, involatile liquid. d: 0.97 kg/l (20°C). Insoluble in water. Viscosity: 126 mPa.s (20°C).
Production:
• *n*-alkanol(C$_8$-C$_{10}$) + trimellitic anhydride (esterification)
Uses:
polyvinyl chloride plasticiser

tri-allate

S-2,3,3-trichloroallyl diisopropylthiocarbamate; [2303-17-5]

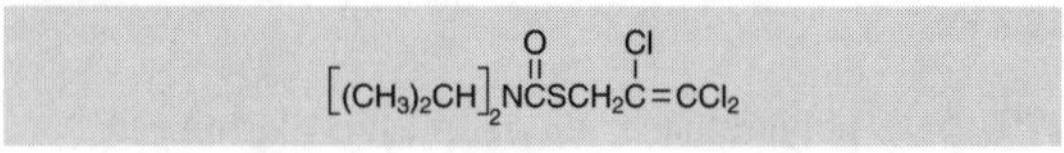

$C_{10}H_{16}Cl_3N_1O_1S_1$. M: 304.67.
Production:
• propargyl alcohol + chlorine + carbonyl sulphide + diisopropylamine (chlorination/dehydrochlorination/thiocarbonylation/dehydrochlorination)
Uses: herbicide

triallylamine

[102-70-5]

$C_9H_{15}N_1$. M: 137.23.
Production:
• allyl chloride + ammonia (amine formation; coproduced with diallylamine/allylamine)
Uses: unsaturated polyester resin comonomer; crosslinking comonomer

triallyl cyanurate

2,4,6-trialloxy-1,3,5-triazine; triallyl isocyanurate; TAC; [101-37-1]

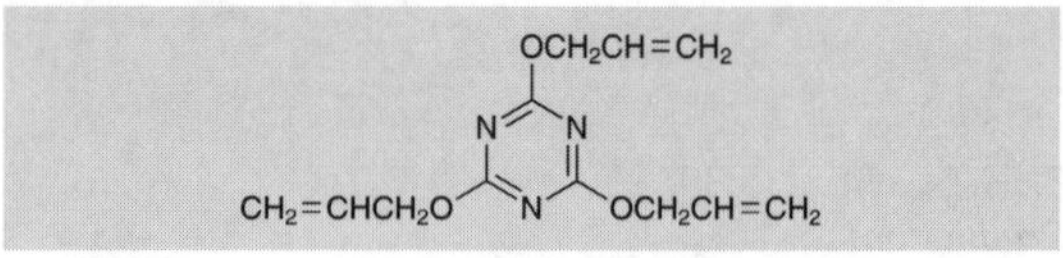

$C_{12}H_{15}N_3O_3$. M: 249.27. Pale yellow crystals/liquid. MP: 27–28°C. d: 1.11 kg/l (30°C). Insoluble in water. Soluble in most organic solvents.
Production:
• allyl chloride + sodium cyanate (dehydrochlorination/condensation)
Uses: heat-resistant unsaturated polyester resin comonomer; adhesion promotion agent; peroxide crosslinking coactivator (vinyl polymers, rubber)

triallyl phosphate

TAP; [1623-19-4]

$C_9H_{15}O_4P_1$. M: 218.19. Colourless liquid. d: 1.06 kg/l (25°C). Slightly soluble in water. Soluble in oxygenated solvents.
Production:
• allyl alcohol + phosphorus oxychloride (dehydrochlorination)
Uses: peroxide crosslinking coactivator

triallyl trimellitate

triallyl benzene-1,2,4-tricarboxylate; TATM; [2694-54-4]

$C_{18}H_{18}O_6$. M: 330.33.
Production:
• allyl alcohol + trimellitic anhydride (esterification)
Uses: peroxide crosslinking coactivator

N,N',N"-triaminoguanidine nitrate
TAGN; [4000-16-2]

$C_1H_9N_7O_3$. M: 167.13.
Production:
• guanidine nitrate + hydrazine (condensation)
Uses: explosives

1,3,5-triamino-2,4,6-trinitrobenzene
TATB; [3058-38-6]

$C_6H_6N_6O_6$. M: 258.15.
Production:
• phloroglucinol + nitric acid, concentrated + ammonia (nitration/amine formation)
Uses: explosives

triamterene
[396-01-0]

$C_{12}H_{11}N_7$. M: 253.27.
Production:
• 5-nitroso-2,4,6-triaminopyrimidine + benzyl cyanide (condensation)
Uses: diuretic drug

triamylamine
tri-*n*-pentylamine; [621-77-2]

$(CH_3CH_2CH_2CH_2CH_2)_3N$

$C_{15}H_{33}N_1$. M: 227.43.
Production:
• *n*-amyl alcohol + ammonia (amine formation)
Derivatives:
perfluorotriamylamine

triazolam
[28911-01-5]

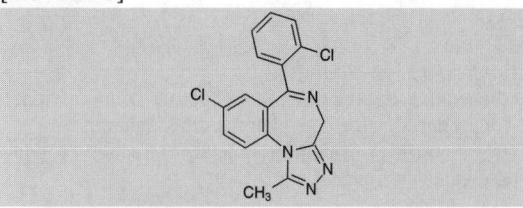

$C_{17}H_{12}Cl_2N_4$. M: 343.23.
Production:
• 2-amino-2',5-dichlorobenzophenone + hydroxylamine sulphate + chloroacetyl chloride + hydrazine + triethyl orthoacetate (oxime formation/amide formation/cyclisation/acid-catalysed rearrangement/reduction/imine formation/condensation)
Uses: hypnotic drug

1,2,4-triazole
[288-88-0]

$C_2H_3N_3$. M: 69.06. Needles. MP: 119–121°C. BP: 260°C with decomposition. Soluble in water and alcohol.
Production:
• formamide + hydrazine (condensation/deammoniation)
• formaldehyde + hydrazine (condensation/diazotisation/reduction)
Derivatives: azocyclotin; bitertanol; diclobutrazol; diniconazole; flusilazole; flutriafol; hexaconazole; myclobutanil; paclobutrazol; penconazole; propiconazole; triadimefon; uniconazole

triazophos
O,O-diethyl *O*-1-phenyl-1H-1,2,4-triazol-3-yl phosphorothioate; [24017-47-8]

$C_{12}H_{16}N_3O_3P_1S_1$. M: 313.31.
Production:
• phenylhydrazine + sodium cyanate + formamide + *O,O*-diethyl phosphorochlorothioate (cyanate addition/condensation/dehydrochlorination)
Uses: acaricide/insecticide/nematicide

tribenzylamine
[620-40-6]
$C_{21}H_{21}N_1$. M: 287.41. White to pale yellow, crystalline solid. MP: 91–94°C. BP: 380–390°C. Slightly soluble in water and alcohol.

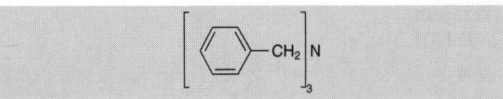

Production:
• benzaldehyde + ammonia (reductive ammoniation; coproduced with benzylamine/dibenzylamine)
Uses: corrosion inhibitor; metal extraction solvent; base-catalysis reagent

2,4,6-tribromoaniline
TBA; [147-82-0]

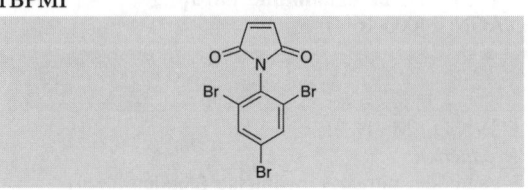

$C_6H_4Br_3N_1$. M: 329.82. Needles. MP: 120–122°C. BP: 300°C. d: 2.35 kg/l (20°C). Insoluble in water. Soluble in oxygenated and chlorinated solvents.
Production:
• aniline + bromine (ring bromination)
Derivatives: 2,4,6-tribromophenyl maleimide

tribromoneopentyl alcohol
2,2,2-tri-(bromomethyl)ethanol; TBNPA

$$HOCH_2-\underset{\underset{CH_2Br}{|}}{\overset{\overset{CH_2Br}{|}}{C}}-CH_2Br$$

$C_5H_9Br_3O_1$. M: 324.83.
Production:
• pentaerythritol + hydrobromic acid (alcohol bromination)
Uses: fire-retarded rigid polyurethane foam/unsaturated polyester resin comonomer

2,4,6-tribromophenol
bromol; tribromophenol; TBP; [118-79-6]

$C_6H_3Br_3O_1$. M: 330.80. Solid. MP: 95–96°C. d: 2.2 kg/l (4°C). Very slightly soluble in water. Soluble in most organic solvents.
Production:
• phenol + bromine (ring bromination)
Derivatives: 2,4,6-tribromophenyl allyl ether
Uses: wood preservative

2,4,6-tribromophenyl allyl ether
TBPAE
$C_9H_7Br_3O_1$. M: 370.87.

Production:
• 2,4,6-tribromophenol + allyl chloride (Williamson synthesis)
Uses: fire-retardant comonomer (expanded polystyrene)

2,4,6-tribromophenyl maleimide
TBPMI

$C_{10}H_4Br_3N_1O_2$. M: 409.86.
Production:
• maleic anhydride + 2,4,6-tribromoaniline (imide formation)
Uses: fire-retarded polystyrene/thermosetting resin

tributoxyethyl phosphate
tris(2-butoxyethyl) phosphate; TBEP; [78-51-3]

$$[CH_3CH_2CH_2CH_2OCH_2CH_2O]_3P{=}O$$

$C_{18}H_{39}O_7P_1$. M: 398.48. Pale yellow liquid. BP: 210–220°C (0.5 kPa). d: 1.02 kg/l (25°C). Insoluble in water. Soluble in most organic liquids.
Production:
• ethylene glycol monobutyl ether + phosphorus trichloride (dehydrochlorination)
Uses: coalescing solvent/plasticiser (acrylic-based polish, gloss paints, adhesives); fire-retardant additive (plastics); antifoam (paints, textiles, paper)

tri-*n*-butyl acetylcitrate
acetyl tri-*n*-butyl citrate; tri-*n*-butyl citrate acetate; tri-*n*-butyl *O*-acetylcitrate; [77-90-7]

$$CH_3CO-\underset{\underset{CH_2COOCH_2CH_2CH_2CH_3}{|}}{\overset{\overset{O}{\overset{||}{C}}\quad CH_2COOCH_2CH_2CH_2CH_3}{\overset{|}{C}COOCH_2CH_2CH_2CH_3}}$$

$C_{20}H_{34}O_8$. M: 402.48. Colourless liquid. BP: 172°C (0.13 kPa). d: 1.05 kg/l (25°C). Insoluble in water.
Production:
• tri-*n*-butyl citrate + acetic anhydride (acetylation)
Uses: plasticiser (rubber, cellulosic resins)

tri-*n*-butylaluminium
TNBA; [1116-70-7]

$$(CH_3CH_2CH_2CH_2)_3Al$$

$C_{12}H_{27}Al_1$. M: 198.33. Colourless liquid. BP: 240°C.

FP: -60°C. d: 0.82 kg/l (25°C). Spontaneously flammable in air. Decomposed by water.
Production:
• triisobutylaluminium + 1-butene (alkyl exchange)
Uses: Ziegler catalyst component

tri-*n*-butylamine
tributylamine; TNBA; [102-82-9]

$$(CH_3CH_2CH_2CH_2)_3N$$

$C_{12}H_{27}N_1$. M: 185.36. Liquid with an unpleasant, amine-like odour. BP: 214°C. FP: -70°C. d: 0.78 kg/l (4°C). Slightly soluble in water. Soluble in oxygenated solvents.
Production:
• *n*-butanol + ammonia (ammoniation; coproduced with di-*n*-butylamine/*n*-butylamine)
Derivatives: perfluorotributylamine; tetra-*n*-butylammonium bromide; tetra-*n*-butylammonium hydrogen sulphate; tri-*n*-butylmethylammonium chloride

tri-*n*-butyl citrate
butyl citrate; tributyl citrate; TBC; [77-94-1]

$$CH_2COOCH_2CH_2CH_2CH_3$$
$$HO-CCOOCH_2CH_2CH_2CH_3$$
$$CH_2COOCH_2CH_2CH_2CH_3$$

$C_{18}H_{32}O_7$. M: 382.50. Liquid. Pour point: -85°C. BP: 170°C (0.13 kPa). d: 1.05 kg/l (20°C).
Production:
• *n*-butanol + citric acid (esterification)
Derivatives:
tri-*n*-butyl acetylcitrate
Uses: plasticiser (lacquers, printing inks)

tri-*n*-butylmethylammonium chloride
TBMAC (Ethyl)

$$(CH_3CH_2CH_2CH_2)_3NCH_3^+ \ Cl^-$$

$C_{13}H_{30}Cl_1N_1$. M: 235.84. Available commercially as a 75% solution in water. BP: 152°C. Pour point: -33°C. d: 0.96 kg/l (20°C).
Production:
• tri-*n*-butylamine + methyl chloride (quaternisation)
Uses:
phase-transfer catalyst

tri-*n*-butyl phosphate
tributyl phosphate; TBP; [126-73-8]

$$(CH_3CH_2CH_2CH_2O)_3P=O$$

$C_{12}H_{27}O_4P_1$. M: 266.32. Colourless liquid. BP: 155–158°C (1.3 kPa). Pour point: -70°C. d: 0.96 kg/l. Insoluble in water. Miscible with most organic solvents.
Production:
• *n*-butanol + phosphorus oxychloride (dehydrochlorination)

Uses: extraction agent (rare earths, uranium, plutonium, phosphoric acid processing); fire-resistant hydraulic fluid; fire-resistant cellulose ester/rubber plasticiser; antifoam

tri-*n*-butylphosphine
TBUP; [998-40-3]

$$\left[CH_3CH_2CH_2CH_2\right]_3P$$

$C_{12}H_{27}P_1$. M: 202.32.
Production:
• 1-butene + phosphine (addition)
Derivatives:
chlorphonium chloride
Uses: hydroformylation catalyst intermediate

S,S,S-tributyl phosphorotrithioate
[150-50-5]

$$(CH_3CH_2CH_2CH_2S)_3P=O$$

$C_{12}H_{27}O_1P_1S_3$. M: 314.51.
Production:
• *n*-butyl mercaptan + phosphorus oxychloride (dehydrochlorination)
Uses: defoliant (cotton)

tributyltin acetate
tri-*n*-butyltin acetate; [56-36-0]

$$(CH_3CH_2CH_2CH_2)_3SnO\overset{O}{\overset{\|}{C}}CH_3$$

$C_{14}H_{30}O_2Sn_1$. M: 349.08. White, waxy solid. MP: 80–83°C. d: 1.27 kg/l. Insoluble in water.
Production:
• tributyltin chloride + acetic acid (dehydrochlorination)
Uses: biocide (marine antifouling paints)

tributyltin chloride
tri-*n*-butyltin chloride; [1461-22-9]

$$(CH_3CH_2CH_2CH_2)_3SnCl$$

$C_{12}H_{27}Cl_1Sn_1$. M: 325.49. Colourless liquid. Insoluble in cold water. Soluble in oxygenated, chlorinated and aromatic solvents. Hydrolysed by hot water.
Production:
• tetra-*n*-butyltin + stannic chloride (Kocheshkov redistribution)
Derivatives:
tributyltin acetate; tributyltin fluoride; tributyltin methacrylate; tri-*n*-butyltin oxide

tributyltin fluoride
tri-*n*-butyltin fluoride; TBTF

$$(CH_3CH_2CH_2CH_2)_3SnF$$

$C_{12}H_{27}F_1Sn_1$. M: 309.04.

Production:
• tributyltin chloride + sodium fluoride (salt formation)
Uses: biocide (marine antifouling paints)

tributyltin methacrylate

$$CH_2=\overset{\overset{O}{\|}}{\underset{\underset{CH_3}{|}}{C}}COSn(CH_2CH_2CH_2CH_3)_3$$

$C_{16}H_{32}O_2Sn_1$. M: 375.13.
Production:
• tributyltin chloride + methacrylic acid (esterification)
Uses: marine antifouling paint resin comonomer

tri-*n*-butyltin oxide

bis(tri-*n*-butyltin)oxide; hexabutyldistannoxane; TBTO; TBT; [56-35-9]

$$(CH_3CH_2CH_2CH_2)_3Sn-O-Sn(CH_2CH_2CH_2CH_3)_3$$

$C_{24}H_{54}O_1Sn_2$. M: 596.07. Yellow liquid. BP: 254°C (6.7 kPa). MP: <-45°C. d: 1.17 kg/l (20°C). Insoluble in water. Soluble in oxygenated solvents.
Production:
• tributyltin chloride + sodium hydroxide (dechlorination)
Uses: biocide (marine antifouling paints); plastics/adhesives biostabiliser; wood preservative

tricalcium phosphate

calcium orthophosphate; calcium phosphate, tribasic; tricalcium bis(orthophosphate); E341(c) (EC); [7758-87-4]

$$Ca_3(PO_4)_2$$

$Ca_3O_8P_2$. M: 310.18. White powder. d: 3.14 kg/l. Insoluble in water and alcohol. Soluble in dilute acid. See also defluorinated apatite.
Production:
• calcium hydroxide + phosphoric acid, pure (salt formation)
Uses: flow conditioner/anticaking agent; mineral supplement (animal feedstuffs, pharmaceuticals); suspension agent (polystyrene production)

tricalcium phosphate, defluorinated

See: apatite, defluorinated

trichlorfon

O,O-dimethyl 1-hydroxy-2,2,2-trichloroethylphosphonate; [52-68-6]

$$Cl_3CCHP(OCH_3)_2 \atop |\ OH$$

$C_4H_8Cl_3O_4P_1$. M: 257.43.

Production:
• chloral + dimethyl phosphite (dehydrochlorination)
Derivatives:
dichlorvos
Uses: anthelmintic drug; insecticide

trichlormethiazide

[133-67-5]

$C_8H_8Cl_3N_3O_4S_2$. M: 380.66.
Production:
• chloral + 5-chloroaniline-2,4-disulphonamide (carbonyl condensation)
Uses:
diuretic/antihypertensive drug

trichloroacetaldehyde *See:* chloral

trichloroacetic acid

TCA; [76-03-9]

$$Cl_3CCOOH$$

$C_2H_1Cl_3O_2$. M: 163.39. White, deliquescent crystals with a pungent odour. MP: 58°C. BP: 198°C. Soluble in water producing highly acidic solutions.
Production:
• acetic acid + chlorine (exhaustive chlorination)
Derivatives:
(*1RS*)-*cis/trans*-3-(2,2-dichlorovinyl)-2,2-dimethylcyclopropanecarboxylic acid; etridiazole; sodium trichloroacetate

1,1,3-trichloroacetone

[921-03-9]

$$ClCH_2\overset{\overset{O}{\|}}{C}CHCl_2$$

$C_3H_3Cl_3O_1$. M: 161.41.
Production:
• methyl γ-chloroacetoacetate (alpha chlorination/decarboxylation; coproduced with 1,3-dichloroacetone)
Derivatives: folic acid; methotrexate

α,2,4-trichloroacetophenone

2-chloro-1-(2,4-dichlorophenyl)ethanone; 2,2′,4′-trichloroacetophenone; [4252-78-2]

$C_8H_5Cl_3O_1$. M: 223.49. Solid.

Production:
- 2,4-dichloroacetophenone (alpha chlorination; coproduced with α,α,2,4-tetrachloroacetophenone)

Derivatives:
econazole; hexaconazole; imazalil; isoconazole; miconazole; penconazole; propiconazole; pyrifenox

2,4,5-trichloroacetophenone
[13061-28-4]

$C_8H_5Cl_3O_1$. M: 223.49.
Production:
- acetophenone + chlorine (ring chlorination; coproduced with 2,4-dichloroacetophenone)

Derivatives: α,α,2,4,5-pentachloroacetophenone

2,4,5-trichloroaniline
[636-30-6]

$C_6H_4Cl_3N_1$. M: 196.47. Needles. MP: 97°C. BP: 270°C. Insoluble in water. Soluble in oxygenated solvents.
Production:
- 2,5-dichloronitrobenzene (ring chlorination/nitro reduction)

Derivatives: Pigment Red 112

1,2,4-trichlorobenzene
[120-82-1]

$C_6H_3Cl_3$. M: 181.45. Crystals. BP: 214°C. MP: 17°C. d: 1.45 kg/l (20°C). Insoluble in water. Soluble in ether and benzene.
Production:
- p-dichlorobenzene (ring chlorination; coproduced with 1,2,4,5-tetrachlorobenzene)

Derivatives: dicamba; iodofenphos; tetradifon

trichlorobutylene oxide
TCBO

$C_4H_5Cl_3O_1$. M: 175.44.

Production:
- allyl alcohol + carbon tetrachloride (free-radical addition/dehydrochlorination)

Uses: fire-retardant comonomer

1,1,1-trichloroethane
methyl chloroform; trichloroethane; Genklene (ICI); [71-55-6]

CH_3CCl_3

$C_2H_3Cl_3$. M: 133.40. Colourless liquid. FP: -38°C. BP: 71–81°C. d: 1.31 kg/l (20°C). Insoluble in water. Miscible with most other solvents. The product usually contains a stabiliser to inhibit reaction with aluminium.
Production:
- 1,1-dichloroethane + chlorine (thermal chlorination; coproduced with 1,1,2-trichloroethane)

Derivatives: 1-chloro-1,1-difluoroethane; 1,1-dichloro-1-fluoroethane; triethyl orthoacetate; trimethyl orthoacetate
Uses: non-flammable solvent (hand/vapour metal degreasing, adhesives, aerosol formulations); solvent (insecticides, polishes, metal-working fluids, surface coatings)

1,1,2-trichloroethane
[79-00-5]

$ClCH_2CHCl_2$

$C_2H_3Cl_3$. M: 133.40. Colourless liquid. BP: 113–114°C. FP: -37°C. d: 1.43 kg/l (25°C). Insoluble in water. Miscible with oxygenated and chlorinated solvents.
Production:
- 1,1-dichloroethane + chlorine (thermal chlorination; coproduced with 1,1,1-trichloroethane)
- vinyl chloride + chlorine (addition)

Derivatives: vinylidene chloride
Uses: speciality solvent

trichloroethylene
tri; tric; trichlor; 1,1,2-trichloroethylene; TCE; Triklone (ICI); [79-01-6]

$ClCH=CCl_2$

$C_2H_1Cl_3$. M: 131.39. Colourless, non-flammable liquid. BR: 86–98°C. FP: -87°C. d: 1.46 kg/l (20°C). Insoluble with water. Miscible with oxygenated solvents. Stabilised grades are produced for vapour cleaning applications.
Production:
- ethylene dichloride + chlorine (chlorination; coproduced with perchloroethylene)
- ethylene dichloride + chlorine + oxygen (oxychlorination/dehydrochlorination; coproduced with perchloroethylene)
- acetylene + chlorine (addition/dehydrochlorination)

Derivatives: captafol; chloroacetic acid; 1-chloro-2,2,2-trifluoroethane

Uses: chain-transfer agent (polyvinyl chloride production); extraction solvent (vegetable oil refining); heat-transfer fluid; non-flammable solvent (dry cleaning, textile scouring, metal degreasing, surface coatings, corrosion preventatives)

trichlorofluoromethane
CFC-11; Freon 11 (Du Pont); R11; [75-69-4]

CFCl₃

$C_1Cl_3F_1$. M: 137.37. Colourless, nonflammable liquid with a mild, ether-like odour. BP: 24°C.
Production:
- carbon tetrachloride + hydrogen fluoride (halogen exchange; coproduced with dichlorodifluoromethane)
- natural gas + chlorine + hydrogen fluoride (Montedison single-step process; coproduced with dichlorodifluoromethane)

Uses: blowing agent (polyurethane foams); dry-cleaning solvent; aerosol propellant; heat-transfer fluid; refrigerant/air conditioning gas

trichloroisocyanuric acid
1,3,5-trichloro-*sym*-triazine-2,4,6-trione; trichloro-*sym*-triazinetrione; TCCA; [87-90-1]

$C_3Cl_3N_3O_3$. M: 232.41. White granules. Solubility in water: 12 g/l water (25°C).
Production:
- cyanuric acid + chlorine (chlorination)

Derivatives: potassium dichloroisocyanurate
Uses: bleaching/sanitising agent (scouring powders, laundry detergents); swimming pool disinfectant

trichloromethanesulphenyl chloride
perchloromethyl mercaptan; [594-42-3]

CCl₃SCl

$C_1Cl_4S_1$. M: 185.88. Pale yellow liquid with a strong, acrid odour. BP: 149°C with decomposition. d: 1.70 kg/l (20°C). Slowly hydrolysed by water. Soluble in most organic solvents.
Production:
- carbon disulphide + chlorine (chlorination)

Derivatives: dichlorofluoromethanesulphenyl chloride; captan; etridiazole; folpet

α-trichloromethylphenyl carbinyl acetate
α-(trichloromethyl)benzyl acetate; [90-17-5]
$C_{10}H_9Cl_3O_2$. M: 267.54. White, crystalline solid with a rose-like odour. MP: 88°C.

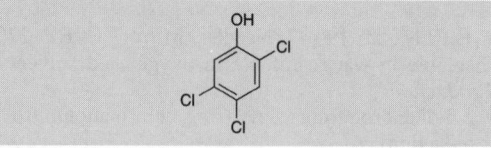

Production:
- benzene + chloral + acetic anhydride (carbonyl addition/esterification)

Uses: fragrance ingredient

trichloromethylsilane
methyltrichlorosilane; [75-79-6]

CH₃SiCl₃

$C_1H_3Cl_3Si_1$. M: 149.48. Colourless liquid. BP: 66°C. d: 1.27 kg/l (25°C). Hydrolysed by water releasing hydrogen chloride.
Production:
- silicon, metallurgical grade + methyl chloride (Direct process; coproduced with chlorotrimethylsilane/dichlorodimethylsilane/dichloromethylsilane)

Derivatives: dichloromethylphenylsilane; methyl triacetoxysilane; silicone resin
Uses: chemical vapour deposition (silicon carbide fibre coating); surface treatment agent (silica)

2,4,5-trichlorophenol
[95-95-4]

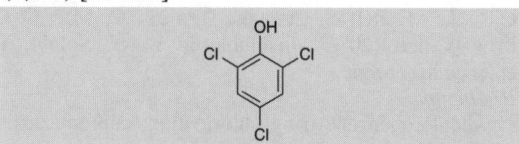

$C_6H_3Cl_3O_1$. M: 197.45. Needles with a chlorophenolic odour. MP: 63–65°C. Sublimes. Slightly soluble in water. Soluble in most organic solvents.
Production:
- 1,2,4,5-tetrachlorobenzene (base-catalysed hydrolysis)

Derivatives: hexachlorophene; 2,4,5-T

2,4,6-trichlorophenol
2,4,6-T; [88-06-2]

$C_6H_3Cl_3O_1$. M: 197.45. Light tan solid. MP: 66°C. BP: 246°C. d: 1.46 kg/l (100°C). Sparingly soluble in water. Soluble in alkali and oxygenated solvents. Also available commercially as a 40% aqueous solution of the sodium salt.
Production:
- phenol + chlorine (ring chlorination; coproduced with 2,4-dichlorophenol)

Derivatives: chloranil; prochloraz
Uses: antiseptic; wood/textile preservative

trichlorophenylsilane
phenyltrichlorosilane; [98-13-5]

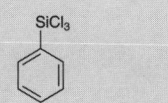

$C_6H_5Cl_3Si_1$. M: 211.56. Colourless liquid. BP: 201°C. d: 1.32 kg/l (20°C). Hydrolysed by water releasing hydrogen chloride.
Production:
• silicon, metallurgical grade + chlorobenzene (Direct process; coproduced with dichlorodiphenylsilane)
Derivatives: silicone resin; trimethoxyphenylsilane

1,2,3-trichloropropane
trichlorohydrin; [96-18-4]

$$ClCH_2CHCH_2Cl$$
(with Cl above central carbon)

$C_3H_5Cl_3$. M: 147.43. Colourless liquid. BP: 156°C. FP: -15°C. d: 1.39 kg/l (20°C). Insoluble in water. Soluble in oxygenated solvents.
Production:
• 1,3-dichloropropene + hydrogen chloride, anhydrous (addition)
Uses: polysulphide rubber comonomer

3,5,6-trichloro-2-pyridone
2-hydroxy-3,5,6-trichloropyridine; 2,3,5-trichloro-6-hydroxypyridine; 3,5,6-trichloro-2-pyridol

$C_5H_2Cl_3N_1O_1$. M: 198.45.
Production:
• dimethyl glutarate + ammonia (imide formation/chlorination/hydrolysis)
Derivatives: chlorpyrifos; chlorpyrifos-methyl; triclopyr

trichlorosilane
[10025-78-2]

$$SiHCl_3$$

$H_1Cl_3Si_1$. M: 135.46. Colourless liquid. BP: 33°C. Decomposes on contact with water. Fumes in air.
Production:
• silicon, metallurgical grade + hydrogen chloride, anhydrous (reaction; coproduced with silicon tetrachloride)
Derivatives: γ-aminopropyltriethoxysilane; γ-chloropropyltrimethoxysilane; β-(3,4-epoxycyclohexyl)ethyltrimethoxysilane; γ-glycidoxypropyltrimethoxysilane; γ-mercaptopropyltrimethoxysilane; γ-methacryloxypropyltrimethoxysilane; silane; silicon, electronic grade; 3-(trimethoxysilyl)propyldimethyloctadecylammonium chloride; vinyltrichlorosilane

α,α,α-trichlorotoluene *See:* benzotrichloride

2,4,6-trichloro-1,3,5-triazine *See:* cyanuric chloride

1,1,1-trichloro-2,2,2-trifluoroethane
[354-58-5]

$$CCl_3CF_3$$

$C_2Cl_3F_3$. M: 187.37.
Production:
• perchloroethylene + hydrogen fluoride (halogen exchange; byproduct of 1,1-dichloro-2,2,2-trifluoroethane production)
Derivatives: 3-(2-chloro-3,3,3-trifluoropropenyl)-2,2-dimethylcyclopropanecarboxylic acid

1,1,2-trichloro-1,2,2-trifluoroethane
trichlorotrifluoroethane; CFC-113; R113; [76-13-1]

$$CFCl_2CF_2Cl$$

$C_2Cl_3F_3$. M: 187.37. Colourless, non-flammable gas. BP: 48°C. d: 1.57 kg/l (20°C). Insoluble in water.
Production:
• perchloroethylene + hydrogen fluoride (fluorination; coproduced with 1,2-dichloro-1,1,2,2-tetrafluoroethane/chloropentafluoroethane/tetrachlorodifluoroethane)
Derivatives: chlorotrifluoroethylene
Uses: dry-cleaning solvent; metal/plastic cleaning solvent; refrigerant gas

triclocarban
1-(3',4'-dichlorophenyl)-3-(4'-chlorophenyl)urea; TCC; [101-20-2]

$C_{13}H_9Cl_3N_2O_1$. M: 315.58.
Production:
• 3,4-dichloroaniline + *p*-chlorophenyl isocyanate (isocyanate addition)
Uses: biocide/antiseptic (soaps, cleaners, cosmetics)

triclopyr
3,5,6-trichloro-2-pyridyloxyacetic acid; [55335-06-3]

$C_7H_4Cl_3N_1O_3$. M: 256.48. Available commercially as the

acid or as the triethylamine salt.
Production:
• 3,5,6-trichloro-2-pyridone + sodium chloroacetate (ether formation)
Derivatives:
fluroxypyr-1-methylheptyl; triclopyr-2-butoxyethyl
Uses: herbicide

triclopyr-2-butoxyethyl
[64470-88-8]

$C_{13}H_{16}Cl_3N_1O_4$. M: 356.64.
Production:
• ethylene glycol monobutyl ether + triclopyr (esterification)
Uses: herbicide

triclosan
2,4,4′-trichloro-2′-hydroxydiphenyl ether; [3380-34-5]

$C_{12}H_7Cl_3O_2$. M: 289.55.
Production:
• 2,4-dichlorophenol + 2,5-dichloronitrobenzene (ether formation/nitro reduction/diazotisation/ hydration)
Uses: disinfectant (soap, detergent sanitisers); toothpaste ingredient

triclosene sodium *See:* sodium dichloroisocyanurate

tricresyl phosphate
tritolyl phosphate; TCP; Disflamoll TKP (Bayer); [1330-78-5]

$C_{21}H_{21}O_4P_1$. M: 368.37. Colourless liquid. BP: 266–272°C (1.3 kPa). Pour point: -30°C. d: 1.16 kg/l (20°C). Insoluble in water. Mixed isomer product.
Production:
• m/p-cresol + phosphorus oxychloride (dehydrochlorination)
Uses:
casein polymer production clarifying agent; extreme-pressure additive (lubricants); fire-resistant hydraulic fluid; fire-resistant plasticiser (adhesives, lacquer, polyvinyl chloride, rubber); petrol/diesel fuel antipreignition additive

tricrotonylidenetetramine
TCT

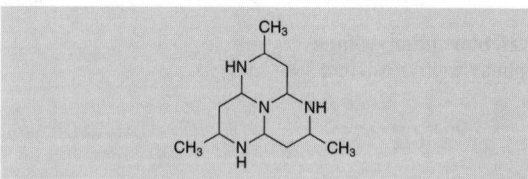

$C_{12}H_{24}N_4$. M: 224.35.
Production:
• crotonaldehyde + ammonia (carbonyl condensation/ addition)
Uses: vulcanisation accelerator

tricyclazole
5-methyl-1,2,4-triazolo[3,4-b]benzothiazole; [41814-78-2]

$C_9H_7N_3S_1$. M: 189.24.
Production:
• o-toluidine + sulphur + carbon disulphide + hydrazine + formic acid (thiocarbonylation/amine formation/condensation)
Uses: fungicide

tricyclohexyltin hydroxide *See:* cyhexatin

n-tridecaldehyde
aldehyde C-13; n-tridecanal; n-tridecyl aldehyde; [10486-19-8]

$$CH_3(CH_2)_{11}CHO$$

$C_{13}H_{26}O_1$. M: 198.35. Colourless liquid with a citrus odour. BP: 156°C (3.0 kPa). MP: 14°C. Insoluble in water. Soluble in alcohol.
Production:
• 1-dodecene + synthesis gas (hydroformylation)
Derivatives: tridemorph
Uses: fragrance ingredient

tridecanol
isotridecanol; tridecyl alcohol

$$C_{12}H_{25}CH_2OH$$

$C_{13}H_{28}O_1$. M: 200.36. Colourless liquid. BP: 245–265°C. d: 0.84 kg/l (20°C). Insoluble in water. Flash point: 118°C (PMCC). Mixed isomer product.
Production:
• dodecene, branched + synthesis gas (hydroformylation)
Derivatives: complex ester oils; diester oils; diisotridecyl adipate; diisotridecyl phthalate; ditridecyl thiodi-

propionate; isotridecanol ethoxylates; isotridecyl methacrylate; isotridecyl-3-oxypropylamine; isotridecyl stearate; sodium bistridecylsulphosuccinate
Uses: metal extraction solvent; oiliness additive (lubricants); solvent

tridemorph
2,6-dimethyl-4-tridecylmorpholine; [81412-43-3]

$C_{19}H_{39}N_1O_1$. M: 297.53. Mixed product. The chain-length distribution is 60–70% C_{13}.
Production:
• 2,6-dimethylmorpholine + *n*-tridecaldehyde (amine formation)
Uses: fungicide

p,p',p''-tri-(2,3-epoxypropoxy)triphenylmethane
Tactix 742 (Dow Chemical)

$C_{28}H_{28}O_6$. M: 460.52.
Production:
• *p*-hydroxybenzaldehyde + phenol + epichlorohydrin (carbonyl condensation/ether formation)
Uses: high performance epoxy resin (composite aircraft bodies and components)

trietazine
2-chloro-4-diethylamino-6-ethylamino-1,3,5-triazine; [1912-26-1]

$C_9H_{16}Cl_1N_5$. M: 229.71.
Production:
• cyanuric chloride + ethylamine + diethylamine (amine formation/amine formation)
Uses: herbicide

triethanolamine
TEA; TELA; [102-71-6]

$C_6H_{15}N_1O_3$. M: 149.20. Colourless, hygroscopic liquid.

with a mild, ammoniacal odour. Available commercially as 99% pure material or as an 85% solution in water. BP: 340°C. FP: 21°C. d: 1.12 kg/l (99% grade, 25°C). Miscible with water and oxygenated solvents. Available commercially as the free base or hydrochloride.
Production:
• ammonia + ethylene oxide (epoxidation; coproduced with monoethanolamine/diethanolamine)
Derivatives:
alkyd resins, water-soluble; polyether polyols, rigid; triethanolamine alkylbenzenesulphonate; triethanolamine lauryl ether sulphate; triethanolamine lauryl sulphate; triethanolamine monooleate ester; triethanolamine oleate diester; triethanolamine phosphate; triethanolamine titanate; triethylenediamine
Uses: cement grinding aid; corrosion inhibitor; polyurethane/thermosetting acrylic resin crosslinking agent; amine soaps (metalworking fluids, general cleaners, hand cleaners, waxes, polishes); agrochemical ingredient; solubiliser/neutraliser/corrosion inhibitor (paints, printing inks); solubiliser (shampoos, toiletries, hair dyes, tints); neutralising agent (powder laundry detergents); photoactivator (printing inks, lacquers); solubiliser/neutralising agent (liquid laundry detergents, dishwashing liquids, cleaners, shampoos); solvent (gas refining, sulphur dioxide extraction)

triethanolamine alkylbenzenesulphonate
TEA-dodecylbenzenesulphonate (CTFA)

$C_{24}H_{45}N_1O_6S_1$. M: 475.69. Yellow-orange, viscous liquid usually sold as a 50–60% solution in water.
Production:
• dodecylbenzenesulphonic acid, linear + triethanolamine (salt formation)
Uses: dry-cleaning detergent; pigment dispersant; surfactant (light-duty liquid cleaners, dishwashing detergents); textile desizing auxiliary

triethanolamine lauryl ether sulphate
TEA-laureth sulphate (CTFA)

n = 2–3. Liquid consisting of a 28–30% solution in water.
Production:
• *n*-alkanol(C_{12}-C_{14}) ethoxylates + triethanolamine (sulphation/salt formation)
Uses: surfactant (shampoos, bubble baths)

triethanolamine lauryl sulphate
TEA-lauryl sulphate (CTFA); [139-96-8]
$C_{18}H_{41}N_1O_7S_1$. M: 415.59. Available commercially as a 40–75% solution in water.

$$CH_3(CH_2)_{11}OSO_3^- \quad {}^+NH(CH_2CH_2OH)_3$$

Production:
- lauryl alcohol, narrow-cut/n-alkanol(C_{12}-C_{13})/ n-alkanol(C_{12}-C_{14})/n-alkanol(C_{12}-C_{18}) + triethanolamine (sulphation/salt formation)

Uses: industrial/firefighting foams; shampoos/bubble baths/toothpaste

triethanolamine monooleate ester

$$CH_3(CH_2)_7CH=CH(CH_2)_7\overset{\overset{O}{||}}{C}OCH_2CH_2N(CH_2CH_2OH)_2$$

$C_{24}H_{47}N_1O_4$. M: 413.65.
Production:
- triethanolamine + oleic acid (esterification)

Uses:
W/O emulsifier (lubricants, polishes, wax emulsions)

triethanolamine oleate diester

$$\left[CH_3(CH_2)_7CH=CH(CH_2)_7\overset{\overset{O}{||}}{C}OCH_2CH_2\right]_2NCH_2CH_2OH$$

$C_{42}H_{79}N_1O_5$. M: 678.09. Liquid. Cloud point: -12---4°C.
Production:
- triethanolamine + oleic acid (esterification)

Uses: lubricant (drawing soaps)

triethanolamine phosphate

$$3(HOCH_2CH_2)_3NH^+ \quad PO_4^{3-}$$

$C_{18}H_{48}N_3O_{13}P_1$. M: 545.56.
Production:
- triethanolamine + phosphoric acid, pure (salt formation)

Uses: corrosion inhibitor (antifreeze)

triethanolamine titanate

diisopropyl bis(triethanolaminotitanate); TEAT

$$\left[(HOCH_2CH_2)_2NCH_2CH_2O\right]_2Ti\left[OCH(CH_3)_2\right]_2$$

$C_{18}H_{42}N_2O_8Ti_1$. M: 462.44. Pale yellow liquid containing 80% active matter in isopropanol. d: 1.07 kg/l (20°C). Soluble in alcohol, aromatic and chlorinated solvents.
Production:
- isopropyl titanate + triethanolamine (transesterification)

Uses: adhesion promotion agent (surface coatings); thixotropic/crosslinking agent (emulsion paints)

1,1,3-triethoxybutane
TEB

$$\underset{\overset{|}{CH_3CHCH_2CH(OC_2H_5)_2}}{OC_2H_5}$$

$C_{10}H_{22}O_3$. M: 190.29.

Production:
- crotonaldehyde + ethanol (Michael addition/acetal formation)

Uses: flotation frothing agent

triethoxyethane *See:* triethyl orthoacetate

triethoxymethane *See:* triethyl orthoformate

triethoxyvinylsilane
vinyltriethoxysilane; [78-08-0]

$$CH_2=CHSi(OC_2H_5)_3$$

$C_8H_{18}O_3Si_1$. M: 190.32. Colourless liquid. BP: 160°C. d: 0.89 kg/l (25°C). Insoluble in water.
Production:
- vinyltrichlorosilane + ethanol (dehydrochlorination)

Uses:
polyethylene crosslinking agent (Sioplas process)

triethyl acetylcitrate
acetyl triethyl citrate; Citroflex A2 (Pfizer); [77-89-4]

$$CH_3CO-\overset{\overset{O \quad CH_2COOCH_2CH_3}{|}}{\underset{\overset{|}{CH_2COOCH_2CH_3}}{C}}COOCH_2CH_3$$

$C_{14}H_{22}O_8$. M: 318.32. Liquid. MP: -50°C. d: 1.14 kg/l (23°C). Insoluble in water.
Production:
- triethyl citrate + acetic anhydride (acetylation)

Uses:
plasticiser (ethyl cellulose, cellulose esters)

triethylaluminium
aluminium triethyl; TEA; [97-93-8]

$$Al(C_2H_5)_3$$

$C_6H_{15}Al_1$. M: 114.17. Colourless liquid. BP: 185°C. FP: -46°C. d: 0.83 kg/l (25°C). Spontaneously ignites on contact with air. Hydrolysed violently by water.
Production:
- aluminium + ethylene + hydrogen (reaction)

Derivatives:
diethyl zinc; ibuprofen
Uses: Ziegler catalyst component (polyolefin production); reagent (Meerwein-Ponndorf reduction)

triethylamine
TEA; [121-44-8]

$$(C_2H_5)_3N$$

$C_6H_{15}N_1$. M: 101.20. Colourless liquid. BP: 89°C. FP: -115°C. d: 0.73 kg/l (4°C). Soluble in water and oxygenated solvents.
Production:
- ethanol + ammonia (amine formation; coproduced with ethylamine/diethylamine)

Derivatives: benzyltriethylammonium chloride; tetraethylammonium bromide; tetraethylammonium chloride; tetraethylammonium hydroxide
Uses: cold-box foundry mould process curing agent; epoxy resin curing agent

triethylbenzylammonium chloride
See: benzyltriethylammonium chloride

triethyl citrate
ethyl citrate; TEC; [77-93-0]

$$CH_2COOC_2H_5$$
$$HO-CCOOC_2H_5$$
$$CH_2COOC_2H_5$$

$C_{12}H_{20}O_7$. M: 276.28. Colourless, involatile liquid. BP: 127°C (0.13 kPa). d: 1.14 kg/l (25°C). Slightly soluble in water. Soluble in oxygenated solvents.
Production:
• ethanol + citric acid (esterification)
Derivatives: triethyl acetylcitrate
Uses: perfume fixative; plasticiser (cellulosic resins, lacquers, printing inks)

triethylenediamine
diaminobicyclooctane; 1,4-diazobicyclo[2.2.2]octane; DABCO (Air Products); TEDA; [280-57-9]

$C_6H_{12}N_2$. M: 112.18. Solid. MP: 160°C. d: 1.14 kg/l (25°C). Soluble in water. Flash point: >38°C (PMCC).
Production:
• triethanolamine + ammonia (dehydrochlorination)
Uses: polyurethane foam catalyst; metal deactivator (lubricants)

triethylene glycol
TEG; [112-27-6]

$$HOCH_2CH_2OCH_2CH_2OCH_2CH_2OH$$

$C_6H_{14}O_4$. M: 150.18. Colourless liquid. BP: 288°C. FP: -7°C. d: 1.12 kg/l (25°C). Viscosity: 37 mPa.s (25°C). Miscible with water. Soluble in oxygenated solvents.
Production:
• ethylene oxide (hydration; coproduced with ethylene glycol/diethylene glycol)
• diethylene glycol + ethylene oxide (epoxidation)
Derivatives: iodoxamic acid; rosin ester gum; triethylene glycol bis[3-(3-*t*-butyl-4-hydroxy-5-methylphenyl)propionate]; triethylene glycol diacetate; triethylene glycol dimethacrylate; triethylene glycol dinitrate; triethylene glycol dipelargonate
Uses: unsaturated polyester resin comonomer; dehydration agent (natural gas processing); plasticiser (polyvinyl alcohol); solvent (printing inks, dyes, pharmaceuticals, cosmetics); tobacco humectant

triethylene glycol bis[3-(3-*t*-butyl-4-hydroxy-5-methylphenyl)propionate]
Irganox 245 (Ciba-Geigy); [36443-68-2]

$C_{34}H_{50}O_8$. M: 586.76.
Production:
• *o*-cresol + isobutylene + triethylene glycol + methyl acrylate (orthoalkylation/Michael addition/transesterification)
Uses: antioxidant (oils, fats, plastics, fibres, rubber)

triethylene glycol diacetate
TEGDA; [111-21-7]

$$CH_3COCH_2CH_2OCH_2CH_2OCH_2CH_2OCCH_3$$

$C_{10}H_{18}O_6$. M: 234.24. Colourless liquid. BP: 300°C. d: 1.11 kg/l (20°C). Saponification value: 480 mg KOH/g. Slightly soluble in water.
Production:
• triethylene glycol + acetic anhydride (acetylation)
Uses: plasticiser (cellulose acetate cigarette filters)

triethylene glycol dimethacrylate
TEDMA; TEGMA

$$CH_2=CC(OCH_2CH_2)_3OCC=CH_2$$
$$CH_3 \quad\quad\quad CH_3$$

$C_{14}H_{22}O_6$. M: 286.32. Colourless liquid with an ester-like odour.
Production:
• triethylene glycol + methyl methacrylate (transesterification)
Uses: polyvinyl chloride plastisol comonomer; acrylic/vinyl resin crosslinking agent

triethylene glycol dimethyl ether
triglyme; [112-49-2]

$$CH_3O(CH_2CH_2O)_3CH_3$$

$C_8H_{18}O_4$. M: 178.23. Liquid. BP: 216°C. MP: -45°C. d: 0.99 kg/l (20°C). Miscible with water and most organic solvents.
Production:
• triethylene glycol monomethyl ether (methylation)
Uses: solubiliser (organic media)

triethylene glycol dinitrate
TEGN; triethylene glycol nitrate

$$O_2NO(CH_2CH_2O)_3NO_2$$

$C_6H_{12}N_2O_8$. M: 240.17.

Production:
• triethylene glycol (nitration)
Uses: alcohol-based diesel fuel cetane improver

triethylene glycol dipelargonate

$$CH_3(CH_2)_7\overset{O}{\underset{|}{C}}(OCH_2CH_2)_3O\overset{O}{\underset{|}{C}}(CH_2)_7CH_3$$

$C_{24}H_{46}O_6$. M: 430.62.
Production:
• triethylene glycol + pelargonic acid (esterification)
Uses: jet engine synthetic lubricant base oil

triethylene glycol monobutyl ether
Butoxytriglycol (Union Carbide); Butyl Triethoxol (ICI); [143-22-6]

$$CH_3CH_2CH_2CH_2(OCH_2CH_2)_3OH$$

$C_{10}H_{22}O_4$. M: 206.29. Colourless liquid. BP: 276°C. FP: -48°C. d: 1.00 kg/l (20°C). Miscible with water.
Production:
• *n*-butanol + ethylene oxide (epoxidation; coproduced with diethylene glycol monobutyl ether/ethylene glycol monobutyl ether)
Derivatives: silicone-polyol block copolymers
Uses: coupling solvent (paints, lacquers, detergents, soluble oils)

triethylene glycol monoethyl ether
ethyl triglycol; Ethoxytriglycol (Union Carbide); Triethoxol (ICI)

$$CH_3CH_2(OCH_2CH_2)_3OH$$

$C_8H_{18}O_4$. M: 178.23. Colourless liquid. MP: 240–250°C. d: 1.02 kg/l (20°C). Miscible with water and most organic solvents. Flash point: 135°C (TOC).
Production:
• ethanol + ethylene oxide (epoxidation; coproduced with diethylene glycol monoethyl ether/ethylene glycol monoethyl ether)
Uses: solvent (lacquers, paints)

triethylene glycol monomethyl ether
methoxytriethylene glycol; methoxytriglycol; methyl triglycol; methyl trigol; [112-35-6]

$$CH_3(OCH_2CH_2)_3OH$$

$C_7H_{16}O_4$. M: 164.21. Colourless liquid. BP: 235°C. Viscosity: 280 cSt (-40°C). Miscible with water and most organic solvents.
Production:
• methanol + ethylene oxide (epoxidation)
Derivatives: triethylene glycol dimethyl ether; tris(triethylene glycol monomethyl ether)borate
Uses: coupling solvent (water-based paints); brake/hydraulic fluid blending component; plasticiser/wetting agent (resins, paints); solvent

triethylenemelamine
2,4,6-tris(1-aziridinyl)-1,3,5-triazine; TEM; Tretamine;

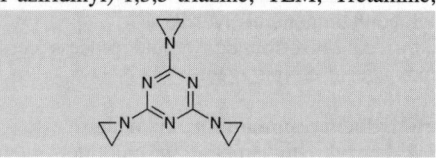

$C_9H_{12}N_6$. M: 204.24. Crystalline solid. Decomposes when heated above 139°C. Soluble in water, oxygenated and chlorinated solvents. Polymerises at ambient temperatures.
Production:
• cyanuric chloride + ethyleneimine (dehydrochlorination)
Uses: textile finishing agent

triethylenephosphoramide
tri-(aziridin-1-yl)phosphine oxide; APO; TEPA; [545-55-1]

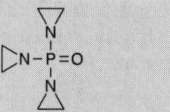

$C_6H_{12}N_3O_1P_1$. M: 173.16. Solid. MP: 41°C. Soluble in water and oxygenated solvents.
Production:
• ethyleneimine + phosphorus oxychloride (dehydrochlorination)
Uses: antineoplastic drug; textile finishing agent

triethylenetetramine
TET; TETA; [112-24-3]

$$H_2NCH_2CH_2NHCH_2CH_2NHCH_2CH_2NH_2$$

$C_6H_{18}N_4$. M: 146.24. Amber liquid with a weak, ammoniacal odour. BP: 260–290°C. Pour point: <-40°C. Miscible with water, oxygenated and aromatic solvents. Immiscible with aliphatic solvents. Flash point: 132°C.
Production:
• ethylene dichloride + ammonia (amine formation; coproduced with ethylenediamine/diethylenetriamine/tetraethylenepentamine/polyethylenepolyamine/piperazine/aminoethylpiperazine)
• ethylenediamine + monoethanolamine (reductive amination; coproduced with diethylenetriamine/tetraethylenepentamine/polyethylenepolyamine)
Derivatives: fatty acid imidazoline polyamines; polyamide resins, non-reactive; polyamide resins, reactive; urea-formaldehyde resins, cationic
Uses: epoxy resin curing agent

N,N',N''-triethylhexahydrotriazine
hexahydro-1,3,5-triethyl-*sym*-triazine; Vancide TH (Vanderbilt Chemical); Trimene base (Uniroyal Chemical); [7779-27-3]

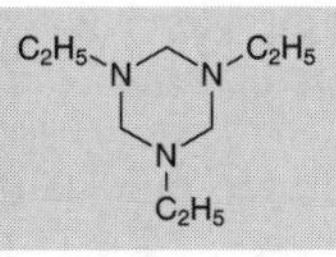

$C_9H_{21}N_3$. M: 171.29.
Production:
• ethylamine + formaldehyde (carbonyl condensation)
Uses: polyurethane foam catalyst; biocide (adhesives, latices, metalworking fluids)

tri-(2-ethylhexyl) phosphate
trioctyl phosphate; TOP; [78-42-2]

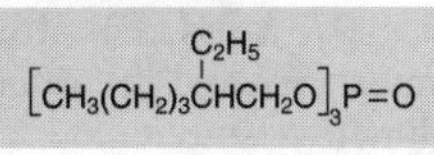

$[CH_3(CH_2)_3CHCH_2O]_3 P{=}O$ with C_2H_5 branch

$C_{24}H_{51}O_4P_1$. M: 434.64. Colourless liquid. BP: 232–236°C (1.3 kPa). d: 0.92 kg/l (20°C). Viscosity: 15 mPa.s (20°C). Insoluble in water.
Production:
• 2-ethylhexanol + phosphorus oxychloride (dehydrochlorination)
Uses: hydrogen peroxide production cosolvent; fire-resistant polyvinyl chloride/cellulose nitrate plasticiser

tri-(2-ethylhexyl) trimellitate
trioctyl trimellitate; TOT; TOTM

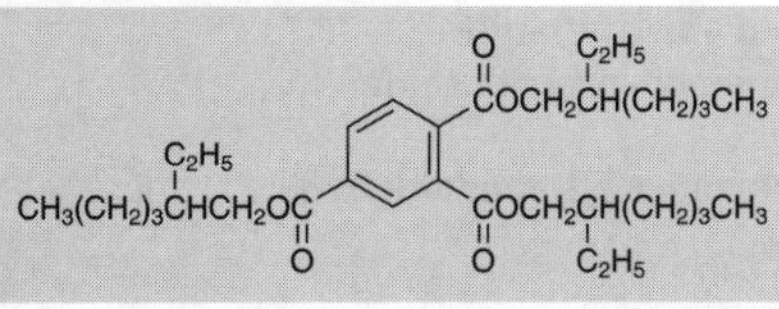

$C_{33}H_{54}O_6$. M: 546.78. Colourless, involatile liquid. d: 0.99 kg/l (20°C). Viscosity: 300 mPa.s (20°C). Insoluble in water.
Production:
• 2-ethylhexanol + trimellitic anhydride (esterification)
Uses: plasticiser (chlorinated plastics/rubber)

triethyl orthoacetate
ethyl orthoacetate; triethoxyethane; [78-39-7]

$CH_3C(OC_2H_5)_3$

$C_8H_{18}O_3$. M: 162.23. Liquid. BP: 142–143°C.
Production:
• acetonitrile + ethanol (reaction)
• 1,1,1-trichloroethane + sodium ethoxide (ether formation)
Derivatives: alprazolam; diazoxide; triazolam

triethyl orthoformate
ethyl orthoformate; triethoxymethane; [122-51-0]

$CH(OC_2H_5)_3$

$C_7H_{16}O_3$. M: 148.21. Liquid with pleasant odour. BP:

146°C. MP: <18°C. d: 0.89 kg/l (20°C). Soluble in oxygenated solvents. Hydrolysed by water.
Production:
• hydrogen cyanide + ethanol (reaction)
• chloroform + sodium ethoxide (ether formation)
Derivatives: allopurinol; 4-amino-5-aminomethyl-2-methylpyrimidine; 4-amino-5-bromomethyl-2-methylpyrimidine hydrobromide; amitraz; benzyl phenylmalonate; diethyl ethoxymethylenemalonate; *N*-(*p*-ethoxycarbonylphenyl)-*N*′-ethyl-*N*′-phenylformamidine; *N*-(*p*-ethoxycarbonylphenyl)-*N*′-methyl-*N*′-phenylformamidine; pyrazophos

triethyl phosphate
TEP; [78-40-0]

$(C_2H_5O)_3P{=}O$

$C_6H_{15}O_4P_1$. M: 182.16. Liquid. BP: 215–216°C. d: 1.07 kg/l (20°C). Soluble in water and oxygenated solvents.
Production:
• ethanol + phosphorus oxychloride (dehydrochlorination)
Uses: ketene production catalyst; fire-retardant/viscosity depressant additive (polyester laminates, cellulosics); peroxide phlegmatising agent

triethyl phosphite
O,O,O-triethyl phosphite; TEPI; [122-52-1]

$(C_2H_5O)_3P$

$C_6H_{15}O_3P_1$. M: 166.16. Colourless liquid. BP: 155–157°C. d: 0.97 kg/l (20°C). Insoluble in water. Soluble in oxygenated solvents.
Production:
• ethanol + phosphorus trichloride (dehydrochlorination)
Derivatives: chlorfenvinfos; Fluorescent Brightener 199
Uses: reagent (Wittig-Horner reactions); organonickel catalyst intermediate

triflic acid *See:* trifluoromethanesulphonic acid

triflumizole
1-[1-[4-chloro-2-(trifluoromethyl)phenylimino]-2-propoxyethyl]-1H-imidazole; [68694-11-1]

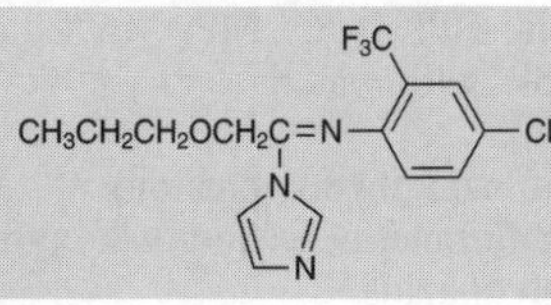

$C_{15}H_{15}Cl_1F_3N_3O_1$. M: 345.74.
Production:
• *n*-propanol + chloroacetaldehyde + 2-amino-5-chlorobenzotrifluoride + imidazole (imide formation/ether formation/chlorination/amine formation)
Uses: fungicide

trifluoperazine
[117-89-5]; [440-17-5] (hydrochloride)

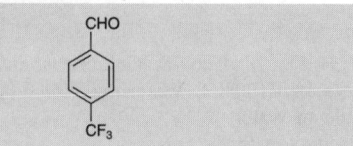

$C_{21}H_{24}F_3N_3S_1$. M: 407.49. Available commercially as the hydrochloride.
Production:
• 2-(trifluoromethyl)phenothiazine + 1-bromo-3-chloropropane + *N*-methylpiperazine (amine formation/amine formation)
Uses: neuroleptic drug

trifluoroacetic acid
perfluoroacetic acid; [76-05-1]

CF₃COOH

$C_2H_1F_3O_2$. M: 114.02. Liquid with a pungent odour. BP: 72°C. MP: -15°C. d: 1.49 kg/l (20°C). Strongly acidic. Soluble in oxygenated solvents.
Production:
• acetic acid + hydrogen fluoride (Simon electrochemical fluorination)
Derivatives: ethyl trifluoroacetate; trifluoroacetic anhydride; 2,2,2-trifluoroethanol
Uses: alkylation/acylation catalyst

trifluoroacetic anhydride
[407-25-0]

(CF₃CO)₂O

$C_4F_6O_3$. M: 210.03. Hygroscopic liquid. BP: 39–40°C. MP: -65°C. Hydrolysed by water and alcohol.
Production:
• trifluoroacetic acid (dehydration)
Derivatives: thiazafluron

2,2,2-trifluoroethanol
[75-89-8]

CF₃CH₂OH

$C_2H_3F_3O_1$. M: 100.03. Colourless liquid with an alcohol-like odour. BP: 74°C. MP: -45°C. d: 1.38 kg/l (25°C). Miscible with water.
Production:
• trifluoroacetic acid (hydrogenation)
Derivatives: isoflurane; poly(fluoroalkoxyphosphazene) elastomers; polythiazide

trifluoromethane
fluoroform; HFC-23; R23; [75-46-7]

CHF₃

$C_1H_1F_3$. M: 70.01. Colourless, liquified gas. BP: -82°C.

MP: -155°C. d: 1.44 kg/l (-80°C). Non-flammable. Very slightly soluble in water.
Production:
• chloroform + hydrogen fluoride (halogen exchange)
Derivatives:
bromotrifluoromethane
Uses: R-503 refrigerant gas component

trifluoromethanesulphonic acid
magic acid; triflic acid; trifluoromethylsulphonic acid; [1493-13-6]

CF₃SO₃H

$C_1H_1F_3O_3S_1$. M: 150.07. Solid. BP: 162°C. MP: 34°C. Miscible with water. Soluble in dimethylformamide, acetonitrile and dimethyl sulphoxide.
Production:
• methanesulphonic acid + hydrogen fluoride (Simon electrochemical fluorination/hydrolysis)
Derivatives: lithium trifluoromethanesulphonate; mefluidide; perfluidone
Uses: esterification/alkylation/hydroisomerisation catalyst (chemical synthesis, petroleum refining)

2-(trifluoromethyl)aniline
See: *o*-aminobenzotrifluoride

3-(trifluoromethyl)aniline
See: *m*-aminobenzotrifluoride

4-(trifluoromethyl)benzaldehyde

$C_8H_5F_3O_1$. M: 174.12. Liquid. BP: 80–81°C (3.3 kPa).
Production:
• *p*-xylene + hydrogen fluoride (side-chain chlorination/halogen exchange/side-chain chlorination/hydration; coproduced with 4-(trifluoromethyl)benzyl alcohol)
Derivatives: hydramethylnon

2-(trifluoromethyl)benzoyl fluoride

$C_8H_4F_4O_1$. M: 192.11.
Production:
• *o*-xylene + hydrogen fluoride (side-chain chlorination/halogen exchange/side-chain chlorination/hydration)
Derivatives: flutolanil

3-(trifluoromethyl)benzoyl fluoride
[328-99-4]

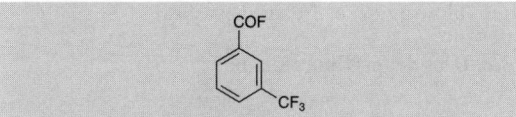

$C_8H_4F_4O_1$. M: 192.11. Liquid. BP: 159–163°C.
Production:
- *m*-xylene + hydrogen fluoride (side-chain chlorination/halogen exchange/side-chain chlorination/hydration)

Derivatives: Vat Blue 30

4-(trifluoromethyl)benzyl alcohol

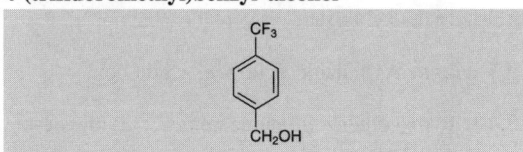

$C_8H_7F_3O_1$. M: 176.14.
Production:
- *p*-xylene + hydrogen fluoride (side-chain chlorination/halogen exchange/side-chain chlorination/hydration; coproduced with 4-(trifluoromethyl)benzaldehyde)

Derivatives: flocoumafen

4-(trifluoromethyl)chlorobenzene
See: p-chlorobenzotrifluoride

3-(trifluoromethyl)phenol
See: m-hydroxybenzotrifluoride

2-(trifluoromethyl)phenothiazine
[92-30-8]

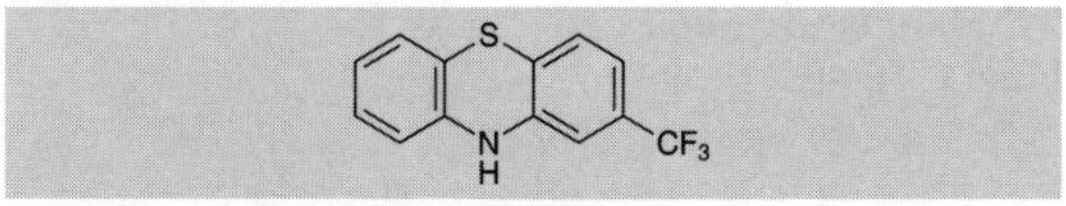

$C_{13}H_8F_3N_1S_1$. M: 267.26.
Production:
- chlorobenzene + *m*-aminobenzotrifluoride + sulphur (amine formation/thionation)

Derivatives:
fluphenazine; trifluoperazine; triflupromazine

3,3,3-trifluoropropylene
3,3,3-trifluoro-1-propene; TFP; [677-21-4]

$$CF_3CH=CH_2$$

$C_3H_3F_3$. M: 96.04. BP: -27°C.
Production:
- chlorotrifluoromethane + ethylene (addition/dehydrochlorination)

Derivatives: dichloromethyl-3,3,3-trifluoropropylsilane

α,α,α-trifluorotoluene *See:* benzotrifluoride

2,4,6-trifluoro-1,3,5-triazine *See:* cyanuric fluoride

trifluperidol
[749-13-3]

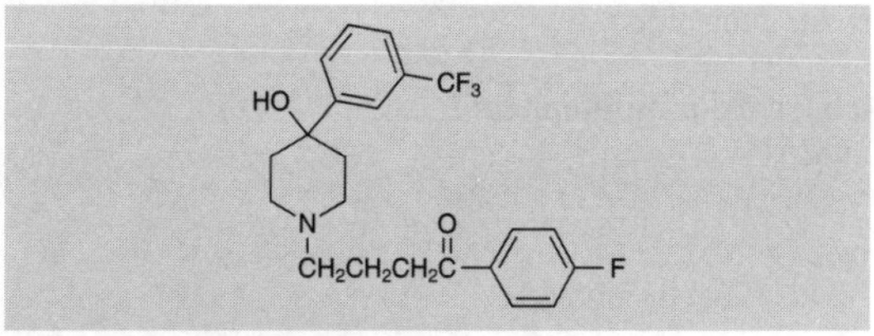

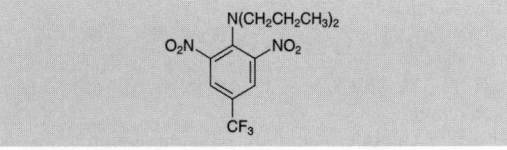

$C_{22}H_{23}F_4N_1O_2$. M: 409.42.
Production:
- *m*-aminobenzotrifluoride + cuprous chloride + 1-benzyl-4-piperidone + 4-chloro-4'-fluoro-butyrophenone (diazotisation/Sandmeyer reaction/Grignard reagent formation/Grignard reaction/amine dealkylation/amine formation)

Uses:
antipsychotic drug

triflupromazine
[146-54-3]; [1098-60-8] (hydrochloride)

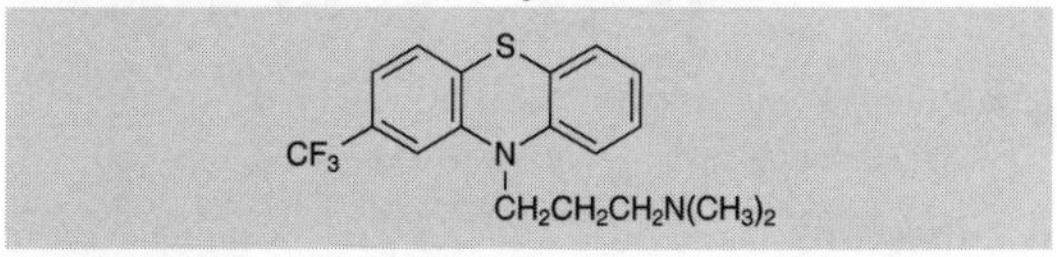

$C_{18}H_{19}F_3N_2S_1$. M: 352.41. Available commercially as the hydrochloride.
Production:
- 2-(trifluoromethyl)phenothiazine + 3-dimethylamino-propyl chloride hydrochloride (amine formation)

Uses: neuroleptic drug

trifluralin
N,N-di-*n*-propyl-2,6-dinitro-4-trifluoromethylaniline; Treflan (Eli Lilly); [1582-09-8]

$C_{13}H_{16}F_3N_3O_4$. M: 335.28.
Production:
- di-*n*-propylamine + 4-chloro-3,5-dinitrobenzo-trifluoride (amine formation)

Uses: herbicide

triforine
1,4-bis(2,2,2-trichloro-1-formamidoethyl)piperazine; [26644-46-2]
$C_{10}H_{14}Cl_6N_4O_2$. M: 434.97.

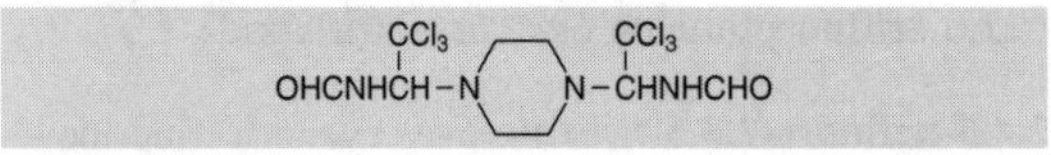

Production:
• chloral + formamide + piperazine (reductive amination/oxidative coupling)
Uses: fungicide

triglycidyl-*p*-aminophenol
TGPAP

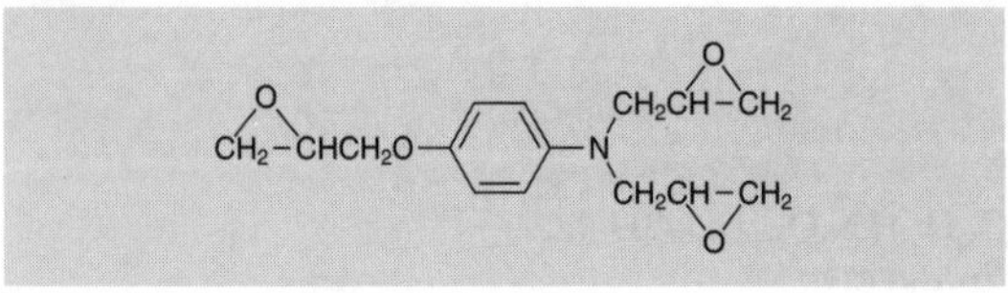

$C_{15}H_{19}N_1O_4$. M: 277.32.
Production:
• *p*-aminophenol + epichlorohydrin (amine formation)
Uses:
epoxy resins (composite aircraft bodies/components)

triglycidyl isocyanurate
TGIC; [2451-62-9]

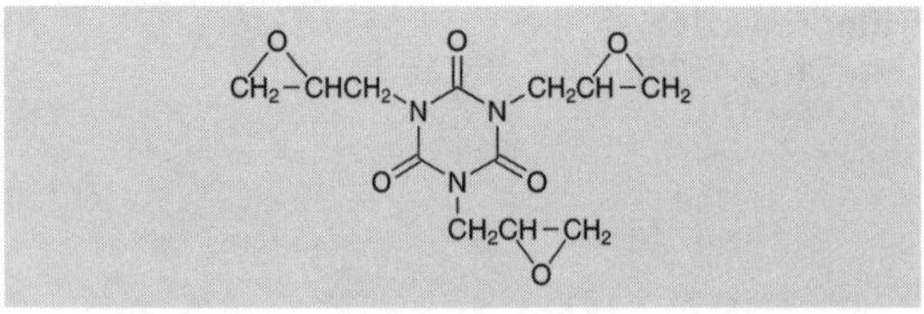

$C_{12}H_{15}N_3O_6$. M: 297.26. White granules. MP: 85–115°C. Epoxy equivalent: 110 g.
Production:
• cyanuric acid + epichlorohydrin (amine formation)
Uses: epoxy resin comonomer (powder coatings, high voltage electrical components)

triglyme *See:* triethylene glycol dimethyl ether

tri-*n*-hexylamine
trihexylamine

$C_{18}H_{39}N_1$. M: 269.52.
Production:
• *n*-hexyl chloride + ammonia (ammoniation)
Derivatives:
perfluorotrihexylamine

trihydrazinotriazine

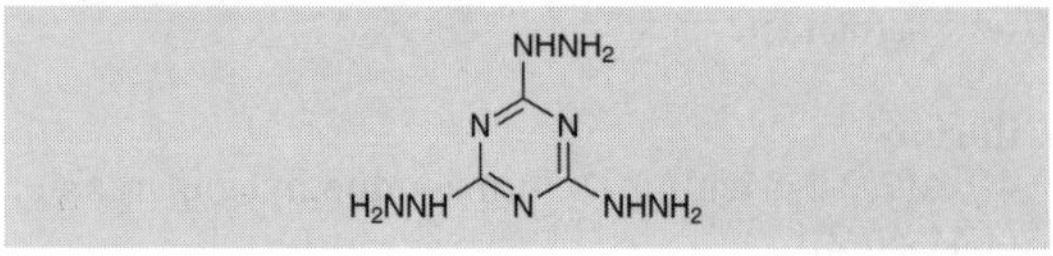

$C_3H_9N_9$. M: 171.16.

Production:
• cyanuric chloride + hydrazine (amine formation)
Uses: blowing agent (foamed plastics)

1,1,ω-trihydroperfluoroalkanol

$H(CF_2CF_2)_nCH_2OH$

n = 1–3.
Production:
• tetrafluoroethylene + methanol (telomerisation; coproduced with 2,2,3,3-tetrafluoropropanol)
Derivatives: poly(fluoroalkoxyphosphazene) elastomers

1,2,3-trihydroxybenzene *See:* pyrogallol

1,3,5-trihydroxybenzene *See:* phloroglucinol

3,4,5-trihydroxybenzoic acid *See:* gallic acid

2,3,4-trihydroxybenzophenone mono-2,1,5-diazoester

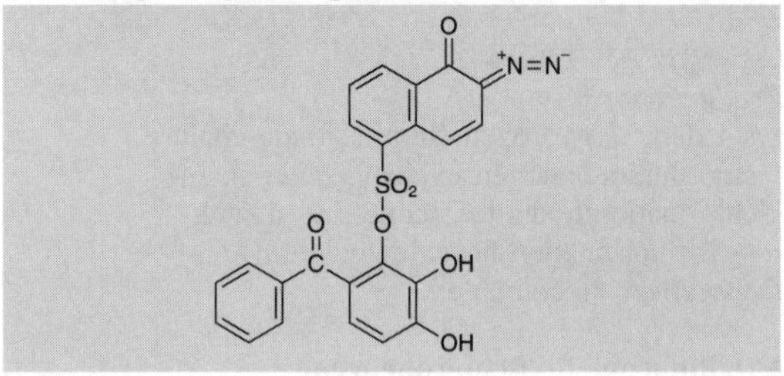

$C_{23}H_{14}N_2O_7S_1$. M: 462.42.
Production:
• pyrogallol + benzoyl chloride + 2-diazo-1-naphthol-5-sulphonic acid chloride (Friedel-Crafts acylation/ ether formation)
Uses: positive photoreprographic plate light sensitiser

triisobutylaluminium
TIBA; [100-99-2]

$[(CH_3)_2CHCH_2]_3Al$

$C_{12}H_{27}Al_1$. M: 198.33. Colourless liquid. Spontaneously flammable in air, emitting dense smoke. BP: 212°C. FP: 1°C. d: 0.78 kg/l (25°C). Reacts with water.
Production:
• aluminium + isobutylene + hydrogen (addition)
Derivatives:
tri-*n*-butylaluminium
Uses: catalyst; Ziegler catalyst component (polyolefin production); thixotropic agent (water-based paints)

triisobutylene *See:* dodecene, branched

triisooctylamine

$(C_7H_{15}CH_2)_3N$

$C_{24}H_{51}N_1$. M: 353.68.

Production:
• isooctanol + ammonia (ammoniation)
Uses: mineral extraction reagent

triisooctyl phosphite

$$(C_7H_{15}CH_2O)_3P$$

$C_{24}H_{51}O_3P_1$. M: 418.64. Colourless liquid. d: 0.89 kg/l (20°C). Insoluble in water.
Production:
• isooctanol + phosphorus trichloride (dehydrochlorination)
Uses: antioxidant (plastics)

triisooctyl trimellitate
TIOTM

$C_{33}H_{54}O_6$. M: 546.78. Colourless, high-boiling liquid. d: 0.99 kg/l (15°C). Viscosity: 300 mPa.s (20°C). Insoluble in water.
Production:
• isooctanol + trimellitic anhydride (esterification)
Uses: plasticiser (polyvinyl chloride, chlorosulphonated rubber)

triisopropanolamine
TIPA; [122-20-3]

$$CH_3$$
$$N(CHCH_2OH)_3$$

$C_9H_{21}N_1O_3$. M: 191.28. White solid with ammoniacal odour. BP: 306°C. FP: 44°C. d: 0.99 kg/l (25°C). Soluble in water, oxygenated and aromatic solvents. The commercial product is a mixture of isomers.
Production:
• ammonia + propylene oxide (epoxidation; coproduced with diisopropanolamine/ monoisopropanolamine)
Uses:
crosslinking agent (rubber); emulsifier/corrosion inhibitor (metalworking fluids); surfactant/solubilising agent

TRIM *See:* trimethylolpropane trimethacrylate

trimedlure
t-butyl 4/5-chloro-2-methylcyclohexanecarboxylate; [12002-53-8]

$C_{12}H_{21}Cl_1O_2$. M: 232.75. Mixed isomer product with a *trans*-configuration of the methyl and carboxyl substituents on the cyclohexane ring.
Production:
• *t*-butanol + crotonic acid + butadiene + thionyl chloride (esterification/Diels-Alder cycloaddition/ isomerisation/chlorination)
Uses: insect pheromone

trimellitic anhydride
benzene-1,2,4-tricarboxylic acid-1,2-anhydride; TMA; [552-30-7]

$C_9H_4O_5$. M: 192.12. Molten liquid or flakes. MP: 161–163°C. Soluble in oxygenated solvents.
Production:
• pseudocumene (liquid-phase oxidation)
Derivatives:
alkyd resins, water-soluble; 1,4-dichlorophthalazine-6-carboxyl chloride; poly(amide-imide); tri-*n*-alkyl(C$_7$-C$_9$) trimellitate; tri-*n*-alkyl(C$_8$-C$_{10}$) trimellitate; triallyl trimellitate; tri-(2-ethylhexyl) trimellitate; triisooctyl trimellitate; trinonyl trimellitate
Uses: heat-cured epoxy resin curing agent; unsaturated polyester resin comonomer

trimer acid
[68937-90-6]; [7049-66-3]
Viscous liquid. d: 1.00 kg/l (25°C). Acid value: 180–190 mg KOH/g. Saponification value: 195–205 mg KOH/g. Mixed product produced by cycloaddition of unsaturated fatty acids. A typical composition is 22% dimer acids, 78% trimer acids.
Production:
• castor oil, dehydrated/tall oil fatty acid (dimerisation/hydrogenation; coproduced with dimer acid/isostearic acid)
Derivatives: polyamide resins, non-reactive; polyamide resins, reactive
Uses: alkyd resin/epoxy ester resin comonomer

trimesic acid
benzene-1,3,5-tricarboxylic acid; [554-95-0]

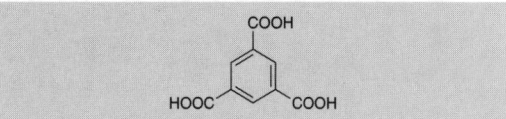

$C_9H_6O_6$. M: 210.14. White, crystalline solid. MP: 345°C. Slightly soluble in water. Soluble in oxygenated solvents.
Production:
• mesitylene (side-chain oxidation)
Uses: unsaturated/saturated polyester resin comonomer

trimethadione
[127-48-0]

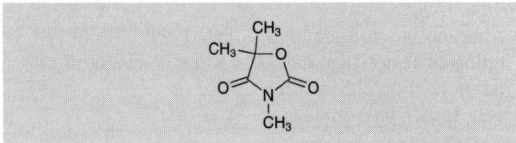

$C_6H_9N_1O_3$. M: 143.15.
Production:
• acetone cyanohydrin + urea + dimethyl sulphate
(nitrile hydrolysis/condensation/methylation)
Uses:
antiepileptic drug

trimethoprim
[738-70-5]

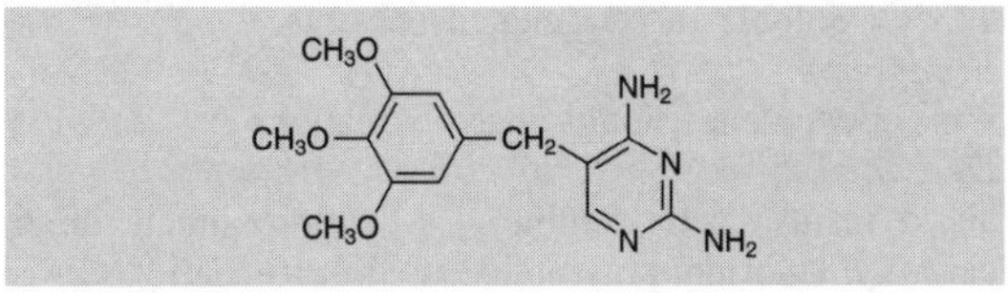

$C_{14}H_{18}N_4O_3$. M: 290.32.
Production:
• 3,4,5-trimethoxybenzaldehyde + 3-methoxypropio-
nitrile + guanidine hydrochloride (carbonyl
condensation/condensation)
Uses: antibacterial drug

3,4,5-trimethoxybenzaldehyde
[86-81-7]

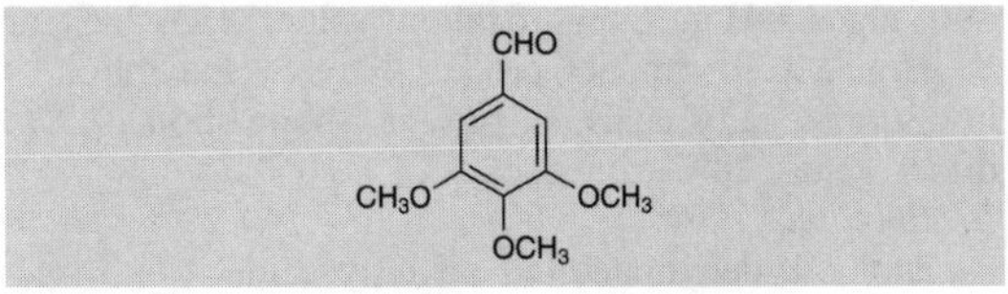

$C_{10}H_{12}O_4$. M: 196.21. Solid. MP: 73–75°C.
Production:
• *p*-hydroxybenzaldehyde + dimethyl sulphate
(sulphonation/alkali fusion/methylation)
Derivatives:
trimethoprim; 3,4,5-trimethoxybenzoic acid

3,4,5-trimethoxybenzoic acid

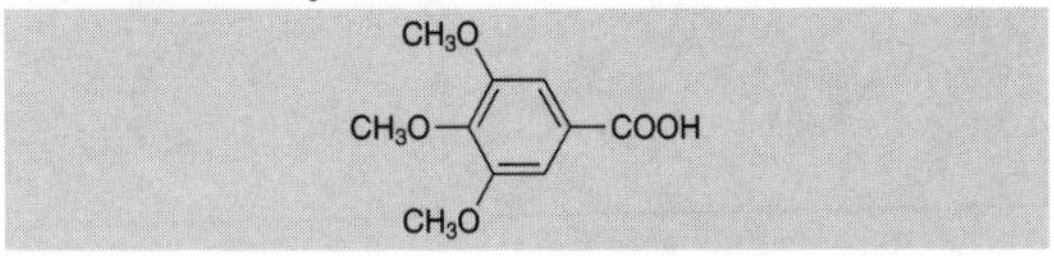

$C_{10}H_{12}O_5$. M: 212.20. Needles. MP: 167°C. Slightly
soluble in water. Soluble in oxygenated solvents.
Production:
• 3,4,5-trimethoxybenzaldehyde (carbonyl oxidation)
Derivatives: dilazep
Uses: pharmaceutical raw material

trimethoxyphenylsilane
phenyltrimethoxysilane; [780-69-8]

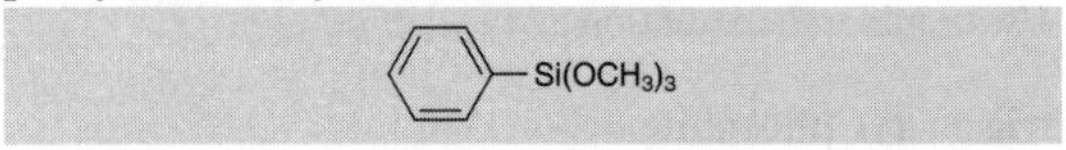

$C_9H_{14}O_3Si_1$. M: 198.30. Colourless liquid. BP: 211°C.
d: 1.06 kg/l (25°C). Insoluble in water. Soluble in oxygenated, chlorinated and aromatic solvents.
Production:
• trichlorophenylsilane + methanol
(dehydrochlorination)
Uses: plastics coupling agent

**3-(trimethoxysilyl)propyldimethyloctadecylammonium
chloride**

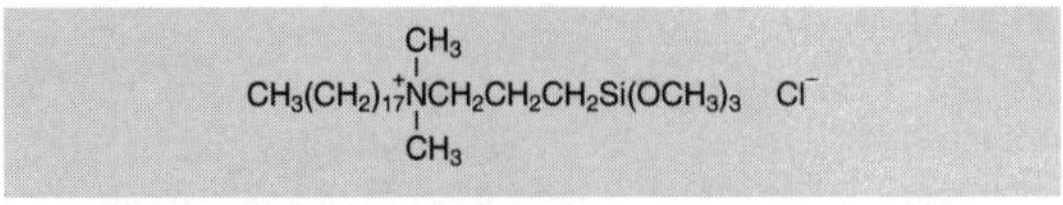

$C_{26}H_{58}Cl_1N_1O_3Si_1$. M: 496.30.
Production:
• dimethylstearylamine + allyl chloride + trichlorosilane + methanol (quaternisation/hydrosilation/
dehydrochlorination)
Uses: biocide (textile treatments)

trimethylacetic acid *See:* pivalic acid

1,1,1-trimethylacetone *See:* pinacolone

trimethyladipic acid
TMA

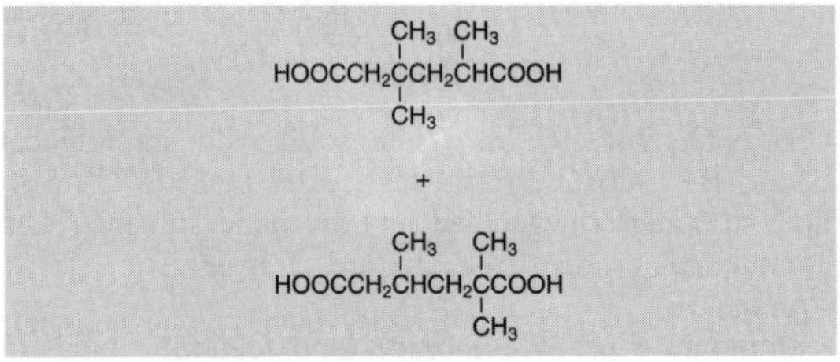

$C_9H_{16}O_4$. M: 188.23. Mixed product containing the
2,2,4- and the 2,4,4-trimethyl isomers.
Production:
• 3,3,5-trimethylcyclohexanone + nitric acid,
concentrated (oxidative cleavage)
Derivatives: diester oils; trimethylhexamethylenediamine; trimethyl valerolactone
Uses: polyester polyol comonomer

trimethylamine
TMA; [75-50-3]

$(CH_3)_3N$

$C_3H_9N_1$. M: 59.11. Liquified gas with an ammoniacal
odour. BP: 3°C. FP: -117°C. d: 0.64 kg/l (4°C). Miscible with water and oxygenated solvents. Soluble in

chlorinated and aromatic solvents. Also available commercially as 25% or 40% aqueous solutions.
Production:
• methanol + ammonia (amine formation; coproduced with methylamine/dimethylamine)
Derivatives:
Basic Red 18; benzyltrimethylammonium chloride; betaine; cetyltrimethylammonium bromide; cetyltrimethylammonium chloride; chlormequat chloride; 3-chloro-2-hydroxypropyltrimethylammonium chloride; choline chloride; 2,3-epoxypropyltrimethylammonium chloride; myristyltrimethylammonium bromide; polystyrene, crosslinked, trimethylbenzylammoniated; tetramethylammonium bromide; tetramethylammonium chloride; tetramethylammonium hydroxide

N,N,N′-trimethylaminoethylethanolamine

$$(CH_3)_2NCH_2CH_2NCH_2CH_2OH$$
with CH$_3$ on the N

$C_7H_{18}N_2O_1$. M: 146.23.
Production:
• aminoethylethanolamine (methylation)
Uses: polyurethane foam catalyst

trimethylammoniumethyl methacrylate chloride
2-methacryloxyethyltrimethylammonium chloride; 2-trimethylammoniumethylmethacrylic chloride; TMAEMC

$$CH_2=CCOCH_2CH_2N(CH_3)_3 \quad Cl^-$$
with O double bond and CH$_3$

$C_9H_{18}Cl_1N_1O_2$. M: 191.70.
Production:
• 2-dimethylaminoethyl methacrylate + methyl chloride (quaternisation)
Derivatives: acrylamide copolymers, cationic

2,4,6-trimethylaniline *See:* mesidine

1,2,4-trimethylbenzene *See:* pseudocumene

1,3,5-trimethylbenzene *See:* mesitylene

trimethylbenzene fraction

C_9H_{12}. M: 120.20. Aromatic hydrocarbon cut in the boiling range 162–176°C. d: 0.88 kg/l (15°C). Flash point: 44°C (ACC).
Production:
• C_{9+} aromatics (fractionation; coproduced with C_{10+} aromatics)
Derivatives: durene; high-boiling aromatic solvents; mesitylene; naphthenic solvents; pseudocumene; xylene, mixed

Uses: solvent (stoving/roller coating paint finishes, printing inks)

trimethylbenzylammonium chloride
See: benzyltrimethylammonium chloride

trimethylbenzylammonium hydroxide
See: benzyltrimethylammonium hydroxide

trimethyl borate
methyl borate; [121-43-7]

$$(CH_3O)_3B$$

$C_3H_9B_1O_3$. M: 103.91. Colourless liquid. BP: 67–68°C. Decomposed by water.
Production:
• methanol + boric acid (esterification)
Derivatives: sodium borohydride
Uses: gaseous brazing/welding flux

trimethylchlorosilane *See:* chlorotrimethylsilane

trimethylcyclohexanol
homomenthol; 3,3,5-trimethylcyclohexanol; [116-02-9]

$C_9H_{18}O_1$. M: 142.24. Available as mixed or *cis*-isomer grades.
Production:
• isophorone (hydrogenation)
Derivatives: cyclandelate; homomenthyl salicylate
Uses: dye levelling agent; solvent

3,3,5-trimethylcyclohexanone

$C_9H_{16}O_1$. M: 140.22.
Production:
• isophorone (hydrogenation)
Derivatives: 1,1-di-(*t*-butylperoxy)-3,3,5-trimethylcyclohexane; trimethyladipic acid
Uses: speciality solvent/levelling agent

trimethyl 3-cyclohexenecarboxaldehyde
isocyclocitral

$C_{10}H_{16}O_1$. M: 152.24.

Production:
- 2-methylpentadiene + crotonaldehyde (Diels-Alder cycloaddition)

Uses: fragrance ingredient

3,5,5-trimethyl-2-cyclohexen-1-one
See: isophorone

2,2,4-trimethyl-1,2-dihydroquinoline, polymeric
1,2-dihydro-2,2,4-trimethylquinoline; TDQP; TMDHQ; TMQ; Flectol H (Monsanto); [26780-96-1]

n = ~3. Mixed product. Amber beads. Softening point: 75°C. Insoluble in water. Miscible with oxygenated and aromatic solvents.

Production:
- aniline + acetone (condensation)

Uses: antioxidant/antiozonant (crosslinked polyethylene, rubber, latex, lubricants)

trimethylene glycol
propane-1,3-diol; 1,3-propylene glycol; [504-63-2]

$$HOCH_2CH_2CH_2OH$$

$C_3H_8O_2$. M: 76.09. Colourless liquid. BP: 213°C. d: 1.05 kg/l (20°C). Miscible with water and oxygenated solvents.

Production:
- water + acrolein (Michael addition/hydrogenation)

Derivatives:
1,3-propylene glycol di-(*p*-aminobenzoate)

Uses: polyurethane polyester polyol comonomer

N,N'-trimethyleneurea *See:* propylene urea

trimethylhexamethylenediamine
TMD

$$H_2NCH_2CH_2CHCH_2CCH_2NH_2 \quad + \quad H_2NCH_2CH_2CCH_2CHCH_2NH_2$$

$C_9H_{22}N_2$. M: 158.29.

Production:
- trimethyladipic acid + ammonia (nitrile formation/ nitrile reduction)

Derivatives:
polyamide 6-(3)T; trimethylhexamethylene diisocyanate

Uses: epoxy resin curing agent

trimethylhexamethylene diisocyanate
TMDI.
$C_{11}H_{18}N_2O_2$. M: 210.27.

$$OCNCH_2CH_2CHCH_2CCH_2NCO \quad + \quad OCNCH_2CH_2CCH_2CHCH_2NCO$$

Production:
- trimethylhexamethylenediamine + phosgene (phosgenation)

Uses: isocyanate component (polyurethane coatings)

3,5,5-trimethylhexanoic acid *See:* isononanoic acid

N,N,N-trimethyl-2-hydroxypropylammonium 2-ethyl-hexanoate

$$(CH_3)_3^+NCH_2CHOH \quad CH_3(CH_2)_3CHCOO^-$$

$C_{14}H_{31}N_1O_3$. M: 261.41.

Production:
- dimethylisopropanolamine + methyl chloride + 2-ethylhexanoic acid (quaternisation/salt formation)

ses: polyurethane foam catalyst

trimethylmyristylammonium bromide
See: myristyltrimethylammonium bromide

trimethylol acetylene urea
See: trimethylolglycoluril

trimethylolethane
ethylidynetrimethanol; 2-hydroxymethyl-2-methyl-1,3-propanediol; TME; [77-85-0]

$$CH_3C(CH_2OH)_3$$

$C_5H_{12}O_3$. M: 120.15. Colourless crystalline solid. Solubility in water: 1.4 kg/l water (25°C). Soluble in oxygenated solvents.

Production:
- propionaldehyde + formaldehyde (aldol condensation/Cannizarro reaction)

Derivatives:
alkyd resins, water-soluble

Uses: short oil/water-soluble alkyd resin comonomer

trimethylolglycoluril
trimethylol acetylene urea; TMDAU

$C_7H_{12}N_4O_5$. M: 232.20.

Production:
- glycoluril + formaldehyde (carbonyl condensation)

Uses:
amino resin crosslinking agent (textile finishes)

trimethylolpropane
TMP; [77-99-6]

CH₃CH₂C(CH₂OH)₃

$C_6H_{14}O_3$. M: 134.18. White solid. MP: 59°C. BP: 295°C. Soluble in water and oxygenated solvents.
Production:
• *n*-butyraldehyde + formaldehyde (aldol condensation/Cannizzaro reaction)
Derivatives: alkyd resins, water-soluble; hexamethylene diisocyanate-trimethylolpropane adduct; polyester resins, carboxylated; polyester resins, hydroxylated; polyether polyols, flexible; polyether polyols, flexible, amine-terminated; polyether polyols, rigid; polyurethane, cast elastomers; toluene diisocyanate-trimethylolpropane adduct; trimethylolpropane diallyl ether; trimethylolpropane triacrylate; trimethylolpropane tri-(caprylate/caprate); trimethylolpropane triheptanoate; trimethylolpropane trimethacrylate; trimethylolpropane trioleate; trimethylolpropane tripelargonate
Uses: alkyd resin comonomer; polyurethane crosslinking agent; reactive diluent (radiation-cured inks, lacquers); polyvinyl chloride heat costabilisers

trimethylolpropane diallyl ether
1,1-dialloxypropanol

CH₂OH
CH₃CH₂C(CH₂OCH₂CH=CH₂)₂

$C_{12}H_{22}O_3$. M: 214.31.
Production:
• trimethylolpropane + allyl chloride (ether formation)
Derivatives: unsaturated polyester resins, coating grades
Uses: unsaturated polyester/vinyl resin comonomer

trimethylolpropane triacrylate
TMPTA

CH₃CH₂C(CH₂OCCH=CH₂)₃

$C_{15}H_{20}O_6$. M: 296.31.
Production:
• trimethylolpropane + acrylic acid (esterification)
Derivatives:
trimethylolpropane tri-(3-aziridinopropionate)
Uses: reactive diluent (radiation-cured inks, lacquers)

trimethylolpropane tri-(3-aziridinopropionate)

CH₃CH₂C[CH₂OCCH₂CH₂N◁]₃

$C_{21}H_{35}N_3O_6$. M: 425.52.
Production:
• trimethylolpropane triacrylate + ethyleneimine (Michael addition)
Uses: crosslinking agent

trimethylolpropane tri-(caprylate/caprate)

CH₃CH₂C[CH₂OC(CH₂)ₙCH₃]₃

n = 6, 8.
Production:
• trimethylolpropane + C_8-C_{10} fatty acids (esterification)
Uses:
lubricant (textile spin finishes, metalworking fluids)

trimethylolpropane triheptanoate

CH₃CH₂C[CH₂OC(CH₂)₅CH₃]₃

$C_{27}H_{50}O_6$. M: 470.69.
Production:
• trimethylolpropane + *n*-heptanoic acid (esterification)
Uses: synthetic lubricant base oils

trimethylolpropane trimethacrylate
TMPTMA; TRIM; [3290-92-4]

CH₃CH₂C[CH₂OCC=CH₂]₃
CH₃

$C_{18}H_{26}O_6$. M: 338.40. Colourless liquid with a slight ether-like odour. d: 1.06 kg/l (25°C). Insoluble in water. Commercial products contain hydroquinone monomethyl ether or similar polymerisation inhibitors.
Production:
• trimethylolpropane + methyl methacrylate (transesterification)
Uses: polymerisable/softened polyvinyl chloride plastisol comonomer; high thermal stability peroxide crosslinking coactivator; reactive diluent (radiation-cured inks, lacquers)

trimethylolpropane trioleate

CH₃CH₂C[CH₂OC(CH₂)₇CH=CH(CH₂)₇CH₃]₃

$C_{60}H_{110}O_6$. M: 927.53. Liquid. Cloud point: -20°C. Saponification value: 183–190 mg KOH/g. Insoluble in water.
Production:
• trimethylolpropane + oleic acid (esterification)
Uses: lubricity additive (metalworking fluids)

trimethylolpropane tripelargonate

CH₃CH₂C[CH₂OC(CH₂)₇CH₃]₃

$C_{33}H_{62}O_6$. M: 554.85. Oil. Pour point: -50°C. Viscosity: 4.5 mm²/s (100°C). Viscosity index: 140. Flash point: 250°C (COC).

Production:
• trimethylolpropane + pelargonic acid (esterification)
Uses:
synthetic lubricant base oils

trimethyl orthoacetate
[1445-45-0]

CH₃C(OCH₃)₃

$C_5H_{12}O_3$. M: 120.15.
Production:
• acetonitrile + methanol (reaction)
• 1,1,1-trichloroethane + sodium methoxide (ether formation)
Derivatives:
bromobutide; methyl 3,3-dimethyl-4-pentenoate

trimethyl orthoformate
[149-73-5]

HC(OCH₃)₃

$C_4H_{10}O_3$. M: 106.12.
Production:
• hydrogen cyanide + methanol (reaction)
• chloroform + sodium methoxide (ether formation)
Derivatives:
1,1,3,3-tetramethoxypropane

2,2,4-trimethyl-1,3-pentanediol
trimethylpentanediol; Texanol; TMPD (Eastman Chemical); [144-19-4]

CH₂OH
(CH₃)₂CHCHC(CH₃)₂
OH

$C_8H_{18}O_2$. M: 146.23. White solid. MP: 46–55°C. BP: 215–235°C. d: 0.93 kg/l (15°C). Slightly soluble in water.
Production:
• isobutyraldehyde (carbonyl condensation/ hydrogenation)
Derivatives:
2,2,4-trimethyl-1,3-pentanediol benzyl phthalate
Uses: coalescing solvent (water-based paints); unsaturated, high-solids polyester resin comonomer (surface coatings)

2,2,4-trimethyl-1,3-pentanediol benzyl phthalate
Santicizer 278 (Monsanto)

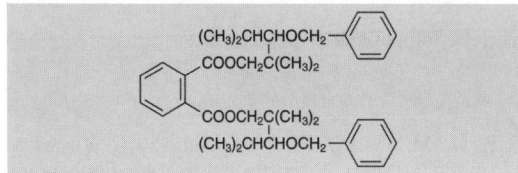

$C_{38}H_{50}O_6$. M: 602.81.

Production:
• 2,2,4-trimethyl-1,3-pentanediol + benzyl chloride + phthalic anhydride (esterification/esterification)
Uses: speciality plasticiser

2,2,4-trimethyl-1,3-pentanediol diisobutyrate
Texanol isobutyrate; TXIB (Eastman Chemical); [6846-50-0]

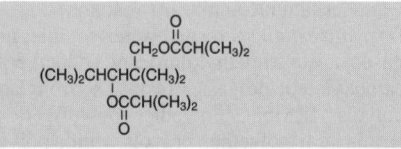

$C_{16}H_{30}O_4$. M: 286.42. Colourless liquid. FP: -70°C. BP: 280°C. d: 0.95 kg/l (20°C).
Production:
• 2,2,4-trimethyl-1,3-pentanediol monoisobutyrate + isobutyric acid (esterification)
Uses:
high-solvation plasticiser (polyvinyl chloride plastisols)

2,2,4-trimethyl-1,3-pentanediol isobutyrate benzoate
Nuoplaz 1046 (Hüls)

CH₂OC
(CH₃)₂CHCHC(CH₃)₂
OCCH(CH₃)₂
O

$C_{19}H_{28}O_4$. M: 320.43.
Production:
• 2,2,4-trimethyl-1,3-pentanediol monoisobutyrate + benzoic acid (esterification)
Uses:
high-solvation plasticiser (polyvinyl chloride plastisols)

2,2,4-trimethyl-1,3-pentanediol monoisobutyrate
Texanol monoisobutyrate (Eastman Chemical)

CH₃   O
(CH₃)₂CHCHCH₂OCCH(CH₃)₂
HO CH₃

$C_{12}H_{24}O_3$. M: 216.32.
Production:
• isobutyraldehyde (carbonyl condensation/Tishchenko reaction)
Derivatives: 2,2,4-trimethyl-1,3-pentanediol diisobutyrate; 2,2,4-trimethyl-1,3-pentanediol isobutyrate benzoate

2,4,4-trimethylpentene
diisobutylene; DIB

CH₃
(CH₃)₃CCH₂C=CH₂

C_8H_{16}. M: 112.22. Mixed product containing 80% 2,4, 4-trimethyl-1-pentene and 20% 2,4,4-trimethyl-2-pent-

ene. Colourless liquid with a pungent odour. BR: 100–105°C. d: 0.72 kg/l (15°C). See also octene, branched.
Production:
- raffinate I (acid-catalysed alkylation; coproduced with raffinate II/dodecene, branched)

Derivatives:
diphenylamine, octylated; isononanoic acid; isooctane; isoparaffin solvents; neohexene; nonanol; *N-t*-octylacrylamide; *t*-octylamine; *p-t*-octylphenol

2,3,5-trimethylphenol
isopseudocumenol; [697-82-5]

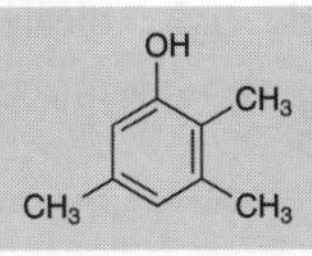

$C_9H_{12}O_1$. M: 136.20. Crystalline solid. MP: 92–95°C. Insoluble in water. Soluble in oxygenated solvents.
Production:
- 3,5-xylenol + formaldehyde (chloromethylation/ reduction)

Derivatives:
etretinate; α-tocopherol

trimethylphenylammonium hydroxide
phenyltrimethylammonium hydroxide; [1899-02-1]

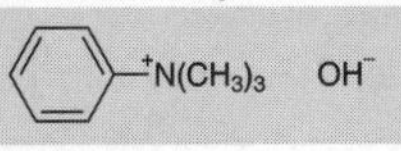

$C_9H_{15}N_1O_1$. M: 153.23.
Production:
- aniline + dimethyl sulphate + calcium hydroxide (methylation/salt formation)

Uses: phase-transfer catalyst; methylation reagent

trimethyl phosphite
O,O,O-trimethyl phosphite; TMPI; [121-45-9]

$(CH_3O)_3P$

$C_3H_9O_3P_1$. M: 124.07. Colourless liquid. BP: 110–112°C. d: 1.05 kg/l (20°C). Hydrolysed by hot water. Soluble in oxygenated solvents.
Production:
- methanol + phosphorus trichloride (dehydrochlorination)

Derivatives: dichlorvos; dicrotophos; dimethyl methylphosphonate; heptenophos; mevinphos; monocrotophos; phosphamidon; tetrachlorvinphos

2,6,10-trimethylundecenal
[141-13-9]

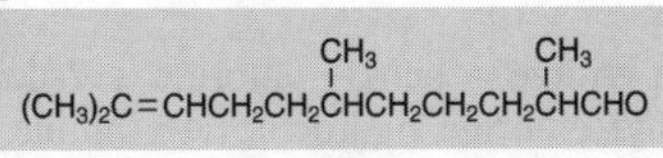

$(CH_3)_2C=CHCH_2CH_2CHCH_2CH_2CH_2CHCHO$

$C_{14}H_{26}O_1$. M: 210.36. Pale yellow liquid with a strong, floral odour. Mixed product consisting mainly of components with a single double-bond in the 3-, 5- or 9-positions.
Production:
- pseudoionone + ethyl chloroacetate (hydrogenation/ Darzens reaction)

Uses: fragrance ingredient

trimethyl valerolactone
Trivalon (Henkel)

$C_8H_{14}O_2$. M: 142.20.
Production:
- trimethyladipic acid (Dieckmann condensation/ decarboxylation/Baeyer-Villiger oxidation)

Uses: fragrance ingredient

trimipramine
[739-71-9]

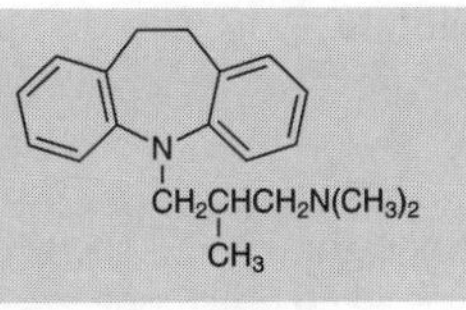

$C_{20}H_{26}N_2$. M: 294.44.
Production:
- iminodibenzyl + 3-dimethylamino-2-methylpropyl chloride hydrochloride (amine formation)

Uses: antidepressant drug

1,3,5-trinitrobenzene
benzite; TNB; [99-35-4]

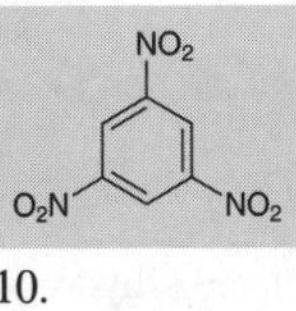

$C_6H_3N_3O_6$. M: 213.10.
Production:
- benzene + nitric acid, concentrated (nitration)

Derivatives:
phloroglucinol
Uses: explosives

2,4,7-trinitrofluorenone
[129-79-3]

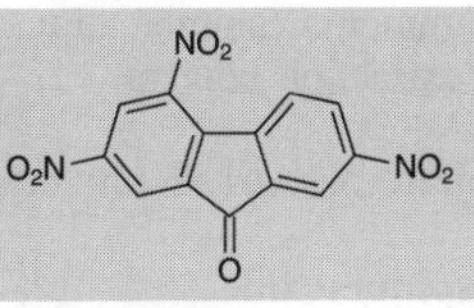

$C_{13}H_5N_3O_7$. M: 315.19.

Production:
• fluorenone (nitration)
Uses: electron acceptor (photoconductive plastics)

2,4,6-trinitrophenol *See:* picric acid

2,4,6-trinitrotoluene
TNT; [118-96-7]

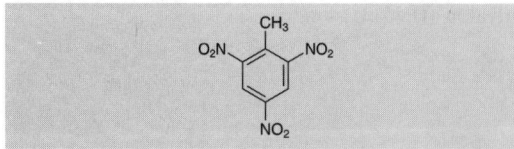

$C_7H_5N_3O_6$. M: 227.13. Yellow needles. MP: 80–82°C. d: 1.65 kg/l (20°C). Insoluble in water. Soluble in acetone and aromatic solvents.
Production:
• toluene (nitration)
Derivatives: hexanitrostilbene
Uses: military explosive

trinonyl trimellitate

$C_{36}H_{60}O_6$. M: 588.87.
Production:
• isononanol/nonanol + trimellitic anhydride (esterification)
Uses: polyvinyl chloride plasticiser

tri-*n*-octylaluminium
[1070-00-4]

$[(CH_2)_7CH_3]_3Al$

$C_{24}H_{51}Al_1$. M: 366.65.
Production:
• aluminium + 1-octene + hydrogen (reaction)
Derivatives: tetra-*n*-octyltin
Uses: polyolefin production catalyst

tri-*n*-octylamine

$[CH_3(CH_2)_7]_3N$

$C_{24}H_{51}N_1$. M: 353.68.
Production:
• *n*-octanol + ammonia (ammoniation)
Uses: mineral extraction reagent

trioctyl phosphate *See:* tri-(2-ethylhexyl) phosphate

tri-*n*-octylphosphine oxide
tri-*n*-octylphosphinic oxide; TOPO; [78-50-2]

$C_{24}H_{51}O_1P_1$. M: 386.64. Solid. MP: 52–55°C. Soluble in hydrocarbons. Insoluble in water.

$[CH_3(CH_2)_7]_3P=O$

Production:
• phosphine + 1-octene + hydrogen peroxide (addition/oxidation)
Uses: extraction agent (uranium ore)

trioctyl trimellitate *See:* tri-(2-ethylhexyl) trimellitate

triolein
glycerol trioleate; glyceryl trioleate; [122-32-7]

$$CH_3(CH_2)_7CH=CH(CH_2)_7COOCH_2$$
$$CH_3(CH_2)_7CH=CH(CH_2)_7COOCH$$
$$CH_3(CH_2)_7CH=CH(CH_2)_7COOCH_2$$

$C_{57}H_{104}O_6$. M: 885.45. Yellow liquid. d: 0.91 kg/l. Cloud point: -10°C. Saponification value: 188–195 mg KOH/g. HLB: 0.8. Insoluble in water. Soluble in chlorinated solvents.
Production:
• oleic acid + glycerol (esterification)
Uses: food emulsifier; lubricity additive (metalworking fluids, textile auxiliaries); solvent (carbon paper, printer ink dyes)

trioxane
metaformaldehyde; 1,3,5-trioxane; [110-88-3]

$C_3H_6O_3$. M: 90.08. Solid. MP: 61–62°C. BP: 115°C. d: 1.17 kg/l (65°C). Soluble in water and oxygenated solvents.
Production:
• formaldehyde (acid-catalysed trimerisation)
Derivatives: polyacetal, copolymers
Uses: stabiliser (chlorinated solvents)

tripelennamine
[91-81-6]; [6138-56-3] (citrate); [154-69-8] (hydrochloride)

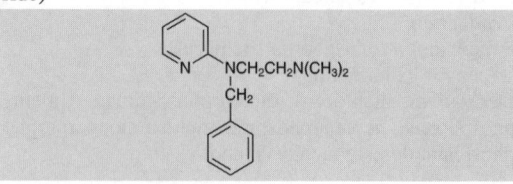

$C_{16}H_{21}N_3$. M: 255.37. Available commercially as the free base, hydrochloride or citrate.
Production:
• 2-aminopyridine + benzyl chloride + 2-dimethylaminoethyl chloride hydrochloride (amine formation/amine formation)
Uses: antihistamine drug

tripentaerythritol

$C_{15}H_{32}O_{10}$. M: 372.41.
Production:
• acetaldehyde + formaldehyde (aldol condensation/
Cannizzaro reaction; byproduct of pentaerythritol
production)
Uses: raw material (synthetic lubricants); polyvinyl
chloride heat costabilisers

tri-*n*-pentylamine *See:* triamylamine

triphenylmethane triisocyanate
p,p′,p″-triisocyanatotriphenylmethane; triphenylmethane-
p,p′,p″-triyl triisocyanate; Desmodur R (Bayer);

$C_{22}H_{13}N_3O_3$. M: 367.36.
Production:
• aniline + phosgene (condensation/phosgenation)
Uses: diene rubber crosslinking agent; polyurethane
boot/shoe adhesives

triphenyl phosphate
TPP; [115-86-6]

$C_{18}H_{15}O_4P_1$. M: 326.29. White, crystalline solid. BP:
247–250°C (1.3 kPa). d: 1.19 kg/l (20°C). Viscosity:
10 mPa.s (20°C). Insoluble in water.
Production:
• phenol + phosphorus oxychloride
(dehydrochlorination)
Uses:
extreme-pressure additive (lubricants); fire-resistant cellulose ester plasticiser

triphenylphosphine
[603-35-0]

$C_{18}H_{15}P_1$. M: 262.29. Crystalline solid. MP: 79–81°C.
d: 1.19 kg/l (25°C). Insoluble in water. Soluble in oxygenated, chlorinated and aromatic solvents.

Production:
• chlorobenzene + phosphorus trichloride +
magnesium (dechlorination)
Uses:
hydroformylation/polymerisation catalyst intermediate

triphenyl phosphite
TPP; [101-02-0]

$C_{18}H_{15}O_3P_1$. M: 310.29.
Production:
• phenol + phosphorus trichloride
(dehydrochlorination)
Uses: polyvinyl chloride heat costabilisers

triphenyl phosphorothionate
TPPT; [597-82-0]

$C_{18}H_{15}O_3P_1S_1$. M: 342.35.
Production:
• phenol + thiophosphoryl chloride
(dehydrochlorination)
Uses: extreme-pressure additive (lubricants)

triphenyltin acetate *See:* fentin acetate

triphenyltin fluoride *See:* fentin fluoride

triphenyltin hydroxide *See:* fentin hydroxide

triple salt acid *See:* phosphotungstomolybdic acid;
phosphomolybdic acid; phosphotungstic acid

triprolidine
[486-12-4]; [550-70-9] (hydrochloride)

$C_{19}H_{22}N_2$. M: 278.40. Available commercially as the
free base or hydrochloride.
Production:
• *p*-methylacetophenone + paraformaldehyde +
pyrrolidine + 2-bromopyridine (Mannich reaction/
Grignard reagent formation/Grignard reaction/
dehydration)
Uses: antihistamine drug

tripropylene glycol
TPG; [13987-01-4]

$$CH_3 \quad CH_3 \quad CH_3$$
$$HOCHCH_2OCHCH_2OCHCH_2OH$$

$C_9H_{20}O_4$. M: 192.26. Colourless liquid. BP: 268°C. d: 1.02 kg/l (20°C). Flash point: 140°C (COC). Miscible with water and oxygenated solvents.
Production:
• propylene oxide (hydration; coproduced with dipropylene glycol/propylene glycol)
Derivatives: tripropylene glycol diacrylate
Uses: brake/hydraulic fluid component; alkyd/unsaturated polyester resin comonomer; polyurethane chain-extender; thickening agent (cosmetics)

tripropylene glycol diacrylate
TPGDA

$$CH_3 \quad CH_3 \quad CH_3$$
$$CH_2=CHCOCH_2CHOCH_2CHOCH_2CHOCCH=CH_2$$
$$O \qquad\qquad\qquad\qquad O$$

$C_{15}H_{24}O_6$. M: 300.34.
Production:
• tripropylene glycol + acrylic acid (esterification)
Uses: reactive diluent (radiation-cured inks, lacquers)

tripropylene glycol monomethyl ether
TPM; Dowfroth 200 (Dow Chemical); [10213-77-1]

$$CH_3 \quad CH_3 \quad CH_3$$
$$CH_3OCHCH_2OCHCH_2OCHCH_2OH$$

$C_{10}H_{22}O_4$. M: 206.29. Colourless liquid. BP: 242°C. Pour point: -78°C. d: 0.96 kg/l (25°C). Miscible with water and most organic solvents.
Production:
• methanol + propylene oxide (epoxidation)
Uses: flotation frothing agent; hydraulic fluid blending component

1,3,5-tris(4-t-butyl-3-hydroxy-2,6-dimethylbenzyl)isocyanurate
1,3,5-tris(4-t-butyl-3-hydroxy-2,6-dimethylbenzyl)-1,3,5-triazine-2,4,6-trione; Cyanox 1790 (American Cyanamid); [40601-76-1]

$C_{42}H_{57}N_3O_6$. M: 699.93.

Production:
• cyanuric acid + formaldehyde + 6-t-butyl-2,4-dimethylphenol (Mannich reaction)
Uses: antioxidant (plastics)

1,1,3-tris(5-t-butyl-4-hydroxy-2-methylphenyl)butane
tri-(butylcresyl)butane (CTFA); 1,1,3-tris(2-methyl-4-hydroxy-5-t-butylphenyl)butane; Topanol CA (ICI); [1843-03-4]

$C_{37}H_{52}O_3$. M: 544.83.
Production:
• 6-t-butyl-m-cresol + crotonaldehyde (carbonyl condensation)
Uses: antioxidant (plastics, rubber, adhesives)

tris(2-chloroethyl) phosphate
Disflamoll TCA (Bayer); Fyrol CEF (Akzo); Genomoll P (Hoechst); TCEP (Courtaulds); [115-96-8]

$$(ClCH_2CH_2O)_3P=O$$

$C_6H_{12}Cl_3O_4P_1$. M: 285.50. Colourless liquid. d: 1.4 kg/l. Insoluble in benzene and water. Soluble in most organic solvents.
Production:
• phosphorus oxychloride + ethylene oxide (epoxidation)
Uses: fire-resistant cellulose ester plasticiser; fire-retardant additive (polyurethane foam)

tris(2-chloroethyl) phosphite
[140-08-9]

$$(ClCH_2CH_2O)_3P$$

$C_6H_{12}Cl_3O_3P_1$. M: 269.50. Colourless, high-boiling liquid. d: 1.35 kg/l (20°C). Hydrolysed by water. Miscible with most organic solvents.
Production:
• phosphorus trichloride + ethylene oxide (epoxidation)
Derivatives:
bis(2-chloroethyl)vinyl phosphonate; ethephon

tris(1-chloro-2-propyl) phosphate
tris(monochloroisopropyl) phosphate; Amgard TMCP (Albright and Wilson); Fyrol PCF (Akzo); TCPP (Courtaulds); [13674-84-5]
$C_9H_{18}Cl_3O_4P_1$. M: 327.57. Colourless liquid with a mild odour. Gradually decomposes when heated over 200°C.

Does not boil. d: 1.29 kg/l (25°C). Insoluble in water. Soluble in most organic solvents.

$$\left[ClCH_2\overset{\underset{\displaystyle CH_3}{\mid}}{C}HO\right]_3 P=O$$

Production:
- phosphorus oxychloride + propylene oxide (epoxidation)

Uses: fire-retardant additive (polyurethane, unsaturated polyester, liquid phenolic resin)

1,3,5-tris(3,5-di-*t*-butyl-4-hydroxybenzyl)isocyanurate

Irganox 3114 (Ciba-Geigy); Vanox GT (Vanderbilt Chemical)

$C_{48}H_{69}N_3O_6$. M: 784.09.
Production:
- cyanuric acid + 2,6-di-*t*-butylphenol + formaldehyde (Mannich reaction)

Uses: antioxidant (plastics)

2,4,6-tris(3,5-di-*t*-butyl-4-hydroxybenzyl)mesitylene

1,3,5-trimethyl-2,4,6-tris(3,5-*t*-butyl-4-hydroxybenzyl)-benzene; Ethanox 330 (Ethyl); Irganox 1330 (Ciba-Geigy); [1709-70-2]

$C_{54}H_{78}O_3$. M: 775.21.
Production:
- mesitylene + 2,6-di-*t*-butylphenol + formaldehyde (Mannich reaction)

Uses:
antioxidant (plastics, rubber)

1,3,5-tris[3-(3,5-di-*t*-butyl-4-hydroxyphenyl)propan-oxyethyl] isocyanurate

Vanox SKT (Vanderbilt Chemical)
$C_{60}H_{87}N_3O_{12}$. M: 1042.37.

Production:
- N,N′,N″-tris(2-hydroxyethyl)hexahydrotriazine + methyl 3,5-di-*t*-butyl-4-hydroxyphenylpropionate (transesterification)

Uses:
antioxidant (plastics)

tris(2,4-di-*t*-butylphenyl) phosphite

Naugard 524 (Uniroyal Chemical); [31570-04-4]

$C_{42}H_{63}O_3P_1$. M: 646.93.
Production:
- 2,4-di-*t*-butylphenol + phosphorus trichloride (dehydrochlorination)

Uses:
antioxidant (plastics)

tris(1,3-dichloro-2-propyl) phosphate

tris(dichloropropyl) phosphate; Amgard TDCP (Albright and Wilson); Fyrol FR-2 (Akzo); [13674-87-8]

$$\left[(ClCH_2)_2CHO\right]_3 P=O$$

$C_9H_{15}Cl_6O_4P_1$. M: 430.91. Clear liquid with a mild odour. Decomposes gradually when heated above 200°C. Does not boil. d: 1.48 kg/l (25°C). Insoluble in water. Soluble in most organic solvents.
Production:
- epichlorohydrin + phosphorus oxychloride (epoxidation)

Uses: fire-retardant additive (polyurethane, unsaturated polyester, liquid phenolic resin)

2,4,6-tris(dimethylaminomethyl)phenol

TDMAMP; [90-72-2]

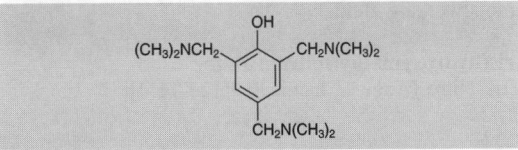

$C_{15}H_{27}N_3O_1$. M: 265.40. Available as the free base or as the 2-ethylhexanoic acid salt.
Production:
- dimethylamine + formaldehyde + phenol (Mannich reaction)

Uses:
polyurethane foam catalyst; epoxy resin curing agent

N,N′,N″-tris(dimethylaminopropyl)hexahydro-1,3,5-triazine

$C_{18}H_{42}N_6$. M: 342.58.
Production:
• 3-dimethylaminopropylamine + formaldehyde
  (carbonyl condensation)
Uses: polyurethane foam catalyst

N,N′,N″-tris(2-hydroxyethyl)hexahydrotriazine
hexahydro-1,3,5-tris(2-hydroxyethyl)-*sym*-triazine; tris-(2-hydroxyethyl)isocyanurate

$C_9H_{21}N_3O_3$. M: 219.29.
Production:
• monoethanolamine + formaldehyde (carbonyl
  condensation)
Derivatives: 1,3,5-tris[3-(3,5-di-*t*-butyl-4-hydroxyphenyl)propanoxyethyl] isocyanurate
Uses: biocide (metalworking fluids, paper coatings, adhesives, paints); comonomer (high temperature plastics)

tris(hydroxymethyl)aminomethane
2-amino-2-(hydroxymethyl)-1,3-propanediol; tromethamine (CTFA); THAM; Tris Amino (Angus); [77-86-1]

$C_4H_{11}N_1O_3$. M: 121.14. Crystalline solid. MP: 171–172°C. Soluble in water forming alkaline solutions. Soluble in alcohol.
Production:
• tris(hydroxymethyl)nitromethane (nitro reduction)
Derivatives: di-(hydroxymethyl) oleyloxazoline; 5-methylol 1-aza-3,7-dioxabicyclo[3,3,0]octane
Uses: emulsifier (creams, lotions, oils, waxes); amino/phenolic resin formaldehyde scavenger; amine soaps (metalworking fluids)

tris(hydroxymethyl)nitromethane
Tris Nitro (Angus Chemical); [126-11-4]

$C_4H_9N_1O_5$. M: 151.11. Sold as solid or as a 50% solution in water. Soluble in water. Insoluble in hydrocarbons.
Production:
• nitromethane + formaldehyde (hydroxymethylation)
Derivatives: tris(hydroxymethyl)aminomethane
Uses: biocide (water, metalworking fluids, latices)

tris(hydroxyphenyl)methane triglycidyl ether
trisepoxy-novolac resins; TEN; Tactix 742 (Dow Chemical)

$C_{28}H_{28}O_6$. M: 460.52.
Production:
• phenol + formaldehyde + epichlorohydrin
  (condensation/ether formation)
Uses: epoxy resins (composite aircraft bodies)

tris(*p*-isocyanatophenyl) thiophosphate
tris(4-isocyanatophenyl) thiophosphate; Desmodur RF (Bayer)

$C_{21}H_{12}N_3O_6P_1S_1$. M: 465.37.
Production:
• *p*-nitrophenol + thiophosphoryl chloride + phosgene
  (dehydrochlorination/nitro reduction/phosgenation)
Uses:
diene rubber crosslinking agent; adhesives primer

tris(isopropylphenyl) phosphate
Reofos (FMC)

$C_{27}H_{33}O_4P_1$. M: 452.53. Mixed isomer product.
Production:
• isopropylphenol + phosphorus oxychloride
  (dehydrochlorination)
Uses: fire-resistant hydraulic fluid; fire-resistant polyvinyl chloride plasticiser

tris(β-methoxyethoxy)vinylsilane
vinyl tris(β-methoxyethoxy)silane; [1067-53-4]

$C_{11}H_{24}O_6Si_1$. M: 280.39.

Production:
• vinyltrichlorosilane + ethylene glycol monomethyl ether (dehydrochlorination)
Uses: plastics coupling agent

tris(nonylphenyl) phosphite
TNPP

$C_{45}H_{69}O_3P_1$. M: 689.01. Colourless, involatile liquid. Pour point: -7°C. d: 0.98 kg/l. Insoluble in water. Soluble in most organic solvents.
Production:
• nonylphenol + phosphorus trichloride (dehydrochlorination)
Uses:
antioxidant (plastics, rubber); polyvinyl chloride heat costabilisers

trisodium hydroxyethylethylenediaminetriacetate
See: hydroxyethylethylenediaminetriacetic acid, trisodium salt

trisodium nitrilotriacetate
sodium nitrilotriacetate; trisodium NTA; [5064-31-3]

$$N(CH_2COO^- \ Na^+)_3$$

$C_6H_6N_1Na_3O_6$. M: 257.09. Available commercially as pure solid or as a solution in water.
Production:
• sodium hydroxide + nitrilotriacetic acid (salt formation)
Uses: sequestrant (household, industrial detergents)

trisodium phosphate
sodium phosphate, tribasic; trisodium orthophosphate; TSP; E339 (EC); [7601-54-9]

$$Na_3PO_4$$

$Na_3O_4P_1$. M: 163.94. White, crystalline powder available in technical or food grades. Soluble in water. Insoluble in alcohol.
Production:
• sodium hydroxide/sodium carbonate + phosphoric acid, pure (salt formation)
• sodium hydroxide + monazite (salt formation/separation; byproduct of thorium dioxide/rare earth oxide, hydrate production)
Derivatives:
trisodium phosphate, chlorinated; zinc phosphate
Uses:
dispersant (easy-cooking cereals); emulsifier (cheese); abrasive metal cleaner ingredient; builder (industrial cleaning formulations); metal phosphatising reagent; softening/conditioning agent (boiler water treatment)

trisodium phosphate, chlorinated
Production:
• trisodium phosphate + sodium hypochlorite (addition)
Uses: bleaching/sanitising agent (household cleaners)

tristearin
glyceryl tristearate; [555-43-1]

$$CH_2OOC(CH_2)_{16}CH_3$$
$$CHOOC(CH_2)_{16}CH_3$$
$$CH_2OOC(CH_2)_{16}CH_3$$

$C_{57}H_{110}O_6$. M: 891.50. White powder or flakes. MP: 55°C. HLB: 1. Insoluble in water. Soluble in chlorinated and aromatic solvents.
Production:
• glycerol + stearic acid (esterification)
Uses: textile processing lubricant; plastics mould release agent; polishing/grinding pastes

tris(triethylene glycol monomethyl ether)borate
methyl triglycol borate

$$(CH_3OCH_2CH_2OCH_2CH_2OCH_2CH_2O)_3B$$

$C_{21}H_{45}B_1O_{12}$. M: 500.39.
Production:
• triethylene glycol monomethyl ether + boric acid (dehydration)
Uses: brake fluid component

trityl chloride
chlorotriphenylmethane; triphenylmethyl chloride; [76-83-5]

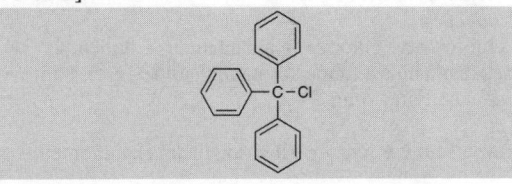

$C_{19}H_{15}Cl_1$. M: 278.78. Hygroscopic solid. MP: 110–114°C. BP: 310°C. Insoluble in water. Soluble in oxygenated, chlorinated and aromatic solvents.
Production:
• benzene + carbon tetrachloride (Friedel-Crafts alkylation)
Uses:
amino/mercapto/alcohol group protection reagent

trixylyl phosphate
trixylenyl phosphate

$C_{24}H_{27}O_4P_1$. M: 410.45. Liquid. Pour point: -60°C. d: 1.14 kg/l. Nonflammable. Insoluble in water.

Production:

- xylenol, mixed + phosphorus oxychloride (dehydrochlorination)

Uses: non-flammable hydraulic fluid (steel works, furnaces, mines); polyvinyl chloride plasticiser

troclosene potassium

See: potassium dichloroisocyanurate

trofosfamide
[22089-22-1]

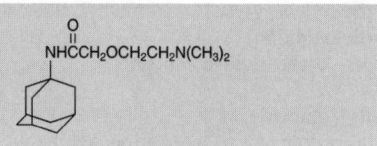

$C_9H_{18}Cl_3N_2O_2P_1$. M: 323.58.
Production:

- diethanolamine + phosphorus oxychloride + 3-(2-chloroethyl)aminopropanol hydrochloride (alcohol chlorination/dehydrochlorination)

Uses:
antineoplastic drug

tromantadine
[53783-83-8]

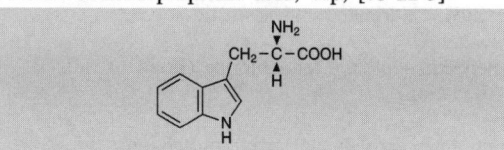

$C_{16}H_{28}N_2O_2$. M: 280.41.
Production:

- chloroacetyl chloride + amantadine + dimethyl-ethanolamine (amide formation/amine formation)

Uses: antiviral drug

tromethamine *See:* tris(hydroxymethyl)aminomethane

L-tryptophan
L-indole-α-aminopropionic acid; Trp; [73-22-3]

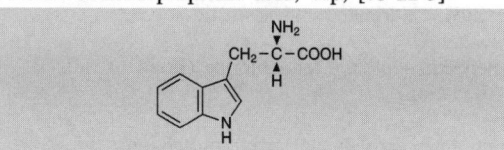

$C_{11}H_{12}N_2O_2$. M: 204.23. Available commercially as the naturally-occurring L(+)-enantiomer. White, crystalline solid. Decomposes on heating above 290°C. Soluble in water.
Production:

- indole + L-serine (enzymatic coupling)
- diethyl 2-(acetamido)malonate + phenylhydrazine + acrolein (Warner-Moe synthesis/enzymatic hydrolysis)

Derivatives: pentagastrin
Uses: infusion solutions/diagnostic aids; raw material (peptide drugs)

TSC *See:* thiosemicarbazide

TSP *See:* calcium triple superphosphate; trisodium phosphate

TSPP *See:* tetrasodium pyrophosphate

TTAB *See:* myristyltrimethylammonium bromide

tung oil

Drying oil extracted from the nuts of cultivated *Aleurites fordii* or *A. montan* shrubs grown in southern USA, Argentina, Africa and China. The oil has a high elaeostearic acid ($C_{18:3}$, conjugated) acid content. d: 9.4 kg/l. Saponification value: 189–197 mg KOH/g. Iodine value: 155–170 g I_2/100 g. The oil is heat-bodied for most applications.
Derivatives: cyclopentadienised oils; maleinised oils; tung oil, heat-bodied
Uses:
drying oil (printing inks); tung oil-phenolic resin (spar varnishes, aluminium decorative/structural/maintenance paints)

tung oil, heat-bodied

Tung oil is mixed with linseed oil and heat-bodied to produce enamel oils which are used in marine paints.
Production:

- tung oil (thermal polymerisation)

Uses: tung oil-coumarone resins (plaster/cement primer paints, aluminium decorative/structural paints)

tungsten
wolfram; [7440-33-7]

W

W_1. M: 183.85. Hard, grey metal. d: 19.3 kg/l. MP: 3,400°C. High electrical conductivity. Shaped by sintering techniques.
Production:

- tungsten trioxide/ammonium paratungstate + hydrogen (hydrogenation)

Derivatives:
tungsten carbide
Uses: cobalt-chromium-tungsten alloys (cemented carbide cutting tools); light filaments; electrical contacts

tungsten carbide
[12070-12-1]

W_nC

n = 1–2. Hard, grey powder. MP: 2,800°C. d: 15.6 kg/l.

Production:
• tungsten/tungsten trioxide + carbon black
  (carburisation)
Uses:
cemented carbide cutting tools; wire-drawing dies

tungsten trioxide
tungsten oxide; tungstic oxide; [1314-35-8]

$$WO_3$$

O_3W_1. M: 231.85. Yellow powder when cold, orange
when hot. Insoluble in water.
Production:
• tungsten ore concentrates + sodium carbonate (ore
  roasting/water leaching/calcination)
• ammonium paratungstate (calcination)
Derivatives:
sodium tungstate; tungsten; tungsten carbide

tungstophosphoric acid *See:* phosphotungstic acid

Turkey red oil *See:* castor oil, sulphated

turmeric *See:* curcumin

turpentine oil, gum
turpentine oil, balsam
Colourless liquid with a mild odour. d: ~0.86 kg/l
(20°C). Comprises mainly α-pinene (65%) and β-pinene (20%). Produced in south-east USA and France.
Production:
• pine gum (fractionation; coproduced with
  dipentene/pine oil/rosin, gum)
Uses: speciality solvent

turpentine oil, sulphate
Colourless liquid with a characteristic odour. d: 0.86
kg/l (20°C). Produced in Canada, USA, Finland, Sweden, Russia, India and China. Comprises mainly α-pinene (65%) and β-pinene (20%). Turpentine oil originating from Scandinavia, India and Russia also contains
3-carene and camphene.
Production:
• sulphate pulp black liquor evaporator condensate
  (separation/fractionation; coproduced with pine oil)
Derivatives: α-pinene; β-pinene; α-terpineol

turpentine oil, wood
turpentine; [8006-64-2]
Colourless liquid with characteristic odour. BP: 155–
167°C. d: ~0.86 kg/l (20°C). Insoluble in water. Soluble in most solvents. The main components of the
oil produced in North America are α-pinene and β-
pinene. Oil from Scandinavia, Russia and elsewhere
also contains 3-carene and camphene. The USA, Canada, Russia, Sweden, Finland, India and China are the
main producing countries.

Production:
• pinewood stumps (steam distillation; coproduced
  with dipentene/pine oil/rosin, wood)
• pyrolysis oil, pinewood (fractionation; coproduced
  with pine oil/wood pitch/tar oil, wood)
Derivatives:
α-pinene; β-pinene; α-terpineol; terpin hydrate
Uses: speciality solvent

turpentine substitute *See:* white spirit

TXIB *See:* 2,2,4-trimethyl-1,3-pentanediol diisobutyrate

tyramine
4-(2-aminoethyl)phenol;   2-(4-hydroxyphenyl)ethylam-
ine; [51-67-2]

HO—⬡—CH₂CH₂NH₂

$C_8H_{11}N_1O_1$. M: 137.19. Crystalline solid. MP: 164°C.
Slightly soluble in water.
Production:
• *p*-hydroxyphenylacetonitrile (nitrile reduction)
Derivatives: bezafibrate
Uses: adrenergic drug

L-tyrosine
L-α-amino-β-(4-hydroxyphenyl)propionic acid; L-β-(4-
hydroxyphenyl)alanine; Tyr; [60-18-4]

HO—⬡—CH₂–C–COOH (with NH₂ above and H below central C)

$C_9H_{11}N_1O_3$. M: 181.20. Available commercially as the
naturally-occurring L(−)-enantiomer. Needles. Decomposed by water when heated above 340°C. d: 1.46
kg/l. Slightly soluble in hot water.
Production:
• animal glue (hydrolysis/extraction; coproduced with
  L-arginine/L-leucine/L-asparagine)
Derivatives:
levothyroxine sodium; oxytocin; thymopentin
Uses: infusion solutions/diagnostic aids; raw material
(peptide drugs)

U

γ-undecalactone
4-hydroxyundecanoic acid lactone; [104-67-6]

CH$_3$(CH$_2$)$_6$

C$_{11}$H$_{20}$O$_2$. M: 184.28. Colourless liquid with a fruity odour. BP: 167–169°C (2.0 kPa). d: 0.94 kg/l (20°C).
Production:
• *n*-octanol + acrylic acid (free-radical addition)
• undecylenic acid (esterification/acid-catalysed rearrangement)
Uses: fragrance/flavouring ingredient

n-undecanal
undecanal; *n*-undecyl aldehyde; [112-44-7]

CH$_3$(CH$_2$)$_9$CHO

C$_{11}$H$_{22}$O$_1$. M: 170.30. Colourless liquid with a floral odour. BP: 117°C (2.4 kPa). d: 0.83 kg/l (20°C). Insoluble in water. Soluble in alcohol.
Production:
• *n*-undecanol (alcohol oxidation)
Derivatives: methylnonylacetaldehyde
Uses: fragrance ingredient

n-undecanol
n-undecyl alcohol; [5332-52-5]

CH$_3$(CH$_2$)$_{10}$OH

C$_{11}$H$_{24}$O$_1$. M: 172.31. Liquid or solid. MP: 16°C. BP: 248–250°C. d: 0.83 kg/l (20°C). Insoluble in water. Soluble in oxygenated solvents.
Production:
• methyl undecylenate (hydrogenation)
Derivatives: *n*-undecanal
Uses: fragrance ingredient

10-undecenal
undecenal; *n*-undecenyl aldehyde; [112-45-8]

CH$_2$=CH(CH$_2$)$_8$CHO

C$_{11}$H$_{20}$O$_1$. M: 168.28. Colourless liquid with a heavy, floral odour. BP: 103°C (0.4 kPa). d: 0.85 kg/l (20°C). Insoluble in water.
Production:
• *n*-undecenyl alcohol (alcohol oxidation)
Uses: fragrance ingredient

n-undecenyl alcohol
alcohol C-11; 10-undecen-1-ol; [112-43-6]
C$_{11}$H$_{22}$O$_1$. M: 170.30. Colourless liquid with a floral odour. BP: 133°C (2.1 kPa). d: 0.85 kg/l (15°C). Insoluble in water.

CH$_2$=CH(CH$_2$)$_8$CH$_2$OH

Production:
• methyl undecylenate (ester reduction)
Derivatives: 10-undecenal
Uses: fragrance ingredient

n-undecenyl aldehyde *See:* 10-undecenal

n-undecyl alcohol *See:* *n*-undecanol

n-undecyl aldehyde *See:* *n*-undecanal

undecylenic acid
10-undecenoic acid; [112-38-9]

CH$_2$=CH(CH$_2$)$_8$COOH

C$_{11}$H$_{20}$O$_2$. M: 184.28. Liquid or solid. BP: 275°C. MP: 24°C. d: 0.91 kg/l (25°C). Insoluble in water. Soluble in oxygenated solvents.
Production:
• methyl undecylenate (ester hydrolysis)
Derivatives: ω-aminoundecanoic acid; γ-undecalactone; zinc undecylenate

uniconazole
1-(4-chlorophenyl)-4,4-dimethyl-2-(1H-1,2,4-triazol-1-yl)pent-1-en-3-ol; [83657-22-1]

OH
(CH$_3$)$_3$CCHC=CH— —Cl
N

C$_{15}$H$_{18}$Cl$_1$N$_3$O$_1$. M: 291.77.
Production:
• α-chloropinacolone + 1,2,4-triazole + *p*-chlorobenzaldehyde (amine formation/carbonyl condensation/carbonyl reduction)
Uses: plant growth regulator

UNN *See:* uranyl nitrate

unsaturated polyester resins, coating grades
Curing is by peroxide, ultra-violet light or electron beam radiation.
Production:
• maleic anhydride/phthalic anhydride + propylene glycol/diethylene glycol + styrene + glycerol α-allyl ether/trimethylolpropane diallyl ether/pentaerythritol triallyl ether (esterification)
Uses:
metal finishing paints (bridges, marine applications); wood finishes (household furniture)

unsaturated polyester resins, general grades
UPR
Colourless liquid comprising 55–65% resin dissolved in styrene. Cured by peroxide catalysts either at ambient or elevated temperatures according to the processing method. Usually reinforced with glass fibre.
Production:
• propylene glycol + maleic anhydride + phthalic anhydride + styrene (esterification)
Uses:
dough moulding compounds (household appliances, vehicle body parts); industrial/agricultural tanks, plant and piping; marble-like work surfaces (kitchens, bathrooms); sheet moulding compounds (vehicle body panels, electrical enclosures, satellite dishes); spray laminated boats/pleasure craft; terrazzo tiles; translucent roofing sheets; binder (industrial flooring/coatings)

unsaturated polyester resins, isophthalate grades
Clear, amber liquid consisting of a 60–70% solution of resin in styrene. Typically cured with methyl ethyl ketone peroxide or benzoyl peroxide. Isophthalate grades of polyester have better chemical resistance than general grades. Polyurethane-modified resins of this type are also available.
Production:
• propylene glycol/diethylene glycol/neopentyl glycol/ethylene glycol + isophthalic acid/maleic anhydride + styrene (polycondensation)
Uses:
unsaturated polyester resin gel coats (boats); glass-reinforced plastics (chemical tanks, pipe, ducting)

UPR
See: unsaturated polyester resins, general grades

uracil
2,4-dihydroxypyrimidine; 2,4-diketopyrimidine; 2,4-oxypyrimidine; [66-22-8]

$C_4H_4N_2O_2$. M: 112.08. White, odourless powder. MP: >300°C. Slightly soluble in water.
Production:
• ethyl formate + ethyl acetate + urea (carbonyl condensation/condensation)
Derivatives:
5-bromopyrimidine; fluorouracil; idoxuridine
Uses: antitumour drug adjunct; sunscreening agent (cosmetics); photographic chemical

uracil-6-carboxylic acid *See:* orotic acid

uranine *See:* fluorescein

uranium dioxide
uranium oxide; [1344-57-6]

UO_2

O_2U_1. M: 270.03. Black, crystalline solid. d: 10.9 kg/l. MP: 2,800°C. Radioactive.
Production:
• uranium hexafluoride, U^{235} enriched (ammonium diuranate or uranyl carbonate process)
Uses: ceramic fuel rods (light water, fast-breeder nuclear reactors)

uranium hexafluoride
[7783-81-5]

UF_6

F_6U_1. M: 352.02. White, crystalline solid. d: 5.09 kg/l. MP: 64.5°C. Sublimes at 56.5°C. Reacts with water forming hydrofluoric acid.
Production:
• uranyl nitrate + hydrogen fluoride + fluorine (wet uranium hexafluoride process)
• uranyl nitrate + hydrogen fluoride + fluorine (wet Comurhex process)
• yellow cake + hydrogen fluoride + fluorine (dry uranium hexafluoride process)
Derivatives: uranium hexafluoride, U^{235} enriched

uranium hexafluoride, U^{235} enriched

$^{235}UF_6$

F_6U_1. M: 352.02. Radioactive.
Production:
• uranium hexafluoride (isotope enrichment)
Derivatives:
uranium dioxide; uranium metal, U^{235} enriched

uranium metal, U^{235} enriched

^{235}U

U_1. M: 238.03. Silvery-white, ductile metal. Radioactive.
Production:
• uranium hexafluoride, U^{235} enriched + hydrogen + magnesium (reduction/reduction)
Uses: nuclear reactor fuel elements

uranyl nitrate
uranium nitrate; yellow salt; UNN; [10102-06-4]

$UO_2(NO_3)_2$

$N_2O_8U_1$. M: 394.03. Available as the hexahydrate. Yellow crystals. d: 2.81 kg/l. MP: 60°C. Soluble in water and oxygenated solvents.
Production:
• nuclear fuel, spent (extraction/separation)
• yellow cake + nitric acid (dissolution)

Derivatives: uranium hexafluoride
Uses: porcelain glaze ingredient

urapidil
[34661-75-1]

$C_{20}H_{29}N_5O_3$. M: 387.49.
Production:
- 6-amino-1,3-dimethyluracil + 1-bromo-3-chloro-
  propane + 1-(2-methoxyphenyl)piperazine
  hydrochloride (amine formation/amine formation)
Uses: antihypertensive drug

urea
carbamide; [57-13-6]

$$H_2NCNH_2$$

$C_1H_4N_2O_1$. M: 60.05. White prills or granules available
in coated or uncoated grades. MP: 132°C. d: 1.32 kg/l
(20°C). Bulk density: 0.74 kg/l. Soluble in water forming alkaline solutions. Soluble in oxygenated solvents.
Production:
- ammonia + carbon dioxide (condensation)
Derivatives:
allantoin; ammonium polyphosphate, solid; azodicarbonamide; barbital; barbituric acid; *N,N'*-bis(methoxymethyl)urone; butalbital; copper phthalocyanine; crotonylidene urea; cyanuric acid; cyclopentobarbital; 2,4-
dichloropyrimidine-5-carboxyl chloride; 1,3-dimethylol-
4,5-dihydroxyethylene urea; dimethylolurea; ethylene
urea; glycoluril; hydantoin; hydramethylnon; *N*-hydr-
oxymethyl-3,4,5,6-tetrahydrophthalimide; D-α-(4-hydr-
oxyphenyl)glycine; isobutylidene urea; melamine; 6-
methyluracil; phenobarbital; phenytoin; potassium cyanate; propylene urea; proquazone; sodium cyanate; sulfadimethoxine; sulphamic acid; thiourea-urea-formaldehyde resins; trimethadione; uracil; urea-formaldehyde-
furfuryl alcohol resins; urea-formaldehyde resins; urea-
formaldehyde resins, anionic; urea-formaldehyde resins,
butylated; urea-formaldehyde resins, cationic; urea peroxide
Uses: airport runway deicing agent; dispersant (animal
glue, proteins); fertiliser; animal feed supplement; plasticiser (starch adhesives)

urea-formaldehyde-furfuryl alcohol resins
Production:
- furfural/furfuryl alcohol + urea + formaldehyde
  (condensation)
Uses:
foundry mould binder

urea-formaldehyde resins
urea resins; UF

$$HO[CH_2NHCNH]_xCH_2OH$$

Thermosetting resins available as a powder or solution
in water. Formed with a 1.3–2.2 molar excess of formaldehyde and cured with an acid catalyst, commonly
ammonium chloride, at 125–160°C.
Production:
- urea + formaldehyde (carbonyl condensation)
Uses: controlled-release fertiliser foam; firelighters;
sound/heat insulation foam; adhesives (chipboard, plywood, furniture); moulding compounds (electrical plugs,
sockets, switches, hairdryer housings, toilet seats, pic-
nicware, buttons, door furniture); wet-strength additive
(paper, starch adhesives); plastic pigments (emulsion
paint); textile finishing agent

urea-formaldehyde resins, anionic

$$HO[CH_2NHCNH]_xCH_2OH$$

Water soluble.
Production:
- urea + formaldehyde + sodium bisulphite (carbonyl
  condensation/sulphonation)
Uses: paper wet-strength additives; textile/leather auxiliary; water-soluble adhesives

urea-formaldehyde resins, butylated

$$CH_3(CH_2)_3O[CH_2NHCNH]_xCH_2O(CH_2)_3CH_3$$

Colourless liquid consisting of resin dissolved in but-
anol. Insoluble in water. Soluble in hydrocarbon solvents.
Production:
- urea + formaldehyde + *n*-butanol (ether formation)
Uses: alkyd-amino acid-cured resins (industrial and
clear wood finishes); alkyd-amino stoving resins (domestic equipment finishes); binder (printing inks)

urea-formaldehyde resins, cationic
Production:
- urea + formaldehyde + ethylenediamine/
  monoethanolamine/diethylenetriamine/triethylene-
  tetramine/guanylurea sulphate/guanidine carbonate/
  diethanolamine (carbonyl condensation)
Uses: paper wet-strength additives

urea peroxide
urea hydrogen peroxide; [124-43-6]

$$(NH_2)_2CO.H_2O_2$$

$C_1H_6N_2O_3$. M: 94.07. White crystals. Soluble in water.

Production:
• urea + hydrogen peroxide (reaction)
Uses:
wax-soluble reagent (pharmaceuticals)

γ-ureidopropyltriethoxysilane

$$\begin{array}{c} NH \\ || \\ H_2NCNHCH_2CH_2CH_2Si(OC_2H_5)_3 \end{array}$$

$C_{10}H_{25}N_3O_3Si_1$. M: 263.42. Available commercially as a 50% solution in methanol. d: 0.98 kg/l (25°C).
Production:
• γ-aminopropyltriethoxysilane + sodium cyanate
  (cyanate addition)
Uses: plastics coupling agent

urethane-acrylate resins

$$CH_2=CCOCH_2CHOCNH-R'-NHCOCHCH_2OCC=CH_2$$

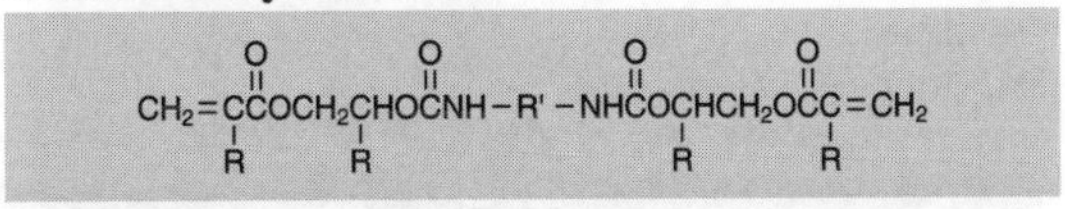

R = H, methyl-. Acrylate-terminated polyurethane pre-polymers. Inks and coatings made with urethane-acrylate resins are characterised by their toughness and their good chemical resistance. Grades based on isophorone isocyanate or hexamethylene isocyanate show less tendency to yellow in light than those made with aromatic isocyanates.
Production:
• toluene diisocyanate/hexamethylene diisocyanate/
  4,4′-diphenylmethane diisocyanate, polymeric/
  isophorone diisocyanate + 2-hydroxyethyl acrylate/
  2-hydroxyethyl methacrylate/2-hydroxypropyl
  acrylate/2-hydroxypropyl methacrylate (isocyanate
  addition)
Uses:
binder (radiation-cured wood/textile finishes, printing inks, paper-foil lacquers)

urethane-alkyd resins
urethane oils
Production:
• linseed oil + glycerol + toluene diisocyanate
  (alcoholysis/isocyanate addition)
Uses:
kitchen/office furniture paints; one-pack urethane alkyd paints (marine varnishes, kitchen/office furniture paints, aluminium-filled paints)

urethane oils *See:* urethane-alkyd resins

V

vacuum residue *See:* short residue

VAE *See:* ethylene-vinyl acetate copolymers, 15% vinyl acetate

Val *See:* L-valine

valdetamide
2,2-diethyl-4-pentenamide; novonal; pentenamide; [512-48-1]

$$CH_2=CHCH_2C(C_2H_5)_2 \overset{\displaystyle CONH_2}{|}$$

$C_9H_{17}N_1O_1$. M: 155.25.
Production:
• ethyl bromide + ethyl cyanoacetate + allyl chloride (dehydrobromination/decarboxylation/dehydrochlorination/nitrile hydration)
Uses: hypnotic drug

valeraldehyde
amyl aldehyde; pentaldehyde; pentanal; *n*-valeraldehyde; valeric aldehyde; [110-62-3]

$$CH_3CH_2CH_2CH_2CHO$$

$C_5H_{10}O_1$. M: 86.13. Colourless liquid. BP: 104°C. FP: -87°C. d: 0.81 kg/l (20°C). Solubility in water: 208 g/l water (20°C).
Production:
• ethylene + synthesis gas (hydroformylation; byproduct of propionaldehyde production)
• pentaldehydes, mixed (separation; coproduced with 2-methylbutyraldehyde)
Derivatives: methyl dihydrojasmonate; valeric acid

valeric acid
pentanoic acid; *n*-pentanoic acid; valerianic acid; [109-52-4]

$$CH_3CH_2CH_2CH_2COOH$$

$C_5H_{10}O_2$. M: 102.13. Colourless liquid with an unpleasant odour. BP: 126–128°C (13.3 kPa). MP: -34°C d: 0.94 kg/l (20°C). Slightly soluble in water. Soluble in oxygenated solvents.
Production:
• valeraldehyde (carbonyl oxidation)
Derivatives:
ethyl valerate; methyl valerate
Uses: pharmaceutical derivatisation reagent

validamycin
validamycin A; [37248-47-8]
$C_{20}H_{35}N_1O_{13}$. M: 497.50.

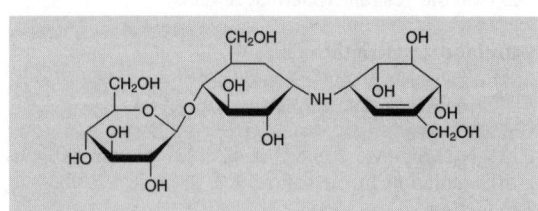

Production:
• microbial fermentation medium + *Streptomyces hygroscopicus* bacteria (fermentation)
Uses: fungicide

D-valine
D-2-aminoisovaleric acid

$$(CH_3)_2CH-\overset{\displaystyle H}{\underset{\displaystyle NH_2}{C}}-COOH$$

$C_5H_{11}N_1O_2$. M: 117.15.
Production:
• DL-valine (acetylation/enzymatic hydrolysis)
Derivatives: D-fluvalinate

DL-valine
α-aminoisovaleric acid; DL-2-aminoisovaleric acid; [516-06-3]

$$(CH_3)_2CHCHCOOH \overset{\displaystyle NH_2}{|}$$

$C_5H_{11}N_1O_2$. M: 117.15. White solid. MP: 298°C with decomposition. Solubility in water: 70 g/l water (25°C).
Production:
• isobutyraldehyde + hydrogen cyanide + ammonia (Strecker synthesis)
Derivatives:
D-valine; L-valine

L-valine
DL-2-aminoisovaleric acid; Val; [72-18-4]

$$(CH_3)_2CH-\overset{\displaystyle NH_2}{\underset{\displaystyle H}{C}}-COOH$$

$C_5H_{11}N_1O_2$. M: 117.15. Available commercially as the naturally-occurring L(+)-enantiomer. Flakes. MP: 315°C (sealed tube). Soluble in water.
Production:
• DL-valine + acetic anhydride + *Aspergillus oryzae* mould (acetylation/enzymatic hydrolysis)
Derivatives: thymopentin
Uses: infusion solutions/diagnostic aids; raw material (peptide drugs)

valproic acid

Depakene (Abbott Laboratories); 2-*n*-propylpentanoic acid; 2-*n*-propylvaleric acid; VPA; [99-66-1]

$(CH_3CH_2CH_2)_2CHCOOH$

$C_8H_{16}O_2$. M: 144.22. Available commercially as the sodium and sodium hydrogen salts.
Production:
- ethyl cyanoacetate + *n*-propyl bromide (dehydrobromination/decarboxylation/nitrile hydrolysis)

Uses: antiepileptic drug

VAM *See:* vinyl acetate

Vamac

See: ethylene-methyl acrylate terpolymer, ionomeric

vamidothion

O,O-dimethyl *S*-2-(1-methylcarbamoylethylthio)ethyl phosphorothioate; [2275-23-2]

$$CH_3NHCCHSCH_2CH_2SP(OCH_3)_2$$
$$\underset{CH_3}{|}$$

$C_8H_{18}N_1O_4P_1S_2$. M: 287.34.
Production:
- ethyl α-chloropropionate + 2-mercaptoethanol + methylamine + *O,O*-dimethyl dithiophosphoric acid (sulphide formation/amide formation/alcohol chlorination/dehydrochlorination)

Uses: acaricide/insecticide

vanadium oxychloride

vanadium oxytrichloride; vanadyl trichloride; [7727-18-6]

$VOCl_3$

$Cl_3O_1V_1$. M: 173.30. Yellow liquid. BP: 127°C. FP: -77°C. d: 1.83 kg/l. Fumes in moist air and reacts with water forming deep-red vanadic acid.
Production:
- vanadium pentoxide + metallurgical coke + chlorine (chlorination)

Uses: ethylene-propylene rubber catalyst component

vanadium pentoxide

[1314-62-1]

V_2O_5

O_5V_2. M: 181.87. Yellow-red crystals. MP: 690°C. d: 3.36 kg/l. Slightly soluble in water.
Production:
- iron-vanadium ore (calcination/water leaching/ solvent extraction/precipitation/calcination)
- spent oil-refining catalysts/boiler fly-ash (solvent extraction/precipitation/calcination)

- phosphoric acid, crude (solvent extraction/ hydrorefining; coproduced with yellow cake)
- uranium ore (leaching/solvent extraction/ hydrorefining; coproduced with yellow cake)

Derivatives: ammonium metavanadate; ferrovanadium; vanadium oxychloride
Uses: oxidation catalyst; ceramic tiles/sanitaryware colorant; glass ingredient

vanadium tetrachloride

[7632-51-1]

VCl_4

Cl_4V_1. M: 192.75. Reddish-brown, oily liquid. MP: 28°C. BP: 154°C. d: 1.82 kg/l (30°C). Hydrolysed by water.
Production:
- ferrovanadium/ferrophosphorus + chlorine (chlorination)

Uses: ethylene-propylene rubber catalyst component

vancomycin

[1404-90-6]

$C_{66}H_{75}Cl_2N_9O_{24}$. M: 1449.28. Complex glycopeptide available as the free base or as the hydrochloride salt.
Production:
- microbial fermentation medium + *Streptomyces orientalis* bacteria (fermentation)

Uses: antibacterial drug

vanilla extract

vanilla
Produced by solvent extraction of vanilla (*Vanilla planifolia* or *V. tahitensis*) beans.
Uses:
flavouring ingredient

vanillic acid

4-hydroxy-3-methoxybenzoic acid; 3-methoxy-4-hydroxybenzoic acid; [121-34-6]

$C_8H_8O_4$. M: 168.15. White needles. MP: 211–213°C. Sublimes on further heating. Slightly soluble in water. Soluble in oxygenated solvents.
Production:
- vanillin (carbonyl oxidation)

Derivatives: ethyl vanillate

vanillin

4-hydroxy-3-methoxybenzaldehyde; 3-methoxy-4-hydroxybenzaldehyde; [121-33-5]
$C_8H_8O_3$. M: 152.15. Colourless crystals. MP: 81–82°C.

BP: 285°C. d: 1.06 kg/l (20°C). Slightly soluble in water. Soluble in oxygenated solvents and aromatics.

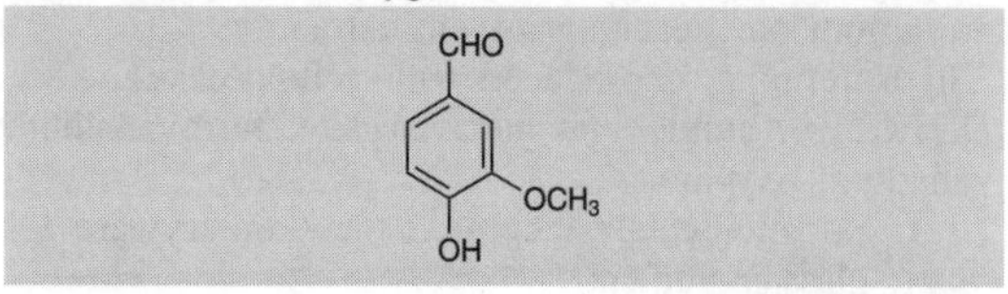

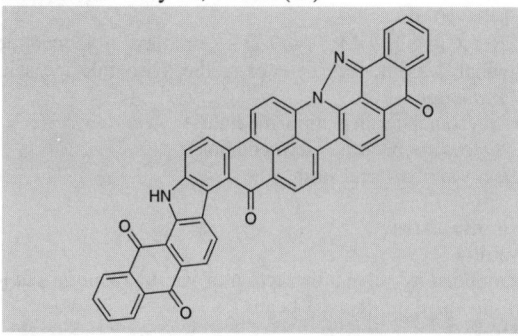

Production:
- guaiacol + glyoxylic acid (carbonyl addition/ oxidation/decarboxylation)
- sulphite pulp waste liquor (oxidative cleavage)
- isoeugenol + ozone (ozonolysis)

Derivatives: 3,4-dihydroxybenzaldehyde; homovanillic acid; levodopa; vanillic acid; veratraldehyde

Uses: electroplating brightening agent; fragrance/flavouring ingredient

vaseline *See:* petroleum jelly

Vat Black 8
Indanthrene Grey M; 71000 (CI)

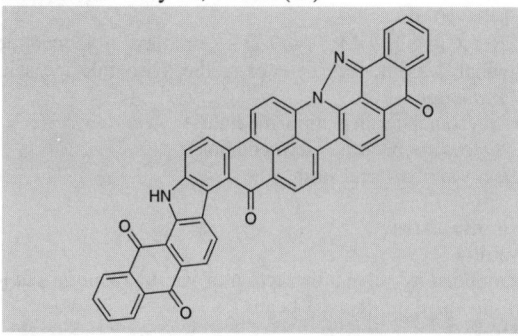

$C_{45}H_{19}N_3O_4$. M: 665.66.
Production:
- 3,9-dibromobenzanthrone + anthrapyrazolone + 1-aminoanthraquinone (condensation)

Uses: dye (cotton, viscose)

Vat Black 25
Olive TA Paste; 69525 (CI); [4395-53-3]

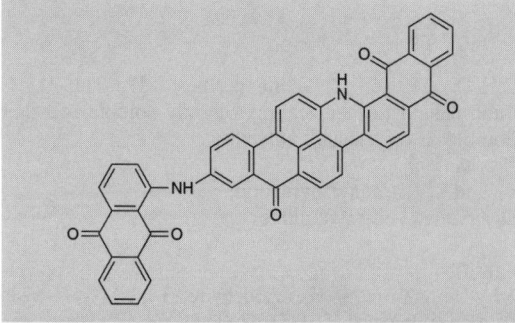

$C_{45}H_{22}N_2O_5$. M: 670.67.

Production:
- 3,9-dibromobenzanthrone + 1-aminoanthraquinone (amine formation/base-catalysed coupling)

Uses: dye (cotton)

Vat Black 27
Indanthrene Olive R; 69005 (CI); [2379-81-9]

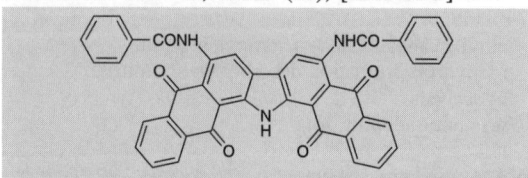

$C_{42}H_{23}N_3O_6$. M: 665.65.
Production:
- 1-amino-4-benzamidoanthraquinone + 1-benzamido-4-chloroanthraquinone (amine formation/ condensation/oxidation)

Uses: dye (cotton, viscose)

Vat Blue 1 *See:* indigo

Vat Blue 4 *See:* indanthrone

Vat Blue 5
Bromindigo Blue 2BD; 73065 (CI)

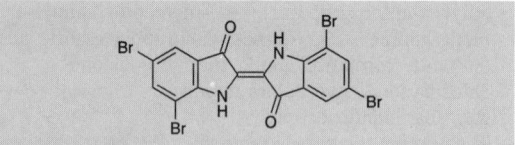

$C_{16}H_6Br_4N_2O_2$. M: 577.86.
Production:
- indigo (ring bromination)

Uses: dye (cotton, viscose, silk)

Vat Blue 6
Indanthrene Blue; Pigment Blue 64 (CI); 69825 (CI)

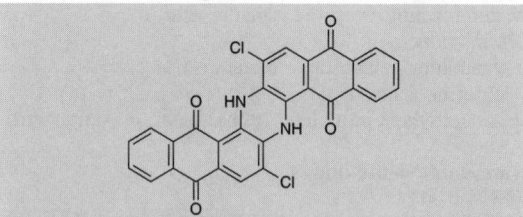

$C_{28}H_{12}Cl_2N_2O_4$. M: 511.33.
Production:
- indanthrone (chlorination)

Uses: vat dye (cotton); pigment (printing inks)

Vat Blue 16
71200 (CI)
$C_{36}H_{18}O_4$. M: 514.54.

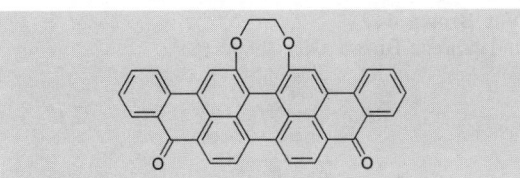

Production:
• 16,17-dihydroxydibenzanthrone + ethylene dibromide (ether formation)
Uses: dye (cotton)

Vat Blue 18
59815 (CI)

$C_{34}H_{13}Cl_3O_2$. M: 559.83.
Production:
• dibenzanthrone (ring chlorination)
Uses: dye (cotton)

Vat Blue 19
59805 (CI)

$C_{34}H_{13}Br_2O_2$. M: 613.28. Mixed product containing an average of 2 bromine atoms per molecule together with 6% sulphur.
Production:
• dibenzanthrone + sulphur (ring bromination/ sulphurisation)
Uses: dye (cotton, viscose)

Vat Blue 20 *See:* dibenzanthrone

Vat Blue 21
Indanthrene Blue HCGK; 67920 (CI)

$C_{29}H_{15}F_3N_2O_4$. M: 512.44.

Production:
• 1-chloro-2-methylanthraquinone + *m*-aminobenzo- trifluoride + benzoyl chloride (side-chain oxidation/amine formation/cyclisation/nitration/ nitro reduction/amide formation)
Uses:
direct dye (cotton, viscose, acetate)

Vat Blue 29
74140 (CI)

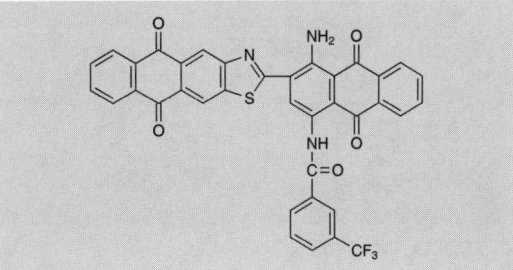

$C_{32}H_{16}Cu_1N_8O_3S_1$. M: 656.15. Mixed product, 25% sul- phonated.
Production:
• copper phthalocyanine (sulphonation)
Uses: dye (cotton, silk)

Vat Blue 30
Indanthrene Blue CLB; 67110 (CI); [6492-78-0]

$C_{37}H_{18}F_3N_3O_5S_1$. M: 673.61.
Production:
• 1-nitroanthraquinone-2-carboxylic acid + sodium hydrosulphide + 2-amino-3-bromoanthraquinone + 3-(trifluoromethyl)benzoyl fluoride (acid chloride formation/thiolation/condensation/nitration/nitro reduction/amide formation)
Uses: dye (cotton)

Vat Blue 42
Hydron Blue G; 53640 (CI)

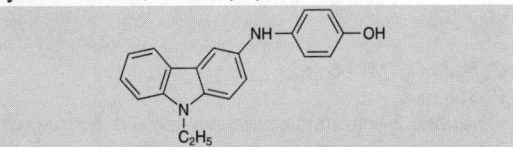

The dye is a mixed, polymeric sulphur complex of the displayed structure. $C_{20}H_{18}N_2O_1$. M: 302.37.

Production:
- *N*-ethylcarbazole + *p*-nitrosophenol + sulphur + sodium sulphide (reductive coupling/polysulphide melt process)

Uses: dye (cotton, viscose)

Vat Blue 43

Hydron Blue R; Vat Blue 47 (CI); 53630 (CI)

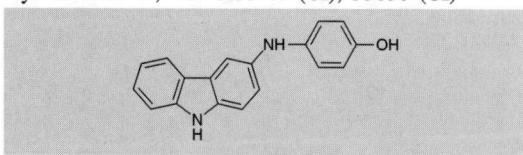

The dye is a mixed, polymeric sulphur complex of the displayed structure. $C_{18}H_{14}N_2O_1$. M: 274.32.
Production:
- carbazole + *p*-nitrosophenol + sulphur + sodium sulphide (reductive coupling/polysulphide bake process)

Uses: dye (cotton, viscose, silk)

Vat Blue 47 *See:* Vat Blue 43

Vat Brown 1

70800 (CI); [2475-33-4]

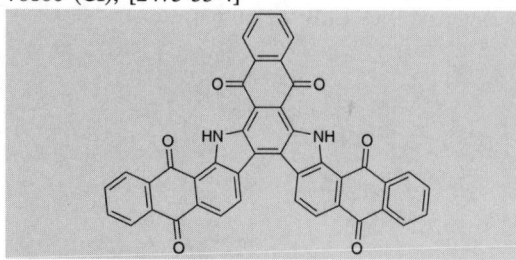

$C_{42}H_{18}N_2O_6$. M: 646.60.
Production:
- 1,4-diaminoanthraquinone + 1-chloroanthraquinone (amine formation/cyclisation)

Uses: dye (cotton, viscose, silk)

Vat Brown 3

69015 (CI); [131-92-0]

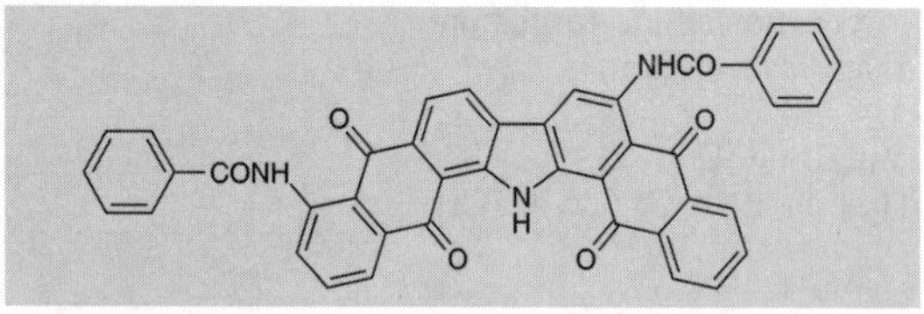

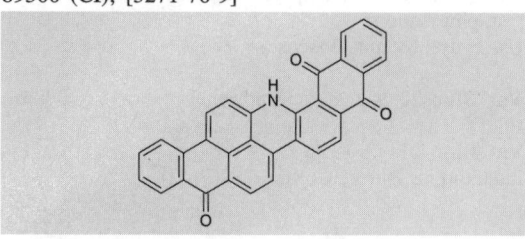

$C_{42}H_{23}N_3O_6$. M: 665.65.
Production:
- 1-amino-5-benzamidoanthraquinone + 1-benzamido-4-chloroanthraquinone (amine formation/oxidative coupling)

Uses: dye (cotton)

Vat Brown 44

Indanthrene Brown GR; 70802 (CI)

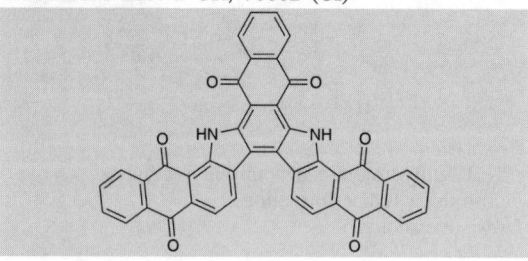

$C_{42}H_{18}N_2O_6$. M: 646.60.
Production:
- 1,4-diaminoanthraquinone + 1-chloroanthraquinone (amine formation/base-catalysed cyclisation)

Uses: dye (cotton)

Vat Green 1

16,17-dimethoxyviolanthrone; Caledon Jade Green; Caledon Jade Green XBN; 59825 (CI); [128-58-5]

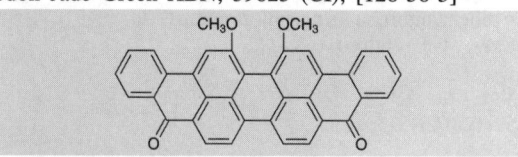

$C_{36}H_{20}O_4$. M: 516.56.
Production:
- 16,17-dihydroxydibenzanthrone + dimethyl sulphate (methylation)

Uses:
dye (cotton, viscose, silk, wool)

Vat Green 3

69500 (CI); [3271-76-9]

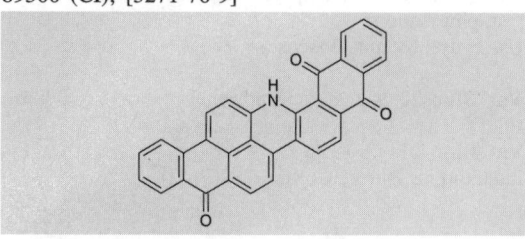

$C_{31}H_{15}N_1O_3$. M: 449.47.
Production:
- 1-aminoanthraquinone + 3-bromobenzanthrone (amine formation/condensation)

Uses: dye (cotton, wool)

Vat Green 7

58825 (CI)
Mixed product of indeterminate structure.
Production:
- anthracene + sulphur (sulphur bake process)

Uses: dye (cotton)

Vat Green 8
Indanthrene Khaki GG; 71050 (CI)

$C_{70}H_{28}N_4O_{10}$. M: 1085.01.
Production:
• 1-aminoanthraquinone + 1,4,5,8-tetrachloro-
anthraquinone (amine formation/acid-catalysed
coupling/oxidation)
Uses:
dye (cotton, silk)

Vat Green 9
59850 (CI)

$C_{34}H_{15}N_1O_4$. M: 501.50.
Production:
• dibenzanthrone (nitration)
Uses: dye (cotton)

Vat Orange 1
dibromodibenzopyrenequinone; Indanthrene Golden Yellow RK; 59105 (CI); [1324-11-4]

$C_{24}H_{10}Br_2O_2$. M: 490.15.
Production:
• dibenzopyrenequinone (ring bromination)
Uses: dye (cotton)

Vat Orange 2
4,12-dibromopyranthrone; Indanthrene Orange RRTS; 59705 (CI); Cibanone Golden Orange 2R (Ciba-Geigy); [1324-35-2]

$C_{30}H_{12}Br_2O_2$. M: 564.24.
Production:
• pyranthrone (ring bromination)
Uses:
dye (cotton, viscose, silk)

Vat Orange 3
dibromoanthranthrone; Pigment Red 168 (CI); 59300 (CI); Helio Fast Scarlet EB (Bayer); Hostaperm Scarlet GO (Hoechst); [4378-61-4]

$C_{22}H_8Br_2O_2$. M: 464.11.
Production:
• naphtholactam (diazotisation/acid-catalysed
coupling/ring bromination)
Uses:
vat dye (cotton); pigment (plastics)

Vat Orange 4 *See:* Pigment Red 216

Vat Orange 5
73335 (CI)

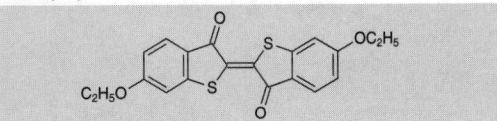

$C_{20}H_{16}O_4S_2$. M: 384.48.
Production:
• *p*-phenetidine + sulphur monochloride + chloroacetic acid + sodium cyanide (Herz route)
Uses:
dye (cotton)

Vat Orange 7
Perinone Orange; Pigment Orange 43 (CI)
$C_{26}H_{12}N_4O_2$. M: 412.42. This product is the *trans*-isomer. The *cis*-isomer is Vat Red 15.
Production:
• naphthalene-1,4,5,8-tetracarboxylic acid + *o*-phenyl-
enediamine (condensation/isomer separation;
coproduced with Vat Red 15)

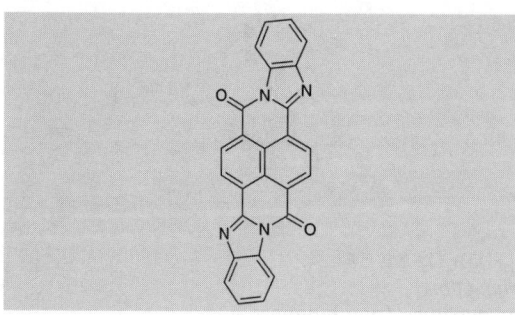

Uses:
vat dye (cotton); pigment (paints, plastics, fibres)

Vat Orange 9 *See:* pyranthrone

Vat Orange 15
69025 (CI); [2379-28-4]

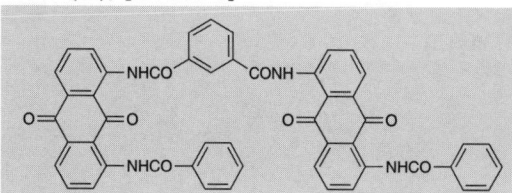

$C_{42}H_{23}N_3O_6$. M: 665.65.
Production:
• 1-amino-5-benzamidoanthraquinone (diazotisation/
Sandmeyer reaction/amine formation/oxidative
coupling)
Uses:
dye (cotton, viscose)

Vat Orange 17
65415 (CI); [6370-77-0]

$C_{50}H_{30}N_4O_8$. M: 814.81.
Production:
• 1-amino-5-benzamidoanthraquinone + 1-amino-
4-benzamidoanthraquinone + isophthaloyl chloride
(amide formation)
Uses: dye (cotton)

Vat Red 1
Hydron Pink FF; 73360 (CI); D&C Red No. 30
(FDC); [2379-74-0]
$C_{18}H_{10}Cl_2O_2S_2$. M: 393.32.
Production:
• *o*-toluidine + sulphur monochloride + chloroacetic
acid + sodium cyanide (Herz route)

Uses: dye (cotton, viscose, silk, wool)

Vat Red 10
67000 (CI); Cibanone Red 2B (Ciba-Geigy)

$C_{29}H_{14}N_2O_5$. M: 470.43.
Production:
• 2-amino-3-bromoanthraquinone +
1-nitroanthraquinone-2-carboxylic acid
(condensation/nitro reduction)
Uses:
dye (cotton, viscose)

Vat Red 13
Pigment Red 195 (CI); 70320 (CI); Cibanone Red 6B
(Ciba-Geigy); [4203-77-4]

$C_{32}H_{22}N_4O_2$. M: 494.56.
Production:
• anthrapyrazolone + diethyl sulphate (oxidative
coupling/ethylation)
Uses:
dye (cotton, silk, wool)

Vat Red 15
Perinone Red; Pigment Red 194 (CI); 71100 (CI)

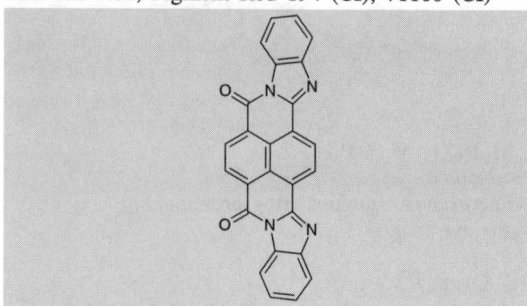

$C_{26}H_{12}N_4O_2$. M: 412.42. Vat Orange 8 is the *trans*-iso-
mer of this product.

Production:
- naphthalene-1,4,5,8-tetracarboxylic acid + *o*-phenylenediamine (condensation/isomer separation; coproduced with Vat Orange 7)

Uses: dye (cotton); pigment (paints, plastics)

Vat Red 23 *See:* Pigment Red 179

Vat Red 28
Cibanone Red G; 65710 (CI)

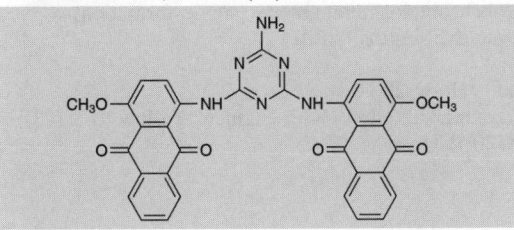

$C_{33}H_{22}N_6O_6$. M: 598.57.
Production:
- cyanuric chloride + ammonia + 1-amino-4-hydroxy-anthraquinone (amine formation/methylation/ammoniation)

Uses: dye (cotton)

Vat Red 29 *See:* Pigment Red 190

Vat Red 32
Pigment Red 189 (CI); 71135 (CI)

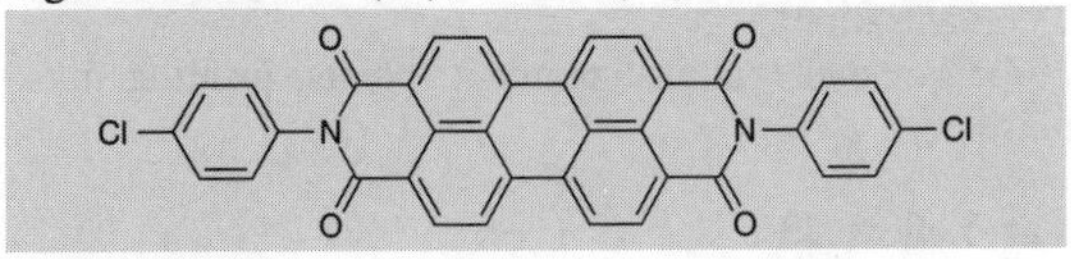

$C_{36}H_{16}Cl_2N_2O_4$. M: 611.45.
Production:
- perylenetetracarboxylic anhydride + *p*-chloroaniline (imide formation)

Uses: dye (cotton)

Vat Red 35
1,2-benzo-5,6-phthaloylacridone; Indanthrene Red RK; 68000 (CI);

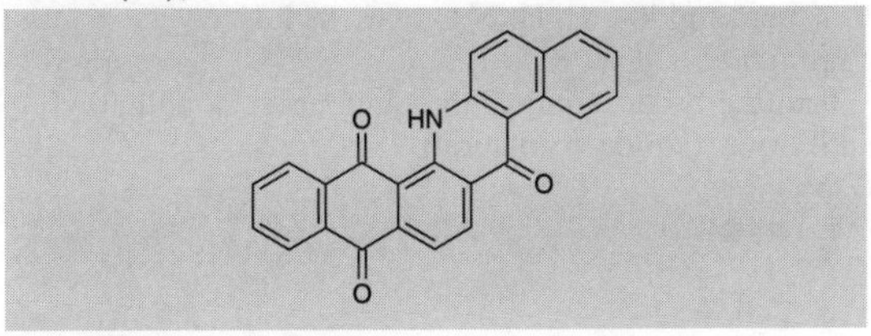

$C_{25}H_{13}N_1O_3$. M: 375.38.
Production:
- 1-chloro-2-methylanthraquinone + Tobias acid (side-chain oxidation/amine formation/condensation)

Uses: dye (cotton, viscose)

Vat Red 41 *See:* thioindigo

Vat Red 48
65205 (CI)

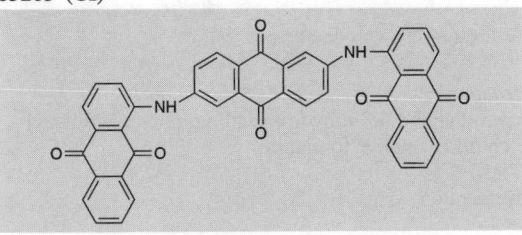

$C_{42}H_{22}N_2O_6$. M: 650.64.
Production:
- anthraquinone-2,6-disulphonic acid + 1-amino-anthraquinone (sulphonate displacement)

Uses:
dye (cotton)

Vat Violet 13
Indanthrene Violet FFBN; 68700 (CI)

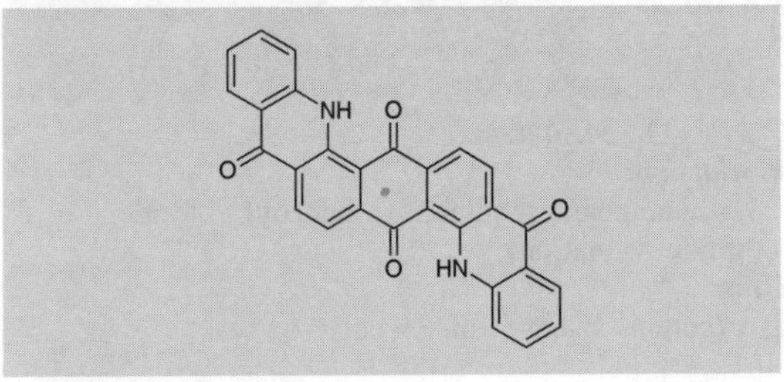

$C_{28}H_{14}N_2O_4$. M: 442.43.
Production:
- anthranilic acid + 1,5-dichloroanthraquinone (amine formation/condensation)

Uses:
dye (cotton, silk)

Vat Violet 15
63355 (CI)

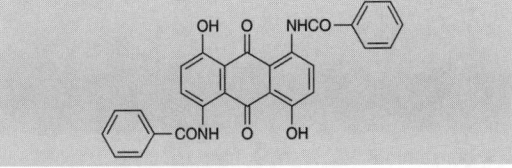

$C_{28}H_{18}N_2O_6$. M: 478.45.
Production:
- 1,5-diamino-4,8-dihydroxyanthraquinone + benzoyl chloride (amide formation)

Uses: dye (cotton, silk)

Vat Violet 17
63365 (CI)
$C_{30}H_{22}N_2O_8$. M: 538.51.

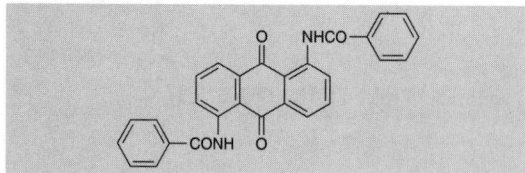

Production:
• 1,5-diamino-4,8-dihydroxyanthraquinone + anisoyl chloride (amine formation)
Uses:
dye (cotton, viscose, silk)

Vat Yellow 1 *See:* flavanthrone

Vat Yellow 3
1,5-dibenzoylaminoanthraquinone; Indanthrene Yellow GK; 61725 (CI)

$C_{28}H_{18}N_2O_4$. M: 446.46.
Production:
• 1,5-diaminoanthraquinone + benzoyl chloride (amide formation)
Uses:
dye (cotton, viscose, silk, wool)

Vat Yellow 4 *See:* dibenzopyrenequinone

Vat Yellow 10
65430 (CI); [2379-76-2]

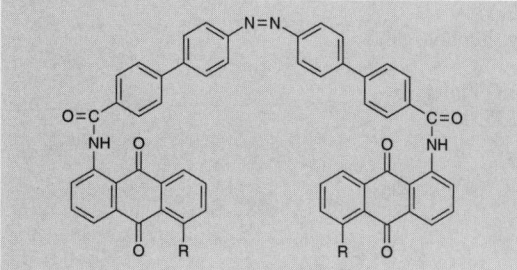

R = benzamido-. $C_{68}H_{42}N_6O_8$. M: 1071.12.
Production:
• biphenyl-4-carboxylic acid + 1-amino-5-benzamidoanthraquinone (nitration/reductive coupling/amide formation)
Uses: dye (cotton)

Vat Yellow 13
65425 (CI)
$C_{50}H_{30}N_4O_8$. M: 814.81.

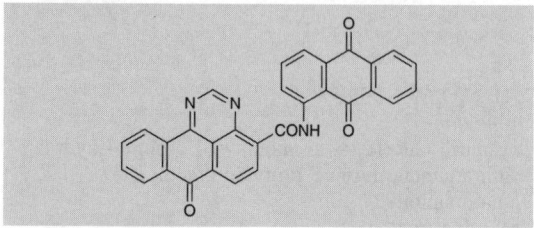

R = benzamido-.
Production:
• terephthaloyl chloride + 1-amino-5-benzamidoanthraquinone (amide formation)
Uses: dye (cotton, silk)

Vat Yellow 20
Indanthrene Yellow 4GF; Pigment Yellow 108 (CI); 68420 (CI)

$C_{30}H_{15}N_3O_4$. M: 481.47.
Production:
• 1-nitroanthraquinone-2-carboxylic acid + 1-amino-anthraquinone + phosgene + dimethylformamide (amide formation/nitro reduction/chlorination/condensation)
Uses: vat dye (cotton); pigment (paints, printing inks, plastics)

Vat Yellow 23
Sabdothrene Yellow 2GW; 65420 (CI)

R = benzamido-. $C_{50}H_{30}N_4O_8$. M: 814.81.
Production:
• 1-amino-5-benzamidoanthraquinone + isophthaloyl chloride (amide formation)
Uses:
dye (cotton)

Vat Yellow 26
65410 (CI)
$C_{36}H_{20}N_2O_6$. M: 576.56.
Production:
• isophthaloyl chloride + 1-aminoanthraquinone (amide formation)

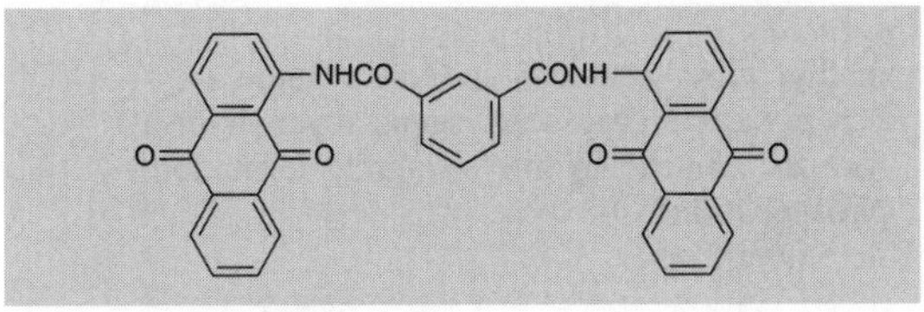

Uses: dye (cotton, viscose)

Vat Yellow 28
69000 (CI); [4229-15-6]

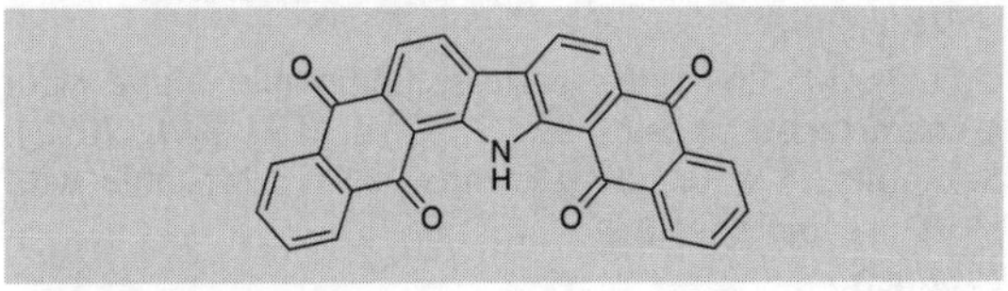

$C_{28}H_{13}N_1O_4$. M: 427.42.
Production:
• 1-aminoanthraquinone + 1-chloroanthraquinone
  (amine formation/acid-catalysed coupling/oxidation)
Uses: dye (cotton, viscose, silk)

VBR *See:* vinyl bromide

VCM *See:* vinyl chloride

VCVDC
See: vinylidene chloride-vinyl chloride copolymers

VDC *See:* vinylidene chloride

VDF *See:* vinylidene fluoride

Vectra *See:* poly(imide-sulphone)

verapamil
[52-53-9]

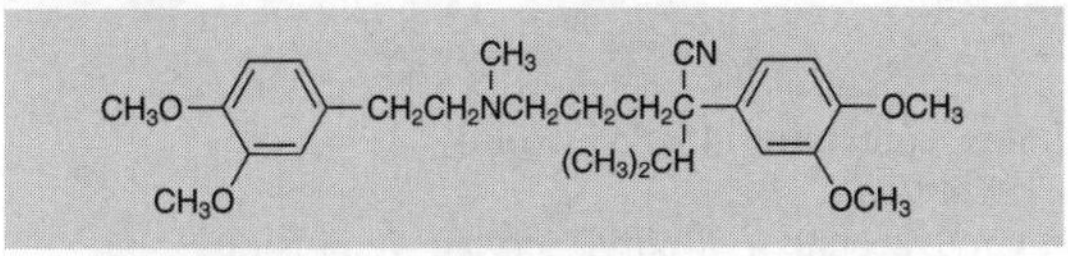

$C_{27}H_{38}N_2O_4$. M: 454.61. Available commercially as the free base or hydrochloride.
Production:
• veratryl cyanide + isopropyl bromide +
  homoveratrylamine + 1-bromo-3-chloropropane
  (dehydrobromination/methylation/amine formation/
  dehydrochlorination)
Uses: antianginal/antiarrhythmic drug

veratraldehyde
3,4-dimethoxybenzaldehyde; vertraldehyde; [120-14-9]
$C_9H_{10}O_3$. M: 166.18. Crystalline solid. MP: 42–45°C.
BP: 281°C. Slightly soluble in hot water. Soluble in oxygenated solvents.

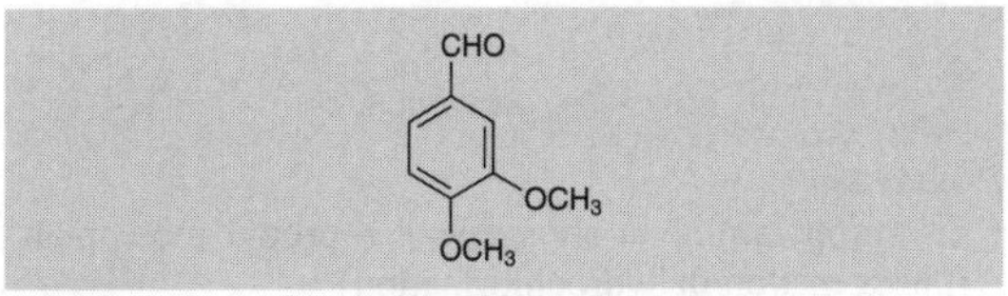

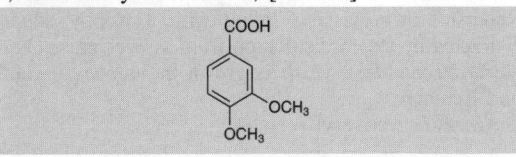

Production:
• vanillin + dimethyl sulphate (ether formation)
Derivatives:
adrenalone; 4-amino-2-chloro-6,7-dimethoxyquinazoline;
epinephrine; veratric acid
Uses: fragrance ingredient

veratric acid
3,4-dimethoxybenzoic acid; [93-07-2]

$C_9H_{10}O_4$. M: 182.18. Needles. MP: 182–184°C. Sublimes. Soluble in hot water and oxygenated solvents.
Production:
• veratraldehyde (carbonyl oxidation)
Derivatives: mebeverine

veratryl cyanide
3,4-dimethoxybenzeneacetonitrile; 3,4-dimethoxybenzyl cyanide; [93-17-4]

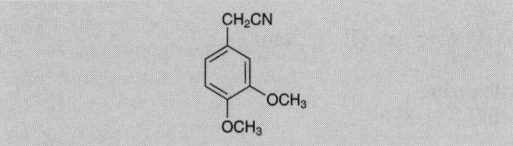

$C_{10}H_{11}N_1O_2$. M: 177.21. Solid. MP: 63–67°C.
Production:
• homoveratric acid + ammonia (nitrile formation)
Derivatives: homoveratrylamine; verapamil

verbena oil, Indian *See:* lemongrass oil

vermiculite
A specific form of mica that exfoliates under heat into thin, lightweight flakes. The main producing countries are USA, Canada and South Africa.
Uses: oil-well drilling mud fluid loss control agent; refractory ceramics ingredient; lightweight concrete aggregate; sound/thermal insulation

vernaldehyde *See:* 1-methyl-4-(4-methyl-3-penten-1-yl)-3-cyclohexenecarboxaldehyde

vernolate
S-propyl dipropylthiocarbamate; [1929-77-7]
$C_{10}H_{21}N_1O_1S_1$. M: 203.35.

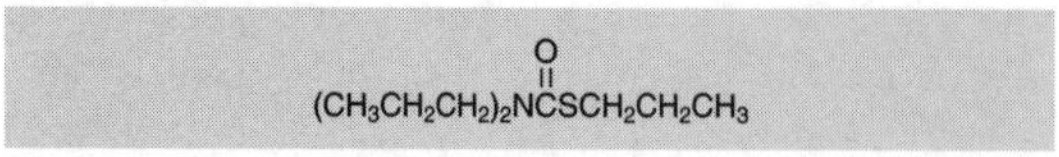

$$(CH_3CH_2CH_2)_2NCSCH_2CH_2CH_3$$

with O double bond on C

Production:
• di-*n*-propylamine + phosgene + *n*-propyl mercaptan (phosgenation/dehydrochlorination)
Uses: herbicide

Versamid *See:* polyamide resins, reactive

vertraldehyde *See:* veratraldehyde

Vespel *See:* polyimide resins

vetiver oil
Reddish-brown, viscous liquid with a woody odour. Extracted by steam distillation from vetiver grass (*Vetiveria zizanioides*) which is grown in Indonesia, Haiti and Reunion.
Derivatives: vetiveryl acetate

vetiveryl acetate
[39850-93-6]
$C_{17}H_{26}O_2$. M: 262.40. Pale yellow liquid with a woody odour. Mixed product.
Production:
• vetiver oil + acetic anhydride (esterification)
Uses: fragrance ingredient/fixative

VFM *See:* vinyl fluoride

VGO *See:* gas oil, vacuum

viloxazine
[46817-91-8]

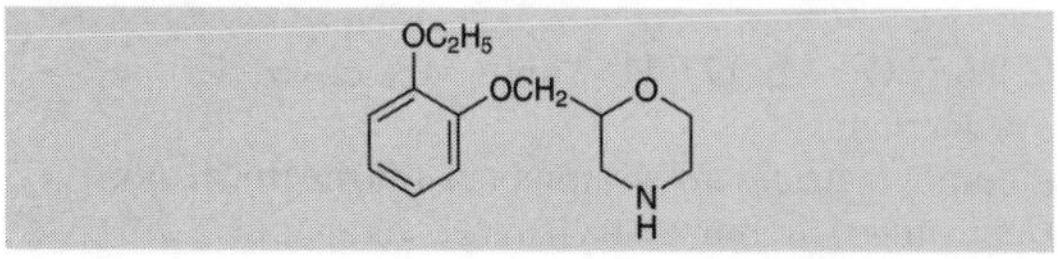

$C_{13}H_{19}N_1O_3$. M: 237.30. Available commercially as the hydrochloride.
Production:
• catechol + diethyl sulphate + epichlorohydrin + monoethanolamine (ethylation/ether formation/epoxidation)
Uses: antidepressant drug

vinclozolin
3-(3,5-dichlorophenyl)-5-methyl-5-vinyl-1,3-oxazolidine-2,4-dione; [50471-44-8]

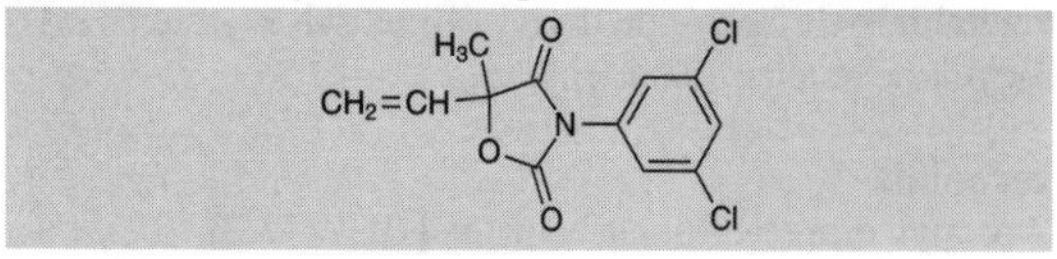

$C_{12}H_9Cl_2N_1O_3$. M: 286.12.

Production:
• methyl vinyl ketone + sodium cyanide + 3,5-dichloroaniline + phosgene (cyanohydrin formation/nitrile hydrolysis/amide formation/phosgenation)
Uses: fungicide

vinyl acetate
VAM; [108-05-4]

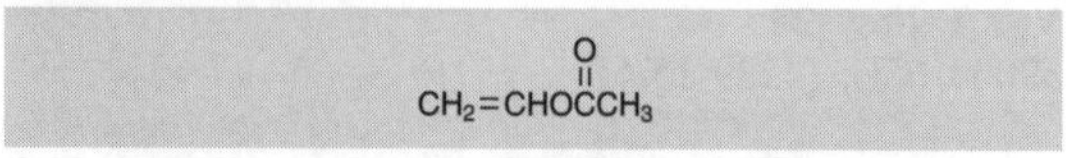

$$CH_2=CHOCCH_3$$

with O double bond

$C_4H_6O_2$. M: 86.09. Colourless, flammable liquid with a characteristic odour. BP: 73°C. d: 0.93 kg/l (20°C). Solubility in water: 20 g/l water (20°C). Miscible with most organic solvents.
Production:
• ethylene + acetic acid (liquid-phase oxidative addition process)
• acetylene + acetic acid (addition)
• ethylene + acetic acid (gas-phase oxidative addition process)
Derivatives: ethylene-vinyl acetate copolymers, <10% vinyl acetate; ethylene-vinyl acetate copolymers, 15% vinyl acetate; ethylene-vinyl acetate copolymers, 18-50% vinyl acetate; ethylene-vinyl acetate copolymers, 40-50% vinyl acetate; ethylene-vinyl alcohol copolymers; polyacrylonitrile; polyvinyl acetate; vinyl acetate-butyl acrylate copolymers; vinyl acetate-crotonic acid copolymers; vinyl acetate-ethylene-vinyl chloride copolymers; vinyl acetate-vinyl neodecanoate copolymers; vinyl chloride-vinyl acetate copolymers; vinylpyrrolidone-vinyl acetate copolymers
Uses: nitrile rubber comonomer

vinyl acetate-butyl acrylate copolymers

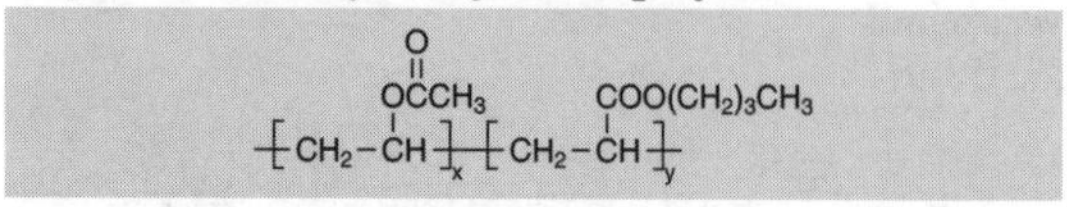

Latex containing 45–55% solids.
Production:
• vinyl acetate + *n*-butyl acrylate (emulsion polymerisation)
Uses: heat-seal coatings; impregnating agent (blinds, upholstery fabrics, knitted fabrics); binder (emulsion paints, paper sizing, textured coatings, wallpaper coatings, fabric wadding)

vinyl acetate-crotonic acid copolymers
poly(vinyl acetate-crotonic acid)

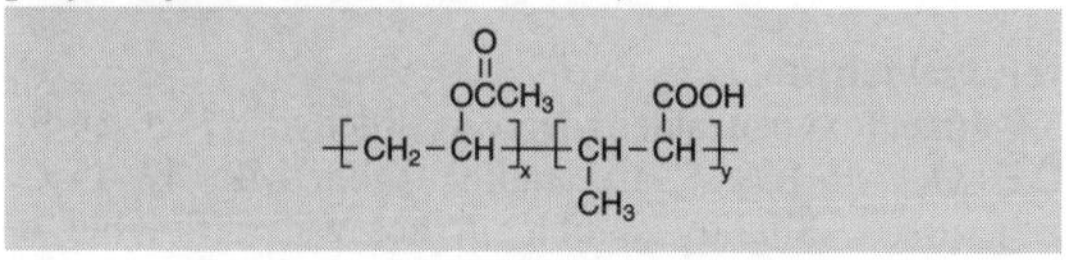

Beads. Softening point: 80–100°C.

Production:
* vinyl acetate + crotonic acid (emulsion polymerisation)

Uses: adhesives

vinyl acetate-ethylene-vinyl chloride copolymers

$$\left[CH_2-CH\right]_{} \left[CH_2-CH_2\right]_m \left[CH_2-CH\right]_n$$
(OCCH$_3$, O; Cl substituents)

Latex containing around 50% solids.
Production:
* vinyl acetate + ethylene + vinyl chloride (emulsion polymerisation)

Uses:
binder (internal/external emulsion paints, paper coatings, fabric coatings, construction adhesives)

vinyl acetate-vinyl neodecanoate copolymers

$$\left[CH_2-CH\right]_x \left[CH_2-CH\right]_y$$
(OCCH$_3$; C$_6$H$_{13}$, CH$_3$-C-CH$_3$, C=O, O substituents)

Latex emulsion containing 50–55% solids. The polymer comprises 65–85% vinyl acetate and 15–35% vinyl neodecanoate. T_g: 17°C.
Production:
* vinyl acetate + vinyl neodecanoate (emulsion polymerisation)

Uses: binder (emulsion paints)

vinyl bromide
VBR; [593-60-2]

$$CH_2=CHBr$$

$C_2H_3Br_1$. M: 106.94. Compressed gas. BP: 16°C. FP: -138°C. d: 1.51 kg/l (15°C). Insoluble in water.
Production:
* acetylene + hydrogen bromide, anhydrous (addition)

Uses: fire-retardant comonomer (textile fibres)

vinyl *n*-butyl ether *See: n*-butyl vinyl ether

N-vinylcarbazole
[1484-13-5]

(structure of N-vinylcarbazole, CH=CH$_2$)

$C_{14}H_{11}N_1$. M: 193.25. Solid. MP: 64–67°C.
Production:
* carbazole + acetylene (amine formation)

Derivatives: polyvinylcarbazole

vinyl chloride
vinyl chloride monomer; VCM; [75-01-4]

$$CH_2=CHCl$$

$C_2H_3Cl_1$. M: 62.49. Colourless gas. BP: -16°C. FP: -154°C. d: 0.97 kg/l (-14°C). Very slightly soluble in water. Miscible with oxygenated and chlorinated solvents.
Production:
* ethylene dichloride (dehydrochlorination)
* acetylene + hydrogen chloride, anhydrous (addition)

Derivatives:
1,1-dichloroethane; (ethylene-vinyl acetate)-vinyl chloride graft copolymers; modacrylic fibre; poly(isobutyl vinyl ether-vinyl chloride); polyvinyl chloride; polyvinyl chloride, high-impact; 1,1,2-trichloroethane; vinyl acetate-ethylene-vinyl chloride copolymers; vinyl chloride-acrylic ester copolymers; vinyl chloride-cyclohexylmaleimide copolymers; vinyl chloride-ethylene copolymers; vinyl chloride-propylene copolymers; vinyl chloride-vinyl acetate copolymers; vinyl fluoride; vinylidene chloride copolymers, latex; vinylidene chloride-vinyl chloride copolymers

vinyl chloride-acrylic ester copolymers
Copolymers containing 75–82% vinyl chloride, 16–24% acrylic ester and a third monomer in some grades.
Production:
* vinyl chloride + methyl acrylate/*n*-butyl acrylate/ 2-ethylhexyl acrylate (emulsion polymerisation)

Uses: fire-resistant coatings; alkyd/epoxy resin additive (textile, paper, magnetic tape coatings); paper sizing

vinyl chloride-cyclohexylmaleimide copolymers
Hostalit LP (Hoechst)

$$\left[CH_2-CH\right]_x \left[C-CH\right]_y$$
(Cl; cyclohexyl-N, O, O, H substituents)

Production:
* vinyl chloride + *N*-cyclohexylmaleimide (polymerisation)

Uses: hot-filled food containers

vinyl chloride-ethylene copolymers

$$\left[CH_2-CH\right]_x \left[CH_2-CH_2\right]_y$$
(Cl substituent)

The polymers also contain a small proportion of a third, functional monomer. Self-extinguishing.
Production:
* vinyl chloride + ethylene (emulsion polymerisation)

Uses: carpetbacking latex; binder (water-based inks, industrial/barrier coatings, paper sizing)

vinyl chloride-propylene copolymers
Sta-Flow (Air Products and Chemical)

Thermoplastic containing 2–10% propylene. An easily moulded, heat-stable form of PVC. d: 1.35–1.40 kg/l. Tensile strength: 50 MPa. Flexural strength: 2,500 MPa.
Production:
• vinyl chloride + propylene (polymerisation)
Uses:
household equipment housings/toys; packaging sheet

vinyl chloride-vinyl acetate copolymers
poly(vinyl chloride-vinyl acetate); PVCA; VC/VAC; [34149-92-3]

Thermoplastics containing 5–20% vinyl acetate. d: 1.37 kg/l.
Production:
• vinyl chloride + vinyl acetate (suspension polymerisation)
Uses: industrial fibres; plasticised compounds (flooring tiles, sheet); rigid compounds (records, drawing equipment, rulers, stencils); binder (marine antifouling paints, metal/plaster/concrete paints, chemically-resistant coatings)

vinyl cyanide *See:* acrylonitrile

4-vinylcyclohexene
butadiene dimer; cyclohexenylethylene; [100-40-3]

C_8H_{12}. M: 108.19. Liquid. BP: 129–131°C. d: 0.83 kg/l (20°C). Insoluble in water.
Production:
• butadiene (Diels-Alder cycloaddition)
Derivatives: dibromoethyldibromocyclohexane; β-(3,4-epoxycyclohexyl)ethyltrimethoxysilane; vinylcyclohexene dioxide

vinylcyclohexene dioxide
Unox Epoxide 206 (Union Carbide); [4223-10-3]

$C_8H_{12}O_2$. M: 140.19. Colourless liquid. d: 1.10 kg/l. Epoxide equivalent: 76 g.

Production:
• 4-vinylcyclohexene + peracetic acid (epoxidation)
Uses: cycloaliphatic epoxy resins

vinyl ester resins
Derakane (Dow Chemical); Diacryl 101 (Akzo)
Liquid comprising methacrylate-terminated epoxy resin prepolymers dissolved in styrene. The resin is cured with peroxide catalysts in the same way as other unsaturated polyester resins. Vinyl esters are characterised by their high strength and elongation performance as well as their resistance to attack by acids and solvents. Special, high-temperature, fire-retarded or high-toughness grades are also available.
Production:
• bisphenol A diglycidyl ether/di-(2-hydroxyethyl)-bisphenol A/epoxy-novolac resins + methacrylic acid/methyl methacrylate + styrene (esterification)
Uses: chemically-resistant, fibre-reinforced piping/tanks

vinyl ethyl ether *See:* ethyl vinyl ether

vinyl fluoride
VF; VFM; [75-02-5]

$C_2H_3F_1$. M: 46.04. Colourless gas with an ethereal odour. BP: -72°C. MP: -160°C. d: 0.78 kg/l (-30°C). Insoluble in water. The commercial product contains a polymerisation inhibitor.
Production:
• acetylene + hydrogen fluoride (addition)
• vinyl chloride + hydrogen fluoride (addition/dehydrochlorination)
Derivatives: polyvinyl fluoride

vinylidene chloride
1,1-dichloroethylene; VC; VDC; [75-35-4]

$C_2H_2Cl_2$. M: 96.95. Colourless, mobile liquid with a characteristic, sweet smell. BP: 31°C. FP: -122°C. d: 1.21 kg/l (20°C). Insoluble in water. Commercial grades contain polymerisation inhibitors.
Production:
• 1,1,2-trichloroethane (dehydrochlorination)
Derivatives:
modacrylic fibre; vinylidene chloride copolymers, latex; vinylidene chloride-methyl acrylate copolymers; vinylidene chloride-vinyl chloride copolymers
Uses: nitrile rubber comonomer

vinylidene chloride copolymers, latex

X = polar group. Latex emulsion containing vinylidene

chloride and 7–50% comonomer. High vinylidene chloride contents are used where low gas or water permeability is required. For improved flexibility or light fastness higher comonomer contents are used.
Production:
• vinylidene chloride + acrylonitrile/methyl methacrylate/vinyl chloride/ethyl acrylate/methyl acrylate (emulsion polymerisation)
Uses: fire-resistant emulsion paints; barrier coatings (paper, film, aluminium foil and board); binder (wallpaper coatings); textile/carpet coatings

vinylidene chloride-methyl acrylate copolymers
Saran MA (Dow Chemical)

$$\left[CH_2-CCl_2\right]_x\left[CH_2-\overset{\displaystyle COOCH_3}{\underset{\displaystyle }{CH}}\right]_y$$

Production:
• vinylidene chloride + methyl acrylate (suspension polymerisation)
Uses: food packaging film

vinylidene chloride-vinyl chloride copolymers
poly(vinylidene chloride-vinyl chloride); VCVDC; Saran (Dow Chemical)

$$\left[CH_2-CCl_2\right]_x\left[CH_2-\overset{\displaystyle Cl}{\underset{\displaystyle }{CH}}\right]_y$$

Thermoplastic consisting of vinylidene chloride polymerised with 10–15% vinyl chloride. d: 1.67–1.71 kg/l. Tensile strength: 60–140 MPa (film), 140–280 MPa (filament). The fibre is characterised by its flexibility, toughness, weather and chemical resistance. The film is produced by casting techniques. It has excellent clarity, is strong with low permeability to gas and water.
Production:
• vinylidene chloride + vinyl chloride (suspension polymerisation)
Uses: filaments (outdoor furniture, vehicle upholstery, agricultural/industrial fabrics, filters); biaxially-oriented film (food packaging); chemical plant components and piping

vinylidene fluoride
1,1-difluoroethylene; VDF; [75-38-7]

$$CH_2=CF_2$$

$C_2H_2F_2$. M: 64.04. Colourless, odourless gas. BP: -86°C. d: 0.61 kg/l (25°C). Slightly soluble in water. Soluble in oxygenated solvents. Flammable.
Production:
• 1-chloro-1,1-difluoroethane (dehydrochlorination)
Derivatives: difluoroethane; hexafluoroisobutylene-vinylidene fluoride copolymers; polyvinylidene fluoride; vinylidene fluoride-hexafluoropropylene copolymers; vinylidene fluoride-hexafluoropropylene-tetrafluoroethylene terpolymers

vinylidene fluoride-hexafluoropropylene copolymers
Viton A (Du Pont)

$$\left[CH_2-CF_2\right]_x\left[CF_2-\overset{\displaystyle CF_3}{\underset{\displaystyle }{CF}}\right]_y$$

Elastomers consisting of 60–85% vinylidene fluoride. The polymer is characterised by its good thermal properties and its chemical resistance.
Production:
• vinylidene fluoride + hexafluoropropylene (polymerisation)
Uses: high performance seals/gaskets (aerospace, aircraft, chemical plant components)

vinylidene fluoride-hexafluoropropylene-tetrafluoroethylene terpolymers
Viton B (Du Pont)

$$\left[CH_2-CF_2\right]_x\left[CF_2-\overset{\displaystyle CF_3}{\underset{\displaystyle }{CF}}\right]_y\left[CF_2-CF_2\right]_z$$

Elastomers characterised by their excellent thermal properties as well as their chemical and solvent resistance.
Production:
• vinylidene fluoride + hexafluoropropylene + tetrafluoroethylene (polymerisation)
Uses: high performance elastomers

N-vinylimidazole
[1072-63-5]

$C_5H_6N_2$. M: 94.11. Liquid. BP: 74–77°C (1.3 kPa). MP: <-50°C. Soluble in water.
Production:
• imidazole + acetylene (ethynylation)
Uses: comonomer/grafting reagent (ashless lubricant dispersants)

vinyl isobutyl ether *See:* isobutyl vinyl ether

vinyl methyl ether *See:* methyl vinyl ether

vinyl methyl ketone *See:* methyl vinyl ketone

vinyl neodecanoate
Veova 10 (Shell)

$$C_6H_{13}\overset{\displaystyle CH_3}{\underset{\displaystyle CH_3}{C}}COOCH=CH_2$$

$C_{12}H_{22}O_2$. M: 198.31. BP: 210°C.
Production:
• neodecanoic acid + acetylene (vinylation)
Derivatives:
vinyl acetate-vinyl neodecanoate copolymers

vinyl propionate
[105-38-4]

$$CH_2=CHOCCH_2CH_3$$
(with O double-bonded above C)

$C_5H_8O_2$. M: 100.11. Liquid. BP: 95°C. d: 0.92 kg/l (20°C). Insoluble in water.
Production:
• acetylene + propionic acid (vinylation)
Derivatives: poly(vinyl propionate)

2-vinylpyridine
[100-69-6]

$C_7H_7N_1$. M: 105.15. Yellow liquid. BP: 158°C. Slightly soluble in water. Soluble in oxygenated and chlorinated solvents.
Production:
• α-picoline + formaldehyde (condensation/dehydration)
Derivatives:
2-ethylpyridine; vinylpyridine copolymers, latex
Uses: acrylic fibre comonomer; grafting reagent (ashless lubricant dispersants)

4-vinylpyridine

$C_7H_7N_1$. M: 105.15.
Production:
• γ-picoline + formaldehyde (condensation/dehydration)
Derivatives: poly(4-vinylpyridine)

vinylpyridine copolymers, latex
pyridine-styrene-butadiene copolymers, latex; VP Latex; PSBR

Latex. Standard grades consist of 15% styrene, 70% butadiene and 15% 2-vinylpyridine.
Production:
• styrene + butadiene + 2-vinylpyridine (emulsion polymerisation)
Uses: tyre cord/drive belt adhesives

N-vinyl-2-pyrrolidone
NVP; [88-12-0]
$C_6H_9N_1O_1$. M: 111.15. Colourless solid or liquid. MP: 14°C. BP: 90–93°C (1.3 kPa).

Production:
• 2-pyrrolidone + acetylene (ethynylation)
Derivatives:
polyvinylpyrrolidone; polyvinylpyrrolidone, crosslinked; vinylpyrrolidone-vinyl acetate copolymers
Uses:
comonomer (water-soluble/hydrophilic polymers); grafting reagent (ashless lubricant dispersants); reactive diluent (radiation-cured inks/lacquers)

vinylpyrrolidone-vinyl acetate copolymers
PVP/VA

Available as 50% solutions in ethanol or isopropanol with the vinyl pyrrolidone:vinyl acetate ratio in the range 70:30 to 20:80.
Production:
• N-vinyl-2-pyrrolidone + vinyl acetate (emulsion polymerisation)
Uses:
film-forming agent (hairsprays, pharmaceutical coatings); protective colloid (emulsion polymerisation); thickening agent (cosmetics); viscosity modifier (coatings, drilling muds, detergents, pigment dispersions)

vinyltoluene
m/p-methylstyrene; methylstyrene; VT; [25013-15-4]

C_9H_{10}. M: 118.18. Colourless liquid. BP: 168°C. FP: -77°C. d: 0.89 kg/l (25°C). Insoluble in water. Miscible with oxygenated solvents. Flash point: 51°C (TCC).
Production:
• toluene + ethylene (Friedel-Crafts alkylation/ dehydrogenation)
Derivatives:
acrylic resins, carboxylated; alkyd resins, styrenated/vinyltoluenated; α-methylstyrene-vinyltoluene copolymers; styrene-acrylic copolymers; vinyltoluene-acrylic copolymers, latex
Uses: polystyrene/alkyd/epoxy ester resin comonomer; reactive diluent (unsaturated polyester resins)

vinyltoluene-acrylic copolymers, latex
Production:
• vinyltoluene + 2-ethylhexyl acrylate (emulsion polymerisation)

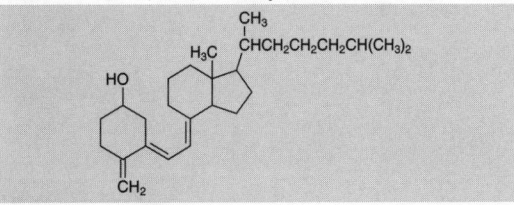

Uses: binder (external masonry paints)

vinyltriacetoxysilane

$CH_2=CHSi(O\overset{O}{\overset{\|}{C}}CH_3)_3$

$C_8H_{12}O_6Si_1$. M: 232.27.
Production:
• vinyltrichlorosilane + acetic acid
  (dehydrochlorination)
Uses: plastics coupling agent

vinyltrichlorosilane
[75-94-5]

$CH_2=CHSiCl_3$

$C_2H_3Cl_3Si_1$. M: 161.49. Pale yellow liquid. BP: 90°C.
d: 1.26 kg/l (25°C). Hydrolysed by water. Flash point:
15°C (COC).
Production:
• trichlorosilane + acetylene (hydrosilation)
Derivatives:
triethoxyvinylsilane; tris(β-methoxyethoxy)vinylsilane;
vinyltriacetoxysilane
Uses: plastics coupling agent

vinyltriethoxysilane
See: triethoxyvinylsilane

vinyl tris(β-methoxyethoxy)silane
See: tris(β-methoxyethoxy)vinylsilane

vinyon *See:* polyvinyl chloride

violanthrone *See:* dibenzanthrone

violet leaf alcohol
2-*trans*-6-*cis*-nonadien-1-ol; [28069-72-9]

$C_9H_{16}O_1$. M: 140.23. Colourless liquid with a strong,
violet odour. BP: 98°C (1.5 kPa). d: 0.86 kg/l (25°C).
Insoluble in water.
Production:
• 3-hexenol + acrolein (chlorination/Grignard
  reaction/rearrangement)
Uses: fragrance ingredient

viscose *See:* sodium cellulose xanthate

viscose rayon *See:* cellulose, regenerated

vitamin A
retinol; vitamin A₁; [68-26-8]; [127-47-9] (acetate ester); [79-81-2] (palmitate ester)

$C_{20}H_{30}O_1$. M: 286.46. Yellowish crystals. MP: 57–58°C.
Insoluble in water. Also available commercially as the
acetate, propionate and palmitate esters.
Production:
• β-C₁₄ aldehyde + methyl pentenynol (Hoffmann-La
  Roche synthesis)
• β-ionone + 3-formylcrotonyl acetate + acetylene
  (BASF synthesis)
Uses: dietary supplement; animal feed additive

vitamin B₁ *See:* thiamine

vitamin B₂ *See:* riboflavin

vitamin B₃ *See:* nicotinic acid; nicotinamide

vitamin B₆ *See:* pyridoxine

vitamin B₁₂
cyanocobalamin (INN); [68-19-9]
$C_{63}H_{88}Co_1N_{14}O_{14}P_1$. M: 1355.38. Pure cyanocobalamin
consists of dark red, hygroscopic crystals. Slightly soluble in water. Soluble in alcohol. More commonly available prediluted in sugar, starch or dicalcium phosphate as a pink powder.
Production:
• microbial fermentation medium + *Streptomyces
  olivaceus* bacteria (fermentation/extraction)
Uses: animal feed additive; dietary supplement

vitamin C *See:* ascorbic acid

vitamin D₂ *See:* calciferol

vitamin D₃
cholecalciferol (INN); 7-dehydrocholesterol; [67-97-0]

$C_{27}H_{44}O_1$. M: 384.65.

Production:
• 7-dehydrocholesterol (photochemical conversion)
Uses: dietary supplement; animal feed additive; pharmaceutical ingredient

vitamin E *See:* α-tocopherol; *See:* tocopherol, mixed

vitamin H *See:* biotin

vitamin K₁
phyloquinone; phytomenadione; [84-80-0]

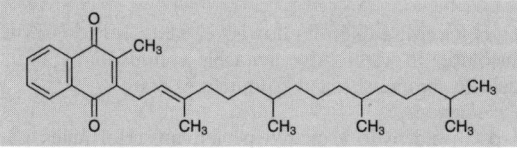

$C_{31}H_{46}O_2$. M: 450.71. The commercial product is a mixture of the *cis* and *trans*-isomers with the *trans*-isomer predominating.
Production:
• menadione + acetic anhydride + phytol (quinone reduction/esterification/orthoalkylation/hydrolysis/dehydrogenation)
Uses: antihaemorrhagic drug

vitamin K₃ *See:* menadione

VLDPE *See:* polyethylene, very low-density

VLO *See:* linseed oil

VPA *See:* valproic acid

VT *See:* vinyltoluene

walnut oil
[8024-09-7]
Brown oil. Produced by expression from the fruit kernel of the walnut (*Juglans*) tree. d: 0.93 kg/l. Insoluble in water. The chain-length distribution is: 17–29% $C_{18:1}$, 73% $C_{18:2}$ and 10–16% $C_{18:3}$.
Uses: cooking/salad oil; drying oil (paints/alkyd resins)

warfarin
4-hydroxy-3-(3-oxo-1-pentylbutyl)coumarin; [81-81-2]

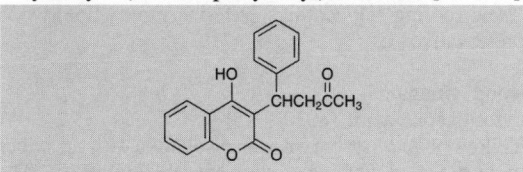

$C_{19}H_{16}O_4$. M: 308.34.
Production:
• benzylideneacetone + 4-hydroxycoumarin (condensation)
Uses: anticoagulant drug; rodenticide

washing soda *See:* sodium carbonate

wash oil *See:* creosote oil

water-glass *See:* sodium silicate

wattle bark extract
tannin
Extract of black wattle (mimosa, *Acacia pycnantha*, *A. mollissima* and *A. binervata*) bark containing about 35% tannin. Australia is the main producing country.
Uses: laking agent (flexographic dye inks); rust conversion formulations; tanning agent

wax, Fischer-Tropsch
n-paraffins (C_{24}-C_{60})
Fischer-Tropsch waxes are supplied in several grades. Sasol provides medium wax (C_{24}–C_{35}) and hard wax (>C_{35}). These products are oxidised or partially saponified to form other grades.
Production:
• synthesis gas (Synthol Fischer-Tropsch process; coproduced with naphtha, light, Synthol/naphtha, heavy/gas oil, light/oxygenates, Fischer-Tropsch, mixed/refinery gas)
• synthesis gas (Arge Fischer-Tropsch process; coproduced with naphtha, heavy/gas oil, light, Arge-/oxygenates, Fischer-Tropsch, mixed/refinery gas)
• synthesis gas (Shell MDS process; coproduced with naphtha, heavy/kerosene/gas oil, light/refinery gas)

Derivatives: wax, oxidised
Uses: candles; electrical insulation; hot melt adhesives; polish/release agents/anticorrosion products; polyvinyl chloride processing lubricant; textile finishing agent

wax, oxidised
[68441-17-8]
Carboxylated hydrocarbon wax. Acid value: 25–30 mg KOH/g. Oxidised wax is relatively easy to emulsify in water.
Production:
• microcrystalline wax/polyethylene wax, high-density/polyethylene wax, low-density/wax, Fischer-Tropsch (air oxidation)
Uses: floor polish/coatings/emulsions ingredient; plastics/resin processing lubricant; textile auxiliaries

wheat germ oil
[8006-95-9]
Yellow liquid. Produced by expression and solvent extraction of wheat germ. d: 0.93 kg/l (25°C). Insoluble in water. Slightly soluble in alcohol.
Uses:
dietary supplement

whey
Byproduct of cheese production. Contains, typically, 5% lactose, 1% protein and 1% fats, salts and lactic acid.
Derivatives:
ethanol; DL-lactic acid; lactose; single cell protein
Uses: animal feed ingredient

white acid *See:* hydrofluoric acid

white arsenic *See:* arsenic trioxide

white lead *See:* lead carbonate, basic

white oil
liquid paraffin
Available as pale yellow, technical-grade oil or colourless, medicinal grade. Chemically the oils consist of alkanes and cycloalkanes with very little aromatics.
Production:
• lubricant oils, distillates + oleum (wet refining process; coproduced with sodium petroleum sulphonate)
Uses: base oil (toiletries, cosmetics, creams, pharmaceuticals); high-boiling lacquer solvent; chewing gum ingredient; lubricant (food handling machinery, textile processing); pesticide adjuvant (horticultural sprays); paper waterproofing agent

white precipitate *See:* mercuric chloride, ammoniated

white spirit
mineral spirits; naphtha, Stoddard solvent; turpentine substitute; VM&P
Hydrocarbon distillation fraction with BP: 140–210°C and an aromatic content of 15–19%. Flash point: >40°C. A number of different fractions within the boiling range are available.
Production:
• naphtha, heavy (fractionation; coproduced with special boiling-point solvents)
Derivatives: white spirit, dearomatised
Uses: solvent (dry-cleaning, metal cleaning, industrial cleaning, paints, varnishes, printing inks, floor polishes, textile printing, cutback bitumen roofing compounds, selective herbicide formulations); extraction solvent (rosin, wax);

white spirit, dearomatised
Exxsol D (Exxon Chemical)
Colourless liquids. Various distillation fractions in the boiling range 140–240°C. d: 0.75–0.78 kg/l. The aromatics content is generally less than 1%. The solvent properties are inferior to standard white spirit but the odour is considerably reduced.
Production:
• white spirit (hydrogenation)
Uses: solvent (paints, printing ink, resins, polishes, household products)

whiting *See:* calcite; calcium carbonate, precipitated

witchhazel extract
Produced by steam distillation of the leaves and bark of wych hazel (*Hamamelis virginiana*).
Uses: astringent drug

wolfram *See:* tungsten

wood creosote
Mixed product containing guaiacol, creosol and related phenols as well as phenol ether.
Production:
• tar oil, wood (alkali extraction)
Uses: expectorant drug; antiseptic; antiskinning agent (oil-based paints, lacquers)

wood pitch
Brown-black solid. Softening point: 40–85°C, depending on grade.
Production:
• wood tar, hardwood (fractionation; coproduced with tar oil, wood)
• pyrolysis oil, pinewood (fractionation; coproduced with turpentine oil, wood/pine oil/tar oil, wood)
Uses: lens grinding adhesive

wood spirit
Dark yellow liquid consisting of methanol with acetic, propionic and butyric acid as the main impurities.
Production:
• pyrolysis oil, hardwood (separation; coproduced with wood vinegar/wood tar, hardwood)
Uses: ethanol/acetic acid denaturant

wood tar, hardwood
Production:
• pyrolysis oil, hardwood (separation; coproduced with wood vinegar/wood spirit)
Derivatives: 3-methyl-2-cyclopenten-2-ol-1-one; maltol; tar oil, wood; wood pitch
Uses: roofing felt/coatings; veterinary medicine; wood preservative

wood vinegar
pyroligneous acid; [8030-97-5]
Yellow or reddish-brown water solution with an odour of acetic acid and wood tar. Miscible in water. The major active constituent of the product is acetic acid.
Production:
• pyrolysis oil, hardwood (separation; coproduced with wood tar, hardwood/wood spirit)
Uses: flavouring ingredient (smoked meats)

xanthan gum

corn sugar gum; xanthan; E415 (EC); [11138-66-2]
White to cream powder. Long-chain polysaccharide gum. Soluble in water producing viscous, highly-pseudoplastic solutions. Unaffected by high or low pH. Insoluble in most organic solvents.
Production:
- microbial fermentation medium + *Xanthomonas campestris* bacteria (fermentation)

Uses:
conditioning agent/stabiliser (toiletries); stabiliser (salad dressing, bakery products, dairy goods); viscosifier (oil-well workover fluids, cleaners, adhesives, pesticides, paint)

xanthinol nicotinate

xanthinol niacinate; [437-74-1]

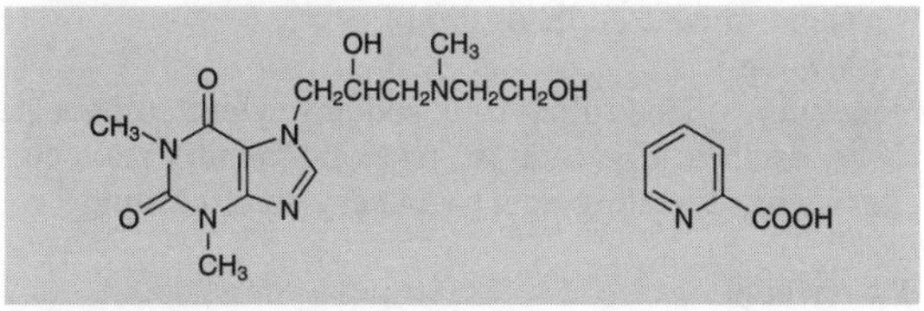

$C_{19}H_{26}N_6O_6$. M: 434.45.
Production:
- methylethanolamine + epichlorohydrin + theophylline + nicotinic acid (epoxidation/amine formation/salt formation)

Uses:
vasodilator drug

xanthotoxin *See:* methoxsalen

xenon

Xe_1. M: 131.30. Colourless gas. BP: -108°C. d: 5.90 g/l (gas).
Production:
- air (cryogenic separation; byproduct of oxygen/nitrogen production)

Uses:
inert filler gas (fluorescent tubes)

xipamide

[14293-44-8]
$C_{15}H_{15}Cl_1N_2O_4S_1$. M: 354.80.
Production:
- *p*-aminosalicylic acid + chlorosulphonic acid + ammonia + 2,6-xylidine (diazotisation/Sandmeyer reaction/chlorosulphonation/sulphonamide formation/amide formation)

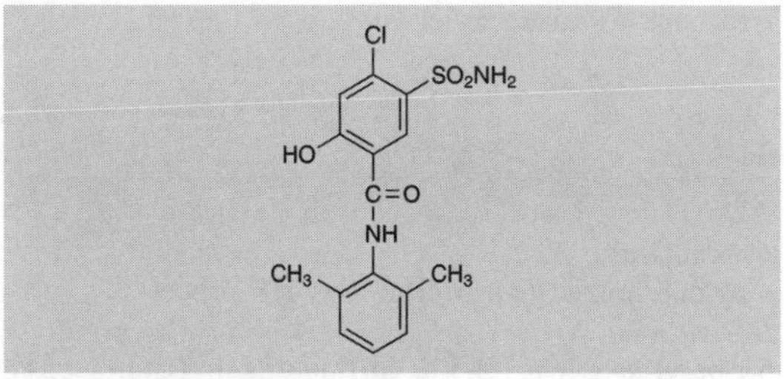

Uses: diuretic drug

XMC *See:* 3,5-xylyl methylcarbamate

XPE *See:* polyethylene, crosslinked

XPS *See:* polystyrene, expandable

XR resin *See:* tetrafluoroethylene-perfluoro(vinyl ether sulphonate) copolymers

XSBR *See:* styrene-butadiene copolymers, carboxylated

xylene, mixed

C_8 aromatics; dimethylbenzene; xylene; xylol; [1330-20-7]

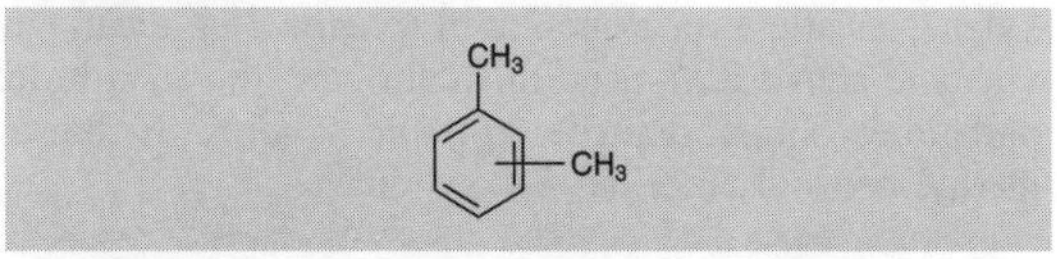

C_8H_{10}. M: 106.17. Colourless liquid with a mild, aromatic odour. BR: 138–141°C. d: 0.87 kg/l (15°C). Insoluble in water. Miscible with most organic solvents. Flash point: 29°C (CC).
Production:
- aromatics, mixed (separation; coproduced with benzene/toluene/C_{9+} aromatics)
- toluene (disproportionation; coproduced with benzene)
- toluene + trimethylbenzene fraction (disproportionation)

Derivatives: ethylbenzene; perfluorodimethylcyclohexane; Solvent Red 27; *m*-xylene; *o*-xylene; *p*-xylene; xylenesulphonic acid
Uses: insecticide carrier; solvent (alkyd resins, acrylic resins, paints, lacquers, printing inks, adhesives)

m-xylene

1,3-dimethylbenzene; MX; [108-38-3]
C_8H_{10}. M: 106.17. Colourless liquid. BP: 137–138°C. MP: -47°C. d: 0.86 kg/l (20°C). Insoluble in water.

Soluble in alcohol. Miscible with ether and hydrocarbon solvents. Impure *m*-xylene is produced by separation of the *o*-xylene and *p*-xylene components of mixed xylenes. The remaining stream is usually isomerised back to mixed xylenes.

Production:
• xylene, mixed (Mitsubishi Gas HF process)
Derivatives:
5-*t*-butyl-*m*-xylene; 3,5-di-(trifluoromethyl)aniline; isophthalic acid; isophthalodinitrile; 3-(trifluoromethyl)-benzoyl fluoride; 3,5-xylenol; 2,4-xylidine; 2,6-xylidine

o-xylene
1,2-dimethylbenzene; [95-47-6]

C_8H_{10}. M: 106.17. Colourless liquid. BP: 144–145°C. FP: -25°C. d: 0.88 kg/l (15°C). Insoluble in water. Miscible with most organic solvents. Flash point: 30°C (TOC).
Production:
• xylene, mixed (fractionation)
Derivatives:
benzophenonetetracarboxylate dianhydride; 4-chloro-*o*-xylene; hexafluoropropane-2,2-bis(phenyl-3′,4′-dicarboxylic acid anhydride); pendimethalin; phthalic anhydride; phthalide; phthalodinitrile; *o*-toluic acid; 2-(trifluoromethyl)benzoyl fluoride; 3,4-xylidine

p-xylene
1,4-dimethylbenzene; [106-42-3]

C_8H_{10}. M: 106.17. Colourless liquid. BP: 138–139°C. FP: 13°C. d: 0.86 kg/l (20°C). Insoluble in water. Miscible with most organic solvents.
Production:
• xylene, mixed (separation)
Derivatives: 1,4-bis(chloromethyl)benzene; dimethyl terephthalate; poly-*p*-xylylene; terephthalic acid; 4-(trifluoromethyl)benzaldehyde; 4-(trifluoromethyl)benzyl alcohol; 2,5-xylidine

xylene diisocyanate, hydrogenated
1,3-bis(isocyanatomethyl)cyclohexane; HXDI
$C_{10}H_8N_2O_2$. M: 188.18.

Production:
• 1,3-bis(aminomethyl)cyclohexane + phosgene (phosgenation)
Uses: polyurethane elastomers/adhesives comonomer

xylenesulphonic acid
[25321-41-9]

$C_8H_{10}O_3S_1$. M: 186.23. Brown liquid, most commonly available as a 60–65% solution in water, but also as 80% and 95% grades.
Production:
• xylene, mixed (sulphonation)
Derivatives:
potassium xylene sulphonate; sodium xylene sulphonate
Uses: esterification catalyst; phenolic foundry resin curing agent; descaling agent (foundry sand castings)

2,4-xylenol
2,4-dimethylphenol; 2,4-DMP

$C_8H_{10}O_1$. M: 122.17. Pale amber liquid. BP: 211°C. d: 1.02 kg/l (20°C). Flash point: 92°C (PMCC). Soluble in oxygenated and aromatic solvents. Slightly soluble in water. Standard commercial grades of 2,4-xylenol are mixtures containing about 55% 2,4-xylenol and 27% 2,5-xylenol. Upgraded material is also sold.
Production:
• xylenol, mixed (fractionation)
Derivatives:
6-*t*-butyl-2,4-dimethylphenol; 2,4-dimethyl-6-(α-methylcyclohexyl)phenol; 2,2′-isobutylidenebis(4,6-dimethylphenol)

2,6-xylenol
2,6-dimethylphenol; [576-26-1]

$C_8H_{10}O_1$. M: 122.17. Needles. MP: 46–49°C. BP: 208°C. Soluble in water and alcohol.

Production:
- phenol + methanol (orthoalkylation; coproduced with *o*-cresol)

Derivatives: mexiletine; poly(phenylene oxide); xylenol, butylated; 2,6-xylidine

3,4-xylenol
3,4-dimethylphenol

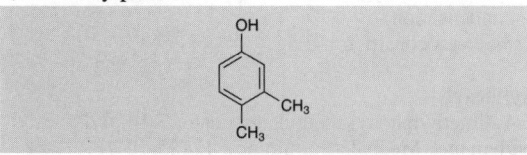

$C_8H_{10}O_1$. M: 122.17. Needles. MP: 65–68°C. BP: 225°C. Slightly soluble in water. Soluble in aromatic solvents.

Production:
- 4-chloro-*o*-xylene (hydrolysis)

Derivatives: 4,4′-oxydiphthalic anhydride; xylylcarb

3,5-xylenol
3,5-dimethylphenol; [108-68-9]

$C_8H_{10}O_1$. M: 122.17. Crystalline solid. BP: 63–65°C. Sublimes above 219°C. Soluble in water and oxygenated solvents.

Production:
- isophorone (dealkylation/dehydrogenation)
- *m*-xylene (sulphonation/alkali fusion)

Derivatives: 4-chloro-3,5-xylenol; methiocarb; 2,3,5-trimethylphenol; 3,5-xylidine; 3,5-xylyl methylcarbamate

xylenol, butylated

$C_{12}H_{18}O_1$. M: 178.27.

Production:
- xylenol, mixed/2,6-xylenol + isobutylene (Friedel-Crafts alkylation)

Uses: antioxidant (motor fuels)

xylenol, mixed
dimethylphenol; [1300-71-6]

$C_8H_{10}O_1$. M: 122.17. Mixed tar acid fraction containing

various xylenol isomers, ethylphenol and higher boiling phenols. BR: 215–230°C. Sparingly soluble in water. Soluble in aqueous alkali, oxygenated and aromatic solvents.

Production:
- cresylic acid (fractionation; coproduced with phenol/*o*-cresol/*m/p*-cresol)

Derivatives: biphenyl; novolac resins; *o*-phenylphenol; trixylyl phosphate; 2,4-xylenol; xylenol, butylated

Uses: alkali-resistant phenolic resin comonomer; disinfectant; froth flotation agent; engine cleaner ingredient; solvent (wire enamels)

2,3-xylidine
2,3-dimethylaniline; [87-59-2]

$C_8H_{11}N_1$. M: 121.19. Liquid. BP: 221–222°C. MP: <-15°C. d: 0.99 kg/l (20°C). Slightly soluble in water. Soluble in oxygenated solvents.

Production:
- *o*-xylene (nitration/nitro reduction; byproduct of 3,4-xylidine production)

Derivatives: mefenamic acid

2,4-xylidine
4-amino-*m*-xylene; 2,4-dimethylaniline; [95-68-1]

$C_8H_{11}N_1$. M: 121.19. Liquid. BP: 214°C. d: 0.98 kg/l (20°C). Slightly soluble in water. Soluble in organic solvents. An impure form, containing 20% of the 2,6-isomer, is used for some applications.

Production:
- *m*-xylene (nitration/nitro reduction; coproduced with 2,6-xylidine)

Derivatives: acetoacet-2,4-xylide; Acid Orange 24; Acid Red 26; amitraz; 3-hydroxy-2-naphth-2′,4′-xylidide; mefluidide; Solvent Orange 7

2,5-xylidine
2,5-dimethylaniline; [95-78-3]

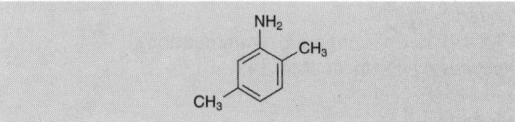

$C_8H_{11}N_1$. M: 121.19. Yellow liquid or solid. MP: 16°C. BP: 214°C. d: 0.98 kg/l (20°C). Slightly soluble in water. Soluble in oxygenated solvents.

Production:
• *p*-xylene (nitration/nitro reduction)
Derivatives:
Direct Yellow 51; Solvent Red 22; Solvent Red 26

2,6-xylidine

2-amino-*m*-xylene; 2,6-dimethylaniline; DMA; [87-62-7]

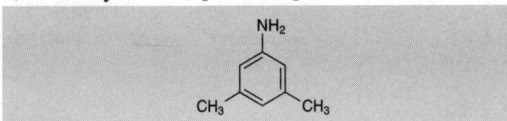

$C_8H_{11}N_1$. M: 121.19. Yellow liquid. BP: 216°C. MP: 11°C. d: 0.98 kg/l (20°C). Slightly soluble in water. Soluble in oxygenated and aromatic solvents. Flash point: 91°C (CC).
Production:
• aniline + methanol (orthoalkylation)
• *m*-xylene (nitration/nitro reduction; coproduced with 2,4-xylidine)
• 2,6-xylenol + ammonia (ammoniation)
Derivatives:
benalaxyl; bupivacaine; denatonium benzoate; dimethachlor; furalaxyl; lidocaine; lidoflazine; mepivacaine; metalaxyl; metazachlor; ofurace; oxadixyl; xipamide

3,4-xylidine

4-amino-1,2-xylene; 3,4-dimethylaniline; [95-64-7]

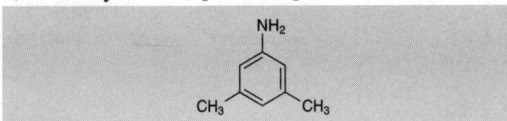

$C_8H_{11}N_1$. M: 121.19. Crystalline solid. MP: 49–51°C. d: 1.08 kg/l (15°C). Slightly soluble in water. Soluble in aromatic solvents.
Production:
• *o*-xylene (nitration/nitro reduction)
Derivatives: riboflavin

3,5-xylidine

3,5-dimethylaniline; [108-69-0]

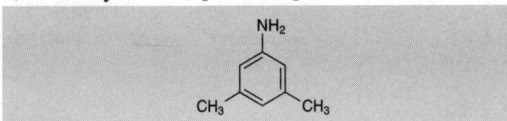

$C_8H_{11}N_1$. M: 121.19.
Production:
• 3,5-xylenol + ammonia (ammoniation)
Derivatives: Pigment Red 149

xylometazoline

[526-36-3]; [1218-35-5] (hydrochloride)
$C_{16}H_{24}N_2$. M: 244.38. Available commercially as the free base or hydrochloride.

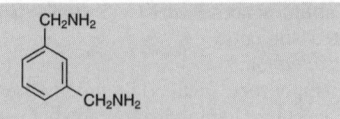

Production:
• 5-*t*-butyl-*m*-xylene + formaldehyde + sodium cyanide + ethylenediamine (cyanomethylation/condensation)
Uses: vasoconstrictor drug

xylylcarb

3,4-dimethylphenyl methylcarbamate; 3,4-xylyl methylcarbamate; Meobal (Sumitomo); [2425-10-7]

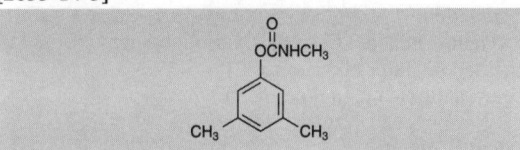

$C_{10}H_{13}N_1O_2$. M: 179.22. Colourless solid. MP: 74°C. Insoluble in water. Soluble in oxygenated solvents.
Production:
• 3,4-xylenol + methyl isocyanate (isocyanate addition)
Uses: insecticide

m-xylylenediamine

1,3-diaminomethylbenzene; *m*-xylenediamine; MXDA; [1477-55-0]

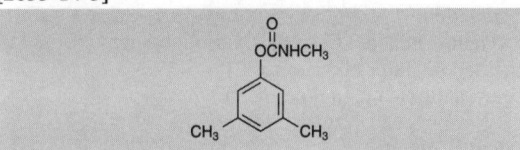

$C_8H_{12}N_2$. M: 136.20. Colourless liquid. FP: 14°C.
Production:
• isophthalodinitrile (nitrile reduction)
Derivatives: 1,3-bis(aminomethyl)cyclohexane; poly-(*m*-xylyleneadipamide)
Uses: polyamide comonomer; epoxy resin curing agent

3,5-xylyl methylcarbamate

3,5-dimethylphenyl methylcarbamate; XMC; [2655-14-3]

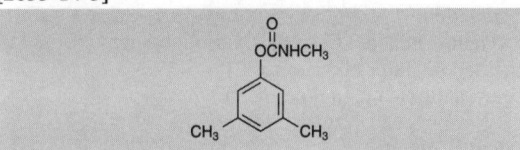

$C_{10}H_{13}N_1O_2$. M: 179.22.
Production:
• 3,5-xylenol + phosgene + methylamine (dehydrochlorination/dehydrochlorination)
Uses: insecticide

yellow cake
ammonium diuranate; sodium diuranate
The term 'yellow cake' is used in referring to the ammonium, sodium, or alkaline earth diuranates used as the starting material for uranium fuel production.
Production:
- uranium ore (leaching/ion-exchange separation/ hydrorefining)
- phosphoric acid, crude (solvent extraction/ hydrorefining; coproduced with vanadium pentoxide)
- uranium ore (leaching/solvent extraction/ hydrorefining; coproduced with vanadium pentoxide)

Derivatives: uranium hexafluoride; uranyl nitrate

yellow prussiate of calcium
See: calcium ferrocyanide

yellow prussiate of potash
See: potassium ferrocyanide

yellow prussiate of soda
See: sodium ferrocyanide

ylang-ylang oil
cananga oil
Yellow liquid with a characteristic floral odour. Produced by steam distillation of *Cananga odorata* flowers. There are several grades available commercially, some of which are produced by fractionation of the crude oil. d: 0.91–0.97 kg/l (20°C). Produced mainly in Indonesia, Madagascar and the Comeros Islands.
Uses: fragrance ingredient (soap, perfumes)

yttrium oxide
[1314-36-9]

$$Y_2O_3$$

O_3Y_2. M: 225.81. Colourless to yellow, crystalline powder. MP: 2,410°C. d: 5.01 kg/l. Insoluble in water.
Production:
- xenotime ore (acid leaching/separation/solvent extraction)

Uses: ceramics additive; phosphor glass ingredient (television, CRT screens); electrical heating/lighting filament raw material

Z

ZBEC *See:* zinc dibenzyldithiocarbamate

ZBED *See:* zinc dibenzyldithiocarbamate

ZDBC *See:* zinc di-*n*-butyldithiocarbamate

ZDBP *See:* zinc di-*n*-butyl dithiophosphate

ZDDP *See:* zinc di-*n*-butyl dithiophosphate; zinc dioctyl dithiophosphate; zinc didodecyl dithiophosphate; zinc dihexyl dithiophosphate; zinc didecyl dithiophosphate

ZDEC *See:* zinc diethyldithiocarbamate

ZDMC *See:* zinc dimethyldithiocarbamate

zein
[9010-66-6]
White or pale yellow powder. d: 1.23 kg/l. Insoluble in water. Soluble in oxygenated solvents. A simple prolamine protein. M: ~38,000.
Production:
• maize gluten (solvent extraction)
Uses:
confectionery coatings; pharmaceutical tablet binder

zeolite, natural
Complex aluminosilicate crystalline polymers, the structures of which are open frameworks containing holes of characteristic size and chemical affinity which can selectively trap small molecules. Commercially exploited zeolite minerals are: clinoptilolite, chabazite, mordenite and erionite. They are mined in several parts of the world, including USA and Japan.
Uses:
construction materials; filler; ion-exchange media

zeolite A
Complex aluminosilicate crystalline polymer with pore openings of 4–5 angstroms in its structure.
Production:
• kaolin + sodium hydroxide (thermal conversion)
• sodium aluminate + sodium silicate (hydrogel process)
Uses:
calcium complexing agent (detergents); drying agent; calcium-exchanged molecular sieves; calcium-exchanged molecular sieves (oxygen-nitrogen separation)

zeolite X
Complex aluminosilicate crystalline polymer with pore openings that are larger than for zeolite A and with a higher Si:Al ratio, making it selective for polar molecules. Also produced in a 'calcium-exchanged' form.
Production:
• sodium aluminate + sodium silicate + potassium hydroxide (thermal rearrangement)
Uses: petroleum catalytic cracking catalyst (rare-earth exchanged); drying agent; calcium-exchanged molecular sieves (oxygen-nitrogen separation); potassium/barium-exchanged molecular sieves (xylene isomer separation)

zeolite Y
Production:
• sodium aluminate + sodium silicate (thermal rearrangement)
Uses: H/Pt/Pd-exchanged catalysts (alkane isomerisation/petroleum hydrocracking); rare earth-exchanged catalysts (petroleum catalytic cracking)

zeolite ZSM 5
zeolite Socony Mobil 5
Production:
• sodium aluminate + sodium silicate + tetramethylammonium hydroxide (thermal rearrangement)
Uses: catalyst (Mobil MTG process, alkane dewaxing, ethylbenzene production, xylene isomerisation)

ZEPC *See:* zinc ethylphenyldithiocarbamate

zeranol
[26538-44-3]

$C_{18}H_{26}O_5$. M: 322.40.
Production:
• mould fermentation medium + *Gibberella zeae* mould (fermentation/extraction/hydrogenation)
Uses: animal growth stimulant

zinc
[7440-66-6]

Zn

Zn_1. M: 65.37. Lustrous, blue-white, ductile metal. d: 7.13 kg/l (25°C). MP: 419°C. BP 907°C.
Production:
• zinc-lead sulphide ores + metallurgical coke (Imperial Smelting process)
• zinc sulphide ore concentrates + metallurgical coke (vertical retort process)

• zinc sulphate (electrolysis)

Derivatives: arsine; brass; cyclopropyl bromide; sodium formaldehyde sulphoxylate; sodium hydrosulphite; zinc ammonium chloride; zinc chloride; zinc oxide; zinc phosphide

Uses: anticorrosion pigment (primer paints); bronze ingredient (coins, bells, statues, pigment); leaded bronze/ manganese bronze/phosphor bronze ingredient (bearings); metal spray coatings; steel galvanising raw material (vehicle bodies, gates, window frames, ladders, pylons); steel sherardising raw material; alcohol reduction/dechlorination reagent; rolled zinc building foil/ battery cans/printing plates; zinc die-casting alloys (model toys, car engine components, handles, locks); zinc electroplating anodes

zinc acetate

zinc diacetate; [557-34-6] (anhydrous); [5970-45-6] (dihydrate)

(CH₃COO)₂Zn

$C_4H_6O_4Zn_1$. M: 183.46. Available as the dihydrate. White, crystalline solid. Loses water of crystallisation when heated over 100°C. Soluble in water forming slightly acidic solutions.
Production:
• zinc oxide + acetic acid (salt formation)
Uses: esterification catalyst; mordant; waterproofing agent; wood preservative

zinc ammonium chloride

[52628-25-8]

ZnCl₂.2NH₄Cl

$H_8Cl_4N_2Zn_1$. M: 243.25. White, crystalline solid. Soluble in water.
Production:
• zinc + ammonia + hydrochloric acid (salt formation)
Uses: galvanising reagent; soldering flux

zinc bacitracin

Zinc salt of the fermented broth containing a mixture of bacitracin polypeptides.
Production:
• microbial fermentation medium + *Bacillus subtilis* bacteria + zinc sulphate (fermentation/salt formation)
Uses: animal feed additive; antibacterial drug

zinc borate

Firebrake ZB (Borax Consolidated); [12513-27-8]

2ZnO.nB₂O₃

n = 1–3. 2ZnO.3B₂O₃.3.5H₂0 is the most common form of zinc borate available commercially. ZnO.B₂O₃.2H₂O and Zn(BO₂)₂ are also sold.

Production:
• zinc sulphate + boric acid (salt formation)
Uses: fire-retardant additive (plastics, paints)

zinc bromide

[7699-45-8]

ZnBr₂

Br_2Zn_1. M: 225.18. White powder. MP: 394°C. d: 4.22 kg/l (4°C). Solubility in water: 3.9 kg/l water (0°C). For oilfield applications zinc bromide is sold as solutions with calcium bromide containing, typically, 77% $ZnBr_2/CaBr_2$ and having a density of 2.3 kg/l.
Production:
• zinc oxide + hydrobromic acid (salt formation)
Uses: oil-well drilling/completion fluids

zinc chloride

[7646-85-7]

ZnCl₂

Cl_2Zn_1. M: 136.28. White, deliquescent granules. d: 2.91 kg/l. MP: 290°C. Solubility in water: 4.32 kg/l (25°C) forming acidic solutions.
Production:
• zinc + chlorine (reaction)
Derivatives: Basic Blue 3; Basic Blue 6; Basic Blue 9; Basic Orange 14; diethyl zinc; lithopone; mancozeb
Uses:
chloromethylation/condensation catalyst; dyeing auxiliary; electroplating bath ingredient; flux; antiseptic/astringent/deodorant preparations; activated charcoal production additive; wood preservative/fireproofing agent

zinc chrome *See:* zinc yellow

zinc cyanide

[557-21-1]

Zn(CN)₂

$C_2N_2Zn_1$. M: 117.40. White, crystalline powder. d: 1.85 kg/l. Insoluble in water. Soluble in sodium cyanide and sodium hydroxide solution.
Production:
• zinc oxide + hydrogen cyanide (salt formation)
Uses: electroplating bath ingredient; reagent (Gatterman reactions)

zinc diamyldithiocarbamate

$\left[(C_5H_{11})_2N\overset{\overset{\textstyle S}{\|}}{C}S\right]_2Zn$

$C_{22}H_{44}N_2S_4Zn_1$. M: 530.23.
Production:
• diamylamine + carbon disulphide + zinc oxide (condensation)
Uses: antiwear additive (gear oils, greases)

zinc dibenzyldithiocarbamate

zinc bis(dibenzyl dithiocarbamate); ZBEC; ZBED; [14726-36-4]

$$\left[\left\langle\bigcirc\right\rangle-CH_2\underset{||}{\overset{S}{NCS}}-Zn-\underset{||}{\overset{S}{SCN}}\,CH_2-\left\langle\bigcirc\right\rangle\right]_2$$

$C_{30}H_{28}N_2S_4Zn_1$. M: 610.19. Creamy-white powder. MP: 185°C. d: 1.1 kg/l. Insoluble in water and hydrocarbon solvents.
Production:
• dibenzylamine + carbon disulphide + zinc oxide (condensation)
Uses: vulcanisation accelerator

zinc di-*n*-butyldithiocarbamate

ZDBC; [136-23-2]

$$\left[(CH_3CH_2CH_2CH_2)_2\underset{||}{\overset{S}{NCS}}\right]_2 Zn$$

$C_{18}H_{36}N_2S_4Zn_1$. M: 474.13. Creamy, white solid. MP: 108°C. d: 1.24 kg/l (20°C).
Production:
• di-*n*-butylamine + carbon disulphide + zinc oxide (condensation)
Uses: antioxidant/antiwear additive (lubricants); vulcanisation accelerator

zinc di-*n*-butyl dithiophosphate

ZDBP; ZDDP

$$\left[(CH_3CH_2CH_2CH_2O)_2\underset{||}{\overset{S}{PS}}\right]_2 Zn$$

$C_{16}H_{36}O_4P_2S_4Zn_1$. M: 548.05.
Production:
• *n*-butanol + phosphorus pentasulphide + zinc oxide (addition/salt formation)
Uses: vulcanisation accelerator

zinc didecyl dithiophosphate

ZDDP

$$\left[(C_{10}H_{21}O)_2\underset{||}{\overset{S}{PS}}\right]_2 Zn$$

$C_{40}H_{84}O_4P_2S_4Zn_1$. M: 884.69.
Production:
• phosphorus pentasulphide + isodecanol + zinc oxide (condensation/salt formation)
Uses:
antiwear additive (hydraulic oils, metalworking fluids)

zinc didodecyl dithiophosphate

ZDDP

$$\left[(C_{12}H_{25}O)_2\underset{||}{\overset{S}{PS}}\right]_2 Zn$$

$C_{48}H_{100}O_4P_2S_4Zn_1$. M: 996.91.

Production:
• phosphorus pentasulphide + *n*-alkanol(C_{12}-C_{13})/ *n*-alkanol(C_{12}-C_{14}) + zinc oxide (addition/ neutralisation)
Uses:
antiwear additive (hydraulic oils, metalworking fluids)

zinc diethyl *See:* diethyl zinc

zinc diethyldithiocarbamate

ZDEC; Ethasan (Monsanto); [14324-55-1]

$$\left[(C_2H_5)_2\underset{||}{\overset{S}{NCS}}\right]_2 Zn$$

$C_{10}H_{20}N_2S_4Zn_1$. M: 361.91.
Production:
• sodium diethyldithiocarbamate + zinc oxide (salt formation)
Uses: preservative (natural rubber latex); vulcanisation accelerator

zinc dihexyl dithiophosphate

ZDDP

$$\left[(C_6H_{13}O)_2\underset{||}{\overset{S}{PS}}\right]_2 Zn$$

$C_{24}H_{52}O_4P_2S_4Zn_1$. M: 660.26.
Production:
• phosphorus pentasulphide + methyl isobutyl carbinol + zinc oxide (addition/neutralisation)
Uses: antiwear additive (lubricants)

zinc dimethyldithiocarbamate

zinc bis(diethyldithiocarbamate); ziram; ZDMC; [137-30-4]

$$\left[(CH_3)_2\underset{||}{\overset{S}{NCS}}\right]_2 Zn$$

$C_6H_{12}N_2S_4Zn_1$. M: 227.68. Colourless powder. MP: 240–244°C. Insoluble in water. Soluble in aqueous alkali, oxygenated and chlorinated solvents.
Production:
• sodium dimethyldithiocarbamate + zinc oxide (salt formation)
Uses: fungicide; biocide (water treatment, paper sizing, adhesives); vulcanisation accelerator

zinc dioctyl dithiophosphate

zinc di-2-ethylhexyl dithiophosphate; ZDDP

$$\left[CH_3(CH_2)_3\overset{C_2H_5}{\overset{|}{CHCH_2O}}\right]_2\underset{||}{\overset{S}{PS^-}}\ \tfrac{1}{2}Zn^{2+}$$

$C_{32}H_{68}O_4P_2S_4Zn_1$. M: 772.47.
Production:
• phosphorus pentasulphide + 2-ethylhexanol/ isooctanol + zinc oxide (condensation)
Uses: oxidation inhibitor/antiwear additive (lubricants)

zinc 2-ethylhexanoate
zinc octoate; [136-53-8]

$$\left[CH_3(CH_2)_3\overset{\overset{\displaystyle C_2H_5}{|}}{CH}COO\right]_2 Zn$$

$C_{16}H_{30}O_4Zn_1$. M: 351.79. Pale yellow liquid. d: 0.90 kg/l. Insoluble in water.
Production:
• 2-ethylhexanoic acid + zinc oxide (salt formation)
Derivatives: cadmium-barium heat stabilisers
Uses: paint drier

zinc ethylphenyldithiocarbamate
zinc bis(N-ethyl-N-phenyl dithiocarbamate); ZEPC; [14634-93-6]

$$\left[\underset{\displaystyle S}{\overset{\displaystyle C_2H_5}{\text{C}_6\text{H}_5-N-C}}\right]_2 Zn$$

$C_{18}H_{20}N_2S_4Zn_1$. M: 458.00.
Production:
• N-ethylaniline + carbon disulphide + zinc oxide (condensation)
Uses: vulcanisation accelerator

zinc ferrite
zinc iron pigment; Pigment Yellow 119 (CI); 77496 (CI); Sicopal Yellow K2395 (BASF); Sicopal Yellow K2595 (BASF)

$$ZnFe_2O_4$$

$Fe_2O_4Zn_1$. M: 241.06. Brown coloured powder.
Production:
• zinc oxide + iron oxide red (calcination)
Uses: plastics colorant

zinc fluoborate
[13826-88-5]

$$Zn(BF_4)_2$$

$B_2F_8Zn_1$. M: 238.97. Available commercially as a 40–50% solution in water.
Production:
• zinc oxide + fluoboric acid (salt formation)
Uses: electroplating bath ingredient

zinc fluoride
[7783-49-5]

$$ZnF_2$$

F_2Zn_1. M: 103.37. White powder. MP: 872°C. d: 4.95 kg/l. Slightly soluble in water.
Production:
• zinc oxide + hydrofluoric acid (salt formation)
Uses: porcelain glaze/enamel ingredient; fluorescent light phosphors; fluorination reagent; galvanising reagent; wood preservative

zinc hexafluorosilicate
zinc fluorosilicate; zinc silicofluoride; [16871-71-9]

$$ZnSiF_6$$

$F_6Si_1Zn_1$. M: 207.45. Available as the hexahydrate. White crystals. d: 2.10 kg/l. Soluble in water forming acidic solutions.
Production:
• zinc oxide + hexafluorosilicic acid (salt formation)
Uses:
concrete surface hardening agents; insect resist agent (wool treatment)

zinc isopropyl xanthate
ZIX; [42590-53-4]

$$\left[(CH_3)_2CH\overset{\overset{\displaystyle S}{||}}{O}C\overset{}{S}\right]_2 Zn$$

$C_8H_{14}O_2S_4Zn_1$. M: 335.83. Creamy-white powder with a characteristic smell. d: 1.5 kg/l. Insoluble in water and hydrocarbon solvents.
Production:
• sodium isopropyl xanthate + zinc sulphate (salt formation)
Uses:
vulcanisation accelerator

zinc laurate
[2452-01-9]

$$\left[CH_3(CH_2)_{10}COO\right]_2 Zn$$

$C_{24}H_{46}O_4Zn_1$. M: 464.00. White powder. MP: 128°C. Slightly soluble in water and alcohol.
Production:
• lauric acid, broad cut + zinc oxide (salt formation)
Uses: polyvinyl chloride heat stabiliser; vulcanisation activator

zinc 2-mercaptobenzimidazole
ZMBI; [3030-80-6]

$C_{14}H_{10}N_4S_2Zn_1$. M: 363.76.
Production:
• 2-mercaptobenzimidazole + zinc oxide (salt formation)
Uses: antioxidant (rubber)

zinc mercaptobenzothiazole
ZMBT

$C_{14}H_8N_2S_4Zn_1$. M: 397.85.

Production:
• 2-mercaptobenzothiazole + zinc sulphate (salt formation)
Uses: vulcanisation accelerator

zinc 2-mercaptomethylbenzimidazole
zinc mercaptomethylbenzimidazole; ZMMBI

$C_{16}H_{14}N_4S_2Zn_1$. M: 391.82.
Production:
• 2-mercaptomethylbenzimidazole + zinc oxide (salt formation)
Uses: antioxidant (rubber)

zinc molybdate, basic
molybdenum white; Moly-White 101 (PMC)

$Mo_1O_4Zn_1$. M: 225.31. White powder. d: 5.06 kg/l. Insoluble in water.
Production:
• zinc oxide + molybdenum trioxide (salt formation)
Uses: anticorrosion pigment (protective paints)

zinc naphthenate
[12001-85-3]
Brown liquid or solid depending on the zinc content which varies in the range 8–16%. Insoluble in water.
Production:
• zinc oxide + naphthenic acid (salt formation)
Uses: corrosion inhibitor (greases, protective oils); paint drier; wood preservative/fungicide

zinc neodecanoate
[27253-29-8]

$C_{20}H_{38}O_4Zn_1$. M: 407.89.
Production:
• zinc oxide + neodecanoic acid (salt formation)
Uses: paint drier

zinc 5-nitroisophthalate

$C_8H_3N_1O_6Zn_1$. M: 274.48.
Production:
• 5-nitroisophthalic acid + zinc oxide (salt formation)
Uses: anticorrosion pigment (protective paints)

zinc octoate *See:* zinc 2-ethylhexanoate

zinc oxide
Chinese White; zinc white; Pigment White 4 (CI); 77947 (CI); [1314-13-2]

O_1Zn_1. M: 81.37.
Production:
• zinc (French air oxidation process)
• zinc oxide concentrates/zinc scrap + coal (American direct process)
• zinc sulphate (calcination)
Derivatives: barium-zinc heat stabilisers; cadmium yellow; cadmium-zinc heat stabilisers; calcium zinc molybdate; cobalt green; ferrite; zinc acetate; zinc bromide; zinc cyanide; zinc diamyldithiocarbamate; zinc dibenzyldithiocarbamate; zinc di-*n*-butyldithiocarbamate; zinc di-*n*-butyl dithiophosphate; zinc didecyl dithiophosphate; zinc didodecyl dithiophosphate; zinc diethyldithiocarbamate; zinc dihexyl dithiophosphate; zinc dimethyldithiocarbamate; zinc dioctyl dithiophosphate; zinc 2-ethylhexanoate; zinc ethylphenyldithiocarbamate; zinc ferrite; zinc fluoborate; zinc fluoride; zinc hexafluorosilicate; zinc laurate; zinc 2-mercaptobenzimidazole; zinc 2-mercaptomethylbenzimidazole; zinc molybdate, basic; zinc naphthenate; zinc neodecanoate; zinc 5-nitroisophthalate; zinc pentamethylenedithiocarbamate; zinc *p*-phenolsulphonate; zinc 2-pyridinethiol-*N*-oxide; zinc rosinate; zinc tetroxychromate; zinc undecylenate; zinc yellow
Uses:
carboxylic latice crosslinking agent; fire-retardant (paper, wood); anticorrosion pigment/biocide (paints); pigment (printing inks, cosmetics); glass/enamel/porcelain raw material; vulcanisation activator

zinc pentamethylenedithiocarbamate
zinc bis(piperidine-1-carbodithionate); Z5MC; ZPD; [13878-54-1]

$C_{12}H_{10}N_2S_4Zn_1$. M: 375.85. Off-white powder. MP: 225°C. d: 1.6 kg/l. Insoluble in water and hydrocarbon solvents. Also sold as an activated mixture with piperidine.
Production:
• piperidine + carbon disulphide + zinc oxide (condensation)
Uses: vulcanisation accelerator

zinc *p*-phenolsulphonate
[127-82-2]
$C_{12}H_{10}O_8S_2Zn_1$. M: 411.70. Available commercially as the octahydrate. White crystals. Loses water of cryst-

allisation when heated above 120°C. Soluble in water forming acidic solutions.

Production:
- *p*-phenolsulphonic acid + zinc oxide (salt formation)

Uses:
astringent drug (medicines, personal-care products)

zinc phosphate
Pigment White 32 (CI); [7779-90-0]

$$Zn_3(PO_4)_2$$

$O_8P_2Zn_3$. M: 386.05. White pigment. d: 3.3 kg/l. Insoluble in water and alcohol.
Production:
- zinc sulphate + trisodium phosphate (precipitation)

Uses: anticorrosion pigment (primer paints)

zinc phosphide
trizinc phosphide; [1314-84-7]

$$Zn_3P_2$$

P_2Zn_3. M: 258.06. Reacts with acid to release phosphine.
Production:
- zinc + phosphorus (reaction)

Uses: rodenticide

zinc 2-pyridinethiol-*N*-oxide
zinc pyridinethione; zinc pyrithione; Omadine (Olin); [13463-41-7]

$C_{10}H_8N_2O_2S_2Zn_1$. M: 317.68.
Production:
- sodium 2-pyridinethiol-*N*-oxide + zinc oxide (salt formation)

Uses: antidandruff agent; biocide (latices)

zinc rosinate
zinc abietate; zinc resinate; zinc resinate; [9010-69-9]
Solid. Softening point: 130–150°C. Zinc content: 2–9%. Mixed zinc/calcium (3:1) rosinates are also available.
Production:
- rosin, wood/rosin, polymerised/rosin, tall oil/rosin, gum/abietic acid + zinc oxide (salt formation)

Uses:
binder (printing inks, oil-based wood varnishes)

zinc silicofluoride *See:* zinc hexafluorosilicate

zinc stearate
[557-05-1]

$$\left[CH_3(CH_2)_{16}COO\right]_2 Zn$$

$C_{36}H_{70}O_4Zn_1$. M: 632.33. White powder. MP: 125°C. d: 1.10 kg/l. Insoluble in water and oxygenated solvents. Soluble in aromatic solvents. The commercial product usually contains 15% zinc oxide.
Production:
- stearic acid + zinc sulphate (salt formation)

Uses: polyvinyl chloride heat stabiliser; cosmetics/pharmaceuticals ingredient; rubber peptising agent/processing aid; amino resins processing lubricant; vulcanisation activator; waterproofing agent (paper, textiles)

zinc sulphate
[7733-02-0]

$$ZnSO_4$$

$O_4S_1Zn_1$. M: 161.43. The commercial product is the monohydrate. White granules or powder. Loses water of crystallisation if heated above 235°C. Soluble in water. Also produced as the heptahydrate, mainly for laboratory purposes.
Production:
- zinc oxide concentrates + sulphuric acid (acid leaching/oxidation/separation/reduction)

Derivatives: lithopone; metiram; propineb; zinc; zinc bacitracin; zinc borate; zinc isopropyl xanthate; zinc mercaptobenzothiazole; zinc oxide; zinc phosphate; zinc stearate; zinc sulphide; zineb
Uses: analytical reagent; fertiliser/animal feed ingredient; mordant; galvanising reagent

zinc sulphide
Pigment White 7 (CI); 77975 (CI); [1314-98-3]

$$ZnS$$

S_1Zn_1. M: 97.43.
Production:
- barium sulphide + zinc sulphate (salt formation)

Uses: flotation depressant (sphalerite ores); fluorescent pigment (paints, plastics)

zinc tetroxychromate
zinc chromate, basic; [49663-84-5]

$$ZnCrO_4.4Zn(OH)_2$$

$H_8Cr_1O_{12}Zn_5$. M: 578.90. Yellow pigment. Soluble in dilute acids and alkalis.
Production:
- zinc oxide + chromic acid (salt formation)

Uses: pigment (etch primer paints)

zinc undecylenate
[557-08-4]
$C_{22}H_{38}O_4Zn_1$. M: 431.91.

$$\left[CH_2 = CH(CH_2)_8COO\right]_2 Zn$$

Production:
• undecylenic acid + zinc oxide (salt formation)
Uses: topical antifungal agent

zinc white *See:* lithopone

zinc yellow
zinc chrome; zinc potassium chromate; Pigment Yellow 36 (CI); [11103-86-9]

$$K_2CrO_4.3ZnCrO_4.ZnO$$

$Cr_4K_2O_{17}Zn_4$. M: 819.64. Greenish-yellow pigment. d: 3.4–3.5 kg/l.
Production:
• zinc oxide + potassium dichromate + sulphuric acid (reaction)
Uses: zinc green pigment component; anticorrosion pigment (primer paints)

zineb
zinc ethylenebis(dithiocarbamate); [12122-67-7]

$$\left[\overset{S}{\underset{\|}{S}} CNHCH_2CH_2NHC\overset{S}{\underset{\|}{S}}Zn \right]_x$$

Complex, polymeric salt of ethylenebis(dithiocarbamic acid) with zinc.
Production:
• nabam + zinc sulphate (salt formation)
Uses: fungicide

ziram *See:* zinc dimethyldithiocarbamate

zircon

$$ZrSiO_4$$

$O_4Si_1Zr_1$. M: 183.31. Zircon is a colourless (when pure), mineral concentrate extracted from beach sands by electrostatic and electromagnetic techniques. d: 4.7 kg/l.
Production:
• mineral sands (separation; coproduced with ilmenite/rutile/monazite)
Derivatives: calcium zirconate; calcium zirconyl silicate; potassium fluorozirconate; sodium zirconylsilicate; zirconia; zirconium tetrachloride
Uses: foundry sands; abrasive; jewellery; opacifying ingredient (pottery glazes); alkali resistant glass raw material; refractory bricks/cement raw material

zirconia
zirconium dioxide; zirconium oxide; [1314-23-4]

$$ZrO_2$$

O_2Zr_1. M: 123.22. White powder. d: 5.73 kg/l. MP: 2,700°C (pure). Refractory ceramics are stabilised with 10–15% calcium or magnesium oxide. Baddeleyite is a natural mineral zirconia found primarily in Brazil and South Africa.
Production:
• zircon (electric arc process/thermal oxidation)
• zircon + calcium oxide + metallurgical coke (plasma arc process)
• calcium zirconyl silicate + sulphuric acid (acid leaching/calcination)
Uses: ceramic tiles/sanitaryware colorant; grinding wheel abrasive; glass polishing compounds; optical/photochromic glass raw material; refractory ceramics (furnace linings, crucibles, electric heating elements)

zirconia, high-purity
zirconium oxide; [1314-23-4]

$$ZrO_2$$

O_2Zr_1. M: 123.22.
Production:
• zirconium hydroxide (calcination)
Derivatives: lead zirconate titanate
Uses: capacitors/thermoelectric devices (fire alarms); catalyst raw material

zirconium
[7440-67-7]

$$Zr$$

Zr_1. M: 91.22. Hard, shiny, ductile metal. MP: 2,125°C. d: 6.51 kg/l. Resistant to air, water, acid, alkali and molten salts because of a protective oxide coating on the surface of the metal. Zirconium needs to be hafnium-free for nuclear rod usage. This is achieved by selective solvent extraction.
Production:
• zirconium tetrachloride + magnesium (Kroll process)
Derivatives: zirconium hydride
Uses: deoxiding agent (non-ferrous metal production); flash bulbs; magnesium alloying ingredient; protective cladding (nuclear fuel rods)

zirconium acetate
[5153-24-2]

$$(CH_3COO)_2Zr(OH)_2$$

$C_4H_8O_6Zr_1$. M: 243.31. Available as an acidic solution containing 22–25% ZrO_2.
Production:
• zirconium carbonate, basic + acetic acid (salt formation)
Uses: starch crosslinking agent (paper/textile sizes); photographic gelatine hardening agent; insolubilising agent (wax emulsion water repellent textile treatments); refractories raw material

zirconium butoxide
zirconium butylate; zirconium tetrabutoxide

$$(CH_3CH_2CH_2CH_2O)_4Zr$$

$C_{16}H_{36}O_4Zr_1$. M: 383.69. Available as a 80% solution in *n*-butanol. Hydrolysed by water.
Production:
* *n*-butanol + zirconium tetrachloride (dehydrochlorination)

Uses: esterification/condensation/polymerisation catalyst; insolubilising agent (textile, leather, paper finishing agents); glass surface treatment agent

zirconium carbonate, basic
zirconyl carbonate; [37356-18-6]

$$mZrO_2.CO_2$$

m = 1–4. White, amorphous powder. Insoluble in water.
Production:
* zirconium sulphate, basic + sodium carbonate (salt formation)

Derivatives: ammonium zirconyl carbonate; potassium fluorozirconate; zirconium acetate; zirconium neodecanoate; zirconium octoate; zirconium oxychloride; zirconium oxynitrate; zirconium sulphate

zirconium hydride
[7704-99-6]

$$ZrH_2$$

H_2Zr_1. M: 93.24. Dark-grey, metallic powder. Ignites on heating above 270°C. d: 5.6 kg/l.
Production:
* zirconium + calcium hydride + hydrogen (reaction)

Uses: hydrogenation catalyst; getter (vacuum/cathode-ray tubes); metal processing agent

zirconium hydroxide
[14475-63-9]

$$Zr(OH)_4$$

$H_4O_4Zr_1$. M: 159.25. White, amorphous powder. d: 3.25 kg/l. Insoluble in water.
Production:
* zirconium sulphate, basic + ammonia (salt formation)

Derivatives:
zirconia, high-purity
Uses: high conductivity ceramics (microwave devices)

zirconium neodecanoate

$$\left[C_6H_{13}\overset{\overset{\displaystyle CH_3}{|}}{\underset{\underset{\displaystyle CH_3}{|}}{C}}COO\right]_2 Zr(OH)_2$$

$C_{20}H_{40}O_6Zr_1$. M: 467.75.

Production:
* neodecanoic acid + zirconium carbonate, basic (salt formation)

Uses: paint drier

zirconium octoate
[15104-99-1]

$$\left[CH_3(CH_2)_3\overset{\overset{\displaystyle C_2H_5}{|}}{CH}COO\right]_2 Zr(OH)_2$$

$C_{16}H_{32}O_6Zr_1$. M: 411.64.
Production:
* 2-ethylhexanoic acid + zirconium carbonate, basic (salt formation)

Uses: paint drier

zirconium oxide See: zirconia; zirconia, high-purity

zirconium oxychloride
zirconyl chloride; [7699-43-6]

$$ZrOCl_2$$

$Cl_2O_1Zr_1$. M: 178.13. Most commonly available as an acidic solution in water containing 36% ZrO_2. Also available (from $ZrCl_4$) as the monohydrate, a white, crystalline solid which loses its water of crystallisation when heated above 150°C. d: 1.91 kg/l. Soluble in water forming acidic solutions.
Production:
* zirconium tetrachloride (hydration)
* zirconium carbonate, basic + hydrochloric acid (salt formation)

Uses:
clay stabiliser (oil-well stimulation); thixotropic oil-well cement component; antiperspirant

zirconium oxynitrate
[13746-89-9]; [13826-66-9]

$$Zr(NO_3)_2(OH)_2$$

$H_2N_2O_8Zr_1$. M: 249.24.
Production:
* zirconium carbonate, basic + nitric acid (salt formation)

Uses:
ceramics ingredient

zirconium phosphate
zirconium orthophosphate; [19764-74-0]
White, amorphous powder with an ill-defined chemical structure. Highly insoluble in water. Decomposes on heating.
Production:
* zirconium sulphate, basic + phosphoric acid, pure (salt formation)

Uses:
ion-exchange catalyst

zirconium sulphate
[14644-61-2]

$$Zr(SO_4)_2$$

$O_8S_2Zr_1$. M: 283.34. Available as an acidic solution in water or as solid (from baddeleyite). The latter is a white, crystalline solid (tetrahydrate) which starts to lose its water of crystallisation when heated above 100°C. Soluble in water forming acidic solutions.
Production:
• baddeleyite + sulphuric acid (acid leaching)
• zirconium carbonate, basic + sulphuric acid (salt formation)
Uses: surface treatment (titanium dioxide pigments); photographic gelatine hardening agent; leather tanning auxiliary

zirconium sulphate, basic
[84583-91-5]

$$mZrO_2.SO_3$$

Complex salt consisting of linear zirconium hydroxide polymers associated with sulphate anions.
Production:
• sodium zirconylsilicate + sulphuric acid (acid leaching)
• calcium zirconate + sulphuric acid (acid leaching/ salt formation/salt formation)
Derivatives: zirconium carbonate, basic; zirconium hydroxide; zirconium phosphate
Uses: tanning agent

zirconium tetrabutoxide *See:* zirconium butoxide

zirconium tetrachloride
zirconium chloride; [10026-11-6]

$$ZrCl_4$$

Cl_4Zr_1. M: 233.03. Crystalline, hygroscopic solid. d: 2.80 kg/l. Sublimes at 331°C. Fumes in moist air. Decomposed by water forming hydrochloric acid.
Production:
• zircon + metallurgical coke + chlorine (thermal reduction/chlorination)
Derivatives:
zirconium; zirconium butoxide; zirconium oxychloride
Uses: alkylation/polymerisation catalyst

ZIX *See:* zinc isopropyl xanthate

ZMBI *See:* zinc 2-mercaptobenzimidazole

ZMBT *See:* zinc mercaptobenzothiazole

Z5MC *See:* zinc pentamethylenedithiocarbamate

ZMMBI *See:* zinc 2-mercaptomethylbenzimidazole

zomepirac
[33369-31-2]

$C_{15}H_{14}Cl_1N_1O_3$. M: 291.73.
Production:
• dimethyl acetonedicarboxylate + chloroacetone + methylamine + *p*-chlorobenzoyl chloride (Hantzsch synthesis/Friedel-Crafts acylation/saponification/ decarboxylation)
Uses: antiphlogistic drug

[77-47-4]	hexachlorocyclopentadiene
[77-48-5]	1,3-dibromo-5,5-dimethylhydantoin
[77-53-2]	cedrol
[77-54-3]	cedryl acetate
[77-58-7]	dibutyltin dilaurate
[77-67-8]	ethosuximide
[77-71-4]	5,5-dimethylhydantoin
[77-73-6]	dicyclopentadiene
[77-78-1]	dimethyl sulphate
[77-83-8]	ethyl methylphenylglycidate
[77-85-0]	trimethylolethane
[77-86-1]	tris(hydroxymethyl)aminomethane
[77-89-4]	triethyl acetylcitrate
[77-90-7]	tri-*n*-butyl acetylcitrate
[77-92-9]	citric acid
[77-93-0]	triethyl citrate
[77-94-1]	tri-*n*-butyl citrate
[77-98-5]	tetraethylammonium hydroxide
[77-99-6]	trimethylolpropane
[78-00-2]	tetraethyl lead
[78-04-6]	dibutyltin maleate
[78-08-0]	triethoxyvinylsilane
[78-10-4]	ethyl silicate
[78-11-5]	pentaerythritol tetranitrate
[78-27-3]	ethynyl cyclohexanol
[78-36-4]	linalyl butyrate
[78-39-7]	triethyl orthoacetate
[78-40-0]	triethyl phosphate
[78-42-2]	tri-(2-ethylhexyl) phosphate
[78-46-6]	di-*n*-butyl butylphosphonate
[78-50-2]	tri-*n*-octylphosphine oxide
[78-51-3]	tributoxyethyl phosphate
[78-59-1]	isophorone
[78-67-1]	2,2′-azobisisobutyronitrile
[78-69-3]	tetrahydrolinalool
[78-70-6]	linalool
[78-77-3]	isobutyl bromide
[78-78-4]	isopentane
[78-79-5]	isoprene
[78-82-0]	isobutyronitrile
[78-83-1]	isobutanol
[78-84-2]	isobutyraldehyde
[78-85-3]	methacrolein
[78-87-5]	propylene dichloride
[78-90-0]	1,2-propanediamine
[78-92-2]	*s*-butanol
[78-93-3]	methyl ethyl ketone
[78-94-4]	methyl vinyl ketone
[78-95-5]	chloroacetone
[78-96-6]	monoisopropanolamine
[79-00-5]	1,1,2-trichloroethane
[79-01-6]	trichloroethylene
[79-03-8]	propionyl chloride
[79-04-9]	chloroacetyl chloride
[79-06-1]	acrylamide
[79-08-3]	bromoacetic acid
[79-09-4]	propionic acid
[79-10-7]	acrylic acid
[79-11-8]	chloroacetic acid
[79-14-1]	glycollic acid
[79-16-3]	*N*-methylacetamide
[79-19-6]	thiosemicarbazide
[79-20-9]	methyl acetate
[79-21-0]	peracetic acid
[79-22-1]	methyl chloroformate

[79-27-6]	tetrabromoethane
[79-30-1]	isobutyroyl chloride
[79-31-2]	isobutyric acid
[79-33-4]	L-lactic acid
[79-35-6]	1,1-dichloro-2,2-difluoroethylene
[79-37-8]	oxalyl chloride
[79-38-9]	chlorotrifluoroethylene
[79-39-0]	methacrylamide
[79-41-4]	methacrylic acid
[79-43-6]	dichloroacetic acid
[79-44-7]	dimethylcarbamoyl chloride
[79-46-9]	2-nitropropane
[79-57-2]	oxytetracycline
[79-63-0]	lanosterol
[79-74-3]	2,5-di-*t*-amylhydroquinone
[79-76-5]	ionone (γ-isomer)
[79-81-2]	vitamin A (palmitate ester)
[79-92-5]	camphene
[79-94-7]	tetrabromobisphenol A
[80-03-5]	acediasulfone
[80-04-6]	4,4′-methylenebiscyclohexanol
[80-05-7]	bisphenol A
[80-09-1]	4,4′-dihydroxydiphenyl sulphone
[80-10-4]	dichlorodiphenylsilane
[80-15-9]	cumene hydroperoxide
[80-17-1]	benzenesulphohydrazide
[80-22-8]	*N*-*n*-butyl-3-amino-4-methoxybenzenesulphon-amide
[80-23-9]	2-amino-4-methylsulphonylphenol
[80-25-1]	menthanyl acetate
[80-26-2]	terpinyl acetate
[80-30-8]	*N*-cyclohexyl-*p*-toluenesulphonamide
[80-35-3]	sulfamethoxypyridazine
[80-39-7]	*N*-ethyl-*p*-toluenesulphonamide
[80-40-0]	ethyl *p*-toluenesulphonate
[80-43-3]	dicumyl peroxide
[80-48-8]	methyl *p*-toluenesulphonate
[80-51-3]	4,4′-oxybis(benzenesulphohydrazide)
[80-54-6]	4-*t*-butyl-α-methylhydrocinnamaldehyde
[80-56-8]	α-pinene
[80-58-0]	α-bromobutyric acid
[80-59-1]	tiglic acid
[80-62-6]	methyl methacrylate
[80-70-6]	tetramethylguanidine
[80-71-7]	3-methyl-2-cyclopenten-2-ol-1-one
[81-04-9]	naphthalene-1,5-disulphonic acid
[81-11-8]	4,4′-diaminostilbene-2,2′-disulphonic acid
[81-13-0]	pantothenol
[81-14-1]	musk ketone
[81-15-2]	musk xylol
[81-16-3]	Tobias acid
[81-21-0]	dicyclopentadiene dioxide
[81-33-4]	perylimide
[81-42-5]	Disperse Violet 28
[81-48-1]	Disperse Blue 72
[81-58-3]	1,4,5,8-tetrachloroanthraquinone
[81-64-1]	quinizarin
[81-77-6]	indanthrone
[81-81-2]	warfarin
[81-82-3]	coumachlor
[81-84-5]	naphthalic anhydride
[81-88-9]	Basic Violet 10
[81-96-9]	3-bromobenzanthrone
[81-98-1]	3,9-dibromobenzanthrone
[82-05-3]	benzanthrone

[82-27-9]	2-amino-1-chloroanthraquinone
[82-38-2]	Disperse Red 9
[82-42-8]	1-chloro-4-hydroxyanthraquinone
[82-44-0]	1-chloroanthraquinone
[82-45-1]	1-aminoanthraquinone
[82-46-2]	1,5-dichloroanthraquinone
[82-48-4]	anthraquinone-1,8-disulphonic acid
[82-66-6]	diphacinone
[82-68-8]	quintozene
[82-75-7]	peri acid
[82-76-8]	N-phenyl-peri acid
[83-07-8]	4-aminoantipyrine
[83-26-1]	pindone
[83-32-9]	acenaphthene
[83-38-5]	2,6-dichlorobenzaldehyde
[83-40-9]	o-cresotic acid
[83-44-3]	deoxycholic acid
[83-48-7]	stigmasterol
[83-56-7]	1,5-naphthalenediol
[83-64-7]	S acid
[83-67-0]	theobromine
[83-79-4]	rotenone
[83-86-3]	phytic acid
[83-88-5]	riboflavin
[83-89-6]	mepacrine
[83-98-7]	orphenadrine
[84-02-6]	prochlorperazine (maleate)
[84-11-7]	9,10-phenanthrenequinone
[84-16-2]	hexestrol
[84-22-0]	tetryzoline
[84-47-9]	2-t-butylanthraquinone
[84-48-0]	anthraquinone-2-sulphonic acid, sodium salt
[84-49-1]	anthraquinone-2,7-disulphonic acid
[84-50-4]	anthraquinone-2,6-disulphonic acid
[84-51-5]	2-ethylanthraquinone
[84-54-8]	2-methylanthraquinone
[84-57-1]	1-(2′,5′-dichloro-4′-sulphophenyl)-3-methyl-pyrazolone
[84-61-7]	dicyclohexyl phthalate
[84-62-8]	diphenyl phthalate
[84-65-1]	anthraquinone
[84-66-2]	diethyl phthalate
[84-69-5]	diisobutyl phthalate
[84-74-2]	di-n-butyl phthalate
[84-80-0]	vitamin K_1
[84-83-3]	Fischer's aldehyde
[84-86-6]	naphthionic acid
[84-87-7]	Nevile-Winther acid
[84-89-9]	1-naphthylamine-5-sulphonic acid
[85-00-7]	diquat dibromide
[85-01-8]	phenanthrene
[85-19-8]	5-chloro-2-hydroxybenzophenone
[85-29-0]	2,4′-dichlorobenzophenone
[85-41-6]	phthalimide
[85-42-7]	hexahydrophthalic anhydride
[85-43-8]	tetrahydrophthalic anhydride
[85-44-9]	phthalic anhydride
[85-47-2]	naphthalene-1-sulphonic acid
[85-52-9]	o-benzoylbenzoic acid
[85-56-3]	2-(4-chlorobenzoyl)benzoic acid
[85-68-7]	n-butyl benzyl phthalate
[85-83-6]	Solvent Red 24
[85-86-9]	Solvent Red 23
[85-91-6]	methyl N-methylanthranilate
[86-12-4]	thenalidine

[86-21-5]	pheniramine
[86-22-6]	brompheniramine
[86-28-2]	N-ethylcarbazole
[86-29-3]	diphenylacetonitrile
[86-39-5]	2-chlorothioxanthone
[86-50-0]	azinphos-methyl
[86-52-2]	1-chloromethylnaphthalene
[86-55-5]	α-naphthoic acid
[86-65-7]	amino-G acid
[86-73-7]	fluorene
[86-74-8]	carbazole
[86-81-7]	3,4,5-trimethoxybenzaldehyde
[86-86-2]	1-naphthylacetamide
[86-87-3]	1-naphthylacetic acid
[86-92-0]	1-(4′-methylphenyl)-3-methylpyrazolone
[86-93-1]	1-phenyl-5-mercaptotetrazole
[86-98-6]	4,7-dichloroquinoline
[87-02-5]	J acid
[87-08-1]	phenoxymethylpenicillin
[87-13-8]	diethyl ethoxymethylenemalonate
[87-17-2]	salicylanilide
[87-18-3]	p-t-butylphenyl salicylate
[87-19-4]	isobutyl salicylate
[87-20-7]	isoamyl salicylate
[87-22-9]	phenethyl salicylate
[87-33-2]	isosorbide dinitrate
[87-42-3]	6-chloropurine
[87-51-4]	indol-3-ylacetic acid
[87-56-9]	mucochloric acid
[87-59-2]	2,3-xylidine
[87-60-5]	2-amino-3-chlorotoluene
[87-62-7]	2,6-xylidine
[87-65-0]	2,6-dichlorophenol
[87-66-1]	pyrogallol
[87-69-4]	tartaric acid
[87-79-6]	L-sorbose
[87-89-8]	inositol
[87-90-1]	trichloroisocyanuric acid
[88-04-0]	4-chloro-3,5-xylenol
[88-05-1]	mesidine
[88-06-2]	2,4,6-trichlorophenol
[88-10-8]	diethylcarbamoyl chloride
[88-12-0]	N-vinyl-2-pyrrolidone
[88-14-2]	2-furoic acid
[88-15-3]	2-acetylthiophene
[88-16-4]	o-chlorobenzotrifluoride
[88-17-5]	o-aminobenzotrifluoride
[88-18-6]	o-t-butylphenol
[88-21-1]	orthanilic acid
[88-23-3]	2-amino-4-chlorophenol-6-sulphonic acid
[88-27-7]	2,6-di-t-butyldimethylamino-p-cresol
[88-39-1]	disodium benzaldehyde-2,4-disulphonate
[88-44-8]	4B acid
[88-51-7]	2B acid
[88-53-9]	5-amino-2-chlorotoluene-4-sulphonic acid
[88-60-8]	6-t-butyl-m-cresol
[88-63-1]	2,4-diaminobenzenesulphonic acid
[88-69-7]	o-isopropylphenol
[88-72-2]	o-nitrotoluene
[88-73-3]	o-chloronitrobenzene
[88-74-4]	o-nitroaniline
[88-75-5]	o-nitrophenol
[88-85-7]	dinoseb
[88-89-1]	picric acid
[88-95-9]	phthaloyl chloride

[94-25-7]	*n*-butyl *p*-aminobenzoate
[94-26-8]	*n*-butyl 4-hydroxybenzoate
[94-34-8]	*N*-(2-cyanoethyl)-*N*-methylaniline
[94-36-0]	benzoyl peroxide
[94-44-0]	benzyl nicotinate
[94-51-9]	dipropylene glycol dibenzoate
[94-59-7]	safrole
[94-70-2]	*o*-phenetidine
[94-74-6]	2-methyl-4-chlorophenoxyacetic acid
[94-75-7]	2,4-D
[94-78-0]	phenazopyridine
[94-80-4]	2,4-D-butyl
[94-81-5]	MCPB-sodium
[94-82-6]	2,4-DB
[94-85-9]	2,5-diethoxyaniline
[94-86-0]	propenylguethol
[94-91-7]	*N,N'*-disalicylidene-1,2-propanediamine
[94-99-5]	2,4-dichlorobenzyl chloride
[95-01-2]	2,4-dihydroxybenzaldehyde
[95-14-7]	benzotriazole
[95-20-5]	2-methylindole
[95-25-0]	chlorzoxazone
[95-31-8]	*N-t*-butyl-2-benzothiazolesulphenamide
[95-33-0]	*N*-cyclohexyl-2-benzothiazolesulphenamide
[95-34-1]	Fluorescent Brightener 133
[95-45-4]	dimethylglyoxime
[95-47-6]	*o*-xylene
[95-48-7]	*o*-cresol
[95-49-8]	*o*-chlorotoluene
[95-50-1]	*o*-dichlorobenzene
[95-51-2]	*o*-chloroaniline
[95-53-4]	*o*-toluidine
[95-54-5]	*o*-phenylenediamine
[95-55-6]	*o*-aminophenol
[95-57-8]	*o*-chlorophenol
[95-63-6]	pseudocumene
[95-64-7]	3,4-xylidine
[95-68-1]	2,4-xylidine
[95-73-8]	2,4-dichlorotoluene
[95-74-9]	4-amino-2-chlorotoluene
[95-75-0]	3,4-dichlorotoluene
[95-76-1]	3,4-dichloroaniline
[95-78-3]	2,5-xylidine
[95-82-9]	2,5-dichloroaniline
[95-83-0]	4-chloro-*o*-phenylenediamine
[95-84-1]	*o*-amino-*p*-cresol
[95-85-2]	2-amino-4-chlorophenol
[95-92-1]	diethyl oxalate
[95-93-2]	durene
[95-95-4]	2,4,5-trichlorophenol
[96-05-9]	allyl methacrylate
[96-09-3]	styrene oxide
[96-10-6]	diethylaluminium chloride
[96-17-3]	2-methylbutyraldehyde
[96-18-4]	1,2,3-trichloropropane
[96-20-8]	2-aminobutanol
[96-22-0]	diethyl ketone
[96-23-1]	glycerol-1,3-dichlorohydrin
[96-24-2]	chlorohydrin
[96-26-4]	dihydroxyacetone
[96-27-5]	thioglycerol
[96-31-1]	*N,N'*-dimethylurea
[96-33-3]	methyl acrylate
[96-34-4]	methyl chloroacetate
[96-45-7]	ethylenethiourea
[96-48-0]	γ-butyrolactone
[96-49-1]	ethylene carbonate
[96-50-4]	2-aminothiazole
[96-54-8]	*N*-methylpyrrole
[96-67-3]	2-amino-4-nitrophenol-6-sulphonic acid
[96-69-5]	4,4'-thiobis(2-*t*-butyl-5-methylphenol)
[96-73-1]	2-chloro-5-nitrobenzenesulphonic acid
[96-76-4]	2,4-di-*t*-butylphenol
[96-80-0]	2-diisopropylaminoethanol
[96-83-3]	iopanoic acid
[96-88-8]	mepivacaine
[96-91-3]	sodium picramate
[96-96-8]	4-amino-3-nitroanisole
[96-99-1]	4-chloro-3-nitrobenzoic acid
[97-00-7]	1-chloro-2,4-dinitrobenzene
[97-02-9]	2,4-dinitroaniline
[97-05-2]	sulphosalicylic acid
[97-08-5]	4-chloro-3-nitrobenzenesulphonyl chloride
[97-18-7]	bithionol
[97-23-4]	dichlorophen
[97-30-3]	α-methylglucoside
[97-35-8]	*N,N*-diethyl-3-amino-4-methoxybenzene-sulphonamide
[97-36-9]	acetoacet-2,4-xylidide
[97-39-2]	di-*o*-tolylguanidine
[97-50-7]	5-chloro-2,4-dimethoxyaniline
[97-52-9]	2-amino-4-nitroanisole
[97-53-0]	eugenol
[97-54-1]	isoeugenol
[97-56-3]	*o*-aminoazotoluene
[97-59-6]	allantoin
[97-61-0]	2-methylvaleric acid
[97-63-2]	ethyl methacrylate
[97-64-3]	ethyl lactate
[97-65-4]	itaconic acid
[97-67-6]	L-malic acid
[97-74-5]	tetramethylthiuram monosulphide
[97-77-8]	tetraethylthiuram disulphide
[97-86-9]	isobutyl methacrylate
[97-88-1]	*n*-butyl methacrylate
[97-89-2]	citronellyl isobutyrate
[97-90-5]	ethylene glycol dimethacrylate
[97-93-8]	triethylaluminium
[97-99-4]	tetrahydrofurfuryl alcohol
[98-00-0]	furfuryl alcohol
[98-01-1]	furfural
[98-02-2]	furfuryl mercaptan
[98-06-6]	*t*-butylbenzene
[98-07-7]	benzotrichloride
[98-08-8]	benzotrifluoride
[98-09-9]	benzenesulphonyl chloride
[98-11-3]	benzenesulphonic acid
[98-13-5]	trichlorophenylsilane
[98-16-8]	*m*-aminobenzotrifluoride
[98-17-9]	*m*-hydroxybenzotrifluoride
[98-19-1]	5-*t*-butyl-*m*-xylene
[98-29-3]	*t*-butylcatechol
[98-32-8]	2-aminophenol-4-sulphonamide
[98-37-3]	2-aminophenol-4-sulphonic acid
[98-44-2]	aniline-2,5-disulphonic acid
[98-50-0]	arsanilic acid
[98-51-1]	*p-t*-butyltoluene
[98-52-2]	4-*t*-butylcyclohexanol
[98-54-4]	*p-t*-butylphenol
[98-55-5]	α-terpineol

[102-56-7]	2,5-dimethoxyaniline
[102-60-3]	tetrahydroxypropyl ethylenediamine
[102-70-5]	triallylamine
[102-71-6]	triethanolamine
[102-76-1]	triacetin
[102-79-4]	N-n-butyldiethanolamine
[102-82-9]	tri-n-butylamine
[102-92-1]	cinnamoyl chloride
[103-01-5]	N-phenylglycine
[103-05-9]	dimethyl phenethyl carbinol
[103-11-7]	2-ethylhexyl acrylate
[103-23-1]	di-(2-ethylhexyl) adipate
[103-24-2]	di-(2-ethylhexyl) azelate
[103-26-4]	methyl cinnamate
[103-27-5]	phenylmercuric propionate
[103-32-2]	N-benzylaniline
[103-34-4]	4,4'-dithiodimorpholine
[103-38-8]	benzyl isovalerate
[103-41-3]	benzyl cinnamate
[103-45-7]	phenethyl acetate
[103-48-0]	phenethyl isobutyrate
[103-49-1]	dibenzylamine
[103-53-7]	phenethyl cinnamate
[103-54-8]	cinnamyl acetate
[103-60-6]	2-phenoxyethyl isobutyrate
[103-64-0]	β-bromostyrene
[103-67-3]	N-benzylmethylamine
[103-69-5]	N-ethylaniline
[103-71-9]	phenyl isocyanate
[103-72-0]	phenyl isothiocyanate
[103-76-4]	N-hydroxyethylpiperazine
[103-79-7]	phenylacetone
[103-80-0]	phenylacetyl chloride
[103-82-2]	phenylacetic acid
[103-83-3]	benzyldimethylamine
[103-84-4]	acetanilide
[103-90-2]	paracetamol
[103-95-7]	cyclamen aldehyde
[103-98-0]	N-lauroyl-p-aminophenol
[103-99-1]	N-stearoyl-p-aminophenol
[104-04-1]	p-nitroacetanilide
[104-09-6]	4-methylphenylacetaldehyde
[104-12-1]	p-chlorophenyl isocyanate
[104-13-2]	p-n-butylaniline
[104-15-4]	p-toluenesulphonic acid
[104-21-2]	anisyl acetate
[104-23-4]	4'-aminoazobenzene-4-sulphonic acid
[104-28-9]	cinoxate
[104-46-1]	anethole
[104-49-4]	p-phenylene diisocyanate
[104-50-7]	γ-octalactone
[104-51-8]	n-butylbenzene
[104-53-0]	3-phenylpropionaldehyde
[104-54-1]	cinnamyl alcohol
[104-55-2]	cinnamaldehyde
[104-61-0]	γ-nonalactone
[104-62-1]	phenethyl formate
[104-67-6]	γ-undecalactone
[104-74-5]	laurylpyridinium chloride
[104-75-6]	2-ethylhexylamine
[104-76-7]	2-ethylhexanol
[104-78-9]	3-diethylaminopropylamine
[104-83-6]	p-chlorobenzyl chloride
[104-86-9]	p-chlorobenzylamine
[104-87-0]	p-methylbenzaldehyde
[104-88-1]	p-chlorobenzaldehyde
[104-90-5]	2-methyl-5-ethylpyridine
[104-91-6]	p-nitrosophenol
[104-93-8]	p-methoxytoluene
[104-94-9]	p-anisidine
[105-11-3]	p-quinonedioxime
[105-13-5]	anisyl alcohol
[105-14-6]	5-diethylamino-2-pentanone
[105-30-6]	2-methylpentanol
[105-34-0]	methyl cyanoacetate
[105-36-2]	ethyl bromoacetate
[105-37-3]	ethyl propionate
[105-38-4]	vinyl propionate
[105-39-5]	ethyl chloroacetate
[105-45-3]	methyl acetoacetate
[105-46-4]	s-butyl acetate
[105-53-3]	diethyl malonate
[105-54-4]	ethyl butyrate
[105-55-5]	diethylthiourea
[105-56-6]	ethyl cyanoacetate
[105-58-8]	diethyl carbonate
[105-59-9]	methyldiethanolamine
[105-60-2]	caprolactam
[105-64-6]	diisopropyl peroxydicarbonate
[105-66-8]	n-propyl butyrate
[105-74-8]	lauroyl peroxide
[105-75-9]	di-n-butyl fumarate
[105-76-0]	di-n-butyl maleate
[105-85-1]	citronellyl formate
[105-86-2]	geranyl formate
[105-87-3]	geranyl acetate
[105-90-8]	geranyl propionate
[105-95-3]	ethylene brassylate
[106-02-5]	15-pentadecanolide
[106-11-6]	diethylene glycol monostearate
[106-12-7]	diethylene glycol monooleate
[106-14-9]	12-hydroxystearic acid
[106-20-7]	di-(2-ethylhexyl)amine
[106-21-8]	tetrahydrogeraniol
[106-23-0]	(±)-citronellal
[106-24-1]	geraniol
[106-25-2]	nerol
[106-27-4]	isoamyl butyrate
[106-29-6]	geranyl butyrate
[106-30-9]	ethyl heptanoate
[106-32-1]	ethyl caprylate
[106-39-8]	p-bromochlorobenzene
[106-40-1]	p-bromoaniline
[106-42-3]	p-xylene
[106-43-4]	p-chlorotoluene
[106-44-5]	p-cresol
[106-46-7]	p-dichlorobenzene
[106-47-8]	p-chloroaniline
[106-48-9]	p-chlorophenol
[106-49-0]	p-toluidine
[106-50-3]	p-phenylenediamine
[106-51-4]	p-benzoquinone
[106-52-5]	4-hydroxy-1-methylpiperidine
[106-58-1]	N,N'-dimethylpiperazine
[106-63-8]	isobutyl acrylate
[106-68-3]	ethyl n-amyl ketone
[106-69-4]	1,2,6-hexanetriol
[106-70-7]	methyl caproate
[106-71-8]	2-cyanoethyl acrylate
[106-75-2]	diethylene glycol bis(chloroformate)

[106-88-7]	1,2-butylene oxide	[108-42-9]	*m*-chloroaniline
[106-89-8]	epichlorohydrin	[108-44-1]	*m*-toluidine
[106-90-1]	glycidyl acrylate	[108-45-2]	*m*-phenylenediamine
[106-91-2]	glycidyl methacrylate	[108-46-3]	resorcinol
[106-92-3]	allyl glycidyl ether	[108-48-5]	2,6-lutidine
[106-93-4]	ethylene dibromide	[108-56-5]	diethyl oxalacetate
[106-94-5]	*n*-propyl bromide	[108-57-6]	divinylbenzene
[106-95-6]	allyl bromide	[108-59-8]	dimethyl malonate
[106-97-8]	*n*-butane	[108-62-3]	metaldehyde
[106-99-0]	butadiene	[108-67-8]	mesitylene
[107-02-8]	acrolein	[108-68-9]	3,5-xylenol
[107-03-9]	*n*-propyl mercaptan	[108-69-0]	3,5-xylidine
[107-05-1]	allyl chloride	[108-73-6]	phloroglucinol
[107-06-2]	ethylene dichloride	[108-77-0]	cyanuric chloride
[107-07-3]	ethylene chlorohydrin	[108-78-1]	melamine
[107-10-8]	*n*-propylamine	[108-80-5]	cyanuric acid
[107-11-9]	allylamine	[108-83-8]	diisobutyl ketone
[107-12-0]	propionitrile	[108-86-1]	bromobenzene
[107-13-1]	acrylonitrile	[108-88-3]	toluene
[107-14-2]	chloroacetonitrile	[108-89-4]	γ-picoline
[107-15-3]	ethylenediamine	[108-90-7]	chlorobenzene
[107-18-6]	allyl alcohol	[108-91-8]	cyclohexylamine
[107-19-7]	propargyl alcohol	[108-93-0]	cyclohexanol
[107-20-0]	chloroacetaldehyde	[108-94-1]	cyclohexanone
[107-21-1]	ethylene glycol	[108-95-2]	phenol
[107-22-2]	glyoxal	[108-98-5]	thiophenol
[107-25-5]	methyl vinyl ether	[108-99-6]	β-picoline
[107-30-2]	chloromethyl methyl ether	[109-00-2]	3-hydroxypyridine
[107-31-3]	methyl formate	[109-01-3]	*N*-methylpiperazine
[107-32-4]	performic acid	[109-02-4]	*N*-methylmorpholine
[107-35-7]	taurine	[109-04-6]	2-bromopyridine
[107-41-5]	hexylene glycol	[109-05-7]	2-methylpiperidine
[107-43-7]	betaine	[109-06-8]	α-picoline
[107-46-0]	hexamethyldisiloxane	[109-09-1]	2-chloropyridine
[107-54-0]	dimethyl hexynol	[109-12-6]	2-aminopyrimidine
[107-56-2]	*O,O*-diisopropyl phosphorodithioic acid	[109-20-6]	geranyl isovalerate
[107-58-4]	*N-t*-butylacrylamide	[109-28-4]	oleamidopropyldimethylamine
[107-71-1]	*t*-butyl peroxyacetate	[109-43-3]	di-*n*-butyl sebacate
[107-75-5]	hydroxycitronellal	[109-46-6]	di-*n*-butylthiourea
[107-87-9]	methyl propyl ketone	[109-52-4]	valeric acid
[107-88-0]	1,3-butanediol	[109-53-5]	isobutyl vinyl ether
[107-91-5]	cyanoacetamide	[109-55-7]	3-dimethylaminopropylamine
[107-92-6]	*n*-butyric acid	[109-57-9]	allylthiourea
[107-95-9]	β-alanine	[109-60-4]	*n*-propyl acetate
[107-96-0]	3-mercaptopropionic acid	[109-61-5]	*n*-propyl chloroformate
[107-97-1]	sarcosine	[109-65-9]	*n*-butyl bromide
[107-98-2]	propylene glycol monomethyl ether	[109-66-0]	*n*-pentane
[108-01-0]	dimethylethanolamine	[109-67-1]	1-pentene
[108-03-2]	1-nitropropane	[109-69-3]	*n*-butyl chloride
[108-05-4]	vinyl acetate	[109-70-6]	1-bromo-3-chloropropane
[108-10-1]	methyl isobutyl ketone	[109-72-8]	*n*-butyllithium
[108-11-2]	methyl isobutyl carbinol	[109-73-9]	*n*-butylamine
[108-16-7]	dimethylisopropanolamine	[109-74-0]	*n*-butyronitrile
[108-18-9]	diisopropylamine	[109-76-2]	1,3-propanediamine
[108-20-3]	diisopropyl ether	[109-77-3]	malononitrile
[108-21-4]	isopropyl acetate	[109-79-5]	*n*-butyl mercaptan
[108-22-5]	isopropenyl acetate	[109-83-1]	methylethanolamine
[108-23-6]	isopropyl chloroformate	[109-86-4]	ethylene glycol monomethyl ether
[108-24-7]	acetic anhydride	[109-89-7]	diethylamine
[108-30-5]	succinic anhydride	[109-90-0]	ethyl isocyanate
[108-31-6]	maleic anhydride	[109-92-2]	ethyl vinyl ether
[108-32-7]	propylene carbonate	[109-94-4]	ethyl formate
[108-38-3]	*m*-xylene	[109-97-7]	pyrrole
[108-39-4]	*m*-cresol	[109-99-9]	tetrahydrofuran
[108-41-8]	*m*-chlorotoluene	[110-00-9]	furan

[112-82-3]	cetyl bromide
[112-84-5]	erucamide
[112-85-6]	behenic acid
[112-90-3]	oleylamine
[112-92-5]	stearyl alcohol
[113-59-7]	chlorprothixene
[113-92-8]	chlorphenamine (hydrogen maleate)
[114-07-8]	erythromycin
[114-26-1]	propoxur
[115-07-1]	propylene
[115-10-6]	dimethyl ether
[115-11-7]	isobutylene
[115-18-4]	2-methyl-3-buten-2-ol
[115-19-5]	methylbutynol
[115-25-3]	octafluorocyclobutane
[115-29-7]	endosulphan
[115-32-2]	dicofol
[115-37-7]	thebaine
[115-38-8]	methylphenobarbital
[115-46-8]	azacyclonol
[115-68-4]	sulfadicramide
[115-69-5]	2-amino-2-methyl-1,3-propanediol
[115-70-8]	2-ethyl-2-aminopropan-1,3-diol
[115-77-5]	pentaerythritol
[115-78-6]	chlorphonium chloride
[115-83-3]	pentaerythritol tetrastearate
[115-86-6]	triphenyl phosphate
[115-90-2]	fensulfothion
[115-95-7]	linalyl acetate
[115-96-8]	tris(2-chloroethyl) phosphate
[115-98-0]	bis(2-chloroethyl)vinyl phosphonate
[115-99-1]	linalyl formate
[116-02-9]	trimethylcyclohexanol
[116-06-3]	aldicarb
[116-09-6]	hydroxyacetone
[116-14-3]	tetrafluoroethylene
[116-15-4]	hexafluoropropylene
[116-29-0]	tetradifon
[116-53-0]	2-methylbutyric acid
[116-63-2]	1-amino-2-naphthol-4-sulphonic acid
[116-71-2]	dibenzanthrone
[116-81-4]	bromamine acid
[116-82-5]	1-amino-2-bromo-4-hydroxyanthraquinone
[117-06-6]	1-amino-5-benzamidoanthraquinone
[117-10-2]	1,8-dihydroxyanthraquinone
[117-12-4]	1,5-dihydroxyanthraquinone
[117-14-6]	anthraquinone-1,5-disulphonic acid
[117-18-0]	tecnazene
[117-34-0]	diphenylacetic acid
[117-42-0]	Koch acid
[117-57-7]	oxyquinaldine carboxylic acid
[117-59-9]	5-hydroxynaphthalene-1-sulphonic acid
[117-61-3]	benzidine-2,2′-disulphonic acid
[117-62-4]	2-naphthylamine-1,5-disulphonic acid
[117-79-3]	2-aminoanthraquinone
[117-80-6]	dichlone
[117-81-7]	di-(2-ethylhexyl) phthalate
[117-82-8]	di-(2-methoxyethyl) phthalate
[117-83-9]	dibutoxyethyl phthalate
[117-89-5]	trifluoperazine
[117-96-4]	amidotrizoic acid
[118-12-7]	Fischer's base
[118-32-1]	G acid
[118-44-5]	N-ethyl-1-naphthylamine
[118-45-6]	4-chlorophthalic anhydride
[118-46-7]	8-amino-2-naphthol
[118-48-9]	isatoic anhydride
[118-52-5]	1,3-dichloro-5,5-dimethylhydantoin
[118-55-8]	phenyl salicylate
[118-58-1]	benzyl salicylate
[118-60-5]	2-ethylhexyl salicylate
[118-71-8]	maltol
[118-74-1]	hexachlorobenzene
[118-75-2]	chloranil
[118-79-6]	2,4,6-tribromophenol
[118-82-1]	4,4′-methylenebis(2,6-di-t-butylphenol)
[118-90-1]	o-toluic acid
[118-91-2]	o-chlorobenzoic acid
[118-92-3]	anthranilic acid
[118-93-4]	o-hydroxyacetophenone
[118-96-7]	2,4,6-trinitrotoluene
[119-06-2]	diisotridecyl phthalate
[119-19-7]	N-phenylgamma acid
[119-27-7]	2,4-dinitroanisole
[119-32-4]	4-amino-3-nitrotoluene
[119-33-5]	m-nitro-p-cresol
[119-36-8]	methyl salicylate
[119-40-4]	N-phenyl-J acid
[119-47-1]	2,2′-methylenebis(4-methyl-6-t-butylphenol)
[119-52-8]	anisoin
[119-53-9]	benzoin
[119-58-4]	4,4′-bis(dimethylamino)benzhydrol
[119-61-9]	benzophenone
[119-64-2]	tetralin
[119-65-3]	isoquinoline
[119-70-0]	4,4′-diaminodiphenylamine-2-sulphonic acid
[119-80-2]	2,2′-dithiodibenzoic acid
[119-84-6]	dihydrocoumarin
[119-90-4]	o-dianisidine
[119-93-7]	o-tolidine
[120-00-3]	4′-amino-2′,5′-diethoxybenzanilide
[120-07-0]	N,N-di-(2-hydroxyethyl)aniline
[120-12-7]	anthracene
[120-14-9]	veratraldehyde
[120-18-3]	naphthalene-2-sulphonic acid
[120-20-7]	homoveratrylamine
[120-21-8]	p-diethylaminobenzaldehyde
[120-23-0]	(2-naphthyloxy)acetic acid
[120-32-1]	o-benzyl-p-chlorophenol
[120-36-5]	dichlorprop
[120-46-7]	dibenzoylmethane
[120-47-8]	ethyl 4-hydroxybenzoate
[120-51-4]	benzyl benzoate
[120-52-5]	dibenzoyl-p-quinonedioxime
[120-55-8]	diethylene glycol dibenzoate
[120-57-0]	piperonal
[120-58-1]	isosafrole
[120-61-6]	dimethyl terephthalate
[120-65-0]	dimethylaminomethylphenol
[120-71-8]	p-cresidine
[120-72-9]	indole
[120-75-2]	2-methylbenzothiazole
[120-78-5]	2,2′-dibenzothiazyl disulphide
[120-80-9]	catechol
[120-82-1]	1,2,4-trichlorobenzene
[120-83-2]	2,4-dichlorophenol
[120-92-3]	cyclopentanone
[120-93-4]	ethylene urea
[121-03-9]	4-nitrotoluene-2-sulphonic acid
[121-19-7]	3-nitro-4-hydroxyphenylarsonic acid

[137-99-5]	dinonylphenol (2,4-isomer)
[138-22-7]	*n*-butyl lactate
[138-37-4]	mafenide (hydrochloride)
[138-39-6]	mafenide
[138-86-3]	dipentene
[138-89-6]	*N,N*-dimethyl-*p*-nitrosoaniline
[139-05-9]	sodium cyclamate
[139-06-0]	calcium cyclamate
[139-08-2]	myristyldimethylbenzylammonium chloride
[139-13-9]	nitrilotriacetic acid
[139-33-3]	ethylenediaminetetraacetic acid, disodium salt
[139-40-2]	propazine
[139-41-3]	sodium dihydroxyethylglycine
[139-62-8]	cyclomethycaine
[139-85-5]	3,4-dihydroxybenzaldehyde
[139-89-9]	hydroxyethylethylenediaminetriacetic acid, trisodium salt
[139-96-8]	triethanolamine lauryl sulphate
[140-01-2]	diethylenetriaminepentaacetic acid, pentasodium salt
[140-08-9]	tris(2-chloroethyl) phosphite
[140-10-3]	cinnamic acid (*trans*-isomer)
[140-11-4]	benzyl acetate
[140-26-1]	phenethyl isovalerate
[140-28-3]	benzathine
[140-29-4]	benzyl cyanide
[140-31-8]	aminoethylpiperazine
[140-53-4]	*p*-chlorobenzyl cyanide
[140-72-7]	cetylpyridinium bromide
[140-80-7]	4-amino-1-diethylaminopentane
[140-88-5]	ethyl acrylate
[140-89-6]	potassium ethyl xanthate
[140-93-2]	sodium isopropyl xanthate
[140-95-4]	dimethylolurea
[141-01-5]	ferrous fumarate
[141-03-7]	di-*n*-butyl succinate
[141-05-9]	diethyl maleate
[141-10-6]	pseudoionone
[141-12-8]	neryl acetate
[141-13-9]	2,6,10-trimethylundecenal
[141-14-0]	citronellyl propionate
[141-18-4]	dibutoxyethyl adipate
[141-20-8]	diethylene glycol monolaurate
[141-22-0]	ricinoleic acid
[141-24-2]	methyl ricinoleate
[141-30-0]	3,6-dichloropyridazine
[141-32-2]	*n*-butyl acrylate
[141-43-5]	monoethanolamine
[141-52-6]	sodium ethoxide
[141-53-7]	sodium formate
[141-66-2]	dicrotophos
[141-75-3]	*n*-butyryl chloride
[141-78-6]	ethyl acetate
[141-79-7]	mesityl oxide
[141-82-2]	malonic acid
[141-86-6]	2,6-diaminopyridine
[141-91-3]	2,6-dimethylmorpholine
[141-92-4]	hydroxycitronellal dimethyl acetal
[141-94-6]	hexetidine
[141-97-9]	ethyl acetoacetate
[142-03-0]	aluminium acetate, basic
[142-16-5]	di-(2-ethylhexyl) maleate
[142-19-8]	allyl enanthate
[142-22-3]	diethylene glycol bis(allyl carbonate)
[142-26-7]	*N*-acetylethanolamine
[142-29-0]	cyclopentene
[142-30-3]	dimethyl hexynediol
[142-45-0]	acetylenedicarboxylic acid
[142-47-2]	monosodium glutamate
[142-59-6]	nabam
[142-62-1]	caproic acid
[142-72-3]	magnesium acetate
[142-73-4]	iminodiacetic acid
[142-77-8]	*n*-butyl oleate
[142-82-5]	heptane
[142-84-7]	di-*n*-propylamine
[142-90-5]	lauryl methacrylate
[142-91-6]	isopropyl palmitate
[142-96-1]	di-*n*-butyl ether
[143-07-7]	lauric acid, narrow cut
[143-08-8]	*n*-nonanol
[143-18-0]	potassium oleate
[143-19-1]	sodium oleate
[143-22-6]	triethylene glycol monobutyl ether
[143-23-7]	bis(hexamethylene)triamine
[143-27-1]	*n*-hexadecylamine
[143-28-2]	oleyl alcohol
[143-33-9]	sodium cyanide
[144-19-4]	2,2,4-trimethyl-1,3-pentanediol
[144-21-8]	disodium methylarsonate
[144-39-8]	linalyl propionate
[144-55-8]	sodium bicarbonate
[144-62-7]	oxalic acid
[144-74-1]	sulfathiazole (sodium salt)
[144-80-9]	sulfacetamide
[144-82-1]	sulfamethizole
[144-83-2]	sulfapyridine
[145-73-3]	endothal-sodium
[146-22-5]	nitrazepam
[146-54-3]	triflupromazine
[146-56-5]	fluphenazine (dihydrochloride)
[147-14-8]	copper phthalocyanine
[147-20-6]	diphenylpyraline
[147-24-0]	diphenhydramine (hydrochloride)
[147-55-7]	pheneticillin
[147-82-0]	2,4,6-tribromoaniline
[147-85-3]	L-proline
[147-93-3]	thiosalicylic acid
[148-18-5]	sodium diethyldithiocarbamate
[148-24-3]	8-hydroxyquinoline
[148-25-4]	chromotropic acid
[148-69-6]	*N*-(2-cyanoethyl)-*N*-ethyl-*m*-toluidine
[148-79-8]	thiabendazole
[148-87-8]	*N*-(2-cyanoethyl)-*N*-ethylaniline
[149-26-8]	disul-sodium
[149-30-4]	2-mercaptobenzothiazole
[149-44-0]	sodium formaldehyde sulphoxylate
[149-57-5]	2-ethylhexanoic acid
[149-64-4]	butylscopolamine bromide
[149-73-5]	trimethyl orthoformate
[149-74-6]	dichloromethylphenylsilane
[149-91-7]	gallic acid
[150-13-0]	*p*-aminobenzoic acid
[150-30-1]	DL-phenylalanine
[150-50-5]	*S,S,S*-tributyl phosphorotrithioate
[150-60-7]	dibenzyl disulphide
[150-75-4]	*N*-methyl-*p*-aminophenol
[150-76-5]	hydroquinone monomethyl ether
[150-84-5]	citronellyl acetate
[150-86-7]	phytol

[150-90-3]	sodium succinate
[151-05-3]	dimethyl benzyl carbinyl acetate
[151-10-0]	resorcinol dimethyl ether
[151-21-3]	sodium lauryl sulphate
[151-50-8]	potassium cyanide
[151-56-4]	ethyleneimine
[151-67-7]	halothane
[151-83-7]	methohexital
[152-02-3]	levallorphan
[152-47-6]	sulfalene
[152-72-7]	acenocoumarol
[153-61-7]	cefalotin
[154-21-2]	lincomycin
[154-41-6]	norephedrine (hydrochloride)
[154-42-7]	thioguanine
[154-69-8]	tripelennamine (hydrochloride)
[155-09-9]	tranylcypromine
[156-38-7]	*p*-hydroxyphenylacetic acid
[156-43-4]	*p*-phenetidine
[156-57-0]	2-mercaptoethylamine hydrochloride
[156-62-7]	calcium cyanamide
[156-87-6]	3-aminopropanol
[206-44-0]	fluoranthene
[256-96-2]	iminostilbene
[280-57-9]	triethylenediamine
[281-23-2]	adamantane
[286-20-4]	cyclohexene oxide
[288-32-4]	imidazole
[288-88-0]	1,2,4-triazole
[298-00-0]	parathion-methyl
[298-02-2]	phorate
[298-04-4]	disulfoton
[298-06-6]	*O,O*-diethyl dithiophosphoric acid
[298-07-7]	bis(2-ethylhexyl) hydrogen phosphate
[298-12-4]	glyoxylic acid
[298-14-6]	potassium bicarbonate
[298-46-4]	carbamazepine
[298-57-7]	cinnarizine
[298-81-7]	methoxsalen
[299-27-4]	potassium gluconate
[299-28-5]	calcium gluconate
[299-29-6]	ferrous gluconate
[299-42-3]	L-ephedrine
[299-42-3]	DL-ephedrine
[299-95-6]	isoprenaline (sulphate)
[300-37-8]	diodone (diethanolamine salt)
[300-62-9]	amphetamine
[300-76-5]	naled
[300-92-5]	aluminium distearate
[301-02-0]	oleamide
[301-04-2]	lead acetate
[301-10-0]	stannous octoate
[301-12-2]	oxydemeton-methyl
[302-01-2]	hydrazine
[302-17-0]	chloral hydrate
[302-72-7]	DL-alanine
[303-07-1]	2,6-dihydroxybenzoic acid
[303-53-7]	cyclobenzaprine
[303-69-5]	prothipendyl
[304-59-6]	Rochelle salt
[306-83-2]	1,1-dichloro-2,2,2-trifluoroethane
[306-94-5]	perfluorodecalin
[307-30-2]	1,1-hydroperfluorooctanol
[309-36-4]	methohexital (sodium salt)
[314-40-9]	bromacil

[315-30-0]	allopurinol
[315-72-0]	opipramol
[317-34-0]	theophylline (ethylenediamine salt)
[319-03-9]	4-fluorophthalic anhydride
[319-86-8]	lindane
[320-51-4]	5-amino-2-chlorobenzotrifluoride
[320-60-5]	2,4-dichlorobenzotrifluoride
[321-14-2]	5-chlorosalicylic acid
[321-55-1]	haloxon
[328-74-5]	3,5-di-(trifluoromethyl)aniline
[328-84-7]	3,4-dichlorobenzotrifluoride
[328-99-4]	3-(trifluoromethyl)benzoyl fluoride
[330-54-1]	diuron
[330-55-2]	linuron
[333-20-0]	potassium thiocyanate
[333-41-5]	diazinon
[334-48-5]	capric acid
[335-67-1]	perfluorooctanoic acid
[338-69-2]	D-alanine
[341-69-5]	orphenadrine (hydrochloride)
[345-92-6]	4,4'-difluorobenzophenone
[346-18-9]	polythiazide
[352-32-9]	*p*-fluorotoluene
[352-93-2]	ethyl sulphide
[353-59-3]	bromochlorodifluoromethane
[354-58-5]	1,1,1-trichloro-2,2,2-trifluoroethane
[355-02-2]	perfluoromethylcyclohexane
[355-43-1]	perfluorohexyl iodide
[355-46-4]	perfluorohexanesulphonic acid
[356-12-7]	fluocinonide
[357-57-3]	brucine
[359-83-1]	pentazocine
[364-62-5]	metoclopramide
[364-98-7]	diazoxide
[365-24-2]	4,4'-difluorobenzhydrol
[366-18-7]	2,2'-bipyridine
[367-21-5]	3-chloro-4-fluoroaniline
[367-25-9]	2,4-difluoroaniline
[367-51-1]	sodium thioglycollate
[371-40-4]	*p*-fluoroaniline
[372-09-8]	cyanoacetic acid
[373-02-4]	nickel acetate
[375-85-9]	perfluoroheptanoic acid
[375-95-1]	perfluorononanoic acid
[378-44-9]	betamethasone
[379-52-2]	fentin fluoride
[382-10-5]	hexafluoroisobutylene
[383-63-1]	ethyl trifluoroacetate
[387-45-1]	2-chloro-6-fluorobenzaldehyde
[389-08-2]	nalidixic acid
[390-64-7]	prenylamine
[393-75-9]	4-chloro-3,5-dinitrobenzotrifluoride
[395-28-8]	isoxsuprine
[396-01-0]	triamterene
[404-82-0]	fenfluramine (hydrochloride)
[407-25-0]	trifluoroacetic anhydride
[409-21-2]	silicon carbide
[420-04-2]	cyanamide
[428-59-1]	hexafluoropropylene oxide
[431-03-8]	diacetyl
[432-08-6]	perfluorotrihexylamine
[434-16-2]	7-dehydrocholesterol
[434-22-0]	19-nortestosterone
[435-97-2]	phenprocoumone
[437-38-7]	fentanyl

[437-74-1]	xanthinol nicotinate	[504-20-1]	phorone
[438-41-5]	chlordiazepoxide (hydrochloride)	[504-24-5]	4-aminopyridine
[438-60-8]	protriptyline	[504-53-0]	distearyl ketone
[439-14-5]	diazepam	[504-63-2]	trimethylene glycol
[440-17-5]	trifluoperazine (hydrochloride)	[505-48-6]	suberic acid
[442-52-4]	clemizole	[506-64-9]	silver cyanide
[443-48-1]	metronidazole	[506-68-3]	cyanogen bromide
[444-27-9]	timonacic	[506-77-4]	cyanogen chloride
[445-03-4]	2-amino-5-chlorobenzotrifluoride	[506-87-6]	ammonium carbonate
[446-86-6]	azathioprine	[506-93-4]	guanidine nitrate
[447-41-6]	buphenine	[507-09-5]	thioacetic acid
[456-42-8]	4-fluorobenzyl chloride	[507-60-8]	scilliroside
[456-59-7]	cyclandelate	[507-70-0]	borneol
[458-24-2]	fenfluramine	[509-86-4]	heptabarbital
[458-37-7]	curcumin	[510-15-6]	chlorobenzilate
[460-00-4]	p-bromofluorobenzene	[512-04-9]	diosgenin
[461-58-5]	dicyandiamide	[512-48-1]	valdetamide
[461-72-3]	hydantoin	[513-35-9]	2-methyl-2-butene
[462-06-6]	fluorobenzene	[513-53-1]	s-butyl mercaptan
[462-08-8]	3-aminopyridine	[513-77-9]	barium carbonate
[463-51-4]	ketene	[513-78-0]	cadmium carbonate
[463-58-1]	carbonyl sulphide	[513-86-0]	acetoin
[463-71-8]	thiophosgene	[514-10-3]	abietic acid
[465-65-6]	naloxone	[515-49-1]	sulfathiourea
[466-97-7]	normorphine	[515-64-0]	sulfisomidine
[466-99-9]	hydromorphone	[515-74-2]	sulphanilic acid (sodium salt)
[467-55-0]	hecogenin	[516-03-0]	ferrous oxalate
[469-21-6]	doxylamine	[516-06-3]	DL-valine
[469-61-4]	α-cedrene	[517-23-7]	2-acetobutyrolactone
[469-62-5]	dextropropoxyphene	[518-47-8]	fluorescein (sodium salt)
[470-82-6]	eucalyptol	[519-37-9]	etofylline
[470-90-6]	chlorfenvinfos	[520-07-0]	phenazone (salicylacetate)
[471-34-1]	calcium carbonate, precipitated	[520-45-6]	dehydroacetic acid
[471-46-5]	oxamide	[522-48-5]	tetryzoline (hydrochloride)
[475-71-8]	flavanthrone	[525-66-6]	propranolol
[479-18-5]	diprophylline	[526-08-9]	sulfaphenazole
[479-27-6]	1,8-diaminonaphthalene	[526-36-3]	xylometazoline
[479-45-8]	tetryl	[526-95-4]	gluconic acid
[479-50-5]	lucanthone	[526-99-8]	mucic acid
[479-92-5]	propyphenazone	[527-07-1]	sodium gluconate
[480-22-8]	anthralin	[527-09-3]	copper gluconate
[482-05-3]	diphenic acid	[527-72-0]	2-thenoic acid
[482-15-5]	isothipendyl	[529-19-1]	o-tolunitrile
[482-89-3]	indigo	[532-03-6]	methocarbamol
[484-23-1]	dihydralazine	[532-27-4]	α-chloroacetophenone
[486-12-4]	triprolidine	[532-32-1]	sodium benzoate
[486-16-8]	carbinoxamine	[532-82-1]	chrysoidine
[486-25-9]	fluorenone	[533-45-9]	clomethiazole
[487-21-8]	lumazine	[533-67-5]	D-2-deoxyribose
[487-48-9]	salacetamide	[533-74-4]	dazomet
[494-19-9]	iminodibenzyl	[533-96-0]	sodium sesquicarbonate
[496-46-8]	glycoluril	[534-07-6]	1,3-dichloroacetone
[496-72-0]	3,4-diaminotoluene	[534-52-1]	4,6-dinitro-o-cresol
[497-19-8]	sodium carbonate	[535-13-7]	ethyl α-chloropropionate
[498-66-8]	norbornene	[535-87-5]	3,5-diaminobenzoic acid
[498-94-2]	isonipecotic acid	[536-21-0]	norfenefrine
[499-75-2]	carvacrol	[536-33-4]	ethionamide
[499-83-2]	dipicolinic acid	[536-60-7]	p-isopropylbenzyl alcohol
[501-52-0]	hydrocinnamic acid	[538-75-0]	dicyclohexylcarbodiimide
[501-53-1]	benzyl chloroformate	[538-93-2]	isobutylbenzene
[502-42-1]	cycloheptanone	[539-08-2]	lactophenetide
[502-44-3]	caprolactone	[539-21-9]	ambazone
[502-98-7]	chloroazodin	[539-82-2]	ethyl valerate
[503-74-2]	isovaleric acid	[539-88-8]	ethyl levulinate
[504-03-0]	2,6-dimethylpiperidine	[540-10-3]	cetyl palmitate

[540-63-6]	1,2-ethanedithiol		[569-85-7]	phenazone (valerate)
[540-69-2]	ammonium formate		[573-01-3]	menadoxime
[540-72-7]	sodium thiocyanate		[576-26-1]	2,6-xylenol
[540-84-1]	isooctane		[576-55-6]	tetrabromo-*o*-cresol
[541-41-3]	ethyl chloroformate		[577-11-7]	sodium di-(2-ethylhexyl)sulphosuccinate
[541-73-1]	*m*-dichlorobenzene		[579-66-8]	2,6-diethylaniline
[542-02-9]	acetoguanamine		[582-25-2]	potassium benzoate
[542-05-2]	acetone-1,3-dicarboxylic acid		[583-17-5]	*o*-hydroxycinnamic acid
[542-08-5]	isopropyl acetoacetate		[583-39-1]	2-mercaptobenzimidazole
[542-18-7]	cyclohexyl chloride		[583-52-8]	potassium oxalate
[542-56-3]	isobutyl nitrite		[583-58-4]	3,4-lutidine
[542-75-6]	1,3-dichloropropene		[583-59-5]	2-methylcyclohexanol (mixed isomers)
[543-27-1]	isobutyl chloroformate		[584-03-2]	1,2-butanediol
[543-39-5]	myrcenol		[584-08-7]	potassium carbonate
[543-82-8]	octodrine		[584-42-9]	Mordant Yellow 1
[544-10-5]	*n*-hexyl chloride		[584-79-2]	bioallethrin
[544-17-2]	calcium formate		[584-79-2]	allethrin
[544-60-5]	ammonium oleate		[584-84-9]	toluene diisocyanate
[544-63-8]	myristic acid		[585-88-6]	maltitol
[544-92-3]	copper cyanide		[586-06-1]	orciprenaline
[545-55-1]	triethylenephosphoramide		[587-61-1]	propyliodone
[547-32-0]	sulfadiazine (sodium salt)		[587-98-4]	Acid Yellow 36
[547-44-4]	sulfacarbamide		[589-18-4]	1-phenylethanol
[548-00-5]	ethyl biscoumacetate		[589-98-0]	3-octanol
[548-57-2]	lucanthone (hydrochloride)		[590-00-1]	potassium sorbate
[548-62-9]	Basic Violet 3		[590-01-2]	*n*-butyl propionate
[548-73-2]	droperidol		[590-28-3]	potassium cyanate
[550-12-9]	sodium 5′-guanylate		[590-46-5]	betaine (hydrochloride)
[550-70-9]	triprolidine (hydrochloride)		[590-86-3]	isovaleraldehyde
[551-16-6]	6-aminopenicillanic acid		[591-27-5]	*m*-aminophenol
[551-27-9]	propicillin		[592-01-8]	calcium cyanide
[551-93-9]	*o*-aminoacetophenone		[592-34-7]	*n*-butyl chloroformate
[552-16-9]	*o*-nitrobenzoic acid		[592-41-6]	1-hexene
[552-22-7]	thymol iodide		[592-42-7]	1,5-hexadiene
[552-30-7]	trimellitic anhydride		[592-45-0]	1,4-hexadiene (*trans*-isomer)
[552-89-6]	*o*-nitrobenzaldehyde		[592-88-1]	diallyl sulphide
[553-69-5]	fenyramidol		[593-29-3]	potassium stearate
[554-13-2]	lithium carbonate		[593-60-2]	vinyl bromide
[554-95-0]	trimesic acid		[593-85-1]	guanidine carbonate
[555-16-8]	*p*-nitrobenzaldehyde		[594-27-4]	tetramethyltin
[555-30-6]	methyldopa		[594-42-3]	trichloromethanesulphenyl chloride
[555-31-7]	aluminium isopropoxide		[594-44-5]	ethanesulphonyl chloride
[555-37-3]	neburon		[595-90-4]	tetraphenyltin
[555-43-1]	tristearin		[597-09-1]	2-ethyl-2-nitro-1,3-propanediol
[556-61-6]	methyl isothiocyanate		[597-82-0]	triphenyl phosphorothionate
[556-67-2]	octamethylcyclotetrasiloxane		[598-21-0]	bromoacetyl bromide
[556-82-1]	3-methyl-2-buten-1-ol		[598-50-5]	*N*-methylurea
[556-88-7]	nitroguanidine		[598-56-1]	*N,N*-dimethylethylamine
[557-04-0]	magnesium stearate		[598-62-9]	manganese carbonate
[557-05-1]	zinc stearate		[598-72-1]	α-bromopropionic acid
[557-08-4]	zinc undecylenate		[598-74-3]	3-methyl-2-butylamine
[557-20-0]	diethyl zinc		[598-78-7]	α-chloropropionic acid
[557-21-1]	zinc cyanide		[598-98-1]	methyl pivalate
[557-34-6]	zinc acetate (anhydrous)		[599-04-2]	pantolactone
[562-09-4]	chlorphenoxamine (hydrochloride)		[599-79-1]	salazosulfapyridine
[562-10-7]	doxylamine (hydrogen succinate)		[599-88-2]	sulfaperin
[563-12-2]	ethion		[602-38-0]	1,5/1,8-dinitronaphthalene (1,8-isomer)
[563-41-7]	semicarbazide hydrochloride		[603-00-9]	proxyphylline
[563-78-0]	2,3-dimethyl-1-butene		[603-35-0]	triphenylphosphine
[563-79-1]	2,3-dimethyl-2-butene		[603-50-9]	bisacodyl
[563-80-4]	methyl isopropyl ketone		[603-64-5]	phenazone (mandelate)
[565-68-4]	methylpentynol		[604-75-1]	oxazepam
[565-80-0]	diisopropyl ketone		[605-70-9]	naphthalene-1,4-dicarboxylic acid
[569-64-2]	Basic Green 4		[605-71-0]	1,5/1,8-dinitronaphthalene (1,5-isomer)
[569-84-6]	phenazone (O-acetylsalicylate)		[606-17-7]	adipiodone

[608-31-1]	2,6-dichloroaniline
[608-93-5]	pentachlorophenol
[609-65-4]	o-chlorobenzoyl chloride
[609-93-8]	2,6-dinitro-p-cresol
[610-14-0]	o-nitrobenzoyl chloride
[611-06-3]	2,4-dichloronitrobenzene
[611-75-6]	bromhexine (hydrochloride)
[613-90-1]	benzoyl cyanide
[614-39-1]	procainamide (hydrochloride)
[614-45-9]	t-butyl peroxybenzoate
[615-05-4]	2,4-diaminoanisole
[615-60-1]	4-chloro-o-xylene
[616-38-6]	dimethyl carbonate
[616-44-4]	3-methylthiophene
[616-45-5]	2-pyrrolidone
[617-45-8]	L-aspartic acid
[617-48-1]	DL-malic acid
[617-89-0]	furfurylamine
[618-41-7]	benzenesulphinic acid
[618-88-2]	5-nitroisophthalic acid
[619-84-1]	p-dimethylaminobenzoic acid
[620-22-4]	m-tolunitrile
[620-40-6]	tribenzylamine
[621-77-2]	triamylamine
[621-82-9]	cinnamic acid
[622-40-2]	4-(2-hydroxyethyl)morpholine
[622-97-9]	p-methylstyrene
[623-25-6]	1,4-bis(chloromethyl)benzene
[623-33-6]	ethyl glycinate hydrochloride
[623-70-1]	ethyl crotonate
[623-73-4]	ethyl diazoacetate
[624-24-8]	methyl valerate
[624-48-6]	dimethyl maleate
[624-83-9]	methyl isocyanate
[625-36-5]	3-chloropropionyl chloride
[625-45-6]	2-methoxyacetic acid
[625-58-1]	nitroethane
[626-17-5]	isophthalodinitrile
[626-23-3]	di-s-butylamine
[626-43-7]	3,5-dichloroaniline
[626-48-2]	6-methyluracil
[626-56-2]	3-methylpiperidine
[627-83-8]	ethylene glycol distearate
[627-93-0]	dimethyl adipate
[628-12-6]	2-methoxyethyl chloroformate
[628-20-6]	4-chlorobutyronitrile
[628-96-6]	ethylene glycol dinitrate
[629-11-8]	1,6-hexanediol
[629-14-1]	ethylene glycol diethyl ether
[630-08-0]	carbon monoxide
[630-93-3]	phenytoin (sodium salt)
[631-61-8]	ammonium acetate
[632-22-4]	tetramethylurea
[632-79-1]	tetrabromophthalic anhydride
[633-96-5]	Acid Orange 7
[634-66-2]	1,2,4,5-tetrachlorobenzene
[635-05-2]	pamaquine
[636-30-6]	2,4,5-trichloroaniline
[636-54-4]	clopamide
[637-07-0]	clofibrate
[637-12-7]	aluminium tristearate
[638-07-3]	ethyl γ-chloroacetoacetate
[638-23-3]	carbocysteine
[640-15-3]	thiometon
[640-19-7]	fluoroacetamide
[643-28-7]	cumidine
[643-65-2]	3-methylbenzophenone
[644-62-2]	meclofenamic acid
[646-06-0]	dioxolane
[646-13-9]	isobutyl stearate
[650-51-1]	sodium trichloroacetate
[651-06-9]	sulfametoxydiazine
[652-67-5]	isosorbide
[654-42-2]	hydroquinone dimethyl ether
[657-24-9]	metformin
[657-27-2]	L-lysine (hydrochloride)
[657-84-1]	sodium p-toluenesulphonate
[659-70-1]	isoamyl isovalerate
[661-19-8]	behenyl alcohol
[665-66-7]	amantadine (hydrochloride)
[671-16-9]	procarbazine
[674-82-8]	diketene
[675-14-9]	cyanuric fluoride
[676-58-4]	methylmagnesium chloride
[677-21-4]	3,3,3-trifluoropropylene
[680-31-9]	hexamethylphosphoramide
[683-10-3]	lauryl betaine
[683-18-1]	dibutyltin dichloride
[684-16-2]	hexafluoroacetone
[689-67-8]	geranylacetone
[691-37-2]	4-methyl-1-pentene
[693-04-9]	n-butylmagnesium chloride
[693-21-0]	diethylene glycol dinitrate
[693-23-2]	1,12-dodecanedioic acid
[693-36-7]	distearyl thiodipropionate
[693-95-8]	4-methylthiazole
[693-98-1]	2-methylimidazole
[694-59-7]	pyridine-N-oxide
[696-23-1]	2-methyl-4-nitroimidazole
[696-44-6]	N-methyl-m-toluidine
[697-82-5]	2,3,5-trimethylphenol
[697-83-6]	5-chloro-2,4,6-trifluoropyrimidine
[699-83-2]	2,6-dihydroxyacetophenone
[700-38-9]	6-nitro-m-cresol
[700-65-2]	norephedrine
[706-14-9]	γ-decalactone
[708-06-5]	2-hydroxy-1-naphthaldehyde
[709-55-7]	etilefrine
[709-98-8]	propanil
[719-59-5]	2-amino-5-chlorobenzophenone
[721-50-6]	prilocaine
[723-46-6]	sulfamethoxazole
[729-99-7]	sulfamoxole
[731-27-1]	tolylfluanid
[732-11-6]	phosmet
[737-31-5]	amidotrizoic acid (sodium salt)
[738-70-5]	trimethoprim
[739-71-9]	trimipramine
[741-58-2]	bensulide
[742-20-1]	cyclopenthiazide
[744-45-6]	diphenyl isophthalate
[749-13-3]	trifluperidol
[753-73-1]	dimethyltin dichloride
[756-79-6]	dimethyl methylphosphonate
[759-94-4]	EPTC
[760-67-8]	2-ethylhexanoyl chloride
[762-04-9]	diethyl phosphite
[763-69-9]	ethyl 3-ethoxypropionate
[765-30-0]	cyclopropylamine
[767-00-0]	p-hydroxybenzonitrile

[1122-62-9]	2-acetylpyridine
[1126-09-6]	ethyl isonipecotinate
[1128-08-1]	dihydrojasmone
[1129-41-5]	metolcarb
[1131-18-6]	5-amino-3-methyl-1-phenylpyrazole
[1134-23-2]	cycloate
[1136-45-4]	5-methyl-3-phenylisoxazole-4-carboxylic acid
[1156-19-0]	tolazamide
[1163-19-5]	decabromodiphenyl oxide
[1166-52-5]	dodecyl gallate
[1172-18-5]	flurazepam (hydrochloride)
[1176-08-5]	phenyltoloxamine (dihydrogen citrate)
[1185-39-3]	2,2-dimethylpentanoic acid
[1186-46-5]	N,N-dimethylguanidine (sulphate)
[1187-93-5]	perfluoro(methyl vinyl ether)
[1189-08-8]	1,3-butanediol dimethacrylate
[1189-71-5]	chlorosulphonyl isocyanate
[1190-63-2]	cetyl stearate
[1192-62-7]	2-acetylfuran
[1194-65-6]	2,6-dichlorobenzonitrile
[1195-79-5]	fenchone
[1199-46-8]	2-amino-4-t-butylphenol
[1210-35-1]	dibenzosuberone
[1218-35-5]	xylometazoline (hydrochloride)
[1222-05-5]	4,5,5,6,7,7-hexamethylindanopyran
[1225-55-4]	protriptyline (hydrochloride)
[1225-60-1]	isothipendyl (hydrochloride)
[1236-99-3]	levomepromazine (hydrochloride)
[1245-44-9]	propicillin (potassium salt)
[1271-19-8]	dicyclopentadienyl titanium dichloride
[1300-71-6]	xylenol, mixed
[1300-72-7]	sodium xylene sulphonate
[1302-42-7]	sodium aluminate
[1302-78-9]	bentonite
[1303-28-2]	arsenic pentoxide
[1303-86-2]	boron oxide
[1303-96-4]	sodium borate
[1304-28-5]	barium oxide
[1304-29-6]	barium peroxide
[1304-56-9]	beryllium oxide
[1304-76-3]	bismuth oxide
[1304-85-4]	bismuth subnitrate
[1305-62-0]	calcium hydroxide
[1305-78-8]	calcium oxide
[1305-79-9]	calcium peroxide
[1306-19-0]	cadmium oxide
[1306-38-3]	cerium oxide
[1307-86-4]	cobalt hydroxide
[1307-96-6]	cobalt oxide
[1308-38-9]	chromium oxide
[1309-32-6]	ammonium fluosilicate
[1309-42-8]	magnesium hydroxide
[1309-48-4]	magnesia, caustic-calcined
[1309-48-4]	magnesia, dead-burned
[1309-60-0]	lead dioxide
[1309-64-4]	antimony trioxide
[1310-53-8]	germanium oxide
[1310-58-3]	potassium hydroxide
[1310-65-2]	lithium hydroxide
[1310-73-2]	sodium hydroxide
[1312-81-8]	lanthanum oxide
[1313-13-9]	manganese dioxide
[1313-27-5]	molybdenum trioxide
[1313-60-6]	sodium peroxide
[1313-82-2]	sodium sulphide
[1313-84-4]	sodium sulphide (nonahydrate)
[1313-97-9]	neodymium oxide
[1313-99-1]	nickel oxide, green
[1314-06-3]	nickel oxide, black
[1314-13-2]	zinc oxide
[1314-23-4]	zirconia
[1314-23-4]	zirconia, high-purity
[1314-35-8]	tungsten trioxide
[1314-36-9]	yttrium oxide
[1314-41-6]	red lead
[1314-56-3]	phosphorus pentoxide
[1314-60-9]	antimony pentoxide
[1314-62-1]	vanadium pentoxide
[1314-80-3]	phosphorus pentasulphide
[1314-84-7]	zinc phosphide
[1314-85-8]	phosphorus sesquisulphide
[1314-98-3]	zinc sulphide
[1315-04-4]	antimony pentasulphide
[1317-25-5]	alcloxa
[1317-33-5]	molybdenum disulphide
[1317-35-7]	manganese tetroxide
[1317-36-8]	litharge
[1317-38-0]	cupric oxide
[1317-39-1]	cuprous oxide
[1317-65-3]	calcite
[1317-97-1]	Pigment Blue 29
[1319-46-6]	lead carbonate, basic
[1320-07-6]	Acid Orange 24
[1321-87-5]	dimethyl octynediol
[1323-65-5]	dinonylphenol
[1324-11-4]	Vat Orange 1
[1324-35-2]	Vat Orange 2
[1326-39-2]	Sulphur Green 9
[1326-40-5]	Sulphur Yellow 9
[1326-47-2]	Sulphur Yellow 1
[1326-49-4]	Sulphur Orange 1
[1326-77-8]	Sulphur Green 1
[1326-82-5]	Sulphur Black 1
[1326-96-1]	Sulphur Red 10
[1327-36-2]	aluminium silicate, precipitated
[1327-53-3]	arsenic trioxide
[1328-53-6]	Pigment Green 7
[1330-20-7]	xylene, mixed
[1330-43-4]	sodium borate (anhydrous)
[1330-78-5]	tricresyl phosphate
[1331-22-2]	methylcyclohexanone
[1332-09-8]	pumice
[1332-37-2]	iron oxide red
[1332-40-7]	copper oxychloride
[1332-58-7]	kaolin
[1332-77-0]	potassium tetraborate
[1333-74-0]	hydrogen
[1333-86-4]	carbon black
[1333-86-4]	acetylene black
[1336-21-6]	ammonia, aqueous
[1338-02-9]	copper naphthenate
[1338-23-4]	methyl ethyl ketone peroxide
[1338-24-5]	naphthenic acid
[1341-49-7]	ammonium bifluoride
[1344-09-8]	sodium silicate
[1344-28-1]	alumina, calcined
[1344-40-7]	lead phosphite, dibasic
[1344-57-6]	uranium dioxide
[1344-67-8]	cupric chloride
[1344-81-6]	calcium polysulphide

[2062-78-4]	pimozide
[2062-84-2]	benperidol
[2067-33-6]	5-bromovaleric acid
[2078-42-4]	2,3,6-TBA-sodium
[2079-00-7]	blasticidin S
[2081-44-9]	nonanol
[2082-79-3]	stearyl 3-(3′,5′-di-*t*-butyl-4′-hydroxyphenyl)-propionate
[2090-05-3]	calcium benzoate
[2104-64-5]	*O*-ethyl *O*-(4-nitrophenyl) phenylphosphono-thioate
[2122-70-5]	ethyl 1-naphthylacetate
[2128-93-0]	*p*-phenylbenzophenone
[2130-56-5]	benzidine-3,3′-dicarboxylic acid
[2136-89-2]	*o*-chlorobenzotrichloride
[2139-47-1]	nifenazone
[2163-80-6]	monosodium methylarsonate
[2164-08-1]	lenacil
[2164-17-2]	fluometuron
[2167-23-9]	2,2-di-(*t*-butylperoxy)butane
[2167-85-3]	pipazetate
[2173-57-1]	β-naphthyl isobutyl ether
[2180-92-9]	bupivacaine
[2192-20-3]	hydroxyzine (dihydrochloride)
[2210-79-9]	*o*-cresyl glycidyl ether
[2212-67-1]	molinate
[2216-51-5]	(−)-menthol
[2222-33-5]	dibenzosuberenone-5
[2226-96-2]	4-hydroxy-2,2,6,6-tetramethylpiperidine
[2227-17-0]	dienochlor
[2234-16-4]	2,4-dichloroacetophenone
[2235-46-3]	*N,N*-diethylacetoacetamide
[2235-54-3]	ammonium lauryl sulphate
[2243-62-1]	1,5-diaminonaphthalene
[2243-76-7]	Mordant Orange 1
[2244-21-5]	potassium dichloroisocyanurate
[2274-66-0]	α,α,2,4-tetrachloroacetophenone
[2275-18-5]	prothoate
[2275-23-2]	vamidothion
[2276-90-6]	iotalamic acid
[2298-13-7]	*o*-aminoazotoluene
[2302-96-7]	Acid Red 13
[2303-17-5]	tri-allate
[2307-68-8]	pentanochlor
[2310-17-0]	phosalone
[2312-35-8]	propargite
[2314-09-2]	flurenol-butyl
[2321-07-5]	fluorescein
[2345-26-8]	geranyl isobutyrate
[2353-45-9]	Food Green 3
[2372-21-6]	*t*-butyl peroxyisopropylcarbonate
[2379-28-4]	Vat Orange 15
[2379-74-0]	Vat Red 1
[2379-76-2]	Vat Yellow 10
[2379-81-9]	Vat Black 27
[2382-96-9]	2-benzoxazolethiol
[2385-77-5]	(+)-citronellal
[2386-87-0]	3,4-epoxycyclohexylmethyl 3,4-epoxycyclo-hexylcarboxylate
[2398-96-1]	tolnaftate
[2399-48-6]	tetrahydrofurfuryl acrylate
[2409-55-4]	2-*t*-butyl-*p*-cresol
[2420-87-3]	biphenyl-3,3′,4,4′-tetracarboxylic dianhydride
[2421-28-5]	benzophenonetetracarboxylate dianhydride
[2425-06-1]	captafol
[2425-10-7]	xylylcarb
[2425-54-9]	myristyl chloride
[2425-79-8]	1,4-butanediol diglycidyl ether
[2426-08-6]	*n*-butyl glycidyl ether
[2429-74-5]	Direct Blue 15
[2432-99-7]	ω-aminoundecanoic acid
[2434-53-9]	6-amino-1-methyluracil
[2438-72-4]	bufexamac
[2439-01-2]	chinomethionat
[2439-10-3]	dodine
[2451-01-6]	terpin hydrate
[2451-62-9]	triglycidyl isocyanurate
[2452-01-9]	zinc laurate
[2459-09-8]	methyl isonicotinate
[2461-15-6]	2-ethylhexyl glycidyl ether
[2461-42-9]	α-naphthyl glycidyl ether
[2475-33-4]	Vat Brown 1
[2475-45-8]	1,4,5,8-tetraaminoanthraquinone
[2475-46-9]	Disperse Blue 3
[2497-18-9]	2-hexenyl acetate
[2500-83-6]	dicyclopentenyl acetate (5-ene isomer)
[2508-72-7]	antazoline (hydrochloride)
[2512-29-0]	Pigment Yellow 1
[2516-95-2]	5-chloro-2-nitrobenzoic acid
[2517-43-3]	3-methoxybutanol
[2524-03-0]	*O,O*-dimethyl phosphorochlorothioate
[2524-04-1]	*O,O*-diethyl phosphorochlorothioate
[2530-85-0]	γ-methacryloxypropyltrimethoxysilane
[2530-87-2]	γ-chloropropyltrimethoxysilane
[2536-31-4]	chlorflurenol-methyl
[2540-82-1]	formothion
[2545-59-7]	2,4,5-T-(2-butoxyethyl)
[2550-26-7]	benzylacetone
[2551-62-4]	sulphur hexafluoride
[2580-78-1]	Reactive Blue 19
[2581-34-2]	4-nitro-*m*-cresol
[2582-30-1]	aminoguanidine bicarbonate
[2593-15-9]	etridiazole
[2595-54-2]	mecarbam
[2597-03-7]	phenthoate
[2609-46-3]	amiloride
[2610-10-8]	Direct Red 80
[2610-11-9]	Direct Red 81
[2613-89-0]	phenylmalonic acid
[2618-25-9]	ioglycamic acid
[2623-23-6]	menthyl acetate ((−) enantiomer)
[2631-37-0]	promecarb
[2631-40-5]	isoprocarb
[2634-33-5]	benzoisothiazolin-3-one
[2636-26-2]	cyanophos
[2642-71-9]	azinphos-ethyl
[2654-58-2]	4,4-dimethyl-1-phenyl-3-pyrazolidinone
[2655-14-3]	3,5-xylyl methylcarbamate
[2664-63-3]	4,4′-thiodiphenol
[2675-77-6]	chloroneb
[2691-41-0]	octogen
[2694-54-4]	triallyl trimellitate
[2696-92-6]	nitrosyl chloride
[2698-41-1]	*o*-chlorobenzalmalononitrile
[2705-87-5]	allyl cyclohexylpropionate
[2709-56-0]	flupenthixol
[2724-58-5]	isostearic acid
[2735-04-8]	2,4-dimethoxyaniline
[2736-23-4]	2,4-dichloro-5-sulphamoylbenzoic acid
[2744-49-2]	Fluorescent Brightener 121

[3874-54-2]	4-chloro-4'-fluorobutyrophenone
[3878-19-1]	fuberidazole
[3886-69-9]	D-α-phenylethylamine
[3919-74-2]	3-(2-chloro-6-fluorophenyl)-5-methyl-isoxazole-4-carboxylic acid
[3919-76-4]	3-(2,6-dichlorophenyl)-5-methyl-isoxazole-4-carboxylic acid
[3926-62-3]	sodium chloroacetate
[3930-20-9]	sotalol
[3947-76-0]	N-methylquinolinium iodide
[3964-81-6]	azatadine
[3982-91-0]	thiophosphoryl chloride
[4000-16-2]	N,N',N''-triaminoguanidine nitrate
[4044-65-9]	bitoscanate
[4051-63-2]	Pigment Red 177
[4065-45-6]	2-hydroxy-4-methoxybenzophenone-5-sulphonic acid
[4075-81-4]	calcium propionate
[4083-64-1]	p-toluenesulphonyl isocyanate
[4093-35-0]	bromopride
[4098-71-9]	isophorone diisocyanate
[4105-12-8]	isocamphylcyclohexanol
[4124-63-4]	mercaptoacetaldehyde
[4147-51-7]	dipropetryn
[4149-06-8]	3-amino-1-phenyl-5-pyrazolone
[4189-44-0]	thiourea dioxide
[4203-77-4]	Vat Red 13
[4205-90-7]	clonidine
[4208-80-4]	Basic Yellow 11
[4221-98-1]	(+)-α-phellandrene
[4223-10-3]	vinylcyclohexene dioxide
[4229-15-6]	Vat Yellow 28
[4252-78-2]	α,2,4-trichloroacetophenone
[4253-22-9]	dibutyltin sulphide
[4253-34-3]	methyl triacetoxysilane
[4261-68-1]	2-diisopropylaminoethyl chloride hydrochloride
[4273-92-1]	4-chloro-2,5-dimethoxy-3'-hydroxy-2'-naphthanilide
[4275-07-4]	butylideneaniline
[4300-97-4]	monochloropivaloyl chloride
[4314-14-1]	Pyrazolone Yellow 3G
[4316-73-8]	sodium sarcosinate
[4316-74-9]	sodium N-methyltaurate
[4333-56-6]	cyclopropyl bromide
[4360-47-8]	cinnamonitrile
[4368-56-3]	Acid Blue 62
[4372-46-7]	pyridoxine (tripalmitate)
[4378-61-4]	Vat Orange 3
[4394-00-7]	niflumic acid
[4394-85-8]	N-formylmorpholine
[4395-53-3]	Vat Black 25
[4403-90-1]	Acid Green 25
[4404-39-1]	Acid Violet 14
[4418-26-2]	dehydroacetic acid (sodium salt)
[4420-74-0]	γ-mercaptopropyltrimethoxysilane
[4433-79-8]	acetoacet-4-chloro-2,5-dimethoxyanilide
[4434-38-2]	Fluorescent Brightener 46
[4452-58-8]	sodium percarbonate
[4454-05-1]	2-methoxydihydropyran
[4474-24-2]	Acid Blue 80
[4482-25-1]	Solvent Brown 12 (hydrochloride)
[4485-12-5]	lithium stearate
[4498-32-2]	dibenzepin
[4553-62-2]	2-methylglutaronitrile
[4584-46-7]	2-dimethylaminoethyl chloride hydrochloride
[4595-59-9]	5-bromopyrimidine
[4602-84-0]	farnesol
[4620-70-6]	t-butylaminoethanol
[4635-59-0]	4-chlorobutyryl chloride
[4658-28-0]	aziprotryne
[4674-50-4]	nootkatone
[4682-36-4]	orphenadrine (hydrogen citrate)
[4691-65-0]	sodium 5'-inosate
[4696-56-4]	calcium laurate
[4697-36-3]	carbenicillin
[4707-47-5]	methyl 3-methylorsellinate
[4711-68-6]	3-hydroxy-2-naphth-p-phenethidide
[4722-98-9]	monoethanolamine lauryl sulphate
[4776-06-1]	fluorosalan
[4800-94-6]	carbenicillin (disodium salt)
[4845-99-2]	brucine (sulphate)
[4846-91-7]	fenoxazoline
[4849-32-5]	karbutilate
[4860-03-1]	cetyl chloride
[4904-61-4]	1,5,9-cyclododecatriene
[4936-47-4]	nifuratel
[4940-11-8]	ethyl maltol
[4945-47-5]	bamipine
[4979-32-2]	N,N-dicyclohexyl-2-benzothiazole-sulphenamide
[5001-32-1]	guanoclor
[5002-47-1]	fluphenazine (decanoate ester)
[5036-02-2]	tetramisole
[5064-31-3]	trisodium nitrilotriacetate
[5089-22-5]	1,4-bis(benzoxazol-2-yl)naphthalene
[5102-83-0]	Pigment Yellow 13
[5104-49-4]	flurbiprofen
[5118-29-6]	melitracen
[5133-19-7]	aloin
[5146-66-7]	geranonitrile
[5153-24-2]	zirconium acetate
[5160-02-1]	Pigment Red 53
[5211-62-1]	o-methoxyphenylacetone
[5216-25-1]	p-chlorobenzotrichloride
[5221-53-4]	dimethirimol
[5232-99-5]	ethyl 2-cyano-3-phenylcinnamate
[5234-68-4]	carboxin
[5250-39-5]	flucloxacillin
[5259-88-1]	oxycarboxin
[5281-04-9]	Pigment Red 57
[5329-14-6]	sulphamic acid
[5332-52-5]	n-undecanol
[5332-73-0]	3-methoxypropylamine
[5337-19-9]	m-nitrobenzenesulphonic acid
[5392-28-9]	2,4,5,6-tetraaminopyrimidine sulphate
[5392-40-5]	citral
[5394-83-2]	10-camphoric acid
[5407-04-5]	3-dimethylaminopropyl chloride hydrochloride
[5413-60-5]	dicyclopentenyl acetate (6-ene isomer)
[5421-46-5]	ammonium thioglycollate
[5423-22-3]	guanidine phosphate, monobasic
[5423-23-4]	guanidine phosphate, dibasic
[5459-58-5]	n-butyl cyanoacetate
[5459-93-8]	N-ethylcyclohexylamine
[5466-77-3]	2-ethylhexyl p-methoxycinnamate
[5469-45-4]	2-acetamidocinnamic acid
[5470-11-1]	hydroxylamine hydrochloride
[5471-51-2]	p-hydroxybenzylacetone
[5521-55-1]	5-methylpyrazine-2-carboxylic acid

[7440-02-0] nickel
[7440-03-1] niobium
[7440-05-3] palladium
[7440-06-4] platinum
[7440-09-7] potassium
[7440-21-3] silicon, electronic grade
[7440-22-4] silver
[7440-23-5] sodium
[7440-25-7] tantalum
[7440-31-5] tin
[7440-32-6] titanium
[7440-33-7] tungsten
[7440-36-0] antimony
[7440-37-1] argon
[7440-38-2] arsenic
[7440-41-7] beryllium
[7440-43-9] cadmium
[7440-47-3] chromium
[7440-48-4] cobalt
[7440-50-8] copper
[7440-56-4] germanium
[7440-57-5] gold
[7440-59-7] helium
[7440-66-6] zinc
[7440-67-7] zirconium
[7440-69-9] bismuth
[7440-70-2] calcium
[7443-70-1] 2-methylcyclohexanol (*cis*-isomer)
[7446-07-3] tellurium dioxide
[7446-08-4] selenium dioxide
[7446-09-5] sulphur dioxide, pure
[7446-11-9] sulphur trioxide
[7446-70-0] aluminium chloride, anhydrous
[7447-40-7] potassium chloride
[7447-41-8] lithium chloride
[7474-05-7] (*S*)-α-chloropropionic acid
[7487-88-9] magnesium sulphate
[7487-94-7] mercuric chloride
[7488-55-3] stannous sulphate
[7491-74-9] piracetam
[7492-67-3] citronelloxyacetaldehyde
[7492-70-8] *n*-butyl *n*-butyryllactate
[7540-51-4] (–)-citronellol
[7542-09-8] cobalt carbonate, basic
[7549-37-3] citral dimethyl acetal
[7550-35-8] lithium bromide
[7550-45-0] titanium tetrachloride
[7553-56-2] iodine
[7558-79-4] disodium phosphate
[7558-80-7] monosodium phosphate
[7560-83-0] *N*-methyldicyclohexylamine
[7575-23-7] pentaerythritol tetrakis(3-mercaptopropionate)
[7580-67-8] lithium hydride
[7601-54-9] trisodium phosphate
[7601-89-0] sodium perchlorate
[7631-86-9] diatomaceous earth
[7631-90-5] sodium bisulphite
[7631-95-0] sodium molybdate
[7631-99-4] sodium nitrate
[7632-00-0] sodium nitrite
[7632-51-1] vanadium tetrachloride
[7637-07-2] boron trifluoride
[7646-69-7] sodium hydride
[7646-78-8] stannic chloride
[7646-79-9] cobalt chloride

[7646-85-7] zinc chloride
[7647-01-0] hydrochloric acid
[7647-01-0] hydrogen chloride, anhydrous
[7647-14-5] sodium chloride, natural
[7647-15-6] sodium bromide
[7647-18-9] antimony pentachloride
[7651-02-7] stearamidopropyldimethylamine
[7664-38-2] phosphoric acid, pure
[7664-39-3] hydrogen fluoride
[7664-41-7] ammonia
[7664-93-9] sulphuric acid
[7681-11-0] potassium iodide
[7681-38-1] sodium bisulphate
[7681-49-4] sodium fluoride
[7681-52-9] sodium hypochlorite
[7681-53-0] sodium hypophosphite
[7681-55-2] sodium iodate
[7681-57-4] sodium metabisulphite
[7681-82-5] sodium iodide
[7681-93-8] pimaricin
[7683-59-2] isoprenaline
[7696-12-0] tetramethrin
[7697-37-2] nitric acid
[7697-37-2] nitric acid, concentrated
[7699-43-6] zirconium oxychloride
[7699-45-8] zinc bromide
[7702-01-4] capryloamphocarboxyglycinate
[7704-34-9] sulphur
[7704-98-5] titanium hydride
[7704-99-6] zirconium hydride
[7705-07-9] titanium trichloride
[7705-08-0] ferric chloride
[7718-54-9] nickel chloride
[7719-09-7] thionyl chloride
[7719-12-2] phosphorus trichloride
[7720-78-7] ferrous sulphate
[7722-64-7] potassium permanganate
[7722-76-1] monoammonium phosphate
[7722-84-1] hydrogen peroxide
[7722-86-3] peroxysulphuric acid
[7722-88-5] tetrasodium pyrophosphate
[7723-14-0] phosphorus
[7723-14-0] phosphorus, red
[7726-95-6] bromine
[7727-18-6] vanadium oxychloride
[7727-21-1] potassium persulphate
[7727-37-9] nitrogen
[7727-43-7] blanc fixe
[7727-54-0] ammonium persulphate
[7727-67-5] sodium tetraphosphate
[7732-18-5] water
[7733-02-0] zinc sulphate
[7738-94-5] chromic acid
[7757-79-1] potassium nitrate
[7757-82-6] sodium sulphate
[7757-83-7] sodium sulphite
[7757-93-9] dicalcium phosphate
[7758-01-2] potassium bromate
[7758-02-3] potassium bromide
[7758-05-6] potassium iodate
[7758-16-9] disodium acid pyrophosphate
[7758-19-2] sodium chlorite
[7758-23-8] monocalcium phosphate
[7758-29-4] sodium tripolyphosphate
[7758-87-4] tricalcium phosphate

[7758-94-3]	ferrous chloride	[7789-79-9]	calcium hypophosphite
[7758-97-6]	chrome yellow	[7790-76-3]	calcium pyrophosphate
[7758-98-7]	copper sulphate	[7790-94-5]	chlorosulphonic acid
[7758-99-8]	copper sulphate (pentahydrate)	[7790-98-9]	ammonium perchlorate
[7761-88-8]	silver nitrate	[7790-99-0]	iodine monochloride
[7772-98-7]	sodium thiosulphate	[7791-13-1]	cobalt chloride
[7772-99-8]	stannous chloride (anhydrous)	[7791-18-6]	magnesium chloride
[7773-01-5]	manganous chloride	[7791-25-5]	sulphuryl chloride
[7773-06-0]	ammonium sulphamate	[7803-51-2]	phosphine
[7775-09-9]	sodium chlorate	[7803-62-5]	silane
[7775-11-3]	sodium chromate	[8000-25-7]	rosemary oil
[7775-14-6]	sodium hydrosulphite	[8000-28-0]	lavender oil
[7775-19-1]	sodium metaborate	[8000-29-1]	citronella oil, Ceylon
[7775-27-1]	sodium persulphate	[8000-29-1]	citronella oil, Java
[7776-28-5]	phytic acid (calcium salt)	[8000-34-8]	clove leaf oil
[7778-18-9]	gypsum	[8000-42-8]	caraway oil
[7778-39-4]	arsenic acid	[8000-66-6]	cardamom oil
[7778-50-9]	potassium dichromate	[8001-22-7]	soyabean oil
[7778-54-3]	calcium hypochlorite	[8001-23-8]	safflower oil
[7778-74-7]	potassium perchlorate	[8001-25-0]	olive oil
[7778-80-5]	potassium sulphate	[8001-26-1]	linseed oil
[7779-27-3]	N,N′,N″-triethylhexahydrotriazine	[8001-29-4]	cottonseed oil
[7779-90-0]	zinc phosphate	[8001-30-7]	maize oil
[7782-41-4]	fluorine	[8001-31-8]	coconut oil
[7782-42-5]	graphite, manufactured	[8001-39-6]	japan wax
[7782-44-7]	oxygen	[8001-69-2]	cod liver oil
[7782-49-2]	selenium	[8001-75-0]	ceresin
[7782-50-5]	chlorine	[8001-78-3]	castor oil, hydrogenated
[7782-78-7]	nitrosyl hydrogen sulphate	[8001-79-4]	castor oil
[7782-92-5]	sodamide	[8002-03-7]	peanut oil
[7783-06-4]	hydrogen sulphide	[8002-09-3]	pine oil
[7783-18-8]	ammonium thiosulphate	[8002-13-9]	rapeseed oil
[7783-20-2]	ammonium sulphate	[8002-26-4]	tall oil fatty acid
[7783-28-0]	diammonium phosphate	[8002-29-7]	anthracene oil
[7783-47-3]	stannous fluoride	[8002-43-5]	lecithin
[7783-49-5]	zinc fluoride	[8002-50-4]	fish oil
[7783-56-4]	antimony trifluoride	[8002-53-7]	montan wax
[7783-60-0]	sulphur tetrafluoride	[8002-64-0]	neatsfoot oil
[7783-61-1]	silicon tetrafluoride	[8002-74-2]	kerosene
[7783-66-6]	iodine pentafluoride	[8002-75-3]	palm oil
[7783-81-5]	uranium hexafluoride	[8003-05-2]	phenylmercuric nitrate, basic
[7783-90-6]	silver chloride	[8003-22-3]	quinophthalone
[7784-13-6]	aluminium chloride, hexahydrate	[8003-34-7]	pyrethrum
[7784-18-1]	aluminium fluoride (anhydrous)	[8003-88-1]	Acid Orange 51
[7784-24-9]	aluminium potassium sulphate (tetracosahydrate)	[8004-87-3]	Basic Violet 1
		[8004-92-0]	Acid Yellow 3
[7784-25-0]	ammonium alum	[8006-40-4]	beeswax (yellow)
[7784-27-2]	aluminium nitrate	[8006-44-8]	candelilla wax
[7784-30-7]	Senegal phosphate	[8006-54-0]	lanolin
[7784-42-1]	arsine	[8006-64-2]	turpentine oil, wood
[7785-23-1]	silver bromide	[8006-78-8]	bay oil
[7785-87-7]	manganese sulphate	[8006-87-9]	sandalwood oil
[7786-81-4]	nickel sulphate	[8006-90-4]	peppermint oil
[7787-59-9]	bismuth oxychloride	[8006-95-9]	wheat germ oil
[7788-97-8]	chromic fluoride (anhydrous)	[8007-02-1]	lemongrass oil
[7789-00-6]	potassium chromate	[8007-08-7]	ginger oil
[7789-04-0]	chromium phosphate	[8007-46-3]	thyme oil
[7789-06-2]	strontium chromate	[8007-70-3]	anise oil
[7789-08-4]	ammonium dichromate	[8008-20-6]	kerosene, deodorised
[7789-21-1]	fluorosulphonic acid	[8008-45-5]	nutmeg oil
[7789-23-3]	potassium fluoride	[8008-52-4]	coriander oil
[7789-29-9]	potassium bifluoride	[8008-56-8]	lemon oil
[7789-38-0]	sodium bromate	[8008-57-9]	orange oil
[7789-41-5]	calcium bromide	[8008-79-5]	spearmint oil
[7789-45-9]	cupric bromide	[8009-03-8]	petroleum jelly

[10099-74-8]	lead nitrate
[10101-39-0]	calcium silicate
[10101-53-8]	chromium sulphate
[10102-06-4]	uranyl nitrate
[10102-18-8]	sodium selenite
[10102-24-6]	lithium silicate
[10102-43-9]	nitric oxide
[10102-71-3]	sodium alum
[10108-64-2]	cadmium chloride
[10118-90-8]	minocycline
[10124-43-3]	cobalt sulphate (anhydrous)
[10141-00-1]	chrome alum
[10143-60-9]	dioctyl octylphosphonate
[10161-34-9]	trenbolone acetate
[10163-15-2]	sodium fluorophosphate
[10169-02-5]	Acid Red 97
[10191-60-3]	*N*-cyanoimido-*S,S*-dimethyldithiocarbamate
[10192-30-0]	ammonium bisulphite
[10196-04-0]	ammonium sulphite
[10206-21-0]	cefacetrile
[10213-77-1]	tripropylene glycol monomethyl ether
[10238-21-8]	glibenclamide
[10262-69-8]	maprotiline
[10265-92-6]	methamidophos
[10287-53-3]	ethyl *p*-dimethylaminobenzoate
[10294-34-5]	boron trichloride
[10294-40-3]	barium chromate
[10294-44-7]	mercurous chloride
[10294-50-5]	cobalt phosphate
[10318-18-0]	DL-cysteine hydrochloride (hydrate)
[10325-94-7]	cadmium nitrate
[10326-41-7]	D-lactic acid
[10347-81-6]	maprotiline (hydrochloride)
[10361-37-2]	barium chloride (anhydrous)
[10380-28-6]	oxine-copper
[10397-75-8]	iocarmic acid
[10402-90-1]	eprazinone
[10433-59-7]	2,4-DB (sodium salt)
[10453-86-8]	resmethrin
[10453-89-1]	(*1RS*)-*cis/trans*-chrysanthemic acid
[10486-19-8]	*n*-tridecaldehyde
[10519-11-6]	decahydro-β-naphthyl acetate
[10540-29-1]	tamoxifen
[10545-99-0]	sulphur dichloride
[10552-74-6]	nitrothal-isopropyl
[10588-01-9]	sodium dichromate
[10591-84-1]	*N,N'*-dimethyldiphenylthiuram disulphide
[10595-72-9]	ditridecyl thiodipropionate
[10605-21-7]	carbendazim
[11061-68-0]	insulin, human
[11099-07-3]	glycerol monostearate (crude grade)
[11103-86-9]	zinc yellow
[11104-88-4]	phosphomolybdic acid
[11108-67-1]	ferroboron
[11110-52-4]	sodium amalgam
[11121-95-2]	ferromolybdenum
[11128-29-3]	potassium pentaborate
[11138-66-2]	xanthan gum
[12001-26-2]	mica
[12001-85-3]	zinc naphthenate
[12002-53-8]	trimedlure
[12013-47-7]	calcium zirconate
[12013-69-3]	calcium plumbate
[12018-01-8]	chromium dioxide
[12027-67-7]	ammonium molybdate

[12036-76-9]	lead sulphate, monobasic
[12037-29-5]	praseodymium oxide
[12042-91-0]	aluminium chlorohydrate
[12045-78-2]	potassium tetraborate (tetrahydrate)
[12047-27-7]	barium titanate
[12058-66-1]	sodium stannate
[12060-58-1]	samarium oxide
[12069-32-8]	boron carbide
[12069-69-1]	copper carbonate, basic
[12070-08-5]	titanium carbide
[12070-12-1]	tungsten carbide
[12075-68-2]	ethylaluminium sesquichloride
[12122-67-7]	zineb
[12124-97-9]	ammonium bromide
[12125-02-9]	ammonium chloride
[12142-33-5]	potassium stannate
[12217-79-7]	Disperse Blue 56
[12221-52-2]	Basic Red 22
[12222-75-2]	Disperse Blue 73
[12223-85-7]	quinophthalone
[12229-13-9]	potassium pentaborate (octahydrate)
[12236-82-7]	Reactive Blue 2
[12262-52-1]	Sulphur Green 11
[12262-58-7]	cyclohexane peroxide
[12270-13-2]	Basic Blue 41
[12397-06-7]	lead sulphate, tribasic
[12427-38-2]	maneb
[12513-27-8]	zinc borate
[12604-57-8]	ferrotungsten
[12604-58-9]	ferrovanadium
[12769-17-4]	Solvent Blue 35
[12769-96-9]	Pigment Violet 15
[12771-68-5]	ancymidol
[12788-93-1]	*n*-butyl phosphoric acid
[13001-39-3]	Fluorescent Brightener 199
[13005-36-2]	potassium phenylacetate
[13042-18-7]	fendiline
[13061-28-4]	2,4,5-trichloroacetophenone
[13071-79-9]	terbufos
[13121-70-5]	cyhexatin
[13138-45-9]	nickel nitrate
[13171-00-1]	4-acetyl-1,1-dimethyl-6-*t*-butylindane
[13171-21-6]	phosphamidon
[13181-17-4]	bromofenoxim
[13194-48-4]	ethoprophos
[13195-64-7]	diisopropyl malonate
[13254-34-7]	2,6-dimethyl-2-heptanol
[13292-46-1]	rifampin
[13327-32-7]	beryllium hydroxide
[13356-08-6]	fenbutatin oxide
[13360-45-7]	chlorbromuron
[13360-57-1]	dimethylsulphamyl chloride
[13360-63-9]	*n*-butylethylamine
[13392-18-2]	fenoterol
[13392-28-4]	rimantidine
[13424-46-9]	lead azide
[13457-18-6]	pyrazophos
[13460-98-5]	theodrenaline
[13463-39-3]	nickel tetracarbonyl
[13463-40-6]	iron pentacarbonyl
[13463-41-7]	zinc 2-pyridinethiol-*N*-oxide
[13463-67-7]	titanium dioxide
[13466-78-9]	3-carene
[13472-45-2]	sodium tungstate
[13477-00-4]	barium chlorate

[17601-94-4]	2-amino-3-bromo-5-nitrobenzonitrile		[22047-49-0]	2-ethylhexyl stearate
[17606-31-4]	bensultap		[22059-60-5]	disopyramide (phosphate)
[17617-23-1]	flurazepam		[22071-15-4]	ketoprofen
[17639-93-9]	methyl α-chloropropionate		[22089-22-1]	trofosfamide
[17671-50-0]	betaine (citrate)		[22204-24-6]	pyrantel (pamoate)
[17696-62-7]	phenyl p-hydroxybenzoate		[22204-53-1]	naproxen
[17796-82-6]	N-(cyclohexylthio)phthalimide		[22212-55-1]	benzoylprop-ethyl
[17804-35-2]	benomyl		[22224-92-6]	fenamiphos
[17863-51-3]	Fluorescent Brightener 9 (cis-isomer)		[22248-79-9]	tetrachlorvinphos
[17902-23-7]	tegafur		[22254-24-6]	ipratropium bromide
[18010-40-7]	bupivacaine (hydrochloride)		[22316-47-8]	clobazam
[18063-03-1]	2,6-difluorobenzamide		[22494-42-4]	diflunisal
[18181-70-9]	iodofenphos		[22583-29-5]	N,N-dimethylguanidine (chloride)
[18181-80-1]	bromopropylate		[22760-18-5]	proquazone
[18282-10-5]	stannic oxide		[22781-23-3]	bendiocarb
[18323-44-9]	clindamycin		[22818-40-2]	D-α-(4-hydroxyphenyl)glycine
[18479-58-8]	dihydromyrcenol		[22839-47-0]	aspartame
[18559-94-9]	salbutamol		[22916-47-8]	miconazole
[18683-91-5]	ambroxol		[22936-75-0]	dimethametryn
[18691-97-9]	methabenzthiazuron		[23031-25-6]	terbutaline
[18694-40-1]	epirizole		[23047-25-8]	lofepramine
[18854-01-8]	isoxathion		[23103-98-2]	pirimicarb
[18997-19-8]	chloromethyl pivalate		[23135-22-0]	oxamyl
[19010-66-3]	lead dimethyldithiocarbamate		[23142-01-0]	pentoxyverine (citrate)
[19044-88-3]	oryzalin		[23184-66-9]	butachlor
[19216-56-9]	prazosin		[23239-41-0]	cefacetrile (sodium salt)
[19321-40-5]	pentaerythritol tetraoleate		[23422-53-9]	formetanate hydrochloride
[19387-91-8]	tinidazole		[23436-19-3]	propylene glycol monoisobutyl ether
[19396-06-6]	polyoxin		[23505-41-1]	pirimiphos-ethyl
[19438-61-0]	4-methylphthalic anhydride		[23560-59-0]	heptenophos
[19480-40-1]	2,4-DB (potassium salt)		[23564-05-8]	thiophanate-methyl
[19562-30-2]	piromidic acid		[23593-75-1]	clotrimazole
[19666-30-9]	oxadiazon		[23598-72-3]	3-(2-chlorophenyl)-5-methylisoxazole-4-carboxylic acid
[19764-74-0]	zirconium phosphate			
[19794-93-5]	trazodone		[23680-84-4]	4-amino-2-chloro-6,7-dimethoxyquinazoline
[19889-37-3]	2-ethyl-2-methylbutanoic acid		[23743-28-4]	sodium 4,4'-bis(4-phenyl-1,2,3-triazol-2-yl)-stilbene-2,2'-disulphonate (disodium salt)
[19937-59-8]	metoxuron			
[20062-22-0]	hexanitrostilbene			
[20139-55-3]	acetoacet-4-chloro-2-methylanilide		[23887-31-2]	clorazepate
[20298-69-5]	2-t-butylcyclohexyl acetate (cis-isomer)		[23947-60-6]	ethirimol
[20298-70-8]	2-t-butylcyclohexyl acetate (trans-isomer)		[23950-58-5]	propyzamide
[20306-75-6]	N-methylacetoacetamide		[23964-58-1]	carticaine
[20338-08-3]	titanium dioxide, hydrate		[24017-47-8]	triazophos
[20354-26-1]	methazole		[24151-93-7]	piperophos
[20380-58-9]	tilidine		[24304-00-5]	aluminium nitride
[20416-09-5]	5-benzyl-3-furylmethyl alcohol		[24307-26-4]	mepiquat chloride
[20427-59-2]	copper hydroxide		[24356-60-3]	cefapirin (sodium salt)
[20432-69-3]	clorazepate		[24468-13-1]	2-ethylhexyl chloroformate
[20514-27-6]	ethyl 1-(4-sulphophenyl)-5-pyrazolone-3-carboxylate		[24526-64-5]	nomifensine
			[24561-10-2]	piperocaine (hydrochloride)
[20548-54-3]	cadmium yellow		[24579-73-5]	propamocarb
[20788-07-2]	resorantel		[24691-80-3]	fenfuram
[20830-75-5]	digoxin		[24717-85-9]	citronellyl tiglate
[20859-73-8]	aluminium phosphide		[24851-98-7]	methyl dihydrojasmonate
[21087-64-9]	metribuzin		[24934-91-6]	chlormephos
[21109-95-5]	barium sulphide		[24937-79-9]	polyvinylidene fluoride
[21260-46-8]	bismuth dimethyldithiocarbamate		[24981-14-4]	polyvinyl fluoride
[21593-23-7]	cefapirin		[25013-15-4]	vinyltoluene
[21645-51-2]	alumina trihydrate		[25013-16-5]	t-butylhydroxyanisole
[21651-19-4]	stannous oxide		[25014-41-9]	polyacrylonitrile
[21725-46-2]	cyanazine		[25038-59-9]	poly(ethylene terephthalate)
[21829-25-4]	nifedipine		[25038-74-8]	polyamide 12
[21908-53-2]	mercuric oxide, red		[25046-79-1]	glisoxepide
[21908-53-2]	mercuric oxide, yellow		[25054-76-6]	oleamidopropyl betaine
[22031-33-0]	N-(2-acetoxyethyl)-N-(2-cyanoethyl)aniline		[25057-89-0]	bentazone
			[25059-80-7]	benazolin-ethyl

[25067-34-9] ethylene-vinyl alcohol copolymers
[25103-52-0] isooctanoic acid
[25154-52-3] nonylphenol
[25155-30-0] sodium dodecylbenzenesulphonate
[25167-67-3] 1-butene
[25168-15-4] 2,4,5-T-isooctyl
[25168-26-7] 2,4-D-isooctyl
[25190-06-1] poly(tetramethylene ether) glycol
[25265-68-3] 2-methyltetrahydrofuran
[25311-71-1] isofenphos
[25319-90-8] MCPA-thioethyl
[25321-41-9] xylenesulphonic acid
[25322-68-3] polyethylene glycol
[25322-69-4] polypropylene glycol
[25366-23-8] thiazafluron
[25377-73-5] dodecenylsuccinic anhydride
[25383-99-7] sodium stearoyl-2-lactylate
[25395-31-7] diacetin
[25523-97-1] chlorphenamine ((+)-enantiomer)
[25639-42-3] methylcyclohexanol
[25717-80-0] molsidomine
[25765-48-4] polyacrylamide, aminomethylated
[25774-02-1] benzyl phenylmalonate
[25875-51-8] robenidine
[25905-14-0] lavandulyl acetate
[25953-19-9] cefazolin
[25954-13-6] fosamine-ammonium
[25956-17-6] Food Red 17
[26002-80-2] phenothrin
[26062-94-2] poly(butylene terephthalate)
[26087-47-8] iprobenfos
[26171-23-3] tolmetin
[26225-79-6] ethofumesate
[26264-58-4] sodium alkylnaphthalene sulphonate (methyl substituent)
[26266-58-0] sorbitan trioleate
[26272-90-2] cetyl chloroformate
[26399-02-0] 2-ethylhexyl oleate
[26399-36-0] profluralin
[26401-97-8] dioctyltin diisooctylthioglycollate
[26403-17-8] isodecanoic acid
[26489-01-0] (±)-citronellol
[26530-20-1] 2-n-octyl-4-isothiazolinone
[26538-44-3] zeranol
[26628-22-8] sodium azide
[26644-46-2] triforine
[26658-19-5] sorbitan tristearate
[26675-46-7] isoflurane
[26718-65-0] mevinphos
[26741-53-7] bis(2,4-di-t-butylphenyl)pentaerythrityl diphosphite
[26774-90-3] epicillin
[26780-96-1] 2,2,4-trimethyl-1,2-dihydroquinoline, polymeric
[26787-78-0] amoxicillin
[26839-75-8] timolol
[26864-56-2] penfluridol
[26896-20-8] neodecanoic acid
[26944-48-9] glibornuride
[26952-21-6] isooctanol
[27031-08-9] sulfaguanole
[27164-46-1] cefazolin (sodium salt)
[27178-16-1] diisodecyl adipate
[27193-86-8] dodecylphenol
[27220-47-9] econazole

[27253-29-8] zinc neodecanoate
[27314-13-2] norflurazon
[27344-41-8] 4,4′-bis(2-sulphostyryl)biphenyl (disodium salt)
[27355-22-2] phthalide
[27458-93-1] isostearyl alcohol
[27523-40-6] isoconazole
[27554-26-3] diisooctyl phthalate
[27761-27-9] N-(4-amino-5-methoxy-2-methyl-phenyl)benzamide
[27813-21-4] tetrahydrophthalimide
[28069-72-9] violet leaf alcohol
[28249-77-6] thiobencarb
[28300-74-5] antimony potassium tartrate
[28330-26-9] maleic hydrazide (sodium salt)
[28395-03-1] bumetanide
[28434-00-6] S-bioallethrin
[28434-01-7] bioresmethrin
[28553-12-0] diisononyl phthalate
[28655-69-8] diazodinitrophenol
[28772-56-7] bromadiolone
[28797-61-7] pirenzepine
[28906-87-8] N,N′-dimethylolethylene urea
[28911-01-5] triazolam
[28924-21-2] 3,5-dibenzoxyacetophenone
[28981-97-7] alprazolam
[29091-05-2] dinitramine
[29091-21-2] prodiamine
[29094-61-9] glipizide
[29104-30-1] benzoximate
[29122-68-7] atenolol
[29171-20-8] dehydrolinalool
[29232-93-7] pirimiphos-methyl
[29806-73-3] 2-ethylhexyl palmitate
[29964-84-9] isodecyl methacrylate
[29973-13-5] ethiofencarb
[30007-47-7] 5-bromo-5-nitro-1,3-dioxane
[30043-49-3] ethidimuron
[30399-84-9] isostearic acid
[30525-89-4] paraformaldehyde
[30560-19-1] acephate
[30864-28-9] methacrifos
[31001-73-7] 2,4-dihydroxybenzophenone 2,1,5-diazoester
[31127-82-9] iodoxamic acid
[31218-83-4] propetamphos
[31329-57-4] naftidrofuryl
[31330-63-9] tetrazene
[31377-23-8] amantadine (sulphate)
[31430-15-6] flubendazole
[31431-39-7] mebendazole
[31556-45-3] isotridecyl stearate
[31566-31-1] glycerol monostearate
[31570-04-4] tris(2,4-di-t-butylphenyl) phosphite
[31637-97-5] etofibrate
[31717-87-0] dodemorph acetate
[31828-71-4] mexiletine
[31879-05-7] fenoprofen
[31895-22-4] thiocyclam hydrogen oxalate
[31906-04-4] 3/4-(4-hydroxy-4-methylpentyl)-3-cyclohexenecarboxaldehyde
[32073-22-6] sodium cumene sulphonate
[32210-23-4] 4-t-butylcyclohexyl acetate
[32360-05-7] stearyl methacrylate
[32388-56-0] 4-acetyl-1,1,6-trimethylethano-octahydronaphthalene

[62587-73-9]	cefsulodin
[62695-55-0]	*t*-butyl peroxy-2-ethylhexanoate
[62850-32-2]	fenothiocarb
[62893-19-0]	cefoperazone
[62924-70-3]	flumetralin
[63148-65-2]	polyvinyl butyral
[63231-60-7]	microcrystalline wax
[63284-71-9]	nuarimol
[63393-93-1]	isopropyl lanolate
[63527-52-6]	cefotaxime
[63721-05-1]	methyl 3,3-dimethyl-4-pentenoate
[63782-90-1]	flamprop-M-isopropyl
[64249-01-0]	anilofos
[64257-84-7]	fenpropathrin
[64470-88-8]	triclopyr-2-butoxyethyl
[64485-93-4]	cefotaxime (sodium salt)
[64902-72-3]	chlorsulfuron
[65085-01-0]	cefmenoxime
[65369-76-8]	1-(3-chlorophenyl)piperazine hydrochloride
[65405-39-2]	dimethylolpropylene urea
[65416-20-8]	*N*-(*p*-ethoxycarbonylphenyl)-*N'*-ethyl-*N'*-phenylformamidine
[65472-88-0]	naftifine
[65907-30-4]	furathiocarb
[66003-55-2]	alloxydim-sodium
[66063-05-6]	pencycuron
[66085-59-4]	nimodipine
[66108-95-0]	iohexol
[66148-78-5]	temocillin
[66215-27-8]	cyromazine
[66230-04-4]	esfenvalerate
[66246-88-6]	penconazole
[66332-96-5]	flutolanil
[66345-62-8]	diclobutrazol
[66357-35-5]	ranitidine
[66373-53-3]	1-(2-methoxyphenyl)piperazine hydrochloride
[66441-23-4]	fenoxaprop-ethyl
[66592-87-8]	cefadroxil
[66841-25-6]	tralomethrin
[67129-08-2]	metazachlor
[67166-49-8]	isostearyl isostearate
[67306-00-7]	fenpropidin
[67306-03-0]	fenpropimorph
[67338-65-2]	benazolin (potassium salt)
[67375-30-8]	cypermethrin
[67434-14-4]	benoxaprofen
[67485-29-4]	hydramethylnon
[67650-82-2]	citronellyl acetate
[67747-09-5]	prochloraz
[68039-35-0]	cedryl methyl ketone
[68083-31-8]	sodium anisaldehyde bisulphite
[68085-85-8]	cyhalothrin
[68140-98-7]	ethyl hydroxymethyl oleyloxazoline
[68153-14-0]	*Ocotea cymbarum* oil
[68228-18-2]	proglinazine-ethyl
[68333-79-9]	ammonium polyphosphate, solid
[68359-37-5]	cyfluthrin
[68391-11-7]	pyridine bases
[68401-81-0]	ceftizoxime
[68411-97-2]	cocoyl sarcosine
[68424-43-1]	lanolin acid
[68425-37-6]	*n*-alkanol(C$_{12}$-C$_{18}$)
[68441-17-8]	wax, oxidised
[68553-81-1]	rice bran oil
[68650-39-5]	cocoamphocarboxyglycinate
[68683-31-8]	dipropylene glycol monosalicylate
[68694-11-1]	triflumizole
[68737-61-1]	dimethyl-3-cyclohexenecarboxaldehyde
[68813-55-8]	oxantel (pamoate salt)
[68844-77-9]	astemizole
[68910-05-4]	polyethylenepolyamine
[68915-31-1]	sodium hexametaphosphate
[68917-70-4]	ouricury wax
[68922-10-1]	citronellyl isovalerate
[68937-90-6]	trimer acid
[68990-63-6]	shark liver oil
[69327-76-0]	buprofezin
[69377-81-7]	fluroxypyr-1-methylheptyl
[69409-94-5]	D-fluvalinate
[69558-55-0]	thymopentin
[69712-56-7]	cefotetan
[69806-50-4]	fluazifop-butyl
[70124-77-5]	flucythrinate
[70288-86-7]	ivermectin
[70331-94-1]	2,2'-oxamidobis[ethyl 3-(3,5-di-*t*-butyl-4-hydroxyphenyl)propionate]
[70356-03-5]	cefaclor
[70458-96-7]	norfloxacin
[70624-18-9]	*N,N'*-bis(2,2,6,6-tetramethyl-4-piperidyl)-1,6-hexamethylenediamine
[71195-58-9]	alfentanil
[71626-11-4]	benalaxyl
[72178-02-0]	fomesafen
[72391-46-9]	chlozolinate
[72558-82-8]	ceftazidime
[73250-68-7]	mefenacet
[73384-59-5]	ceftriaxone
[73886-28-9]	heptopargil
[74051-80-2]	sethoxydim
[74070-46-5]	aclonifen
[74115-24-5]	clofentezine
[74144-37-9]	L-asparagine (sulphate)
[74222-97-2]	sulfometuron-methyl
[74223-64-6]	metsulfuron-methyl
[74398-41-7]	hexabromocyclododecane
[74431-23-5]	imipenem
[74499-03-9]	oxytocin (dihydrogen citrate)
[74525-36-3]	prothipendyl (hydrochloride)
[74712-19-9]	bromobutide
[74782-23-3]	oxabetrinil
[75738-58-8]	cefmenoxime (hydrochloride)
[75847-73-3]	enalapril
[76095-16-4]	enalapril (maleate)
[76547-98-3]	lisinopril
[76578-14-8]	quizalofop-ethyl
[76674-21-0]	flutriafol
[76738-62-0]	paclobutrazol
[77182-82-2]	glufosinate-ammonium
[77501-90-7]	fluoroglycofen-ethyl
[77732-09-3]	oxadixyl
[78110-38-0]	aztreonam
[78587-05-0]	hexythiazox
[79127-80-3]	fenoxycarb
[79241-46-6]	fluazifop-P-butyl
[79277-27-3]	thiafensulfuron-methyl
[79538-03-7]	tetrafluoro-*p*-methylbenzyl alcohol
[79538-32-2]	tefluthrin
[79983-71-4]	hexaconazole
[80370-33-8]	4-tolyl-2,1,5-diazoester
[81334-34-1]	imazamethabenz-methyl

Abbreviations

ACC	Abel Closed Cup
BP	boiling point
BR	boiling range
CAS	Chemical Abstracts Service
CC	closed cup
CFA	copper ferrocyanide
CI	Colour Index
COC	Cleveland open cup
CTFA	Cosmetics, Toiletries and Fragrance Association
d	density
EC	European Commission
EO	ethylene oxide
FAO	UN Food and Agriculture Organisation
FDA	US Food and Drug Administration
FP	freezing point
HLB	hydrophilic-lypophilic balance
M	molecular weight
MP	melting point
NSE	non self-emulsifiable
OC	open cup
PMCC	Pensky-Martens closed cup
PMTA	phosphomolybdotungstic acid
PO	propylene oxide
SE	self-emulsifiable
TOC	Tag open cup
WHO	World Health Organisation